ENGINEERING GRAPHICS AND DESIGN

WITH GRAPHICAL ANALYSIS

LOUIS GARY LAMIT
De Anza College

KATHLEEN L. KITTO
Western Washington University

With Illustrations by
John I. Shull and John J. Higgins

WEST PUBLISHING COMPANY
Minneapolis/St. Paul
New York
Los Angeles
San Francisco

TO MY FATHER, LOUIS JOSEPH LAMIT, WHO WORKED AT CHRYSLER CORPORATION FOR 42 YEARS AS A MECHANICAL ENGINEER AND WHO HELPED ME GET MY FIRST JOB IN ENGINEERING AND DESIGN AS A DRAFTER WHEN I WAS 16 YEARS OLD.

Louis Gary Lamit

TO THOSE WHOSE ACTIONS HAVE MADE ME A BETTER AND STRONGER PERSON.

Kathleen L. Kitto

PRODUCTION CREDITS

Cover Images: Leonardo da Vinci's sketch of a "helix," considered to be the first helicopter © The Granger Collection. Used with permission. Helicopter solid model courtesy of MCAD.

Text and Endsheet Design: LightSource Images, Minneapolis

Copyedit: Elliot Simon & Associates

Photo Research: Beaura K. Ringrose

Production Assistance: Lynette D'Amico; Maren Hoven, Helland Hoven

Page Layout: Geri Davis, The Davis Group, Inc.

Composition: Carlisle Communications

Technical Graphic Services: Publication Services, Inc.

Photo and Illustration Credits follow the Index.

Production, Printing, and Binding by West Publishing Company

TEXT IS PRINTED ON 10% POST CONSUMER RECYCLED PAPER

British Library Cataloguing-in-Publication Data. A catalogue record for this book is available from the British Library.

610 Opperman Drive
P.O. Box 64526
St. Paul, MN 55164-0526
1-800-328-9352

Printed in the United States of America

04 03 02 01 00 99 98 97 8 7 6 5 4 3 2 1 0

Library of Congress Cataloging-in-Publication Data
Lamit, Louis Gary, 1949–
Engineering graphics and design, with graphical analysis / Louis Gary Lamit, Kathleen L. Kitto.
p. cm.
Includes index.
ISBN 0-314-06733-7 (hard : alk. paper)
1. Engineering graphics. 2. Engineering design. I. Kitto, Kathleen L. II. Title.
T353.L263 1997
604.2—dc20 96-2078
CIP

ABOUT THE AUTHORS

LOUIS GARY LAMIT is the former department head of drafting and CAD facility manager and is currently an instructor at De Anza College in Cupertino, California, where he teaches AutoCad-based and Pro/ENGINEER-based computer-aided drafting and design as well as basic drafting.

Mr. Lamit has worked as a drafter, designer, numerical control (NC) programmer, and engineer in the automotive, aircraft, and piping industries. A majority of his work experience is in the area of mechanical and piping design. Mr. Lamit started as a drafter in Detroit (as a job shopper) working for the automobile industry doing tooling, dies, jigs and fixture layout, and detailing at Koltanbar Engineering, Tool Engineering, Time Engineering, and Premier Engineering for Chrysler, Ford, AMC, and Fisher Body. Mr. Lamit has worked at Remington Arms and Pratt & Whitney Aircraft as a designer, and at Boeing Aircraft and Kollmorgan Optics as an NC programmer and aircraft engineer.

Since leaving industry, Mr. Lamit has taught at all levels (Melby Junior High School, Warren, Michigan; Carroll County Vocational Technical School, Carrollton, Georgia; Heald Engineering College, San Francisco; Cogswell Polytechnical College, San Francisco and Cupertino, California; Mission College, Santa Clara, California; Santa Rosa Junior College, Santa Rosa, California; Northern Kentucky University, Highland Heights, Kentucky; and De Anza College, Cupertino, California).

Mr. Lamit has written a number of textbooks, including *Industrial Model Building* (1981), *Piping Drafting and Design* (1981), *Descriptive Geometry* (1983), and *Pipe Fitting and Piping Handbook* (1984) for Prentice-Hall; and *Drafting for Electronics* (3rd ed., 1997) and *CADD* (1987), for Charles Merrill (Macmillian Publishing). *Technical Drawing and Design* (1994) and *Principals of Engineering Drawing* (with Kathleen L. Kitto, 1994) were published by West Publishing Company. Mr. Lamit has also written a number of articles, booklets, problem sheets, worksheets, and workbooks, and presented papers and tutorials in technical areas associated with physical modeling, piping, electronics, CAD, and descriptive geometry.

Mr. Lamit received a BS degree from Western Michigan University in 1970 and did masters work at Wayne State University and Michigan State University. He has also done graduate work at University of California at Berkeley and holds an NC programming certificate from Boeing Aircraft.

KATHLEEN L. KITTO is Chair of the Engineering Technology Department at Western Washington University in Bellingham, Washington. She is a professor in the Manufacturing Engineering Technology program and teaches courses in engineering graphics, robotics and automated systems, computed-integrated manufacturing, machine design, computer-aided-engineering tools and related basic engineering mechanics courses.

Ms. Kitto has designed a high-temperature test facility to study the high-temperature creep behavior of refractories and ceramics used in magnetohydrodynamic (MHD) air preheaters. As well as completing mechanical designs, she designed the instrumentation for the high-temperature test facility and other test facilities. Also in industry, she worked on flow loops and instrumentation for large-scale, one-of-a-kind commercial lasers.

Ms. Kitto has taught at Montana College of Mineral Science and Technology in Butte, Montana, at Bellevue Community College in Bellevue, Washington, and at Western Washington University. At Western Washington University her research has focused on the adaptation and design of devices for differently abled children and adults. She is the faculty advisor for the student chapters of both the American Society of Mechanical Engineers and the Society of Manufacturing Engineers. Both student clubs have received numerous national awards and recognition. Her recent research has also involved the high-temperature ceramic materials for a new thermophotovoltaic generator.

Ms. Kitto received MS and BS degrees (with high honors) in metallurgical engineering from Montana College of Mineral Science and Technology. She is an active member of the American Society of Mechanical Engineers, the Society of Manufacturing Engineers, the Rehabilitation Society of North America, and the American Association of Engineering Educators. She has published over 20 scholarly papers and is author of another text with L. Gary Lamit, *Principles of Engineering Drawing* (1994, West). She is a member of Western Washington University's Faculty Senate Executive Committee, Academic Coordinating Commission, Expository Writing Committee, and Scholastic Standing Committee.

BRIEF CONTENTS

CONTENTS

COMPARISON OF ANSI Y14.1 DRAWING FORMAT SIZES WITH ISO PAPER SIZES

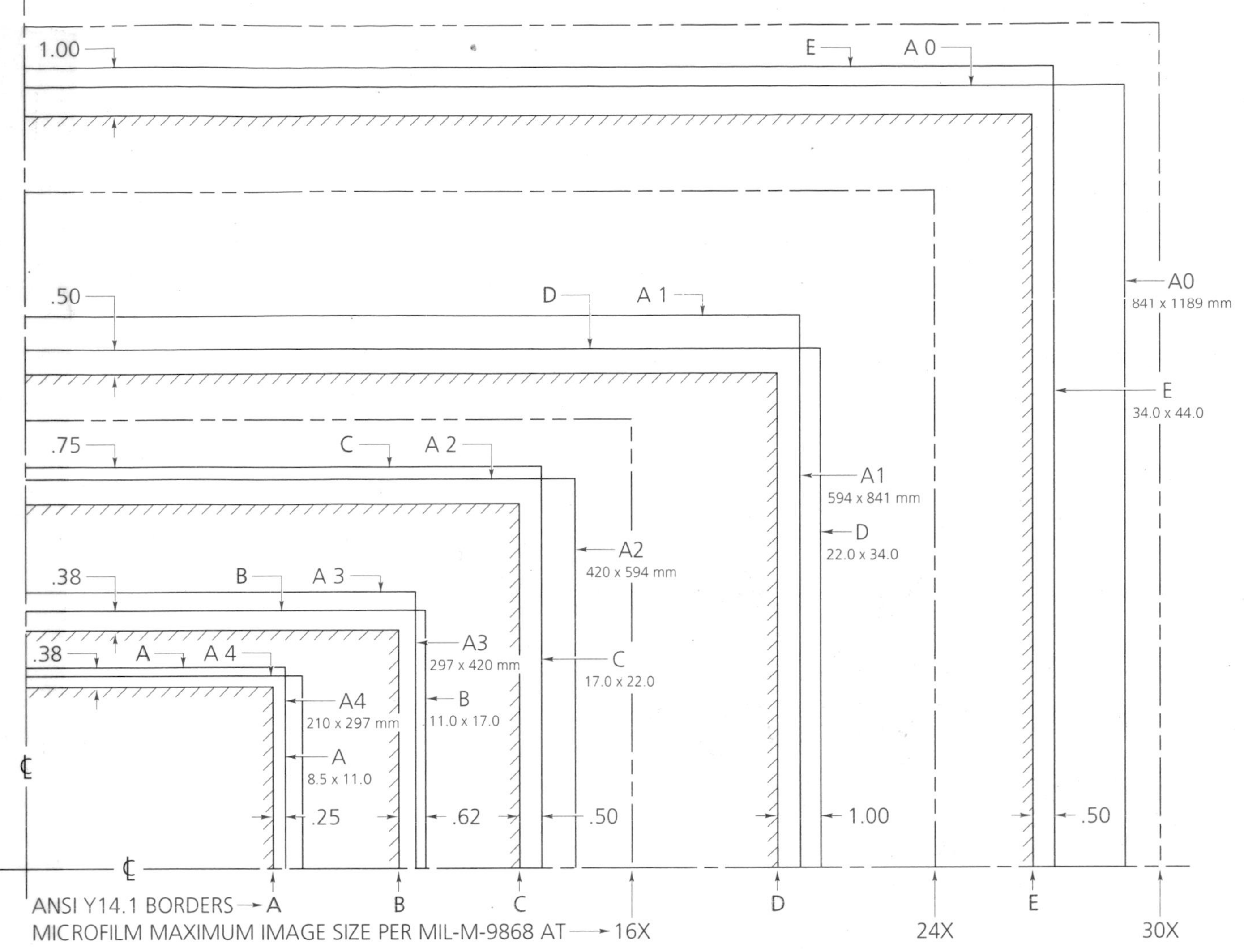

ENGINEERING GRAPHICS AND DESIGN

WITH GRAPHICAL ANALYSIS

PREFACE

Engineering Graphics and Design with Graphical Analysis and *Fundamentals of Engineering Graphics and Design* were exciting, rewarding projects that presented us with many challenges. Both books are comprehensive and are intended for use with one- or two-semester/quarter courses in engineering design graphics or engineering graphics. Because of their comprehensive nature, they will also serve as an excellent reference for practicing engineers and other professionals in the field.

Perhaps the most difficult question to answer during the development of the text was what to exclude. Computers have changed the way engineers and designers "do" design and engineering. Parametric solid modeling and geometric dimensioning and tolerancing is increasingly important in design, especially in world-class facilities. However, the fundamental subjects—such as the engineering design method, orthographic projection, and descriptive geometry—are still the foundations for any course in engineering graphics and design.

The text contains a wide variety of current industry drawings and 3D solid models. Engineering graphics is a discipline that is ever changing and evolving. Orthographic projections and 3D solid models are both important components of the same equation. Engineering graphics is a communication tool for engineers and design professionals. Modern students must be well versed in all aspects of engineering and its tools if they are to become effective leaders in an increasingly competitive world marketplace. The goal of every engineering drawing, model, or database is to get the part made correctly—the first time. Enhanced tools make enhanced design efforts possible. This leads to better products being produced in shorter times to market. The products have built-in quality, rather than inspected-out defects. Without the appropriate part definition and control, the part simply cannot be produced effectively or efficiently.

TEXT ORGANIZATION

Engineering Graphics and Design with Graphical Analysis is organized into six parts that follow a logical progression of fundamental topics and advanced subjects. Those students using the *Fundamentals* textbook will have five of these same six parts available to study. Part One, Engineering and Design, covers the basics of the engineering design method and the use of computers in design engineering and manufacturing. A fifth chapter in that section, Parametric Design, shows how parametric design can help to streamline the basic engineering design process. Part Two, Basic Graphical Materials and Procedures, introduces the traditional fundamental engineering graphics topics of equipment, materials, and techniques; lettering and annotation; geometric constructions; and sketching. Part Three, Drawing Basics, covers the basic multiview drawing subjects, sections, auxiliary views, and pictorials. Part Four, Processes and Documentation, introduces the students to manufacturing processes, dimensioning, and the fundamentals of geometric dimensioning and tolerancing. Part Five, Mechanical Parts, Procedures, and Layout, contains chapters on threads and fasteners; springs; gears, shafts, and bearings; and cams. Part Five also covers working drawings, welding drawings, and an introduction to fluid power. The final section of *Engineering Graphics and Design with Graphical Analysis,* Part Six, Engineering Graphical Analysis, is a comprehensive treatment of descriptive geometry techniques and vector analysis that concludes with a chapter containing several suggestions for design projects.

A three-part comprehensive appendix contains useful engineering design information and can serve as a course reference guide. Appendix A, Glossaries, contains mechanical and CAD/CAM glossaries. Appendix B, Abbreviations and Standards, gives general abbreviations and ANSI and Canadian Standards. Appendix C, Standard Catalog Parts and Reference Material, provides information on such items as threads, drills, bolts, screws, nuts, washers, rivets, retaining rings, pins, bushings, and keys. It also lists sheet metal gages, structural shapes and sizes, and fits and tolerances.

The following outline represents the organization of the text:

PART ONE Engineering and Design
- Chapter 1 Introduction to Engineering Graphics and Design
- Chapter 2 Design Engineering
- Chapter 3 The Design Process
- Chapter 4 Computers in Engineering Design and Manufacturing
- Chapter 5 Parametric Design

ILLUSTRATIONS IN THE TEXT

Unlike many of the traditional texts that have only one style of drawing, this text is dedicated to letting the student see what the world of design and engineering is like. Most projects are from industry and have been manufactured within the last few years. Drawings in the text include a wide range of manual illustrations and engineering details, CAD-plotted projects using pen, electrostatic, and laser plotters, professional technical illustrations, and 3D solid models. The variety of drawing types and styles found in the text include the following.

- *Instructional drawings* were created by professional illustrators to introduce a concept or guide a student through a series of steps to accomplish a specific construction or lay out a part. These are done with CAD and manual technical illustration techniques.
- *Industry drawings* have been drawn directly from company sources, no changes have been made. Some are CAD and some are manual drawings.
- *Example art* illustrates a concept and is normally redrawn from an industry source.
- *Exercises* are placed at the end of each chapter. Each exercise is on an 8½ × 11 in. "A"-size sheet with a .25 in. grid.
- *Problems* are found at the end of most chapters and include a variety of CAD, sketch-quality projects, and manually drawn instrument drawings. Problems range from simple "A"-size one-view drawings to multiple-view "D"-size projects. Problems can be completed as 2D or 3D CAD or solid modeling, instrument, or sketch assignments.

TEXT FEATURES

A variety of traditional and innovative features are incorporated in the text.

- Performance-based *learning objectives* begin each chapter.
- *Industry-based drawings and design examples* are used throughout the text.
- *Sketching* has been integrated into most of the chapters. Chapter 9 is devoted entirely to sketching. Other chapters in the text have many sketching examples, problems, or exercises. In fact, all the exercises could be assigned as sketching projects.
- A number of *innovative chapters* are included:
  Chapter 2 Design Engineering
  Chapter 3 The Design Process
  Chapter 4 Computers in Engineering Design and Manufacturing
  Chapter 5 Parametric Design
  Chapter 13 Pictorials: 3D Representations and 3D Modeling
  Chapter 16 Geometric Dimensioning and Tolerancing
  In *Engineering Graphics and Design with Graphical Analysis* only:
  Chapter 29 Vector Analysis
  Chapter 30 Design Projects
- *Industrial-based "Focus On . . . " boxes* describe historical engineering design information or special engineering

concepts as they relate to the material in each chapter. These boxes contain photographs or illustrations that present the concept visually or to explain the historical significance of the material.

- *"Applying Parametric Design" boxes* show how parametric design can help to create 3D solid models during the design and engineering phase of product design.
- The *Chapter Quiz* includes eight true-or-false, eight fill-in-the blank, and eight short-answer review questions. Answers to all quiz questions are given in the solutions manual.
- *Chapter Exercises* at the end of each chapter are designed to be completed at specific intervals in the chapter. The exercises are suggested at logical stopping points within each chapter so the student can understand the material in increments.
- *Chapter Problems* close every appropriate chapter. They are numerous and of sufficient level of difficulty to provide real-world examples of industrial projects or to teach instructional concepts. Simple to advanced projects are provided in most chapters.
- The text ends with a *comprehensive appendix,* which was designed to be used in industry as a reference for the practicing engineer or designer.

SUPPLEMENTS

In addition to the text, a series of ancillaries is available to make the transition to a new text as comfortable as possible.

- *Transparency acetates* (about 200) and *transparency masters* (about 200) provide the instructor with a comprehensive set of lecture materials that can be used to display the chapter concepts via overhead projector.
- The *Solutions Manual* (by James Wilson) offers answers to all text quiz questions and solutions to most of the exercises and problems found at the end of each chapter. The solutions manual is also available as AutoCAD disks.
- A selection of *workbooks, worksheets, and problem sheets* offers additional drawing exercises for the student. A workbook by Kenneth I. Stibolt primarily emphasizes manual methods. Two sets of worksheets and problem sheets have been prepared by L. Gary Lamit. One is geared to the chapter Problems in the text; the other offers full-sized versions of the 1/4-page-grid Exercises. The workbooks, worksheets, and problem sheets can be purchased separately, or they can be bought shrink-wrapped with the text, at a significant savings. Ask your West sales representative about other workbooks and supplements available for instructors.

ACKNOWLEDGMENTS

We would like to thank the following for their contributions of illustrations:

Rachael Svit
Elena Verne
Irene Guerrero
Valerie Prouty
Jaime Guerrero
Dennis Wahler
John Shull
John Higgins
Pat Scheetz
Dick Finn
Jamse Gee
Ken Louie
Phillip Christensen
Gary Donaldson
Mike Healy
Boris Zanneli
David Givins
Joshua Hutchinson
Hafizullah Obaidi
Michael Cachero
Jeff Fenton
Jay Romiti
Jose Uribe
Dave Patine
John Ramalo
Ernie Antin
Eric Schuler

We also thank Dave Patine at Parametric Technology, who provided a wealth of support for the text, including Pro/ENGINEER software and hundreds of slides. Autodesk provided their usual complete assistance, including AutoCAD Designer and AutoCAD 13, and a great many slides and drawings. The Proto-Draft Modules shown in many of the figures were provided by South-Western Publishing Company.

The following reviewers of this text provided meaningful and insightful suggestions that added to the completed book:

Vera Anand
Clemson University

James D. Bethune
Boston University

David M. Fischer
New Hampshire Technical College—Manchester

Kathryn Holliday-Darr
Penn State at Erie-Behrend

Hamid Khan
Ball State University

Paul G. Menz
Cumberland County College

John G. Nee
Central Michigan University

Mike Schnurr
Hillsborough Community College

Ed Wheeler
University of Tennessee-Martin

Thank you to James Wilson for providing the Solutions Manual.

We are also grateful to all the administrators, staff, and students at De Anza College and Western Washington University who encouraged us and supported us. Elliot Simon deserves special acknowledgement for his hands-on role in the manuscript copyedit.

A special word of thanks is offered to the many individuals at West Publishing Company who have made substantial contributions to make this book a success. Mary Verrill, thank you for your hours and hours of patience and devotion to this huge project. Chris Conty, thank you for making the project a reality. A special thank you to Liz Riedel for always being there for us and listening for countless hours; this project would have never come to be without your unceasing support and deep friendship.

L. Gary Lamit
Kathleen L. Kitto

ENGINEERING AND DESIGN

Chapter 1

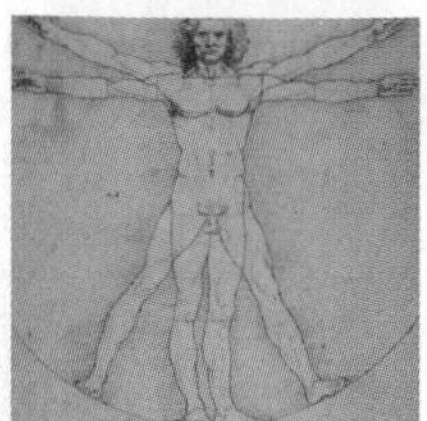

INTRODUCTION TO ENGINEERING GRAPHICS AND DESIGN

LEARNING OBJECTIVES

Upon completion of this chapter you will be able to:

1. Recognize that engineering graphics allows graphical representation of ideas.
2. Compare career fields in engineering, and understand how engineers and designers use engineering graphics to communicate ideas.
3. Define common terms used in engineering graphics.
4. Understand the transitions in engineering graphics that have taken place from ancient Roman construction projects to modern concurrent engineering projects.
5. Understand and identify technical drawing types and design stages.
6. Understand the role of descriptive geometry in solving three-dimensional problems.
7. Identify the various standards of practice used in engineering graphics and design.

1.1 INTRODUCTION

Engineering graphics and design use graphic language to communicate ideas. This language, developed and used by engineers, designers, and drafters, serves as an essential tool from the beginning of a product's development to its production. How do we communicate ideas graphically? What are the components of this graphic language? What is a good drawing? This text will answer these questions by covering the basics of engineering graphics and engineering design.

Engineering graphics is a *language* or a *tool,* not a specialized field. Engineers use this tool to create and produce a variety of products—from consumer items to highly specialized technical products for the aerospace industry. Engineering drawings play an essential role in design, manufacturing, processing, and production. Every industrial nation employs a large number of engineers and designers. Literally millions of jobs in the United States and Canada depend on technical communication in some way.

Engineering drawings are geometric representations of an idea or product that must be processed, manufactured, or constructed. The engineering-and-design process is used to define, establish, and create. The engineer, the designer, and the drafter use drawings to communicate technical information to each other and from the design office to the manufacturing floor. All machines, devices, and products are graphically designed before they are manufactured. The cost, the intricacy, and the manufacturability of the item are considered during the beginning of the design stage. Approximately 75% of the cost to produce a part are fixed in the design stage. After the design has been refined, engineering drawings are used to communicate the design data.

You should not look on engineering graphics and design as an end in itself or as an island of information. Design drawings and models are only the first step in the long and

FIGURE 1.1 An Engineering and Design Office

complicated process of product development, production, and manufacture.

Engineering drawings may be prepared either on drafting boards using traditional engineering drawing instruments or with computers. A solid model of the product might be created before any manufacturing is considered. It is not uncommon to see computer-aided design and drafting (CAD) systems interspersed among drafting tables (Fig. 1.1). Some companies still use traditional engineering drawing in portions of their design process. All large companies, such as IBM, General Motors, Hewlett Packard (Fig. 1.2), and Ford have converted entirely to computer-aided design/computer-aided manufacturing (CAD/CAM) systems.

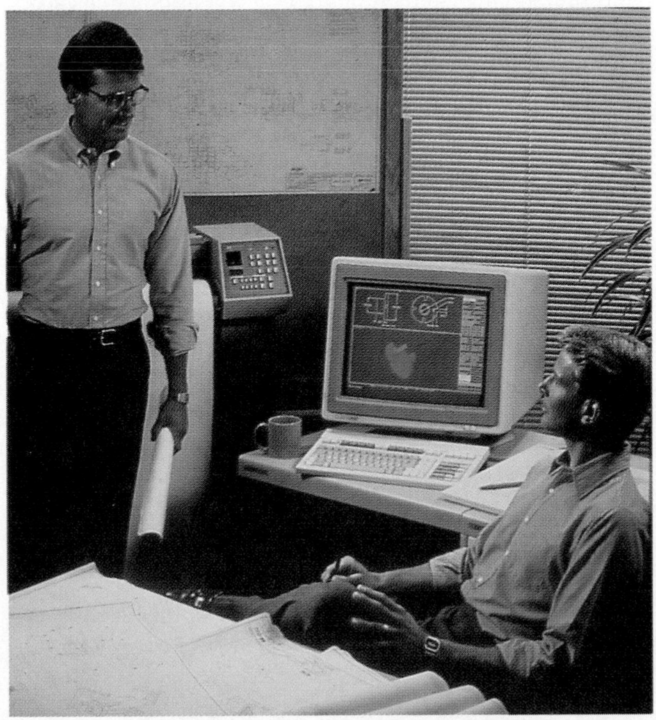

FIGURE 1.2 CAD System

1.2 CAREERS IN ENGINEERING GRAPHICS

There are many sequences you can follow in careers that use engineering graphics and design. Figure 1.3 shows traditional job categories in technical drawing and the path from drafting trainee to design supervisor for a career in drafting and design. The following list shows job categories and responsibilities for various engineering and drafting careers that make use of engineering graphics:

Job Category	*Responsibility*
Chief Engineer	Management
Engineer	Conceptual design
	Ideas
	Calculation and verification
Designer	Design ideas
	Physical layout
Layout designer	Assemblies
	Finalization of design
Detailer	Basic drawings
	Details
	Dimensioning
Checker	Checking of all drawings and designs
Technical illustrator	Presentation drawings
	Manuals
	Publication-quality art

The traditional starting point for a career in drafting and design is the *drafting trainee* (Fig. 1.3). The drafting trainee normally has had high school or beginning-level college courses in drafting, math, and related technical subjects. Some drafting trainees start at the apprentice level, with no drafting experience.

Typically, the first step on the path to a career in drafting and design is to obtain a certificate at a technical school or a one- to two-year associate degree at a community or technical college that offers a drafting and design degree. With this education you enter the job market as a *drafter/detailer* or a *junior drafter*. The entry level depends on the quality of the degree program and the graduate's experience. The junior drafter is required to know considerably more than the drafting trainee. Mastery is essential in the use of instruments, materials, and drafting techniques, including lettering, geometric construction, freehand sketching, projection techniques, sectioning, dimensioning, and tolerancing. The primary responsibility of the junior drafter is to prepare detail drawings.

The *senior drafter* (or *layout designer*) position requires a minimum of two to five years' experience in a particular engineering discipline. Layout designers refine the engineer's and designer's sketches, including investigating alternate design possibilities. Layout designers are required to understand drafting conventions and standards, know how to determine clearances and fits, and make the calculations

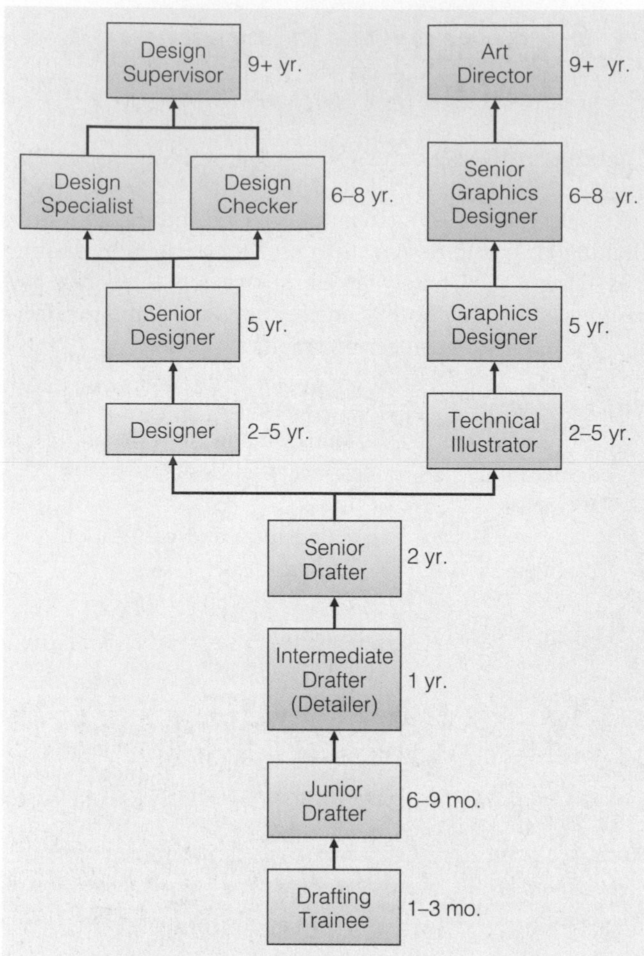

FIGURE 1.3 **Flowchart for a Career in Drafting and Design**

necessary for an accurate design. Knowledge and understanding of shop practices, procedures, manufacturing techniques, and basic production methods are important. After two to seven years' experience, the layout designer may qualify as a junior designer or a designer. A designer is called on to refine designs established by engineers.

Senior designers are in charge of a design group. The senior designer has between six and twenty years of experience as a designer in a particular field. The senior designer works directly with engineers and checkers.

Checkers are responsible for the accuracy of the finished drawings. They review the drawings for clarity, completeness, production feasibility, and cost effectiveness. Checkers review all mathematical computations. A checker is schooled in all standards and conventions for a particular engineering discipline. The checker takes the original design sketches, drawing layouts, and detail drawings of the project and makes sure they are consistent, accurate, and complete.

The ultimate legal responsibility for a project rests with the *engineering team*. Engineers graduate in four or five years from degree programs specific to particular disciplines: mechanical, civil, electrical, chemical, metallurgical, etc. Engineers typically complete at least one course or course sequence in engineering graphics before graduation. Many engineers today go on to complete advanced degrees in their discipline. Engineers must be *registered* in their state to certify certain projects. The *design supervisor* coordinates, supervises, and schedules work assignments.

Computers have changed the way engineers do engineering. Today, it is not uncommon for an engineer to be working on a CAD station to complete an initial solid model design for a project. **Parametric** CAD programs are found increasingly in all stages of design engineering. The concurrent engineering environment calls for design for manufacturing (DFM) to be considered during the initial design phase. Parametric CAD programs facilitate this effort. Engineers, industrial designers, technologists, and drafters work together from project inception to ensure a high-quality, manufacturable product.

The basic knowledge required for a particular engineering project is acquired through a combination of schooling and industrial experience. The technology used in today's engineering design environment is changing rapidly. New features are constantly added to each design program. The pressure to compete in world-class manufacturing has pushed the need to complete projects from engineering design to production in a much shorter time. A product late to market is often worthless in today's face-paced environment.

You should attempt to gain exposure and training on different CAD software and hardware packages. Pay particular attention to both two-dimensional (2D) and three-dimensional (3D) CAD packages. Experience in solid modeling and parametric design are also particularly important today. A knowledge of computer-aided manufacturing and rapid prototyping (stereolithography) will also help a career. Of course, strong written and oral communication skills are essential for a successful engineering career.

1.3 TERMS OF THE PROFESSION

This text uses terms that are common in engineering and design. Some of the most important terms follow.

Computer-aided design and drafting or computer-aided design (CAD) The use of the computer to design a part and to produce engineering drawings. Two-dimensional CAD is confined to the layout and graphic representation of parts using traditional standard industry conventions. Drawings are *representations* of a part plotted on paper. Whereas 2D CAD is limited to detailing and drafting, 3D CAD, or solid modeling, is usually the starting point for design (Fig. 1.4).

Engineering design graphics The use of graphical communication in the design process. Engineering drawings represent design ideas, configurations, specifications, and analyses for many different kinds of engineering projects.

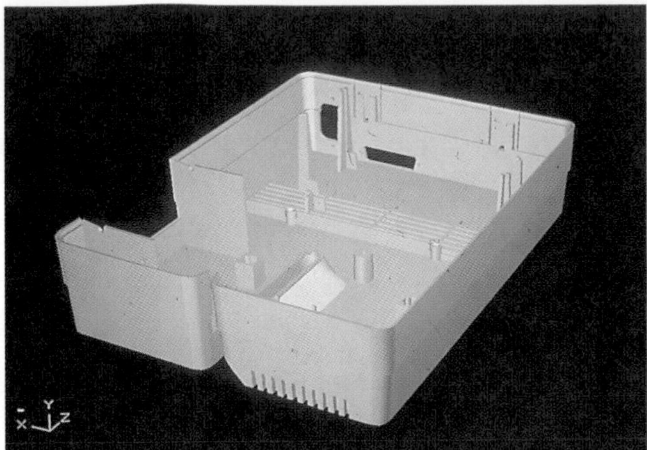

FIGURE 1.4 3D Mold Design

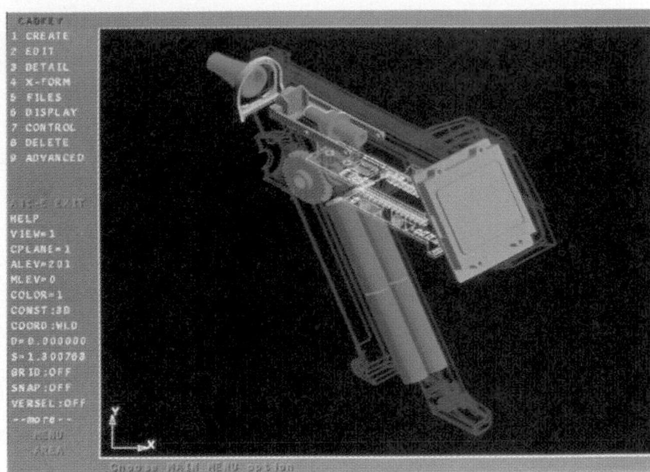

FIGURE 1.6 Solid Model of an Assembly

Manual drafting (instrument drawing) The kind of drafting done on a drafting board using paper, pencil, and drawing instruments. Each chapter in the text covers a specific area of manual and CAD procedures used in engineering graphics. In this text, *manual drafting* is confined to the creation of drawings via traditional instruments, not a computer.

Modeling As used throughout the text, describes the design stage of constructing a 3D physical model or an electronic 3D model of a part. A model can be created via physical modeling (Fig. 1.5) and/or by computer modeling (Figs. 1.6 and 1.7) using 3D CAD systems and parametric modelers. With 3D CAD models, you can investigate a variety of designs, model the mechanical response of the designs on the system, and complete other analyses (Fig. 1.8). Physical modeling is used to create a lifelike scale model of the part.

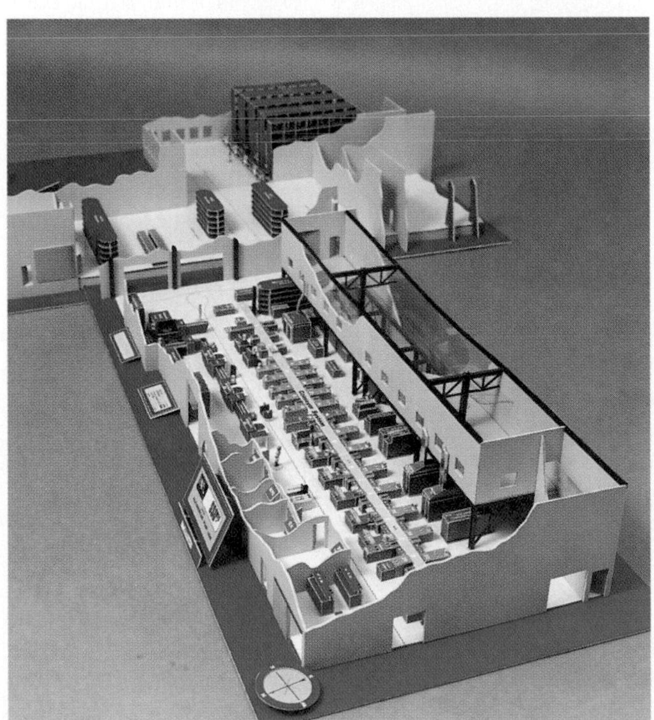

FIGURE 1.5 Scale Physical Model of the Advanced Electronics Assembly Facility

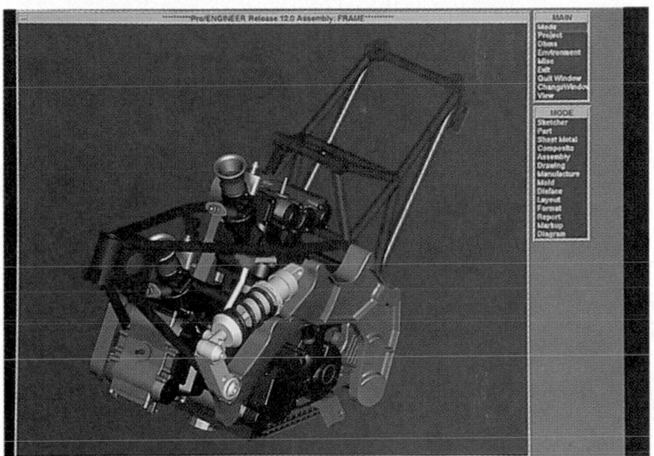

FIGURE 1.7 Shaded Solid Model

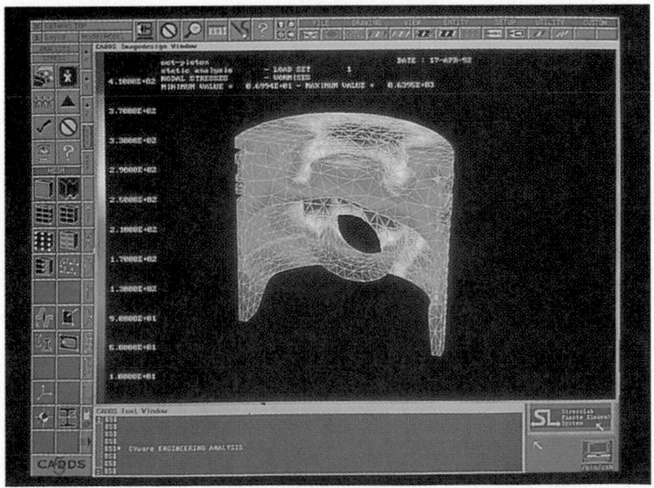

FIGURE 1.8 3D Design Model Used for Engineering Analysis

Technical drawing Encompasses all forms of graphic communication: manual, mechanical, freehand, instrument, and computer-generated drawings used by the engineer, designer, or drafter to express and to develop technical designs for manufacturing, production, or construction.

Technical illustration The use of artistic methods and pictorial techniques to represent a part or a system for use by nontechnical personnel. Technical illustrations are used widely in service, parts, owner's, and other types of manuals. Sales and advertising also use technical illustrations.

Technical sketching The use of freehand graphics to create drawings and pictorial representations of ideas. It is one of the most important tools available to the engineer and designer to express creative ideas and preliminary design solutions.

1.4 THE HISTORY OF ENGINEERING DRAWING

Technical drawings have been employed throughout history to communicate ideas. Some of the earliest evidence of the use of drawings comes from the construction of the ancient pyramids and temples, with drawings dating to as far back as 1400 B.C. Drawings were used in ancient Rome to display bridge designs and other construction projects. Leonardo DaVinci employed pictorial sketches to develop and explore different inventions and designs.

The beginning of modern technical drawing dates back to the early 1800s. Until that time, graphic communication was more artistic in nature and used pen, ink, and color washes to display pictorial graphic images of a product or construction projects. By the 1900s, drawings were used for the production and manufacture of a wide variety of industrial products. Engineers were learning how to mass-produce products and how to communicate engineering designs more effectively with engineering drawings.

A series of standards and conventions was established to aid the transfer of information between the engineering/design department and manufacturing/production or construction. Communication between companies, industries, and countries was also made easier by standardization. Today, we have a very strict, standardized method of displaying graphic information.

Before the mid-1800s, instruments for graphical representation were limited to measuring scales, the compass, dividers, paper, and ink. Ink was replaced by the pencil. The T-square evolved into the parallel bar and then into the drafting machine. The newest tool in engineering design and drafting is 2D and 3D CAD systems.

1.5 TYPES OF DRAWINGS: ARTISTIC AND TECHNICAL

Drawing is a tool used by engineers and industrial designers to design a product, solve a problem, or produce a product. Almost everything around us began as an idea and then as a drawing: the buildings in which we live and work; the appliances in our homes—dishwashers, can openers, dryers, toasters; our means of transportation—cars, trains, ships, airplanes; our systems that support life—plumbing, electricity; even what we wear was conceived and brought into being by the effective use of engineering drawings. Few items get manufactured or produced without an engineering drawing.

There are two types of drawings: *artistic* and *technical.* Artistic drawings are outside the scope of this text. Though technical illustrations (Figs. 1.9 and 1.10) use artistic techniques, an artistic drawing has many techniques and expres-

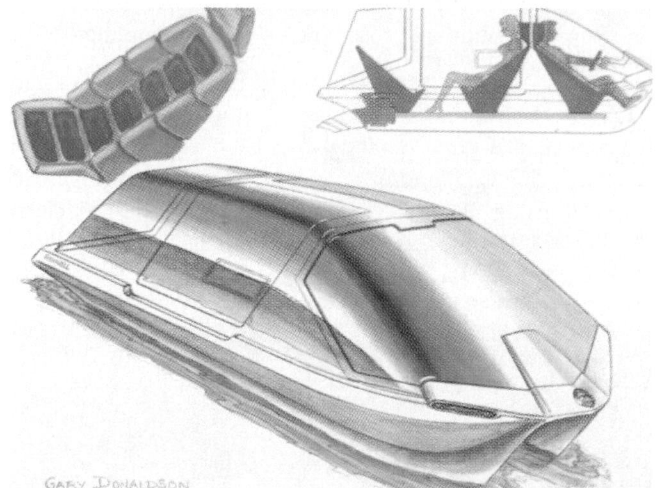

FIGURE 1.9 A Technical Illustration

FIGURE 1.10 A Technical Illustration of a Space Station

sions not used in technical drawings. First of all, whereas an artistic drawing is usually interpreted differently by everyone who sees it, a technical drawing must communicate the same message to every user or reader of the drawing. To limit the interpretation to only one possible conclusion, the technical drawing is controlled by accepted standards, drawing "conventions," and projection techniques.

Engineering drawings are used to transfer technical information. The drawing must contain all information required to bring the concept, product, or idea into reality. Dimensions, notes, views, and specifications are required for a complete drawing. Technical drawings must contain everything needed for proper interpretation of the design, because design and manufacturing may be located far apart—often in different countries.

1.6 TYPES OF TECHNICAL DRAWINGS

This text is concerned primarily with engineering drawings of mechanical parts—machined parts, castings, and weldments. Various types of drawings are associated with mechanical design and engineering. The following are considered standard types of drawings in industry.

Design sketches Sketches are initial design ideas, requirements, calculations, and concepts, and are used to convey the design parameters to the layout designer.

Layout drawings Layout drawings are made to develop the initial design. They must show all the information needed to make detail drawings or assembly drawings.

Assembly drawings Assembly drawings show a number of detail parts or subassemblies that are joined together to perform a specific function.

Detail drawings A detail drawing relays all the information needed to determine the final form of a part. It must show a complete and exact description of the part, including shapes, dimensions, tolerances, surface finish, and heat treatment, either specified or implied.

Casting drawings Casting drawings are usually not required, and the normal practice is to show the necessary casting dimension along with the machining dimensions on the detail drawing. When a separate casting drawing is used, it contains only information needed for casting, but no dimensions for machining or finishing.

Fabrication drawings Fabrication drawings are created for parts with permanently fixed pieces. The method of fastening is called out on the drawing with symbols or by other standard methods. Welded and riveted parts require fabrication drawings.

1.7 THE DESIGN PROCESS

The design process (Fig. 1.11) starts with a concept or an idea. The *first stage* of a project begins with the identification of a particular need for a product. Many times, the product is identified by a need in industry, government, the military, or the private sector.

The *second stage* involves the creation of a variety of options or design ideas. These ideas may be in the form of sketches, and include mathematical computations. The *third stage* is the refinement of the preliminary designs. Possible solutions to the problem are identified.

The *fourth stage* involves refinement and selection of a particular design. Here the project is put in a more formal, finalized state using assembly drawings and models. This stage requires close attention to how the part is to be manufactured and produced [**design for manufacturability (DFM)**].

In the *fifth stage,* detail drawings are prepared. The result is a complete set of working drawings. The *sixth stage* in the design process is the manufacturing and production of a product, or the construction of a system. In manufacturing, design and layout time is allocated for producing dies, tools, jigs, and fixtures.

During the design process, the engineers and designers

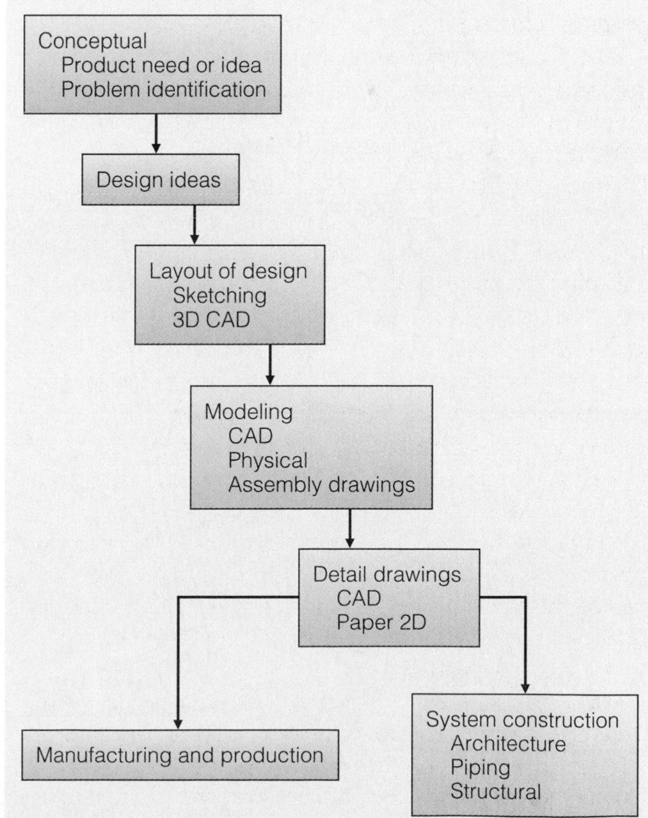

FIGURE 1.11 The Design Process

Focus On . . .

THE DESIGN PROCESS

Even as you read this text, new ideas to give you new sources of pleasure or new sources of frustration are being conceived. Engineers create systems, devices, and processes useful to and sought after by our society. The process by which these goals are achieved in engineering design is a planned sequence of events.

It has been said that "necessity is the mother of invention." Need is the motivating factor in most designs. When Levi Strauss first made what became known as blue jeans, they didn't have the rivets at the pockets. In 1872, Levi was contacted by a tailor from Reno, Nevada, who had started riveting the pants he made for his customers. The two men decided to patent this new innovation and in 1873 were awarded the first patent for pocket rivets.

The patent certificate for rivets on jeans.

Sometimes design is an accident. In 1878, a Procter & Gamble worker forgot to turn off the machine that stirred the soap. The soap that resulted had a lot of air bubbles and was so light it could float. He had just invented Ivory soap, by accident!

Curiosity sometimes drives design. The design of the microwave oven came about because Percy Spencer was curious about the amount of heat that was generated from magnetrons, the tubes used in radar during World War II. He could warm his hands by holding them close to the magnetrons. It was not until he found candy melted in his coat pocket that the idea of using the microwave to cook entered his mind. Many experiments later, the *high-frequency dielectric heating apparatus*—a microwave oven!—was invented. Spencer obtained a patent for it in 1953. Today, microwave ovens are an integral part of home, work, and school—all because Spencer was curious.

For years, we have dreamed about "smart homes." Imagine all the electrical appliances in your home connected so they electronically communicate with each other. As you return home, your house "senses" your arrival, opens the garage door, unlocks the house, turns on the lights, and turns on the television to your favorite program. As we approach the age when this is indeed possible, it is also easy to imagine the amount of information and technology that is needed to produce such a system.

If a design is to be a success and not a frustration, it must be simple and easy to operate, no matter how much information or technology is used. The designer must be able to transmit precise, clear instructions to the user. Much of our technology today makes devices simpler to use, but requires reams of documentation in the development stage. Information management and our ability to communicate will determine whether our future designs are a joy or a frustrating mess of words and wires.

The microwave was born out of curiosity.

encounter many situations where traditional visualization techniques and a mastery of the principles of projection are used in the solution of complex engineering and technical problems. The ability to analyze a specific problem, visualize its spatial considerations, and translate the problem into a viable graphic projection is essential for the engineer. Descriptive geometry is important to this process.

1.8 DESCRIPTIVE GEOMETRY

Descriptive geometry (see Part Six) uses orthographic projection to solve 3D problems with a 2D graphics procedure. Descriptive geometry applications establish the proper representation and relationships of geometric features. These views provide an accurate graphic method to establish information such as true shape and true length. Figure 1.12 shows a descriptive geometry solution to calculating the angle formed by two intersecting planes. The relationship of elements, such as the true distance between a line and a point or the angle between two planes, is a typical descriptive geometry problem.

Engineering graphics, technical drawing, and descriptive geometry share many of the same techniques and are not distinctly different, since each includes and encompasses the others. Two-dimensional mechanical drawing is actually elementary descriptive geometry. Constructions in descriptive geometry are done using orthographic projection techniques. Descriptive geometry has been part of most engineers' education for many years. Gaspard Monge developed the principles of descriptive geometry as a set of projection methods and techniques that are the basis for technical

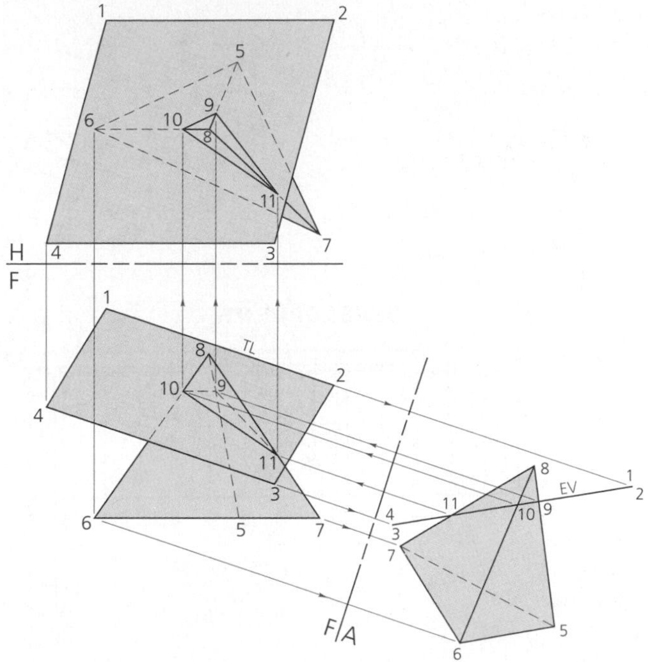

FIGURE 1.13 Intersection Problem

drawing education. A text on engineering graphics, therefore, is a book based on the principles of descriptive geometry.

The study of descriptive geometry includes intersections and developments. Intersections can be completed manually (Fig. 1.13) or on a CAD system using surface models (Fig. 1.14) or solid models. Developments are constructed manually (Fig. 1.15), or the process can be automated via advanced CAD systems. Intersections and developments are covered in detail in Chapters 27 and 28.

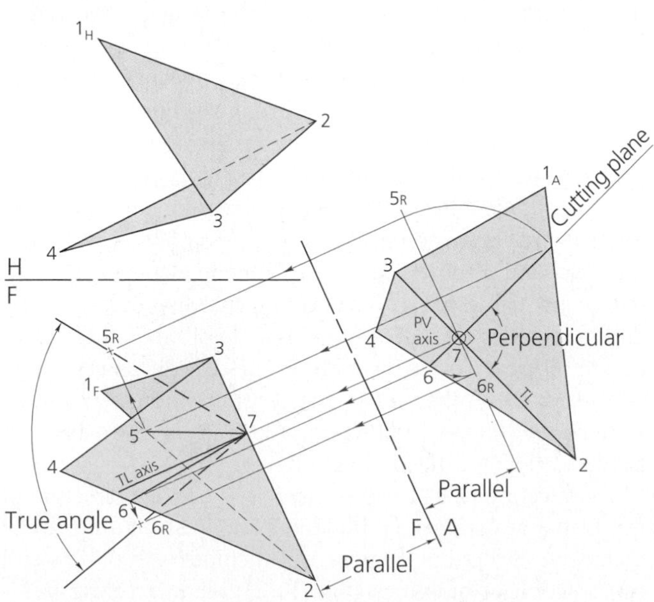

FIGURE 1.12 Descriptive Geometry Problem

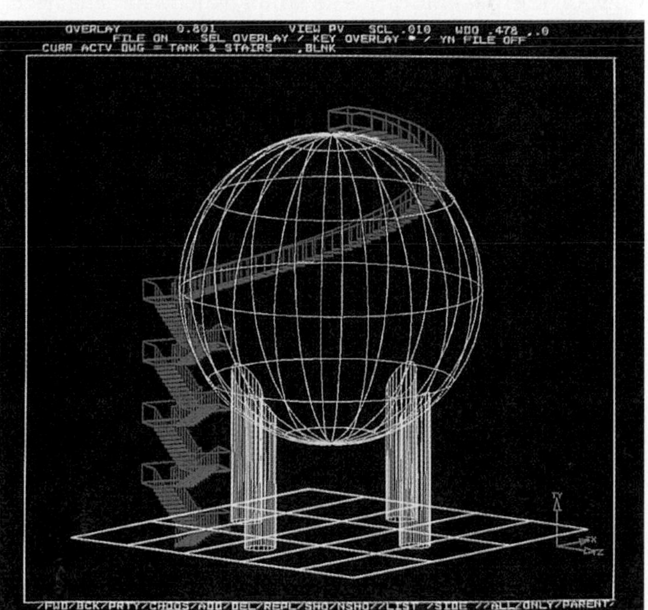

FIGURE 1.14 3D Design of a Holding Tank. Surface modeling was used to solve for the intersection of the four cylindrical legs and the spherical tank.

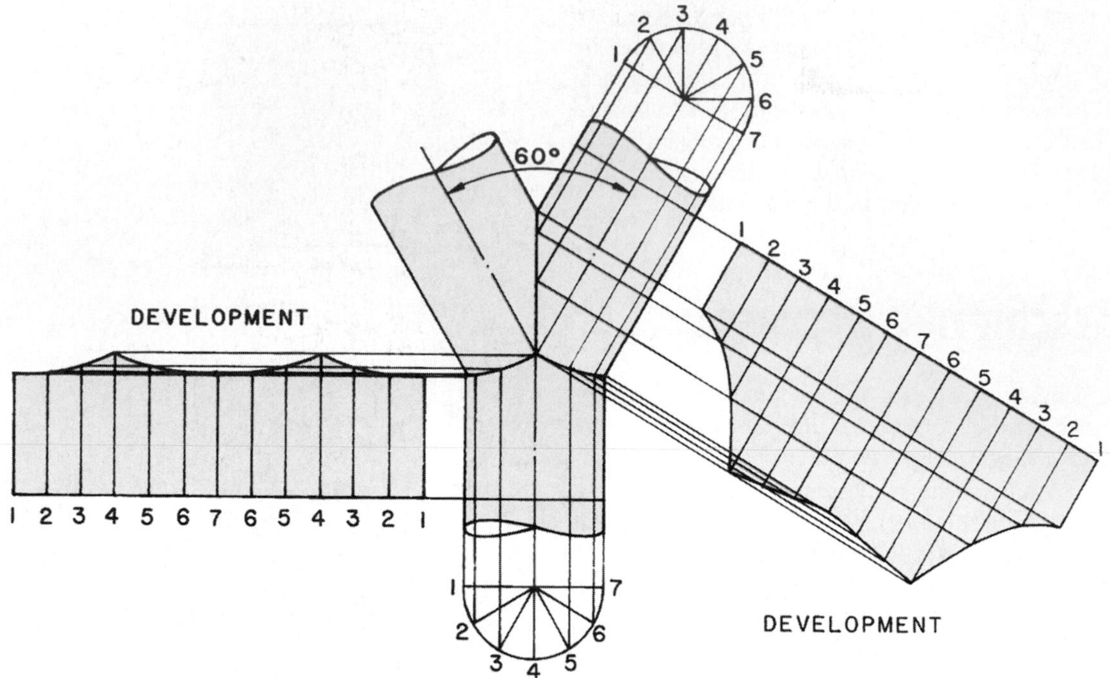

FIGURE 1.15 Development Problem

1.9 CAREER FIELDS IN INDUSTRY

Engineers and designers are employed in a variety of engineering fields: civil, electronic, chemical, ceramic, manufacturing, mechanical, nuclear, solar, petrochemical, mining, and metallurgical engineering. All of these fields employ designers and drafters to refine ideas and bring the design to completion. The following list provides an overview of the possible fields of employment for engineers, designers, and drafters:

Mechanical
Product design
Manufacturing design: jigs and fixtures, dies, assemblies, and details

Electronic-Electrical
Circuits, printed circuit boards
Integrated circuits
Electrical, electromechanical
Computers

Applications for Electronic and Mechanical Design
Marine
Aerospace
Transportation
Mining

Architectural, Engineering, and Construction (AE&C)
Civil: facilities, dams, airports, roads, mapping
Structural: buildings, plants, power generation
Piping: solar, nuclear, chemical, process, power, hydroelectric
Architecture: Commercial, residential, landscape

Technical Illustration
Product literature: advertising, sales, presentation, service manuals, display

In mechanical engineering, designers and engineers make assembly drawings of jigs, fixtures, dies, and other types of manufacturing aids to create and produce machine parts and new mechanical designs (Fig. 1.16). This is one of the largest employment areas for an engineer or a designer. The mechanical engineer is concerned with the conceptual development and the engineering calculations (designs) involved in creating and developing mechanical devices, including items to be used in machinery, automobiles, mechanical equipment (Fig. 1.17), and aerospace products (Fig. 1.18).

Architectural engineering and construction is comprised primarily of civil engineering, structural design, piping design, and architecture. Civil engineering and mapping employ engineers and designers to develop highways, roads, railways, and airports. Sewage treatment plants, water systems, and dams are all created by civil engineers. Piping design includes such diverse fields as fossil fuel power plant design, nuclear power plants (Fig. 1.19), solar power, and a wide range of other areas that require industrial piping systems used in the production of chemicals, petrochemical products (Fig. 1.20), food, and beverages.

Architecture (Fig. 1.21) is the design and construction of residential or commercial buildings (larger structures can be included). Structural engineering includes the design and construction of buildings (Fig. 1.22), manufacturing facilities, airport terminals, and power plants, to name a few.

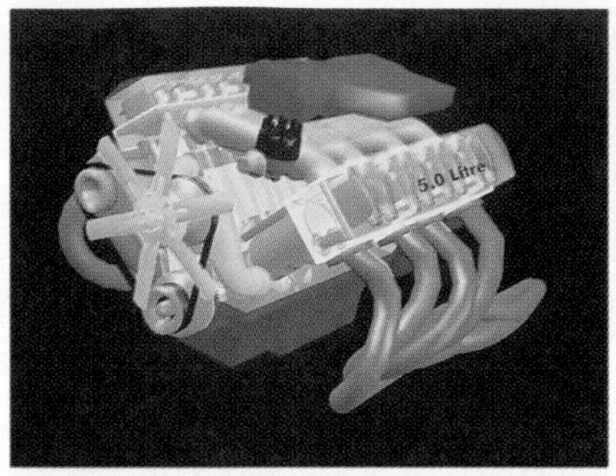

FIGURE 1.16 3D Mechanical Design

FIGURE 1.17 Earthmover Tractor

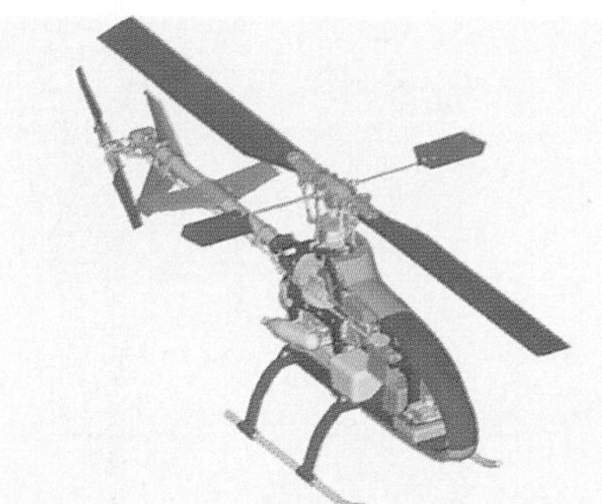
FIGURE 1.18 3D Model of an Experimental Helicopter

FIGURE 1.19 Diablo Canyon Nuclear Power Plant

FIGURE 1.20 Petrochemical Facility

FIGURE 1.21 Architectural Design

FIGURE 1.22 Construction of a Corporate Office Facility

FIGURE 1.23 Power Transmission Lines

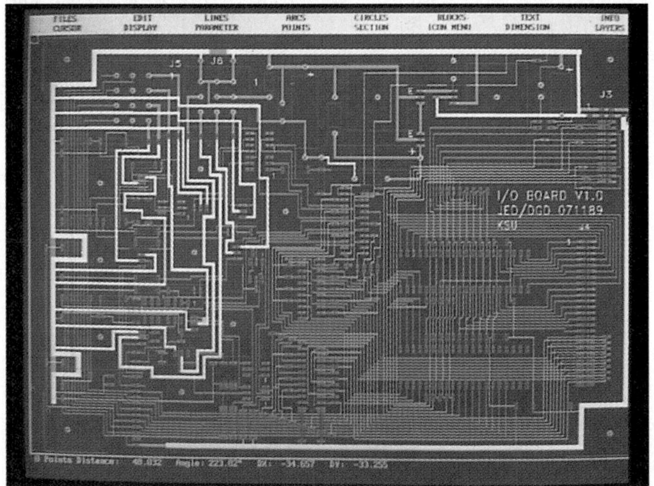

FIGURE 1.24 Printed Circuit Board Design

Electronic and electrical engineering includes the layout of power systems for generation, transmission (Fig. 1.23), and utilization of electrical energy, circuits and the design of printed circuit boards (Fig. 1.24), integrated circuits (Fig. 1.25), and computer products. Electrical engineering concentrates on power generation and the utilization of electrical energy. Electronic engineering, on the other hand, covers smaller devices, consumer electronics, circuit design, embedded microprocessors, integrated circuit design, and computer applications.

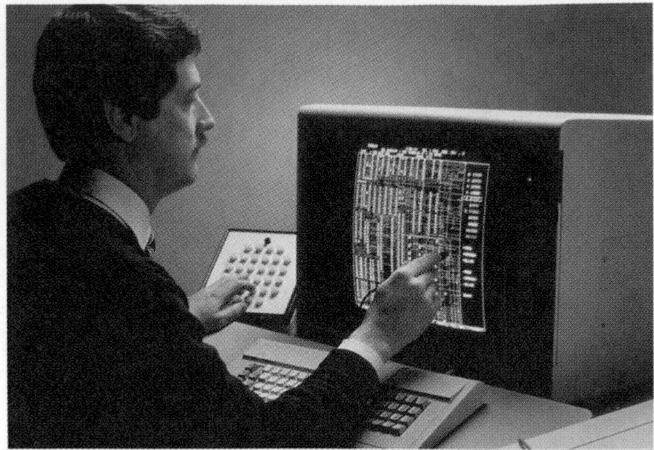

FIGURE 1.25 Integrated Circuit Design

FIGURE 1.26 Technical Illustration

Mining engineering, aerospace engineering, and transportation engineering all use combinations of mechanical, electronic, and electrical designs.

Technical illustration (Fig. 1.26) is an area where the artistic and mechanical aspects of drafting and design merge. Technical illustrations are pictorial drawings, needed for manuals, of products, buildings, or other items.

This text is concerned primarily with mechanical design. Mechanical design and engineering are important because they involve the production of devices and designs for a variety of applications. Marine engineering includes the design and manufacture of marine vessels (Figs. 1.27 and 1.28). Aerospace engineering includes the design of engines and other mechanical devices. Transportation engineering includes the design of automobiles, trucks, buses, and trains, and their individual components, and requires extensive mechanical design (Fig. 1.29).

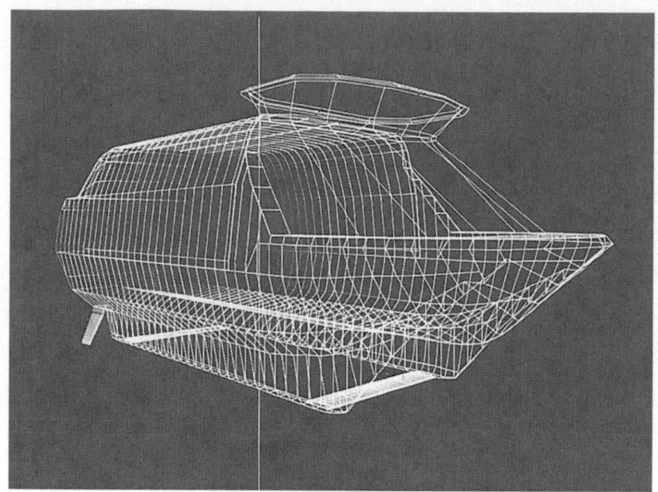

FIGURE 1.27 Marine Vessel Design

(a) Wheel

FIGURE 1.28 Physical Model of a Marine Vessel

(b) 3D design of a wheel using CAD

FIGURE 1.29 3D Computer-Aided Design

1.10 COMPUTERS AND ENGINEERING DRAWING

Computer-integrated manufacturing (CIM) is the integration of all phases of production, from design to manufacturing, using the computer. Computers have changed the way engineers do engineering and has profoundly altered the factory floor (Fig. 1.30). **Computer-aided engineering (CAE), computer-aided manufacturing (CAM),** and CAD are collectively called **computer-integrated manufacturing (CIM).** The term **CAD/CAM** refers to the use of computers to integrate the design and production process to improve productivity. CAM includes: **numerical control (NC), computer numerical control (CNC)** (Fig. 1.31), and **direct numerical control (DNC)** machining and the use of **robotics** in manufacturing.

FIGURE 1.30 Computer Control on the Factory Floor

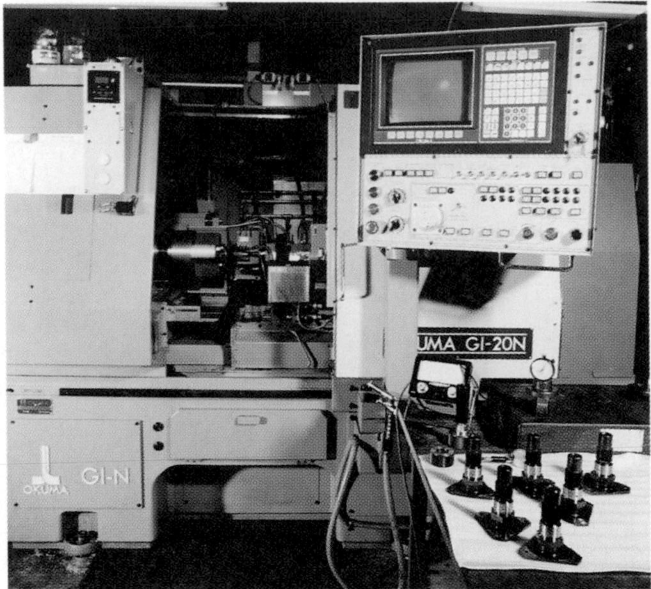

FIGURE 1.31 CNC Machining

FIGURE 1.32 Personal Computer CAD System

The use and integration of computers in all phases of the design-through-manufacturing process and their significance to the new concurrent engineering environment are extremely important to the future of engineering and industrial design. Descriptive geometry, projection techniques, drafting conventions, and dimensioning standards apply to drawings and models completed manually and with the computer. Orthographic projections will still be used on the production floor, regardless of how the part was designed initially. Solid models will continue to aid in the visualization process in the entire design-through-manufacturing process.

1.11 COMPUTER-AIDED DESIGN

CAD involves any type of design activity that uses the computer to develop, analyze, modify, or enhance an engineering design. CAD systems are based on interactive computer graphics. The engineer creates an image on the monitor by entering commands at the computer (Fig. 1.32) and by interacting with the computer program. In many systems, the image is formed from basic geometries/entities/primitives—points, lines, circles, arcs, splines, cylinders, boxes, prismatic solids, torroids, etc. The entities can be easily modified—enlarged or reduced in size, moved to another location, rotated, mirrored, copied, etc. By using different manipulations, the required details of the graphic image are created.

CAD *design* refers to the establishment and definition of the 3D database; CAD *drafting* involves primarily defining, refining, and manipulating the *same* database to provide certain kinds of information. CAM and CIM apply and utilize the same database as was initially created. This concept is at the heart of concurrent engineering. Concurrent engineering is sometimes called *simultaneous* engineering because manufacturing and design are considered simultaneously.

As an engineer or a designer using a CAD system, you must be able to understand the system's *hardware* configuration and its *software* capabilities. CAD/CAM systems are designed to be operated as purchased, and programming ability is not required. However, you can program them to customize them for your particular needs. In any case, you must be familiar with the following:

1. Drafting standards
2. Engineering-discipline-specific conventions
3. Particular industrial applications: mechanical, piping, electrical, electronics, electromechanical, civil, structural, or architectural
4. Software characteristics of your CAD system

It must be stressed that CAD is an engineering and design *tool.* The method of creating engineering graphics has changed, not the content. Regardless of the type of system, the most common form of output remains the "drawing."

1.12 STANDARDS

Many agencies control the standards used in engineering and design. **American National Standards Institute (ANSI)**, the **Department of Defense (DOD)** standards, and the **military standards (MIL)** are the three most used standards in the United States. The **International Standards Organization (ISO)** standards and **Japanese standards (JIS)** are also used in many companies.

ANSI standards are available to engineers and designers at their place of employment. It is important to become familiar with these standards. ANSI-Y14 contains information on drafting practices, dimensioning, projection, descriptive geometry, geometric tolerancing, and a wide variety of other areas associated with engineering and design.

Standards are used because drawings are a standard form of communication between individuals, departments, companies, and countries. They communicate design requirements. If standards are followed, each drawing will mean the same thing to everyone who reads and uses it. The real purpose of a drawing is eventually to get the part made correctly. A drawing that no one understands is worthless.

Some companies have not adopted ANSI standards, are using older standards, or have not updated all of their older drawings to the newer standards. Always be aware of this when reviewing drawings. This text uses ANSI standards as a basis for its drawings, conventions, practices, and instructional methodology. All projects completed from the book are to be drawn using the latest revisions of ANSI standards, conventions, and drawing practices.

1.13 STANDARDS OF MEASUREMENT

The United States is the only major industrial country in the world still using feet, inches, and decimal equivalents. However, many large companies, such as Ford, IBM, John Deere, General Motors, Honeywell, and most electronic, medical instrument, and computer manufacturers, have converted completely to the metric system that is called **Système Internationale (SI).** The English system units are now called **U.S. customary units.**

Because you may encounter both measurement systems on the job, this text uses a balanced approach and applies both systems. Piping, architecture, and structural engineering use units of feet, inches, and fractions, in most cases. The standard of measurement for metric drawings is the millimeter. The U.S. decimal-inch unit is used on many of the illustrations and on many of the exercises and problems at the end of the chapters. In some cases, your instructor may wish you to convert the units of measurement from one system to another.

1.14 ORGANIZATION OF THE TEXT

This text is organized into six parts. Part One covers the basics of engineering and design: introduction to engineering graphics (Chapter 1), design engineering (Chapter 2), the design process (Chapter 3), computers in engineering design and manufacturing (Chapter 4), and parametric design (Chapter 5).

Part Two covers basic graphical materials and procedures: equipment, materials, and techniques for engineering graphics (Chapter 6), lettering and annotation (Chapter 7), geometric constructions (Chapter 8), and sketching (Chapter 9).

Part Three covers drawing basics: multiview drawing (Chapter 10), sections (Chapter 11), auxiliary views (Chapter 12), and pictorials (Chapter 13).

Part Four covers processes and documentation: manufacturing processes (Chapter 14), dimensioning (Chapter 15), and geometric dimensioning and tolerancing (Chapter 16).

Part Five covers mechanical parts, procedures, and layout: threads and fasteners (Chapter 17), springs (Chapter 18), gears, shafts, and bearings (Chapter 19), cams (Chapter 20), fluid power (Chapter 21), welding drawings (Chapter 22), and working drawings (Chapter 23).

Part Six covers engineering graphical analysis: points and lines (Chapter 24), planes (Chapter 25), revolutions (Chapter 26), intersections (Chapter 27), developments (Chapter 28), vector analysis (Chapter 29), and design projects (Chapter 30).

The main body of the text is followed by four appendixes. In Appendix A you will find three glossaries: mechanical, CAD/CAM, and parametric design. Appendix B contains abbreviations, standards, and general abbreviations. Appendix C presents catalog parts and reference material: threads, twist drills, bolts, screws, nuts, washers, rivets and retaining rings, pins, bushings, Woodruff keys, sheet metal gages, structural shapes and sizes, fits, and tolerances. Consult the appendixes when working on projects from the text.

Each chapter in the text has the same sequence. They start with an introduction and continue with an explanation of the material to be covered. Chapter objectives introduce the chapter.

At the end of each chapter is a quiz composed of "True or False," "Fill in the Blanks," and "Answer the Following" questions. In Chapters 6–29, the quiz is followed by exercises and problems. The exercises are designed to be completed at specific intervals. You will be prompted at certain places within each chapter to complete the corresponding exercises, which test your knowledge of the material just covered. All exercises are presented on a grid format using .25 in. units, and can be transferred directly without the use of dimensions to an $8\frac{1}{2} \times 11$ in. "A"-size grid-lined sheet of paper. If metrics are preferred, use metric grid paper with appropriate divisions. The problems can be assigned in many different ways—as sketches, ink drawings, manual drawings, or CAD projects. Unlike the exercises, which are confined to an $8\frac{1}{2} \times 11$ in. "A"-size format, the size of paper depends on the project requirements.

QUIZ

True or False

1. CAD systems and drafting boards may be in mixed use in engineering offices and firms.
2. Engineering or technical drawings were used to communicate technical ideas only in the twentieth century.
3. Artistic drawings are used extensively to communicate ideas in engineering.
4. CIM doesn't really involve computers in design or on the manufacturing floor.
5. Descriptive geometry and engineering graphics are totally separate fields.
6. CAD systems are based on interactive computer graphics.
7. An extensive knowledge of computer programming is needed to use CAD effectively.
8. There are literally millions of jobs in manufacturing and engineering that depend on engineering graphics in some way.

Fill in the Blanks

9. __________ __________ is the term used to describe the use of graphical communication in the design process.
10. The two main types of drawings are: __________ and __________.
11. __________ __________ use artistic methods and pictorial techniques to represent a part or system for use by nontechnical personnel.
12. __________ __________ __________ is the integration of all phases of production, from design to manufacturing, using the computer.
13. Technical __________ is the use of freehand graphics to create drawings.
14. __________ involves any type of design activity that uses the computer to develop, analyze, modify, or enhance an engineering design.
15. __________, __________, and __________ are three different agencies that control the standards for engineering drawing in the United States.
16. __________ __________ is completed on a drafting board using paper, pencil, and drawing instruments.

Answer the Following

17. Describe why CAE, CAD, CAM, and CAD/CAM are collectively called CIM.
18. Describe at least two different engineering disciplines and the types of job they entail.
19. Explain how technical illustration differs from engineering drawing.
20. Explain why standards are important in engineering graphics.
21. Explain and describe the basic concepts involved in the design process.
22. What types of problems are solved by the use of descriptive geometry techniques?
23. What is the difference between a casting drawing and a fabrication drawing?
24. How has the computer changed engineering and engineering graphics?

DESIGN ENGINEERING

Chapter 2

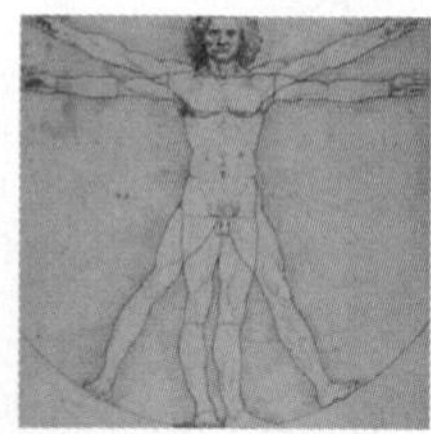

LEARNING OBJECTIVES

Upon completion of this chapter you will be able to:

1. Understand the basics of both product engineering and manufacturing engineering.
2. Understand the role of the design engineer in the design process.
3. Develop an understanding of the fundamentals of system design.
4. Understand product design parameters.
5. Understand the factors involved in product design optimization.
6. Understand the fundamentals of product design considerations.
7. Develop a working knowledge of the design tree.

2.1 INTRODUCTION

Engineering design encompasses both **product engineering** and **manufacturing engineering.** Product and manufacturing engineering include a wide range of activities, from the creative description of the item to its production. To design and produce a product efficiently, the **manufacturability** of the part must be built into the design from the beginning. In **design for manufacturability (DFM),** the manufacturability of an item is considered from the very beginning of the project. (DFM is covered in more detail in Chapter 3.) Quality of the product must be built into the part, not inspected out during the production process. Service of the part should be easy, effective, and efficient. The materials used during the production of the part should be recyclable and remanufacturable. Product engineering and the manufacturing engineering of a successful project integrates many activities:

Product Engineering

Product description
Specifications
Models
- Test
- Prototype
- Fit and function
- Presentation

Analysis
- Stress/strain
- Fatigue/corrosion
- Movement/kinematics
- Load—forces/dynamics
- Heat—energy/thermodynamics

Layout and detail drawings
Redesign

Manufacturing Engineering

Production method
Costs
Quantity
Tooling
- Dies
- Tools
- Jigs and fixtures
- Inspection gages

Robot workcells
Material management and movement
Ordering
Production planning
Manpower requirements
Testing
Inspection
Quality control
Distribution
- Packaging
- Shipping
- Storing/stacking

Facility management

(a) Bicycle design

(b) Rear wheel of bicycle

FIGURE 2.1 Bicycle

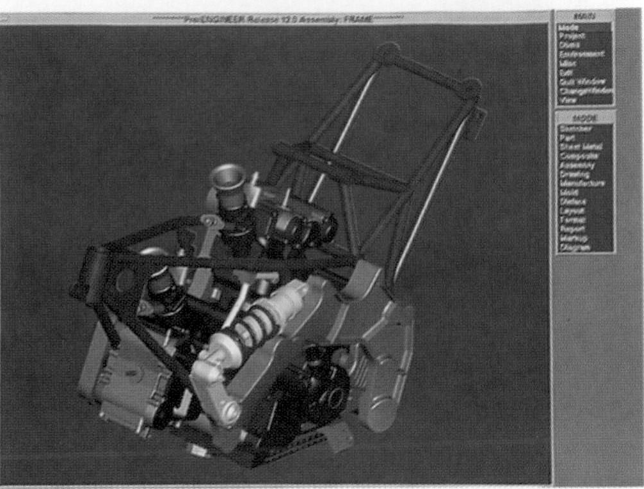

FIGURE 2.2 Motorcycle Engine

The end result of the design activity is the most useful and economic product or system. To achieve success, the engineer/designer must consider multiple factors and make decisions based on compromises. Seldom is a design everything the engineer wanted when the project began. A successful design is one that is functional and manufacturable and that serves the needs of the customer. The product must also come to market at the appropriate time. A product too late to market is usually a failure. As competition increases worldwide, time to market becomes critical.

Designs are functional when they satisfy a need and are available to the customer (Fig. 2.1) in some form or quantity that is cost effective to produce and use and is profitable for the company. Before a design is accepted, such as that of a motorcycle engine (Fig. 2.2), it must be tested and researched thoroughly. After the development and testing of a product or mechanical design, the design data are released to the factory for production.

2.2 THE DESIGN ENGINEER AND DESIGNING

Designers use their education and experience to invent new products, create new systems, or take existing products or systems and add innovations. The design process involves creativity and the ability to discover new solutions to existing problems or to invent new products to fill a need. Being a designer has less to do with natural talent than with cultivating an eye for detail, accumulating knowledge from education, and gathering experience from designing.

Designing is an intellectual activity that has no hard-and-fast rules. Most good designers develop their expertise through experience. The best designers keep their minds open to new concepts and learn from co-workers, journals, magazines, and past failures. They are well informed; they choose the best features from several approaches for their designs. When they approach a new problem, they study existing, related designs to try and understand the rationale behind their creation.

Since the item being designed or invented often does not exist before the process starts, product design (Fig. 2.3) demands more creativity. Product design involves the creation of commercially profitable, useful, or desirable items and devices. Mechanical design includes a wide range of industrial products (Fig. 2.4) and tools used in manufacturing (jigs and fixtures, dies, molds). The systems designer is a problem solver and innovator. He or she combines existing standard parts in a unique functional manner, to satisfy a need or industrial requirement.

During the design process, the designer uses many different types of documents and consults a variety of

(a) Mouseman—right-hand and left-hand designs

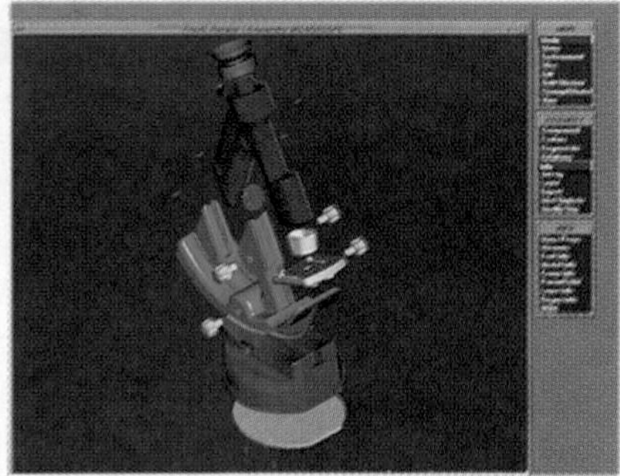

(b) Microscope

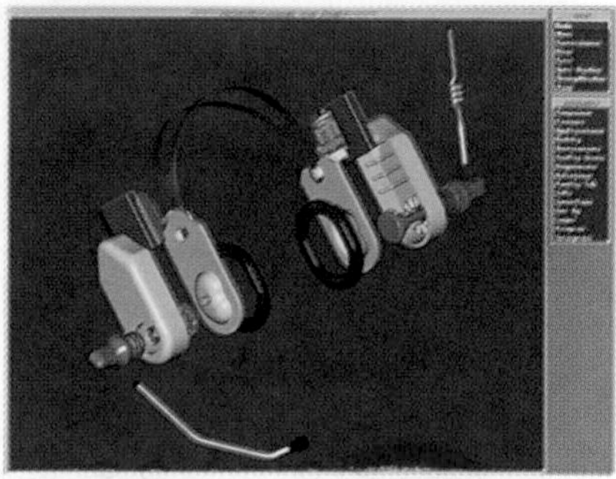

(c) Headset

FIGURE 2.3 **Product Design**

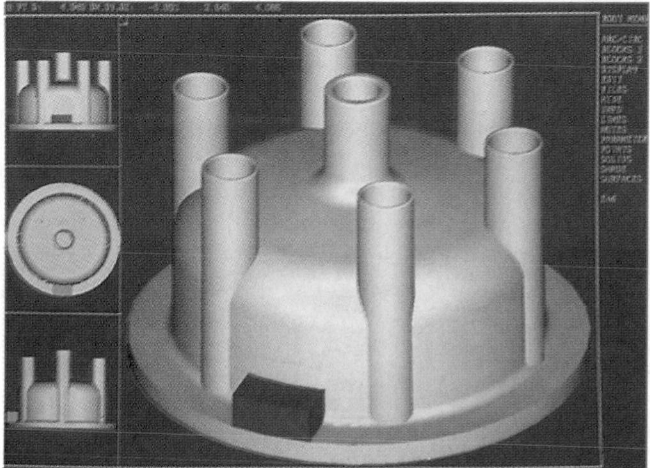

FIGURE 2.4 **Design of a Distributor Cap**

specialists (Fig. 2.5). Customers communicate their needs through the contract and program office, which in turn releases the job to the engineering team. During the design process the engineer has many responsibilities, including:

- Geometric arrangement of the components or design configuration
- Effects of motion, forces, shear, and environment
- Human capabilities, limitations, and requirements (human factors)
- Manufacturing and production processes
- Material selection

To understand a design situation (Fig. 2.6) and bring the problem to a successful conclusion, the engineer needs basic creative instincts, an inquisitive mind, and the ability to communicate verbally (in written form) and graphically. Successful design engineer traits include the following:

- Intuition
- Good communication skills—written, oral, graphic
- Open mind to problem-solving
- Inquisitive mind
- Understanding of fundamental design principles

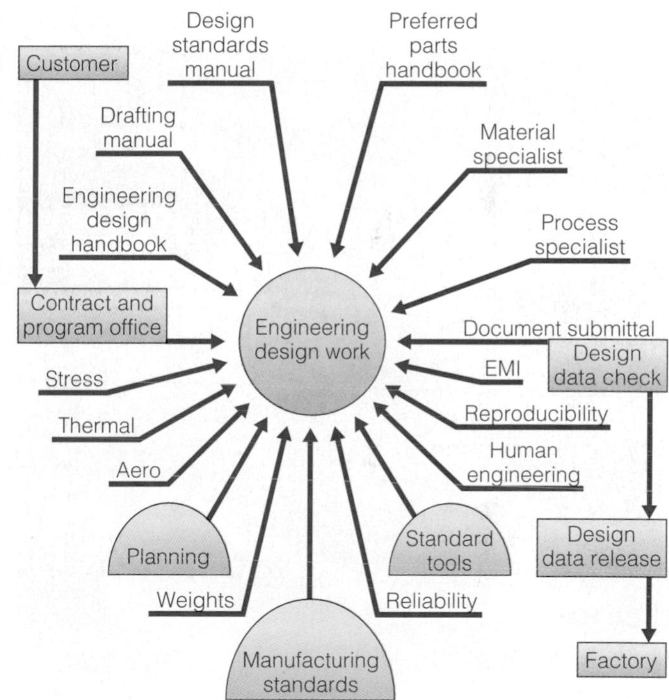

FIGURE 2.5 **Engineering Design Flow Diagram**

- Ability to integrate and balance several ideas and solutions
- Ability to do self-evaluation
- Concentration skills
- Visualization skills
- Ability to think and communicate in 3D
- Mathematical skills

Cultivating successful designer traits can be done by 2D sketching, 3D visualization techniques, and the scrutiny of existing mechanical items and products. Developing creative mental skills, encouraging an investigative mind, practicing

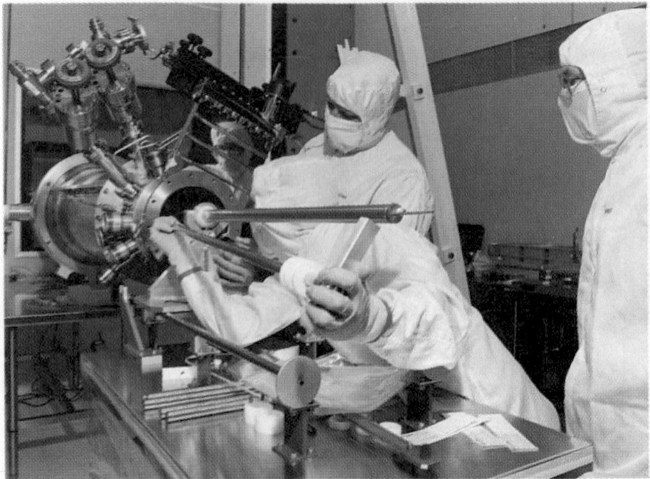

FIGURE 2.6 Electronics Alignment Assembly in a Clean Room

FIGURE 2.7 Space Station Illustration—Structure and Solar Panels

written and oral descriptions of designs, and specific organizational skills are also essential.

The space program (Fig. 2.7) is an excellent example of where engineers had to create new designs for exploration in entirely unique environments. Space exploration required engineers who were not captive to preconceived notions or a limited vision, or who were afraid to push the frontiers of knowledge.

2.3 SYSTEMS DESIGN

Systems design and engineering involve a variety of engineering disciplines that use standard parts in an assembled configuration to accomplish a task. Systems design revolves around the use of standardized parts that can be assembled in unique ways to solve particular problems or meet specialized needs. Each system is a combination of parts designed to fit into a specialized environment. Many systems are themselves combinations of systems. A building, for example, is not just a structural and architectural system; the typical building has a structural system to support it, a plumbing and piping system to provide water and remove waste, a gas system for heating, an electronics system for communications and security, an electrical system for power and lighting, a heating distribution system, a mechanical system for moving people and materials, and a ventilation and air conditioning system for controlling the temperature and air filtration of the structure. The larger the building, the more complex the systems.

Power generation systems, construction/structural systems, mass transportation systems (public and military), and electronic systems, including computers, are all system designs. The nuclear plant in Figure 2.8 is an example of a combination of structural, mechanical, and electronic sys-

FIGURE 2.8 Nuclear Plant Containment Area

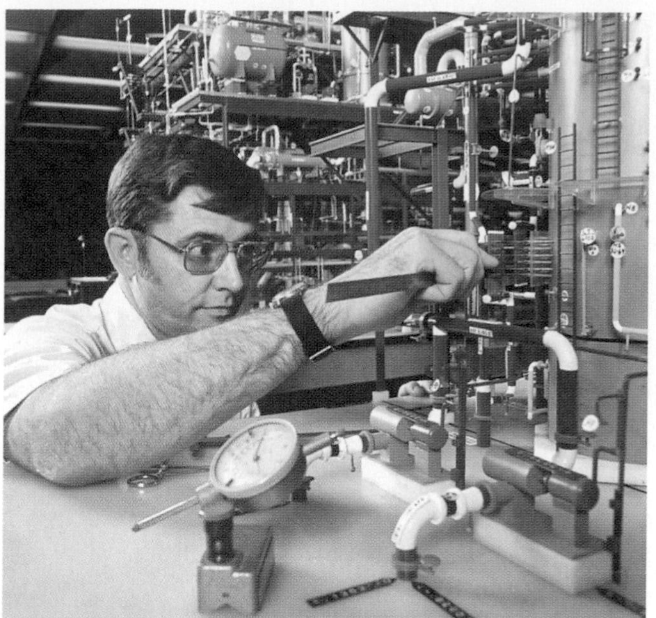

FIGURE 2.9 Petrochemical Plant Model

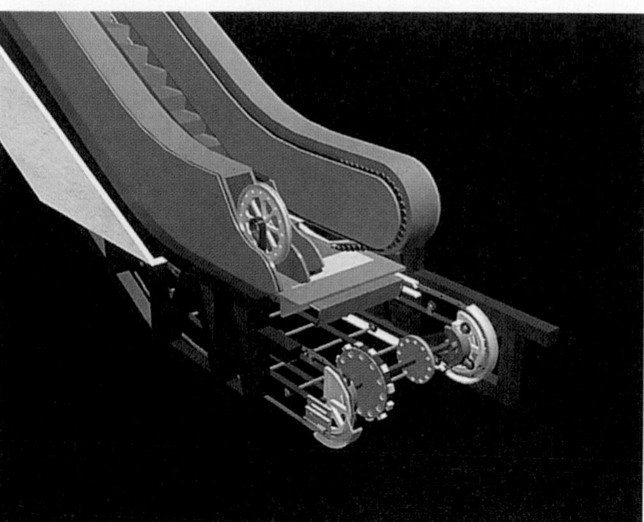

FIGURE 2.11 Escalator Design

tems. The petrochemical plant model shown in Figure 2.9 is an example of a system for producing consumable energy products. A refinery is composed of electrical, heating and ventilation, structural, mechanical, electronic, instrumentation, and piping systems—all integrated into a complex facility.

2.4 PRODUCT AND INDUSTRIAL DESIGN

Product design is accomplished by an industrial designer working in conjunction with the engineering, manufacturing, and marketing departments to develop and create a useful and profitable product. Products are mass-produced for consumer, educational, or industrial markets. Figure 2.10 shows an example of an industrial product whose function is far more important than its visual appeal: the oscilloscope, which is sold to industry, military, and educational markets. The escalator shown in Figure 2.11 is an example of a solid model design for the commercial market. The gas generator in Figure 2.12 is the kind of product that has both individual consumer and industrial markets. Since its design is functional and mechanical in nature, we could say that it is more of an industrial product. The pointing device used for computer input [Fig. 2.3(a)] is an example of a consumer product.

FIGURE 2.10 Oscilloscope

FIGURE 2.12 10 kW Gas Generator Mockup

2.5 PRODUCT DESIGN PARAMETERS

All design decisions must be made after careful consideration of the factors (design parameters) influencing the product. Product design parameters (Fig. 2.13) determine manufacturing and production methods and include the following:

- Weight
- Texture
- Material
- Color
- Symmetry
- Repetition
- Size
- Balance

Each design parameter affects the other parameters. For instance, the weight of the product is influenced by its material and size; the color will be influenced by the material; the material influences the texture or surface quality. Since the texture of a product may in some cases be more important than other factors, the surface feel or texture requirements, in return, affect the material choice. The weight and size of a product affect its ease of use.

The shape of a product should be considered with regard to its symmetry, proportion, repetition, and balance. Geometric proportions that are pleasing to the eye and appear balanced can give a repetitive shape to the part. Automotive design is a good illustration of this point. As shown in Figure 2.14, curves, lines, and contours all influence the balance and symmetry of a product. Remember, the best-selling product is not always the best product. An extremely reliable, completely functional, long-lasting product will not necessarily sell if it is also poorly proportioned and unappealing in color and shape. All of the listed factors are interdependent. A good designer determines the proper mix, based on their relative importance to the project.

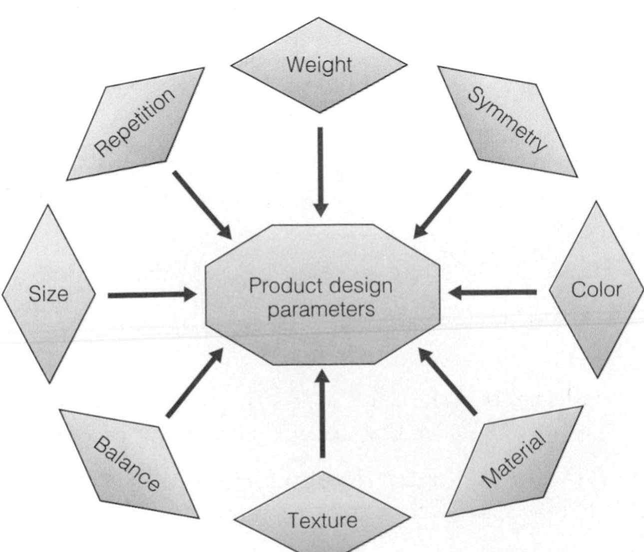

FIGURE 2.13 Product Design Parameters

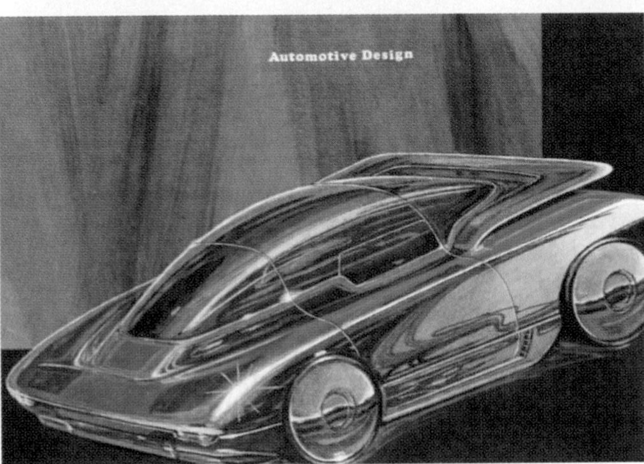

FIGURE 2.14 Two Examples of Geometric Proportion in Automotive Design

The forceps in Figure 2.15 are an example of a small product. Though normally considered a medical instrument, this clamping device can be found in industrial workplaces and in the home. This product must be strong, lightweight, balanced, corrosion resistant, and come in a variety of sizes and shapes. Since the main surgical requirement is that it be sterilizable, its color is not important. The material itself dictates most of its characteristics. Stainless steel satisfies the design requirements.

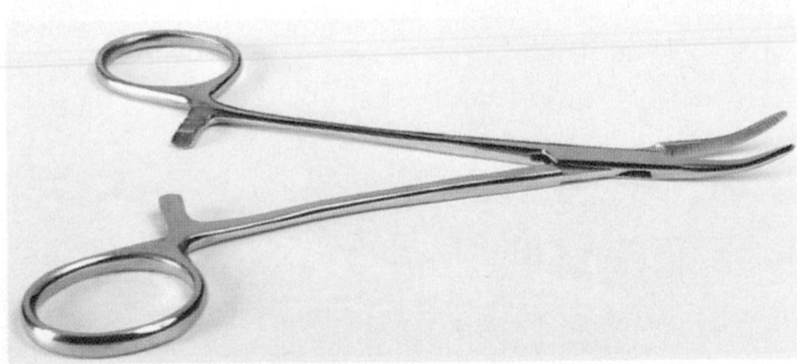

FIGURE 2.15 Forceps

2.6 DESIGN CONSIDERATIONS

Design considerations require proper and timely decisions by engineers. A careful and systematic overview of a product's design considerations will lead to a successful final product.

The calipers in Figure 2.16 are an example of a product that was designed for a very specific function. Calipers are used by designers, engineers, machinists, and others involved in the manufacturing process. Calipers must be accurate, lightweight, sturdy, simple to use, easy to handle, unbreakable within limits, have an extremely long life, and not be affected by the environment. Inaccurate, corrodible, or breakable calipers would not sell. Obviously, the function of this product is the foremost concern—it must measure something accurately. This functional consideration determines the material choice; nonmetals would be inappropriate, since they would not allow for the accuracy required of the finished product. Appearance is not a major consideration. The requirement for corrosion resistance limits the material choices, as will the strength considerations.

Design considerations include the following:

- **Function**
- **Constraints**
- **Materials**
- **Appearance**
- **Environmental effect on product and product on environment**
- **Product life**
- **Reliability**
- **Safety requirements**
- **Standardization and interchangeability of components**
- **Maintenance and service requirements**
- **Costs**

Function. The actual functions of a product must be defined early in the design process. Unnecessary functions or extra features (sometimes called "bells and whistles") should be eliminated if they do not substantially increase the value or salability of the product. The designer must determine whether the product could serve more than the original function described by the customer. Could the product be less complicated? Could it serve more than one purpose?

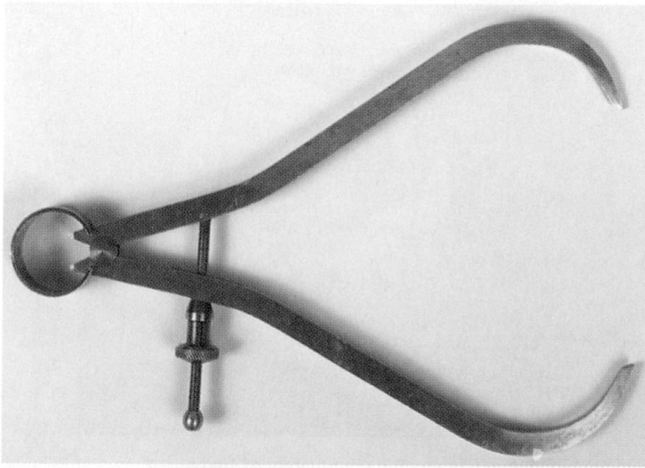

FIGURE 2.16 Calipers

The function of a product will always be its primary consideration. If the product does not function properly, then it is not marketable. The function of a product will be influenced by its complexity. A basic rule is to minimize the *complexity of a design*. The simpler a product, the easier and cheaper it is to manufacture. Strength requirements will be influenced by the product's function. Reducing rotational stress, bending, and other complex movements is the goal. The designer considers these factors when designing for strength. Interference between moving parts is also an aspect of function. The function of a product determines the movements and how many individual parts are required. *Attempt to minimize the number of parts in a design.*

Constraints. *Design for simplicity* within the constraints. What are the **constraints** of the project? Are the size, weight, and volume of the product adequate? Could they be reduced to create a better design? The projected cost of the product is also a constraint. A "widget" that performs 24 different functions but costs five times more than the consumer will pay is not a well-designed product. Size, weight, and volume will be influenced by handling, shipping, and marketing considerations.

The size of a product will also be influenced by who uses the item. A child's hand is smaller than an adult's, and, in most cases, a woman's hand will be smaller than a man's. If the item is gender-determined (used by only one sex), then marketing research defines many of the constraints.

Materials. The **material** used for the design is determined by a multitude of factors. In fact, much of the success of a design might be determined by the material choice. The following is a partial list of material properties that are considered during the design process:

Strength A measure of a material's capacity to resist different types of forces.

Elasticity The stiffness of a material and its capacity to resist deflection under load; stress is related to strain by the **elastic constant.**

Ductility The ability of a metal to deform before fracturing.

Fatigue When a material fails after many repeated load cycles.

Bearing characteristics The suitability of a material to be used as an element resting on another part and in motion.

Hardness and brittleness The opposite of ductility; a characteristic of a material to resist penetration.

Damping The ability of a material to dissipate energy caused by vibration.

Temperature range The effective range within which the material properties will be suitable.

Toughness The ability of a material to absorb energy before fracturing.

Resilience or elasticity The ability of a material to store energy when deforming permanently.

Wearing The ability of a material to withstand rubbing motion (frictional loads), causing removal of material.

Corrosion The ability of a material to resist deterioration caused by a reaction to environmental conditions.

Toxicity The possibility of producing a poisonous effect; material safety data sheets (MSDS) are now required documentation for products.

Machinability The relative ability of a material to be machined.

Forgeability The ability of a material to be forged.

Formability The ability of a material to be formed.

Castability The ability of a material to be cast.

Weldability The ease with which a material can be welded.

Many times, the function of the item determines the material; in other cases, there is more leeway in the material choice. The material that best suits the design and manufacturing requirements is sometimes a compromise. **Availability** is also a factor in material selection. An exotic material may be the best choice; but if it is hard to procure, another material may be better for adequate production runs.

Appearance. Appearance is one of the most important considerations in consumer product design and usually the least important for industrial product design. The look, feel, shape (symmetry, modernness, roundness, smoothness), and eye appeal of a product have to be considered early in the design phase. Sometimes, for the successful marketing of a product, the function and other characteristics will be less important than the appearance.

Environment. The effect of the product on the environment is now more important than at any other time in history. Industrial history is full of examples of how profit took precedence over protection of the environment. In most places, an environmental impact report is mandatory for large systems design.

The effects of the environment on the product are also a concern for the designer, as with the tractor in Figure 2.17. The effects of temperature variations during operation must be considered in the design phase of a product. Dust and dirt must be excluded from many products to ensure proper operation. Vibration also affects the operation and life of a product and, therefore, must be limited by dampening devices and other methods. The moisture level in an operating environment will be a concern for many products; excess moisture can cause corrosion. Designing any product starts with an understanding of when, how, by whom, and where the product is to be used.

FIGURE 2.17 Case Tractor

The oscilloscope (Fig. 2.10) was designed to be carried. The electronics inside must be shielded properly by the packaging. Heat must be allowed to escape from the package. Therefore, vents are provided in the sheet metal on the sides of the package. The ruggedness of the product will obviously influence its reliability, life, and what effects the environment has on its operation.

The space shuttle was designed to withstand heat that reaches thousands of degrees while it leaves and reenters the atmosphere. The shuttle tiles had to be made of ceramics that could handle this type of repeated environmental assault. Most of the shuttle's components were designed to operate in a dust-free environment. Therefore, the manufacturing and assembly stages of production for its components were done in clean rooms.

The space telescope in Figure 2.18 must be cooled to eliminate its own heat radiation, which could interfere with

FIGURE 2.18 Infrared Astronomical Satellite

infrared reception from the stars. The telescope and its associated measuring equipment were designed to be cooled to 4°F above absolute zero. Environmental considerations are one of the most demanding aspects of this design.

Product Life. The **operation life** of a product is its time of operation before it fails. The **shelf life** of a product is the period of time it can be in storage and still operate correctly. The designer can influence the life of a product by choice of material, features, manufacturing methods, and assembly methods. Often, it is the intention of the designer to have the product wear out at a given life length.

An industrial product's life may be longer and provide for easier replacement of worn parts. The tractor in Figure 2.17 is an example of a product designed to be maintained over a long period of use.

The Viking lander (Fig. 2.19) had to have an extremely long life in order to operate effectively in a hostile environment. Service, replacement, and maintenance were not considered in this design because the lander could not be reached to perform those functions. The original parts had to have extremely long operational lifetimes and had to operate error-free for an extended period while undergoing extensive environmental attack—temperature variation, dust, and solar radiation. In other words, it had to be extremely reliable.

Reliability. The reliability of a product is influenced by its number of moving parts, its complexity, and its sensitivity to the environment. **Reliability** is a product's ability to function properly during each operation. Reliability affects both the life and the cost of the product. An unreliable product will not enjoy continued sales. Each product is designed to have adequate reliability to last the average expected life. The higher the quality of the components in a product, the longer its life and the higher its reliability. However, it is not cost-effective to design something whose components are more reliable than the item itself. Parts designed for the military and for space exploration must have the highest reliability.

FIGURE 2.19 Viking Lander

Safety. Safety involves the correct performance of a product. Some sensitive or dangerous products have fail-safe designs so as to prevent any injury or harm to the environment. **Fail-safe** means that a product incorporates features for automatically counteracting the effect of an anticipated possible source of breakdown. Products can be dangerous when they do not perform correctly, when they are operated incorrectly, or when they are performing correctly but with insufficient protection for the operator. Each of these three considerations influences the design. The first and last are the easiest to prevent: Protective shields, housings, and guards can be incorporated into the design. The product can be rigorously tested for safe operation and incorporation of any safety features.

Standardization and Interchangeability. By using standard, off-the-shelf items, the cost of the product can be reduced. Systems design is, in reality, the assembly of standard components in unique configurations that accomplish a specific task—such as producing power or creating a chemical. Products also benefit from the incorporation of standard parts in their design. The use of standard parts and previously designed parts is an important factor in DFM, thereby saving time and cost.

The ability of a unit to use similar parts or have different components that can be substituted is called interchangeability. The product is designed so that different sizes of fasteners or other standard components can be used. This will reduce the production costs and eliminate possible shortage problems and delays in production.

Maintenance. *Design for simplicity* in disassembly and maintenance. Some, if not most, products are now designed as throwaways. Design with recycling in mind whenever the product is to be a throwaway.

Products that require repair, service, and maintenance are designed to be disassembled at specific intervals of operation or stages of wear; therefore, design for disassembly. Providing clearance for tools and hands during maintenance and repair is a consideration for many industrial products. As an example, the valve in Figure 2.20 is designed to allow for the removal of the handwheel, stem, bonnet, and disk to replace the composition ring. This service can be accomplished without cutting or disassembling the pipeline.

Costs. The number of parts produced could influence the cost of a product. In general, the greater the quantity manufactured, the lower the overall unit cost of the product. If you had to purchase each part separately, the average automobile would cost about 100 times more than it does now, as most of us have experienced when we needed a repair on our car. Most consumer products can be made much more cheaply by producing large quantities. Industry

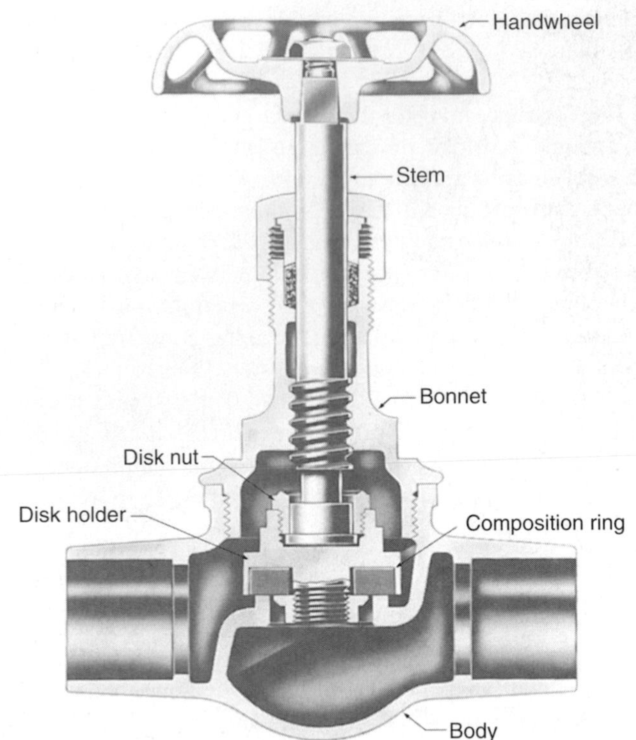

FIGURE 2.20 Composition Disk Globe Valve

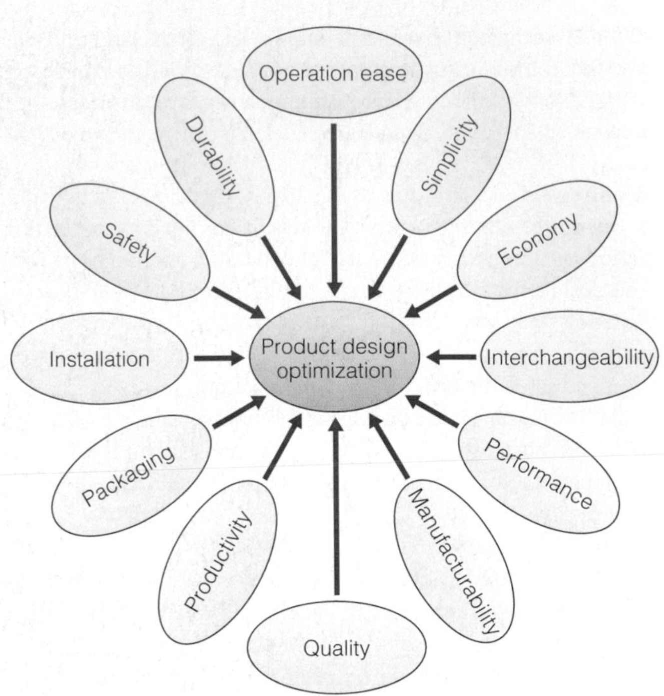

FIGURE 2.21 Product Design Optimization

has realized that they must hold down costs and at the same time increase quality. The designer can be an important factor in this equation. Materials, manufacturing methods, equipment, and labor all affect the cost of a product.

The design, production, and marketing costs of a product must be estimated early in the design process to bring the product to market and make a fair return on the investment. Designing in quality instead of inspecting out problems will ensure a greater profit and a better product.

2.7 PRODUCT DESIGN OPTIMIZATION

The optimum product is created when all factors are properly analyzed and balanced. Figure 2.21 shows the twelve major influences that, when properly considered, will yield a superior product. This process is called product optimization. Each of the twelve factors affects the success of the product. A good designer factors in each to develop an optimum product.

The pipe insulation covers shown in Figure 2.22 were designed according to many of these factors. Durability, quality, economy, performance, simplicity, installation ease, interchangeability, safety, and manufacturability were all considered in the design and production of the covers. Although the insulation of a pipeline (Fig. 2.23) that uses covers does not require the aesthetic considerations required of consumer products, it does demand proper industrial considerations that will affect design and production.

FIGURE 2.22 Zestron Pipe Insulation Covers

FIGURE 2.23 Pipe Insulation

2.8 THE DESIGN TREE

The design tree (Fig. 2.24) is useful in analyzing a particular project. The design tree can serve to illustrate the decision process during the crucial initial design or redesign phase of a project. Although the physical configuration, materials, manufacturing methods, assembly procedures, and equipment costs may be altered and balanced between selections, stages occur during the design of a new product in which equal function, quality, and performance levels can be obtained. The goal is to maximize the product's advantages while maintaining the critical specifications.

The design tree starts with the trunk (product idea). The two main branches are the material selection and the physical configuration. The left limb in the illustration depicts the material choices and splits at metal and nonmetal. Many questions must be answered at this juncture. If metal is chosen, what grades and types should be considered? If nonmetal is considered the best choice, the same questions are asked. The physical shape of the product will be determined by taking the right branch and selecting its size, shape, and features. The branching process can continue to include possible modifications and enhancements. The design tree can also help to see where a particular option or feature may actually threaten the product's integrity.

2.9 DESIGN EXAMPLE

Engineers and designers are pushed to the very edge of engineering design technology when designing visionary vehicles and experiments for the space program. **Gravity Probe B** (Figs. 2.25 and 2.26), an experiment first conceived over 30 years ago, is an example of how engineers, futurists, and designers have sought to use new technology to search for proof for Einstein's theory of relativity. Designers, engineers, and scientists have invented new technologies and given many demonstrations of new devices to work toward the launch of Gravity Probe B.

In 1959—only two years into the space age—three scientists at Stanford University conceived the idea of searching for proof of Einstein's theory of relativity in the only environment possible for the experiment—space. An adventuresome idea such as this is, of course, often the starting point

FIGURE 2.24 The Design Tree

FIGURE 2.25 Overview of the Design of Gravity Probe B

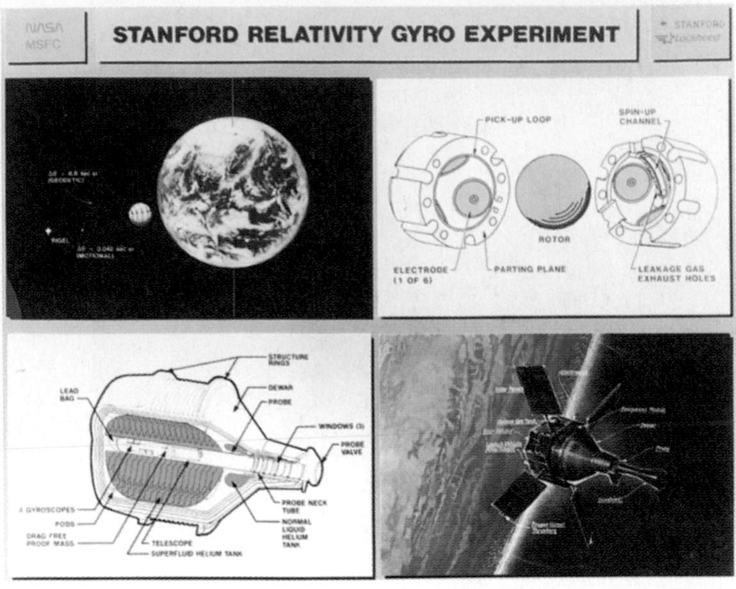

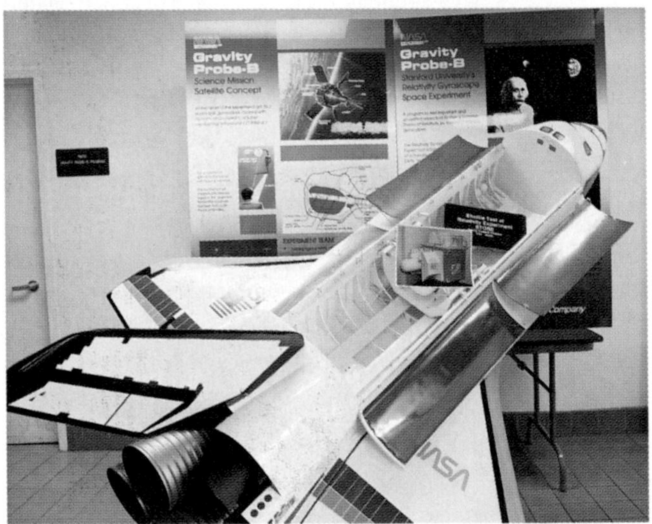

FIGURE 2.26 Electronic Test of Gravity Probe B to Be Flown in the Open Chamber of the Space Shuttle

for many great engineering designs. In the 1960s, research for the project was funded, but NASA clearly saw the success of the project as improbable. The designers had to invent four near-perfect gyroscopes to measure a very tiny effect in space, equivalent to looking for something the size of a human hair from ten miles away. However, by 1989 the designers had overcome so many obstacles that Gravity Probe B was widely recognized as one of the most important fundamental physics experiments ever to be undertaken.

Newton claimed that gravity is a force that is transmitted instantaneously—even over great distances. Einstein disagreed and worked out his theories of special relativity by which nothing can travel faster than the speed of light. Einstein proposed in 1916 that gravity is not a force, but a field that warps space and time in his four-dimensional universe (time being the fourth dimension). Newton said that the planets orbit the sun because a gravitational force holds them in orbit. Einstein said that each planet really travels in a straight line, but its path is elliptical because it is moving in curved space. Of course, most modern theories on the cosmos rely on Einstein's theories. Parts of Einstein's theories, however, remain largely untested. Therefore, not everyone is convinced that Einstein was *completely* right. No one has ever observed gravitational radiation, for example.

A phenomenon known as "frame dragging" is also predicted by Einstein's theory of general relativity. It is this effect that Gravity Probe B is designed to measure (Fig. 2.27). By that theory, a large object, such as Earth, drags space-time with it as it spins. The Stanford researchers' idea was to line up gyroscopes on a distant star and then see if Earth's rotation would drag space and time around with it; this would alter the spin of the gyroscopes (gyros). If Newton is right, the gyros will stay lined up on the star forever; if Einstein is right, the gyros' spin should change slightly over a period of time. However, the instruments will have to measure a tiny angle of 42 milliarc-seconds a year to find the effect. If the Earth is really dragging space around it as it rotates, the axis of the gyro will swivel at a rate of one full turn in 25 million years.

The design of the experiment itself calls for four near-perfect gyros that can function in near-zero gravity at near-zero temperatures in a near-perfect vacuum in near-zero magnetic fields. The gyros will be near-perfect spheres of quartz about the size of tennis balls (each sphere being round to a millionth of an inch). Vibrations during the experiment could ruin the experiment. Each sphere is coated with a thin film of superconducting material, allowing the gyros to be suspended in a magnetic field. To make the design challenge more complex, the position would be fixed on a star 300,000 light-years away! The small signal that will be detected must be transmitted by satellite error free and immune from outside errors of all sorts.

FIGURE 2.27 Airlock and Dewar Stand Vacuum Testing of Electronics for Gravity Probe B

The design team eventually found a way to produce the world's roundest gyroscopes, a drag-free satellite, a refrigerated capsule to hold helium in place and cool it for two years, and a method for detecting the small change in spin with superconductor technology. Special clean rooms were designed just for the project (Fig. 2.28), as were special rooms for assembly and storage of the project. In order for the rotor ball in the gyroscope to be a superconductive, the engineers have developed a dewar, a large vacuum-bottle-like container that will provide the near-absolute-zero temperatures needed for the gyroscope. New composite materials were employed for the assemblies. Each piece or assembly that was developed had to be meticulously cleaned (Fig. 2.29) and tested in vacuum containers (Fig. 2.30) and cold chambers (Fig. 2.31) developed especially for the project. Electronic testing of some of the probe equipment will be sent up in the space shuttle in approximately 1996 (Fig. 2.32). The 3-ton-payload drag-free satellite is scheduled to be launched in 1999 on a Delta rocket. The satellite has been now renamed the Relativity Mission. Gravity Probe A, in June 1976, was a suborbital flight of an atomic clock to test the equivalence of gravitational and inertial mass.

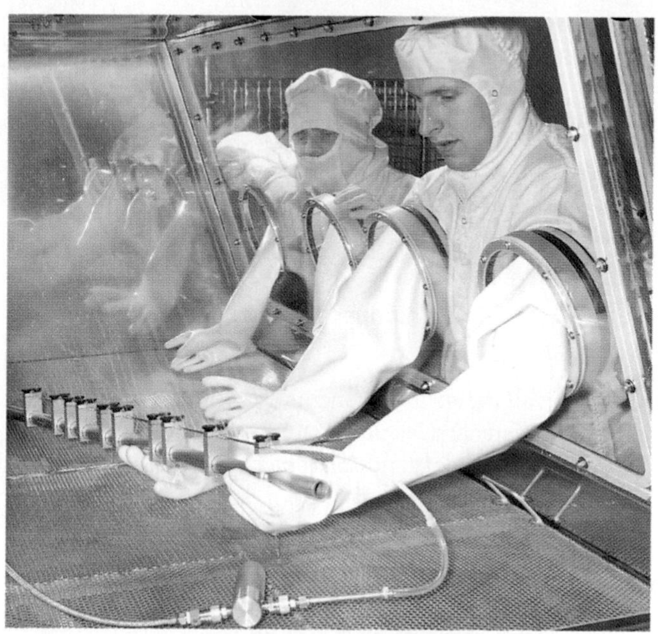

FIGURE 2.29 Precision Cleaning of Flexible Bellows Tubes for Electronic Controls

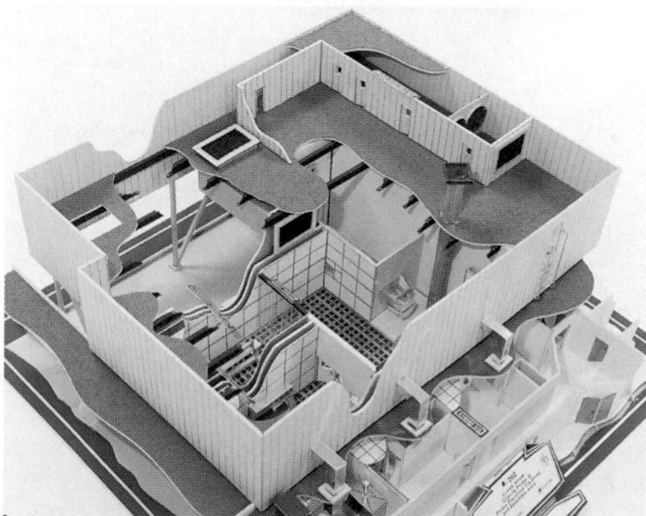

FIGURE 2.28 Scale Model of a Precision Clean Room Used to Assemble Probe Parts

FIGURE 2.30 Airlock Chamber for Testing Electronics and Composites

FIGURE 2.31 Cold Chamber for Testing Probe Segments

As with all design, components and test facilities began as ideas that were first sketched to communicate ideas (Fig. 2.33) and to understand placement of components and sizes. Preliminary plans (Fig. 2.34) and manufacturing assembly plans (Fig. 2.35) were developed before the components or facilities could be manufactured (Fig. 2.36). For most components of Gravity Probe B and the associated test facilities, every idea was new and untried. Design iterations were many. Test followed test. New concepts and new theories were developed. Each design concept pushed the limits of known applications.

Not all engineering and design is as sophisticated as those involved in Gravity Probe B. However, all engineering and design follows the same methodology and considerations.

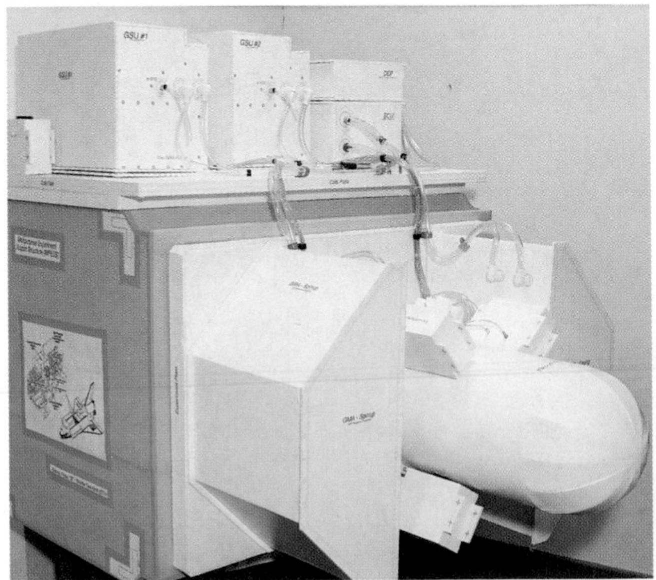

FIGURE 2.32 Scale Model of Electronic Testing of the Probe to Be Sent Up in the Space Shuttle

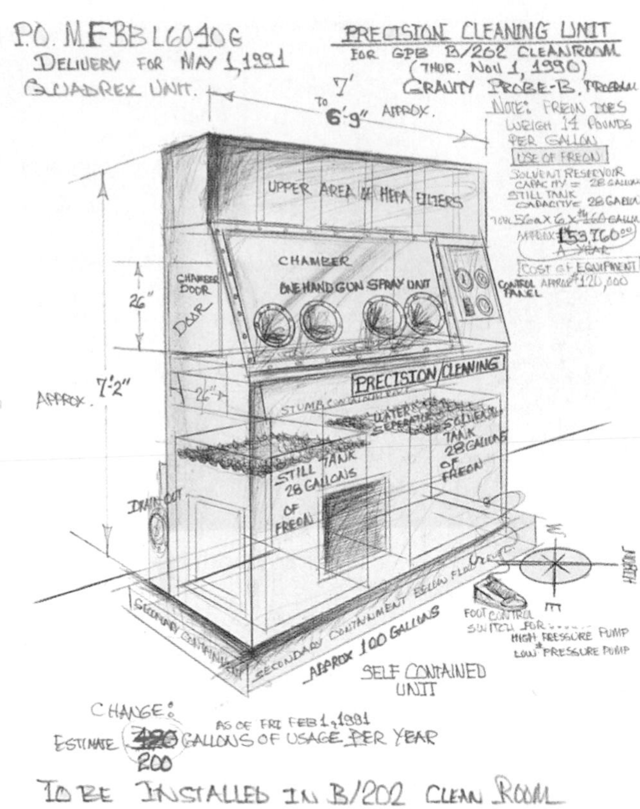

FIGURE 2.33 Sketch of a Precision Cleaning Apparatus

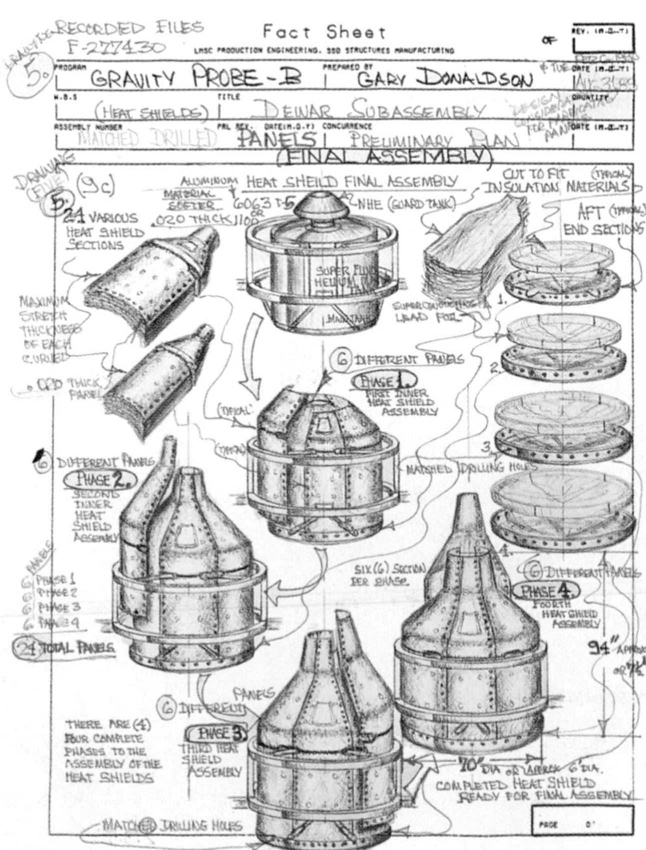

FIGURE 2.34 Plans for the Heat Shields of the Dewar

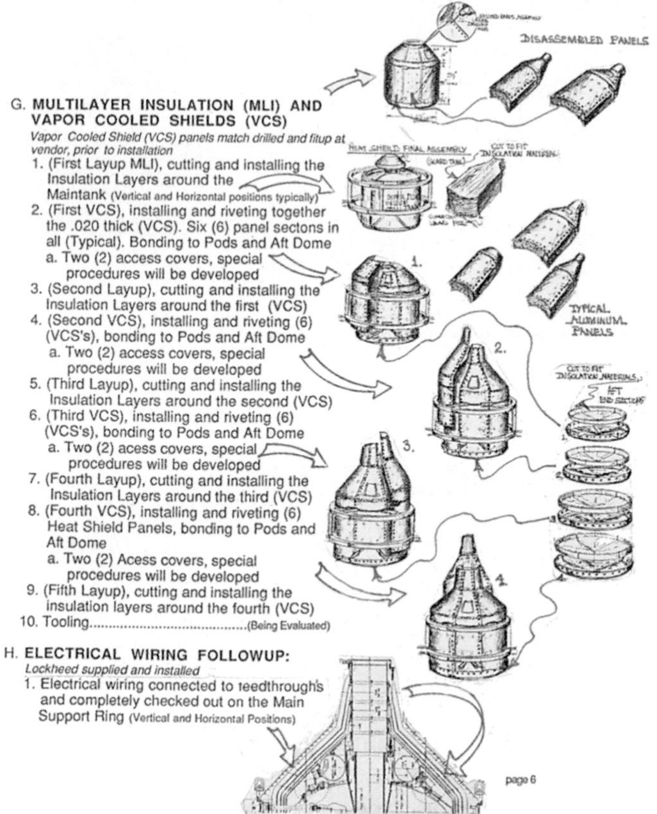

FIGURE 2.35 Partial Manufacturing Assembly Plan for the Dewar

FIGURE 2.36 Precision Cleaning Unit

QUIZ

True or False

1. Product design is usually completed without considering how to manufacture the product.
2. Systems engineering is relatively unimportant.
3. Function is the most determining factor in design.
4. Recyclability is not considered when the product is designed to be a "throwaway."
5. Project cost and profit margin are two of the most important factors in any design.
6. Reliability is the length of time a product will operate properly.
7. Weight is never important when designing a product for the industrial sector.
8. "Off-the-shelf" refers to a mechanical item that is too large for shelf storage.

Fill in the Blanks

9. The __________ __________ can be used to illustrate the decision process during design or redesign.
10. The shape of a product should be considered with regard to its symmetry, __________ , __________ , and __________.
11. Durability, life, quality, economy, and simplicity are all factors in product __________ __________.
12. The __________ __________ can be used to describe and determine the material and configuration requirements of a design.
13. Products that must be disassembled after specific hours of operation must be __________ __________ __________.
14. The __________ product is created when all factors are properly analyzed and balanced.
15. Design parameters include weight, size, __________ , __________ , __________ , color, __________ , and __________.
16. __________ __________ __________ is an experiment designed to help prove Einstein's theory of relativity.

Answer the Following

17. Compare systems design with product design. Describe both, and explain their differences.
18. Name ten factors that influence design at the onset of a project.
19. Describe the components involved in product engineering.
20. Describe the components involved in manufacturing engineering.
21. Describe concepts involved in the design tree.
22. Describe the role of constraints and function in the design process.
23. Explain in detail the concept of *design for manufacturability*.
24. Explain the purpose of the Gravity Probe B experiment.

THE DESIGN PROCESS

Chapter 3

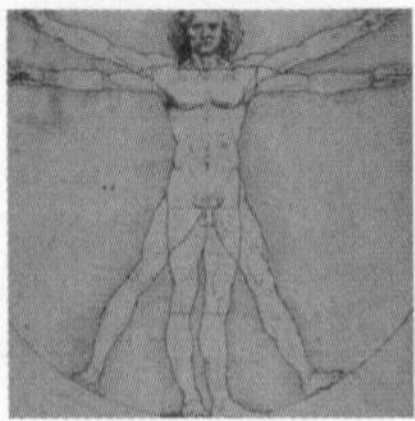

LEARNING OBJECTIVES

Upon completion of this chapter you will be able to:

1. Understand the role of the engineer in the design process.
2. Interpret the criteria for product and manufacturing engineering that result in design for manufacturability.
3. Analyze and utilize the stages involved in the design process while recognizing their flexibility.
4. Develop an understanding of critical-path scheduling and just-in-time production concepts.
5. Integrate CAD applications into the design process.
6. Understand the role that solid modeling and CAD play in the efficient design of a manufactured product.

3.1 INTRODUCTION

The design process is an organized, interactive engineering activity that results in a well-defined concept and a specific plan to turn that concept into reality. The design process is a logical and planned sequence by which an individual or a team can develop a solution to a specific problem. The stages in the design process described here are not intended to be rules or procedures that are appropriate for all design situations; consider them a guide to the design process.

Though the end product is specified in the form of drawings, computer images, sketches, and engineering specifications, designing involves more than simply putting a drawing together and having the part made in the shop. Designing is an interactive process with planned steps and checkpoints. Every design involves solving a particular problem, analyzing what is needed to do the job, and planning the series of steps and activities that will transform the concept into a concrete object. Each design involves making choices in materials, instrumentation, manufacturing processes, and fabrication personnel. Finally, every design should have the input of a team, each member of which can offer advice, assistance, guidance, constructive critiques, and support.

With the advent of **design for manufacturability (DFM),** the design process now incorporates procedures and considerations formerly left only to manufacturing. Throughout this chapter you will be introduced to a variety of DFM concepts and ideas that will show the design process to be a fluid and dynamic way to integrate manufacturability into the design. With DFM, manufacturing is considered at the beginning of the design process. Since as much as 70% of the manufacturing cost of a part is fixed during design, DFM is an important concept. For more information, see *Design for Manufacturability* by David M. Anderson (CIM Press, Lafayette, CA).

Few people understand the complexity of a particular product or the amount of effort required to bring a product to market. Figure 3.1 presents an example of a complex

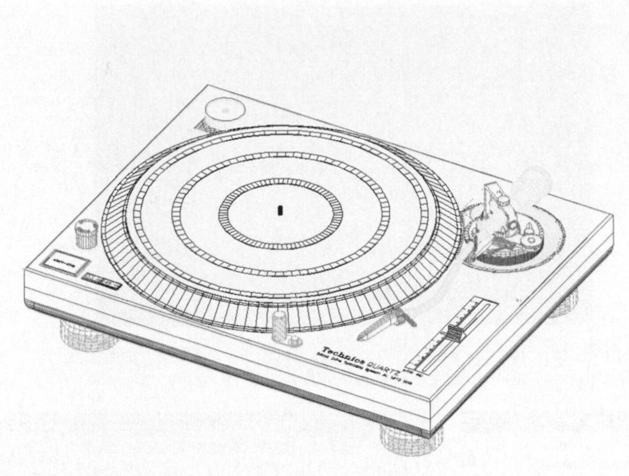

(a) Design of assembly using 3D wireframe modeling

(b) Same assembly shown with AutoShade

FIGURE 3.1 **Design Via a Solid Modeler**

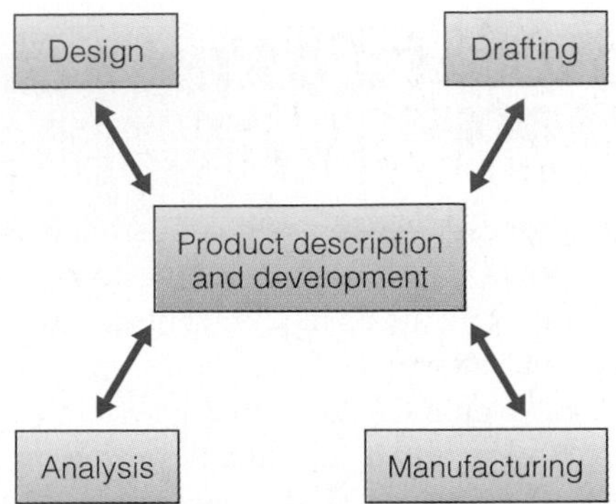

FIGURE 3.2 **Product Description and Development**

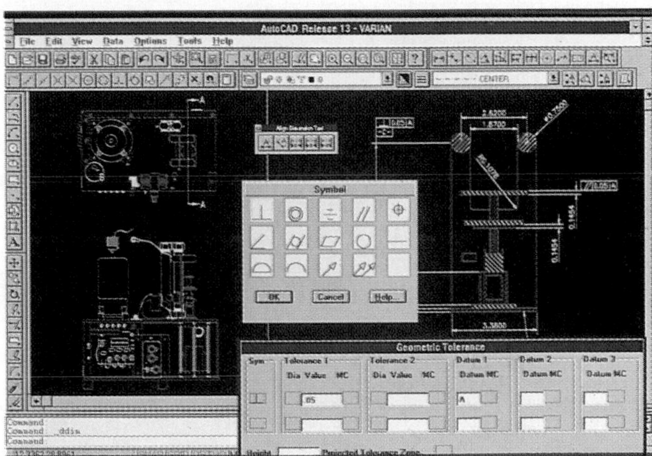

FIGURE 3.3 **Using CAD in the Design Process**

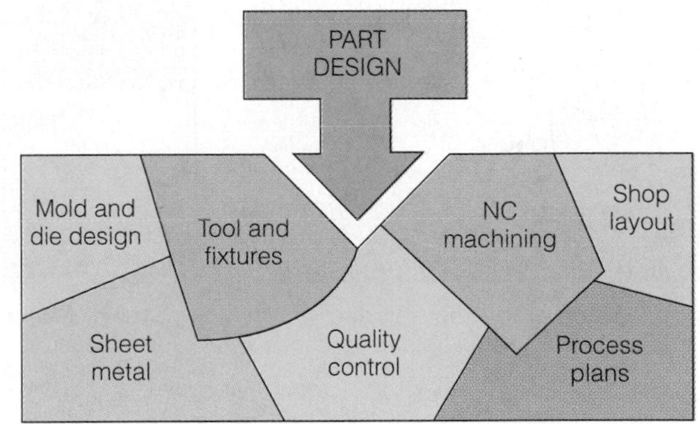

FIGURE 3.4 **Part Design Using CAD**

assembly designed on a solid modeling system. The complexity of a typical system design, such as a nuclear power plant, a petrochemical facility, or an industrial building, is more obvious. But even in these types of projects, the general public does not fathom the complexity of and the time devoted to the design process.

A typical consumer product, such as a household appliance or a hand tool, can appear deceptively simple. In reality, however, the design concerns, engineering requirements, and manufacturing procedures are extremely complicated and time-consuming. Obviously, all products are the result of many hours of intense work. Product description and development include design, drafting, analysis, and manufacturing (Fig. 3.2). If the part design is generated on a CAD system (Fig. 3.3), it can be used in all subsequent stages of the design-through-manufacturing sequence (Fig. 3.4).

It is impossible to describe how to design every item. It has been said that you cannot teach engineering design, but a thorough presentation of design concepts leading to the understanding of the conceptualization process involved in design and mastery of the stages involved in the design process will lay a solid foundation for anyone aspiring to become a design engineer. Specific design parameters for a product or system are mastered on the job through the accumulation of experience.

The two main divisions of engineering design are systems design and product design. Although systems design is an important field, a majority of this text is devoted to product and mechanical design techniques. Therefore, this chapter is primarily a detailed analysis of the design process as it relates to product development and mechanical design.

3.2 OVERVIEW OF THE DESIGN PROCESS

The **design process** begins when a customer expresses a need for a product. Working with the customer, you define the project and formulate its requirements. Figure 3.5 shows the design, analysis, and manufacture of a commercial product—a saw—on a CAD/CAM/CAE system (Intergraph). Many steps are required to design and manufacture a complicated product such as the saw shown in the figure.

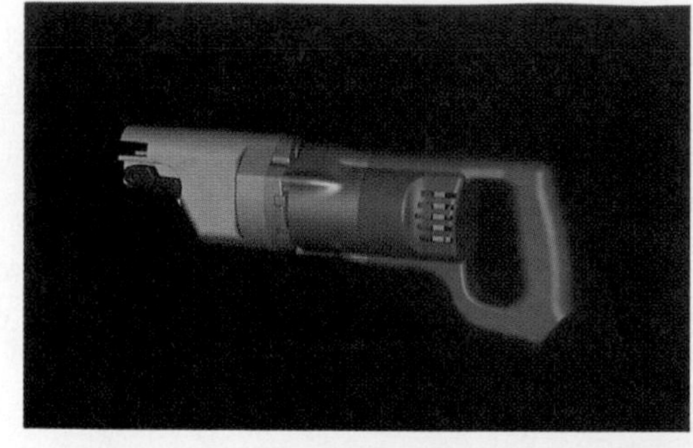

(a) Intergraph engineering modeling system (EMS) enhances mechanical design productivity with solid modeling tools

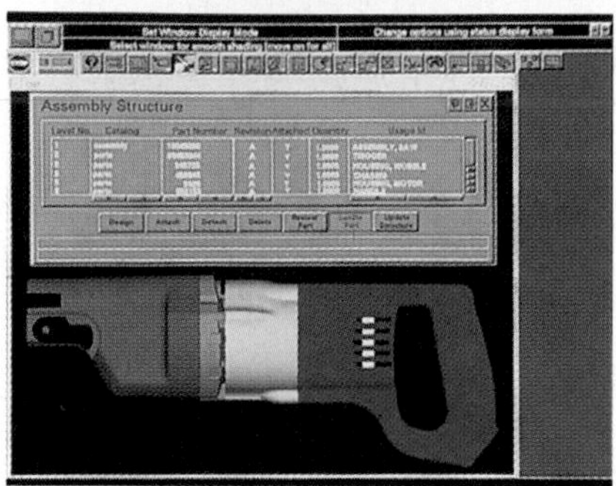

(b) EMS data management software produces bills of material and automatically generates single-level parts lists for drawings

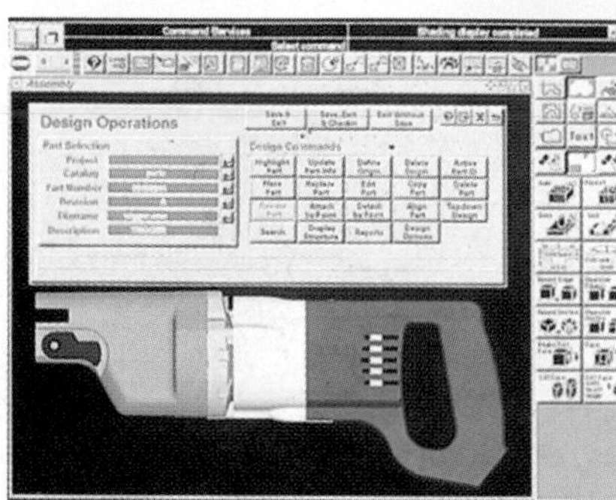

(c) EMS forms make it easy to select parts and add them to an assembly; a design engineer can choose either top-down or bottom-up design

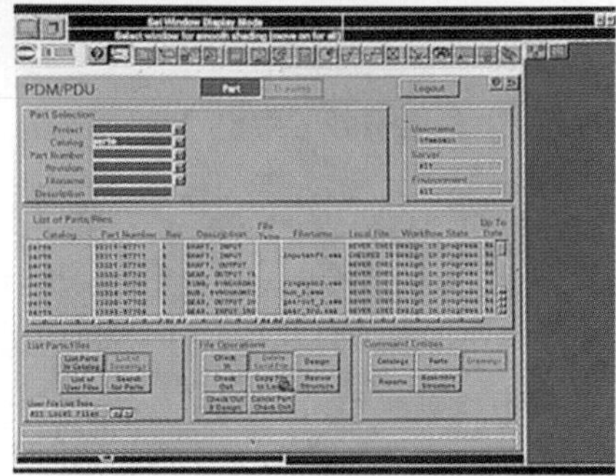

(d) EMS data management system simplifies file management with component check-in and check-out, file location tracking, archiving, retrieval, and security

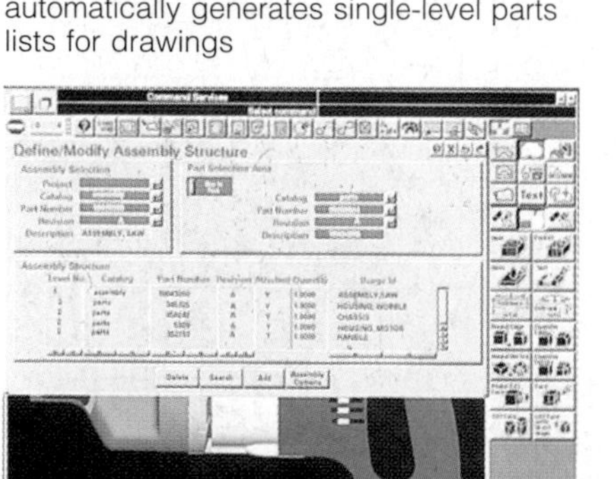

(e) EMS data management software provides a single product structure and central controls that link development teams with a shared information resource

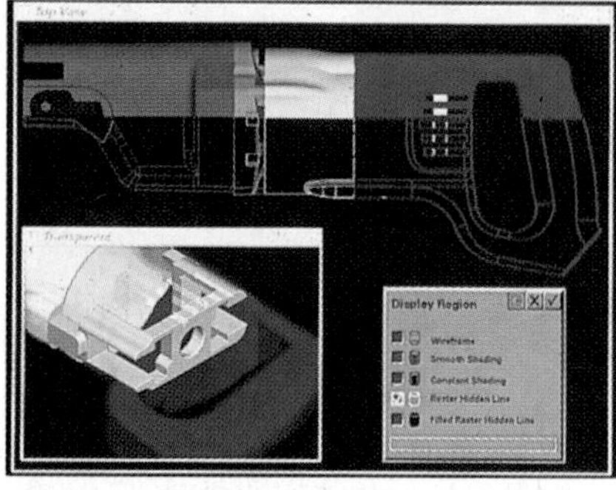

(f) Sharing data with engineering design, Intergraph industrial design products couple product styling with engineering processes

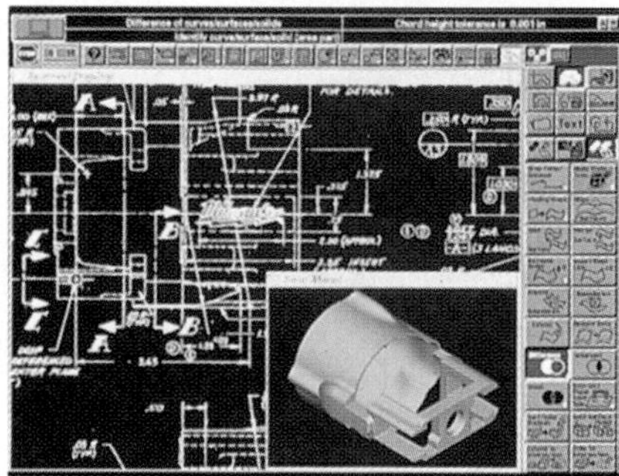

(g) With Intergraph's EMS, existing drawings are electronically scanned and can be used for reference or modified for new uses

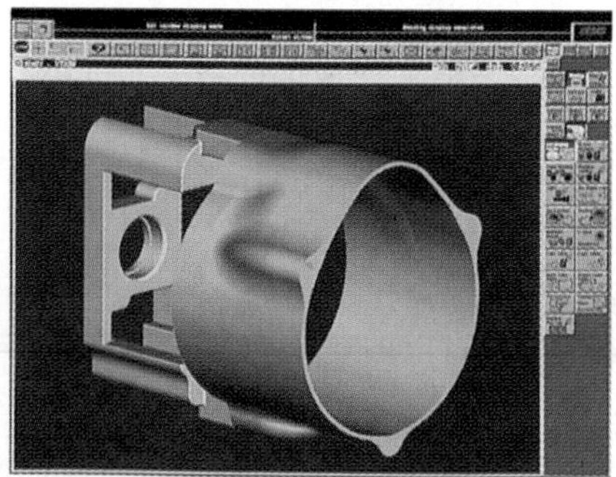

(h) The master model supplies Intergraphs's full suite of downstream applications with complete data, eliminating translation and re-creation

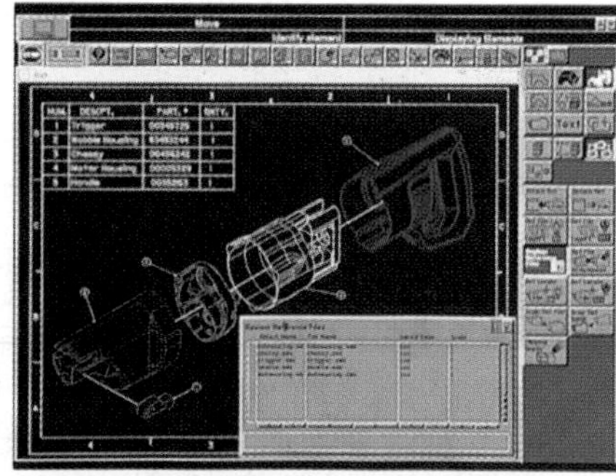

(i) Using Intergraph, read-only design files ensure parts' mating and enable designers to share information while designing different parts of an assembly

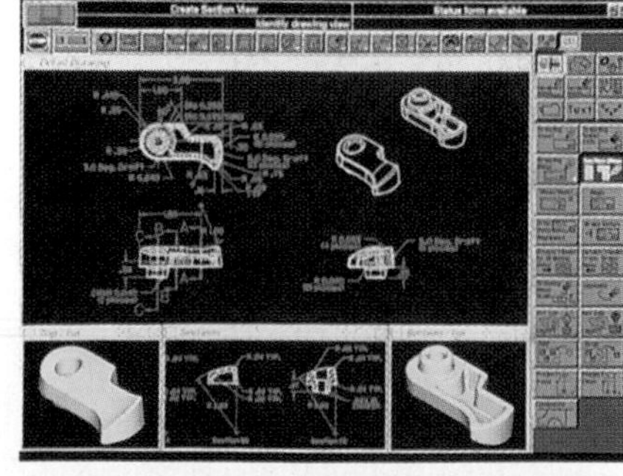

(j) For detailing, in Intergraph, the design software includes dimensions and creates section views, which are automatically updated to incorporate model modifications

FIGURE 3.5 Design Example—a Saw

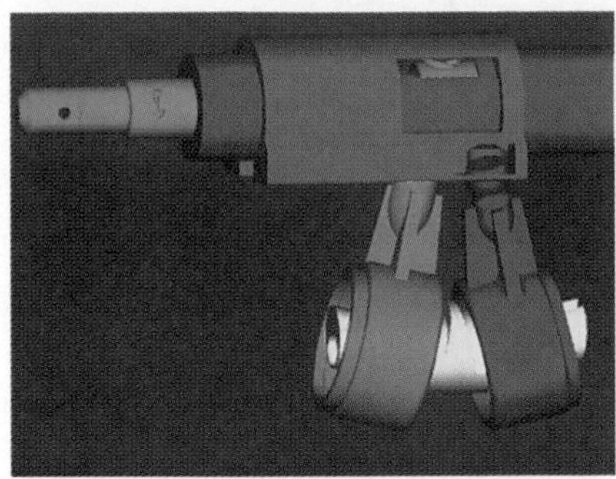

(k) Shaded models in EMS show the relationship and relative motion of mating parts and assemblies

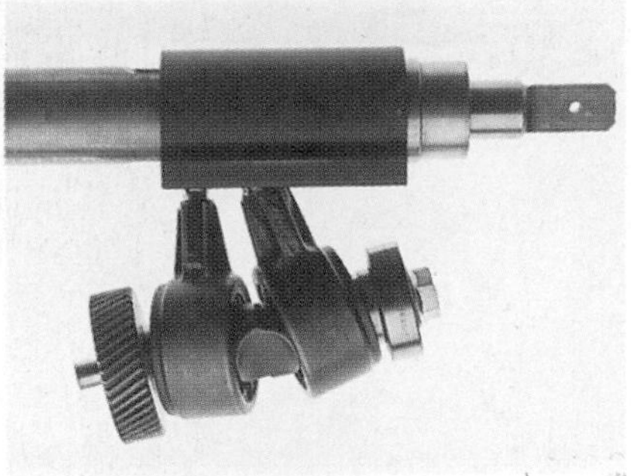

(l) Machined assembly showing actual part geometry and motion

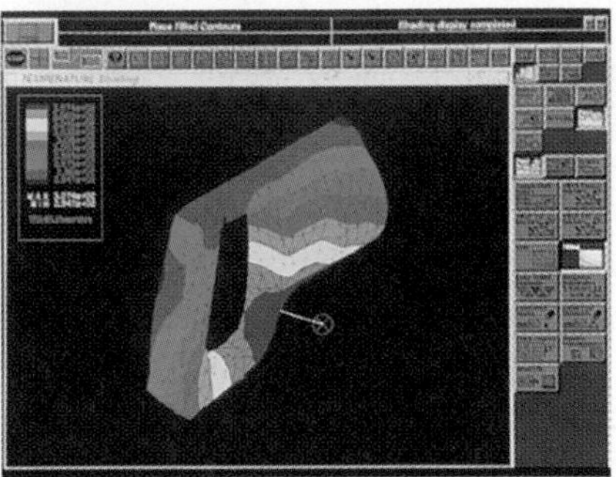

(m) EMS plastics injection analysis software analyzes the effects of time, temperature, and pressure on the flow of molten plastic

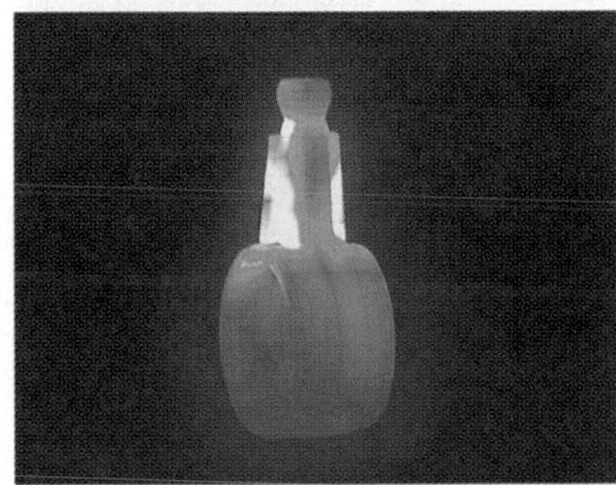

(n) Intergraph finite element analysis software enables engineers to perform structural analysis of complex components

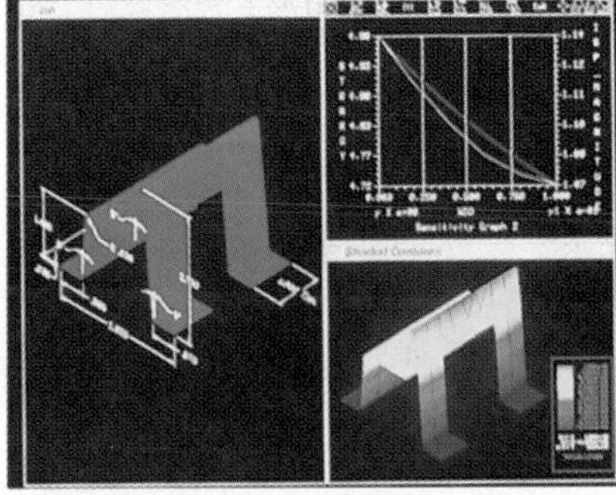

(o) Based on user-defined variables, constraints, and goals, closed-loop design optimization software evaluates design variations to determine the best solution in EMS

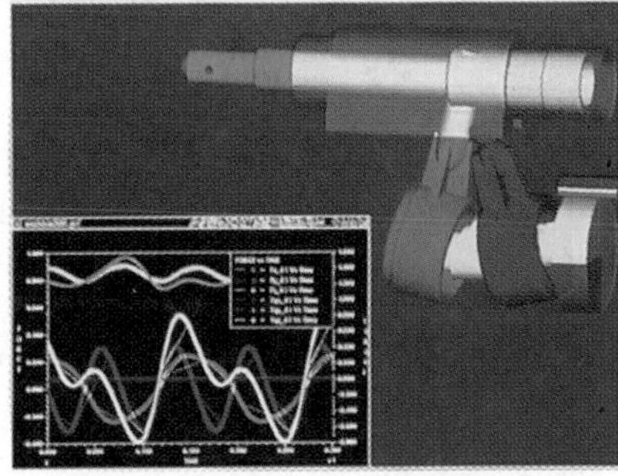

(p) Mechanical systems analysis software in EMS helps study mechanism performance, including interference and the way forces change during operation

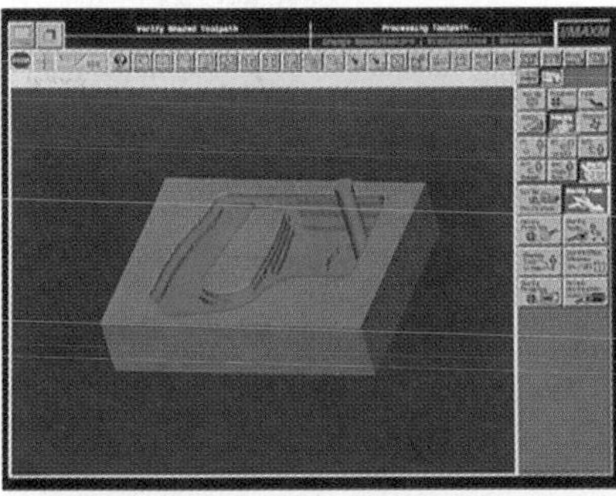

(q) Three-axis milling in roughing mode maximizes machining efficiency and prepares a part for finishing in EMS. Animated simulation helps verify machining processes

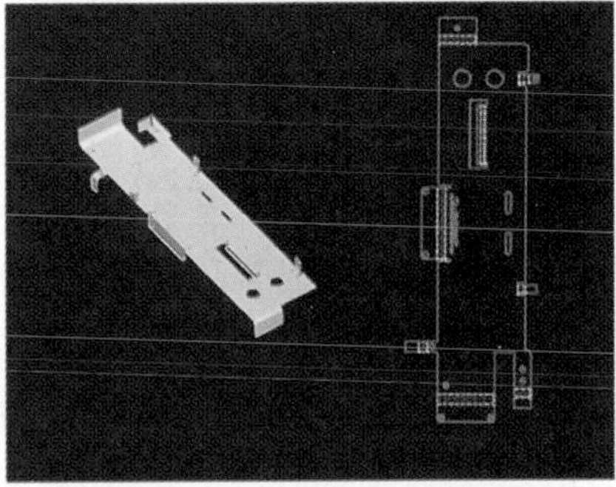

(r) Reducing design-to-manufacture turnaround time, flat-pattern development software develops flat patterns for a variety of 3D shapes in EMS

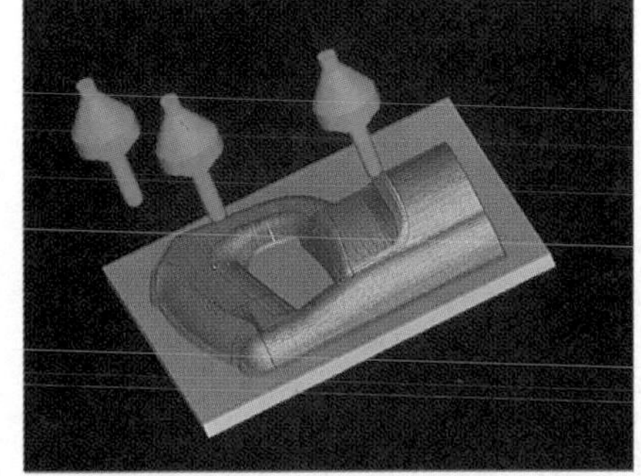

(s) Directly linked with design data, Intergraph manufacturing software generates and verifies milling toolpaths

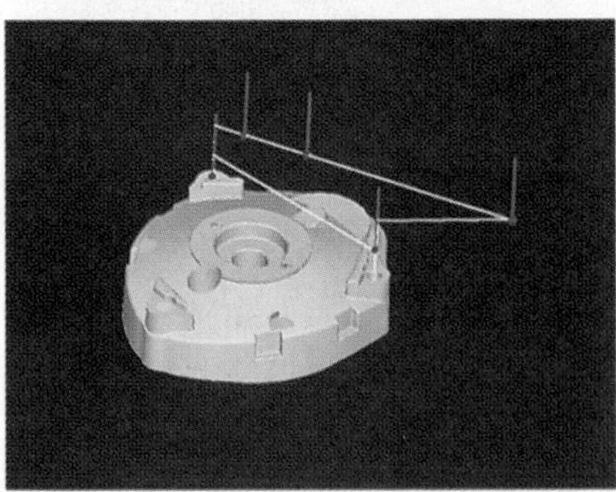

(t) Integrating design, manufacturing, and quality control, Intergraph Coordinate Measuring Machine (CMM) software accesses design files directly for measuring free-form and geometric features

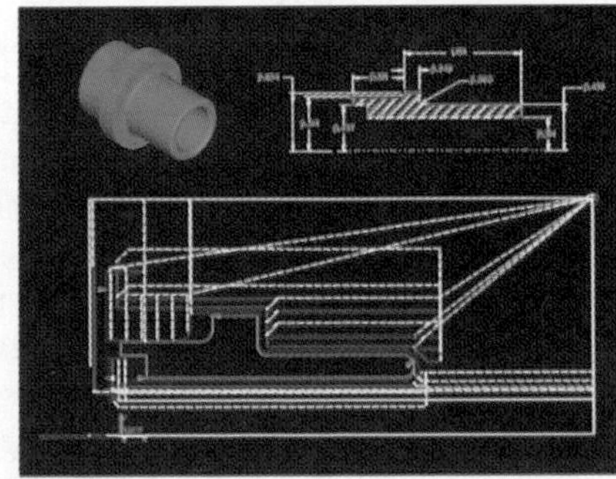

(u) Intergraph's lathe option creates turning, grooving, and threading toolpaths according to model geometry

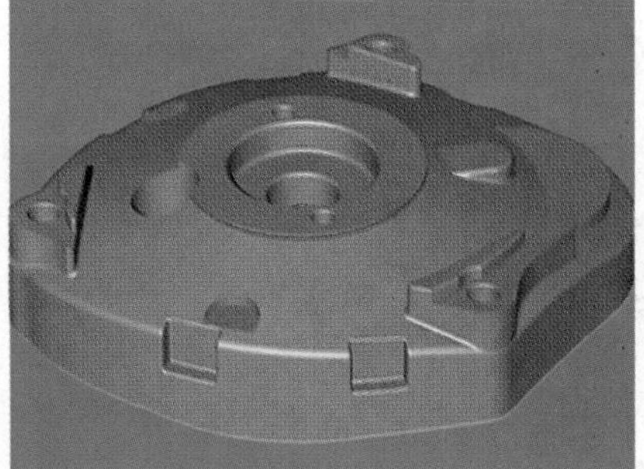

(v) Shaded solid model in EMS shows detail of part design

FIGURE 3.5 Design Example—a Saw—*Continued*

(w) Using Intergraph's EMS, shading of solid models makes part creation and visualization easier

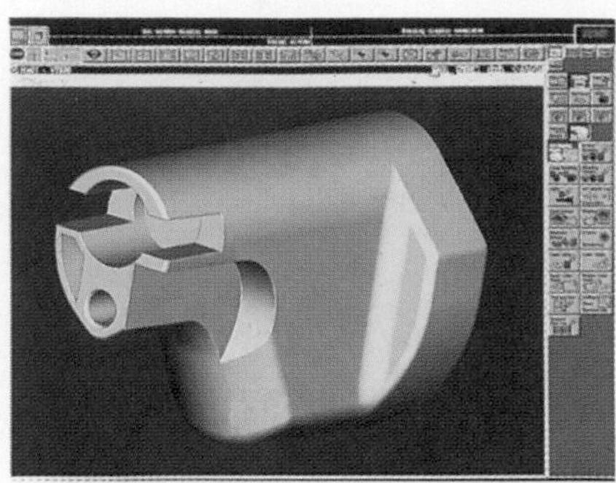

(x) Complex components are easier to visualize using a shaded solid model in Intergraph's EMS

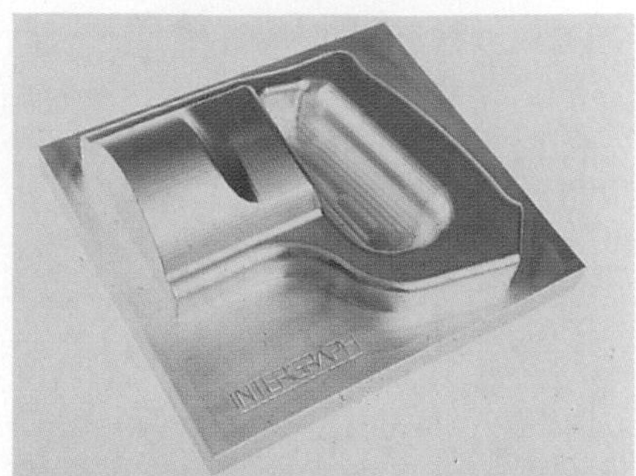

(y) CNC toolpaths are created in EMS to speed the production of rough-cut molds and components

(z) Machining operations are made easier using one 3D design database

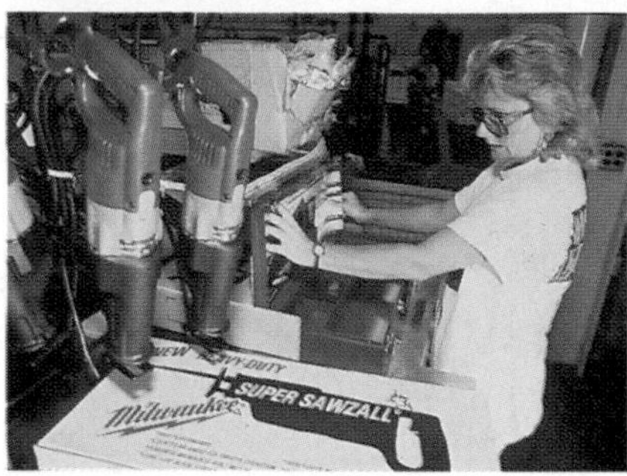

(aa) Inspection, quality control, and packaging are simplified by using one 3D solid model design database for the entire assembly

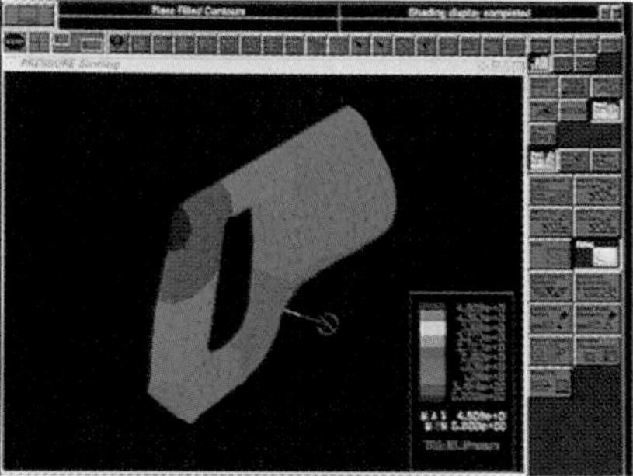

(bb) Finite element modeling and plastics injection molding analysis are part of the EMS system. Shaded contours show stress or temperature distributions.

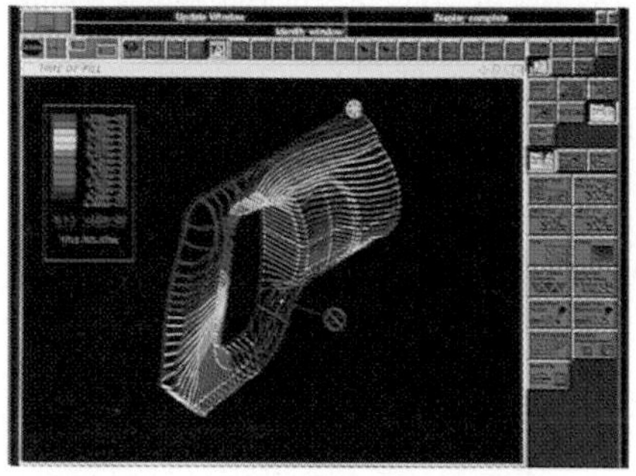

(cc) Finite element modeling and plastics injection molding analysis can also be shown in EMS with iso lines

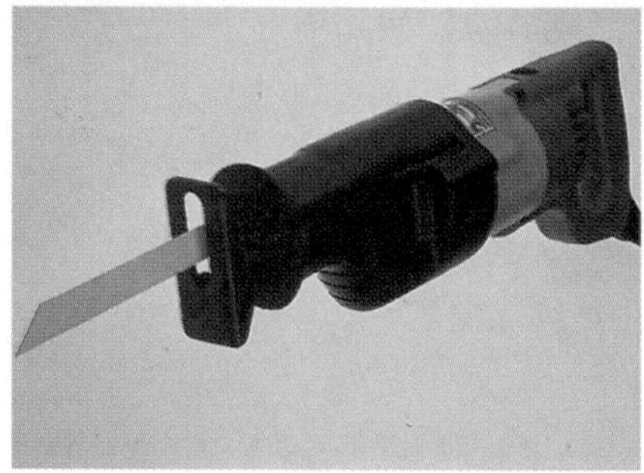

(dd) Product design is integrated in Intergraph's EMS software

(ee) Part designed via EMS shown in use

FIGURE 3.5 Design Example—a Saw—*Continued*

The design process to complete such a product and bring it to market involves a series of steps. Though in most cases the design steps are unique to each product, there are general steps and guidelines by which every project can develop and produce a product.

For simplicity, the design process has been separated into eight individual stages (Fig. 3.6). This is not to be taken as a set of hard-and-fast steps or rules. The actual design process is more flexible and is not as linear as described here. *Design for manufacturability* requires the eight stages to be considered, not separately, but as an integrated whole in which each "stage" is constantly being considered within every other stage. Many of the eight stages presented here are performed simultaneously by the design/manufacturing team. The stages do not always flow in a straight line from 1 through 8. Sometimes there are different stages or more or fewer stages. Remember, these are theoretical divisions of tasks. Manufacturing always comes after the engineering and analysis, but *manufacturing decisions and capabilities are integrated into the preliminary design and engineering stage.*

The flow diagram of Figure 3.6 shows various stages in the design process. The general flow is from top to bottom, as the arrows beneath each box indicate. The flow lines and arrows on the left and the right sides of the illustration flow from the bottom up. On the left side, for instance, we see that consulting the marketing and sales division influences problem identification (1), evaluation (3), and the design choice (5). On the right side of the figure, we see that

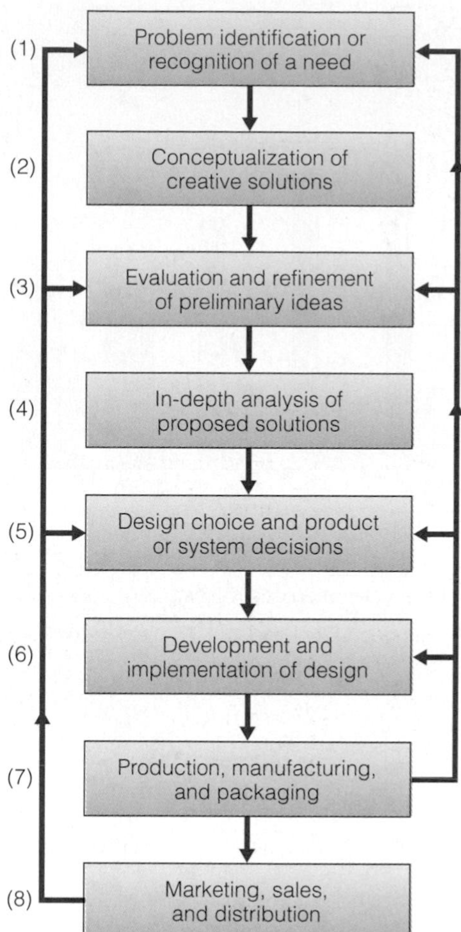

FIGURE 3.6 Stages in the Design Process

manufacturing (7) affects almost every other stage in the process. The rest of this chapter will take each stage in sequence and indicate the specific influencing factors and tasks associated with it.

3.3 PROBLEM IDENTIFICATION OR RECOGNITION OF NEEDS

The design process starts with the **identification** of a problem (Fig. 3.7), an observed need, or a potential new idea for a product or system. Problem identification or recognition of need is the starting point of all design efforts. The identification or recognition stage requires the designer or design team to be thoroughly acquainted with the problem or need. You should attempt to answer the following at this stage of the project:

- *Who* needs it?
- *What* is needed?
- *Where* is it needed?
- *When* is it needed?
- *Why* is it needed?
- *How* many are needed?

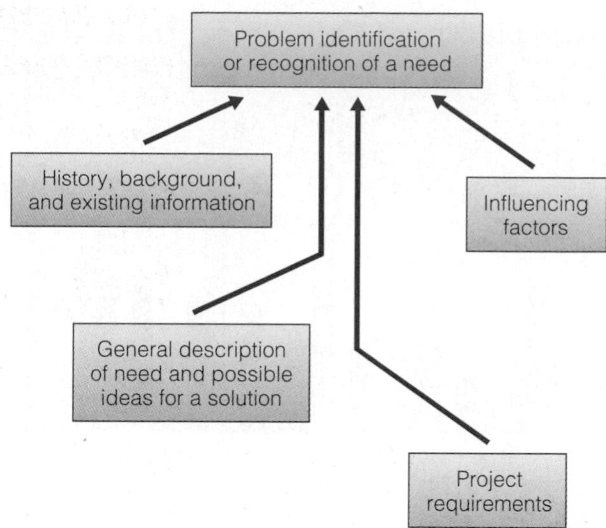

FIGURE 3.7 Stage 1 in the Design Process

History, Background, and Existing Information. The **background** of the project is presented to the design team by a concerned party: the company management, an outside client, or a company inventor who has a new idea. The marketing department may be asked to do a survey on the potential for a particular product. For example, suppose a computer company that has a well-received product line servicing the private sector with personal computers wishes to enter the engineering workstation market. Surveys may be needed to determine the total sales of computers in that sector and create a forecast for the future. The marketing and research department will probably create a series of charts and graphs to present their findings visually. The company's management, along with the design team, then discusses the potential for their firm to enter—and be successful in—this market. Figure 3.8(a) presents a graphical analysis of the market forecast shown in Figure 3.8(b).

A number of questions can be asked at this stage of the process:

- What exists now?
- How was the problem faced in the past?
- Is this a new problem?

The answers to these questions may be incomplete at this stage; in fact, they may create more questions.

General Description of Needs and Possible Ideas for Solutions. The **general description** of and possible solutions to the problem flow from a series of meetings conducted with the design team. Let us say a company that has been manufacturing small residential plumbing valves and medium-sized industrial valves has an opportunity to bid on a large job requiring pipeline-sized valves (Fig. 3.9). The new product line will affect the manufacturing equipment, facility space, manpower requirements, shipping, and storage areas of the firm. The size of the valve alone may necessitate a total retooling of the facility. The job may also

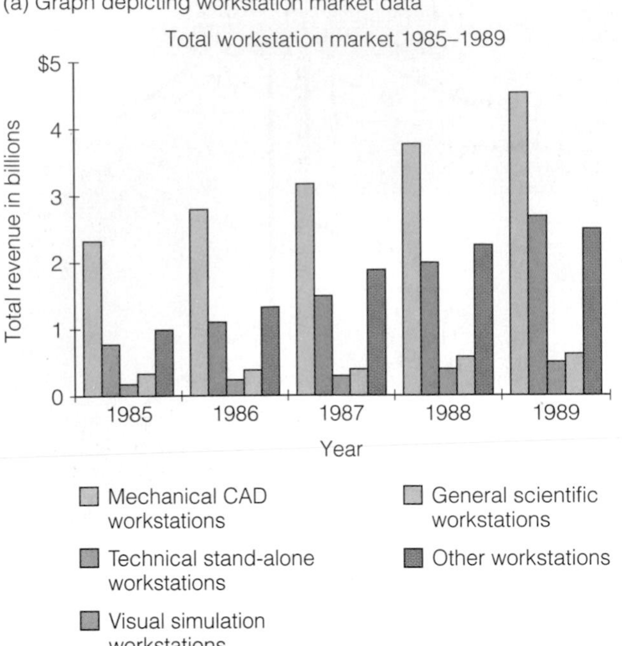

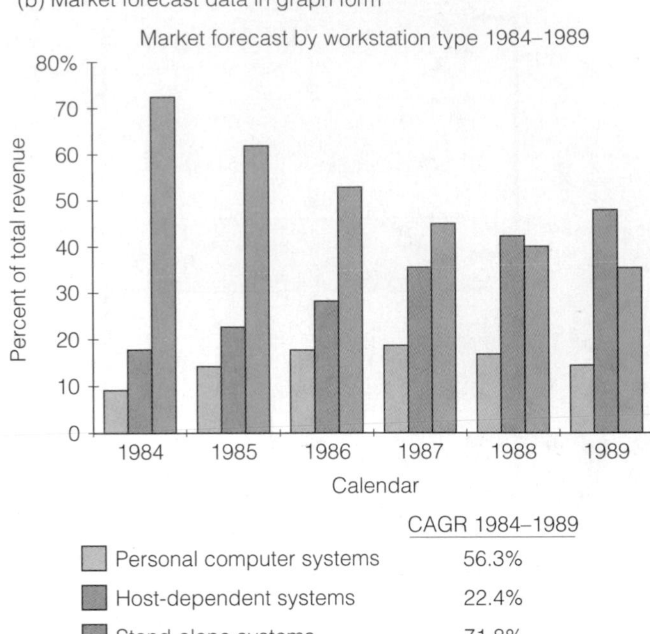

FIGURE 3.8 **Example of a Market Analysis**

be a one-time opportunity and have little continued sales after the project is complete. The economics of the project is of primary concern. How will it affect existing product lines? Is it worth the risk? Will the company turn a profit for its effort? Will the company be able to sustain a continued presence in this market after the project is complete?

FIGURE 3.9 **48 in. Gate Valve for TransAlaska Pipeline**

Influencing Factors. The design of a product or system does not happen in a vacuum. All products and systems have an effect on the users of the product or system and, possibly, on society in general. The cost of a project determines its feasibility. All factors that may influence the total cost and the economic feasibility of the design must be considered before the project is initiated.

Environmental constraints and concerns may be important for many product designs. Systems design is influenced by the environmental constraints and effects imposed on it by the government and special interest groups. The design of a power plant, chemical facility, hydroelectric plant, bridge, housing complex, or building, to name a few, is defined by the acceptable effect it has on the environment. An environmental impact report may be needed before much of the design effort is begun. The valve of Figure 3.9 is on the TransAlaska pipeline (Fig. 3.10). Environmental impact reports were a major part of the design effort and were used to convince the public that the pipeline was feasible and safe. The actual conditions under which the pipeline and valves operate stretched the limits of pipeline technology.

The economics of a particular solution must be understood at an early part of this stage. Can the product or system make money? Is the existing budget adequate? Will the project involve new markets, or will the product be replacing an existing one? When economics is concerned, input from all other departments is important. The marketing and manufacturing departments have considerable input that must be integrated into the total economic analysis of the project if it is to be successful.

Project Requirements. Basic parameters can be identified at this stage. All ideas and suggestions should be recorded as

FIGURE 3.10 **Gate Valve Being Installed on the TransAlaska Pipeline**

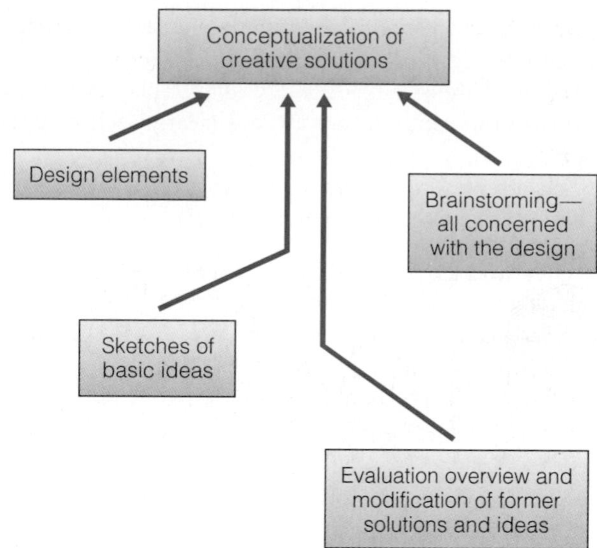

FIGURE 3.11 **Stage 2 in the Design Process**

notes and rough sketches. The project's size, shape, color, material, and general configuration can be discussed. No decisions should be made at this point. Requirements dictated by a client or purchaser of the product or system must be added to the list of known influencing factors and project requirements. If a project must be a certain color or weight, this must be understood at the earliest stage of the process. If the product is to be produced efficiently, design for manufacturability must be integrated into the project from the outset.

3.4 CONCEPTUALIZATION OF CREATIVE SOLUTIONS

Before the design process goes any further, **creative possibilities** for a solution to the design problem should purposely be investigated. Knowing background information and the research on pertinent data helps the designer see clearly the range of possible answers to the design problem.

This second stage (Fig. 3.11) includes researching every available source of information about the project. Each of the design elements listed in Stage 1 is now analyzed thoroughly. The influencing factors, general parameters, and project requirements are used to investigate possible solutions. Even at this stage, attempt should not be made to find a complete final solution. Data from outside sources is integrated into the design process during this stage. Former solutions to the same or a similar problem can be discussed and expanded on now.

Although the past experience and education of a designer are extremely important for the success of a project, proper research on all existing information on the subject is no less important. Since the research process helps build a professional "database" that can be tapped for other projects, a new or inexperienced designer benefits from any existing information. Oddly enough, it is not the lack of background sources but the overabundance of information that is a problem. The design engineer must differentiate between what is useful and important and what is unessential. The following list provides some sources for acquiring information on a design problem:

- Textbooks
- Periodicals—technical magazines
- Library search
- Engineering standards
- Technical reports
- Published papers presented at conferences
- Manufacturing specifications
- Catalogs of parts
- Patents
- Handbooks
- Previous designs in the company
- Co-workers—other designers and engineers

Design Elements. The **elements of design** must be identified by the design engineer early in this stage of the project. The identification and classification of design elements helps to clarify and divide important or vital elements from minor or nonvital concerns. A creative choice for a design solution must flow from a deep understanding of the design elements related to the project. Listing the design elements helps clear up any misconceptions regarding the project. The following is a list of steps that will help identify the design elements:

1. Define the *basic design problems* relevant to the solution.
2. Define the *secondary design problems* that are not the designer's concern but that still need to be solved.
3. Identify *perceived problems* that are not really important. This alleviates false concerns.
4. Identify *obstructions* to the design, i.e., significant ob-

stacles to the design solution that must be avoided or circumvented.

5. Find and discuss all *hidden difficulties*. These are obstructions to the solution that are not clearly seen or understood.
6. Scrutinize any *hindrances* to the design that are really not important enough to justify much time.

Sketches and Layouts of Basic Ideas. Although a few rough sketches may have been made during Stage 1, more developed sketches and pictorial layouts (Fig. 3.12) now can help define any preliminary ideas better. All notes and preliminary sketches should be kept on file. Nothing created at this stage should be destroyed. Sketches and layouts help refine the design. They also define physical aspects of the problem and help spin off creative or new solutions. All those concerned with the project should bring the notes and sketches developed to this point to the next meeting, where a short brainstorming session may introduce creative solutions to the problem.

Brainstorming. A brainstorming session would be appropriate at this time. **Brainstorming** is a group problem-solving technique that elicits a spontaneous contribution of ideas from all members of the group. No idea is rejected at this point, and all members of the group are considered equal. Ideas are not explored in depth at this time. All suggestions are recorded, to be used later to develop certain ideas. The acceptance of the project or design choice is a long way off at this stage of the project. Creative solutions are given as much merit as practical or obvious solutions.

Many aspects of the design background must be understood *before* the brainstorming session so that it does not become a useless exercise. Brainstorming may help find a unique or unthought of set of possibilities. Multiple products or variations of one product or solution should be thoroughly investigated before the next stage.

Review and Modification. After the brainstorming session, all notes, sketches, surveys, marketing analysis, and research data should be reviewed. Any ideas that show no merit are filed at this point. The basic thrust of the design effort starts to take shape. Many possible answers to the problem are still considered, but a basic or general idea of the direction of the project will be sought so as not to linger at this stage.

3.5 EVALUATION AND REFINEMENT OF IDEAS

The **evaluation** of possible solutions and their **refinement** into an end product (Fig. 3.13) is done at Stage 3. Refinement of a design is more restrictive at this point. More than one solution is still pursued, but the basic parameters of the project have been used to control the breadth of the design effort. An analysis of the project includes graphical analysis via descriptive geometry, statics, and vector analysis. Human factors engineering is also an aspect of this analysis.

Creative Choices and Alternative Size and Shape. Before a formal proposal is formulated, a number of possibilities for the project should be sketched and evaluated to determine size and shape. The basic parameters determined here help define the engineering and scientific analysis needed and what must be understood before the final decision on design choice is made.

The size and shape of the design will narrow the choice of materials. Specific design requirements, elements, and parameters are now solidified into a complete description of the problem and the thrust of a solution.

Comparative Analysis of Design Possibilities. To be successful, the analysis of a problem must include both its requirements and its limitations, in order. The restraints and limitations of a design problem help define the boundaries of the solution. Any analysis of the data gathered to this time must include the possibility of a compromise solution to the

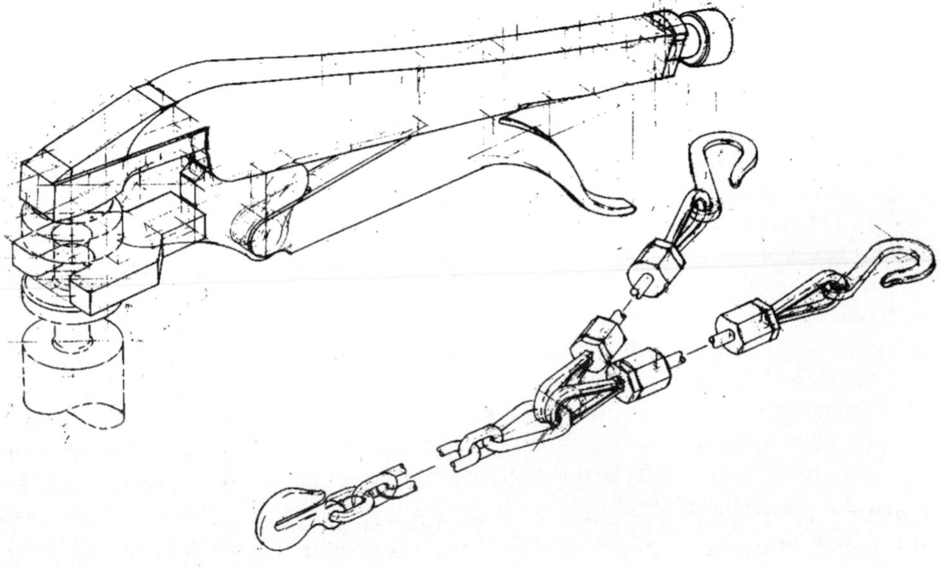

FIGURE 3.12 Pictorial Layout

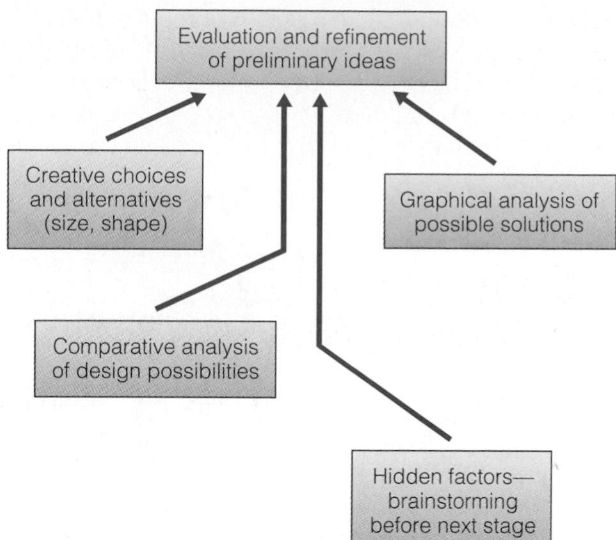

FIGURE 3.13 Stage 3 in the Design Process

problem. From this analysis, a decision must be made to proceed with any graphical analysis that may be needed to define the project better.

Graphical Analysis of Possible Solutions. Engineering analysis includes the use of graphics to define a number of possible solutions and analyze them using descriptive geometry, vector analysis, layout drawings, and 3D modeling with a CAD system. Figure 3.14 is an example of the use of descriptive geometry to find a clearance between a pipeline and a fixed point in space. Piping systems, as in Figure 3.15, are one part of a complete plant. The interferences between pipelines and other systems (e.g., electrical, heating/cooling) and the structure require a detailed analysis. Sketches and

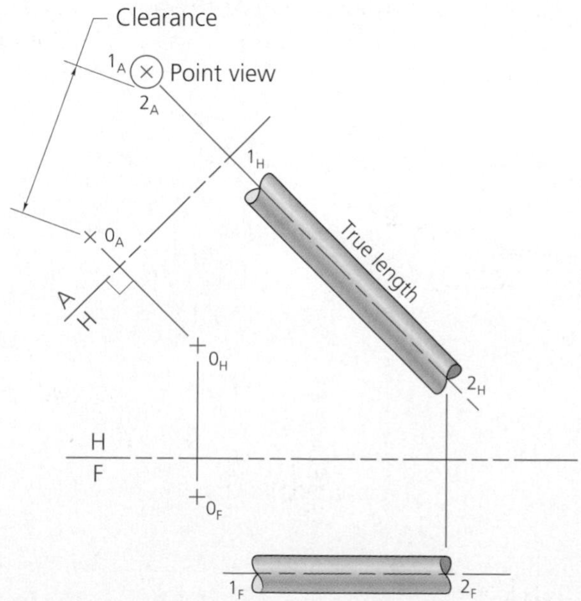

FIGURE 3.14 Descriptive Geometry Problem-Solving for the Shortest Distance Between a Pipe and a Fixed Point

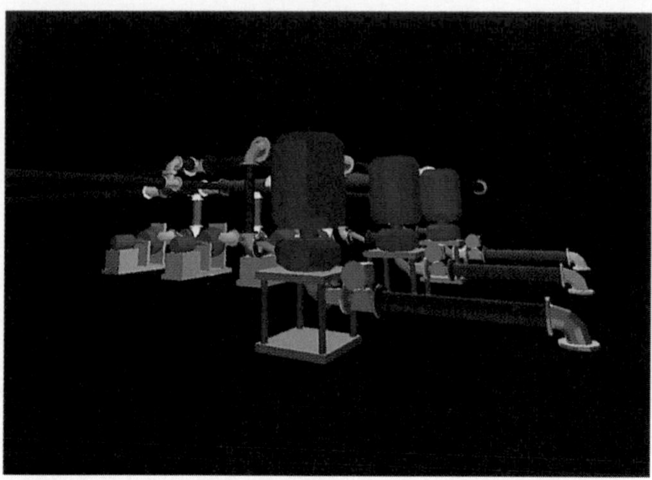

FIGURE 3.15 Shaded Image of Piping and Equipment

descriptive geometry drawings are created with instruments or on a computer—to scale. A selection of the "best possible solutions" is rendered for **graphic analysis.**

Human Engineering and Graphical Analysis. Product design includes consideration of human engineering requirements. Human engineering involves analyzing how people are affected by performing specific tasks and the man–machine interface. The first concern is normally referred to as ergonomics and the second as human factors. Both are important to the successful design of a product or a system.

Ergonomics is concerned primarily with the study of physiological responses to physically demanding work; environmental stress caused by temperature, noise, and lighting; motor skills for assembly; and visual-monitoring tasks. *Human factors* is the modeling of the human body in a work-related setting. Human factors data is useful in the design of a factory workstation in order to provide a comfortable environment and thereby increase work output and decrease job stress. As an example, three views of a man at work are shown in Figure 3.16. The seating and standing heights of a typical male, the comfortable reaching distance from both positions, and the maximum and minimum working area are defined graphically. Industrial design requires the study of body dimensions and movements. Simple products, such as hand tools, to complex system products, such as automobiles, require extensive use of human factors and ergonomic studies and recommendations.

Human engineering also considers a person's behavior within a work environment. The interaction of workers with their tools, equipment, or workstation is the focus of human engineering design. Strength capabilities relative to the equipment and workplace design are also essential factors in a sound and functional design. Much of the human engineering design research has come from the space program. The space program spawned the first intensive study of human physiology of man in the healthy state. Many of the tasks associated with space travel required intensive study of adverse environments to create appropriate designs for equipment and living. The restrictive work environment of a

ELEVATION VIEW — STANDING

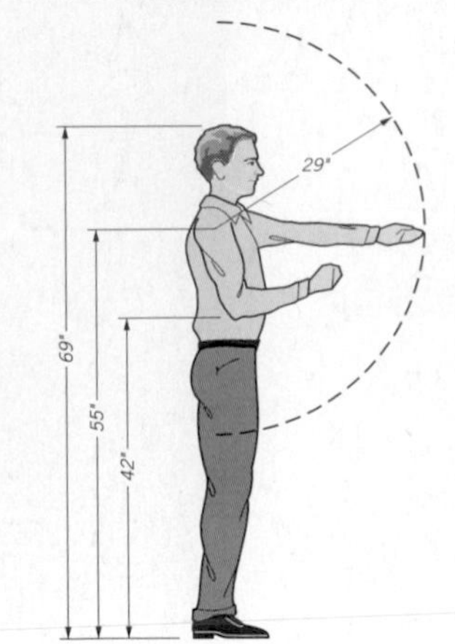

ELEVATION VIEW — SEATED

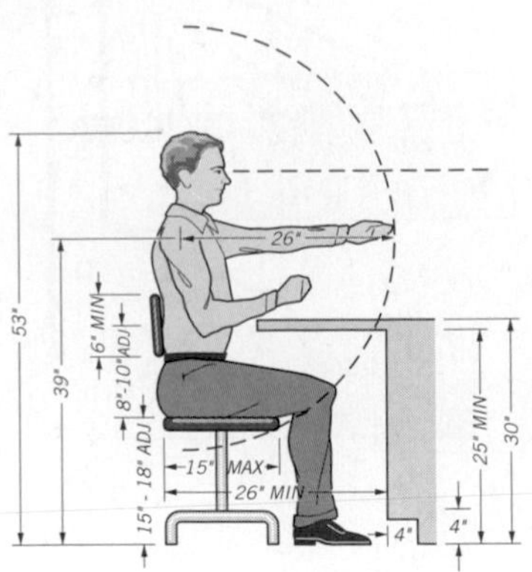

PLAN VIEW

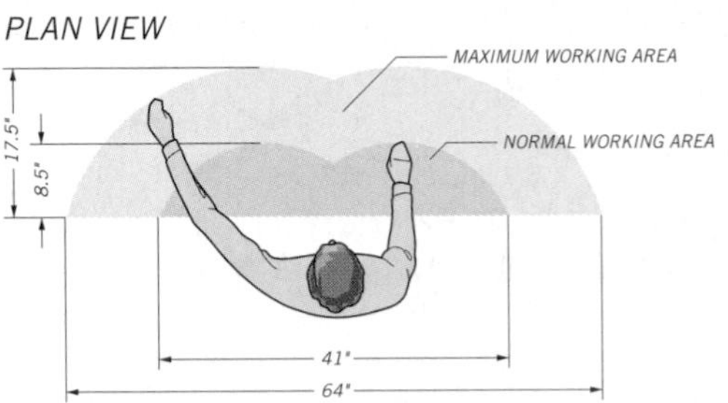

NOTES

1. SOURCE, HUMAN FACTORS IN ENGINEERING AND DESIGN, E. J. McCORMICK 4TH EDITION, McGRAW HILL
2. POPULATION SOURCE, NATIONAL HEALTH SURVEY, USPHS PUBLICATION 1000, SERIES 11, NO. 8, JUNE 1985
3. IN GENERAL, DESIGN WORK STATIONS TO ACCOMMODATE A 95TH PERCENTILE MALE WHILE ALLOWING REACH FOR A 5TH PERCENTILE FEMALE.

TECHNOLOGY GROUP STAFF ENGINEERING	
TITLE 50TH PERCENTILE MALE HUMAN FACTORS DATA	
DEPT NA LEVEL NA	TEKTRONIX, INC. BEAVERTON, OR.
SCALE 1/2" = 1"	
NAME J. GONZALES	APPROVED:
DATE 31 OCT 81	

FIGURE 3.16 Male Human Factors Data

spaceship required designs incorporating the findings of research on human factors and ergonomics.

The human factors dummy in Figure 3.17 was used to design an ejection seat for an airplane. The dummy, attired in a pressurization suit, is fitted into an ejection seat for engineering tests. Notice the foot clamps, arm guards, and stabilizing fins on the seat. The seat was designed by engineers to have a stable supersonic ejection with maximum projection for the pilot.

The design of products and systems used and operated by people incorporates human factors analysis as an important part of the research-and-analysis stage of the project. Typically, the operation of a system or product must incorporate the following objectives:

1. Minimize the possibility of injury caused by improper use of the product or system. Designs must incorporate safety features that make normal usage error-free. Avoiding injury to others adjacent to the user of the product is also important, as is anticipating misuse of the product.
2. The design should be as efficient as possible. Limiting user fatigue and stress due to repetition is essential to proper design.
3. Systems or products should be designed with physical attractiveness, operational ease, and error-free operation in mind. These factors contribute to overall user satisfaction and to the desire to purchase and maintain the unit.
4. The product or system should be designed with a positive, efficient, and functional user interface.

FIGURE 3.17 Human Factors Dummy

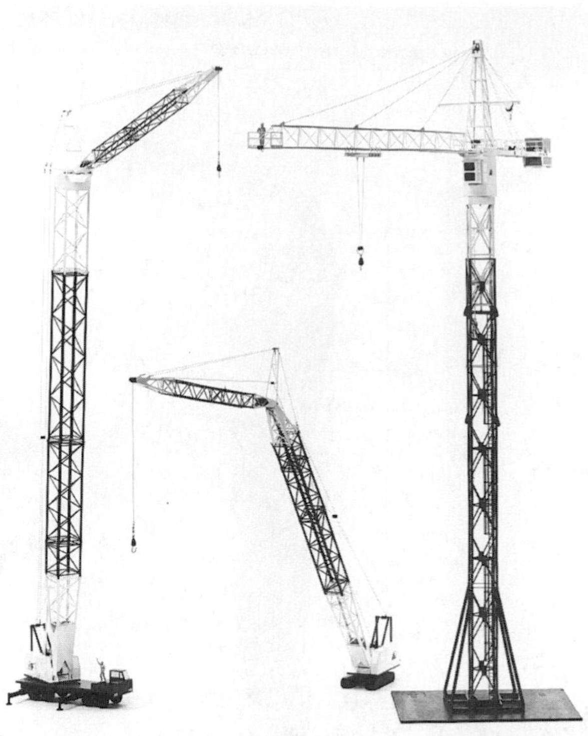

FIGURE 3.18 Model of a Crane

5. Products and systems must be designed to prevent catastrophic failure and must fail in a relatively safe mode at the end of their useful life. The end of a product's useful life must come with subtle and safe warnings.

FIGURE 3.19 Model of a Pipe-Laying Ship

The designing of controls for crane operation is an example of a system that requires the study and analysis of human engineering. The cranes in Figures 3.18 and 3.19 are operated by a center-post joystick. The design of such a control starts with the establishment of the physical movements required by the operator and of the variations in a typical operator's body dimensions. Figure 3.20 shows a set of sketches that helped establish the maximum movements

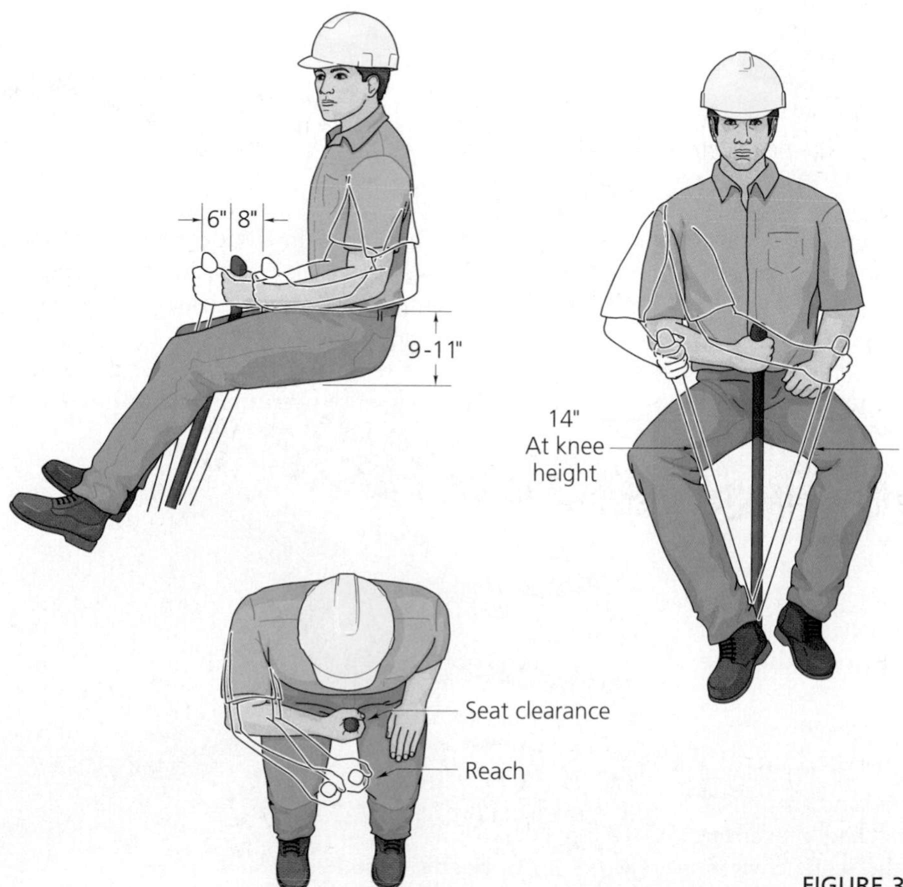

FIGURE 3.20 Control Stick Movement Studies

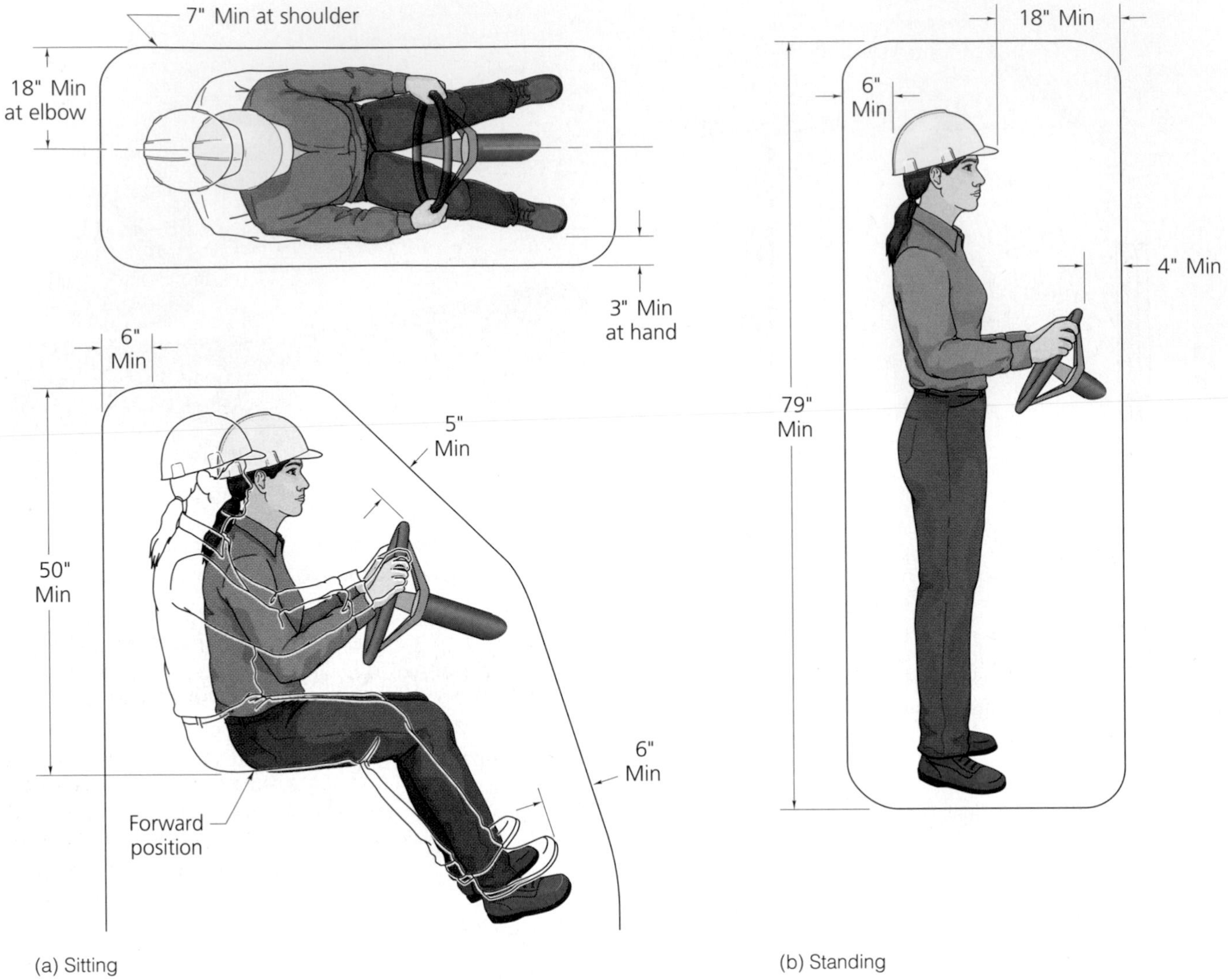

(a) Sitting

(b) Standing

FIGURE 3.21 Human Factors Study of a Cab Design

required for proper operation. Reach, seat clearance, stick height, lateral movement, and arm height are graphically described in this illustration. The given dimensions are rough estimates of the design requirements that were refined in a later step.

Descriptive geometry methods were used to solve graphically for potential interferences and to verify the degrees of freedom of movement of the control stick. If someone was supposed to be able to drive the operator's cab, then the human factors and ergonomic studies would include design of a space envelope [Figs. 3.21(a) and (b)]. The cab is designed for optimal, comfortable operation and safety during movement over rough surfaces. The determination of whether the operator was to stand or to sit would also have to be made at this stage of the design.

Product Design and Human Factors. The mechanical factors, anthropometric (human dimensions) and anatomical considerations (body and limb rotational and movement characteristics), ergonomic factors, and the work environment must also be considered in the design of consumer products. Hand tools require the study and utilization of these principles. The tools must be designed to be strong, functional, easy to carry, safe to operate, easy to store, compact, insulated from electrical shock, and slip resistant.

The design of the long-nose pliers in Figure 3.22 required

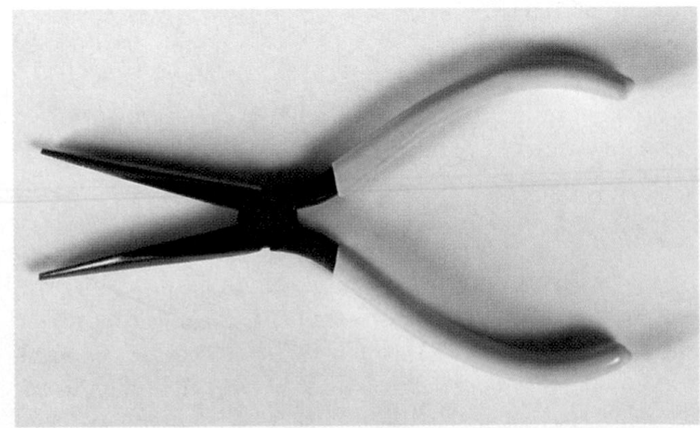

FIGURE 3.22 Needle-Nose Pliers

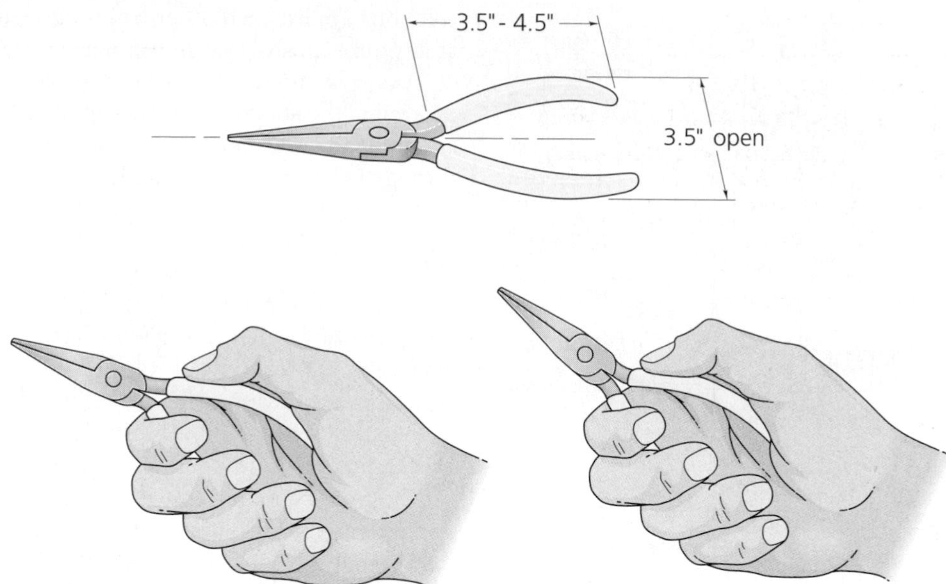

FIGURE 3.23 Design Studies of Pliers Handles

the designer to align the center of gravity with the grasping hand so that the user does not have to overcome rotational movement, or torque, of the tool. The tool handle is oriented so the user's wrist remains in the most comfortable and natural position while applying force. The sketches in Figure 3.23 show variations in designs for handle orientation. The handle must be long enough to accommodate the average hand so that the user's grip includes all fingers and provides proper leverage during operation. And yet, the maximum handle spread must not be so great that a small hand could not fully open the tool's jaws during operation.

Hidden Factors. What possible factors may have been overlooked in the design? Are there any aspects of the design that are suspect? If these and other such pertinent questions are not satisfactorily answered, the design team should go back to the beginning of the design process and review each step. The design proposal cannot be accepted without the consensus of the total team and all departments in the company. Solutions to any problems must be solved here, not later when they could prove costly.

A variety of pertinent questions should be honestly and openly discussed at this point in the project:

- What could go wrong?
- Will the product work?
- Will it sell?
- Will the company lose money?

Often, at this juncture the business managers will determine that although the product will sell, the company cannot, with its current assets, produce the item. A startup company may then be formed, with the design team becoming the core of a new company. The impact of potential failure is minimized while success produces a diversification of assets.

3.6 IN-DEPTH ANALYSIS OF PROPOSED SOLUTIONS

The **analysis and evaluation** (Fig. 3.24) of possible design solutions is normally done through a thorough investigation of the data that pertains to it. The use of graphs, charts, and diagrams can greatly improve this analysis and help in communicating the data to others involved in the project. Data can be categorized into three types: **survey data,** gathered by the marketing department evaluating a design's possible acceptance by the public; **design data,** gathered by analyzing the performance characteristics of the test model; and **comparison data,** used to balance two or more design

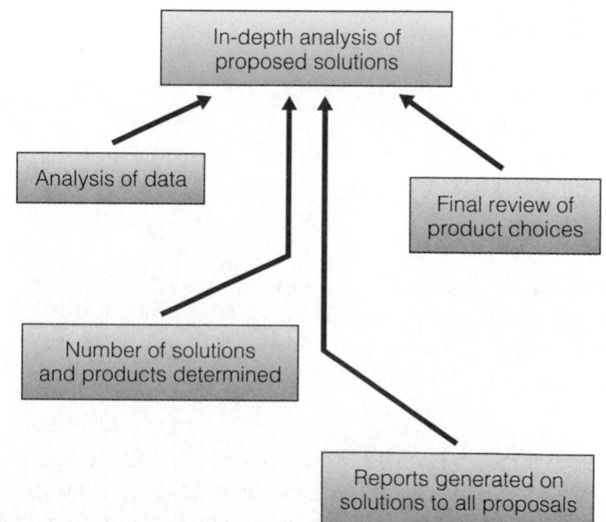

FIGURE 3.24 Stage 4 in the Design Process

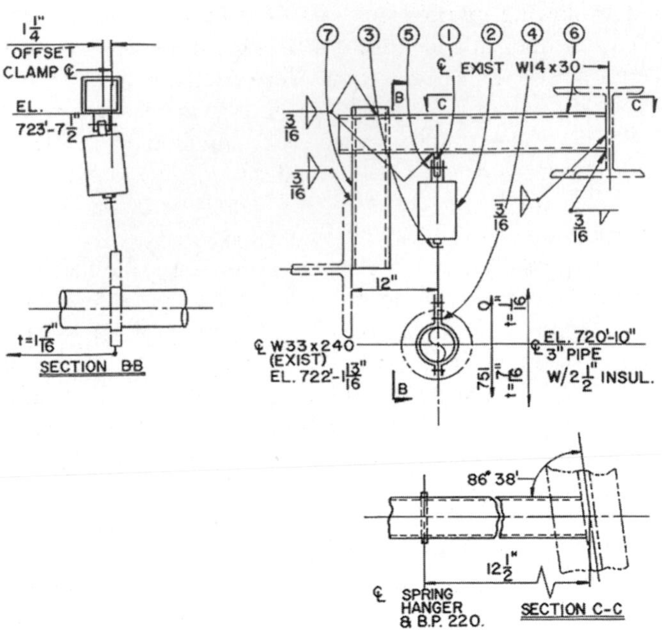

FIGURE 3.25 Spring Hanger Used in Pipe Support Design

solutions against each other based on material, manufacturability, or exclusive design features.

Data presented graphically can also help a designer determine the adequacy of a design based on environmental conditions or the reaction of the materials to stresses created during operation. As an example, consider piping systems. A typical piping system is designed to operate under specific temperatures. A steam line or a chemical process line may have a high operating temperature. The designer must create a piping system that not only transfers the line contents from one place to another, but also is flexible enough to handle expansion and contraction of the system during operation. Pipe supports must handle the full weight of the system and at the same time allow for restricted movement of the line caused by thermal expansion or earthquakes.

The pipe support shown in Figure 3.25 incorporates a spring hanger in its design. Spring hangers can adjust the load of the pipe and allow for limited safe movement. The graph in Figure 3.26 was used in the design of the pipe support. The thermal expansion of a pipe for a steam line at various temperatures is graphed. Six separate materials have been plotted. The expansion characteristics of the pipeline being designed are determined so as to meet the operating conditions.

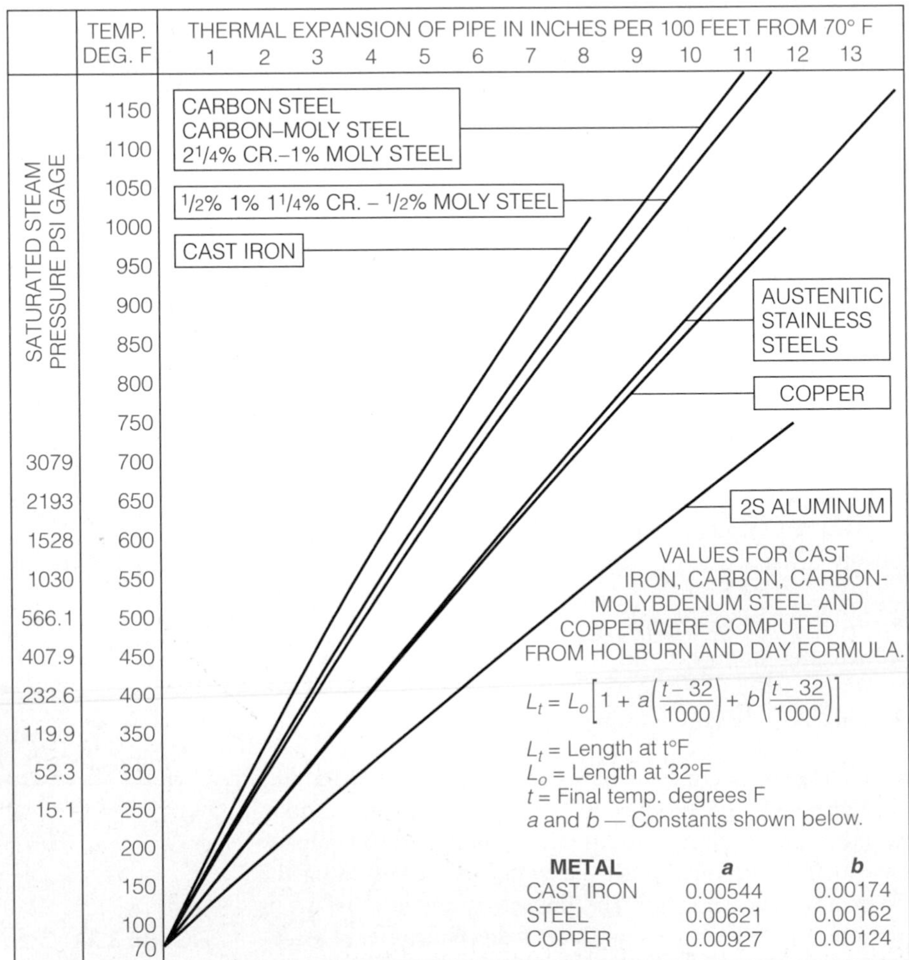

FIGURE 3.26 Thermal Expansion of Pipe

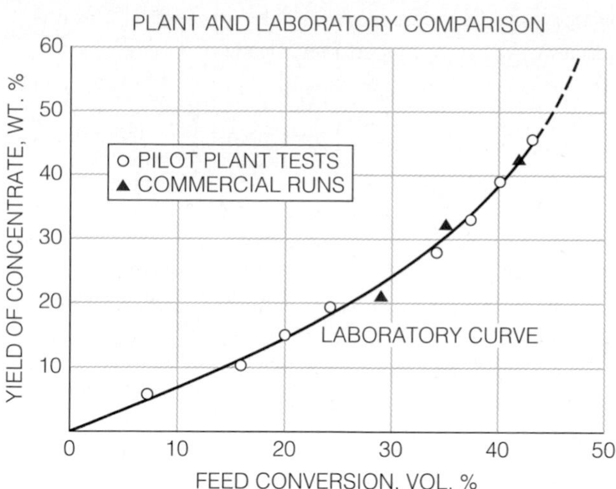

FIGURE 3.27 Graph Layout for Publications

Analysis of Data. Marketing data is useful in identifying features and capabilities desired by the public. Marketing data will, at times, drive the project design. The performance characteristics of a possible design solution are determined by analyzing the data generated from hardware testing. The use of graphs and charts is an integral part of this process.

Graphs and Charts. Throughout this text, information about the fundamentals of drafting and design is displayed in **graphs, charts,** and **diagrams.** Most technical graphs are plotted on preprinted grid paper. All graphs must contain the following information: axes or scale lines, major divisions, a brief title, designators on axes, units, one or more curves, and captions or notes (Fig. 3.27). Sometimes, in addition to this information, plotting symbols (data representation points) are required. A graph should be able to stand alone—that is, be easily understood without extensive explanation. Figures 3.28 and 3.29 show some of the do's and don'ts associated with creating a graph.

The importance of drawing clear, easily understood graphs should not be overlooked. Much of the information needed to do a design is shown in graphical form. This information includes characteristic performance curves of devices, stress input response curves of devices and entire systems, relationships of one quantity to another, waveforms, thermal expansion of items, and project schedules.

Graphical data is sometimes represented by noncircular curves, as in Figure 3.29. Graph lines are plotted on a given grid pattern on rectangular coordinate paper, representing two variables. When a CAD system is used for the graph, spline or smooth curves are used to connect the data points. The horizontal coordinate on a graph is usually plotted as the independent variable, and the dependent variable is plotted vertically. The horizontal, or **X,** axis is called the **abscissa** and the vertical, or **Y,** axis, the **ordinate.** The origin of the data may be located at one of a number of different places on the graph, such as the lower left corner of the graph, with 0, 0, as in Figure 3.29, or the center, as in Figure 3.30.

Figure 3.31 shows lines and symbols on a graph. Clear, accurate graphs and charts are essential for communicating

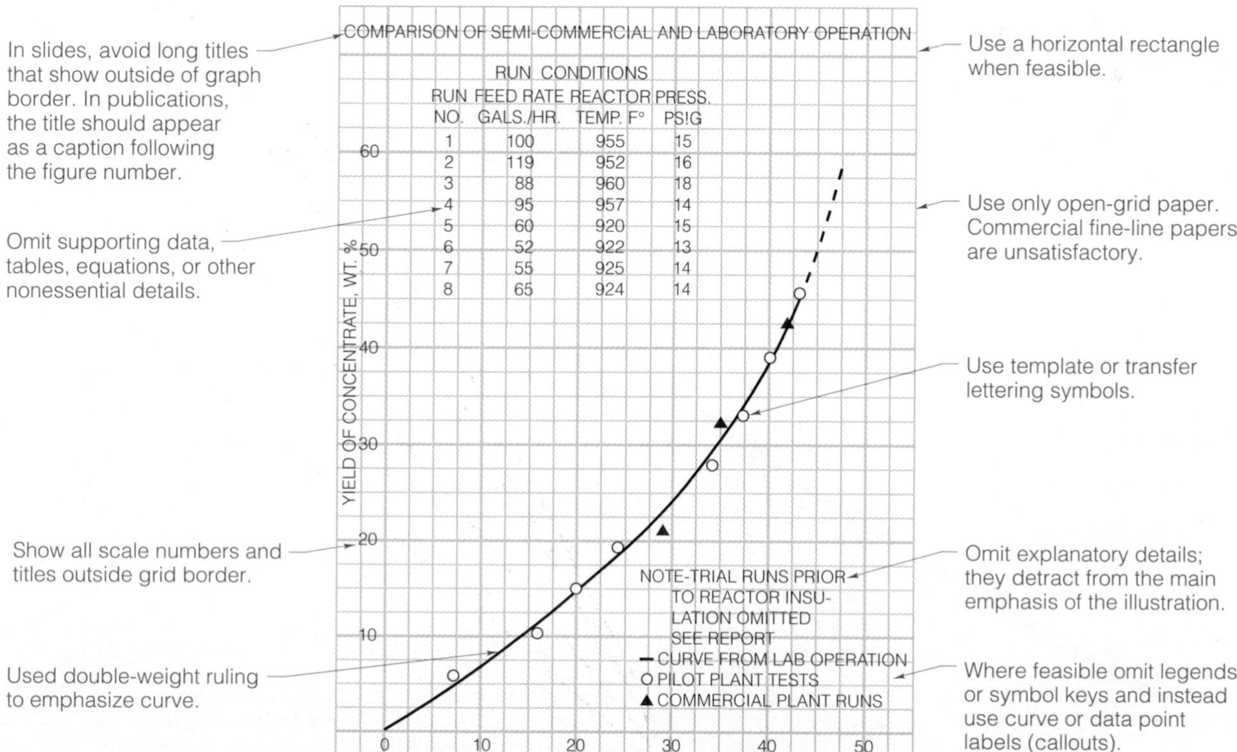

FIGURE 3.28 Example of Poor Illustration of Graph

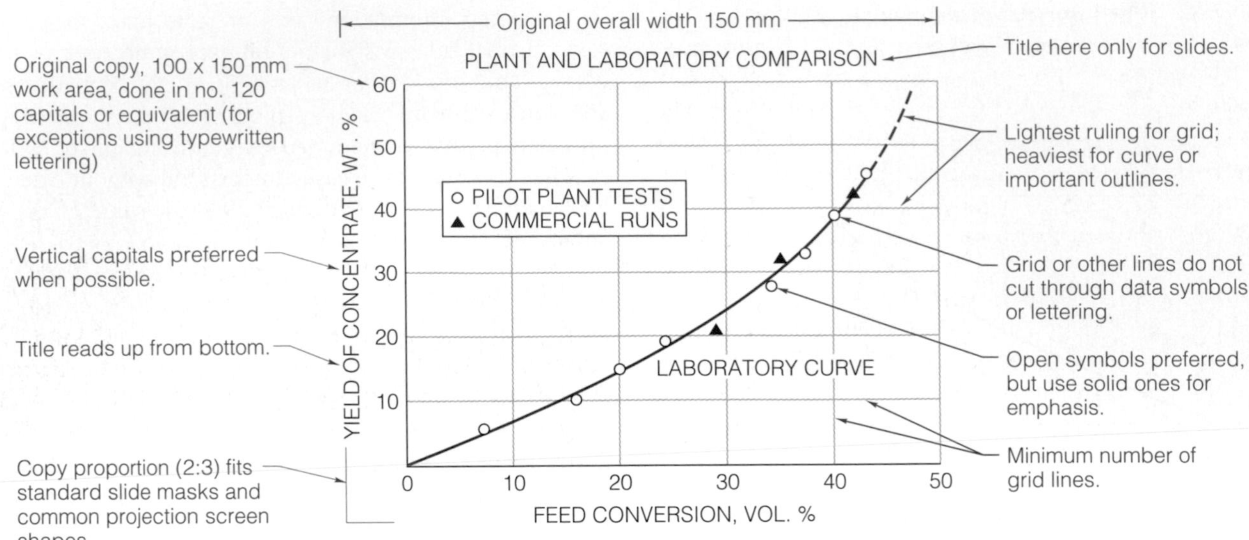

FIGURE 3.29 Example of a Good Illustration of a Graph

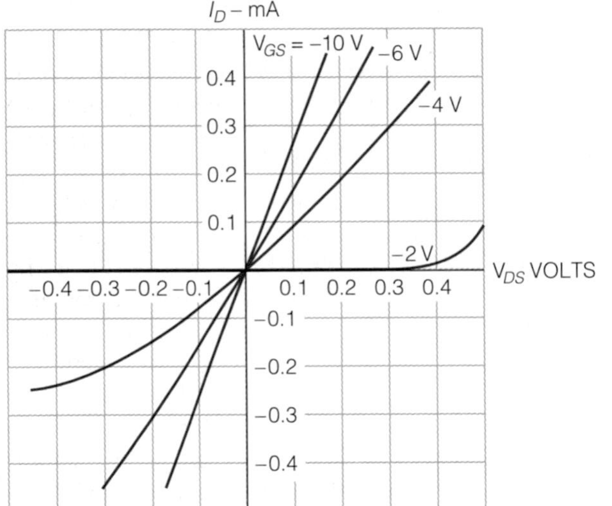

FIGURE 3.30 Voltage Versus Current Characteristics for an FET

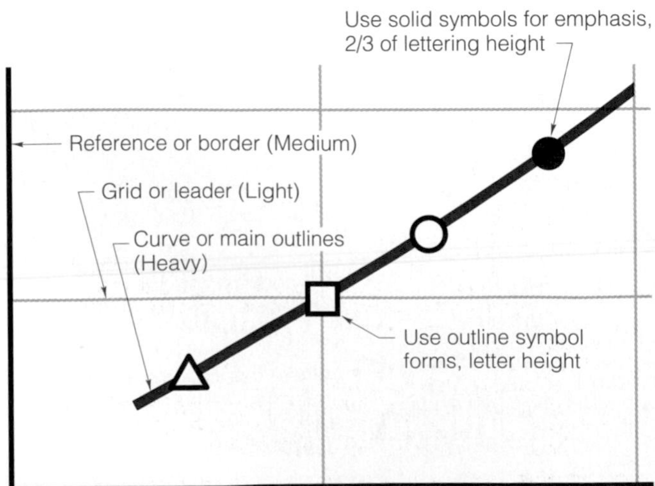

FIGURE 3.31 Lines and Symbols on Graphs

data in this stage of the design process. At present, almost all graphs and charts are generated with the help of a computer (Fig. 3.32).

(a)

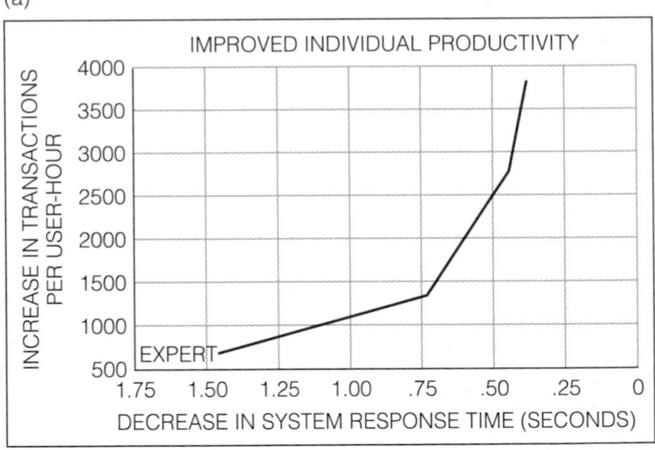

(b)

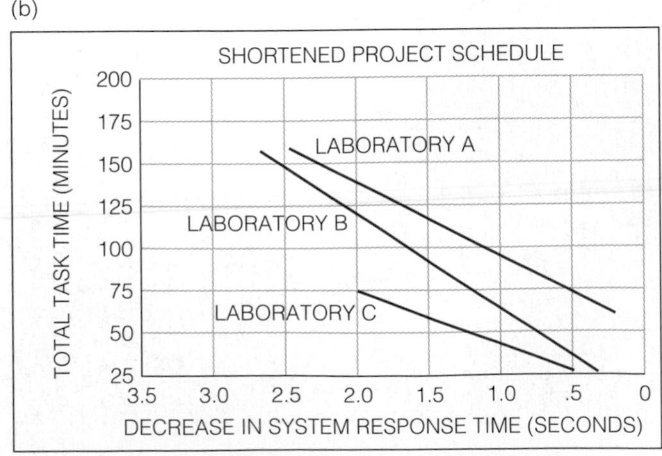

FIGURE 3.32 Computer-Generated Graphs

Number of Solutions and Products Determined. The process of creating a new design always gives rise to more than one solution. Often the different solutions involve trade-offs between cost, reliability, and time. Manufacturability concepts and procedures help ensure a design that is functional, cost-effective, and timely. If the design process has given birth to more than one solution or product, then it should be determined whether or not the project needs to be separated into different proposals. Each possible solution may produce a valid, marketable item. A record of each design possibility should be kept, including all sketches, written descriptions, and other data. It is appropriate to investigate more than one solution at a time. If a team is working on a project, it may need to be divided into subunits, with each subunit investigating different solutions. A variety of different designs should be created and developed to a point where they are sufficiently defined. They should then be evaluated and compared during the next stage of the project. Duplication by competing teams should be minimized by the sharing of data and resources.

The model of a hovercraft in Figure 3.33 is one of many design solutions being investigated by a ship building company. The surface-effect ship, in Figure 3.34, is a more detailed design alternative. The Coast Guard hovercraft shown in Figure 3.35 is a full-scale test prototype. The design of simple products or complex systems (like the hovercraft) requires a complete analysis of design alternatives and a comparison of performance capabilities, before production.

Reports Generated on Solutions to All Proposals. Technical reports containing design data on each possible solution must be generated at this point in the process. All pertinent factors, both positive and negative, must be clearly defined before the project is developed further. The design team does not want to enter the decision stage of the project ill prepared or with incomplete findings. Management will not pursue a project that is poorly defined. Properly presented projects need complete graphic descriptions and well-written reports.

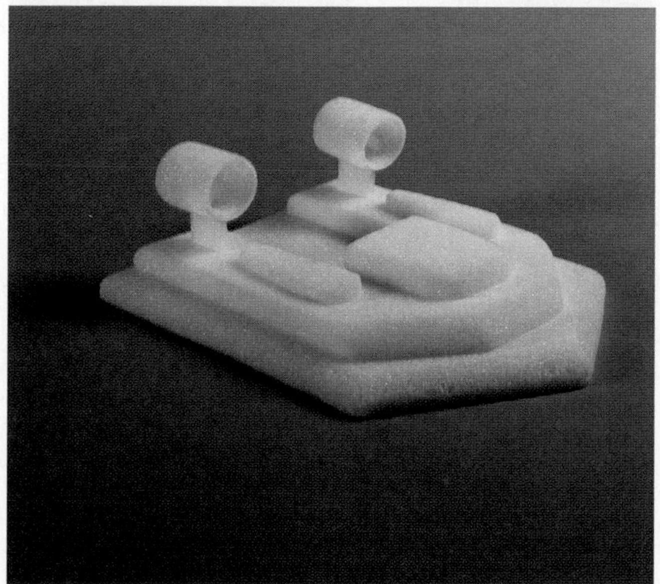

FIGURE 3.33 Model of a Hovercraft Produced by Carving Art Foam

FIGURE 3.34 Surface-Effect Ship Model

Final Review of Product Choices. The design department must evaluate each of the possible solutions before submitting their findings and suggestions to the management during Stage 5. Two or more design solutions should be prepared by the design team. During a team meeting, each of the designs should be compared. The merits of each design solution should be presented clearly, as should any drawbacks to the design. Each of the features incorporated into the design should be compared to those of other possible solutions. A list should be prepared ranking the relative importance of each feature.

Materials, manufacturing, and facility requirements should be discussed at this meeting to balance each solution's effectiveness against others, based on cost and company capabilities. At this point, select the best designs and prepare for the next stage of the project.

FIGURE 3.35 Coast Guard Hovercraft Test Model

3.7 DESIGN CHOICE AND PRODUCT OR SYSTEM DECISIONS

After all the data have been gathered on the design problem and the remaining possible solutions have been clearly defined, the fifth and last stage in the decision process is addressed (Fig. 3.36). Management has the final say on which project design solution to pursue. The designers, engineers, and other company personnel involved in the project present their findings and design choices to management for a decision. The choice depends on many variables. A project may even be abandoned at this point, or more than one product or solution may be accepted.

The development and design of supersonic aircraft required extensive research leading to new and unconventionally shaped wings to offset the effects of the abrupt and erratic changes in air flows encountered at the speed of sound. One of the solutions was the swept-back wing shown in Figure 3.37 being prepared for experiments. Resembling the tip of an arrow, this wing is more efficient because of the sharp reduction in the drag created by the formation of shock waves at and near the speed of sound. Earlier designs for wings were also modeled and tested in a wind tunnel to determine their in-flight characteristics. Each of these was eventually incorporated into modern military and commercial aircraft. The sharp wing style was also tested in a full-size mockup, shown in a wind tunnel experiment in Figure 3.38. The eventual prototype aircraft, shown in Figure 3.39, was the world's largest experimental aircraft. The B70 project was never produced because of cost, materials research, government decisions, and improvements in the accuracy of ICBMs, which made the aircraft obsolete. The development work was later used in the design of the Concord supersonic transport. The Stealth bomber (Fig. 3.40) involved technology and research developed for previous aircraft, but also incorporated special high-tech materials and design concepts to enable it to fly undetected by conventional radar.

At present, a revival of interest in supersonic transport is occurring. The years of research and development that seemed for naught may eventually bring an efficient, well-designed product to the market—a supersonic aircraft for commercial passengers.

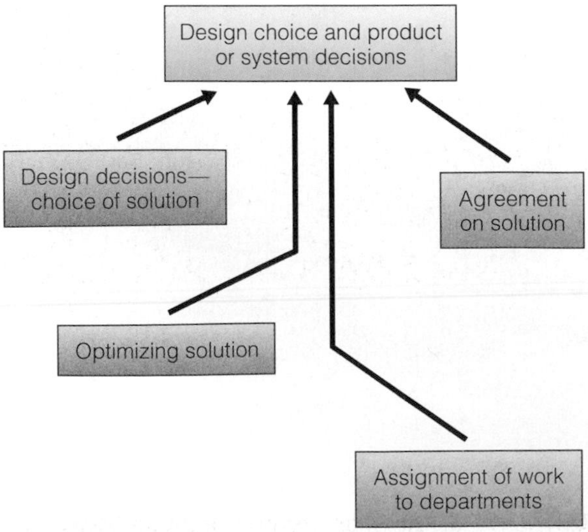

Design choice and product or system decisions

Design decisions—choice of solution

Agreement on solution

Optimizing solution

Assignment of work to departments

FIGURE 3.36 Stage 5 in the Design Process

FIGURE 3.37 Model Being Prepared for Research and Development of Air Flows and Wing

FIGURE 3.38 Aircraft Model Being Prepared for Wind Tunnel Studies

FIGURE 3.39 World's Largest Experimental Test Aircraft

Over the last twenty years, new materials such as composites have been developed. A new generation of materials will fly with the X-30, an experimental plane that will pioneer hypersonic travel in the late 1990s. To withstand the environmental impact of travel at 17,000 mph (Mach 2.5) and an orbit near that of the present-day space shuttle, carbon composite materials coated with ceramics will be used.

Sometimes a design concept exceeds the known capabilities of science and technology. In this case, the development of the design may have to wait for the technology to catch up with the concept. History has many examples of designs that were developed before they could be effectively, safely, and profitably brought to market. The former Soviet Union's 2000-mph transport and the French-English Concorde jet may have been premature efforts, considering design flaws and cost of operation.

Design Decisions. A complete technical report on each solution must be submitted at this juncture by the design group. The report consists of a design proposal and a timetable for completion of the project. All pertinent data regarding the design solutions must accompany the proposal, including cost analysis, time studies, capital requirements (personnel, equipment, and facility), design layouts, and other materials that may help in the decision process.

The management decision team, which includes members from the design, manufacturing, and marketing departments, evaluates the merits of each solution submitted by the design department. The evaluations of competing designs consider the following:

Design Comparison

- Capability to satisfy the original statement of the design intent and project definition
- Cost, manufacturability, and reliability
- Design requirements for precision (which will affect cost), operating efficiency/flexibility, maintenance projections, and environmental impact
- Material and manufacturing processes
- Effect of configuration and complexity on manufacturing costs

After each of these is satisfactorily investigated, the management team can decide on the design choice or choices. The design team then proceeds to the next stage, optimizing the selected design.

Optimizing Solution. The design team further develops and refines the selected design. The selection of materials,

FIGURE 3.40 Stealth Bomber on Computer Screen (left) and in Flight (above)

processes, and other design requirements can be further refined at this stage. Each feature and capability of the design should be analyzed and evaluated. Any changes should be made at this point so that, during Stage 6 (development and implementation), there are no drastic changes in the design that hinder its completion. Any new desirable features or capabilities should be evaluated. A list of concerns and considerations should include the following:

Design Refinements

- Should any new or desired features be added at this time?
- Should the effective life of the design be extended or decreased?
- Are there any aspects of the design's appearance that need to be changed or defined better?
- Based on the design's potential configuration and operating conditions, what materials should be considered acceptable?
- Is the design manufacturable?
- What are the basic cost parameters for the design?
- Can the design be more flexible and interchangeable without cost increases?
- What are the tolerance requirements?
- Have the stress factors and alignment problems that may be encountered been determined?
- Has the need for study models, prototypes, and test models for motion, stress, or other design studies been established?

Agreement on Solution. After the choice of solutions is determined, it is important that all of the concerns of each department be addressed. A consensus must be reached on the acceptability of the solution. There should be complete agreement as to the direction and choice of management's decision. Reservations by one or more of the departments in the company about the product's feasibility are addressed and eliminated at this time, so as not to undermine the design's success. All basic features and design requirements are now solidified into an accepted solution.

Assignment of Work. The project work schedule is determined after the final design is chosen and the **project launch** is given the go-ahead by management. Several methods of project scheduling are used in industry. One method is the **Project Evaluation and Review Technique (PERT)**, for coordinating the many activities associated with a successful design project. All departments must be coordinated efficiently to move the project from design through production smoothly and error free.

The success of the project depends on this coordination. At the project launch, each department is given specific work assignments and time requirements. The **critical-path method** of scheduling project work assignments is used in conjunction with PERT to control the project. The critical-path method was used in the design and manufacturing of the trackball input device to be discussed in Section 3.11, Design Project Example.

3.8 DEVELOPMENT AND IMPLEMENTATION OF DESIGN

The development and implementation stage of the design process includes the drawing, modeling, testing, analysis, and refinement of the design (Fig. 3.41). The actual documentation of the project can be done manually or on a CAD system.

Physical models are used for design and testing (Fig. 3.42). Actual full-scale prototypes, developed from design drawings, are used to test for strength and design flaws. The rotor mount test in Figure 3.43 focused on that portion of the prototype design. Other models are used for testing different aspects of the design.

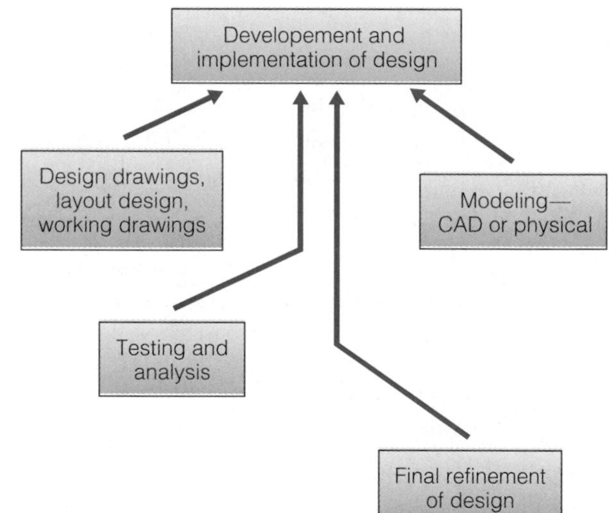

FIGURE 3.41 Stage 6 in the Design Process

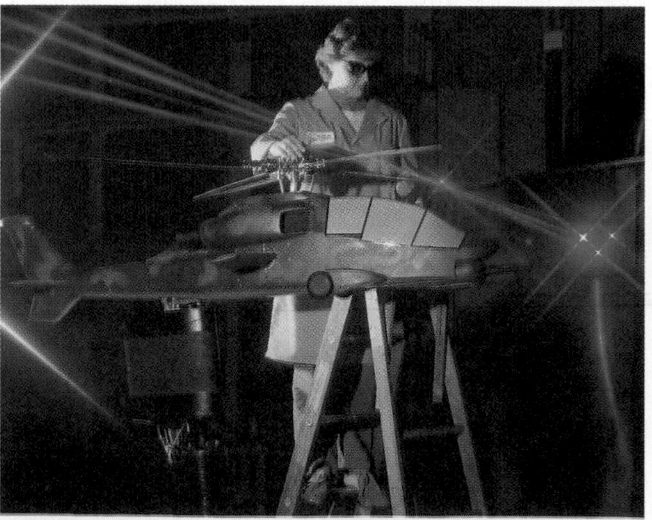

FIGURE 3.42 Test Being Prepared for the Scale Model of a Helicopter

FIGURE 3.43 Rotor Test

FIGURE 3.44 Space Shuttle Design

The design and development of a project takes many forms while it weaves through a series of trials and errors, testing, and refinement. The space shuttle started as a design concept and proposal. The pictorial rendering in Figure 3.44 is quite unlike the final vehicle. The original designs were drawn, modeled, tested, and refined many times before design completion.

Stage 6 in the design process is the heart of all design efforts. It is when most of the work is done and the project brought to fruition. All previous steps must have been accomplished effectively for this step to be successful. If the system or product was not properly identified, the research was not conducted correctly, alternative solutions were not developed and analyzed, the analysis of all data was inadequate, and all departments involved in the project were not incorporated in the first five stages, the development and implementation of the design might not come to successful conclusion. The sixth stage starts with the creation of design drawings, either manually or with a CAD system.

Design, Layout, and Working Drawings. At this step in the design process, it is important for all preliminary work to be complete and for the design to have been accepted. No major changes in the design should be implemented at this point. The acceptance of the project by all parties is essential.

A majority of this text is devoted to this stage of the design process. Manual or CAD-generated technical drawings or models are the primary means of communicating design and manufacturing information at this time. Drawings are also required before the construction of physical models: test, prototype, mock-ups, presentation, process, system, or product.

Similar designs and previous work are useful guides for product improvement design work. The designer must be familiar with existing documents. There are many situations where the redesign of an existing item or refitting of an existing system necessitates the use of older drawings that have been completed under previous standards. Most design work rarely involves original design work from concept to production, but is instead a continual evolution of an existing product. Each member of a design team works only on a small portion of the total effort.

Physical Models. **Models** are used throughout the industry as scaled representations of systems design and for refinement and testing of product designs. A **systems model** shows an installation: components, structure, and instrumentation. A model provides a better understanding of any installation and can be used as a tool for design and checking. Product models are employed in many stages of the design process to establish scale, appearance, and function of a product. Scale models of tractor-trailer designs are shown in Figure 3.45.

The designer can request a model at almost any stage of the design process. The type of models requested depends on the product or system and the availability of modeling facilities. Outside vendors are, at times, called on to complete a model. Regardless of who does the modeling or where, the designer will be an important part of its creation.

Engineering systems models are a design tool that can eliminate unnecessary problems, bad design, inefficient

FIGURE 3.45 Tractor-Trailer Design Models

planning, and other expensive, time-loss situations. They are used throughout the petrochemical, nuclear, and conventional power-generation industries. They are also encountered in food and beverage processing, pulp and paper manufacture, pharmaceutical processing, and other fields of systems design. Product design uses models throughout the design process, including research and development.

When working with a three-dimensional model (Fig. 3.46), the designer can visualize the design sequences and operations necessary for the project. This may not be possible when using a large assortment of drawings.

Models are most advantageous as a working tool, from the beginning stages of a project through the entire design phase. The beginning or preliminary models may look nothing like the final design model. Many intermediate stages may be needed to provide the 3D information for solving problems that may be encountered.

A **mock-up model** is a full-size replica of a proposed design, used primarily to refine the appearance of the product: its size, configuration, color, and artistic considerations. This type of model is not often involved in movement or operation design.

Product models are found more often in mechanical engineering fields to help design various parts of machinery or other mechanical devices, such as components that must be manufactured. In some cases, such models are built to a scale larger than that of the project itself.

Prototype models are basically similar to product models, but are sometimes working simulations of the product. In the case of an airplane, the company might build an actual, full-scale prototype to gain knowledge of its aerodynamic characteristics, and also to estimate public acceptance and sales. Some prototype models are mock-ups of the eventual product. Three-dimensional prototypes are sometimes required in the design of mechanisms to test their performance and capabilities. A prototype will often be close to the same configuration as the finished product. Therefore, the prototype model is used in the project design stage, after much of the design data has already been determined and the choice of designs made. Prototypes are tested under typical operating conditions of the proposed product.

FIGURE 3.46 Working with a 3D Plant Model

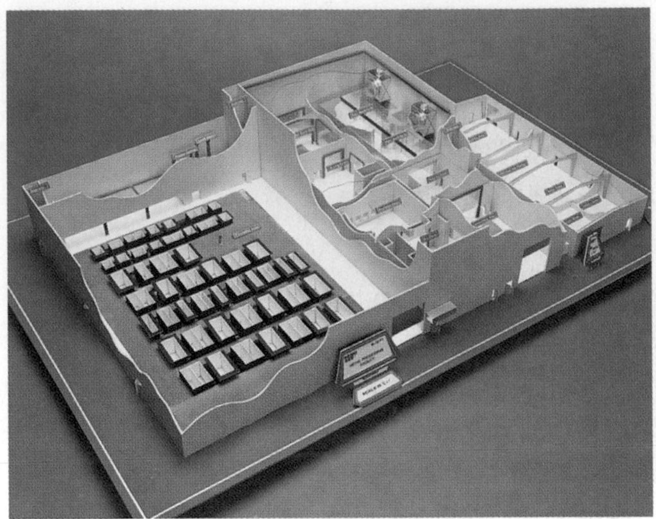

FIGURE 3.47 Scale Model of Metals and Spray Painting Facility

Presentation models, such as the one in Figure 3.47, are created to display a project, building, product, or design to the general public, or for sales.

CAD Modeling. Modeling with a 3D CAD system allows the designer to create multiple options for a design. A CAD model can be altered much easier than a layout on paper or a physical model. The CAD model can be used in every phase of the design decision process.

Three-dimensional modeling capabilities are grouped into four basic categories: 3D wireframe models, 3D surface models, hybrids of these first two types, and solid models.

Wireframe Models As the name signifies, a wireframe model is one in which the part geometry is represented by interconnected edges (Fig. 3.48). These edges may be lines, arcs, or splines. Most CAD systems with 2D drafting capabilities can create 2D wireframe models for 2D numerical control or to generate drawings. Three-dimensional systems, however, provide better modeling capability than the 2D systems.

Three-dimensional wireframe models (Fig. 3.49) have the same basic elements as the 2D model but add the **Z** coordinates. Visualization is much better with the 3D wireframe model than with the 2D wireframe model, and it is easier to use.

Surface Models Three-dimensional surface models are con-

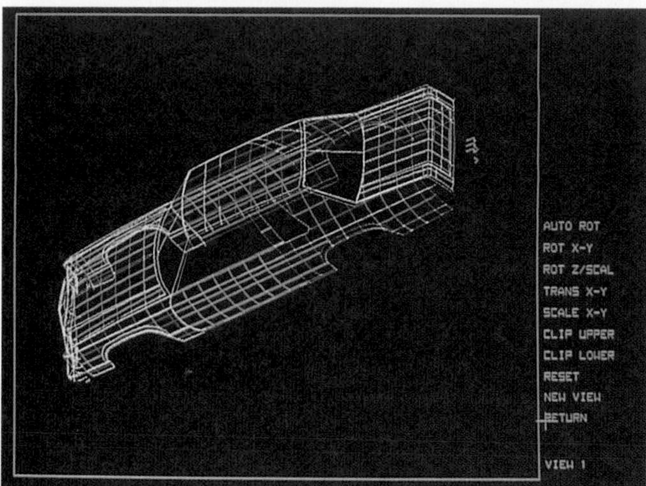

FIGURE 3.48 Wireframe Model of a Car

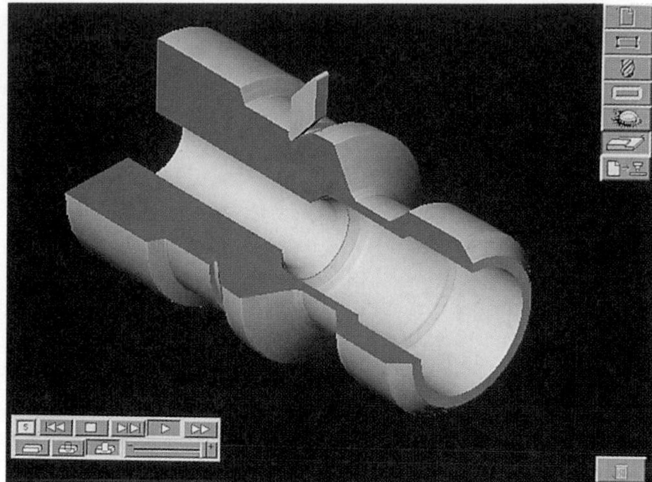

FIGURE 3.50 3D CAD Geometry Creation with Virtual Gibbs Features

structed by stretching a transparent membrane over the wireframe model. These membranes then become the faces of the model. The faces may be simple surfaces, such as planes, cylinders, and spheres, or more complex surfaces, such as ruled surfaces, extrusions, rotations of spline curves, and sculpted surfaces.

Three-dimensional surface models (Fig. 3.50) can represent shapes that are difficult to construct with wireframes, for example, styled surfaces, such as the outer skins of automobiles, and function surfaces, such as turbine blades and gears.

Hybrid Models Most 3D modeling systems on the market are a combination of wireframe and surface modeling. The addition of the surfaces eliminates some of the deficiencies of the wireframe model. Specifically, the model can be unambiguous and complete.

Solid Models The major requirement of a solid modeler is that it be able to construct an unambiguous representation of parts or assemblies (Fig. 3.51). Constructive solid geometry (CSG), boundary representation (b-rep), and parametric modeling are the three popular methods for creating a solid model.

A solid design model (Fig. 3.50) forms the master representation of a part, instead of the engineering drawing. The main output of a design office is a solid model of the part together with all the associated information contained on the engineering drawing. Engineering drawings are a secondary function when this system is used. In particular, the drawings, if required, are generated from the model. The combination of a solid model and the necessary tolerance and associated technical data is called the product model. Functions downstream of the design office take the product model as their primary input.

Physical Models from a CAD Database. Conceptual models are an important part of the product design process.

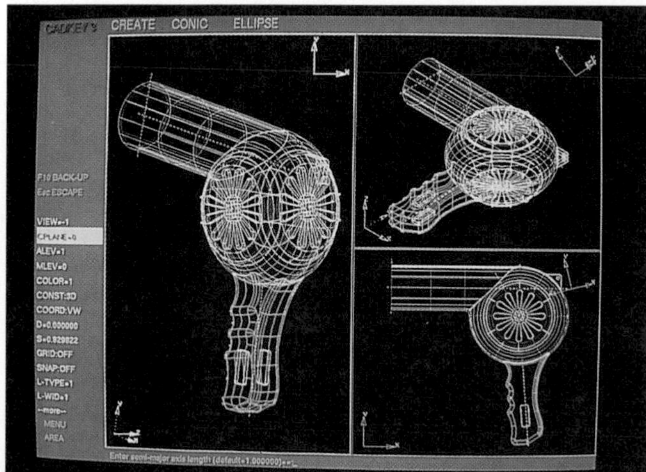

FIGURE 3.49 3D Wireframe Design Model of a Hairdryer

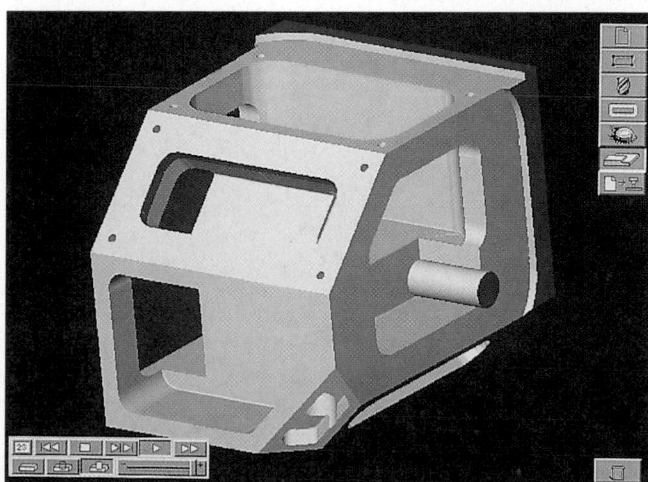

FIGURE 3.51 3D Real-Time Cut Part Rendering with Virtual Gibbs System

Industrial designers and packaging engineers get a computer representation of their idea via CAD/CAM/CAE. Sometimes, however, seeing the part on a 2D high-resolution graphic screen, or even on the stereoscopic monitors that project a 3D view, is not enough. The "soft" touch of the physical model can bring a design to life, sometimes revealing unanticipated problems. By quickly forming 3D conceptual models from design ideas, engineers can evaluate a design, demonstrate its feasibility, and sell the concept.

Building conceptual models, prototypes, and patterns for castings are necessary steps in product design—but expensive and time-consuming, often accounting for over half of the design effort. **Rapid prototyping (RP)** is currently changing the way products are designed and brought to market. The ability to create plastic model parts (Fig. 3.52) in a matter of hours without tooling, using the same CAD database created while designing the part on the CAD system, is revolutionizing design. CAD/CAM/CAE software, chemistry, laser, and optical scanning technologies have been combined to form this unique process. Rapid prototyping, which creates 3D plastic parts from CAD/CAM/CAE data in a matter of hours, is producing parts for the automotive, aerospace, computer, medical, consumer, and electronic components industries. Applications of this technology include conceptual designs, prototypes, testing models, and casting master patterns.

Conventional model making proves to be time-consuming and expensive. Typically, a design engineer creates a 3D model on a mechanical CAD system or on a drafting table. Then paper drawings are plotted and passed to a model maker, who interprets them to create a prototype. Traditional methods include creating models from wood, clay, or a block of solid material, which is sculpted, cut, or machined.

Stereolithography, one of the most common rapid prototyping methods in industry today, is used to make conceptual models, plastic prototypes, soft tooling for silicone and sand molds, and patterns for metal castings (Fig. 3.52). Models created with stereolithography help to visualize designs, to verify engineering changes, and to check form, fit, and function.

Stereolithography Process. A 3D model database produced on a CAD format is sliced into a stack of thin layers using the stereolithography software. The layers are then redrawn on the surface of a vat of liquid photopolymer by a computer-controlled ultraviolet laser projector. Via a stereolithography apparatus (SLA), solid or surface data (from a CAD database) are sliced by software into very thin cross sections. A laser then generates a small, intense spot of ultraviolet (UV) light that is moved across the top of a vat of liquid photopolymer by a computer-controlled optical scanning system. The laser changes the liquid photopolymer to a solid wherever it touches, as it prints precisely each cross section. A vertical elevator system lowers the newly formed layer, while a recoating and leveling system establishes the next layer's thickness. Successive cross sections, each of which adheres to the one below it, are built one on top of another to form the part, from the bottom up. After the last layer is made, the part is removed from the SLA and given a high-intensity flood of UV light to complete the polymerization process. The part can then be finished by sanding, sand blasting, painting, or dying.

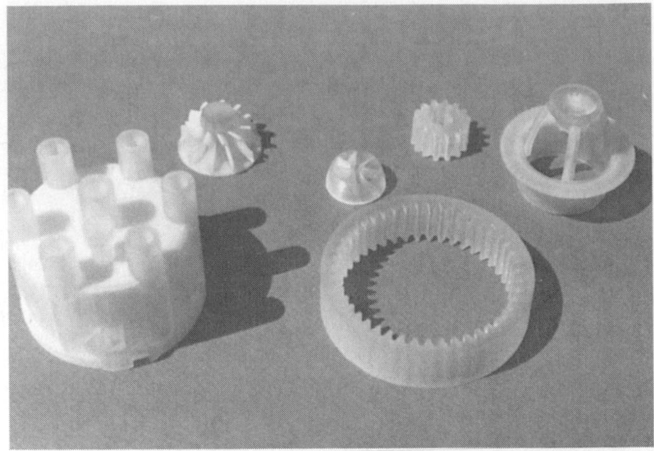

FIGURE 3.52 Parts Produced via Stereolithography

Testing and Analysis. One of the primary responsibilities of the designer is to create a design that will withstand the stresses under which the product, part, or system is to function. If the design is to be operated safely, the proper strength becomes the designer's major concern. The size and configuration of a structural member, the ability of the part to withstand loads without breaking, deforming, or fracturing, the safe design of rotating machinery, the shielding of radical temperatures in operation of a system, and the stress produced by the application of external stress during operation are all in the domain of the designer. After the product or system is designed, it must undergo testing and analysis. Lab testing for strength of materials and finite-element analysis using a CAD system (Fig. 3.53) are both used throughout industry to determine the adequacy of the design.

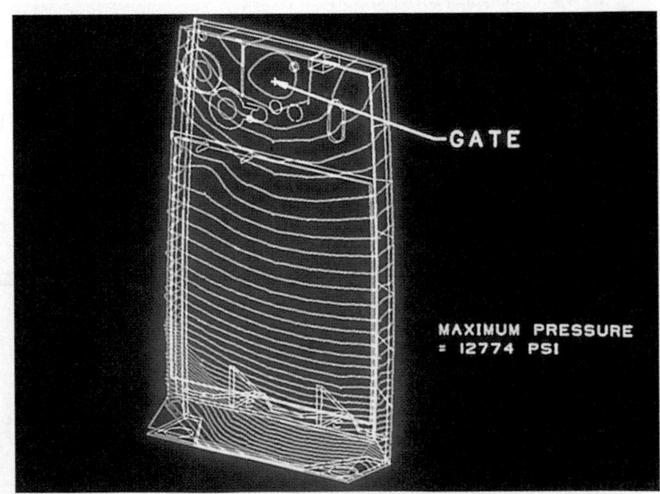

FIGURE 3.53 Wireframe Model of a Mold Part During Analysis

Focus On . . .

STEREOLITHOGRAPHY IN THE DESIGN PROCESS

Stereolithography was invented in 1984, was patented in 1986, and became commercially available in early 1988. In 1989 only one commercial product was available. Today more than a dozen models are available from at least six manufacturers. In that brief time, stereolithography has moved from being primarily a visualization tool to a product by which several design iterations can be made and some limited tooling and prototype parts (see figure) can be produced. For example, stereolithography parts can be used in place of wax models for patterns in investment casting.

Stereolithography can produce a solid object from a CAD model (surface or solid) (see figure) quickly and efficiently by directing ultraviolet laser radiation onto a liquid photopolymer. The photopolymer hardens when exposed to this laser beam. Each pass produces a hard polymer down to a certain depth. The platform on which the exposed polymer sits is lowered after each pass, sending the hardened polymer under the surface of the liquid bath. The part is built up layer by layer. The designer can hold and examine a real object at any stage in the design process. Changes in the CAD file can be quickly translated into a new solid object. The cost of each prototype (see figure) is significantly lower than when produced by more traditional methods, so that design iterations are quicker. More radical designs can be considered as well.

The first stereolithography systems produced parts that were fragile and brittle. Today the parts are stronger and tougher. Initial systems had a part accuracy that was poor and could exceed 0.050 in. New resins and changes in the software have reduced part error to 0.010 in. or less. Most errors are within 0.005 in. After a part is produced, it must be cleaned and postcured. Liquid resin that clings to the part is wiped off, and the part is placed in a solvent cleaning system. Postcuring finishes the polymerization process and increases the part's strength. Small parts are cured in an hour or two, but large parts may require up to 10 hours. To become functional models, prototypes may be polished, painted, or spray-metal coated.

Many successful commercial companies (see figure) today use rapid prototyping stereolithography systems to evaluate a design and reduce the time to market for commercial products. For example, Motorola has built over 8000 models to date at about one-tenth the cost of conventional prototypes and saved over $2 million. Delivery time for a part at Motorola is only 18–20 hours. Automatic generation of tooling is the next challenge for stereolithography systems.

Solid model of shaver.

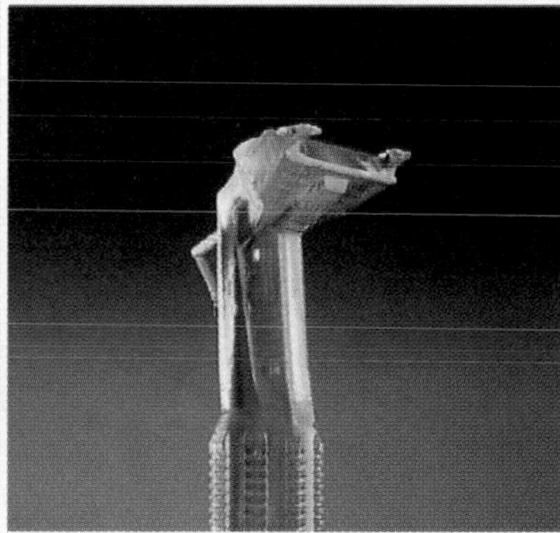

Stereolithography prototype model.

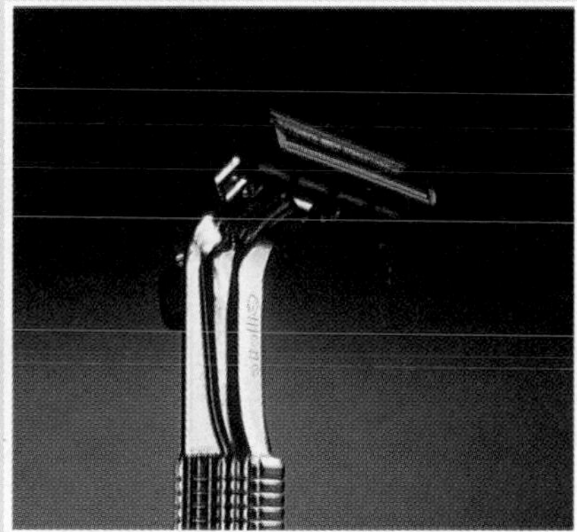

Final part.

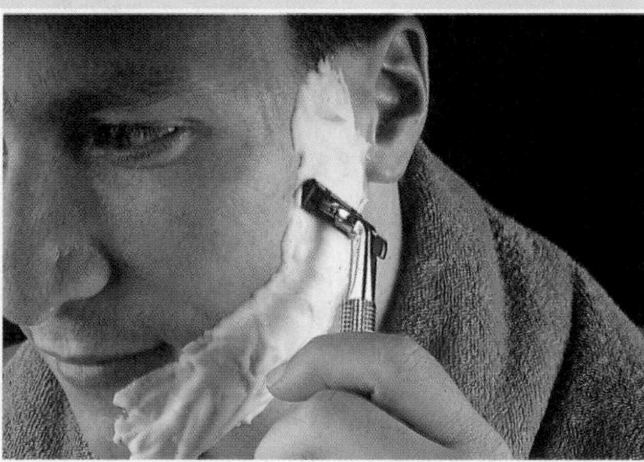

Shaving with the product.

Finite-Element Method. To design an optimal structure or to determine the cause of failure after manufacture, design engineers commonly employ computerized design and analysis methods. One such method, which is supported by the CAD system, is the **finite-element method** (FEM, sometimes finite-element analysis, FEA). The finite-element method is an engineering tool that mathematically simulates the behavior of a part. Via FEM, the designer can determine the amount and location of stress in a design, without building a test prototype.

A typical finite-element modeling program allows the designer/engineer to create the model, prepare it for analysis, and then graphically display the results. As an integral part of a CAD system, the FEM program takes full advantage of all graphics and dynamics features. It also uses part information (since the part design information already exists), thus reducing the likelihood of errors and speeding the entire analysis cycle. Finite-element analysis starts with finite-element modeling.

Finite-element analysis is the second part of the finite-element method. It is generally a mainframe computer program that analyzes the information from the text file to determine the amount and location of stress. Mass properties, including weight, volume, and center of gravity, can also be calculated (Fig. 3.54).

Once the analysis is performed, numerical results are returned to the CAD system and the finite-element analysis postprocessing phase begins. This involves reviewing the analysis results, determining problem areas, and modifying the design.

Final Refinement of Design. The finalization of a design will begin at this point in the design sequence. After the basic design decisions have established an acceptable product, and it has been drawn, modeled, and tested, the final design refinements are made. Any alterations and refinements in this stage require many hours of manual drawing changes or alteration of the design database on a CAD system.

When complete, the final design is evaluated for potential new technology, innovation, and patent possibilities. A patent can be granted for a process or a unique invention or discovery. A patent is granted only to an individual, not to a company. The patent law states, "Any person who invents or discovers any new and useful process, machine, manufacture, composition of matter, or any new or useful improvement thereto, may obtain a patent." A patent is established with a written description of the invention or process, normally accompanied by drawings.

Patent drawings—on standard patent drawing sheets—must be included as one portion of a patent application. Figure 3.55 shows a patent drawing. Inking is required, and shading is normally used to show the invention realistically. The patent drawing will be the last drawing created for a

FIGURE 3.54 Finite-Element Modeling and Analysis Using a CAD System

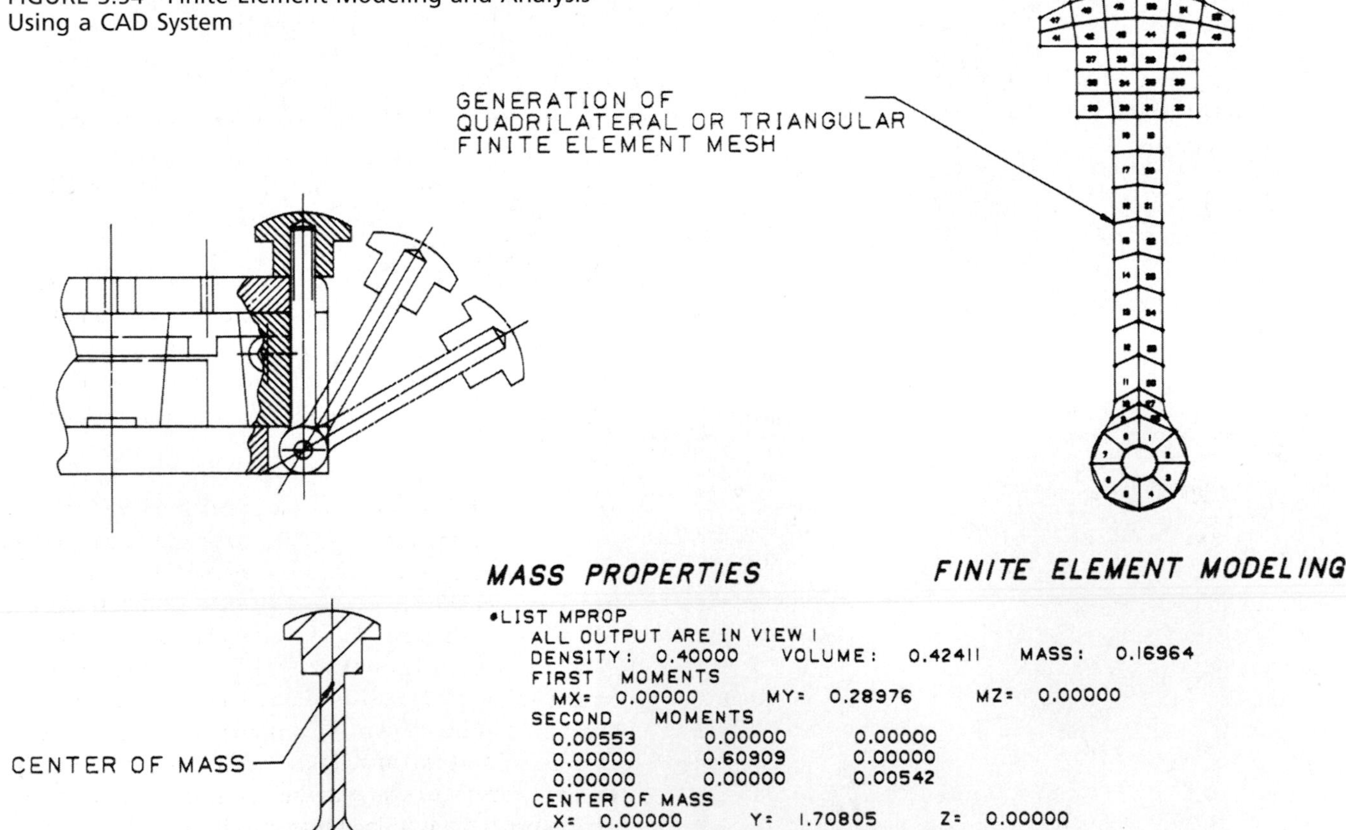

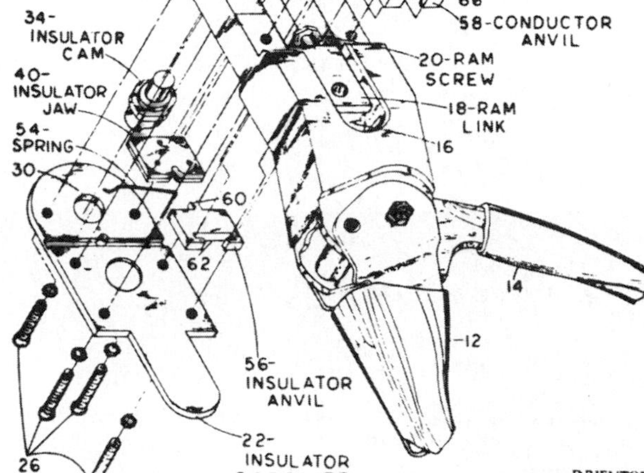

FIGURE 3.55 Patent Drawing

design project. (Once a product is designed, other drawings may be required for tooling and production.) A patent drawing should be very general and present concepts only, not specific size, shape, or material details, in order to prevent theft of the idea. The patent secures to the inventor exclusive production rights for up to fourteen years.

3.9 PRODUCTION, MANUFACTURING, AND PACKAGING

At this point in the design processes, Stage 7 (Fig. 3.56), the design must be presented to all interested, involved, and essential parties. The presentation will involve the designers, engineers, and other company personnel. The configuration of the design is presented in drawings, renderings, and possibly a prototype or presentation model. All aspects of the design are discussed at this meeting. The limitations, restraints, and capabilities of the design, as well as the new or improved features, problems in the product design pro-

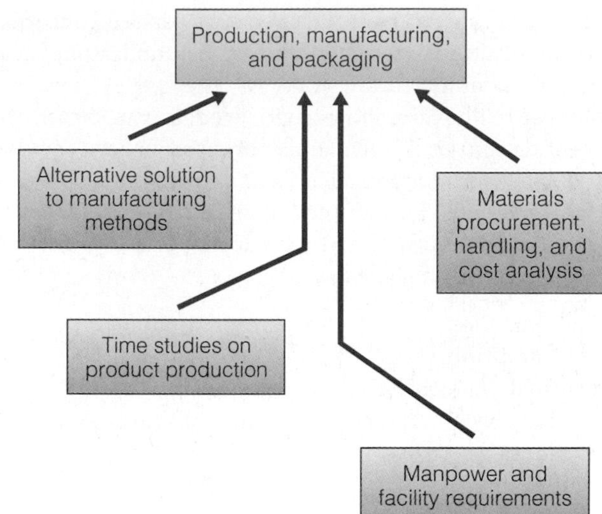

FIGURE 3.56 Stage 7 in the Design Process

cess, and validation of all research, scientific, and engineering aspects of the project, must be available so questions can be answered, decisions defended, and the appropriateness of the developed design demonstrated. Graphs, charts, notes, sketches, models (of rejected design alternatives), and design calculations used to establish the solution may all be needed at this meeting. The production department will require much of this information to establish manufacturing requirements and a production schedule.

Detail drawings of each aspect of the product, assemblies, and any other graphic documentation are complete at this stage. Remember, this is not the first time these parties have been consulted about the design. There has been continuous communication throughout the design process, and, although this is the seventh step in a formal explanation of the design process, the flow of information has been back and forth between these steps throughout the process.

Manufacturing Considerations in Design. The design of a particular part or product usually determines the material and the manufacturing process. Failure to understand the limits and possibilities of the material and the manufacturing options will doom the project from the start. Design for manufacturability is therefore essential to the success of a product. The stress, vibration, environmental operating conditions, tolerance requirements, and surface finish are determined during previous stages in the design process. Therefore, by the time the material selection and the manufacturing methods are selected, they are almost defined by default. The decisions by the designers at this stage are merely refinements. An overview of possible materials and processes to be used must include an understanding of the capabilities and limitations of each one. The engineer must be familiar with these capabilities and limitations in order to select the proper material and the manufacturing method.

Of course, the selection of materials in Stage 5 determines many of the methods used in manufacturing the part or product. Comprehensive solid modeling packages incorporate many features to help the engineer understand and model the manufacturing process. The steps shown in Figure 3.57 illustrate how solid models can assist the engineer design the CNC manufacturing sequence. The part itself helps determine the material and, therefore, the manufacturing methods. Each of the following factors is critical to the manufacturability of a particular material and must be considered during this design stage:

- **Size** limitation
- **Configuration**
- **Thermal** characteristics
- **Tolerance** requirements
- **Hardness**
- **Weight** limits
- Required ultimate **strength**
- **Elasticity**
- Surface **texture**—roughness
- **Precision**

A variety of manufacturing processes is available. The choice of a process is determined by the part's material and whether or not the process will create an acceptable part. Regardless of the process or the material, the designer should design to maximize efficiency and cost-effectiveness. The following processes are used in manufacturing and will be covered in more detail in Chapter 14:

- Machining
  - drilling
  - boring
  - milling
  - planing
  - reaming
  - broaching
  - turning
- Welding
- Casting
- Forging
- Forming
- Stamping
- Extruding
- Bending

Assembly of the part is partially determined by material selection. The estimated maximum number of parts and the minimum run also affect selection of the process. Since a simple part is easier to create and assemble, the part's

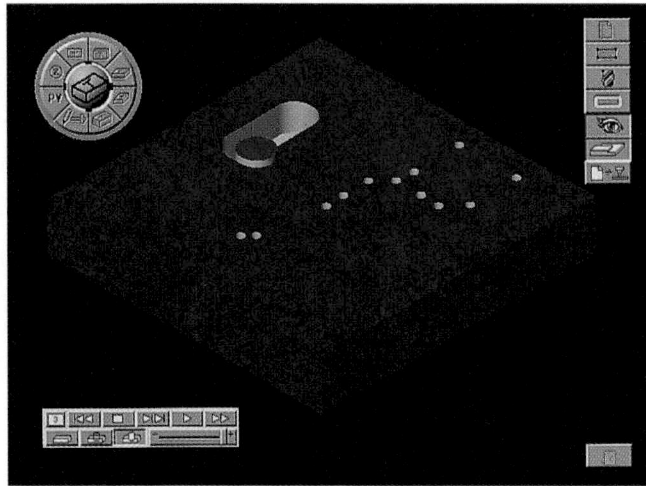

(a) 3D cut part rendering shows a preview of the part as it is machined

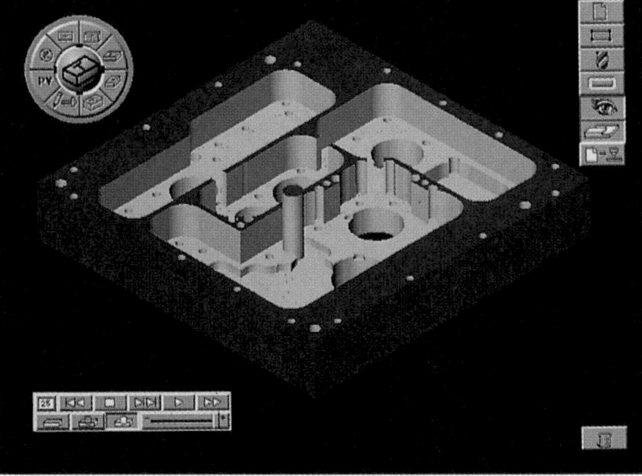

(c) Yellow highlights any number of individual operations for maximum contrast and visibility

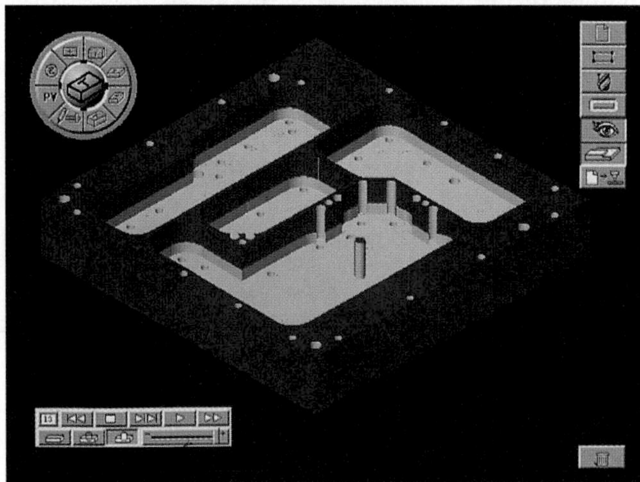

(b) Red flags any noncutting surface of the tool that hits the material

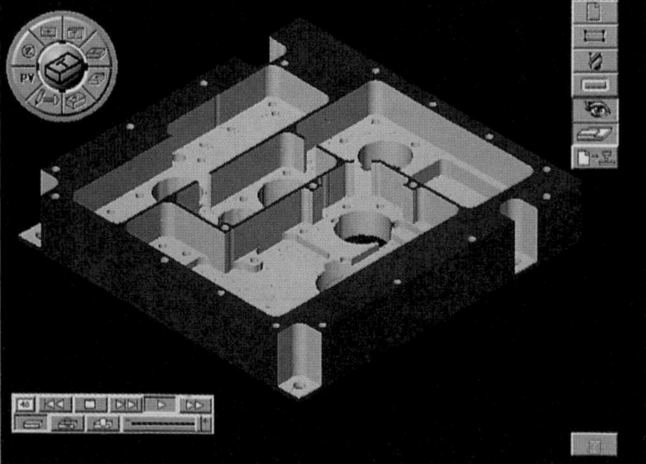

(d) Viewing the part as a rendered image at the computer makes it easy to detect errors and reduce wasted machine time and scrap

FIGURE 3.57 Using Solid Modeling and CNC Machining to Produce a Part

complexity influences selection as well. Manufacturing assembly processes include:

- Brazing
- Riveting
- Bolting
- Welding
- Gluing

The following is a partial list of concerns and suggestions for the designer. If these conditions are met, the chance of designing a successful, manufacturable part is greatly increased.

1. Design for standard machines and processes.
2. Design within the cost-effective limits of available and effective manufacturing procedures.
3. Design to limit the number of manufacturing processes.
4. Design to permit efficient production in acceptable quantities and within time requirements.
5. Design for the most cost-effective process that will deliver a product meeting the design parameters.
6. Design for ease of assembly

Although the preceding discussion centers on the designer's responsibilities and the design requirements, it should be understood that the actual selection of manufacturing processes should be made by the manufacturing engineer in conjunction with the product designer.

Alternate Solutions to Manufacturing Methods. *Automated manufacturing* is the design of a product or part so that it can be readily manufactured, fabricated, assembled, handled, tested, quality controlled, packaged, stored, and shipped using automated methods. Since much of today's manufacturing involves robot and automated assembly systems, the part itself should be designed to facilitate these methods. A typical engineer has always been concerned with materials and manufacturing methods, including fabrication and assembly. Increased productivity requirements, brought on by foreign competition and concern for profitability, have made automated manufacturing methods essential to the survival of a company. Ever-increasing overhead, labor, and material costs have driven industry's desire to automate. An understanding of the new methods of robotic production and automated manufacturing methods requires the knowledge of their capabilities as well as their shortcomings. Figure 3.58 shows the influences of automation on the design process.

As a new concept, material, or process becomes known, you can begin to compile a list that will help in the design process of a particular project. Material considerations, processes, automated technology, and other factors can be listed to help create the optimum design. If design rules and autofacturing tips are to be up to date and useful, they will be in a constant state of flux. As data for a project becomes known, you should incorporate it into the design rule list for a project. Automated manufacturing design often includes designing for simplicity. Remember, the more complex a part, the more difficult it is to autofacture; a simple part will require less manipulation by a robot. Thus, keeping the

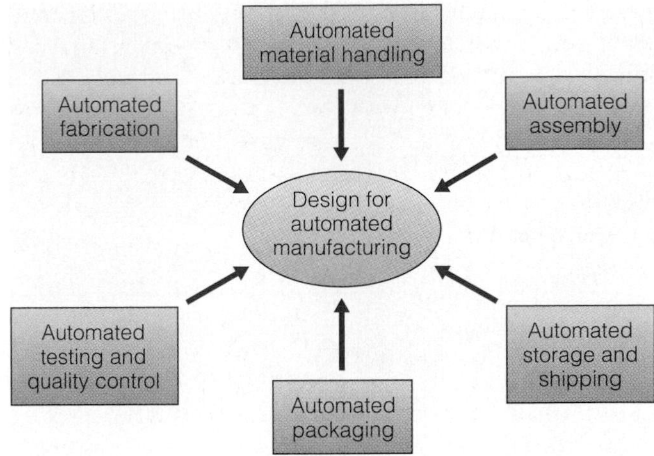

FIGURE 3.58 Design for Automated Manufacturing

robot's movements short and efficient will decrease production time. The design of the part will influence the robot's required movements [Fig. 3.59(a)].

Designing for elimination of obstructions is another consideration [Fig. 3.59(b)]. Automated assembly and the incorporation of robots in the manufacturing process requires that obstructions be kept to a minimum so that the robotic arm and end-effector can move freely during material handling [Fig. 3.59(c)], part positioning [Fig. 3.59(d)], and part removal.

Designing with automated manufacturing in mind takes more initial design time, but you will be rewarded with a more efficient, cost-effective, and better product. The following checklist can maximize the results of your design effort.

1. Incorporate every design aid available to reduce manufacturing costs, without adversely influencing the product's essential features.
2. Understand the basic capabilities and limitations of your in-house production and outside vendors' capabilities pertaining to the part's manufacturing and materials.
3. Determine the manufacturing methods—whether manual production, automated production, or a combination of the two—early in the design process so as to maximize the successful creation of the product.
4. Use a design review process that maximizes the effect of any design rules created in the design process. Be willing to review the results and redefine. Keep an open mind about the material, the process, and the automated manufacturing methods.
5. Keep up to date on new and developing automated processes, machinery, time-and-production studies, advanced materials, and technology.

Time Studies on Product Production. Studies are required of all processes needed to produce a part. The rate of production has a direct effect on the profitability of a product. **Time studies** are conducted to optimize a product's manufacturing cycle. Material handling, production

(a) The workcell can be designed for welding, assembly, machine loading, and other manufacturing operations. The robot is performing material-handling operations.

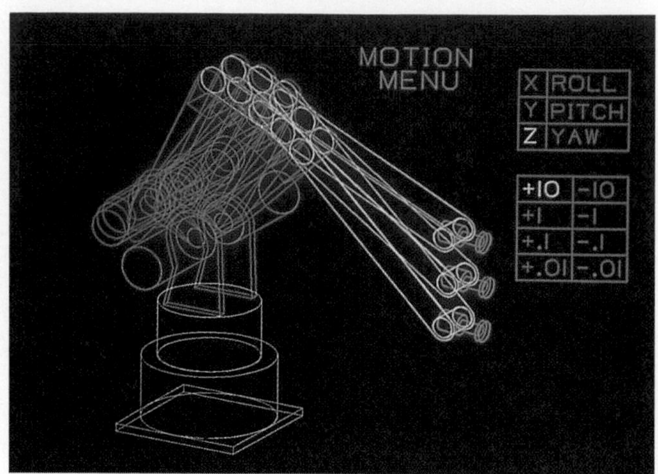

(c) Using the motion menu feature, workcell designers can analyze and simulate robot motion. The screen view shows the superimposed robot images.

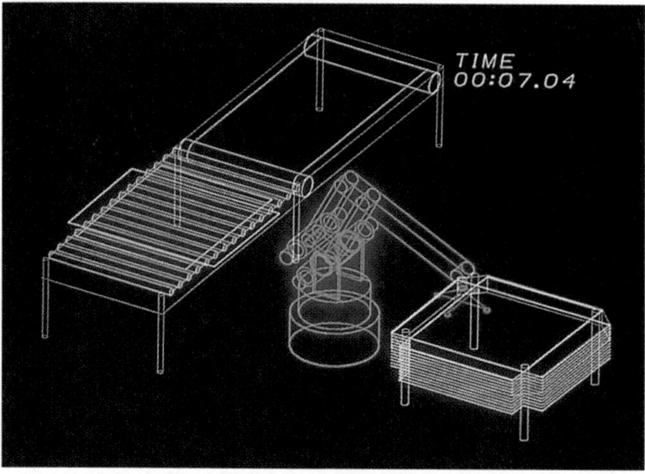

(b) During robot simulation, workcell cycle time is displayed on the screen. Throughout the simulation, the software allows the operator to check workcell design elements—interferences, motion of the robot, end-effector, interaction of workcell components.

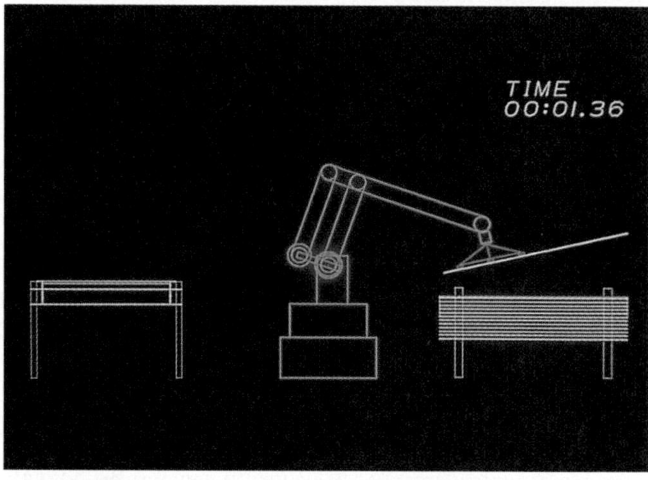

(d) The robotic workcell was designed via simulation software. The conveyor (*left*), indexing pallet (*right*), and robot (*center*) are drawn with the robot library.

FIGURE 3.59 Robots

elapsed time (manufacturing and assembly), and part removal (and transportation) are all in this study. Time analysis affects the determination of manufacturing methods, assembly fastening choice, and, sometimes, the material itself.

Materials Procurement, Handling, and Cost Analysis. The **availability** of a material or standard part will influence its selection as much as will design requirements. **Material procurement** and handling are an essential part of the total design effort. If the specified standard part is temporarily out of stock or not available, a product can be delayed in the manufacturing stage.

The designer must be aware of the material cost, as well as its availability. The increased cost of substituting one material for another at the manufacturing stage can completely destroy the product's profitability. The introduction of **just-in-time** manufacturing, where the traditional warehousing of large amounts of materials and standard parts is limited by efficient management of the procurement of the materials and parts and their arrival at the manufacturing station exactly when needed in the assembly or production process, requires extensive coordination of all departments. The manufacturing facility must be able to procure, store, and handle the material and standard parts if the production run is to be trouble free.

Manpower and Facility Requirements. Often, a company's facility and workforce will determine when and where the part or product should be made and assembled. The design process includes decisions based on available space, machinery, and trained personnel. One pressing problem in many industries is the lack of an educated, trainable workforce. The implementation of automated methods has been influenced by this lack of high-quality personnel, as well as by foreign competition. The use of robots in the manufacturing stage will also affect personnel, facility, and equipment considerations.

Robots and Manufacturing. Robots (Fig. 3.59) are increasingly used for efficient, safe, cost-effective manufacturing processes, including material and finished-product handling and storage, as well as the actual processes involved in the production of the item. CAD robotics packages are a computer-aided design and manufacturing (CAD/CAM) tool for robotic simulation and robot workcell design. Much of all robotics workcell design is simulated remotely on a CAD system before it is used on the factory floor.

A robot workcell consists of the robot itself, robot end-effectors (hands), part orienters, the part being operated on, fixtures, and the surrounding equipment with which the robot interacts. By means of a robot-simulator package, automation engineers can consult libraries of robots and equipment to design a workcell and simulate actual robot motion within the cell. From the simulation, an engineer can accurately determine the workcell cycle time and check for interferences in the motion of the robot with other workcell components.

Industrial Packaging. The field of packaging design includes design of boxes to hold consumer items such as perfume, electronic products, food products, and general household items. It also includes industrial packaging for mechanical and electronic designs (sheet metal enclosures). The artistic design of boxes for consumer items is considered under Stage 8. Here, the discussion is confined to sheet metal enclosures required for mechanical and electronic systems.

A typical sheet metal design can be created, in 3D, on a CAD system (Fig. 3.60). The 3D model sheet metal designs can be automatically unfolded in a flat pattern development (Fig. 3.61).

The enclosure for any mechanical or electronic system considers the many factors that influence other areas of design. Space requirements, safety, function, operation, service, and environmental conditions are all determining factors. Most of these requirements are known early in the design process so as to provide sufficient leeway in the packaging when this step is reached.

FIGURE 3.60 Example of Sheet Metal Used in Industrial Packaging

FIGURE 3.61 Sheet Metal Flat Pattern Development Using 3D CAD

3.10 MARKETING, SALES, AND DISTRIBUTION

Marketing, sales, and distribution (Stage 8 in the design process) are an essential aspect of the total design effort (Fig. 3.62). The product or system may never exist without a thorough economic analysis. The cost of advertising, marketing, packaging, shipping, and distribution greatly affects the cost to bring the product to market. The input of the sales and marketing department, the packaging department, and the shipping and storage facility makes the important connection to the real world of business and affects profit margin. Many products that have been brought to market without a proper understanding of the business aspects of the design process are doomed to fail—even good products.

Advertising, Budgets, and Marketing Direction. The marketing department may participate in preliminary project work. Marketing is responsible for an accurate product survey before the product is designed. A poor design decision with respect to customer needs would leave the marketing department with the job of selling an unusable or undesirable product. Sometimes an advertising campaign can create a need for a product in the minds of the public or sell an inferior product. In general, marketing will help determine many product function requirements before the final design is accepted. Surveys that help determine the need, size, color, shape, feel, and acceptable cost can be completed well before the engineers and designers are through with their work. The rough preliminary ideas of an

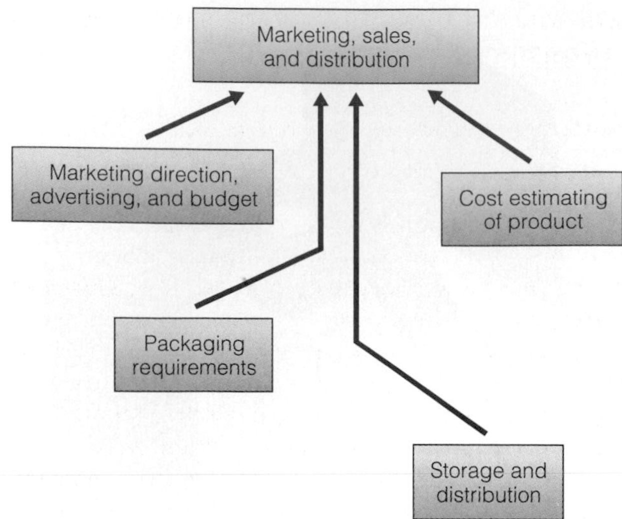

FIGURE 3.62 Stage 8 in the Design Process

inventor/engineer/designer may be refined and altered by the input of the marketing department.

Cost Estimating of Product. The **cost analysis** of the product includes the expenses generated by the engineering, design, manufacturing, sales, and shipping departments. Each department must submit a detailed cost estimate for the man-hours, materials, and overhead cost for each stage of the design development process in which it is involved. Design costs include modeling and drafting; sales costs include advertising and marketing; packaging costs include art design and box design. Since manufacturing cost includes personnel, equipment, facility, and material considerations, it may be the largest single cost item of the product.

Product **cost estimation** affects many of the other departments' decisions. The choice of materials, the choice of manufacturing methods (such as fastening), the choice of packaging materials and art design, and the level and extent of sales and advertising are all influenced by the item's cost and profit margin. Cost estimating includes how long it takes to generate an acceptable return and how many items must be sold before the product is considered an economic success.

Packaging Requirements. The design of a product does not end with the product itself. Without proper presentation, the product may fail to achieve the required sales to be successful. **Packaging** is almost as important as the product, especially in the world of mass marketing and international sales.

Packaging also includes new concepts of green-packaging (environmental packaging)—using biodegradable packaging and eliminating overpackaging. Too much packaging creates unnecessary amounts of waste when the product is used.

A simple box may not be so simple. As a matter of fact, it can be rather complex. Size must be considered, along with shape, printed text, color, art, and competition from other boxes. Most packaging for consumer products must be designed for appearance as well as function.

Although packaging is normally part of Stage 7, most of the design input about appearance comes from the advertising and marketing departments. The actual design of the dies and patterns is the domain of the manufacturing group. The marketing department, in conjunction with the packaging designers assigned to the manufacturing department, must agree on a box design that is functional, attractive, and producible, within cost restraints.

Designing a box with a specific purpose can be even more complex—French fry boxes have unusual shapes and curves; deodorant boxes use die cuts to display the product inside; and medicine boxes are designed to be tamper resistant. Technology is minimizing complications while providing greater control, particularly over prototyping, through CAD/CAM.

Software programs have been designed specifically for the packaging industry. Software is available that offers a library of parametric designs for creating standard box configurations. The designer simply provides appropriate dimensions to any box design (for example, the standard reverse tuck—a common design with simple end flaps connected to the front of one side of the box and the back of the other side to tuck it closed), and the CAD program automatically draws the required shape.

CAM programs can send instructions to devices such as a plotter. This machine cuts out the box and makes creases at the folds of the prototype, saving hours of tedious work. Instructions can also be sent to a laser that cuts a plywood die to hold the steel rules used to cut multiple boxes once the final design is determined.

Once the individual box design is complete [Fig. 3.63(a)], copies are nested together [Fig. 3.63(b)], mirroring and duplicating the images and interlocking them like jigsaw puzzle pieces to produce as many boxes as possible from a single sheet of cardboard. The software performs automatic bridging, a technique in which gaps are left during the process of cutting the plywood so that it doesn't fall apart. The die manufacturer then inserts steel blades into the plywood, bridging the gaps with blades so that the boxes will fall out like shapes from a cookie cutter.

One potential for CAD/CAM packaging lies with large food and pharmaceutical companies that want more direct control over the prototyping phase for the hundreds of packages fabricated for their products. By combining packaging software with devices such as a PLANTAGRAM, in which a shelf environment is recreated, designers can see how the box will look against the competition. The decision can then be finalized before the die is cast.

While the ability to connect CAD box design to CAM machining has been available for some time, the concept of integrating the process with packaging graphics is a new idea that offers major advantages. The capability to prepare the entire design [Fig. 3.63(c)], including the structure, graphics, and machine codes, on a single computer not only

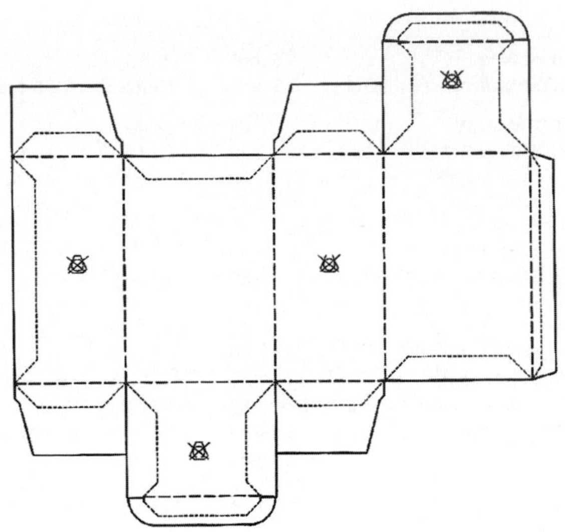

(a) Die design using Ovation CAD/CAM

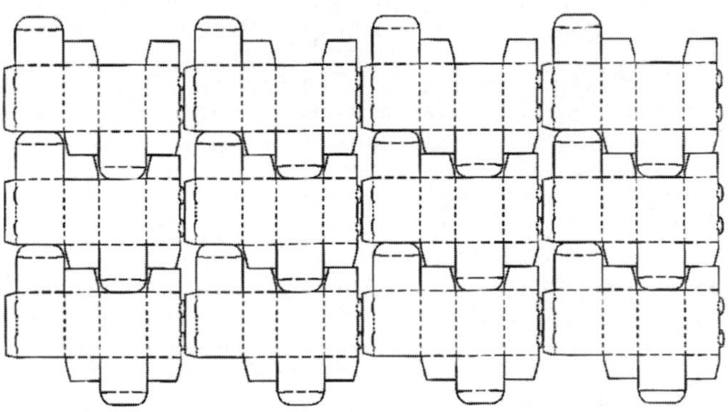

(b) Nested design layout

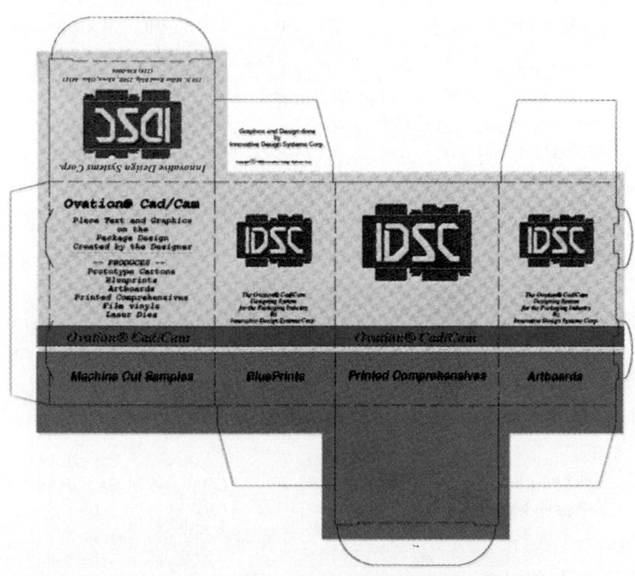

(c) Package graphics

FIGURE 3.63 Packaging Design Example

speeds and simplifies the prototyping phase, it also eliminates expensive mistakes.

Shipping and Distribution. **Just-in-time (JIT)** manufacturing is a process in which the component parts of a system design arrive at the assembly line station at the time of installation. This requires careful control of materials, equipment, and fabrication processes and subassembly transportation to the site at the appropriate time. **Field fabrication** of system parts also depends on the timely arrival of appropriate materials. The planners of any project have most of the responsibility for this stage of the project. The designers and the procurement department must be in constant communication at almost every stage to prevent shortfalls or overstocking of supplies. It is the coordination between all involved departments that makes a project meet both time constraints and cost estimates.

Shipping and distribution of a product includes storing and warehousing the product. Many times, a consumer product's timely arrival on the market greatly affects its sales. If the greatest sales opportunity occurs in the three months before Christmas, what would happen if the product showed up on store shelves on December 28?

The shipping department must be aware of the product's size and weight and any other factors that would influence the method of shipment. Is the product fragile? Is it bulky? Will it be affected by heat or cold? Is it perishable? Does it need any special considerations, such as refrigeration? If the product is to be stored at the facility, will there be enough warehouse space? Should the warehouse be automated to handle the product with robotic systems? How many of the product should be available at any one time? These are all questions that must be asked early in the design process and solved by the time this last stage is reached.

The quantity of items to be handled and stored is also an important consideration. Design for stacking whenever possible. If the product is to be shipped to the general public, contracting with outside shipping sources must also be done. Other concerns at this stage include: Will the product be shipped overseas? If so, are there any packaging, duty, tariff, or handling factors that must be considered? As we can see, designing for storing, stacking, and shipping goes far beyond just how to move the product from the manufacturing and packaging facility to the trucking dock.

Illustrations for Presentation, Sales, Advertising, and Catalogs. Pictorial illustrations are used in this stage of the design process to present the product, system, or concept to a nontechnical or purchasing audience. Renderings of products and concepts provide a realistic illustration of the proposed item. Renderings and models help introduce a product, concept, or system design to the general public or an interested potential customer. Using the 3D CAD database, an illustrator can now create a pictorial illustration without redrawing the assembly or part.

3.11 DESIGN PROJECT EXAMPLE

The device shown in Figure 3.64(a) is an example of a well-designed consumer product created on a CAD system. Logitech manufactures a variety of mouse devices for computers. You may even have one of their products in your school on your CAD system. Over the years the designers at Logitech became aware of some of the shortcomings of the traditional mouse. Since the ball is on the bottom of a typical mouse, the user must move the device across a flat surface. This meant that the mouse must always rest on a clean, flat pad or other acceptable surface. The position of the mouse, either on the right or the left of the computer, is dependent on whether the user is right-handed or left-handed. If the surface is not flat and clean, the mouse is susceptible to skipping. The user always has to have the device lying flat.

The new device solved many of these problems. The ball was moved to the top of the device to be rotated by the user's hand, not by contact between the ball and a flat surface. The user was now free to hold the input device in her or his hands. Of course, since it could be operated by either hand without a flat area, the device did not have to be on the right or left side of the computer. Logitech called this product Trackman.

The **critical-path method** of scheduling is documented in Figure 3.64(b). Here, a computer program was used to keep track of the critical and noncritical tasks in the design sequence. The major headings are:

- Product management
- Mechanical design
- Software development
- Software quality assurance (QA)
- Publications
- Product engineering
- Test engineering
- Materials
- Manufacturing

Each of the major headings is subdivided into specific tasks. The duration of each task is estimated and noted as its *Duration Time*. The *Resource* of each task was the specific

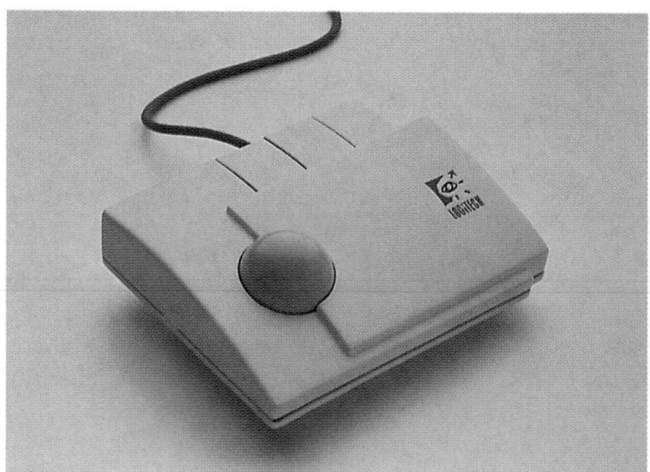

(a) Trackman roller ball mouse

Heading Task Resource	Dur	Schd Start	Schd Finish	Status
TRACKMAN.PJ	148	03-27-89<	10-24-89	
PRODUCT MGMT	51	05-01-89	07-14-89	In Prog.
Rel Wood Model	0	05-01-89	05-01-89	Comp./Crit.
Rel Prototype	0	05-26-89	05-26-89	Comp./Crit.
Rel SalesForecst	0	06-01-89<	06-01-89	Comp./Crit.
Rel IntlShipInfo	0	07-14-89<	07-14-89	Scheduled
MECHANICAL DSGN	140	03-27-89	10-12-89	In Prog.
Rel Case Drawing	0	05-17-89	05-17-89	Comp./Crit.
Rel PWAPartsList	0	06-21-89	06-21-89	Comp./Crit.
SubmitPCBartwork	0	06-13-89<	06-13-89	Comp./Crit.
Rel PCB Layout	0	06-26-89	06-26-89	Comp./Crit.
Tooling	69	03-27-89<	07-07-89	Comp./Crit.
Tooling Support	69	03-27-89	07-07-89	Comp./Crit.
Josef	69	03-27-89	07-07-89	Critical
Rec CaseIsArtcl	0	07-07-89	07-07-89	Comp./Crit.
Rel Proto to Pkg	0	07-13-89	07-13-89	Comp./Crit.
Debug Parts	1w	07-10-89	07-14-89	In Prog.
Josef	1w	07-10-89	07-14-89	
Make 60 PCB's	13	06-27-89	07-17-89	In Prog./Crit.
Rec PWA Componts	0	07-14-89<	07-14-89	Scheduled
Rec 60 PWA's	0	07-27-89	07-27-89	Schd./Crit.
Build DVT1 Units	1w	07-28-89	08-03-89	Schd./Crit.
Rel DVT1 Units	0	08-03-89	08-03-89	Schd./Crit.
Run DVT1 Test	2w	08-04-89	08-17-89	Schd./Crit.
Josef	2w	08-04-89	08-17-89	Critical
Run DVT2 Test	1w	08-18-89	08-24-89	Scheduled
Josef	1w	08-18-89	08-24-89	
Texture Tool	1w	08-25-89	08-31-89	Scheduled
Make PVT units	3	09-01-89	09-06-89	Scheduled
Evaluate PVT	2w	09-22-89	10-05-89	Schd./Crit.
Mftr M-P Units	1w	10-06-89	10-12-89	Schd./Crit.
SOFTWARE DEVELOP	94	05-01-89	09-13-89	In Prog.
Rel Prelim Spec	0	05-05-89	05-05-89	Comp./Crit.
Rel Final Spec	0	07-14-89	07-14-89	Scheduled
Driver	56	05-01-89	07-20-89	In Prog.
Trackball Driver	1w	05-01-89<	05-05-89	Comp./Crit.
Joe	1w	05-01-89	05-05-89	Critical
Control Panel	4w	05-01-89<	06-29-89	Comp./Crit.
Bang	4w	05-01-89	06-29-89	Critical
Dual Mode-Driver	2w	06-15-89	07-06-89	Comp./Crit.
Joe	2w	06-15-89	07-06-89	Critical
WORD Fix	16	06-19-89	07-14-89	In Prog.
Mark	16	06-19-89	07-14-89	
ADI Driver	1w	07-14-89	07-20-89	Scheduled
Mark	1w	07-14-89	07-20-89	
Rel for Alpha	0	07-14-89	07-14-89	Scheduled
Alpha Test	8	07-14-89	07-25-89	Scheduled
Rel for Beta	0	07-25-89	07-25-89	Scheduled
Beta Evaluation	4w	08-09-89	09-06-89	Scheduled
Rel for Final	0	09-13-89	09-13-89	Scheduled
SOFTWARE QA	54	07-07-89	09-22-89	In Prog.
Alpha Phase	12	07-07-89	07-25-89	In Prog.
Rec A-Materials	4	07-07-89	07-14-89	In Prog.
Rec Alpha Manual	0	07-07-89	07-07-89	Comp./Crit.
Rec Mouse Units	0	07-14-89	07-14-89	Scheduled
Rec Alpha SW	0	07-14-89	07-14-89	Scheduled
Run Alpha Test	8	07-14-89	07-25-89	Scheduled
Luis	8	07-14-89	07-25-89	
Manual FdbackDue	0	07-17-89	07-17-89	Scheduled
Beta Phase	30	07-25-89	09-06-89	Scheduled
Rec B-Materials	7	07-25-89	08-03-89	Scheduled
Rec Beta SW	0	07-25-89	07-25-89	Scheduled
Rec Beta Manuals	0	07-27-89	07-27-89	Scheduled

(b) Critical-path schedule for Trackman roller ball mouse

FIGURE 3.64 Trackman Mouse

Heading Task Resource	Dur	Schd Start	Schd Finish	Status
Reca Beta HW	0	08-03-89	08-03-89	Scheduled
Run Beta Test	23	08-04-89	09-06-89	Scheduled
Luis	23	08-04-89	09-06-89	
Mail Materials	3	08-04-89	08-08-89	Scheduled
Angie	3	08-04-89	08-08-89	
Beta Evaluation	4w	08-09-89	09-06-89	Scheduled
Final Phase	7	09-13-89	09-22-89	Scheduled
Rec Final SW	0	09-13-89	09-13-89	Scheduled
Run Final Tests	1w	09-14-89	09-20-89	Scheduled
Rel Master Disks	0	09-20-89	09-22-89	Scheduled
Write SWQA Reprt	2	09-21-89	09-22-89	Scheduled
PUBLICATIONS	103	05-05-89	10-03-89	In Prog.
Rec Prelim Spec	0	05-05-89	05-05-89	Comp./Crit.
Rec Final Spec	0	07-14-89	07-14-89	Scheduled
Getting Started	77	05-17-89	09-06-89	In Prog.
Alpha Phase	49	05-17-89	07-27-89	In Prog.
Write Alpha	7w	05-17-89	07-07-89	Comp./Crit.
Bob G.	7w	05-17-89	07-07-89	Critical
Release Alpha	0	07-07-89	07-07-89	Comp./Crit.
AlphaFeedbackDue	0	07-17-89<	07-17-89	Scheduled
Correct Alpha	8	07-18-89	07-27-89	Scheduled
Rob G.	8	07-18-89	07-27-89	
Beta Phase	28	07-27-89	09-06-89	Scheduled
Release Beta	0	07-27-89	07-27-89	Scheduled
Beta FeedbackDue	0	08-03-89	08-03-89	Scheduled
Correct Beta	2w	08-04-89	08-17-89	Scheduled
Bob G.	2w	08-04-89	08-17-89	
Beta Test	4w	08-09-89	09-06-89	Scheduled
Final Phase	7	08-17-89	08-28-89	Scheduled
Rel Final Doc	0	08-17-89	08-17-89	Scheduled
Final Review	2	08-18-89	08-21-89	Scheduled
Correct Final	1w	08-22-89	08-28-89	Scheduled
Bob G.	1w	08-22-89	08-28-89	
Blueline #1	1w	08-29-89	09-05-89	Scheduled
Blueline #2	1w	09-06-89	09-12-89	Scheduled
Print Manuals	3w	09-13-89	10-03-89	Scheduled
PRODUCT ENG'G	114	05-02-89	10-12-89	In Prog.
Rec. PCB Artwork	0	07-14-89	07-14-89	Scheduled
Rec TrackManUnit	0	08-04-89	08-04-89	Scheduled
Rec Master Disks	0	09-20-89	09-20-89	Scheduled
Rec SWQA Report	0	09-22-89	09-22-89	Scheduled
Rec HWTestReprts	0	10-09-89	10-09-89	Scheduled
Rec Blueline #2	0	09-12-89	09-12-89	Scheduled
BOM	78	06-21-89	10-12-89	In Prog.
Rec PrePartsList	0	06-21-89	06-21-89	Comp./Crit.
Prepare Pre BOM	2	06-22-89	06-23-89	Comp./Crit.
Issue Prelim BOM	0	06-28-89	06-28-89	Comp./Crit.
ECO Final BOM	0	10-12-89	10-12-89	Scheduled
HWQA Testing	7	08-04-89	08-14-89	Scheduled
Run HWQA Test	1w	08-04-89	08-10-89	Scheduled
Write HWQA Reprt	2	08-11-89	08-14-89	Scheduled
Safety Tests	42	08-04	10-03-89	Scheduled
FCC Test	2	08-04-89	08-07-89	Scheduled
Rec FCC Approval	0	08-07-89	08-07-89	Scheduled
UL Test	6w	08-04-89	09-15-89	Scheduled
Rec Ul Approval	0	09-15-89	09-15-89	Scheduled
Rec FCC Letter	0	10-03-89	10-03-89	Scheduled
Packaging	89	05-02-89	09-07-89	In Prog.
Rec Wood Model	0	05-02-89	05-02-89	Comp./Crit.
Rec Drawings: MD	0	05-18-89	05-18-89	Comp./Crit.

Heading Task Resource	Dur	Schd Start	Schd Finish	Status
Tray	66	05-26-89	08-30-89	In Prog.
RecTrckballProto	0	05-26-89	05-26-89	Comp./Crit.
Make Proto Drwgs	2w	05-26-89	06-14-89	Comp./Crit.
Build Tooling	4w	07-17-89	08-11-89	Scheduled
Rec Hand Samples	0	08-11-89	08-11-89	Scheduled
Approve Samples	1w	08-14-89	08-18-89	Scheduled
Finalize Drwgs	3	08-21-89	08-23-89	Scheduled
Manufacture Tray	1w	08-24-89	08-30-89	Scheduled
Carton	62	06-09-89	09-07-89	In Prog.
Define Packaging	2w	06-09-89	06-15-89	Comp./Crit.
Rec Hand Sample	0	07-13-89	07-13-89	Comp./Crit.
Sample Approved	0	07-14-89	07-14-89	Scheduled
Draw PackageSpec	1	07-14-89	07-14-89	Scheduled
Make Die Vinyl	3	07-17-89	07-19-89	Scheduled
Rel Die Vinyl	0	07-19-89	07-19-89	Scheduled
Rec 1st Articles	0	08-11-89	08-11-89	Scheduled
Approve 1stArtcl	3	08-14-89	08-16-89	Scheduled
Artwork	20	07-19-89	08-16-89	Scheduled
Rec Die Vinyl	0	07-19-89	07-19-89	Scheduled
Design Artwork	20	07-20-89	08-16-89	Scheduled
Beth	20	07-20-89	08-16-89	
Rel Films	0	08-16-89	08-16-89	Scheduled
Die—	10	07-27-89	08-09-89	Scheduled
PURCHASING				
Select Vendor	1w	07-27-89	08-02-89	Scheduled
Carol B.	1w	07-27-89	08-02-89	
Make Die	1w	08-08-89	08-09-89	Scheduled
Carol B.	1w	08-03-89	08-09-89	
Mftr Carton	3w	08-17-89	09-07-89	Scheduled
ECO	40	08-17-89	10-12-89	Scheduled
Process PWA ECO	2	08-18-89	08-21-89	Schd./Crit.
Approve PWA ECO	1	08-22-89	08-22-89	Schd./Crit.
Process Pkg ECO	2	08-17-89	08-18-89	Scheduled
Approve Pkg ECO	1	08-21-89	08-21-89	Scheduled
Process SW ECO	2	09-25-89	09-26-89	Scheduled
Approve SW ECO	1	09-27-89	09-27-89	Scheduled
Process FinalECO	2	10-10-89	10-11-89	Scheduled
Approve FinalECO	1	10-12-89	10-12-89	Scheduled
TEST ENGINEERING	99	05-18-89	10-09-89	In Prog.
Case Evaluation	5	08-17-89	08-24-89	Scheduled
Rec Plastics	0	08-17-89	08-17-89	Scheduled
Eval Plastics	1w	08-18-89	08-24-89	Scheduled
PCB Evaluation	2	07-17-89	07-19-89	Scheduled
Rec PCB	0	07-17-89	07-17-89	Scheduled
Evaluate PCB	2	07-18-89	07-19-89	Scheduled
Product Testers	73	05-18-89	08-31-89	In Prog.
Develop Plan	7	05-18-89<	07-14-89	In Prog.
Bus BON Test	35	07-14-89	08-31-89	Scheduled
Rec PCB Layout	0	07-14-89	07-14-89	Scheduled
Layout & Design	4w	07-14-89	08-10-89	Scheduled
Build Fixture	3w	08-11-89	08-31-89	Scheduled
Bus Test Ready	0	08-31-89	08-31-89	Scheduled
Serial BON Test	35	07-14-89	08-31-89	Scheduled
Rec PCB Layout	0	07-14-89	07-14-89	Scheduled
Layout & Design	4w	07-14-89	08-10-89	Scheduled
Build Fixture	3w	08-11-89	08-31-89	Scheduled
Serial TestReady	0	08-31-89	08-31-89	Scheduled

(b) Critical-path schedule for Trackman roller ball mouse—*Continues*

FIGURE 3.64 Trackman Mouse—*Continues*

Heading Task Resource	Dur	Schd Start	Schd Finish	Status
Final Test	35	07-14-89	08-31-89	Scheduled
Rec Case Drawing	0	07-14-89	07-14-89	Scheduled
Layout & Design	4w	07-14-89	08-10-89	Scheduled
Build Fixture	3w	08-11-89	08-31-89	Scheduled
Final Test Ready	0	08-31-89	08-31-89	Scheduled
PVT—Trackball	12	09-22-89	10-09-89	Scheduled
PVT Build	1w	09-22-89	09-28-89	Scheduled
PVT Evaluation	1w	09-29-89	10-05-89	Scheduled
Give PWA Approvl	0	10-05-89	10-05-89	Scheduled
Write PVT Report	2	10-06-89	10-09-89	Scheduled
MATERIALS	59	07-14-89	10-05-89	Scheduled
Rel MPSO		07-14-89	07-14-89	Scheduled
Rel PWA Schedule	0	07-20-89	07-20-89	Scheduled
Rel SW DupeSched	0	07-27-89	07-27-89	Scheduled
SW Duplication	5	09-27-89	10-04-89	Scheduled
Rec SW ECO Aprvl	0	09-27-89	09-27-89	Scheduled
Duplicate Disks	1w	09-28-89	10-04-89	Scheduled
PWA Builds	31	08-22-89	10-05-89	Scheduled
PWA PreProd	21	08-22-89	09-21-89	Schd./Crit.
PWA ECO Approval	0	08-22-89	08-22-89	Schd./Crit.
PCB Artwork>Mftr	0	08-22-89	08-22-89	Schd./Crit.
Make 300Barebrds	2w	08-23-89	09-06-89	Schd./Crit.
QC Bareboards	2	09-07-89	09-08-89	Schd./Crit.
Kit 300 PWAs	1	09-11-89	09-11-89	Schd./Crit.
Make PWAs	6	09-12-89	09-19-89	Schd./Crit.
QC PWAs	2	09-20-89	09-21-89	Schd./Crit.
PWA MassProd	31	08-22-89	10-05-89	Scheduled
PWA ECO Approval	0	08-22-89	08-22-89	Scheduled
Make Bareboards2	4w	08-23-89	09-20-89	Scheduled
Rec Bareboards 2	0	09-20-89	09-20-89	Scheduled
QC Bareboards	2	09-21-89	09-22-89	Scheduled
Kit PWAs 2	1	09-25-89	09-25-89	Scheduled
Make PWAs 2	6	09-26-89	10-03-89	Scheduled
QC PWAs 2	2	10-04-89	10-05-89	Scheduled
Intl. Shipping	40	07-14-89	09-08-89	Scheduled
Rec IntlShipInfo	0	07-14-89	07-14-89	Scheduled
Prepare Applictn	2w	07-14-89	07-27-89	Scheduled
License Approval	6w	07-28-89	09-08-89	Scheduled
Rec Approval	0	09-08-89	09-08-89	Scheduled
MANUFACTURING	47	08-18-89	10-24-89	Schd./Crit.
Rel AssemblyPlan	0	08-18-89<	08-18-89	Scheduled
Preproduction	24	08-31-89	10-05-89	Scheduled
Rec Test Equip	0	08-31-89	08-31-89	Scheduled
Rec Cases	0	09-08-89	09-08-89	Scheduled
Rec PWA's #1	0	09-21-89	09-21-89	Schd./Crit.
Run PreProductn	2w	09-22-89	10-05-89	Schd./Crit.
PreProductn Done	0	10-05-89	10-05-89	Scheduled
Mass-Production	33	09-07-89	10-24-89	Schd./Crit.
Final ECO Approval	0	10-12-89	10-12-89	Scheduled
Rec Packaging	0	09-07-89	09-07-89	Scheduled
Rec SW Diskettes	0	10-04-89	10-04-89	Scheduled
Rec PWA's #2	0	10-05-89	10-05-89	Scheduled
Rec Final Manual	0	10-03-89	10-03-89	Scheduled
Rec Cases	0	10-12-89	10-12-89	Schd./Crit.
Run MassProductn	1w	10-16-89	10-20-89	Schd./Crit.
Inspect FinalPkg	2	10-23-89	10-24-89	Schd./Crit.
MassProductnDone	0	10-24-89	10-24-89	Schd./Crit.
PRODUCT AVAIL:	0	10-24-89	10-24-89	Schd./Crit.

(b) Critical-path schedule for Trackman roller ball mouse–*Continued*

FIGURE 3.64 Trackman Mouse—*Continued*

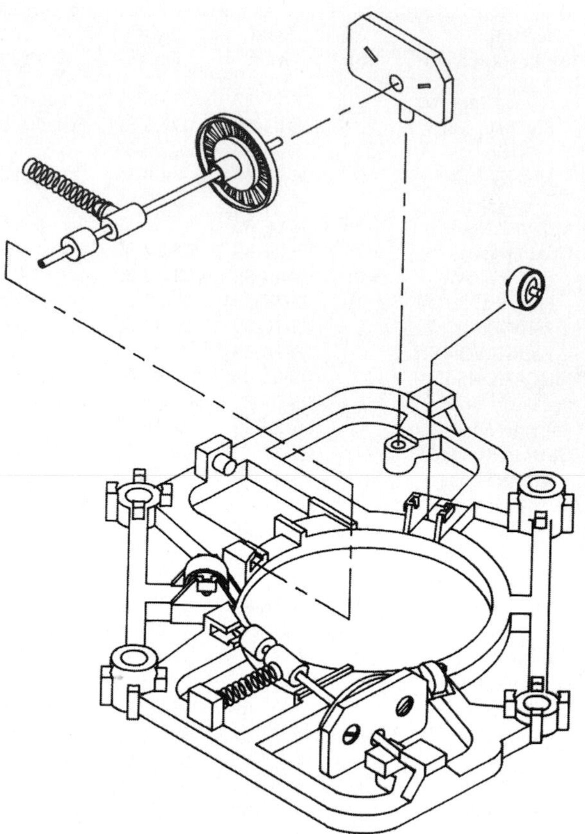

(c) Trackball subassembly

FIGURE 3.64 Trackman Mouse—*Continued*

employee assigned to oversee and complete the task by the scheduled date. The *Scheduled Start* and *Scheduled Finish* dates were also noted on this list. Last, the *Status* was tracked for each task. *In Progress, Scheduled,* and *Completed* notations are shown, as well as whether or not this was a critical task. For the product to be on the market before Christmas, all tasks had to be completed by 10-24-89. The critical-path method of scheduling project tasks throughout the design-through-manufacturing process is used in many companies.

Figure 3.64(c) is an enlargement of the subassembly skeleton (part 4). Figure 3.64(d) shows the assembly of Trackman. Figure 3.64(e) is the detail of the Tball skeleton, which is part of the subassembly (part 4). Figure 3.64(f) is the detail of the top enclosure (part 1). Figure 3.64(g) is the detail of the bottom enclosure (part 2), and Figure 3.64(h) is the detail of the button plate. Trackman was designed completely on an AutoCAD system and is an excellent example of the critical-path method of scheduling project activities and using CAD in the design process.

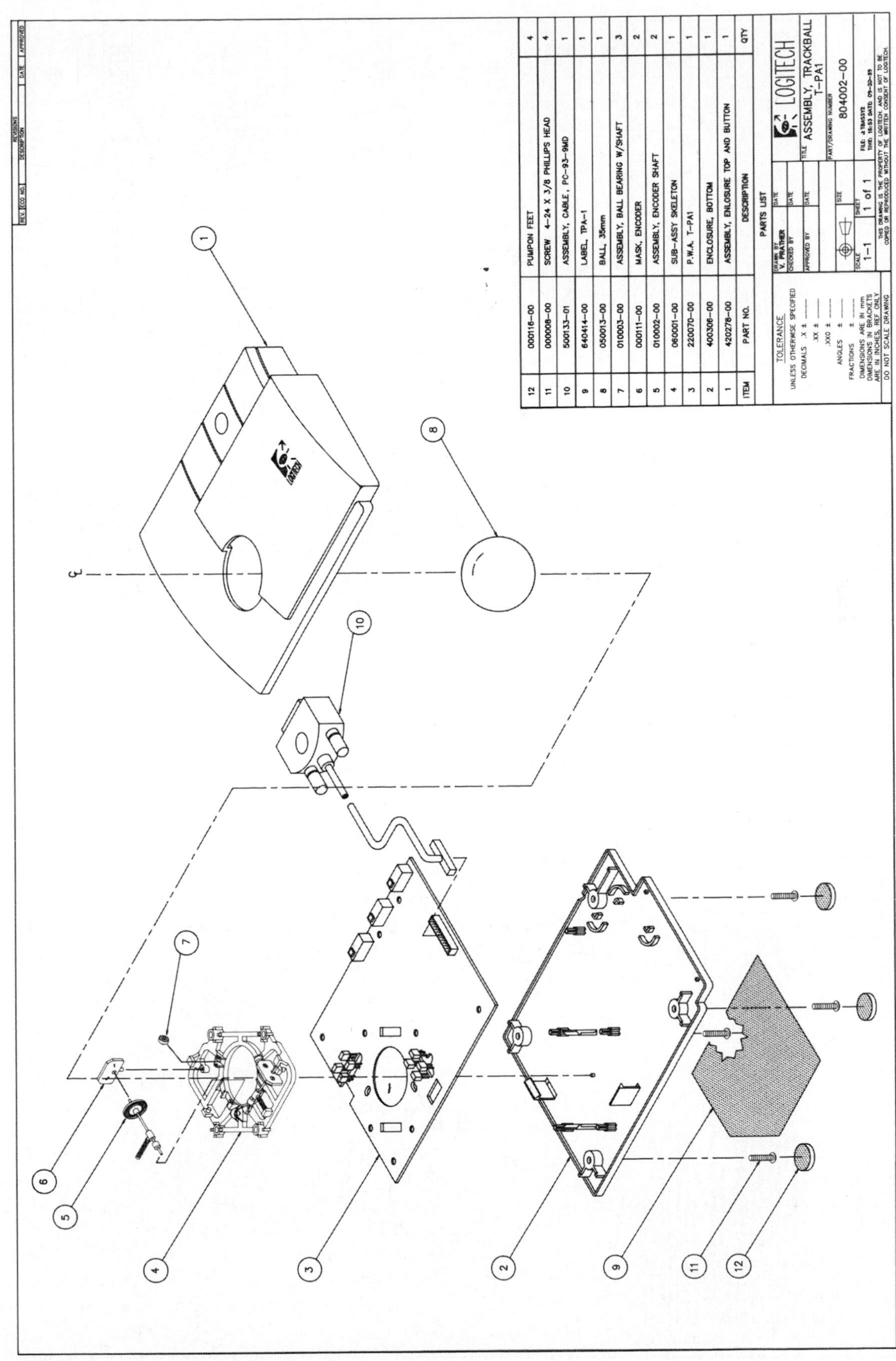

(d) Trackball assembly

FIGURE 3.64 Trackman Mouse—*Continues*

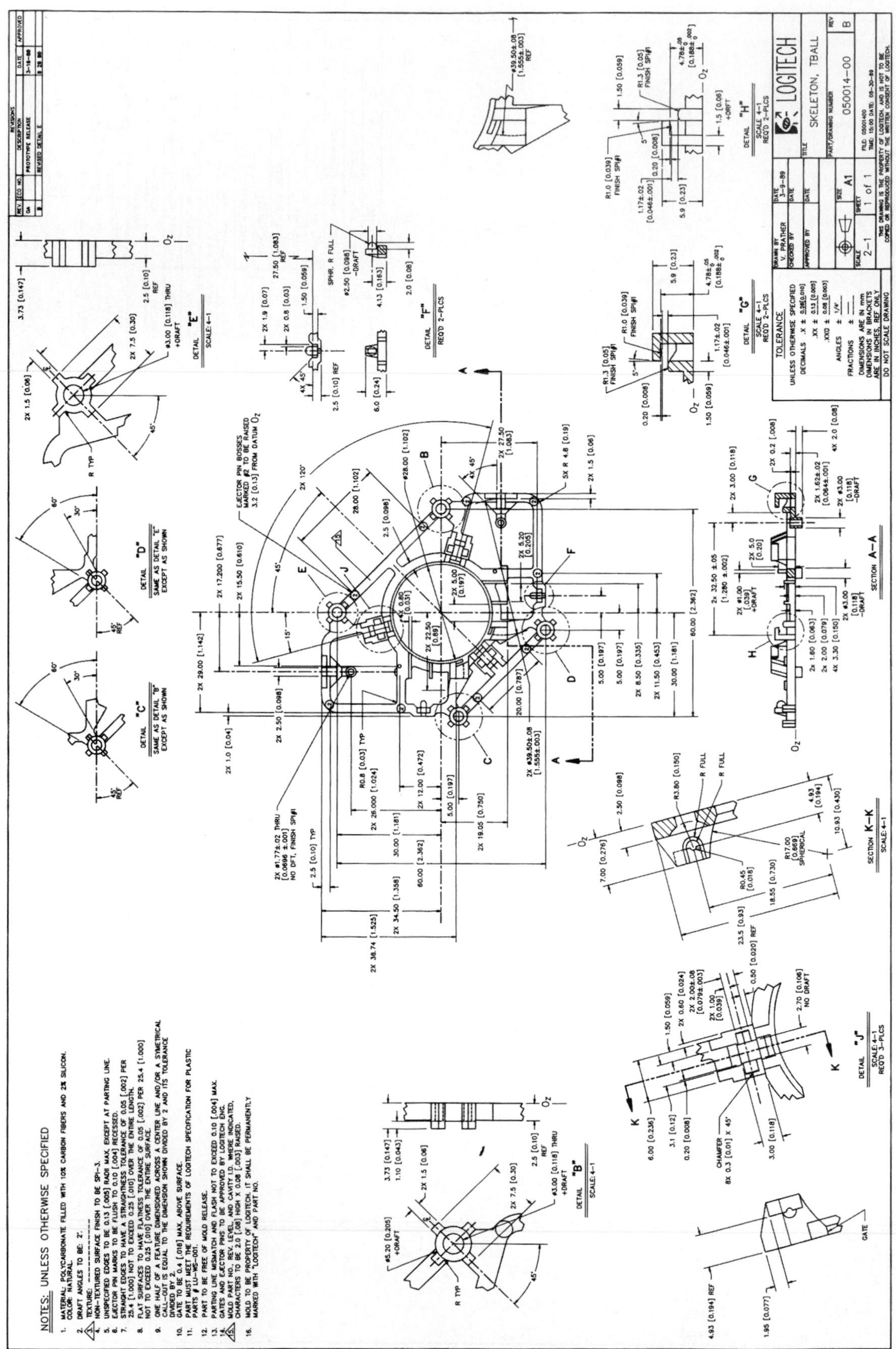

(e) Detail of skeleton, Trackball

FIGURE 3.64 Trackman Mouse—*Continued*

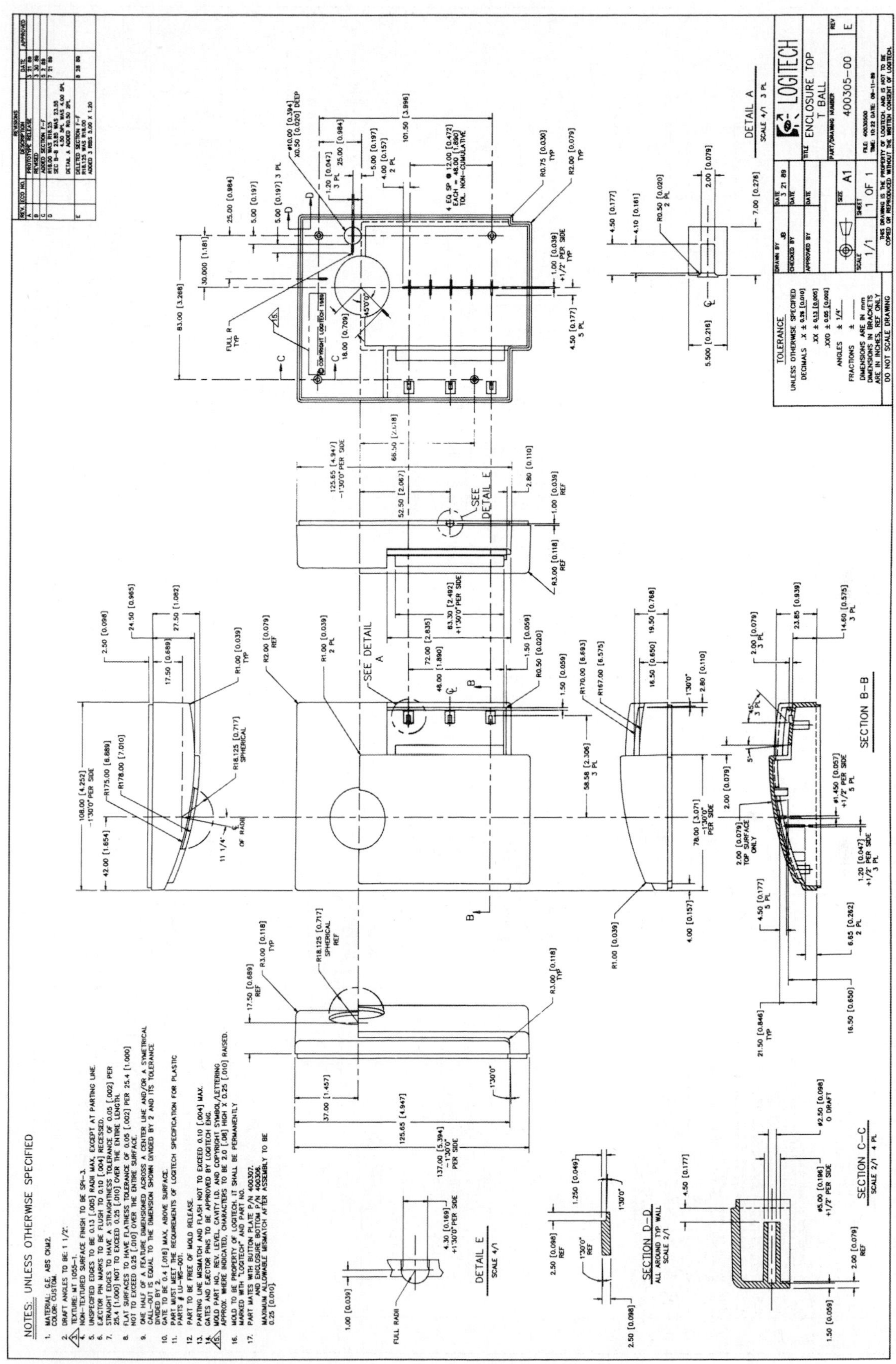

(f) Top enclosure of Trackball

FIGURE 3.64 Trackman Mouse—*Continues*

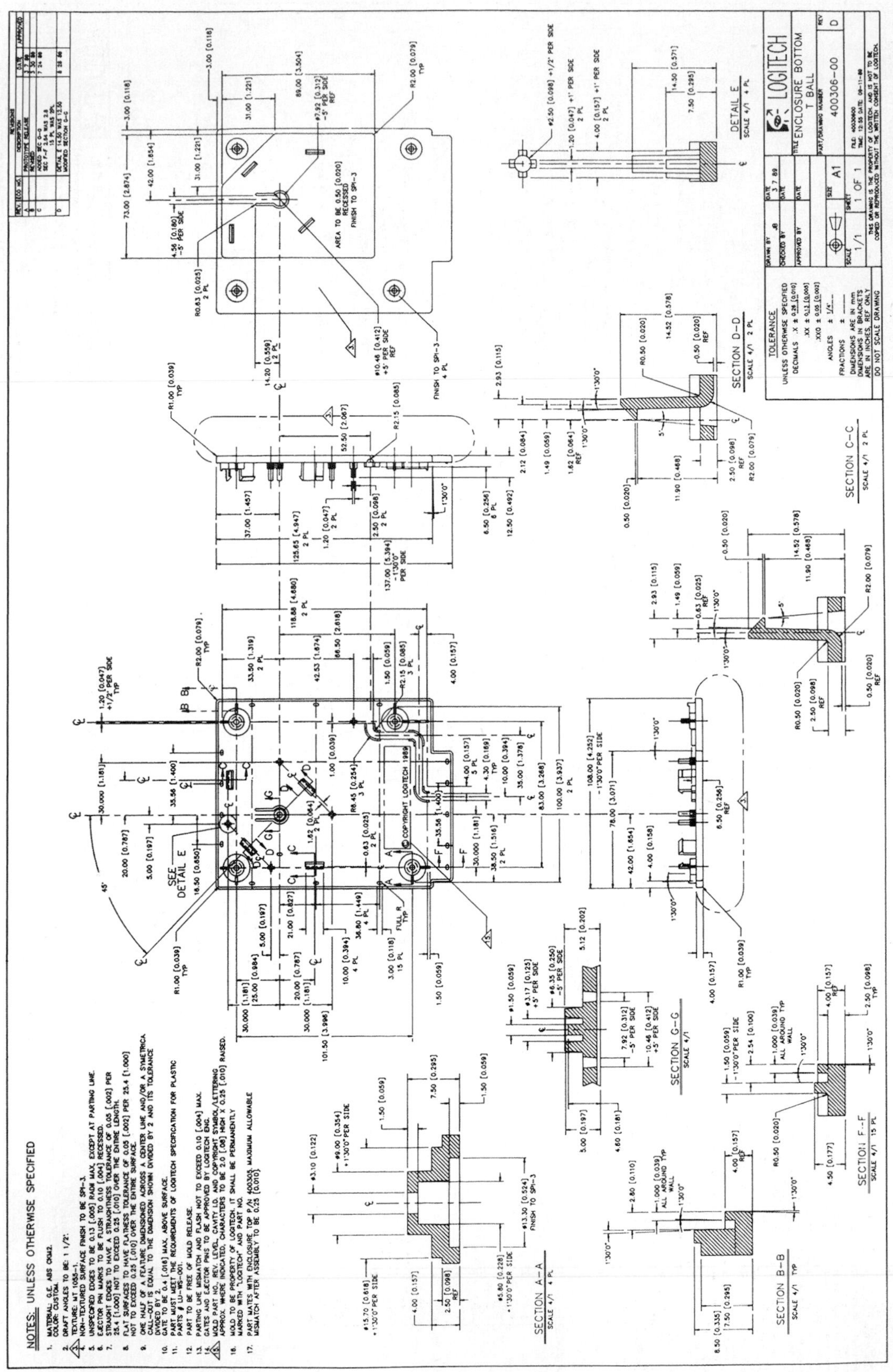

(g) Bottom enclosure of Trackball

FIGURE 3.64 Trackman Mouse—*Continued*

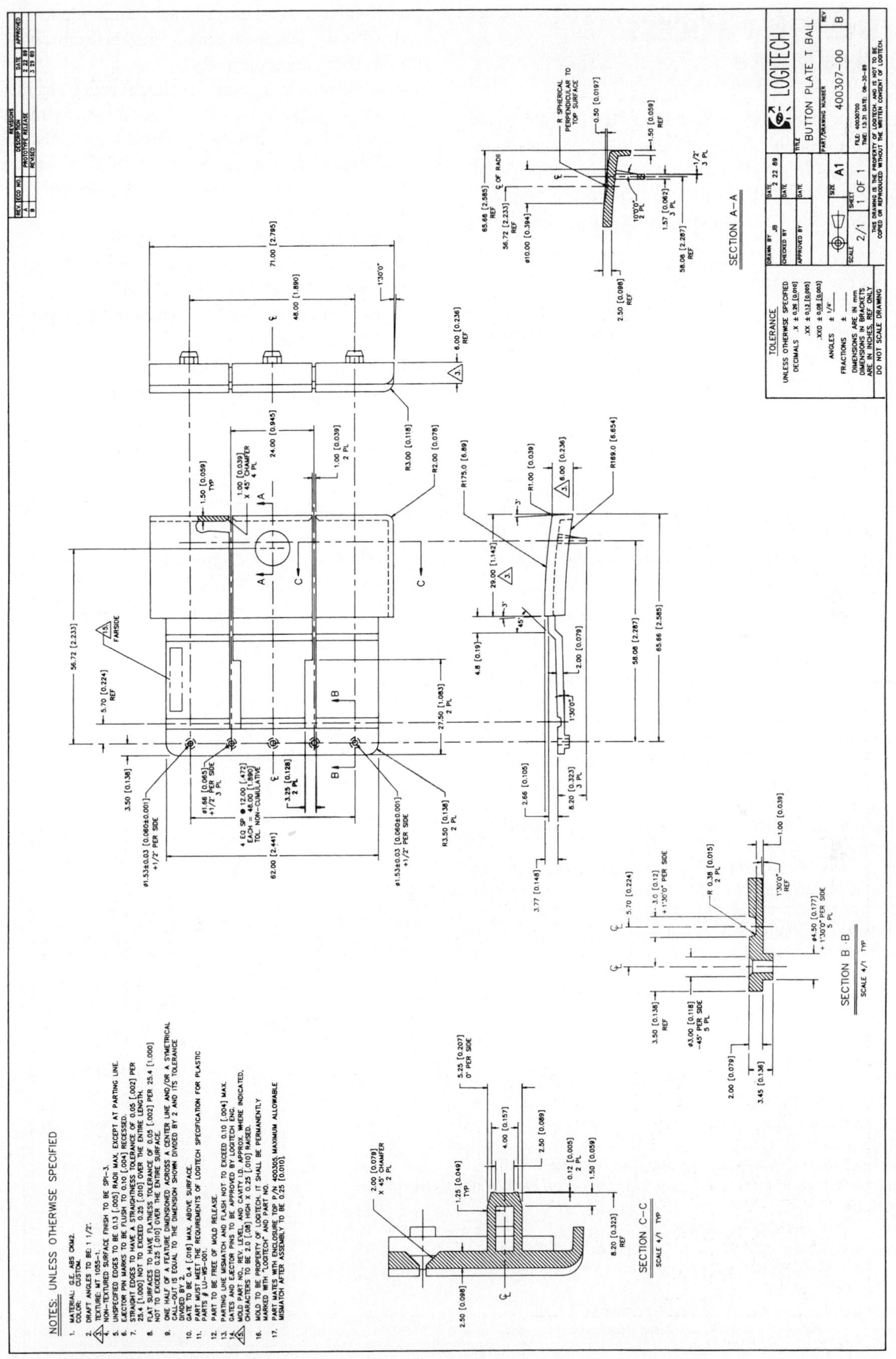

(h) Button plate for Trackball

FIGURE 3.64 Trackman Mouse—*Continued*

3.12 DESIGN PROCESS SUMMARY

The design process summary is included here as a guide and is hardly definitive. Table 3.1 gives a product design checklist. Use it as a guide only, because not all parts apply to all designs. It is recommended that any projects completed from this text use the checklist as a guide during the design process.

Design Process Summary

1. *Identification*: Defining the design objective
   a. Make a list of known facts and existing information.
   b. Ask the following questions: What? Why? Where? Whom? How? When?
2. *Conceptualization*: Brainstorming, creative solutions
   a. How many ways can it be solved?
   b. Thought starters, make a list of values.
   c. Similarities, environmental requirements
   d. Checklist, brainstorming, material options
   e. Is there a simpler way?
3. *Evaluation*: Application, functional requirements, synthesis
   a. What makes the design good—economy, simplicity, reliability, durability, usefulness, attractiveness, manufacturability, easy to promote in sales, easy to service?
   b. What are the alternatives to the design?
4. *Decision*: Design optimization
   a. What materials should be used?
   b. Should the parts be interchangeable?
   c. Should we use standard parts?
   d. Is it an economical manufacturing process?
   e. How easy is it to operate?
5. *Development*: Implementation of design
   a. Create working drawings and details.
   b. Model the part—CAD, physical, types, number of models.

TABLE 3.1 Product Design Checklist

A. Customer Requirements	Comment	Yes	No
1. Functionality			
a. Does the product meet customer requirements?			
b. Does it deliver the required performance?			
c. Does it satisfy emergency conditions?			
d. Have the important functions of the overall system and subsystems been agreed on?			
e. Is there a consensus between customers and designers?			
2. Safety Provisions			
a. Were provisions made for both intended use and foreseeable misuse?			
b. Was the product analyzed for hazards?			
c. Are there interlocks and safety devices?			
d. Does it meet applicable DOE and ME safety standards?			
e. Are complete safety instructions provided?			
f. Are warning, hazard, and severity signs properly identified?			
g. Have all possible radiation, toxicity, or corrosivity problems been considered?			
h. Was the product subjected to overstress tests?			
i. Has Hazards Control reviewed the design?			
j. Are there any high-voltage, high-pressure, or high-explosive sources?			
k. Are there other stored-energy sources?			
3. Operation and Maintenance Provisions Requested by Customer			
a. Does the product come with clear and concise instructions?			
b. Is it simple to operate?			
c. Are the controls operable and understandable?			
d. Does the product accommodate differing physical characteristics of operators?			
e. Is it easily maintained?			
f. Will spare parts be available?			
g. Can product be misused?			
h. Are operating or maintenance manuals needed?			
i. Are controls foolproof, so a hazardous condition cannot be inadvertently created?			
4. Cost and Schedule Requirements			
a. What is the basic cost to design and produce the product?			
b. What will the cost be over the total life of the product?			
c. What will spare parts cost?			
d. What are the major cost items and drivers?			
e. Could cost savings be realized with alternate designs?			
f. Are costs reasonable and realistic?			
g. Has a detailed schedule been determined for the design release or for long lead-term items?			

c. Check the design.
d. Testing and analysis—modeling, debugging
e. Improve and redesign for aesthetic or functional refinements.

6. *Production*: Manufacturing, packaging, handling the product
    a. Facility needs
    b. Personnel requirements
    c. Materials and processes for manufacturing
    d. Packaging design
    e. Material handling and product handling
7. *Marketing*: Sales and distribution
    a. Staff training
    b. Servicing the product
    c. Low maintenance costs, customer acceptance
    d. Sales strategy on how to present
    e. Product and main features
    f. Distribution of the product: Who? How?

TABLE 3.1 Product Design Checklist—*Continued*

A. Customer Requirements—*Continued*	**Comment**	**Yes**	**No**
5. Potential Environmental Effects on Product Performance and Reliability a. Could the product be affected by any of the following extremes at the customer's place of business: i. Voltage surges? ii. Service water hardness? iii. Pressure? iv. Temperature? v. External vibration? vi. External shock? vii. Ambient temperature? vii. Humidity? ix. Magnetic or electrical fields? x. Ambient sound? xi. Weather? b. Will operation be affected if the product is contaminated by foreign materials (sand, grit, oil, lint, dirt, etc.)? c. Will it be affected by corrosive ambients (salt, humid air, sea water, acids, cooling fluids, etc.)? d. Can radio interference affect operation? e. Can radiation affect the product? f. Can supplementary products (detergents, bleaches, oils, grease, solvents, lubricants, etc.) affect the product? g. How would an earthquake affect the product? 6. Potential Product Effect on Customer's Personnel and Environment a. Does the product have a pleasant appearance? Is it compatible with its surroundings? b. Is it noisy? c. Does it give off objectionable odors? d. Will it affect the temperature of the area it is used in? Will it affect other equipment? e. Does it vibrate? f. Does it produce objectionable light? g. Does it emit radiation? h. Does the exhaust give off noxious fumes? i. Will waste materials require special disposal? Have provisions been made for their handling, storage, and shipping? 7. Reliability and Performance Provisions a. Is the estimated reliability adequate? b. Was the reliability estimating method valid? c. Could performance deteriorate with wear or environmental change? d. Are the controls stable? e. What were the design provisions for minimizing likely failures? f. Have the methods of calibration and determining the performance been verified? g. Have emergency shutdown provision been provided for? h. Have provisions been made for power or water supply failures? i. Are there provisions for periodic inspection and in-sevice nondestructive evaluation?			

Continued

TABLE 3.1 Product Design Checklist—*Continued*

B. Good Design Practices			
1. Parts Breakdown a. Can several parts be combined into one? b. Can cost savings be realized by breaking a complex part into smaller, simpler, or less costly components? c. Is the Bill of Materials structure logical? d. Will the Bill of Materials suit the needs of manufacturing personnel? e. Is the drawing numbering system logical? 2. Safety Practices a. Does the product conform to the Design Safety Standards Manual? b. Is it free of sharp edges, burrs, or corners? c. Are the safety factors reasonable and defensible? d. Is a Safety Note needed? Has it been prepared according to the DSS? e. Is an Operational Safety Procedure needed? f. Has a failure modes and effects analysis been performed? g. Was a fault-tree analysis performed? h. Were all likely hazards identified and eliminated? 3. Assembly and Installation a. Can any part be assembled incorrectly? b. Is the assembly sequence simple and logical? c. Is there space for tooling access, insertion, etc.? d. Can likely repairs be diagnosed without disassembly? e. Are special tools needed for assembly and installation? f. Are common fasteners used? g. Will corrosion be readily apparent? If not, can the design be changed to ensure visibility? h. Will the method of inspection really validate the correctness of the assembly or installation work? i. Are written assembly or installation procedures required? 4. Parts and Components a. Does the design make use of proven standardized parts (fasteners, washers, clips, connectors, snap rings, etc) b. Are the raw materials specified in standard sizes, types, or forms (e.g., standard plate or sheet metal thicknesses, rod sizes, composition)? c. Are standard parts or raw materials readily available in the shop where the design will be fabricated? d. Were the components proven by use in an earlier, related design? 5. Design Selection a. Was the design scope properly defined? b. Were the selection criteria properly balanced and valid? c. Did the criteria respect customer requirements? d. Were alternate designs, concepts, or processes identified and documented? 6. Measurements and Control a. What needs to be measured, recorded, monitored, or alarmed? Why? b. What alternate sensors can be considered? c. What functions are to be controlled? Why? How? d. What provisions were made for instrumentation recalibration? e. How should data be recorded? f. Have requirements for resolution, repetition, and accuracy of measurements been determined? g. What should be automated? Why? How? h. How and when should instruments or controls be tested? i. How can you tell when controls are working properly? 7. Nondestructive Evaluation a. Are nondestructive evaluation inspections required? b. Are appropriate techniques and equipment available? c. If not, can the design be modified? d. If not, can new NDE equipment or techniques be developed?			
C. Minimizing Costs			
1. Has an engineering analysis been performed to investigate: a. The use of alternate, less expensive materials? b. Redesigning to reduce initial costs?			

TABLE 3.1 Product Design Checklist—*Continued*

C. Minimizing Costs—*Continued*			
c. The cost of maintenance, repairs, or operation? 2. How reliable is the cost estimate? 3. Is a service warranty provided by the manufacturer? a. Is the manufacturer's reputation for service good? b. How quickly will service be provided? 4. Have manufacturing and production costs been optimized: a. To utilize existing processes, equipment, and facilities? b. To minimize tooling costs? c. To make the most use of standard parts? d. To utilize more efficient new processes, equipment, and facilities? e. To minimize inspection and testing? 5. Can an alternate component be procured with a substantially better warranty?			
D. Improving Reliability			
1. Are the maximum stresses within limits through the full range of travel, load, voltage, etc.? 2. Are the safety factors used reasonable? 3. Is the design as simple as possible? 4. Were failure modes or critical elements analyzed? 5. Did you make optimum use of standard, proven components and subassemblies? 6. Was the reliability data of similar devices considered? 7. Were design integrity tests successfully completed (life, safety, simulated stress environments, etc.)? 8. Are drawings clear and unambiguous? 9. Is the equipment available when needed? 10. Were steps taken to minimize electrolysis, corrosion, dirt, etc.?			
E. Manufacturability and Production			
1. Does the design use existing equipment for fabrication, finishing, assembly, inspection, calibration, testing, packaging, etc.? 2. If not, are new processes, equipment, and facilities more effective? 3. Does the design avoid hazardous operations? 4. Are tool and piece costs optimized? 5. Does the design use existing acceptable tooling where possible? 6. Does it permit maximum standardization? 7. Are the tolerances and surface finishes specified consistent with acceptable processes and equipment? 8. Does the design correct or avoid known manufacturing problems? 9. Are the operations requiring special skills, new equipment, or special attention minimized? 10. Are critical dimensions or parameters to be controlled during procurement and manufacturing clearly identified? 11. Do the materials specified conform to standards? 12. Are specifications clearly and completely described on drawings? 13. Could inspection be accomplished easier and cheaper by changing the design?			
F. Shipping and Storage Requirements			
1. Will the product be transported with standard packaging? 2. Is additional special packing material required? 3. Will the package withstand applicable transportation tests for: a. Shock? b. Vibration? c. Temperature extremes? d. Humidity extremes? e. Handling equipment? f. Sand and dust? 4. Have you considered the available transport and storage equipment? 5. Has the shape and size of packaged product been optimized for rail and truck transportation?			

Continued

TABLE 3.1 Product Design Checklist—*Continued*

F. Shipping and Storage Requirements—*Continued*			
6. Are clear instructions for handling and lifting provided on the outside of the package? 7. How will used packaging material be disposed of? 8. How will moveable parts be secured during transport?			
G. Maintenance and Serviceability			
1. Are there any potential safety hazards during installation, repair, disassembly, or maintenance? 2. Is special test or service equipment needed? If so, have provisions been made to procure it? 3. Can the product be satisfactorily installed quickly? 4. Are items requiring frequent maintenance easily accessible? 5. Are new or nonstandard items minimized? 6. Are servicing instructions clear? Are they adequate? Are they the result of a fault-tree analysis or failure mode and effects analysis? 7. How will performance be verified after repair? 8. Are periodic nondestructive inspections required?			
H. Applicable Laws and Agency Requirements			
1. Does the product comply with applicable laws and agency requirements such as: a. Local ordinances? b. State or federal laws? c. Environmental Protection Agency laws and guidelines? d. Department of Energy (DOE) guidelines? e. Department of Transportation (DOT) rules for shipping? f. Others? 2. Does the product comply with applicable agency standards or guidelines such as: a. Underwriter's Laboratory (UL)? b. American Gas Association? c. Military specifications? d. Environmental Protection Agency (EPA)? e. Occupational Safety and Health Act (OSHA)? f. Consumer Product Safety Act? g. American National Standards Institute (ANSI)? h. American Society of Mechanical Engineers (ASME)? i. National Electronics Manufacturers Association (NEMA)? j. Institute of Electrical and Electronics Engineers (IEEE)? k. American Welding Society? l. DOE or others? 3. Are permits required for installation or operation, e.g., for venting gas or hazardous material?			
I. Patient and Classification Requirements			
1. Has a search been conducted to learn of recent related patents? 2. For patent protection, have any inventions been promptly disclosed? 3. Is any portion of the design, analysis, or documentation classified? Has an authorized classifier reviewed the preliminary and final designs? 4. Have steps been taken to safeguard the classified information? Are all personnel working on classified portions aware of the rules regarding the handling, dissemination, and disposal of classified information?			
J. Human Factors			
1. Are controls and displays well organized? 2. Are controls conveniently located for efficient operation? 3. Can monitoring or diagnostic devices be easily and accurately read? 4. Are instructions clear, legible, and complete? 5. Can all operations be performed safely without danger to the user or the product? 6. Have the physiological and psychological characteristics (age, education, size, strength, or handicap) of the user been considered? 7. Can maintenance be performed easily? 8. Have the human factors of similar devices been analyzed?			

Continued

TABLE 3.1 **Product Design Checklist**

A. Customer Requirements	Comment	Yes	No
1. Functionality a. Does the product meet customer requirements? b. Does it deliver the required performance? c. Does it satisfy emergency conditions? d. Have the important functions of the overall system and subsystems been agreed on? e. Is there a consensus between customers and designers? 2. Safety Provisions a. Were provisions made for both intended use and foreseeable misuse? b. Was the product analyzed for hazards? c. Are there interlocks and safety devices? d. Does it meet applicable DOE and ME safety standards? e. Are complete safety instructions provided? f. Are warning, hazard, and severity signs properly identified? g. Have all possible radiation, toxicity, or corrosivity problems been considered? h. Was the product subjected to overstress tests? i. Has Hazards Control reviewed the design? j. Are there any high-voltage, high-pressure, or high-explosive sources? k. Are there other stored-energy sources? 3. Operation and Maintenance Provisions Requested by Customer a. Does the product come with clear and concise instructions? b. Is it simple to operate? c. Are the controls operable and understandable? d. Does the product accommodate differing physical characteristics of operators? e. Is it easily maintained? f. Will spare parts be available?			

QUIZ

True or False

1. The design process is a series of eight rules that should be followed exactly.
2. All designs developed by a company's design team eventually get manufactured or produced.
3. Human engineering is the study of people and how they engineer/design projects in industry.
4. Human factors play an important role in all product design.
5. It is not important to have a brainstorming session during product design.
6. Ergonomics considers how humans interact with their work environment.
7. Automation is never considered during design of the manufacturing process.
8. In DFM, manufacturing is considered right from the start of the design sequence.

Fill in the Blanks

9. __________ design uses standard components arranged in a unique configuration.
10. __________ __________ is the first stage of the design process.
11. __________ design and __________ design are the two main divisions of design projects.
12. The effects of motion, heat, __________, and environment are some of a designer's concerns.
13. Machinability, castability, __________, __________, and __________ environment are all factors in the selection of the material for a product.
14. Stereolithography is one of the most common __________ __________ methods used in industry today.
15. Human factors is the modeling of the __________ __________ in a work-related setting.
16. __________-__________-__________ manufacturing is a process in which the component parts of a system design arrive at the assembly line station at the time of installation.

Answer the Following

17. Describe the use of models in the design process.
18. How are graphs and charts used in the design process?
19. What is human engineering, and how do human factors and ergonomics influence design?
20. What is DFM, and how does it affect the design process?
21. List six sources of information available to the designer.
22. What is critical-path scheduling?
23. Name and describe each of the stages of the design process.
24. What is stereolithography? How is it used in the design process?

COMPUTERS IN ENGINEERING DESIGN AND MANUFACTURING

Chapter 4

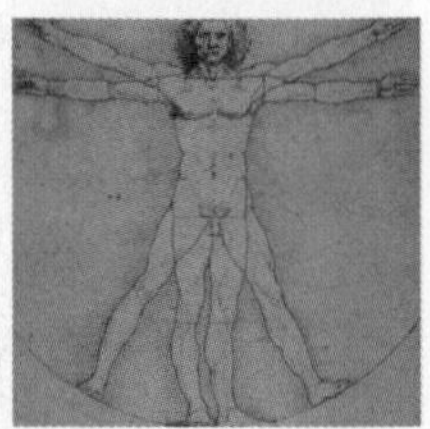

LEARNING OBJECTIVES

Upon completion of this chapter you will be able to:

1. Recognize the significance of computer-integrated manufacturing (CIM) in modern production.
2. Define CAD/CAM hardware and software as well as their respective configurations and capabilities.
3. Understand the role hardware plays in CAD/CAM, CIM, and computer-aided engineering (CAE).
4. Demonstrate an understanding of how data is stored on magnetic disk, magnetic tape, and CD's and in the computer itself.
5. Identify the components of a CAD workstation and their functions.
6. Develop a broad understanding of applications software.
7. Demonstrate knowledge of computer numerical control (CNC) part programming and of robotic integration into the manufacturing production process.

4.1 INTRODUCTION

Anyone wishing to enter industry as an engineer or a designer must be familiar with how profoundly the computer is altering the factory floor and the engineering office (Fig. 4.1). **Computer-aided engineering (CAE), computer-aided manufacturing (CAM),** and **computer-aided design and drafting (CAD)** are collectively called **computer-integrated manufacturing (CIM).** CIM refers to the integration of all phases of production, from design to manufacturing, via the computer. The term **CAD/CAM** refers to the use of computers to integrate the design and production process to improve productivity. CAM includes **computer numerical control (CNC)** machining (Fig. 4.2) and the integration of robotics into manufacturing and production.

In the 1990s, the role of CAM in a CAD/CAM environment will continue to increase, especially as an integrator in helping firms achieve the benefits of computer-integrated manufacturing. The CIM concept encompasses many manufacturing, computer-based automation applications. CIM can be thought of as a closed-loop feedback system whose primary inputs are product requirements and whose primary outputs are finished products. CIM is comprised of a combination of software and hardware for product design, production planning/control, and manufacturing processes.

CAD/CAM is the primary CIM integrator for computer-based applications in manufacturing. CAD/CAM's integration ability rests on a foundation of common engineering and manufacturing information. This allows engineering to define a part model (Fig. 4.3) and manufacturing to use that same definition to produce the product.

Product design simplification and other factory simplifications, such as **just-in-time (JIT)** programs, are normally completed before large-scale integration is introduced in a company. JIT programs are developed to bring the correct

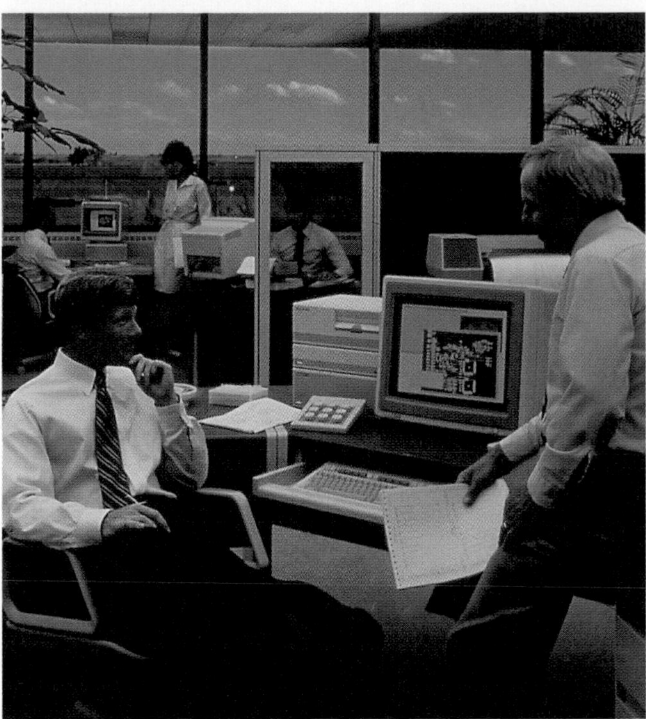

FIGURE 4.1 Design and Engineering Office

FIGURE 4.2 CNC Machining Center

part or material to the appropriate place at the required time. This eliminates excessive and costly warehousing of material and parts and streamlines the production and materials/parts handling process. JIT programs depend on parts standardization: The fewer the part variations and types of parts, the simpler the flow of material and parts within the factory. JIT programs therefore reduce the **work-in-progress (WIP)** inventory. This is why **design for manufacturability (DFM)** is usually the first step when initiating a CIM program. DFM simplifies designs, reduces the number of part types, and thus streamlines the flow of parts in a factory.

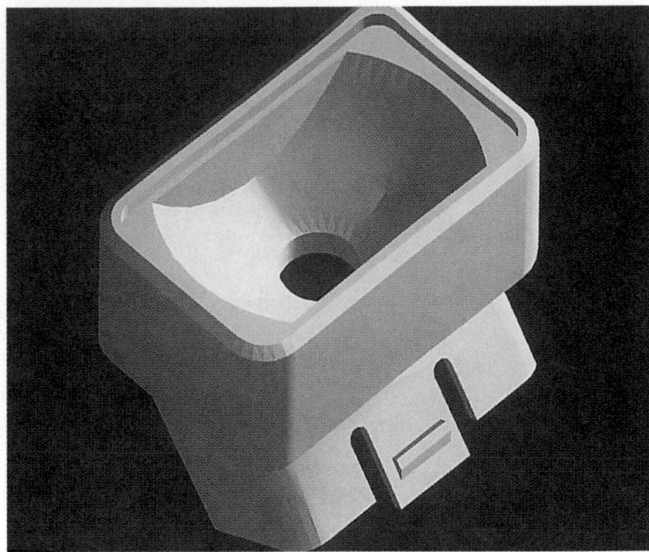

FIGURE 4.3 3D Part Design

The method of design determines how well the design fits into a CIM environment. CAD easily flows into CAM; but once the factory is dependent on CAD input, it will be less able to accept manual designs.

CIM also encompasses flexible manufacturing processes and procedures. Flexible manufacturing depends on parts commonality programs, which strive to minimize the number of part types and maximize commonality throughout the product line. If a factory (Fig. 4.4) is to be flexible, every manufacturing workstation must be able to work on a wide range of products. This is possible only when the parts are common enough so as always to be available where needed. Standardization of design features is also required for flexible manufacturing. Different parts will be traveling along the same materials handling systems and will be built by the

FIGURE 4.4 Computerized Advanced Electronic Assembly and Inspection Stations

FIGURE 4.5 Flexible Manufacturing System

same tools and equipment. Figure 4.5 shows a factory employing a flexible manufacturing system for production. In it, a number of manufacturing workstations are linked by a *materials handling system that moves the part from station to station, where one or more machining or processing operations are performed.*

Design for manufacturability, just-in-time programs, flexible manufacturing, and other automation concepts are driven by the original CAD input. Automation using CIM places constraints on the design based on DFM principles. Because the trend is toward more sophisticated factories, good DFM practices will be required by the designer and should be understood by engineers. The extensive use and integration of the computer in the design and manufacturing process will continue to increase throughout your career in industry.

4.2 CAD TECHNOLOGY

Engineers and designers create their designs electronically with a CAD system, view the designs on a display (Fig. 4.6), make quick and easy revisions, and then command the system to draw the design on a plotter. The completed parts [Figs. 4.6(a) and (b)] can be combined in an assembly [Fig. 4.6(c)] and displayed as shaded models [Fig. 4.6(d)]. Interactive graphics means the ability to perform graphics operations directly on the computer with immediate feedback. You need not be a computer programmer or typist to use a CAD system effectively. However, good typing skills do improve command input. Built-in programming knowledge of some CAD programs using EDIT and AutoLISP is also helpful.

The CAD operator also has constant access to processors and storage units that provide all the capabilities of a calculator and all the reference information of a library: Data is supplied for both trigonometric and geometric construction. Symbols, patterns, drawing segments, minidrawings, and even complete drawings can be stored and reused. You can electronically erase selected portions, shrink or enlarge a part's geometry, copy and edit portions of existing parts, and mirror, copy, and rotate complete parts or selected geometry. To accomplish this, a combination of hardware and software is required.

Hardware includes tablets, display devices, keyboards, input devices, processors, data storage components, plotters, printers, and all the other physical parts of a complete system. The hardware itself does nothing unless directed to do so by a set of instructions.

Software includes the sets of instructions that control the hardware. Software is usually provided by the CAD manufacturer and is already stored on the computer or available on disks, ready for use.

The input, processing, output, and storage hardware elements are interconnected via cables or telecommunications. Interactive CAD is either a stand-alone system or a processor with remote input/output units attached, such as on a PC-based CAD system (Fig. 4.7). System configuration and component terminology vary among CAD manufacturers.

An operator of a CAD system must be able to understand the system's hardware configuration and its software capabilities. The following is essential in order to understand and use a CAD system effectively in engineering design:

1. Knowledge of drafting standards and procedures
2. Specific engineering discipline conventions
3. Actual industrial applications
4. Software language for a particular CAD system package

Software programs are available for all areas of engineering and design. Most systems can be mastered with training, but the specifics of the design area (piping, architecture, electronics, mechanical, structural, etc.) must be learned through a combination of education and experience.

The heart of any CAD system is the design **terminal** or **workstation** (Figs. 4.7 and 4.8). Here, the engineer/designer interacts with the system to develop a part design in detail, monitoring the work constantly on a display screen. By issuing commands to the system and responding to messages from the system, you create a design by manipulating, modifying, and refining it. Once the design is final, a command to the system will make a hard copy or guide computer-controlled machine tools in manufacturing and testing the part. *Hard copy* can be any level of graphics, from a simple check copy to a full-scale ink plot of the drawing on vellum paper. The PC-based system in Figure 4.7 is linked to a pen plotter for outputting drawings.

As a design is developed, the software accumulates and stores product-related data—identifying the precise location, dimensions, descriptive text, and other properties of every element that helps define the new part. Using the design data, the system can perform complex engineering analyses, generate special lists and reports, and detect and flag (note/indicate) design flaws before the part is manufactured.

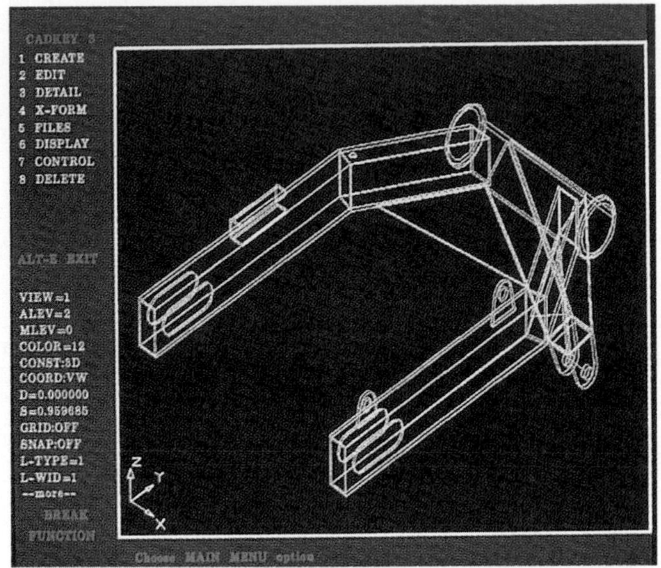

(a) 3D part design (wireframe)

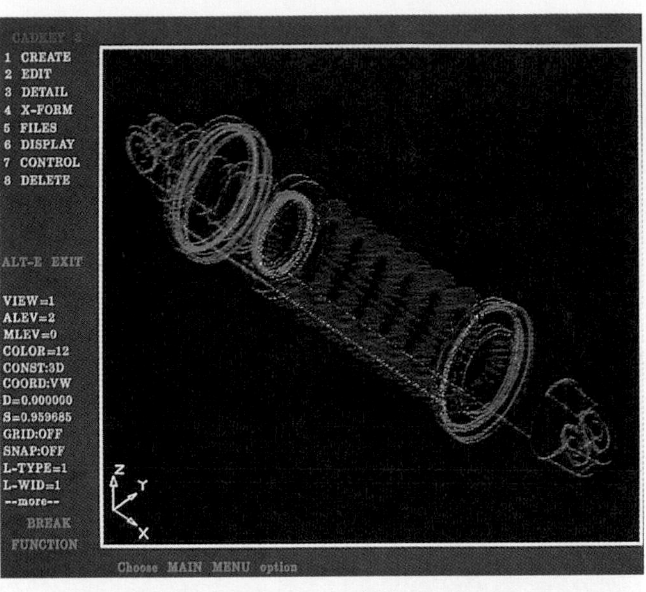

(b) Wireframe model of subpart

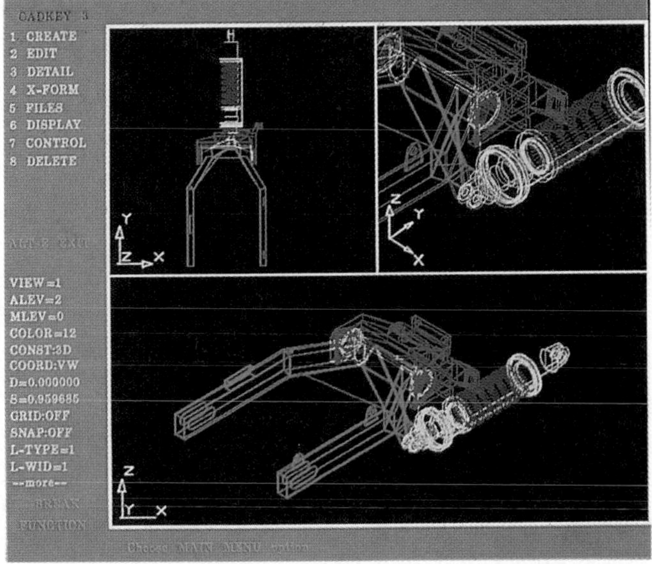

(c) Wireframe assembly

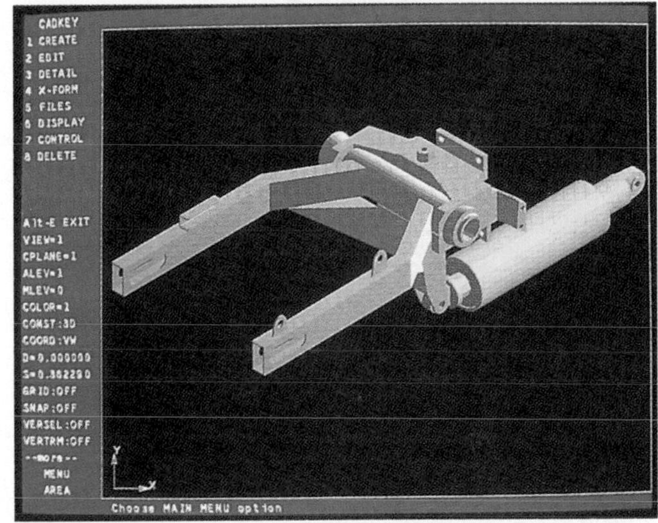

(d) Shaded assembly

FIGURE 4.6 Part Design and Assemblies

4.3 HARDWARE AND SOFTWARE

CAD systems vary in size, capability, and cost. Engineering firms select the computers and software based on their needs and funds available to buy them. The range is from personal computers (PCs) to large mainframes. Some companies need the systems for drafting and design. Others use the systems for CAD/CAM, analysis, fabrication, and testing.

The stand-alone personal computers (Fig. 4.7) have an integral **central processing unit (CPU).** The CPU for the CAD system in Figure 4.7 is housed in a separate floor cabinet. The CPU is the brain; it figures out what the software directions are telling it to do. Inside the brain is a section for **read-only memory (ROM).** ROM cannot be changed or edited easily. There is also a **random-access memory (RAM)** section where the data gets changed and edited. The CPU, ROM, and RAM are on the inside. On the outside are the various devices for putting data into the CPU. The monitor looks like a TV screen. The function keys on the keyboard (F1, F2, etc.) are shorthand versions of commands. The keyboard is another way to input commands—by typing.

A **digitizer** is a table or tablet with pictures, words, or icons of items from which to choose.

RAM is also considered volatile because it can remember the data stored in it only as long as power is applied. Once the power has been removed, the memory promptly forgets, and the next time power is applied it must be taught all over

FIGURE 4.7 Engineering Workstation with Tower CPU Located Under the Table Surface

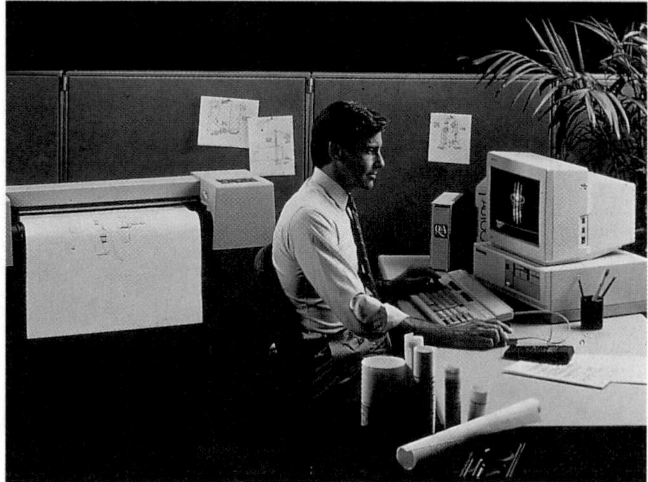

FIGURE 4.8 Drafting Station, Including CAD System and Plotter

again. This is like having a series of lights, each controlled by a button. When you press down any combination of buttons, the corresponding lights come on; when you release the buttons, the lights go off. All data is stored in the RAM as a series of 1's and 0's called **bits.** This is again like the light bulbs, where a 1 is on and a 0 is off. Eight bits make up a **byte,** which is the smallest unit for describing a letter or number. The amount of memory in a computer is measured in bytes. Sixty-four megabytes (Mbytes) represent 64 × 1,024,000 bytes, or 65,536,000 letters, or about 100,000 typewritten pages. An **M** (meaning "mega" or "million") is shorthand for 1,024,000. The typical PC CAD system requires 16 Mbytes or more of RAM.

ROM is like RAM, but the data is not lost when the power is turned off. ROM has many uses. ROM is small compared to RAM. ROM contains hardware configuration data and basic instructions about where the CPU looks for startup data. After the power is turned on, the computer must be given a detailed instruction, that is, where to get the incoming data (from which peripheral device). It must then be fed specific information, that is, what to do with the incoming data (what kind of calculation or other process). These instructions are in the ROM and are never erased.

On a **networked system,** several people can work simultaneously on different parts (making a drawing or model of a project), each providing information from his or her own terminal (Fig. 4.1). It is not uncommon to have eight or more people working on different aspects of the project, each on a different phase of development—such as design, engineering analysis, drafting, or manufacturing—for a single product or for many different products all tied together by the network.

The most common type of CAD system is PC-based. Macintosh, Intel 486 PCs, Pentiums, or clones now compete with workstation-based or terminal systems (Fig. 4.7). AutoCAD, CADKEY, VersaCAD, and Personal Designer software packages are PC-based systems typically found in schools and throughout industry. ProENGINEER is available for high-end PCs.

4.3.1 Operation

A typical CAD system makes possible simple yet powerful interaction between you and the computer. Just by pointing an electronic pen, a puck, or a mouse to a premarked, touch-sensitive drawing tablet or by picking an option from a pull-down menu, you can give the system drafting commands, such as **DRAW** or **ERASE**. You can create, modify, and refine the design interactively, viewing the emerging work on a graphics display. With a single stroke of the pen or keyboard input, you can move, magnify, mirror, rotate, copy, stretch, or otherwise manipulate the entire design or any portion of it.

The system lets you know, by a message on the screen, if there is a procedural error. Via the keyboard, electronic pen, and drawing tablet, you can ask the system to retrieve automatically any previously completed drawing needed for reference, as well as the standard design symbols expected to be used. Symbols and completed designs are all stored in the computer's data bank (memory or database), where they are instantly available. The online library speeds up the design process by eliminating unnecessary redrafting of commonly used components and subassemblies.

4.3.2 Documentation

As a part is designed on the system, its physical dimensions are defined, along with the attributes of its various components. This data, filed in the computer's memory, can later serve many other nongraphical needs. For example, the

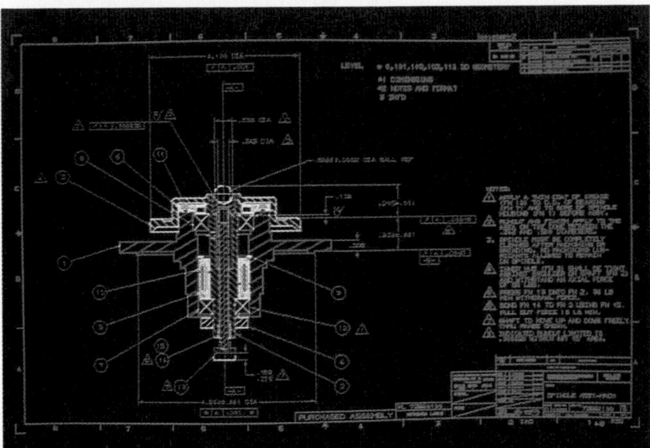

FIGURE 4.9 Engineering Documentation Is Important to Production

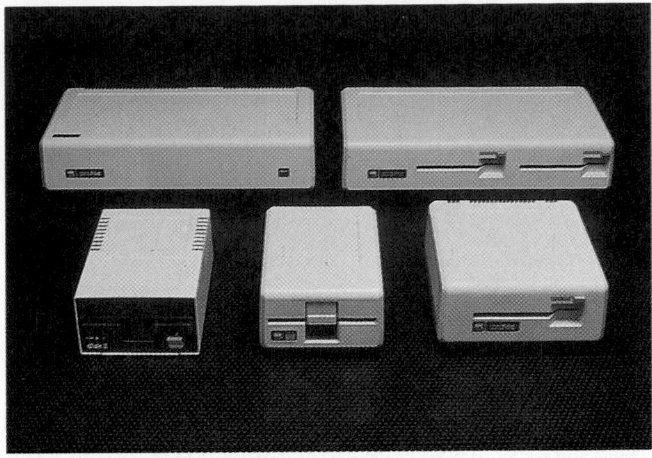

FIGURE 4.10 Floppy and Hard Disk Drives

materials part-number data can help generate bills of materials (Fig. 4.9) for production control.

The CAD database can be used directly by CNC machine tools and equipment for quality control and product testing. Other computer programs can help engineers check for interferences or tolerances, generate models for engineering analyses, and calculate areas, volumes, and weights for the product under development. All these nongraphic capabilities are automatic by-products of the CAD/CAM design process.

4.3.3 Memory/Storage

On mainframe computers and minicomputers, data may be stored in four ways:

- Magnetic disks (which are configured like stacked long-playing records but have much more storage capacity) contain data in a form quickly accessible to the system.
- Magnetic tapes (resembling reel-to-reel audiotapes) are used for semiactive storage.
- CDs are now available that have read and write capabilities.
- The computer itself has a storage capacity, although data is seldom stored there for extended periods.

System commands, utility instructions, and computational procedures are usually stored on disks. Seldom-used reference data is typically stored on magnetic tape. On PC-based systems, storage is accomplished with internal or external hard drives, WORM optical disks, tape drives, or on 3.5 in. or 5.25 in. floppy disks. Figure 4.10 shows a variety of PC disk drives and hard drives.

Symbol libraries, drawing segments, whole drawings, design models, and submodels complete with text are stored on magnetic tape (if inactive or waiting for scheduled revisions) or on disks (if needed for reference at an adjoining workstation or another CAD system). A completed drawing is placed on a portion of disk storage where it can be found rapidly by the system.

4.3.4 CAD Workstations

The **engineering and CAD workstation** (Fig. 4.11) may include a digitizer (which converts graphics to digits) and a monitor with alphanumeric keyboard. This is the control center for active work input. If a mouse is used, the system may not have a digitizer tablet.

The digitizer is wired so that the location of each place on its surface can be sent electronically to the processor by pushing the input button on the crosshair device to indicate a particular point. In the processor, all information is in digits (0 or 1); the digitizer changes graphics (lines and points) to digits. The processor then uses its calculating power to change the lines as the designer or engineer indicates and then reproduces them on the monitor. A typical interactive CAD workstation serves several functions:

- Interface to the host computer, either a large mainframe or local minicomputer
- Digital descriptions of a drawing, possibly stored locally
- Generation of a steady image on the display through its own local memory or by other means

FIGURE 4.11 Engineering Workstations

- Translation of computer instructions into operating functions and routing of commands for the various function generators
- Operator input devices for communicating with the computer: data tablets, mouse, light pen, digitizer table, cursor controls, or function keys

To carry out these functions, some form of display and an alphanumeric keyboard must be available.

4.3.5 Display Devices

All CAD systems use some kind of display device (monitor). There may be two screens, one alphanumeric (letters and numbers), the other graphic (pictures) (Fig. 4.11). This image can be produced by a number of available devices. One such device is the **cathode ray tube (CRT),** which is similar to a television, oscilloscope, or radar. CRTs are available in many sizes and configurations and with various capabilities.

FIGURE 4.12 CAD System Using a Keyboard and a Separate Function Box

4.4 INPUT DEVICES

Input devices enable you to communicate with a computer without the need to learn programming. Through these devices you can pick a function, enter text and numerical data, insert and manipulate geometry, modify the graphics, and even detail the finished part. All CAD systems have at least one operator input device. Many systems have several such devices, each for a different function. Alphanumeric keyboards, function boxes, electronic pens, light pens, trackballs, mice, joysticks, graphics tablets, and digitizing tables are used with CAD systems.

4.4.1 Keyboards and Function Boxes

In addition to the pen, mouse, or puck, you can communicate with the system through a **keyboard.** Using a combination of numbers and simple phrases, you can type **X, Y, Z** coordinates, enter text for drawing annotation, and initiate graphics processing commands. Several kinds of alphanumeric keyboards are commonly employed with CAD/CAM graphics terminals. The conventional typewriter-like alphanumeric keyboard allows you to enter commands, symbols, and text, as well as to request information. One of the most important functions of the keyboard is annotation, the process of inserting text (words and numbers) on a drawing.

The keyboard can enter messages consisting of letters, numbers, mathematical computations, and other symbols into computer storage. As the message or text is composed, it is displayed on the screen for verification or editing before the content is entered into the computer's main storage. The keyboard also can control the screen location of a movable cursor symbol (dash, blinking box, small cross, full-screen cross, or other marker) that is displayed where the next character will be entered. Keyboards may also include special graphics buttons called function keys.

In many cases, the CAD terminal is equipped with a separate box containing program-controlled push buttons (called a **function box** or **button box**). The function box can be integrated into the main keyboard or housed separately, as in Figure 4.12. The number of function keys varies from about 8 to 80. The function identified with each button is generally under computer control and can be changed as the program progresses or when a new application program is activated on the system. In some systems, the buttons can be labeled with an overlay, and the overlay can be changed with each application program. The use of function keys is easily mastered and their meanings quickly memorized. In other applications, the buttons are simply numbered and the function of each button is included in a user-selectable **menu.**

4.4.2 Graphics Tablet and Digitizing

One common input device is the **graphics tablet.** Graphics tablets and tables are electronic units that consist of a rectangular grid of horizontal and vertical lines integrated into a flat drafting-tablelike surface. Generators within the tablet pulse the lines, producing discrete code signals in response to an electronic pen, a puck, or a mouse device moved by the designer. The computer determines the location of the pointing device by decoding the signal. This decoded information is displayed on the CRT as **X** and **Y** coordinates. A line or spot (cursor symbol) corresponding to the input device position appears on the screen.

Most data tablets allow some separation between the pen and the tablet surface. That is, the pen need not be in contact with the tablet surface. Therefore, a paper drawing or other sheet can be placed on the data tablet, enabling you

Focus On . . .

COMPUTER-INTEGRATED MANUFACTURING

Computer-integrated manufacturing (CIM) is a system in which all the functions needed in design, purchasing, manufacturing, inventory, and marketing of products are networked together. The computer information database is shared by everyone, eliminating duplication of information. The software that controls such a system must be refined and perfected, but many companies already have the key components of such a system in place.

One of the major components of CIM is the flexible manufacturing system (FMS), in which computer numerically controlled (CNC) machines are used with robots and part transfer vehicles to move a part from raw stock, through all machining steps and assembly, until it becomes a finished part. A software base controls the entire sequence.

Manufacturing cells.

The four major components of FMS are CNC machines, the coordinate measuring machines (CMM), robots, and part and tool transfer vehicles. This system can run unattended if it is supported properly. Worn tools are not a problem because of the online monitoring system. Inspection is completed with the CMM. Electronic gaging probes measure the features of the part, and the computer compares the results with the limits stored in the database.

Robots load and unload materials and parts to the manufacturing cell. The tool and material transfer vehicles shuttle workpieces and tool magazines from inventory and to specific machines. These vehicles can be automatic guided vehicles (AGVs) or wire-guided, air cushion, or hardware-guided vehicles.

AGVs are not connected to hardware, and rely on onboard sensors and programs to establish their paths. A wire buried in the factory floor defines the path of travel for wire-guided vehicles. The air cushion vehicle glides on an air cushion and is guided by external hardware. Unfortunately, any debris on the floor will stop the air cushion vehicle. The hardware-guided vehicle runs on a track or rail. It is very reliable, but hardly flexible.

The American manufacturing industry has taken a hard look at what must be done to compete with ambitious programs under way in Japan and in Europe. Executives from a review program concluded that we need to make our factories "agile," link them together by computers, and collaborate.

CIM will certainly play the key role as industry strives to eliminate paperwork, eliminate duplication of effort, reduce development-to-product cycle time, and improve quality and customer satisfaction. Much development is still needed before we have a true CIM environment.

---

to translate drawing coordinates into digital form. This process is called **digitizing.** This digitizing feature is very important in many computer-aided design and data analysis applications. Digitizers are devices that convert coordinate information into numeric form readable by a digital computer. Some CAD systems use a sheet overlay to develop unique menus for program control.

Some CAD systems now run with Windows-based software, as shown in Figure 4.13. These systems are normally equipped with a mouse-type input device for quick and simple selection of the Windows options.

A tablet without menu options is simply a **data tablet.** This type of graphics tablet has a surface area that corresponds to the display area of the CRT. By moving a hand-held puck with input buttons, you can position the display cursor symbol on the CRT. Instead of a tablet menu, a **display menu** appears on the CRT (Fig. 4.14). Menu commands are entered by positioning the symbol cursor over the desired menu function displayed on the screen and pressing an input button.

Digitizing tables are used by some companies to input 2D sketches into the system directly (Fig. 4.15). Flow diagrams, block diagrams, schematic diagrams, logic diagrams for electronics, and piping diagrams for piping design lend themselves to direct digitizing.

4.4.3 Light Pen and Electronic Pen

The **light pen** is a pen-shaped electrophoto-optical device that allows you to identify a particular element directly on the display screen or to select a particular function from the

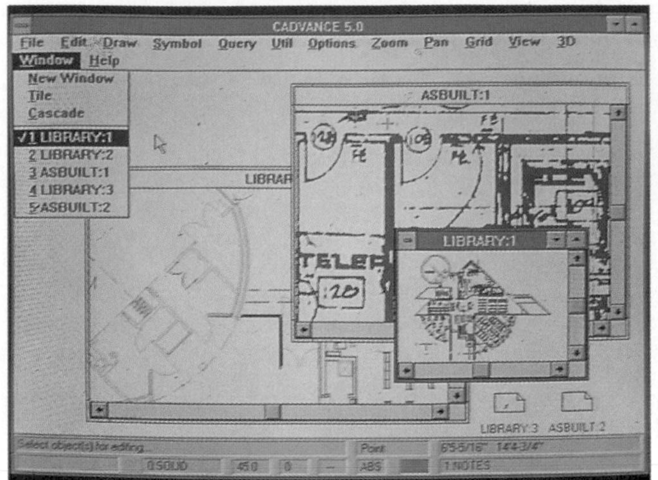

(a) Assessing part libraries via Windows

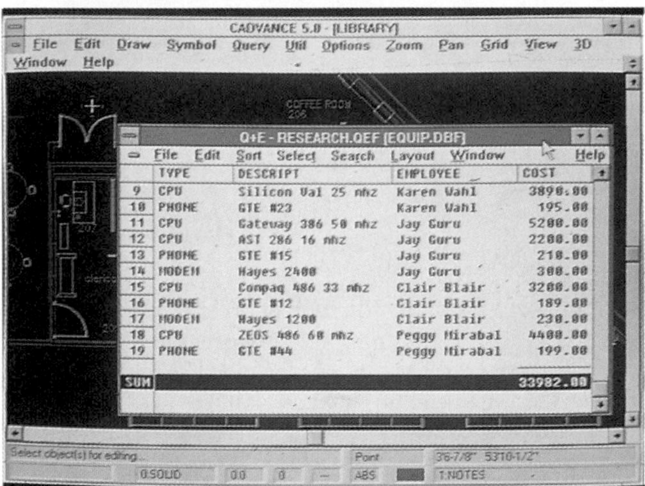

(b) Equipment list for office (displayed with Windows)

FIGURE 4.13 CADVANCE CAD System Using Windows-Based Software

FIGURE 4.15 Large Digitizing Table Being Used to Input a Sketch

FIGURE 4.16 CAD System Using a Pen

menu. An **electronic pen** (Fig. 4.16) is restricted to coordinating input or menu selections and cannot be used to draw on the display device. A light pen, however, can be used to draw on the CRT display surface. Few systems today employ a light pen. Most CAD stations input information via electronic pen, puck, or mouse (using a screen menu).

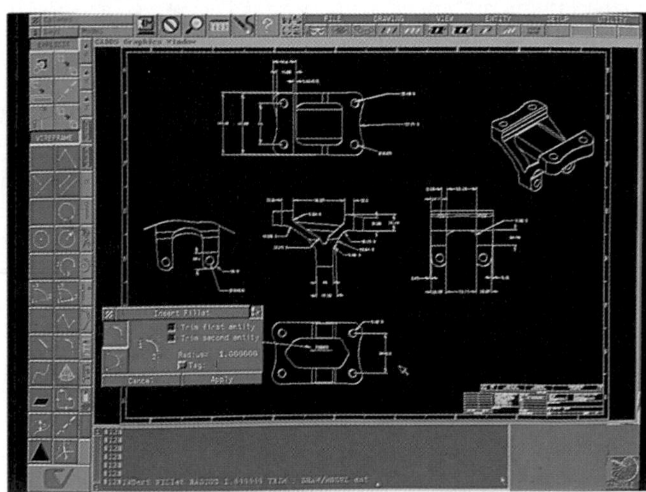

FIGURE 4.14 Screen Menu

4.4.4 Pointing Devices

Besides pens, various special **cursor controls** are available for CAD systems, including the trackball, the joystick, and the mouse. Figure 4.17 shows a variety of pointing devices available for CAD systems, including roller ball and mouse types. Each of these data entry devices can be used by the engineer to enter coordinates manually in specific **X, Y,** and **Z** registers. The trackball mechanically couples a control element to both the X and Y generators so that a single motion can drive both transducers simultaneously (operating like a mouse). The trackball uses a rolling ball to drive the transducers. The **joystick** is similar to the trackball except that it is moved by a small, batlike handle.

Most PC-based CAD systems can be operated with a **mouse** as their primary means of input (Fig. 4.18). A mouse

FIGURE 4.17 Pointing Devices

is moved along a flat surface (a pad or table); its movement controls the position of the screen cursor. Buttons on the mouse allow you to input the screen menu selections and to pick locations on the screen.

4.4.5 Menus

A **menu** template overlay for a digitizer is an input device consisting of command squares on a digitizing surface (such as a tablet or table) or on the screen. A menu eliminates the need for the keyboard for entering graphical or common command data. A menu tablet allows the selection of the most commonly used tasks for a particular design field. General drawing menus are available for constructing simple to complex graphics. New menus can be changed or created as required.

To utilize a menu (Fig. 4.19), you simply place the pointing device over the desired command and press the cursor button or the function key. Most systems have commands that allow frequently changed parameter options (such as letter heights and slant) to be displayed on the alphanumeric screen for operator inspection or modification.

The menu shows the commonly used symbols and commands. Since not all symbols can be placed on a menu, a typical system is capable of creating and holding a large **drafting library.** A library contains all the needed symbols, drawings, or figures for a particular engineering field: nuts, bolts, screws, electrical symbols, welding symbols, or component outlines. It is basically an unlimited template. The drafting library can be added to or subtracted from as necessary. An engineer typically collects and customizes figures or symbols from the drafting library, creates any special figures that will be needed repeatedly, and assembles them into special menus. Some companies supply drawings on disk and even 3D models of their products to serve as templates for a library of parts.

Although the number of figures may be limited because of size and space, the number of menus is unlimited. The

(a)

(b)

FIGURE 4.18 CAD Systems That Use a Mouse as the Only Input Device

FIGURE 4.19 Tablet and Pen

typical menu item is inserted with a minimum of keystrokes. Each symbol can be inserted at any angle or scale. The symbol or figure can be as simple as an electronic diagram symbol or as complex as a complete printed circuit board. Once the menu symbol or figure is created, it can be stored and used any number of times in other drawings.

4.5 OUTPUT/HARDCOPY DEVICES

Output from CAD systems comes in many forms. The most common is a drawing just like the one created on a drafting board. This drawing, which is a copy of what is on the screen, is created by a plotter (Fig. 4.20). Output can also be a copy of what is on the screen, called a **hard copy.** A hard copy normally comes from a printer or plotter attached directly to the workstation. A drawing not only can be obtained from a plotter, but can also be drawn on microfilm. This is called **computer output microfilm (COM).**

Hard-copy and output devices include printers, plotters, and photocopy equipment. Printers provide the user with alphanumeric readouts and material lists. The plotter allows you to produce ink drawings on paper, vellum, or drafting film in a multitude of colors. Some plotters are limited by the size of the plotting surface. Although they are limited to standard paper widths, others can plot drawings of any length. Pen plotters can use ballpoint pens, felt-tip pens, liquid ink pens, or pencils. Check copies are normally run with inexpensive ballpoint pens. Original high-quality drawings are plotted with India ink and liquid ink pens. When plotting a drawing, you have a number of options: to scale the drawing, rotate it, select the colors to plot, or even substitute different line widths. Not all pen plotters have these options. Various plotters are available, including drum plotters, flatbed plotters, electrostatic plotters, digitizer plotters, and laser plotters.

FIGURE 4.20 3D Models. Three-dimensional models from a computer screen can be easily coverted back to two dimensions to make hard-copy displays.

4.5.1 Plotters

In a CAD system, plotters and displays complement each other. A display is capable of presenting a picture rapidly so that you can react to it, perhaps making changes interactively. A **plotter,** on the other hand, can make large, highly accurate drawings, but more slowly (Fig. 4.21). Displays are used to make the initial decisions, while plotters make the record copies.

The accuracy of plotted output can be considerably higher than the apparent accuracy and quality of the image on the display. A computer defines all graphics as coordinate points. Therefore, all graphics on a CAD system are made of straight-line elements. The closer the points of a curve are spaced, the better a system's **resolution.** *Resolution is the smallest spacing between points on a graphic device at which the points can be detected as distinct.* The degree of resolution influences the quality of the drawing plot, since curves appear as a series of straight lines if the resolution is poor.

4.5.2 Pen Plotters

Typical CAD systems use an electromechanical **pen plotter** to plot data and make engineering drawings. Two basic kinds of pen plotters are in current use. The earliest and perhaps most widely used type is the **drum plotter** (Fig. 4.21). Plotting paper is wrapped around the drum, and the drum is rotated by a digital stepping motor. The rotation provides one deflection axis, while the pen, mounted on a gantry across the drum, provides the other deflection axis. The only other basic control, besides **X** and **Y** deflection, is

FIGURE 4.21 Drum Plotters

the control to move the pen up and down. Drum plotters are available in sizes that range from $8\frac{1}{2}$ in. to more than 42 in. wide. They make plots quickly and of unlimited length. The smaller drum plotters make lines in incremental steps, approximately .005–.01 in. apart, with plotting rates of around 5 in. per second. A typical drum plotter uses either ballpoint, felt-tip, or ink pens.

As the name suggests, a **flatbed plotter** has a flat, horizontal drawing surface, with the paper lying flat, suitable for highly accurate, top-quality drawings. On most flatbed plotters, the pens move and the paper remains stationary. Flatbed plotters were introduced to satisfy the need for high-quality images and large drawing sizes. Now plotters ranging from about $8\frac{1}{2} \times 11$ in. to as much as 4 ft wide × 12 ft long are available.

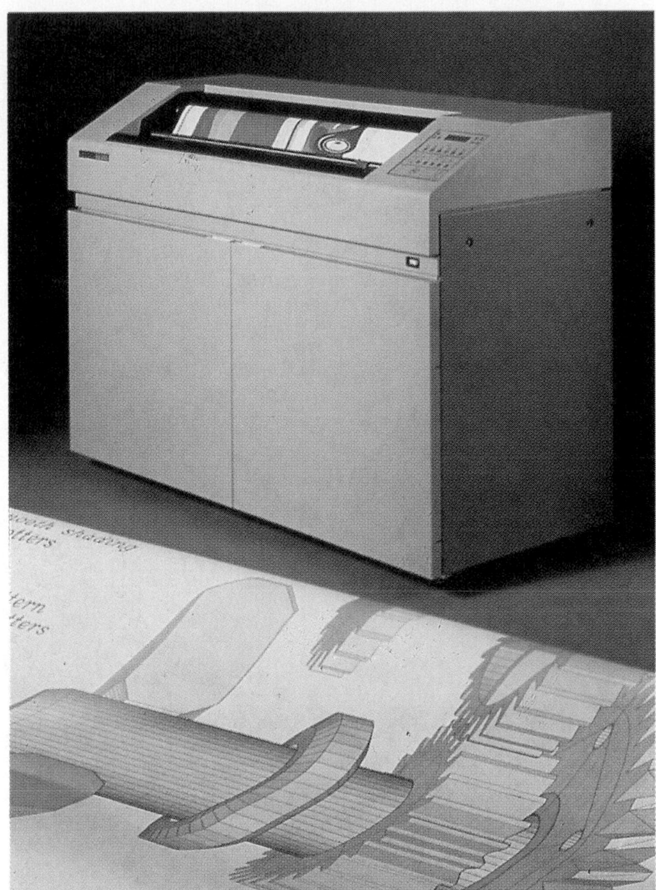

FIGURE 4.22 Electrostatic Plotter

4.5.3 Electrostatic Plotters

In the past, **electrostatic plotters** were used primarily for quick-look capability. However, electrostatic plotters are now of such high quality that they are selected as one of the primary output devices for CAD/CAM systems.

While it takes seconds (or even fractions of a second) to display an image on the CRT, the time required to plot that same drawing on a precision plotter may be several minutes. Plotting twenty to thirty times faster than pen plotters, electrostatic plotters can plot a square foot of data in a few seconds.

All electrostatic plotters (Fig. 4.22) share a similar operating principle: Voltage is applied to an array of densely spaced writing nibs embedded in a stationary writing head. The nibs selectively create minute electrostatic dots on the paper as the paper passes over the writing head. The paper is then exposed to liquid toner to produce a visible, permanent image.

The electrostatic plotter retains the advantage of the drum plotter that drawings can be of unlimited length. Electrostatic plotters are available up to 6 ft in width. A further advantage is that the electrostatic plotter can be used very effectively as a high-speed line printer (up to 1200 lines per minute).

FIGURE 4.23 Scanner

4.5.4 Photoplotter

Photoplotters, the most accurate type of plotter, are chosen where extreme accuracy takes precedence over the cost of the unit. Printed circuit board art masters are normally created with this type of plotter. A light beam is used to "plot" the drawing on light-sensitive film.

4.5.5 Scanners

Scanners can produce high-quality reproductions of photographs, line drawings, or technical illustrations (Fig. 4.23). This technology is employed in desktop publishing, and to produce and merge graphics with word processing for technical reports, technical and service manuals, and various other output.

4.5.6 Printers

A **printer** is a computer-operated typewriter providing the user with hard copy of alphanumeric data. Printers are used as a quick screen dump for reviewing graphics and for producing parts lists and other nongraphic output. Many types of printers are available. The quality of typeface and the speed of printing are two of the most important features of a printer. **Letter-quality printers** are slower and do not plot any type of graphics. Although the quality of the typeface is poor, **dot matrix printers** are extremely fast and plot limited-quality graphics. **Ink-jet printers** [Fig. 4.24(a)] and **laser printers** [Fig. 4.24(b)] are also available for high-quality printing needs as well as high-quality graphics. Printers acting as hard-copy devices with CAD systems must be able to process graphics.

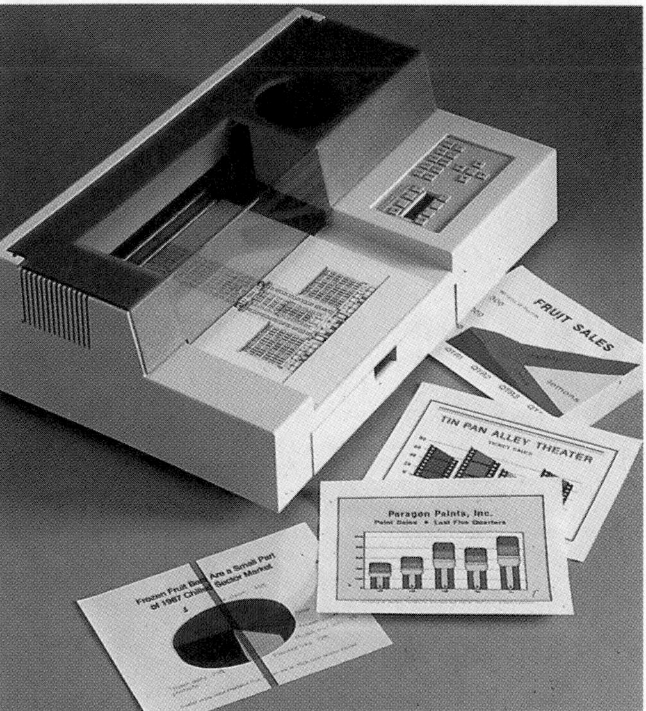

(a) HP Ink-Jet

(b) HP Laserjet 4

FIGURE 4.24 Printers

4.6 CAD/CAM SOFTWARE

Software is the programmed instructions that tell the processor what to do. Programming that is built into the microchips (integrated circuits) and printed circuit boards of the computer is called **firmware.**

Many CAD systems come from the manufacturer preprogrammed. Knowledge of programming is not needed to use a CAD system; you just turn it on and the system is ready for use. Software orders the computer to direct the flow of input data either into working storage or to the disk for instant recall. Software also helps the computer retrieve input data for processing.

4.6.1 Applications Software

A typical CAD **application software** package does not require the designer or engineer to be a computer programmer. CAD systems are designed to free designers from the time-consuming task of programming so that they can concentrate on the design capabilities of the system. On the other hand, any person using an application program must be familiar with the standards and the conventions in that technical field. It is very important for the young engineer to understand that, no matter what the level of sophistication, the hardware and the software are only there to aid the user in design and drafting tasks. As an engineer or designer, you must know about the application and what procedures are applicable to that area. Excellent software packages have been developed for civil and mapping engineering, structural engineering, architectural engineering, piping engineering, mechanical engineering, electronics, technical illustration, and a variety of other areas. The use of CAD in these technical areas has enhanced design and streamlined engineering. But the designer or engineer must still know all of the particulars of the application area. CAD as a tool is cost-effective only in the hands of a knowledgeable, well-educated user.

Generally, the manufacturer of the CAD/CAM system supplies programs for basic-level creation of 2D and 3D drawings. Additional programs may be supplied by the manufacturer to do engineering analysis or help the designers learn special system functions. A typical drawing software package allows the designer to construct all the traditional drafting graphics using standard conventions and practices. The difference lies in the automated capabilities imbedded in the system and the availability of specific applications programs.

Some CAD vendors offer a general CAD software package for constructing symbols, menus, standards, and conventions for any engineering area. This type of software allows other vendors of applications programs to write software for a technical area such as printed circuit board (PCB) design and architecture, using the generic software as the base. Other CAD systems are totally dedicated to one or just a limited number of applications, for example, integrated circuit design, PCB design, or mechanical drafting.

An excellent exercise would be to investigate what other areas of industry and business utilize CAD capabilities. For instance, chemists are using CAD to create new drugs (this field is actually called computer-aided drug design). The 1985 Indy race winner drove a car that was designed on a CAD system. Once you start to look into the present-day uses of CAD, the future possibilities seem unlimited.

4.6.2 Electronic Applications

One of the most important applications for CAD is **integrated circuit** and **printed circuit board (PCB)** design and documentation. All integrated circuit design is done on a computer. CAD increases productivity by automating and integrating the key steps in the design and production of integrated circuits and PCBs. The typical PCB program (Fig. 4.25) uses automatic and manual editing modes to design the entire board, from the drawing of the schematic to the final manufacturing and testing stages (Figs. 4.26 and 4.27). Schematics, text, and board geometry are entered interactively into the system. Automatic assignment, placement, and routing routines are used to complete the design of the board. A variety of PCB sizes and types can be designed. Manual input can override the automatic routines.

The automatic routing of PCBs is complemented by software to place components on the board automatically. Because of the increasing density of boards and complexity of circuits, this is an important feature for development. The CAD system also provides control tapes for numerically controlled drilling and insertion machines for use during the production and manufacturing of circuit boards.

For the development department, there are special problems both in design and in preparing the necessary documentation for manufacturing. Designing the printed board entails overcoming spatial restrictions and layout constraints. Designing the equipment housing requires consideration of cooling arrangements, protection against shocks and vibrations, provision of easy access for servicing, and, at the same time, satisfaction of styling requirements. This is called electronic packaging design.

CAD systems can automate and integrate the key steps in the design, documentation, and design-rules-checking of wiring diagrams. It reduces the time and expense required to capture, check, update, and extract design information. This capability is applied to many types of diagrams: logic, schematic, wire harness, and interconnection.

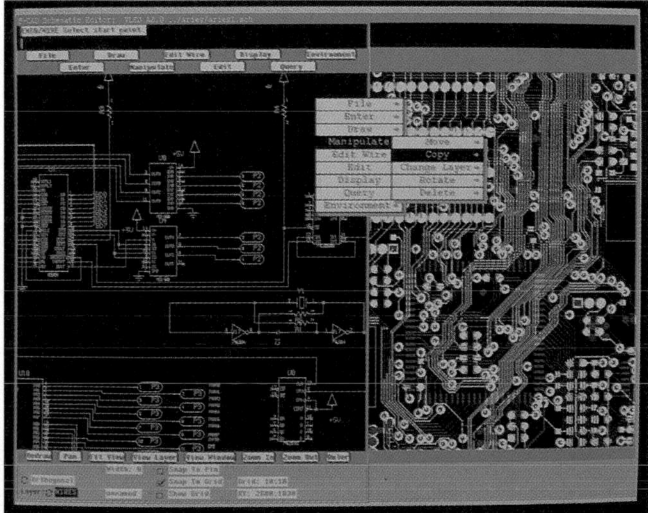

FIGURE 4.25 Printed Circuit Board (PCB) Design

FIGURE 4.26 PCB Design on an Engineering Workstation

4.6.3 Architecture and Construction Applications

Applications are available for building designs on a CAD system, including **architectural design** (Fig. 4.28 a, b, and c). You can design the structure, display and detail the appropriate views, and use color shading to show how the

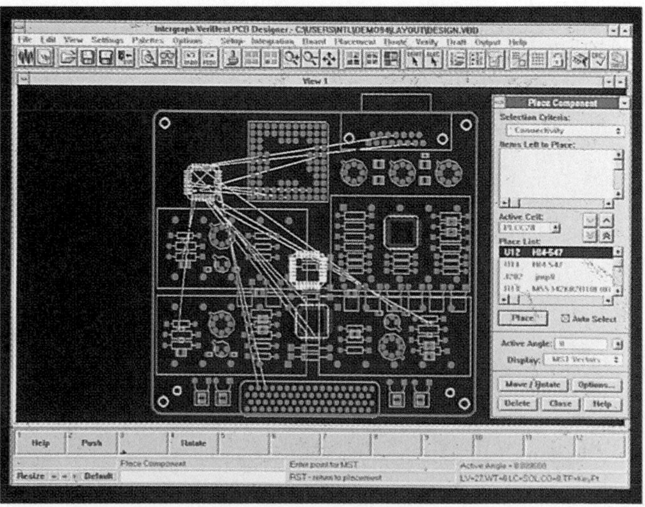

FIGURE 4.27 PCB Design and Editing

(a) Architectural design using AutoCAD

(b) Shaded model

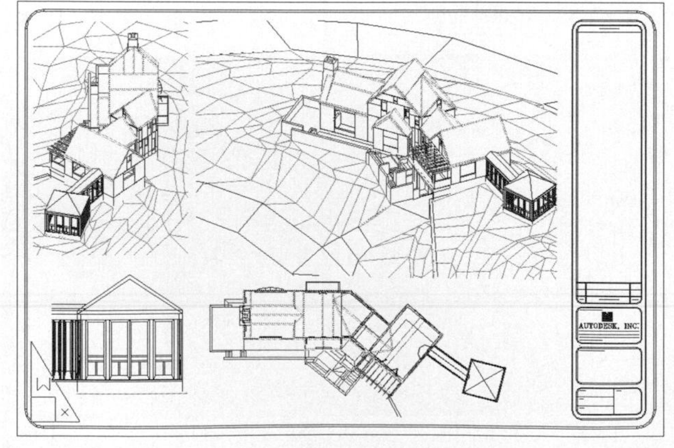

(c) Wireframe model

FIGURE 4.28 Architectural Design

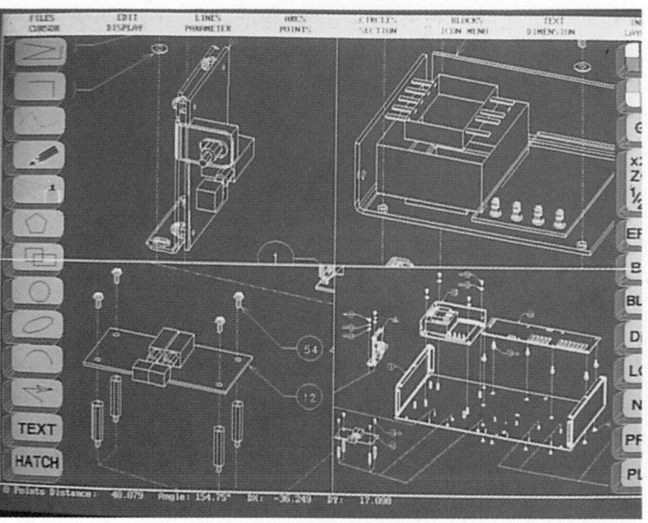

FIGURE 4.29 Electronic Packaging Design

building would appear realistically. This eliminates the need to model the building physically or do a rendering.

Electronic packaging design (Fig. 4.29), space planning, duct work, electrical layout, and plumbing can also be completed. The system allows the integration of such disciplines and permits you to develop several design alternatives for a particular project, including possible landscaping schemes.

4.6.4 Structural Design and Engineering Applications

Structural design, layout, and detailing are important applications for which CAD has been used effectively in the building industry to improve design and decrease drafting time (Fig. 4.30). The designer inputs the structural grid,

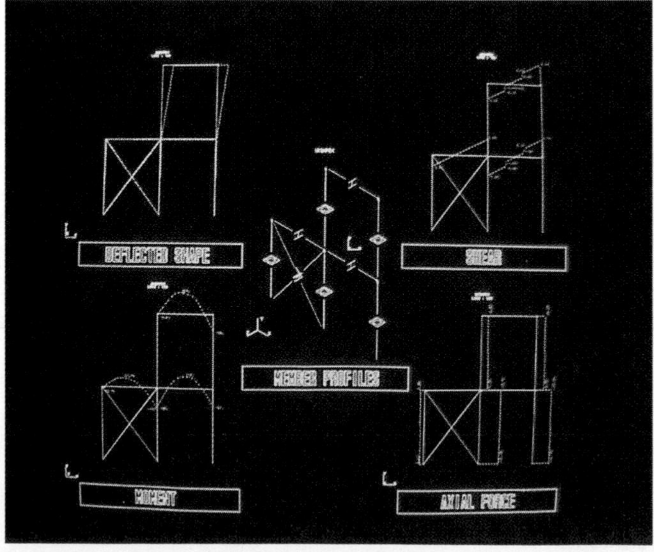

FIGURE 4.30 Structural Steel Design and Drafting

geometry, and member properties. The member profiles can then be graphically checked before analysis begins. After the structural analysis is performed, the results can be displayed using moment, sheer, axial force, and deflected shape diagrams. Color and layering capabilities help in analysis and in differentiating between structural element types and sizes.

4.6.5 Civil Engineering and Mapping Applications

Civil engineering and **mapping** [Fig. 4.31(a)] features include site selection, site preparation, digital terrain modeling, earth work calculations, and contour mapping. Other mapping capabilities allow utility companies and municipalities to plan distribution networks and to manage accurately assets widely distributed throughout large geographic areas [Fig. 4.31(b)].

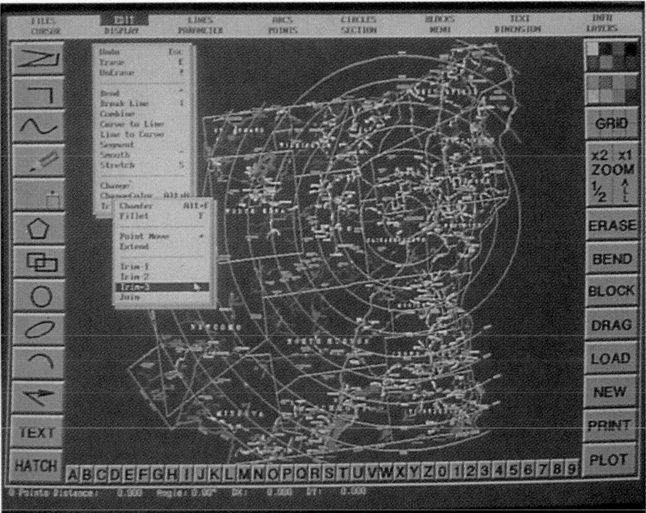

(a)

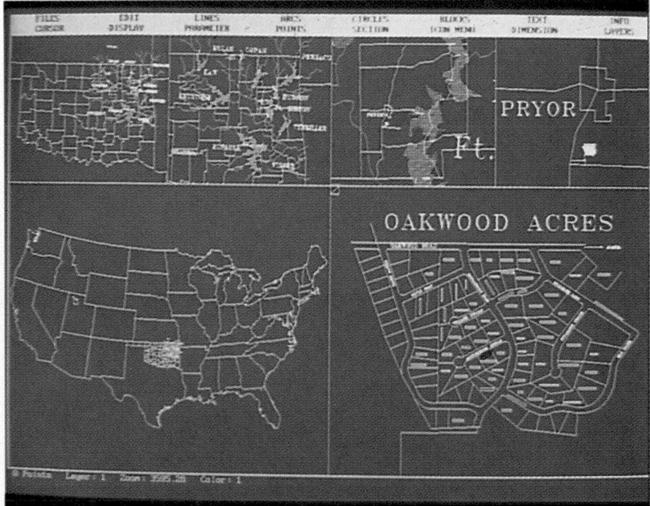

(b)

FIGURE 4.31 Mapping Layout with DesignCAD

The CAD system provides a tool for analysis and design coupled with actual cost estimates. You can automatically design and estimate costs of a runoff water collection system by selecting the minimum pipe sizes required and the minimum pipe slope, calculating flow line and elevation data, and segregating the quantities into bid item costs for the specified layout and flow input to each manhole. This design tool allows the engineer to process several layouts and system modifications, including full cost estimates, in less time than would be spent to design one layout conventionally without cost estimates.

4.6.6 Piping and Plant Design

Plant design CAD programs permit the extraction of a wide range of drawings and reports directly from the stored information, including flow diagrams, isometrics, spools, pipe fabrication, pipe supports, plan, elevation, and section drawings, solid views, from–to lists, bills of materials, and formatted lists. With a 3D CAD system, designs for process and power plants can be created as a true 3D model on the system [Fig. 4.32(a)]. The 3D model facilitates revisions, graphics manipulations, and analysis, such as piping interference checks. These checks pinpoint interferences between plant components early in the design cycle. The 3D model provides hidden line removal to enhance the visual representation of the model [Fig. 4.32(b)]. The designer can recognize and rectify potential plant problems early in the design phase, eliminating costly and time-consuming construction delays.

4.6.7 Mechanical Design Applications

A majority of CAD software packages have mechanical design and detailing capabilities. Besides 3D modeling of mechanical parts, mechanical software packages have many drafting and detailing capabilities to add dimensional information, notes, and labels to your drawings. You can also manipulate your drawings of the model for aesthetic reasons or for visual clarification (Fig. 4.33). These manipulation features include choosing a variety of line fonts (patterns), erasing hidden lines, defining any type or number of views, inserting dual dimensions, defining ANSI, JIS, or ISO standards, sectioning, and crosshatching. One of the most important tasks handled by a CAD system is the updating of existing mechanical designs and drawings, since this can be accomplished quickly and easily compared to manual methods.

Mechanical design includes a wide variety of products and machinery. Aerospace design is one of the most important uses of mechanical CAD, and many of the software packages employed in mechanical design were developed by aerospace companies such as Lockheed and McDonnell Douglas. McDonnell Douglas Unigraphics software running on HP 9000 computers is used in the design and manufac-

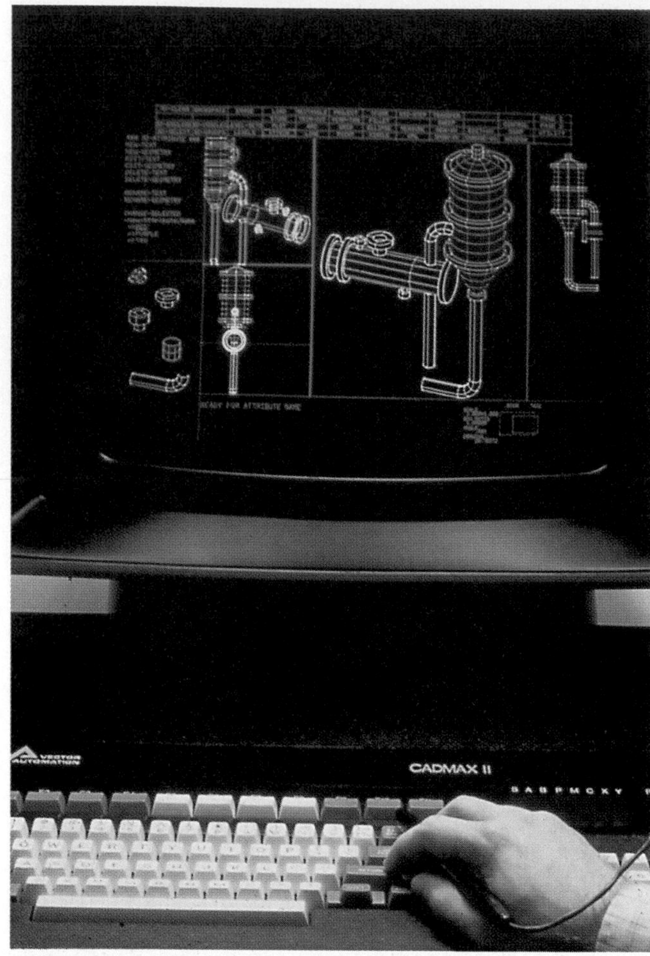

(a) Piping design (wireframe)

(b) Piping design using 3D CAD (surface model with shading)

FIGURE 4.32 3D Piping Design

ture of the NOTAR helicopter shown in Figure 4.34(a). McDonnell Douglas Helicopter Company uses DFM principles in the development of turbine parts [Fig. 4.34(b)].

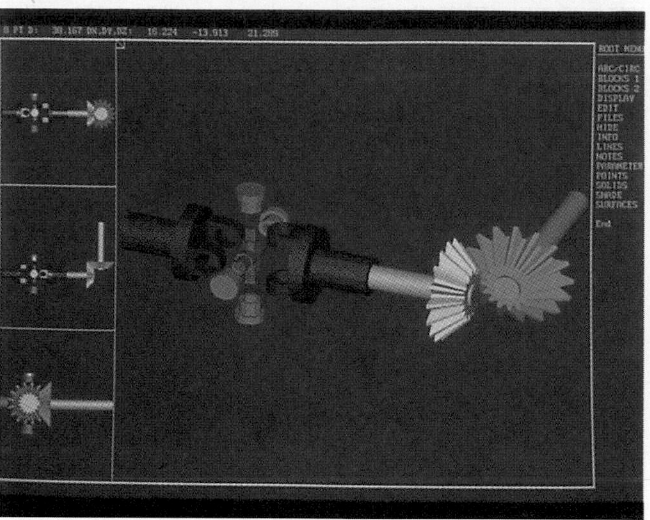

(a) Helical Gear Design

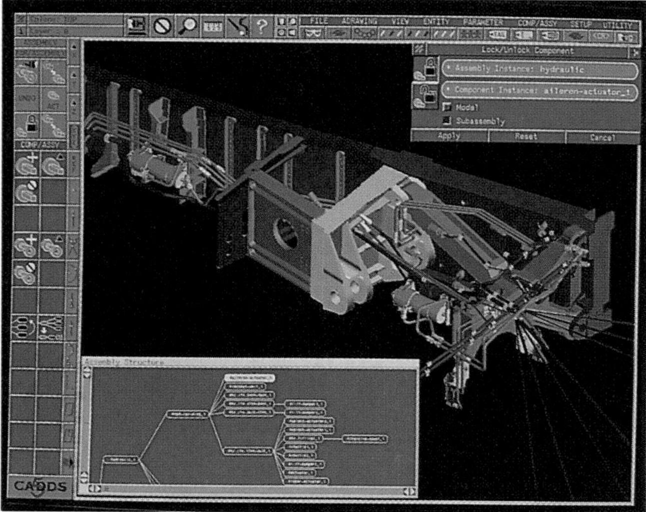

(b) Electrical Routing

FIGURE 4.33 3D Solid Modeling

4.6.8 Product Design and Development

CAD systems provide a means to explore any number of design ideas for new products, such as the motorcycle in Figure 4.35(a) or the aerospace design in Figure 4.35(b). Since exploring design alternatives with CAD systems is much faster than with manual methods, more exploration is possible in the same amount of time. These designs are eventually refined into one finished model. Figure 4.36 shows a phone design created with CADAM software. The phone is shown as a solid model, with the arm and hand of the user modeled to enable study of the product in relationship to the person using it. The use of color and shading along with 3D models of the proposed product aids in rendering and illustrating the product for consumer display.

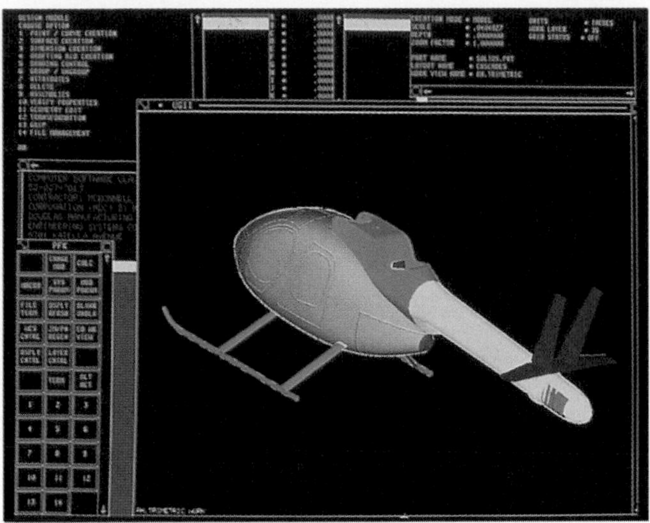
(a) Helicopter design

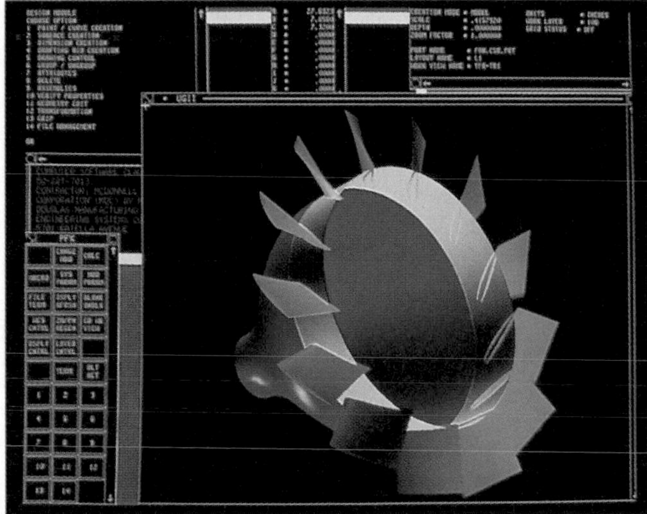
(b) Turbine design

FIGURE 4.34 3D Modeling

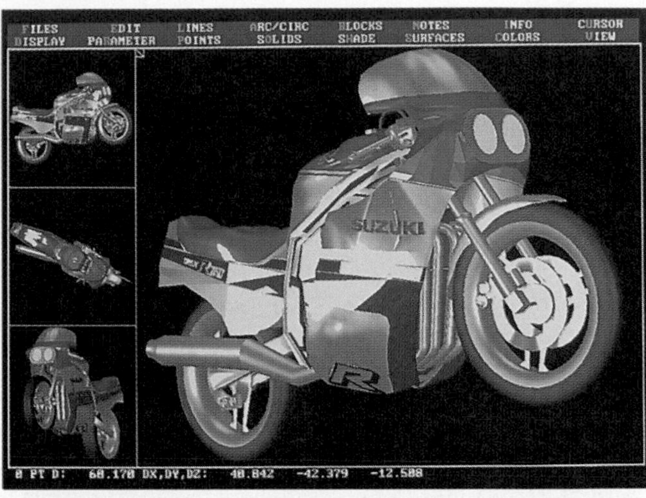

(a) Motorcycle

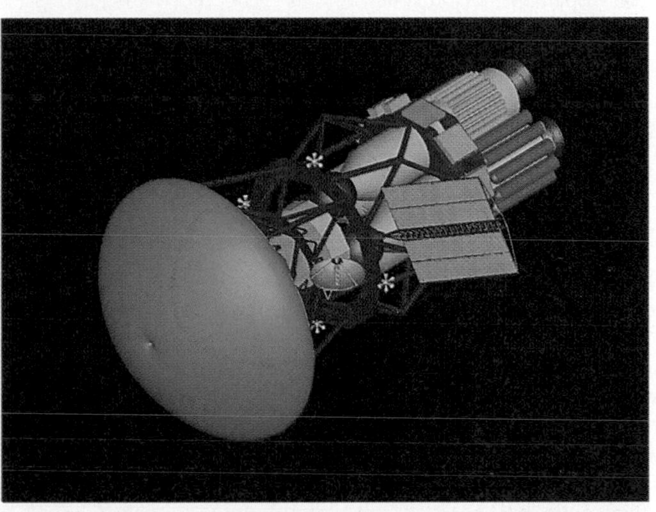
(b) Aerospace

FIGURE 4.35 Product Design Using 3D CAD

4.6.9 Technical Illustration

Technical illustration can be done with a 2D or 3D system. The fact that the original 3D model database can be used to generate the illustration instead of redrawing the part is an advantage of the 3D system (Fig. 4.37). The generation of sales literature is also expedited with CAD, especially when the different departments within a company can all share a common 3D model database.

4.6.10 FEM and FEA Applications

To design an optimal structure or to determine the cause of failure in service, design engineers commonly use computerized design and analysis methods. CAD/CAM systems may have a **finite-element modeling and meshing (FEM)** pack-

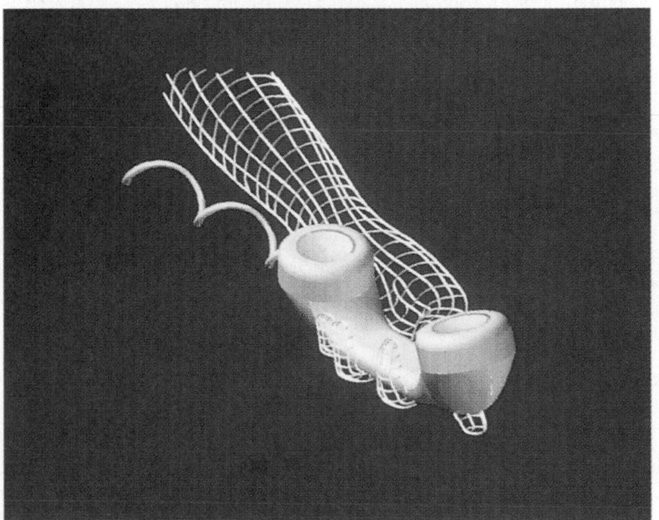
FIGURE 4.36 Product Design and Display

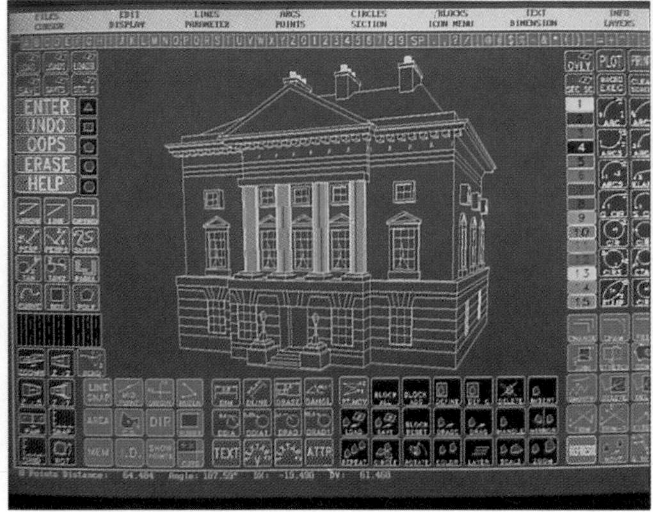

(a) Building illustration

(b) Aircraft illustration

FIGURE 4.37 Technical Illustration Using DesignCAD

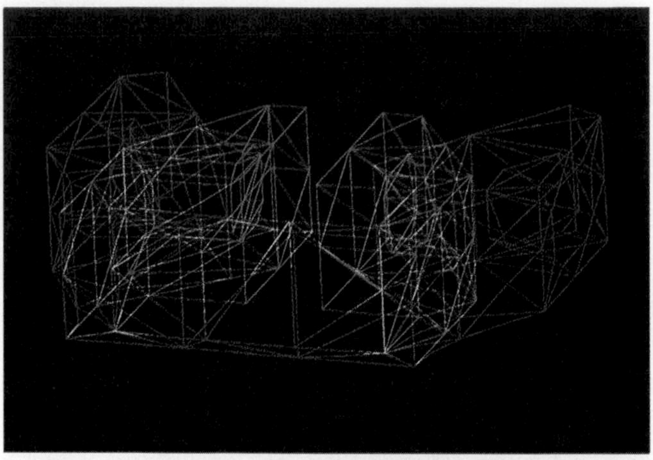

(a) FEM

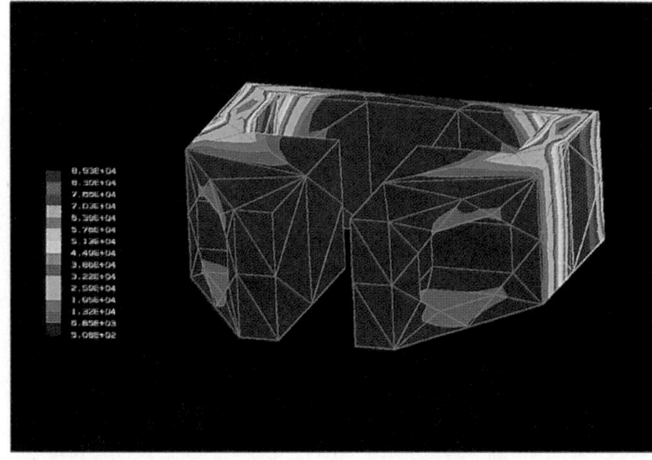

(b) FEA

FIGURE 4.38 Engineering Analysis

age that allows you to create the model, prepare it for analysis, and then graphically display the results.

Finite-element modeling and meshing [Fig. 4.38(a)] involves subdividing a structure into a network of simple elements that have easily definable characteristics. A mesh, which is comprised of associative grid points (nodes) and elements, is generated. Then you interactively define material properties, boundary conditions, and loads (such as forces/moments, pressures, and displacements) applied to the structure.

Most CAD systems significantly aid the design engineer in design detailing and in the verification of the functionality and mechanical resistance of complex parts by employing **finite-element analysis (FEA)** methods interfaced to the 3D model of the structure. FEA methods may be set up to calculate thermal stresses [Fig. 4.38(b)] in addition to loads or to model the behavior of the construction material in its elastic or elastoplastic domain.

4.6.11 Computer-Aided Manufacturing Applications

CAD helps to create or modify a design. **CAM** manages and controls the operations of a manufacturing facility. The integration of computer-aided design and computer-aided manufacturing eliminates duplication of effort by the engineering and manufacturing or production departments. An engineering model (Fig. 4.39) created on a graphics terminal simultaneously defines the source geometry (points, lines, planes, etc.) that otherwise must be manually derived from the drawing before the product is manufactured.

In an optimal CAD/CAM integrated system the production process is computerized, from the original graphics input to the manufacture of the part on a numerically controlled machine. Shop production drawings may at times be entirely eliminated with this process. By producing the source geometry directly from the engineering data, the programmer can extract accurate geometric data, replicating the definition of the part to be manufactured (Fig. 4.40).

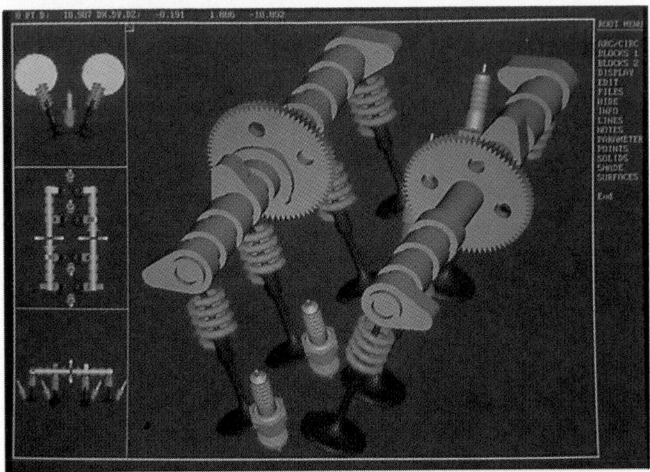

(a) Cam shaft assembly

(b) 3D design of a crank shaft

FIGURE 4.39 **3D Design of Cams**

(a) Mold

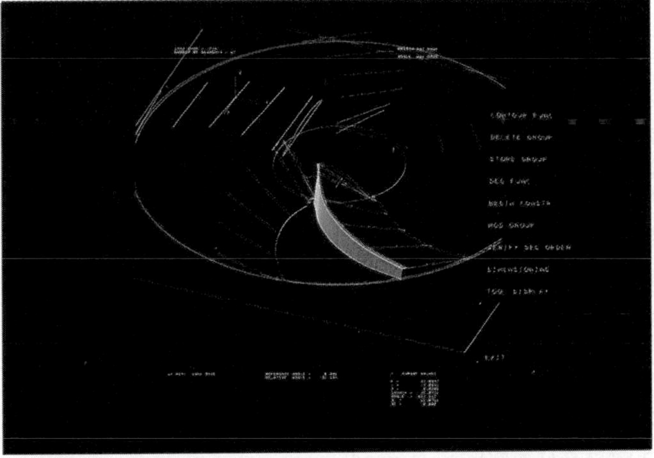

(b) Cutter Paths

FIGURE 4.40 **3D Mold Design**

CAM speeds the manufacturing process by using the same common information initially created in the design and drafting cycle. This information, representing the part (or model) design, is also used by the manufacturing group. The system serves all applications, promotes standardization to enhance management control, accumulates (rather than randomly collecting) manufacturing information, and reduces redundancy and errors.

4.6.12 Computer Numerical Control Part Programming

Since the geometry of the part is defined in the CAD/CAM system, there is no need to go through the process of extracting the part geometry from the drawings. The geometry is already given, precisely as specified. Since the designer is provided with visual verification of every step in the process, the graphic display and interactive nature of the system eliminate the need to envision the cutter path. Many CAD/CAM systems provide this graphical approach to computer numerical control (CNC). CNC involves generating tool paths and producing machine control data for a variety of machining operations (Fig. 4.40). CNC machines (Fig. 4.41) perform their machining operations automatically by using the instructions contained on punched tape or derived directly from the engineering database by the computers. Figure 4.41(a) shows an example of a horizontal CNC machining center, and Figure 4.41(b) shows a vertical CNC machining center. In Figure 4.42, an example of a CNC turning center is provided. Each of these machines uses the CAD-generated engineering database for programming the part machining requirements.

The programmer (Fig. 4.42) defines cutting tools, creates a tool library, and retrieves these tools later to create tool path information. Because CAM packages support most cutting tool configurations, programmers can describe most types of generally used cutting tools. The system also prompts the user to define machining characteristics, such as retract and clearance plane, cutting depth, feed rate (rate of travel), and spindle speed (rate of spindle rotation). The

(a) Horizontal CNC machining center

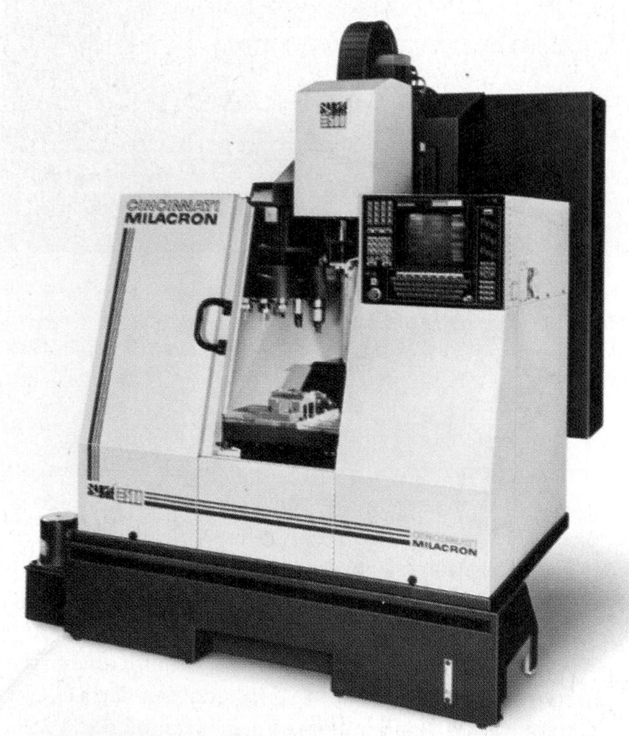

(b) Vertical CNC machining center

FIGURE 4.41 **Computer Numerical Control Machining**

cutter position (**X** and **Z** positions in Fig. 4.43) and all other machining information are displayed on the CNC control center while the machining is in progress.

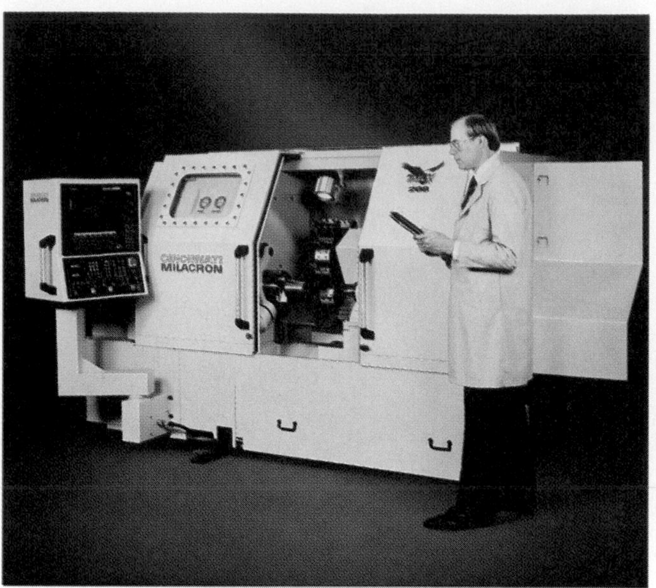

FIGURE 4.42 **CNC Turning Center**

FIGURE 4.43 **CNC Control Panel**

4.6.13 Robotic Applications and CAD

Robotics is the integration of computer-controlled robots into the manufacturing production process. Industrial robots are used to move, manipulate, position, weld, and machine. Robots are controlled by a microprocessor and are normally composed of a separate, stand-alone computer station, the robot mechanism itself, and an electrical hydraulic power unit (Fig. 4.44).

FIGURE 4.44 Industrial Robot

A robot is a reprogrammable, multifunction manipulator designed to move material, parts, tools, or specialized devices through variable, programmed motions for the performance of a variety of tasks. This definition can be expanded to include the control and synchronization of the equipment with which the robot works. This capability can eliminate the need for humans to work in an environment that may be hazardous.

The integration of CAD/CAM and robotics results in increased productivity for robotic implementation activities. The **robotic workcell** contains all the physical equipment needed to create a functioning robot application. In addition to the robot, a workcell can have special fixturing, other automated machines (CNC machines, coordinate measuring machines, or visual inspection equipment), materials handling devices, part-presentation equipment, and robot grippers.

The equipment in the workcell must be arranged so that the robot work envelope includes all required device areas. CAD/CAM is perfect for designing the equipment layout (Fig. 4.45). Libraries of workcell components can be stored on the CAD/CAM system and recalled when needed. For example, a robot library could contain commercial robots along with their work envelopes. Robot movement can be programmed, displayed, and checked directly on the CAD system (Fig. 4.46).

Robotics represents a stage in the engineering, design, drafting, manufacturing, and production sequence. As can be seen, the computer and its related technology play an essential part in the present and future of industrial design. From the days of T-squares and wooden pencils, the technology of engineering design techniques has been continually evolving, making the process of product design and manufacturing increasingly more creative and streamlined.

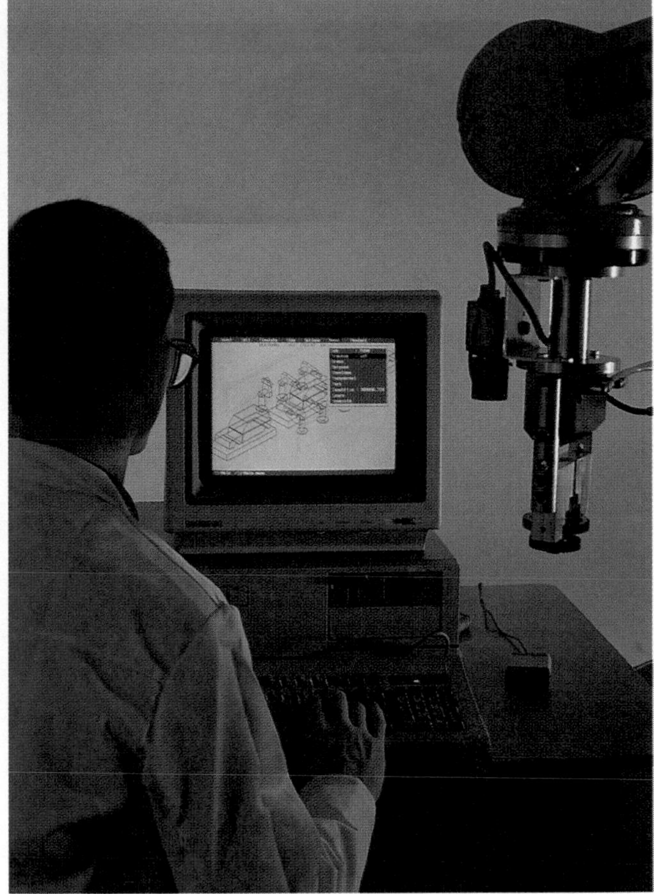

FIGURE 4.45 On-Screen Robot Programming (Off-Line Programming)

The need for manual methods of drafting and drawing will never be totally replaced. But the use of computer-assisted methods will continue to influence the type, quality, and pace of industry.

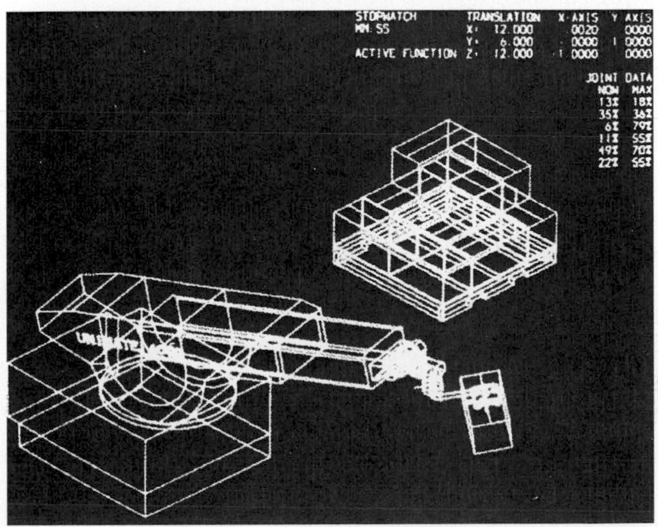

FIGURE 4.46 Robotic Workcell Design

QUIZ

True or False

1. Hardware includes instructions to do specific CAD commands to manipulate the display.
2. CAD systems require the operator to have programming ability.
3. The CPU of a CAD system performs all data manipulation required to construct, calculate, process, and store a drawing or engineering design.
4. Interactive CAD means that the system requires little or no input from the operator.
5. Resolution is the smallest spacing between points on a graphics display at which the points can be detected as distinct.
6. Robots can be viewed and controlled directly on a CAD/CAM system.
7. Electrostatic plotters are the most accurate hard-copy device.
8. Systems software allows the user to complete drawings in specific engineering fields, such as piping and electronics.

Fill in the Blanks

9. __________, __________, __________, and __________ are four applications areas of CAD software.
10. Industrial __________ are used to move, manipulate, position, weld, and assemble items in the manufacturing cycle.
11. A design workstation normally includes a __________, __________, __________, __________, and a __________.
12. Electrostatic __________, __________, __________, and printers are hard-copy devices.
13. The CPU is shared by a number of __________ on a __________ CAD system.
14. The __________ is the movable screen "marker," usually a blinking box, crosshair, or other symbol.
15. Keyboards, __________ boxes, __________ balls, __________ sticks, __________, and __________ tables are all types of operator input devices.
16. A __________ is an input device consisting of command spaces on a digitizing surface such as a data tablet, digitizing tablet, or digitizing table.

Answer the Following

17. Name six typical input devices.
18. Name five typical output devices.
19. What are function keyboards, and how do they differ from terminal keyboards?
20. What is the difference between a printer and a plotter? What are the capabilities of both pieces of equipment?
21. Name three types of plotters, and explain their uses.
22. What is applications software? Name five types.
23. What is the difference between a display menu (online menu) and a tablet menu?
24. Define "CIM" and explain how it relates to the total design-through-manufacturing cycle.

PARAMETRIC DESIGN

Chapter 5

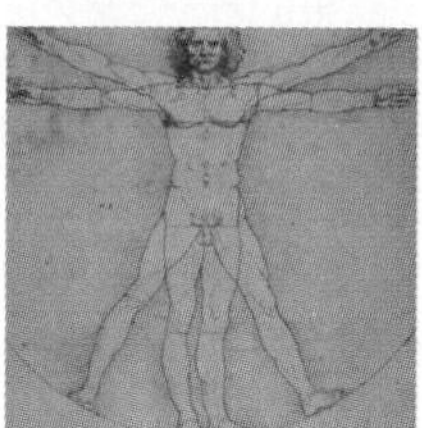

LEARNING OBJECTIVES

Upon completion of this chapter you will be able to:

1. Understand the basic processes involved in parametric feature-based design.
2. Describe the steps in the design process when using a parametric CAD/CAM/CAE system.
3. Understand the function and application of the sketcher in creating base and construction features.
4. Explain how features are used to create a design.
5. Show how parts are designed and then combined into assemblies.
6. Explore the automated generation of details and drawings using parametric design.
7. Understand the use of datum features to model a part.
8. Discover several methods of capturing design intent in parametric modeling.
9. See how a feature-based CAD/CAM system can successfully incorporate engineering knowledge into the solid model.

5.1 INTRODUCTION

This chapter introduces the basic parametric design concepts for creating and documenting individual parts and assemblies. **Parametric** can be defined as *any set of physical properties whose values determine the characteristics or behavior of something.* **Parametric design** enables you to generate a variety of information about your design—its mass properties, a drawing, or a base model. To get this information, you must first model your part design (Fig. 5.1). The part in this figure was modeled with **Pro/ENGINEER™** from **Parametric Technology Corporation.** The part is a solid model and is displayed in two windows on the screen. The primary screen displays the model with a mesh on its surfaces. The mesh functions in variety of engineering applications and capabilities, including engineering analysis of force, moment, and displacement.

This chapter is intended to acquaint you with parametric modeling philosophies. Throughout the remainder of the

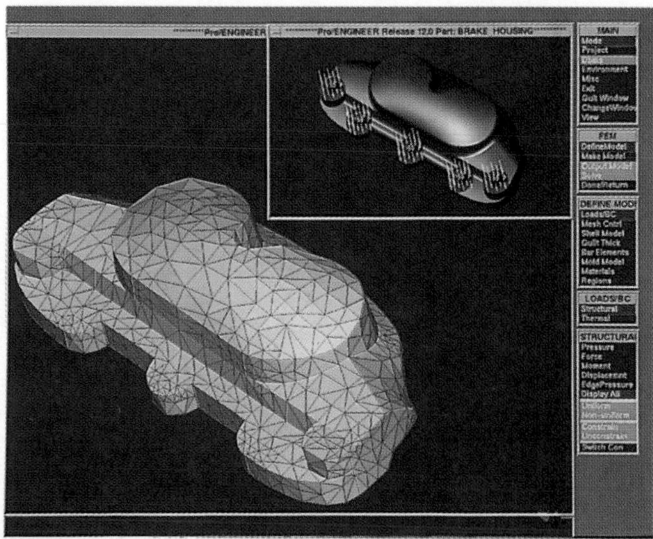

FIGURE 5.1 Part Modeled Using Pro/ENGINEER and Displayed with Pro/MESH

text, a series of **Applying Parametric Design** boxes are introduced to illustrate parametric design ideas for each chapter. *With the exception of this chapter,* all Applying Parametric Design boxes are based entirely on Pro/ENGINEER. This chapter will use an **AutoCAD's Designer™** example in its Applying Parametric Design box.

The following methodologies are the principal aspects of successful parametric solid modeling.

Feature-Based Modeling. Parametric design represents solid models as combinations of engineering features (Fig. 5.2). This chapter introduces the various types of features, along with an example of their combination into a part model.

Creating Assemblies. Just as features are combined into parts, parts may be combined into assemblies, as shown in Figure 5.3, where the race car design incorporates a large number of parts, subassemblies, and a final assembly. This chapter will briefly discuss the hierarchical relationships of assembled parts, as well as the creation of new parts within an assembly model.

Capturing Design Intent. Several methods of capturing design intent in parametric modeling are presented in this chapter. To be able to incorporate engineering knowledge successfully into the solid model is an essential aspect of parametric modeling (Fig. 5.4). This ensures that critical parameters are satisfied as your design evolves.

The diagram in Figure 5.5 illustrates the role of each of the methodologies in the modeling process.

5.1.1 Modeling vs. Drafting

A primary and essential difference between parametric design and traditional computer-aided drafting systems is that parametric design models are three-dimensional. Designs increas-

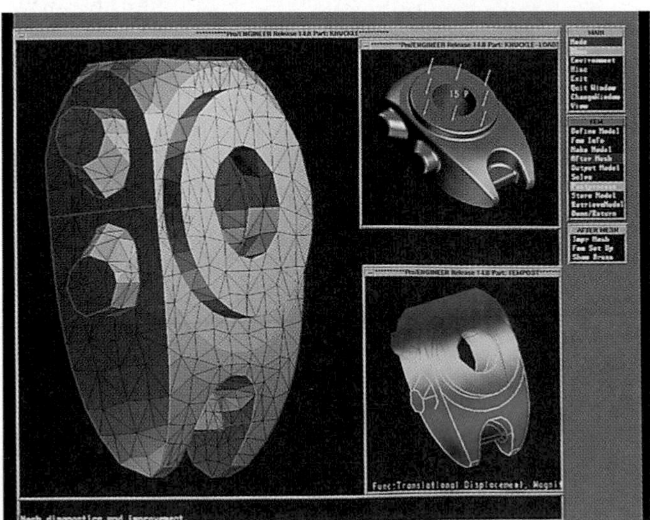

FIGURE 5.2 Analysis Performed on a Part Model Using Pro/ENGINEER

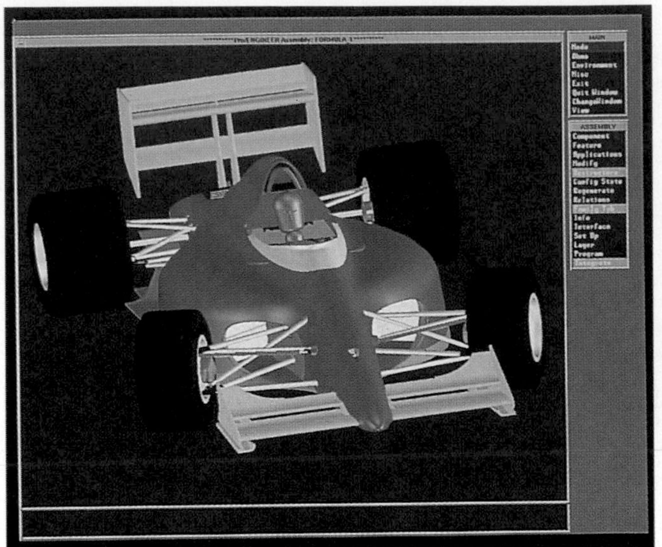

(a) Complete race car

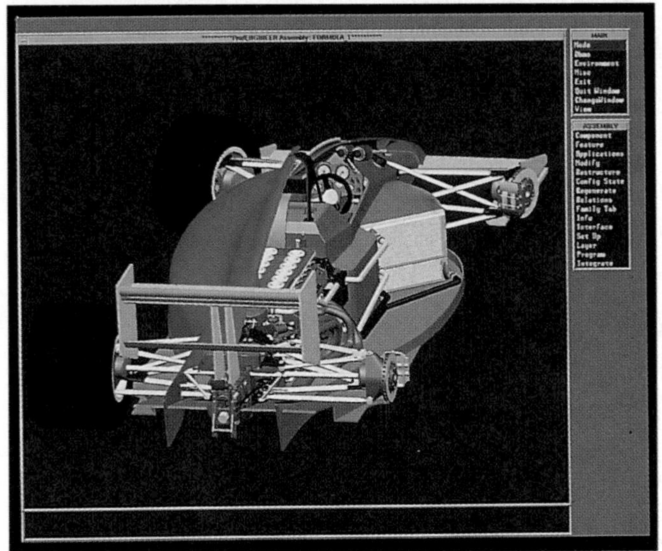

(b) Half of car body removed to see interior

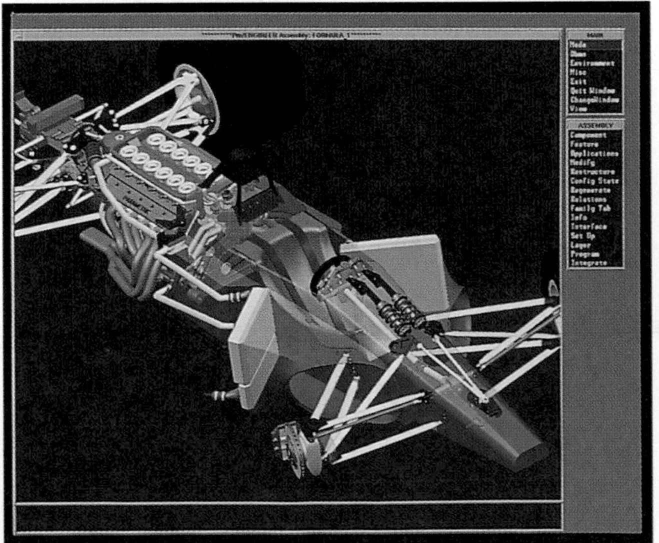

(c) Subassembly

FIGURE 5.3 Race Car Modeled with Pro/ENGINEER

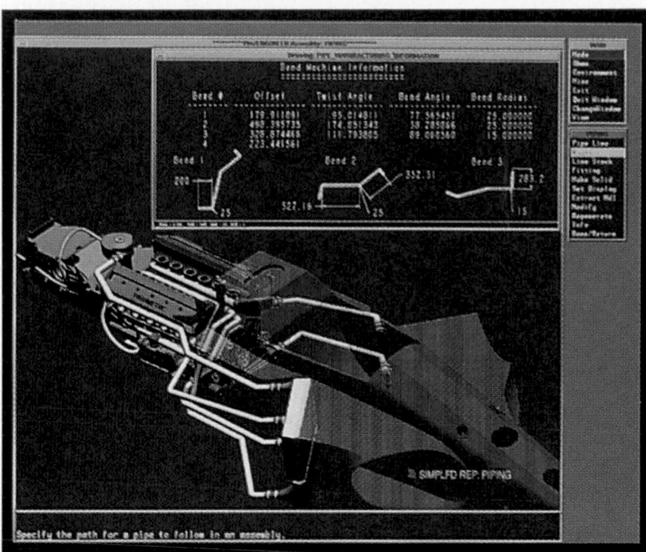

(d) Exhaust piping and bend analysis

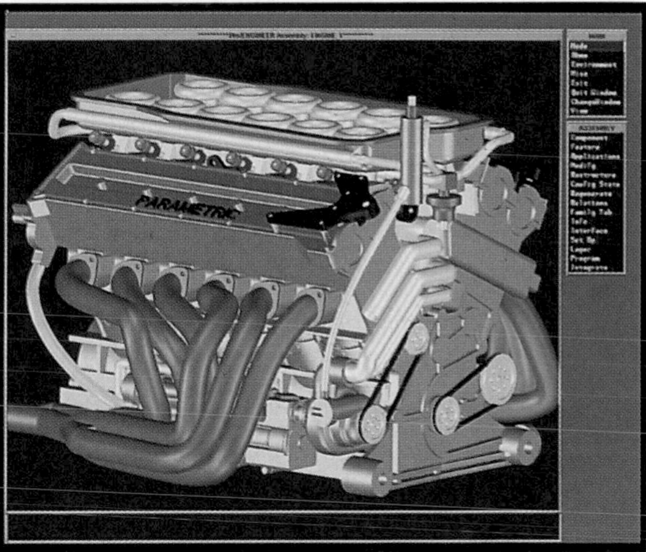

(e) Engine

FIGURE 5.3 Race Car Modeled with Pro/ENGINEER—*Continued*

ingly are represented in the form of solid models that capture design intent as well as design geometry. Engineering designs today are frequently constructed as mathematical solid models instead of as 2D drawings. A solid model is one that represents a shape as a 3D object having mass properties.

There are two main reasons for the move to solid models. First, solid-modeling packages can serve as an easy means of portraying parts for study by cross-functional concurrent-engineering teams. The solid model can be understood by even nontechnical members of the team, such as those from the marketing and sales departments.

Second, the capabilities of solid modelers have been upgraded so the model can represent not only the geometry of part being designed, but also the intent of the designer. This is of most significance when the designer needs to make changes to the part geometry. Far fewer changes will be necessary in later-generation parametric solid models that capture design intent than in previous CAD/CAM modeling software.

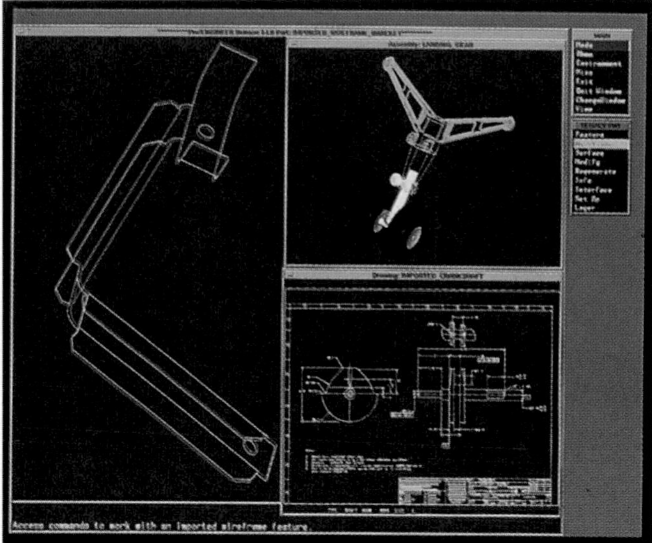

FIGURE 5.4 Parametric Design Using Pro/ENGINEER

In parametric design, drawings are produced as views of the model, rather than the other way around. Parametric design models are not so much drawn as *sculpted* from solid volumes of materials.

5.1.2 Parametric Design Overview

To begin the design process, analyze your design. Before any work is started, take time and *tap* into your own knowledge bank and others that are available. The acronym **TAP** (**t**hink, **a**nalyze, **p**lan) can remind you of these three steps so essential to any engineering design process in which you may be involved.

Break your overall design down into its basic components, building blocks, or primary features. Identify the most fundamental feature of the part as the first feature, or base feature, to sketch. A variety of **base features** can be modeled using the commands *protrusion-extrude, revolve, sweep,* and *blend.* **Sketched features** (*neck, flange,* and *cut*) and pick-and-place features, called **referenced features,** complete the design (*holes, rounds,* and *chamfers*). With the **sketcher,** you use familiar 2D entities (points, lines, circles, arcs, splines, ellipses). There is no need to be concerned with the accuracy of the sketch. Lines can be of differing angles, arcs and circles can have unequal radii, and dimensions and relationships can be sketched without regard to the actual part dimension. In fact, exaggerating the difference between features that are similar but not exactly the same is actually a better practice when using the sketcher.

The system helps to apply logical geometric constraints to the sketch. **Constraints** clean up the sketch geometry according to the system assumptions. **Geometry assumptions** and constraints close ends of connected lines, align parallel lines, and snap sketched lines to the horizontal and vertical. Additional constraints are added through **parametric dimensions** to control the size and shape of the feature. For parts with more than one feature, these steps can create additional parametric features.

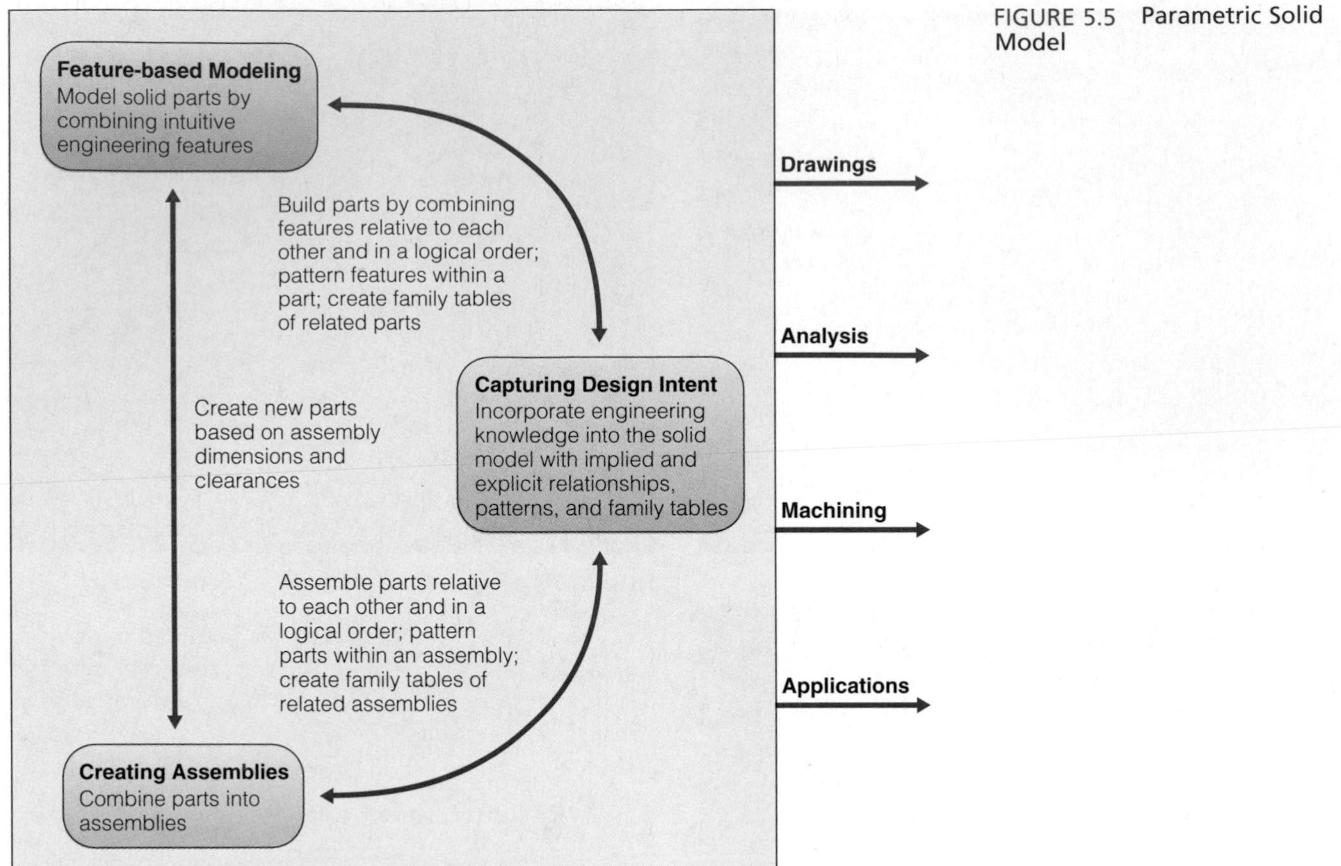
Feature-based Modeling
Model solid parts by combining intuitive engineering features
Build parts by combining features relative to each other and in a logical order; pattern features within a part; create family tables of related parts
Create new parts based on assembly dimensions and clearances
Capturing Design Intent
Incorporate engineering knowledge into the solid model with implied and explicit relationships, patterns, and family tables
Assemble parts relative to each other and in a logical order; pattern parts within an assembly; create family tables of related assemblies
Creating Assemblies
Combine parts into assemblies
Drawings
Analysis
Machining
Applications

FIGURE 5.5 Parametric Solid Model

5.2 FEATURE-BASED MODELING

Features are the basic building blocks for building a part. Features "understand" their fit and function—they have "smarts" built in. For example, a hole or neck or cut feature knows its shape and part location and that it has a negative volume. As you modify a feature, the entire part automatically updates after regeneration. The idea behind feature-based modeling is that the designer construct a part so it is composed of individual features that describe how the geometry is supposed to behave in the event its dimensions change, which happens quite often in industry, as in the case of a design change.

The easiest way to explain feature-based modeling is to contrast it with older solid-modeling methods. One example is that of creating a hole in a part. Older solid modelers used **constructive solid geometry (CSG)** to define such a feature. Here, the designer would define a simple cylinder having the diameter of the desired hole and long enough to extend through the part. Then the system would be told to perform a **Boolean** difference operation between the part and the cylinder. The result would be a hole in the part having the diameter of the cylinder (Fig. 5.6).

A problem arises with this approach if the part is later modified, for instance, if the part must be thicker. If the designer did not make the cylindrical space long enough to extend through the new thicker part, the result will be a model of a blind hole (not all the way through the part feature). The model captured the geometry specified by the designer, but it did not capture the intent, which in this case is a thru-hole.

A designer working in a feature-based modeler would approach the thru-hole differently. A feature called a thru-hole would be defined such that no matter what the thickness dimension of the part, the hole extends completely through it.

Modelers also let the designer suppress features temporarily, as a means of making it easier to change the part geometry. It is also possible to modify previously defined features, or to define new features using combinations of old features. Systems prompt the designer for input during the defining of the feature. Inputs may include positional constraints, relational definitions, and other factors. Feature-based modelers also allow designers to define features pertaining not only to geometry, but also to steps involved in downstream analysis and manufacturing.

The term **parametric modeling** describes the capturing of design operations as they take place, as well as future modifying and editing that takes place on the design. The order of the design operations is significant. Suppose a designer specifies that two surfaces—surface 1 and surface 2—are parallel to each other. Then, if surface 1 moves, surface 2 moves along with it to maintain the specified design relationship. Surface 2 is a **child** of surface 1 in this example. Parametric modelers allow the designer to **reorder** the steps in the part's creation.

The "chunks" of solid material from which parametric

FIGURE 5.6 Feature-Based Modeling

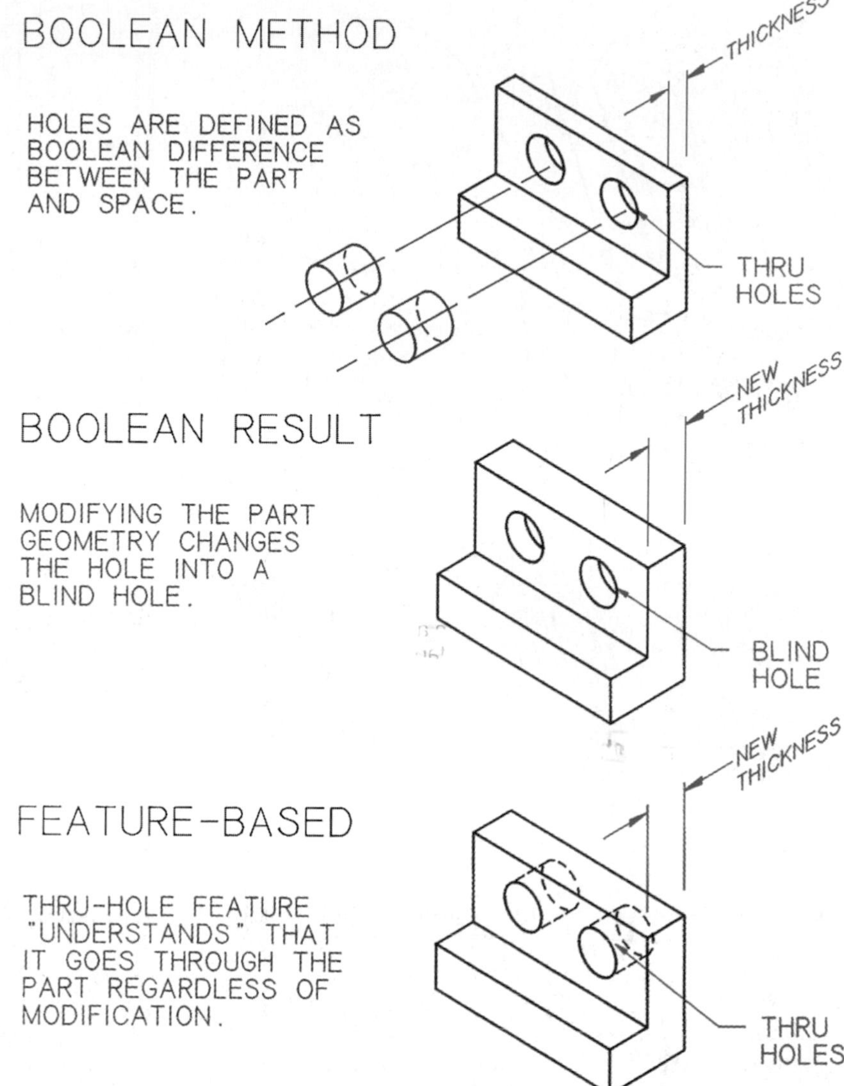
BOOLEAN METHOD
HOLES ARE DEFINED AS BOOLEAN DIFFERENCE BETWEEN THE PART AND SPACE.
THICKNESS
THRU HOLES
BOOLEAN RESULT
MODIFYING THE PART GEOMETRY CHANGES THE HOLE INTO A BLIND HOLE.
NEW THICKNESS
BLIND HOLE
FEATURE-BASED
THRU-HOLE FEATURE "UNDERSTANDS" THAT IT GOES THROUGH THE PART REGARDLESS OF MODIFICATION.
NEW THICKNESS
THRU HOLES

design models are constructed are called features. Features generally fall into one of the following categories.

Base Feature. The base feature may be either a sketched feature or datum plane(s) referencing the default coordinate system. The base feature is important because all future model geometry will reference it directly or indirectly; it becomes the root feature. Changes to the base feature will affect the geometry of the entire model (Fig. 5.7).

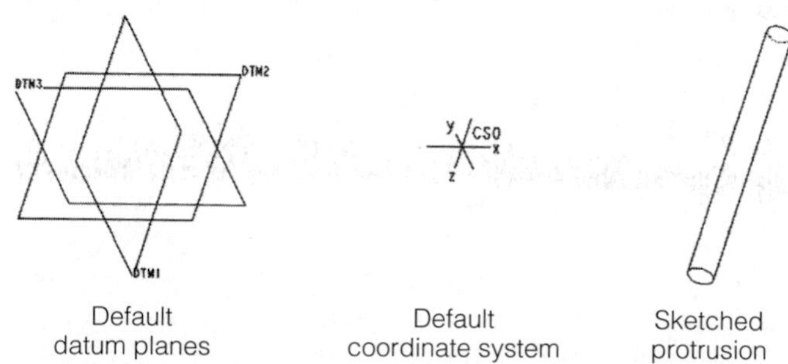
DTM3
DTM2
DTM1
CS0
Default datum planes
Default coordinate system
Sketched protrusion

FIGURE 5.7 Base Features

Sketched Features. Sketched features are created by extruding, revolving, blending, or sweeping a sketched cross section. Material may be added or removed by protruding or cutting the feature from the existing model (Fig. 5.8).

Referenced Features. Referenced features reference existing geometry and employ an inherent form; they need not be sketched. Some examples of referenced features are rounds, drilled holes, and shells (Fig. 5.9).

Datum Features. Datum features, such as planes, axes, curves, and points, generally help provide sketching planes and contour references for sketched and referenced features. Datum features do not have physical volume or mass, and may be visually hidden without affecting solid geometry (Fig. 5.10).

The various types of features are used as building blocks in the progressive creation of solid parts. Figure 5.11 demonstrates this process.

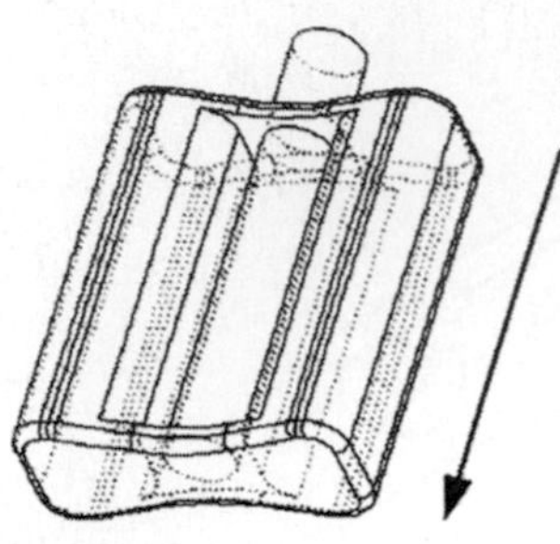

Extrude:
Pedal created by extruding bow-shaped section

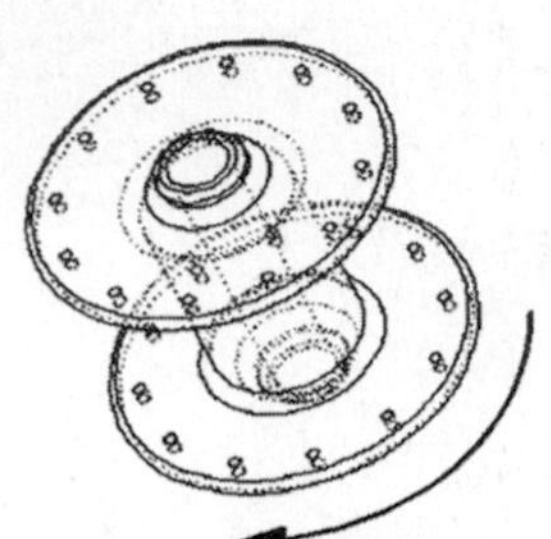

Revolve:
Hub created by revolving sections

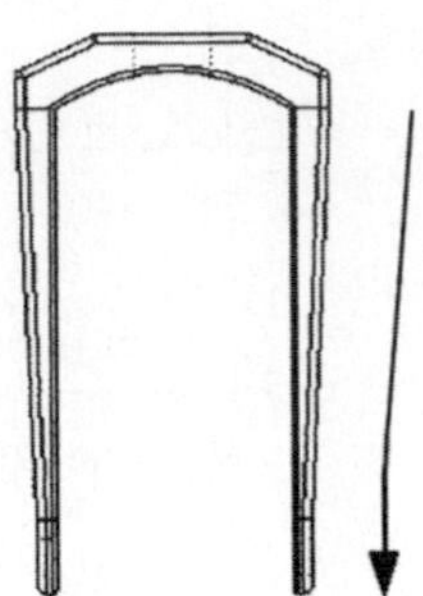

Blend:
Fork created by blending several cross sections

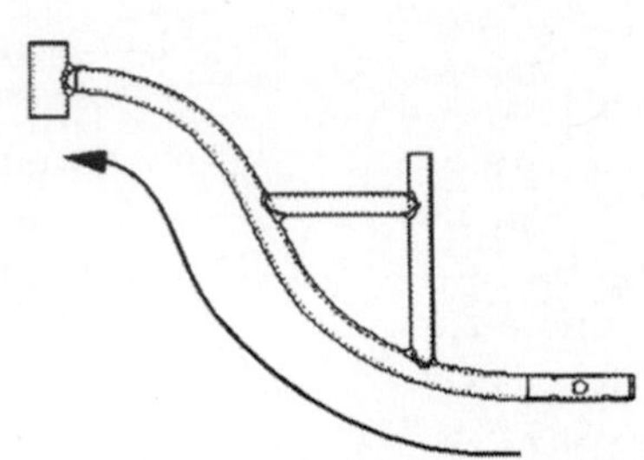

Sweep:
Frame created by sweeping cross section along shown trajectory

FIGURE 5.8 Sketched Features

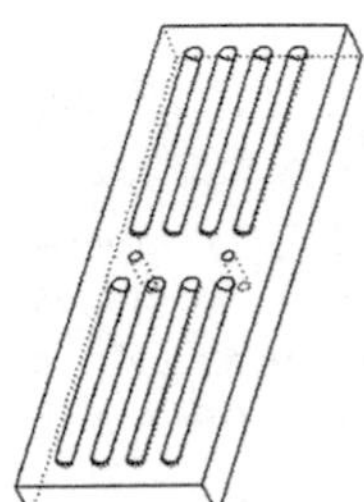

Rounds feature references edges and surfaces, removing material to a specified radius

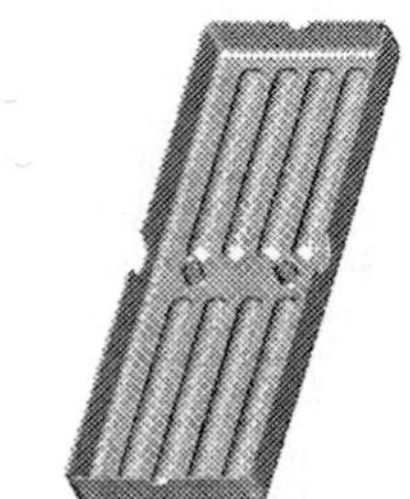

Shell feature references outer surfaces, reducing thickness to a specified value

FIGURE 5.9 Referenced Features

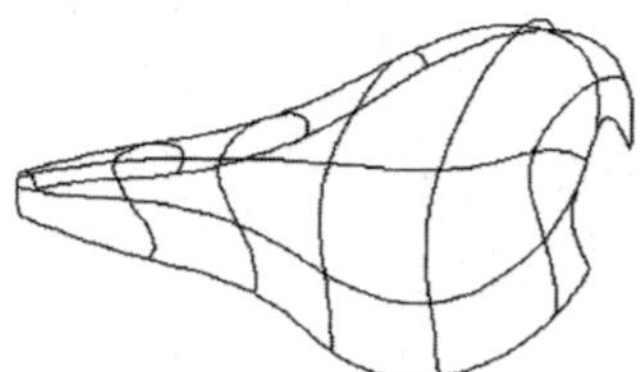

Web of datum curves used to control surface contour

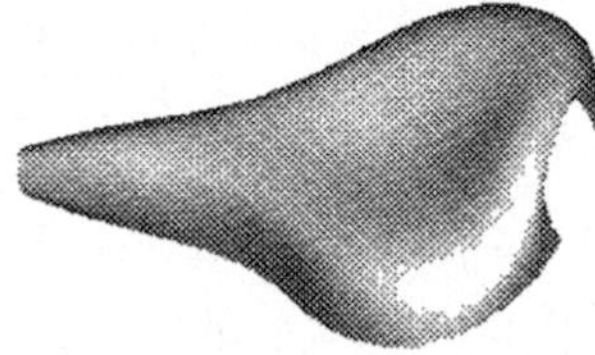

Seat created by enclosing volume with additional surfaces and filling with solid material

FIGURE 5.10 Datum Curves

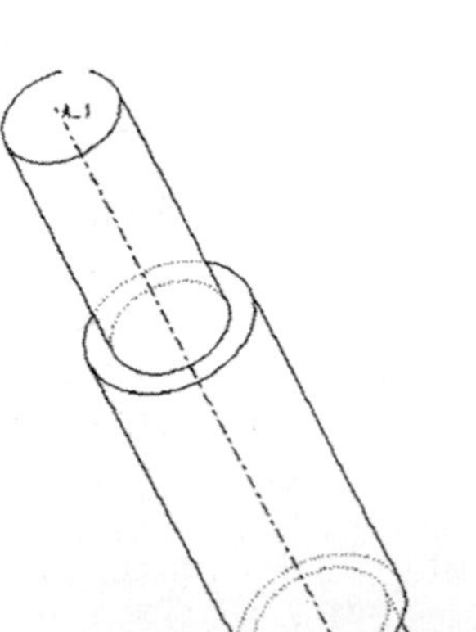

Base feature:
Revolved protrusion from sketched cross section

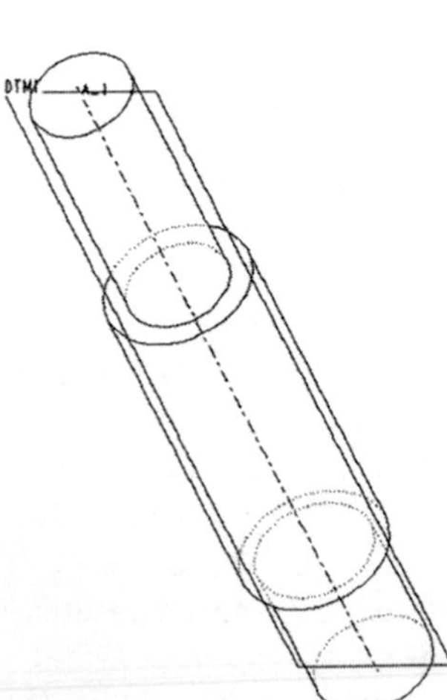

Datum features:
Datum plane created at zero offset normal to Z axis of default coordinate system

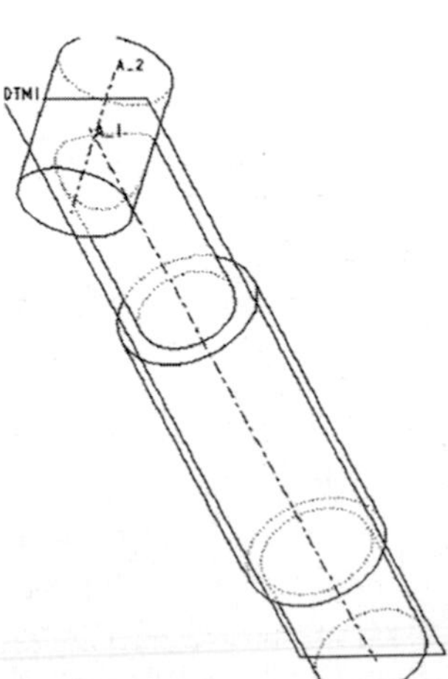

Sketched feature:
Extruded protrusion sketched on datum plane with center aligned to top of base feature

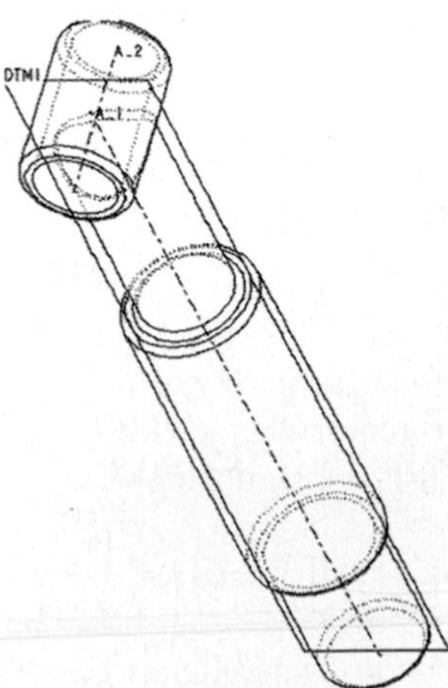

Referenced features:
Hole drilled coaxially through top protrusion; rounds created along sharp edges

FIGURE 5.11 Features

5.2.1 Establishing Part Features

The design of any part requires that the part be *confined, restricted, constrained, and referenced.* In parametric design the easiest method to establish and control the geometry of your part design is to use three datum planes (see Chapters 15 and 16). The system allows you to use the **primary datum** to start your base feature. By creating the default datum planes (DTM1, DTM2, and DTM3 in Pro/ENGINEER) you can constrain your design in all three directions (see Fig. 5.7). Try a simple exercise: Put a book on the floor of a room in your house or school. This establishes **datum A,** or the primary datum plane (DTM3 for Pro/ENGINEER in most cases). Now slide the book up to a wall near the corner of the room. This establishes **datum B,** the **secondary datum** plane (DTM2 for most cases in Pro/ENGINEER). Choose the longest or second most important surface. Lastly, shove the book up against the other wall. You have now established **datum C,** or the **tertiary datum** plane (DTM1 in most cases with Pro/ENGINEER). The book is now constrained by three plane surfaces (walls). With a couple of clamps you can secure the part and machine it as if it were on a milling table (Figs. 5.12 and 5.13).

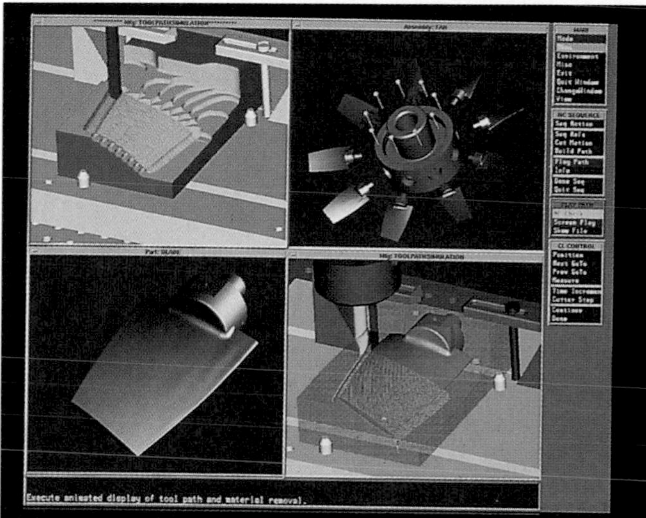

FIGURE 5.12 Machining Using Pro/ENGINEER and Pro/MANUFACTURING

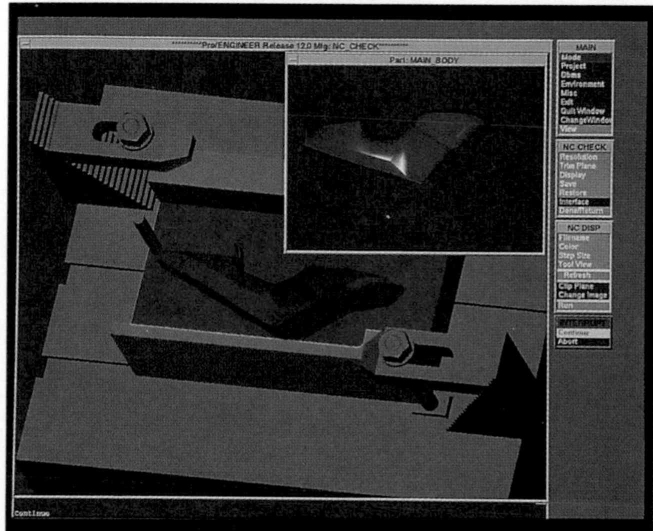

FIGURE 5.13 Pro/MANUFACTURING and Machining Fixtures

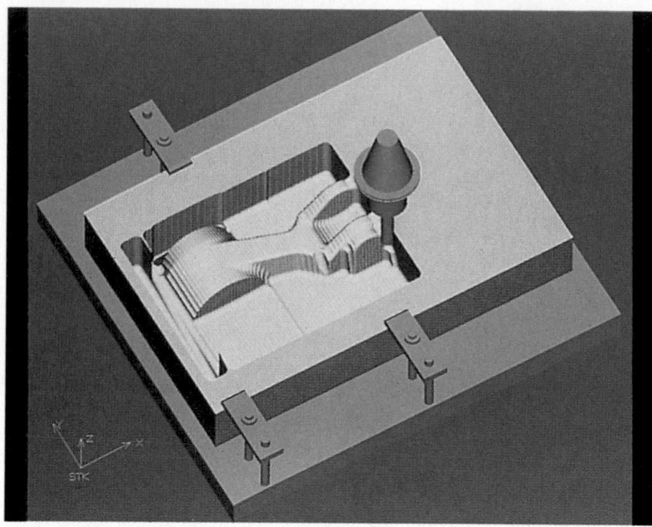

FIGURE 5.14 Visually Machining a Part Using CGTECH™ Software

Although this exercise and description is simplified and will not work for some parts, it does demonstrate how to establish your part in space using datums. You may use any of the datums as sketching planes or for that matter any of the part surfaces for construction geometry. Any number of other datums can be introduced into the part as required for feature creation, assembly operations, or manufacturing applications (Fig. 5.14).

5.2.2 Datum Features and Datum Planes

Datum features are planes, axes, and points by which you place geometric features on the active part. There are three types of datum features: *datum planes, datum axes, and datum points.* You can display all types of datum features, but they do not define the surfaces or edges of the part or add to its mass properties.

Datum planes are infinite planes located in 3D model mode and associated with the part that was active at the time of their creation. To select a datum plane, you can pick on its name or pick anywhere on the planar square.

Datum planes are *parametric*—geometrically associated with the part. Parametric datum planes are associated with and dependent on the edges, surfaces, vertices, and axes of a part. For example, a datum plane placed parallel to a planar face and on the edge of a part moves whenever the edge moves and rotates about the edge if the face moves. As you create parametric datum planes, you determine the relationship to the active part by defining combinations of a placement option that link the datum plane to the part.

Focus On . . .

DISPLAYING PART MACHINING

Before a part is manufactured on a machine using expensive and time-consuming methods, we can now display the cutter, cutter path, machining sequence, and material removal of a part directly on the CRT (see figure). Multiple-axis milling modules for cylindrical parts like roller dies, and drum cams (see figure), EDM wire capabilities (see figure), and multiaxis turning for lathe parts (see figure) are all available in today's high-technology manufacturing.

The volume and local milling of a part on a CAD/CAM system can be displayed and plotted for verification (see figure). In this last figure we can see how easy it is to analyze the programmed cutting sequence and the removal of material for a typical part. Here, a large tool is used to remove a majority of the material through volume milling. The next step involves having a smaller cutting tool finish the pocket and remove the leftover material.

Full visual verification and control of all tool motion are now possible. These new tools are making the process of designing and manufacturing a part quicker, highly efficient, and extremely precise.

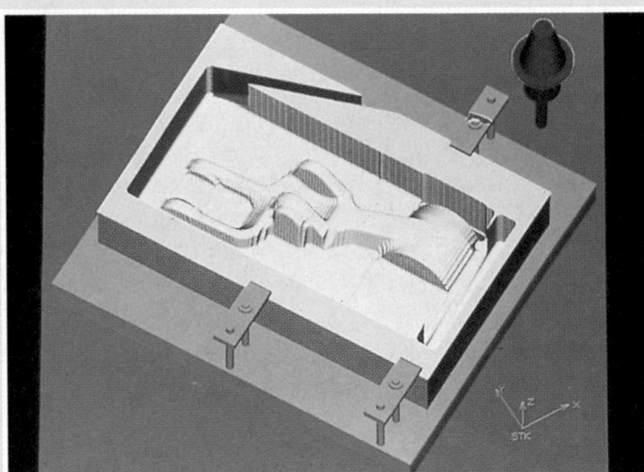

Displaying cutter, workpiece, and material removal using CGTECH™ software.

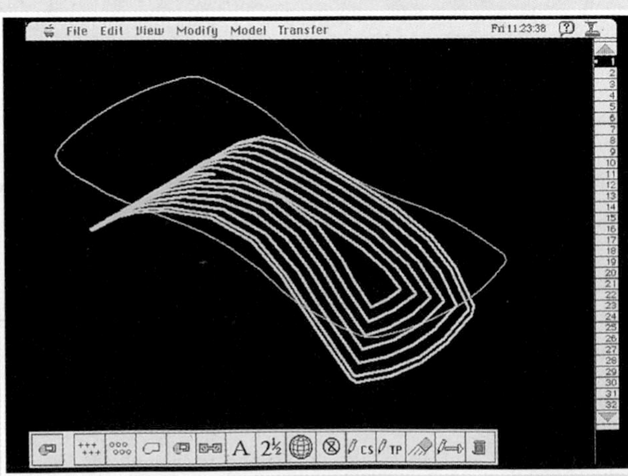

Four-axis milling using Gibbs CAM software.

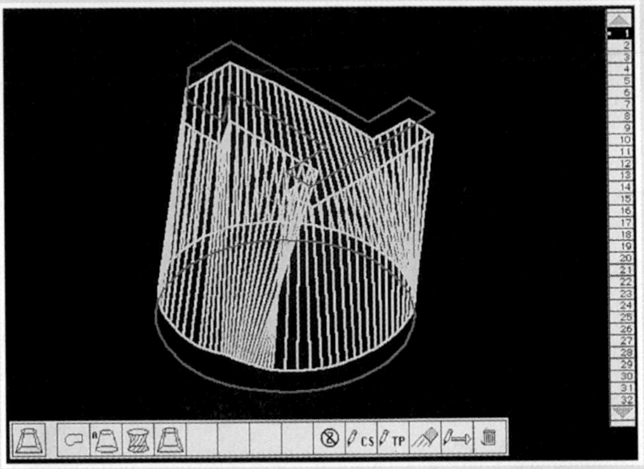

Wire EDM using Gibbs CAM software.

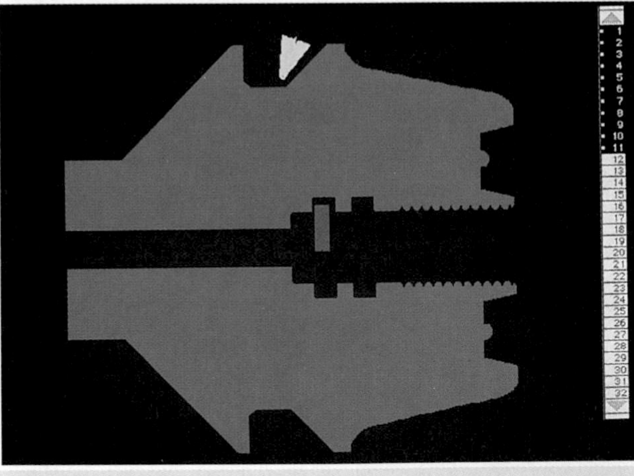

Multi-Axis turning using Gibbs CAM software.

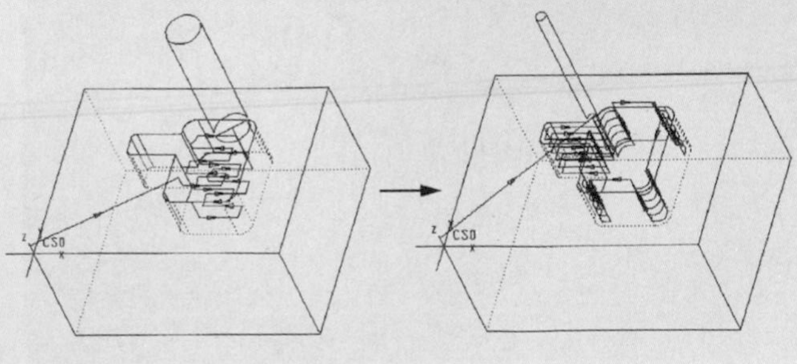

Milling.

Datum planes can create a reference on a part where one does not already exist. For example, you can sketch or place features on a datum plane when there is no appropriate planar surface. You can also dimension to a datum plane as if it were an edge. When you are constructing an assembly, you can use datums with assembly commands.

A datum is created by specifying constraints that locate it with respect to existing geometry. For example, a datum plane might be made to pass through the axis of a hole (Fig. 5.15) and parallel to a planar surface. Figure 5.15(a) shows a model of a clamp without hidden lines. Figure 5.15(b) displays the same part with hidden lines. And Fig. 15.15(c) displays the datum planes. DTM1, 2, and 3 are default datums used to create the base feature. DTM4 and 5 were introduced parallel to DTM1 and 3, respectively, and placed at the center of the part. These datums were used to locate the countersunk hole. Chosen constraints must locate the datum plane relative to the model without ambiguity.

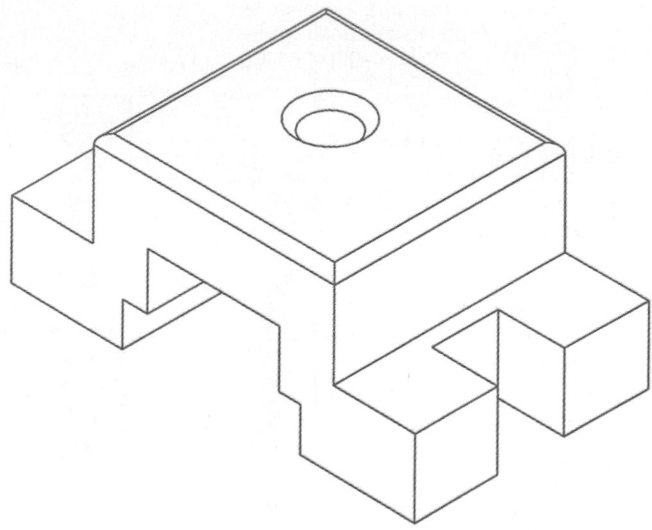

FIGURE 5.15(a) Clamp

5.3 PARENT–CHILD RELATIONSHIPS

Because solid modeling is a cumulative process, certain features must, by necessity, precede others. Those that follow must rely on previously defined features for dimensional and geometric references. The relationships between features and those that reference them are termed **parent–child relationships** (Fig. 5.16). Because children reference parents, features can exist without children, but children cannot exist without their parents.

The parent–child relationship is one of the most powerful aspects of parametric design. When a parent feature is modified, its children are automatically recreated to reflect the changes in the parent feature's geometry. It is therefore essential to reference feature dimensions so that design modifications are correctly propagated through the model. As an example, the modification to the length of a part is automatically propagated through the part and will affect all children of the modified feature.

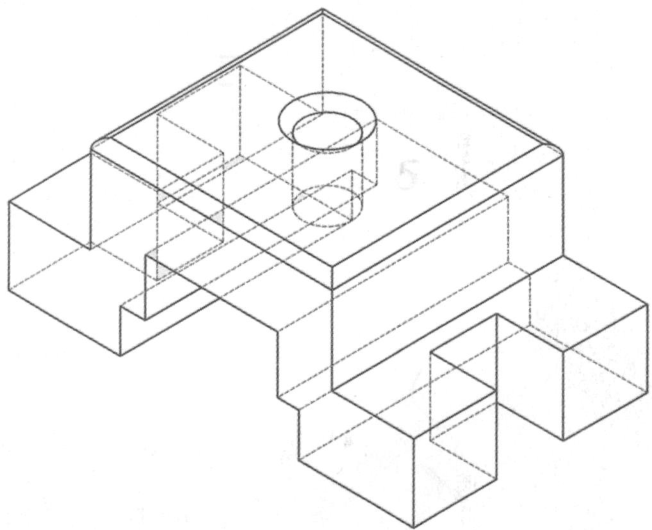

FIGURE 5.15(b) Clamp Displayed with Hidden Lines

5.4 ASSEMBLIES

Just as parts are created from related features, so **assemblies** are created from related parts [Fig. 5.17(a)]. The progressive combination of parts and features into an assembly creates parent–child relationships based on the references used to assemble each component [Fig. 5.17(b)].

Just as features can reference part geometry, parametric design also allows creation of parts referencing assembly geometry. Assembly mode (Fig. 5.18) allows the designer to both fit parts together and design parts based on how they should fit together. Figure 5.18(a) shows the completed assembly of the motorcycle. In Figure 5.18(b) the outer

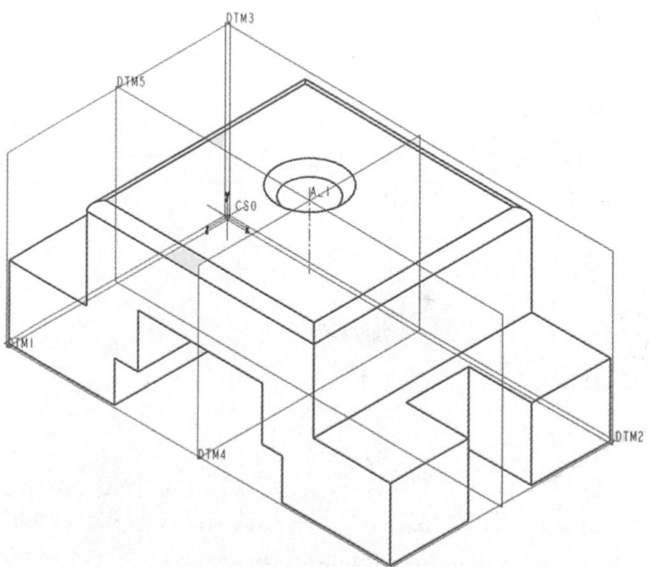

FIGURE 5.15(c) Clamp with Datum Features Displayed

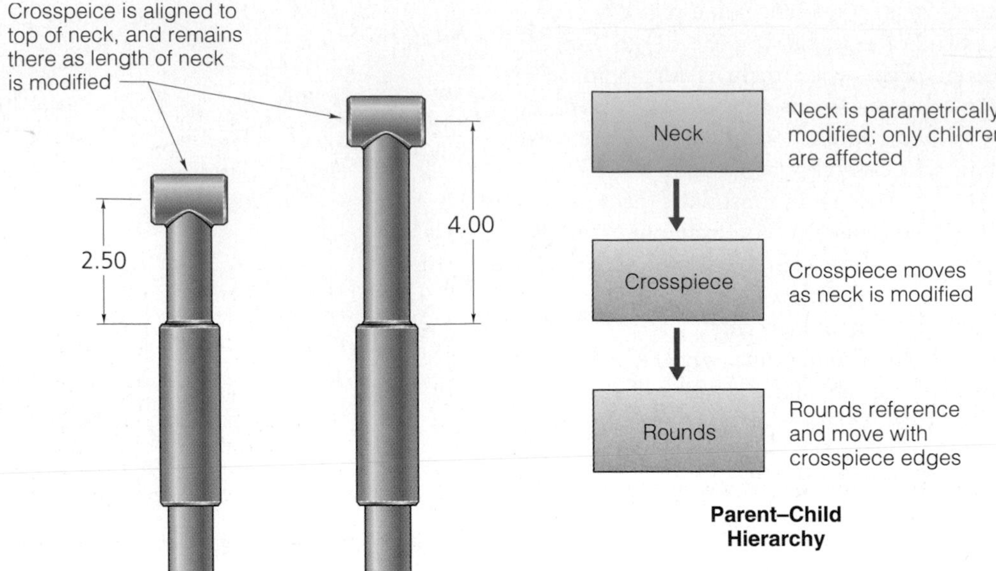
Crosspeice is aligned to top of neck, and remains there as length of neck is modified
2.50
4.00
Neck
Neck is parametrically modified; only children are affected
Crosspiece
Crosspiece moves as neck is modified
Rounds
Rounds reference and move with crosspiece edges
Parent–Child Hierarchy

FIGURE 5.16 Parent–Child Hierarchy

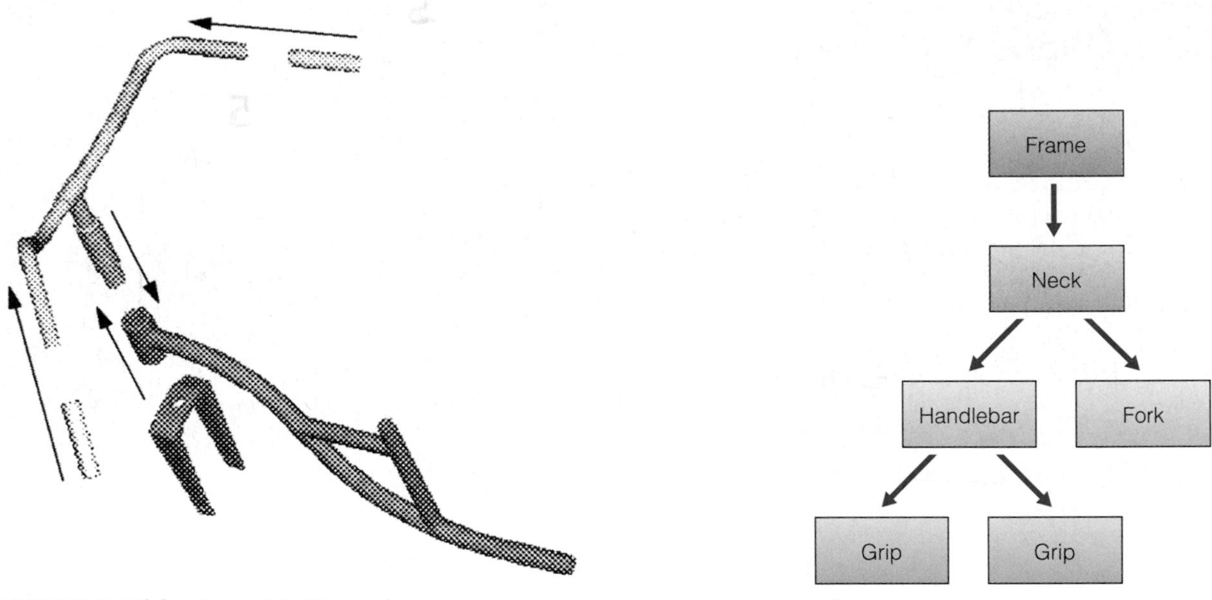
Frame
Neck
Handlebar
Fork
Grip
Grip

FIGURE 5.17(a) Assembly Hierarchy

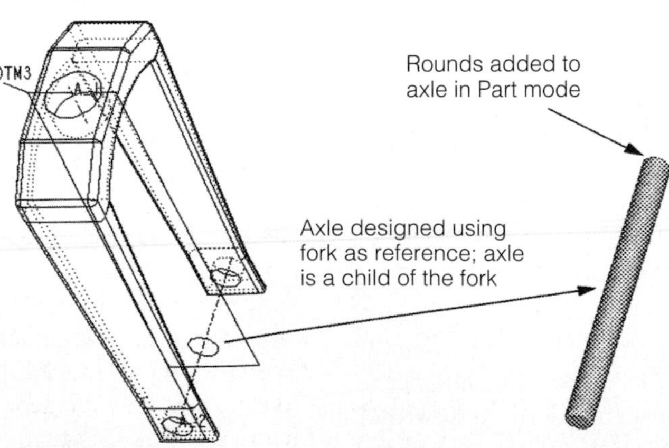
DTM3
Rounds added to axle in Part mode
Axle designed using fork as reference; axle is a child of the fork

FIGURE 5.17(b) Assemblies and Components

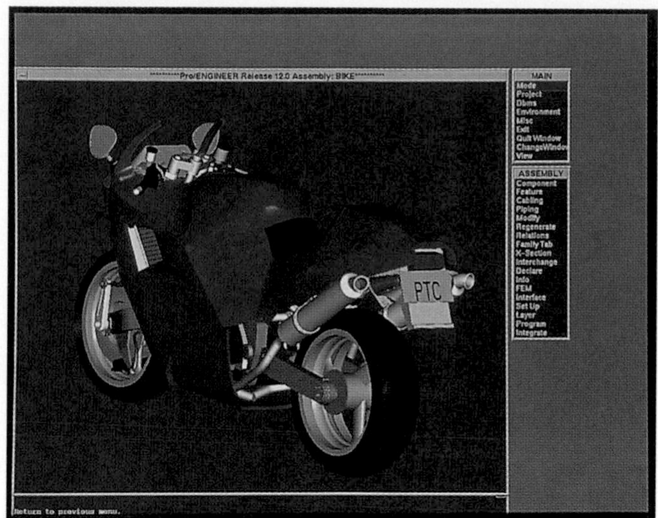

FIGURE 5.18(a) Motorcycle Assembly

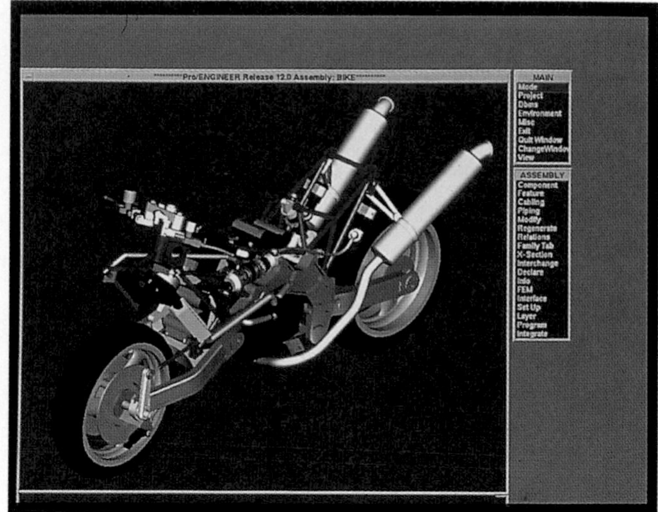

FIGURE 5.18(b) Motorcycle with Body Shell Removed

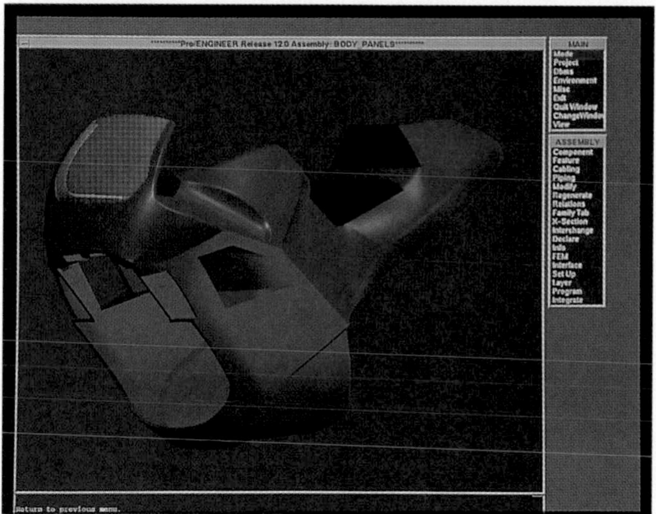

FIGURE 5.18(c) Body Panel Assembly

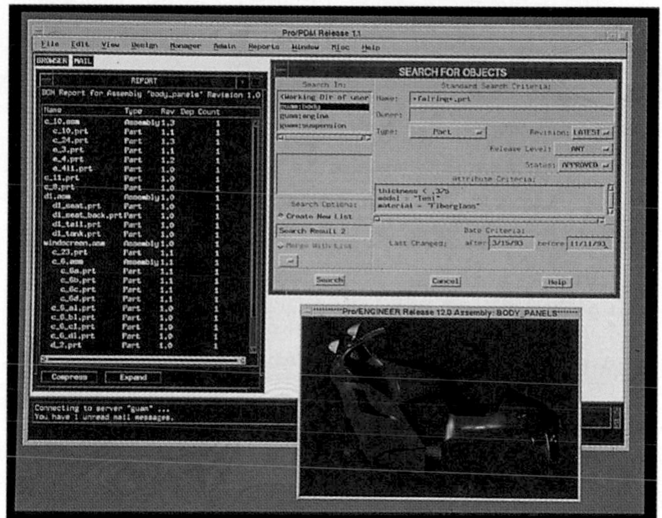

FIGURE 5.18(d) Bill of Materials

molded body panel subassembly [Fig. 5.18(c)] has been removed to view the engine and other components. In Figure 5.18(d) a report is being generated on the removed subassembly. Here, a bill of materials (BOM) is generated for the body panels.

5.5 CAPTURING DESIGN INTENT

A valuable aspect of any design tool is its ability to **render** the design and at the same time capture its **intent.** Parametric methods depend on the sequence of operations used to construct the design. The software maintains a *history of changes* the designer makes in specific parameters. The point of capturing this history is to keep track of operations that depend on each other. Whenever the system is told to change a specific dimension, it can update all operations that are referenced to that dimension.

For example, a circle representing a bolt hole may be constructed so that it is always concentric to a circular slot. If the slot moves, so does the bolt circle. Parameters are usually displayed in terms of dimensions or labels, and serve as the mechanism by which geometry is changed. The designer can change parameters manually by changing a dimension or by referencing them to a variable in an equation (**relation**) that is solved either by the modeling program itself or by external programs such as spreadsheets.

Parametric modeling is particularly useful in modeling whole **families** of similar parts and in rapidly modifying complex 3D designs. It is most effective in working with designs where changes are likely to consist of dimensional changes rather than radically different geometries.

Feature-based modeling, as already discussed, refers to the construction of geometry as a combination of **form features.** The designer specifies features in engineering terms, such as holes, slots, or bosses, rather than geometric

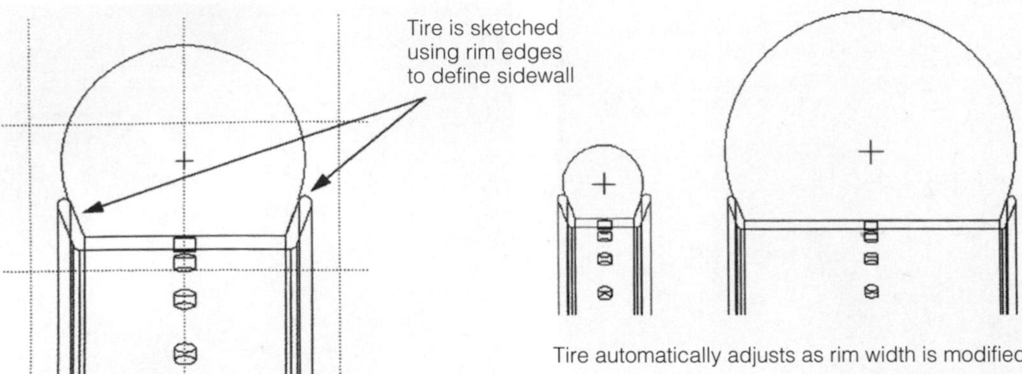

FIGURE 5.19 Section Sketch of Tire and Rim

terms, such as circles or boxes. Features can also store nongraphic information useful in activities such as a drafting, NC, finite-element analysis, and kinematics analysis.

The concept behind capturing design intent is to incorporate engineering knowledge into a model by establishing and preserving certain geometrical relationships. The wall thickness of a pressure vessel, for example, should be proportional to its surface area and should remain so even as its size changes. Parametric design captures these relationships in several ways.

Implicit Relationships. Implicit relationships occur when new model geometry is sketched and dimensioned relative to existing features and parts. An implicit relationship is established, for instance, when the section sketch of a tire (Fig. 5.19) uses rim edges for reference.

Patterns. Design features often follow a geometrically predictable pattern. Features and parts are patterned in parametric design by referencing either construction dimensions or existing patterns. One example of patterning is a wheel hub with spokes (Fig. 5.20). First the spoke holes are radially patterned. The spokes can then be strung by referencing this pattern. Any modification of a pattern member affects all members of that pattern. This helps capture design intent by preserving the duplicate geometry of pattern members.

Explicit Relations. Whereas implicit relationships are merely implied by creating a feature, an explicit relation is entered mathematically by the user. This equation relates part and feature dimensions in the desired manner. An explicit relation might be used, for example, to ensure that any number of spoke holes will be spaced evenly around a wheel hub (Fig. 5.21).

Family Tables. Family tables can create part families from generic models by tabulating dimensions or the presence of certain features or parts. A family table might be used, for example, to catalog a series of wheel rims of varying width and diameter (Fig. 5.22).

Modeling serves to incorporate the features and parts of a complex design while properly capturing design intent to provide flexibility in modification. Each parametric design model may be seen as a careful synthesis of physical and intellectual design (Fig. 5.23).

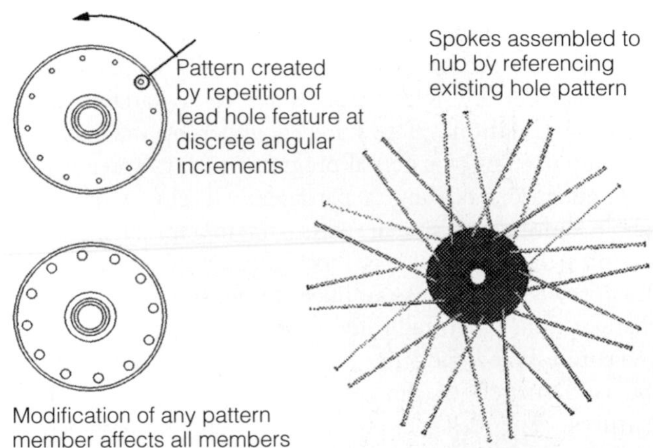

FIGURE 5.20 Wheel Hub with Spokes Designed via a Pattern

5.6 THE SKETCHER ENVIRONMENT

Sketcher techniques are used in many areas of parametric design. The aim of the **sketcher**, like that of parametric design, is to enable the quick and simple creation of geometry for your model. The sketcher requires you to create and dimension this geometry, but during the sketching process you do not have to be concerned with dimensional sizes or the creation of perfect and accurate geometry. Creating sections in sketcher mode is easy to do, and there are only a few steps to remember.

1. **Sketch the section geometry.** Use sketcher tools to create the section geometry.

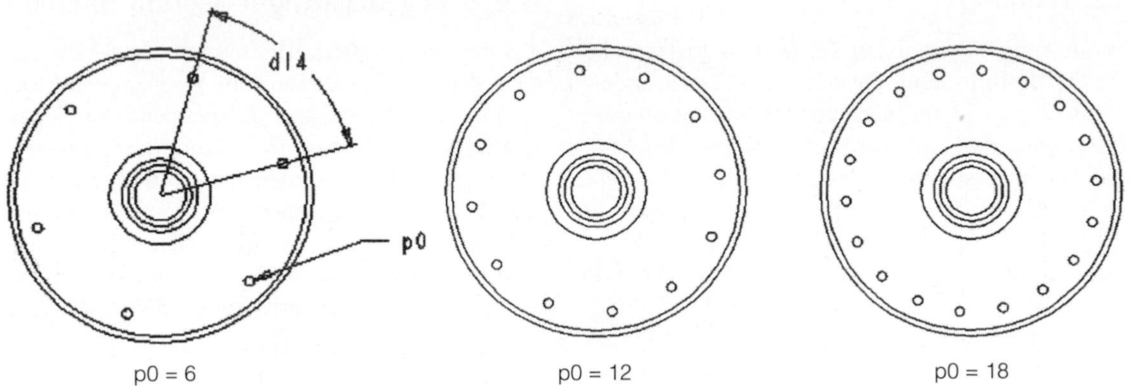
d14
p0
p0 = 6
p0 = 12
p0 = 18
Relation: d14 = 360/p0
Where: d14 = angular separation between pattern instances
p0 = number of pattern instances

FIGURE 5.21 Relations and Feature Creation

2. **Dimension and align the section.** Use a dimensioning scheme that you want to see in a drawing or that makes sense for controlling the characteristics of the section. Align the section geometry to a datum feature or to a part feature.
3. **Regenerate the section.** Regeneration solves the section sketch based on your dimensioning scheme.
4. **Add section relations.** Add relations to control the behavior of your section.

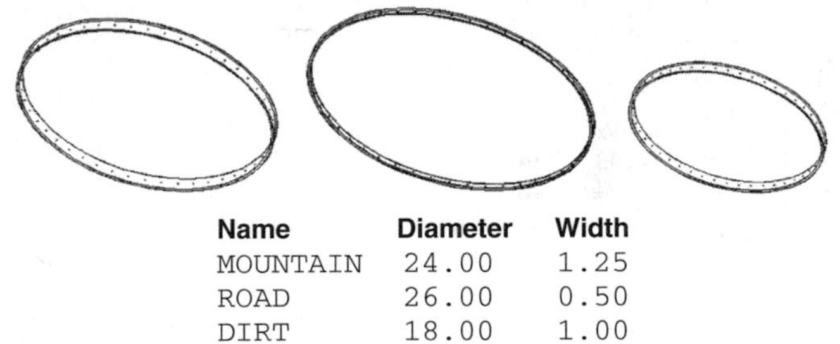

Name	Diameter	Width
MOUNTAIN	24.00	1.25
ROAD	26.00	0.50
DIRT	18.00	1.00

FIGURE 5.22 Family Table

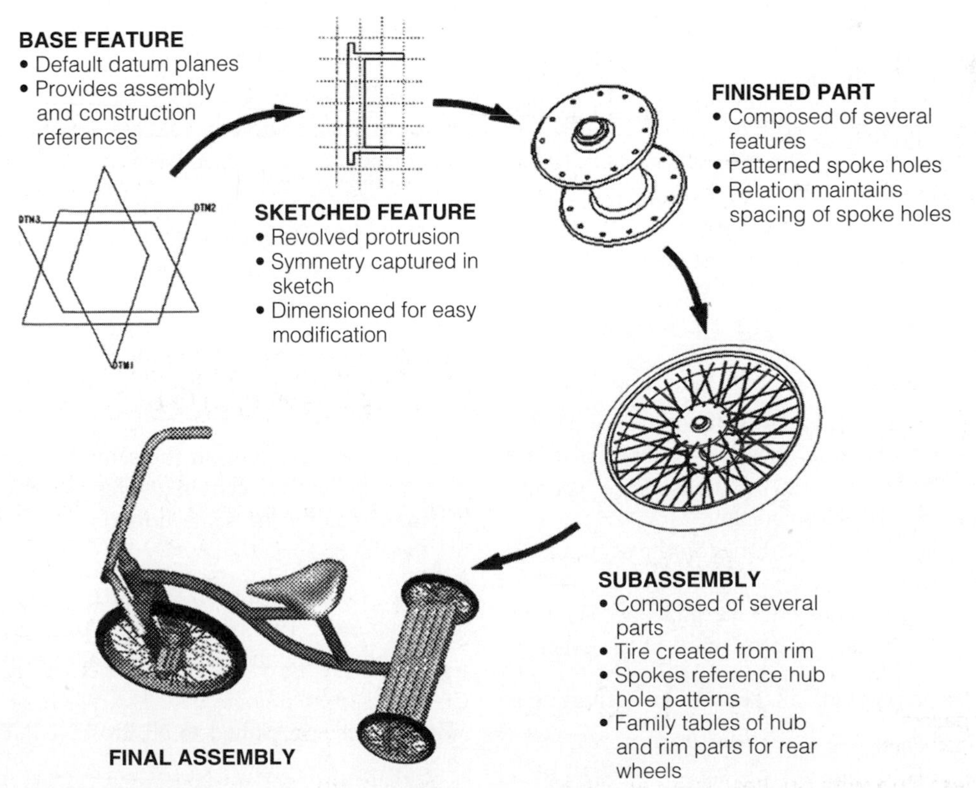
BASE FEATURE
• Default datum planes
• Provides assembly and construction references
DTM3
DTM2
DTM1
SKETCHED FEATURE
• Revolved protrusion
• Symmetry captured in sketch
• Dimensioned for easy modification
FINISHED PART
• Composed of several features
• Patterned spoke holes
• Relation maintains spacing of spoke holes
SUBASSEMBLY
• Composed of several parts
• Tire created from rim
• Spokes reference hub hole patterns
• Family tables of hub and rim parts for rear wheels
FINAL ASSEMBLY

FIGURE 5.23 Parametric Design

5.6.1 The Sketcher

Sketcher mode serves to establish 2D sections that are the basis for the 3D feature being created. In order to understand just how powerful the sketcher is on a parametric design system, you need only look at what the sketching process has been throughout the ages. *Sketching is a way, simply and efficiently, to establish the basic design and intent of a designer-engineer* on paper, and now possible on a CRT.

In the past, designers have sketched on paper, showing lines, arcs, circles, and other geometric shapes in rough, simplified outline and internal forms. The sketched shapes are assumed to be what they *sort of* look like. Round shapes approximating a circle are assumed by the sketch reader to be circles, curved shapes are assumed to be arcs, and lines drawn straight up or down are assumed to be vertical. Lines drawn left to right are assumed to be horizontal. Lines sketched at an angle are straight lines that are angled. Dimensions roughly sketched on a less than perfect drawing of a part are assumed to represent the exact perfect shape desired by the person sketching. All this seems obvious to most people involved in engineering design. But now we have a whole new tool. With the introduction of parametric design we can sketch on the screen and allow the system to make all the assumptions that were traditionally made by a person creating a sketch or reading a sketch. These assumptions include, but are not limited to, the following: symmetry, tangency, parallelism, perpendicularity, equal angles, same-size arcs and circles, coincident centers, colinerarity.

AutoCAD Designer compares your sketch with a set of **rules.** AutoCAD Designer cleans up the sketch after it finds a group of rules that fit the sketch. If AutoCAD Designer exhausts all possible rules without solving the sketch, your sketch is underconstrained. As an example, AutoCAD Designer parametric-based system applies the following rules to a sketch, in the following order.

1. A line sketched nearly horizontal is horizontal.
2. A line sketched nearly vertical is vertical.
3. Two arcs or an arc/circle and a line sketched nearly tangent are tangent.
4. Two arcs or circles whose centers are sketched nearly coincident are concentric.
5. Two lines sketched nearly overlaying along the same line as each other are collinear. Lines sketched nearly parallel are parallel. Lines sketched nearly perpendicular are perpendicular. The lines must be attached for perpendicularity to be inferred automatically.
6. Any arcs and circle sketched with nearly the same radius have the same radius.
7. Geometric forms (lines, arcs, etc.) are attached using the endpoint of one form and the near point of the other.

All parametric design systems make similar assumptions when sketching.

5.6.2 Regenerating a Section Sketch

During regeneration, the system checks to make sure it understands your dimensioning scheme and that you have created a complete and independent set of parameters. It analyzes your section based on the geometry you have sketched and the dimensions you have created. In the absence of explicit dimensions, implicit information based on the sketch may be used. Here is a table of implicit information that Pro/ENGINEER uses to regenerate a section (you can see the similarity to AutoCAD's Designer).

Rule: Equal radius/diameter
Description: If two or more arcs or circles are sketched with approximately the same radius, they are assigned the same radius value.

Rule: Symmetry
Description: Entities sketched symmetrically about a centerline are assigned equal values with respect to the center line.

Rule: Horizontal and vertical lines
Description: Lines that are approximately horizontal or vertical are considered to be exactly so.

Rule: Parallel and perpendicular lines
Description: Lines that are sketched approximately parallel or perpendicular are considered to be exactly so.

Rule: Tangency
Description: Entities sketched approximately tangent to arcs or circles are assumed to be tangent.

Rule: 90°, 180°, 270° arcs
Description: Arcs are considered to be multiples of 90° if they are sketched with approximately horizontal or vertical tangents at the endpoints.

Rule: Collinearity
Description: Segments that are approximately collinear are considered to be exactly so.

Rule: Equal segment lengths
Description: Segments of unknown length are assigned a length equal to that of a known segment of approximately the same length.

Rule: Point entities lying on other entities
Description: Point entities that lie approximately on lines, arcs, or circles are considered to be exactly on them.

Rule: Centers lying on the same horizontal
Description: Two centers of arcs or circles that lie approximately along the same horizontal direction are set to be exactly so.

Rule: Centers lying on the same vertical
Description: Two centers of arcs or circles that lie approximately along the same vertical direction are set to be exactly so.

These rules are applied to all Pro/ENGINEER sketches.

The following section provides an example of the sequence of steps involved in modeling with Pro/ENGINEER. Though different systems use different command names, the capabilities, and in many cases the steps, are the same. Note that the following part would take an experienced designer 3–5 minutes to create.

5.6.3 Creating a Part Using Sketched and "Pick and Place" Geometry

The premise of the sketcher in parametric feature-based design is to create quick-and-simple geometry for your model. The sketching process enables you to create and dimension the geometry for a feature or set of features on your design. Remember, during the sketching process you need *not* concern yourself with creating perfect geometry or accurate dimension values. You might modify your dimensions later in the design process.

In Figure 5.24 the creation of a simple part is described. After the **units of measurement, default datums,** and other **setups** are performed, the sketcher is entered by selecting a feature type. Here the feature to be used as the base feature is an **extruded protrusion.** The default datums [Fig. 5.24(a)] are used to select the sketching plane and orient the sketch. DTM3 is the sketch plane. A sketched section can start the model. The following commands were given.

Figure 5.24(a). Using the datum planes to set up and orient the sketch.

Feature--Create--Datum--Default
Feature--Create--Datum--Coordinate System--Default
Feature--Create--Solid--Protrusion--Extrude--Solid--Single--One Side--Blind--Plane (pick DTM3)**--Okay--Top** (pick DTM2)

Figure 5.24(b) and Figure 5.24(c). Drawing lines with the sketcher. Note that the lines are not perfectly oriented (vertically or horizontally). They are drawn in approximately the desired shape of the base protrusion, with no regard to actual size.

Sketch--Line (sketch the geometry as shown)
Regenerate (system asks you to locate with respect to the part)
Alignment (align the ends of lines to the datums and the lines along the datums to the datums themselves)

Figure 5.24(d). Dimensioned sketch has **symbols** for dimensions, since it has not been regenerated yet.

Dimension (add required dimensions to locate the geometry to the datum planes and describe the features of the geometry)

Figure 5.24(e). Regenerated and aligned sketch has sketch dimension values (which are not correct at this stage).

Regenerate (system responds with "Regeneration completed successfully")

Figure 5.24(f). Modify the dimension values to reflect the correct design requirements. Notice that after the regeneration the section geometry looks quite different from the original sketch!

Modify (pick each dimension in succession and change the value to the required size)
Regenerate

Figure 5.24(g) and Figure 5.24(h). Enter depth of the protrusion (here 5.00). The system responds with "**PROTRUSION** has been created successfully." Show the part in a pictorial view and change it to isometric projection.

View--Default (displays the part in a rotated projection)
Environment--Isometric
View--Default

Figure 5.24(i) and Figure 5.24(j). The base feature is now complete. You may modify any dimension at this stage of the design. Let's change the depth of the part from 5.00 to 6.00.

Modify (pick a line on the part—all the protrusions features will be displayed)
Modify (pick the depth dimension 5.00 and type the new value 6.00)
Regenerate (the model will update itself using the new depth)

Figure 5.24(k). Now let us create a thru-hole on the angled surface. The hole will have a 1.25 diameter and will be placed at the center of the plane. The hole command can be a pick-and-place feature or a sketched feature. We will use the pick-and-place version. Note that the hole will be a child of the surface on which it is created and of surfaces from which it is located.

Feature--Create--Hole--Single--Linear--Straight--One Side--Thru All (enter diameter: 1.25)
(select placement plane—choose the angled surface)
(select two edges, axes, planar surfaces, or datums for dimensioning—select DTM3 and give a value of 3.00)
(select the second reference—select the front lower edge line of the angled surface and give a value of 2.00. Note that 2.00 will only place the hole near the plain center. Later you can modify this value, after you get the system to provide the length of the angled edge line.)

Figure 5.24(l) and Figure 5.24(m). Using the system **Info** command we can get the exact length of the angled edge line and use this dimension to modify the placement of the hole. At the same time, change the size of the hole to ∅1.500.

Info--Measure--Vertex (pick the ends of the angled line—the system gives the distance as 3.60555)
Modify (pick the hole—the system displays the diameter and the location dimensions of the hole. Pick the ∅1.25 dimension and change its value to ∅1.500. Next pick the 2.00 dimension and change it to 3.60555/2. This will make it half the length of the edge line.
Regenerate

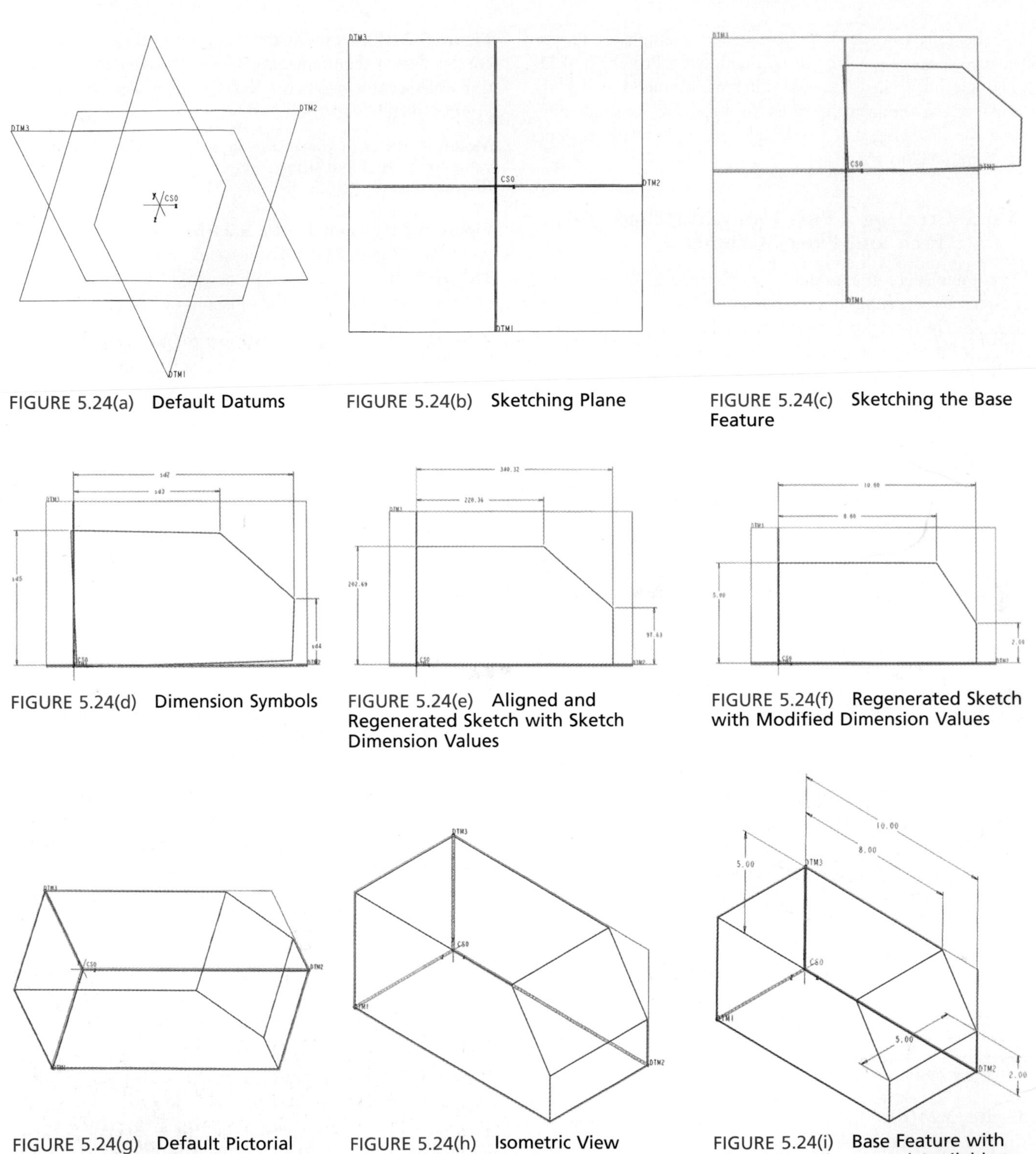

FIGURE 5.24(a) **Default Datums**

FIGURE 5.24(b) **Sketching Plane**

FIGURE 5.24(c) **Sketching the Base Feature**

FIGURE 5.24(d) **Dimension Symbols**

FIGURE 5.24(e) **Aligned and Regenerated Sketch with Sketch Dimension Values**

FIGURE 5.24(f) **Regenerated Sketch with Modified Dimension Values**

FIGURE 5.24(g) **Default Pictorial View**

FIGURE 5.24(h) **Isometric View**

FIGURE 5.24(i) **Base Feature with Dimensions Shown and Available to Modify**

Figure 5.24(n) and Figure 5.24(o). The hole needs a chamfer of 45° × .20. Add the chamfer using the chamfer feature. The chamfer is a pick-and-place feature. The chamfer is a child of the hole.

Feature--Create--Chamfer--Edge--45xd (enter chamfer dimension for d:.2) (select one or more edges to chamfer—pick the holes edge twice—both sides, since the hole is split in half when using Pro/ENGINEER)

Figure 5.24(p). Lastly, we will shade the part.

View--Cosmetic--Colors--Define--Set (define new colors and set the surfaces)
Shade--Display

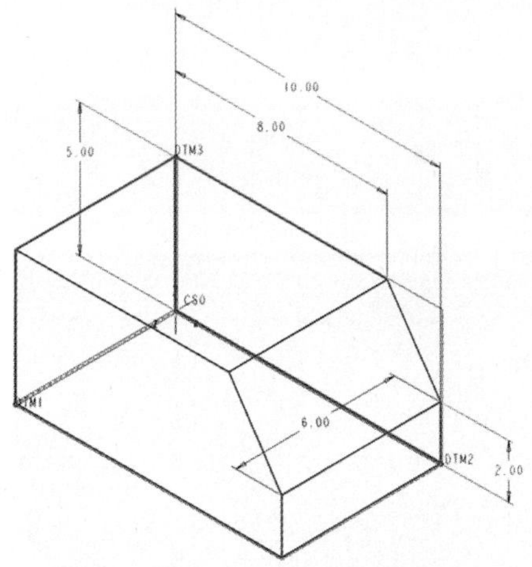

FIGURE 5.24(j) Modifying the Depth Dimension from 5.00 to 6.00

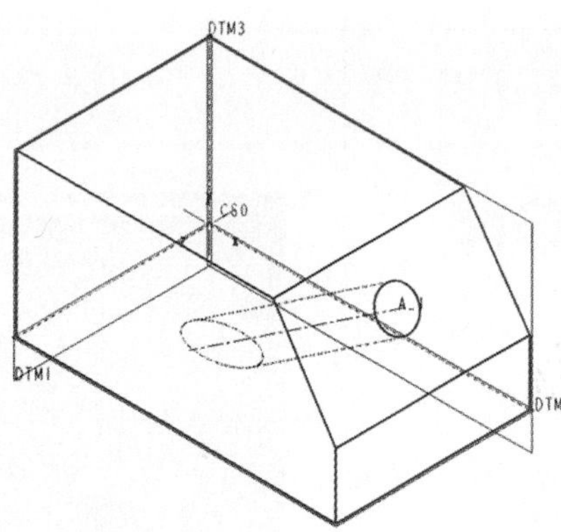

FIGURE 5.24(k) Adding a Hole to the Angled Surface

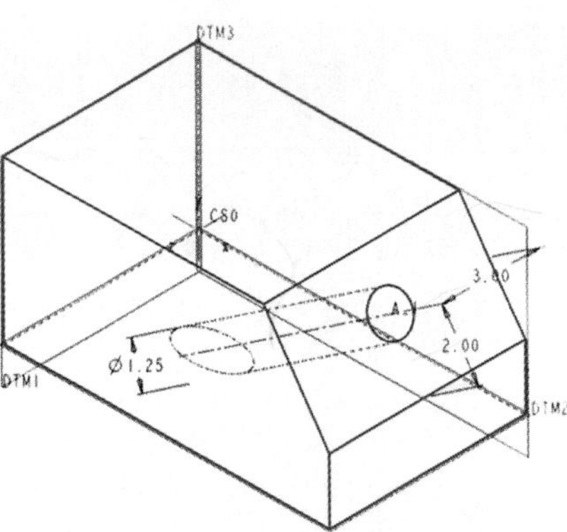

FIGURE 5.24(l) Hole Dimensions Available for Modification

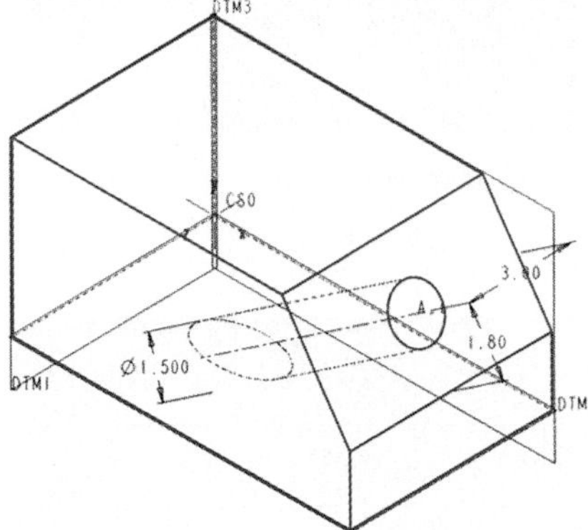

FIGURE 5.24(m) Modifying the Hole Diameter from ∅ 1.25 to ∅ 1.50

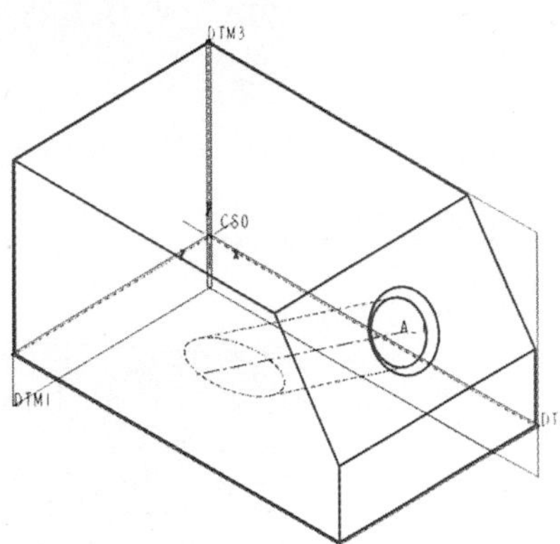

FIGURE 5.24(n) Adding a Chamfer Feature

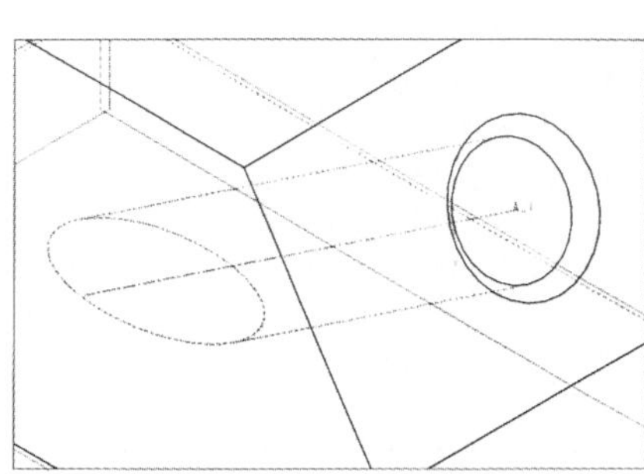

FIGURE 5.24(o) Enlarged View of Chamfer

FIGURE 5.24(p) Shaded Part

5.7 GENERATING DRAWINGS

You can create **drawings** of all parametric design models (Fig. 5.25) or by importing files from other systems. All model views in the drawing are **associative:** If you change a dimensional value in one view, other drawing views update accordingly. Moreover, drawings are associated with their parent models: Any dimensional changes made to a drawing are automatically reflected in the model; any changes made to the model (i.e., addition of features, deletion of features,

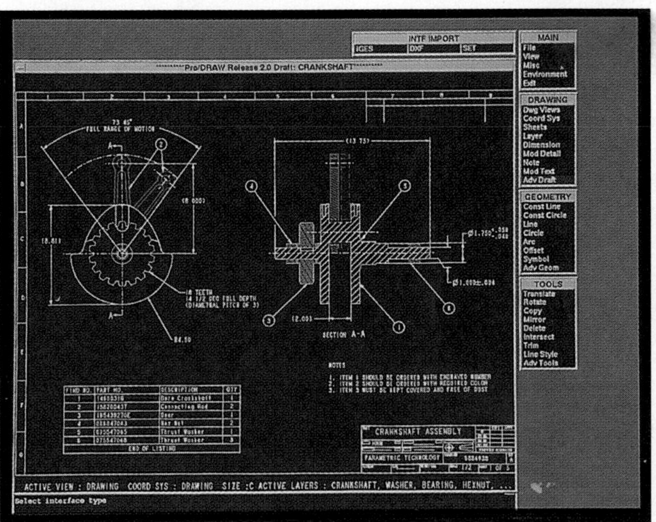

FIGURE 5.25 Dimensioned Drawing Created with Pro/DRAW

Applying Parametric Design . . .

PARAMETRIC DESIGN ON PC'S

This chapter will overview Pro/ENGINEER™ and the Applying Parametric Design boxes from Chapters 6–29. But there are many high-quality parametric design systems available on the market. AutoCAD Designer is a low-cost parametric-based system that can be added on to the latest version of AutoCAD. It is affordable and will allow you to experience parametric design on a PC. Computervision, SDRC's IDEAS, IBM, and Pro/ENGINEER are a few of the dominant high-end parametric design systems found throughout industry. Ford, Chrysler, John Deere, FMC, Boeing, and Lockheed are some of the many companies switching to high-end parametric design systems. If training on these systems is unavailable at a local college, AutoCAD Designer will provide all of the basics that can be learned at home on your PC.

AutoCAD's Designer™ lets you generate many types of information about your design—its mass properties, a drawing, or a base model (Fig. A is a solid model of the Dremel Gun body). To get this information, you must first model the parts that make up the design. To begin the design process, analyze your design. Then break it down into its basic components, or building blocks. Next, identify the most fundamental feature of the part as the first feature to sketch.

Features are the basic building blocks you use to build a part. AutoCAD Designer features "understand" their fit and function. For example, a hole feature knows its shape and part location and that it has a negative volume. So to create a hole in a solid, all you have to do is input a specific position as the place where you want to put the hole. Also, when you edit a feature, the entire part automatically updates in a logical way. The Dremel Gun body has a number of such holes incorporated into its design.

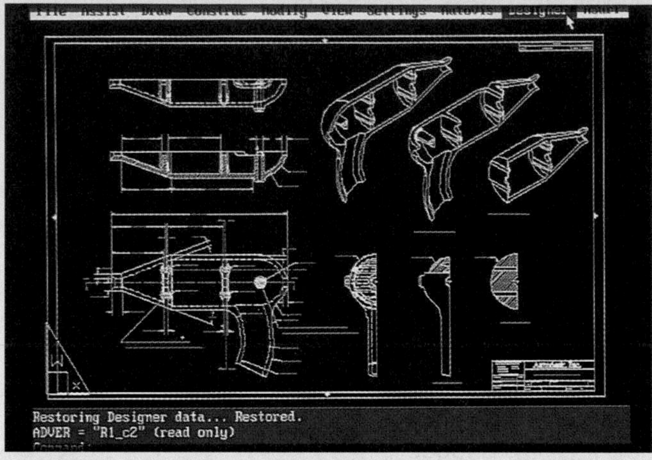

FIGURE B Detail Drawing of Dremel Body with Multiple Dimensions and Sections

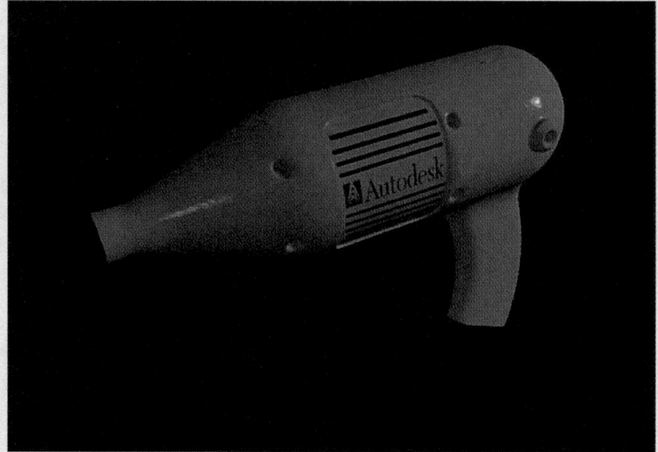

FIGURE C Assembly of Dremel Gun

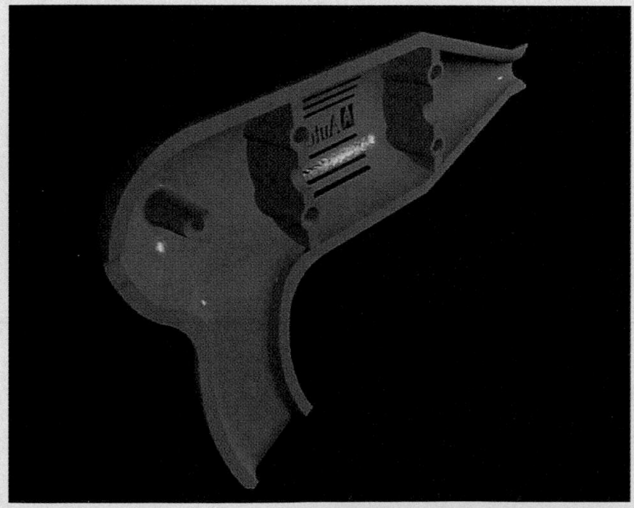

FIGURE A Solid Parametric Model of the Dremel Gun Body

FIGURE D Exploded Assembly of Dremel Gun

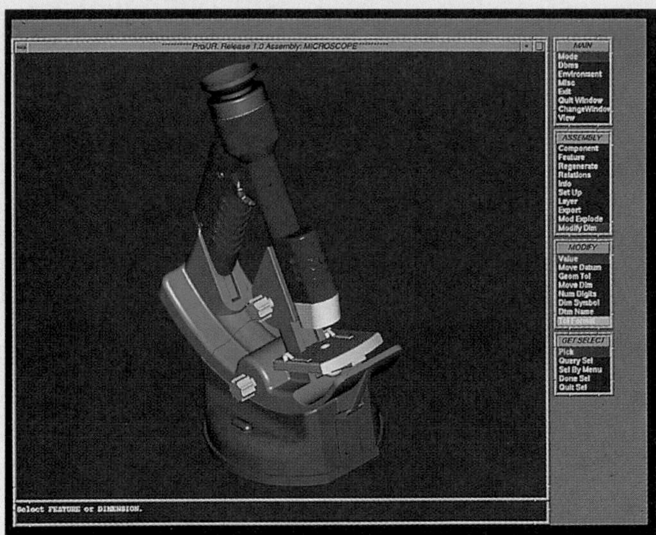

FIGURE E **Solid Model of Microscope**

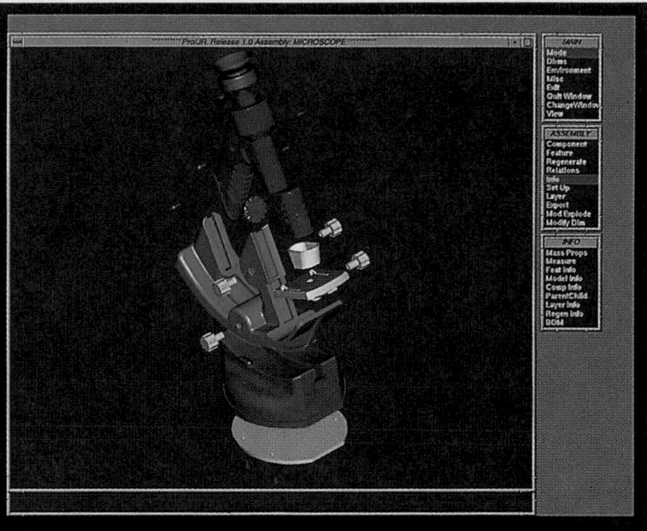

FIGURE H **Exploded Solid Model of Microscope**

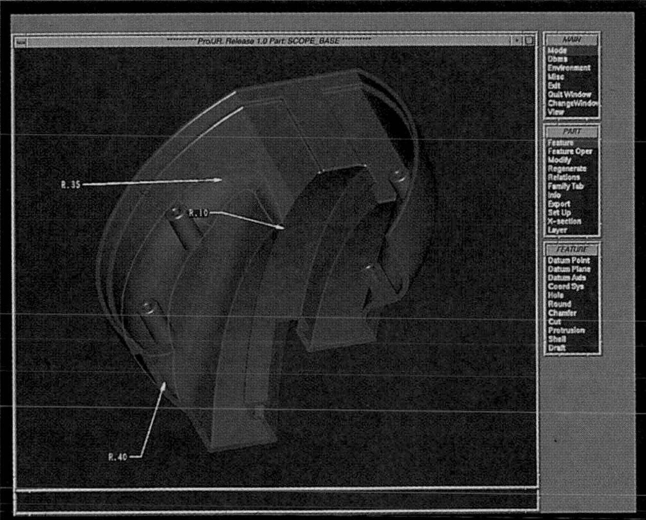

FIGURE F **Shelled Model of the Microscope Base**

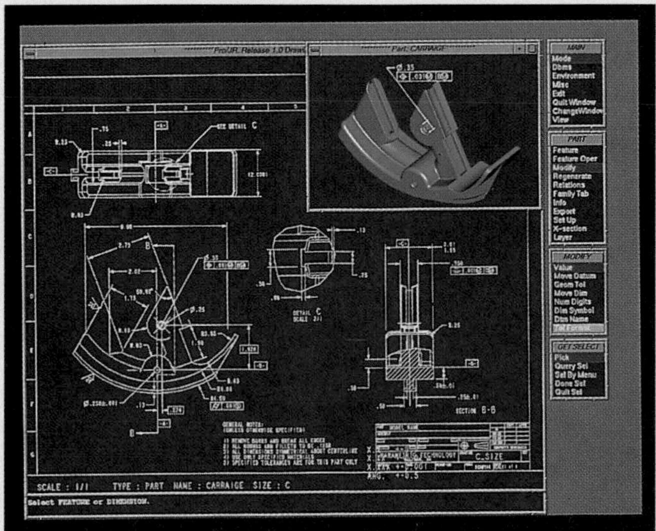

FIGURE G **Detail Drawing of Microscope Component**

In sketching your features, you can use many of the AutoCAD 2D entities as you normally would. However, you don't have to be concerned with the accuracy of the sketch. Lines can be off angle, arcs can have unequal radii, and overall dimensions and relationships can be incorrect. Simple commands help apply logical geometric constraints to the sketch. These constraints clean up the sketch geometry according to the current system settings. The constraints close endpoints, align parallel lines, and snap entities to horizontal and vertical angles. Additional constraints and parametric dimensions are applied to control the size and shape of the feature.

You can begin documentation of a finished part at anytime using the AutoCAD Designer drawing commands. By identifying the drawing views, AutoCAD Designer automatically removes hidden lines and places the feature dimensions on the drawing. A series of sections of the Dremel Gun body is shown in Figure B, along with dimensions required for manufacture. If you make changes to the part and add dimensions and features, AutoCAD Designer updates the drawing along with the part.

Multiple parts are combined to build an assembly that is tied together through global parameters. Figure C shows a completely assembled Dremel tool. You can also create assembly drawings the same way you create parts drawings; and as shown in Figure D, exploded views of the assembly are easily displayed.

Pro/JR.™, from **Parametric Technology Corp.**, is a parametric, feature-based solid-modeling system for the design through documentation of mechanical parts and assemblies (see Fig. E, a solid model of a microscope). The Pro/JR.'s full associativity ensures that a change made anywhere is reflected in all engineering stages of the design-through-manufacturing sequence. This is an entry-level version of Pro/ENGINEER. Pro/JR. is a more expensive PC-based parametric design system than AutoCAD's Designer. But for companies wishing to move from drafting-orientated 2D-3D systems to the more advanced capabilities of 3D parametric modeling, this is an excellent midrange system.

(Continues)

(Continued)

Pro/JR. enables engineers and designers to design parts quickly and easily by selecting "pick and place" features from a menu or by creating sketched features directly on the part. The shelled component of the microscope base (see Fig. F) is an example of a part created via the shell command in Pro/JR.

After a part is modeled with Pro/JR., fully associative drawings are created directly from the design model. Any changes made to the drawing will automatically be reflected in the solid model. Likewise, changes to the model are captured in the drawing. Figure G shows a detail drawing of one piece of the microscope. Drawings are created from the design model without the necessity of drafting views and creating traditional 2D drawings of the part. Pro/JR., as with Pro/ENGINEER, has built-in ANSI or ISO standards for displaying appropriate design-driven dimensions and geometric tolerancing feature specifications. Assembly models and drawings created with Pro/JR. can be displayed in an exploded state to expose hidden components, as shown in Figure H in the exploded view of the microscope model.

Regardless of the parametric design system available to you as an engineering student or as an employee of a design engineering company, this technology will be the primary form of engineering communication and documentation in the near future. Any available training on a parametric design system will greatly enhance your marketability as a beginning engineer or designer.

dimensional changes, etc.) in Part, Sheet Metal, Assembly, or Manufacturing mode are also automatically reflected in the corresponding drawings.

This section describes drawing mode for Pro/ENGINEER, and how to create and manage drawings.

5.7.1 Drawing Mode and Basic Parametric Design

Drawing mode in parametric design provides you the basic ability to document solid models in drawings that share a two-way associativity with the model. *Any changes that are made to the model in Part or Assembly mode will automatically cause the drawing to update and reflect the changes. Any changes made to the model in Drawing mode will be immediately visible on the model in Part and Assembly modes.* Basic Pro/ENGINEER (without the optional module Pro/DETAIL) allows you to create drawing views of one or more models in a number of standard view types and to dimension them. In addition, you can annotate the drawing, manipulate the dimensions, and use layers to manage the display of different items on the drawing.

The optional module **Pro/DETAIL** may be used to extend the drawing capability, or as a stand-alone module for creating, viewing, and annotating models and drawings (Fig. 5.26). Pro/DETAIL supports additional view types and multisheets, and offers commands for manipulating items in the drawing and adding and modifying different kinds of textural and symbolic information. In addition, the abilities to customize engineering drawings with sketched geometry, create custom drawing formats, and make numerous cosmetic changes to the drawing are available.

Drawing parameters are saved with each individual drawing and drawing format. Drawing parameters determine the height of dimension and note text, text orientation, geometric tolerance standards, font properties, drafting standards, and arrow lengths. Parameter values are given defaults by the system.

When you regenerate a drawing, the drawing and the model that it represents are recreated, not simply redrawn. This means that if any of the model's dimension values were changed while in drawing model, regenerating the drawing causes the model to update these changes. The regenerated drawing displays the updated model and any changes that were made to it.

5.7.2 Storing Drawings

Some of the entities and information that you can create or modify in a drawing are saved with the model, rather than with the drawing. This is important to be aware of, since such changes made to the drawing may affect the model that it documents. An example of this occurs when you set a dimension as basic. The dimension becomes theoretically exact, and any tolerances this dimension had are removed.

Strictly *cosmetic* information is saved with the drawing; this information includes:

- All draft entities
- The view in which an entity is displayed
- The placement of an entity on the sheet

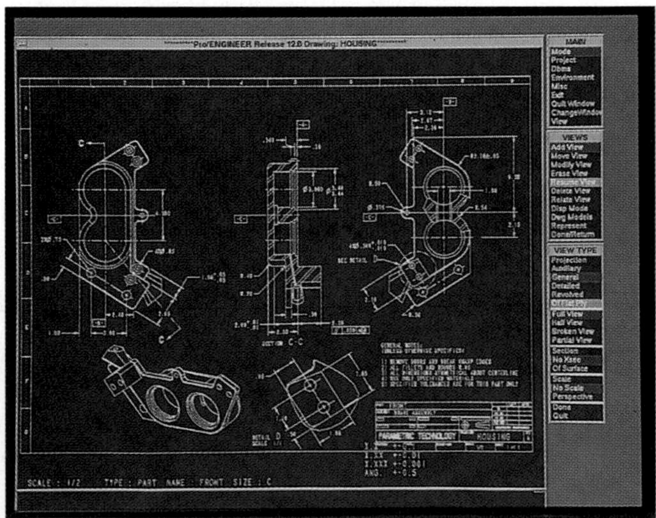

FIGURE 5.26 Detail Drawing Created with Pro/DETAIL

- Jogs and breaks in leaders and dimension lines
- The insertion of dimensions in notes
- The font, height, width, and slant angle of text

However, much of the information added to a drawing is saved with the model; this includes:

- Geometric tolerances (can also be saved in the drawing)
- Dimension information (reference and driven dimensions also), including:
  - Additional text
  - Standard/ordinate dimension type
  - Attached geometric tolerance list
  - Attached set datum or axis reference
  - Value and tolerance information
  - The difference between the primary and secondary units, when explicitly set by the user
  - Basic and inspection attributes
- Set datum and axis information
- Datum target point information
- Surface finishes, including type and value
- Layer membership information for all entities in the model

Whenever you save a drawing after making changes that affect the model, the model is saved with the drawing.

Reports can also be generated from the part or assembly. The race car in Figure 5.27(a) and Figure 5.27(b) is an example of a complex product design documented with a parametric design system. The body design [Fig. 5.27(c)], engine [Fig. 5.27(d)], and internal systems [Fig. 5.27(e)] contain the complete design database required to produce the vehicle. Information about the design can be extracted graphically using drawings and through the generation of reports [Fig. 5.27(f)].

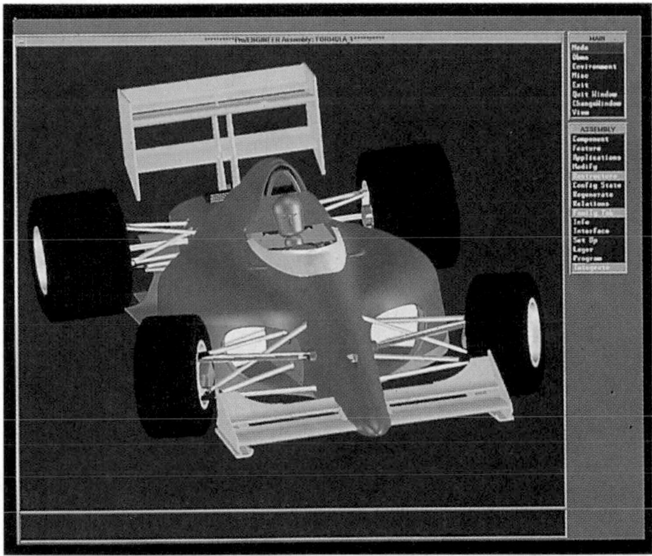

FIGURE 5.27(a) Indy Race Car Designed with Pro/ENGINEER

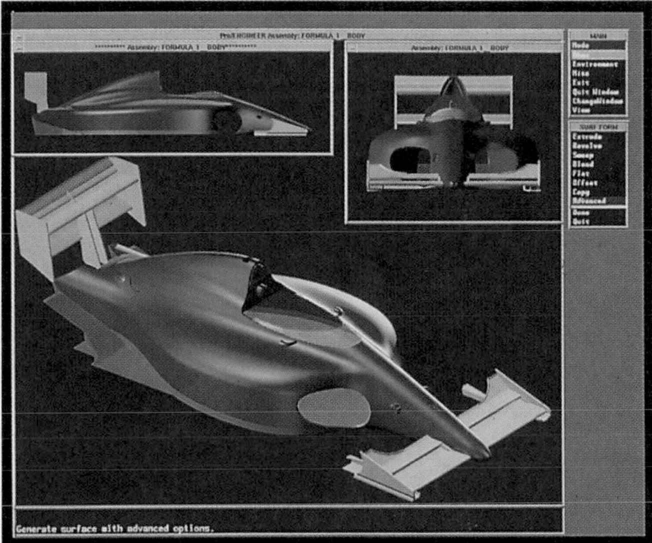

FIGURE 5.27(c) Indy Car Body Design

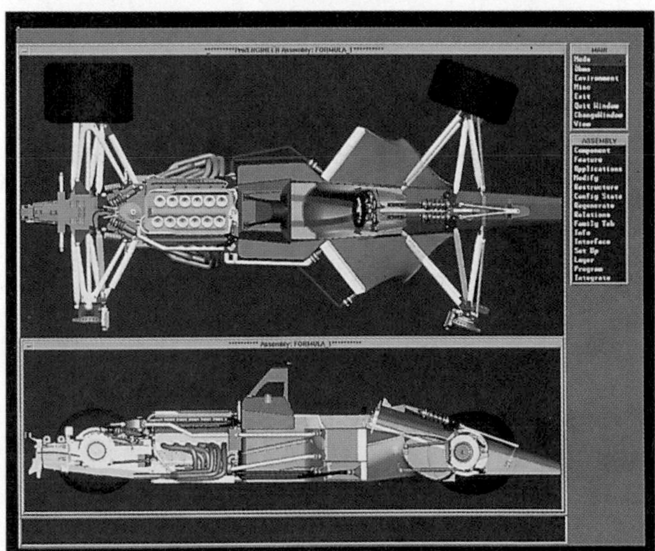

FIGURE 5.27(b) Internal View of Indy Car

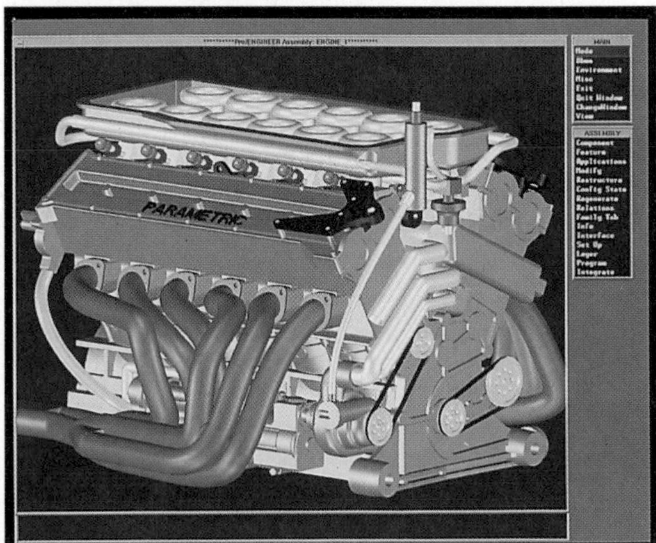

FIGURE 5.27(d) Indy Car Engine

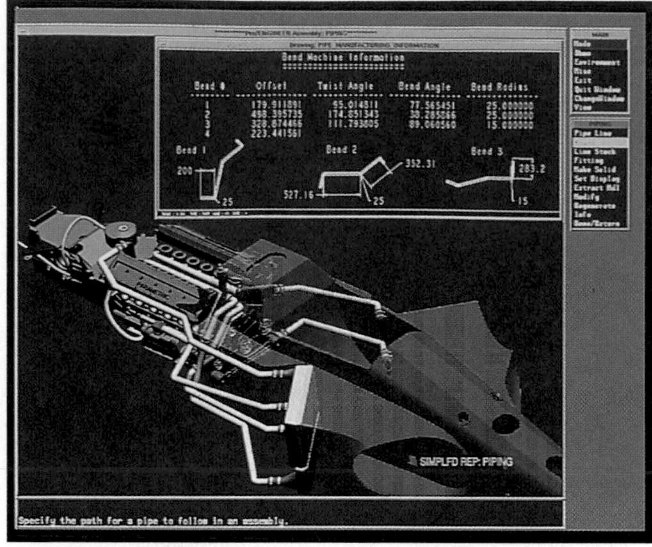

FIGURE 5.27(e) Indy Car Internal Systems

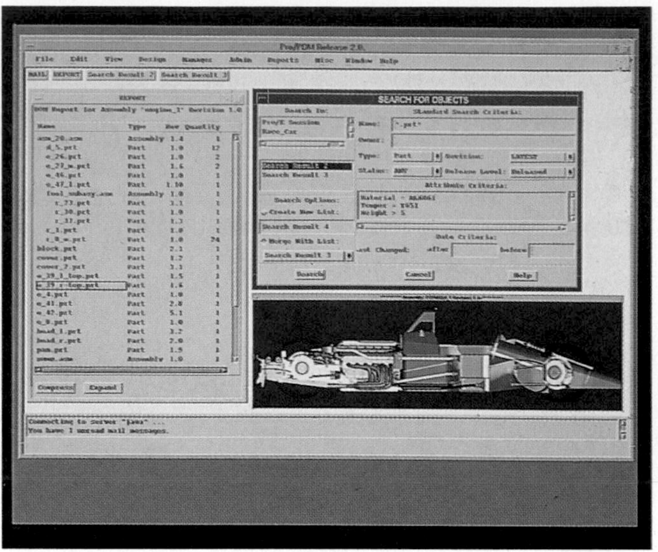

FIGURE 5.27(f) Generating Design Reports for Indy Car

5.8 MANUFACTURING AND PARAMETRIC DESIGN

Parametric design systems also provide the tools to program and simulate numerical control manufacturing processes (Fig. 5.28). The information created can be quickly updated should the engineering design model change. NC programs in the form of ASCII CL data files, tool lists, operation reports, and in-process geometry can be generated.

Pro/MANUFACTURING software will create the data necessary to drive an NC machine tool to machine a part (Fig. 5.29). It does this by providing the tools to let the manufacturing engineer follow a logical sequence of steps to progress from a design model to an ASCII CL data file that can be postprocessed into NC machine data (Fig. 5.30).

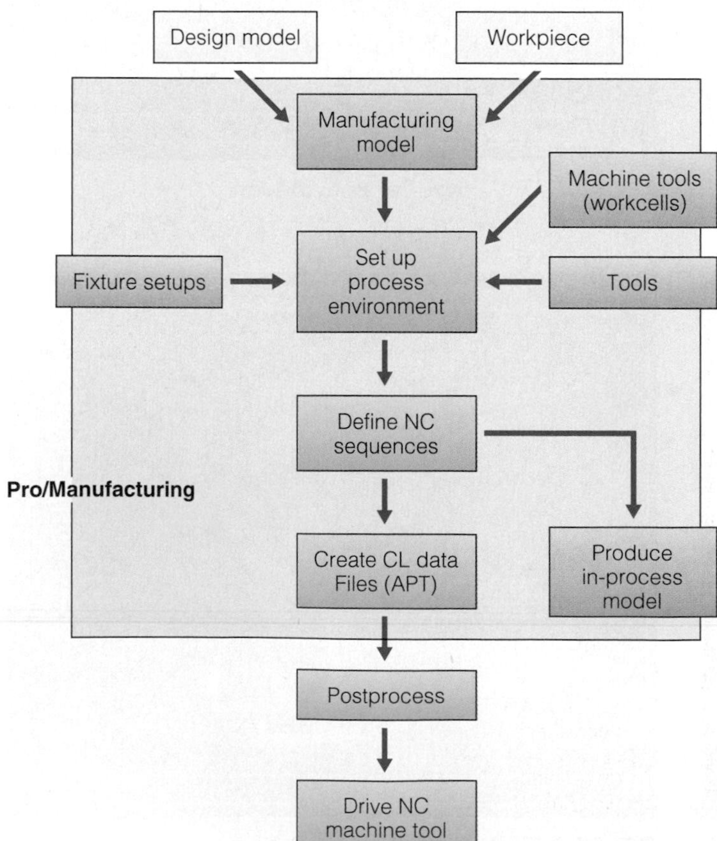

FIGURE 5.28 Pro/MANUFACTURING

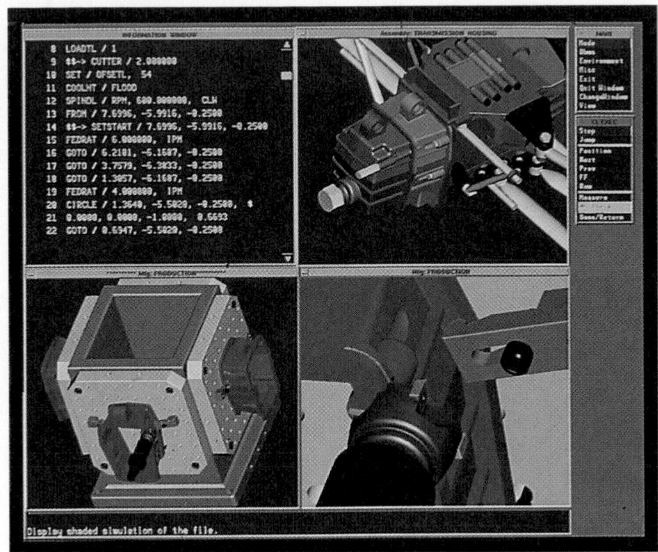

FIGURE 5.29 Fixturing and Part Machining

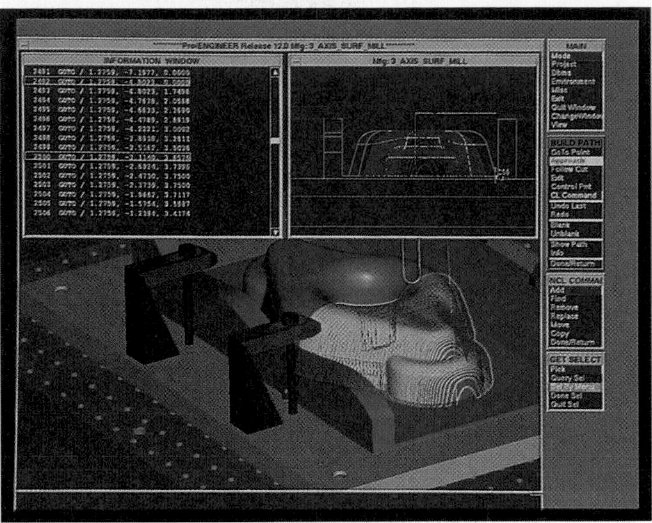

FIGURE 5.30 Part, Fixture, and NC Program

5.8.1 Design Model

The Pro/ENGINEER **design model**, representing the finished product, is the basis for all engineering (Fig. 5.31) and manufacturing (Fig. 5.32) operations. Features, surfaces, and edges are selected on the design model as references for each manufacturing operation (Fig. 5.33). Referencing the geometry of the design model sets up a parametric relationship between the design model and the workpiece. Because of this relationship, when the design model is changed, all associated manufacturing operations are updated to reflect the change. Parts, assemblies, and sheet metal parts may be used as design models.

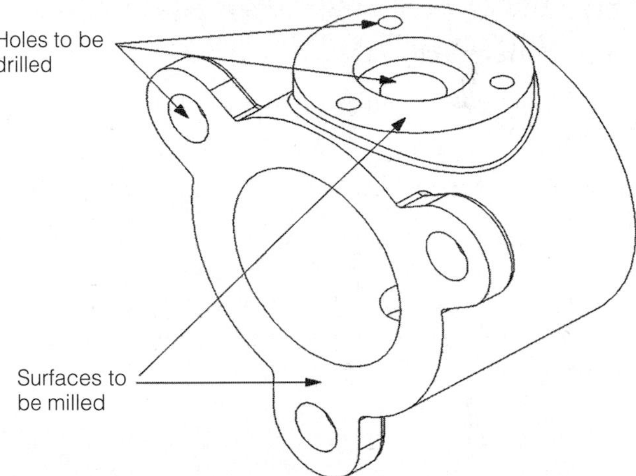

FIGURE 5.32 The Design Model—A Valve Housing

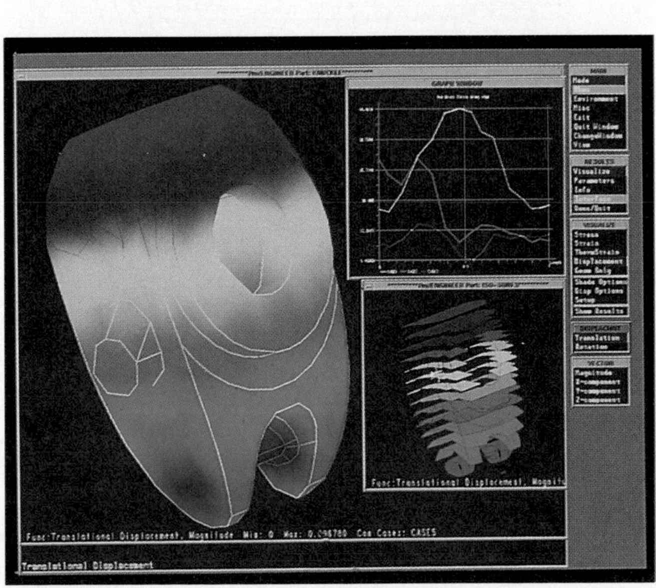

FIGURE 5.31 Engineering Analysis and the Design Model

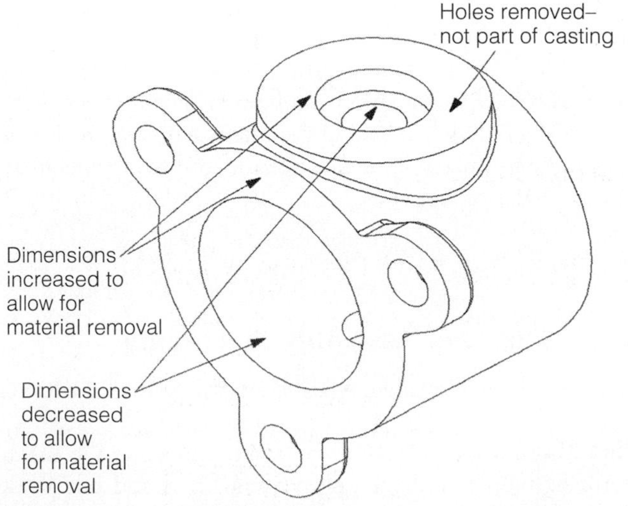

FIGURE 5.33 The Workpiece—A Casting

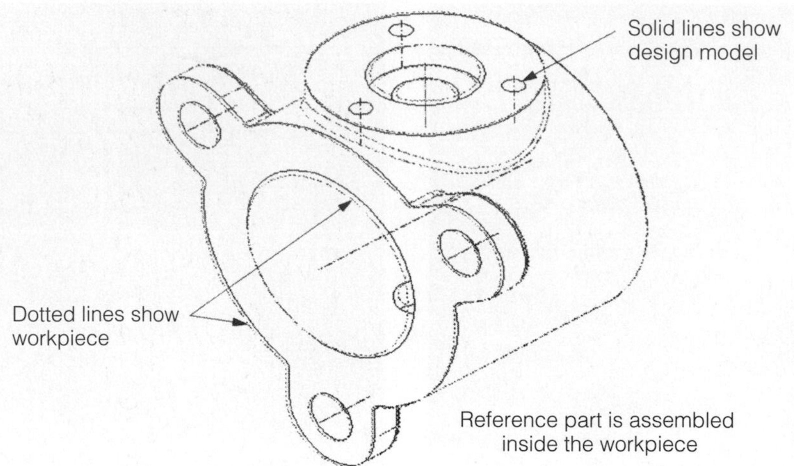
Solid lines show
design model
Dotted lines show
workpiece
Reference part is assembled
inside the workpiece

FIGURE 5.34 The Manufacturing Assembly

5.8.2 Workpiece

The **workpiece** represents the raw stock that is going to be machined by the manufacturing operations. The workpiece can represent any form of raw stock: bar stock, a casting (Fig. 5.33), etc. It may easily be created by copying the design model and modifying the dimensions or deleting/suppressing features to represent the real workpiece. As a part model, the workpiece can be manipulated as any other; it can exist as an instance of a part family table; it can be modified, redefined, etc.

5.8.3 Manufacturing Model

A regular **manufacturing model** consists of a *design model* (also called "reference part" since it is used as reference for creating NC sequences) and a *workpiece* assembled together (Fig. 5.34). As the manufacturing process is developed, the material removal simulation can be performed on the workpiece. Generally, at the end of the manufacturing process the workpiece geometry should be coincident with the geometry of the design model.

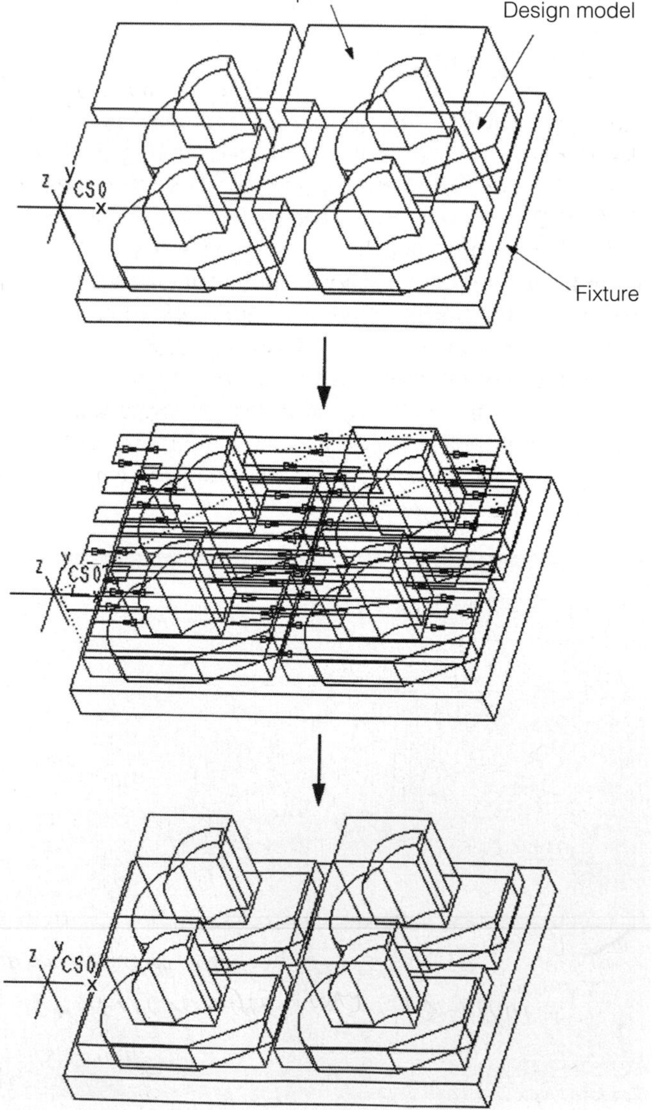
Workpiece
Design model
Fixture
CS0

FIGURE 5.35 Machining Multiple Workpieces

5.8.4 Part and Assembly Machining

These are the two separate types of **Pro/MANUFACTURING.**

Part Machining. Acts on the assumption that the manufacturing model contains one reference part and one workpiece (also a part). Multipart manufacturing (Fig. 5.35) allows you to assemble multiple design models and workpieces, but they are automatically merged upon assembly so that the manufacturing model still consists of one reference part and one workpiece.

Assembly Machining. No assumptions are made by the system as to the manufacturing model configuration. The manufacturing model can be an assembly of any level of complexity (with subassemblies, etc.), and can contain any number of independent workpiece and/or reference models. It can also contain other components that may be part of the manufacturing assembly but have no direct effect on the actual material removal process (i.e., the turntable, clamp, etc.).

Once the manufacturing model [Fig. 5.36(a)] is created, part and assembly machining use similar techniques to develop the manufacturing process [Fig. 36(b)]. The major difference between part and assembly machining is that in part machining all the components of the manufacturing process(operations, workcells, NC sequence, etc.) are *part features that belong to the workpiece,* while in assembly machining these are *assembly features that belong to the manufacturing assembly* (Fig. 5.36(c)].

Besides machining, a variety of other manufacturing processes can be accomplished with help of the original design model database. Die design (Fig. 5.37), mold design (Fig. 5.38), and casting design (Fig. 5.39) are all available on Pro/ENGINEER, along with many other high-level systems.

While working through the various chapters of this text, try to keep in mind the capabilities of parametric design and how they differ from traditional manual drafting and design and from traditional CAD/CAM systems. However, regardless of the system, method, or level of sophistication of the design and engineering process, the knowledge contained in the chapters covering dimensioning, springs, fasteners, gears, and other standard engineering and design applications will remain important to learn.

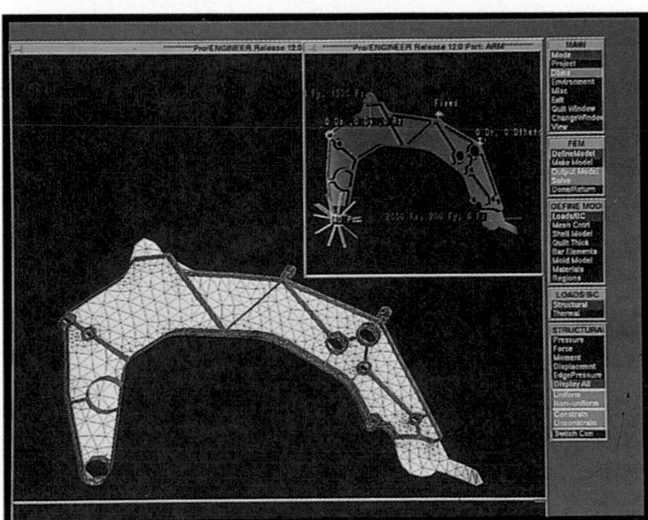

FIGURE 5.36(a) Manufacturing Model

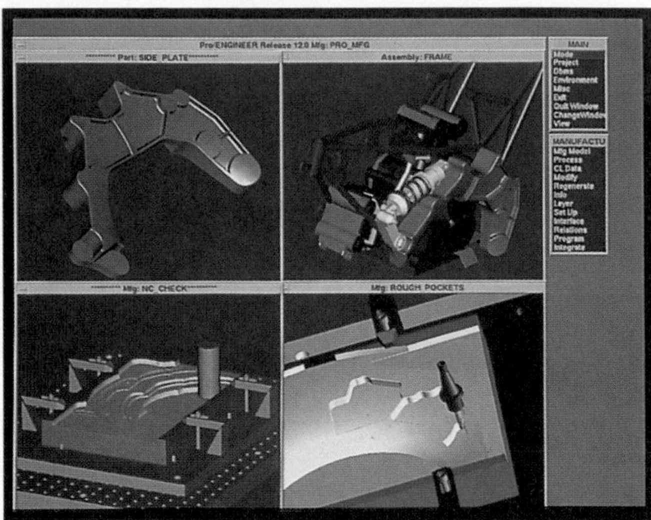

FIGURE 5.36(b) Manufacturing Processes

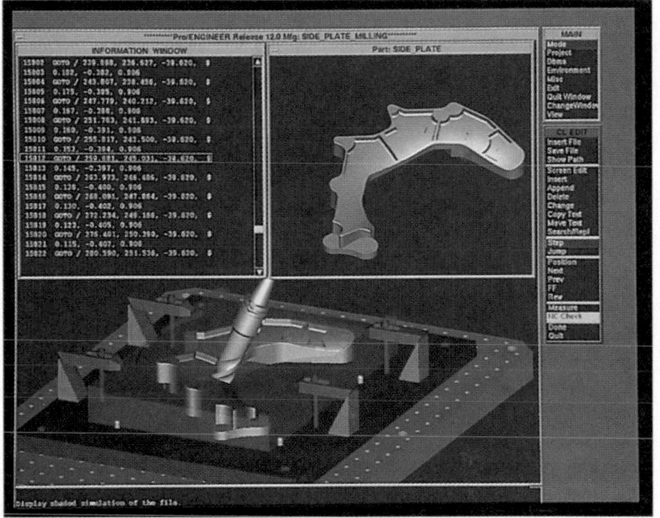

FIGURE 5.36(c) Manufacturing Assembly

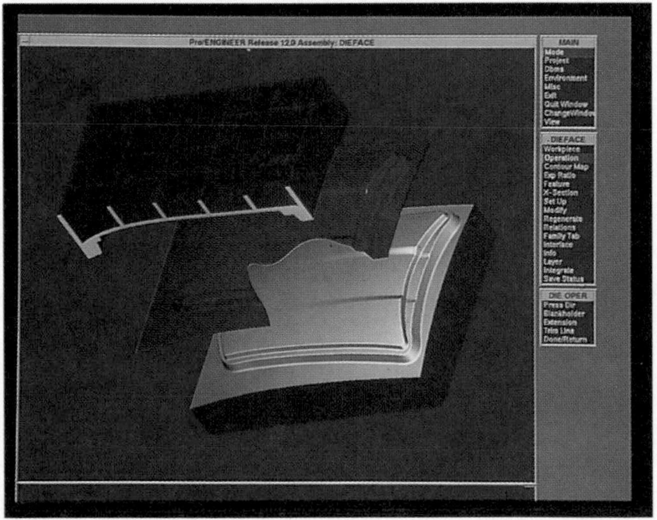

FIGURE 5.37 Pro/DIEDESIGN

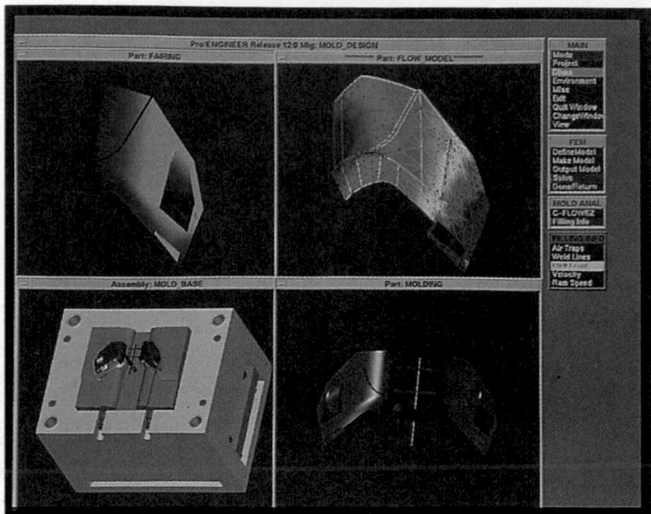

FIGURE 5.38 Pro/MOLDESIGN

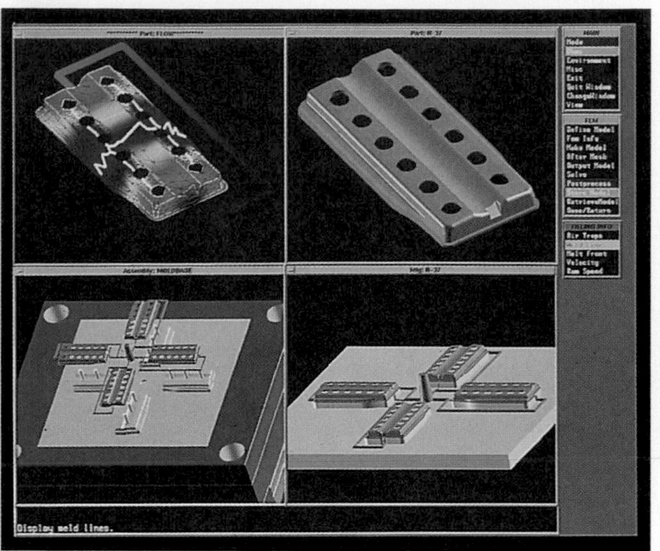

FIGURE 5.39 Pro/CASTING

QUIZ

True or False

1. Parametric design starts with the creation of drawings that represent the 3D shape of the part and proceeds toward a manufacturing 3D model.
2. Sketching in parametric design is very similar to sketching on paper.
3. Extrusions, revolved protrusions, and sketched outlines of parts are just three of many "pick and place" geometry items available with parametric modeling.
4. *Collinearity* describes a situation in which two outlines are exactly the same, because they are divided by a centerline shared by both.
5. Any arcs and circles sketched with nearly the same radius have the exact same radius.
6. The design model represents the finished product and serves as the basis for all engineering and manufacturing operations.
7. Parametric modeling is the capturing of design operations as they take place, as well as future modifying and editing that take place on the design.
8. *Feature-based modeling* refers to the construction of geometries as a combination of form features.

Fill in the Blanks

9. ______ ______ are used to create a reference on a part where one does not already exist.
10. ______ features are created by extruding, revolving, blending, or sweeping a cross section.
11. The design of any part requires that the part be ______, ______, constrained, and ______.
12. There are three types of datum features: ______ ______, ______ ______, and ______ ______.
13. ______ ______ allows you to assemble multiple design models, and workpieces are automatically merged upon ______ so that the manufacturing model still consists of one reference part and one workpiece.
14. ______ can also be generated from the part or ______.
15. The ______ ______ can be an assembly of any level of complexity and can contain any number of independent workpiece and reference models.
16. ______-______ relationships are an important factor in parametric modeling.

Answer the Following

17. Give the primary reasons for using solid models.
18. What are *referenced features* in parametric modeling?
19. Explain what is meant by a *workpiece*.
20. Discuss in your own words *parent–child* relationships.
21. What does *capturing design intent* mean in parametric modeling?
22. Define *drawing parameters*.
23. What is *feature-based modeling?*

Part Two

BASIC GRAPHICAL MATERIALS AND PROCEDURES

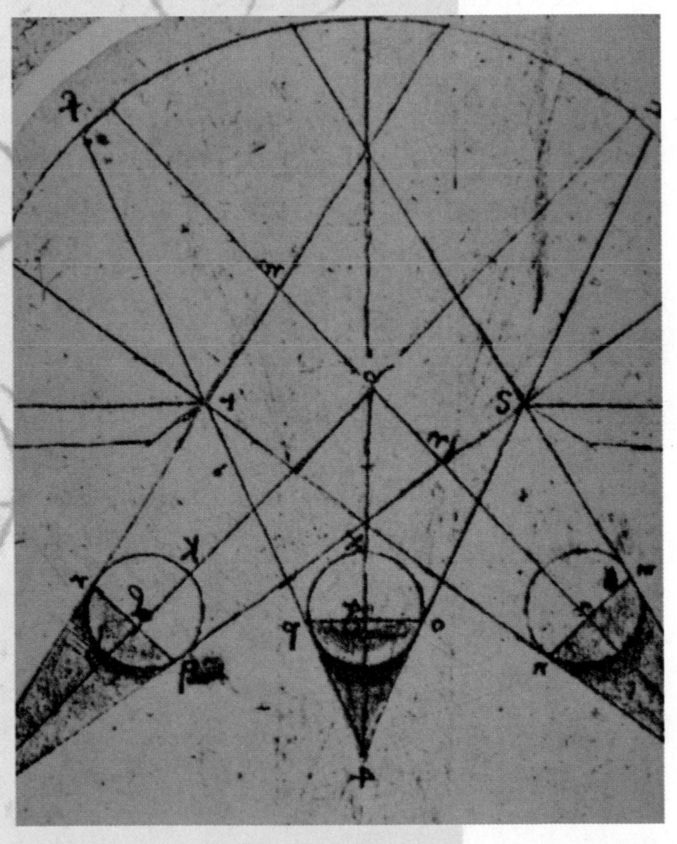

EQUIPMENT, MATERIALS, AND TECHNIQUES FOR ENGINEERING GRAPHICS

Chapter 6

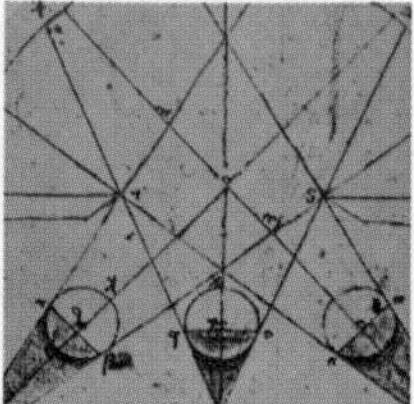

LEARNING OBJECTIVES

Upon completion of this chapter you will be able to:

1. Identify equipment and general drafting tools used in technical drawing.
2. Produce drawings with a variety of drafting instruments.
3. Exhibit knowledge of engineering drawing media and standard drawing formats.
4. Develop the ability to produce ANSI standard line types while recognizing preferred line precedence.
5. Master techniques for drawing construction and printable lines and curves.
6. Use triangles to draw a number of standard angles.
7. Understand the types of scales used on engineering drawings.

6.1 INTRODUCTION

Engineering drawing tools (Fig. 6.1) are used in all fields of engineering and design. Although CAD systems are found increasingly in industry, traditional (manual) drawing techniques and tools are still employed and will continue to be so for the foreseeable future. Therefore, as an aspiring designer or engineer, you must understand these procedures thoroughly and be familiar with drawing tools and techniques. Every engineering office uses—with varying degrees of sophistication—the equipment described in this chapter. The simple lead holder and the complex electronic pen are both important in the design process and share the same purpose.

This chapter covers equipment, instruments, materials, and drawing techniques used in the engineering office. **Equipment** includes drawing boards, drafting machines, print machines, T-squares, triangles, templates, and computer-aided design hardware. **Instruments** are precision-manufactured drawing tools, such as the compass and dividers, in all their variations. **Materials** comprise drawing media (vellum and drafting film) and related support items, such as grid underlays, preprinted title blocks, transfer drafting aids, and print paper.

Techniques are the methods used by the drafter to complete a drawing; they are covered at the end of this chapter. This chapter's primary focus is on equipment and tools and on the methods and techniques of creating a drawing manually. Engineers and designers must know how to use their equipment, instruments, and materials to communicate effectively. The originator and the reader of an

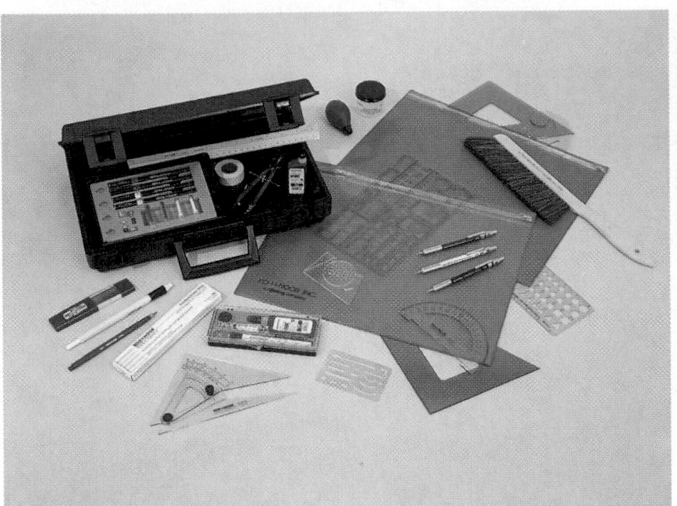

FIGURE 6.1 Drafting Tools

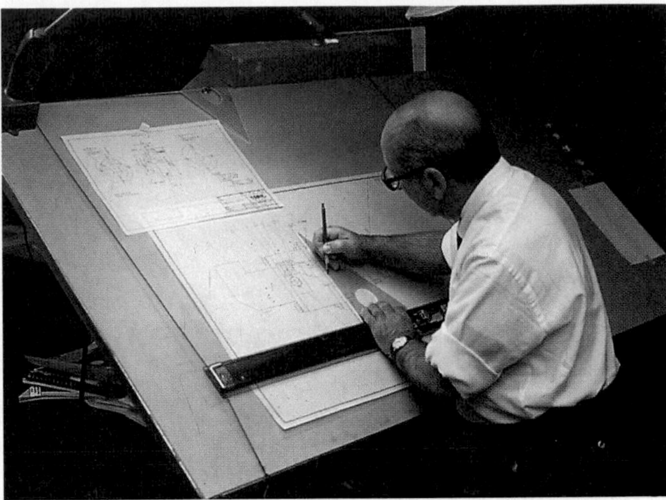

FIGURE 6.2 Drafting Table with Parallel Bar

engineering drawing must understand the procedures, conventions, and concepts used in the drawing. In all fields of engineering drawing and design, symbols, linework, projection procedures, and notation must be in accordance with standard conventions.

6.2 EQUIPMENT

The most important and conspicuous piece of equipment in any engineering office is the **drafting table.** Originally, all engineering drawing was done on flat-surfaced wood drawing boards. Normally, one or more edges were cut as straight and square as possible, creating a "straightedge" that the drafter could use to guide a T-square. Today, board sizes range from hand-carried versions to large-format standalone tables. The table in Figure 6.2 is vertically adjustable and can be tilted to any comfortable angle. Modern tables may be power operated. Whatever the drafting table's size or material, the table surface must have a pliable cover. This can be Borco vinyl (or linoleum) or some other plastic or vinyl covering that permits drafting without destroying the table surface or marring the drawing medium.

Light tables are also used throughout industry to prepare printed circuit artwork, draw pictorial illustrations, and do tracing. Normally, the drawing surface is an opaque glass or plastic sheet that scatters the rays from the light source. Figure 6.3 shows a modern light table and reference desk. Here the tabletop and the light mechanism are an integral part of the drawing surface.

6.2.1 Storage and Reproduction Equipment

After a project is drawn, regardless of the method, it must be stored and reproduced. Frequently, drawings are stored as paper originals and prints in multiple-drawer cabinets and in tube storage systems. Because drawings must be cataloged and available for several departments, this method of storage is time-consuming and requires considerable office space, but it is still widely used.

FIGURE 6.3 Light Table Used for Electronic Circuit Layout

Drawings can also be stored on **microfilm** and **microfiche.** Computer graphics systems enable the user to reproduce, almost instantaneously, design data stored on disk or tape. Another form of reprographics uses 35-mm micrographic **aperture cards** or **design data cards** (Fig. 6.4). Design data systems are used with manually produced drawings or with CAD drawings. When a new or revised drawing is checked and ready for release, it is taken to a processor camera (Fig. 6.5). In seconds, a master data card (an accurately reduced version of the original drawing) is produced. Multiple copies of the data card are then made from the original, for distribution. You can review the drawing with a display device.

Aperture data cards enable the user to make prints quickly, with several reductions and enlargement options. The copier shown in Figure 6.4 can copy a drawing on various kinds of paper and instantly switch enlargement sizes. The copy paper is manually fed into the front of the copier, and the viewing screen allows easy monitoring.

FIGURE 6.4 Aperture Card Drawing Reproduction System

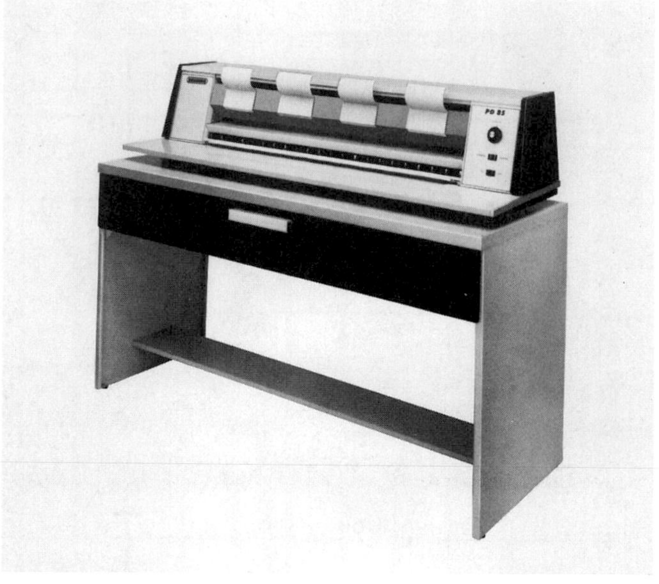

FIGURE 6.6 Whiteprinter

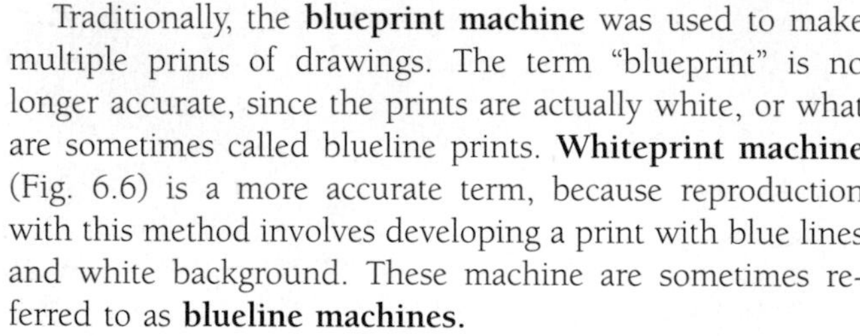

Traditionally, the **blueprint machine** was used to make multiple prints of drawings. The term "blueprint" is no longer accurate, since the prints are actually white, or what are sometimes called blueline prints. **Whiteprint machine** (Fig. 6.6) is a more accurate term, because reproduction with this method involves developing a print with blue lines and white background. These machine are sometimes referred to as **blueline machines.**

When a drawing is completed on a CAD system, it is reproduced with a hard-copy device such as a photocopier or a plotter. The pen plotting method allows the reproduction of an accurate original every time the drawing is plotted. Multiple copies can then be made from a whiteprinter or from input to a data card system.

6.2.2 Straightedges

Originally, the primary horizontal straightedge device used in engineering drawing was the **T-square** (Fig. 6.7). This piece of equipment is still found in a few classrooms and for personal drafting. Because the T-square is the most difficult to manage of all straightedge drawing devices, it is said that "if you can draw with a T-square you can draw with anything." If you must learn by using a T-square, you will be glad to know that once you master it, other straightedges will be easier. Wielding a T-square is difficult because it is the easiest to misalign of all straightedge devices. The bar portion of the T is placed along the edge of a drawing board or table. Parallel horizontal lines are drawn with the length

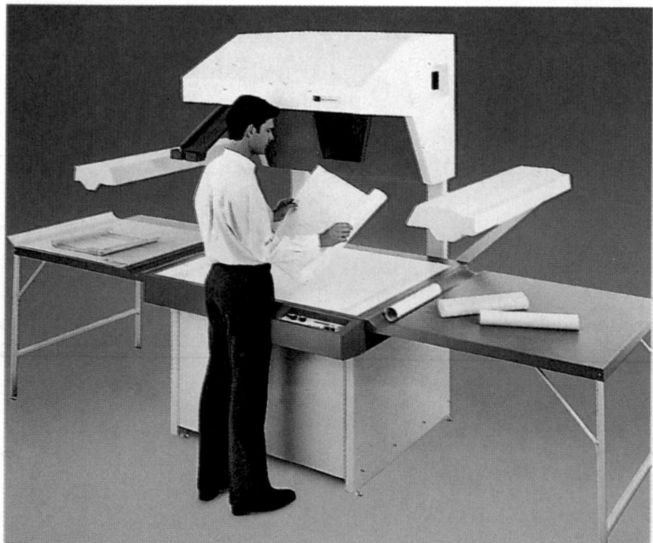

FIGURE 6.5 Microfilm Processor Camera

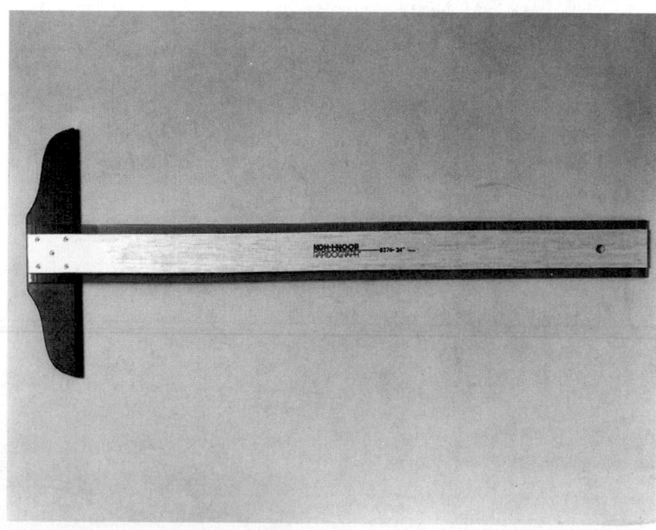

FIGURE 6.7 T-square

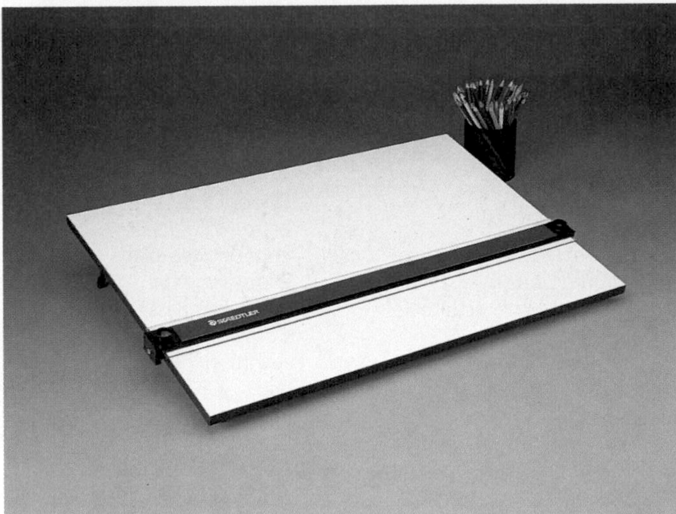

FIGURE 6.8 A Parallel Straightedge

of the T-square, and parallel vertical lines are drawn with a triangle placed against the top edge of the horizontal bar. Obviously, if the T-square and the table edge are not aligned properly, your linework will be inconsistent.

The **parallel straightedge** (Fig. 6.8) is found throughout industry, especially for large drawings such as those required in architecture, piping design, and civil-mapping engineering. The parallel straightedge is attached to the drawing table by a series of cables and pulleys. It remains parallel or at a preset angle to the drawing table as it is moved up or down on the table surface. Parallel straightedges are excellent tools when the drawing consists of long, straight, parallel horizontal lines.

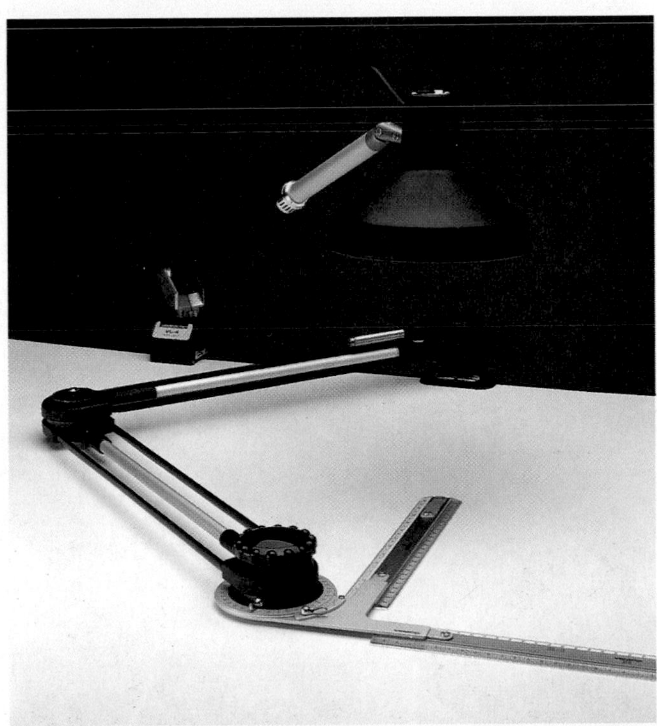

FIGURE 6.9 Arm Drafting Machine

FIGURE 6.10 A Drafter Using a Track Drafting Machine

The **drafting machine** comes in two standard versions: the drafting arm type (Fig. 6.9) and the track type (Fig. 6.10). The track type is the more accurate. Drafting machines are mounted on drawing tables, as shown in these figures. The control head on the drafting machine can be rotated to any angle and set by pushing a button to lock at increments of 15°. It must be hand-locked for intermediate angles. When using a drafting machine, or any straightedge, avoid dragging the equipment across the drawing.

Drafting machines (Fig. 6.11) take the place of triangles, protractors, and scales, but you must still know how to use all types of equipment and instruments.

Regardless of the type of drawing table and straightedge,

FIGURE 6.11 Drafting or Drawing with an Arm Drafting Machine

proper lighting is also essential for relaxed, unstrained work with manual drawing techniques. Since the CRT screen is easier to read if it is shaded from external light sources, lighting requirements are different when using a CAD system.

6.3 GENERAL ENGINEERING DRAWING TOOLS

Traditional manual engineering drawing requires a variety of small tools, instruments, and equipment (Fig. 6.1), for example, special templates, triangles, pencils, lead holders, and technical inking pens. The quality of your engineering drawing is directly influenced by the range and quality of your tools and equipment. This is not to say that expensive, high-quality tools, by themselves, will draw the project. But good-quality tools are beneficial for fast, efficient, and precise linework and projection.

Engineering drawing kits are available from a variety of reputable companies that are sufficient for most classes in engineering drawing. However, precision, high-quality tools and instruments can be purchased individually. Table 6.1 lists standard engineering drawing tools you can buy. Essential items are distinguished from optional items, which can be added as needed.

TABLE 6.1 Equipment

Essential Items	Optional Items
Pencils (grades 4H, 3H, 2H, H, HB)	Lead holders
Sandpaper block	Thin-line pencil
Erasers	Electric eraser
Dusting pad or powder	Adjustable triangle
Erasing shield	Symbol templates
Drafting tape	Lettering guide
Drafting brush	Lettering template
Scales (metric, architect, mechanical, civil)	Drop compass
Protractor	Beam compass
30°/60° triangle	Compass inking attachment
45° triangle	Technical inking pens
Irregular curves	Ink
Templates (circle and ellipse)	Ink eraser
Bow compass	Lettering set
Dividers	Grid paper
Drafting board	Drafting table
Straightedge (T-square, parallel straightedge)	Flexible curve
Calculator	Drafting machine
Paper (vellum, drawing film)	

6.3.1 Pencil Leads and Pencils

Drawing **pencils** are graded by the hardness of their lead. The hardness of the lead determines the kind of line that can be drawn. A hard lead can make a very sharp, thin line, but it will lack the darkness and density necessary to make a good print. A soft lead will make dark lines, but it is very difficult to keep sharp. "H" lead grades are used for engineering drawing on vellum. The "H" grades are, from hardest to softest: 9H, 8H, 7H, 6H, 5H, 4H, 3H, 2H, H, F, and HB (Fig. 6.12). The recommended hardness for lead used on vinyl-topped engineering drawing boards with a good grade of paper are:

- 6H–3H for layout and construction lines
- H–HB for reproducible (printable) lines
- H–HB for lettering

The appropriate hardness of lead, combined with proper drawing techniques, will help produce good, reproducible drawings with sharp, dense lines that make good prints. The skills required to use engineering drawing tools and equipment comes only through practice. Engineering drawing is a skill that must be cultivated throughout your career, not just in school.

Engineering drawing pencils are made in three types: the

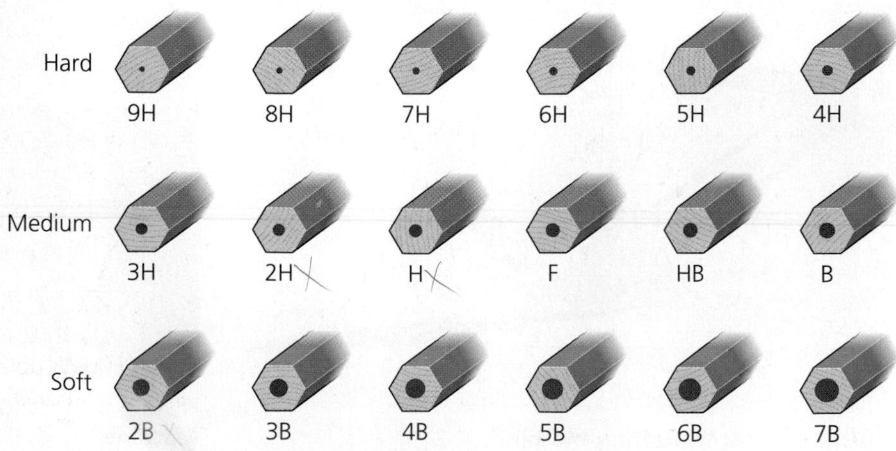

FIGURE 6.12 Pencil Lead Types

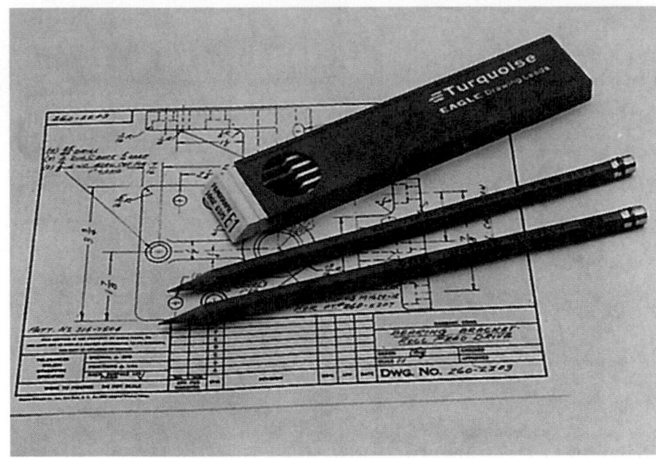

FIGURE 6.13 Drawing Pencils and Leads

familiar **wood pencil** (Fig. 6.13), the **mechanical lead holder,** which uses engineering drawing leads, and the **fine-line mechanical pencil.**

The mechanical lead holder holds a single piece of lead (Fig. 6.14). Having more than one lead holder available with a variety of leads makes it easy to change line weights and types. This drawing tool is easily sharpened, and increases the speed, consistency, and ease of engineering drawing. The mechanical pencil allows the length of exposed lead to be adjusted, both for sharpening and for drawing, without decreasing the length of the holder, which is what happens when sharpening a wood pencil.

The automatic drawing pencil (fine-line pencil) is excellent for drawing lines and letters of consistent width. It never requires sharpening. Automatic drawing pencils come in metric sizes: 0.3, 0.5, 0.7, and 0.9 mm (Fig. 6.15). These sizes are used to draw the typical line weights, 0.25–0.35 mm (centerlines, dimension lines, construction lines), 0.5–0.7 mm (object lines, diagram lines, hidden lines), and 0.7–0.9 mm (cutting plane lines, border lines). Unlike the mechanical engineering drawing pencil, the fine-line pencil holds only one thickness of lead, so you must purchase a number of them. Of course, if you are using a small-width fine-line pencil, you can make the line any width desired by thickening the line. The thinner the lead, however, the more frequently it breaks. Fine-line pencils are sometimes difficult to use with lettering guides and templates.

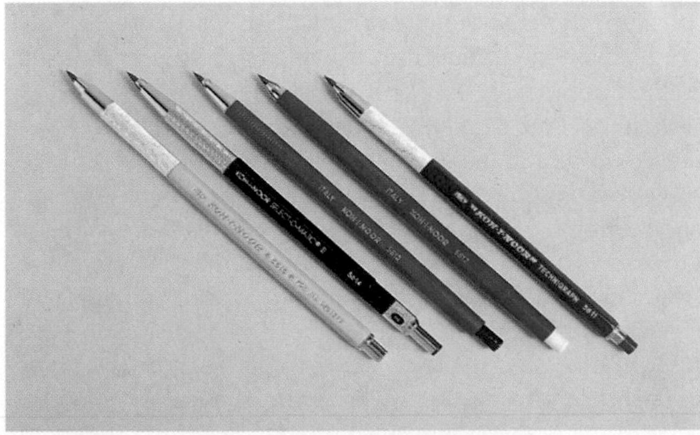

FIGURE 6.14 Mechanical Lead Holders

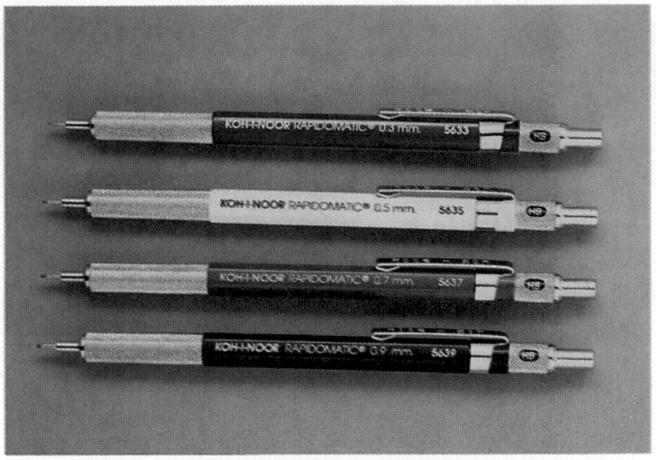

FIGURE 6.15 Fine-Line Mechanical Pencils

Regardless of which type of drawing pencil you choose, purchase a variety of leads (Fig. 6.12). Standard leads for vellum range from soft and dark (6B, 5B, 4B, 2B, B, HB, and F) to the medium hard and dark (H, 2H, 3H). The hardest and lightest types are 4H, 5H, 6H, 7H, 8H, and 9H. In general, only the medium leads are used: 2H and 3H for construction lines and blocking in a drawing, H for darkened finished lines. Some drafters prefer HB for finished lines (printable), but great care must be taken to ensure that the drawing is kept clean and unsmudged. To attain a good-quality reproduction, all lines must block light if a whiteprint machine is used, and they must be dark, crisp, and thick enough to be recorded by a camera if a photocopier or an aperture card machine is used. Plastic leads are employed on drawing film. Plastic leads come in three grades: E1, K, and CF.

6.3.2 Pencil Sharpeners/Pointers

Mechanical lead holders and wood pencils require frequent sharpening or pointing. A sharp conical point is needed to make the thin erasable lines required for construction lines. With the lead holder, the lead is sharpened with a pencil pointer that sharpens only the lead; the wood pencil must have the wood cut away before it is sharpened with a engineering drawing pencil sharpener or a knife (Fig. 6.16).

For darkened finished linework, the pencil point is dulled slightly on scrap paper to avoid frequent breaking and for drawing wide lines. *To maintain the line thickness, the pencil or lead holder should be rotated as the line is drawn.* A sharpened, then slightly dulled lead point is required for lettering. The advantage of a fine-line pencil is that the lead never needs sharpening.

The **pencil pointer** sharpens by cutting away only the lead, and produces a uniform conical shape with a rather long taper. The taper should be three to four times the

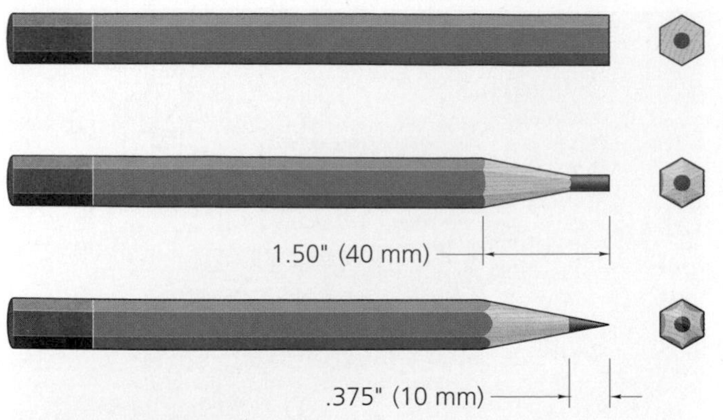

FIGURE 6.16 Sharpening Wood Pencils

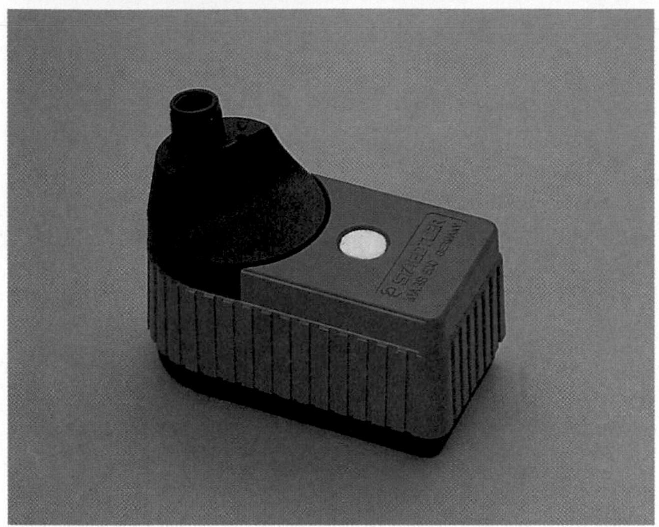

FIGURE 6.17 Mechanical Pencil Sharpener

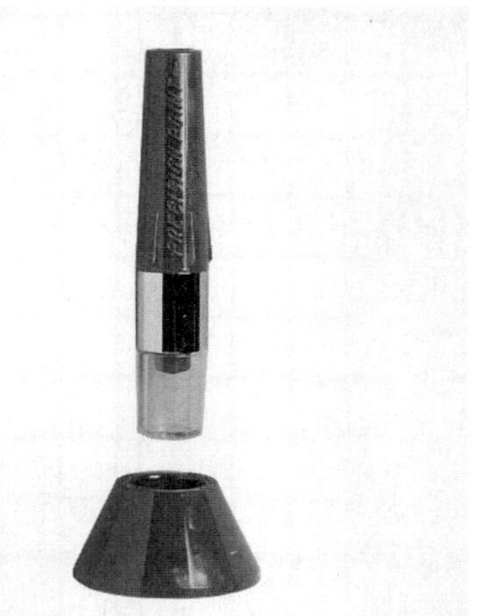

FIGURE 6.18 Sharpener

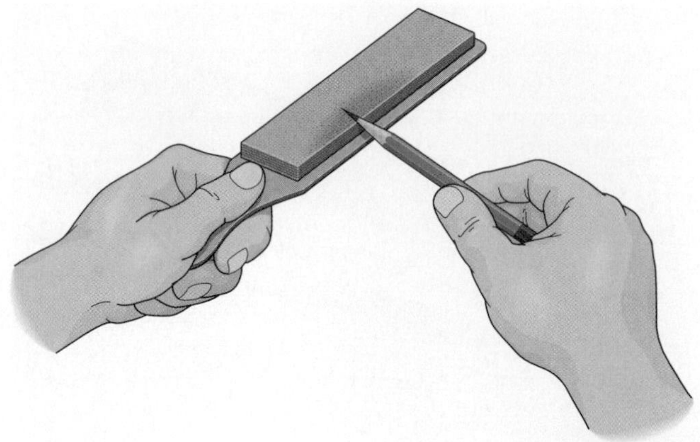

FIGURE 6.19 Sharpening a Pencil with a Sandpaper Block

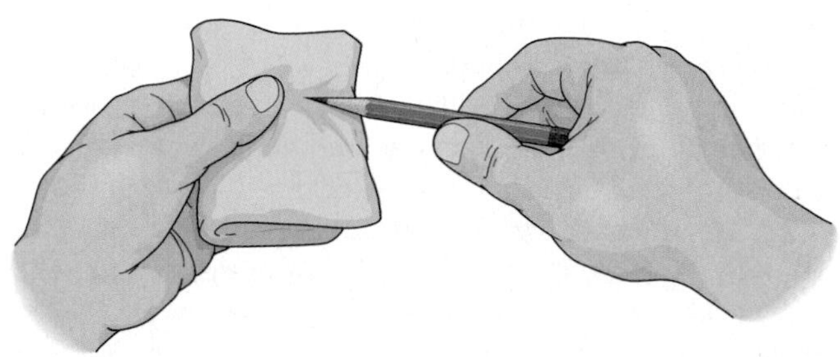

FIGURE 6.20 Cleaning a Pencil Tip

diameter of the lead. Several good pointers are available that use a ribbed cylindrical metal cutter. Depending on the type of pointer, the pencil or lead holder is put into a hole in the cover and rotated around the cutter (Fig. 6.17). Figure 6.18 shows an inexpensive hand-held pointer for mechanical lead holders.

Another sharpening device for wood pencils and lead holders is the **sandpaper pad/block.** The pencil or lead holder is rotated as the point is sanded (Fig. 6.19). A sandpaper pad can also sharpen lead points on compasses. Compass leads are sharpened as wedge shapes instead of conical points in order to keep the edge sharper longer. After sanding the lead, wipe it clean with a soft cloth or tissue (Fig. 6.20).

6.3.3 Erasers and Erasing Shields

Erasing is a necessary part of engineering drawing and, when done properly, enables you to improve and correct drawings easily (Fig. 6.21). The **eraser** should have good "pick-up" power without smudging. Eraser selection is based primarily on the engineering drawing medium you are using (vellum, film, etc.).

Erasers come in many shapes and sizes, from hand-held to electric, and in many grades. Pink Pearl, white composite, and Art Gum erasers are used for both paper (vellum) and engineering drawing film. Special vinyl erasers are available for erasing inked drawings on engineering drawing film. Note that ink is extremely hard to erase on paper. An **electric eraser** (Fig. 6.22) is essential in this situation, but great care is required to avoid rubbing holes in the paper. Care should also be taken when using an electric eraser on engineering drawing film since it tends to destroy the tooth, or surface, of the engineering drawing film. To erase ink drawings completed on film, apply a small amount of

FIGURE 6.21 Erasing

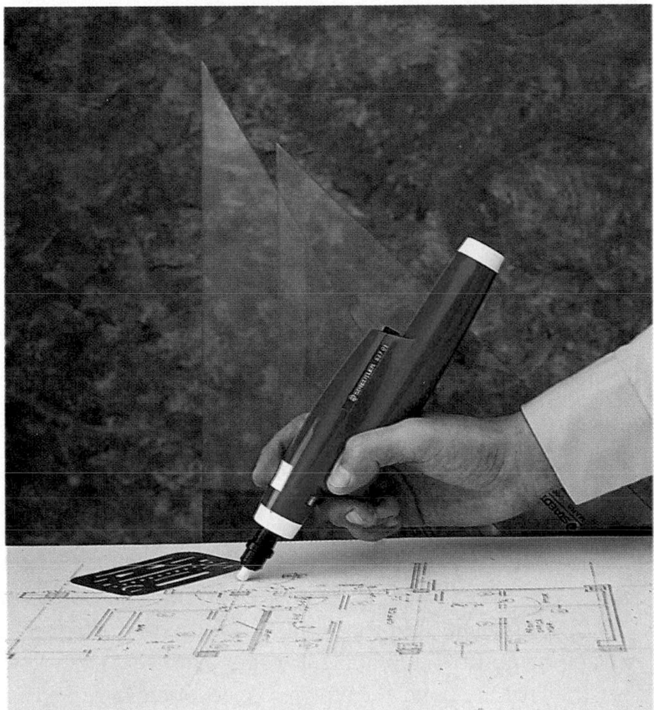

FIGURE 6.22 Electric Eraser

FIGURE 6.23 Erasing Shield

moisture to a vinyl eraser and carefully rub the area to be erased.

To protect adjacent areas of the drawing that are to remain, most erasing is done through the perforations of a stainless steel erasing shield (Fig. 6.23). The **erasing shield** is held firmly in place on the drawing with one hand while the other hand erases through a selected opening (Fig. 6.24). Care must be taken not to erase other areas through adjacent openings.

Eraser crumbs should immediately be swept from the drawing with the engineering **drawing brush** (Fig. 6.25). The crumbs should not be rubbed with the hand—each graphite-laden crumb will act as a dull pencil and make smudges. Figure 6.26 shows an engineering drawing and a brush.

A dry cleaning pad (an erasing dust pad) is another way to keep drawings clean and unsmudged. **Dry cleaning**

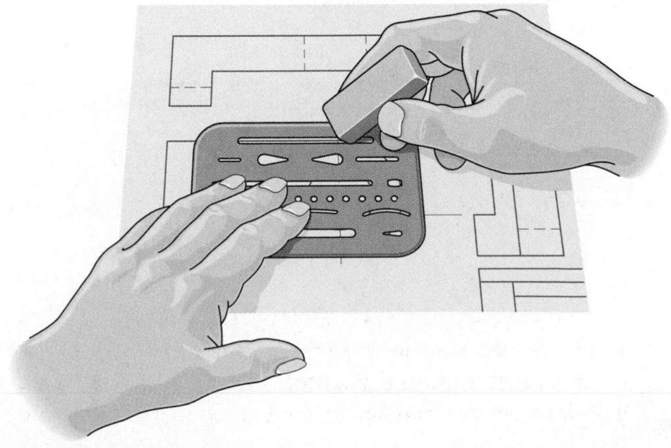

FIGURE 6.24 Using an Erasing Shield

FIGURE 6.25 Brushing the Drawing

FIGURE 6.26 Drafting Brush

pads, which contain finely ground eraser pieces and powder, can remove dirt and leftover crumbled graphite deposited during drawing and lettering. Do not drag a dry cleaning pad across the drawing. Instead, after a small portion of the drawing is complete, lightly pat the linework and lettering. Then, with a brush, sweep the drawing clean of powder and dirt. Although you must be careful not to lighten the lines and lettering too much by rubbing, frequent patting and dusting ensure a higher-quality drawing. Never use a dry cleaning pad when inking with technical pens. Some designers cover the entire drawing with a very light layer of erasing powder; others find this method messy and uncomfortable. Try different methods in order to discover which works best for you.

6.4 DRAWING SCALES

All instrument drawings are drawn accurately at one size, which may be a reduced or an enlarged size, so that all features of the part are in proportion. Such a drawing is said to be drawn *"to scale."* Some mechanical drawings are drawn to a reduced size, and some are drawn to an enlarged size. CAD drawings are drawn 1:1 (full size) and plotted at any convenient size or scale. Table 6.2 compares the four basic scales.

Since construction projects—piping, structural, architecture, and civil—are large and the paper size is small, all of these drawings are done at a reduced scale. Some mechanical drawings are also drawn to a reduced size. The instrument used to measure and layout these drawings is called a **scale** (not a ruler—a ruler makes only full-size measurements).

Certain scales are used in construction work: the civil engineer's scale, the architect's scale, and the metric scale for

TABLE 6.2 Scales

Architect's Scale	Mechanical Engineer's Scale	Civil Engineer's Scale	Metric Scale
$\frac{3}{32}$	1 in. = 1 in. (full size)	10 divisions/unit	1:10
$\frac{1}{8}$	$\frac{1}{2}$ in. = 1 in. ($\frac{1}{2}$ size)	20 divisions/unit	1:20
$\frac{3}{16}$	$\frac{1}{4}$ in. = 1 in. ($\frac{1}{4}$ size)	30 divisions/unit	1:25
$\frac{1}{4}$	$\frac{1}{8}$ in. = 1 in. ($\frac{1}{8}$ size)	40 divisions/unit	1:33.3
$\frac{1}{2}$		50 divisions/unit	1:50
1		60 divisions/unit	1:75
$1\frac{1}{2}$		80 divisions/unit	1:100
3			1:150

Focus On . . .

REPRODUCTION EQUIPMENT

You have probably heard the term *blueprint* to describe an engineering drawing. Blueprinting is a reproduction technique that was, for many years, the only way to duplicate engineering drawings. It is a photographic process in which the original drawing is the negative. The paper for the duplicate print is treated with chemicals that are sensitive to light. After the paper is exposed, it passes through a developing or fixing bath and is then rinsed and dried. The end product is a print (the same size) with blue background paper and white lines.

As more and more engineering drawings were created, it became evident that a new reproduction process that was fast, exact, cost effective, and simple was needed. Considering the number of hours invested in engineering drawings, it seems reasonable that people would also invest many hours trying to create the best reproduction process for those valuable drawings.

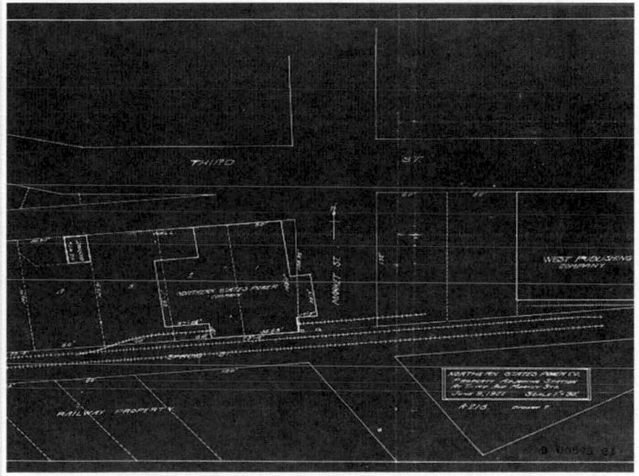

Early reproduction process (blueprint).

The *diazo process* was the answer. This process produces a positive print with dark lines on a white background. Light is transmitted through the original onto chemically treated paper. Developing is completed by one of three processes: dry (utilizing an ammonia vapor), moist (transferring an ammonia solution to the print), or pressure (a thin film of activator is deposited on the exposed paper). You can easily read marks and notations made directly on the print with this method. Unfortunately, the prints soil easily and the life of a print is relatively short.

The next evolution in reproduction equipment was developed from an idea that originated in 1937. In that year, a young law student named Chester Carlson developed a method called *xerography* to make copies. (The word *xerography* comes from the Greek words for "dry" and "writing.") A copy made by this method became known as a Xerox. No doubt you have also heard of Xerox, the company that developed and marketed this process throughout the world. Of course, it was only a matter of time until reproduction equipment was made large enough for copying drawings. This process can produce a copy not only from an original, but also from a copy. Enlarged or reduced-size copies are also possible.

Today, a copy of a computer-generated drawing can be produced with a laser printer/plotter. A laser plotter uses a laser to form areas of static charge to attract metallic powder to the paper. The process produces sharp, clear prints, is extremely fast, and is inexpensive enough to be used in small engineering offices. Laser printers have become an integral part of the engineering workplace.

When you walk into an engineering firm today, you could see a diazo print, a Xerox print, or a print produced with a laser plotter. Regardless of the method used to produce the print, many engineers, designers, and drafters ask for a "blueprint" of the latest product or assembly even though blue paper with white lines hasn't been around for many years.

Whatever the next evolution is in reproduction equipment, it will probably be faster, more accurate, easier to use, and more economical—just like all the other versions. Yet whatever process we use, we will probably call the print a "blueprint."

Sl projects. The engineer's scale is for drawing very large objects, for example, earthworks, roads, and surveys of property. The architect's scale is for drawing buildings and structures. Generally, the basic shape of each of these scales is either two-sided and flat or triangular (Fig. 6.27), and each is about twelve inches long. The triangular shape makes six surfaces available for the different-sized scales. Figure 6.28 shows the five most common types of scales.

The markings on scales are arranged in two ways: *fully divided* and *open divided.* Fully divided scales, throughout their length, have each main unit of measurement completely divided, like the familiar foot ruler, on which each inch is divided into sixteenths. The engineer's and the metric scale are normally fully divided. Open divided scales have

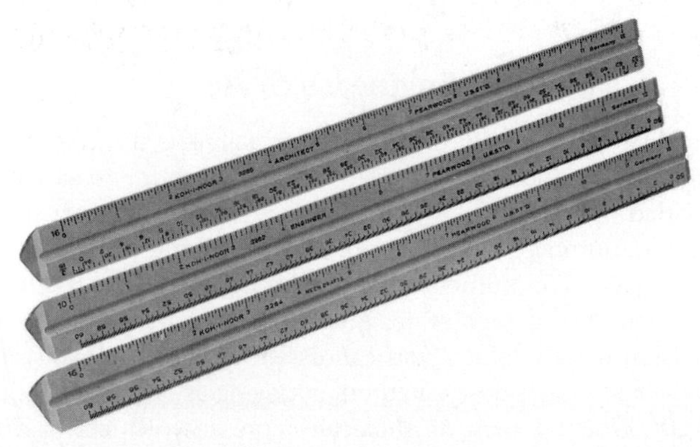

FIGURE 6.27 **Triangular and Flat Scales**

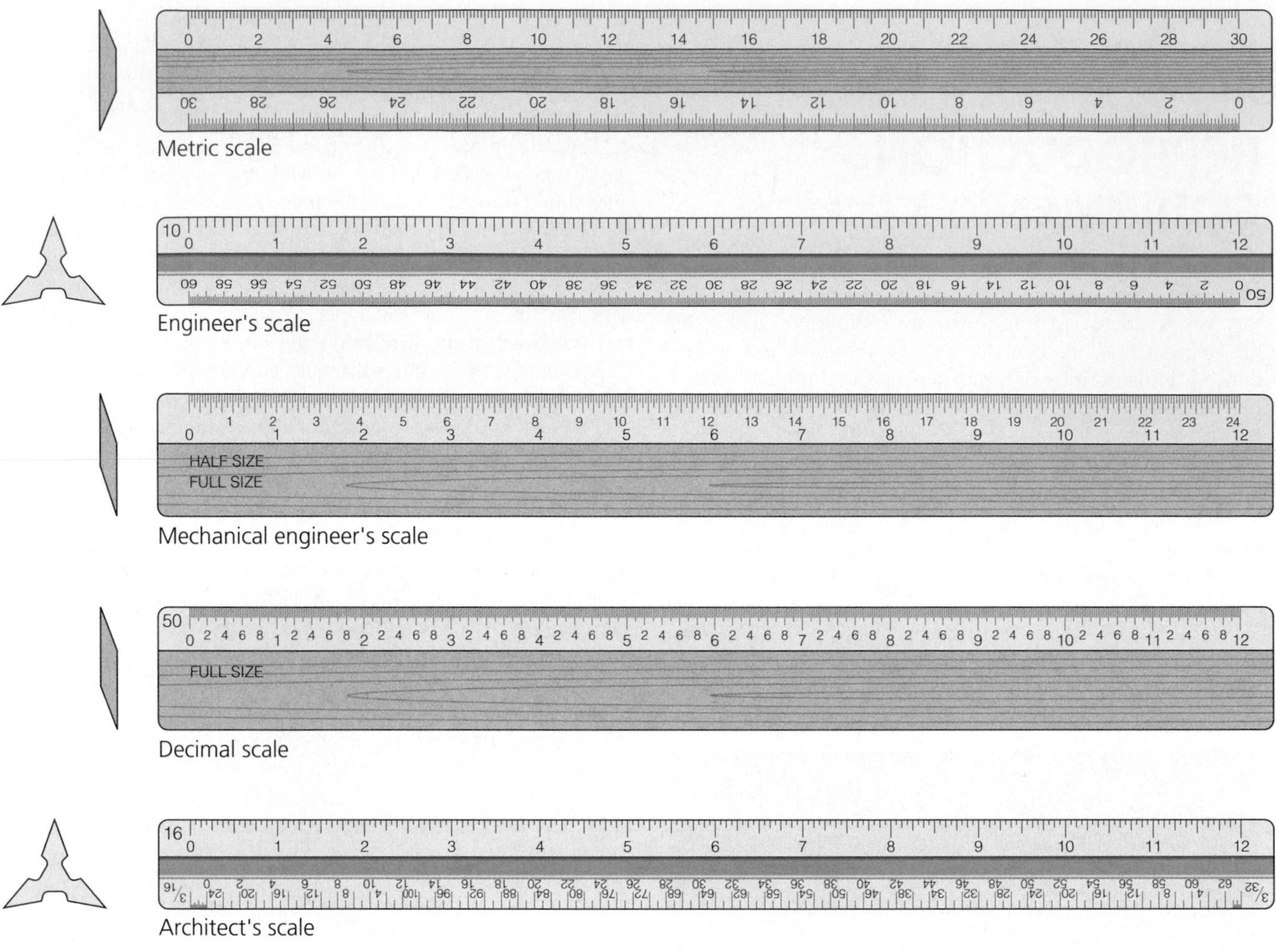

FIGURE 6.28 Five Types of Drawing Scales

each main unit of the scale undivided, except for a fully divided extra main unit at the zero end of the scale. The architect's scale is open divided.

The scale is a precision instrument and, with proper use, will produce consistent drawings. Remember, the scale is a measuring instrument, not a drawing instrument; do not draw on the edge of the scale (unless it is one of the two scales of the engineering drawing machine). Scales edges are not designed for drawing.

6.4.1 The Civil Engineer's Scale

The **engineer's scale** (triangular) normally has six scales that are fully divided. Three-sided civil engineering scales are divided into 10, 20, 30, 40, 50, and 60 divisions per inch and are numbered at each tenth division along the length of each scale. The number of divisions per inch is marked at the zero end of each scale. Although in normal usage each division equals 1 foot, you can assign any unit to the scale divisions. This is designated on a drawing as, for instance, 1″ = 20′, where 1 inch on the scale represents 20 feet of real size. This scale can also be used as a decimal scale, where, for example, 1″ = 2′ and each division represents one-tenth of a foot on the 20 scale, or 1″ = 200′ and each division represents 10 feet on the 20 scale. The other scales can be used similarly. Figure 6.29 shows measurements taken along the civil engineer's scale. Here, .50, 3.60, and 4.90 in. are shown measured on the full-size inch scale, which has increments of 10. These measurements could be in feet if the desired scale were 1″ = 1′.

6.4.2 The Architect's Scale

The **architect's scale** (Fig. 6.30) has a "foot ruler" full-size scale on one surface and ten different reduced-size open divided scales. The open divided scale uses only 1-foot units reading in one direction from the zero end, with a fully divided 1-foot unit reading in the opposite direction. Therefore, the number of feet is read along the length of the scale and the number of inches is read in the fully divided unit at the zero end of that same scale. Both numbers become larger with increasing distance from the zero end.

Each scale is identified by a number or a fraction at its zero end. This number does not represent a proportion of

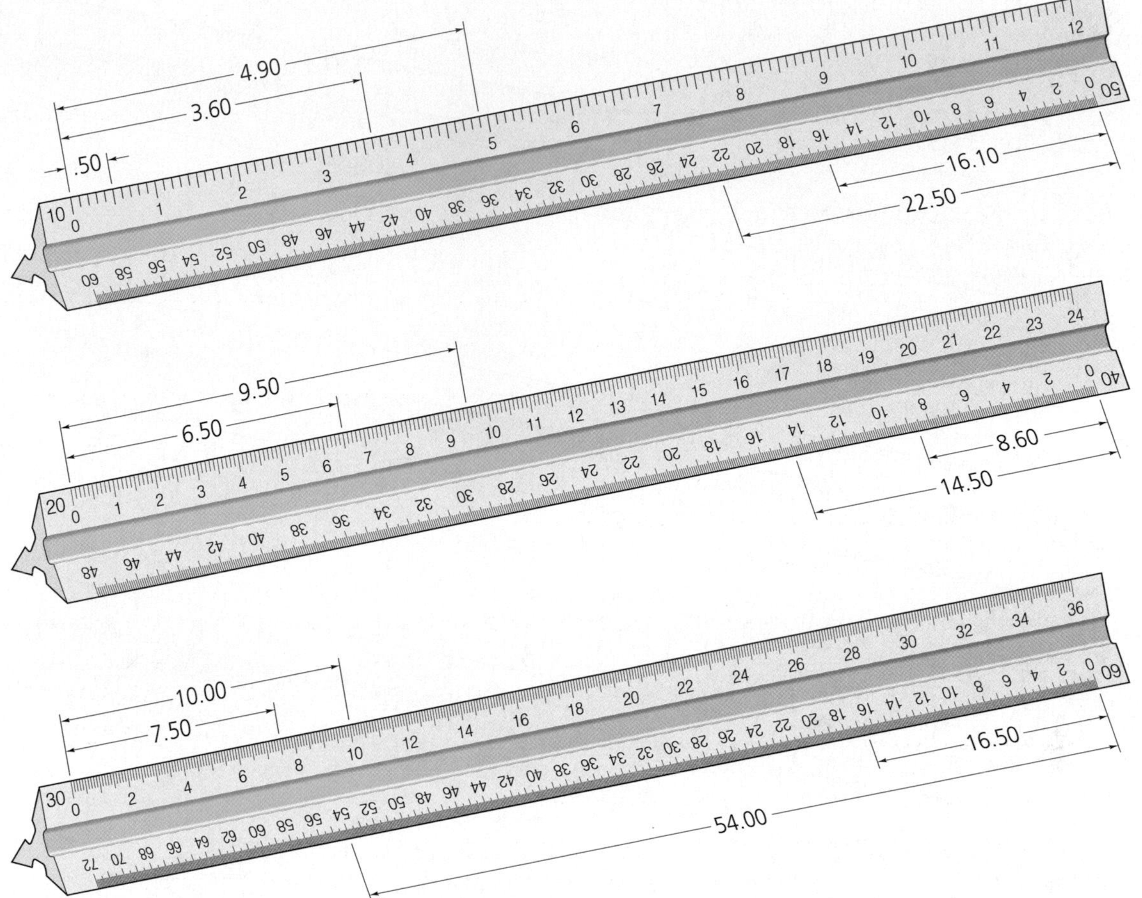

FIGURE 6.29 Civil Engineer's Scale

size but is an abbreviation for the unit of length in inches that represents 1 foot of real size. Figure 6.30 shows measurements taken along the architect's scale.

Some Architect's Scale Abbreviations

Abbreviation	Meaning	Proportion
3	3″ = 1′0″	$\frac{1}{4}$ size
$1\frac{1}{2}$	$1\frac{1}{2}$″ = 1′0″	$\frac{1}{8}$ size
1	1″ = 1′0″	$\frac{1}{12}$ size
$\frac{3}{4}$	$\frac{3}{4}$″ = 1′0″	$\frac{1}{16}$ size
$\frac{1}{2}$	$\frac{1}{2}$″ = 1′0″	$\frac{1}{24}$ size
$\frac{3}{8}$	$\frac{3}{8}$″ = 1′0″	$\frac{1}{32}$ size
$\frac{1}{4}$	$\frac{1}{4}$″ = 1′0″	$\frac{1}{48}$ size

Each of the ten open divided scale surfaces has two scales printed on it, reading in different directions from each end. Each pair of scales has a 1:2 size ratio and is $3-1\frac{1}{2}$, $1-\frac{1}{2}$, $\frac{3}{4}-\frac{3}{8}$, $\frac{1}{4}-\frac{1}{8}$, and $\frac{1}{36}-\frac{3}{32}$. In the smaller of the two scales, the "foot" numbers are nearer the working edge of the scale. Also, both scales have alternate foot markers (numbered on the larger scale), whereas the other foot markers are for only the smaller scale.

On the $\frac{1}{4}$ and the $\frac{3}{16}$ scales, only the even-numbered are numbered; on the $\frac{1}{8}$ and $\frac{3}{32}$ scales, only the markers divisible by 4 are numbered. Care must be used in making correct readings from all of these foot markers.

The fully divided 1-foot unit at the zero end of each scale is divided into inches and fractions of an inch and is read from the zero. The number of divisions varies with the unit of length that represents 1 foot. The value of the smallest unit varies from $\frac{1}{8}$ in. for the 3 scale to 2 in. for the $\frac{1}{8}$ and $\frac{3}{32}$ scales. Study the various scales to become familiar with the smallest units on each. The lengths of the dividing lines vary to make reading the scales easier. The 3, 6, and 9 in. marks are numbered on the 1 and $\frac{1}{2}$ scales, and each inch is marked on the 3 scale.

In Figure 6.30, $3\frac{9}{16}$ in. and $4\frac{1}{2}$ in. have been set off on the full-size inch scale (16), which is divided into increments of $\frac{1}{16}$ in. A variety of other measurements is provided on each of the other scale edges.

6.4.3 The Mechanical Engineer's Scale

The **mechanical engineer's scale** (Fig. 6.31) is normally two-sided and flat. One side, the full inch scale, is divided into either decimal units of .10 in. or as many as fifty divisions (every .02 in.). The opposite side is half scale (1:2). This scale also comes in a triangular version.

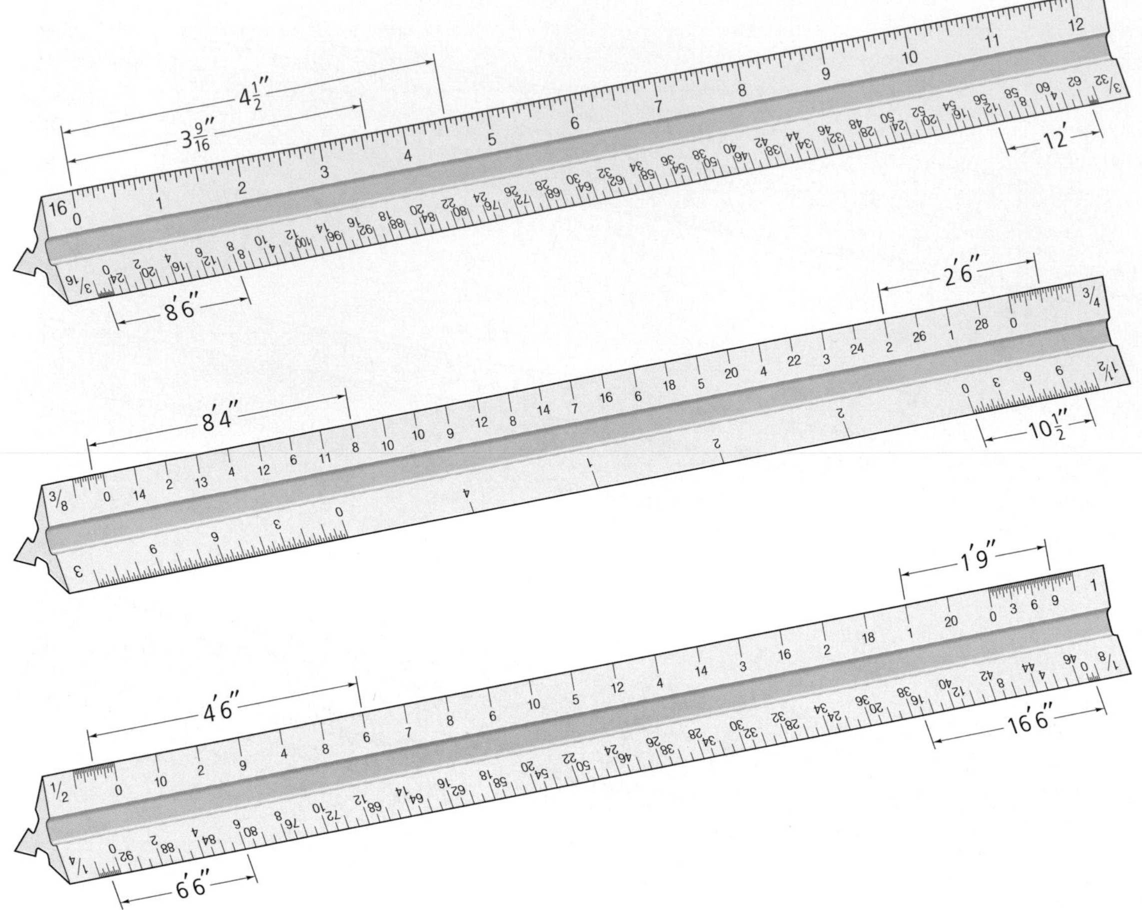

FIGURE 6.30 **Architect's Scale**

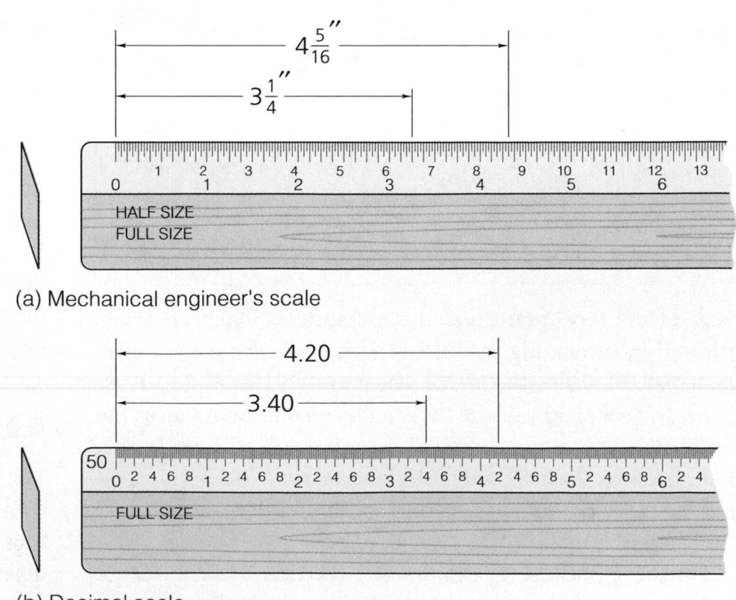

(a) Mechanical engineer's scale

(b) Decimal scale

FIGURE 6.31 **Mechanical Engineer's Scale**

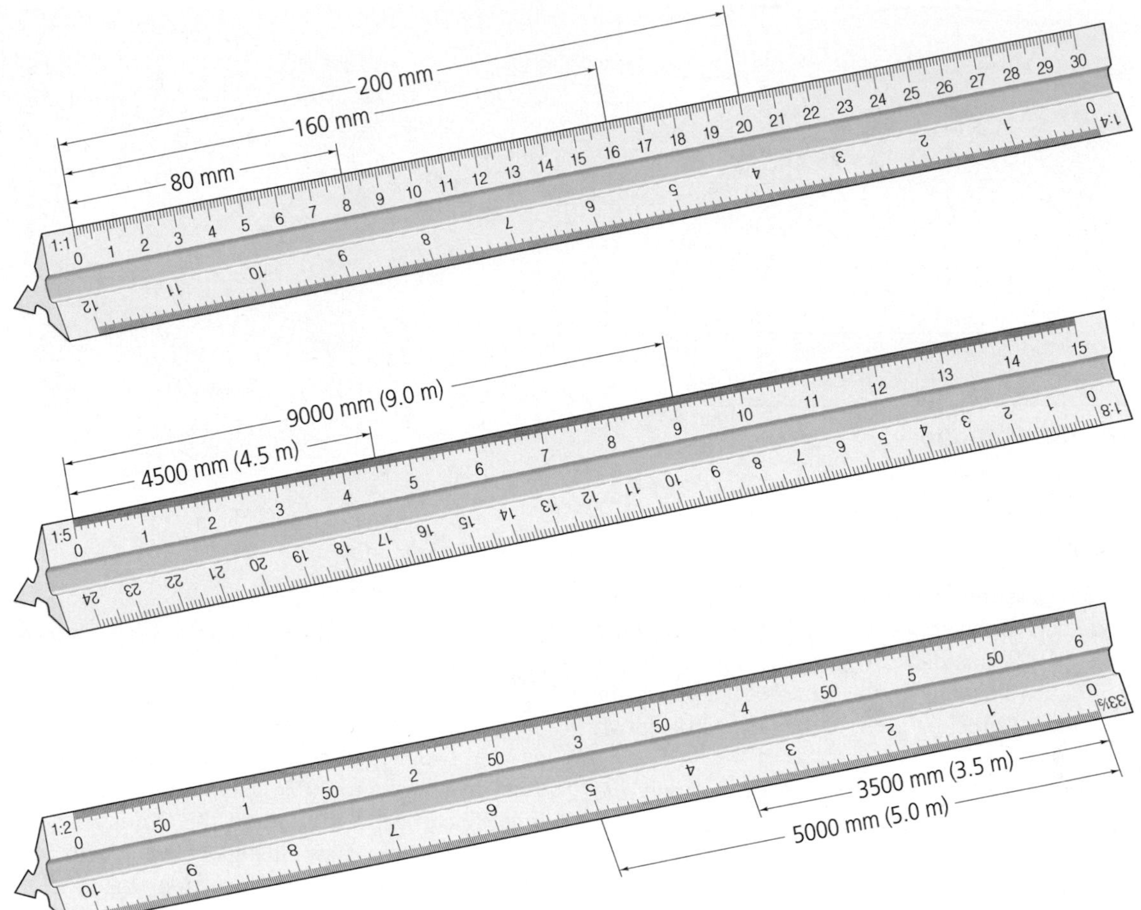

FIGURE 6.32 Triangular Metric Scale

Figure 6.31 also shows a sixteenth scale used by mechanical engineers. This scale is flat and has a full-scale fractionally divided scale on one side and a half-size fractionally divided scale on the other side. Figure 6.31(a) demonstrates full-size inch measurements $4\frac{5}{16}$ and $3\frac{1}{4}$ in.; Figure 6.31(b) shows 4.20 and 3.40 full-size decimal-inch measurements.

6.4.4 The Metric Scale

Metric units, also called **Sl units (Système Intemationale d'Unites),** are measured with a metric scale (Fig. 6.32). Many different versions of metric scales are available. To convert customary-unit (inch decimal and inch fraction) drawings, multiply the inch value by 25.4 to get the metric equivalent (1 in. = 25.4 mm) (or use tables provided on the inside front left cover of the text). As an example, 6.50 in. × 25.4 mm/in. = 63.5 mm. To change a metric value into decimal inches, divide by 25.4. As an example, 50 mm ÷ 25.4 mm/in. = 1.96 in.

The full-size metric scale is divided into major units of centimeters and smaller units of millimeters. There are 10 millimeters in each centimeter. Metric units, in full size as well as in reductions and enlargements, are being used more and more in all forms of design work. To many, the metric scale is much easier to master and use than decimal-inch or fraction-inch scales. Figure 6.32 shows a triangular metric scale with measurements. To set off 80 mm full size (1:1), start at the zero end of the 1:1 scale (Fig. 6.32) and count to the right until you get to the 8 (8 cm = 80 mm). On the 1:5 scale ratio, the 4.5 mark on the scale gives you 4500 mm, or 4.5 m.

This text has been designed for use with all types of scales. Many of the problems, and all of the exercises, in the text are not dimensioned, allowing your instructor to choose the unit of measurement. Use of different scales is highly recommended.

6.5 DRAWING TOOLS

Drawing tools include a variety of items to create geometric figures, measure and layout constructions, and establish features as a drawing of a part. These include protractors, triangles, and templates.

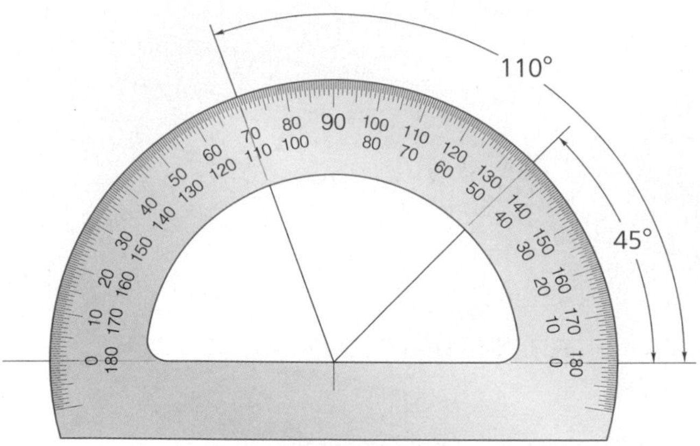

FIGURE 6.33 180° Protractor

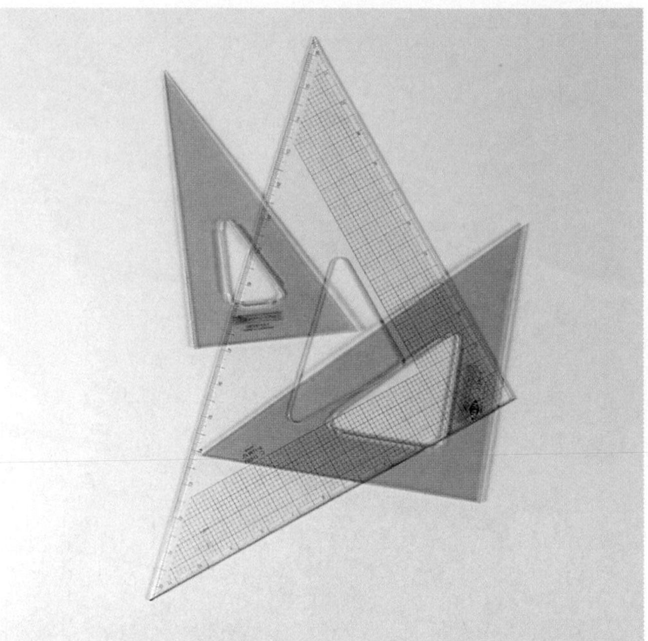

FIGURE 6.34 Triangles

6.5.1 Protractors

The **protractor** measures angles instead of lines. A 360° protractor (circular) is the easiest to use. Figure 6.33 shows a 180° protractor. Protractors can measure existing angles and can lay out lines at an angle. The center of the protractor is aligned with the intersecting point of the lines to be drawn or measured.

Note that the drafting machine can replace not only the straightedge, the triangle, and the scale, but also the protractor. However, a circular protractor is still an excellent investment, whether you have access to a drafting machine or not. Since it is easy to misread angle measurements when drawing with a drafting machine or an adjustable triangle, use of a protractor is recommended. Features of a part drawn at angles, regardless of the method of construction, should always be checked with a protractor.

6.5.2 Triangles

The standard **triangles** (Fig. 6.34) are the 45° triangle, the 30°/60° triangle, and the adjustable triangle. Triangles are positioned with a straightedge as a horizontal baseline and then used to draw a vertical line. When a drafting machine is available, triangles are unnecessary. But for productivity, triangles are extremely useful in conjunction with a drafting machine. The vertical scale of a drafting machine is difficult to keep 90° (perpendicular) to the horizontal scale; triangles used with drafting machines eliminate this problem.

The **45° triangle** is used to draw lines at an angle of 45° with the baseline. The **30°/60° triangle** is used to create lines at 30° or 60° with the baseline. Together the two triangles create angles of 15° and 75°. Combinations of the 45° and the 30°/60° triangle divide the 360° of a full circle into twenty-four 15° segments. Other angles are drawn with an adjustable triangle or with the aid of a protractor.

The **adjustable triangle** (Fig. 6.35) is the same as a 45° triangle when closed, but can be opened to form two parallel edges. The amount of opening of the triangle is measured by a protractor scale that reads from 0° to 45° and then doubles back from 45° to 90°. Zero-degree to 45° angles are formed by the two edges at the "open" corner of the triangle. Forty-five degree to 90° angles are formed by the sides at the "hinge" corner. By rotating the adjustable triangle into position, you can draw all angles. Check with a protractor all the measurements and constructions made with an adjustable triangle, because it is very easy to make a mistake with an adjustable triangle. For example, 40° and 50° have the

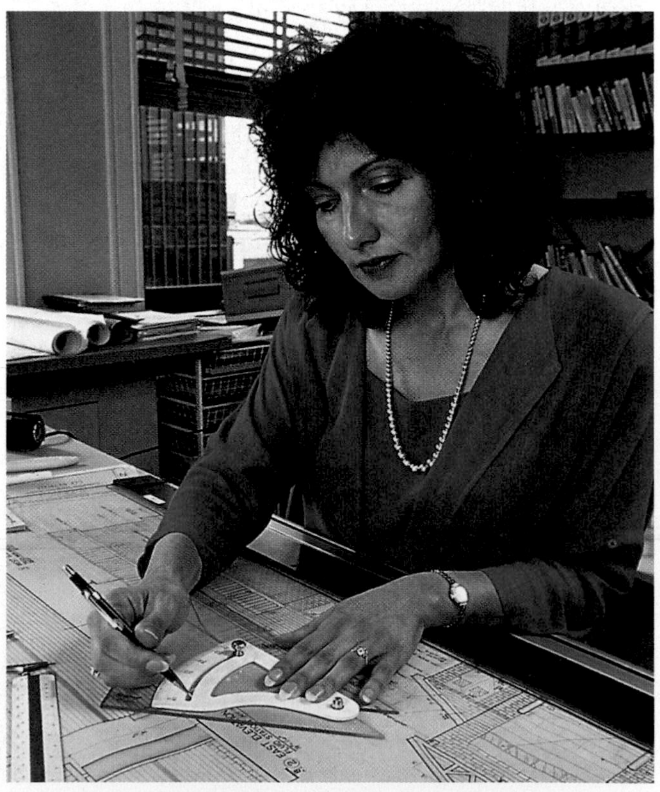

FIGURE 6.35 Using an Adjustable Triangle

same setting, so the angle you establish depends on which side of the triangle is touching the straightedge. The New Draft™ shown in Figure 6.36 is a combination of a 45° triangle, a 30°/60° triangle, and a template.

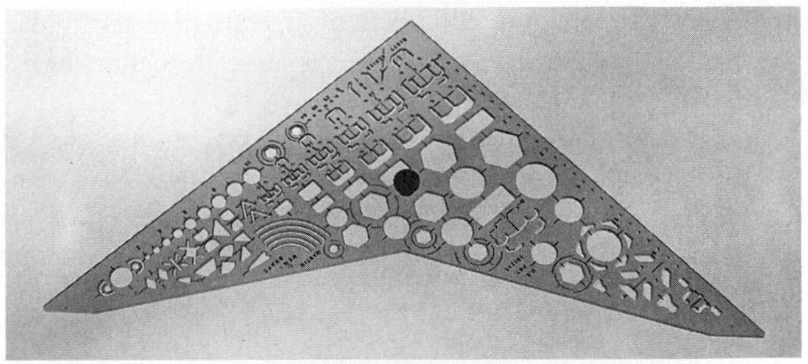

FIGURE 6.36 New Draft™ Template Triangle

6.5.3 Templates

A **template** is a tool for drawing shapes of varying sizes. Standard templates (Fig. 6.37) are essential for the quick,

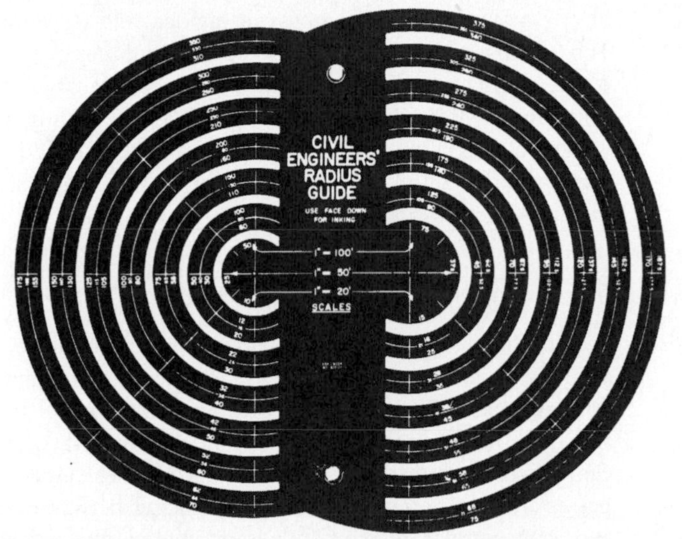

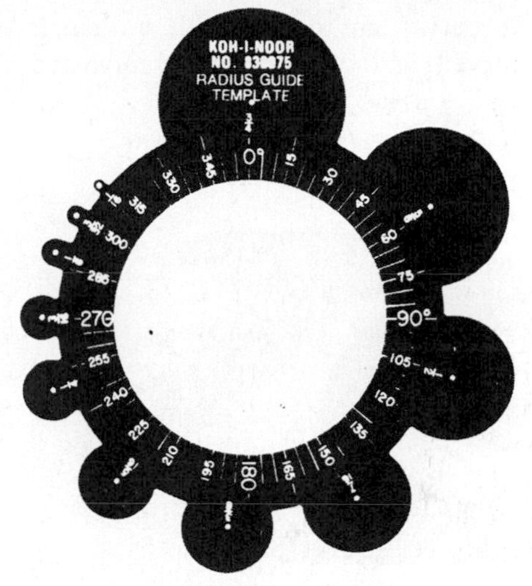

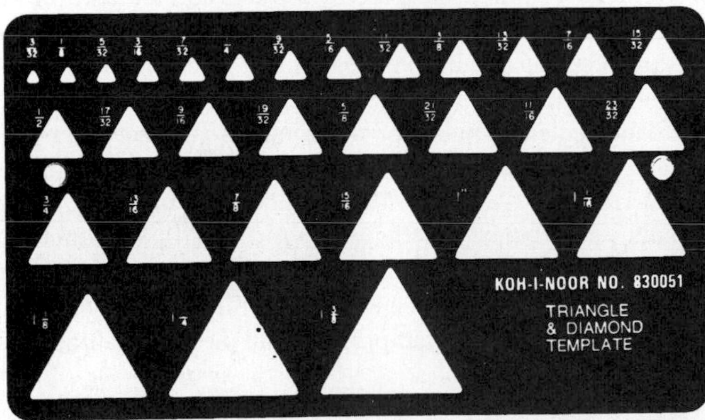

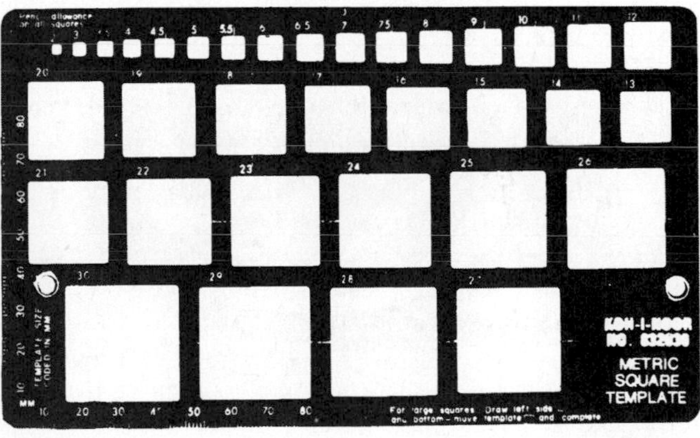

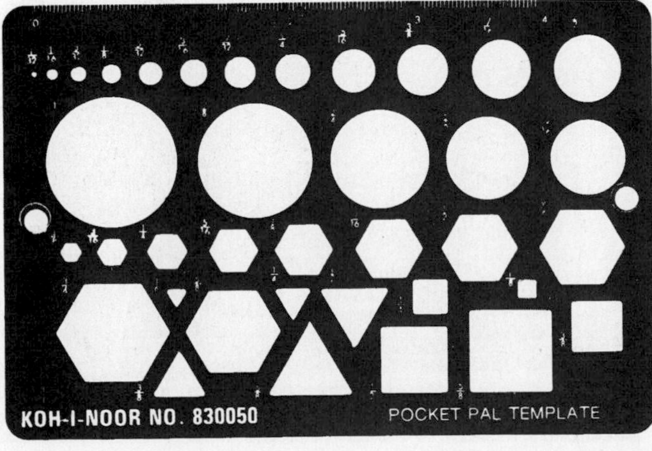

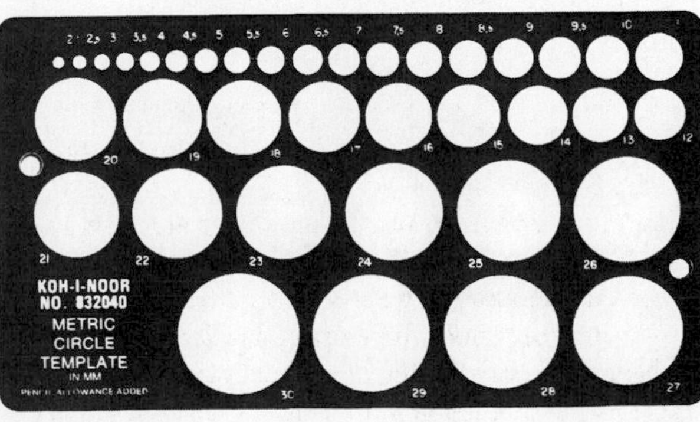

FIGURE 6.37 Templates

easy construction of circular, square, rectangular, triangular, elliptical, and symbolic shapes. Templates are better than a compass for small-diameter circles.

Circle templates, one of the most common types of templates in engineering drawing, come in all standard sizes for U.S. and metric units. After you master the essentials of linework and compass work, you will use templates for all standard-shape construction.

6.5.4 Irregular Curves

Noncircular curves are drawn with a French curve or **irregular curve** (Fig. 6.38) or a flexible curve as a guide, but the guide fits the curve only for a short distance. Noncircular curves are difficult to draw since they must be equal in width to the straight lines with which they blend to produce a uniform drawing.

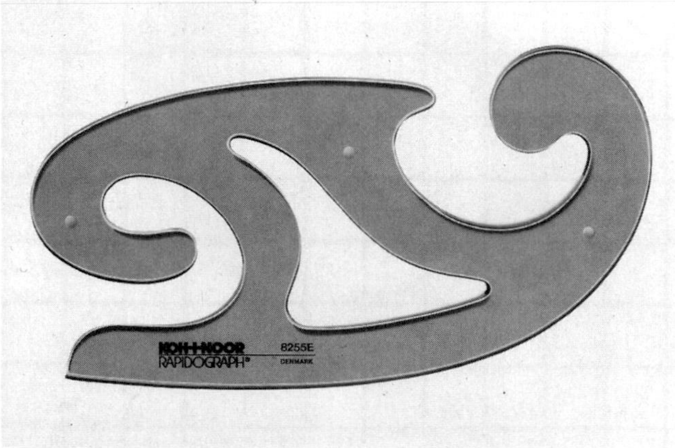

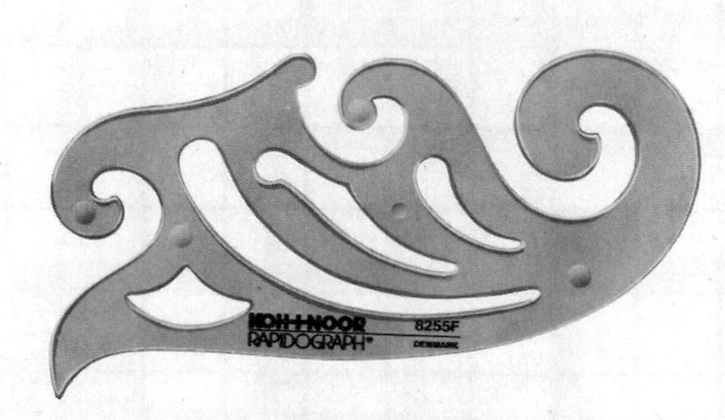

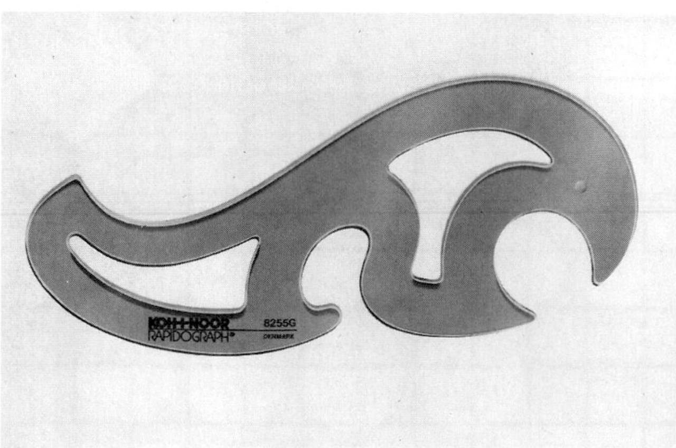

FIGURE 6.38 Irregular Curves

6.6 INSTRUMENTS

Instruments include all forms of *compasses, dividers,* and *inking tools.* The drafting instrument set (Fig. 6.39) consists of one or two sizes of compass, a divider, and accessories. The compass is used to draw circles and circular arcs. Although many types of drafting sets are available, they normally contain such obsolete items as the ruling pen, which has been replaced by the technical pen. You need only purchase a medium-sized, high-quality bow compass and medium-sized dividers in most cases.

6.6.1 Bow Compass and Dividers

A good bow compass and dividers are essential to the accurate construction of all forms of engineering drawings. A **bow compass** (Fig. 6.40) has a center thumbwheel to set and hold the spacing between the center point and the lead. Compasses without such a center thumbwheel and compasses that do not rigidly hold the spacing between point and lead are not recommended for engineering drawing. **Dividers** (Fig. 6.41) lack a center wheel and are used to set off measurements from one view to another quickly. This is extremely valuable in the construction of mechanical drawings and for descriptive geometry.

The centering point for the compass is either a tapered point or a short needle point projecting from a wider shaft that creates a "shoulder." The shoulder acts as a limit to the point's penetration into the paper and board. To restrict the compass point from penetrating the drawing medium and to provide a stable, secure centering point from which to swing an arc or a circle, you can place a small piece of drafting tape

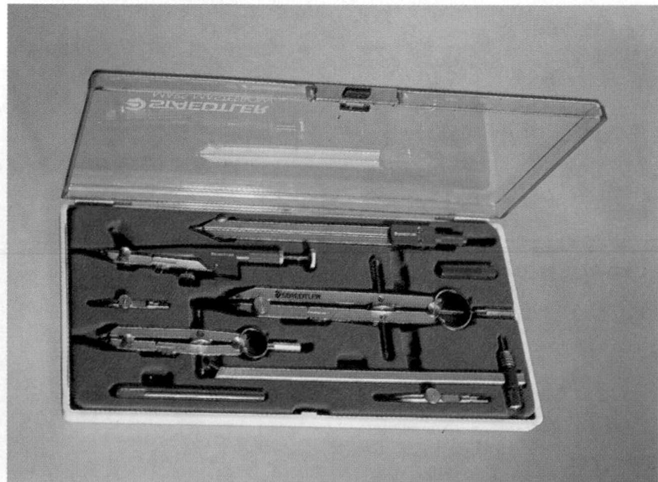

FIGURE 6.39 Drafting Instruments

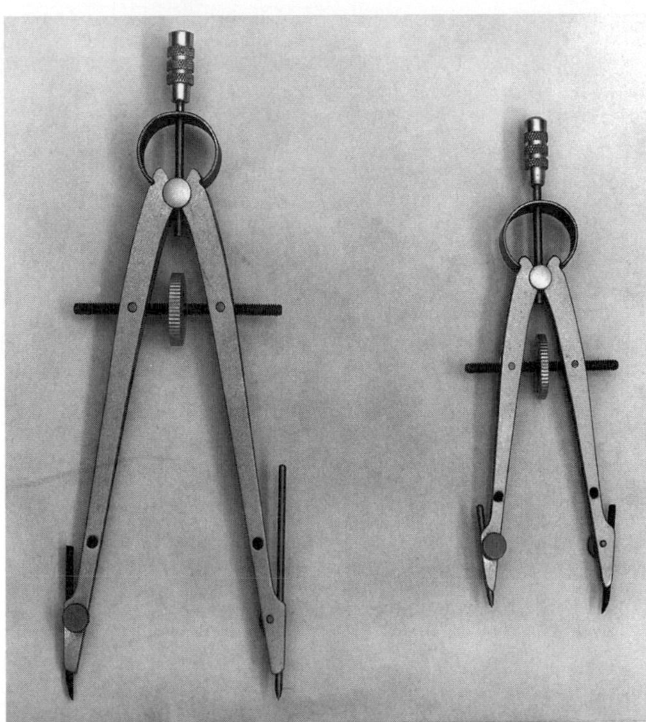

FIGURE 6.40 Bow Compasses

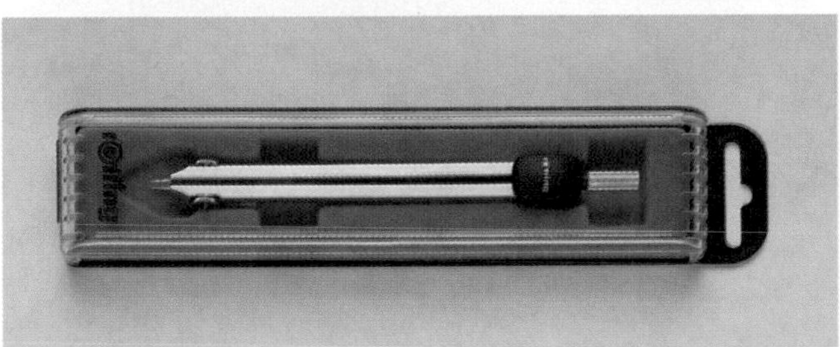

FIGURE 6.41 Dividers

(or dot) on the drawing at the center of the arc or circle to be drawn and then draw construction centerlines over the tape. Circles smaller than .50 in. (12 mm) are much easier to draw with a template or a drop bow compass than with a large- or medium-sized compass. *Use templates whenever possible.* A compass is best for odd-sized and large circles and for construction techniques.

The compass lead should be a piece of the drafting pencil lead (same grade lead or softer). Then both straight and curved lines will be drawn with the same lead and it will be easier to maintain uniformity. The lead is secured in the compass with about $\frac{1}{8}$ in. (9 mm) exposed and is sharpened with a sandpaper block (Fig. 6.42). Use care when sharpening the lead to keep the line through the point and the lead perpendicular to the sandpaper. Make a flat cut that leaves an oval surface, called a *bevel.* The bevel should be about three times as long as the diameter of the lead. The resulting point is chisel-shaped and should have about the same taper, when viewed from the side, as the drafting pencil. Do not try to adjust the lead in the compass after it is sharpened because it is almost impossible to reposition the chisel shape properly. The centering point is adjusted so that the midpoint of the needle point is even with the end of the lead. The beveled end can be on either side of the lead (Fig. 6.43), though usually it is put on the outside. To create a thin, dark curve, both sides of the lead may be beveled, which also creates a longer-lasting point/edge but is harder to maintain.

Dividers come with two identical tapered metal points. Some drafters prefer to replace one metal point with a piece of 4H lead. The lead point can be used to set off dimensions (especially for descriptive geometry), instead of using the two metal points, which tend to mar the drafting medium.

FIGURE 6.42 Sharpening the Lead of a Compass

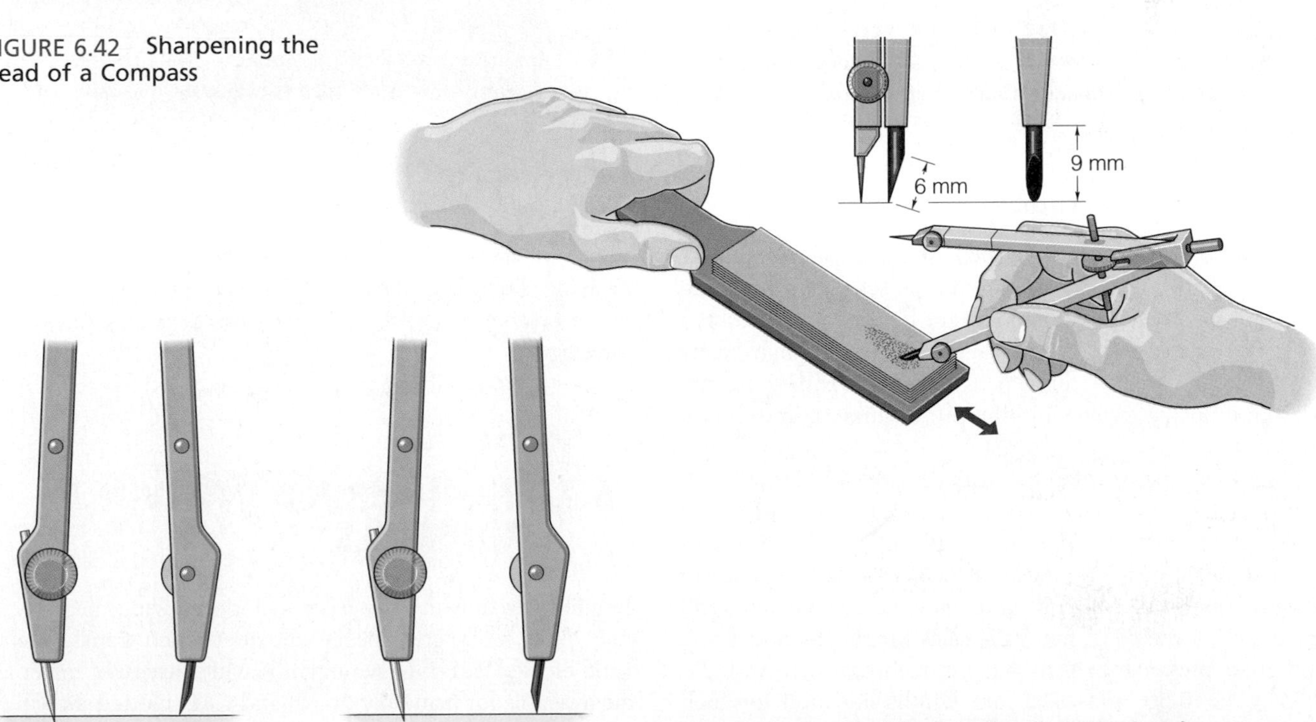

FIGURE 6.43 Positioning the Compass Lead

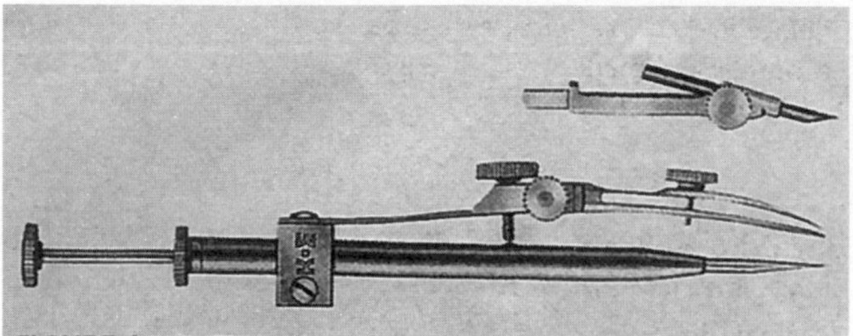

FIGURE 6.44 Drop Compass

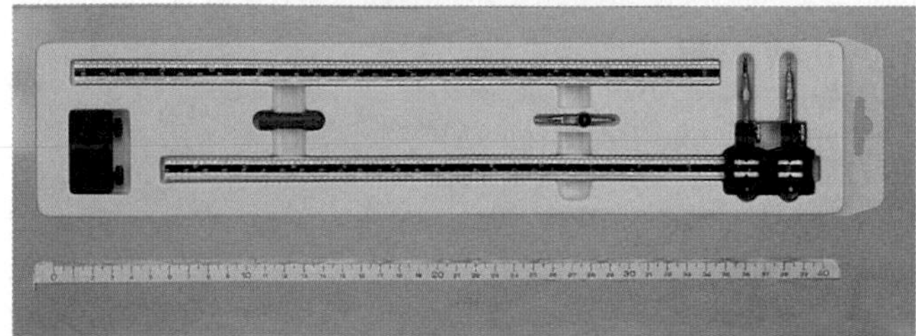

FIGURE 6.45 Beam Compass

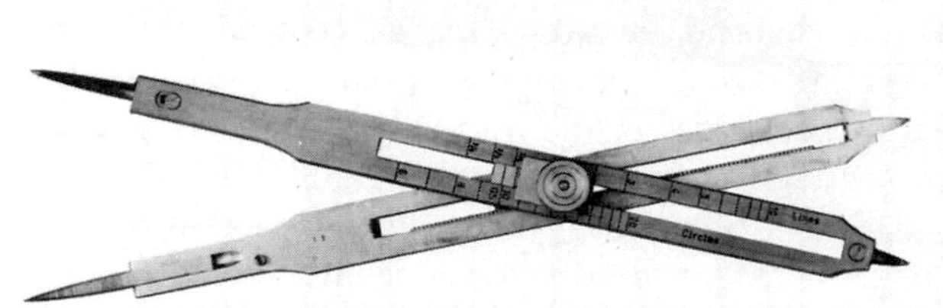

FIGURE 6.46 Proportional Dividers

For special drawing needs, three useful tools are available: the *drop compass* (Fig. 6.44) for very small, accurate circles; the *beam compass* (Fig. 6.45) for very large circles and arcs; and *proportional dividers* (Fig. 6.46) for reductions and enlargements.

6.6.2 Inking Instruments

Most compasses have inking-pen or technical-pen attachments. When you purchase a compass set, attempt to find one equipped with an attachment for holding a *technical pen* (Fig. 6.47), not a nib-type ruling pen. Although many drafting sets contain ruling pens (Fig. 6.39), they are not used in industry, so we will limit our discussion to technical pens.

Technical pens, like the sets shown in Figure 6.48, although expensive, have replaced all other forms of inking tools. Technical pens come in a wide range of pen widths (diameters) (Fig. 6.49), and each pen width corresponds to a metric thickness. Inked projects may include diagrams and pictorials for technical manuals, sales brochures, and graph and chart presentations. In general, technical pens in 0.25, 0.35, 0.45, 0.50, and 0.70 mm widths are used for such drawing. *Though it is a poor practice, manual inking is also used by some companies to make minor corrections on CAD-plotted drawings.*

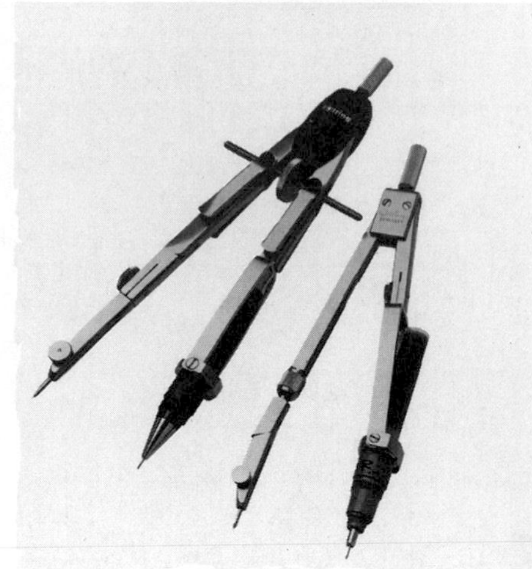

FIGURE 6.47 Bow Compass with Technical Pen Attachment

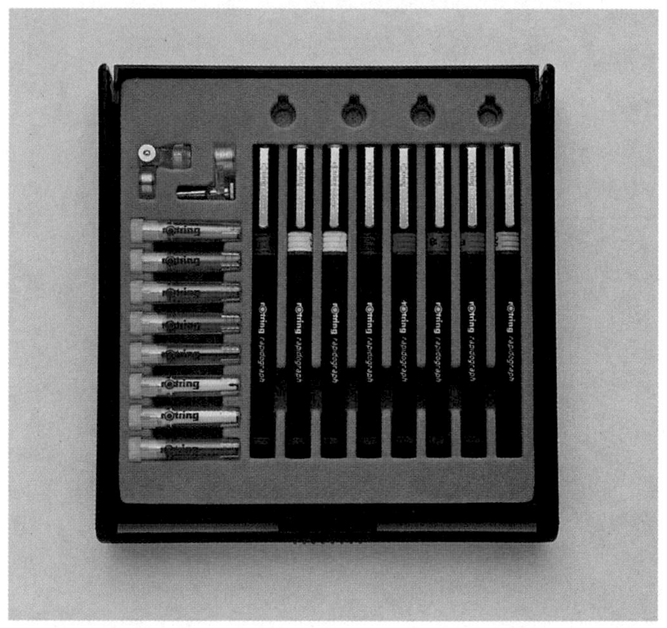

FIGURE 6.48 Technical Pens

6.7 ENGINEERING DRAWING MATERIALS

Engineering drawing materials include drawing media (vellum, film, sepia, grid sheets) and preprinted transfer items (title blocks, lettering, symbols). A wide variety of materials are available for manually drawn and CAD-plotted drawings.

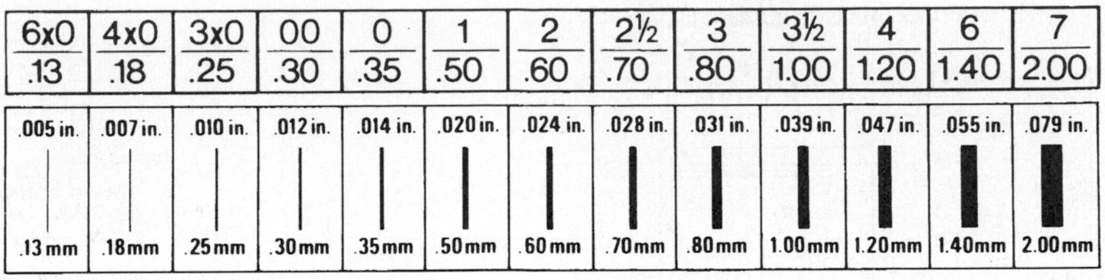

6x0	4x0	3x0	00	0	1	2	2½	3	3½	4	6	7
.13	.18	.25	.30	.35	.50	.60	.70	.80	1.00	1.20	1.40	2.00

.005 in.	.007 in.	.010 in.	.012 in.	.014 in.	.020 in.	.024 in.	.028 in.	.031 in.	.039 in.	.047 in.	.055 in.	.079 in.
.13 mm	.18 mm	.25 mm	.30 mm	.35 mm	.50 mm	.60 mm	.70 mm	.80 mm	1.00 mm	1.20 mm	1.40 mm	2.00 mm

FIGURE 6.49 Technical Pen Sizes

6.7.1 Engineering Drawing Media

Traditional engineering drawing media that are transparent enough to be whiteprinted include vellum and drafting film. Drawing **vellum** is a high-quality, translucent paper. Paper used for the diazo reproduction process must allow light to shine through (i.e., be translucent). In addition, pencil on vellum is easily erased, and vellum also takes ink well.

Drafting film is made of durable, high-quality polyester sheets. This medium is excellent for ink and also for plastic lead and combination leads. Special leads and erasers are available for use on drafting film. Although film is expensive compared to vellum, you should have some experience drawing on it with graphite lead, plastic lead, and ink. Vellum and drafting film are available in a plain version or a version with fine, nonreproducible-blue grids.

Vellum and film are secured to the drawing table with drafting tape. **Drafting tape** (or drafting dots) is a high-quality version of masking tape that is designed not to pull the finish off the paper surface.

6.7.2 Drawing Sheet Size and Format

Vellum and film come in standard sheet sizes and rolls. Table 6.3 compares International and ANSI drawing sizes. Rolls of paper and film are available in widths of 30, 36, 42, and 54 inches and in lengths of 25 feet or more. International standards establish a series of paper sizes based on width-to-length proportions. Figure 6.50 illustrates the various ANSI sheet sizes. (This same figure appears on the inside back right cover.) The margins shown in Figure 6.50 produce net drawing areas that are well within the sheet sizes of both standards. Drawing formats made to this standard can be reproduced on either U.S. or international sheet sizes by contact printing and microfilm projection methods. Most U.S. companies purchase preprinted standard sheets in ISO or ANSI specifications. Figure 6.51 compares the ISO and ANSI drawing formats.

Standardization of drawing size and location of format features on drawing forms provides definite advantages for the design office in the areas of readability, handling, filing, and reproduction. If companies are to share drawings successfully, similar items of information must be in the same location on all drawings and the information must be recorded in the same manner. Sheet size and format are covered in ANSI Standard Y14.1.

TABLE 6.3 Drawing Sheet Sizes

American National Standard Y14.1, in.	International Standard, mm
A $8\frac{1}{2} \times 11$	A4 210 × 297
B 11 × 17	A3 297 × 420
C 17 × 22	A2 470 × 594
D 22 × 34	A1 594 × 841
E 34 × 44	A0 841 × 1189
F 28 × 40	

6.7.3 Drawing Formats

The size and style of lettering on **drawing formats** (within title blocks) is to be in accordance with ANSI Y14.2M. To provide contrasting divisions between major elements of the format, the following guide should be used on all projects taken from this text.

Thick lines: 0.7 to 0.9 mm (approximately .03 in.)

- Borderline
- Outline of principal blocks
- Main division of blocks

Medium lines: 0.45 to 0.5 mm (approximately .02 in.)

- Minor divisions of the title block

6.7.4 Title Blocks

The **title block** is one of the most important parts of the drawing. The title block is usually located in the lower right corner of the format. Normally, it includes spaces for the following information:

- Company/school name
- Project title/part name/job number
- Scale
- Drawn by
- Material specification
- Date
- Checked by
- Sheet number
- Drawing number
- Standard company tolerances (sheet tolerance)
- Revision box

Figure 6.52 shows the ANSI standard title block layouts for A–K sheet sizes. Title blocks are discussed in detail in Chapter 23.

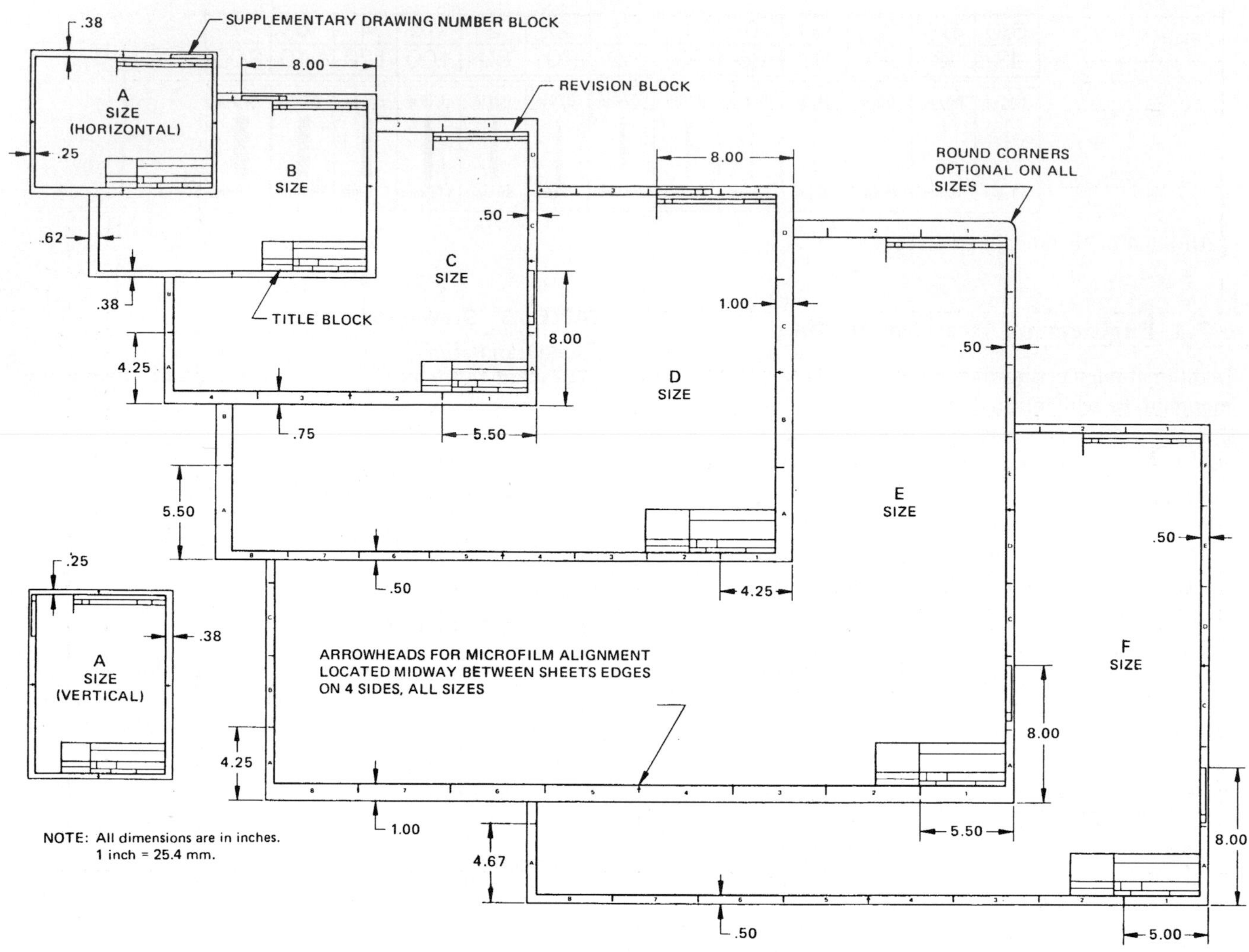

Size Designation	Width (Vertical)	Length (Horizontal)	Margin		International Designation	Width		Length	
			Vertical	Horizontal		mm	in.	mm	in.
A (Horiz)	8.5	11.0	0.38	0.25	A0	841	33.11	1189	46.11
A (Vert)	11.0	8.5	0.25	0.38	—	—	—	—	—
B	11.0	17.0	0.38	0.62	A1	594	23.39	841	33.11
C	17.0	22.0	0.75	0.50	A2	420	16.54	594	23.39
D	22.0	34.0	0.50	1.00	A3	297	11.69	420	16.54
E	34.0	44.0	1.00	0.50	A4	210	8.27	297	11.69

FIGURE 6.50 **Flat Size Formats**

6.8 BASIC ENGINEERING DRAWING TECHNIQUES

When graphics are used to communicate engineering, design, production, and manufacturing data, high-quality drawing skills are essential. Drawings must be neat and accurate. Lettering and linework must be precise, dark, and of high quality. This section covers the basics of *linework*. It presents procedures and techniques to help you develop high-quality drawing skills.

6.8.1 Lines

All drawings are made of **lines.** The control you have over the pencil or pen and the techniques you use determine the quality of the drawing and the accuracy of the graphic communication. The conscientious designer or engineer

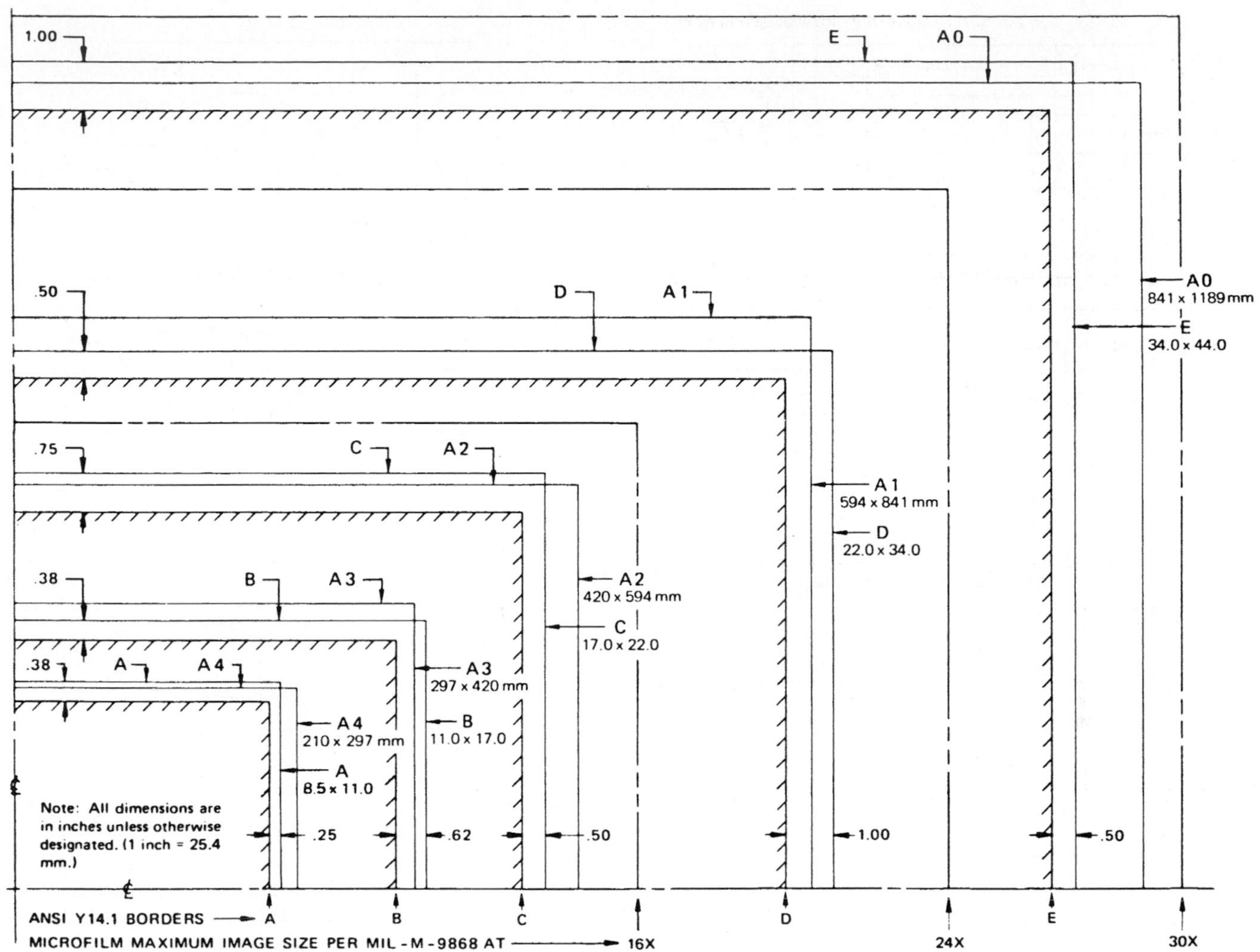

FIGURE 6.51 Comparison of ANSI Y14.1 Drawing Format Sizes with ISO Paper Sizes

constantly strives to improve his or her technique through practice and attention to detail. The characteristics of all lines on a drawing are that they be black, clean-cut, precise, and opaque, with sufficient contrast in thickness between line types. The most important aspect is to convey the precise understanding of the process, the intent, and the content of a drawing. Understanding how lines function and what they mean is particularly important.

Lines (Fig. 6.53) and their relationships are important concerns of engineering graphics. A *line* is considered to have length but no width. A straight line is the shortest distance between two points and is the type of line implied by the word "line." A line that bends is called a *curve.*

Parallel lines are equally spaced along their entire length, becoming neither closer together nor farther apart. The symbol for parallel lines is // (Fig. 6.53). *Perpendicular lines* are at an angle of 90° to each other and can be intersecting or nonintersecting (Fig. 6.53). The symbol for perpendicular lines is ⊥.

The lines in engineering drawings are drawn with different widths to provide specific information. Each line type is actually a symbol that represents a function or idea or communicates a special situation. What thickness to draw any line is determined by what it represents and the smallest size to which it will be reduced. To avoid confusion, lines representing the same function must be the same thickness throughout a single drawing. The minimum spacing between parallel lines is determined by how much the drawing will be reduced. Two parallel lines that are placed too close will merge when the drawing is reduced—this is called *fill-in,* a situation that must be avoided. Normally, .06 in. (1.5 mm) minimum parallel spacing meets reduction requirements for most drawings.

The following list describes traditional line thickness used on engineering drawings.

1. **Fine lines.** Thin, black lines used to provide information about the drawing or to construct the drawing. These include dimension lines, leader lines, extension lines, centerlines, and construction lines.
2. **Medium lines.** Medium-width, solid, black lines used to outline planes, lines, surfaces, and solid shapes Medium lines are also used for hidden (dashed) lines.

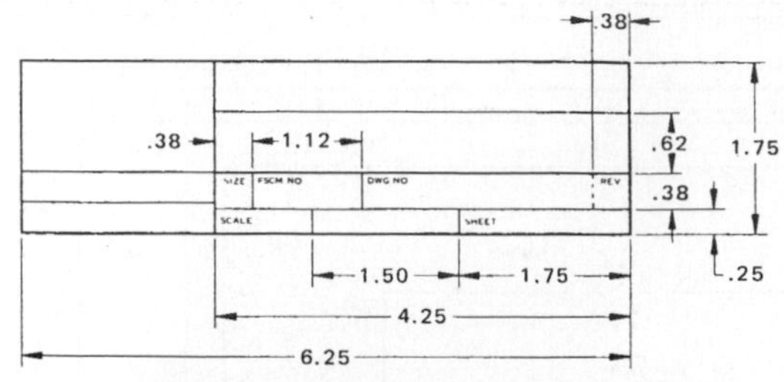

NOTE: All dimensions are in inches. 1 inch = 25.4 mm.
TITLE BLOCK FOR A, B, C, AND G – SIZES

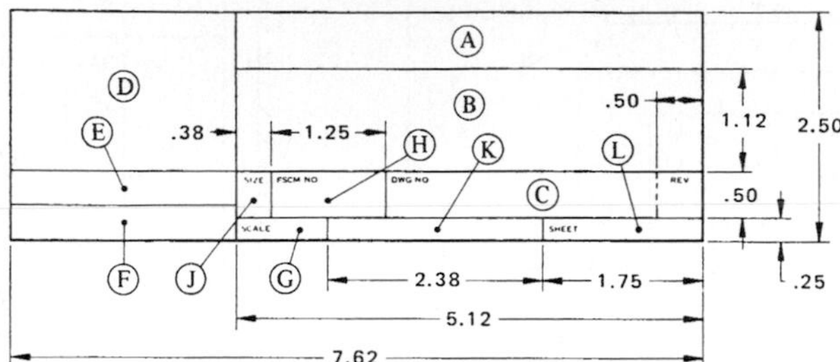

NOTE: All dimensions are in inches. 1 inch = 25.4 mm.
TITLE BLOCK FOR D, E, F, H, J, AND K – SIZES

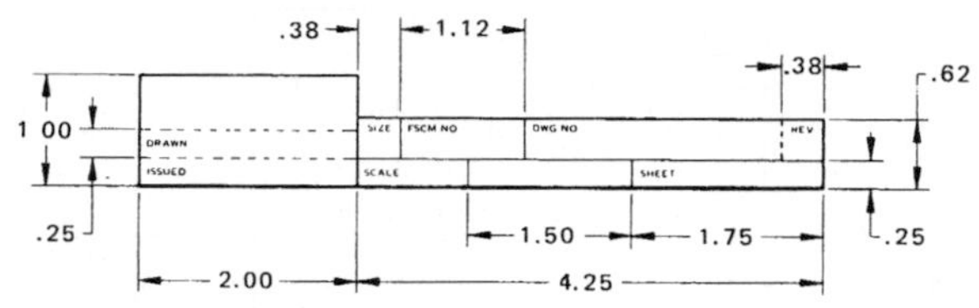

NOTE: All dimensions are in inches. 1 inch = 25.4 mm.
CONTINUATION SHEET TITLE BLOCK FOR A, B, C, and G – SIZES

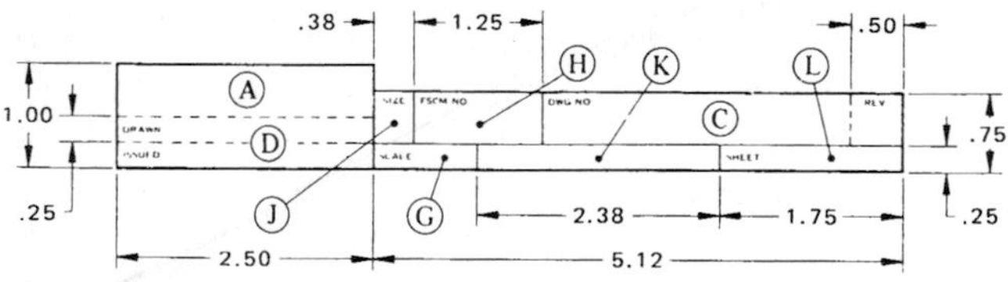

NOTE: All dimensions are in inches. 1 inch = 25.4 mm.
CONTINUATION SHEET TITLE BLOCK FOR D, E, F, H, J, AND K – SIZES

FIGURE 6.52 **ANSI Title Block Dimensions**

3. **Heavy lines.** Solid, thick, black lines used for the border, cutting plane lines, and break lines.

The newest ANSI standard suggests only two line-thickness choices—thin and thick. All lines listed under 1 and 2 from the preceding list are now drawn with thin lines, and all lines listed under 3 are drawn with thick lines. Many companies still use the three line thicknesses shown in the list.

6.8.2 Line Types

Line types and conventions for mechanical drawings are covered in ANSI Standard Y14.2M (Fig. 6.54). Figure 6.55 provides examples of each type of line. Every line on your drawing has a meaning. In other words, lines are *symbols* that mean specific things. The line type determines if the line is part of the part or conveys information about the part.

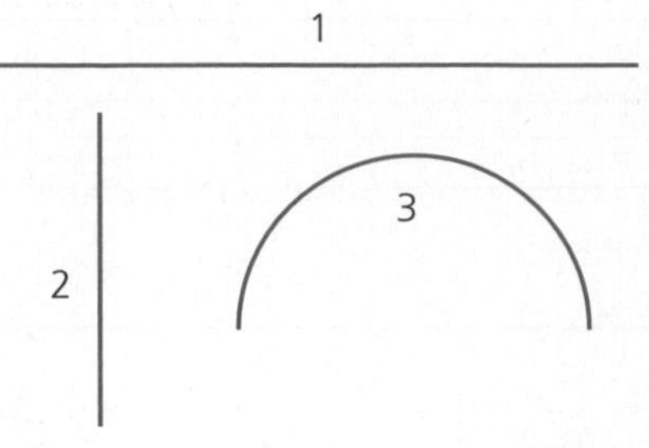

Lines, 1 (horizontal), 2 (vertical), 3 (curved)

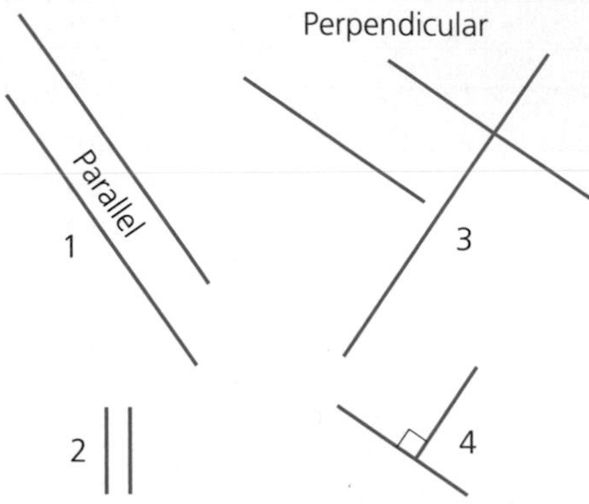

Parallel and perpendicular lines

FIGURE 6.53 **Orientation of Lines**

A *visible object line* represents the visible edges of the part. A *hidden line* is a dashed line that represents an edge that does not show because it is behind another feature of the part. Part description is composed of these two types of lines.

Other lines convey information about the part but are not lines of the part itself. In this category are *section lines, cutting-plane lines, centerlines, dimension lines, extension lines,* and *phantom lines.*

Besides having different configurations, such as dashes and spaces, each line type has a weight (thickness). The following list gives the suggested weight (thickness) of lines on your drawing.

THICK	
Visible object line	0.60 to 0.70 mm
Cutting-plane line	0 70 to 0.90 mm
Border line	0.70 to 0.90 mm
Break line	0.45 to 0.70 mm
THIN	
Hidden line	0.45 to 0.50 mm
Section line	0.25 to 0.30 mm
Centerline	0.30 to 0.35 mm
Dimension line	0.30 to 0.35 mm
Phantom line	0.45 to 0.50 mm
Break line	0.45 to 0.70 mm

Visible Object Lines. Visible object lines are thick lines that represent the visible edges and contours of a part. Since visible lines are the most important lines, they must stand

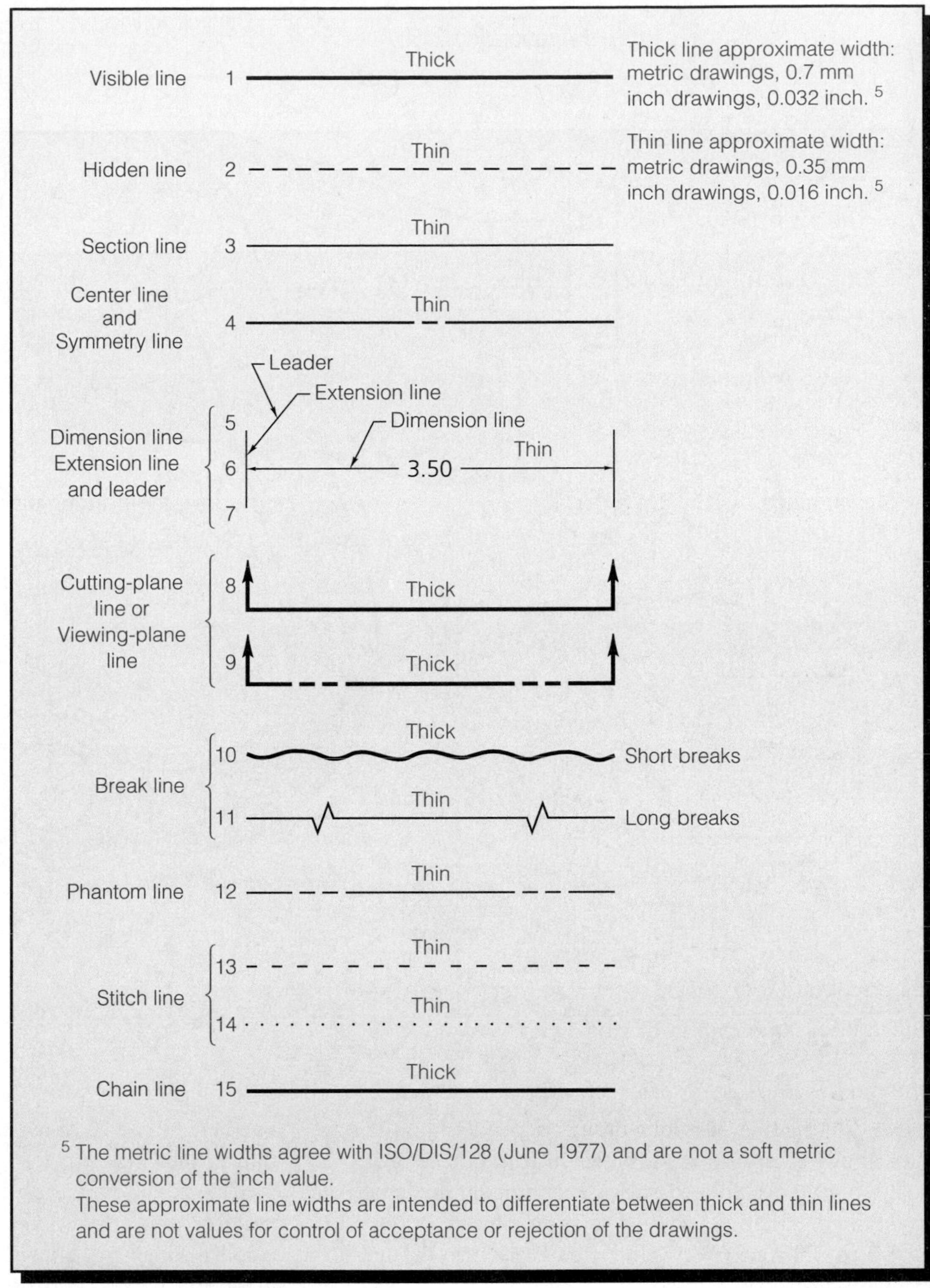

FIGURE 6.54 Standard Line Types and Thicknesses

out from all other secondary lines on the drawing. In mechanical drawing, visible lines are normally drawn about .032 in. thick (between 0.6 and 0.7 mm).

Hidden Lines. Hidden lines are short, thin dashes, approximately .12 in. (3.0 mm) long, spaced about .03 to .06 in. (0.7 to 1.5 mm) apart. They show the hidden features of a part. Hidden lines should always begin and end with a dash, except when a dash would form a continuation of a visible line.

Dashes always meet at corners, and a hidden arc should start with dashes at the tangent points. When the arc is small, the length of the dash may be modified to maintain a uniform and neat appearance. Excessive hidden lines are difficult to follow. Therefore, only lines or features that add to the clearness and the conciseness of the drawing are shown; confusing and conflicting hidden lines should be eliminated. If hidden lines do not adequately define a part's configuration, a section should be taken (see Chapter 11). Whenever possible, hidden lines are eliminated from the sectioned portion of a drawing. Hidden lines are drawn approximately .017 in. (0.45 to 0.50 mm) thick (see Chapter 10).

Centerlines. Centerlines are thin, long and short dashes, alternately and evenly spaced, with long dashes placed at

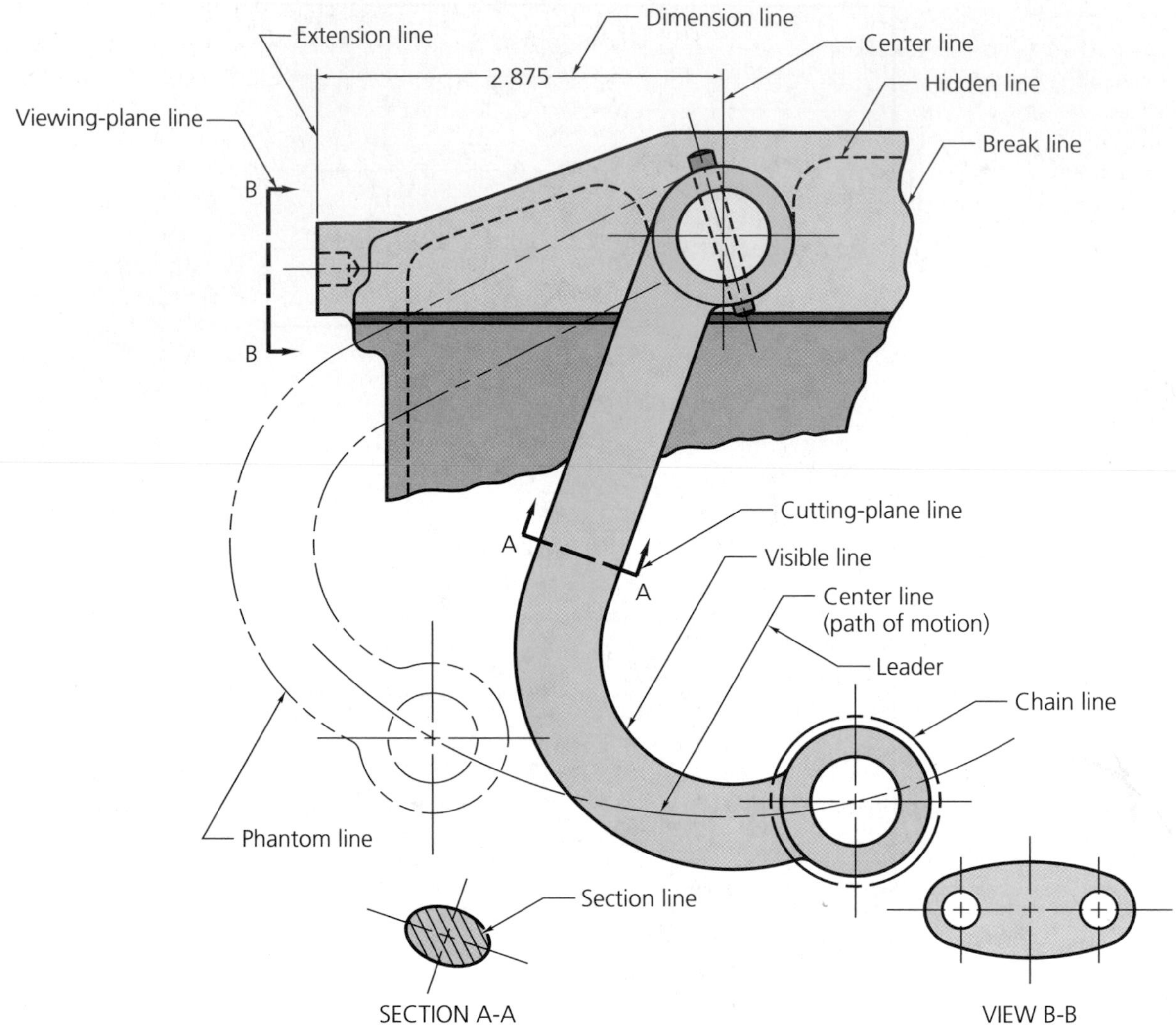

FIGURE 6.55 **Application of Line Types**

each end of the line. The long dash is dependent on the size of the drawing and normally varies in length from .75 to 2 in. (20 to 50 mm). Short dashes, depending on the length of the required centerline, should be approximately .06 to .12 in. (1.5 to 3.0 mm). Very short centerlines may be unbroken, with dashes at both ends.

Centerlines indicate the axes of symmetrical parts of features, bolt circles, paths of motion, and pitch circles. They should extend about .12 in. (3 mm) beyond the outline of symmetry, unless they are used as extension lines for dimensioning. Every circle, and some arcs, should have two centerlines that intersect at the center of their short dashes. Centerlines are usually drawn about .012 in. (0.3 mm) thick.

Dimension Lines. Dimension lines are thin lines that show the extent and the direction of dimensions. Space for a single line of numerals is provided by a break in the dimension line. However, on horizontal line dimensions, when two lines of numerals are used in the form of limits, one may be placed above and the other below an unbroken dimension line.

If possible, dimension lines are aligned and grouped for uniform appearance and ease of reading. For example, parallel dimension lines should be spaced no less than .25 in. (6 mm) apart, and no dimension line should be closer than .38 in. (10 mm) to the outline of a part feature [.50 in. (12 mm) is the preferred distance].

All dimension lines terminate with an arrowhead on mechanical engineering drawings, with a slash or a dot in architecture. The preferred ending is the arrowhead. Arrowheads are drawn with a 1:3 ratio (width is $\frac{1}{3}$ the length). The actual size is determined by the drawing scale, the total drawing size and area used, and the reduction requirements. Avoid large, elaborate arrowheads. Dimension lines are drawn the same thickness as centerlines, .012 in. (0.3 mm). See Chapter 15 for complete information on dimensions.

Extension Lines. Extension lines indicate the termination of a dimension. An extension line must not touch the feature from which it extends, but should start approximately .04 to .06 in. (2 mm) from the feature being dimensioned and extend the same amount beyond the arrow side of the last dimension line. When extension lines cross other extension lines, dimension lines, leader lines, or object lines, they are usually not broken. When extension lines cross dimension lines close to an arrowhead, breaking the extension line is recommended, for clarity. Extension lines are drawn at the same thickness as dimension lines and centerlines, .012 in. (0.3 mm).

Leader Lines. A leader line is a continuous straight line that extends at an angle from a note, a dimension, or other reference to a feature. An arrowhead touches the feature at that end of the leader. At the note end, a horizontal bar .25 in. (6 mm) long terminates the leader approximately .12 in. (3 mm) away from midheight of the note's lettering, at either the beginning or the end of the first line. Leaders should not be bent to underline the note or dimension. Unless unavoidable, leaders should not be bent in any way except to form the horizontal terminating bar at the note end of the leader.

Leaders usually do not cross. Leaders or extension lines may cross an outline of a part or extension lines if necessary, but they usually remain continuous and unbroken at the point of intersection. When a leader is directed to a circle or a circular arc, its direction should be *radial*. Leader lines are drawn the same thickness as centerlines, dimension lines, and extension lines, .12 in. (0.3 mm).

Section Lines. Section lines are thin, uniformly spaced lines that indicate the exposed cut surfaces of a part in a sectional view. Spacing should be approximately .10 in. (3 mm) and at an angle of 45°. The spacing is dependent on the reduction percentage of the drawing. Section lines are drawn slightly thinner than centerlines and dimension lines, .01 in. (0.25 mm) (see Chapter 11).

Phantom Lines. Phantom lines consist of medium-thin, long and short dashes. They indicate alternate positions of moving parts, adjacent positions of related parts, and repeated details. They can also show the cast, or the rough shape, of a part before machining. The line starts and ends with the long dash of .60 in. (15 mm), with about .06 in. (1.5 mm) space between the long and short dashes. A phantom line is drawn approximately as thick as a hidden line, .016 in. (0.45 mm). Phantom lines are drawn similar to centerlines, except they have two short dashes between each long dash. The short dashes are drawn approximately .12 in. (0.3 mm) or longer, depending on the size of the drawing and the reduction requirements. In some cases, as when showing alternate or related positions of parts, or when a part is the workpiece on a jig and fixture assembly, the phantom line is drawn in red.

Cutting-Plane Lines and Viewing-Plane Lines. Cutting-plane lines and viewing-plane lines consist of thick, long and short dashes. These lines indicate the location of cutting planes for sectional views and the viewing positions for removed partial views. Cutting-plane lines start and stop with long dashes—.60 in. (15 mm) or longer. The short dashes are approximately .25 in. (6 mm) long, with about .12 in. (3 mm) of space between them. An alternative method uses medium-length [.38 in. (9 mm)] dashed lines for the total cutting plane. Both methods are acceptable. Cutting plane lines are normally drawn with a thickness of about .032 in. (0.70 mm) and are the thickest lines on a drawing (see Chapter 11 on sectioning).

Break Lines. Break lines are thick, freehand, continuous, ragged lines used to limit a broken view, a partial view, or a broken section. For long breaks, where space is limited, a neat break may be made with long, medium-thickness, ruled dashes joined by freehand zigzags. For short breaks, the lines are drawn thicker, the same as cutting plane lines, .03 in (0.7 mm). Long break lines are about as thick as thin lines, .017 in. (0.45 to 0.50 mm) (see Chapter 11).

Construction Lines. Construction lines lay out the part's features and locate the dimensions. They are very thin, light gray lines. Normally, 6H–3H lead is used for construction lines. In most cases, excess construction lines are erased before the part is darkened. When construction lines are drawn with nonreproducible-blue lead, they do not require erasing.

6.8.3 Precedence of Lines

Whenever lines coincide in a view, certain ones take precedence. Since the visible features of a part (object lines) are represented by thick solid lines, they take precedence over all other lines. If a centerline and a cutting plane coincide, the more important one should take precedence. Normally the cutting-plane line, drawn with a thicker weight, will take precedence. The following list gives the preferred *precedence of lines* on your drawing:

1. Visible (object) lines
2. Hidden (dashed) lines
3. Cutting-plane lines
4. Centerlines
5. Break lines
6. Dimension and extension lines
7. Section lines

6.8.4 Placing the Paper or Drafting Film on the Board

Drafting paper is placed on the board in a position that will allow you to use the drawing tools properly and to be comfortable while drawing. This position is approximately halfway up on the board and either near the working edge of the board or centered.

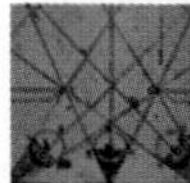

Applying Parametric Design . . .

DRAWING FORMATS

Drawing formats are user-defined drawing sheet layouts. A drawing format can be used by any number of drawings. It may also be modified or replaced in a drawing at any time.

There are two types of drawing formats: standard and sketched. Standard formats (see Fig. A) consist of draft entities, not model entities. You can select the desired format size from a list of standard drawing sizes [A–F size and A0–A4 size (see Fig. B)], or create a new size by entering values for length and width.

FIGURE A Standard Format Using a Table

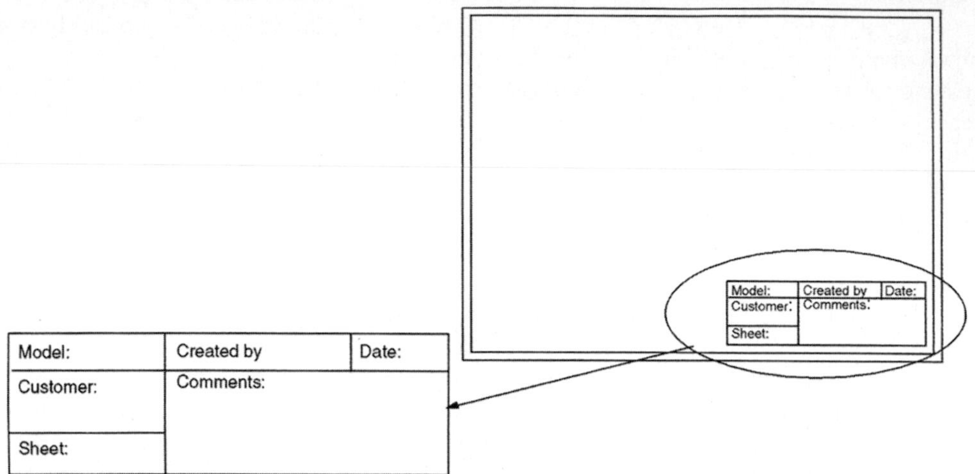

FIGURE B Standard Formats Created in Format Mode

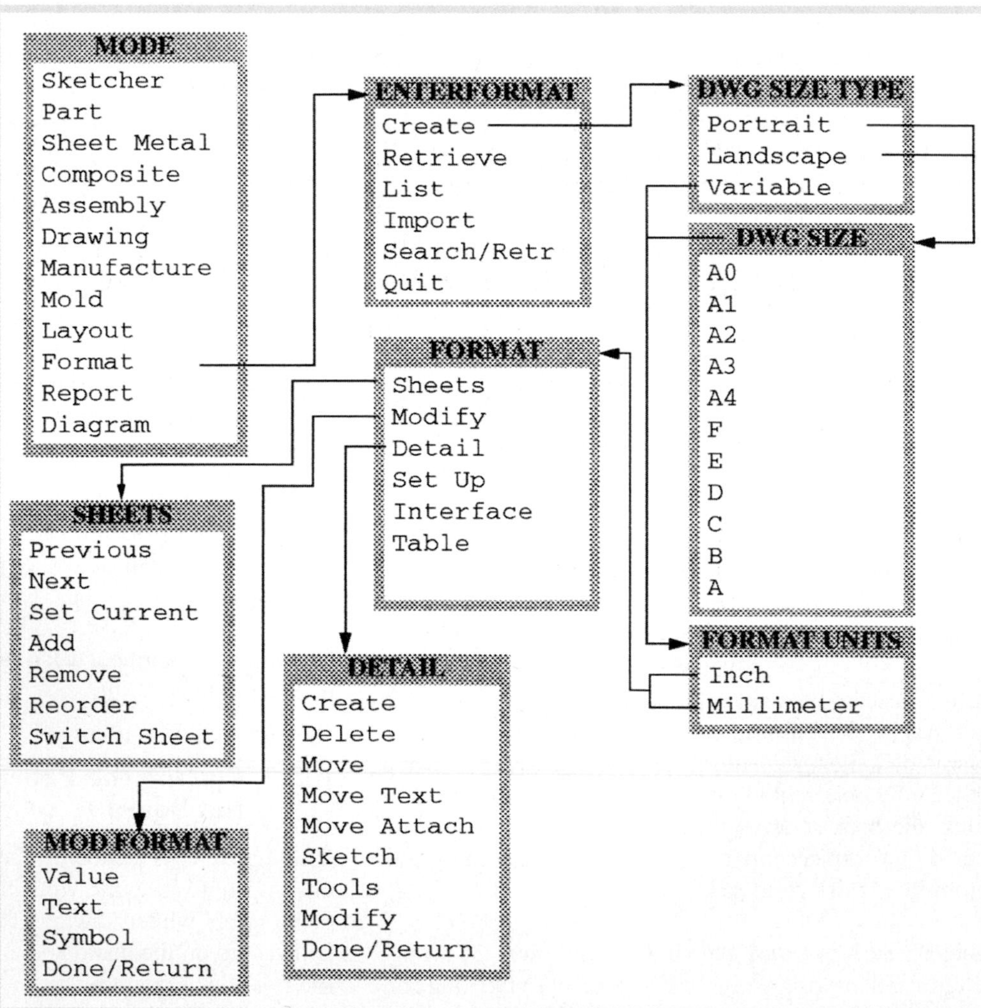

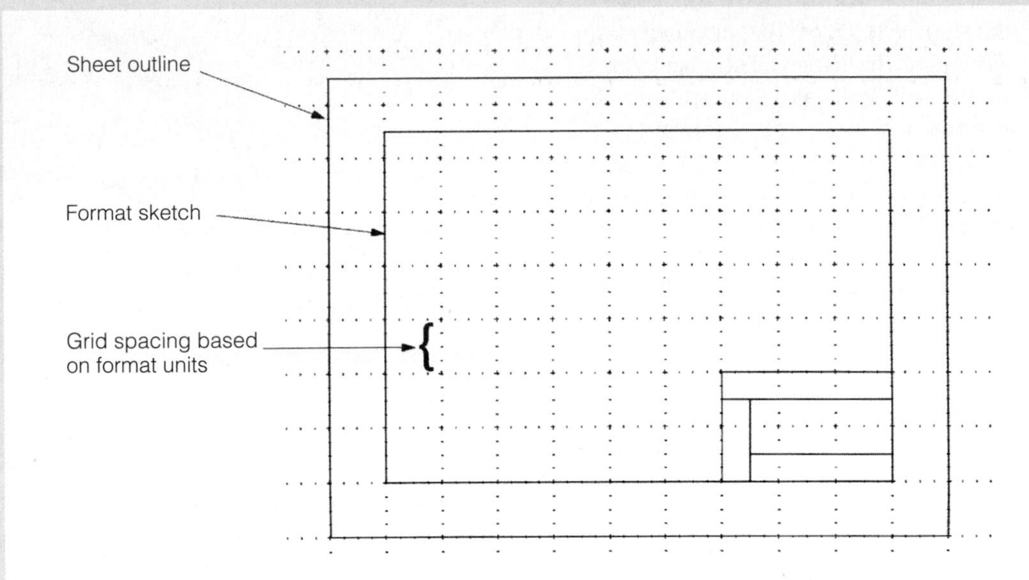

FIGURE C Sketching a Standard Format

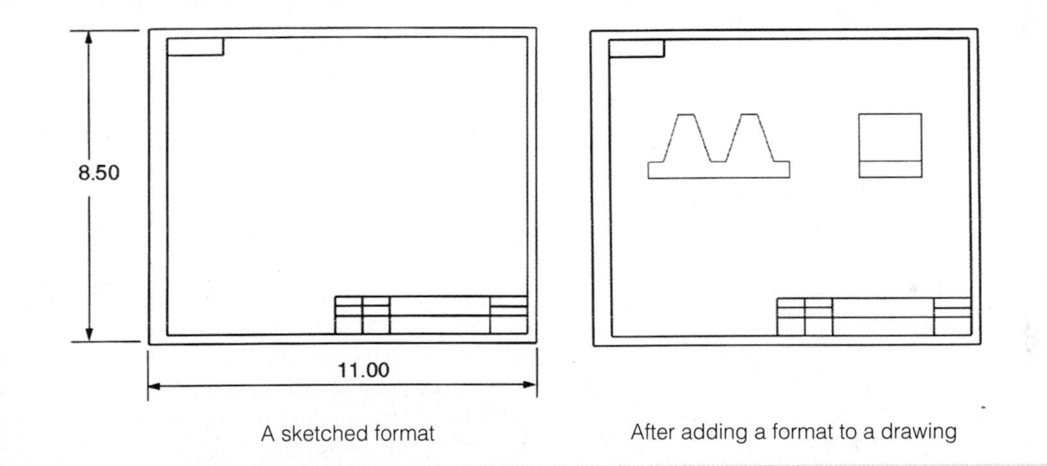

FIGURE D A Sketched Format

Sketched formats (see Fig. C), created in sketcher mode, may be parametrically modified, enabling you to create nonstandard-size formats or families of formats. They can consist of note text, symbols, tables, and drafting geometry, including drafting cross sections and filled areas.

With Pro/ENGINEER you are able to do the following:

- Create draft geometry, notes.
- Move, mirror, copy, group, translate, and intersect geometry.
- Use and modify the draft grid.
- Enter user attributes.
- Create drawing tables.
- Use interface tools to create plot, DXF, SET, and IGES files.
- Import IGES, DXF, and SET files into the format.
- Create user-defined line styles.
- Create, use, and modify symbols.
- Include drafting cross sections in a format.

Regardless of whether you use a standard format or a sketched format, the format is added to a drawing created from a specified view of a parametric 3D model. The sketched format shown here (see Fig. D) was added to the drawing of the part. The system automatically fits a sketched format to the proper size piece of paper. Views and draft entities are scaled accordingly.

When using a T-square, the working edge of the board is the side against which the head of the T-square rests (normally the left side). With the paper positioned near it, the head of the T-square will make full contact with the working edge of the board in all necessary drawing positions. In addition, the blade of the T-square is slightly flexible and "gives" as pressure is applied when drawing. Placing the paper near the working edge of the board allows the T-square to be used with minimum bending of the blade.

When using a parallel straightedge or a drafting machine, the bottom of the paper is aligned first and the corners are then taped.

Unless standard-format preprinted sheets are available, the piece of drawing paper is always about 1 inch larger in width and height than the size of the final sheet. This excess paper is trimmed off when the sheet is complete. (A completed sheet is called a drawing.)

After it is cut from the roll, the paper is placed on the board with its curl down (unless the paper has a "tooth" side that cannot be reversed). This keeps the edges of the paper from being accidentally torn—for instance, by a triangle corner. The paper is square with the board and taped down with small strips of drafting tape—.5 × 1.00 in. is sufficient, or you can use drafting dots. One-half of each strip of tape is attached to the paper first, and then, after the paper is pulled snug (but not stretched), the tape is pressed onto the drawing board. You can hold the paper in position by laying the straightedge across it and holding the straightedge down with the left arm while taping with the right hand. After the two top corners are taped, the straightedge can be released. Then tape the bottom corners. When properly taped down, the paper clings tightly to the board without wrinkles, loose edges, or signs of stretching. Rubbing the edges of the masking tape with your fingernail will make it stick better and make it less likely to roll up under the straightedge and triangles.

Once the paper is taped in position, trim lines are drawn using a straightedge and triangles (corresponding to a standard drawing format). Upon completion of the drawing, the excess paper is trimmed. The trim lines will be the edges of the completed drawing. Standard sheet sizes do not need trimming.

6.9 INSTRUMENT DRAWINGS

Drawings with straight lines that have been drawn with the aid of a T-square, a straightedge, or a drafting machine and triangle are known as **instrument drawings.** These are carefully drawn to an accurate size. Lines of each type are uniform in width and density. The lines begin and end so as to form square corners and intersections.

You should first find the exact center of the sheet by drawing diagonals (connecting opposite corners). This will help center the work on a layout drawing.

Drafting a line in an instrument drawing is a two-step process that requires two different kinds of lines to be drawn. First, the position and the length of the line are determined, and then the line is drawn with correct width and density. The first line, for positioning, is drawn thin and light gray and is called a **construction line.** You may prefer to lay out your work with a nonreproducible-blue lead. After the line's position has been verified and its length measured and marked (Fig. 6.56), a second line is drawn exactly over the first line. This second line is drawn dense and uniform and is called a **printable line.** The part or project being drawn is completely blocked in (laid out) before darkening any lines.

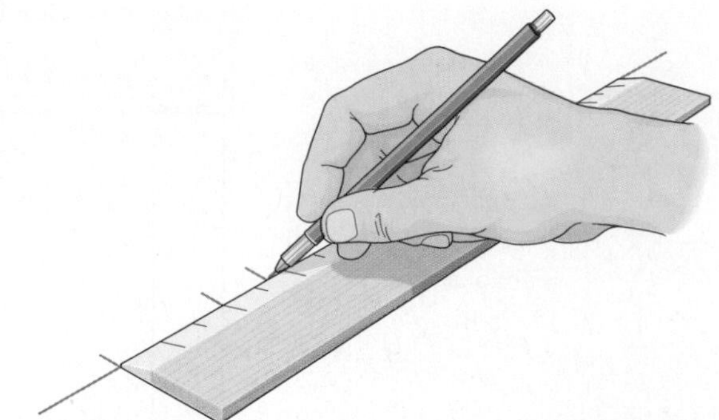

FIGURE 6.56 Measuring with a Scale

Construction lines are used to construct or lay out the drawing. Construction lines may extend somewhat beyond the corners and intersections of the part's outline. Construction lines are thin and gray, and they are cleaned up after the drawing is complete if they will print. Nonreproducible-blue lines do not require erasing since they will not reproduce when the drawing is printed with a whiteprint machine. Printable lines are drawn, with 2H, H, or HB lead, at different widths to show different kinds of information.

Unless company (or school) practice allows construction lines to remain on the finished drawing, any extra lines used for construction purposes are erased before the drawing is darkened. Ask your instructor which method to follow before you complete a project.

6.9.1 Techniques for Drawing Lines

All engineering drawings are created using triangles and/or some form of straightedge. Vertical lines are constructed with a straightedge and triangle or a drafting machine. Horizontal lines are drawn with a straightedge that will give consistently parallel lines. Curved lines are drawn with a compass, a template, or an irregular curve. Lines are not formed freehand; only lettering is drawn freehand.

A properly drawn line is uniform for its entire length. When using a wood pencil or a lead holder, you can make a line consistent in two ways:

1. Incline the pencil or the lead holder so it makes an angle of about 60° with the surface of the paper. Pull the pencil in the direction in which it is leaning (Fig. 6.57). Keep the pencil at a consistent angle as you draw the line.

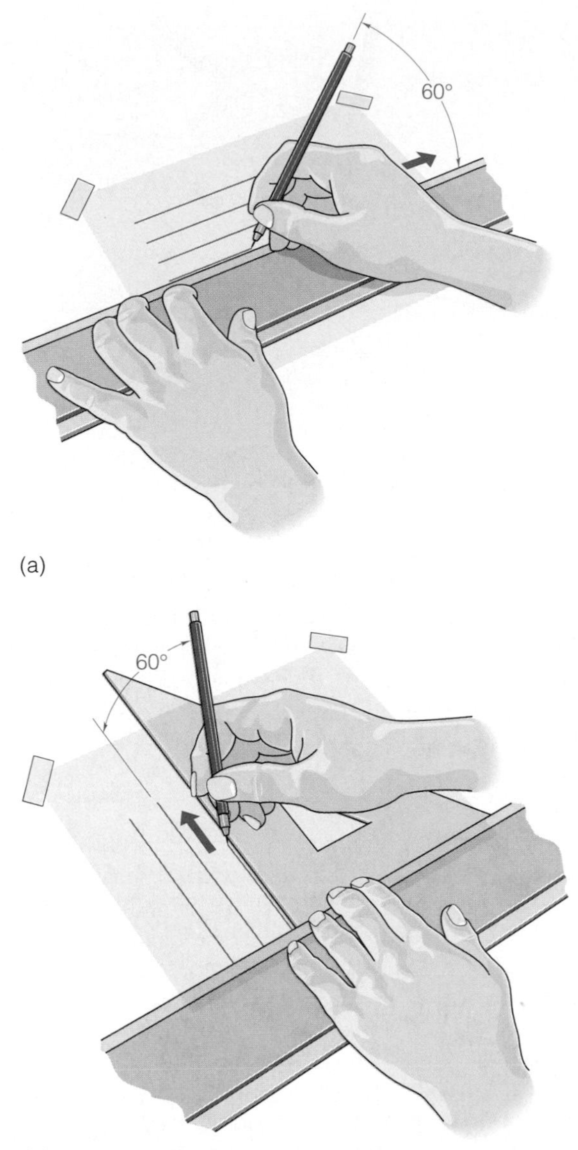

FIGURE 6.57 **Angling the Pencil While Drawing**

2. Rotate the pencil or the lead holder slowly as the line is drawn, to maintain a semisharp conical point. This will enable you to control the thickness and the quality of the line.

These techniques take practice but will soon become automatic. Your lines will be uniform from end to end and from one line to another. Fine-line pencils are held straight (vertical to the board) instead of at an angle and usually do not need to be rotated.

Since most drawings are reduced or enlarged when reproduced, the correct use of line weights and line techniques is essential. Because even the smallest mistake can be magnified, special care must be taken on drawings that are to be enlarged; otherwise the mistake will also be enlarged. On drawings that are to be reduced—for example, printed circuit artwork drawings that are normally drawn at 2:1 or 4:1 enlargements—reduction will clean up and minimize any small problems. However, accuracy is still important, regardless of the scale. Do not rely on reduction to hide any poorly constructed areas of your drawing.

How well lines print is determined by their density—that is, their ability to block light. Density is controlled by the hardness/softness of the lead and by the pressure applied while the line is being drawn. The width and the sharpness of the line are determined by the size of the point touching the paper. A sharpened pencil point should be smoothed and rounded on scratch paper after being repointed. It can also be resharpened on scratch paper. Uniform lines require uniform point preparation.

Fine-line lead holders are available in a variety of different lead thicknesses. A 0.5 and 0.7 mm lead holder with H or 2H leads is good for lettering and linework. Construction lines can be drawn with 0.3 and 0.4 mm fine-line pencils with 3H or 6H leads or nonreproducible-blue leads. These instruments require no sharpening and help maintain a high-quality, consistently uniform line.

Construction lines are drawn with the greatest accuracy possible. To achieve accuracy, place the pencil point on the paper where the line is to be drawn. Then carefully move the straightedge or triangle up to it so as to just touch the pencil point without moving it. Draw a construction line with the pencil point riding along the top edge of the straightedge. Tilt the pencil slightly away from the straightedge. Pull the pencil; do not push it, except when using a fine-line pencil.

6.9.2 Pencil Position for Printable Lines

Once the lines, corners, and intersections have been positioned and verified using construction lines, the figure must be redrawn with printable lines. These are drawn exactly over the construction lines, even though they will not extend the full length of the construction lines. Printable lines will make sharp corners and intersections.

Drawing one line exactly over another is not difficult with the proper technique. Let the pencil lead ride along the top edge of the straightedge (or triangle) by tilting the pencil slightly toward the straightedge. This will move the point slightly away from the straightedge so that both edges of the line are visible as it is being drawn. Also, the construction line is completely visible ahead of the point, so it is easy to see that it has been completely covered by the printable line. It is usually necessary to go over a printable line a couple of times in order to build up enough density to make sharp, clear prints. Again, the wood pencil and the lead holder are pulled (never pushed—they may tear the paper). A consistent line width is maintained by touching up the lead point as often as necessary.

Drawing a straight line while guiding the lead along the top edge of the straightedge requires practice and technique. First, if the point is to stay the same distance from the straightedge as it is being rotated, the pencil point must be prepared with a smooth cone shape—no flat spots. Second, the angle that the pencil tilts over the straightedge, as seen when viewed parallel to the straightedge, must be kept

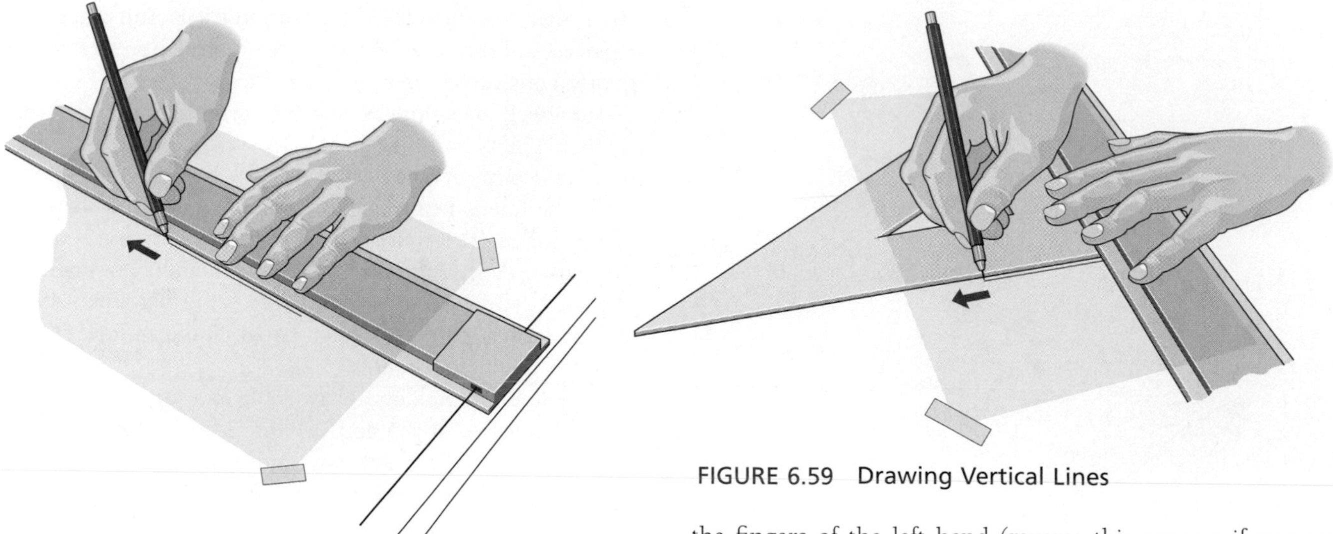

FIGURE 6.58 Drawing Horizontal Lines

FIGURE 6.59 Drawing Vertical Lines

uniform by proper wrist and arm action. This technique will become automatic with a little practice.

6.9.3 Drawing Horizontal Lines

Horizontal lines are drawn with the T-square, the parallel bar, or the drafting machine. Place the pencil point at the desired position of the horizontal line and move the straightedge up to the point, just touching it. When the straightedge is positioned, hold it with the free hand and forearm. This will minimize the deflection of the blade (when using the T-square or a drafting machine) as the line is drawn. Employing the previously discussed techniques, draw the line from left to right (Fig. 6.58). Horizontal lines are always drawn along the top edge of the straightedge. This places the straightedge between the hand and the paper and helps keep the drawing clean.

As any line is drawn, some graphite "chalks" off the point and lies as dust on the drawing. To avoid smearing this graphite dust, frequently blow or brush the dust off the drawing. Always use a drafting brush, never your hand (Fig. 6.25.) Graphite dust is the source of almost all "dirt" on drawings. All drawing equipment is lifted from the board before being moved. If you drag the equipment or instruments across the drawing, you will smear the linework and dirty the drawing. Keep the board, your hands, equipment, and instruments clean to minimize smearing your linework.

6.9.4 Drawing Vertical Lines

Vertical lines are drawn with the vertical edge of any triangle (or the vertical scale of the drafting machine). Position the straightedge and the triangle at the desired spot, with the vertical edge of the triangle to the left (Fig. 6.59). Then place the pencil point at the desired position of the vertical line and move the triangle up to the point, just touching it. This is done by holding the straightedge with the left hand and forearm and positioning the triangle with the fingers of the left hand (reverse this process if you are left-handed). Draw the line from bottom to top using the construction line or printable line technique.

Vertical lines are usually drawn with an upward motion along the left edge of the triangle. This places the triangle between the hand and the paper and helps keep the drawing clean. When drawing a construction line, change only the angle of the pencil. (Twist your body slightly in a counterclockwise direction to achieve a more comfortable position for printable lines.) You can also draw on the right side of the triangle, pulling the pencil toward you. The goal is a clean, accurate, and quickly constructed drawing. Your method of achieving this may differ slightly.

6.9.5 Drawing Lines at an Angle

Sloping lines (angled lines) are drawn much like vertical lines except that the sloping edge of the triangle, adjustable triangle, or drafting machine is used. Lines that slope toward the upper right corner of the board are easily drawn. Sloping lines must first be accurately measured and laid out with construction lines. Check the angle with a protractor before darkening. Figure 6.60 shows how to use a 45° triangle and a 30°/60° triangle to draw a variety of angles when used singly and together. Separately or in combination, the two triangles can achieve any 15° angle increment—15°, 30°, 45°, 60°, 75°, or 90°.

To draw parallel lines (Fig. 6.61), draw the first line as required and then slide the triangle in the direction of the second line. Establish the exact position of the line and complete the construction. Any other parallel lines can be drawn the same way.

Perpendicular lines (Fig. 6.62) are drawn similarly to parallel lines. The exception is that instead of sliding the triangle, you flip the triangle so the edge you were drawing on is now perpendicular to the first line.

6.9.6 Making Accurate Measurements

Accurate drafting is possible only with accurate use of the scale in marking measurements. The thickness of the edge of

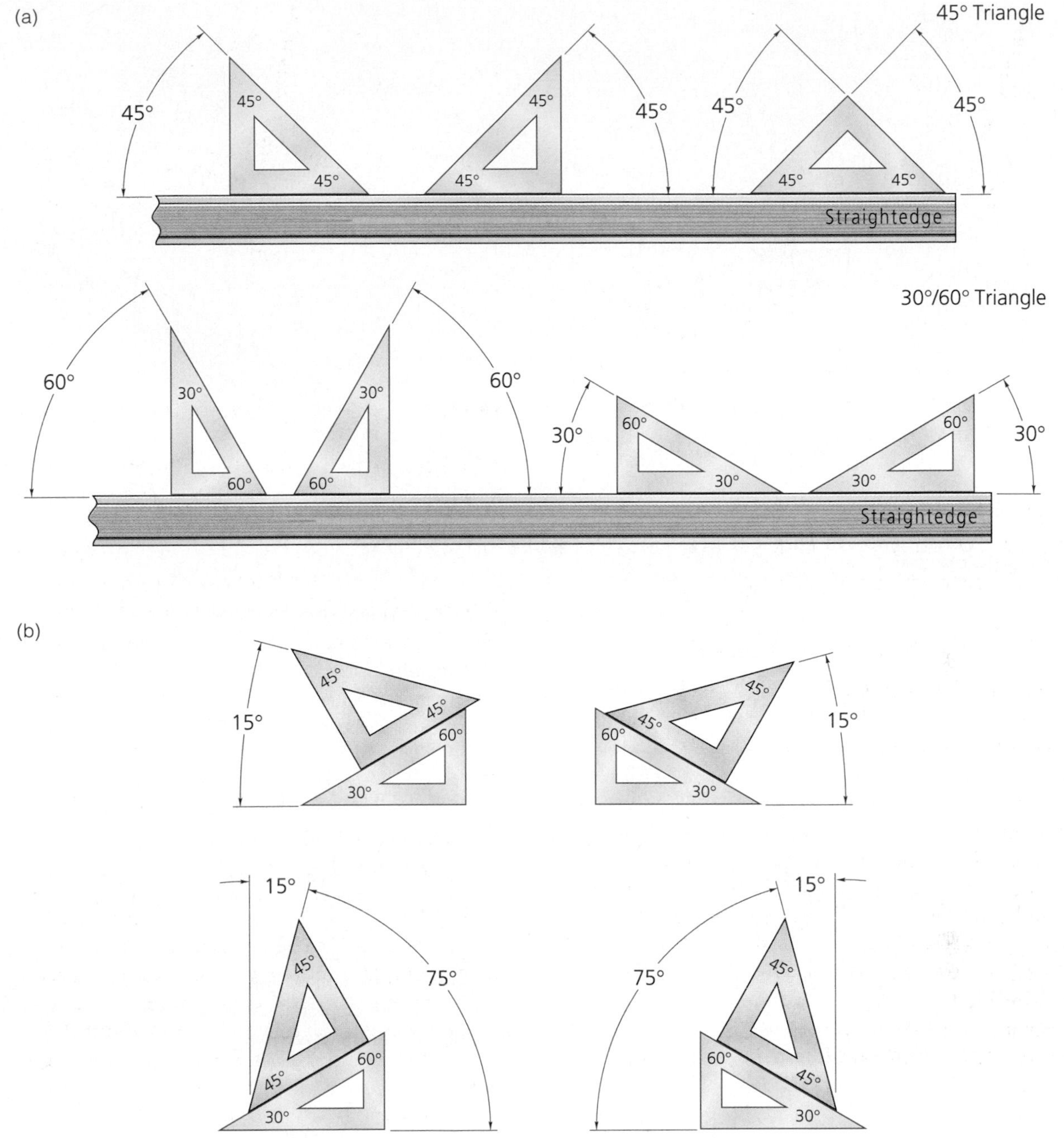

FIGURE 6.60 **Drawing Sloping (Angled) Lines with Triangles**

the scale and the distance from the mark on the scale to the surface of the paper is a physical limitation of your scale's accuracy. The most accurate measurements are made by sighting along a line that is perpendicular to the paper.

All scale readings should be marked on the paper with a short, thin dash (Fig. 6.63). This dash is easily seen after the scale is removed and the straightedge is positioned to use the measurement. Errors in measurement are seldom discovered until much work has been done, at which point the only way to correct them is to erase and redraw. Measurements put down as dots are too often lost, and many incorrect lines have been drawn from specks of dust.

If a number of measurements are to be put down end-to-end, all of them should be measured from the same point. If the measurements are put down by moving the scale for each measurement to the end of the previous one, an accumulation of errors may result in a large error. Remember, a series of successive dimensions is equal to the dimensions' arithmetic total and must be drawn that way.

6.9.7 Using Dividers

Dividers are used to transfer dimensions and measurements. They are *not* for setting off distances when cumulative errors could result; the scale is how to measure divisions in these cases.

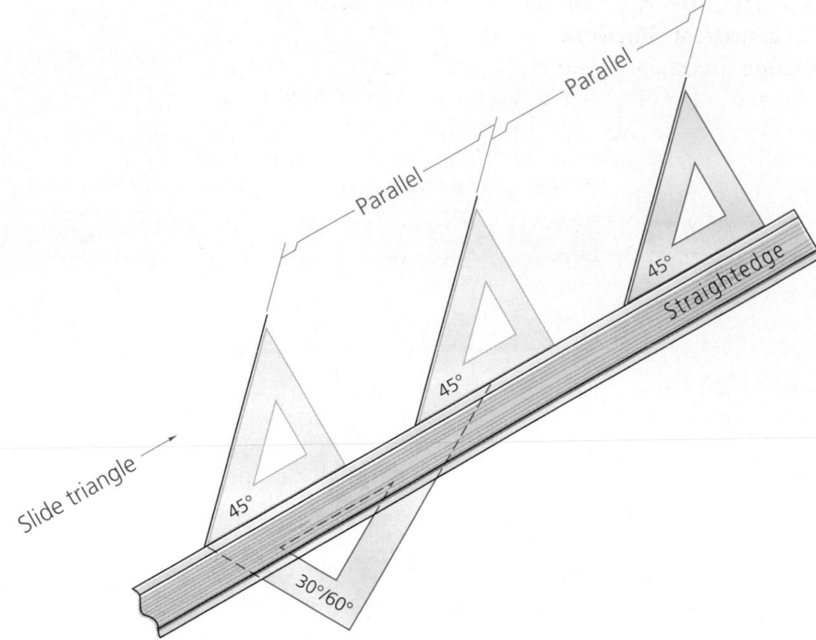

FIGURE 6.61 Construction of Parallel Lines Using Triangles

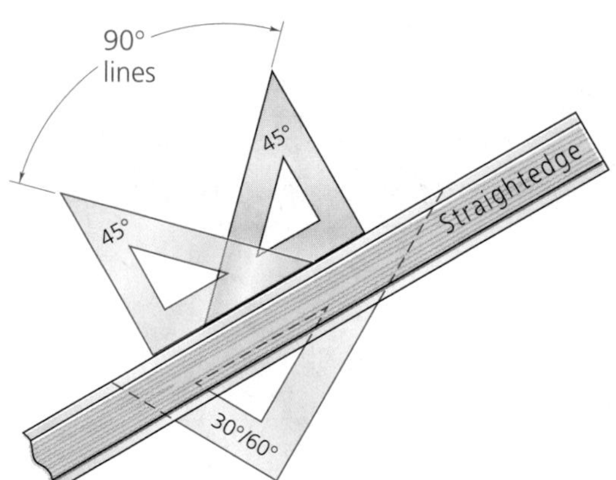

FIGURE 6.62 Construction of Perpendicular Lines Using Triangles

Dividers (Fig. 6.64) are held, adjusted, and manipulated with one hand. Measurements can be taken from an existing view or from a scale. Dividers are one of the most important instruments for quick construction of accurate drawings and are essential for solving descriptive geometry problems.

6.9.8 Drawing Curved Lines

Arcs, circles, and other **curved lines** require special linework techniques. The compass lead is fixed in the compass and cannot be rotated, therefore it requires frequent repointing. Noncircular curves are drawn with a French curve or an irregular curve (Fig. 6.38) or a flexible curve as a guide, but the guide fits the curve only for a short distance. Moreover, curves must be drawn equal in width to the straight lines to produce a uniform drawing.

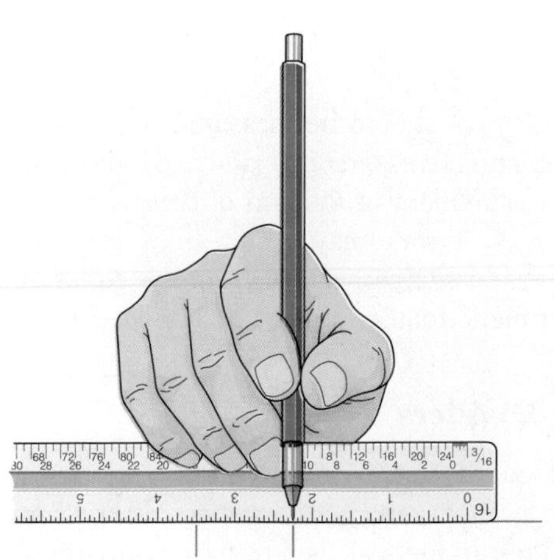

FIGURE 6.63 Measurements with a Scale

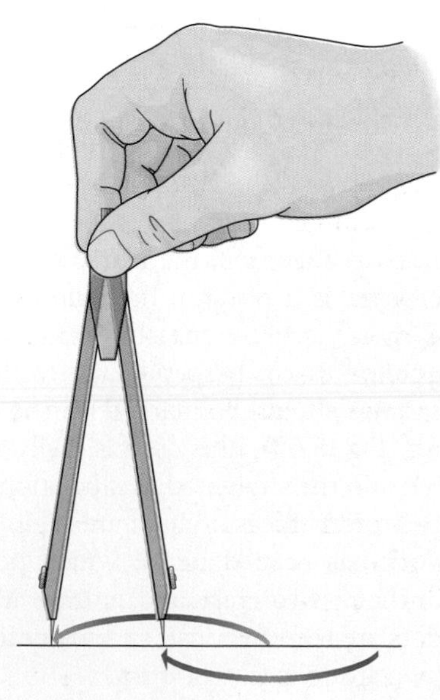

FIGURE 6.64 Using Dividers

The use of the compass and the irregular curve to create dark, consistent linework is typically one of the most frustrating aspects of mastering engineering drawing. Circle, ellipse, and other curved templates are available in standard sizes. These excellent tools can be helpful for many constructions, though they are somewhat limited in sizes and shapes and are relatively expensive if you need to purchase more than a few. Wait to practice curves with templates until you have mastered the compass and the irregular curve.

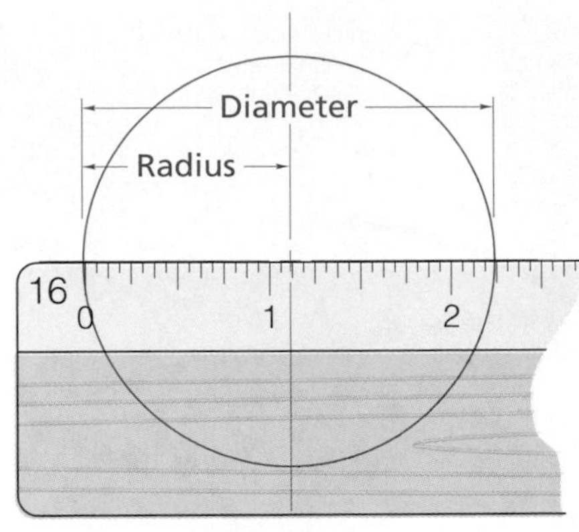

FIGURE 6.65 Measuring a Circle

6.9.9 Using the Bow Compass

As mentioned in the section on instruments, the compass lead in a bow compass should be a short piece of the *same lead* as in the drafting pencil. The lead that comes with the compass is usually unsatisfactory and should be discarded. By using the same lead, both straight and curved lines will be drawn uniformly. Recall that the lead is secured in the compass with about $\frac{1}{8}$ in. (0.9 mm) exposed, and it is sharpened with a sandpaper pad (Fig. 6.42). (Remember, sandpaper pads are very messy and should be kept off of the drawing board and in a plastic bag.) Exercise care in sharpening the lead to keep the line through the point and the lead perpendicular to the sandpaper and to make a flat cut that gives an oval surface. This surface should be about three times as long as the diameter of the lead. The sides of this oval can be lightly sanded. When viewed from the side, the resulting "point" is chisel shaped and should have about the same taper as the cone-shaped taper of the drafting pencil. Because it is almost impossible to reposition the chisel shape properly, the lead in the compass is not adjusted after it has been sharpened. The chisel point should be touched up on scratch paper, and the centering point should be adjusted so that the midpoint of the needle point portion is even with the end of the lead. This adjustment ensures that the point makes proper contact with the paper. The compass can now be adjusted to the required radius and used to draw an arc or a circle.

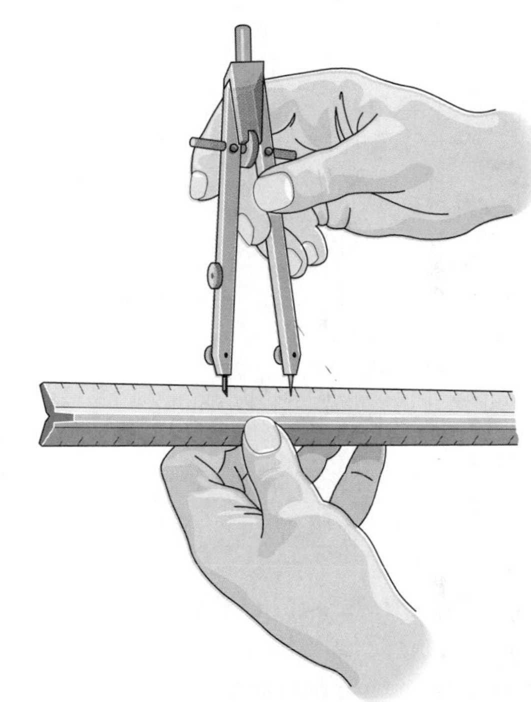
FIGURE 6.66 Setting the Compass Radius

On a construction line drawn on scratch paper, a distance equal to the radius of the circle or arc to be drawn is measured. The compass is set to this distance and a construction circle is drawn. When the diameter of the circle is measured, the reading should be twice that of the given radius. To get an accurate diameter reading, the measurement must be taken along a line that passes through the center point of the circle (Fig. 6.65). Any difference between the measured diameter and twice the given radius is twice the error of the compass setting. In Figure 6.66, the compass is being set by using the scale. This is not the easiest or most accurate method, but it is faster.

The width of the line drawn is determined by the thickness of the lead at the bevel. As a circle is drawn, the point shortens and the line widens. Therefore, a circle is started with a line somewhat narrower than desired. The line is redrawn until it is the correct width and density. A longer taper will hold a line width longer than a short stubby taper.

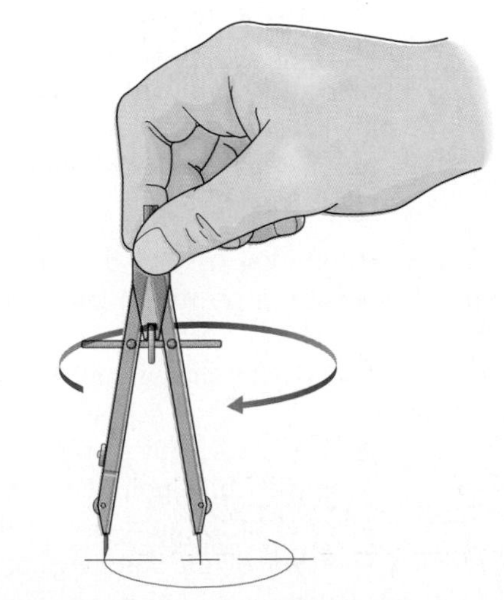
FIGURE 6.67 Using the Bow Compass

Figure 6.67 shows the proper method of constructing a

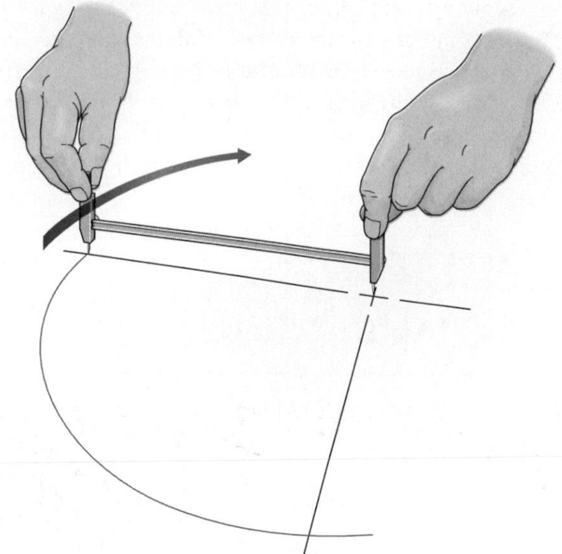

FIGURE 6.68 Using the Beam Compass

circle with a bow compass. First, draw the circle with a thin dark line. Then thicken it by resetting the radius slightly and drawing another curve touching the first one. This method ensures crisp, black lines of the appropriate thickness. Of course, this method is of no use for drawing a hidden (dashed) line. Dashed curves are drawn with a slightly dulled compass lead point and only one pass to complete the circle.

The beam compass (Fig. 6.68) is used when a large-diameter circle or arc is required. Both hands are required to draw a circle with this instrument.

6.9.10 Using the Irregular Curve

Noncircular curves require the **irregular curve** (see Fig. 6.38) to make smooth, printable lines. Examples of such curves are the ellipse—an angular view of a circle—the helix, and spirals. Irregular curves are manufactured in many shapes and sizes.

Curves that are drawn with the irregular curve are usually determined by first plotting a series of points that are known to lie on the curve. Then a curve is drawn that includes all of these points. Figure 6.69 illustrates the use of the irregular curve. Good results can be obtained by following these steps:

1. Lightly sketch a smooth line freehand to include the plotted points. It is easier to set the irregular curve to a line than it is to match a series of points.
2. Set the irregular curve so that it matches a part of the line (at least three points).
3. Draw the line that fits the curve, but stop a little before the end of the fit (before the third point).
4. Reset the irregular curve to fit the next part of the curve and draw the next portion of the line. Again, the last portion of fit is not drawn.

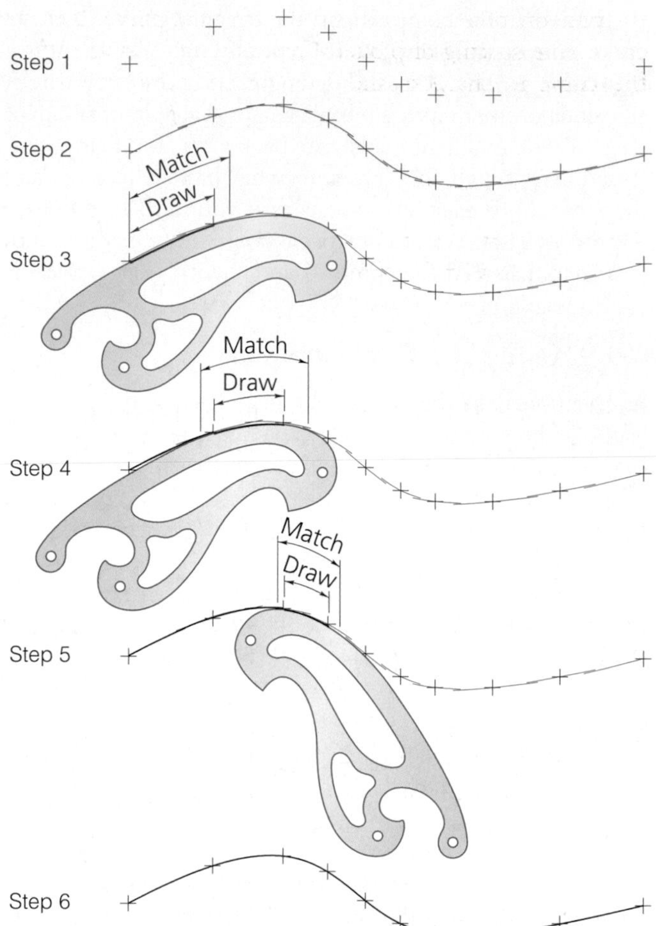

FIGURE 6.69 Using the Irregular Curve

5. Repeat this process until the curve is complete.

If the sketched curve and the first series of matching the irregular curve to the sketched line are all done on a tracing paper overlay, then the result will be much neater. The ends of each segment of the line are marked as the line matches the irregular curve. Then the same fits can be used in the next step. When all fits are made, the tracing paper overlay is placed under the drawing and carefully aligned with the curve under the plotted points. The curve is traced onto the drawing with the irregular curve marked on the overlay. This technique has two advantages. First, all fits are made on throwaway paper, where erasures can easily be made without erasing the plotted points. Second, before the final drawing of the curve, the accuracy of fit can be seen when the overlay is positioned under the drawing.

The overlay technique is particularly valuable when the curve is symmetrical. For example, an ellipse has four identical curves—two are mirror images of the other two. All are symmetrical about the major and minor axes. It is necessary to fit only one of these curves, then this fit is duplicated on the other three.

If a smooth curve is desired, the plotting of the points of an irregular curve is particularly important. A small error in the position of a point can easily cause irregularities in the curve. The spacing of plotted points should be small where the curve is sharpest and long where the curve is the straightest.

6.9.11 Keeping Your Drawings Clean

All drawings attract dirt. How much dirt is determined by your habits as a drafter. Cleanliness does not just happen; it is the result of developing correct habits. Procedures and techniques that will keep your drawings clean include the following.

Keep your hands clean. Periodically wash your hands to remove accumulations of graphite, perspiration, body oils, and dirt.

Keep your equipment clean. Periodically wash with soap and water all tools that touch the paper. Tools that contain wood or metal should be cleaned with a damp sponge; when they become soiled, they must also be scrubbed. The drawing surface should be cleaned regularly.

Clean up graphite dust. Most dirt on a drawing is actually graphite. Repeated and consistent use of the drafting brush and the dust pad to remove this graphite dust, before other tools smear it around, will contribute significantly to cleaner drawings. Always brush after erasing.

Keep your pencil point clean. The pencil pointer leaves dust clinging to the lead. Some pointers also push shavings up into the pencil's jaws. If the dust and the shavings are not removed before drawing starts, they will drop onto the drawing. Thus, after each sharpening, lightly tap the pencil on the side of the desk to dislodge any shavings and then wipe the lead on a piece of tissue. Poking the lead point into a piece of Styrofoam also works well.

Keep your paper clean. Proper use of the straightedge and triangle always places these instruments between your hands and the paper. Even clean hands will put body oils onto the paper; this has a magnetic effect on dirt. When lettering, place a sheet of clean paper under your hands to keep the drawing cleaner.

6.9.12 Inking Drawings

Ink is frequently used on drafting film or vellum. Drawings used in product literature, technical manuals, and pictorial illustrations are normally inked to get good photographic quality.

Ink drawings must first be laid out with construction lines and then inked. It is very difficult to ink a drawing while laying it out. Light tables are excellent for inking and tracing drawings. Because ink tends to flow between surfaces and to smear lines, triangles and templates must be raised from the drawing when inking a line. Specially designed equipment with a ledge or with inking risers prevents the equipment from being flush with the paper.

Ink drawings are prepared with technical pens (Fig. 6.70). Keeping the technical pen almost vertical helps prevent uneven and ragged linework (Fig. 6.71). If possible, no more than one pass should be made for thin and medium lines. Extremely thick lines are drawn with an appropriate pen size. If a thinner pen is used to thicken the line in stages, better results may be obtained.

The ink should be completely dry before you start another portion of the drawing. Some drafters prefer to ink all horizontal lines from the top of the sheet downward and then from left to right. Ink lines should be erased very

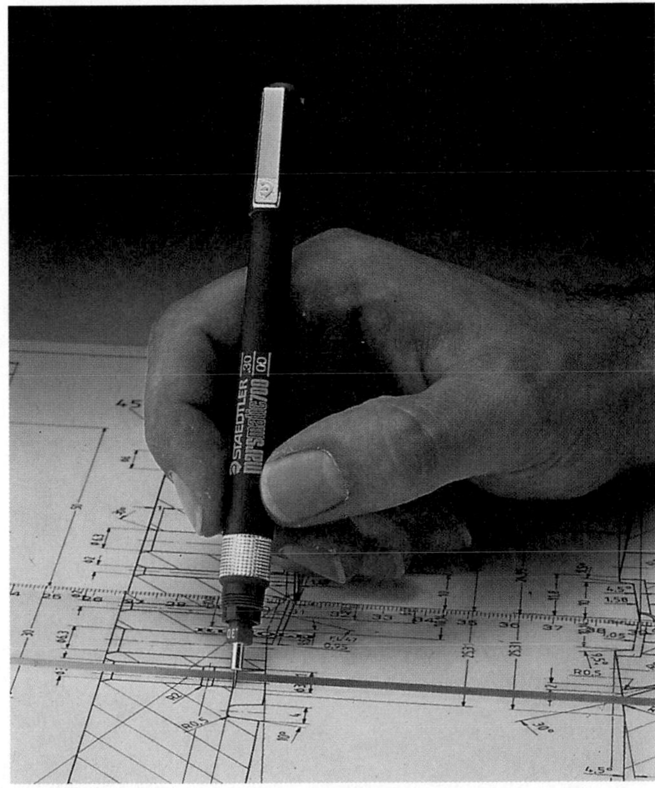

FIGURE 6.70 Inking with a Technical Pen

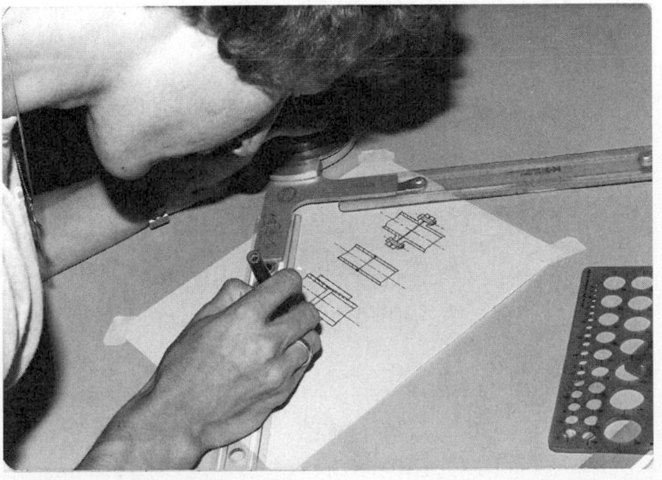

FIGURE 6.71 Inking

carefully, especially on vellum or other types of paper. You can easily erase ink from drafting film with the proper type of eraser and a small amount of moisture. As in pencil drawings, the surrounding lines should be protected while erasing.

You May Complete Exercises 6.1 Through 6.12 at This Time

QUIZ

True or False

1. Plastic leads are used on vellum.
2. 5H and 6H leads are used to darken the final drawing.
3. Construction lines drawn with nonreproducible-blue lead do not require erasing before the drawing is darkened.
4. The title block is always placed in the lower left-hand corner of the sheet.
5. Hidden lines always take precedence over centerlines.
6. Object lines are thin, black, and approximately 0.35 mm.
7. Break lines are normally drawn freehand.
8. A dry cleaning pad is used to remove graphite from a newly sharpened pencil.

Fill in the Blanks

9. A sandpaper pad is used to ______.
10. Dry cleaning pads are used to ______ and ______ a drawing.
11. An architect's scale is ______ divided.
12. ______ and ______ curves are used to draw odd-sized circular curves and arcs.
13. Technical pens should be held ______.
14. A mechanical engineer's scale is ______ divided.
15. Always draw on the ______ side of the straightedge.
16. Incline lead holders at ______ degrees to the drafting board when drawing.

Answer the Following

17. Describe the process of drawing a vertical instrument line.
18. Describe three ways to keep your drawing clean.
19. Explain how to sharpen and prepare a wooden pencil for drawing an instrument line.
20. Describe the process of drawing an irregular curve.
21. Describe the two primary types of drawing media used in drafting.
22. What does the term *precedence of lines* mean?
23. What line widths are used on a drafting format and title block?
24. Name five types of information included in a title block.

EXERCISES

Transfer the given information to an "A"-size sheet of .25 in. grid paper. Complete all views, and solve for proper visibility, including centerlines, object lines, and hidden lines. Exercises that are not assigned by the instructor can be sketched in the text to provide practice and to enhance understanding of the preceding instructional material.

After Completing the Chapter You May Draw the Assigned Exercises

Exercise 6.1 Draw the given design.

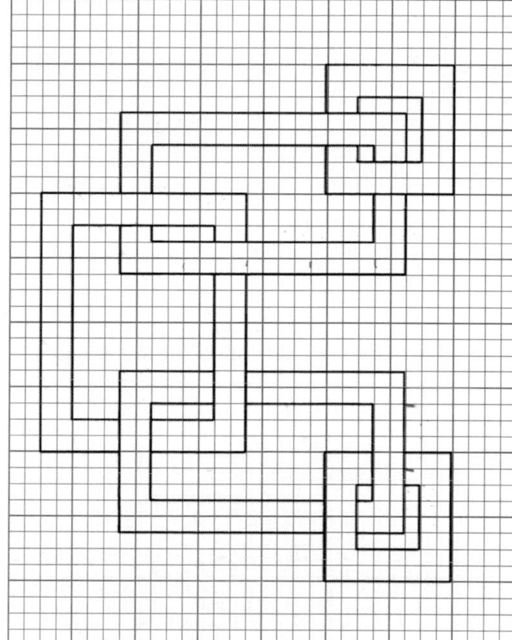

EXERCISE 6.1

Exercise 6.2 Draw the cover plate.

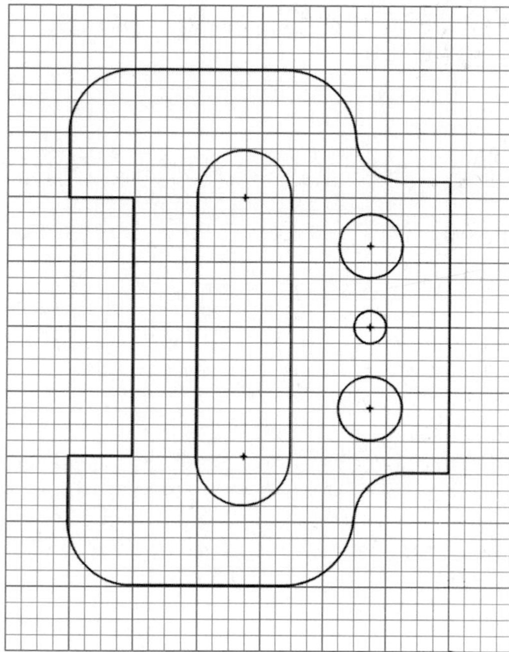

EXERCISE 6.2

Exercise 6.3 Draw the gage plate.

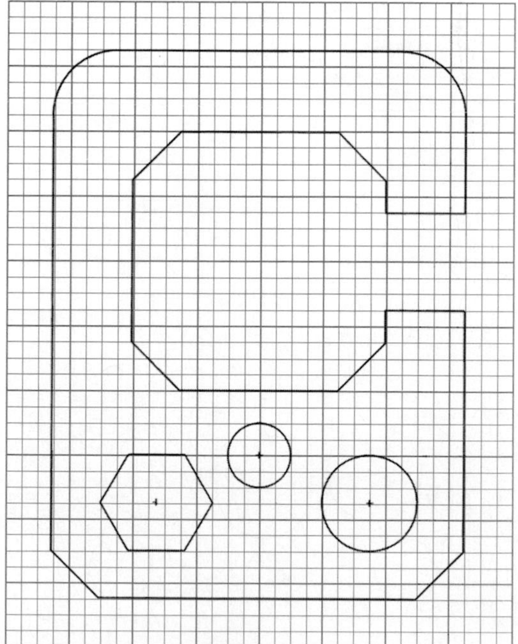

EXERCISE 6.3

Exercise 6.4 Draw the design.

EXERCISE 6.4

Exercise 6.5 Draw the two gaskets.

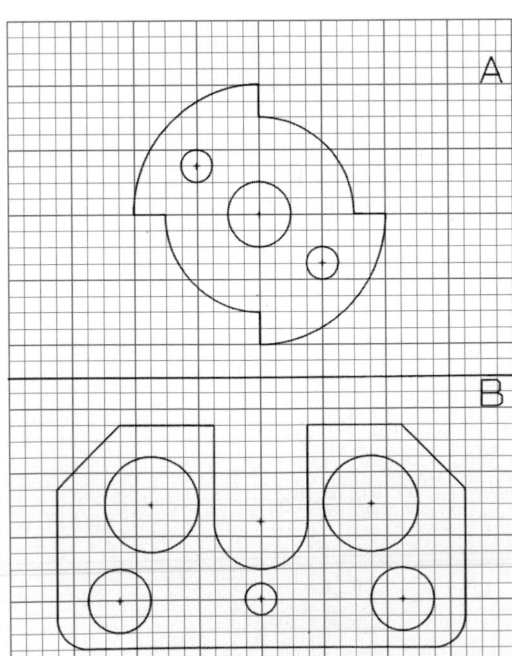

EXERCISE 6.5

Exercise 6.6 Draw the two cover plates.

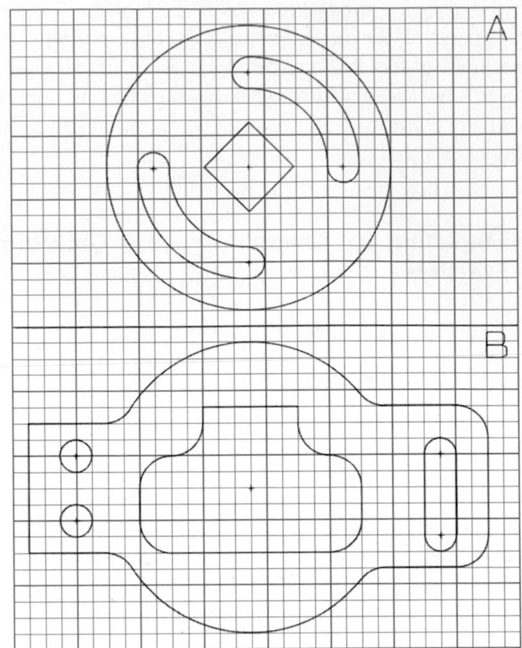

EXERCISE 6.6

Exercise 6.7 Draw the complete cone check and guide.

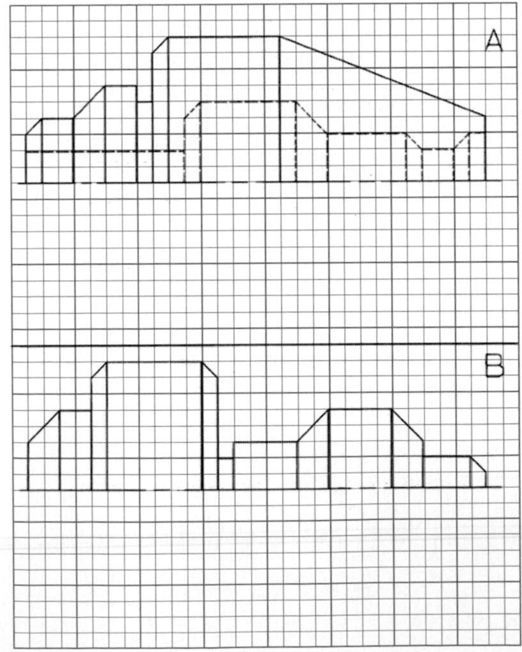

EXERCISE 6.7

Exercise 6.8 Draw the two guides.

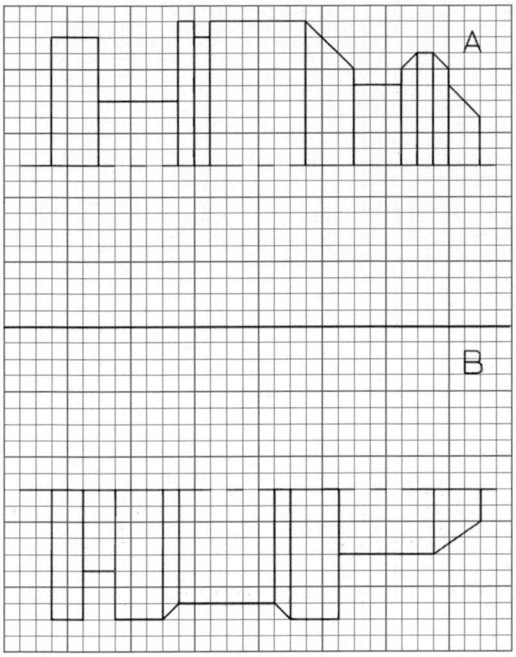

A

B

EXERCISE 6.8

Exercise 6.9 Draw the control plate.

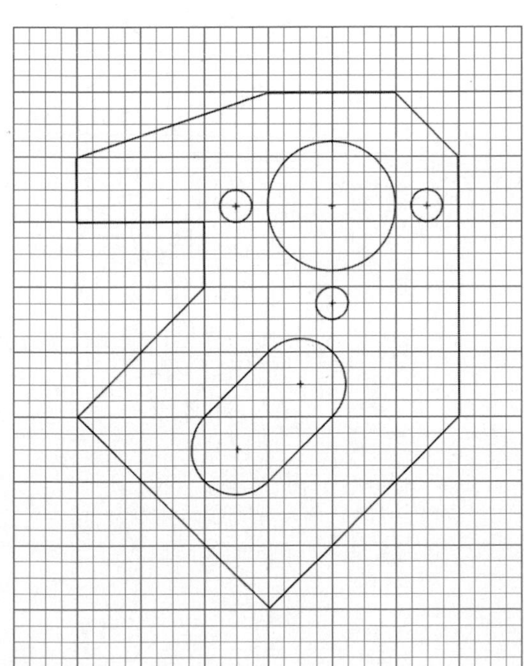

EXERCISE 6.9

Exercise 6.10 Draw the disk guide.

EXERCISE 6.10

Exercise 6.11 Draw the mount surface.

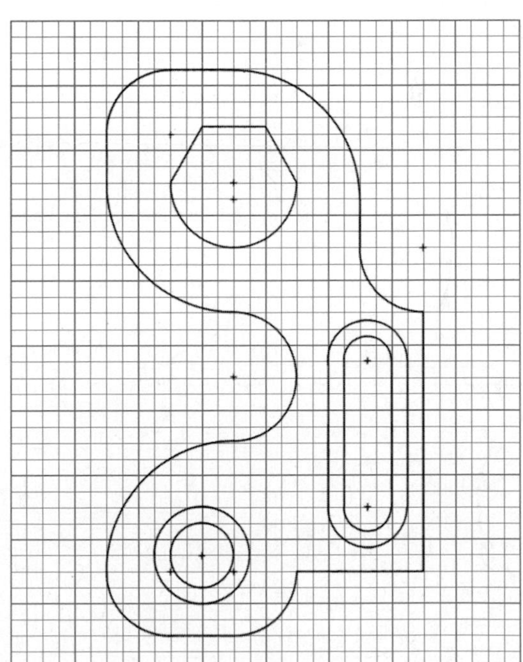

EXERCISE 6.11

Exercise 6.12 Draw the tube gasket.

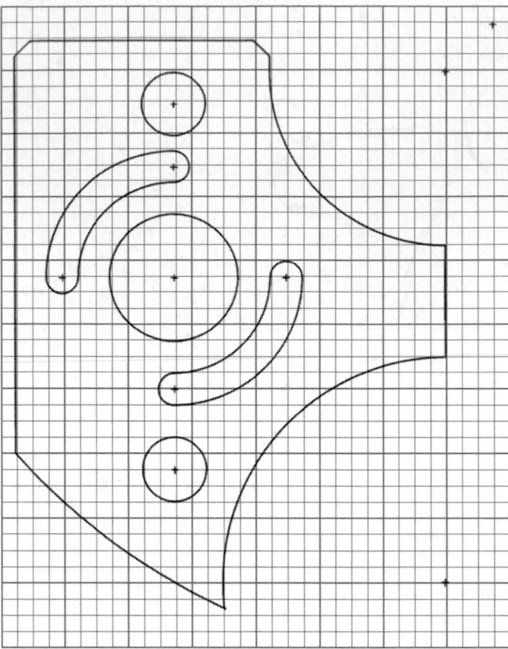

EXERCISE 6.12

PROBLEMS

Problems 6.1(A) Through (K) Draw each problem assigned by the instructor on an "A"-size sheet, one drawing per sheet. Establish measurements by using one of the three scales provided. Your instructor may request enlarged or reduced drawings as needed.

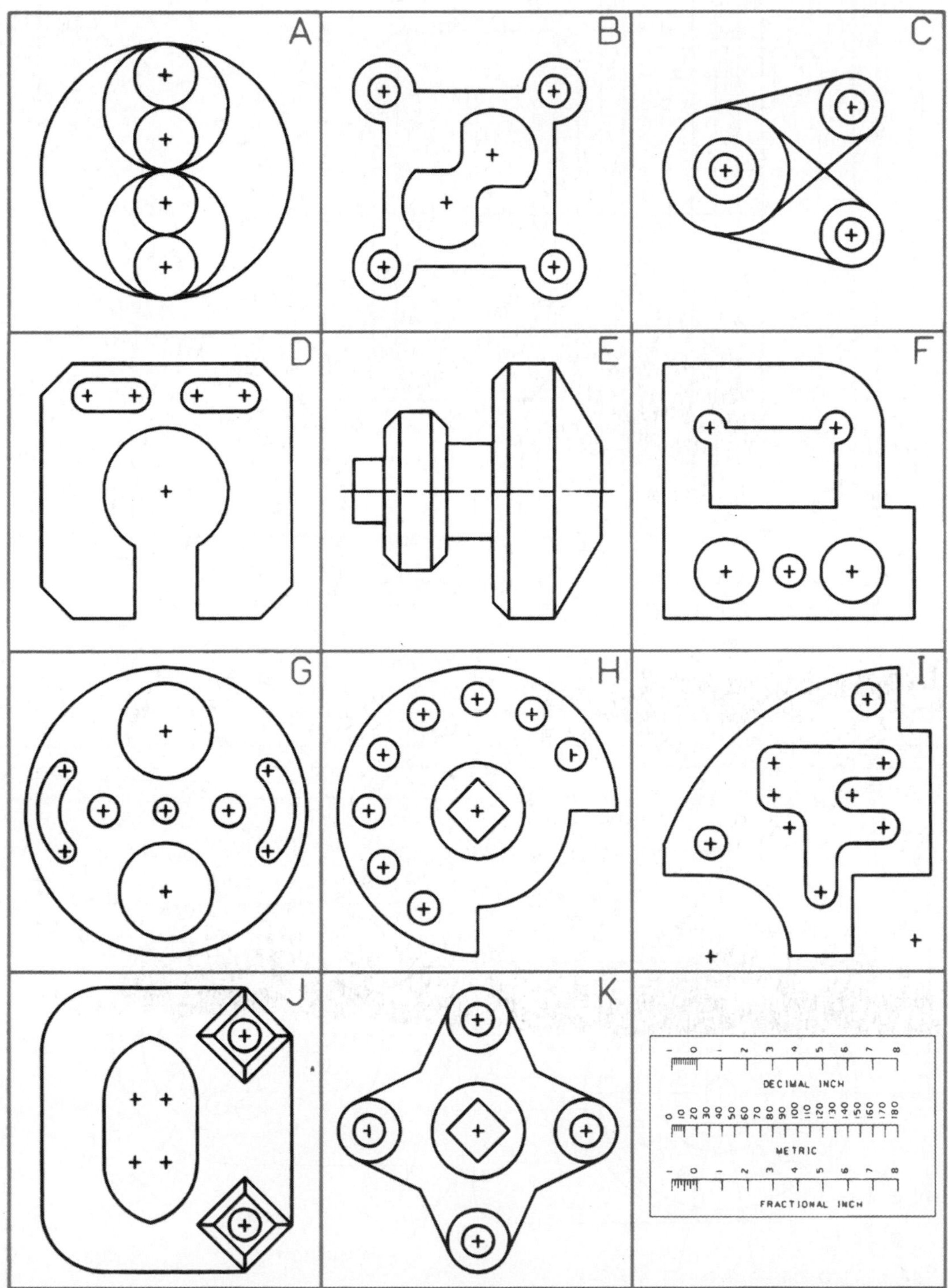

PROBLEM 6.1

Problem 6.2

An "A"-size drawing format is called for in this project. Redraw the given object. Do not dimension.

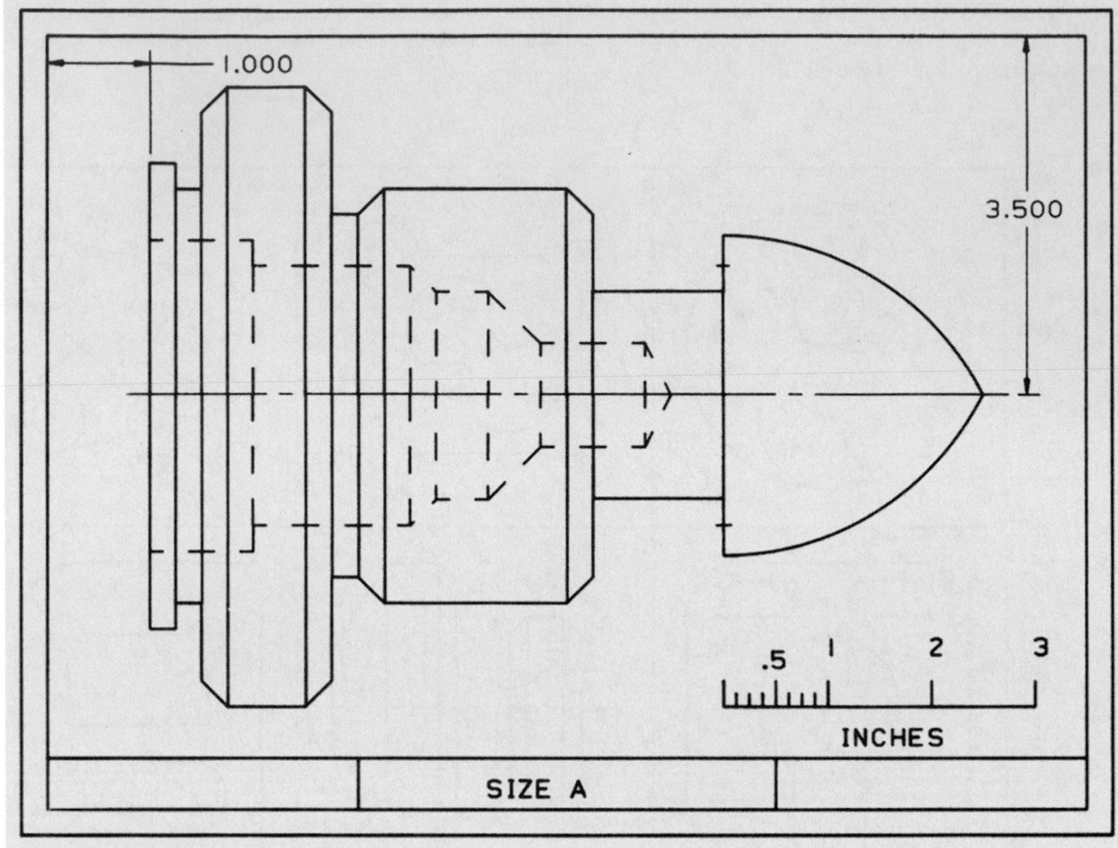

PROBLEM 6.2

Problem 6.3 Using a "B"-size sheet, redraw the part. This is an ISO (International Standards Organization—see Chapter 1) standard drawing using metric dimensions (millimeters). Do not dimension. This drawing includes the diameter symbol ∅ and the square symbol □.

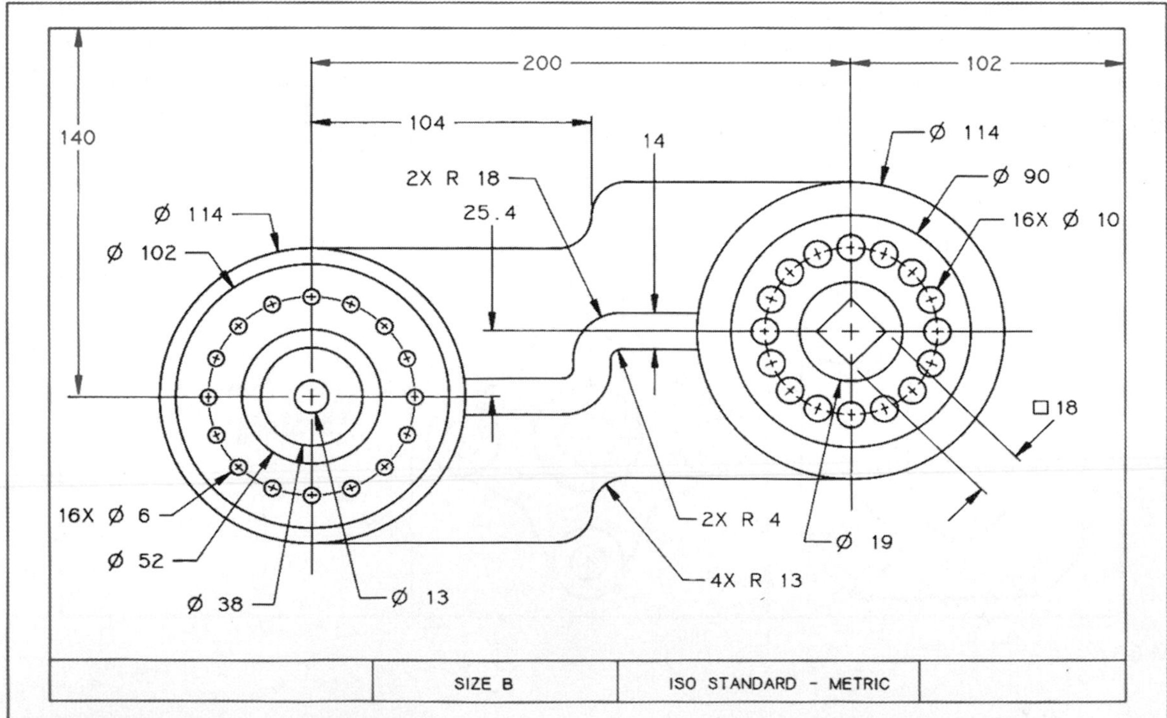

PROBLEM 6.3 Assembly Plate

Problem 6.4 Using a "C"-size sheet, draw the part as shown. Dimension only if assigned by the instructor. (This project is difficult; information contained in Chapter 8 concerning tangent arcs may be helpful.)

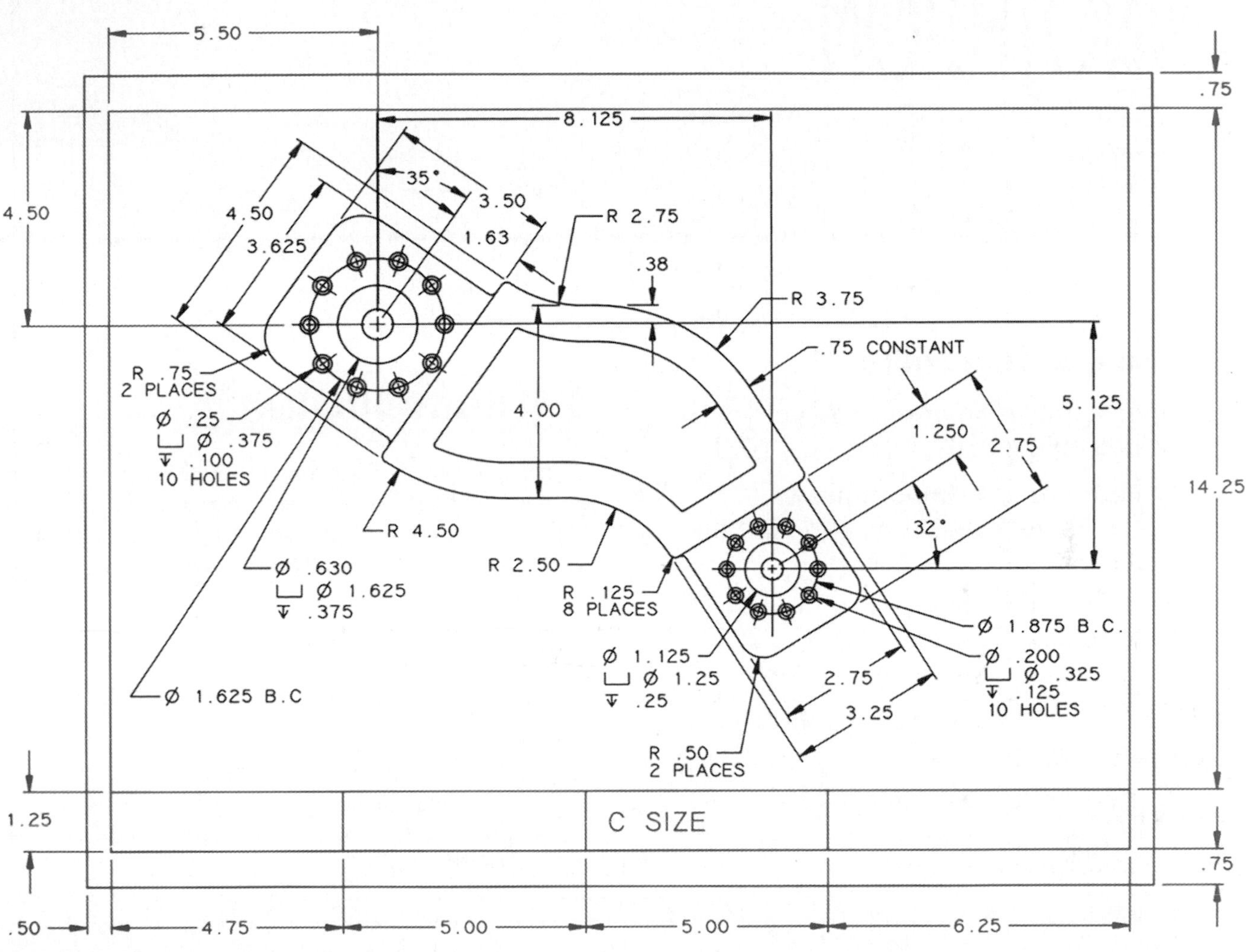

PROBLEM 6.4 Arm

LETTERING AND ANNOTATION

Chapter 7

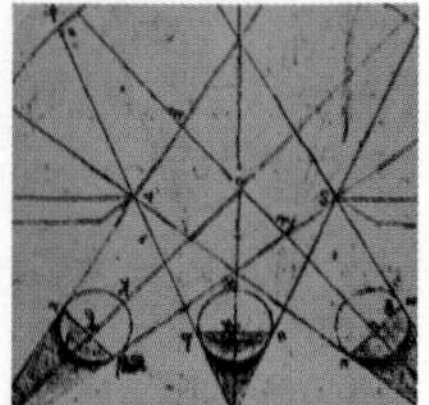

LEARNING OBJECTIVES

Upon completion of this chapter you will be able to:

1. Recognize the importance of freehand, mechanical, and machine lettering.
2. Differentiate between common lettering styles.
3. Develop the ability to use guidelines and lettering guides to determine lettering heights.
4. Produce standard single-stroke, uppercase Gothic characters with uniform size and spacing.
5. Identify and use mechanical lettering aids.
6. Identify machine lettering techniques.
7. Create annotations using a CAD system.

7.1 INTRODUCTION

Engineering drawings are never complete until they are explained by labels, dimensions, notations, and titles (Fig. 7.1). This information is either carefully lettered freehand or inserted using a **TEXT** or **DIMENSION** command when done on a CAD system.

All designers and engineers should master the art of freehand lettering. Through the study of letter forms and the direction of strokes, and with consistent practicing of lettering styles, an acceptable quality and style of lettering can be developed. The importance of good lettering cannot be overemphasized. Lettering can *make or break* an otherwise excellent drawing. In engineering and design, sloppy or misplaced lettering causes misconceptions and inaccurate communication of data.

CAD-generated drawings allow the engineer to access the database and therefore request the system to provide extra information, clarification, and verification of a part. Because drawings generated on the board can only be "read," the written information about the part, in the form of notes, labels, and dimensions, is of great importance. This is not to say that the written information on a CAD drawing is any less important. With a CAD system you can recall the part drawing and verify a location of a feature, check a dimension, or list out information about the part, but all written information is still important. However, manual lettering must stand completely on its own.

7.2 LETTERING METHODS AND STYLES

Lettering can be done by any of three separate methods: (1) manual (freehand), (2) mechanical, and (3) machine. Table

FIGURE 7.1 An Engineering Drawing

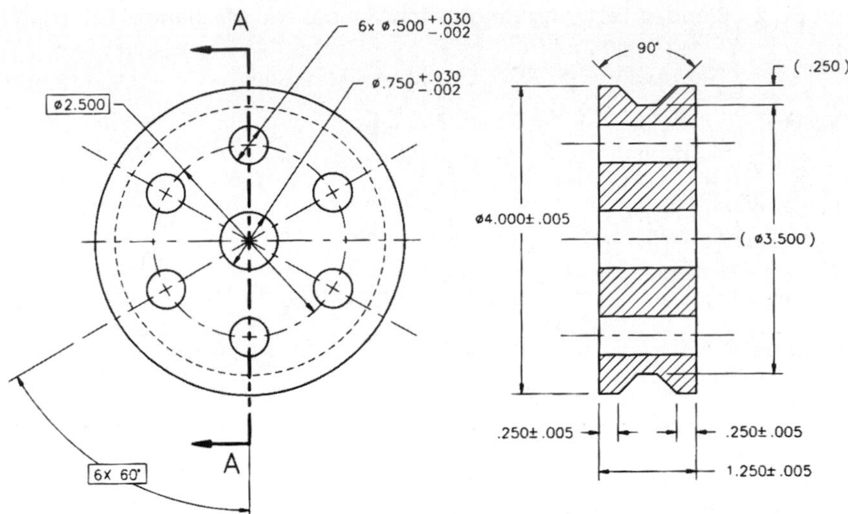

TABLE 7.1 Lettering Methods

Types of Letters	Manual	Mechanical	Machine
Vertical	Freehand	Template	Typewriter
Inclined	Lettering aid	WRICO	Printer
Uppercase	(slot guide)	Leroy	Dry transfer
Lowercase		Letterguide	Phototypesetter
		Varigraph	CAD
		Kroy	

7.1 lists the three categories along with a few types of equipment and the techniques associated with each group.

A wide variety of lettering styles, or fonts, are available. A **font** is an assortment of type all of one size and style. For most engineering disciplines, the *single-stroke uppercase Gothic alphabet* is used. The Gothic alphabet does not have short bars, or **serifs,** at the ends of strokes as does the Roman alphabet. Figure 7.2 shows a few of the many fonts commercially available in phototypesetting and printing processes and in dry transfer letters. Note that the vertical uppercase DRAFTING STANDARD font is available.

Lettering of titles, subtitles, drawing numbers, and other uses may be made freehand, by typewriter, or with the aid of mechanical lettering devices such as templates and lettering machines. Regardless of the method used, all characters must conform with the recommended Gothic style and must be legible in full- or reduced-size copy by any accepted method of reproduction. The quality of your lettering after reduction will depend on the legibility of the original lettering and its height. The recommended minimum freehand and mechanical lettering heights for various size drawings are given in Table 7.2.

American Typewriter Condensed
American Typewriter Condensed Bold
CooperBl.Ital
CooperBlk.Out.
COPPERPLATE
DAVIDA
Dom Casual
Eurostile Med.Ex.
Eurostile Bold Ext.
Fette Fraktur
Folio Light
Folio Medium
Folio Bold
Folio Ex. Bold
Folio Bold Cond.
Gregorian
Helvetica Oblique
Helvetica Rounded
Meather Regular
MESQUITE REGULAR

FIGURE 7.2 Examples of Lettering Fonts

7.3 MANUAL LETTERING

Many drawings are still made and revised with freehand lettering techniques. Both **vertical lettering** (Fig. 7.3) and **inclined lettering** (Fig. 7.4) are found throughout industry. Vertical lettering is preferred since it reduces and microfilms better than inclined lettering. Still, inclined lettering is easier for some to master and normally is faster to complete. Most companies accept only vertical lettering. At times, you may be called on to complete or revise an existing drawing. If you are given such a task, try to match the existing lettering style.

Uppercase letters are used for all lettering on drawings unless lowercase letters are required to conform with other established standards, equipment nomenclature, or marking. Lowercase lettering is seldom found on engineering draw-

TABLE 7.2 Blended Lettering Heights for Manual and Mechanical Lettering (Uppercase Letters)

Project	Size of Drawing	Height of Manual Letters, U.S. (Metric) Units	Height of Mechanical Letters, U.S. (Metric) Units
Numbers in a title block	A–C*	.250 in., $\frac{1}{4}$ in. (7 mm)	.240 in. (7 mm)
	D and above*	.312 in., $\frac{5}{16}$ in. (7 mm)	.290 in. (7 mm)
Title, section lettering	A–F	.250 in., $\frac{1}{4}$ in. (7 mm)	.240 in. (7 mm)
Zone letters and numerals in borders	A–F	.188 in., $\frac{3}{16}$ in. (5 mm)	.175 in. (5 mm)
Lettering in dimensions, tolerances, notes, tables, limits	A–C D and above	.125 in., $\frac{1}{8}$ in. (3.5 mm) .156 in., $\frac{5}{32}$ in. (5 mm)	.120 in. (3.5 mm) .140 in. (5 mm)

*Drawing sizes: A = $8\frac{1}{2} \times 11$ in., B = 11×17 in., C = 17×22 in., D = 22×34 in.

ABCDEFGHIJKLMNOP
QRSTUVWXYZ&
1234567890

FIGURE 7.3 ANSI Standard Vertical Upper- and Lowercase Lettering

ABCDEFGHIJKLMNOP
QRSTUVWXYZ&
1234567890

FIGURE 7.4 ANSI Standard Inclined Upper- and Lowercase Lettering

ABCDEFGHIJKLMNO
PQRSTUVWXYZ
1234567890

FIGURE 7.5 ANSI Standard Microfont Alphabet

ings except for the drawing *notes,* since long columns of uppercase characters are not as pleasing to the eye and are harder to read. The use of lowercase lettering is specified in company standards when acceptable. In general, only uppercase Gothic lettering is required on mechanical and electronic drawings. Piping, architectural, structural, and civil drawings sometimes employ lowercase lettering.

Though the recommended font style is single-stroke Gothic, adaptations such as the **Gothic-style Microfont alphabet** are also acceptable (Fig. 7.5). The Microfont alphabet is suggested for drawings requiring microfilm reproduction.

7.3.1 Guidelines and Lettering Heights

Freehand lettering requires guidelines at the top and bottom of the letters to determine the height of lettering on the drawing. Guidelines are not necessary if you use grid underlay or fadeout grid paper, but you should avoid using grid underlay until you have gained some experience with lettering from hand-drawn guidelines.

Guidelines (Fig. 7.6) are very thin, sharp, light gray, and drawn with 6H–3H grade lead or with nonreproducible-blue lead. Since most lettering is done with capital letters and whole numbers, only two guidelines are necessary. Guidelines can be drawn with a straightedge or with the aid of a line-spacing guide, such as the AMES lettering guide (Fig. 7.7) or the Braddock-Rowe triangle. For dimensions, notes, and labels, most lettering is between .125 and .156 in. high (in U.S. decimal units) or between 3.5 and 5 mm high (in SI units). Lettering height is determined by the drawing format size. For all problems in the text, use the standards for lettering heights and guideline spacing shown in Table 7.2. Lettering heights in the table correspond to *Conventions and Lettering* from the American National Standards Institute. (Metric sizes are not U.S. conversions.)

The distance between lines of lettering on manually drawn projects for notes and labels is equal to the full height of the letter being used. This spacing is best for reproducible, legible letters if they will be reduced and/or enlarged (for instance, when a microfilmed drawing is returned to its original size). When upper- and lowercase lettering is used

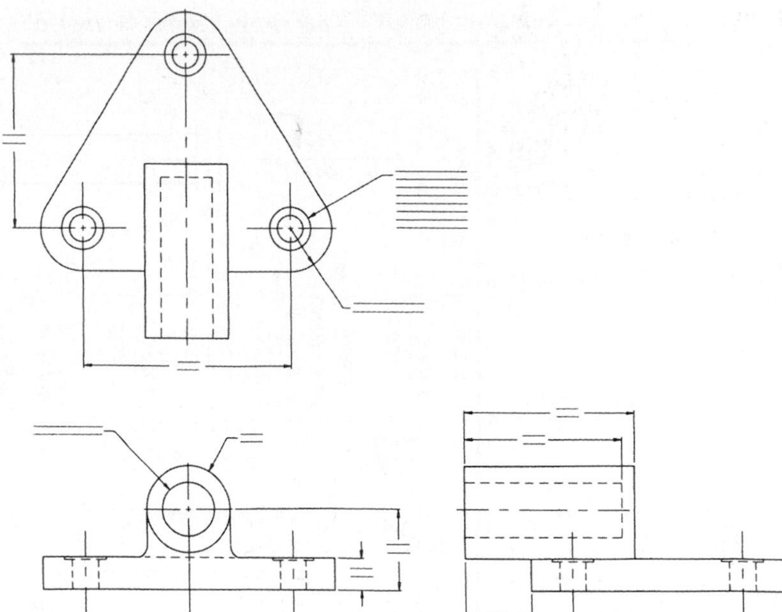

FIGURE 7.6 Mechanical Drawing with Guidelines

on "D"-size sheets and larger, the minimum uppercase height is a minimum of 5 mm for metric drawings and .156 in. for U.S. decimal-inch drawings. This will provide for legible enlargement for microfilmed drawings. Figure 7.8 is an example of a well-lettered "D"-size drawing of a refinery layout. This project was lettered freehand without guidelines, since it was drawn on a nonreproducible-blue grid sheet. Note that the designer had to letter the drawing from two directions. The drawing remained taped to the board, and the designer had to turn his or her body to complete the project. With a CAD system, the drawing's text can be rotated as it is inserted.

The **freehand lettering guide** is shown in Figure 7.9. This device eliminates the need for guidelines, since it limits the height of the lettering to the space within the slots. Lettering aids tend to flatten the upper and lower portions of some letters. Do not use lettering guides while attempting to learn and perfect freehand lettering. Guidelines are also unnecessary when you use vellum, or drafting film, with nonreproducible grid lines. The grid spacing (if the correct size) can be used as guidelines for the lettering. Guidelines are also unnecessary when you use a lettering template.

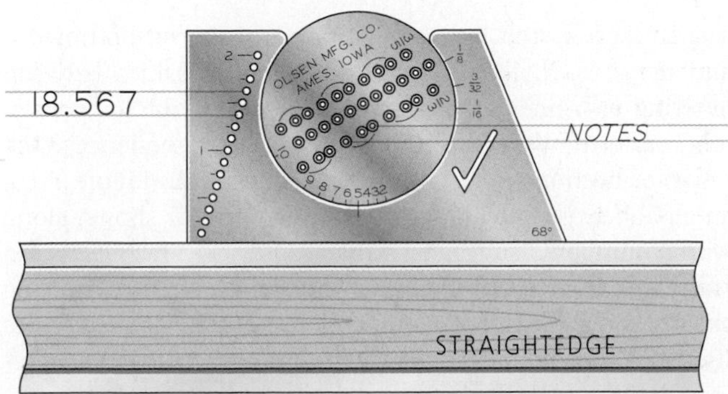

FIGURE 7.7 AMES Lettering Guide

You may wish to use vertical or inclined guidelines (Fig. 7.10) when practicing lettering, until some consistency is achieved. Vertical or inclined guidelines are *not* used on drawings.

Except when special emphasis is required, lettering should not be underlined. If underlining is required, it should not be less than 1.5 mm (.06 in.) below the lettering.

7.3.2 Pencil Technique

Freehand lettering places a requirement on linework that is different from that possible with instrument lines. Instrument lines are made more dense when the construction line is traced. For most people, it is impossible to trace freehand lettering consistently. Therefore, engineers and designers must draw lettering of the proper density in only one stroke. To help get the proper density, a soft lead is used. Depending on your preference, the H, HB, or F lead can be used with good results for all lettering.

Soft lead contributes to the dirt on the drawing because it "chalks" more easily. Frequent use of a brush is necessary. Due to its tendency to smear, lettering is usually the last step in the completion of a drawing. When lettering, do not let your hand come in contact with the drawing surface. Always place a sheet of clean paper between your hand and the drawing medium. This will help keep the drawing free of body oils and dirt as well as prevent smearing of the linework (Fig. 7.11).

Since it requires no sharpening, the fine-line pencil is an excellent lettering device. A 0.5 or 0.7 mm fine-line pencil is used for lettering when available. Rotating your pencil or lead holder minimizes depletion of the point and helps maintain consistency of character width.

By now you have developed lifelong habits regarding how to hold a pencil and how to form each character. The suggested hand orientation (Fig. 7.11) is provided to help

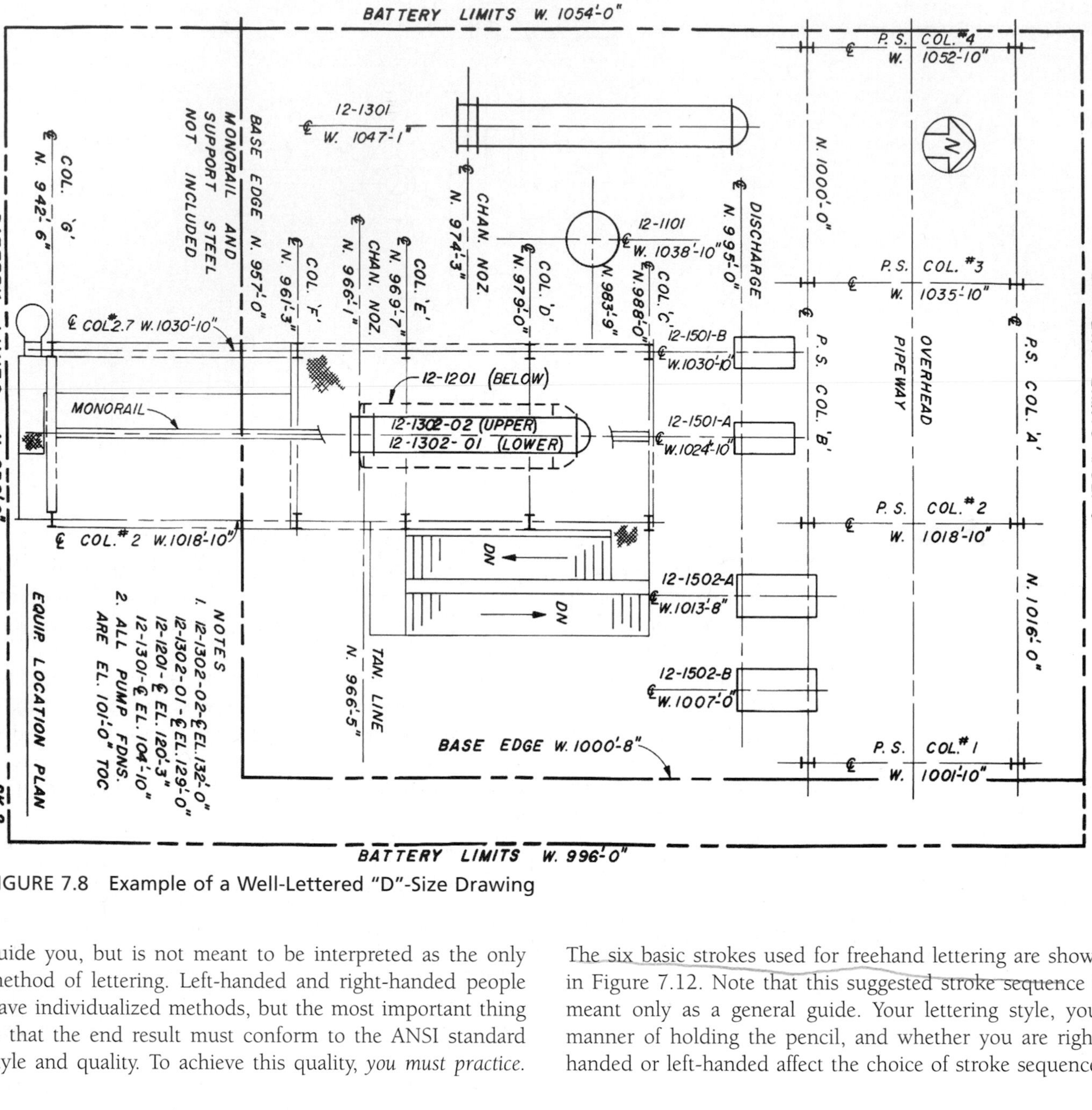

FIGURE 7.8 Example of a Well-Lettered "D"-Size Drawing

guide you, but is not meant to be interpreted as the only method of lettering. Left-handed and right-handed people have individualized methods, but the most important thing is that the end result must conform to the ANSI standard style and quality. To achieve this quality, *you must practice.*

FIGURE 7.9 Freehand Lettering Aid

The six basic strokes used for freehand lettering are shown in Figure 7.12. Note that this suggested stroke sequence is meant only as a general guide. Your lettering style, your manner of holding the pencil, and whether you are right-handed or left-handed affect the choice of stroke sequence.

7.3.3 Lettering Strokes, Uniformity, and Form

The strokes of your letters must be consistent in both width and density. Obviously, variation in the densities between lettering and linework must be avoided. Strive for consistent, uniform, well-spaced letters. The stroke sequence is the same for both inclined and vertical lettering. In Figure 7.13, an alphabet of vertical and inclined lettering is shown along with a numbered suggested stroke sequence. This figure also highlights typical problems in forming letters. Lettering examples are provided below each comment. The examples used are reference designations found on electronic drawings. Note that guidelines were used throughout.

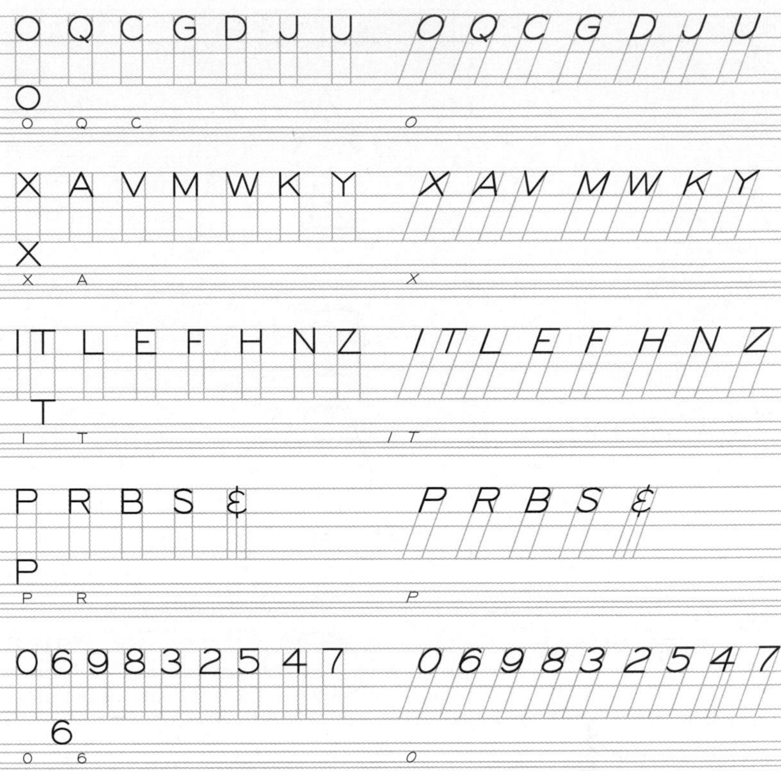

FIGURE 7.10 Using Horizontal and Vertical (or Inclined) Guidelines for Lettering Practice

FIGURE 7.11 Hand Position When Lettering

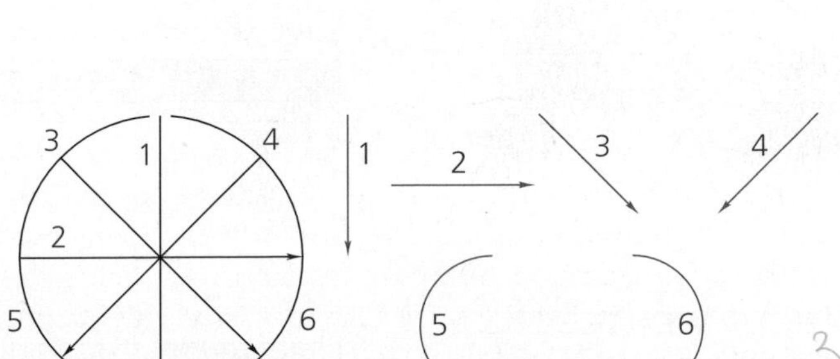

FIGURE 7.12 Basic Lettering Strokes

The grid pattern shown in Figure 7.13 gives the ideal width-and-height relationship for single-stroke Gothic lettering. All characters are six units in height and vary in width from the 1 and I to the W and M.

In Figure 7.14, the typical slant angle used for inclined lettering is shown. Any angle between 90° (vertical) and 65° is acceptable unless an individual company has a preferred practice. Left-handers sometimes slant their lettering backwards 1° to 5°. This method should be used only if it falls within your company's (or class's) standard practice.

Strive to develop a lettering style that is comfortable and that communicates the necessary engineering data without confusion and mistakes. It is very important to catch bad habits early in order not to ingrain them in your lettering style. Please note that in the beginning it is important to eliminate any individualized style, until your lettering becomes clear, concise, dark, and well formed. Through practice, a more attractive personal style will emerge and become your own.

7.3.4 Spacing

Spacing is done by eye to create a pleasing and orderly set of words or numbers. The spacing between letters in a word is as important as the spacing between words. The background area between characters should *appear* equal even though it's not. The spacing between words should be a minimum of six units wide, that is, the width of the widest letter, such as W or M. The spacing between letters varies because the

CHARACTER	COMMENTS AND EXAMPLES	INCORRECT	POSSIBLE MISTAKES
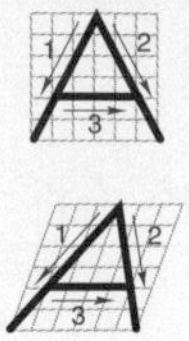 A (vertical); A (inclined)	MAKE UPPER PART LARGER THAN BOTTOM PART. ADAPTER, CONNECTOR (CP)	A	4
 B (vertical); B (inclined)	LOWER PART SLIGHTLY LARGER THAN UPPER PART. BARRIER PHOTOCELL (V) BLOCK, CONNECTING (TB)	B	8
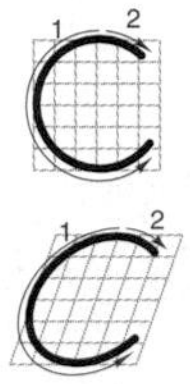 C (vertical); C (inclined)	FULL OPEN AREA, ELLIPTICAL LETTER BODY. COUPLER, DIRECTIONAL (DC) CUTOUT, FUSE (F)	C	O
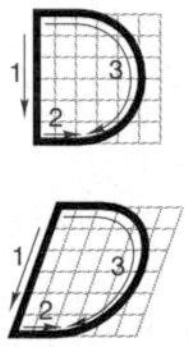 D (vertical); D (inclined)	HORIZONTAL BARS AND STRAIGHT LINE BACK. DIODE, SEMICONDUCTOR (CR) DELAY FUNCTION (DL)	D	O
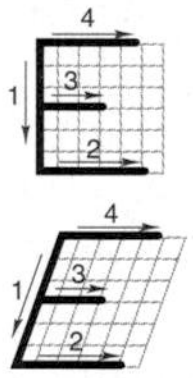 E (vertical); E (inclined)	SHORT BAR SLIGHTLY ABOVE CENTERLINE. ELECTRONIC MULTIPLIER (A) EQUALIZER, NETWORK, EQUALIZING (EQ)	E E	L
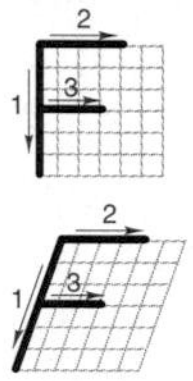 F (vertical); F (inclined)	SHORT BAR SLIGHTLY ABOVE CENTERLINE. FIELD EFFECT TRANSISTOR (Q) FUSE HOLDER (X)	F F	T E
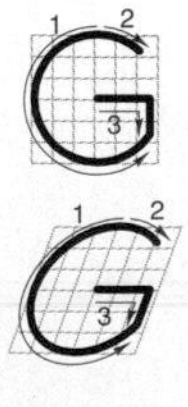 G (vertical); G (inclined)	BASED ON TRUE ELLIPSE, SHORT HORIZONTAL LINE ABOVE CENTERLINE. GENERATOR (G) GAP (HORN, PROJECTIVE, OR SPHERE) (E)	G G G	C O 6
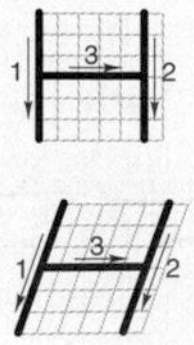 H (vertical); H (inclined)	BAR SLIGHTLY ABOVE CENTERLINE. HARDWARE (COMMON FASTENERS, ETC.) (H) HEADSET, ELECTRICAL (HT)	H H	

FIGURE 7.13 Stroke Sequence, Comments, Examples, and Possible Errors in Lettering

CHARACTER	COMMENTS AND EXAMPLES	INCORRECT	POSSIBLE MISTAKES
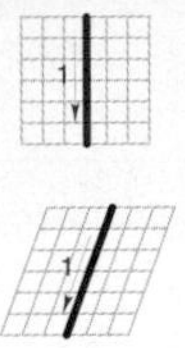 I	NO SERIFS, EXCEPT WHEN NEXT TO NUMBER ONE (I). INDUCTOR (L) INDICATOR (EXCEPT METER OR THERMOMETER) (DS)	I 1	
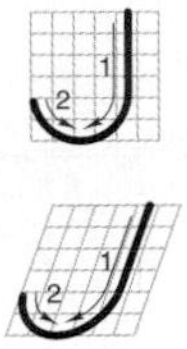 J	WIDE FULL HOOK WITH NO SERIFS. JUNCTION (COAXIAL)	J J	
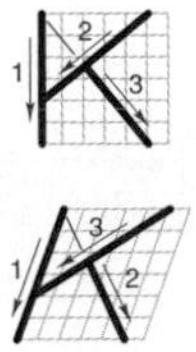 K	EXTEND LOWER BRANCH FROM UPPER BRANCH. WAVE GUIDE (CP) JACK (J)	K K	R
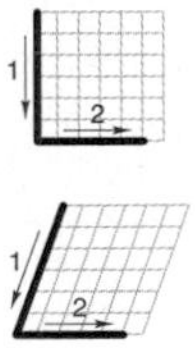 L	MAKE BOTH LINES STRAIGHT. LOOP ANTENNA (E)	L	
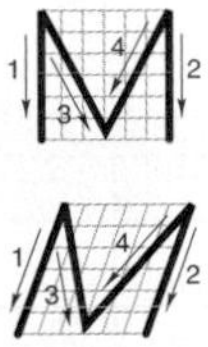 M	NOT AS WIDE AS W: CENTER PART EXTENDS TO BOTTOM OF LETTER. MICROCIRCUIT (U) MULTIPLIER, ELECTRONIC (A)	M M	
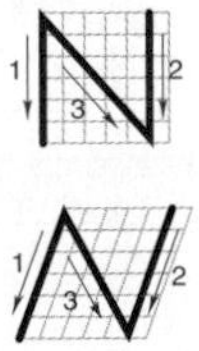 N	DO NOT CRAM LINES TOGETHER. NETWORK, EQUALIZING (HY) DIODE, TUNNEL (CR)	N N	U V
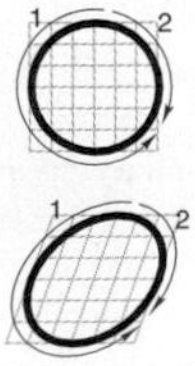 O	FULL TRUE ELLIPSE. OSCILLOGRAPH (M) OSCILLOSCOPE (M)	O O	C Q 6
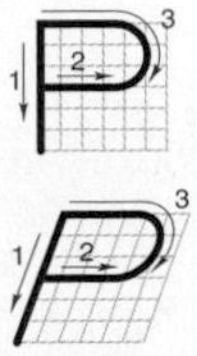 P	MIDDLE BAR INTERSECTS AT LETTER S MIDDLE. PHOTODIODE (CR) POTENTIOMETER (R)	P P	K T D

FIGURE 7.13 Stroke Sequence, Comments, Examples, and Possible Errors in Lettering—*Continues*

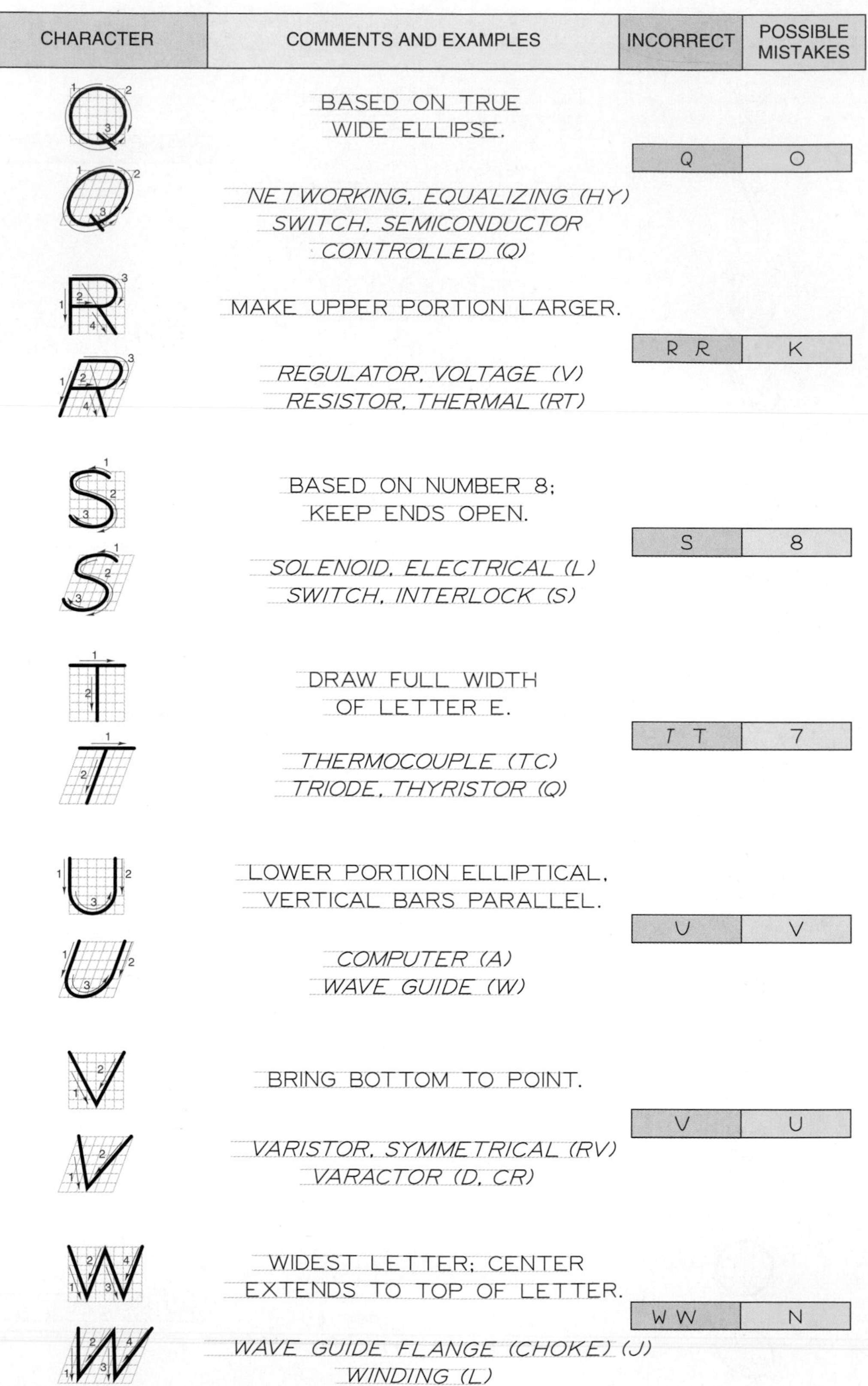

CHARACTER
COMMENTS AND EXAMPLES
INCORRECT
POSSIBLE MISTAKES
BASED ON TRUE WIDE ELLIPSE.
Q
O
NETWORKING, EQUALIZING (HY)
SWITCH, SEMICONDUCTOR CONTROLLED (Q)
MAKE UPPER PORTION LARGER.
R R
K
REGULATOR, VOLTAGE (V)
RESISTOR, THERMAL (RT)
BASED ON NUMBER 8; KEEP ENDS OPEN.
S
8
SOLENOID, ELECTRICAL (L)
SWITCH, INTERLOCK (S)
DRAW FULL WIDTH OF LETTER E.
T T
7
THERMOCOUPLE (TC)
TRIODE, THYRISTOR (Q)
LOWER PORTION ELLIPTICAL. VERTICAL BARS PARALLEL.
U
V
COMPUTER (A)
WAVE GUIDE (W)
BRING BOTTOM TO POINT.
V
U
VARISTOR, SYMMETRICAL (RV)
VARACTOR (D, CR)
WIDEST LETTER; CENTER EXTENDS TO TOP OF LETTER.
W W
N
WAVE GUIDE FLANGE (CHOKE) (J)
WINDING (L)

FIGURE 7.13 Stroke Sequence, Comments, Examples, and Possible Errors in Lettering—*Continued*

CHARACTER	COMMENTS AND EXAMPLES	INCORRECT	POSSIBLE MISTAKES
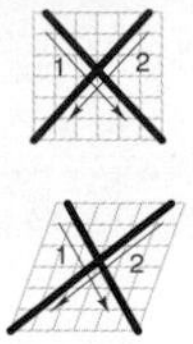 X	CROSS LINES ABOVE CENTERLINE. *LAMP HOLDER (X)* *INDICATOR (EXCEPT METER* *OR THERMOMETER (DS)*	X	
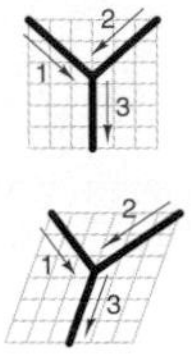 Y	UPPER PART MEETS BELOW CENTER. *R R RELAY (K)* *POWER SUPPLY (PS)*	Y Y	V T
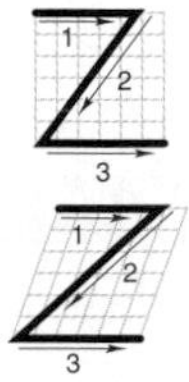 Z	HORIZONTAL LINES PARALLEL. *TUNER, E-H (Z)* *NETWORK, PHASE CHANGING (Z)*	Z	2
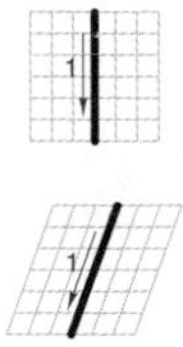 1	SAME AS LETTER I. *10,000 OHMS* *Q4 2N1011*	1 1	7
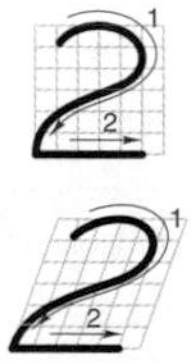 2	BASED ON NUMBER 8; OPEN HOOK. *Q1 2N1925 1200 OHMS*	2 2	Z
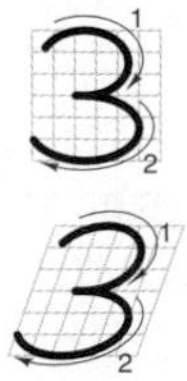 3	BASED ON NUMBER 8; UPPER PART SMALLER THAN LOWER. *VM103 1N673*	3 3	8 5
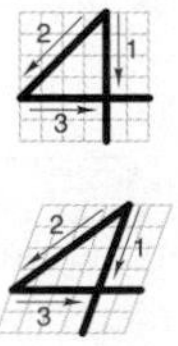 4	HORIZONTAL BAR BELOW CENTER OF FIGURE. *TB103/4-22G/R 2N38974*	4 4 4	7 9 H

FIGURE 7.13 Stroke Sequence, Comments, Examples, and Possible Errors in Lettering—*Continues*

CHARACTER	COMMENTS AND EXAMPLES	INCORRECT	POSSIBLE MISTAKES
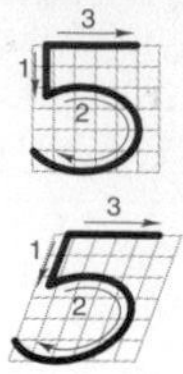 5	BASED ON ELLIPSE; KEEP WIDE. XQ2-5 1.5 MS	5 5	6 3 S
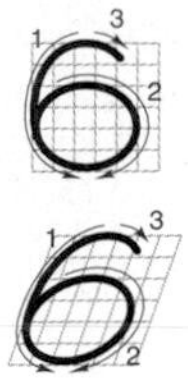 6	BASED ON ELLIPSE; OPEN. 42-020-6 68,000 OHMS	6	8
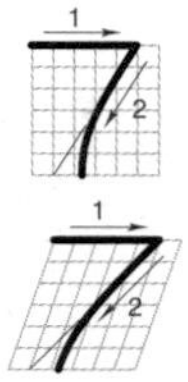 7	KEEP AS WIDE AS LETTER E. 4.7 K 47,000 OHMS	7 7 7	I
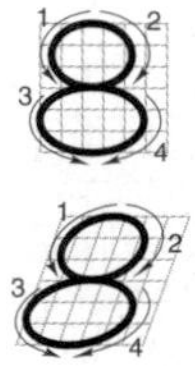 8	BASED ON ELLIPSE; KEEP WIDE. 3N58 IN678	8 8 8	B
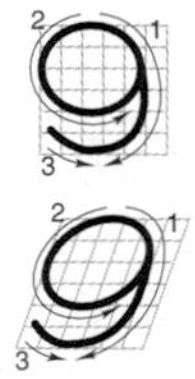 9	COMPOSED OF TWO ELLIPSES; KEEP FULL. QI 2N195 3.9 K	9	8
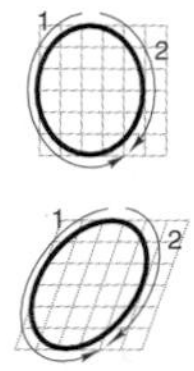 0	SAME AS LETTER D. 5473,000 OHMS 120 K	0	Q

FIGURE 7.13 Stroke Sequence, Comments, Examples, and Possible Errors in Lettering—*Continued*

shapes of the adjacent letters vary. Spacing for letters and words should correspond to the following specifications (Fig. 7.15):

- Background areas between letters in words are separated by approximately equal areas.
- Spacing for numerals separated by a decimal point (5.375, 2.54 mm, etc.) is a minimum of two-thirds of the character height used for the lettering.
- Spaces between words are approximately equal and a minimum of .06 in. (1.5 mm). A full character height for horizontal word spacing is suggested.
- The horizontal space between lines of lettering is at least half the height of the characters, but preferably one full character height of space is left between lines.
- Sentences are separated by at least one full character height and preferably two character heights if space permits.

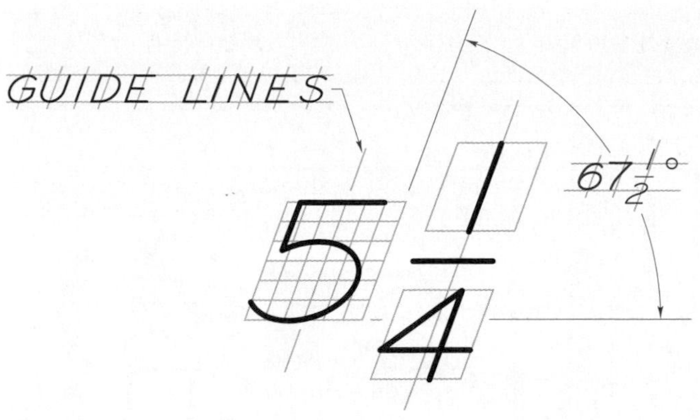

FIGURE 7.14 Using Guidelines for Inclined Lettering

FIGURE 7.15 Spacing of Letters and Words

7.3.5 Lowercase Lettering

Lowercase lettering as shown in Figure 7.16 is seldom used except for construction drawings. Lowercase lettering, whether inclined or vertical, requires extra guidelines. Guidelines for the *waistline* (top of main body of letter) and *baseline* (bottom of main body of letter), as well as for ascender and descender lines, are added to the drawing before the letters are drawn. *Ascender lines,* or cap lines, designate the top of strokes for letters that extend above the waistline, such as b, d, f, h, k, and l. *Descender lines,* or drop lines, designate the bottom of strokes for letters below the baseline, such as g, j, p, and y.

7.3.6 Fractions on Drawings

Most drawings are dimensioned with decimal-inch or metric units. These are easier, more accurate, and quicker to draw, since all numbers are placed between two equally spaced guidelines. For some drawings, the tolerance and accuracy required for manufacturing and construction is loose enough to permit fraction dimensioning, such as for sheet metal work. Fractions are also widely used in piping, civil, architectural, and structural design.

In Figure 7.17, the height ratio of fraction number to whole number is provided. When a drawing is to be reduced, the size of lettering may need to be larger than normal for accurate enlargement (enlargement from reduction size). *The ANSI standard on lettering states that the height*

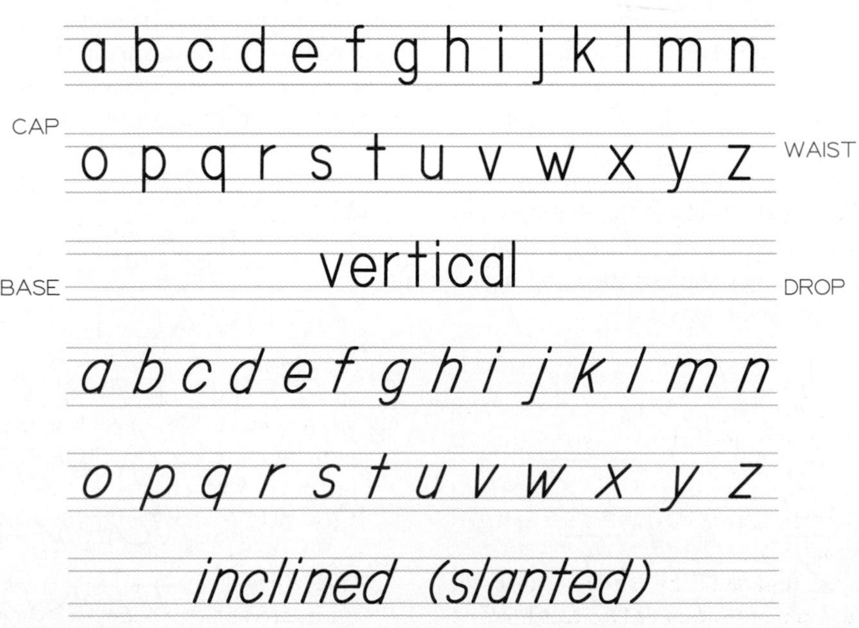

FIGURE 7.16 Lowercase Lettering

Focus On . . .

THE ALPHABET

The alphabet developed as a result of man's need to record events. In fact, our modern alphabet had its origin in Egyptian hieroglyphics. The word *hieroglyphics* means "picture writing" and is the oldest and most primitive of all writing. Some of the letters of the Roman alphabet in use today can be traced back to these crude pictures.

The Greeks adopted symbology from the Phoenicians, who had developed a 22-letter alphabet in about 1500 B.C. The adopted system evolved into two distinct alphabets in two parts of Greece. The Western type became the Latin alphabet (about 700 B.C.) and was used throughout the Old World. (The modern English word for *alphabet* comes from the first two letters of the Greek alphabet, *alpha* and *beta*.) The original Roman alphabet of twenty-three characters has remained unchanged except that characters have been added.

People began communicating with each other through all forms of written communication once the alphabet was accepted. Unfortunately, books, even from the earliest times, were prepared by the laborious method of hand-copying onto papyrus, parchment, or vellum. The scribes cut quills and made ink from gum and lampblack. Before the fall of the Roman Empire, the copying of books was a thriving and important industry. When Rome fell, the rich patrons of literature were scattered and their libraries were left to be burned. Monks, fearful that all literature would be lost, took on as part of their religious duties the task of copying classical and religious books.

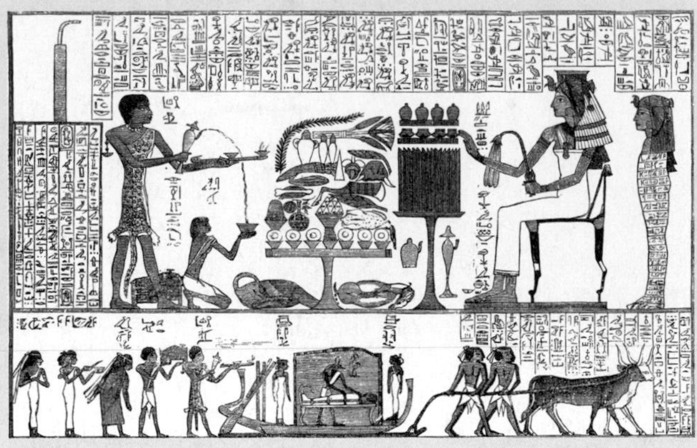

Hieroglyphics.

About fifty years before Columbus discovered America, Johannes Gutenberg revolutionized graphic communications. Gutenberg, in Mainz, Germany, perfected a way to cast individual letters. As a young man, he had studied the arduous task of scribes and wanted to invent a mechanical printing process to make the scribes' work easier and to make books more accessible. Until his time, all lettering was done by hand and it was left to the individual as to how each letter was made or decorated.

By three years after he started, Gutenberg had printed 200 copies of the Bible. Thirty of these were printed on a paper made from animal skins. These thirty copies used the hides of about 10,000 calves!

of the fraction number should be the same as that for the whole number. Most engineering books, and many companies, however, suggest the relationship shown in Figure 7.17.

The division line of the common fraction is drawn parallel to the direction in which the dimension reads and is separated from the numerals by a minimum of 1.5 mm (.06 in.) of space. The numbers must not touch the fraction division bar. The division bar is drawn horizontally between the numbers and not at an angle, except in notes, where the angled division bar is acceptable. Some company standards allow the angled division bar, but it is not an ANSI standard.

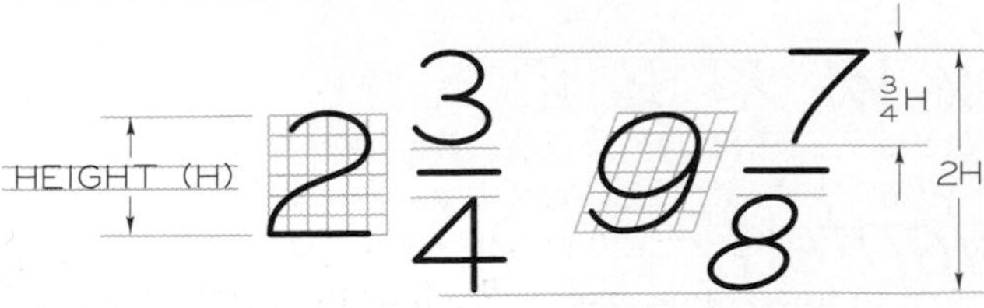

FIGURE 7.17 Fractions

7.3.7 Lettering Composition

Various special circumstances affect the composition and placement of letters on a drawing. Expanded (extended), compressed, stopline, centered, and symmetrical lettering are found on many types of diagrams and drawings. Figure 7.18 shows examples of compressed and extended letters. Note that these variations are easily accomplished using a

CONDENSED LETTERING

NORMAL LETTERING

EXTENDED LETTERING

CONDENSED

NORMAL

EXTENDED

FIGURE 7.18 Lettering Variations

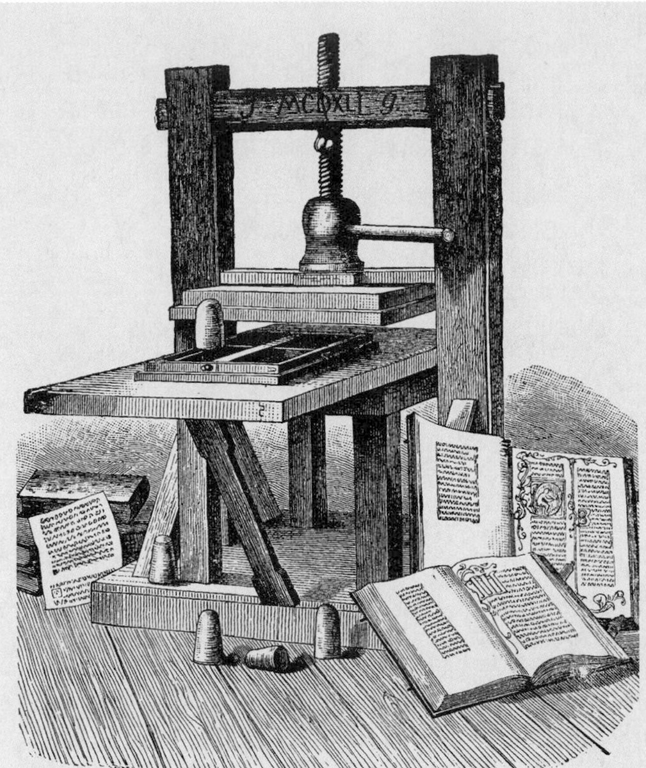

A Guttenberg printing press.

During the Industrial Revolution, the printing press needed for production was invented. Now with the printing process, more books could be printed and more people could afford to own them. Gutenberg's dream was realized at last!

It seems inconceivable not to know an alphabet or to have printed books. Even though we don't think much about our alphabet, most of what we do to communicate with each other is based on standard alphabets and printed material.

The computer is now the basis for another revolution in communications. The operators of modern CAD systems have a variety of *fonts* to choose from when inserting text into their drawings. A font is a series of patterns created by the CAD program to represent specific letters in certain styles (roman, italic, or script, for example). The font of the text can be changed at will. Computers can virtually link offices together across the country and the world. Regardless of how fast or sophisticated the method or the style of the text, our modern alphabet remains the basis for the way we communicate in written form.

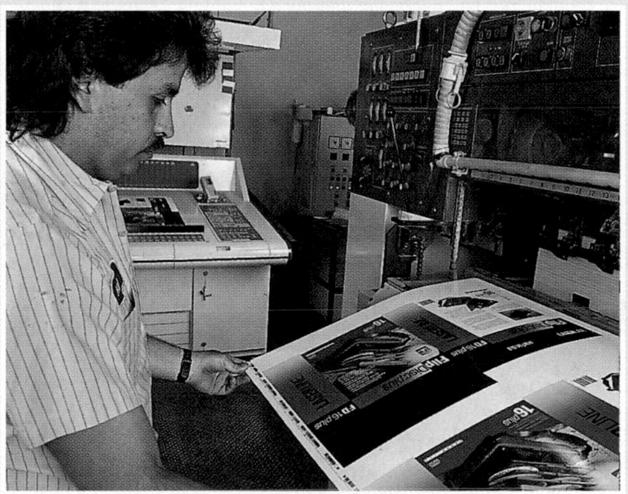

A modern printing shop.

CAD system, since the lettering font, height, width, slant, and justification can be selected by the user.

By drawing letters and numerals in groups, going from simple to complex, you will learn an easy way to practice on the forms that you need to improve without having to letter the whole alphabet. The following groupings can be used during practice:

- Straight lines only
  A, E, F, H, I, K, L, M, N, T, V, W, X, Y, Z, 1, 4
- Straight and curved lines
  B, D, J, P, U, 2, 5, 7
- Curved lines only
  C, G, O, Q, S, 3, 6, 8, 9, 0

Stopline lettering is used on some drawings and charts. In most cases, lettering is *left-justified* (aligned on the left in a column). When lettering must stop along a given line or at a specific point it is called *right-justified.* Since the letters are normally drawn from left to right, right-justified freehand lettering (stopline lettering) is somewhat difficult to do. Stopline lettering is drawn from right to left.

The stability of lettering construction is very important to lettering composition. How does the lettering or number look on the paper? The construction of each letter and number is extremely important. This includes proportion, stability, uniformity, balance, consistency, thickness, and density. The combination of these factors to make notes is called *composition.* The beauty of machine lettering lies in its ability to do all the variations automatically.

7.3.8 Lists and Notes

Traditionally, notes have been placed above the drawing's title block area on the far right. The newest ANSI standards have reversed the placement of notes. *Notes are now to be placed on the lower left or the upper left of the drawing.* However, many companies still follow the older practice of placing notes above the title block on the right side of the

REF NO	COMPONENT	PART NO
R-401	33K	216480
R-402	24K	216477
R-403	9.1K	216467
R-404	33	549978
R-405	100K	216491
R-406	430K	216731
R-407	7.5K	216465
R-408	100	595359
R-409	1K	216445
R-410	5.1K	216461
R-411	15K	216472
R-412	47K	216484
R-413	100K	216491
R-414	680	216442
J	JUMPER	1207833
C-421	.15/35 MFD	491255
C-422	150 PF DISC	1207587
C-423	3.3/35 MFD	1207585
C-424	.47/35 MFD	1208599
C-425	.33/35 MFD	1208591
C-426	2.2/35 MFD	1208601
C-427	.0068/100 MFD	492500
C-428	.0027/100 MFD	491309
C-429	150 PF DISC	1207587
Q-441	GREEN	1207577
Q-442	GREEN	1207577
Q-443	BLACK	1207601

FIGURE 7.19 Hand-Lettered Parts List

NOTES:

1 MARK PER MIL-STD-130 APPROXIMATELY WHERE SHOWN, .093 HIGH CHARACTERS USING ITEM 48

2 SOLDER IN ACCORDANCE WITH NHB5300.4 (3A-1)

3 PARTIAL REFERENCE DESIGNATIONS ARE SHOWN FOR COMPLETE DESIGNATIONS PREFIX WITH UNIT NUMBER AND SUBASSEMBLY DESIGNATIONS

4 ELECTROSTATIC DEVICE, HANDLE PER DOD-STD-1686

5 TORQUE 2-2.5 INCH LBS

6 FINISH: CONFORMAL COAT PER GEN-PS5205 EXCEPT CONNECTOR AND DESIGNATED AREAS SHOWN

7 BOND ITEM 67 TO ITEM 1 PRIOR TO POPULATION OF CARD ASSEMBLY PER GEN-PS5402 CLASS 7

8 APPLY FILLET TO COMPONENTS INDICATED AFTER CONFORMAL COATING PER GEN-PS5402 CL II

FIGURE 7.20 Hand-Lettered Notes Added to Preprinted Company Notes

drawing. Hand-lettered lists (Fig. 7.19) and notes are time-consuming and tiring. Preprinted standard notes are easy to apply, and simplify the process of constructing long lists of notes. The notes in Figure 7.20 are standard preprinted company notes; 7 and 8 were added freehand.

You May Complete Exercises 7.1 Through 7.4 at This Time

7.4 MECHANICAL LETTERING AIDS

One of the most common lettering devices found in any engineering room is the **template.** Although freehand lettering is the rule rather than the exception on manually drawn projects, templates are used on some drawings. Templates are available for almost any size and style of lettering, and can be adapted for ink as well as pencil use (Fig. 7.21). The beauty of a template lies in its ability to produce repeatable,

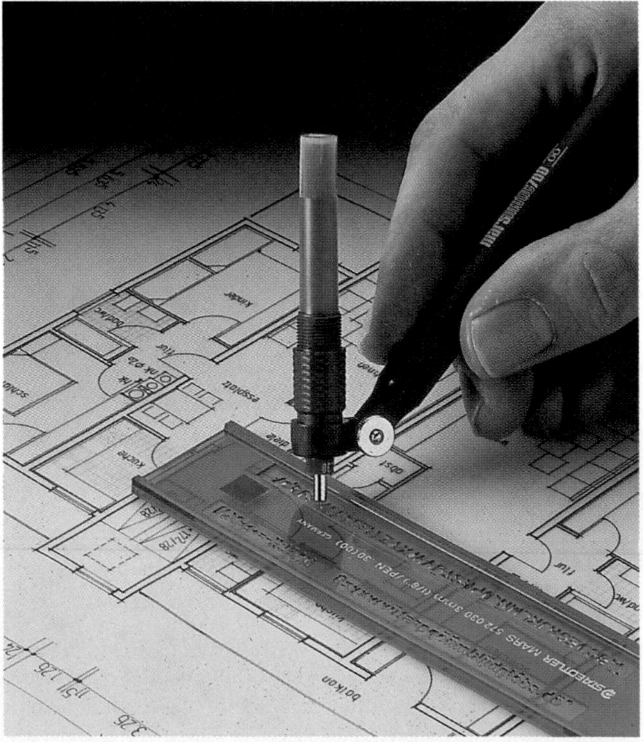

FIGURE 7.21 Lettering Guide Template

uniform letters and numerals. Template lettering, however, takes considerably more time than freehand lettering (Fig. 7.22).

With a template, guidelines are unnecessary. But a template must rest against a straightedge while in use so that all the letters are aligned properly. Template lettering is used on drawings that are inked, in title blocks, and for section letter identification. The major drawback of templates is that it is hard to ink perfectly formed letters without a great deal of practice. The pencil or inking pen must be kept almost perpendicular to the paper while the letters are drawn. The Koh-I-Noor Rapidometric Guide template in Figure 7.21 is an example of a template designed to be used for inking. Note that the inset drawing shows how the template shelf does not come in contact with the drawing surface. Thin stick-on pads may also be fastened to the bottom of templates and triangles. This eliminates potential smearing of the ink.

The **Leroy** lettering set uses a scriber and a template with a slot guide to produce close-to-perfect letters (Fig. 7.23). The scriber can be adjusted to alter the slant of the lettering. The drawing in Figure 7.24 was lettered with a Leroy set.

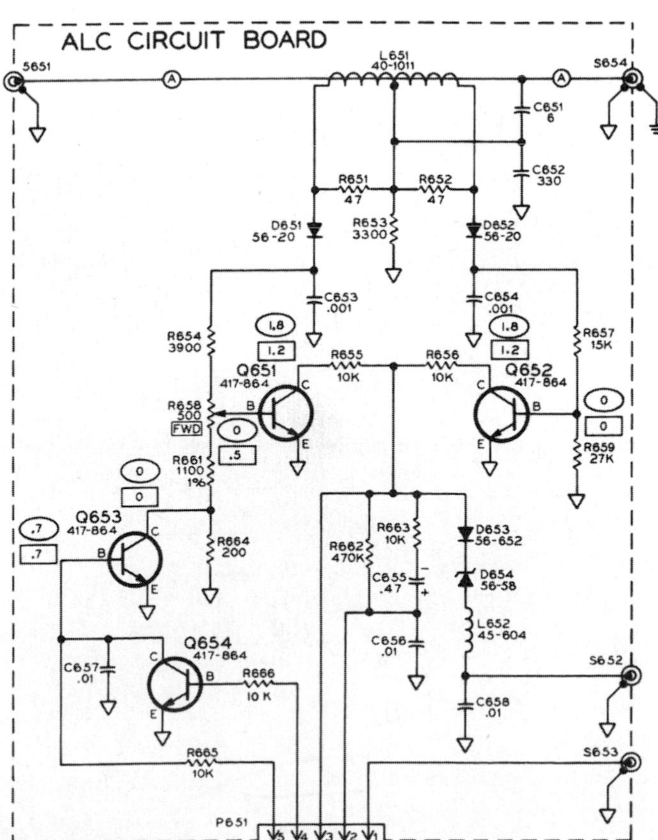

FIGURE 7.22 Template-Lettered Diagram

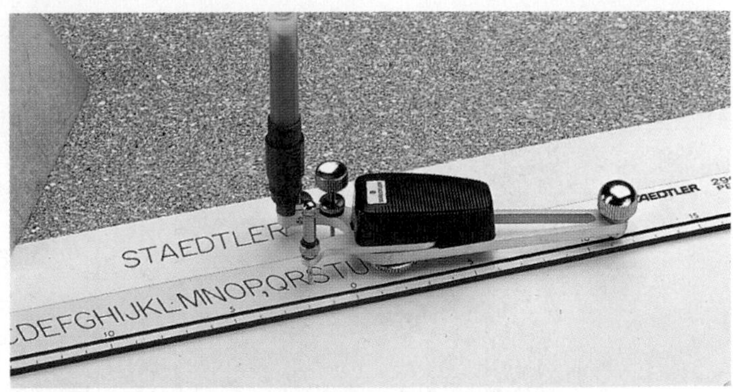

FIGURE 7.23 Lettering with a Leroy Set

Skill in using a lettering template and scriber can only be gained through practice. The most difficult part of lettering systems is mastering the spacing of characters.

All hand-operated lettering systems are expensive and take more time than traditional freehand lettering. Mechanical lettering devices and the inking of drawings are usually limited to drawings for publication. Manuals, catalogs, and sales literature require more precise lettering and linework than design, detailing, and assembly drawings.

Mechanical lettering devices enable you to make slightly smaller letters than manual techniques. (See Table 7.2 to compare sizes.) The variation in recommended minimum standard letter heights between freehand and mechanical devices is needed because freehand lettering does not reduce and enlarge as accurately as mechanically drawn characters.

7.5 MACHINE LETTERING DEVICES

In the past, typewriters with specially designed carriages and Gothic typefaces were sometimes used on A-, B-, and C-sized sheets. Figure 7.25 shows a panel drawing where the labels have been typed. Oddly enough, freehand lettering was used for markings on the panel itself. When using the typewriter for lettering, a special inking ribbon must be employed so that the characters do not smear.

Dry transfer lettering and **appliqués** are normally confined to artwork or headings (Fig. 7.26). It is time-consuming to apply each letter or number separately. The Kroy lettering system (Fig. 7.27) or the Merlin lettering system allows you to dial a sequence of letters or numbers, as required. The result is a dry adhesive-backed strip for easy attachment to the drawing. Notes, headings, and titles are easy to apply with this system (Fig. 7.28). The drawing in Figure 7.29 was lettered with a Kroy system.

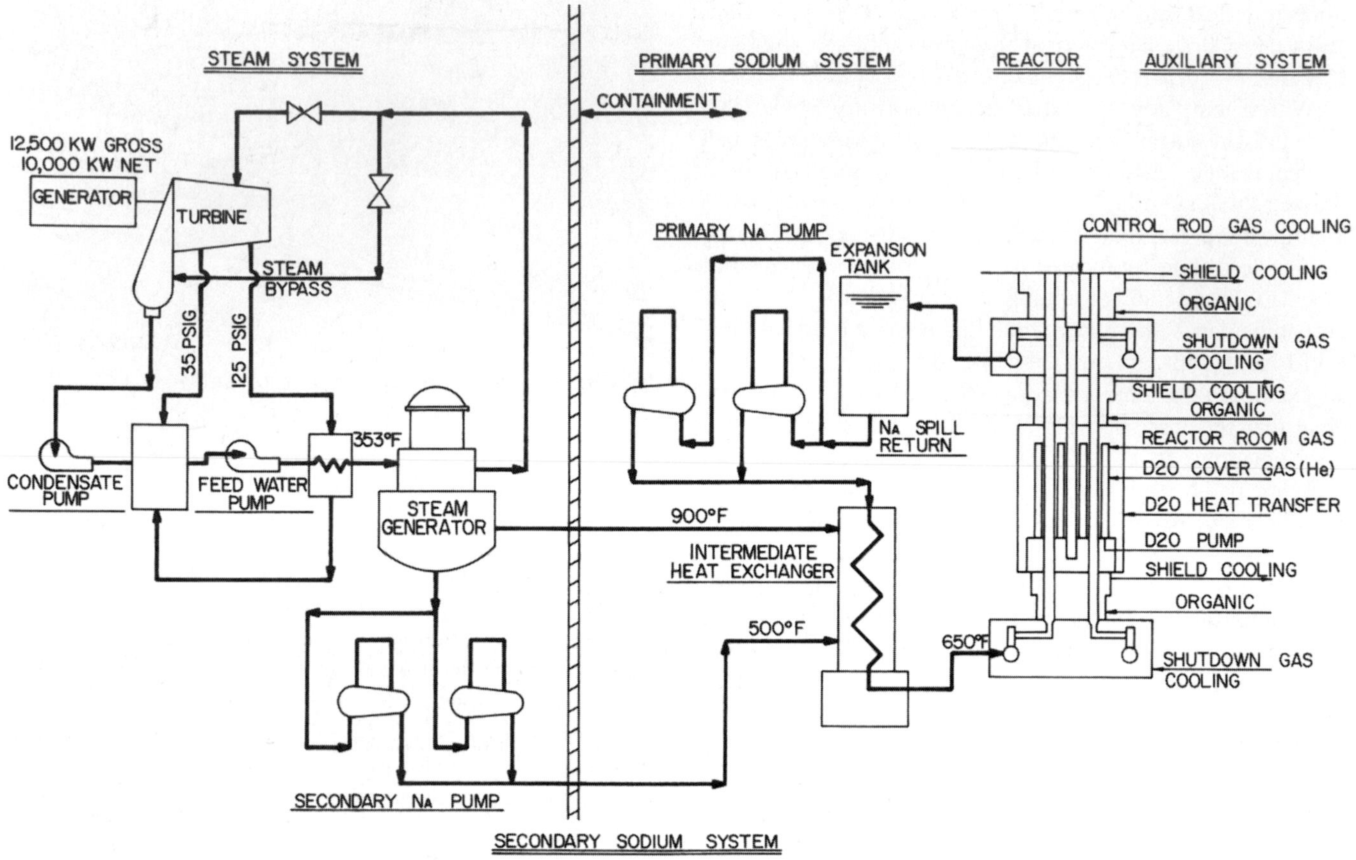

STEAM SYSTEM
PRIMARY SODIUM SYSTEM
REACTOR
AUXILIARY SYSTEM
CONTAINMENT
12,500 KW GROSS
10,000 KW NET
GENERATOR
TURBINE
STEAM
BYPASS
35 PSIG
125 PSIG
CONDENSATE
PUMP
FEED WATER
PUMP
353°F
STEAM
GENERATOR
PRIMARY NA PUMP
EXPANSION
TANK
NA SPILL
RETURN
900°F
INTERMEDIATE
HEAT EXCHANGER
500°F
650°F
CONTROL ROD GAS COOLING
SHIELD COOLING
ORGANIC
SHUTDOWN GAS
COOLING
SHIELD COOLING
ORGANIC
REACTOR ROOM GAS
D20 COVER GAS(He)
D20 HEAT TRANSFER
D20 PUMP
SHIELD COOLING
ORGANIC
SHUTDOWN GAS
COOLING
SECONDARY NA PUMP
SECONDARY SODIUM SYSTEM

FIGURE 7.24 Drawing Lettered with a Leroy Set

24V+ 24V- COM COM +6V -6V
Yellow
Green
Black
White
Red
Black
AC ON
AC OFF
RT
RT
-6
Brown
Thermistor
Terminals
AC
24
+6
F3,
-6V output
F1, Input A-C
F2,
+6V output
F4,
24V output
Logic
080-2442
-6V Series
Regulator
080-2439
Voltage Adjustment
Potentiometers R114
24V Series Regulator
080-2440
+6VPass Unit
& Current Sense
080-2440
+6V Pass Unit Card
080-2441
+6V, 24V Pass
Unit Card 080-2441
Voltage Adjustment
Potentiometer R114
+6V Series Regulator
080-2439

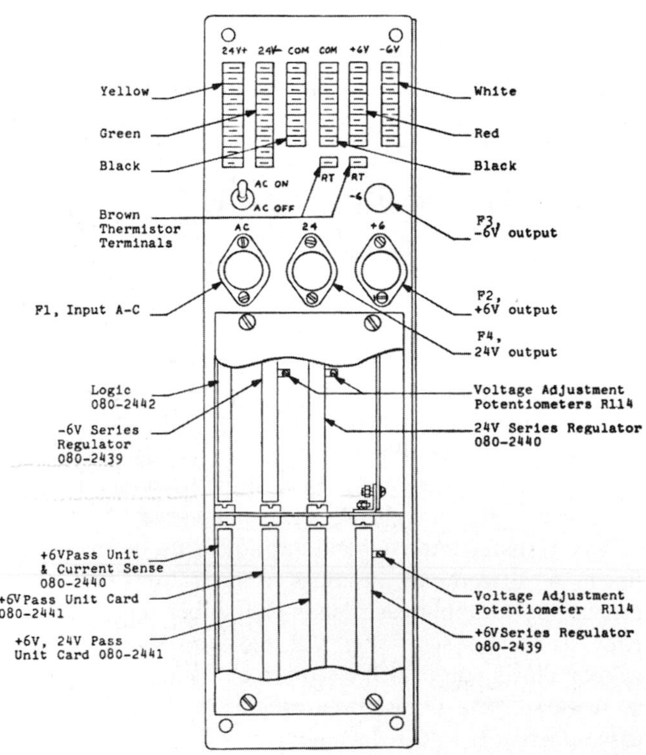

FIGURE 7.25 Typed Lettering on a Service Manual Panel Drawing

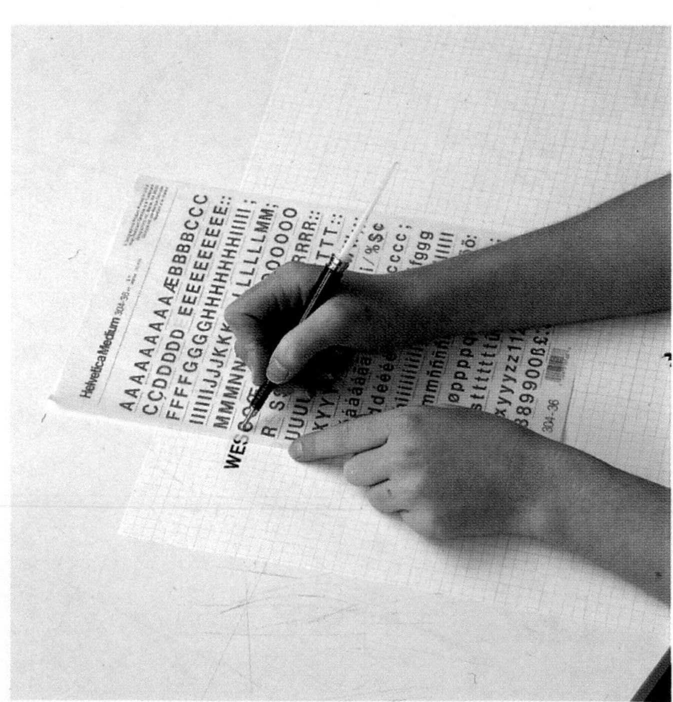

FIGURE 7.26 Transfer Lettering

FIGURE 7.27 Kroy Lettering Systems

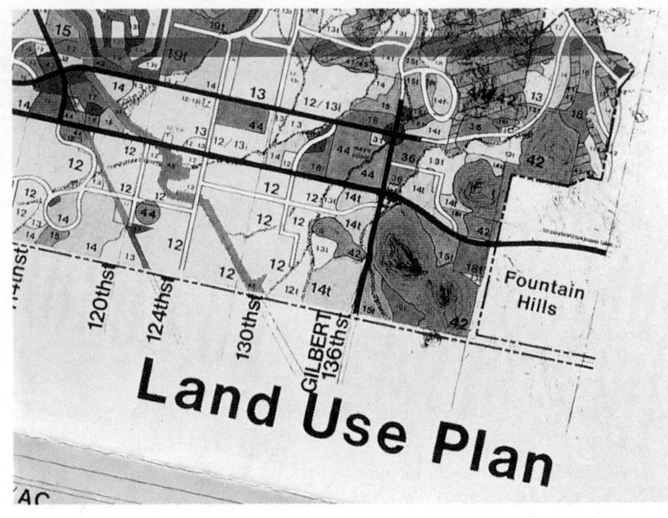

FIGURE 7.28 Kroy Lettering Applied to a Drawing

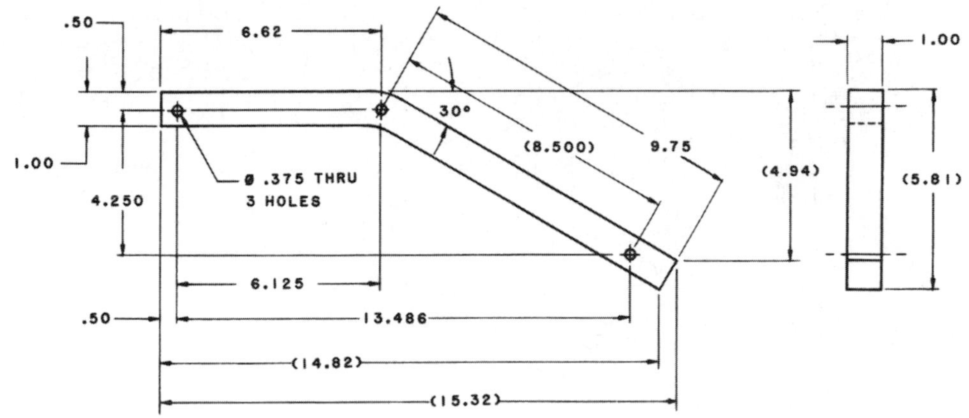

FIGURE 7.29 Kroy-Lettered Drawing

Phototypesetting and **printing** are used for publication-level artwork and drawings when quality is extremely important. Figure 7.30 is an example of phototypeset lettering on an illustration of a pressure vessel module.

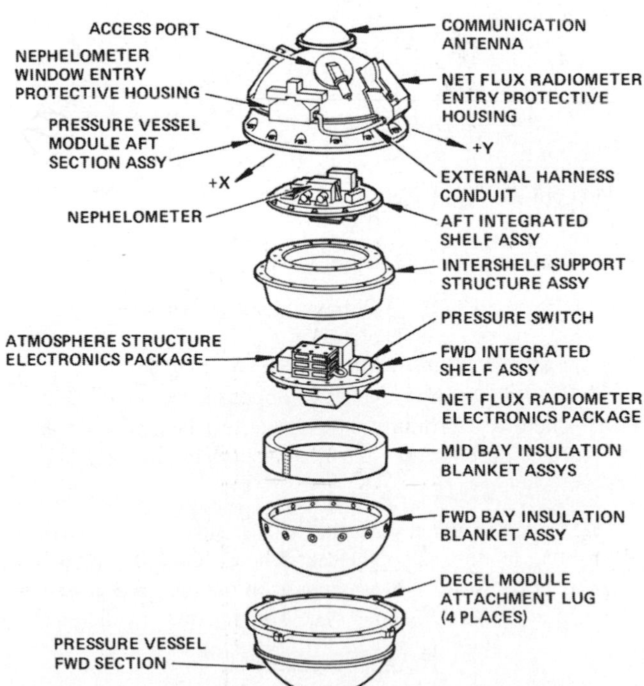

FIGURE 7.30 Typeset Lettering Used on a Technical Illustration

7.6 LETTERING WITH A CAD SYSTEM

The speed of lettering with a CAD system is only limited by the efficiency and speed of the engineer or designer entering the data at the terminal keyboard. CAD systems allow for almost unlimited lettering fonts and sizes. Figure 7.31 shows examples of CAD fonts and character modification.

CAD systems have the capability to letter at any angle, with any inclination to the vertical, and at almost any

Applying Parametric Design . . .

TEXT AND NOTES ON MODELS AND DRAWINGS

When modeling (see Fig. A), **text** can be included in a sketch for extruded protrusions and cuts, trimming surfaces, and cosmetic features. The characters in an extruded feature must use the "font3d" font for Pro/ENGINEER. For cosmetic features, any font may be used; this is done by modifying the text *after* creating the sketch.

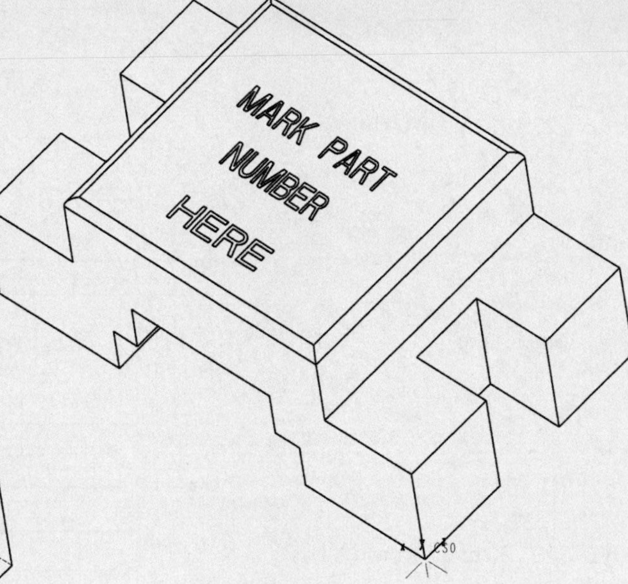

FIGURE B Parametric Model with Extruded Text

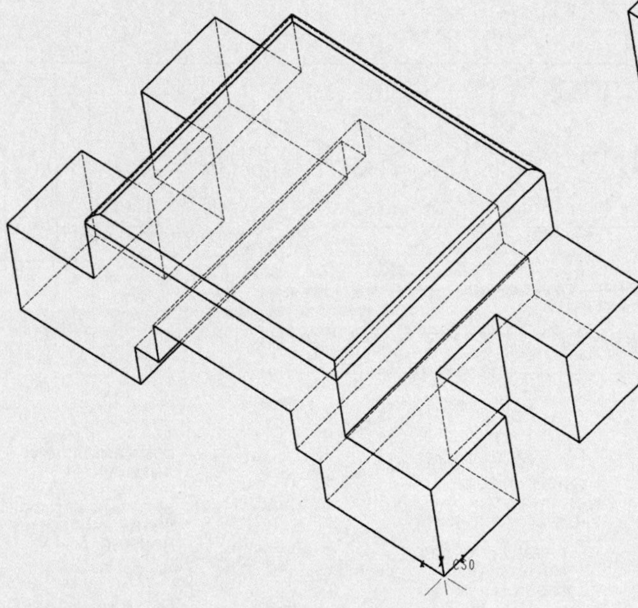

FIGURE A Model of Part

To include a text entry in a sketch:

1. From the GEOMETRY menu, choose **Text.**
2. Enter a single line of up to 79 characters of text. (Here, MARK PART NUMBER HERE was used.)
3. Place the text by picking two opposite corners of a text box. [The box determines the original text height, width factor, and location. After the text is placed, the box becomes invisible (see Fig. B).]

Dimension the text to the part or sketcher geometry (see Fig. C). To dimension the text, choose **Dimension** from the SKETCHER menu, pick anywhere on the text, pick a geometry entity, and place the dimension. The dimension will be created from the text origin (the lower left corner of the text box). The clamp has extruded lettering on its top face.

In Drawing Mode, **Notes** can be part of a dimension, be attached to one or many edges on the model, or float "free" (see Fig. D). You can add notes via the keyboard or by reading them from a text file. Notes are created with the default values (height, font, etc.) specified in the drawing setup file.

To add notes to the drawing, choose **Create** from the DETAIL menu and **Note** from the DETAIL ITEM menu. The NOTE TYPES menu will appear, allowing you to select options for the note you will create:

> **No Leader/Leader/On Item**—Create a note with or without a leader.
> **Enter/File**—Enter the note from the keyboard, or read the note from a text file.
> **Horizontal/Vertical/Angular**—Create a horizontal or vertical note, or enter an angular value between 0° and 359°.
> **Standard**—Create notes with multiple leaders.

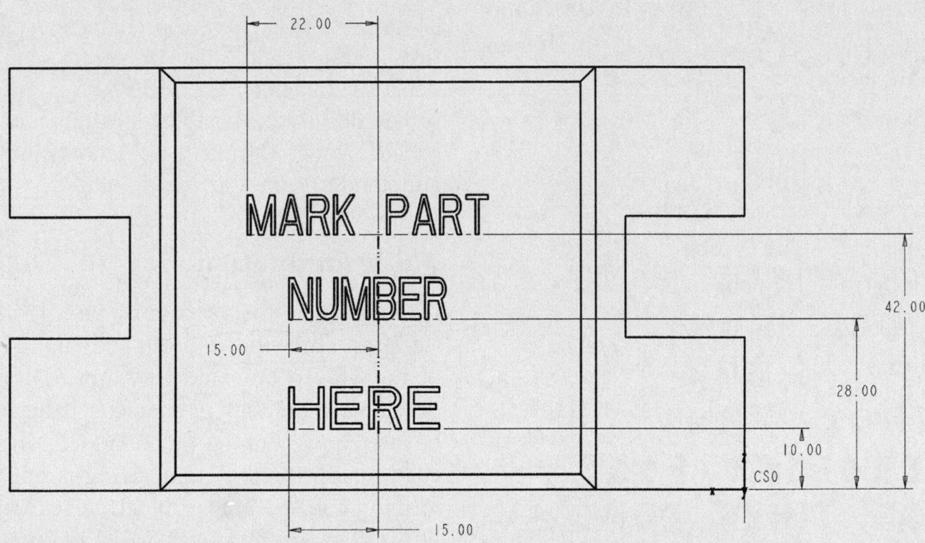

FIGURE C **Dimensioning Text Entities in Sketcher**

> **Normal Leader**—Create a note with a leader that is normal to an entity.
> **Tangent Leader**—Create a note that is tangent to an entity.
> **Left/Center/Right/Default**—Create the note text as left-, center-, or right-justified (see Fig. E). **Default** will be left-justified.

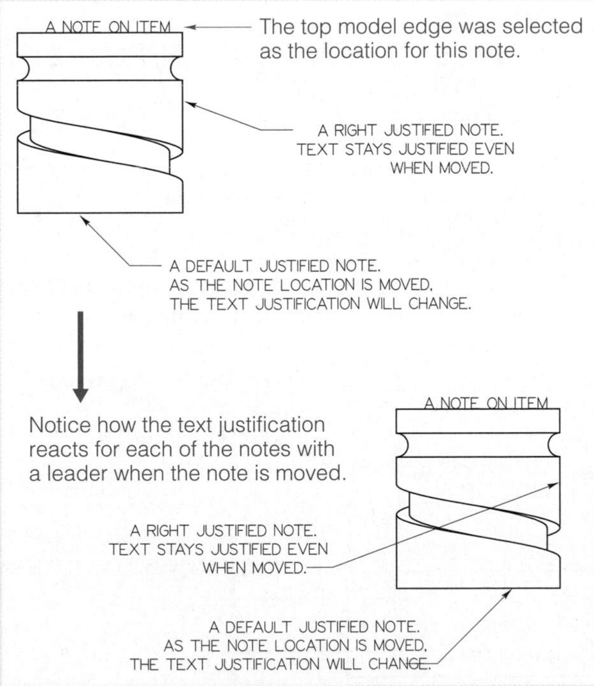

FIGURE D **Note Text Justification**

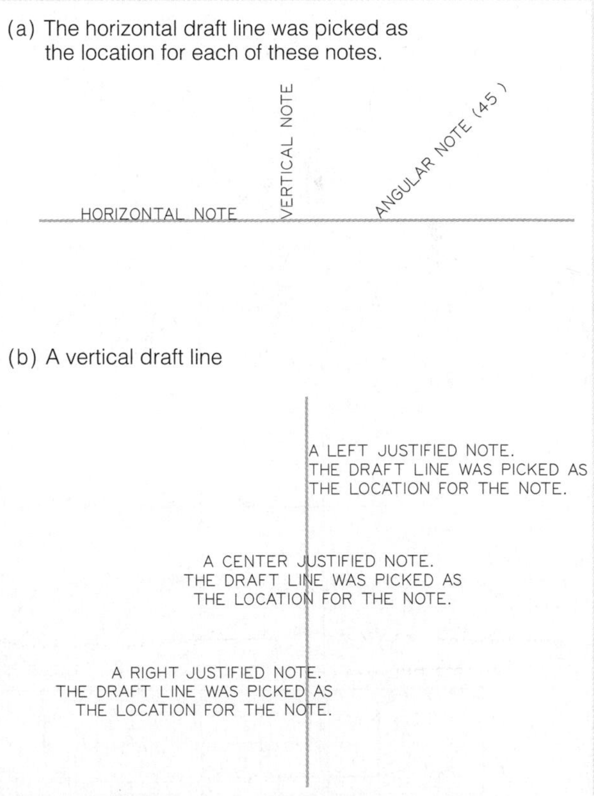

FIGURE E **Text Angle and Justification**

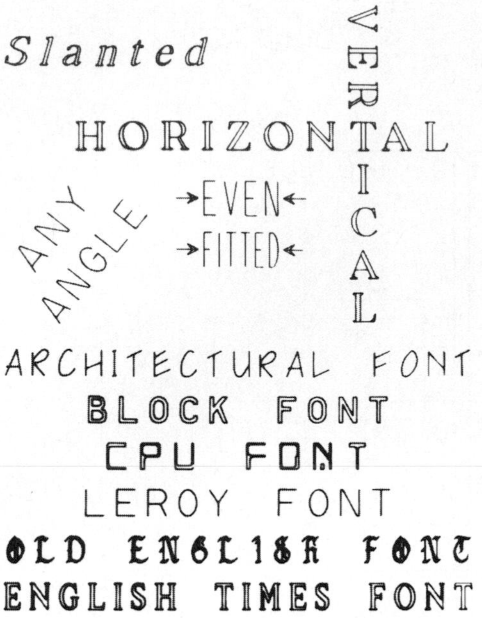

Slanted

VERTICAL

HORIZONTAL

ANY ANGLE

→EVEN←

→FITTED←

ARCHITECTURAL FONT

BLOCK FONT

CPU FONT

LEROY FONT

OLD ENGLISH FONT

ENGLISH TIMES FONT

FIGURE 7.31 CAD Fonts and Character Modification

character height or width. Figure 7.32 is an example of an engineering drawing created on a CAD system. Notice the clarity of the lettering for the dimensioning and notes.

On a CAD system, the character spacing, position, and justification (right, left, or center) are easily selected as default parameters. The **SETVARS** command in AutoCAD is sometimes used to establish defaults for the lettering (**TEXT**) on a drawing. Normally, all defaults are selected before the annotation of the drawing is started.

7.6.1 Annotation

Annotation is the process of placing words and numbers (text) on a drawing. You can add text to a drawing by means of the **TEXT** command in AutoCAD. Text entities can be drawn with a variety of character patterns, or fonts, and can be stretched, compressed, obliqued, angled, slanted, thickened, or mirrored. A **text string** is one or more characters forming a single unit or block. A text string can contain as little as one text character or can be composed of many lines or paragraphs of text. CAD systems allow text to be saved in the same manner used to file a part or drawing. The **text file** (or block) can then be recalled and reused on any drawing. This ability is particularly helpful when a company uses the same set of notes or instructions for a number of parts.

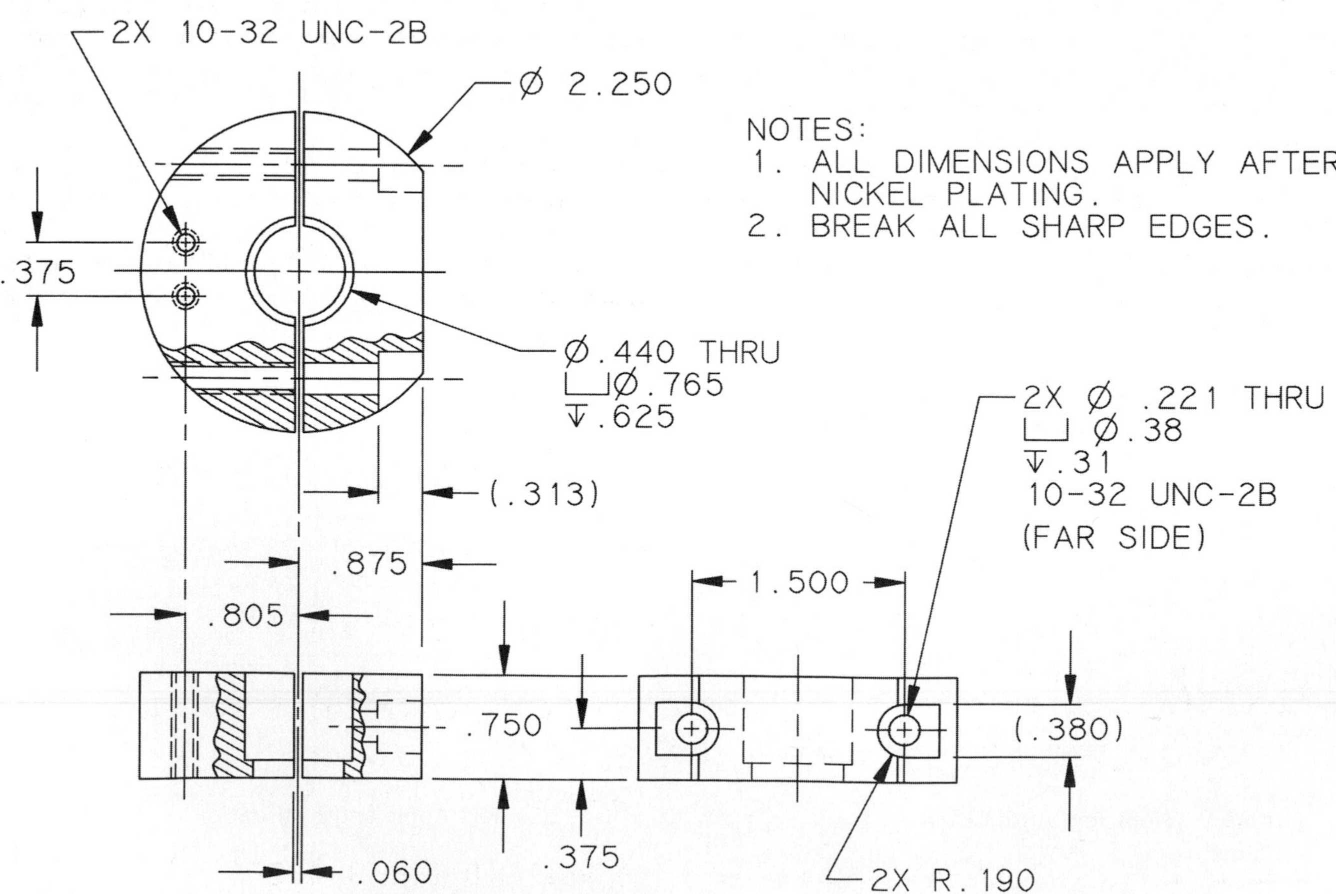

FIGURE 7.32 An Engineering Drawing with CAD Lettering

FIGURE 7.33 Text Justification

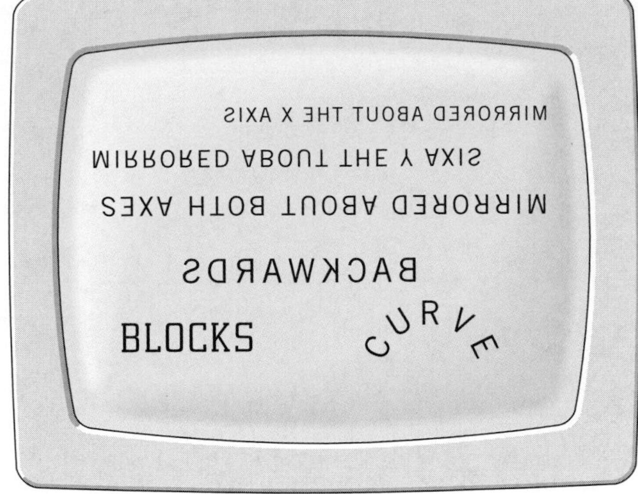

FIGURE 7.35 Text Variations

7.6.2 Text Justification and Height

Text is ordinarily left-justified at the starting point specified; that is, the left end of the text baseline is placed at the starting point. Right-justified (stopline) text aligns the text with the right side, as shown in Figure 7.33, where left-justified, center-justified, and aligned text samples are also given.

The text height specifies, in drawing units, how far above the baseline the capital letters extend. On some systems the height is specified by designating a point; the height will be the distance between this and the starting point. The height, width, slant, and angle can also be determined by the user (Fig. 7.34). Figure 7.35 shows a few text examples that can be created with some systems: mirrored, curved, block, and backwards. Lowercase lettering must be specified before inserting the text, because the default for many systems is uppercase characters.

7.6.3 Text Styles and Fonts

A text font defines the pattern used to draw text characters. Fonts are referred to as **STYLES** in AutoCAD. Text entities can be drawn using any number of character fonts. Several such fonts are supplied with most CAD software; samples of six AutoCAD styles are shown in Figure 7.36.

Many systems have a variety of text fonts available on the screen or tablet menu for quick and easy insertion on the drawing. A tablet menu can be used for selecting a text font, changing the font style of an existing text string, and inserting text with variations of height, width, thickness, angle, slant, and justification.

On many systems the default values have been set for standard drafting text (Fig. 7.37), and the user can change the values before adding text to the drawing. The **TEXT STYLE** command in AutoCAD affects all text, including the parameters for the text characters used in dimensions. The

FIGURE 7.34 Slanted, Angled, Tall, and Wide Text

ROMAN SIMPLEX 1 2 3 4 5

ITALIC TRIPLEX 1 2 3 4 5

MONOTEXT 1 2 3 4 5

GOTHIC ENGLISH 1 2 3 4 5

SCRIPT COMPLEX 1 2 3 4 5

STANDARD 1 2 3 4 5

FIGURE 7.36 Text Fonts (Styles)

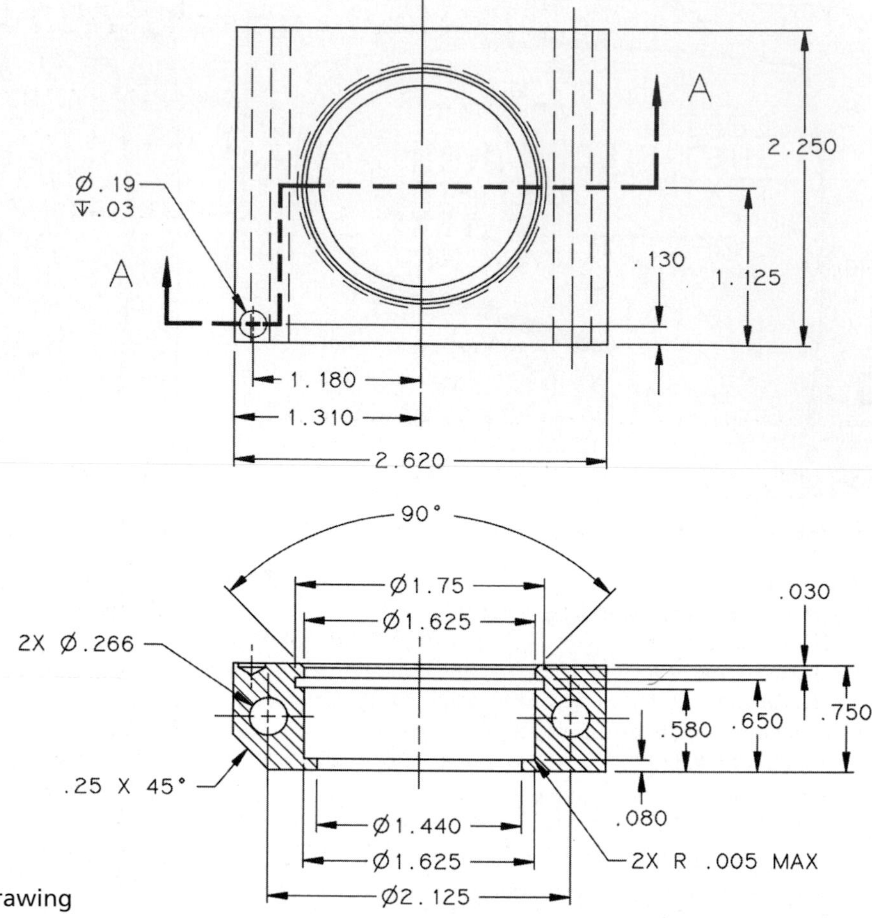

FIGURE 7.37 CAD-Drawn Engineering Drawing

STYLE command prompts you for the specific information that will set the defaults for the text. The **STYLE** command was used to set the text parameters for Figure 7.38.

```
Command: STYLE
Text Style (or ?) <default>: MONOTEXT
Existing Style.
Font file <default>: <RETURN>
Height <default>: .250
Width factor <default>: <RETURN>
Obliquing factor <default>: <RETURN>
Backwards? <N>: <RETURN>
Upside-down? <N>: <RETURN>
Vertical? <N>: <RETURN>
(MONOTEXT is now the current text style)
```

7.6.4 Entering Text on a Drawing

The process for entering text on a drawing involves picking the **TEXT** command and then digitizing the location (or giving coordinates) of the required text. You can add multiple positions of the same text by simply digitizing more than one location for the string.

Before the text can be drawn, you may have to determine the desired text height, the rotation angle from the baseline, and the text string itself. AutoCAD prompts you for this information when using the **DTEXT** command. The following **DTEXT** command was used after **STYLE** to insert the text in Figure 7.38:

```
Command: DTEXT
Start point or Align/Center/Fit/Middle/
Right/Style: <PICK LOCATION>
Height <.250>: <RETURN>
Rotation angle <default>: <RETURN>
Text: <RETURN>
NOTES: UNLESS OTHERWISE SPECIFIED
1. MATERIAL: ALUMINUM, AA ALLOY 6061-T6
2. ALL FILLETS AND ROUNDS R.25
3. BREAK ALL CORNERS
4. PERMANENT MARK PART NO. 000-000345-001
```

Whether using a CAD system or one of the many different lettering aids described in this chapter, mastering freehand lettering is still essential. Engineering and design sketches and other types of written communications require the mastery of freehand lettering to ensure proper and correct transferring of data. Regardless of future innovations in technology, handwritten communication will always be necessary for the designer and engineer in industry.

```
NOTES: UNLESS OTHERWISE SPECIFIED

1. MATERIAL: ALUMINUM, AA ALLOY 6061-T6
2. ALL FILLETS AND ROUNDS R.25
3. BREAK ALL CORNERS
4. PERMANENT MARK PART NO. 000-000345-001
```

FIGURE 7.38 Text Entered with AutoCAD

QUIZ

True or False

1. Inclined lettering, .25 in. high, is preferred on mechanical drawings.
2. When hand-lettering a drawing, the distance between lines is equal to the specified character height.
3. The space between words should be a full four units or equal to the letter J.
4. Vertical lettering is preferred over inclined lettering, since it reduces better.
5. Vertical and inclined lettering should not be mixed on one drawing.
6. CAD systems eliminate the need to master freehand lettering.
7. There are eight basic strokes for forming letters and numbers.
8. Guidelines need only be used when learning how to letter.

Fill in the Blanks

9. Lettering is divided into three methods: ________, ________, and ________.
10. Guidelines must be used when hand-lettering except when using ________ paper.
11. The ANSI standard on lettering states that the height of a fraction number should be ________ to the whole number.
12. Notes and dimensions should be at least ________ in height on a "D"-size drawing.
13. Inclined lettering should be approximately ________ degrees.
14. Stopline lettering is the same as ________.
15. ANSI lists and notes are placed in the ________ or ________ side of the drawing.
16. Templates and lettering guides should always be placed against a ________ when lettering.

Answer the Following

17. What ANSI standard covers lettering on engineering drawings?
18. When is lowercase lettering used, and on what type of drawings?
19. When are machine lettering devices normally used for a drawing?
20. Define the term *text font.*
21. Explain the difference between manual, mechanical, and machine lettering.
22. What is annotation?
23. Name five types of lettering characteristics available on CAD systems.
24. List the reasons for mastering manual lettering.

EXERCISES

Exercises may be assigned as freehand, template, or machine-lettering projects. Transfer the given information to an "A"-size sheet of .25 in. grid paper.

After Reading the Chapter Through Section 7.3.8, You May Complete the Following Exercises

Exercise 7.1 Practice lettering using the standard stroke sequence. You may add vertical or inclined guidelines for this exercise.

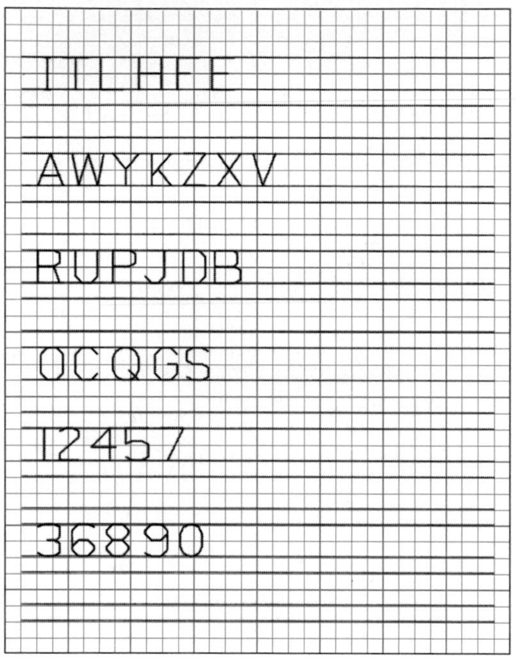

EXERCISE 7.1

Exercise 7.2 Letter the sentence and the notes three times each.

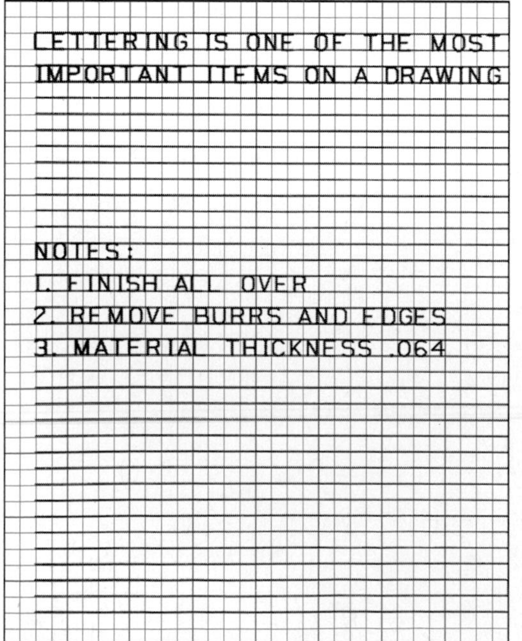

EXERCISE 7.2

Exercise 7.3 Letter the page as shown using compressed and extended lettering.

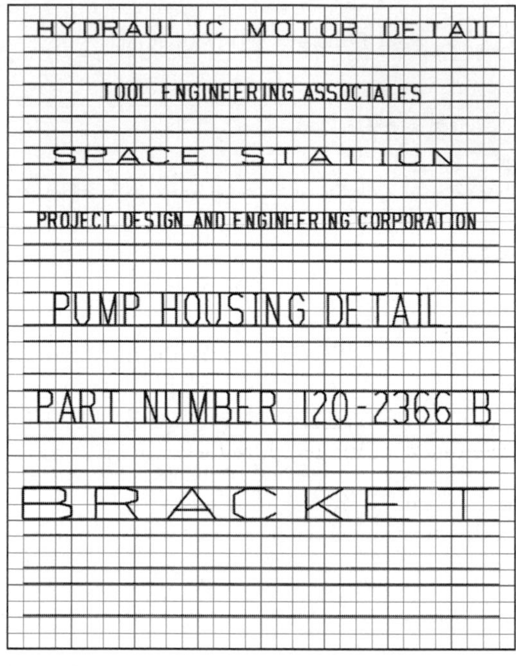

EXERCISE 7.3

Exercise 7.4 Letter the drawing notes as shown using right-justified, left-justified, and center-justified lettering.

BREAK ALL SHARP CORNERS
REMOVE BURRS
SURFACE ROUGHNESS 750

DEDENDUM
ROOT DIAMETER
ADDENDUM
PITCH DIAMETER

PREMIER DRAFTING AND DESIGN
CORPORATION

EXERCISE 7.4

PROBLEMS

Problem 7.1 Using the layout sheet provided nearby, complete the lettering assignment as shown. Use this example to lay out the drawing format for the following problems.

Problem 7.2 Letter each of the following twice, using compressed and extended, vertical, .5 in. or 12 mm height, uppercase lettering. See Problem 7.1 for the page layout, or use the Problem Sheets.

ANGLE BRACKET ASSEMBLY
PUMP HOUSING DETAIL
DESIGN AND ENGINEERING, INC.

Problem 7.3 Letter the following note three times at 4 mm height in vertical uppercase lettering.

HEAT TREATMENT:
MC QUAID-EHN GRAIN SIZE 5-8 HEAT TO 1550 DEGREES F AND QUENCH IN OIL. DRAW TO BRINELL HARDNESS 241-285. 100% BRINELL REQUIRED

Problem 7.4 Letter the following note three times using .25 in. high inclined letters. Instructor may assign project to be inked using a lettering template or a Leroy set.

NOTE:
1. LOCATING POINTS TO BE CASE FLAT AND SMOOTH
2. CAST FEATURES ARE DETERMINED BY BASIC DIMENSIONS IN RELATION TO LOCATING SURFACES.

Problem 7.5 Letter the following specifications using vertical, mixed uppercase and lowercase characters .156 in. or 4 mm in height.

1. Casting to be pressure tight when tested at 100 P.S.I.
2. Finish all over 125 μin.
3. Do not apply piece mark.
4. Material thickness .125 in.

Problem 7.6 Reletter the parts list in Figure 7.19 using vertical uppercase lettering.

Problem 7.7 Using a CAD system, letter the notes in Figure 7.20.

Problem 7.8 Set up an "A"-size drawing as in Figure 7.10, and fill the entire page with lettering.

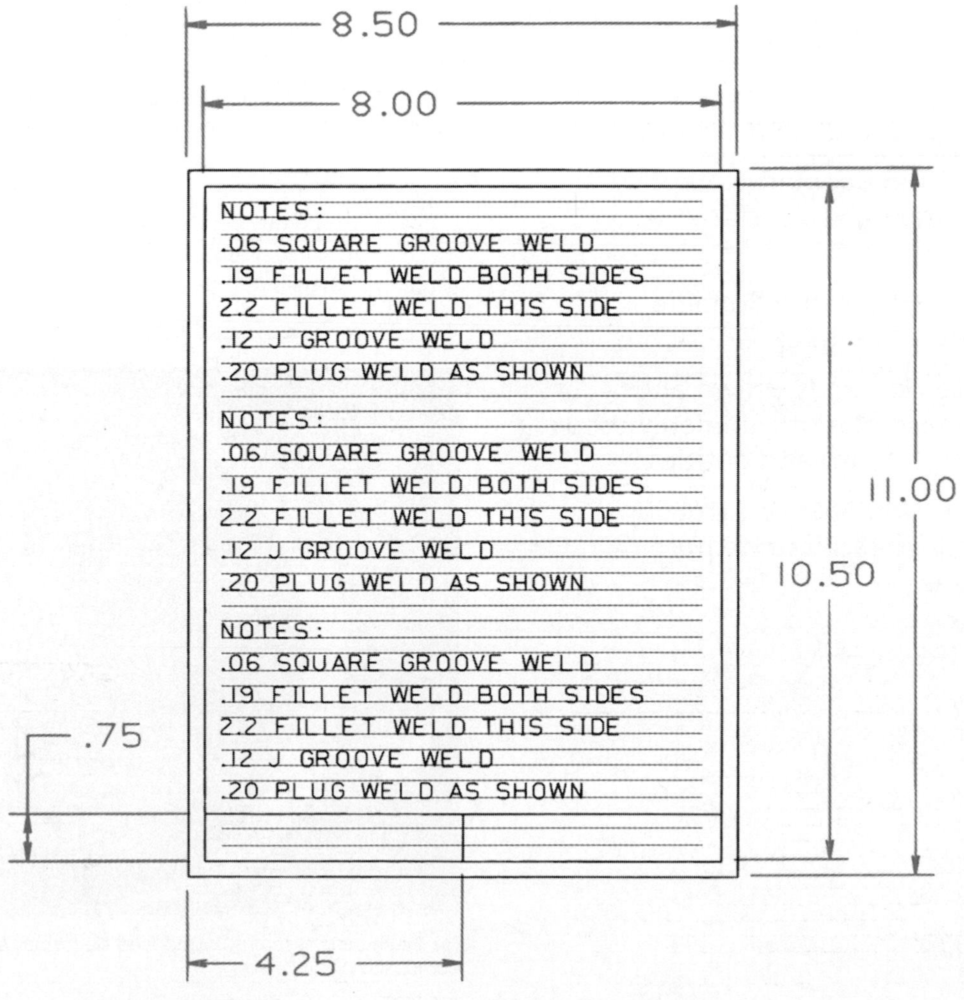

PROBLEM 7.1

GEOMETRIC CONSTRUCTIONS

Chapter 8

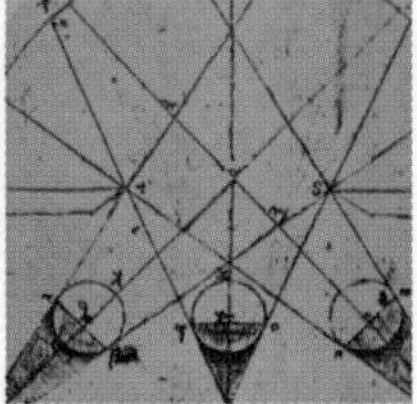

LEARNING OBJECTIVES

Upon completion of this chapter you will be able to:

1. Develop the ability to interpret graphic solutions to common geometrical problems.
2. Define and construct, via manual and CAD methods, plane geometric shapes: points, lines, curves, polygons, angles, and circles.
3. Define solid geometric shapes: polyhedra, curved surfaces, and warped surfaces.
4. Apply basic construction line drawing techniques.
5. Produce uniformly drawn and scaled examples of commonly used geometric forms and entities.
6. Employ geometric construction methods to facilitate feature locations.

8.1 INTRODUCTION

Geometric construction is a procedure for drawing figures and shapes that requires only the tools of drafting, including traditional drawing instruments and equipment and the new tools of computer hardware and software. Regardless of the tools, geometric construction requires an understanding of geometric shapes and the mechanics of their construction, as well as the ability to solve problems visually. Geometric construction emphasizes scale, uniformity of linework, and smooth joining of lines and curves when done manually. Such constructions are used extensively in industry. For example, the gravity probe assembly in Figure 8.1(a) is composed almost entirely of circular-cylindrical shapes; the stairway in Figure 8.1(b) is a cylindrical helix; and the mechanical subassembly in Figure 8.1(c) uses a variety of geometric shapes.

(a) Neck tube assembly composed of copper support rings and composite plastic insert

FIGURE 8.1 Geometry in Design

(b) Helical stairway

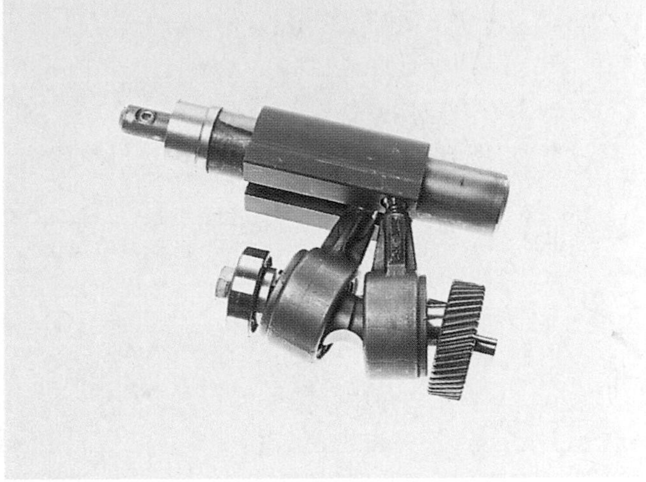

(c) Subassembly

FIGURE 8.1 Geometry in Design—*Continued*

8.2 GEOMETRIC FORMS

Geometric forms include a wide range of shapes and figures: **squares, triangles, arcs** and **circles, solids,** and **single-curved, double-curved,** and **warped surfaces.** The following sections provide step-by-step procedures for manually constructing common geometric forms.

8.2.1 Points and Lines

Geometric forms and shapes are points connected by lines. The **point** is the primary geometric unit in graphical construction. All projections of lines, planes, surfaces, and solids can be physically located and manipulated by identifying a series of points. These points locate ends of straight lines or are placed along a curved line to establish the line in space. Since a point exists at one position in space, it is located in space by establishing it in two or more adjacent views. (**Views** of points, lines, and other shapes are introduced in Chapter 9.)

A **line** is a series of points in space, and has magnitude (length) but not width. Although a line may be located by establishing any two points and although it may have a specified length, all lines can be extended.

Lines are used to draw edges of plane surfaces and solid shapes. A **straight line** is the shortest distance between two points. The word *line* usually refers to a straight line. A line that bends is a *curve.* When two lines are in the same plane, either they are parallel or they intersect. **Parallel lines,** symbolized by //, are the same distance apart along their entire length. Lines that intersect at an angle of 90° are **perpendicular lines,** symbolized by ⊥. Figure 8.2 shows various types of lines. Geometric constructions require you to draw arcs, circles, and other *curved lines* that use specific linework techniques.

8.2.2 Polygons

A **polygon** is a planar closed figure that has three or more straight sides. A **regular polygon** has all sides of equal length and all angles of equal size. A regular polygon can be inscribed within a circle, with corners touching the circle, or it can be circumscribed about a circle, with sides touching the circle.

A **triangle** is a three-sided polygon. The sum of its interior angles always equals 180°. In Figure 8.2, the **equilateral triangle** has equal sides and equal angles and is a regular polygon. The second type of triangle is an **isosceles triangle.** It has two equal sides and two equal angles; the unequal side is the base, and the corner opposite the unequal side is the **apex,** or **vertex.** A line drawn through the apex to the base divides an isosceles triangle into two equal triangles. **Scalene triangles** have unequal angles and unequal sides.

A **quadrilateral** is a four-sided polygon. The sum of its interior angles is 360°. Figure 8.2 shows the six types of quadrilaterals. The first four quadrilaterals have opposite sides that are equal in length and are called **parallelograms.** The first parallelogram is a **square**, because all sides and angles are equal. The second parallelogram is a **rectangle** because its opposite sides are equal and its angles are all the same. The third parallelogram is a **rhombus.** It has four equal sides and its opposite angles are equal. The fourth

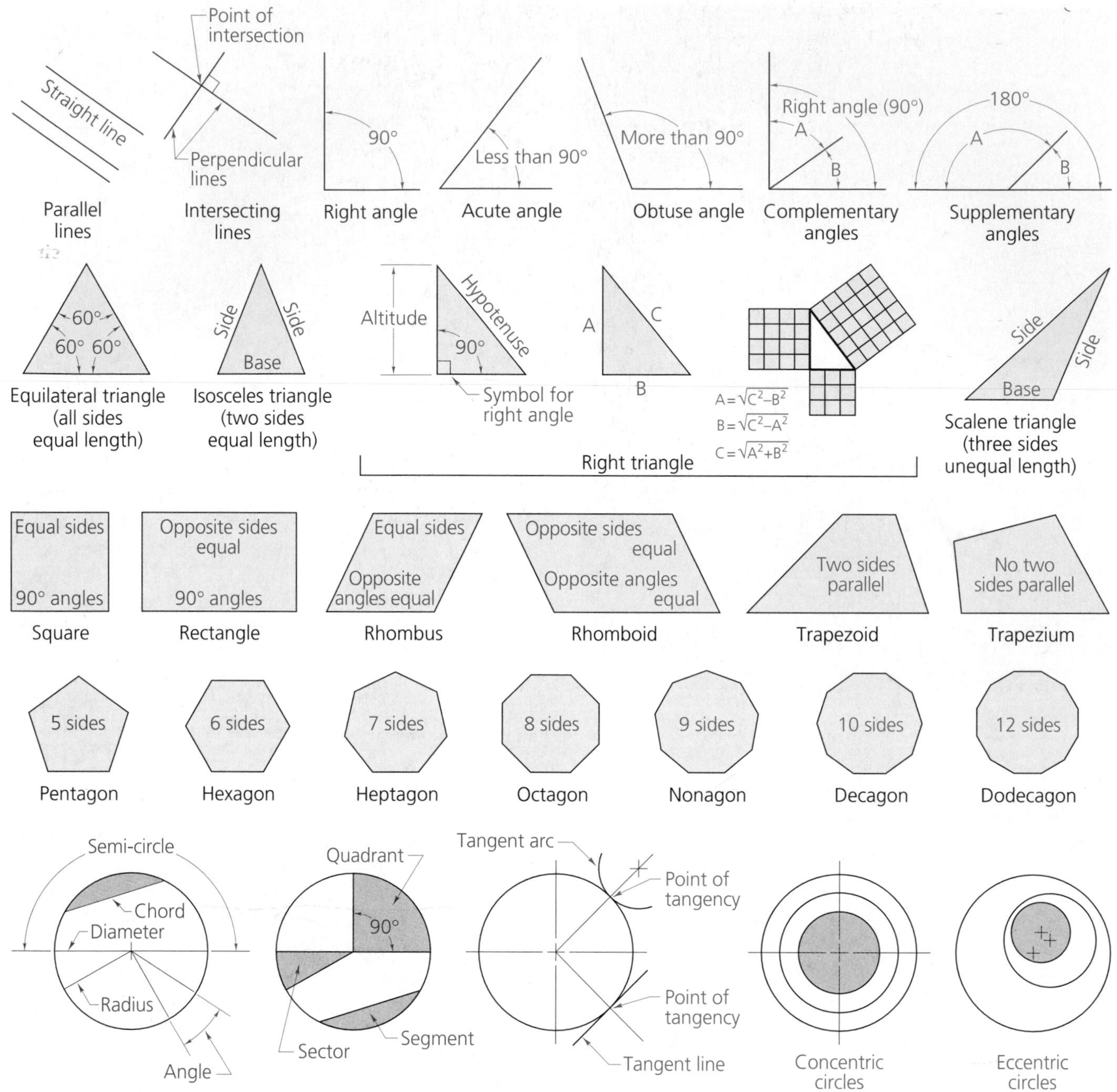

FIGURE 8.2 Geometric Shapes and Items

parallelogram, a **rhomboid,** has opposite sides parallel and opposite angles equal. A **trapezoid** has two sides parallel. When a quadrilateral has no two sides parallel it is called a **trapezium.**

Figure 8.2 also includes seven other regular polygons: **pentagon** (five sides), **hexagon** (six sides), **heptagon** (seven sides), **octagon** (eight sides), **nonagon** (nine sides), **decagon** (ten sides), and **dodecagon** (twelve sides).

8.2.3 Angles and Circles

Angles, represented by the symbol ∠, are formed by two intersecting lines (Fig. 8.3). The angle measurement of the distance between lines is typically expressed in degrees and sometimes in radians.

Various Types of Angles (Fig. 8.3)

Acute angle Less than 90°.

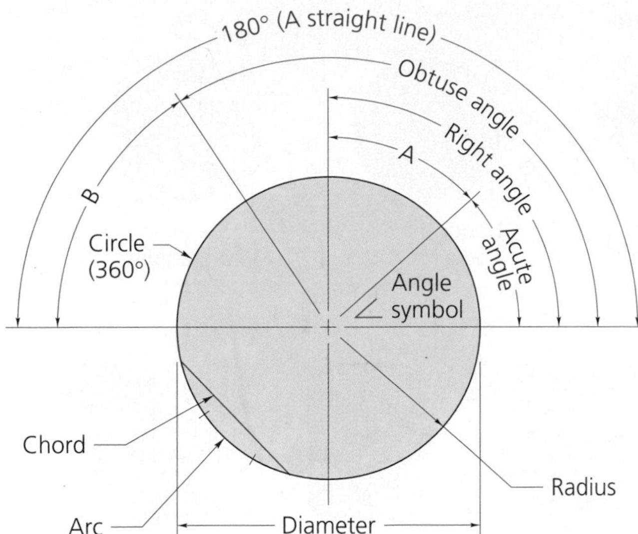

FIGURE 8.3 Angles and Circles

Right angle 90°, formed by two perpendicular lines.

Obtuse angle More than 90° but less than 180°.

180° angle A **straight line.**

Complementary angles Two angles whose sum is 90°.

Supplementary angles Two angles whose sum is 180°.

Circles represent holes and solid round shapes on drawings. A full circle is 360°.

Parts of a Circle (Fig. 8.3)

Circumference The distance around the circle.

Diameter The distance measured from edge to edge and through the center of the circle.

Radius One-half the diameter, measured from the center of the circle to the circumference.

Chord A straight line that connects two points on the circle's circumference.

Arc A continuous portion of the circumference, from one fixed point along it to another.

Concentric circles Have different radii but the same center point.

Eccentric circles Have different center points and different radii.

8.2.4 Polyhedra

Polyhedra (Fig. 8.4) are solids formed by plane surfaces. Every surface (face) of each form is a polygon. **Prisms** are polyhedra that have two parallel polygon-shaped ends and sides that are parallelograms. The **cube** is a polyhedron that has six equal sides. A **pyramid** is a polyhedron that has a polygon for a base and triangles with a common vertex for faces. A **tetrahedron** is a pyramid that has four equal sides. Figure 8.4 also illustrates a **right pyramid**, a **truncated pyramid**, and an **oblique pyramid.**

8.2.5 Curved Surfaces

Curved surfaces are divided into two categories: **single curved** (also called **ruled surfaces**) and **double curved.** Forms that are bounded by single-curved surfaces include **cones** and **cylinders.** Variations of cones include the **right cone**, the **frustum of a cone**, the **oblique cone**, and the **truncated cone.** Figure 8.4 also shows a **right cylinder** and an **oblique cylinder.** Double-curved surfaces (Fig. 8.4) are generated by moving a curved line about a straight-line axis and include a **sphere**, a **torus**, and an **ellipsoid.**

Figure 8.5(a–e) presents examples of solid shapes used in the parametric design of parts. Can you see the prism, cylinder, and sphere shapes and their intersections? The parametric solid model of the shaft in Figure 8.5(c) and its accompaning drawing in (d) provide an example of a part design created almost entirely out of cylinders (revolved solids). The parametric model in Figure 8.5(e) is an example of an unfolded flat pattern of a sheet metal part. The part's solid shapes are all prisms except for the hole (circle) being added to the model at this stage in the design.

8.3 DRAWING GEOMETRIC CONSTRUCTIONS

The following sections present step-by-step instructions for drawing geometric constructions, including parallel lines, perpendicular lines, angles, circles, polygons, tangencies, tangent arcs, curves, conics, involutes, spirals, and helices.

8.3.1 Drawing Parallel and Perpendicular Lines

Parallel and perpendicular lines are easily constructed using a straightedge and a triangle. In Figure 8.6 an adjustable triangle is used in the construction, but it could be any triangle. *Position 1* is the first line drawn. Use the following steps.

1. Move the triangle along the straightedge to *position* 2 and draw a parallel line.
2. Rotate the triangle to *position* 3. Then draw a line perpendicular to the first two lines, on the same edge of the triangle that you used before it was rotated.

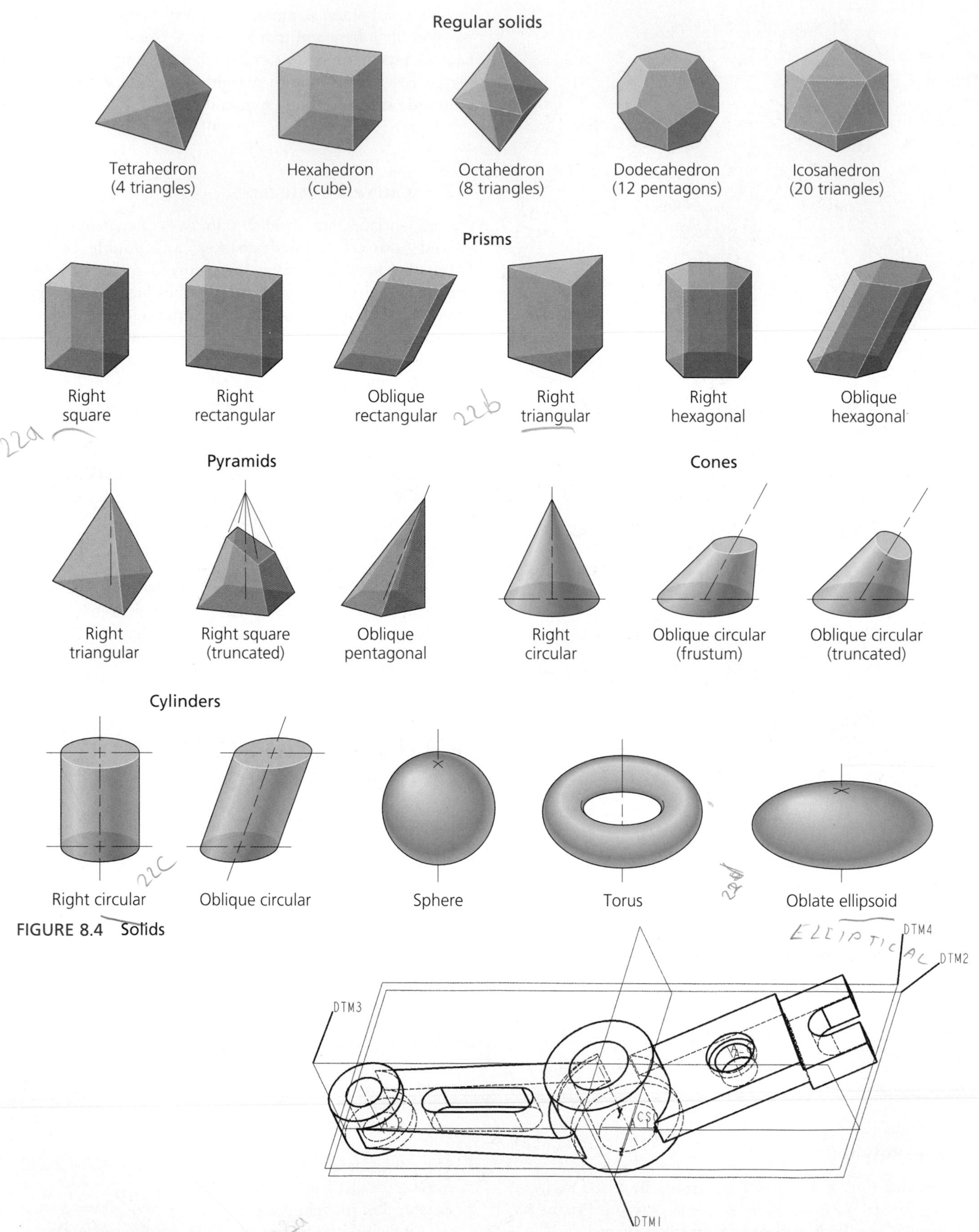

FIGURE 8.4 Solids

(a) Parametric solid model of arm

FIGURE 8.5 Solid Shapes and Modeling

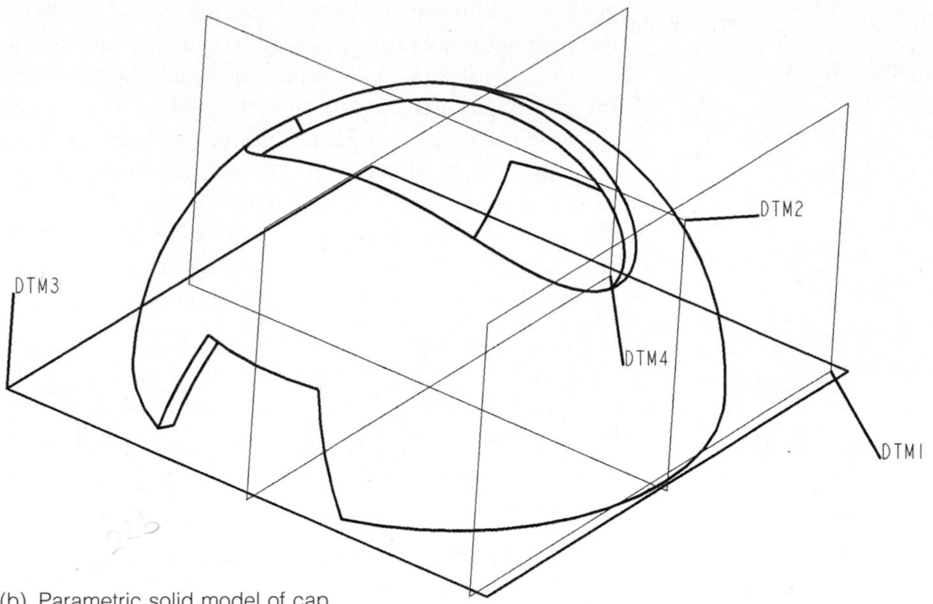

(b) Parametric solid model of cap

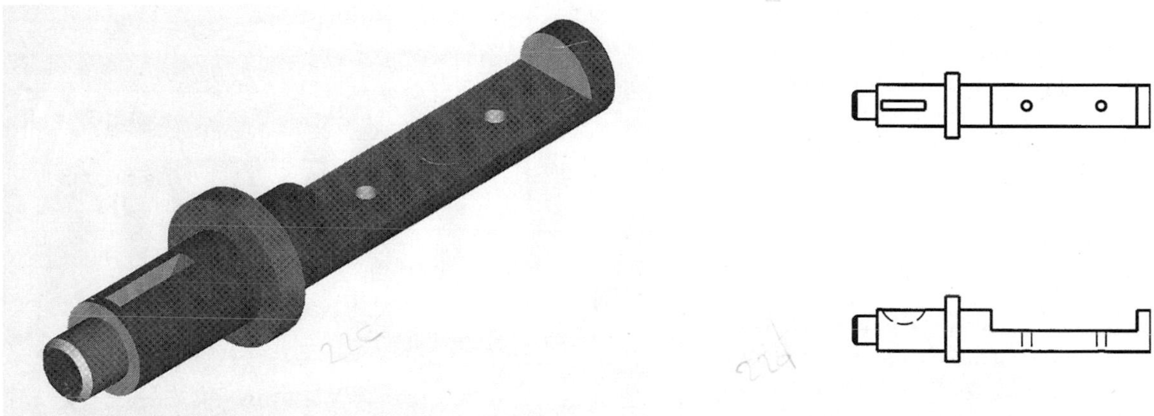

(c) Parametric solid model of shaft

(d) Parametric drawing of shaft

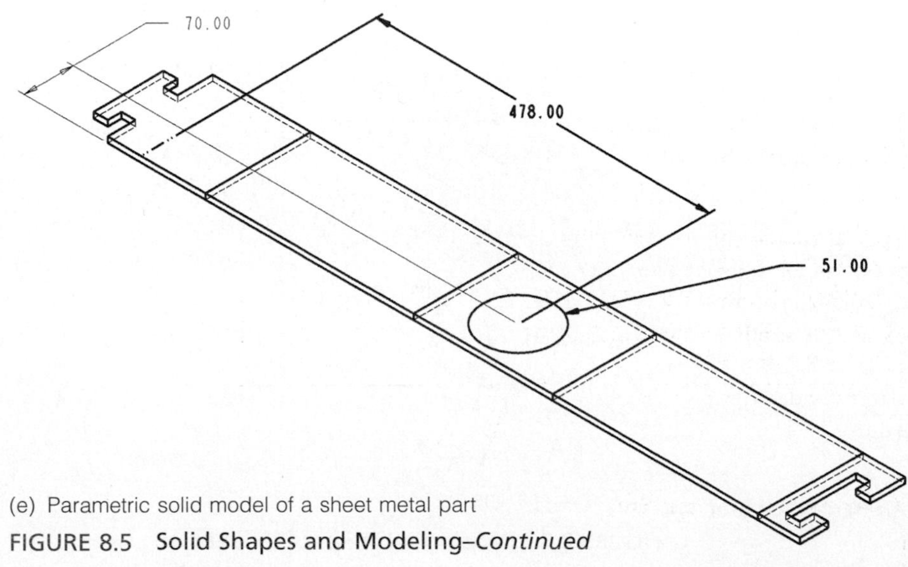

(e) Parametric solid model of a sheet metal part

FIGURE 8.5 Solid Shapes and Modeling–*Continued*

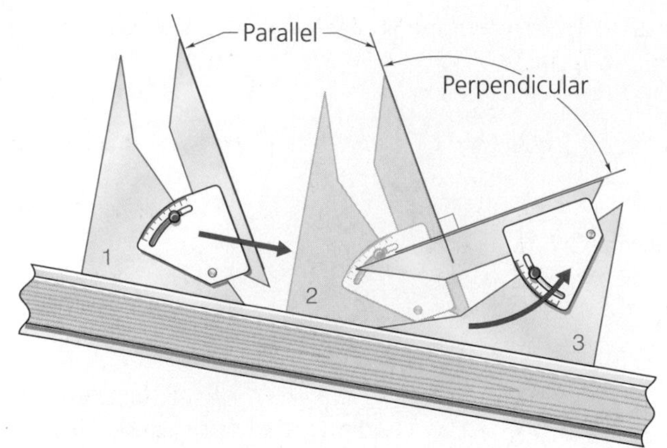

FIGURE 8.6 Drawing Parallel and Perpendicular Lines

8.3.2 Dividing a Line into Equal or Proportional Parts

One way to divide a line is to calculate its length, divide the length by the number of required parts, and then use the result to mark the divisions. However, this method accumulates error. A better way to divide a line equally or proportionally is by one of the following methods.

Figure 8.7(a) illustrates the **parallel-line method** for dividing a line equally. Any type of scale and unit of measurement will do. To simplify the construction and measuring, choose the most convenient unit type and scale. In Figure 8.7(a), line AB is to be divided into eleven equal segments. Use the following steps.

Parallel-Line Method [Fig. 8.7(a)]

1. Draw a construction line AC that starts at either end of line AB. This line is any convenient length (slightly longer works well). Angle A should not be less than 20° or more than 45° or it will be hard to project the divisions from the construction line AC to the original line AB.
2. Find a scale that will divide line AB into approximately the number of parts needed, and mark these divisions on line AC. Here, the full-size inch scale was used, with $\frac{1}{2}$ inch marking each division. There are now eleven equal divisions from A to D that lie on line AC.
3. Set the triangle to draw a construction line from point D to point B. Then through each of the remaining ten divisions draw construction lines parallel to line BD by moving the triangle along the straightedge.

It is also possible to use dividers for step 2 to divide the construction lines into the required number of equal parts.

In the **vertical-line method** [Fig. 8.7(b)], all of the projection lines are vertical and are drawn with a straightedge and any triangle. Any type of scale and unit of measurement can be used. Line AB is to be divided into seven equal parts. Use the following procedure.

Vertical-Line Method [Fig. 8.7(b)]

1. Draw a vertical construction line BC through point B of line AB.
2. With point A as the pivot point, position a scale that gives the required number of divisions and equally divides the distance from point A to some point on line BC. Here full-scale U.S. customary units were used—a $\frac{1}{2}$ in. unit of the scale corresponds to each division—to mark points 1 through 7. It is necessary to use a scale whose overall length of seven units is longer than the line AB.
3. Using the vertical side of a triangle, draw construction lines from points 1 through 7 to line AB. This establishes seven equally spaced segments along line AB.

With the vertical-line and parallel-line methods, there is no need to make measurements that are less than one easily measured unit, regardless of the mathematical value of the resulting divisions. The scale serves only to measure equal units; any scale that will do so can be used.

8.3.3 Proportional Division of a Line

You may occasionally need to divide a line into parts that are in a specified proportion to each other. For instance, if a line must be divided so the first part is three times as long as the

(1)

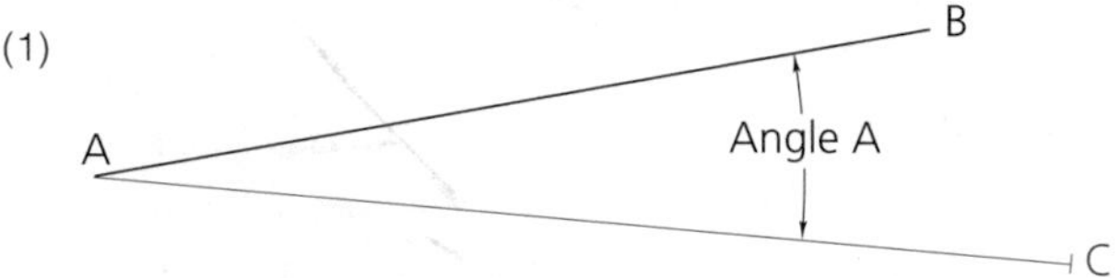

(2)

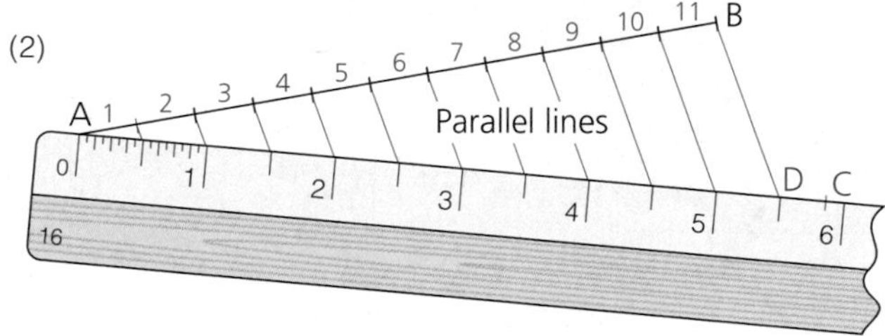

(a) The parallel-line method

(1)

(2)

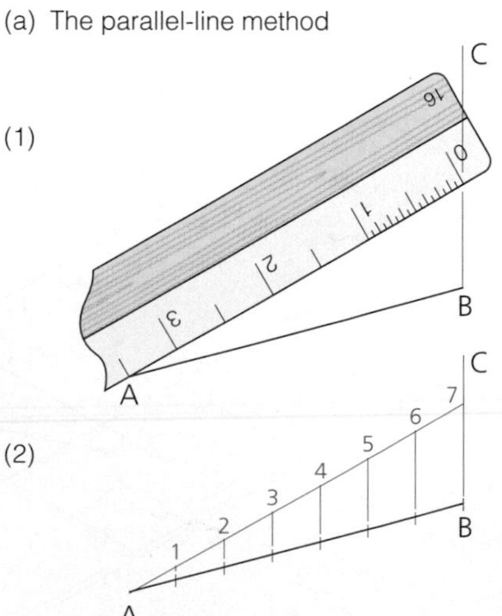

(b) The vertical-line method

FIGURE 8.7 Dividing a Line into Equal Parts

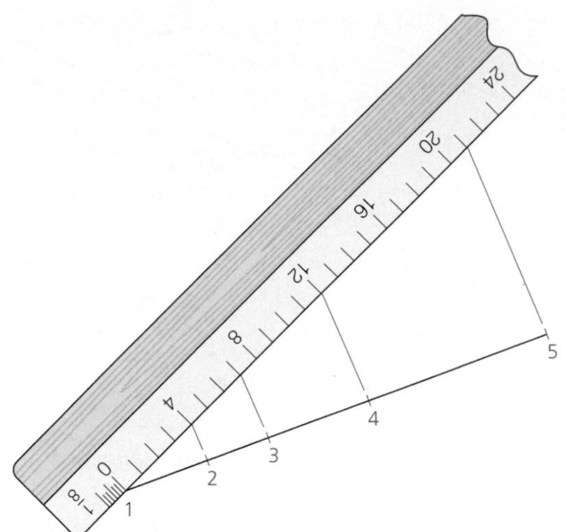

FIGURE 8.8 Proportional Division of a Line

second part, this ratio is written as 3:1 and is read as "three parts to one part" or "three to one." To divide a line proportionally, you use a method similar to that for dividing a line into equal parts.

Figure 8.8 illustrates dividing a line into four parts that have proportions of 4:3:5:9. The following steps are used.

1. Add the proportions of the parts: 4 + 3 + 5 + 9 = 21. This is the number of equal parts that are to be measured on the scale.
2. Draw a construction line at an angle to, and longer than, the given line. Set the scale to make 21 equal divisions. Make the first mark at 4 units, add 3 units, and make the second mark at 7 units; add 5 more units and make the third mark at 12 units. Add 9 units to bring the total to 21 units.
3. Project these marks to position points 2, 3, 4, and 5 on the given line using the parallel-line method. This creates line segments in proportions of 4:3:5:9.

8.3.4 Bisectors for Lines and Angles

A **perpendicular bisector** of a line *divides that line into two equal parts.* A perpendicular bisector can be constructed with only compass and straightedge (Fig. 8.9) by using the following steps.

Bisecting a Line (Fig. 8.9)

1. Set the compass at radius (R) equal to a distance greater than one-half of AB.
2. Using points A and B as centers, draw intersecting arcs to establish intersection points 1 and 2.
3. Draw construction line 1-2 by connecting the two new points. Line 1-2 intersects line AB at its midpoint and is perpendicular to it.

Figure 8.10 shows how to *divide an angle into two equal parts.* Lines AB and BC intersect and form angle ABC. Use the following steps.

Bisecting an Angle (Fig. 8.10)

1. Set the compass to any convenient radius. For small angles and short lines, extend the lines that form the angle. With point B (vertex) as the center, draw an arc (radius R) that locates points 1 and 2. The length of B1 is equal to B2.
2. Using the radius R, draw arcs from points 1 and 2. Point 3 is the intersection of these two arcs.
3. Draw line 3B. This is the bisector of the angle.

8.3.5 Locating the Center of a Known Circle

The perpendicular bisector of a chord of a circle passes through the center of the circle. If a significant portion of a circle is known, its center can be located by establishing the perpendicular bisectors of any two chords of the circle. In Figure 8.11, chords 1-2, 2-3, and 3-1 form a triangle inside the circle. Bisectors of two of these chords cross at the center of the circle (point C). The third perpendicular bisector, though not necessary, serves as a check.

8.3.6 Constructing a Circle Through Three Given Points

Using the procedure for constructing a perpendicular bisector of a line, you can construct a circle through three given

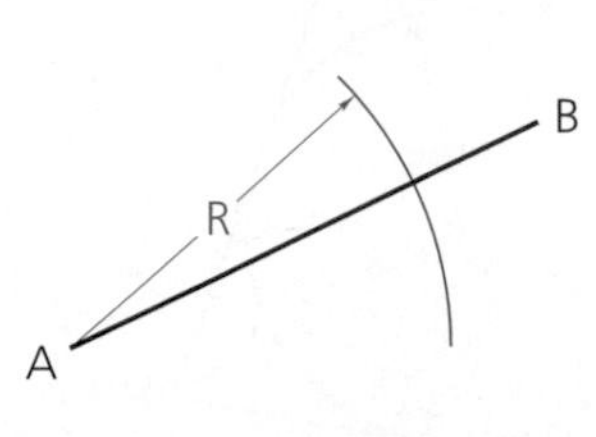

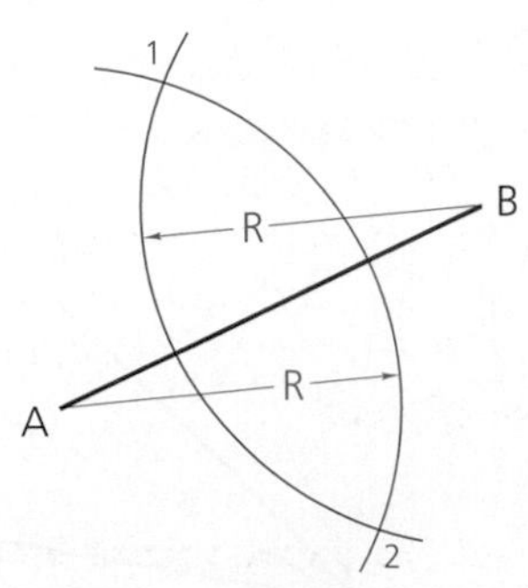

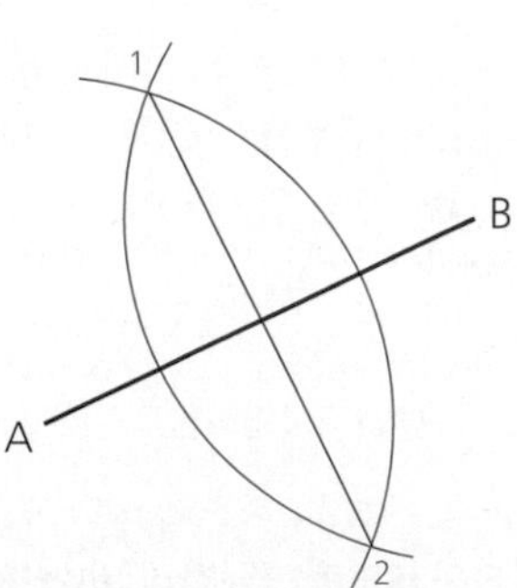

FIGURE 8.9 Bisecting a Line 1 2 3

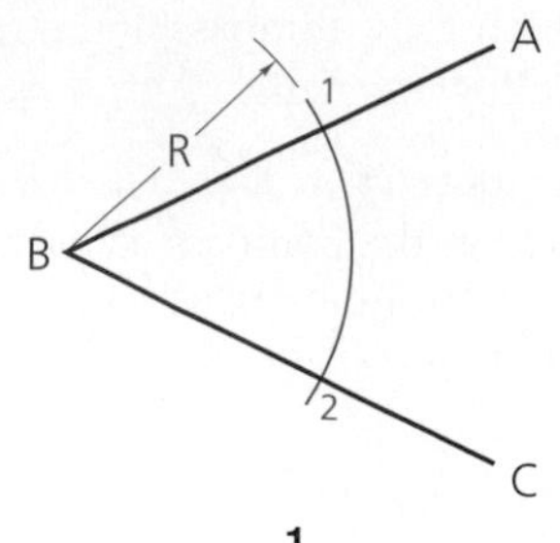

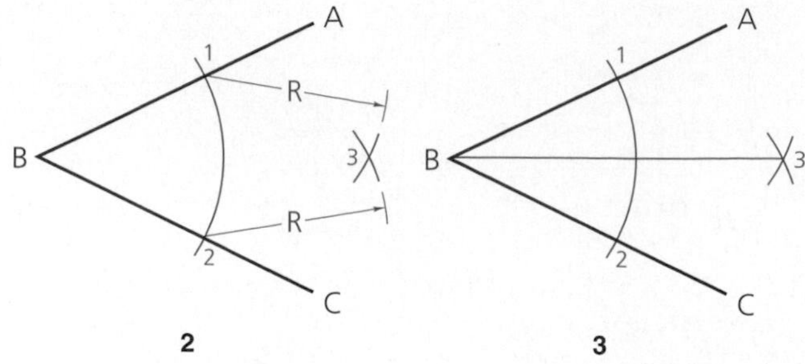

FIGURE 8.10 Bisecting an Angle

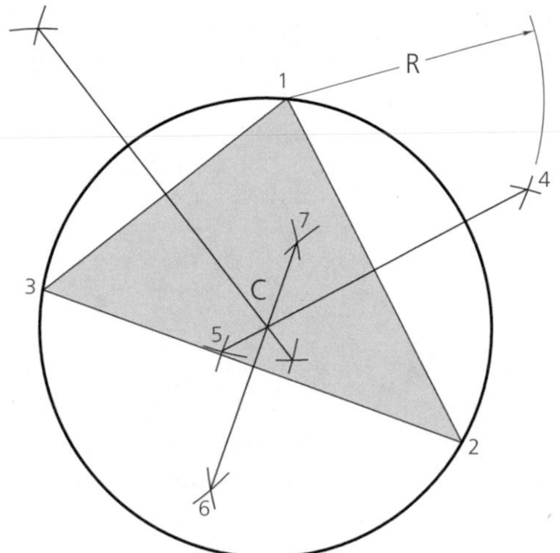

FIGURE 8.11 Finding the Center of a Circle

points in space. Figure 8.12 shows points 1, 2, and 3. The following steps were used.

1. Connect the three points with lines, and then construct perpendicular bisectors for any two chords of the circle (lines 1-2 and 1-3 here). The perpendicular bisectors intersect at the center of the required circle (C).
2. Draw the circle using as the radius the distance from C to any of the three points (C-1, C-2, or C-3).
3. Check the solution by drawing a perpendicular bisector through chord 2-3.

8.3.7 Inscribed Circle of a Triangle

An **inscribed circle of a triangle** is a circle that is tangent to (touches) each side of the triangle. Figure 8.13 illustrates the procedure for constructing the inscribed circle of a triangle. The given triangle is represented by points 1-2-3. The following steps were used.

1. Find the center of the circle by bisecting a minimum of two of the triangle's angles. The angle at point 1 is bisected by drawing arc RA to establish points 4 and 5 (RA is any convenient length).
2. From points 4 and 5, draw equal arcs (RB). Point 6 is the intersection of the two arcs.
3. Draw line 1-6 to establish the bisector of the angle, and extend this line beyond point 6.
4. Bisect the angle at point 2 by drawing arc RC to locate points 7 and 8.

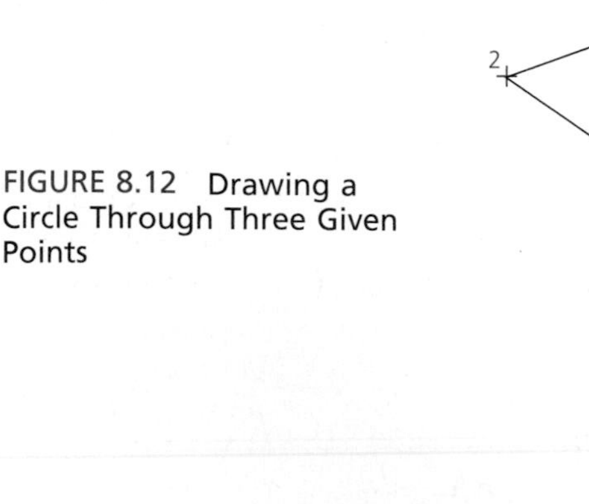

FIGURE 8.12 Drawing a Circle Through Three Given Points

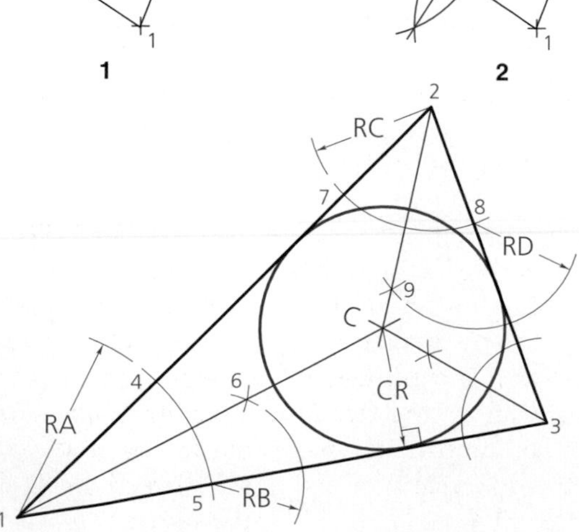

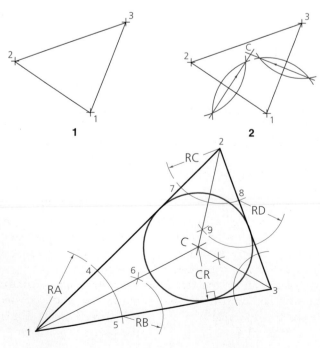

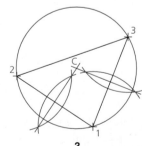

FIGURE 8.13 The Inscribed Circle of a Triangle

5. Establish point 9 by drawing equal arcs (RD) from points 7 and 8.
6. Draw a line from point 2 through point 9, and extend it to intersect the first bisector. The intersection of these two lines determines the center of the circle (C). To check the accuracy of this point, construct a third bisector that will also meet at point C.
7. Draw a line from point C perpendicular to one of the triangle's sides (side 1-3 here) to determine radius CR.
8. To complete the solution, draw the inscribed circle using C as the center and distance CR as the radius.

8.3.8 Circumscribed Circle of a Triangle

A **circumscribed circle of a triangle** touches the three vertex points of a triangle. Constructing a circumscribed circle of a triangle uses the method for constructing a circle through three given points. In Figure 8.11, the perpendicular bisectors of sides 1-2, 2-3, and 1-3 have been drawn. The intersection of the perpendicular bisectors 4-5 and 6-7 establish the center of the circle (C). A third perpendicular bisector (of line 1-3) can be drawn to check for accuracy. The radius of the circle is the distance from C to any of the three points on the triangle (C-1, C-2, or C-3).

8.3.9 Drawing a Triangle with Sides Given

Drawing a triangle, given the sides, is called **triangulation.** Use lines A, B, and C in Figure 8.14 to construct a triangle via the following steps.

1. A, B, and C are given.
2. Draw the baseline (C) and swing an arc as shown.
3. Swing arc B from the end of line C. The intersection of arcs A and B determines the vertex of the triangle.
4. Draw lines A and B.

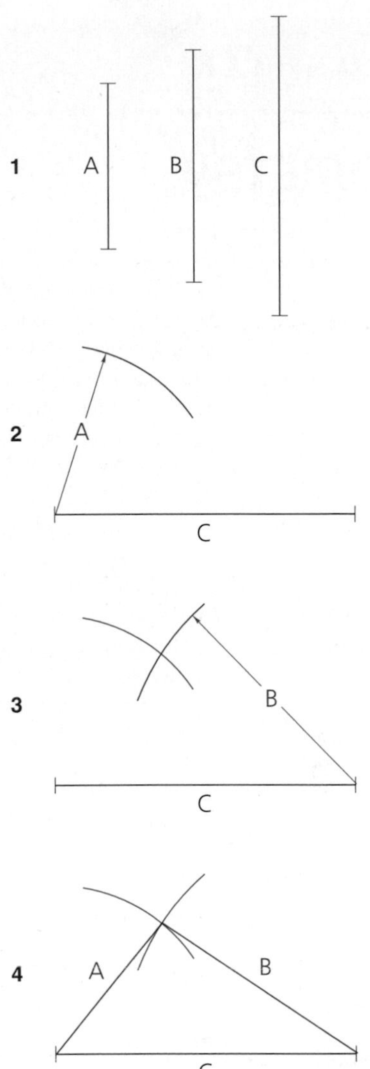

FIGURE 8.14 Drawing a Triangle with Sides Given

8.4 REGULAR POLYGON CONSTRUCTION

Polygons are closed figures having three or more sides. **Regular polygons** have equal-length sides and equal angles. All regular polygons can be *inscribed* within a circle and can also be *circumscribed* about the outside of a circle. (In this case, the circle drawn tangent to the polygon's sides is inscribed in the polygon.)

To draw a particular regular polygon, you must have at least one dimension. The two dimensions that are used for even-number-sided figures (squares, hexagons, octagons, etc.) are *across corners* and *across flats.* Across corners is the maximum measurable straight-line distance across the figure and is equal to the diameter of its circumscribing circle. Across flats is the minimum measurable straight-line distance across the figure and is equal to the diameter of its inscribed circle.

8.4.1 Constructing an Equilateral Triangle

The simplest type of regular polygon is the **equilateral triangle,** which has three equal sides and three equal angles (60°). Figure 8.15 shows the steps used to construct an equilateral triangle.

1. Given the length of one side of the triangle (line 1-2), draw the baseline.
2. From endpoints 1 and 2, draw arcs using the side length as the radius. The intersection of the arcs establishes the vertex of the triangle

Another way to construct an equilateral triangle is to lay out the baseline and then use a 60° triangle to draw each side [Fig. 8.15(3)]. The intersection of the sides establishes the vertex.

Focus On . . .

GEOMETRY

If you want to study the properties of figures and the relationships between points, lines, angles, surfaces, and solids, you study *geometry*. Geometry actually means "earth measurement." The name can be traced back to the way in which people first used those concepts. Practical geometry grew out of the needs of the Egyptians to survey their land to reestablish land boundaries after periodic flooding of the Nile. The flooding itself left a rich and sought-after soil. The workers who made these measurements became known as "rope stretchers" because they used ropes to do their measuring. The Egyptians also relied on geometry to help build their temples and pyramids.

Around 600 B.C., the Greeks returned from their travels through Egypt and brought with them their first knowledge of geometry. Thales, the most famous of those returning from Egypt, was the first to show the truth of a geometric relationship by showing that it followed in a logical and orderly fashion from a set of universally accepted statements (axioms or postulates). You may remember axioms and proofs from your geometry class.

Thales's student, Pythagoras, established a society in Italy that was devoted to the study of geometry and arithmetic. His most famous work was the theorem that bears his name. His influence was felt for centuries. Every student of geometry and trigonometry knows the Pythagorean theorem, which relates the lengths of the three sides of a right triangle ($a^2 + b^2 = c^2$). The side opposite the right angle is the longest side, or the hypotenuse (c). The other two sides, a and b, are the sides opposite the other two angles in the triangle.

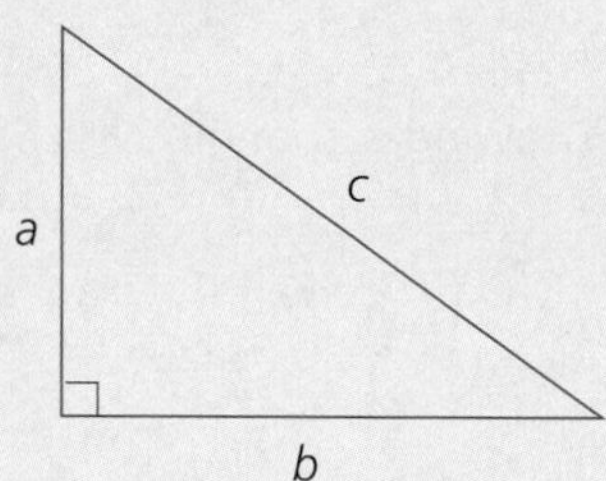

The Pythagorean theorem. In a right triangle with sides a and b and hypotenuse c, $a^2 + b^2 = c^2$.

While the early Greeks and others were able to make great contributions, it was not until 1796 that a great advancement was made in geometry. A 19-year-old German, Carl Friedrich Gauss, proved it was possible to construct a regular 17-sided polygon using a compass and a rule. The Greeks had only been able to construct regular polygons of 3, 4, 5, 6, 8, 10, and 15 sides. The 17-sided polygon was a major breakthrough. In 1799, Gauss was awarded a Ph.D. for developing the first proof of the fundamental theorem of algebra.

It may be difficult to appreciate how each contribution to geometry made engineering graphics possible. Even the most sophisticated CAD system makes use of fundamental geometric principles that were developed long ago. Operators of modern CAD systems can use the **POLYGON** command to create regular polygons of any number of sides (17 sides or 1000 sides, for example).

What started out as a way to measure the earth evolved into a discipline that is the key to solving most engineering problems. All the geometric constructions used today in drafting were developed by individuals building on previous developments of others. No doubt, humankind will continue building on the past for the future.

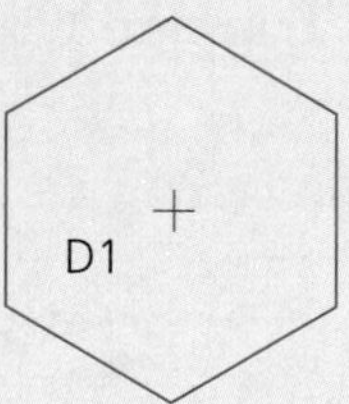

```
Command: POLYGON
Number of sides: 8
Edge of/<Center of Polygon>: D1
Inscribed in circle/Circumscribed about
circle: C
Radius of circle: .75
```

The POLYGON command using an AutoCAD system.

8.4.2 Constructing a Square

A **square** has four equal sides and four equal angles. Figure 8.16 shows a square inscribed within a circle; the circle's diameter equals the distance across the inscribed square's corners. Figure 8.16 also shows a circle inscribed within a square; the circle's diameter equals the side of the square. Three methods can be used to construct a square.

In Figure 8.16(1), the base is drawn using the side length. Then an arc R is drawn using point 1 as the center and line 1-2 as the length. The intersection of the arc with a vertical line extended from point 1 establishes the height of the square. The square is then completed.

In Figure 8.16(2), the baseline is drawn and a 45° triangle is used to draw lines diagonally through points 1 and 2 to establish points 3 and 4. Points 3 and 4 are at the intersection of the diagonals and lines drawn vertically through points 1 and 2.

Figure 8.16(3) uses a circle template or a compass to draw inscribed and circumscribed circles to construct a

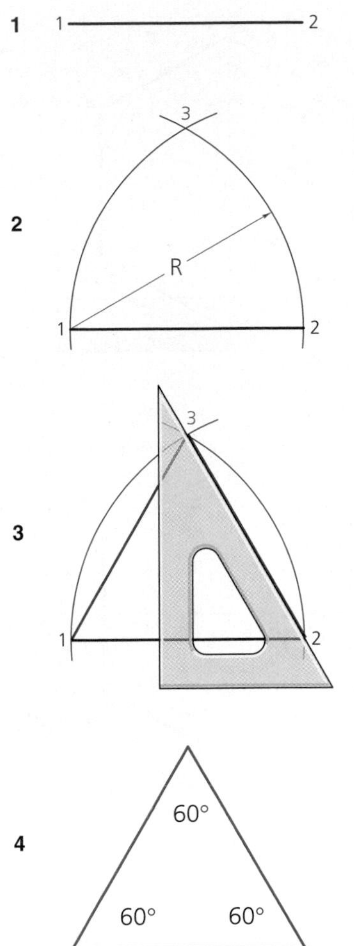

FIGURE 8.15 **Drawing an Equilateral Triangle**

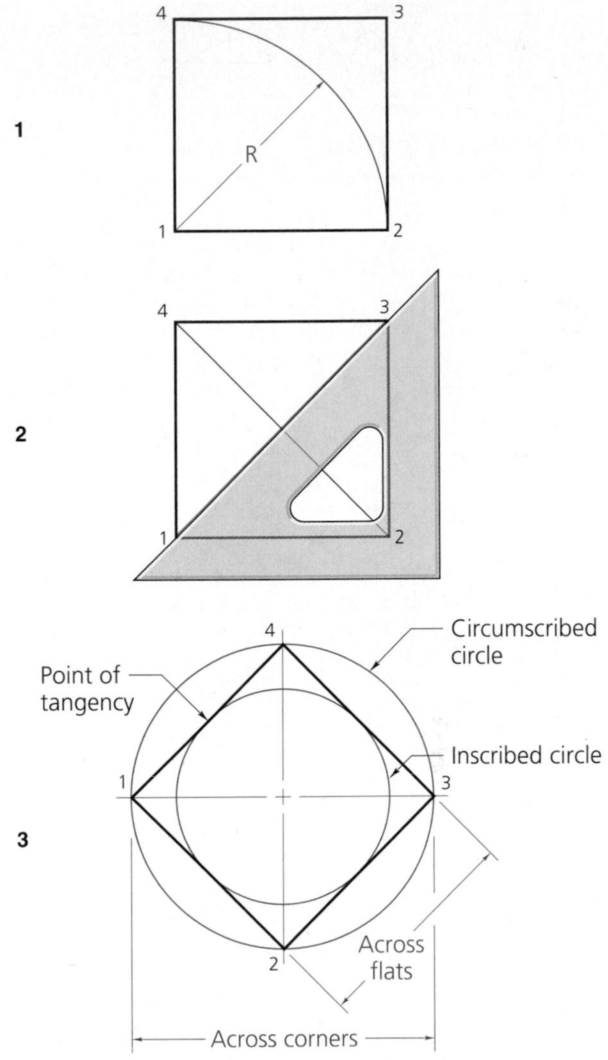

FIGURE 8.16 **Drawing a Square**

square. The point of tangency is where the square's sides touch the circumference.

8.4.3 Constructing a Pentagon

A **regular pentagon** has five equal sides and five equal angles. Figure 8.17 illustrates how to draw a pentagon (the diameter of the circumscribing circle is given).

1. Draw the centerlines of the figure, and then draw the circle. The center of the circle is point 0.
2. Find point 2 by bisecting line 0-1. Radius R (2-3) is used to establish point 4 on the vertical centerline. The distance from point 3 to point 4 (radius R2) is then used to locate point 5 on the circumference of the circle
3. Draw side 3-5. Use radius R2 from point 5 to establish point 6. Then use R2 to establish the remaining sides of the pentagon.

8.4.4 Constructing a Hexagon

A **regular hexagon** has six equal sides and six equal angles. Figure 8.18 shows how to construct a hexagon. In this figure, the distance across the flats was known. The distance across the flats is equal to the diameter of the inscribing circle. The following steps were used.

1. Locate the center of the hexagon.
2. Draw a circle equal to the distance across the flats, then, with a 30° angle, construct tangents to the circle.

If you know the distance across the corners, then draw the circumscribed circle first and mark off each side length along the circumference, using a distance equal to the radius of the circle (use dividers) [Fig. 8.19(a)]. Figure 8.19(b) shows an alternative method for producing a hexagon.

8.4.5 Constructing an Octagon

A **regular octagon** has eight equal sides and eight equal angles. To draw an octagon with the distance across the corners known, draw the circumscribed circle first and then mark off the side lengths around the circumference. If you

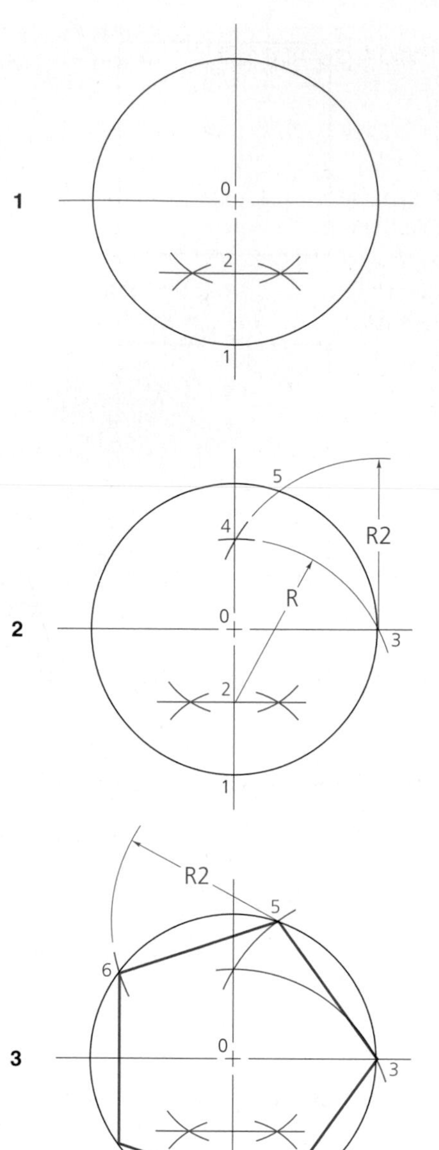

FIGURE 8.17 Drawing a Pentagon

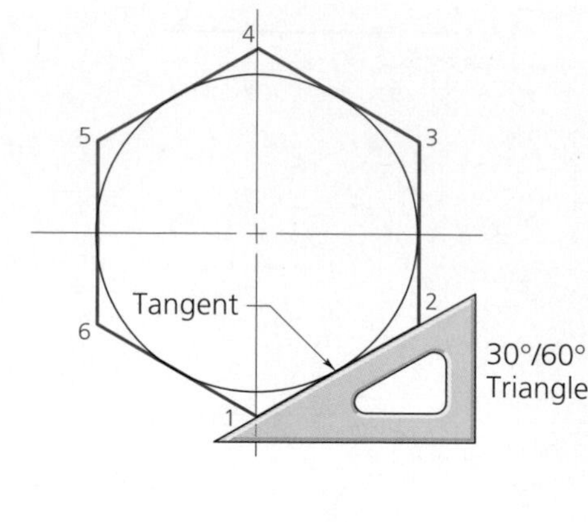

(a)

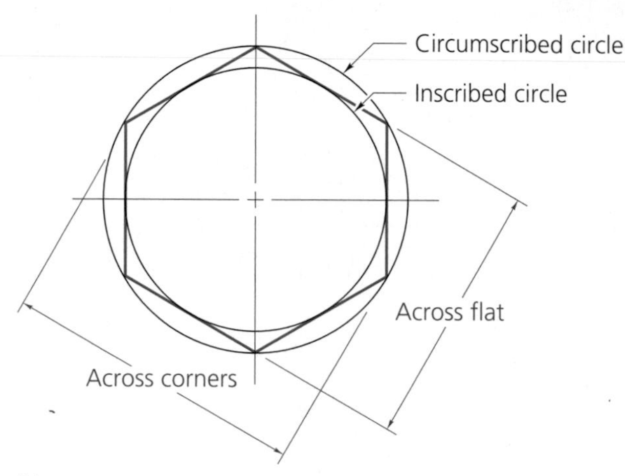

(b)

FIGURE 8.18 Drawing a Hexagon Using Inscribed and Circumscribed Circles

know the distance across the flats, then use a 45° triangle to draw tangent lines to establish the eight sides (Fig. 8.20).

8.4.6 Constructing a Regular Polygon with a Specific Number of Sides

To construct a **regular polygon** with a specific number of sides, divide the given diameter of the circumscribing circle via the parallel-line method described earlier (Fig. 8.21). A polygon with seven sides is used as an example. The following steps were used.

1. Construct an equilateral triangle (0-7-8) with the diameter (0-7) as one of its sides.
2. Draw a line from the apex (point 8) through the second point on the line (point 2).

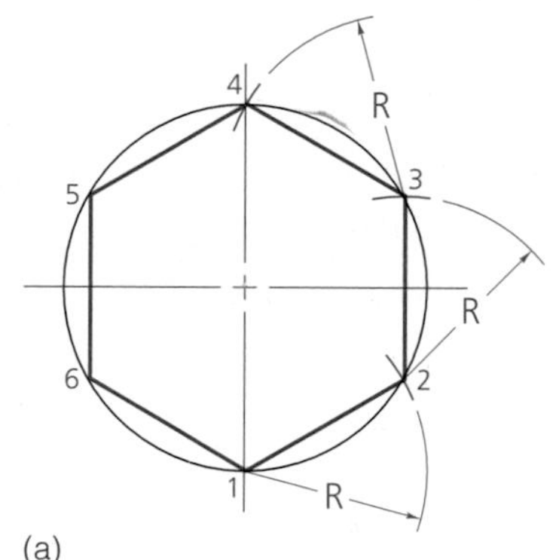

(a)

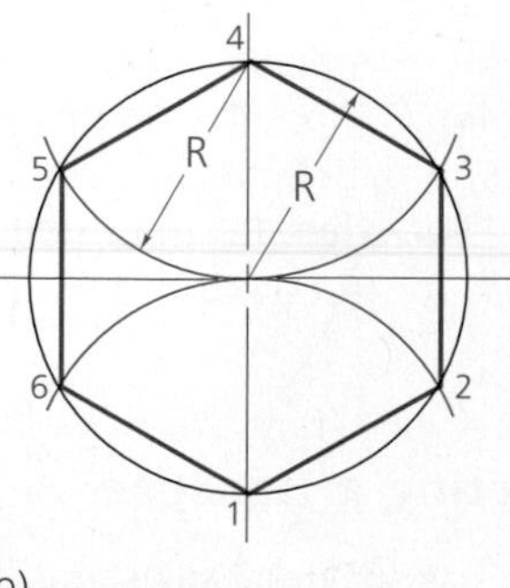

(b)

FIGURE 8.19 Drawing a Hexagon

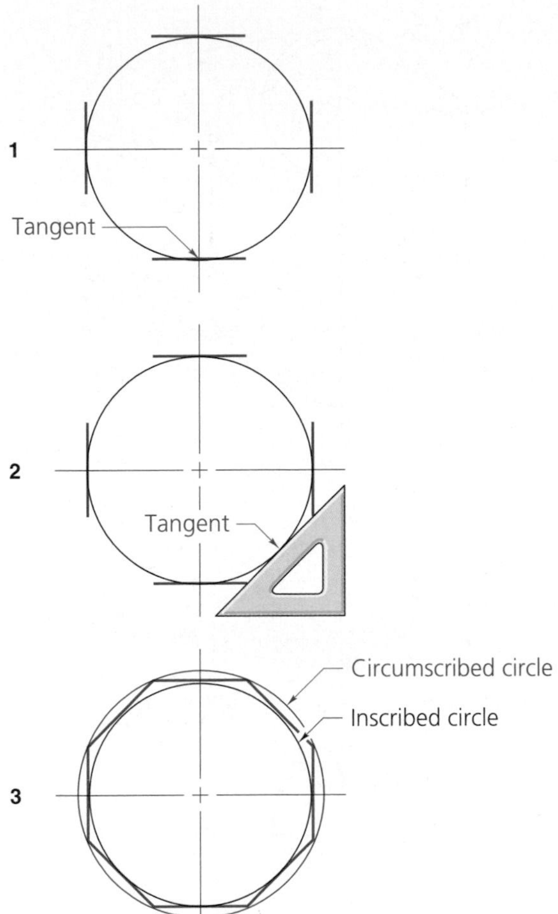

FIGURE 8.20 Drawing an Octagon

3. Extend line 8-2 until it intersects the circle at point 9. Radius 0-9 will be the size of each side of the figure.
4. Using radius 0-9, mark off the corners of the polygon, then connect the points.

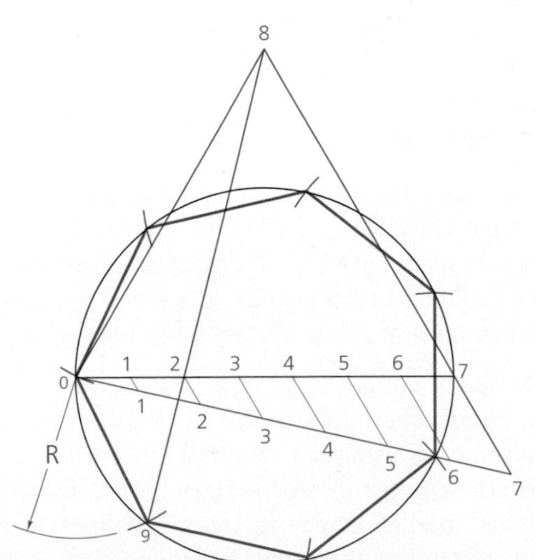

FIGURE 8.21 Drawing a Regular Polygon

8.5 TANGENCIES

An arc that touches a line at only one point is tangent to that line, and the line is tangent to the arc. Two curves can also be tangent. The line and the arc touch at only one place even if they are extended. If a line and an arc are tangent, (1) the tangent line is perpendicular to the radius of the arc at the point of tangency, and (2) the center of the arc is on a line that is perpendicular to the tangent line and extends from the point of tangency.

Figure 8.22 illustrates principle 1. To draw a line tangent to the circle at point 1, draw radius C1. Construct line AB perpendicular to the radius line C1 passing through point 1. Line AB is tangent to the circle at point 1.

Figure 8.23 illustrates principle 2. To draw a circle tangent to a given line, first project a line perpendicular to the given line AB from point T (tangent point). The center of the circle will be on this line. Locate the center point by marking off an arc from point T, using the radius of the circle. Using the same radius (line CT), draw the tangent circle.

8.5.1 Line Tangent to Two Circles

Figure 8.24 illustrates the procedure for finding the points of tangency between a line and two circles. A line can be

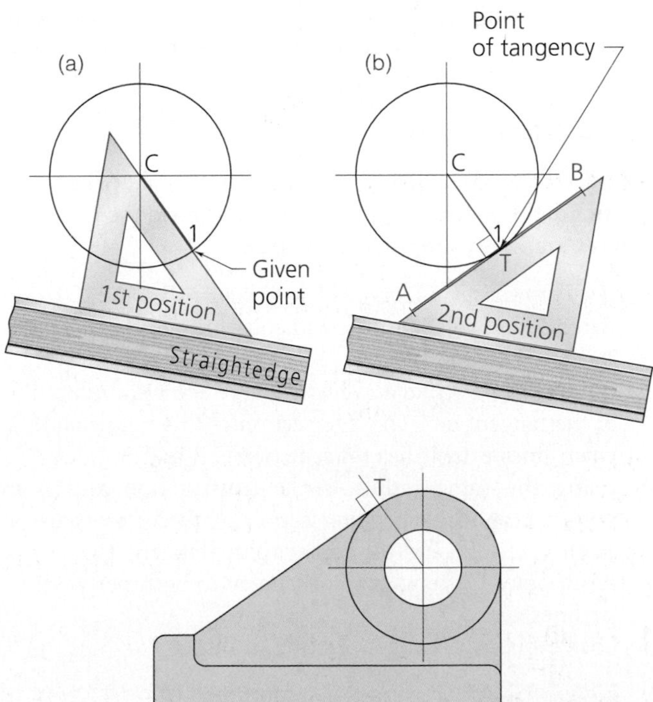

FIGURE 8.22 Drawing a Line Tangent to a Circle

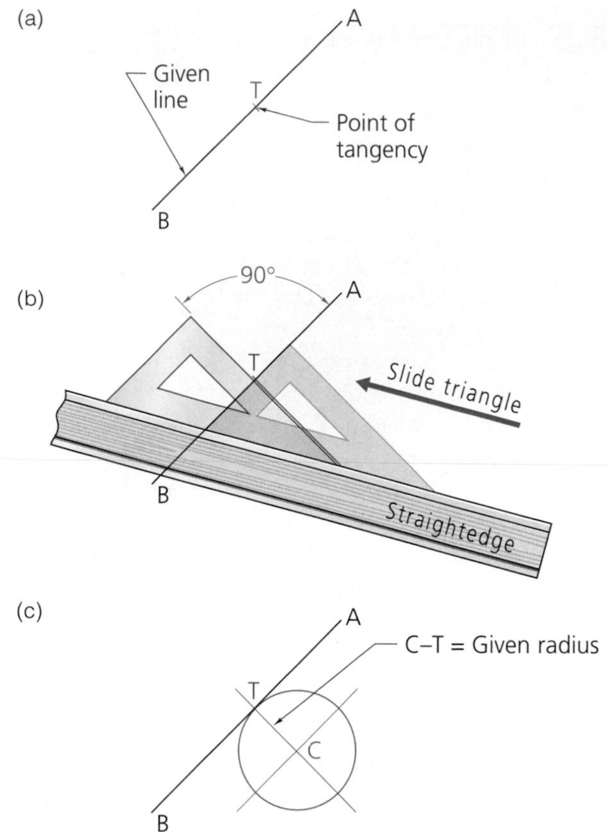

FIGURE 8.23 Drawing a Circle Tangent to a Line

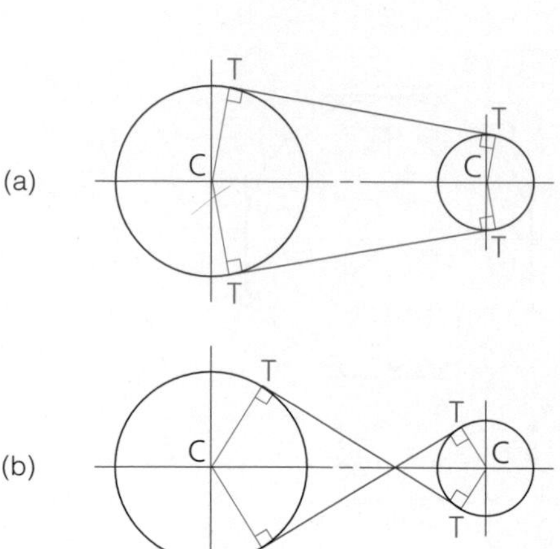

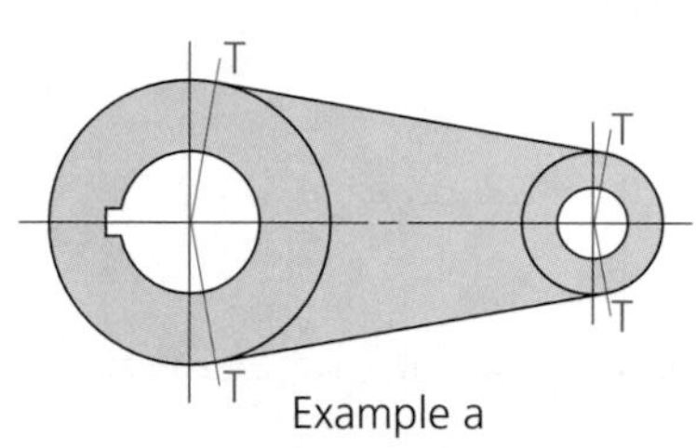

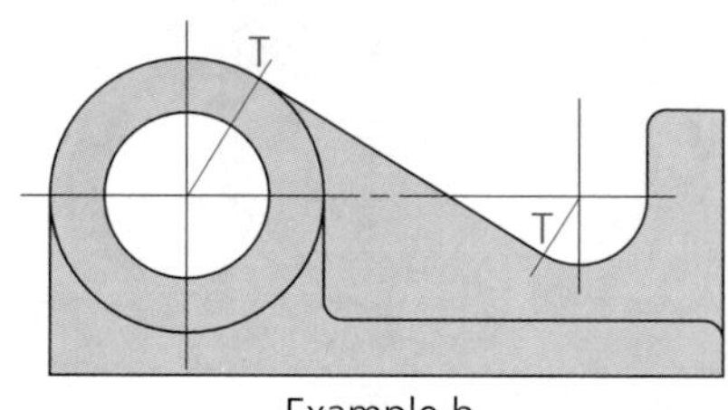

FIGURE 8.24 Tangencies of a Line and Two Circles

tangent to two circles, as shown in Figure 8.24(a) and (b). Four tangency positions are possible. In Figure 8.24(a), the lines are tangent to the outside of the circles. This is called an **open belt tangent.** In Figure 8.24(b), the lines form a **closed belt tangent.** In both examples, the circles are given. The construction is the same as for Figure 8.22.

8.5.2 Tangent Arcs

There are two methods for drawing an **arc between two perpendicular lines.** Figure 8.25(a) illustrates the construction of arc 2-3 using only a compass.

For Perpendicular Lines, with a Compass [Fig. 8.25(a)]

1. Extend the two given perpendicular lines to meet at point 1.
2. From point 1 strike a radius equal to the required radius of the tangent arc. The intersection of this radius and the given lines establishes tangent points 2 and 3.
3. Using the same radius, strike construction arcs from points 2 and 3. The intersection of these two arcs, at point C, establishes the center of the tangent arc.
4. From point C, draw arc 2-3 tangent to both perpendicular lines.
5. Locate points of tangency on both lines.

Figure 8.25(b) illustrates a second method.

For Perpendicular Lines, Without a Compass [Fig. 8.25(b)]

1. Extend the given perpendicular lines so they meet at point 1.
2. Draw a parallel line distance R from each of the given lines using the required tangent arc radius for dimension R. Point C is at the intersection of these two lines.
3. Locate tangent points 2 and 3 by extending construction lines from C perpendicular to the given lines.
4. From center point C, draw the required tangent arc from point 2 to point 3

To draw arcs that are tangent to nonperpendicular lines, use the same procedure as in Figure 8.25(b). This method is for lines at acute angles (Fig. 8.26) or at obtuse angles (Fig. 8.27). In Figures 8.26 and 8.27, the given lines have been extended to meet at point 1. Use the following steps.

For Nonperpendicular Lines [Figs. 8.26 and 8.27]

1. Draw construction lines parallel to and at distance R from the given lines using the required tangent arc radius.
2. Where these two lines intersect (point C), draw construction lines perpendicular to the given lines to establish points 2 and 3 as the points of tangency.

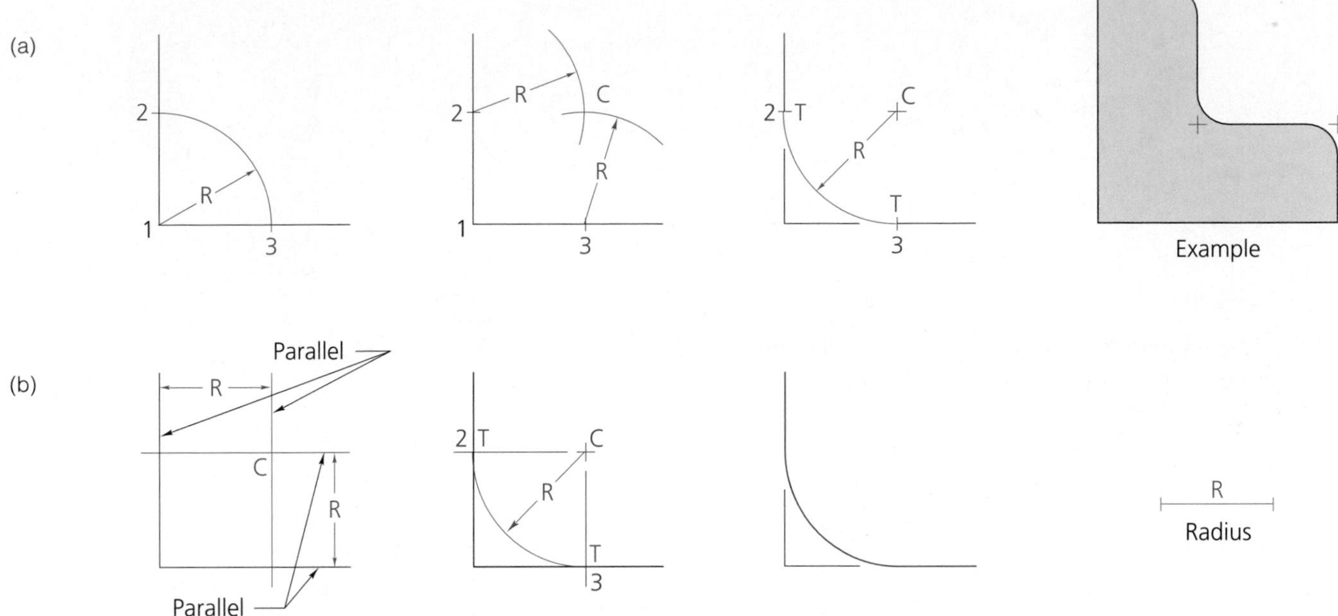

FIGURE 8.25 Drawing an Arc Tangent to Two Perpendicular Lines

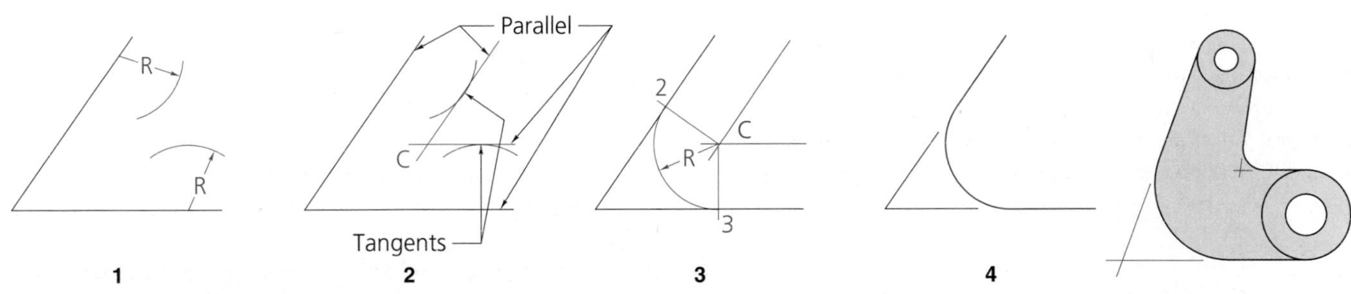

FIGURE 8.26 Drawing an Arc Tangent to Two Lines Forming an Acute Angle

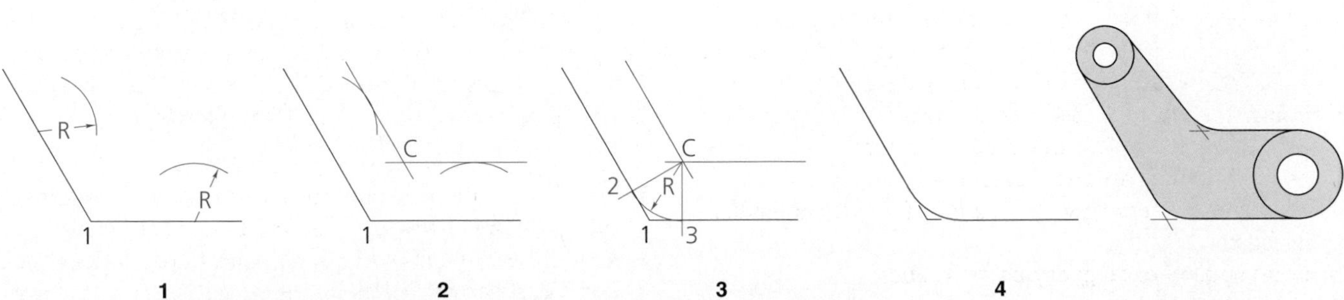

FIGURE 8.27 Drawing an Arc Tangent to Two Lines Forming an Obtuse Angle

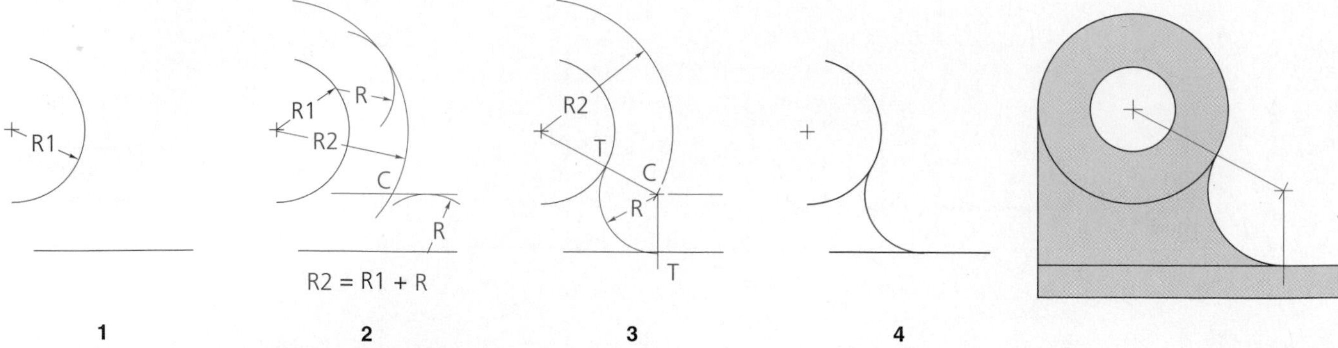

FIGURE 8.28 Drawing an Arc Tangent to a Line and an Arc

3. Draw radius R from point 2 to point 3 to establish an arc tangent to both given lines.
4. Darken the lines and the arc to form a smooth, continuous figure.

8.5.3 Drawing an Arc Tangent to a Line and an Arc

To construct an arc tangent to a line on one side and an arc on the other (Fig. 8.28), use the following procedure. The line and the arc are given along with the required radius R for the tangent arc.

1. Draw the given line and arc.
2. Draw a construction line parallel to and at distance R from the given line. Add R and R1 to establish R2. Use R2 to swing a construction arc until it intersects the construction line at point C.
3. Using R, swing an arc tangent to the line and the given arc. Use C as the center point.
4. Draw construction lines from the center of the given arc to C and from C perpendicular to the given line. These construction lines locate the points of tangency (T).
5. Darken the line and the arcs, forming a smooth, consistent line

8.5.4 Drawing an Arc Tangent to Two Arcs

To construct an arc tangent to two arcs or circles, lay out the given arcs as shown in Figure 8.29. Here R1 and R2 are given along with the distance between their centers. The radius length (R) of the tangent arc is also provided.

1. Add the radius length R to R1. Use this length to draw a construction arc.
2. Add R to R2 and draw another construction arc. The two construction arcs intersect at C.
3. Using the given radius length (R), draw the tangent arc with C as the center.
4. Locate the point of tangency (T) by drawing a line from C

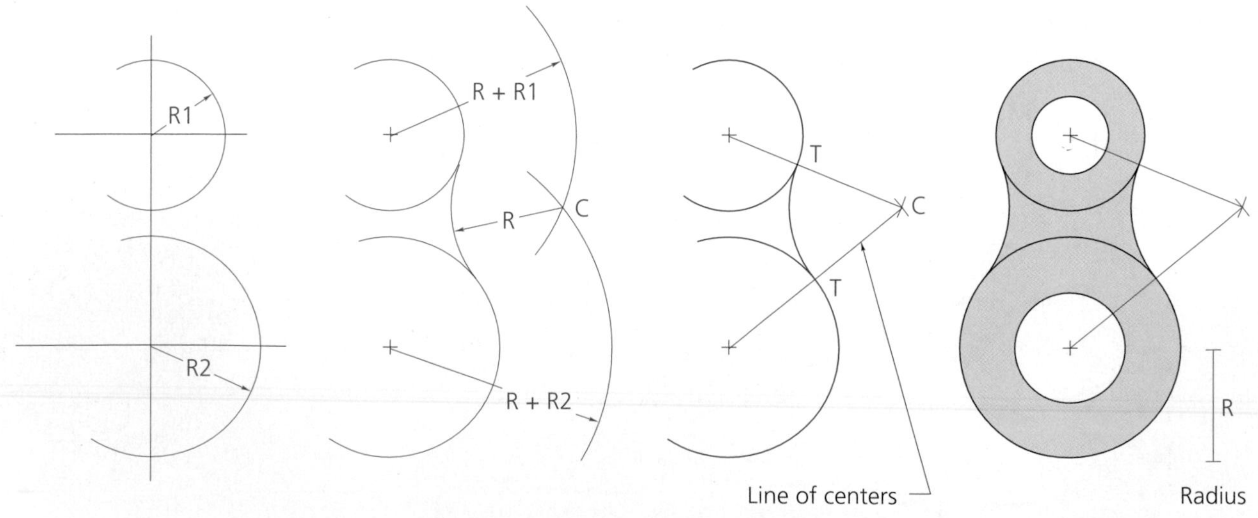

FIGURE 8.29 Drawing an Arc Tangent to Two Arcs

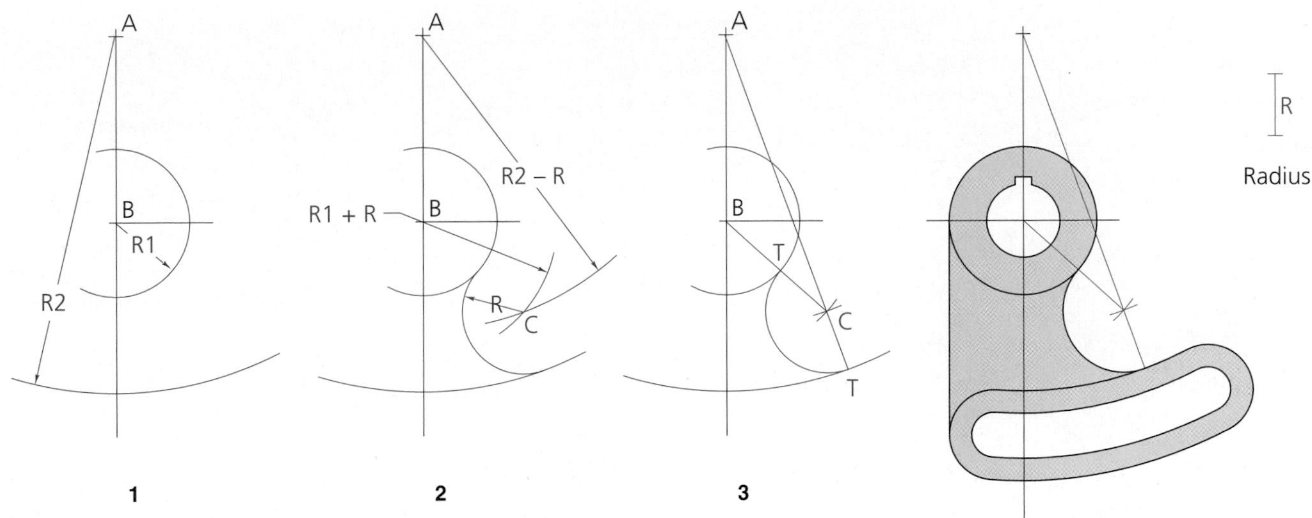

FIGURE 8.30 Constructing a Tangent Arc Between Two Arcs

to each center of the given arcs. This line is called the **line of centers.**

8.5.5 Drawing an Arc Tangent to Two Arcs with One Arc Enclosed

In Figure 8.30, a tangent arc joins two arcs. In this example, the tangent arc becomes tangent to the inside of one arc and tangent to the outside of the other. The arcs are given along with their centers, A and B. The radius length (R) of the tangent arc is also provided. The following method is used.

1. Locate centers A and B, and construct the two given arcs, Rl and R2.
2. *Add* R and R1 and use this length to draw a construction arc from B. *Subtract* R from R2, and use this length to draw a construction arc from A. The intersection of these two construction arcs locates C. Using the given tangent arc radius (R), draw an arc from C tangent to both given arcs.
3. Locate the point of tangency by drawing a line (line of centers) from A through C until it intersects the large arc at T. Locate the other point of tangency (T) by drawing a line from B to C.

8.5.6 Drawing an Arc Tangent to Two Arcs and Enclosing Both

In Figure 8.31, the tangent arc encloses both given arcs. R1, R2, A, and B are given along with the tangent arc radius R. The tangent arc is drawn by using the following steps:

1. Lay out the two given arcs as shown in the figure (R1 and R2).

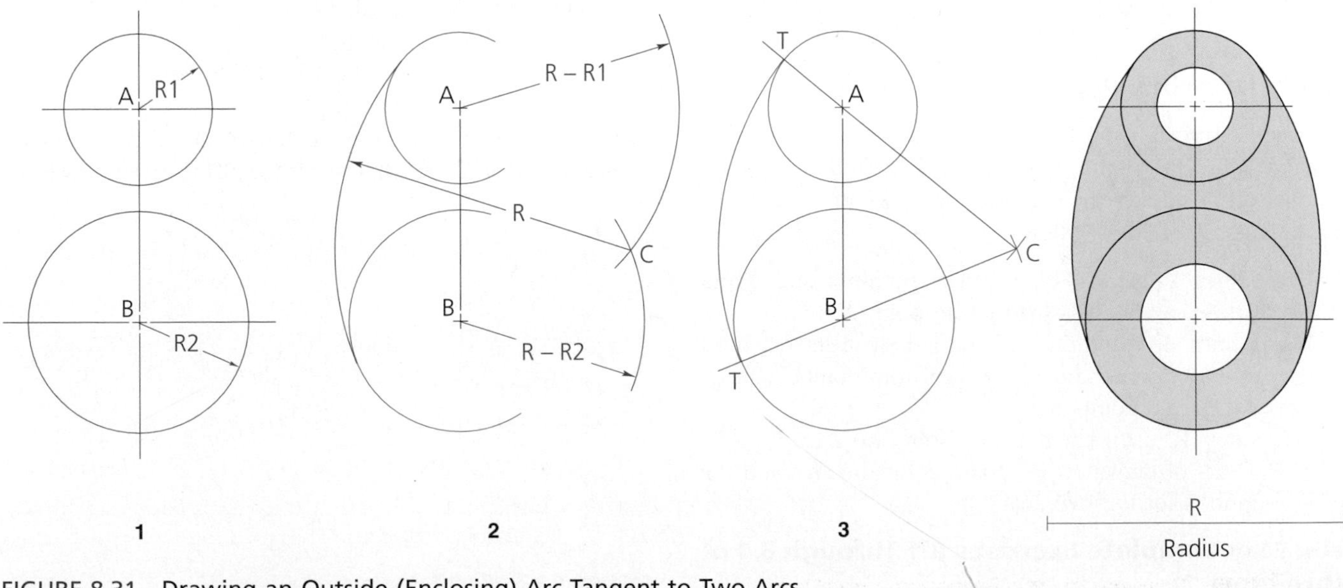

FIGURE 8.31 Drawing an Outside (Enclosing) Arc Tangent to Two Arcs

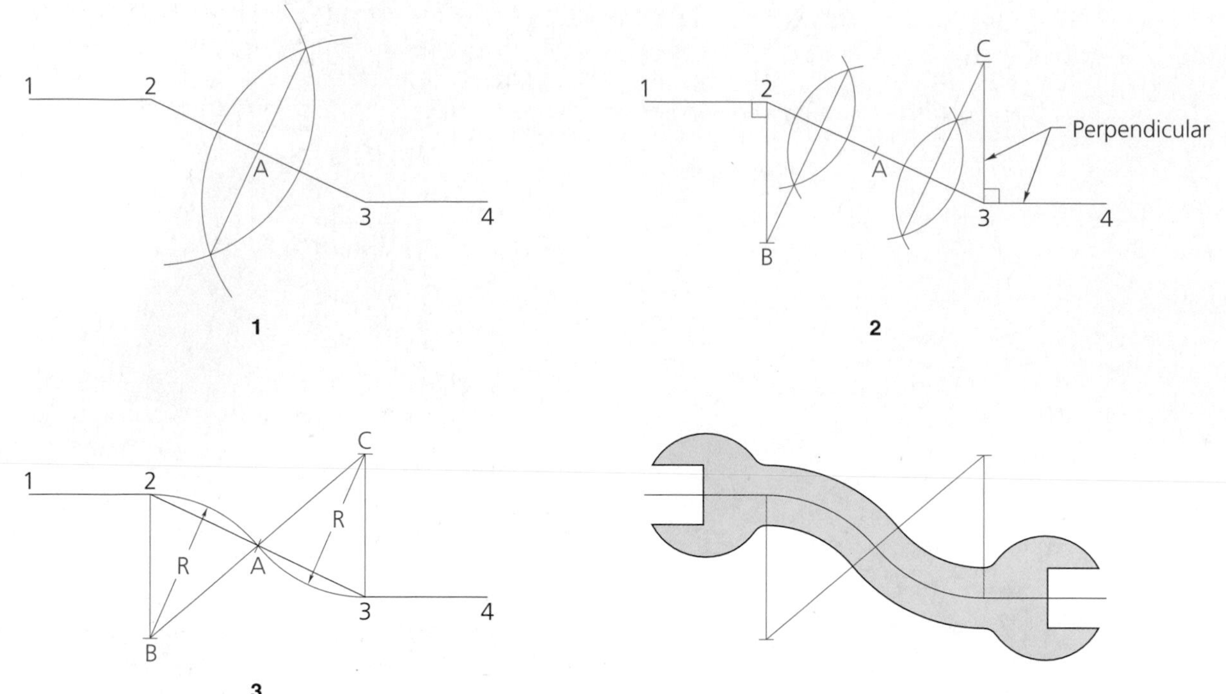

FIGURE 8.32 Drawing an Ogee Curve

2. Find C by first subtracting the radius length R1 from R. Use this length to draw a construction arc. Subtract R2 from R and draw another construction arc. The intersection of these two arcs locates C. Using R, draw an arc with C as its center and its ends tangent to the two given arcs.
3. Determine the exact point of tangency by drawing construction lines from C to A and from C to B, extending both until they intersect the arc, as shown. The intersection of these lines and the two given arcs locates the two tangent points (T).

8.5.7 Drawing Ogee Curves

An **ogee curve** is used to connect two parallel lines with tangent arcs. In Figure 8.32, lines 1-2 and 3-4, their parallel distance, and their location in space are given. The curve is constructed as follows.

1. Draw lines 1-2 and 3-4. Connect points 2 and 3 and bisect this new line (2-3) to locate point A.
2. Bisect lines 2-A and 3-A. Extend these bisectors until they intersect perpendiculars drawn from points 2 and 3. This will locate points B and C.
3. Draw arcs (R) using the distance from B to 2 (or C to 3). The points of tangency are 2 and 3 for the arcs and the lines, and A for the two arcs.

You May Complete Exercises 8.1 Through 8.4 at This Time

8.5.8 Rectifying Circles, Arcs, and Curves

Circles and arcs can be laid out (*rectified*) along a straight line. Their true length (circumference or arc length) is layed off along a straight line. All rectification is approximate but is still graphically acceptable within limits.

To **rectify** the circumference of a circle means to find the circumference graphically. In Figure 8.33, the circumference of the circle has been established by rectification.

1. Draw line 2-5 tangent to the bottom of the circle and exactly three times its diameter.
2. Draw line C-3 at an angle of 30°.
3. Draw line 3-4 perpendicular to the vertical centerline (line 1-2) of the circle.
4. Connect point 4 to point 5. Line 4-5 will be approximately equal to the circumference of the given circle.

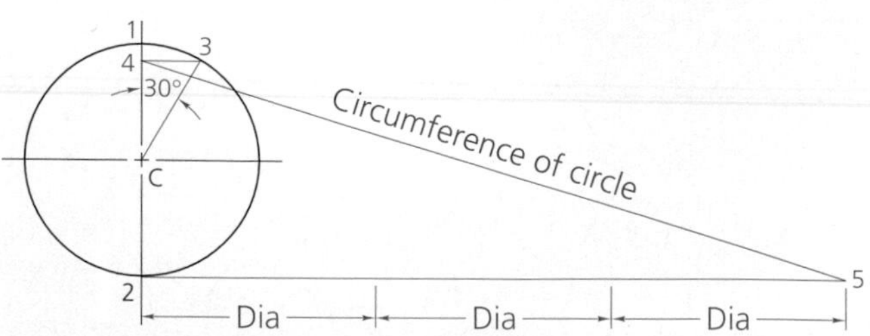

FIGURE 8.33 Rectifying a Circle

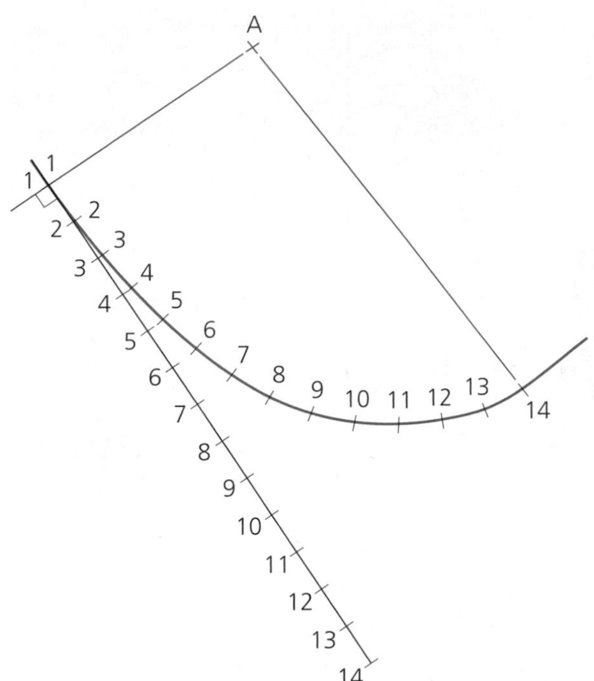

FIGURE 8.34 Rectification of an Arc

8.5.9 Approximate Rectification of an Arc

To rectify an arc or curved line, start by drawing a line tangent to one end. In Figure 8.34, the line was drawn tangent to the curved line at point 1. (Note that it is not necessary to have point A, although it does help to establish the exact tangent points.) The following steps are used.

1. Use dividers to mark off very small equal distances along the curve. The smaller the distance, the more accurate the approximation because each distance will be the chord measurement of its corresponding arc segment and, therefore, will be somewhat shorter than the arc's true length.
2. Starting at the opposite end of the arc, away from the side with the tangent line, mark off equal chords, point 14 to point 13, 13 to 12, 12 to 11, 11 to 10, and so on. Continue marking off each division until less than one full space remains, which is at point 2 in the given example.
3. Without lifting the dividers, start dividing the tangent line into the same number of segments, 2 to 3, 3 to 4, 4 to 5, and so on. The tangent line 1 - 14 will approximately equal the length of the given arc.

8.6 CONIC SECTIONS

A **right circular cone** is one in which the altitude and the axis coincide (the axis is perpendicular to the base). The intersection of a plane and a right circular cone is called a *conic section*. Five possible sections can result from this intersection (Fig. 8.35). The shapes formed by the sections are:

1. *Parabola* A plane (EV 1) passes parallel to a true-length element (edge) of the cone, forming the same base angle (angle between the base and the edge) and resulting in a parabola.

2. *Hyperbola* A plane (EV 2) passing through a cone, parallel to the altitude and perpendicular to the base, results in a hyperbola.

3. *Ellipse* A plane (EV 3) that cuts all the elements of the cone but is not perpendicular to the axis forms a true ellipse.

4. *Triangle* A plane that passes through the vertex and is parallel to the axis cuts an isosceles (or equilateral) triangle (front view).

5. *Circle* A plane that passes perpendicular to the axis forms a circular intersection. In Figure 8.35, a series of horizontal cutting planes have been introduced in the frontal (front) view, which project as circles in the horizontal (top) view.

8.6.1 Intersection of a Cone and a Plane

The **intersection of a cone and a plane** is established by passing a series of horizontal cutting planes through the cone (perpendicular to its axis). In Figure 8.35, the front and top views of the cone are shown along with the edge view of three planes that intersect it. To find the top view and the true shape of each intersection, use the following steps.

1. In the front view, pass a series of evenly spaced horizontal cutting planes through the cone, CP1 through CP12.
2. Each cutting plane projects as a circle in the horizontal view.
3. EV 1 intersects cutting planes 3 through 12 in the frontal view. Project intersection points to the top view. The intersection of EV 1 and the cone forms a parabola (1).
4. The true shape of the parabola is seen in a view projected parallel to EV 1. Draw the centerline of the parabola parallel to EV 1, and project the intersection points of the plane (EV 1) and each cutting plane from the front view. Distances are transferred from the horizontal view, as in dimension A.
5. Repeat steps 3 and 4 to establish the intersection of EV 2 and EV 3 with the cone. EV 2 projects as a line in the top view and as hyperbola in a true-shape view (2). EV 3 forms an ellipse in the top view and projects as a true-size ellipse in view (3).

8.6.2 Constructing an Ellipse

Two methods for constructing an **ellipse** are covered in this section: the **concentric-circle method** and the **four-center**

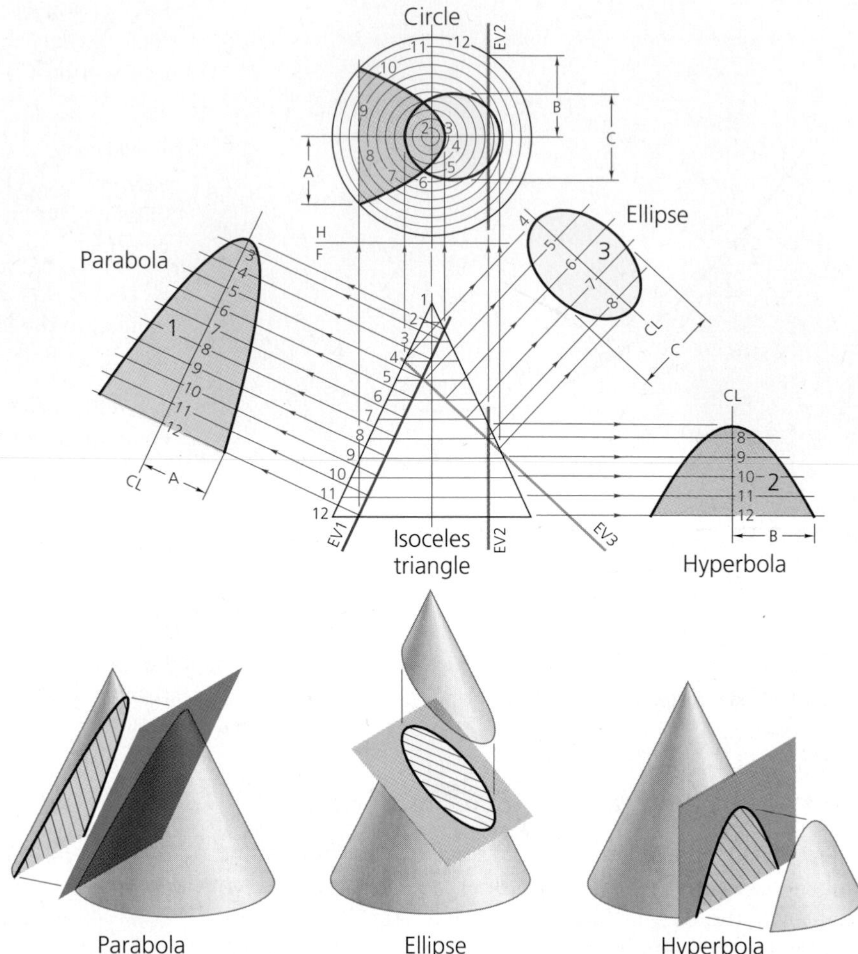

FIGURE 8.35 Conic Sections

method. Both methods are useful for constructing oddly sized or large ellipses. And both *approximate* the shape of a true ellipse. Figure 8.36 illustrates the concentric-circle method of constructing an ellipse.

Concentric-Circle Method (Fig. 8.36)

1. Given the major axis A-B and the minor axis C-D, draw concentric circles (circles of a different size with the same center point) using the axes as diameters.
2. Divide the circles into an equal number of sections. Figure 8.36 uses twelve equal divisions.
3. Where each line crosses the inner circle (point 2 or 5), draw a line parallel to the major axis; where the same line crosses the outer circle (point 1 or 4), draw a line parallel to the minor axis. The point of intersection of these two lines (point 3 or 6) will be on the ellipse.
4. Repeat this process for each division of the circles. Use an irregular curve to connect the points smoothly. It is accurate in direct proportion to the number of divisions used and points located.

Figure 8.37 shows the approximate method, also called the four-center method, for constructing an ellipse.

Approximate (Four-Center) Method (Fig. 8.37)

1. With the major axis (A-B) and the minor axis (C-D) given, connect points B and C.

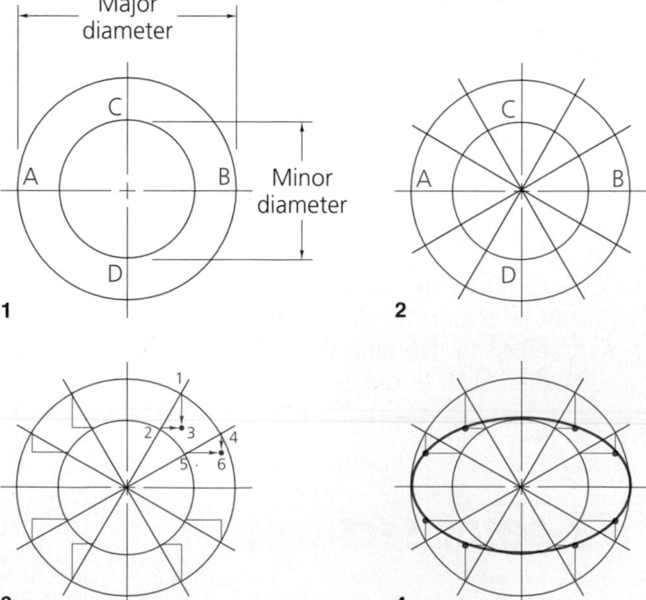

FIGURE 8.36 Drawing an Ellipse Using the Concentric-Circle Method

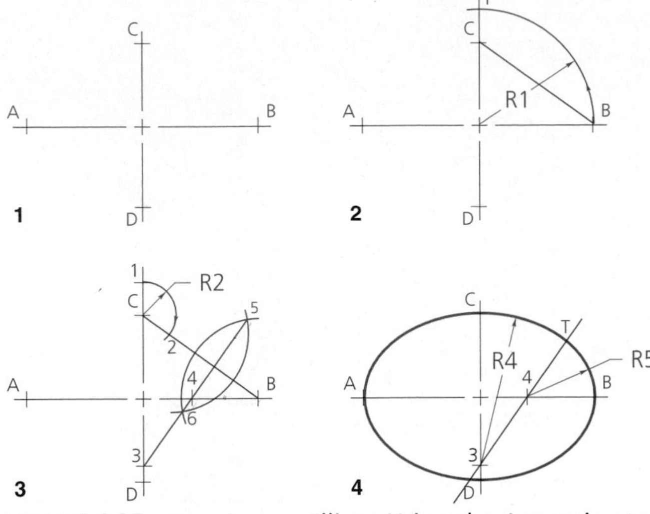

FIGURE 8.37 Drawing an Ellipse Using the Approximate Method (Four-Center Method)

2. Using the distance from the center of the ellipse to point B as the radius, strike arc R1. Point 1 is the intersection of R1 and the extended minor axis.
3. The distance from point C to point 1 establishes R2. Draw arc R2 so it intersects line B-C at point 2.
4. Bisect line B-2 and extend the bisector 5-6 so it crosses the minor axis at point 3. Point 3 is the center point for radius R4.
5. Where bisector 5-6 crosses the major axis (point 4), draw radius R5 to establish the sides of the ellipse at point A and point B. R4 is the radius for the upper and lower arcs at points C and D of the ellipse.

These two methods work best when *the minor axis is at least 75% of the major axis.* When the minor axis is too small in comparison to the major axis, the top and bottom of the ellipse are flattened. The closer the major axis and the minor axis are in length, the more accurate the ellipse.

8.6.3 Constructing a Parabola Using a Rectangle or Parallelogram

A **parabola** is the result of an intersection between a cone and a plane passed parallel to one of its elements. It is a plane curve, generated by a point moving so that its distance from a fixed point, known as the *focus,* is always equal to its distance from a fixed line. Parabolas are used in the design of surfaces that need to reflect sound or light in a specific manner. The construction of a parabola is demonstrated with a rectangle in Figure 8.38(a) and with a parallelogram in Figure 8.38(b).

1. Divide side BC into an even number of equal parts and side AB into half as many equal parts.
2. Connect the points along AB and CD to E.
3. Draw parallel lines from the points along BC to where they intersect the lines drawn in step 2. The intersection points are points along the parabola's curve.
4. Connect the intersection points using an irregular curve. The greater the number of divisions, the greater the accuracy of the curve.

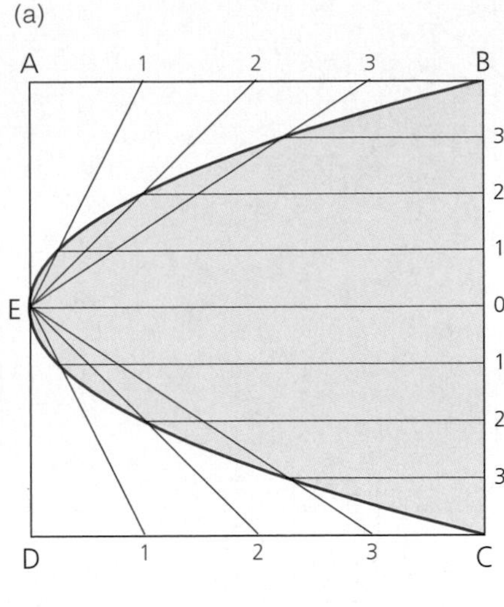

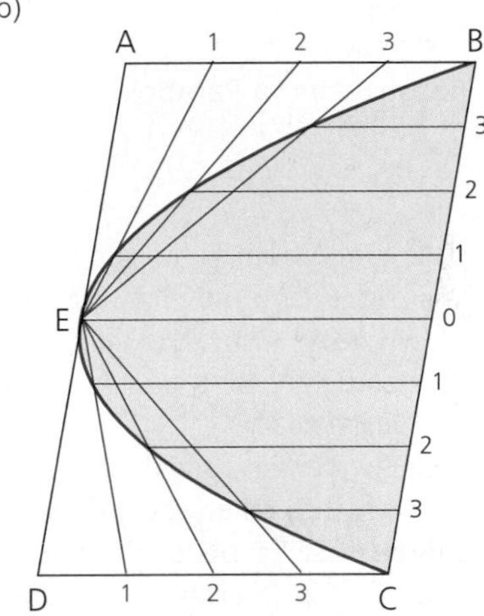

FIGURE 8.38 Drawing a Parabola

8.6.4 Constructing a Parabola by Establishing the Intersection of a Plane and a Cone

Figure 8.39 illustrates the step-by-step procedure for constructing a parabola by establishing the intersection of a plane and a cone.

1. Draw the given cone and the intersecting plane in the front and top views. A parabola is formed by an intersecting plane that is parallel to one of the cone's elements-edge lines (front view).
2. Draw any number of concentric circles in the top view. The greater the number of circles, the greater the accuracy of the parabola. [Figure 8.39(b) uses only two circles in order to provide a clearer picture of the process.]

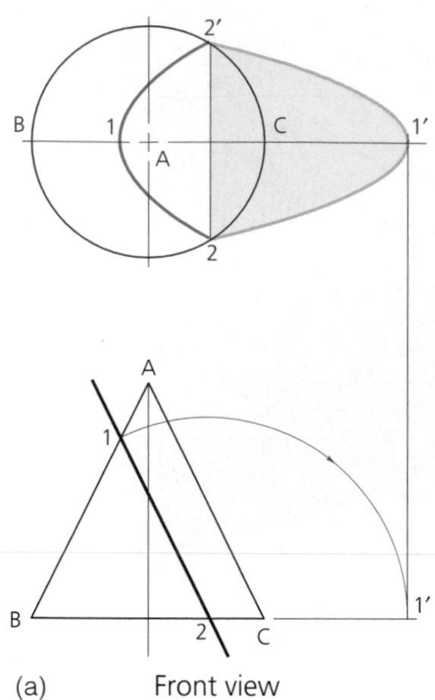

(a) Front view

(b)

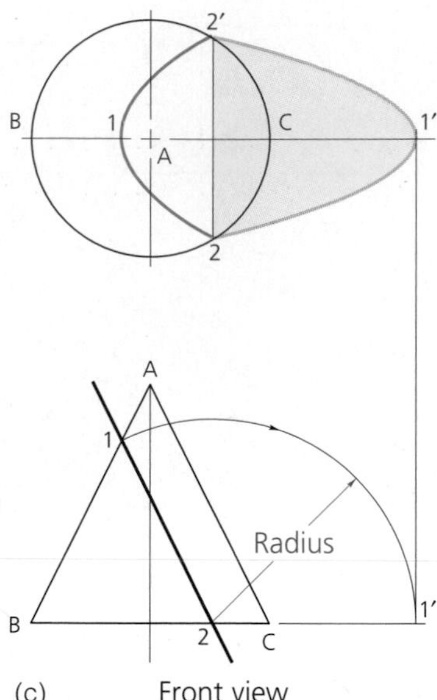

(c) Front view

FIGURE 8.39 Constructing a Parabola

3. Project the circle to the front view. The intersection of the circle (seen as an edge) and the plane establishes points X and Y in the front view
4. Project points X and Y to the top view and complete the top view of the parabola.
5. Using point 2 as the center, draw arcs using lengths 2-Y, 2-X, and 2-1 until they intersect the base plane in the front view. Project these points to the top view.
6. Draw horizontal lines from each intersecting point in the top view until they intersect with corresponding points projected from the front view.
7. Connect these points to form the true view of the parabola.

8.6.5 Connecting Two Points with a Parabolic Curve

Figure 8.40 shows three parabolic curves. In each case, points X, Y, and 0 are given. The following steps are used for the construction.

1. Draw lines X-0 and Y-0.
2. Divide each line into the same number of equal parts, and number the divisions.
3. Connect the corresponding points with construction lines.
4. Sketch a smooth curve that is tangent to each of the elements, as shown.
5. Use an irregular curve to draw the curve.

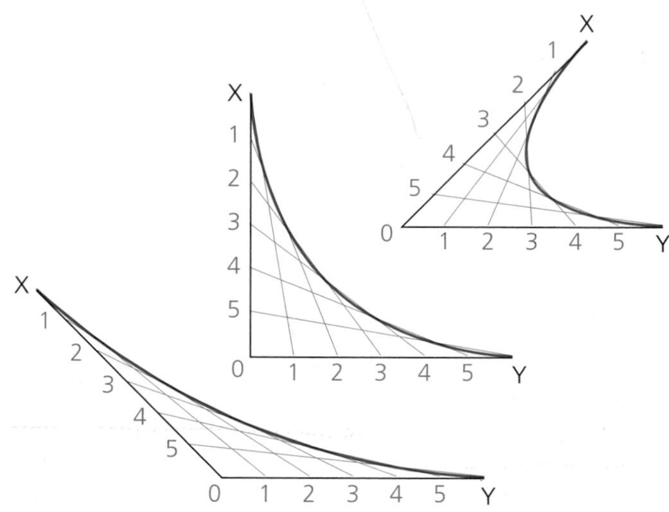

FIGURE 8.40 Drawing Parabolic Curves

8.6.6 Constructing a Hyperbola

A **hyperbola** is a plane surface (curve) that is formed by the intersection of a right circular cone and a vertical plane. Figure 8.41 illustrates the procedure for drawing a hyperbola:

1. Draw the cone and the plane in the top and front views [Fig. 8.41(a)].
2. Construct a number of planes parallel to the base [Fig. 8.41(b)]. These planes form concentric circles when they intersect the cone (top view). The greater the number of planes, the greater the accuracy of the hyperbola.
3. In the front view, the intersection of each edge of the planes intersects the vertical plane and establishes four points in the top view: X, X′, Y, and Y′.
4. The vertical plane appears as an edge in the top view.

(a)

(b)

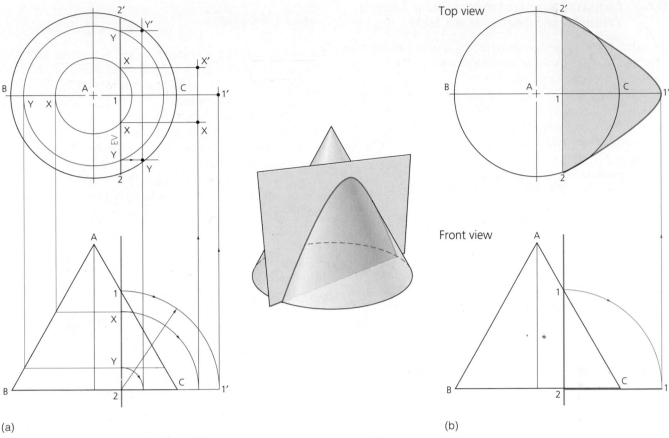

FIGURE 8.41 **Constructing a Hyperbola**

Draw horizontal construction lines from each intersecting point as shown in Figure 8.41(b).

5. Draw the required arcs in the front view until they intersect the base plane of the cone. Project these points to the top view.
6. The intersection of corresponding points establishes points on the hyperbola in the top view.
7. Use an irregular curve to draw the curve.

8.6.7 Drawing a Spiral of Archimedes

A **spiral of Archimedes** is a plane curve generated by a point moving away from or toward a fixed point at a constant rate while a radial line from the fixed point rotates at a constant speed. Figure 8.42 shows a spiral of Archimedes. To draw one, use the following steps.

1. Draw centerlines with a center point at 0, as shown.
2. Establish an equal number of angles; twelve angles of 30° each were used in the example.
3. Divide any line into the same number of equal divisions; in the example, line 0-12 is used (divisions A through L).
4. Draw the construction arcs from each point to the corresponding angle.
5. Each intersection of an arc and an angle establishes one point of the spiral.
6. Use an irregular curve to connect the points.

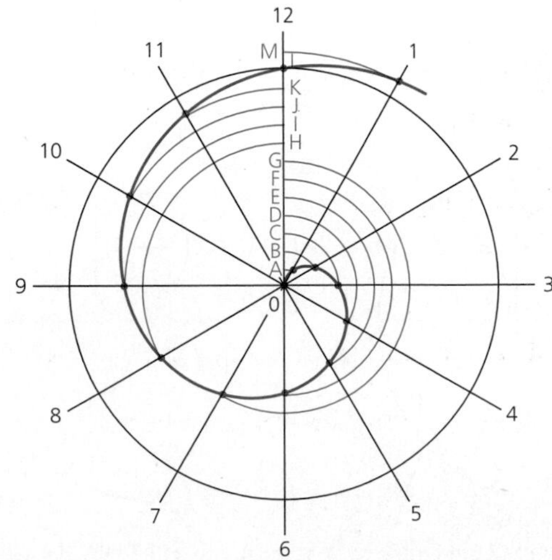

FIGURE 8.42 **Drawing a Spiral of Archimedes**

8.6.8 Constructing an Involute of a Line, a Triangle, a Square, or a Circle

An **involute** is a plane curve traced by a point on a thread kept taut as it is unwound from another curve. Figure 8.43 shows four kinds of involutes.

In Figure 8.43(a), the **involute of a line** is constructed by first drawing the given line 1-2. Point 2 becomes the center of the first arc (radius 1-2), point 1 the center of the second arc (radius 1-3), and point 3 the center of the third arc (radius 3-4).

The **involute of a triangle** is constructed by drawing the triangle [Fig. 8.43(b)]. Use point 3 as the center of the first arc (radius 3-1). Extend lines 2-3, 1-2, and 3-1. Use point 2 as the center of the second arc (radius 2-4) and point 1 as the center of the next arc (radius 1-5).

The **involute of a square** is constructed by drawing the square and extending each side line [Fig. 8.43(c)]. Point 4 becomes the center of the first arc (radius 4-1), point 3 the center of the second arc (radius 3-5), point 2 the center of the third arc (radius 2-6), and point 1 the center of the fourth arc (radius 1-7).

The **involute of a circle** is constructed by drawing the circle and dividing it into equal angles [Fig. 8.43(d)]. Draw tangent construction lines from the end of each angle. Mark off along each tangent the length of each circular arc. Use an irregular curve to connect the endpoints of the arc and tangent lines with a smooth curve.

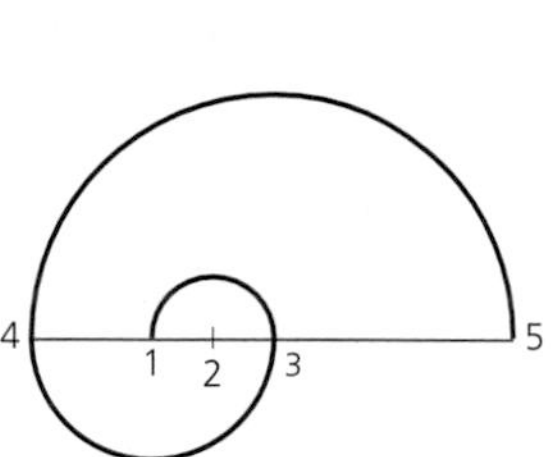

(a) Involute of a line

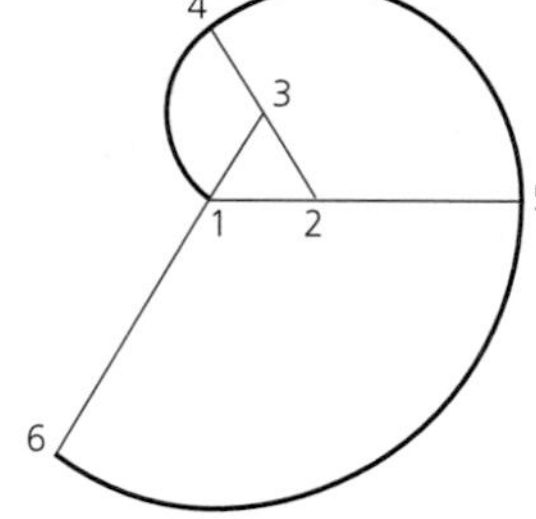

(b) Involute of a triangle

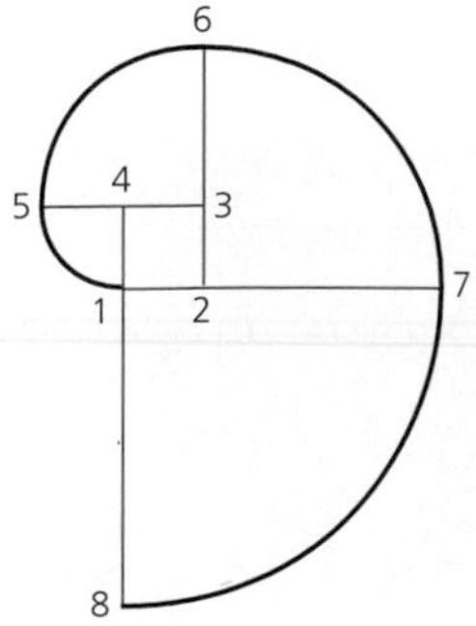

(c) Involute of a square

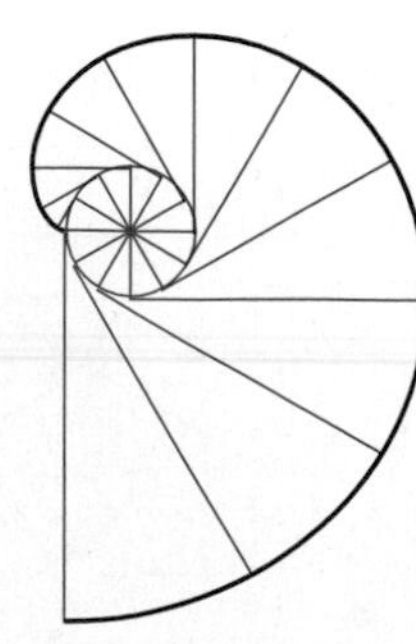

(d) Involute of a circle

FIGURE 8.43 Drawing Involutes

8.7 HELICES

A **cylindrical helix** is a double-curved line drawn by tracing the movement of a point as it revolves about the axis of a cylinder. Figure 8.44 shows two revolved positions of a cylindrical helix modeled in 3D. The resulting curve is traced on the cylinder by the revolution of a point crossing its right sections at a constant oblique angle. The point must travel about the cylinder at a uniform linear and angular rate. The linear distance (parallel to the axis) traveled in one complete turn is called the **lead.** This type of helix is called a cylindrical helix. A variety of industrial products are based on the cylindrical helix, including fasteners and springs. The stairway in Figure 8.1(b) was designed with a cylindrical helix.

If the point moves about a line that intersects the axis, it is a **conical helix.** The generating point's distance from the axis line changes at a uniform rate. A helix can be either *right-handed* or *left-handed.*

8.7.1 Constructing a Helix

The techniques for constructing a cylindrical helix and a conical helix use the same steps. Start the construction by radially dividing the end view (curve) into an equal number of parts (Fig. 8.45). The lead is divided into the same number of parts. Use the following steps.

1. Draw the right-handed cylindrical helix by first dividing the circular end view into equal divisions. Also divide the lead into equal parts (sixteen were used in the example).
2. Label the points on both views.
3. Project the end view divisions to the front view as vertical elements on the surface of the cylinder. In the front view, establish a series of points on the surface of the cylinder. Each point represents a position of the generating point as it rotates about the axis.
4. You can develop the cylindrical helix by unrolling the cylinder's surface. The helix line is a straight line on the

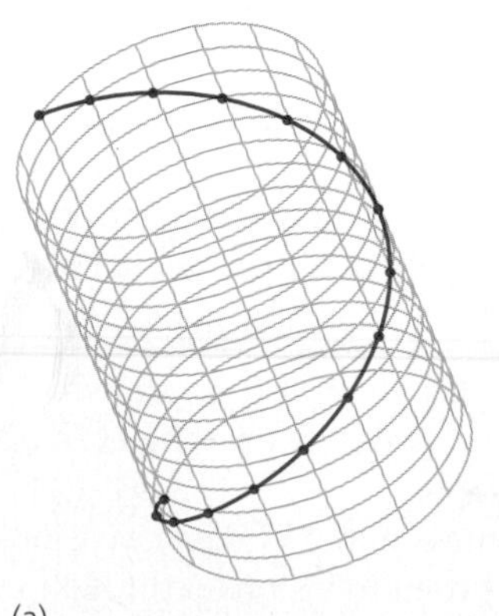

(a)

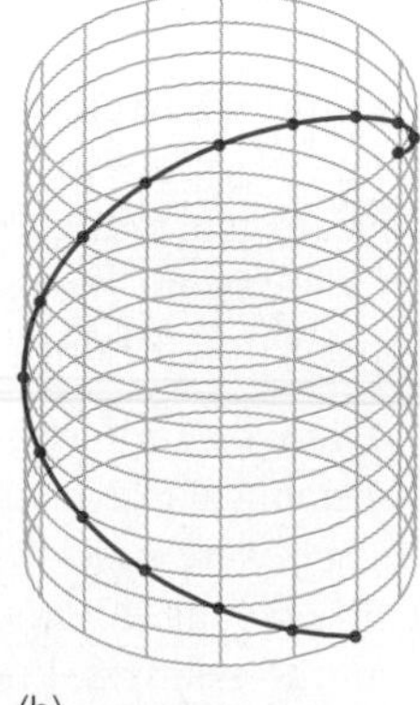

(b)

FIGURE 8.44 3D Model of a Cylindrical Helix

FIGURE 8.45 Drawing a Cylindrical Helix

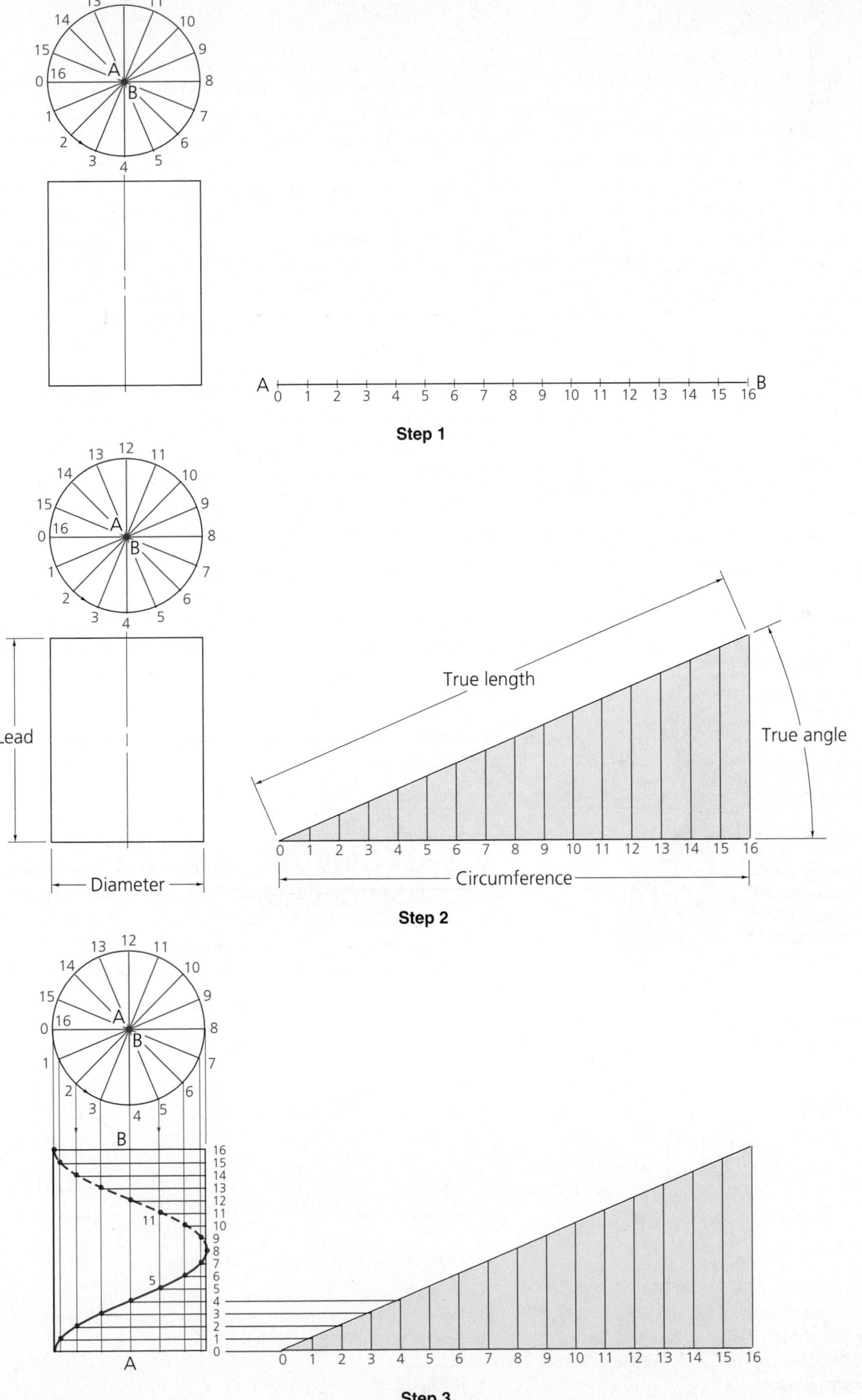

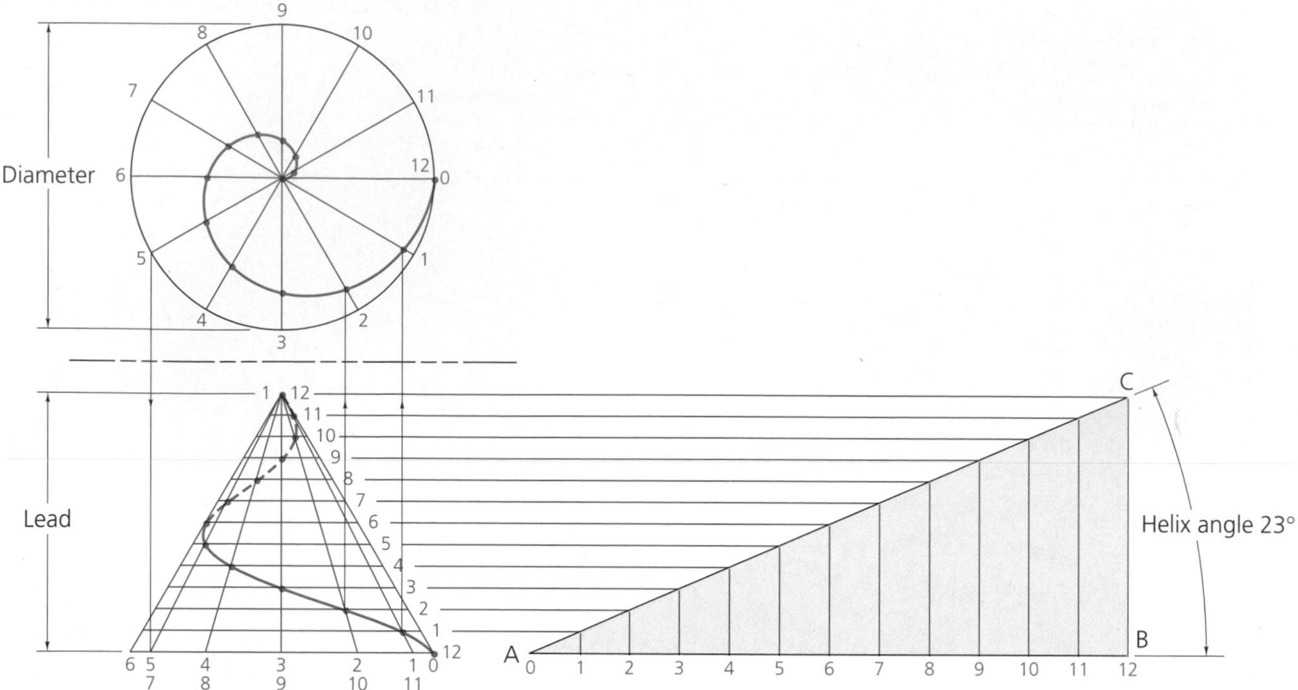

(a) Drawing a conical helix

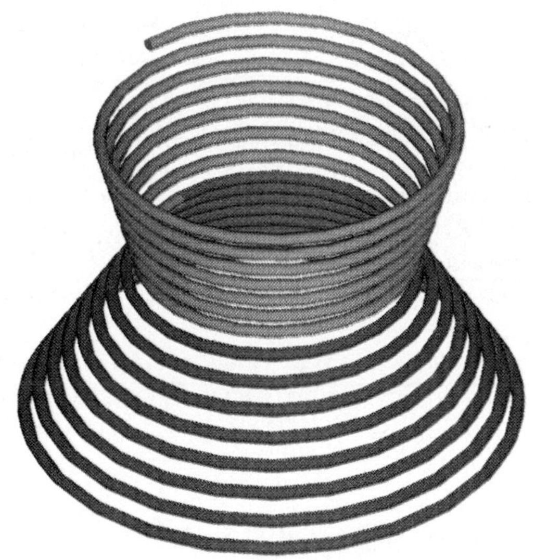

(b) Parametric model of helical spring design

FIGURE 8.46 Conical Helices

development. The angle the helix line makes with the baseline is called the **helix angle** (true angle).

To construct a conical helix, you must know its *taper angle* (angle between the cone's axis and an element on the cone surface) and lead. In Figure 8.46(a), the lead and the circle divisions are established as for a cylindrical helix. Elements determined in the top (end) view appear in the front view as straight lines, intersecting the vertex of the cone. Lead elements are drawn as horizontal lines. Points on the surface of the cone are located at the intersection of related elements. Figure 8.46(b) is an example of a helical design created with a parametric modeling system

You May Complete Exercises 8.5 Through 8.8 at This Time

8.8 GEOMETRIC CONSTRUCTION USING CAD

In CAD, anything placed on a drawing is a geometry **item**, or **entity.** Basic geometric entities include points, lines, arcs, and circles (Figs. 8.47 and 8.48). Entities are used to create

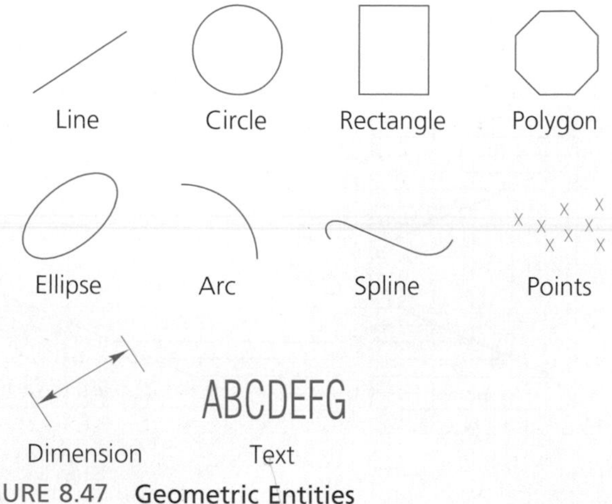

FIGURE 8.47 Geometric Entities

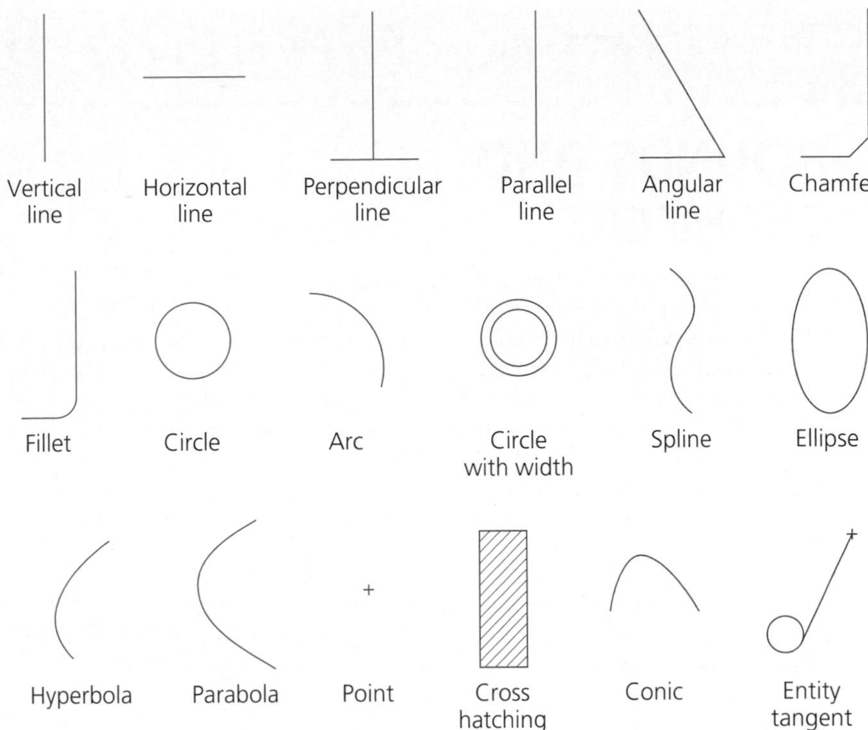

FIGURE 8.48 **Additional Geometric Entities**

any type of geometric feature. These CAD-based constructions can be substituted for many of the geometric constructions introduced in the first portion of this chapter. Of course, you still need to understand fundamental construction techniques to complete drawings on CAD systems. The techniques described for CAD systems are similar for all systems, but differ in the command names used. The commands presented here are for AutoCAD.

8.8.1 Location of Geometry

There are three ways to define a location on a drawing in CAD: (1) by digitizing the location (**free digitizing**), (2) by entering the location's coordinates via the computer keyboard or menu (**explicit entry**), or (3) by snapping to a location on an entity using a **reference,** which AutoCAD calls object snaps (**OSNAPS**). **OSNAPS** can specify a location on existing geometry. For example, the endpoint, center, or midpoint of an entity and the intersection of two entities (Fig. 8.49) are object snaps.

8.8.2 Basic Construction

Regardless of whether a 2D or 3D system is used, creating the geometry is the first step in drawing a *part* with a CAD system. The basic construction instructions are used to create geometry entities such as lines, arcs, and circles. Entities are the building blocks of every part. To construct geometry, the system must know the location, the size, and the appearance of the entity. To specify an entity's size, a value is given and the explicit coordinates are either typed or defined by freehand digitizing.

OSNAP options (Fig. 8.49) enable the creation of geometry relative to an existing entity; either the **ENDPOINT**, **MIDPOINT**, or **CENTER** of an entity can be referenced. The intersection of two entities can also be referenced with an **OSNAP** option (**INT**ersection). Lines have two **OSNAPS**, **END**points and a **MID**point. Circles and arcs have at least one **END**point and a **CEN**ter.

A CAD program assists your drawing efforts by finding many points automatically. For example, a typical problem in manual drafting and geometric construction is to find the

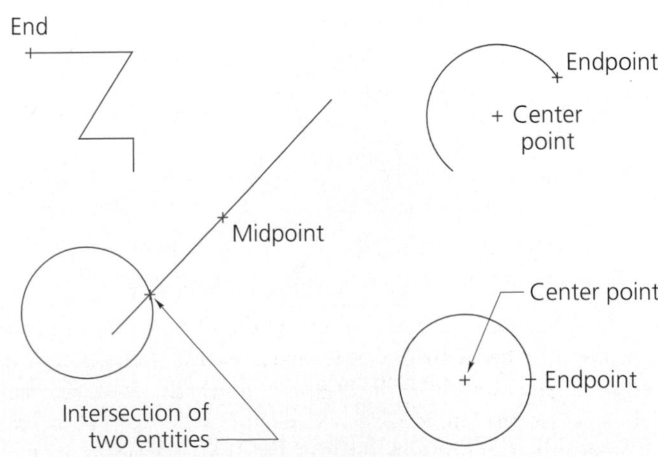

FIGURE 8.49 **Geometry Terminology**

Applying Parametric Design . . .

ROUNDS AND CHAMFERS

A variety of geometric shapes and constructions are accomplished automatically with a CAD system using parametric modeling. **Chamfers** and **rounds** (fillets/tangent arcs) are created automatically at selected edges of the part. Tangent arcs are introduced as rounds between two adjacent surfaces of the solid model. Chamfers are created between abutting edges of two surfaces on the solid model. There is no need to construct this geometry with 2D commands or manually. Understanding the choice and options for creating these two types of features requires knowledge of the traditional methods in 2D CAD and manual drawing.

The **Rounds** option creates a fillet or a round on an edge, that is, a smooth transition with a circular profile between two adjacent surfaces. Rounds should be added as late in the design as possible. There are cases where rounds should be added early; but in general, wait until later to add the rounds. You might also choose to place all rounds on a layer and suppress that layer to speed up your working session.

There are four basic types of rounds to consider, *edge, edge to surface, remove surface,* and *surface to surface.* Much of the time, you'll create **Edge** rounds. These do not remove surfaces (i.e., replace a planar surface with a rounded surface) but only smooth the hard edges between two adjacent surfaces. These rounds can:

- Be *constant* (single radius for all selected edges) or *variable* (have different radii specified at edge vertices *and* datum points)
- Have radius values of zero
- Have a radius value *determined* by a datum point or edge vertex
- Be of circular or conic cross section

Edge-Surf rounds (see Fig. A) create a transitional surface between an edge and a selected surface (tangent to the latter), having the same effect as rolling a ball bearing along an inside corner.

Remove Surf rounds (see Fig. B) can completely replace a surface with a rounded surface. The radius is automatically determined from the selected edges and surfaces adjacent to the one being replaced.

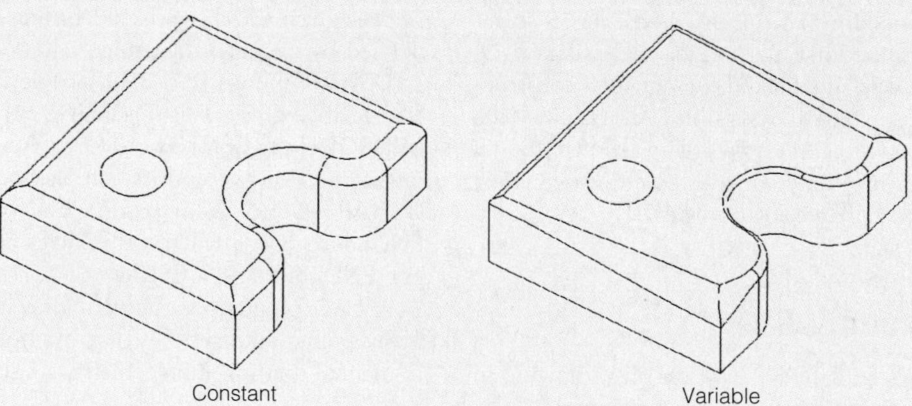
Constant
Variable

FIGURE A "Edge Round" Examples

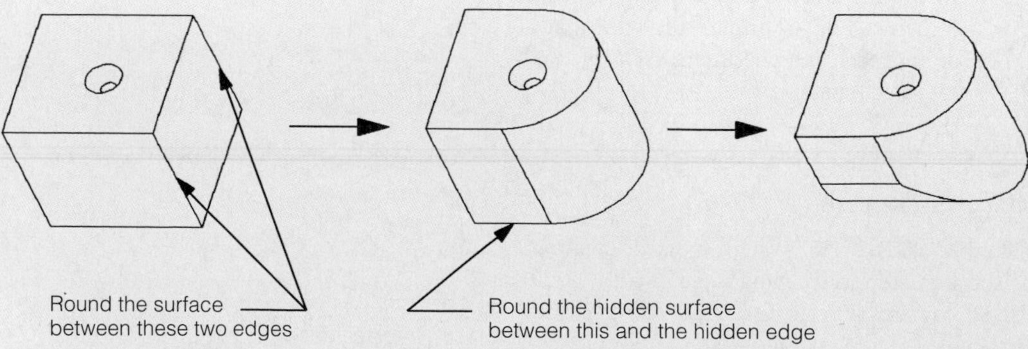
Round the surface between these two edges
Round the hidden surface between this and the hidden edge

FIGURE B "Remove Surface Round" Examples

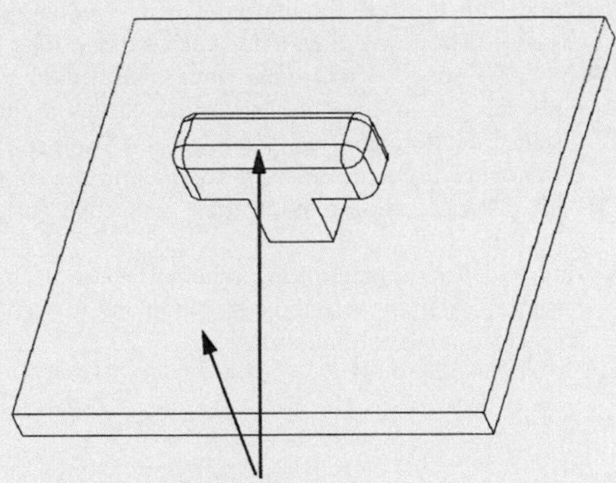

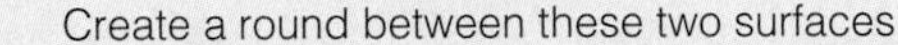
Create a round between these two surfaces

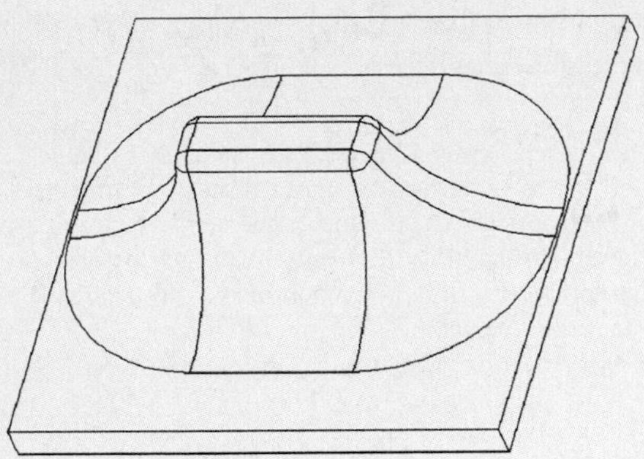
Surface-to-surface round created

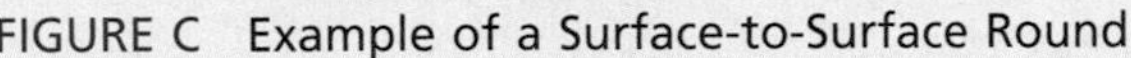
FIGURE C Example of a Surface-to-Surface Round

Surf-Surf (surface-to-surface) rounds (see Fig. C) are used to form transitional surfaces across multiple surfaces that don't necessarily share a common edge. They can add and remove material at the same time. These rounds are always of constant radius.

Use the **Edge** command specifically when creating rounds that do not completely remove adjacent surfaces.

A constant-radius round uses a single radius for all selected edges.

To Create a Constant-Radius Round

1. Choose **Round** form the SOLID menu.
2. Choose **Edge** and **Constant**, and **Circular** or **Conic**, and then Done.
3. Pick the edges to be rounded. Use any combination of the EDGE SELECT menu commands.
4. Enter the radius of the round using the RADIUS VALUE menu options.

The angle part provided here (see Fig. D) has two edges that require a round. The **Round** command is given, and the two edges are selected with the resulting round (see Fig. E). One round is on the outside edge of the part (a round) and the other provides a rounded internal feature (a fillet). The values of the rounds could be the same or different and can be modified at any stage of the design. Note that the rounds are children of the two surfaces that they connect.

An **edge chamfer** removes a flat section of material from a

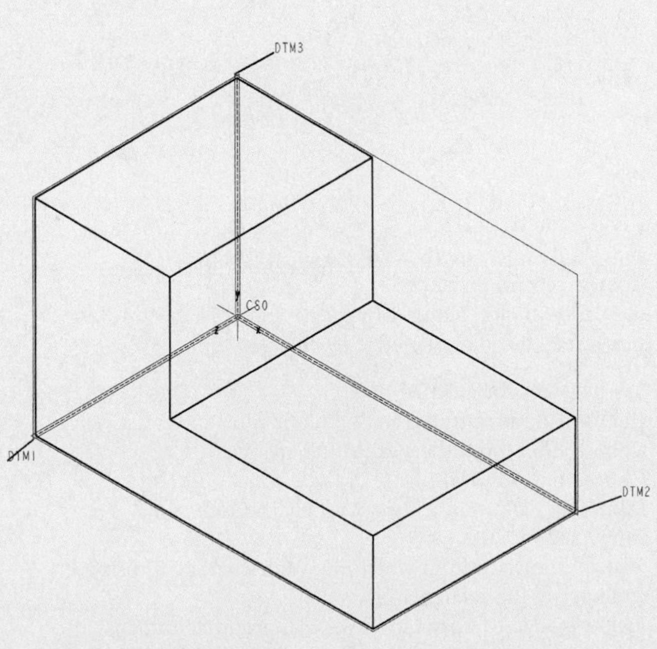
DTM3
CSO
DTM1
DTM2

FIGURE D Angle Part

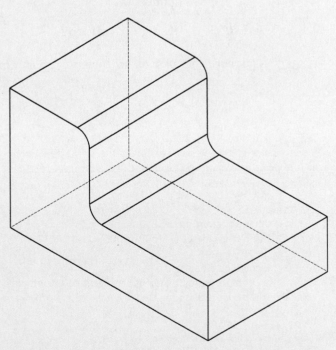

FIGURE E Adding Fillets and Rounds with the Round Command

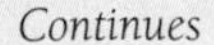
Continues

selected edge to create a beveled surface between the two original surfaces common to that edge. Multiple edges may be selected. There are four dimensioning schemes for edge chamfers (see Fig. F):

> **45 × d** This dimensioning scheme creates a chamfer that is at an angle of 45° to both surfaces and a distance d from the edge along each surface. The distance is the only dimension to appear when modified. 45 × d chamfers can only be created on an edge formed by the intersection of two perpendicular surfaces.

> **d × d** This dimensioning scheme creates a chamfer that is a distance d from the edge along each surface. The distance is the only dimension to appear when modified.

> **d1 × d2** This dimensioning scheme creates a chamfer at a distance d1 from the selected edge along one surface and a distance d2 from the selected edge along the other surface. Both distances appear along their respective surfaces when modified.

> **Ang × d** This dimensioning scheme creates a chamfer at a distance d from the selected edge along one adjacent surface at a specified angle to that surface.

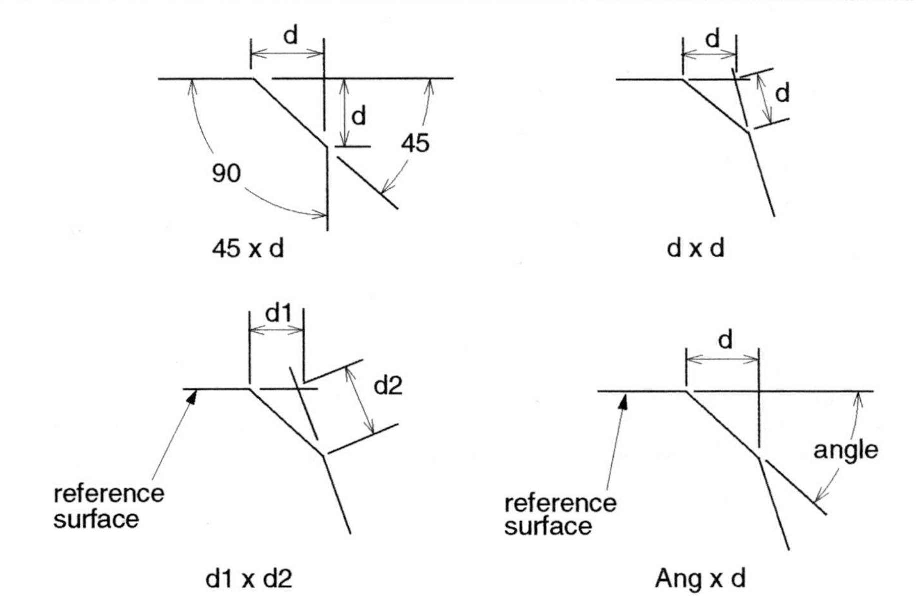

FIGURE F Chamfer Dimensioning Schemes

These schemes appear as options under the CHAMFER menu, which appears as soon as you choose **Edge** from the CHAMFER menu.

To Create a **45 × d** *and* **d × d** *Edge Chamfer*

1. Choose **Chamfer** from the SOLID menu.
2. Choose **Edge** from the CHAMFER menu.
3. Choose the **45 × d** or **d × d.**
4. Enter the chamfer dimension.
5. Select the edges to chamfer. Remember that for a **45 × d** edge chamfer, the surfaces bounding an edge must be at 90° to each other.

To Create a **d1 × d2** *Chamfer*

1. Choose **Chamfer** from the SOLID menu.
2. Choose **Edge** from the CHAMFER menu.
3. Choose the **d1 × d2.**
4. Input a distance along a surface to be selected.
5. Input a second distance.
6. Pick the surface along which the first distance will be measured, and pick the edge to chamfer.

To Create an **Ang × d** *Chamfer*

1. Choose **Chamfer** from the SOLID menu.
2. Choose **Edge** from the CHAMFER menu.
3. Choose the **Ang × d.**
4. Input an angle from a surface to be selected.
5. Input distance.
6. Select the surface from which the values will be measured, and specify the reference.
7. Pick the edge to chamfer and the appropriate dimensioning references.

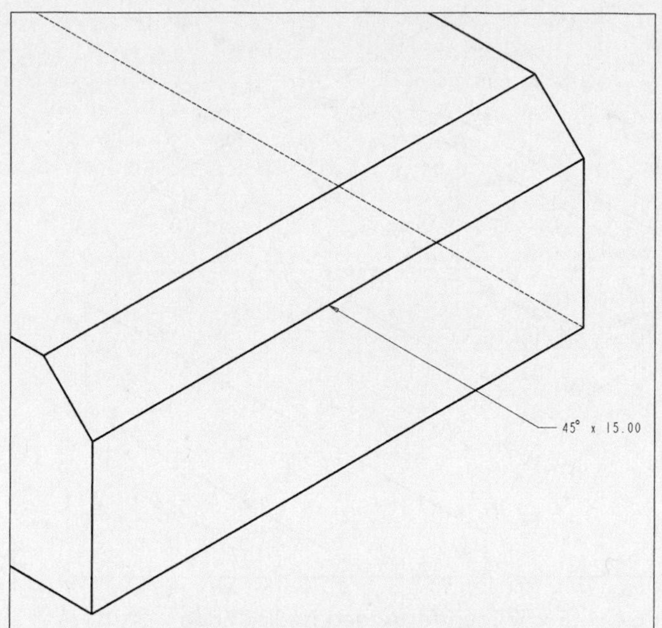

FIGURE G Adding a 45 × 15 Chamfer Feature to the Front Edge of the Part

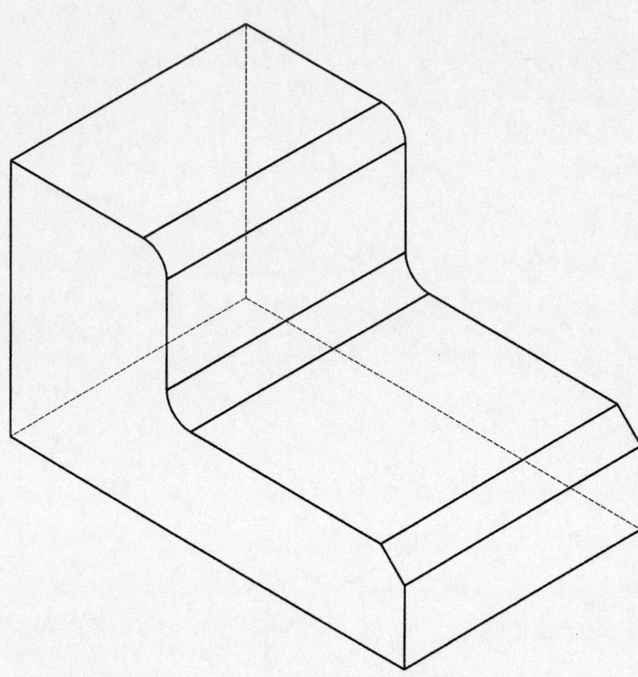

FIGURE H Part with Chamfer and Rounds

The **45 × d** option (see Fig. G) was used to chamfer the front edge of the angle part (see Fig. H). The next feature added to the part is a slot. The slot is created, dimensioned, and regenerated in the **sketcher** (see Fig. I). The slot is created thru the part (see Fig. J). A 45 × 5 chamfer is added to the upper edge of the slot (see Fig. K). The chamfer is then modified to 45 × 10 (see Fig. L). The finished part (see Fig. M) has rounds, a chamfer, and a chamfered slot.

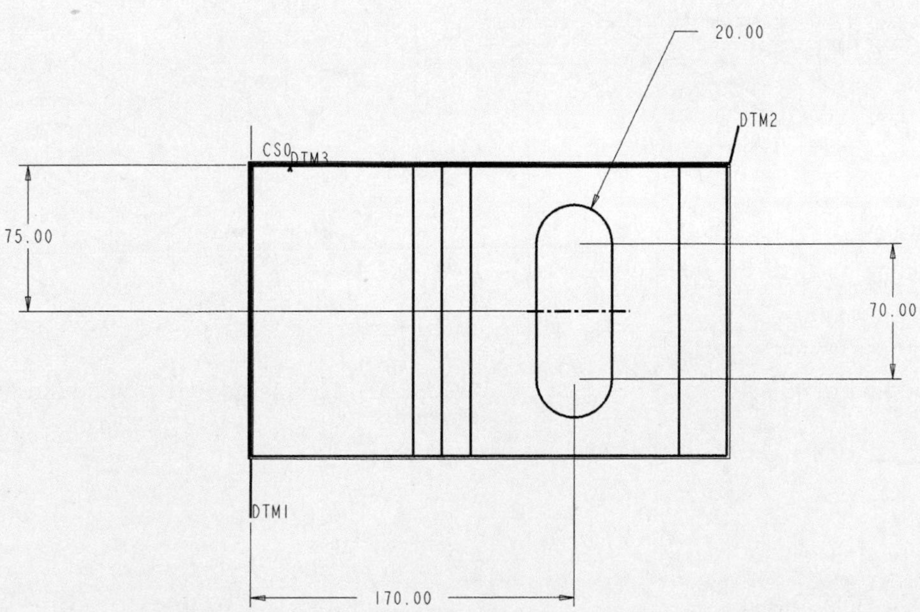

FIGURE I Creating the Slot in the Sketcher

Continues

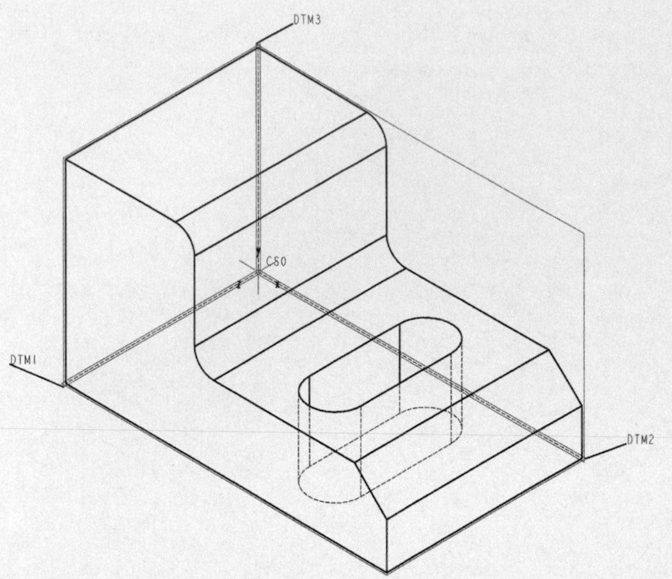

FIGURE J Part with Slot

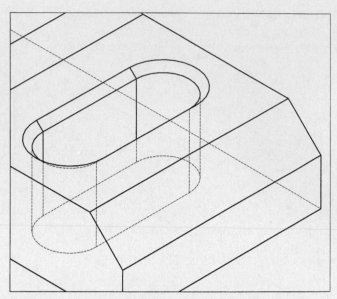

FIGURE K 45 × 5 Chamfer Added to Slot Edge

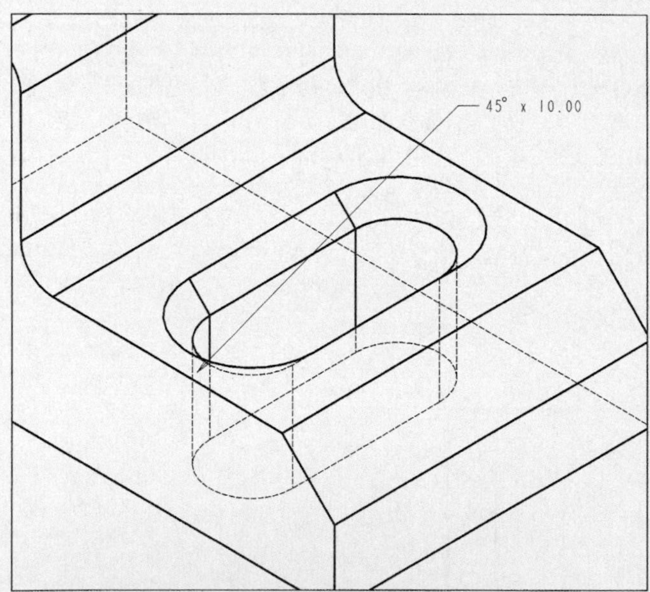

FIGURE L Chamfer Modified to 45 × 10

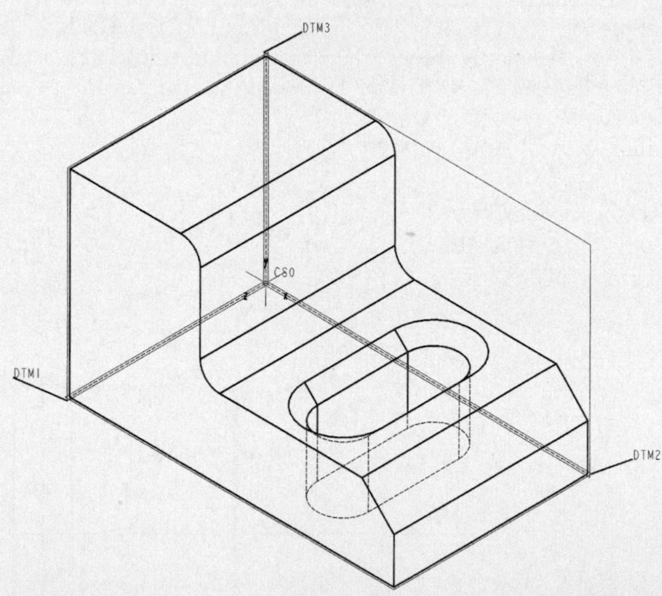

FIGURE M Completed Part with Rounds, Slot, and Chamfers

(Continued)

center of a circle or an arc. The **POINT** command using the **CEN**ter **OSNAP** reference will automatically put a point at the center of a circle.

In the following discussion, any commands or options to commands enclosed by brackets < > are the **defaults** for that command.

8.9 GEOMETRY ENTITIES

In CAD, the term **geometry entity** includes geometric forms, groups, figures, text, labels, dimensions, and cross-hatching. As an engineer or designer, you will specify the shape, size, color, and location of entities. Figures 8.47 and 8.48 show a range of geometry entities available on CAD systems.

8.9.1 Points

As discussed in the first part of this chapter, points are the simplest entities; they serve as references or as placement coordinates for other entities. You can use a digitizer or the keyboard to enter coordinate values and the **POINT** command to place a point at the specified location. Each point has an **X** and a **Y** coordinate (and a **Z** coordinate in 3D).

In Figure 8.50, three points have been drawn by free digitizing: **D1, D2,** and **D3.** Free digitizing is the same as *picking* a position on the tablet or with a mouse. The "BEFORE" illustration [Fig. 8.50(a)] indicates the digitized locations with an **x** at each location. In the "AFTER" illustration [Figure 8.50(b)], the three points are indicated by crosses (+). A variety of point styles are available; here the cross was previously selected using AutoCAD's **SETVAR** option for **PDMODE** set to 2. The following AutoCAD command was used:

`Command:` **POINT** (give the **POINT** command by typing or from the screen menu)
`Point:` **D1, D2, D3** (pick three positions; use <RETURN> between picks to reenter the **POINT** command)
`Command:` **REDRAW** (repaints the screen and shows the points as a cross)

8.9.2 Lines

Lines are entities that connect two endpoints of a line segment. Each point has **X** and **Y** coordinates (and a **Z** coordinate if you are using a 3D CAD system). Endpoints may be specified explicitly or referenced from existing geometry.

You can use the **LINE** command to create a line, a series of connected lines, or several separate lines. When connected lines are created, the endpoint of one line is also the start point of the next line. Lines that can be created include:

- A series of connected lines
- A closed region with connected lines (using **CLOSE** at end of command)
- A horizontal or a vertical line (using **ORTHO**)
- A line at an angle to an existing line
- A line parallel or perpendicular to an existing line
- A line tangent to a circle, a line, or a point

In Figure 8.51 a line was created by free digitizing. A series of connected lines was created in Figure 8.52 using the same command, except that **D3** and **D4** were picked instead of hitting <RETURN> at the second **To Point** prompt. The following command was used in Figure 8.52:

`Command:` **LINE**
`From Point:` **D1** (pick the starting position)
`To Point:` **D2** (pick the ending position of the line)
`To Point:` <RETURN> (ends the command)

Drawing a Horizontal or Vertical Line. You can create a horizontal or a vertical line by first turning on the orthogonal (**ORTHO**) option. This option limits your movement to the **X** and **Y** axes from your last location. Figure 8.53 shows a horizontal line created using the **LINE** command with **ORTHO** turned on. The first digitize (pick) established the starting point of the line, and the second digitize established the direction and length.

Drawing a vertical line is similar to creating a horizontal line, except that the line is aligned with the **Y** axis instead of the **X** axis. In Figure 8.54, the **LINE** command was selected and two points were digitized to create a vertical line. The first point established the line's starting point, and the second point established the line's direction and distance.

(a) Before

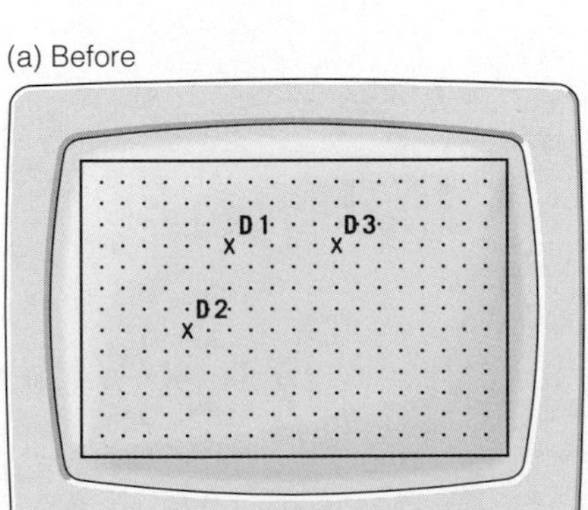

(b) After

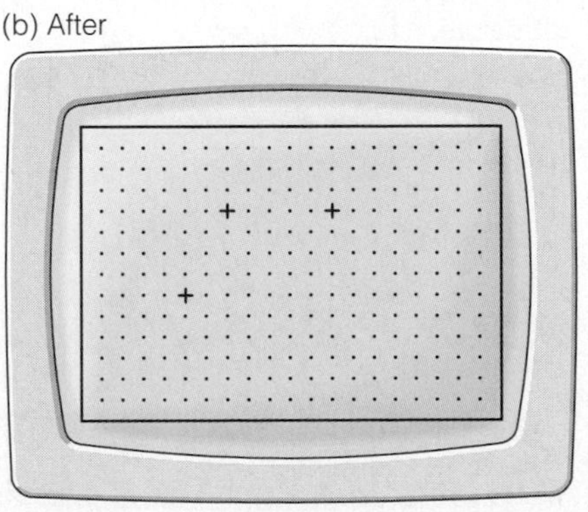

FIGURE 8.50 Drawing Points

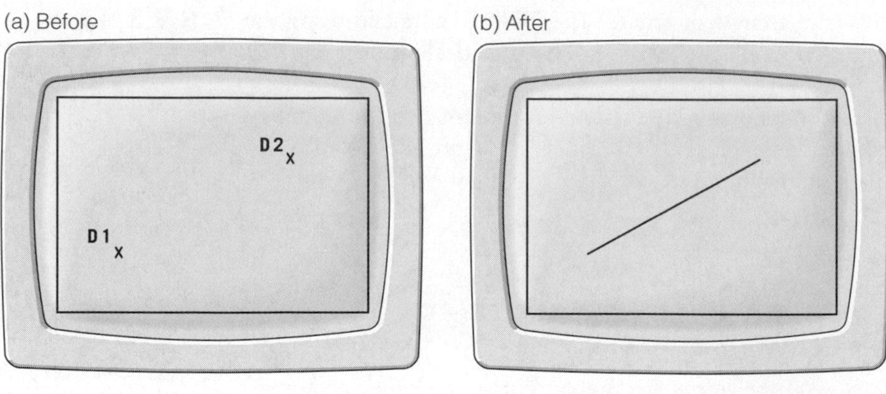

FIGURE 8.51 Drawing a Line

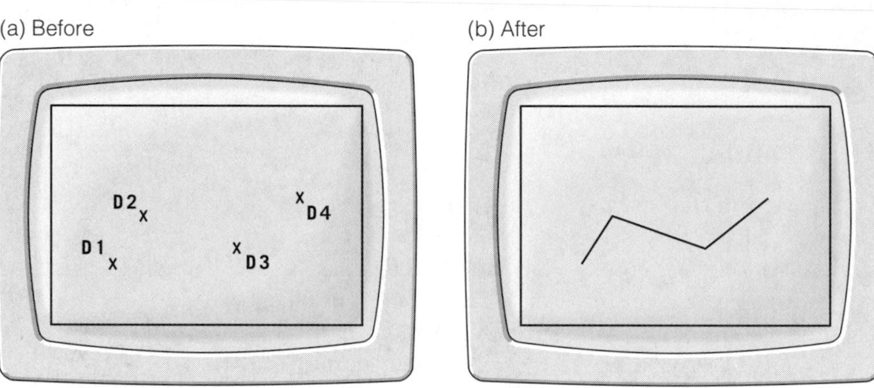

FIGURE 8.52 Drawing Multiple Lines

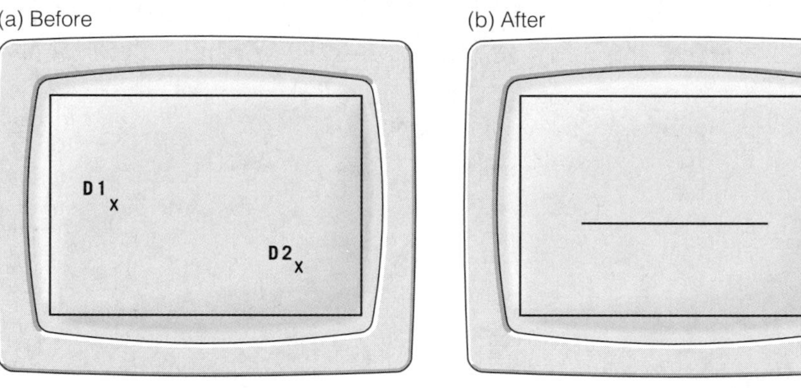

FIGURE 8.53 Drawing a Horizontal Line

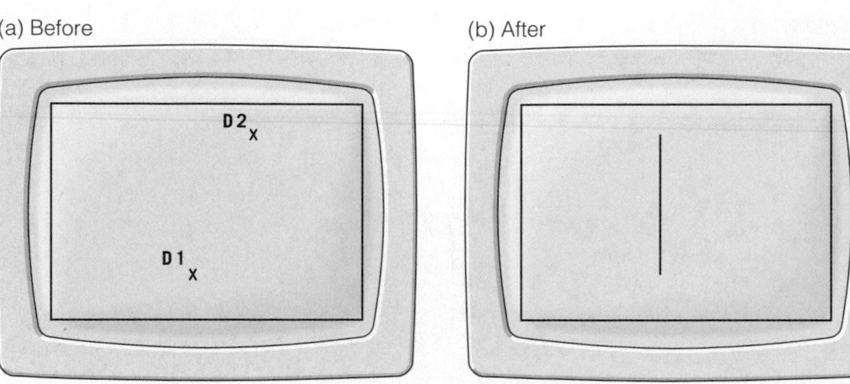

FIGURE 8.54 Drawing a Vertical Line

(a) Before

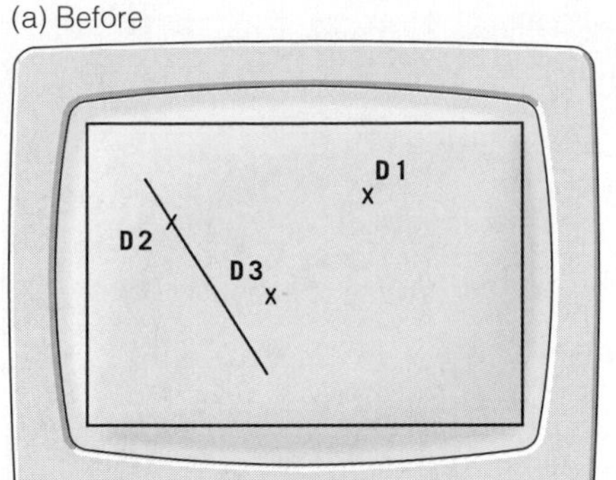

(b) After

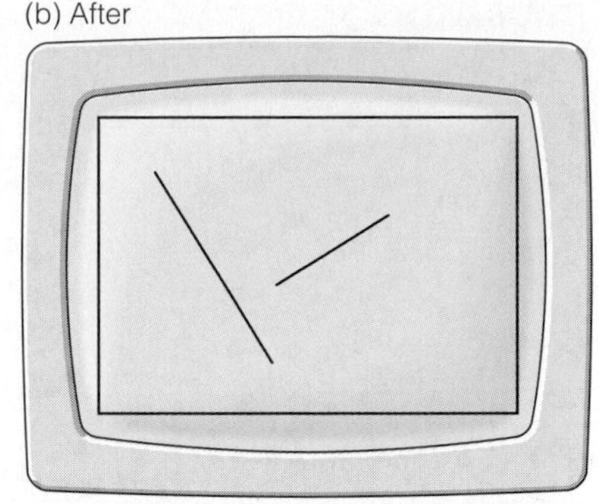

FIGURE 8.55 Drawing a Line Perpendicular to an Existing Line

Drawing a Perpendicular Line. You can draw a line perpendicular to an existing line using the **LINE** command in conjunction with the perpendicular (**PER**) **OSNAP**. Figure 8.55 shows a line that was created perpendicular to an existing line. The **LINE** command was selected as follows:

`Command:` **LINE**
`From point:` **D1** (digitize the location of the line's starting point)
`To point: per` (pick the **OSNAP PER** option)
of **D2** (pick the line)
`To point:` **D3** (digitize the location of the endpoint of the line)

Drawing a Tangent Line. To create a line tangent to an arc or a circle, use the **OSNAP** tangent option (**TAN**). In Figure 8.56, the **LINE** command was selected. Point **D1** was the starting point (at the end of the existing line), and **D2** identified the circle to which the line is to be tangent. Because two tangency positions are possible for each circle, the digitized points must be near the point of tangency (the side you wish the line to connect to the circle). The following command was used:

`Command:` **LINE**
`From point:` **END** (select the **OSNAP END**)
of **D1** (pick near the end of the line)
`To point:` **TAN** (select the **OSNAP TAN**)
of **D2** (select the circle on the side of the desired tangency)

8.9.3 Circles

Using a CAD system, a circle has its start point and endpoint at the 3 o'clock position and its origin at the center. You can create circles in several different ways, depending on the type of information available. You can give three digitized circumference points, the radius or diameter value, or digitize the radius or diameter.

Drawing Circles by Specifying Three Points on the Circumference. Figure 8.57 shows a circle created with the **CIRCLE** command and three digitizes (**D1**, **D2**, and **D3**), which define three points on the circle's circumference. The following command was used:

`Command:` **CIRCLE**
`3P/2P/TTR/<Center point>: 3P` (pick the three-point option)
`First point on circumference:` **D1**
`Second point on circumference:` **D2**
`Third point on circumference:` **D3**

Drawing Circles by Digitizing the Diameter. CAD systems can create a circle by calculating the circle's diameter from the distance between two digitized locations. Figure 8.58 illustrates a circle created with the **CIRCLE** command and two digitized points (**D1** and **D2**), which established opposite points (the diameter) on the circle's circumference.

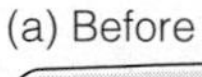

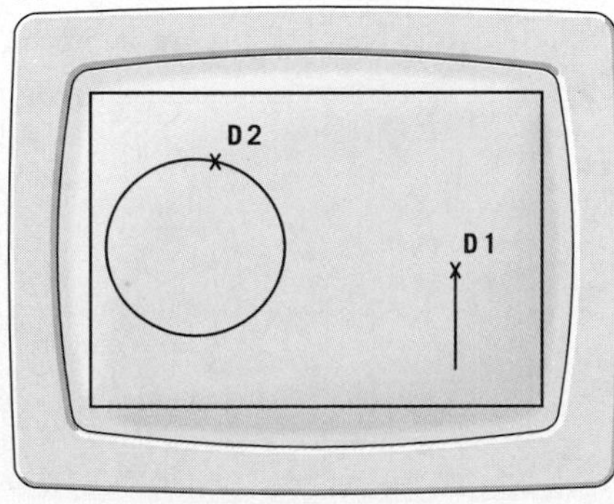

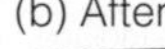

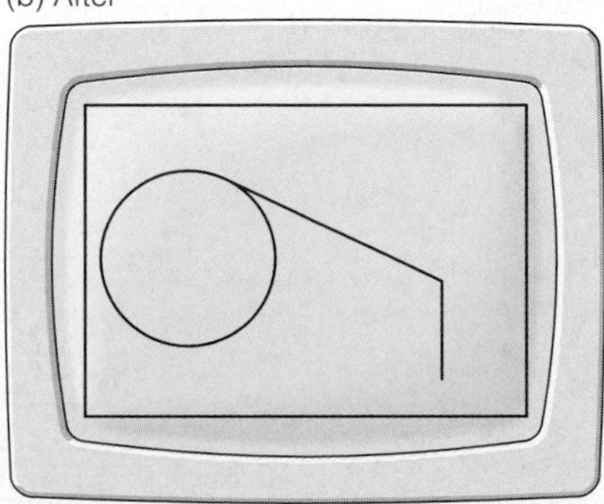

FIGURE 8.56 Drawing a Line Tangent to a Circle and at the End of an Existing Line

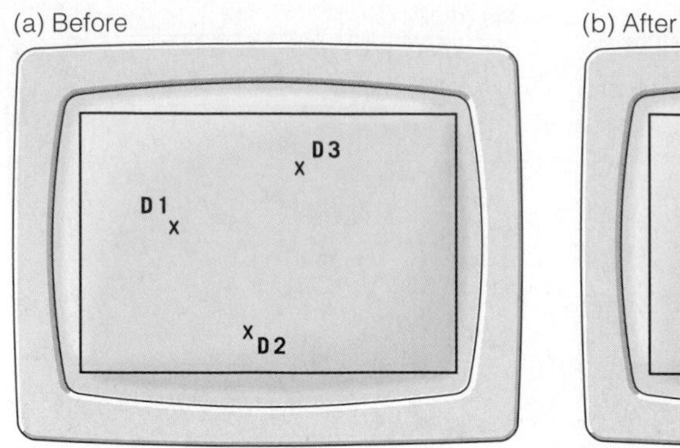

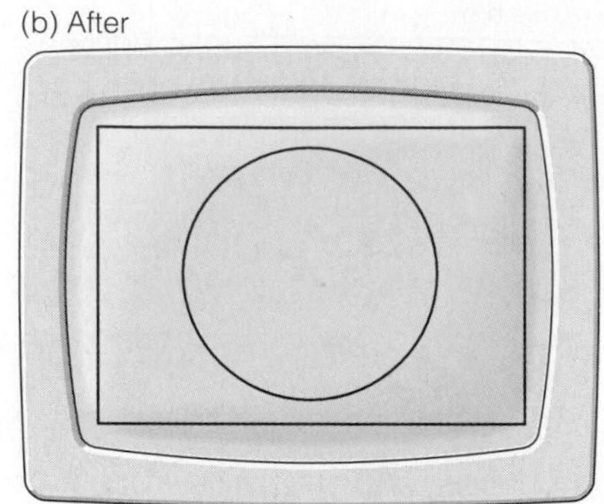

FIGURE 8.57 Drawing a Three-Point Circle

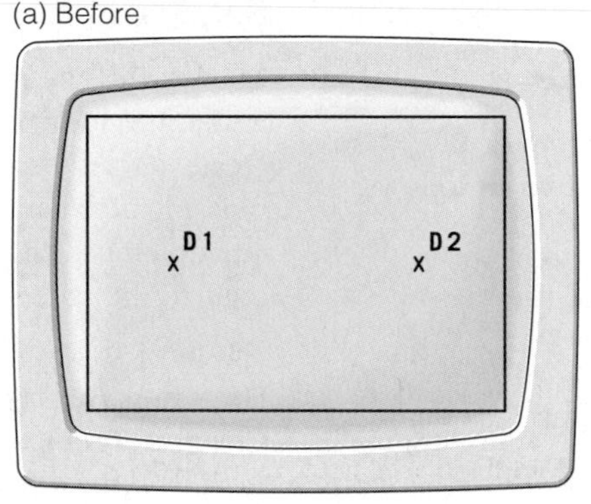

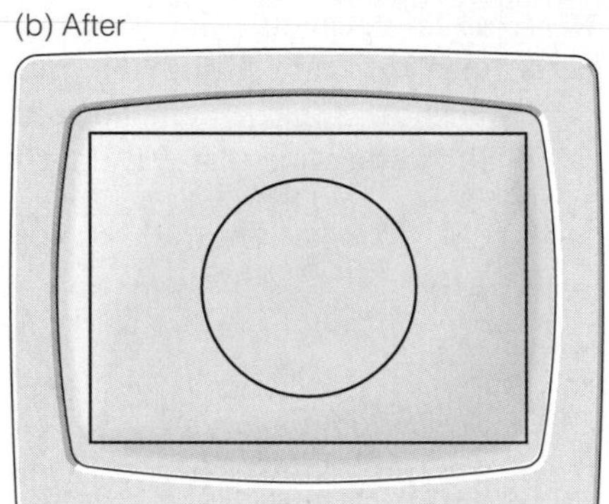

FIGURE 8.58 Drawing a Circle by Digitizing a Diameter

The following command was used:

Command: **CIRCLE**
3P/2P/TTR/<Center point>: 2P (pick the two-point option)
First point on diameter: **D1**
Second point on diameter: **D2**

Drawing Circles by Digitizing the Radius. CAD systems can create a circle by calculating the circle's radius from two digitized locations. In Figure 8.59, the **CIRCLE** command was selected along with two digitized locations. Point **D1** established the circle's center, and **D2** identified a point on the circumference. The following command was used:

Command: **CIRCLE**
3P/2P/TTR/<Center point>: **D1** (pick the center of the circle)
Diameter/<Radius>: **R** (pick radius option)
Radius: **D2** (digitize location)

Specifying a Diameter or a Radius. You can also specify a circle's diameter or radius by entering an explicit value. Only one digitized point is required for creating a circle when the diameter or the radius value is known (Fig. 8.60).

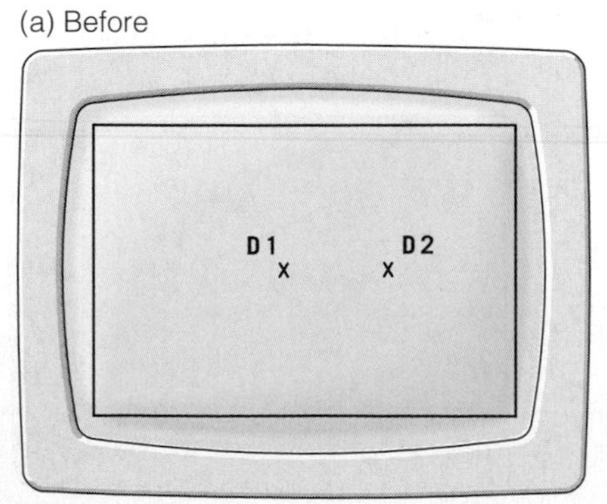

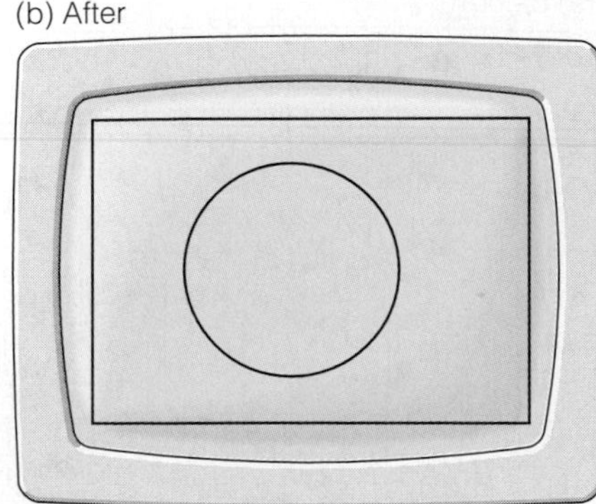

FIGURE 8.59 Drawing a Circle by Digitizing a Radius

(a) Before

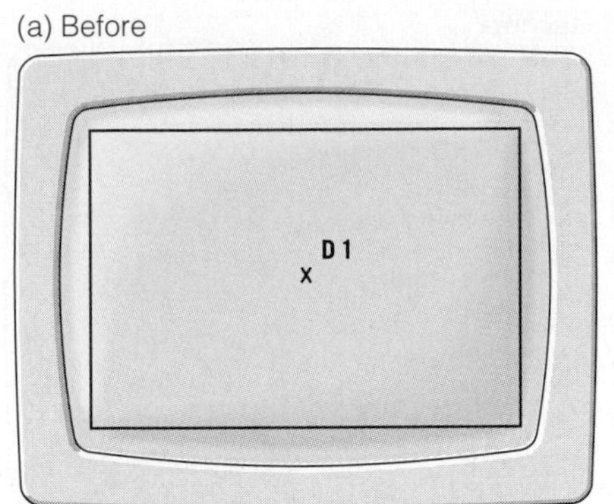

(b) After

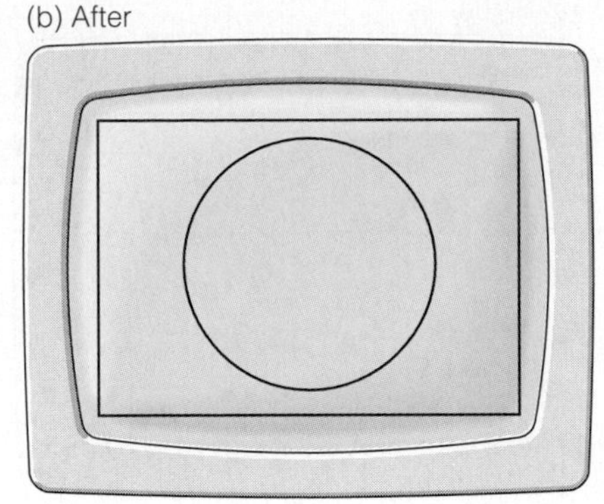

FIGURE 8.60 Drawing a Circle by Specifying the Radius Value

The following command was used:

Command: **CIRCLE**
3P/2P/TTR/<Center of circle>: **D1** (center of circle)
Diameter/<Radius>: **3.00** (radius value)

8.9.4 Arcs

There are many ways to create an arc, including specifying the start point, specifying a point on the arc's path, and specifying the endpoint. The system creates the arc in the direction in which the points were digitized. AutoCAD lets you create an arc many different ways, only two of which we will present here.

Drawing Arcs by Digitizing Three Locations. Figure 8.61 shows an arc created using the **ARC** command and three digitizes. Point **D1** established the arc's starting point, **D2** is a point on the arc, and **D3** is the endpoint. The following command was used:

Command: **ARC**
Center/::Start point>: **D1**
Center/End/Second point>: **D2**
Endpoint: **D3**

Drawing Arcs by Specifying the Center, the Starting Point, and the Endpoint. Figure 8.62 illustrates an arc that was created using the **ARC** command along with specifying the center point, the starting point, and the endpoint. The following command was used:

Command: **ARC**
Center/<Start point>: **C** (pick center option)
of **D1** (digitize center of arc)
Start point: **D2** (digitize start point)
Angle/Length/<Endpoint>: **D3** (digitize the endpoint of the arc)

Drawing Tangent Arcs. A tangent arc is also called a *fillet*. A fillet is an arc created tangent to existing geometry. The **FILLET** command is used to construct tangent arcs. A fillet of a specified size is created by entering the diameter or the radius value. Fillets may be created with respect to points, lines, circles, and arcs. In Figure 8.63, the **FILLET** command was specified and the two lines were picked. In Figure 8.64, the following command was used to create the fillet:

Command: **FILLET**
Polyline/Radius/<Select first object>: R (select R for radius)
Enter fillet radius: **1.50** (set the radius default)
Command: <RETURN> (reenter the command)
FILLET Polyline/Radius/<Select first object>: **D1** (pick first entity)
Select second object: **D2** (pick second entity)

(a) Before

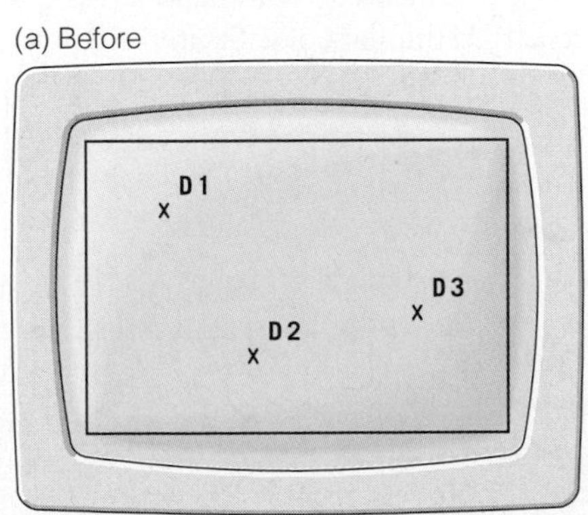

(b) After

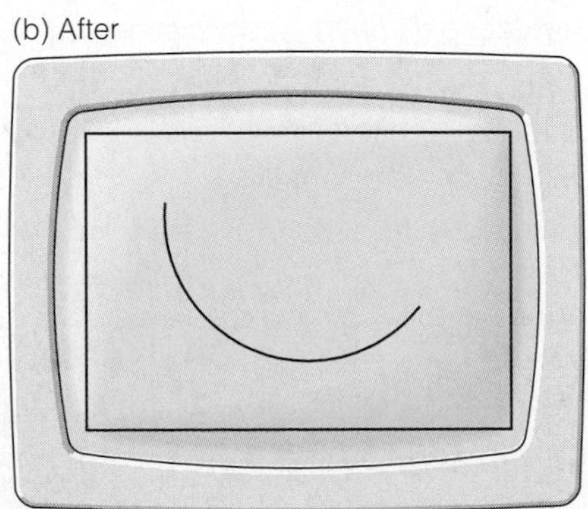

FIGURE 8.61 Drawing an Arc Through Three Digitized Points

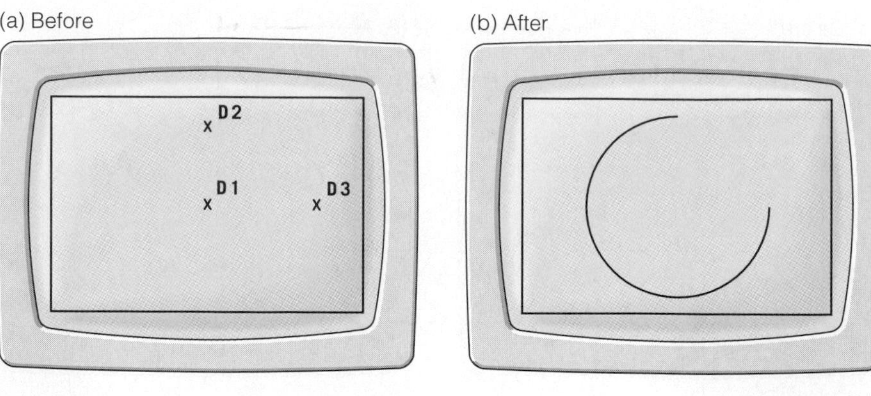

FIGURE 8.62 **Drawing an Arc**

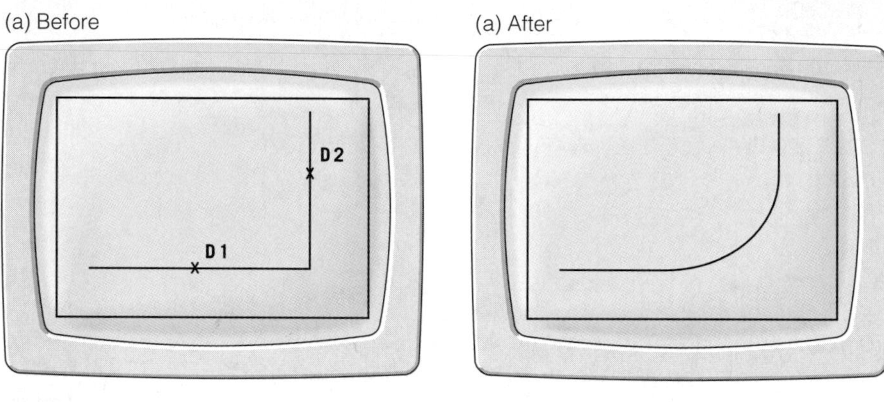

FIGURE 8.63 **Drawing a Fillet Between Two Lines**

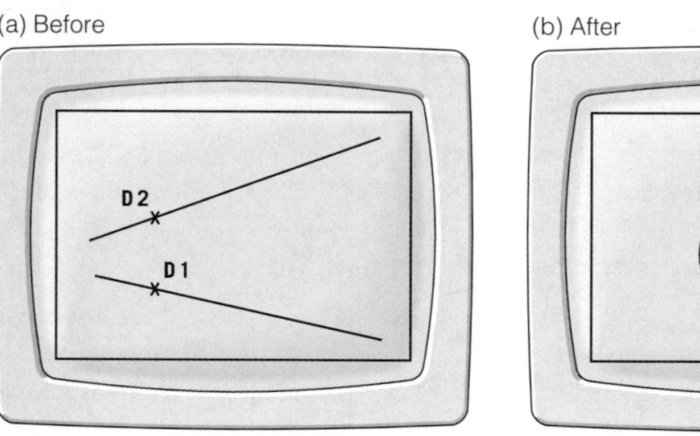

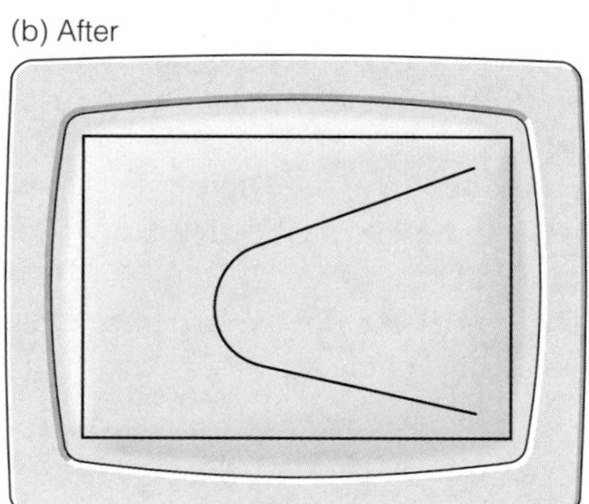

FIGURE 8.64 **Drawing a Fillet**

8.9.5 Drawing Ellipses

An ellipse is an elongated circle. Mathematically, it is defined as a cone intersected by a plane and therefore can be referred to as a conic. CAD systems draw perfect ellipses. In the following example, the **ELLIPSE** command is used to create an ellipse with a major axis of 50 mm and a minor axis of 40 mm.

```
Command: ELLIPSE
<Axis endpoint 1>/Center: C (pick C for center)
Center of ellipse: (digitize location for center of ellipse)
Axis endpoint: @25>0.00 (pick polar point for half the major axis at 0°)
<Other axis endpoint>/Rotation:
@ 20< 270 (pick polar point for half the minor axis at 270°)
```

8.9.6 Drawing Polygons

Many CAD systems have a command that allows the automatic creation of a polygon. With AutoCAD the **POLYGON** command can be used to draw a polygon of any number of sides and of any size. The following command creates a hexagon with distance across the flats of 1.00 in.:

```
Command: POLYGON
Number of sides: 6 (enter number of sides)
Edge of/<Center of Polygon>: (digitize center of polygon)
Inscribed in circle/Circumscribed about circle: C (pick circumscribed)
Radius of circle: 1.00 (distance across flats)
```

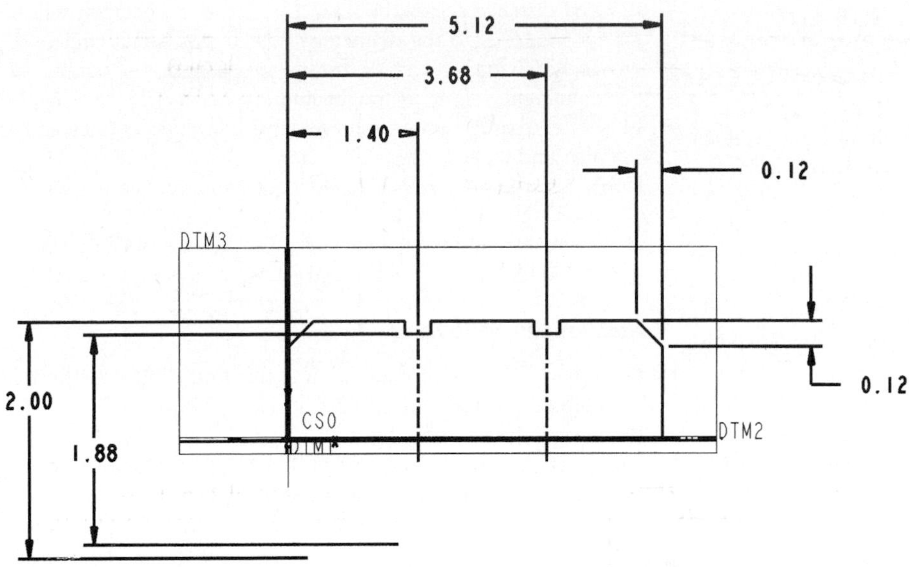

(a) Sketch geometry and dimensions

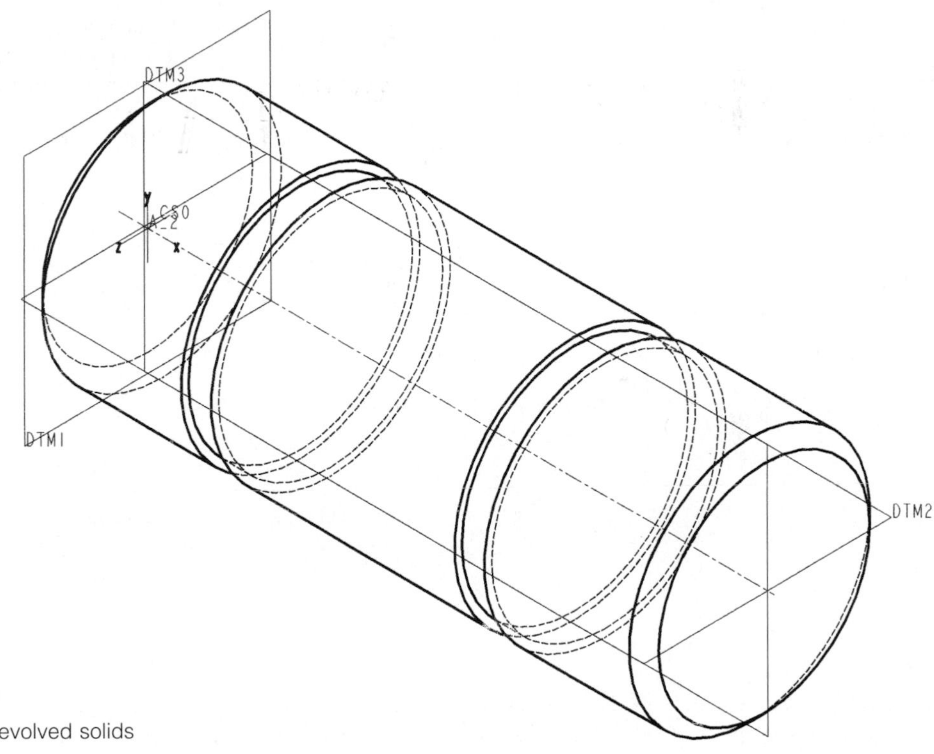

(b) Parametric solid model containing all revolved solids

FIGURE 8.65 **Parametric Geometry**

It is important for an engineer to master the manual procedures and techniques introduced in this chapter. Many of the manual construction techniques are needed when drafting and designing projects in industry, even when a CAD system is available. In Figure 8.65(a) and (b) we can see how the part's design was created by sketching a simple geometric shape (parametric modeling) of the outline (section) and adding dimensions. The pin was created by revolving the section 360° about a sketched centerline. Because of the simplicity of parametric modeling, the pin was modeled in less than 3 minutes!

QUIZ

True or False

1. Both hyperbolas and cones are generated from conic sections
2. In helix construction, the distance traveled by one point for one revolution measured parallel to the axis is called the lead.
3. The concentric method of ellipse construction is more accurate than using a template.
4. Tangent arcs are basically the same thing as fillets.
5. Squares, hexagons, pentagons, and ellipses are regular polygons.
6. A circle can be used to construct all forms of regular polygons.
7. A bisector of a line or an angle divides the line or angle into an equal number of parts.
8. A regular polygon has equal angles.

Fill in the Blanks

9. All geometric forms are composed of __________ and their __________.
10. __________ are used to divide lines into __________ __________ parts.
11. An __________ circle of a triangle will touch all __________ sides.
12. The distance across the __________ of an octagon will be __________ to the diameter of the __________ circle.
13. To __________ a circle means to __________ out its circumference along a straight line.
14. A __________ arc is a curve connecting two entities and is also known as a __________.
15. __________ are equally spaced along their entire length.
16. Geometric forms include: __________, __________, and __________.

Answer the Following

17. When is it appropriate to use the four-center method of ellipse construction?
18. Give a simple definition of a line and a curve.
19. What are the five types of figures that result from the intersection of a cone and a plane?
20. Define a cylindrical helix and a conical helix.
21. Why would the graphical method of dividing a line be more accurate than the mathematical method?
22. Name four solid shapes commonly used in industry.
23. Why is it important to learn the manual method of constructing geometric forms such as ellipses instead of just using templates?
24. Describe an industrial application of geometric construction.

EXERCISES

Exercises may be assigned as sketching, instrument, or CAD projects. Transfer the given information to an "A"-size sheet of .25 in. grid paper. Complete all views, and solve for proper visibility, including centerlines, object lines, and hidden lines. Exercises that are not assigned by the instructor can be sketched in the text to provide practice and to enhance understanding of the preceding instructional material.

After Reading the Chapter Through Section 8.5.7, You May Complete Exercises 8.1 Through 8.4

Exercise 8.1(A) Bisect the line, the angle, and the arc.

Exercise 8.1(B) Divide line 1 into eleven equal parts using the graphical method. Divide line 2 into seven equal parts and line 3 into proportional parts having ratios of 3:2:5.

Exercise 8.1(C) Construct a hexagon inside and an octagon around the outside of the given circle.

Exercise 8.1(D) Draw every possible tangency for the three circles.

Exercise 8.2(A) Draw a 40 mm radius arc (fillet) between the connected lines. Connect the two lines with a tangent arc (fillet) using a 25 mm radius.

Exercise 8.2(B) Draw a 2 in. radius or a 50 mm radius arc (fillet) between the circle and the line.

Exercise 8.2(C) Construct a 3 in. or a 70 mm inside arc (fillet) on the top right side of the two circles. Draw a 5 in. or a 120 mm outside (enclosing) arc connecting the two circles on the bottom left.

Exercise 8.2(D) Draw an S-shaped curve using the given lines and points.

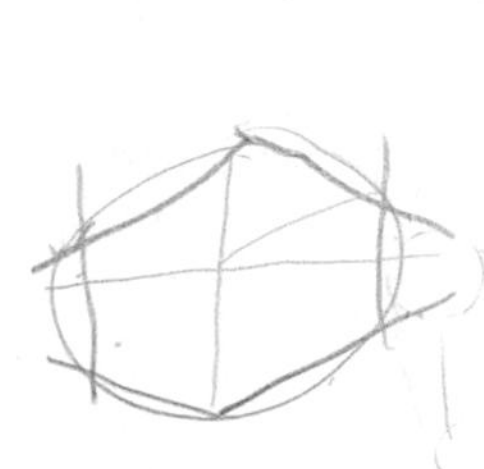

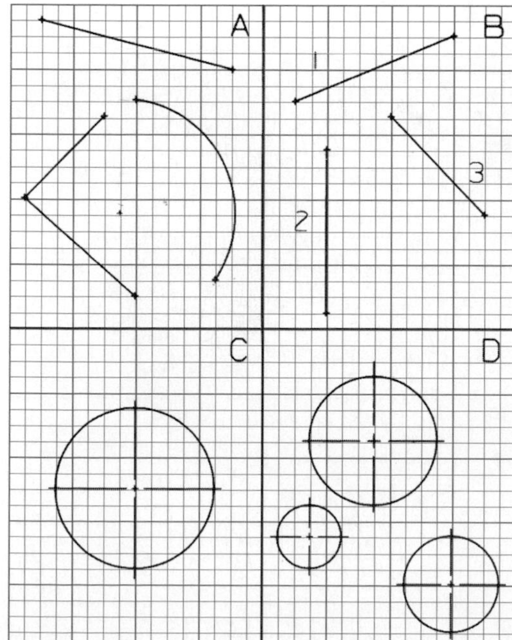

EXERCISE 8.1

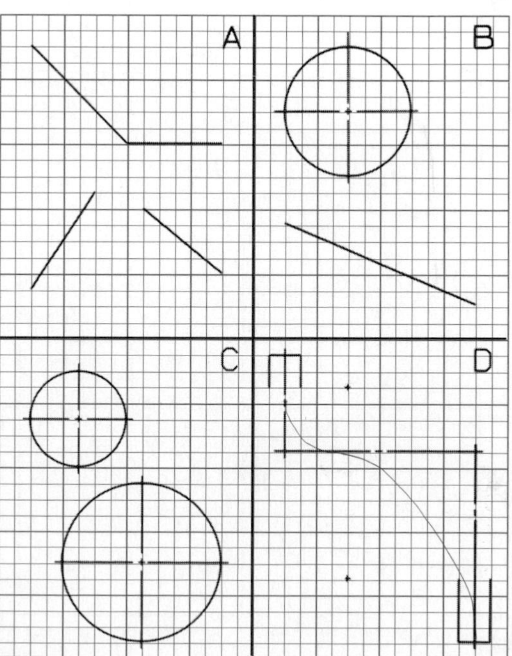

EXERCISE 8.2

Exercise 8.3(A) Given two circles of 2.25 and 3.75 in., draw an ellipse via the concentric-circle method. For a metric problem, use diameters of 70 and 90 mm.

Exercise 8.3(B) Given a major diameter of 4.75 in. and a minor diameter of 3.50 in., draw an ellipse using the four-center method. Draw the ellipse so that the major diameter is vertical. Use 120 and 80 mm for a metric problem.

Exercise 8.3(C) Given circles 2.50 and 3.5 in. in diameter, draw an ellipse via the approximate method. Use 60 and 80 mm for a metric problem.

Exercise 8.3(D) Draw two identical ellipses. Use the concentric-circle method for one and the four-center method for the other. Make 4.5 in. the vertical diameter and 2.75 in. the minor (horizontal in this case) diameter. If metrics are selected as the unit of measurement, use 110 and 70 mm. Compare the two methods for quality and accuracy.

Exercise 8.4(A) and (B) Draw the two figures using geometric construction techniques covered in the chapter.

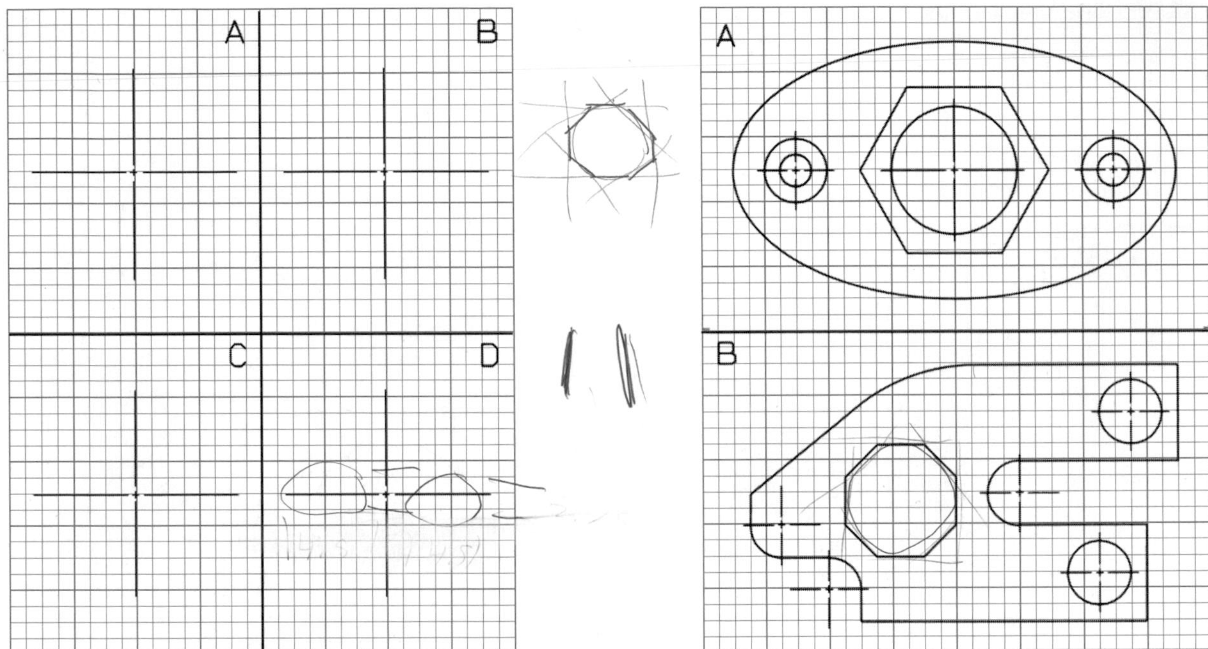

EXERCISE 8.3

EXERCISE 8.4

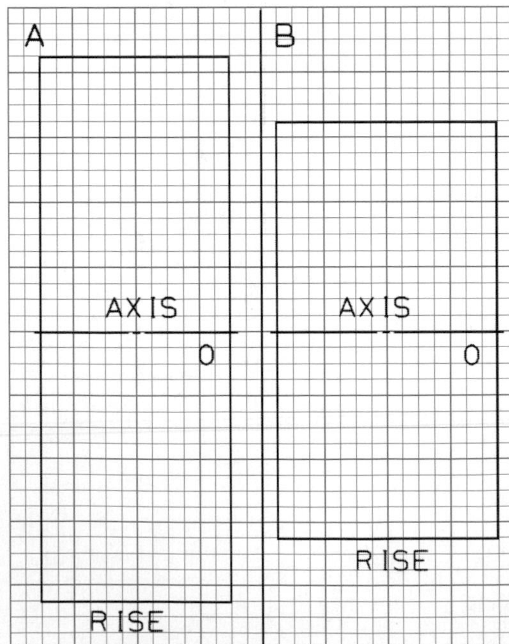

EXERCISE 8.5

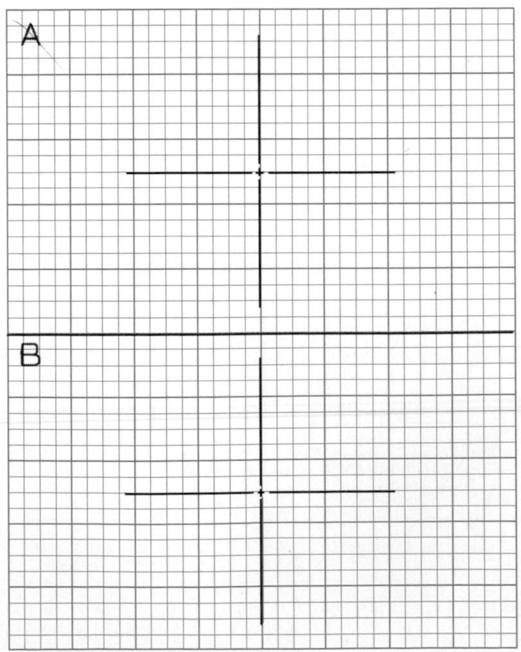

EXERCISE 8.6

After Reading the Chapter Through Section 8.7.1, You May Complete the Following Exercises

Exercise 8.5(A) and (B) Given the rectangle, the rise, and the axis, draw a parabola for each of the problems.

Exercise 8.6(A) or (B) Draw a hyperbola using a 4 in. (or 100 mm) diameter for the cone base and a height of 4 in. (or 100 mm). Pass a cutting plane vertically through the cone 1 in. (or 25 mm) to the right of the cone's vertical axis. For (B) use 5 in. (or 120 mm) as the base diameter and 4.5 in. (or 110 mm) as the cone's height. Draw the cutting plane vertically through the cone at 1.35 in. (or 35 mm) to the left of the cone's axis. Only one of these two problems can be done on the exercise page since the opposite space will be needed for construction.

Exercise 8.7(A) and (B) Construct a spiral of Archimedes. Start at the center and use a line [vertical in (A) and horizontal in (B)] as the beginning line for marking off the divisions. Draw the spiral clockwise in A and counterclockwise in B.

Exercise 8.8(A) Using the given cylinder for the diameter and the height, draw a right-handed helix with a lead of 3 in. Start the helix at the middle of the cylinder at the base where the axis line crosses the baseline

Exercise 8.8(B) Use the given cone diameter and height to construct a left-handed conical helix. Start the helix on the lower left of the base line. Use a lead of 2.5 in.

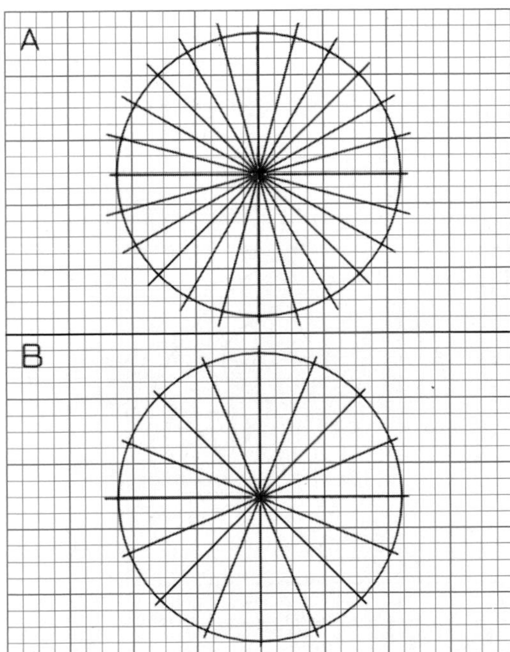

EXERCISE 8.7

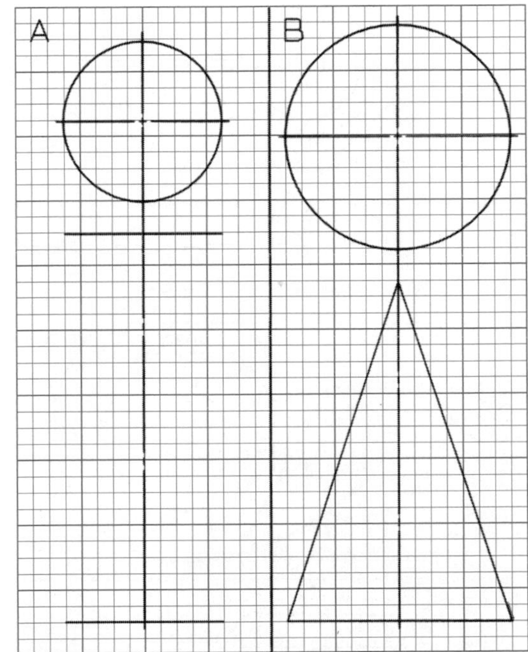

EXERCISE 8.8

PROBLEMS

Dimensions are provided for construction of each figure. They are not to be considered correct per ANSI standards. Do not dimension without the instructor's approval.

Problems 8.1 (A) through (G) Transfer the problems to an appropriate-size drawing format (one per drawing). Use one of the three scales provided. For Problem 8.1(D) the handle of the wrench is to be 1.50 in. (or 40 mm) in width throughout the ogee curve.

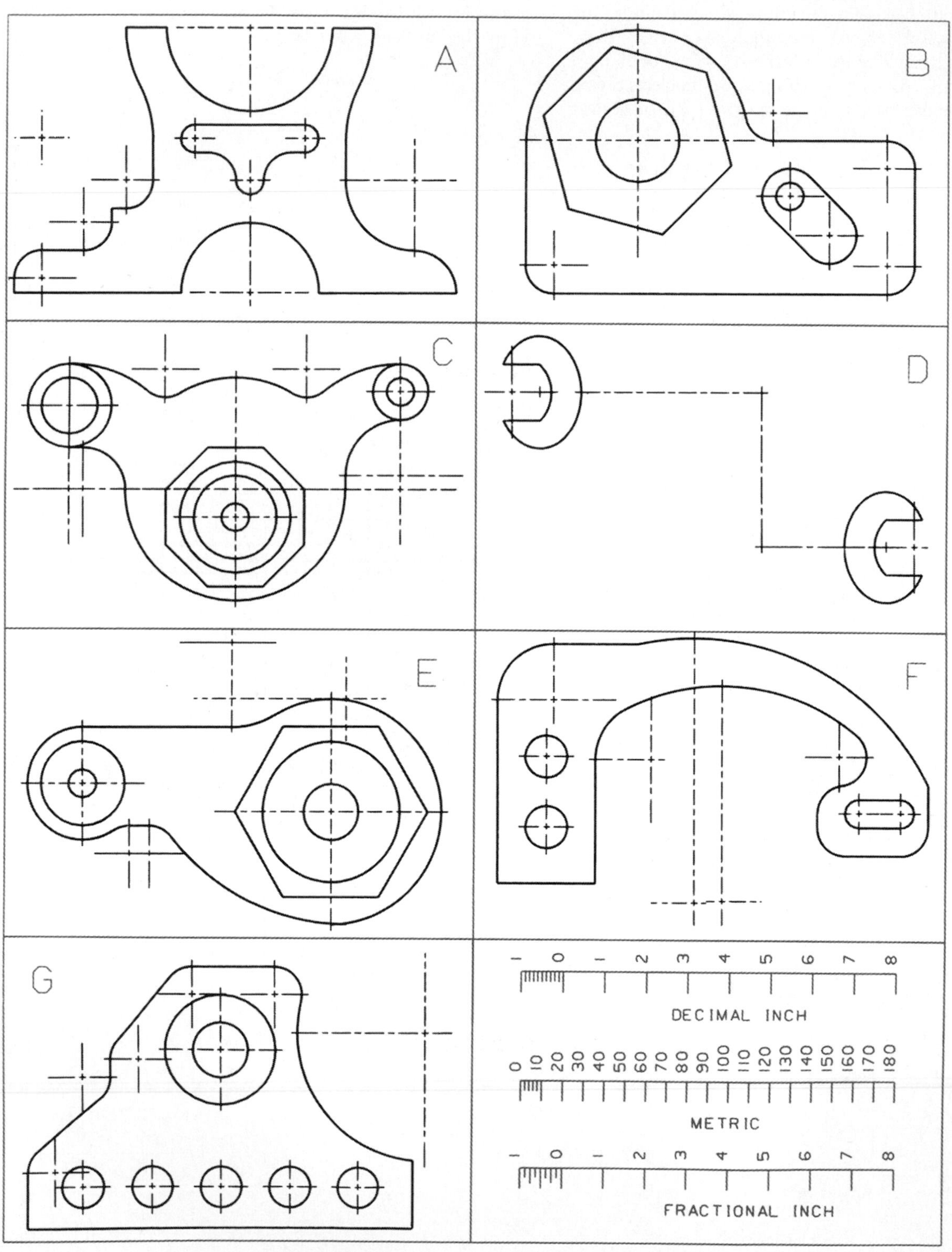

PROBLEM 8.1

Problems 8.2 through 8.13 Draw each of the assigned problems on separate sheets. For Problem 8.6 the 7.500 and the 8.00 radius arcs can be located by extending the centerline of the slot vertically.

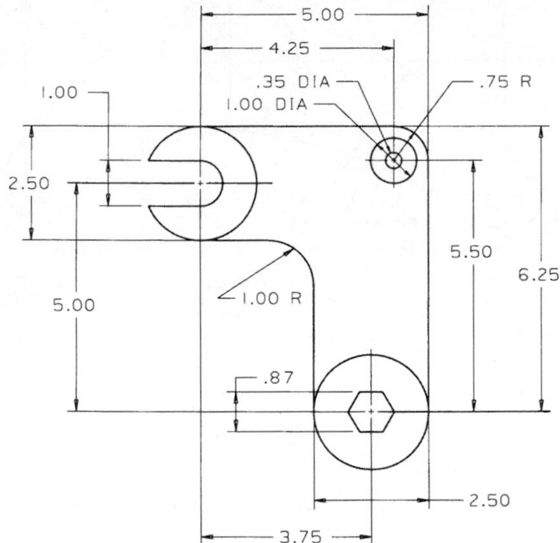

PROBLEM 8.2

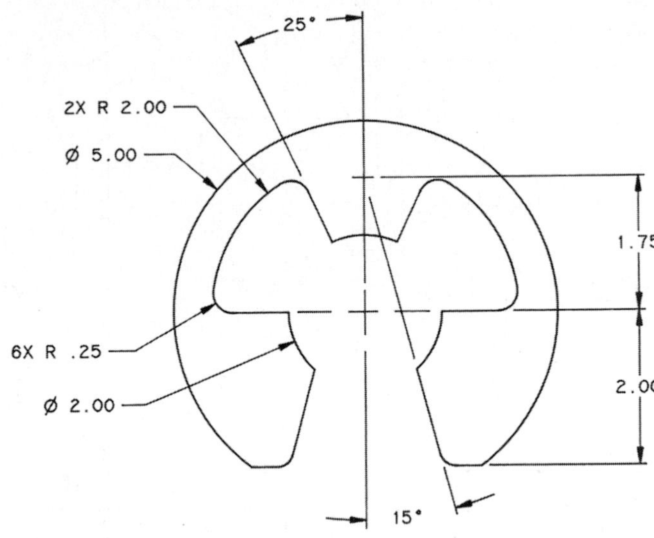

PROBLEM 8.4

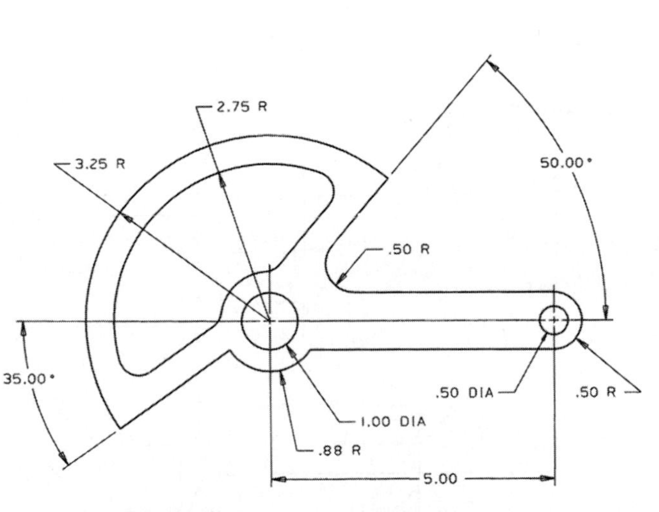

PROBLEM 8.3

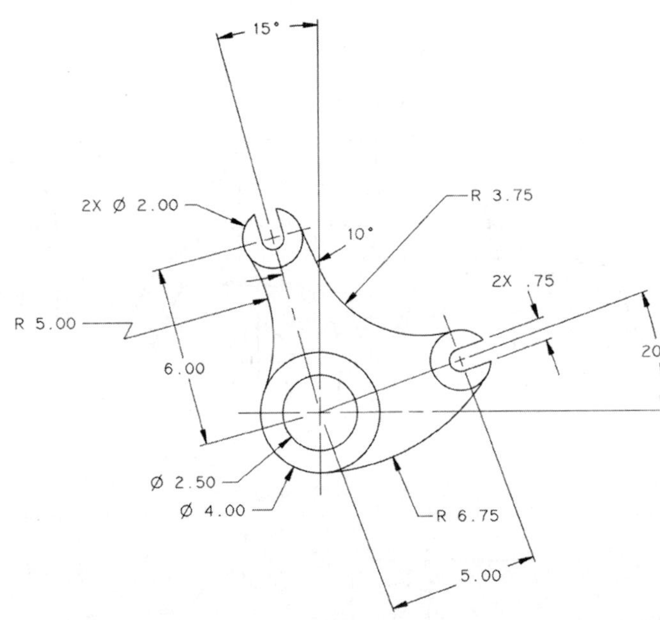

PROBLEM 8.5

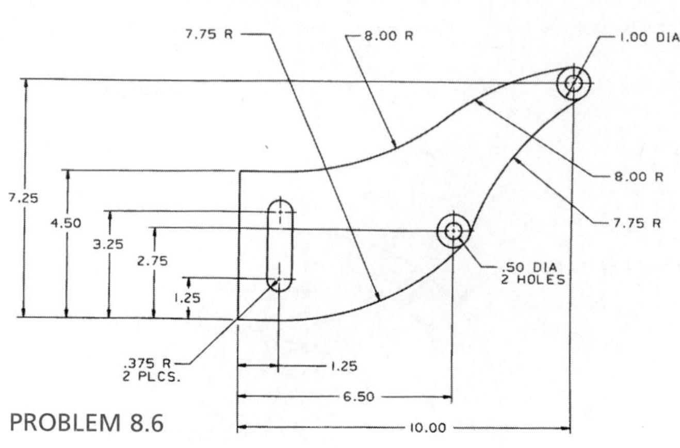

PROBLEM 8.6

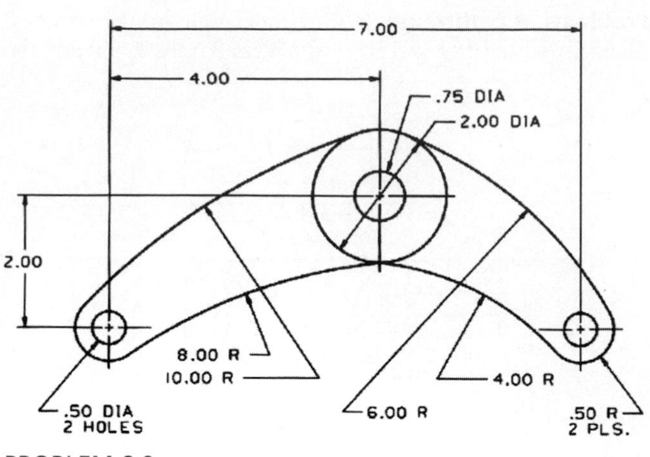

PROBLEM 8.9

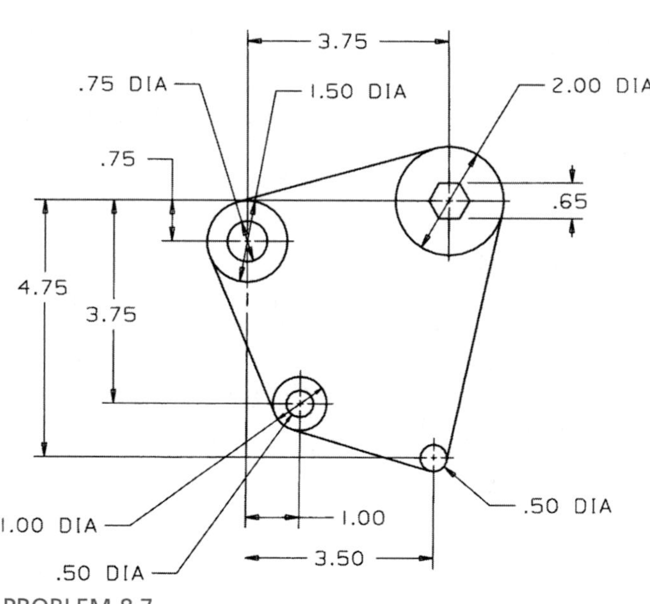

PROBLEM 8.7

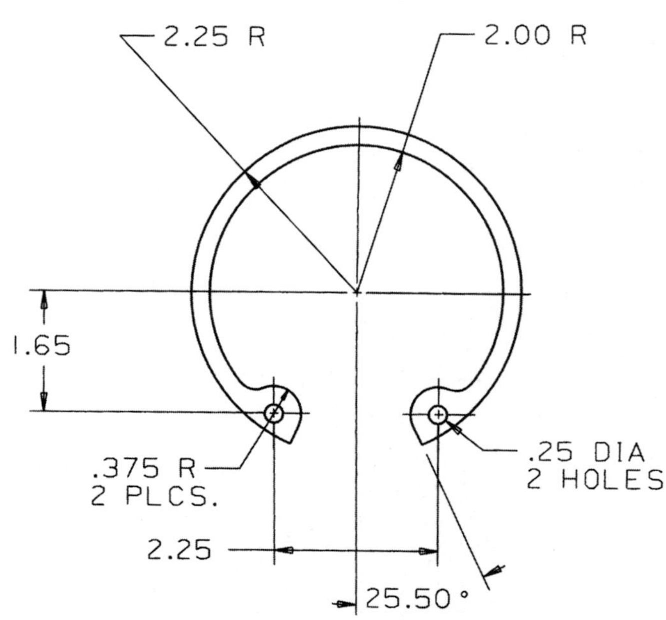

PROBLEM 8.10

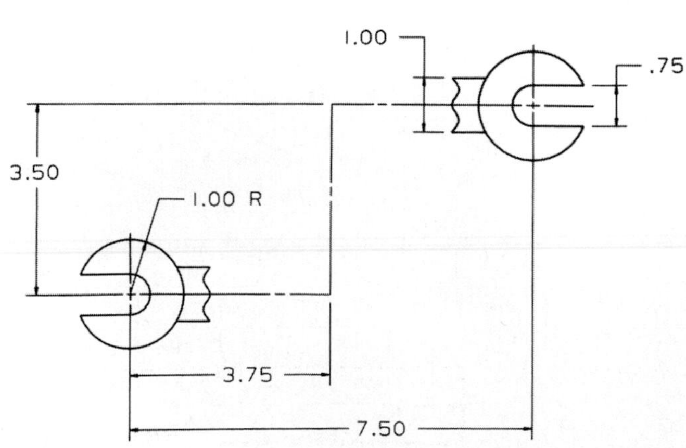

PROBLEM 8.8

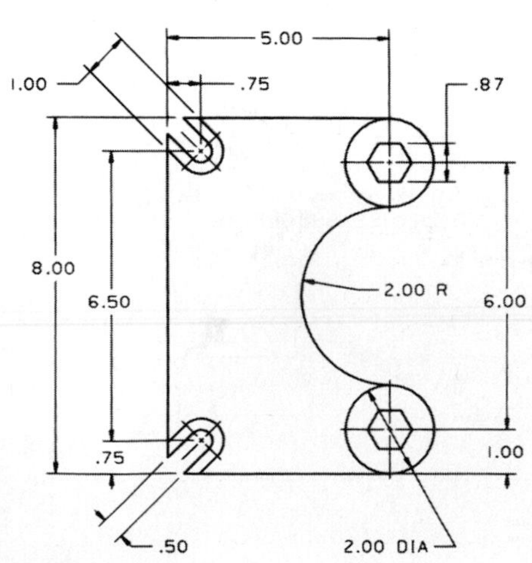

PROBLEM 8.11

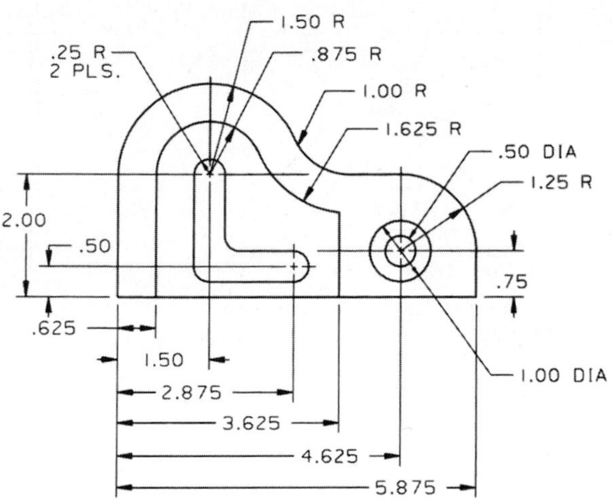

PROBLEM 8.12

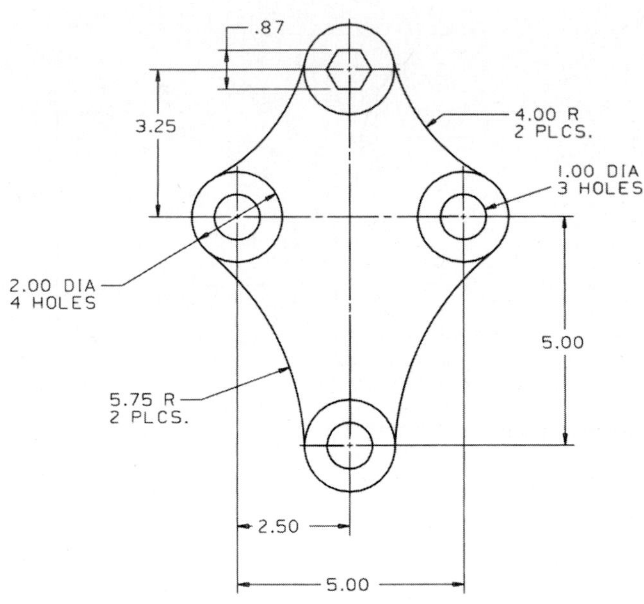

PROBLEM 8.13

Problems 8.14 through 8.24 Draw each of the projects on appropriate-size drawing format. These problems use metric measurements. Draw only the front view for Problems 8.23 and 8.24.

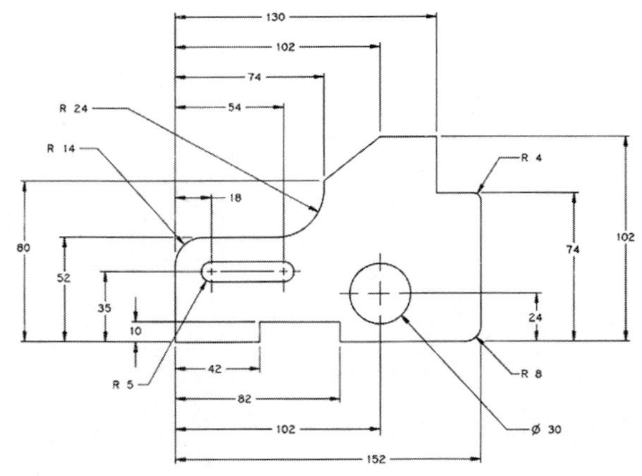

PROBLEM 8.14

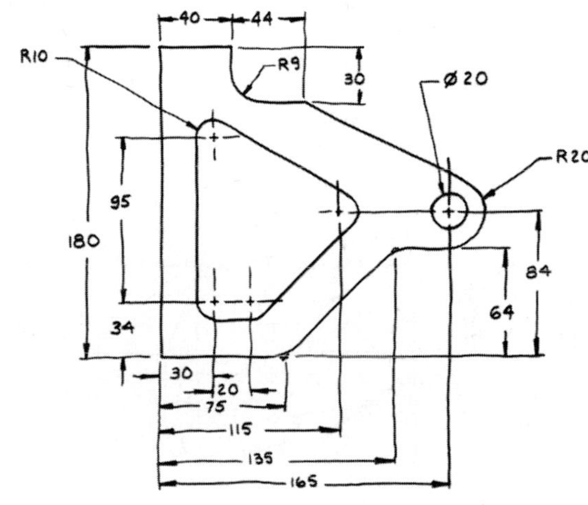

PROBLEM 8.16

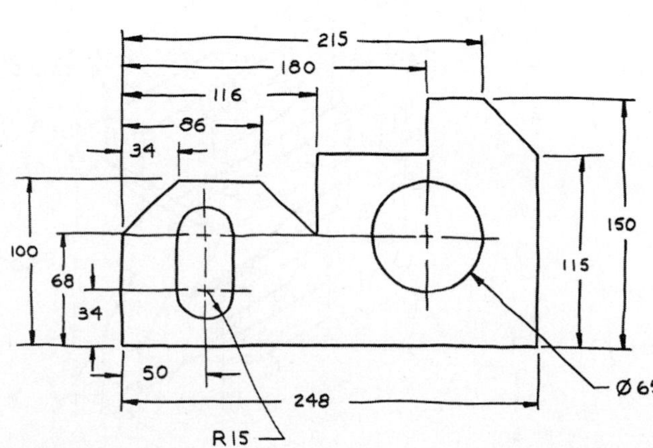

PROBLEM 8.15

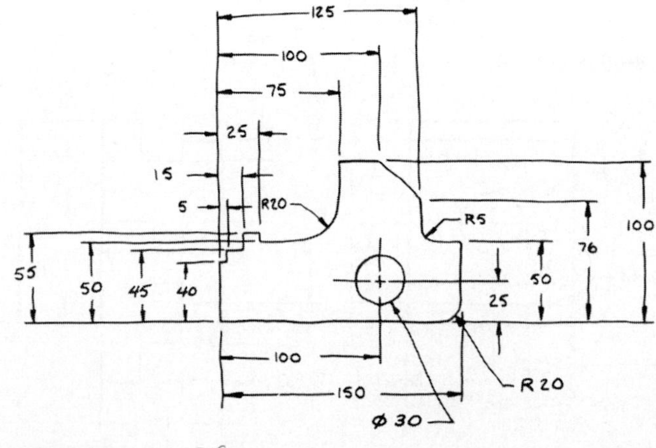

PROBLEM 8.17

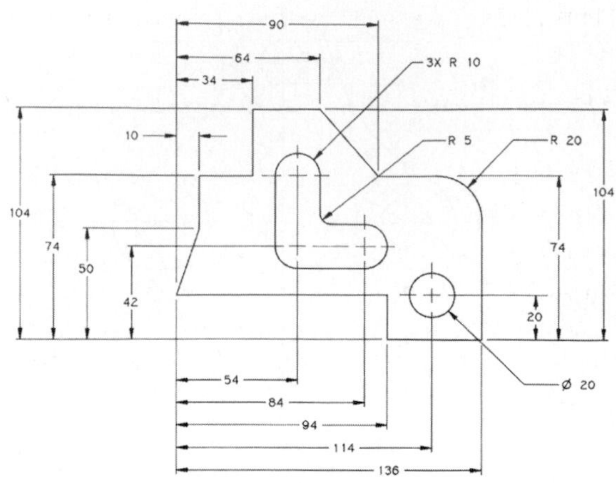

PROBLEM 8.18

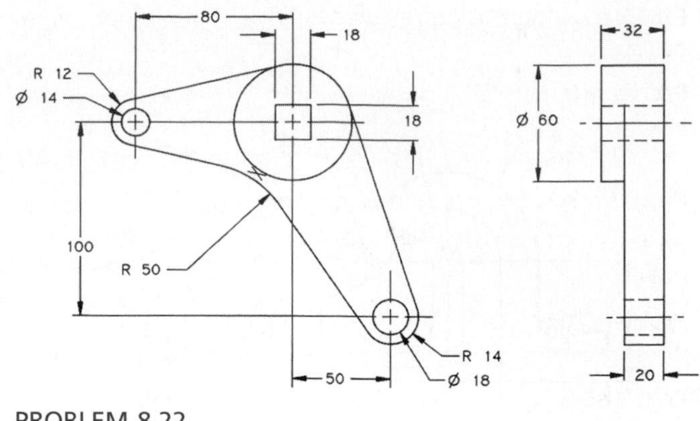

PROBLEM 8.22

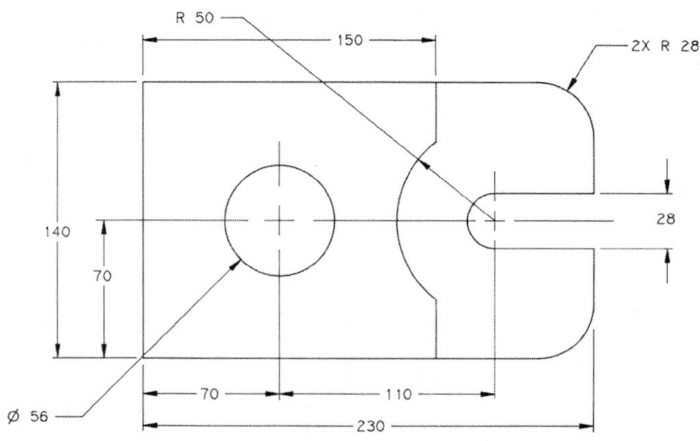

PROBLEM 8.19

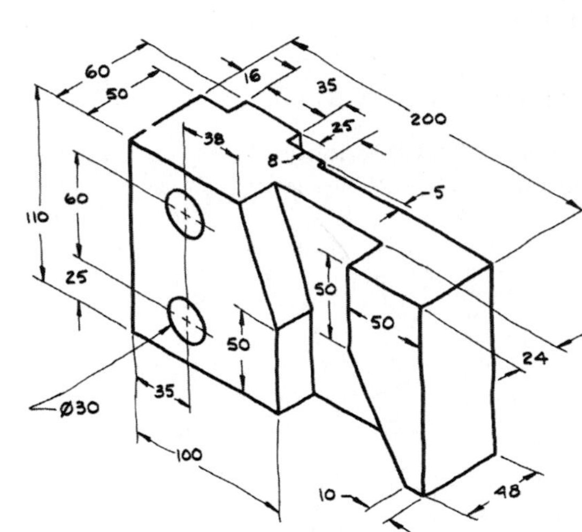

PROBLEM 8.23

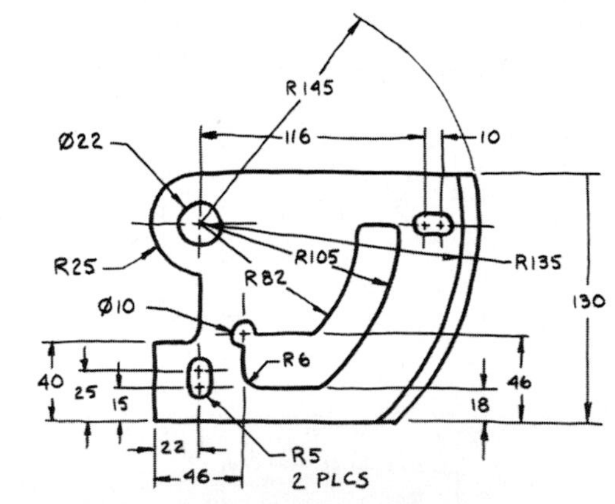

PROBLEM 8.20

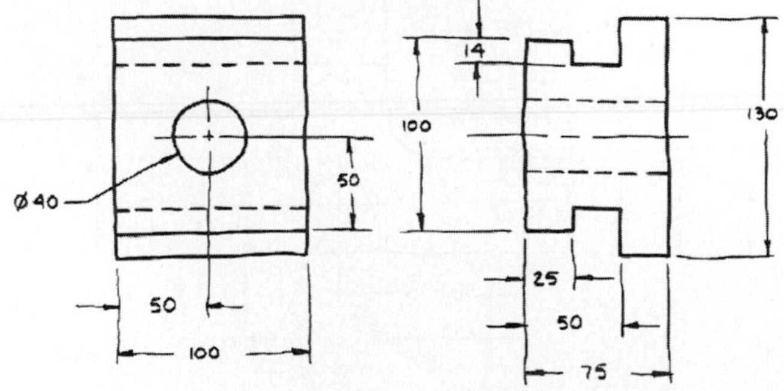

PROBLEM 8.21

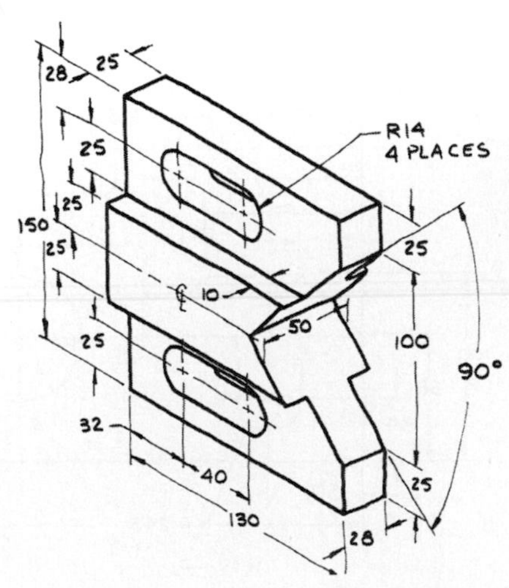

PROBLEM 8.24

Problem 8.25 Divide a 5 in. (120 mm) line into five equal parts.

Problem 8.26 Construct bisectors of the angles of a triangle having a ratio of 3:5:6 units for the sides. Use centimeters or inches as the units.

Problem 8.27 Bisect a 55° angle.

Problem 8.28 Draw a triangle having sides with the proportions 3:4:5.

Problem 8.29 Draw a hexagon that is 3 in. (or 70 mm) across the flats.

Problem 8.30 Draw a hexagon that is 75 mm across the corners.

Problem 8.31 Construct a seven-sided regular polygon in a 5 in. (120 mm) diameter circle.

Problem 8.32 Find the center of a 4 in. (or 100 mm) circle.

Problem 8.33 Connect two lines forming a 35° angle with a radius arc of 1.00 in. (or 25 mm).

Problem 8.34 Connect two perpendicular lines with a radius arc of 1.00 in. (or 30 mm).

Problem 8.35 Draw an ellipse having a major axis of 70 mm and a minor axis of 50 mm.

Problem 8.36 Construct the inscribed circle of a 2 × 3.5 × 4 unit triangle.

Problem 8.37 Draw a circumscribed-circle triangle. Use centimeters as units.

Problem 8.38 Find the center of a 4 in. (or 100 mm) circle by perpendicular bisectors. Rectify the circle.

Problem 8.39 Draw a cylindrical helix having an 80 mm diameter base, a height of 140 mm, and a lead of 50 mm. Draw it as a right-handed helix.

Problem 8.40 Draw a left-handed conical helix with a base diameter of 3 in. (or 70 mm), a height of 4.5 in. (or 110 mm), and a lead of 2.5 in. (or 60 mm).

Problem 8.41 Draw a spiral of Archimedes using a 5 in. (or 120 mm) diameter with angles of 30° and .125 in. (or 10 mm) divisions.

SKETCHING

Chapter 9

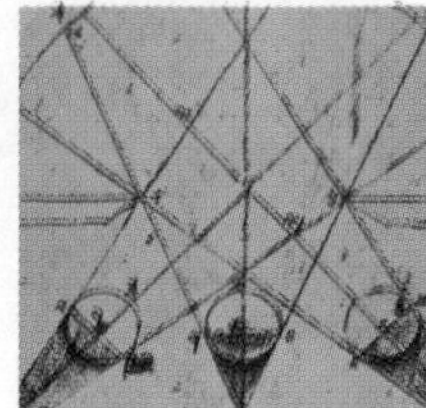

LEARNING OBJECTIVES

Upon completion of this chapter you will be able to:

1. Understand how sketches are used to transform design concepts into visual communication.
2. Recognize the importance of proper proportioning and thorough dimensioning.
3. Develop skills and techniques required to sketch engineering designs efficiently.
4. Demonstrate an understanding of multiview projection and selection of views.
5. Produce isometric, oblique, and multiview engineering sketches.

9.1 INTRODUCTION

Because sketching is one of the primary ways to communicate graphic ideas in the engineering community, the ability to sketch is essential and useful for all designers and engineers. A **sketch** is often employed to convey original design ideas. For example, it is not unusual to see members of a design team making freehand sketches to clarify the design of three-dimensional parts or to explore alternative configurations for an assembly. Figure 9.1 shows a manufacturing sketch depicting the process stages involved in machining and welding a neck cylinder. The design sketch of an assembly normally shows the general configuration of the part or assembly along with callouts, notes, and basic overall and setup dimensions.

Engineers and designers sketch preliminary ideas. Drafters or layout designers then refine those original ideas and requirements and produce drawings. There are three primary types of sketches: pictorial, multiview, and diagrammatic.

Sketching is usually done at any location that has a flat surface. The materials and tools used most often for sketching are paper (preferably grid paper), soft lead pencils, and an eraser. The grid on grid paper speeds the construction of any sketch. Sometimes it is necessary to evolve a layout through a series of sketches. Figure 9.2 shows the evolution of such a layout through the following stages: preliminary (rough) sketch (a), refined sketch (b), and the final CAD drawing (c).

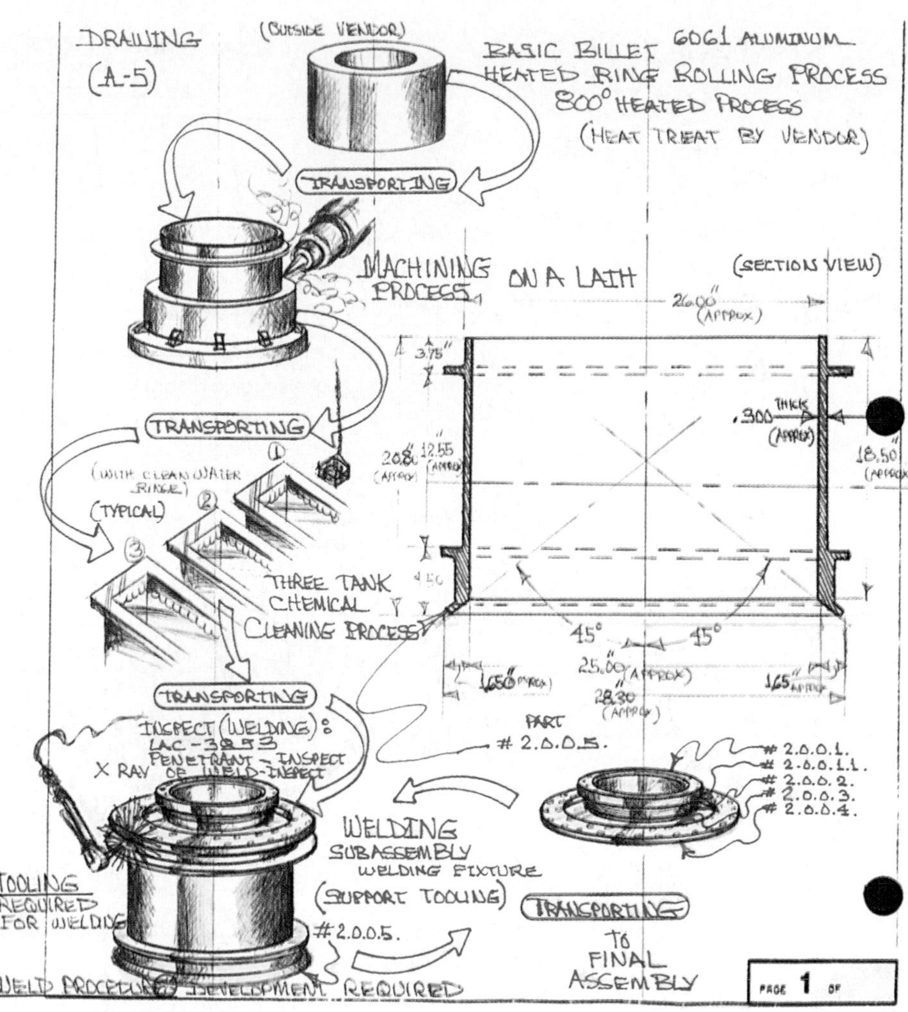

FIGURE 9.1 Sketch of Manufacturing Sequence

9.2 MATERIALS AND EQUIPMENT USED IN SKETCHING

Only a few basic items and materials are required for sketching. Any sketch pad should be grid lined or have a crosshatched underlay grid sheet that can be placed beneath the transparent sketch paper. Nonreproducing grid sheets are also available. Isometric grid-lined paper is available for pictorial sketching. Posterboard grid formats include isometric, oblique, orthographic, and a variety of perspective formats. Figure 9.3 illustrates a simple part sketched on isometric grid paper. This grid paper has, in addition to the 30° receding lines in both directions, vertical and horizontal lines for multiview projection. Grid squares are very useful in maintaining the proper proportion for a part because it is easy to count grid squares while sketching.

9.2.1 Drawing Size When Sketching

While the size of a particular sketch is usually unimportant, conveying the proper proportions of the part in a sketch is essential. Using grid paper helps to ensure that the sketch is in the proper proportion. Sketches are seldom drawn full size. However, sketches, like all other drawings, must be dimensioned. *Drawings of every type should not be measured, but "read."* **"Reading"** a drawing means you should be able to find every dimension for every feature of the part and use that information in later stages of the project. The one exception to the dimensioning rule is when the drawing is a diagram (e.g., as in Fig. 9.2). Diagrams tell a story and do not represent parts or objects. Two-dimensional diagrams can be measured and digitized when using a CAD system.

9.2.2 Line Types Used in Sketching

The line types and widths used in freehand sketches are the same as those used in instrument drawing (ANSI-standard line weights, types, and symbols). The line quality in a sketch

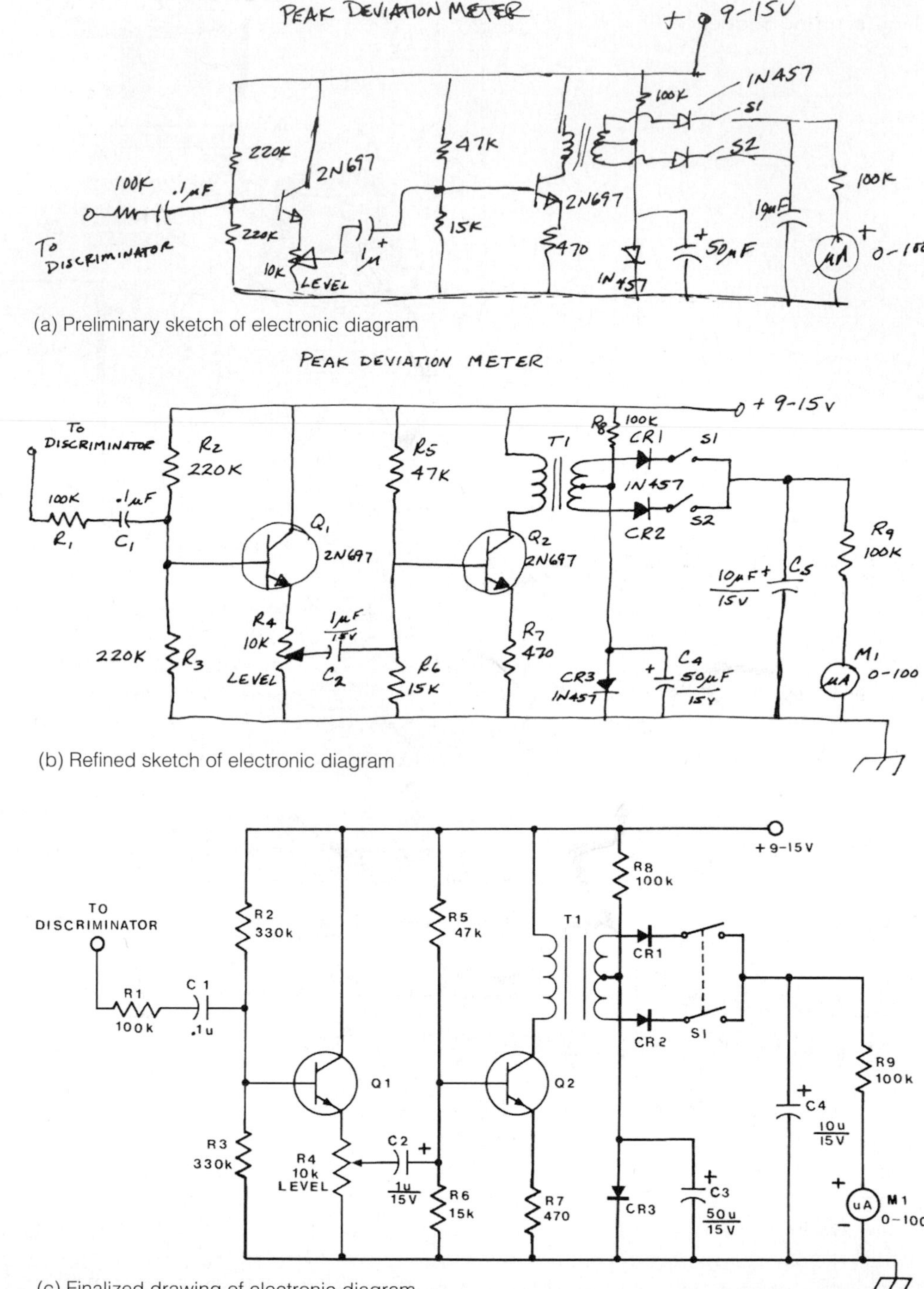

(a) Preliminary sketch of electronic diagram

(b) Refined sketch of electronic diagram

FIGURE 9.2 Sketching Steps (c) Finalized drawing of electronic diagram

is not perfect. Figure 9.4 shows the typical range of line types that may be encountered in sketches. Cutting-plane lines are the widest; object and hidden lines are medium thickness; extension, dimension, centerline, phantom, and section lines are thin lines. Lines should be equally black, as in instrument drawing. Construction lines are usually not removed. Lettering must be clear and easy to read.

Sketching skills are developed over a period of time through practice and effort, and should be cultivated throughout your career. Speed in sketching is not important while you are learning the basic techniques. However, later on, sketching with ease and speed will enhance your ability to communicate graphic ideas efficiently.

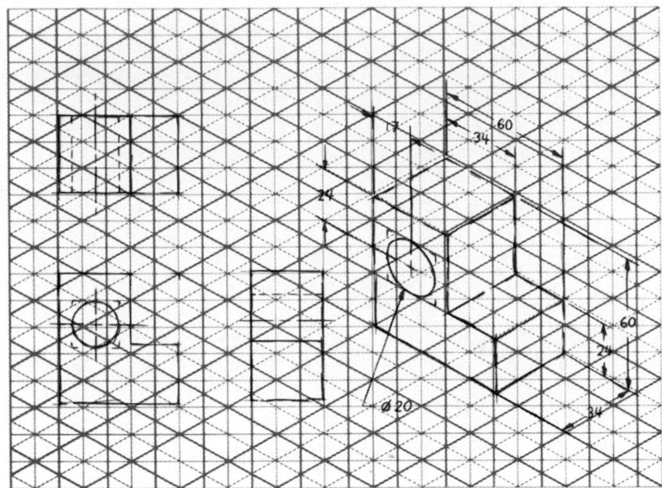

FIGURE 9.3 Grid Paper and Sketching

9.3 SKETCHING TECHNIQUES

When sketching, *hold your pencil at an angle to the paper.* As shown in Figure 9.5, 50° to 60° is recommended for straight lines, and 30° to 45° for circles and arcs. *Rotate your pencil while sketching,* to help maintain a conical point and reduce the time required for sharpening. You may prefer to sketch with fine-line mechanical pencils (0.7 to 0.9 mm, with H or HB lead).

Hold the pencil 1.5 to 2 in. (30 to 50 mm) from the tip, as shown in Figure 9.6. Some drafters prefer to hold the pencil in flat position, as demonstrated in Figure 9.7. Remember, it is not the intent of this text to change the way you hold your pencil. The information in this section is provided to help develop sketching skills. Left-handers may hold their pencils at different angles and orientations.

9.3.1 Sketching Horizontal Lines and Vertical Lines

Horizontal lines are drawn by locating the endpoints and connecting them with a line. Draw lines using construction lines first and, later, after the design is close to completion, go back and darken them. The pencil is moved from left to right (Fig. 9.8). Use short strokes, but try to avoid "feathering" the lines. Pull a wood pencil or lead holder to avoid ripping the paper surface. The lead in fine-line mechanical pencils breaks easily, so you should push them. Some designers leave a small space (gap) between each line segment (the space is unnecessary with grid paper).

Vertical lines are drawn with the same general technique. For vertical lines, move the pencil from the top toward the

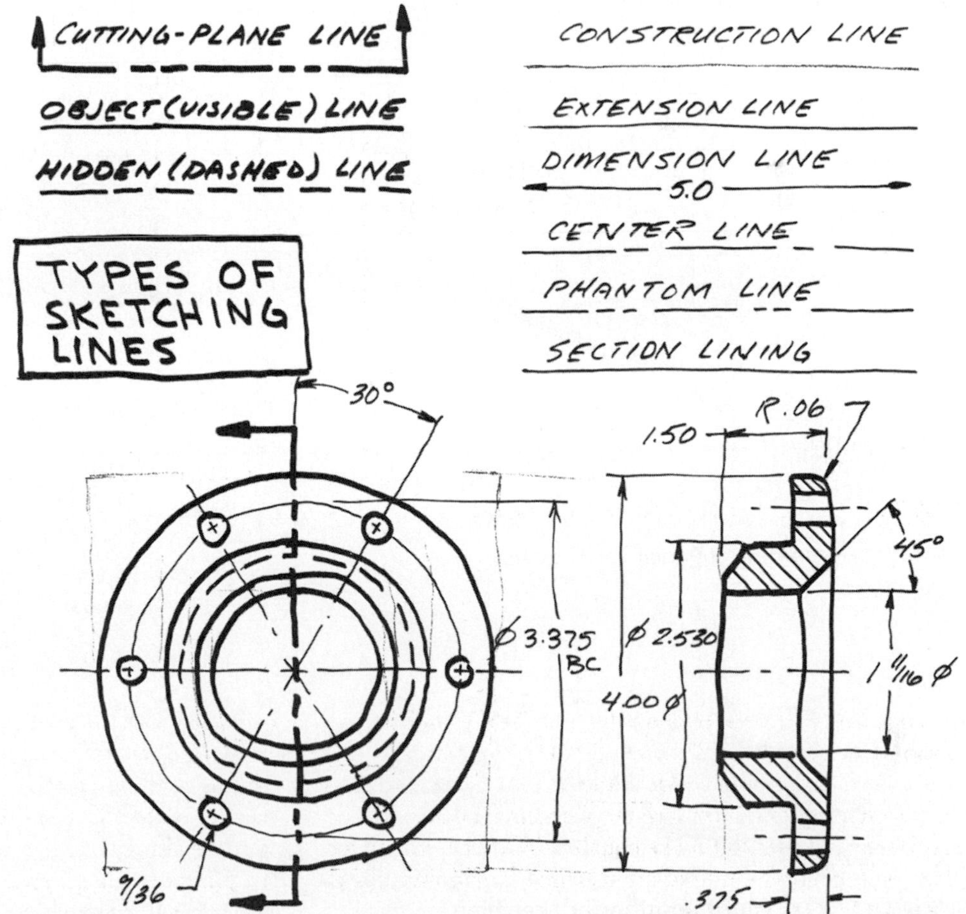

FIGURE 9.4 Line Types for Sketches

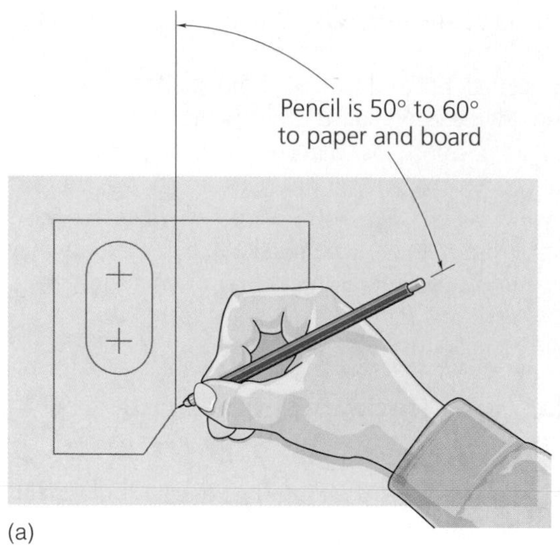
Pencil is 50° to 60°
to paper and board

(a)

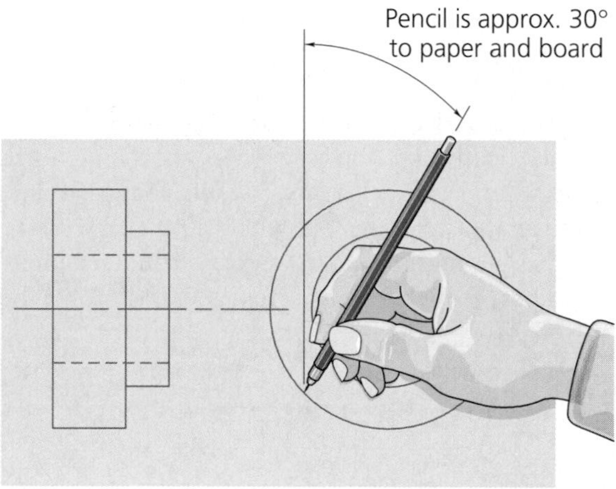
Pencil is approx. 30°
to paper and board

(b)

FIGURE 9.5 Angle of Pencil When Sketching

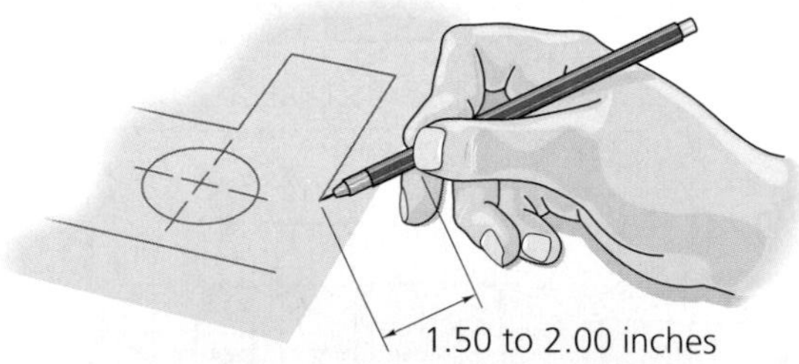
1.50 to 2.00 inches

FIGURE 9.6 Holding a Pencil for Sketching

FIGURE 9.7 Flat Pencil Position for Sketching

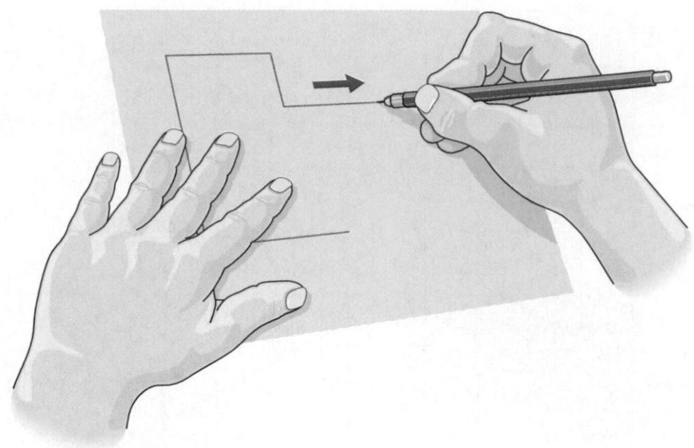

FIGURE 9.8 Sketching Horizontal Lines

bottom of the paper (Fig. 9.9). Again, grid paper helps ensure that the drawn lines will be vertical. Turn the paper to any convenient position to help speed the process. Some designers prefer to move the pencil away from the body from bottom to top or left to right. Try different methods to find the one that works best for you.

9.3.2 Sketching Inclined Lines

Angled lines are drawn by establishing the endpoints, lightly sketching the line, and finally darkening the line. Sketch inclined lines away from you if they are angled to the right (Fig. 9.10) or toward you (or turn the paper) if they are

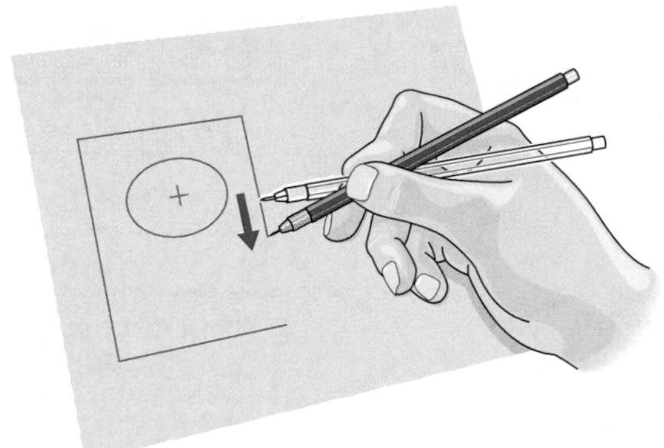

FIGURE 9.9 Sketching Vertical Lines

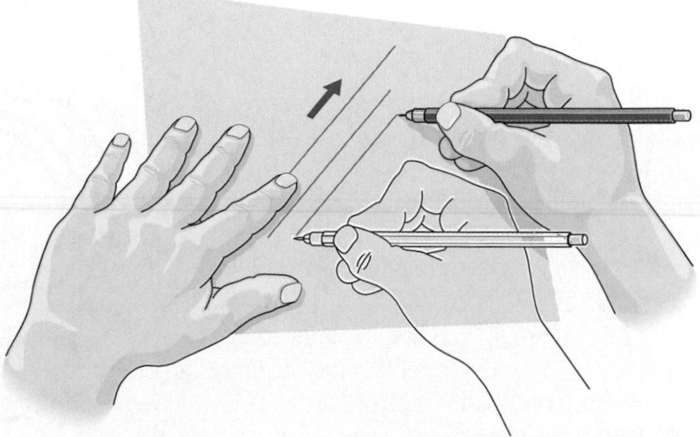

FIGURE 9.10 Sketching Inclined Lines

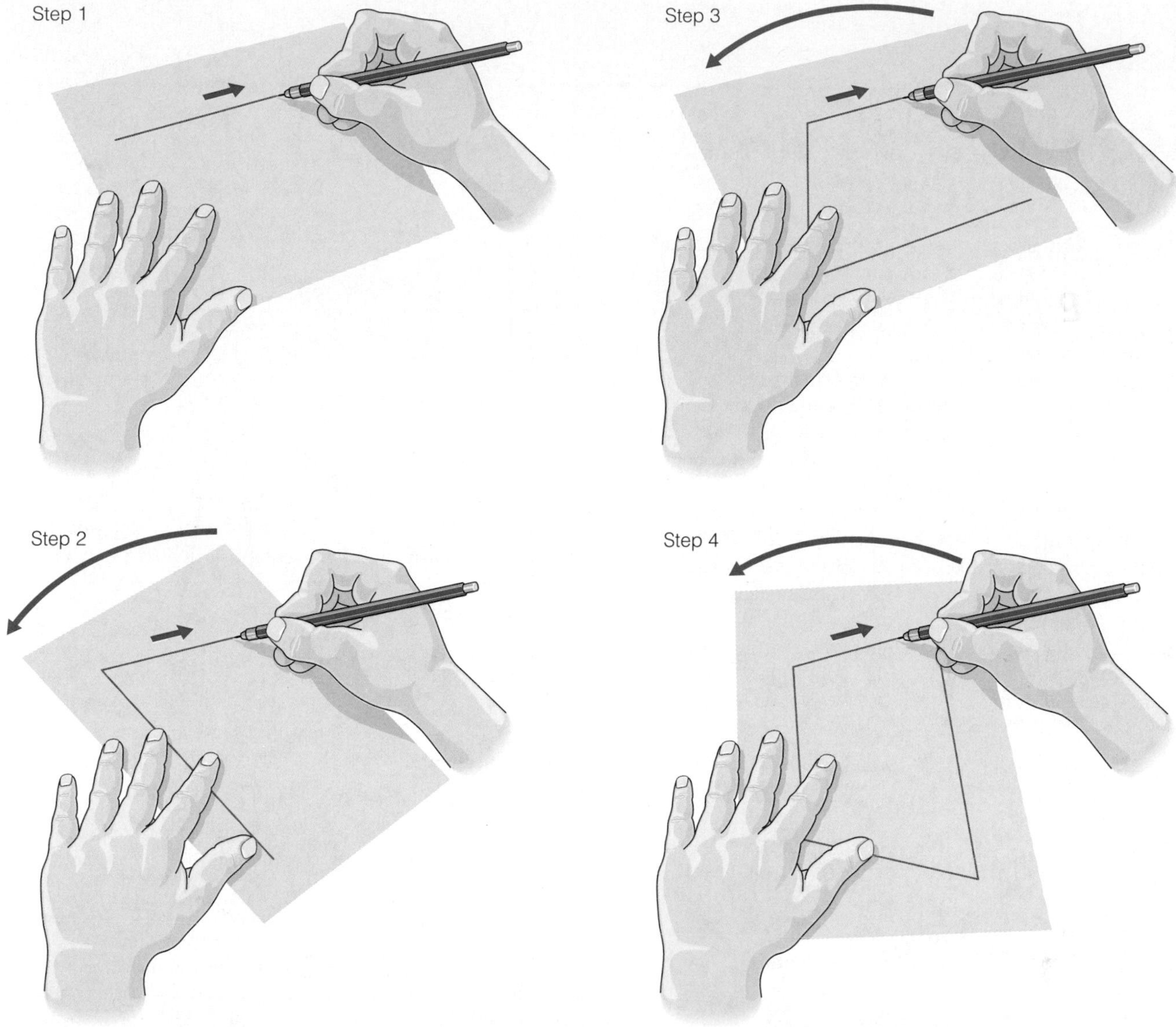

Step 1

Step 3

Step 2

Step 4

FIGURE 9.11 **Sketching by Turning Paper Counterclockwise**

angled to the left. Use the opposite technique if you are left-handed.

Since horizontal lines are the easiest to draw, turn the paper so the line you are sketching is close to horizontal (Fig. 9.11). However, large sketches are often taped to the table, so you should also learn to sketch without turning the paper. If your sketch is small or it is attached to a sketch pad or clipboard, you can turn the sketch at any convenient angle, as shown in Figure 9.12.

Angles can be estimated by drawing two lines perpendicular (90°) to one another. Bisecting this angle gives a 45° measurement. Similarly, dividing the 45° angle into three divisions provides a 15° angle and a 30° angle (Fig. 9.13). Always locate the endpoints of a line by dimensions.

FIGURE 9.12 **Turning Paper May Make Sketching Easier**

Focus On . . .

LEONARDO DA VINCI, "THE SKETCHER"

Sketches, illustrations, and technical drawings visually represent the designer's ideas so they may be understood by others. The thought required to sketch an idea and the discussion of ideas with others are good ways to refine proposed solutions to engineering problems.

Prehistoric people recorded their experiences by drawing on cave walls. These cave drawings showed hunting scenes and included people, animals, and tools such as spears and arrows. Who knows, they may have even believed these drawings had the power to make events come true.

A freehand sketch has always been a fast and easy way to put on paper ideas formulated in the mind. Leonardo da Vinci sketched hundreds of plans for his inventions. Today, manufactured parts often begin with a freehand sketch.

You probably think of Leonardo da Vinci as one of the greatest painters of the Italian Renaissance. It is true that he was trained to be a painter and he did produce some of the world's greatest paintings, including the *Mona Lisa.* He also designed machines that were far ahead of his time, such as a flying machine and a parachute. He became one of the most versatile geniuses in history because of his achievements, including scientific inventions.

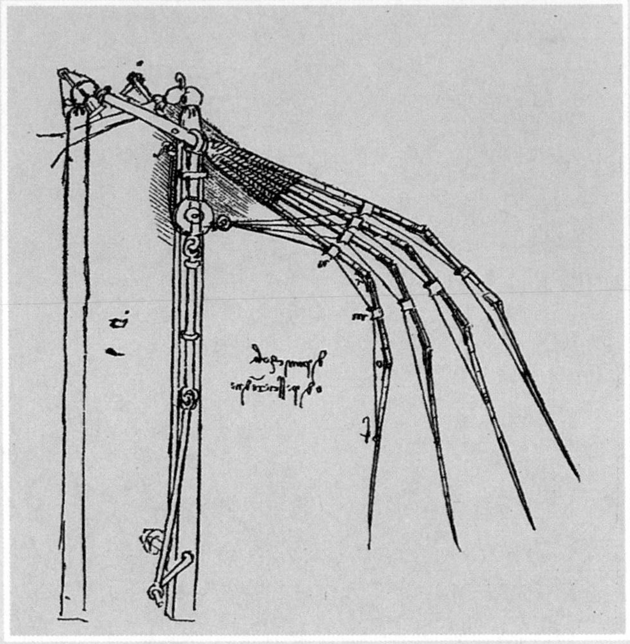

A mechanical sketch of a flying mechanism by Leonardo da Vinci.

In approximately 1482, Leonardo went to Milan to be the court artist to the Duke of Milan. One of his duties was as a military engineer. He designed artillery and the diversion of rivers. He also designed sets for court pageants. When he was forced to leave that post because of the French invasion, he returned to Florence to serve as a military engineer to that court. During this time, he traveled throughout central Italy preparing sketches for maps that would become important to the history of cartography. Although he never did construct a building, he was held in the highest esteem as an architect. He drew plans ranging from the dome of the Milan cathedral to an enormous bridge over the Bosporus.

During his later years, Leonardo did little painting; instead he produced many sketches of experimental machines and other inventions. These rank among his greatest masterpieces because of their sense of motion and his use of shade and shadows.

Leonardo recorded his ideas in several notebooks, many of which include sketches and drawings that reveal his skill as a drafter and designer. About 4200 pages of his notebooks still exist. However, should you decide to read them, be sure to bring a mirror. Leonardo wrote his notes backwards!

If all engineers, designers, and drafters recorded their ideas in a similar diligent and elegant fashion, we too might be well known for our graphic communications skills. Leonardo showed us all the value of a sketch or two. His, of course, were also masterpieces.

Leonardo's backward notes.

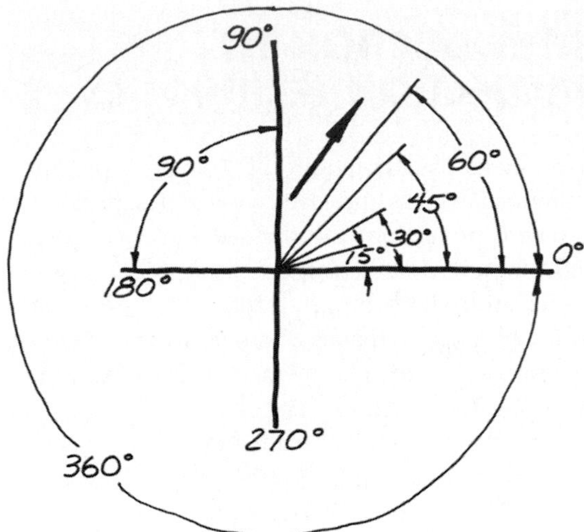

FIGURE 9.13 Typical Angles Used in Sketching

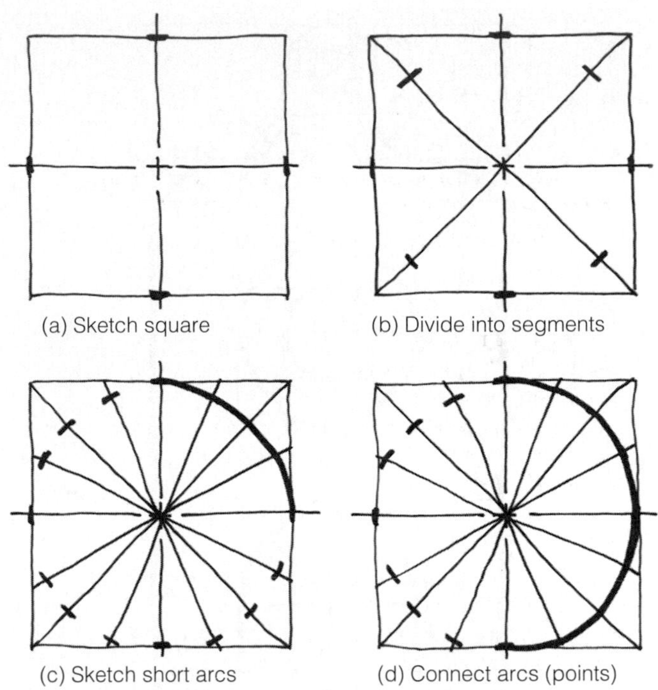

FIGURE 9.14 Sketching a Circle

9.3.3 Sketching Arcs and Circles

Learning to sketch arcs and circles can be frustrating. Always start by locating the center point of the circle or arc, then draw the centerlines of the circle. Measure or estimate the size of the circle, and lay out the diameter along the centerlines, as shown in Figure 9.14. Block out the circle by drawing a square that encompasses it [Fig. 9.14(a)]. Next, draw diagonals and lay out the diameter on the diagonals [Fig. 9.14(b)]. If the circle is large, divide the circle into smaller segments and measure the diameter [Fig. 9.14(c)]. Connect the points by sketching short arcs to complete the circle [Fig. 9.14(d)]. If the sketch is small, rotating the paper helps keep the circle round (Fig. 9.15).

Use the same general technique to sketch arcs. In Figure 9.16, several arcs and circles were required. Centerlines were used for every arc and circle, and all circles and arcs were blocked before they were drawn.

Freehand sketching of irregular curves involves establishing an adequate number of points along the curve and then connecting the points with a smooth curve. A lightly sketched construction curve is drawn first; then the irregular curve is darkened. Grid paper makes it easier to establish the control line points (Fig. 9.17).

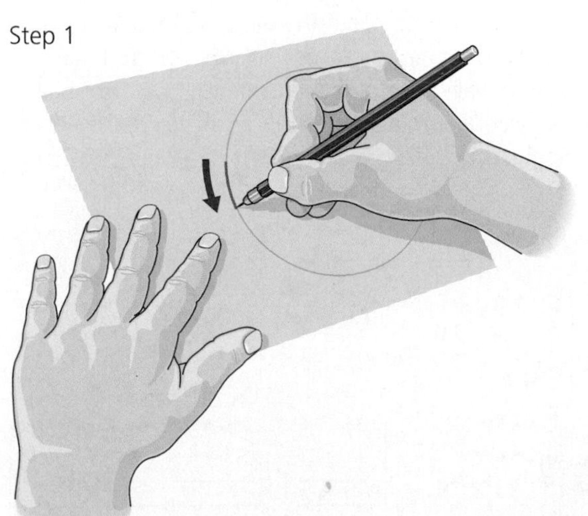

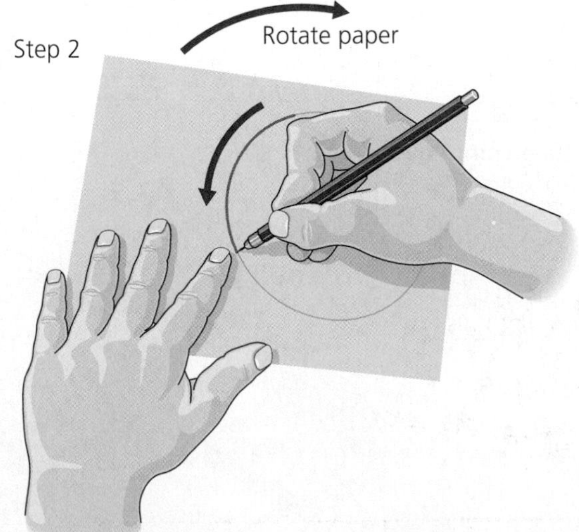

FIGURE 9.15 Sketching Circles by Rotating the Paper

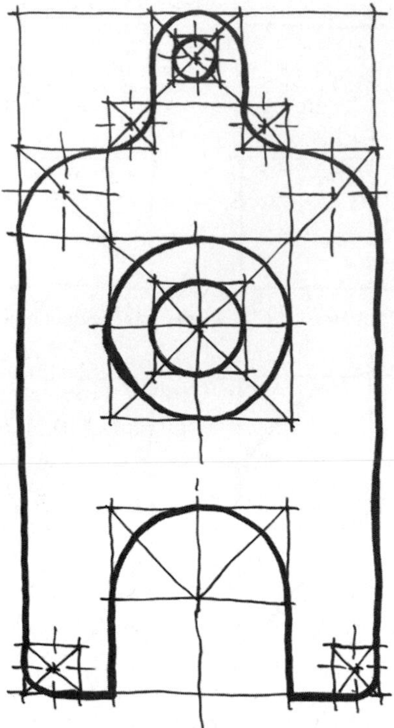

FIGURE 9.16 Blocking Out Circular Shapes When Sketching

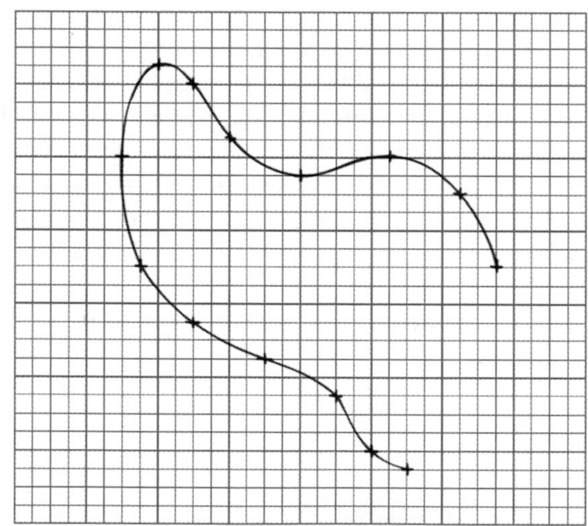

FIGURE 9.17 Sketching Irregular Curves

9.4 INTRODUCTION TO PROJECTION TECHNIQUES

Technical operations usually require 2D (paper) representations to communicate ideas and give physical descriptions of 3D shapes. These projections are divided into two categories, *pictorial* and *multiview*. **Pictorials** simulate 3D views of the part, while **multiviews** are 2D projections of the part. This simple division separates single-view drawings (pictorials—oblique, isometric, and perspective) from multiview drawings.

Chapter 10 covers multiview drawing in great depth. Chapter 13 provides in-depth coverage of all types of pictorial projection methods. This chapter introduces the types of projection associated with freehand sketching and how a sketch is used in industry.

Often, engineering working drawings are multiviews, while pictorials are used for technical illustrations. In sketching, however, both types may help refine design concepts. Figure 9.18 shows each of the four projection types for an angle block. Pictorial projections are single-view drawings that may serve as rough sketches of preliminary ideas, but they do not always lend themselves to communicating exact technical details. *Perspective* projections are constructed with projecting lines that converge at a point. Although this method provides the most lifelike appearance of the part, it does not show true dimensions. *Oblique* pictorials distort the depth of the part. The *isometric* method, which uses full-scale dimensions for all lines that are vertical or parallel to the axes, is the most common and useful method for engineering sketching.

Multiview drawings are not lifelike, because they show the parts in more than one view and are projections. Multiview projection presents the object's top, front, and sides in related adjacent views. The theory behind orthographic projection is that the object is rotated by turning it to the appropriate view. For example, rotating it 90° sideways provides a side view. In Figure 9.19, the part was rotated to the right, so the resulting view is a right side view. The three-view drawing (bottom) shows the part aligned between views. The three principal views (top, front, and side) can be used to project any number of needed views to provide engineering data. An *auxiliary* view is any projection

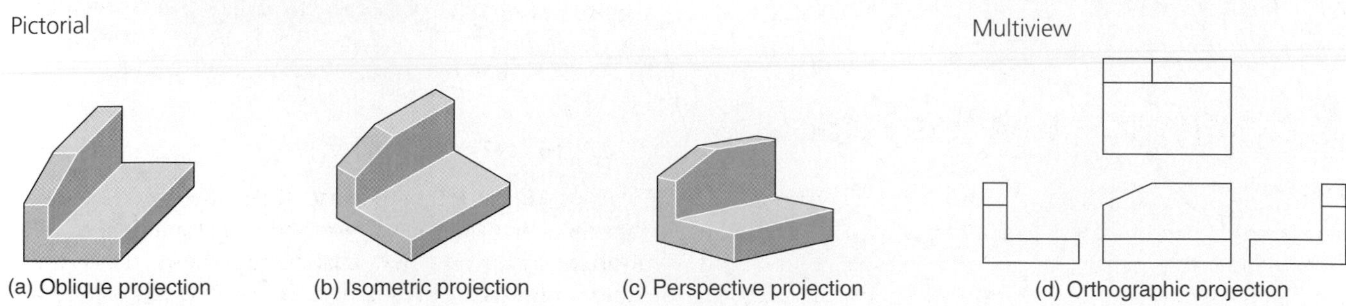

FIGURE 9.18 Projection Methods

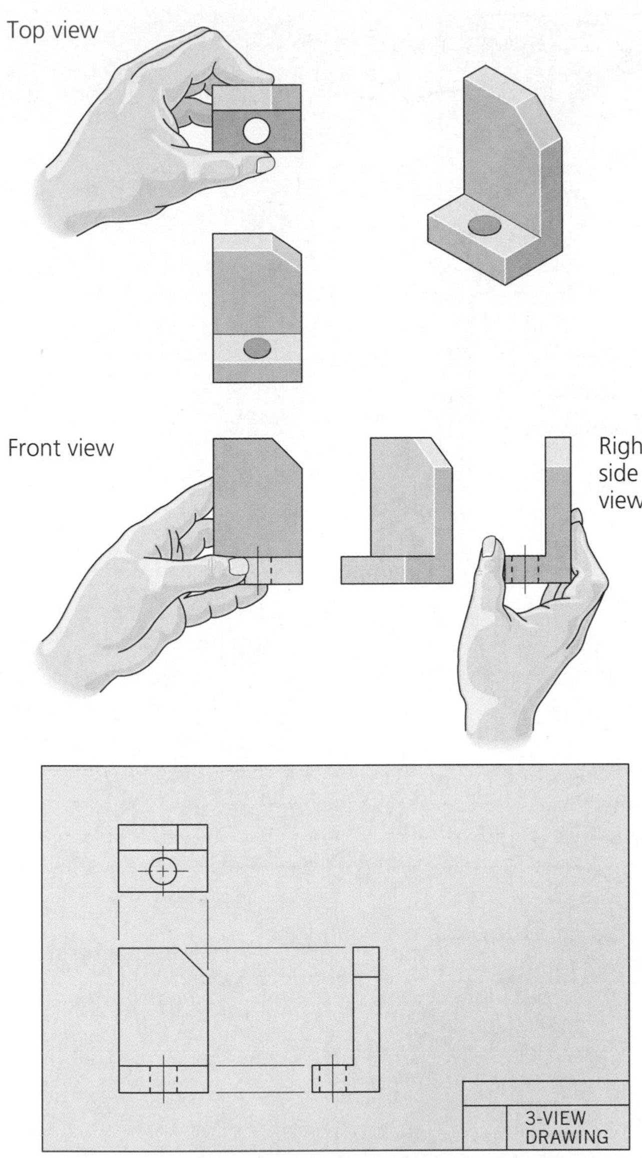

FIGURE 9.19 Three-View Orthographic Projection

other than one of the six principal views (top, front, right side, left side, back, and bottom).

In some cases, the combination of pictorial and multiview sketches define the part or assembly better than would just one method. In Figure 9.20 the sketch of the manufacturing processes required to produce a tank are described with a pictorial isometric sketch and a cutaway section view of the tank's interior.

9.5 MULTIVIEW PROJECTION

Multiview projection describes a part's features and dimensions in one or more views that are projected at 90° angles to each other (Fig. 9.21). This is the primary projection method in engineering work. Figure 9.22 shows a multiview sketch that communicates ideas, dimensions, and shapes for the manufacture of a rocker arm. The front and right side views are shown in the two-view sketch.

Multiview drawing uses orthographic projection to establish the spatial relationship of points, lines, planes, or solid shapes. Two methods are involved: the *normal method* and the *glass box method.* In the normal (natural) method, the object is viewed perpendicular to each of its three primary surfaces.

9.5.1 The Glass Box and Hinge Lines

In the glass box method, you imagine that the part is enclosed in a transparent box. A view of the part is established on its corresponding **glass box** surface (plane) by perpendicular projectors originating at each point on the object and extending to the box surface [Fig. 9.23(a)]. The glass box is hinged so that it can be unfolded onto one flat plane (the paper) [Fig. 9.23(b)]. Each projection shares a dimension with its adjacent view. For example, the top and front views share the width dimension. In this method, all six sides are revolved outward so that they are in the plane of the paper. All except the back plane are hinged to the front plane. The back plane, when used, is normally revolved from the left side view. Each plane is parallel to the plane opposite from it before it is revolved around its hinge line.

A **hinge line,** often referred to as a **folding line,** is the line of intersection between any two adjacent image planes (Fig. 9.24). The left side, front, right side, and back are all elevation views and show the height dimension. The top and bottom surfaces are in the horizontal plane. The depth dimension, width dimension, front, and back are established there. Each image plane (surface of the glass box) is connected at right angles to an adjacent view. For example, the top view is hinged to the front view, as is the right side view. Hinge lines are not shown on technical drawings or sketches.

In the United States and Canada, the six principal views of a part are drawn through third-angle projection, in which the line of sight goes through the image plane to the object (Fig. 9.25). Assume that the object is projected back along the line of sight to the image plane. The line of sight is at a right angle to the projection plane and is assumed to originate at infinity. To visualize this, place the plane between you and the object. Your position changes with every view so that your line of sight is always at a right angle to each image plane. A point is projected on the image plane where its projector (line of sight) pierces that image plane. Point 1 in Figures 9.24 and 9.25 is located on the part and is projected onto the three primary image planes.

9.5.2 Selection of Views

Selecting the proper views and their orientations requires consideration of the actual part and its natural or assembled position. The front view customarily shows the primary features of the part in elevation. Selection of the top view is usually obvious. It is best to use the minimum number of

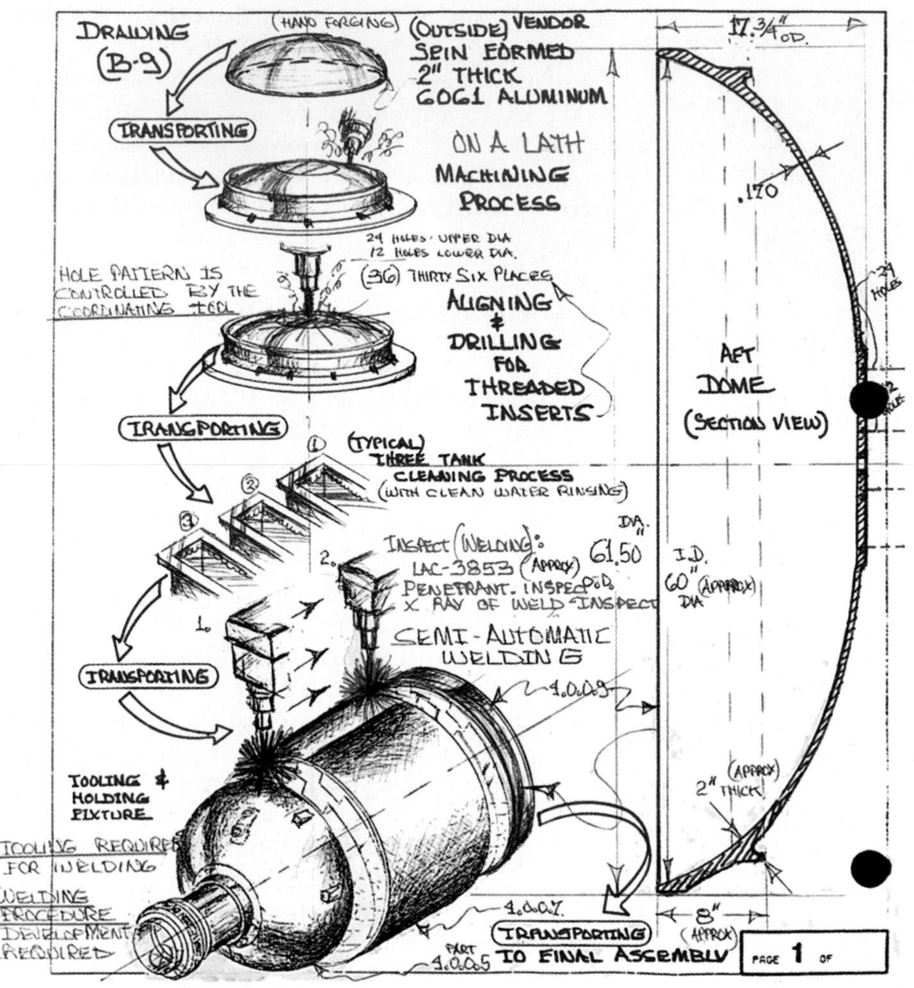

FIGURE 9.20 Manufacturing Sequence Sketch

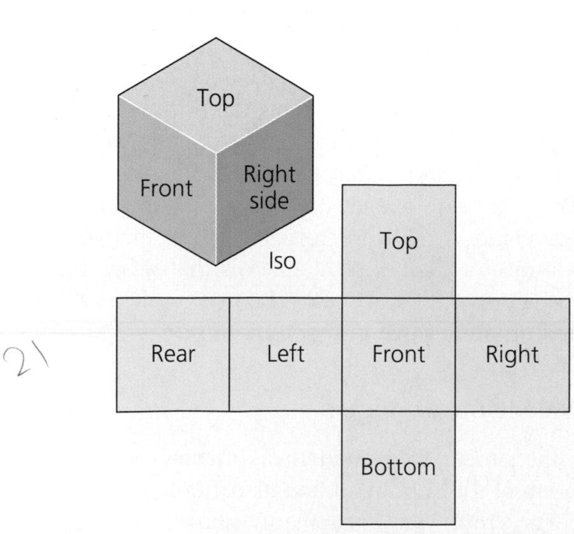

FIGURE 9.21 The Six Standard Views of an Object Plus an Isometric View

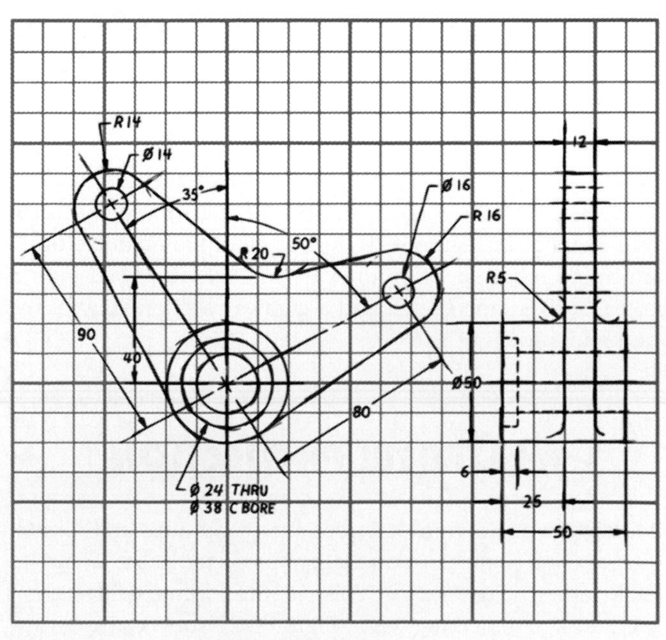

FIGURE 9.22 Two-View Drawing

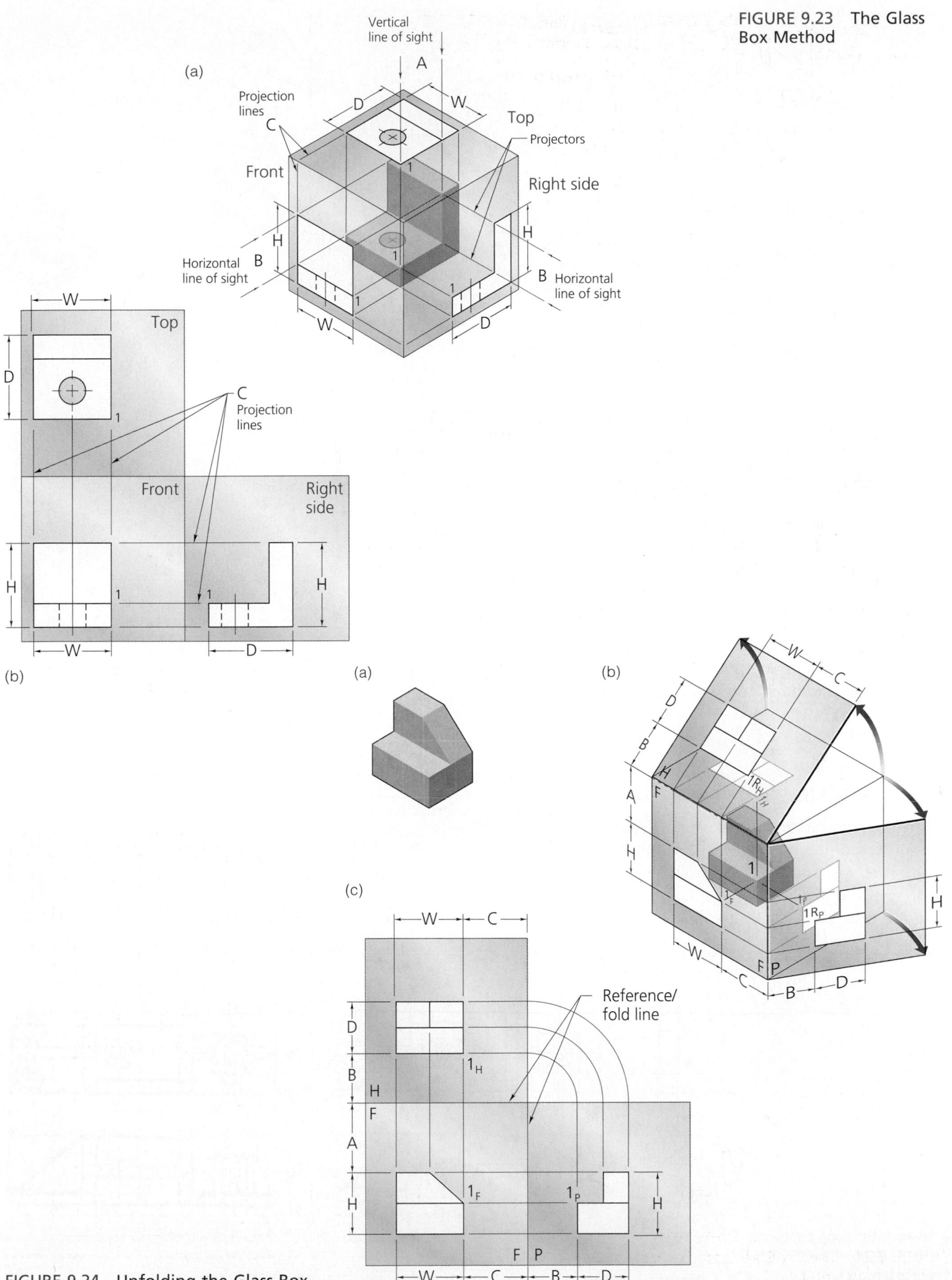

FIGURE 9.23 The Glass Box Method

FIGURE 9.24 Unfolding the Glass Box

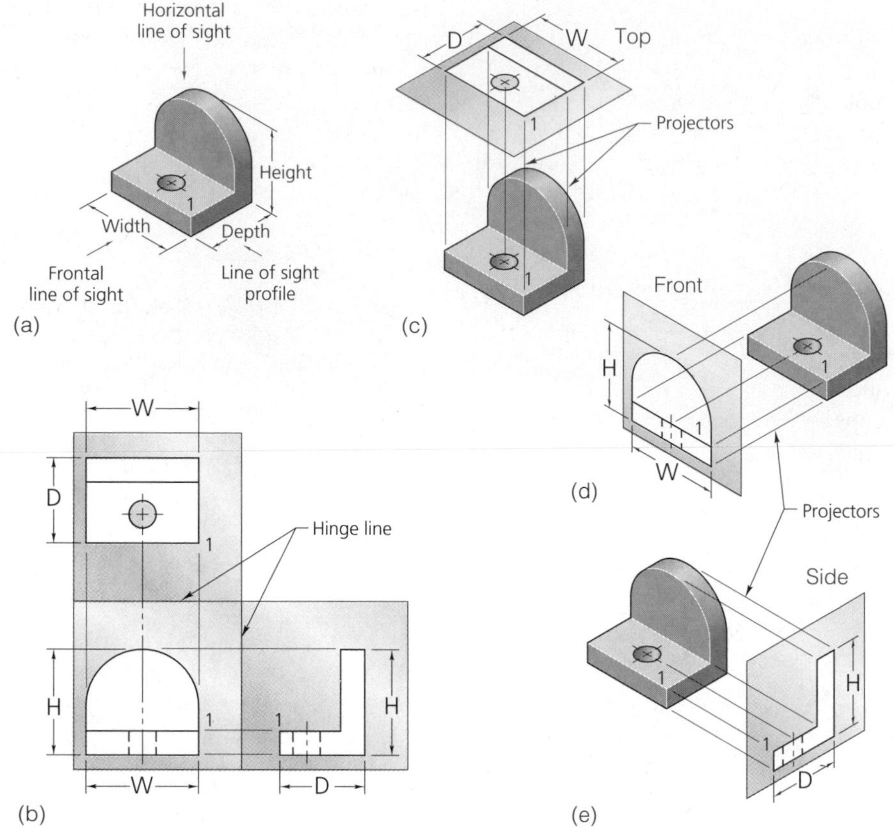

FIGURE 9.25 **Line of Sight for Views**

views necessary to describe the object completely. For example, only one or two views are needed for cylindrical parts because the diameter dimension will describe width and depth, and features along the length are described in the longitudinal view (Fig. 9.26). Engineering sketches generally require at least two views.

9.5.3 Multiview Sketching

Figure 9.26 shows the three stages of sketching. The overall dimensions of the part were blocked out first in each view. Centerlines were added to establish circular or symmetrical aspects of the part. Next, the spring coils were drawn with construction lines. Finally, the lines were darkened. Figure 9.27 shows these same steps applied to a two-view mechanical part.

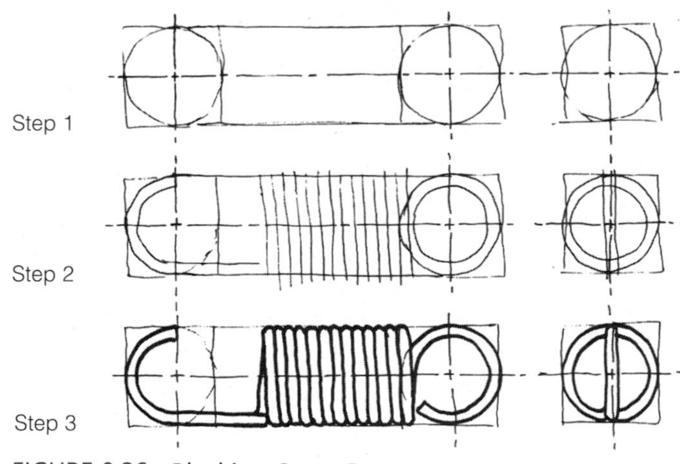

FIGURE 9.26 **Blocking Out a Part**

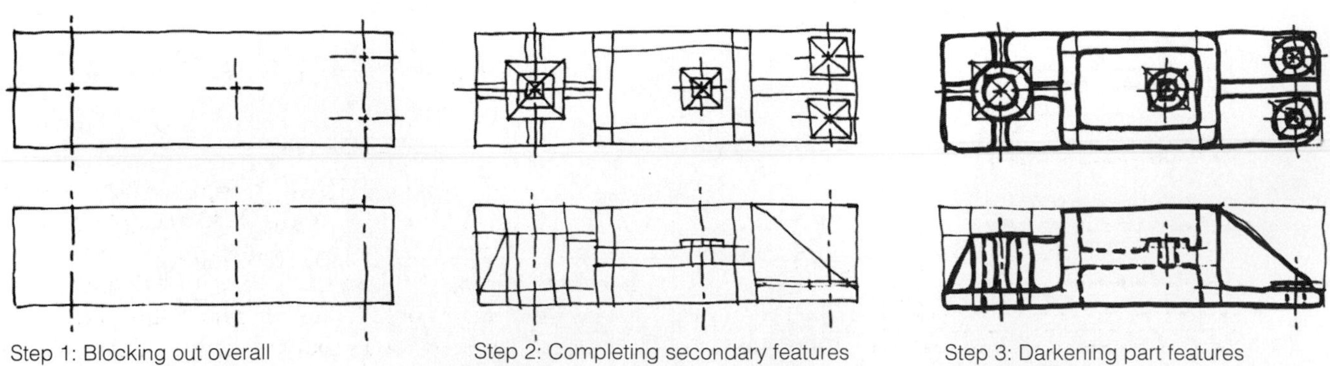

FIGURE 9.27 **Blocking Out a Two-View Sketch**

Figure 9.28 is a multiview sketch of a part that required all three views. Each view is "in line" with its adjacent view, as are all the features of the part. Adjacent views of edges, holes, and other shapes are established by projecting lines between the views. Construction lines are extended view to view. Since alignment of the views is critical in multiview sketching, grid paper makes the sketching process easier and faster.

Sketches are not complete without dimensions. In Figure 9.29 a three-view sketch is shown along with the completed mechanical detail. Both the sketch and the finished detail incorporate the dimensions that are required to manufacture the part accurately. In reality, either the detail or the sketch could have been used to manufacture the part with the same result.

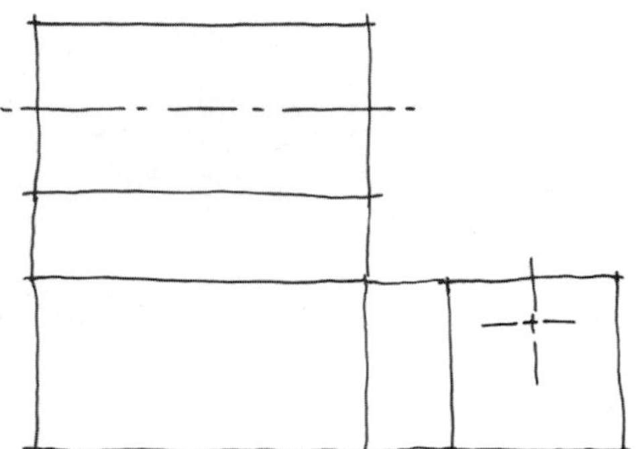

Step 1: Blocking out overall dimensions

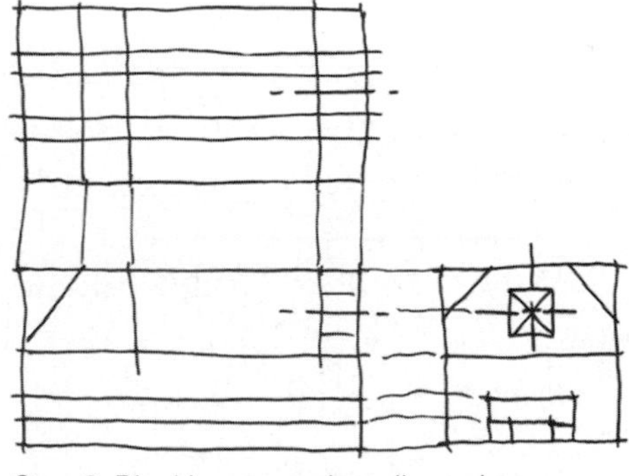

Step 2: Blocking secondary dimensions

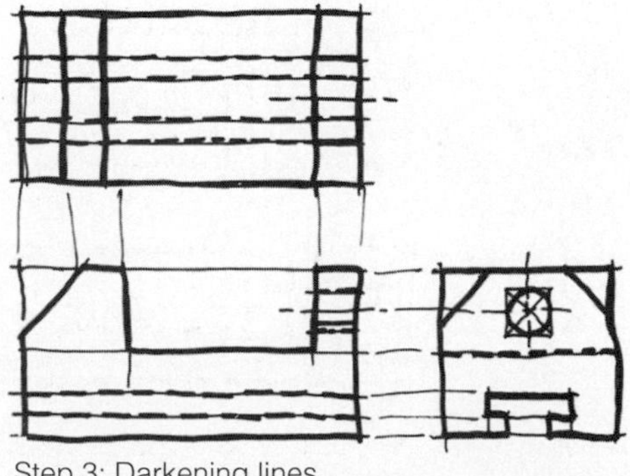

Step 3: Darkening lines

FIGURE 9.28 Blocking Out a Three-View Sketch

Because of the widespread use of computers in technical work, computer-aided design is now involved in many projects. However, sketching is and will continue to be the most effective and most popular way to communicate graphic ideas. Many companies now use a correctly dimensioned engineering sketch to speed the drafting stage of the design through the manufacturing cycle. This is called *simplified drafting* and has gained widespread acceptance in our highly competitive world.

You May Complete Exercises 9.1 Through 9.4 at This Time

9.6 PICTORIAL PROJECTION

Pictorial drawings are widely used for display illustrations and product literature. Isometric drawing is the most common pictorial technique. Pictorial projection includes isometric, oblique, and perspective methods.

Isometric projection is based on the theory that a cube representing the projection axes is rotated until its front face is 45° to the frontal plane and then is tipped forward or downward at an angle of 35°16′. All three primary faces are displayed equally. In Figure 9.30 the part has been enclosed in a glass box and projected onto each of its corresponding surfaces. The viewing plane 1-2-3 is parallel to the projection plane. This is an isometric view. In true isometric projection, the three axes make equal angles with the projection plane and all three axes are equally foreshortened and make equal angles of 120°. A true isometric projection is about 81% the size of an isometric drawing. In actual industry practice, isometric drawing, not isometric projection, is employed.

Isometric drawing is commonly used in sketching (Fig. 9.31). Isometric drawings are constructed along three axes, one vertical and the other two at 30° to the horizontal, going both right and left (isometric axes, Fig. 9.32). All lines in isometric drawings that are on or parallel to the three axes are drawn true length and are isometric lines. Lines not on or parallel to the axes are constructed with offset dimensions and are called nonisometric lines. Nonisometric lines are not true length.

9.6.1 Isometric Construction

Isometric construction using the box method is illustrated in Figure 9.33. The procedure for drawing an isometric box is shown in Figure 9.33(a) using 30° triangles. Starting at point A, the three axes are drawn. The edges of the box are constructed from the height, width, and depth. In an isometric drawing the dimensions are not foreshortened.

After the part is boxed in, the remainder of the drawing is completed. Dividers (or a scale) are used to transfer dimensions shown in Figure 9.33(c) to the isometric view of Figure 9.33(b). All measurements are taken along isometric

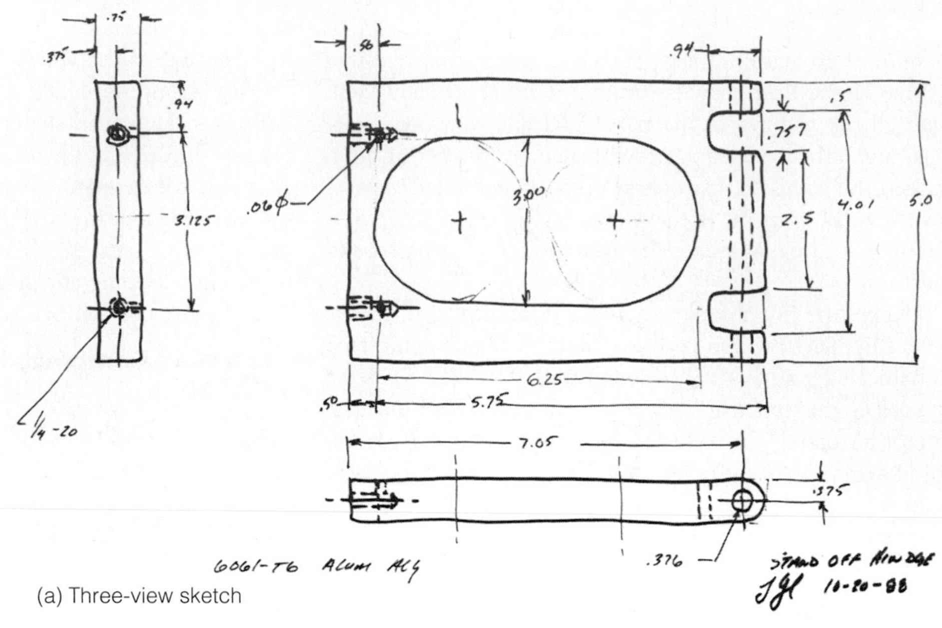

(a) Three-view sketch

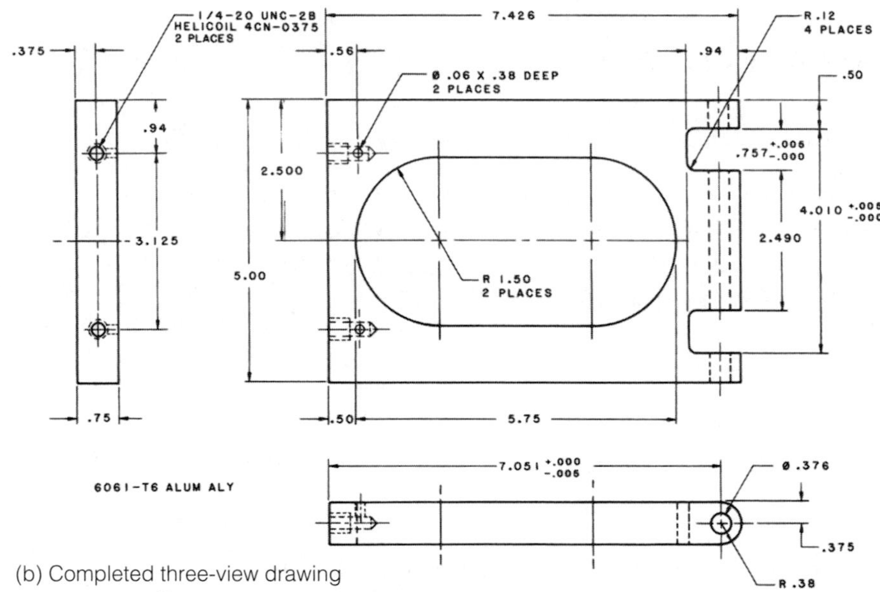

FIGURE 9.29 View Alignment

(b) Completed three-view drawing

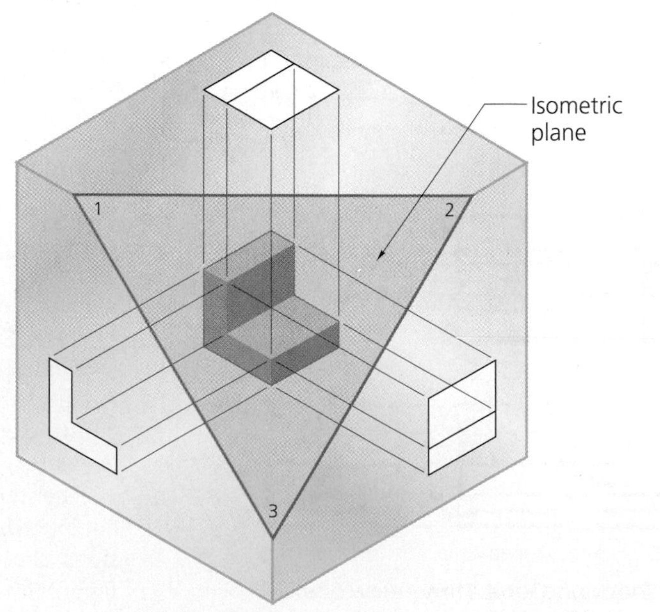

FIGURE 9.30 Isometric Projection

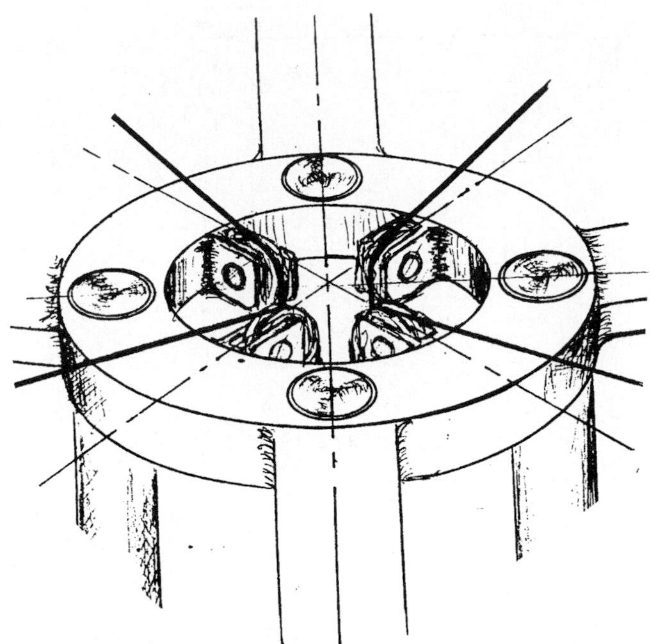

FIGURE 9.31 Isometric Sketch

lines. Dimension D1 is measured along the vertical axis; dimensions D2, D3, and D4 are in the horizontal plane and are measured along or parallel to one of the receding axes. After the centerlines are located, the circles and arcs are drawn.

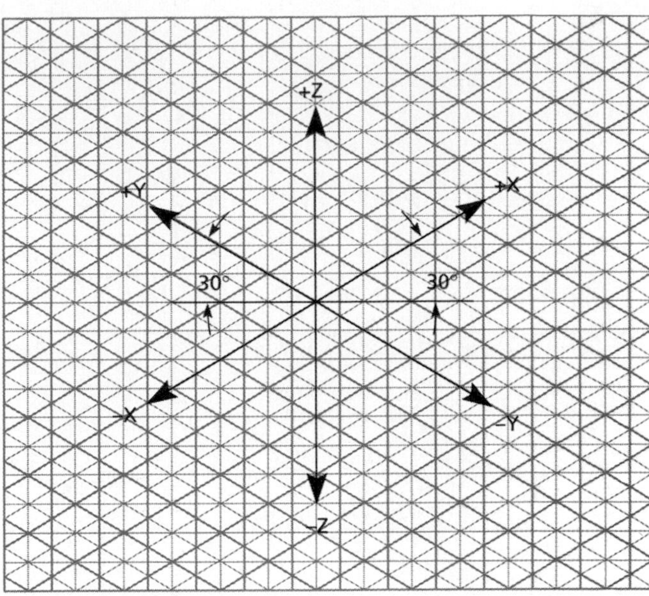

FIGURE 9.32 Isometric Axes

9.6.2 Isometric Angles

Because of the distortion created by the isometric view, few angles appear as true angles. Angles appear larger or smaller than true size and must be established by offset dimensions. For example, the plane in Figure 9.34 has angles of 45° and 30°, both of which are constructed from offset dimensions,

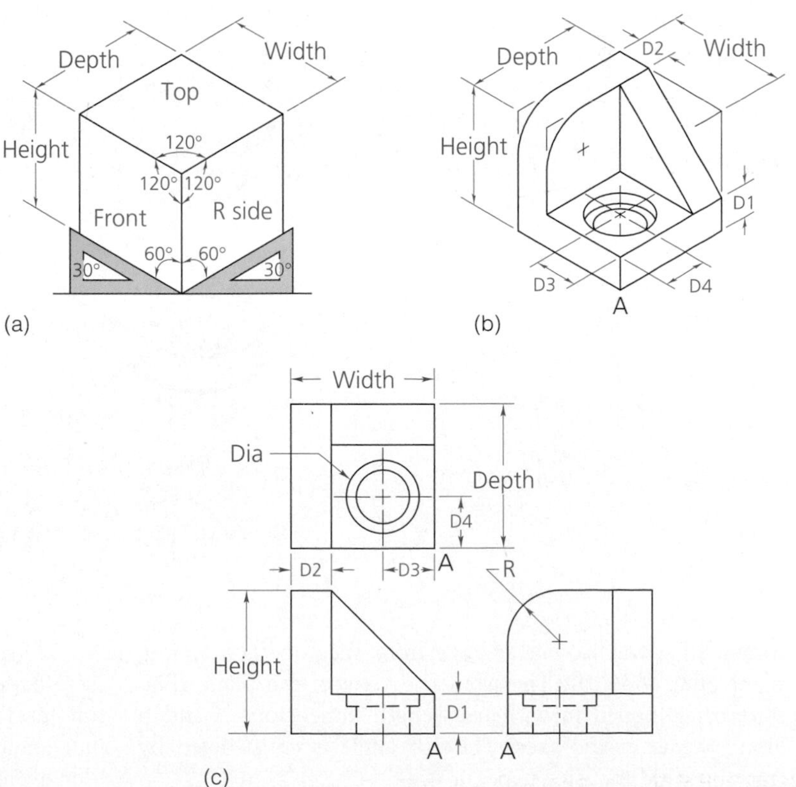

FIGURE 9.33 Isometric Projection

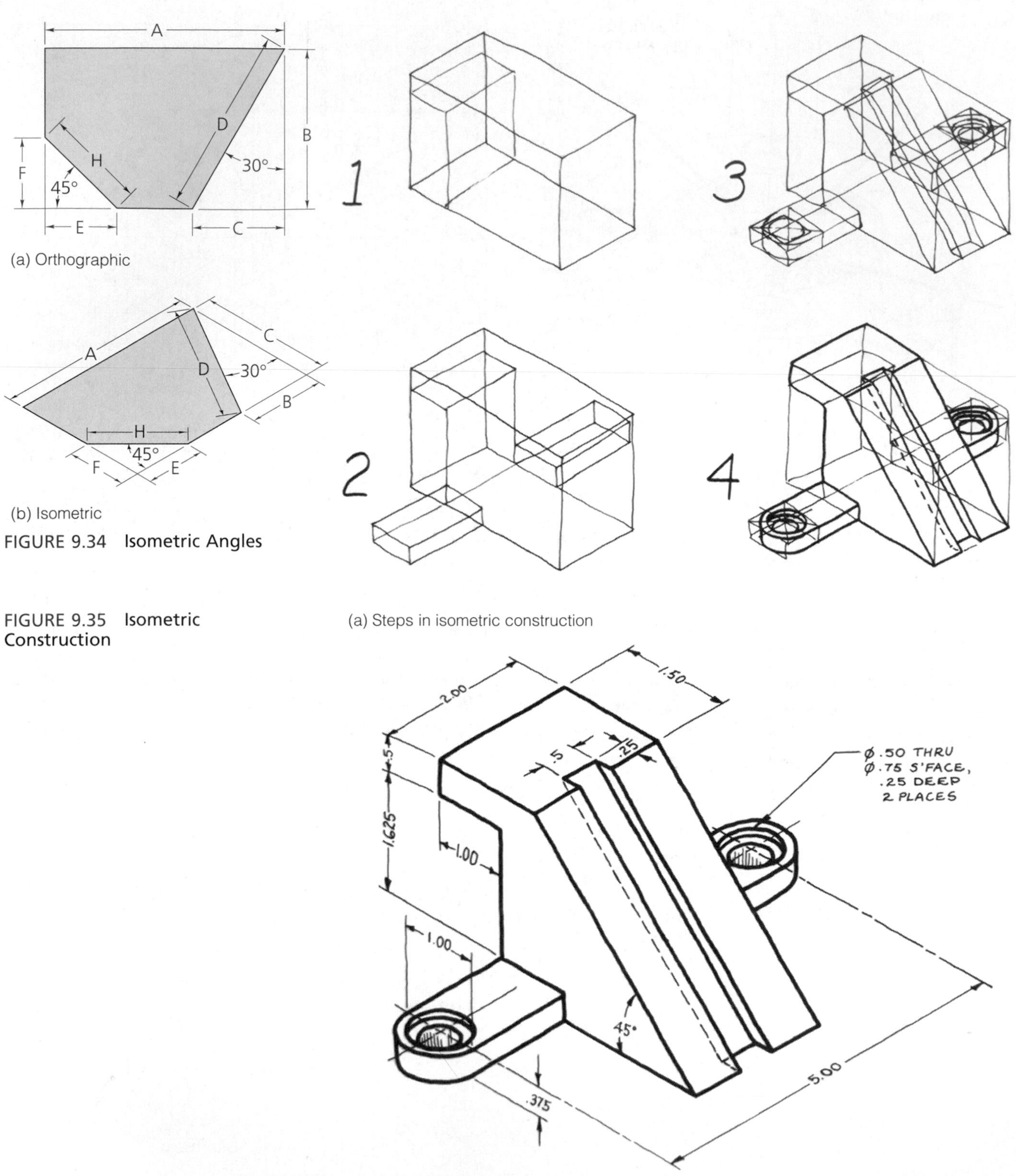

(a) Orthographic

(b) Isometric

FIGURE 9.34 Isometric Angles

FIGURE 9.35 Isometric Construction

(a) Steps in isometric construction

(b) Completed sketch with dimensions

measured along isometric lines from the top view of the plane [Fig. 9.34(a)]. The isometric view of the plane [Fig. 9.34(b)] is boxed in with true-length dimensions A and B along the isometric axes. The 30° angle is constructed by transferring dimension C.

The part in Figure 9.35 has an angled surface. To draw the part in an isometric view, it is necessary to use offset dimensions to establish the endpoints of the edges that are at an angle. Endpoint dimensions can be taken along true-length lines.

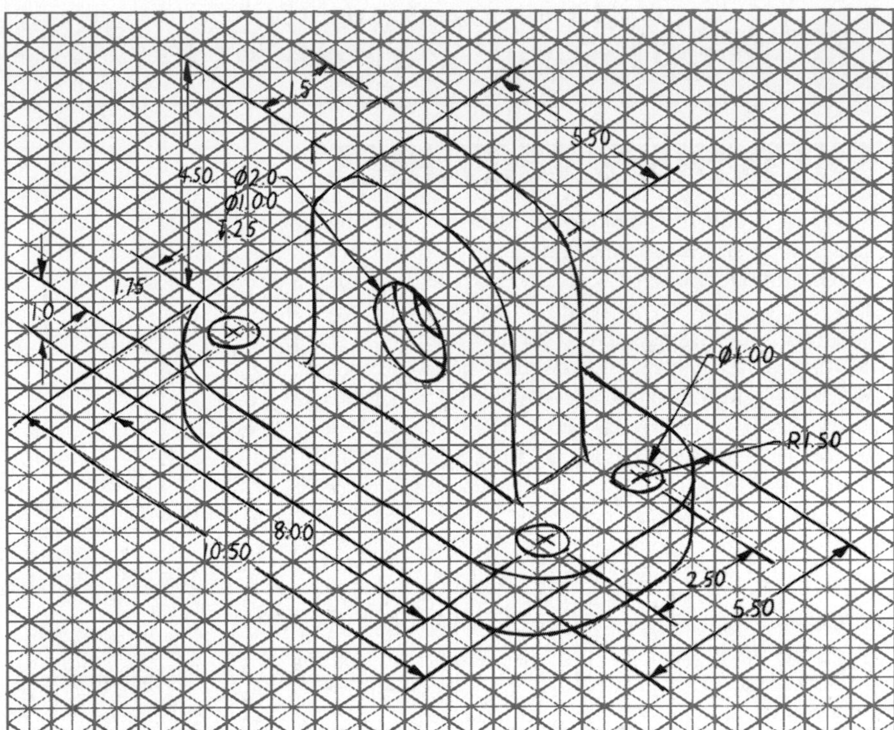

FIGURE 9.36 Isometric Sketch Using Grid Paper

9.6.3 Isometric Circles and Arcs

Circles and circular arcs on isometric drawings appear elliptical (Fig. 9.36) unless they fall exactly on or parallel to the isometric viewing plane. Many methods are employed to construct isometric ellipses: template, trammel, four-center, and point plotting. For sketches, freehand techniques are sufficient (you can also use a template).

The four-center method (Fig. 9.37) does not create a perfect ellipse, but is accurate enough for most purposes. This method is used to draw circles or arcs on any isometric face (Fig. 9.38):

1. Draw lines DA and DC along the two receding axes (at 30°). Draw line AB parallel to DC, and line CB parallel to

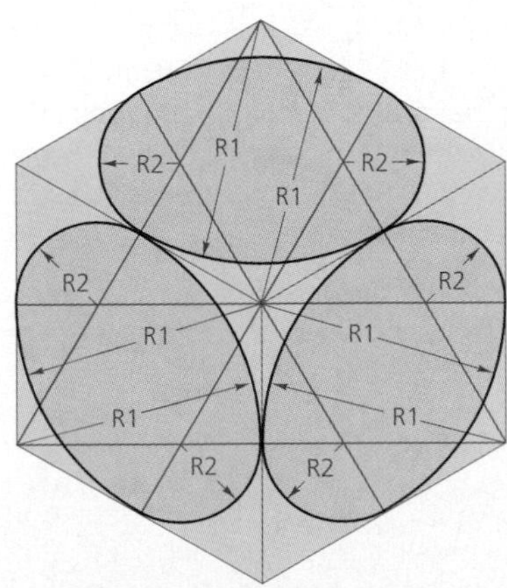

FIGURE 9.37 Isometric Ellipses Drawn by the Four-Center Method

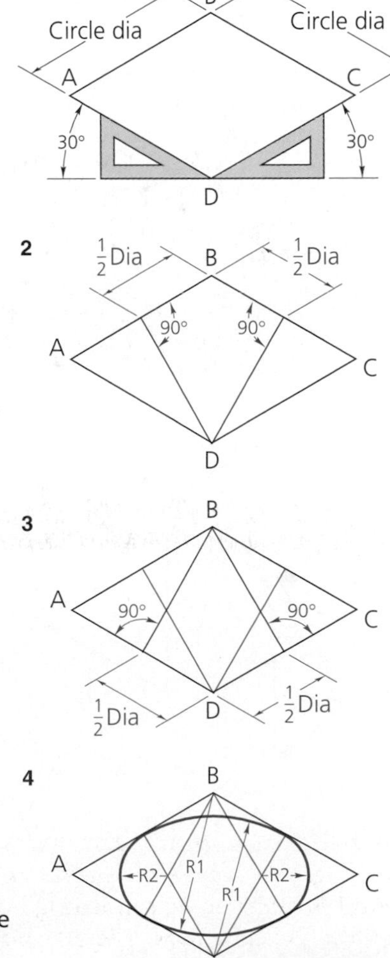

FIGURE 9.38 Ellipse Construction for Isometric Drawings

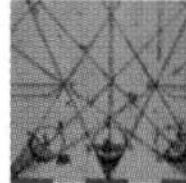

Applying Parametric Design . . .

SKETCHING FEATURES

Sketching is done in the **Sketcher.** Almost all traditional lines, circles, arcs, and their variations can be accomplished on the screen without the need to create exact and perfectly constructed geometry. The system will assume a variety of conditions, such as tangency, similar sizes for same-type geometry, parallelism, perpendicularity, verticality, horizontality, touching endpoints, tangent points, and symmetry. The simple part in Figure A was created by sketching lines and arcs.

You can create two types of **lines:** geometry lines and centerlines. Geometry lines are used to create feature geometry. Centerlines are used to define the axis of revolution of a revolved feature, to define a line of symmetry within a section, or to create construction lines. To sketch lines:

1. Choose Line from the GEOMETRY menu. The LINE TYPE menu appears.
2. Choose Geometry or Centerline from the top portion of the menu to indicate the type of line you want.
3. Choose a command from the bottom portion of the menu to indicate how you wish to create the line:

2 Points Create a line by picking the start point and the endpoint. Geometry lines created with this command will automatically be chained together.

Parallel Pick an existing line to determine the new line's direction, then pick the start point and the endpoint. For a centerline, only a single pick is needed to determine the parallel placement of the line, and the ends of the centerline will be chosen to fit model or section outlines.

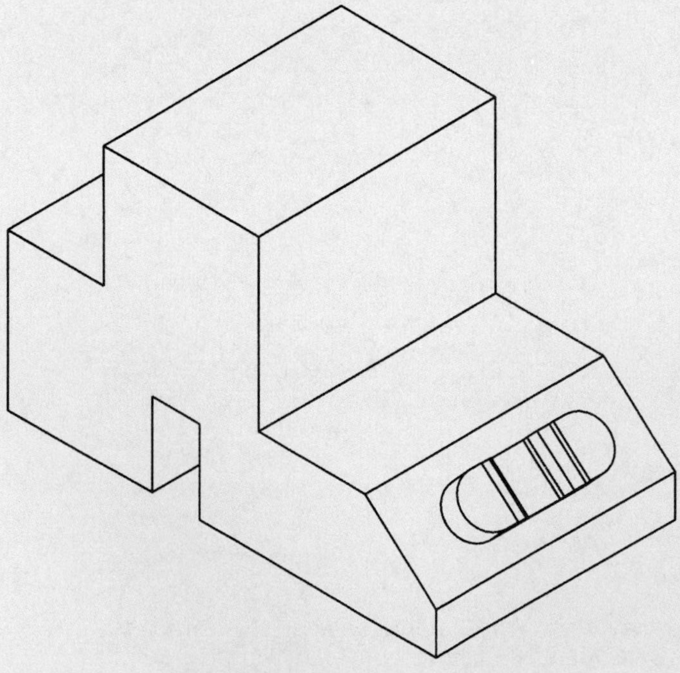

FIGURE A Modeled Part

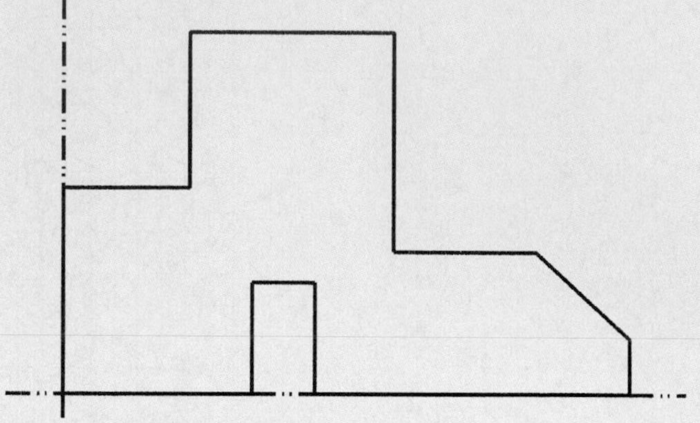

FIGURE B Sketched Outline of Part Using Lines

Perpendicular Pick an existing line to determine the new line's direction, then pick the start point and the endpoint. For a centerline, only a single pick is needed to determine the perpendicular placement of the line, and the ends of the centerline will be chosen to fit model or section outlines.

Tangent Pick an endpoint of an arc or spline to start the new line and determine its direction, then pick the endpoint of the line. For a centerline, only a single pick is needed to determine the tangent placement of the line, and the ends of the centerline will be chosen to fit model or section outlines.

2 Tangent Pick two arcs, splines, or circles to determine the direction of the new line. The line is automatically created between the selected entities. A 2 Tangent line created to construction entities will not split the entity. This button is the model and stays selected until you explicitly select another command. A 2 Tangent centerline, created as a 2 Tangent line defined with two circles, will not split the circles.

Pnt/Tangent Pick a point anywhere in the current section, then pick an arc, spline, or circle to which the line must be tangent. The line will be created automatically.

Horizontal Creates a line that is horizontal relative to the orientation of the section. For a geometry line, the endpoint is automatically the starting point of a chained vertical line. For a centerline, only a single pick is needed to determine the vertical locations of the line.

Vertical Creates a line that is vertical relative to the orientation of the section. For a geometry line, the endpoint is automatically the starting point of a chained horizontal line. For a centerline, only a single pick is needed to determine the vertical locations of the line.

The lines for the outline of the part shown in Figure B are sketched without regard to actual sizes. After the lines are sketched, dimensions are added (see Fig. C). The part is aligned to the default datum planes (see Fig. D). After

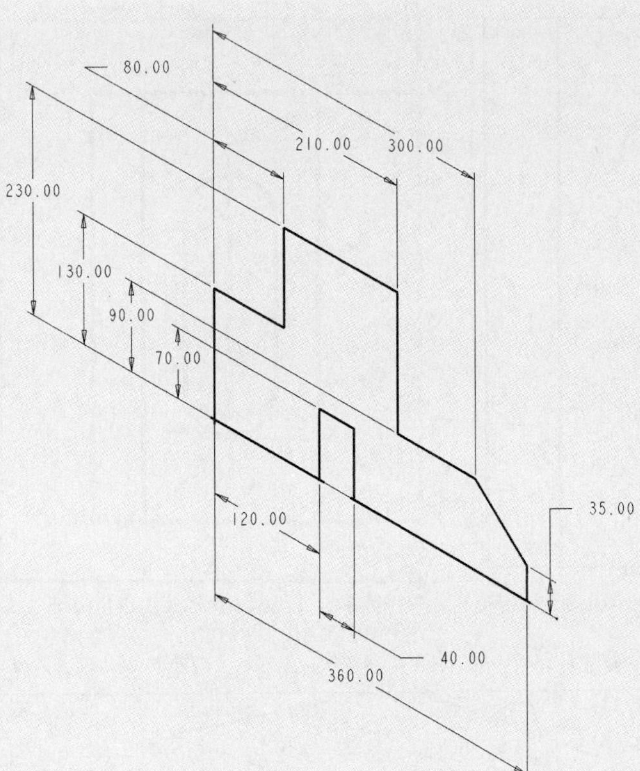

FIGURE C Dimensions Added to the Sketch

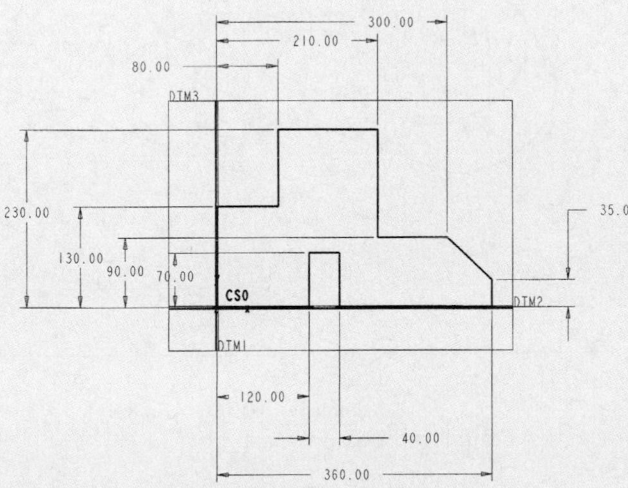

FIGURE D Part Aligned and Constrained by the Default Planes

regeneration, the depth of the part is input and the extruded protrusion base feature is complete (see Fig. E).

The next feature to be created lies on the angled surface (Fig. F). The slanted plane is used as the sketching plane and an arc is placed via one of the available options (Fig. G). The opposite arc is then sketched (Fig. H). The lines between the arcs and a **centerline** complete the sketch (Fig. I). Dimensions are added to the sketch and modified to the design values (Fig. J). The depth of the protrusion is given and the feature is complete (Fig. K).

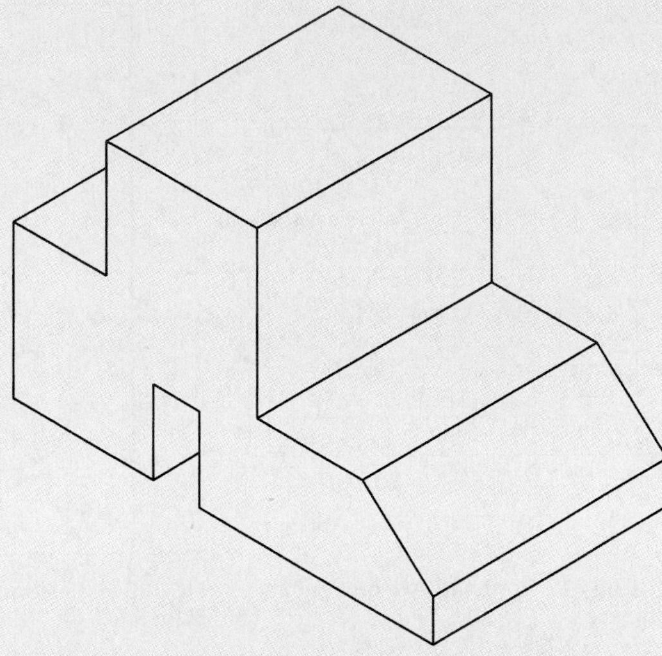

FIGURE E Extruded Protrusion Base Feature

Arcs are sketched via the menu or the mouse. To sketch arcs:

1. Choose Arc from the GEOMETRY menu. The ARC TYPE menu appears.
2. Choose one of the following options from the ARC TYPE menu:

Tangent End This is the same as creating an arc with Mouse Sketch, except you must use the left mouse button. Pick an

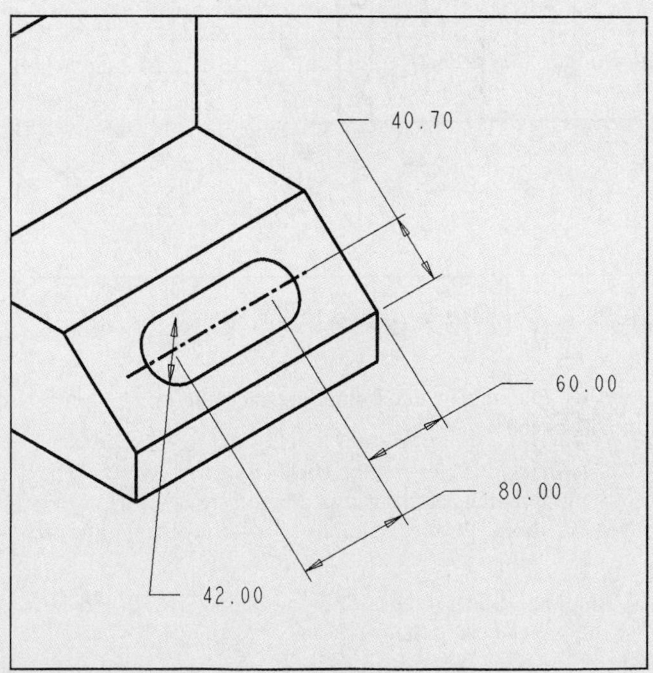

FIGURE F Sketched Boss Feature Showing Lines and Arcs

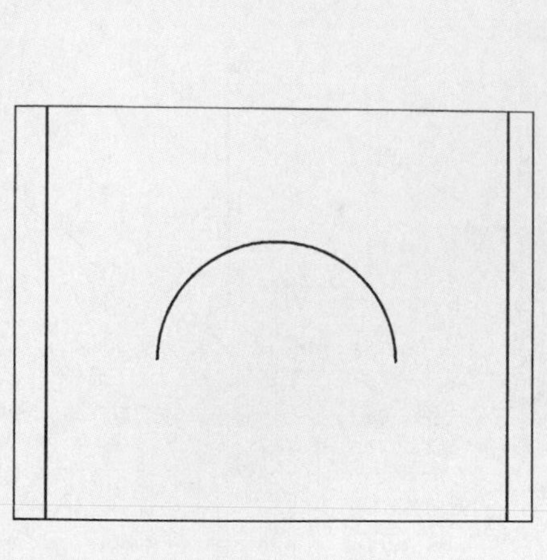

FIGURE G Sketched Arc on Angled Surface

FIGURE H Second Arc Added to the Sketch

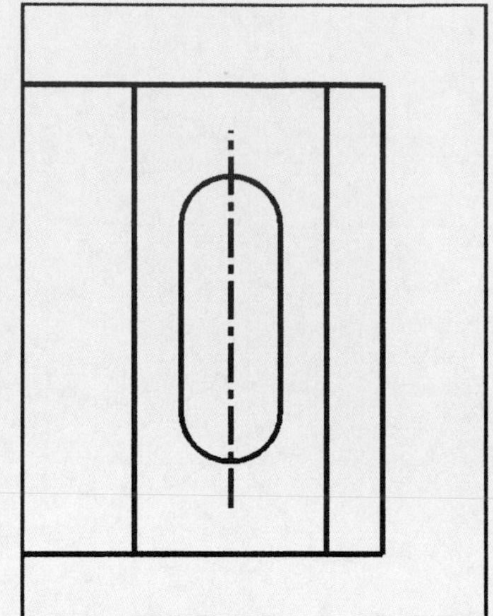

FIGURE I Lines and Centerline Added to the Sketch

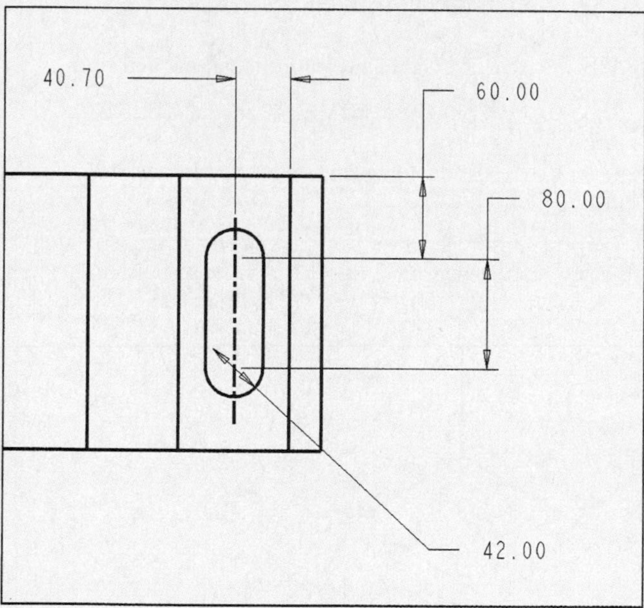

FIGURE J Dimensions Added to the Sketch

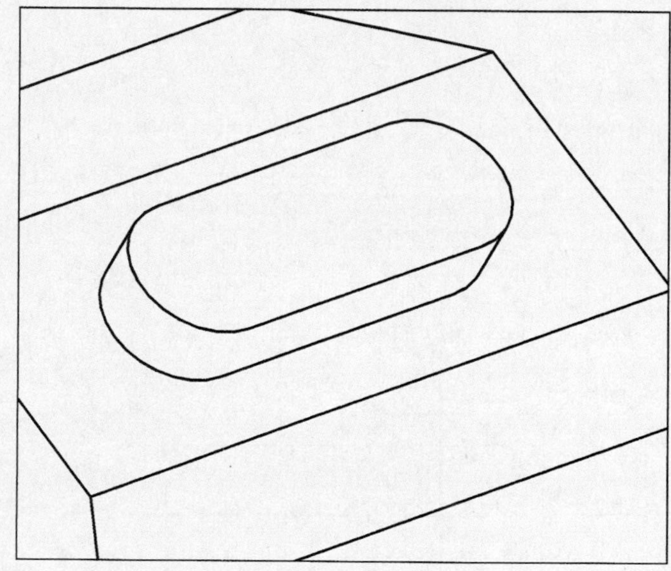

FIGURE K Completed Boss Feature

end of an entity to determine tangency, then pick the endpoints of the arc.

Concentric Pick an existing circle or arc as a reference, then pick the endpoints of the new arc. As you create the arc, a radial line will appear through its center to assist in aligning the endpoint.

3 Tangent Select three entities for the new arc to be tangent to, then create the arc in the same direction as the reference picks.

Fillet Pick two entities between which to create a tangent arc.

Ctr/Ends Pick the center point of the arc, then pick the arc's endpoints.

3 Points Pick the endpoints of the arc, then pick a point on the arc.

The last feature of the part is crated by sketching the slot cut on the edge of the boss protrusion (see Fig. L). The dimensions for the cut are added and then modified to their correct design values (Fig. M). The slot feature will go through the boss feature (Fig. N). The completed slotted boss is shown pictorially (Fig. O). The part is now complete and is displayed as a shaded model (Fig. P).

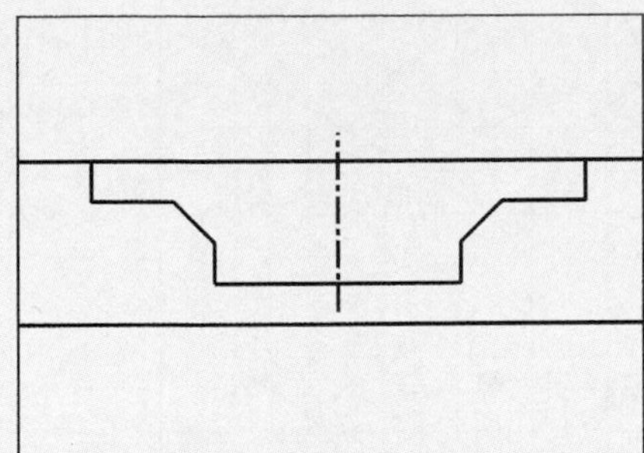

FIGURE L Sketched Cut Using Lines

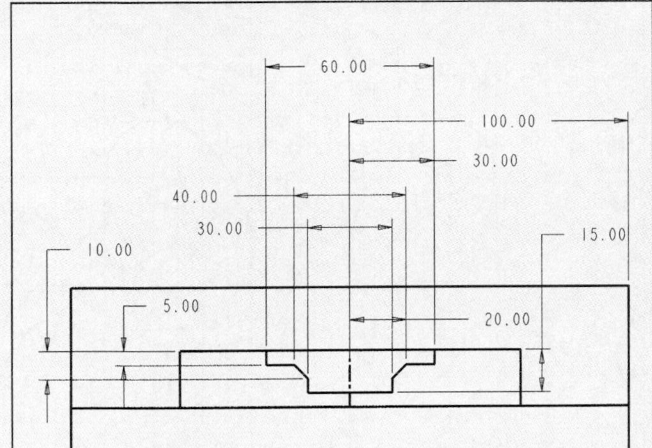

FIGURE M Slot Dimensions Added and Modified

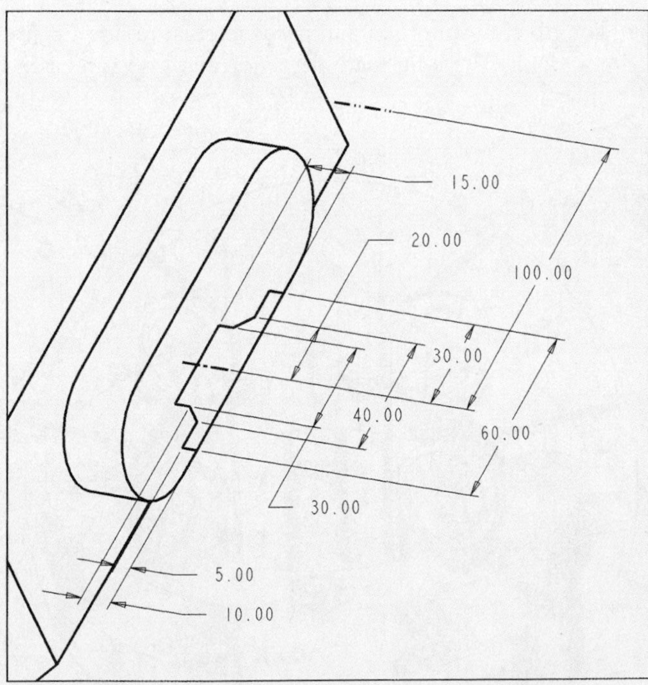

FIGURE N Pictorial of Slot Sketch and Dimensions

This part (Fig. Q) is an example of the type of modeling that can be accomplished with just two simple types of geometry, lines and arcs.

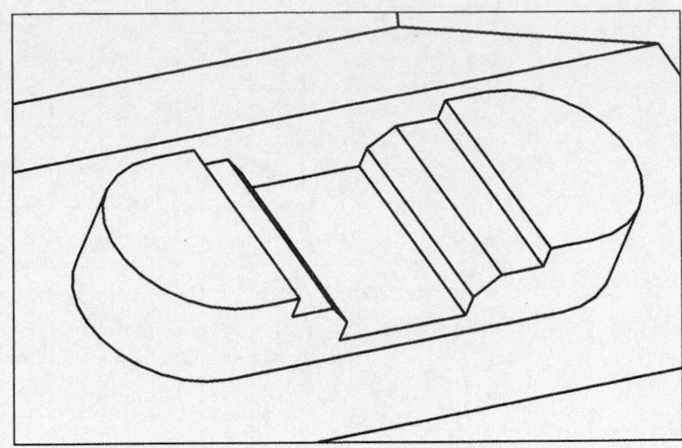

FIGURE O Pictorial View of Completed Boss

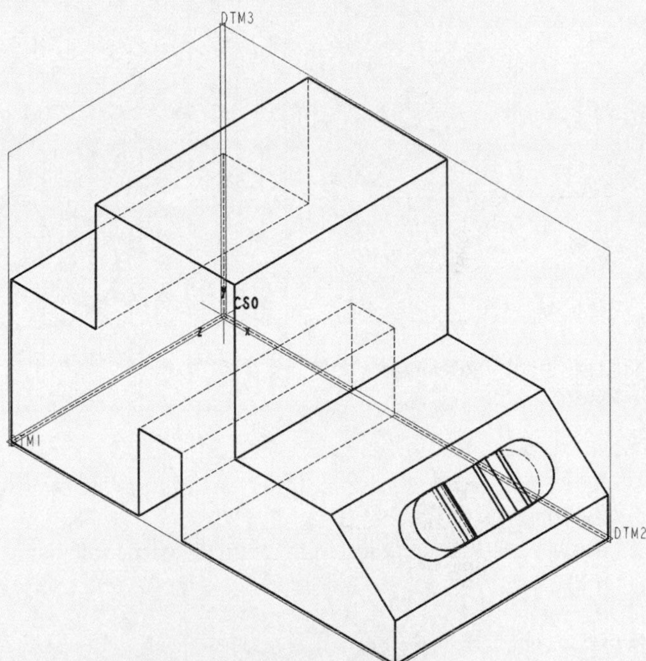

FIGURE P Completed Part

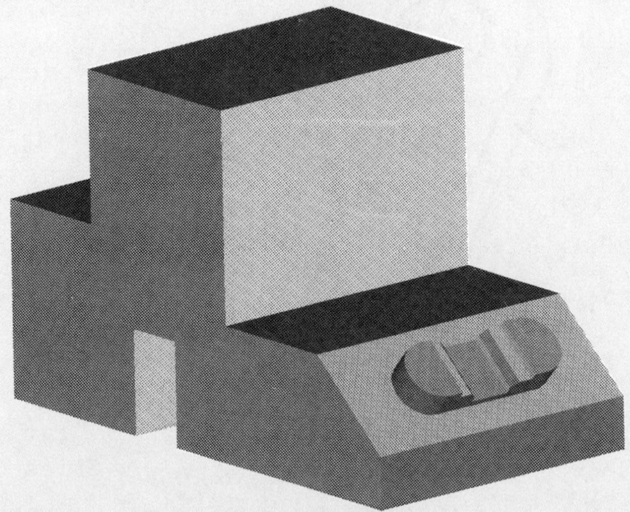

FIGURE Q Shaded Display of Part

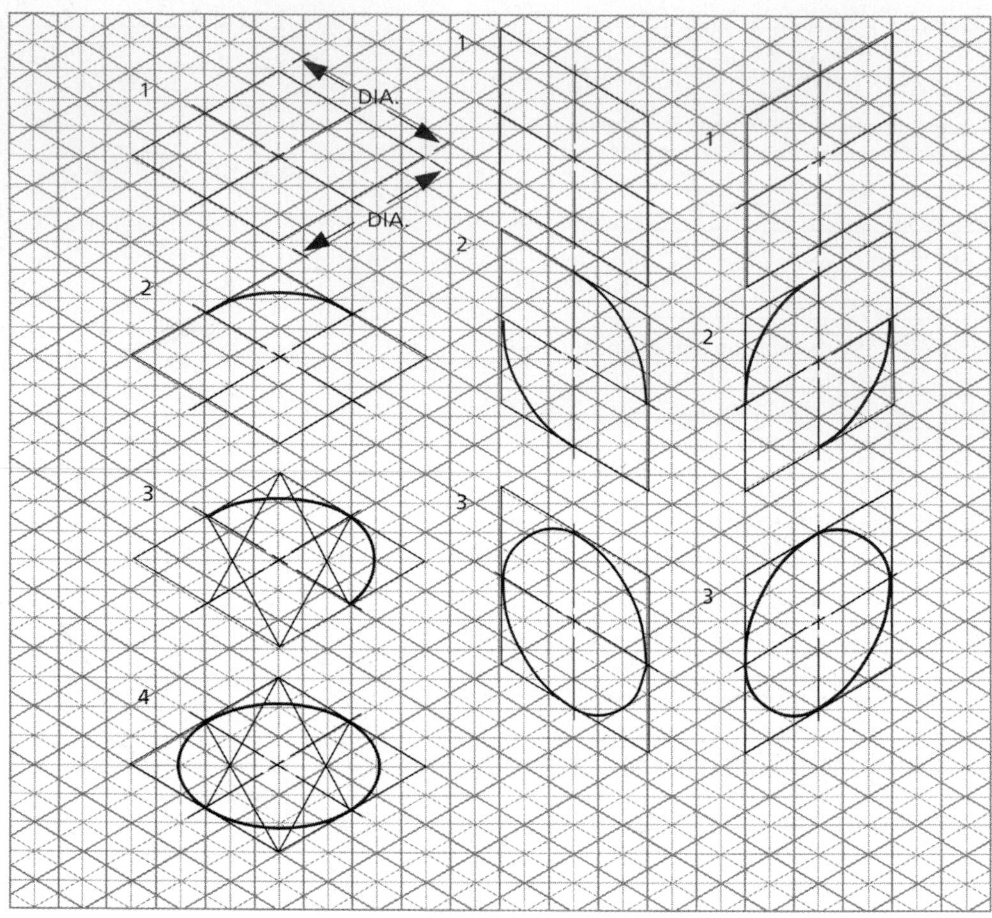

FIGURE 9.39 Sketched Isometric Arcs

AD. *The isometric square has sides equal to the diameter of the circle.*

2. Draw construction lines from point D perpendicular to line AB at its midpoint and perpendicular to line CB at its midpoint. These lines are perpendicular bisectors of each side.

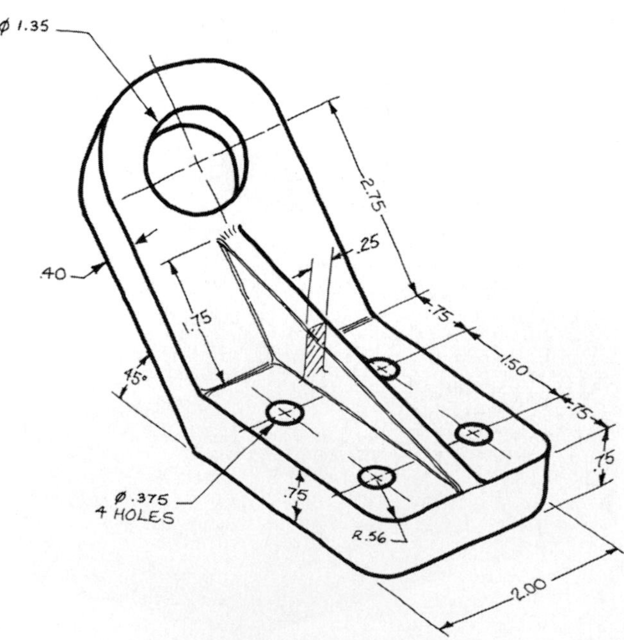

FIGURE 9.40 Isometric Sketch of Part

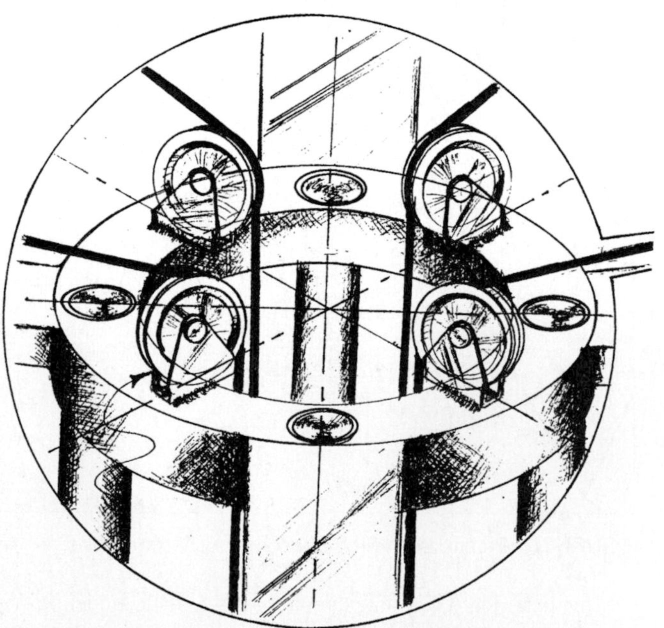

FIGURE 9.41 Isometric Sketch of Pulley System Showing a Variety of Circular Parts Not in an Isometric Plane

3. Repeat step 2 using point B and lines AD and CD
4. Use points D and B to construct arcs R1. R2 originates at the intersection of the perpendicular bisectors.

Isometric ellipses are easily sketched using this method (Fig. 9.39). Circles, arcs, or curves that do not lie in isometric planes, as in Figures 9.40 and 9.41, must be plotted with offset dimensions. A series of points is established along the curved outline (see Chapter 13). Offset dimensions for these points are transferred to the isometric drawing and are laid off along isometric lines.

The last step in any sketch is to provide the required dimensions. Figure 9.42 shows a sketch of a mechanical part, along with the finished detail.

9.7 OBLIQUE PROJECTION

Oblique drawings are produced from parallel projectors that are angular to the projection plane. The primary difference between isometric and oblique is that a receding axis is required for oblique drawings. The other surface is drawn true shape and size. The three axes are vertical (+Z), horizontal (+Y), and receding (+X) (Fig. 9.43). In oblique projection the front face of the part is placed parallel to the image plane. The other faces of the part are on receding axes (1° to 89°), as shown in Figure 9.44. Here, the front face of the block and the diameter of the hole are drawn true shape and size.

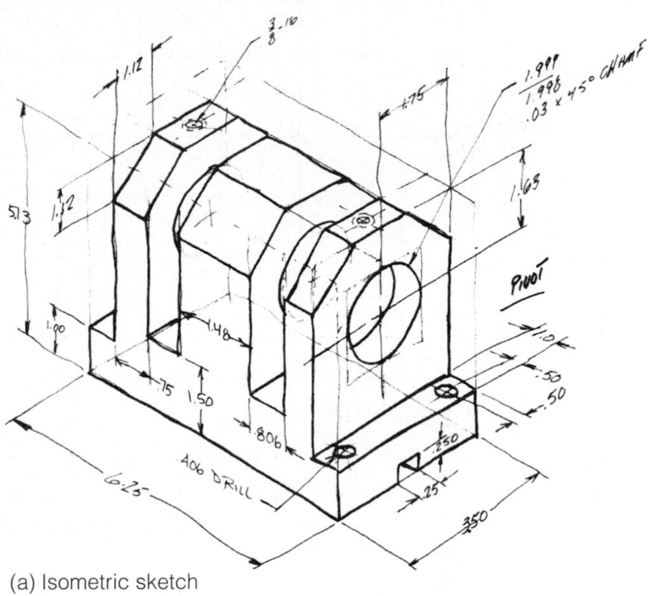
(a) Isometric sketch

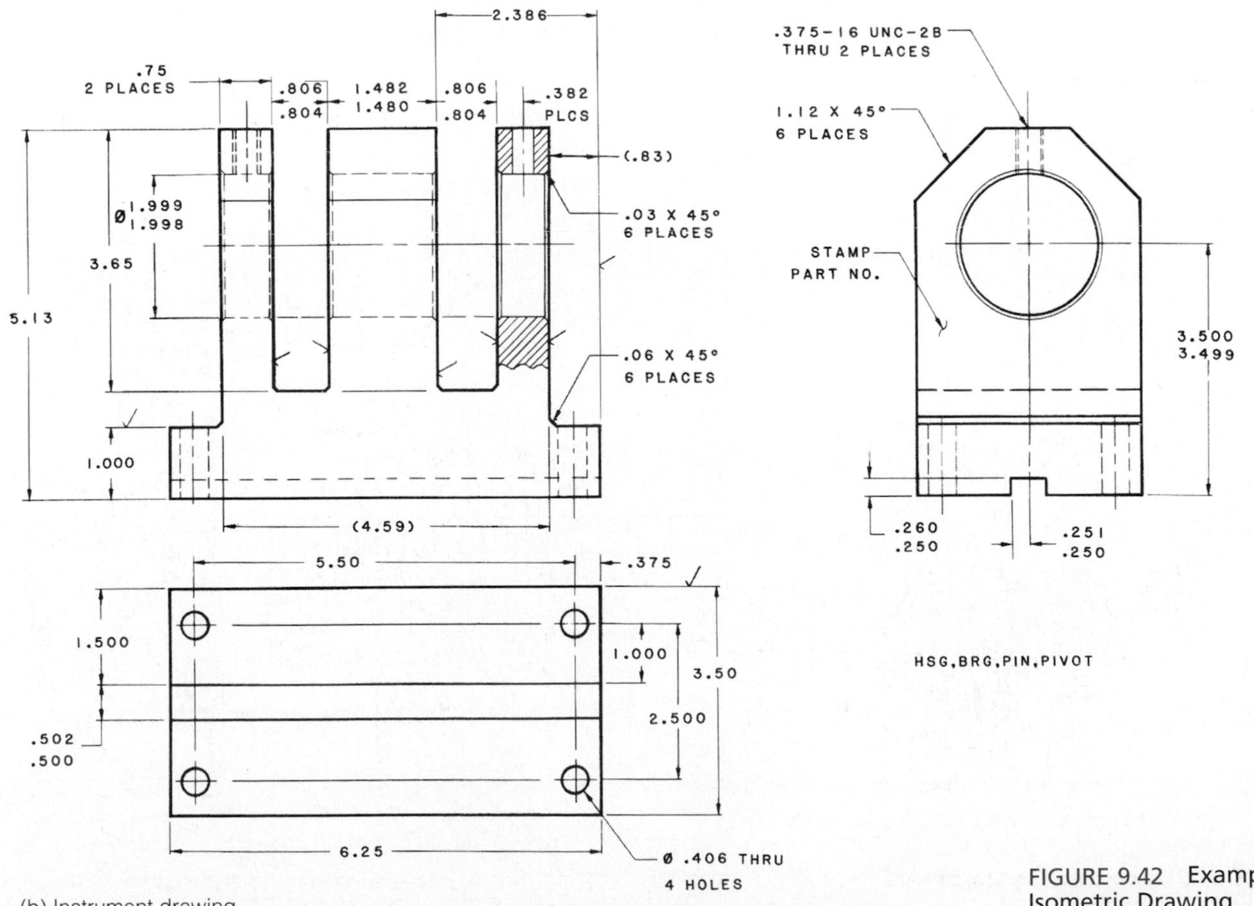

(b) Instrument drawing

FIGURE 9.42 Examples of Isometric Drawing

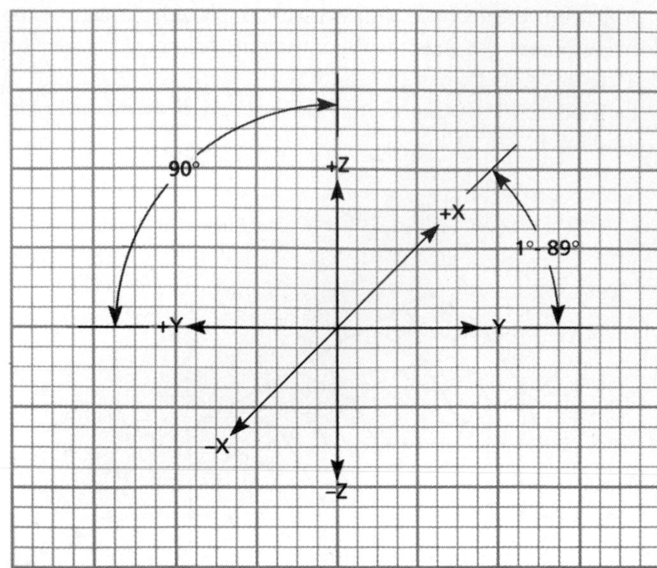

FIGURE 9.43 Oblique Axes

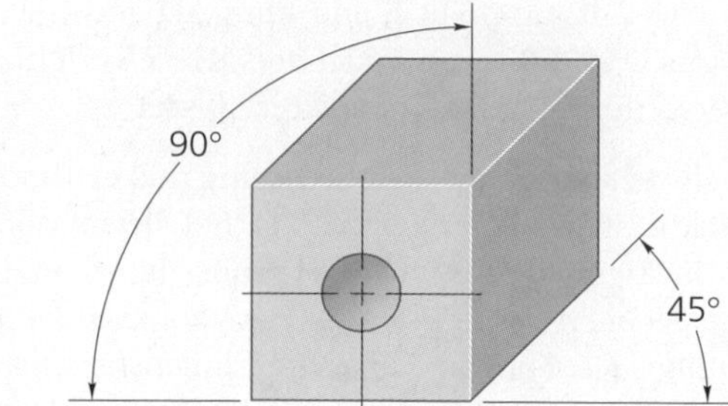

FIGURE 9.44 Oblique Projection

The two basic categories of oblique projection are *cavalier* and *cabinet* (Fig. 9.45). In a cavalier projection (a), receding lines are not foreshortened (full scale). In a cabinet projection (b), the receding lines have been foreshortened one-half their original length ($\frac{1}{2}$ scale). The most common angles are 15°, 30°, 45°, 60°, and 75°. The most common angle for the receding axis is 45°.

Parts drawn with oblique projection are oriented so that the surface with the most curved features lies in the front plane.

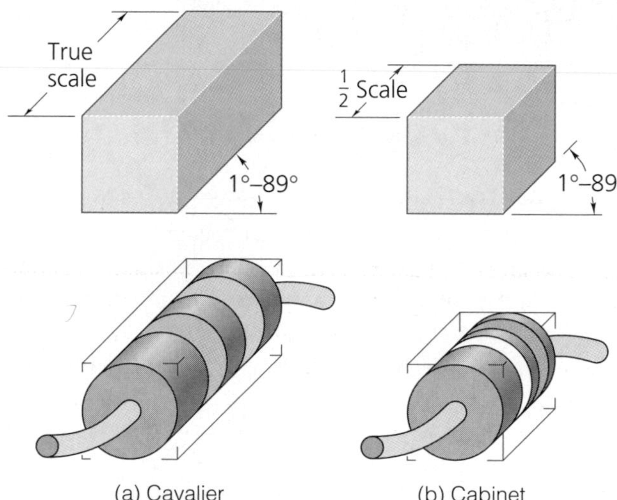

FIGURE 9.45 Oblique Projection

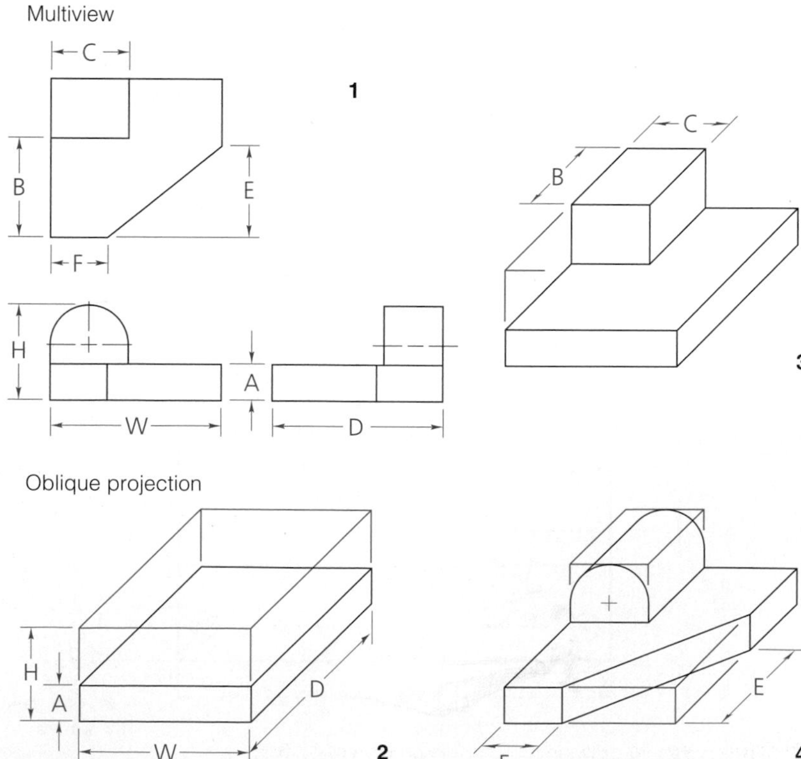

FIGURE 9.46 Construction Steps in Oblique Projection

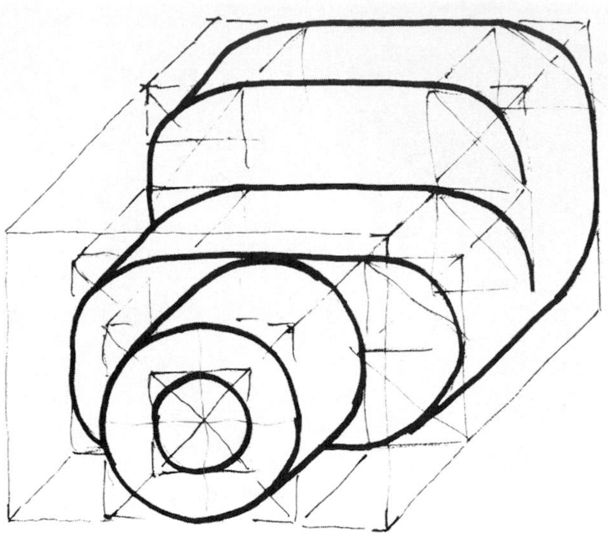

FIGURE 9.47 Oblique Sketch

Circles and arcs are true projections in this position. Oblique projection is extremely useful for parts with parallel curved or irregular features. The construction process for inclined lines and planes is similar to that for isometric drawings: Locate each feature's endpoints along lines that are parallel to one of the axes. For slanted surfaces, locate both ends of the surface and connect the points.

In Figure 9.46 the following steps were used in the construction of the part:

1. Transfer each true-length dimension from the multiview drawing to the oblique view.
2. Establish the overall dimensions of the part using the height, width, and length dimensions, and block out the part as shown (45 ° was used as the receding angle). Use dimension A to establish the top surface of the part.
3. Use dimensions B and C to locate and establish the circular lug of the part. Dimension C is the diameter of the circular feature.
4. Set off dimensions E and F along their respective edges, and draw the corner cut as shown. Then draw the circular curve using the center point, and darken the part.

9.7.1 Oblique Sketching

Start the oblique sketch as you would a multiview or isometric drawing: Block out the overall dimensions, each feature, and box in the curves (Fig. 9.47). Figure 9.48 shows the four steps in oblique sketching: (1) Block out the part, starting with the front or the rear face, and establish the width and the height. (2) Establish the depth of each face, and then *carve out* the primary features. (3) Locate each circular form with centerlines, and box in the curves. (4) Complete the sketch by finalizing the features and darkening

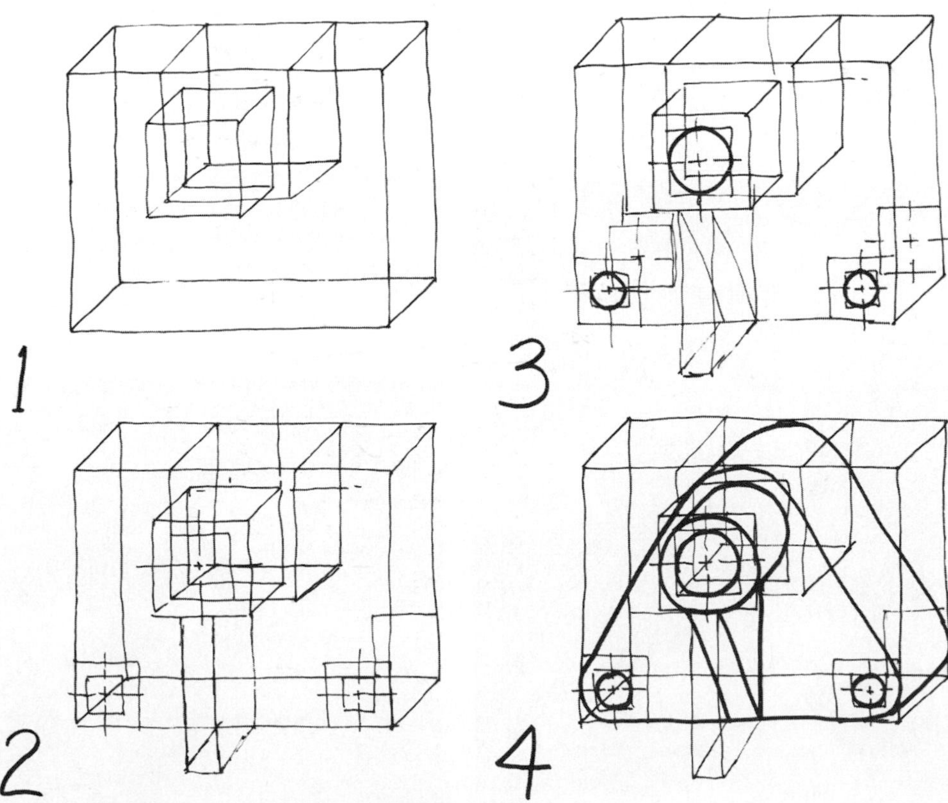

FIGURE 9.48 Step-by-Step Oblique Construction

in all object lines. Normally, hidden edges and surfaces are not shown. In most instances, construction lines are left on the sketch or only slightly dimmed before darkening the object lines.

You May Complete Exercises 9.5 Through 9.8 at This Time

9.8 CAD AND SKETCHING

Sketches are utilized in three ways when a CAD system is used for engineering and design:

- Directly on the CAD system using a sketch or sketcher command
- To lay out diagrams that will later be digitized, usually on grid paper
- As a designer's or engineer's tool for graphically exploring a design on paper before using the system

The typical CAD workstation has an area next to it dedicated as a reference surface (Fig. 9.49). Here, the designer or engineer uses the time-proven method of freehand sketching during the initial design stages of a project. Sketches enable you to develop and explore ideas and to design alternatives. The sketch can then serve as a reference for 3D CAD modeling or 2D CAD drawing and detailing.

Freehand sketching directly on the CAD system is also possible with some computer graphics systems, though this capability is still somewhat limited. By turning on construction lines on one layer and using a different color, you can sketch directly on the system. The layer with the construction lines is turned off before plotting the sketch.

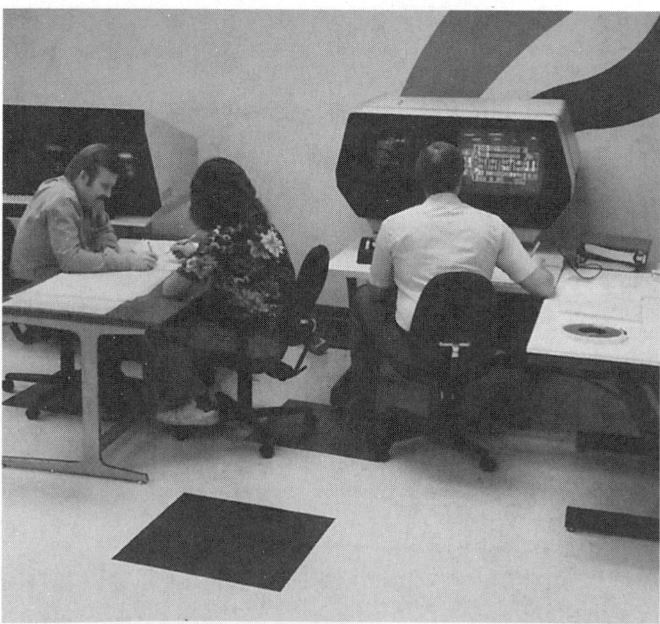

FIGURE 9.49 **Designers Sketching at a Reference Table Next to a CAD/CAM Workstation**

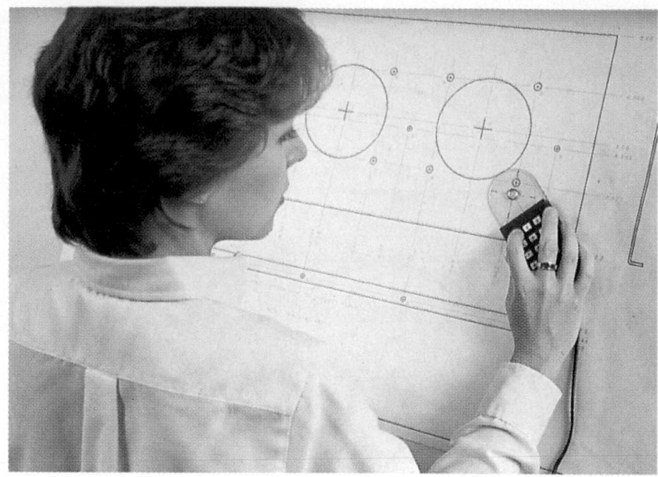

FIGURE 9.50 **Digitizing a Sketch Drawn on Grid Paper**

Digitizing existing drawings and diagrams (Fig 9.50) can be done directly from a freehand sketch with the proper equipment. A digitizing table is used to input existing instrument drawings or freehand sketches. Freehand sketches are normally completed on grid paper and then taped to the digitizing surface. The drafter can establish any scale for the project. The drawing or sketch is then digitized (Fig. 9.51) using a puck, pen, or other input device to create the 2D drawing.

Besides the digitizing of sketches, some CAD systems have the ability to create sketches via specific commands. The **SKETCH** command on AutoCAD permits freehand drawings to be created as part of a drawing. Freehand drawings are distinguished from normal AutoCAD drawings in that they are automatically entered as the puck, mouse, or pen is moved, rather than being built from points, lines, arcs, etc. Freehand drawing via a CAD system is best suited for such items as signatures (Fig. 9.52), map contour lines, and other types of irregular material.

The freehand drawing facility captures your sketching as a series of lines. You can perform limited editing on these

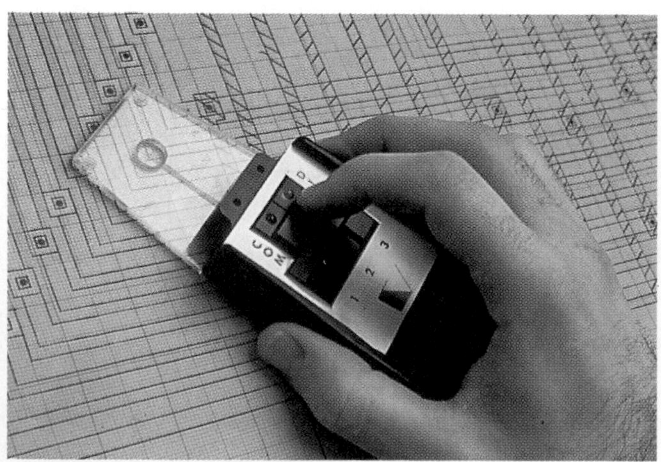

FIGURE 9.51 **Digitizing a 2D Sketch**

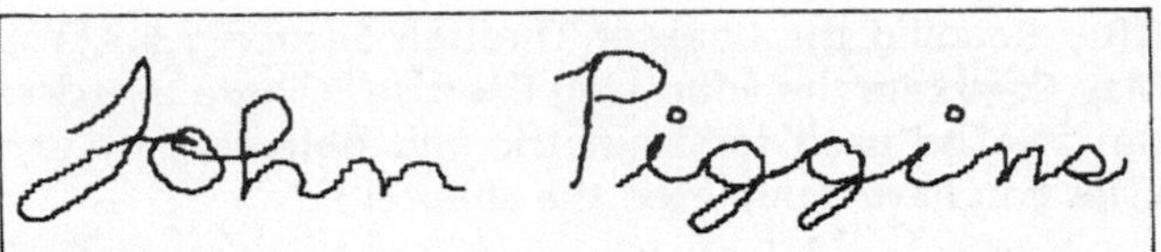

FIGURE 9.52 **Signature Drawn with AutoCAD's SKETCH Command**

lines before recording them in the AutoCAD drawing database. Once recorded, all the normal facilities of AutoCAD can be used on the freehand material—you can move it, delete all or part of it, make it part of a **Block,** and so forth.

Freehand drawings can be made only with a pointing device (digitizing tablet, mouse, pen, etc.). Freehand drawing, especially with very fine accuracy, generates a large number of lines. Although every effort is made to reduce the number of lines generated (by combining lines in the same direction), it is possible in 20 seconds of freehand sketching to create a drawing with as many lines as a normal drawing that took 20 hours to enter.

To complete a simple freehand sketch, turn **Ortho, Snap,** and **Tablet** modes off and enter the **SKETCH** command:

```
Command: SKETCH
Record increment <current>:
```

You determine the increment distance based on the drawing size and the required resolution. Enter the distance, in drawing units, over which movement of the pen or puck justifies generating a line segment. The smaller the distance, the more accurate (smoother) the sketch, but also the larger the database storage involved. In general, 0.1 will generate a reasonably high-resolution sketch on AutoCAD. This method of sketching is not as fast or as accurate as freehand sketching on grid paper. The final sketch with a CAD system tends to have jagged lines, as in Figure 9.52, where the signature is not very smooth, even though an increment of 0.05 was specified.

For the foreseeable future, sketching will remain a freehand manual process, as it has been since humans "scribbled" on cave walls and flat stones, used sticks to scratch construction ideas in sand, and drew engineering marvels on parchment and papyrus.

QUIZ

True or False

1. The most common angles for sketching oblique drawings are 15°, 20°, 25°, and 40°.
2. When drawing a circle, it is common practice to rotate the paper.
3. When blocking in a circle or an isometric ellipse, the sides are equal to the diameter.
4. 6H lead is best for sketching.
5. Sketch vertical lines starting from the bottom and move up.
6. Never show centerlines for round or curved portions of a part if it is drawn as an oblique or isometric projection.
7. Pictorial sketches are essential to the design process because they allow the designer to explore different possibilities, shapes, and orientations of the part.
8. Grid paper should be used whenever possible when sketching.

Fill in the Blanks

9. __________ or __________ lead is the best grade for sketching.
10. The pencil is held about __________ from the __________ when sketching.
11. Right-handed drafters draw horizontal lines by moving the pencil from __________ to __________.
12. Circles are sketched by first drawing a __________
13. __________ and __________ lines are used to lay out the outline of a part before darkening the lines.
14. __________ and __________ lines are sketched by moving the pencil from __________ to __________.
15. __________, __________, and __________ are used to represent a part pictorially during the __________ stage of a project.
16. __________ lines are drawn vertical or receding at __________ degrees to the horizontal for isometric drawings.

Answer the Following

17. List the steps in sketching a circle.
18. Describe the difference between isometric and oblique projection.
19. How is sketching used in conjunction with CAD in the design process?
20. How would you sketch an ellipse that lies in the horizontal plane?
21. What are the six standard views? Which views are most commonly represented on an orthographic drawing?
22. Why are parts always blocked out before darkening the lines?
23. How does the shape of a part help determine the use of isometric or oblique projection techniques?
24. Describe the process of sketching irregular curves.

EXERCISES

Transfer the given information to an "A"-size sheet of .25 in. grid paper. Complete all views, and solve for proper visibility, including centerlines, object lines, and hidden lines. Exercises that are not assigned by the instructor can be sketched in the text to provide practice and to enhance understanding of the preceding instructional material.

After Reading the Chapter Through Section 9.5.3, You May Complete the Following Exercises (These exercises can also be used for isometric and oblique problems after you have completed the chapter.)

Exercise 9.1 Sketch the one-view drawing.
Exercise 9.2 Sketch the two-view drawing.
Exercise 9.3 Sketch the circular part.
Exercise 9.4 Sketch the two-view section drawing.

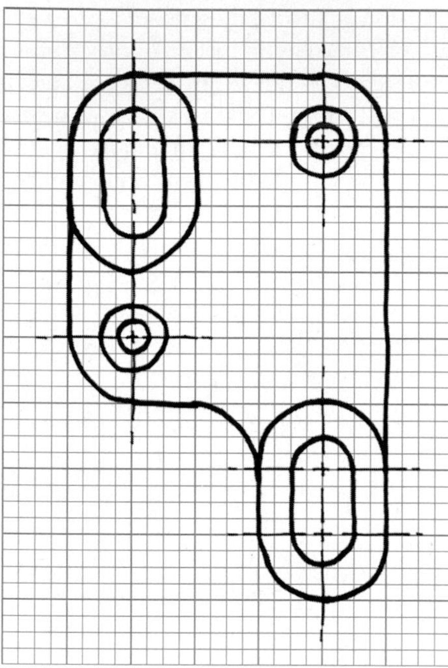

EXERCISE 9.1

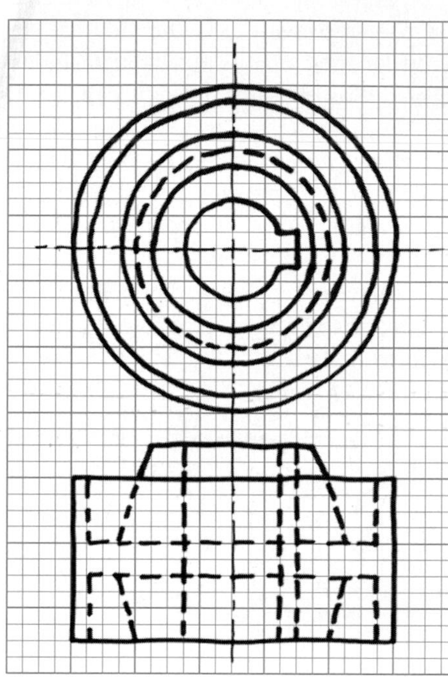

EXERCISE 9.3

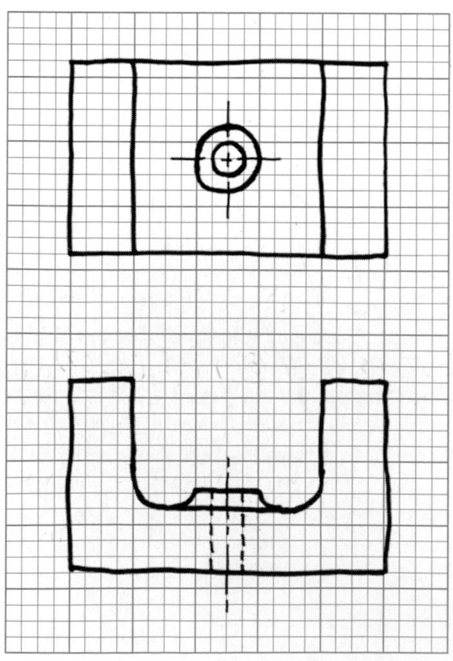

EXERCISE 9.2

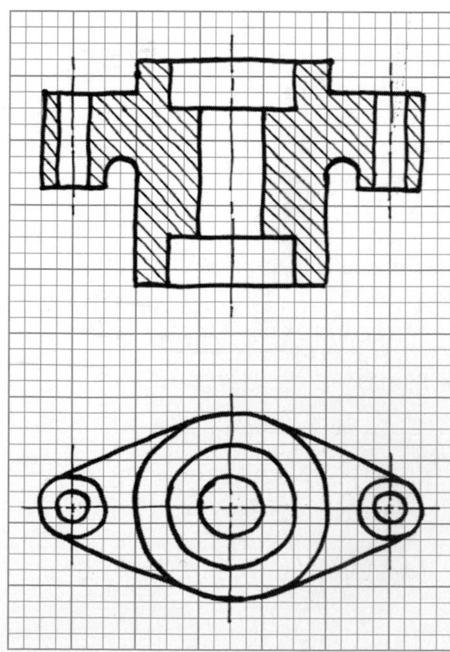

EXERCISE 9.4

After Reading the Chapter Through Section 9.7.1, You May Complete the Following Exercises

Exercise 9.5 Sketch the three-view part, and complete an isometric sketch of the part on isometric grid paper.
Exercise 9.6 Sketch an isometric view of the part on isometric grid paper, and complete a two-view drawing.

Exercise 9.7 Sketch an isometric view of the part on isometric grid paper. Also complete a three-view drawing.
Exercise 9.8 Sketch an oblique cabinet view of the part (use 45°), and complete a two-view drawing project at two times the book scale.

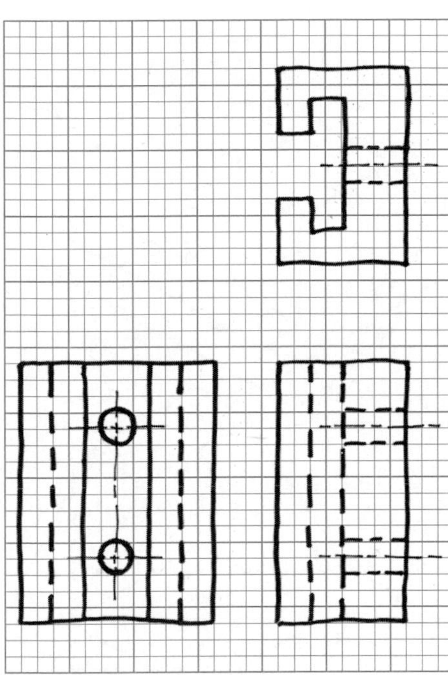

EXERCISE 9.5

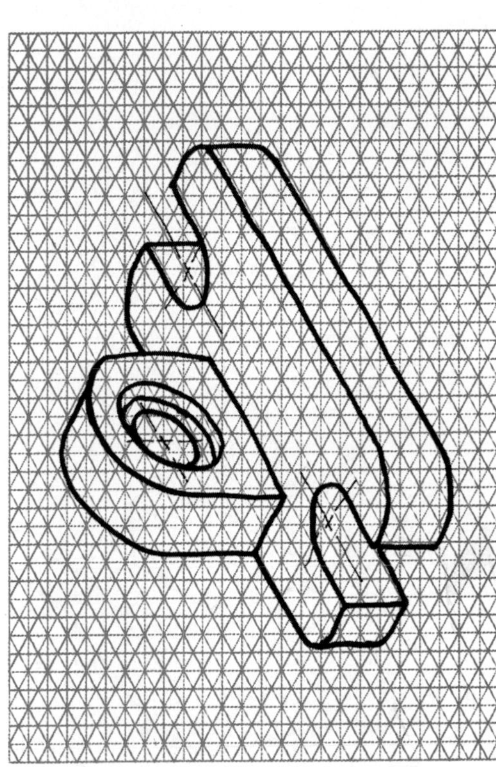

EXERCISE 9.7

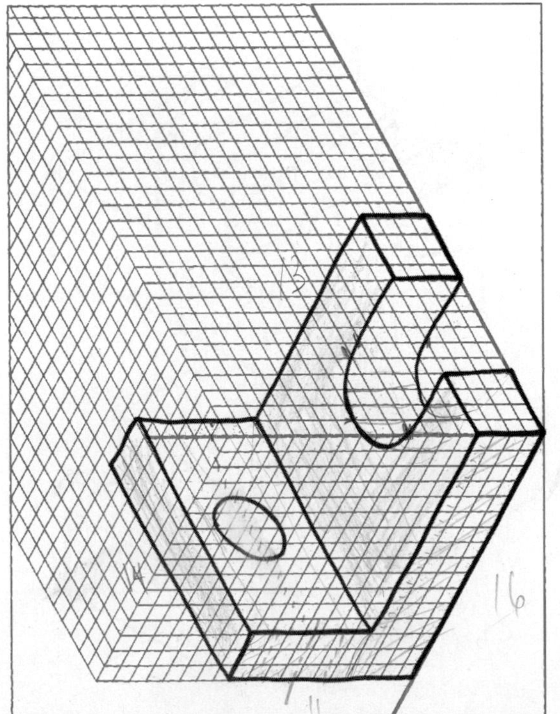

EXERCISE 9.6

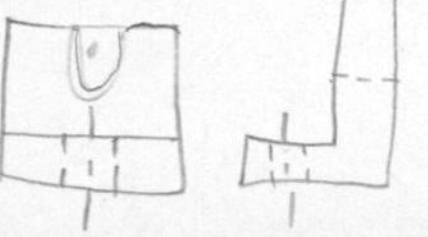

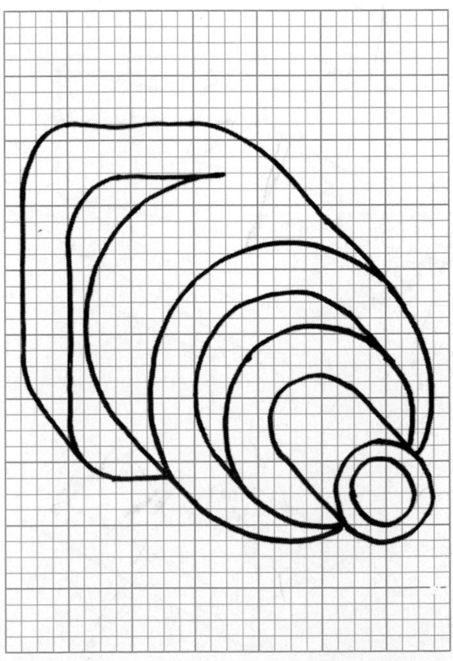

EXERCISE 9.8

PROBLEMS

Problems 9.1(A) through (H) Freehand sketch the assigned problems using multiview projection. Draw the projects at two times the book scale. Problems can be drawn using any units type. Two or three views may be required for the problem.

Problems 9.2(A) through (I) Same as Problem 9.1.

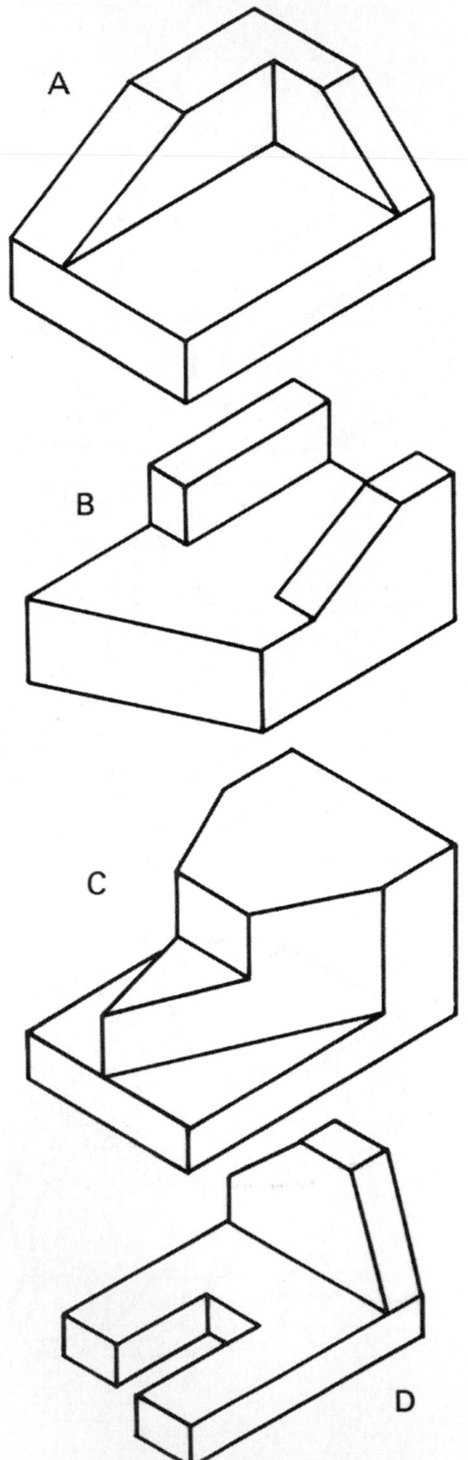

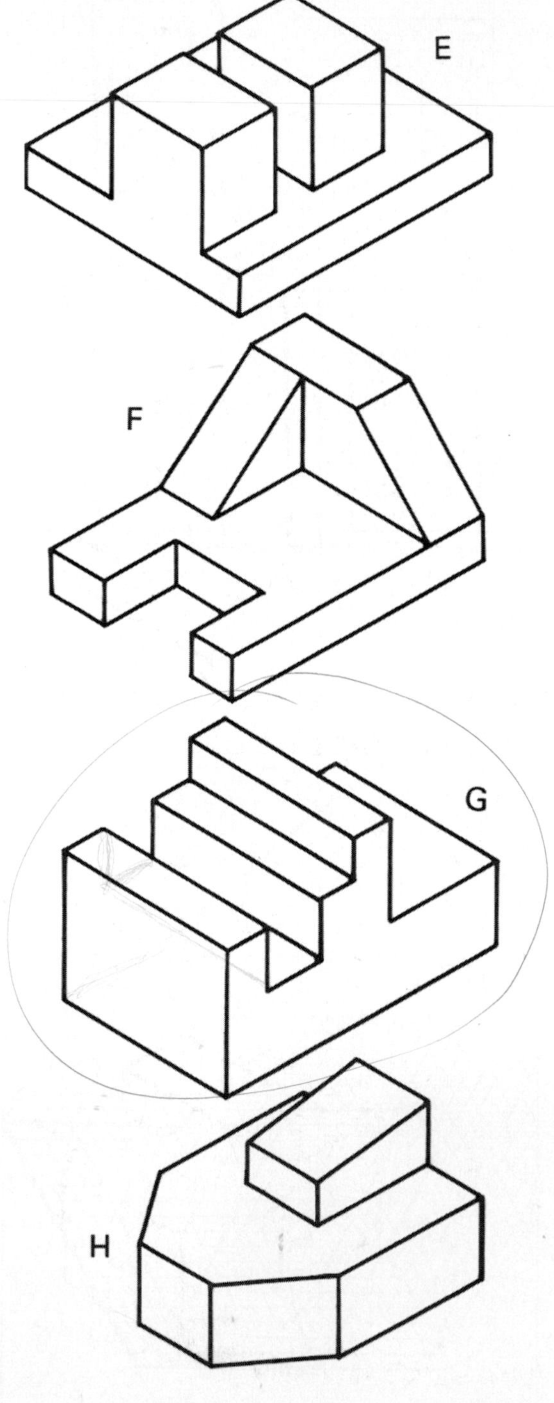

PROBLEMS 9.1(A) THROUGH (H)

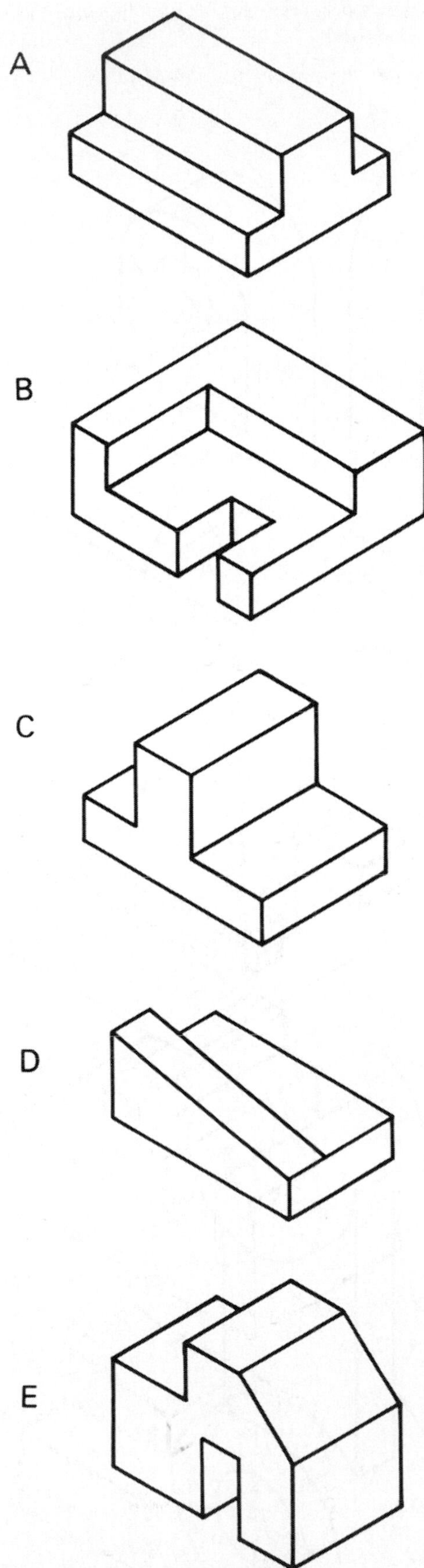

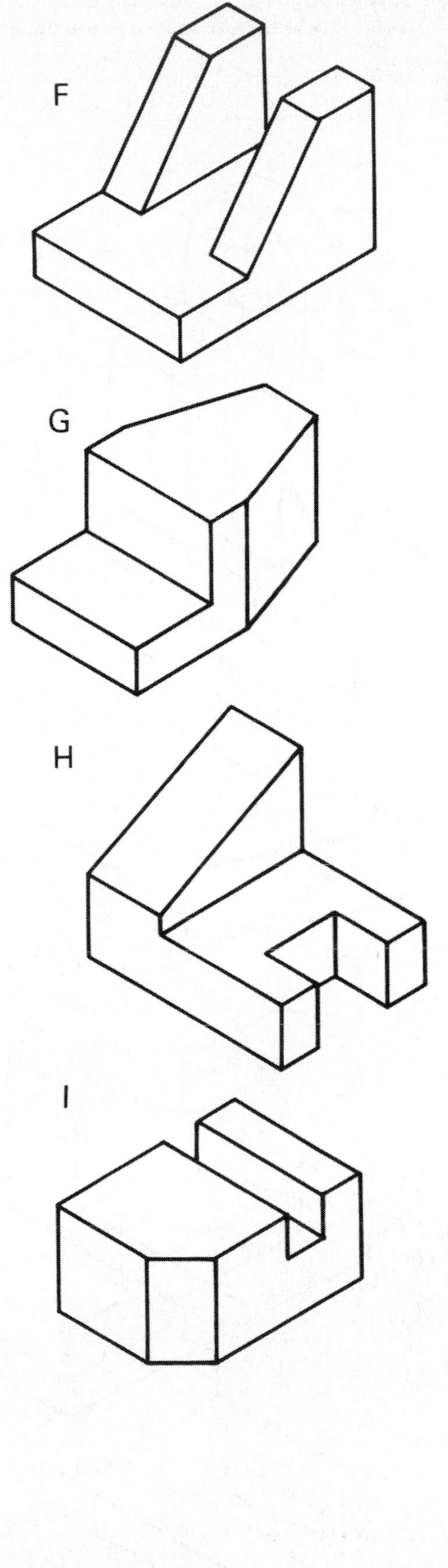

PROBLEMS 9.2(A) THROUGH (H)

Problem 9.3(A) through (G) Using freehand sketching, draw each of the assigned problems. Use oblique projection. Be careful to choose the proper surface for the front face of the part. Draw at two times book scale.

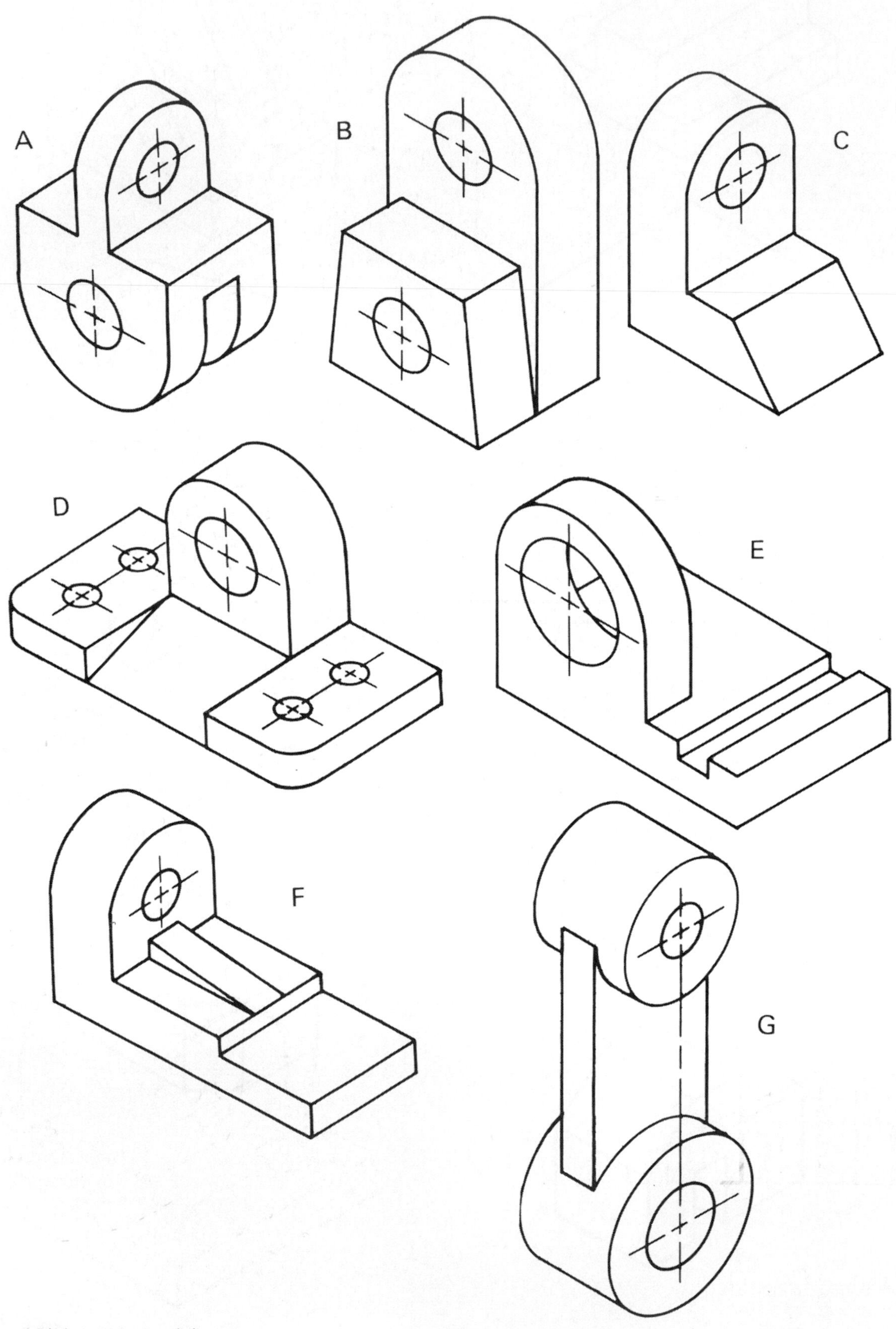

PROBLEMS 9.3(A) THROUGH (G)

Problems 9.4(A) through (C) Complete the three views of each problem. On the same sheet sketch an isometric view. Draw at two times book scale.

Problems 9.4(D) through (F) Sketch three views of each problem. Draw at two times the book scale.

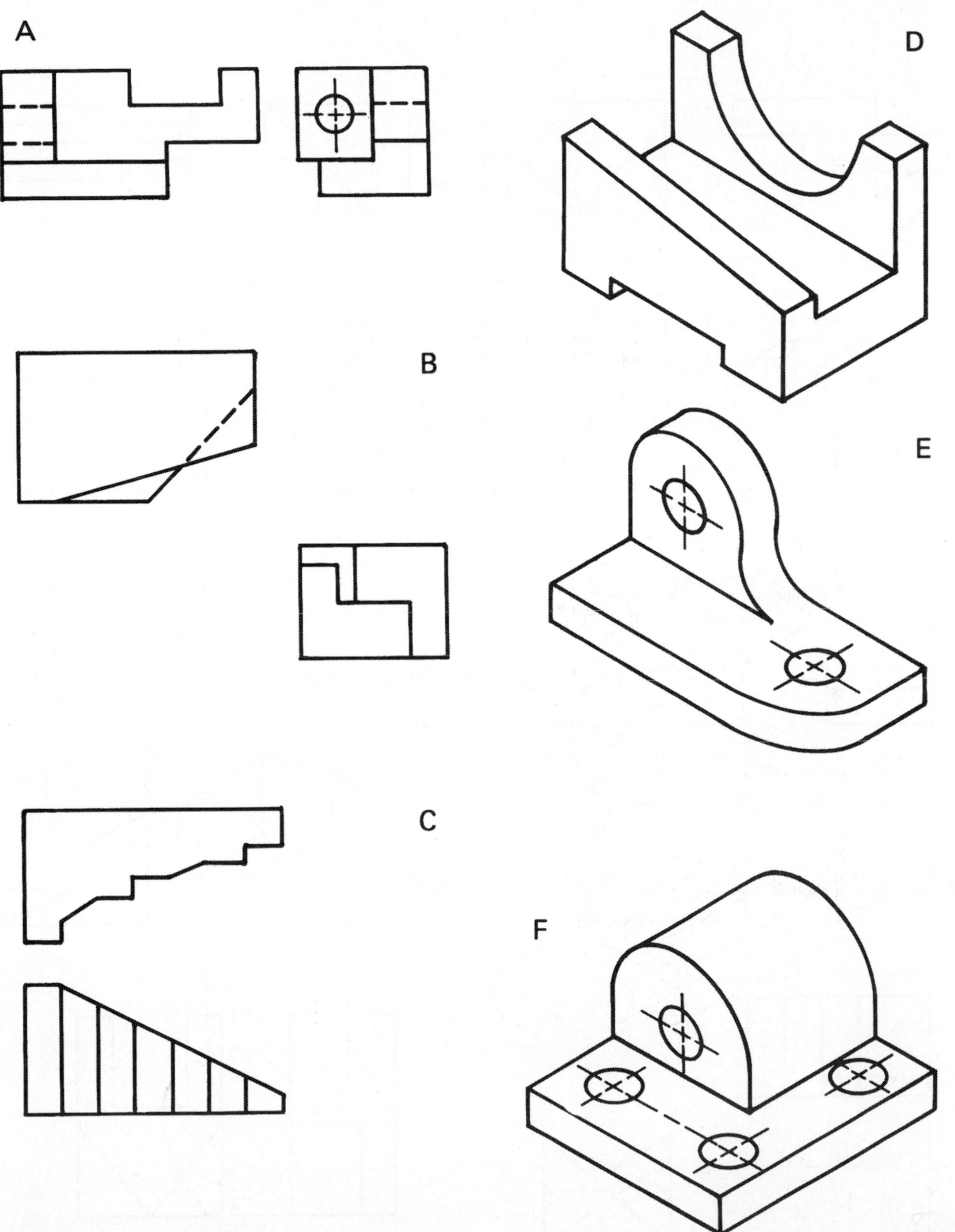

PROBLEMS 9.4(A) THROUGH (F)

Problem 9.5(A) through (J) Complete the given views and project a third view of each problem. Do an isometric sketch of each problem on a separate sheet of paper. Draw at three times the book scale. The isometric sketch will help you solve for the three views of the part.

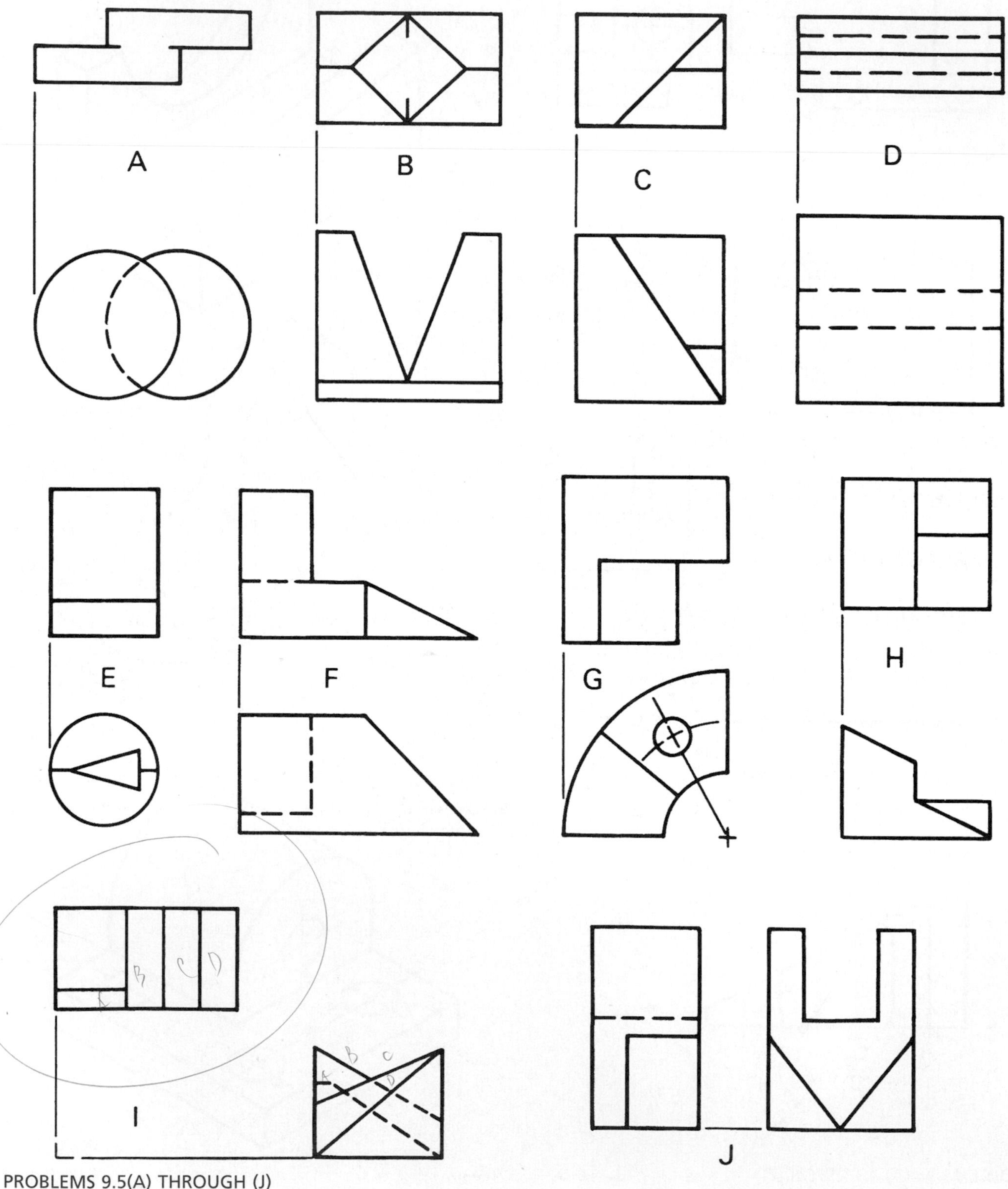

PROBLEMS 9.5(A) THROUGH (J)

DRAWING BASICS

FIGURE 10.4 Multiview Drawing

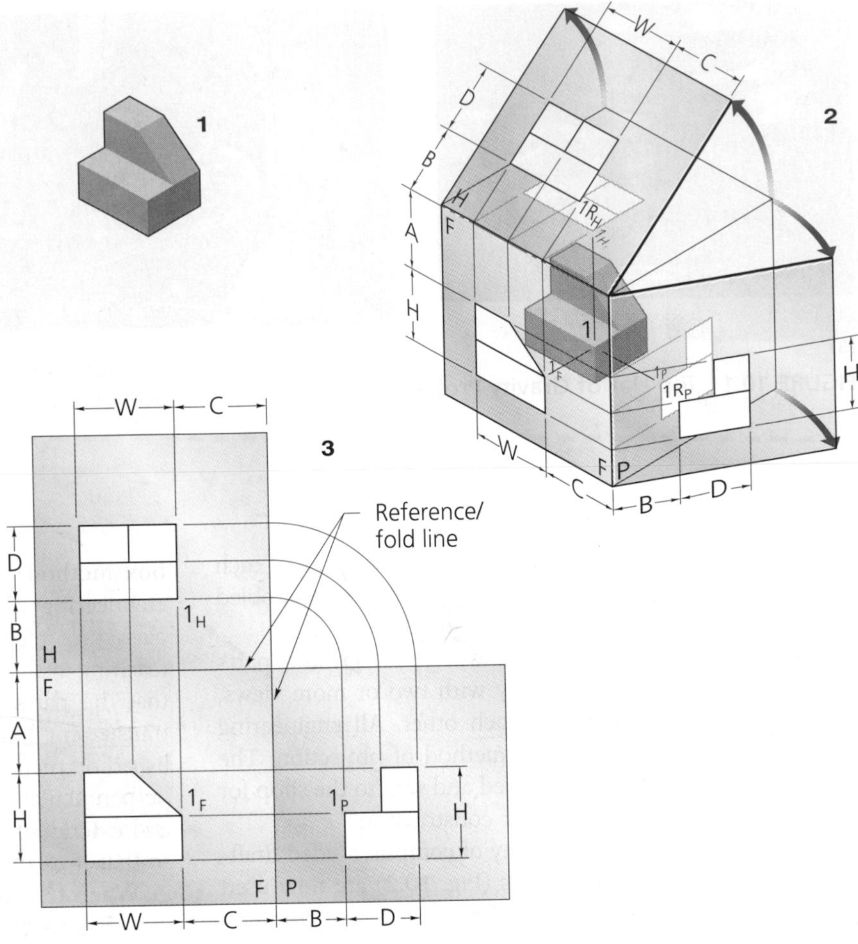

10.2 ORTHOGRAPHIC PROJECTION

Orthographic projection may be defined as a system of drawing composed of images formed by *projectors* extended from a part perpendicular to the desired planes of projection. The figure outlined on one of the projection planes, called an **orthographic view**, shows the true size and shape of a surface parallel to the projection plane (area ABCD with hole in Fig. 10.5). If an area is not parallel to the plane, the view of the area will be foreshortened (area BCEF in Fig. 10.5).

The glass box method of projection for a part is illustrated in its closed (folded) position and open (unfolded) position in Figure 10.6. The part has been theoretically enclosed in the transparent box. The following concepts are used throughout this chapter and the text.

Lines

A = **Vertical lines of sight**
B = **Horizontal lines of sight**
C = **Projection lines**

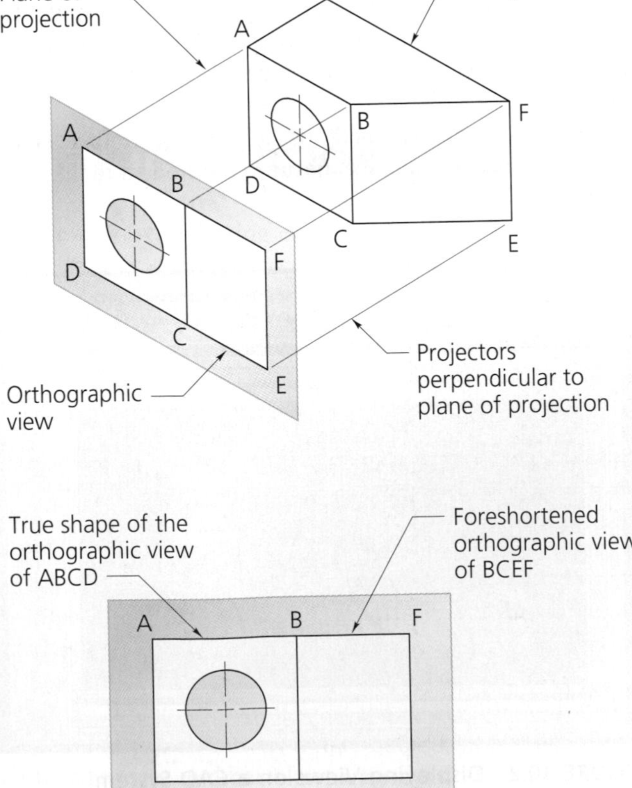

FIGURE 10.5 Third-Angle Orthographic Projection

Dimensions
D = Depth
H = Height
W = Width

Image Planes (Principal Projection Planes)
F = Front (frontal plane)
H = Top (horizontal plane)
P = Side (profile plane)

10.2.1 Line of Sight

When a part is projected onto an image plane, it creates a **"view"** of that part. *The lines of sight represent the direction from which the part is viewed* (Fig. 10.6). The vertical lines of sight (A) and horizontal lines of sight (B) are assumed to originate at infinity. The **line of sight** is always perpendicular to the image (projection) plane, represented by the surfaces of the glass box (top, front, and right side). **Projection lines** (C) connect the same point on the image plane from view to view, always at right angles to the adjacent view.

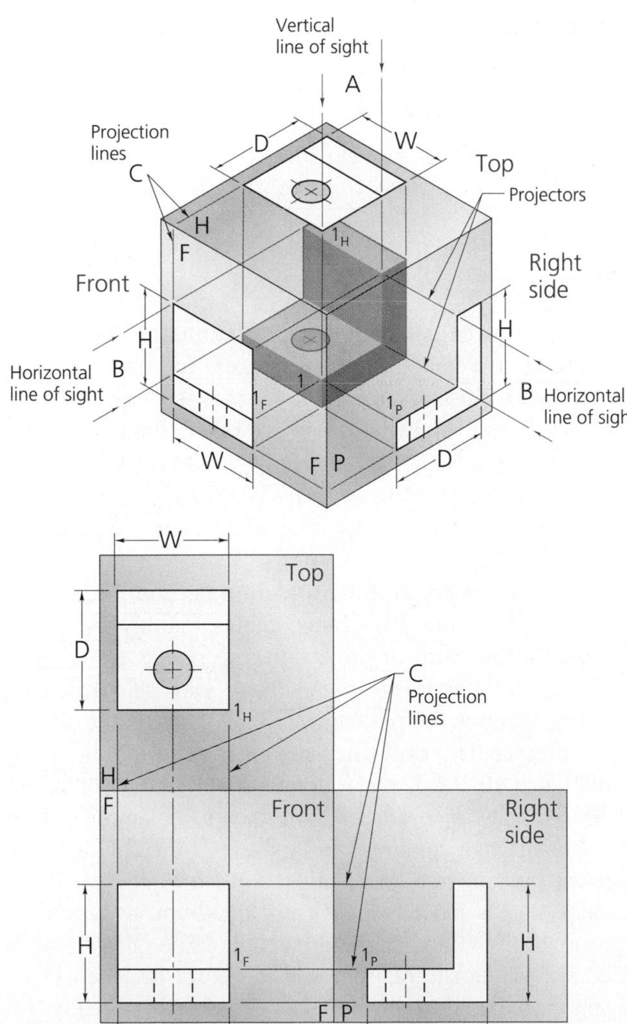

FIGURE 10.6 Orthographic Projection of a Part

A point is projected onto the image plane where its line of sight pierces that image plane. In Figure 10.6, point 1, which represents a corner of the part, has been projected onto the three primary image planes. Where it intersects the horizontal plane (top image plane), it is identified as 1_H. Where it intersects the frontal plane (front image plane), it is identified as I_F. Where it intersects the profile plane (right side image plane), it is labeled l_P. The multiview drawing in Figure 10.6 shows the position of the unfolded image planes, which now lie in the same plane as the paper.

In Figure 10.7(a), the line of sight for each view is shown. These lines of sight establish the direction of viewing that the observer will take when completing the view. Figure 10.7(b) shows the three views properly aligned. In Figures 10.7(c), (d), and (e), the top, front, and side views are broken apart and analyzed separately. All points on each surface of the part are projected onto their corresponding image plane (view). The view of the part is created where these projectors pierce the image plane.

10.3 THE SIX PRINCIPAL VIEWS

When the glass box is opened, its six sides are revolved outward so that they lie in the plane of the paper. Except for the back plane, all are hinged to the front plane. The back plane is normally revolved from the left side view, but it can also be hinged to the right side view. Each image plane, before it is revolved around its hinged fold line (reference line), is perpendicular to its adjacent image plane and parallel to the image plane across from it.

A **fold line** is the line of intersection between any hinged (adjacent) image planes. The left side, front, right side, and back are all **elevation views.** Each is vertical. In these views, the height dimension, elevation, and top and bottom of the view can be determined and dimensioned. The top and bottom planes are in the horizontal plane. The depth dimension, width dimension, and front and back are established in these two horizontal planes.

In most cases, the top, front, and right sides are required. These are sometimes referred to as the horizontal plane, H (top); frontal plane, F (front); and profile plane, P (side). These planes are the three **principal projection planes,** or **views.**

In Figure 10.8(a), the glass box is shown pictorially before it is revolved. The top, front, and bottom are in line vertically, and the left side, front, right side, and back are aligned horizontally. An exception to this alignment is when the glass box is revolved around the top (horizontal) view. This rotation is advantageous when the part has much greater depth than height.

When using directions to establish the location of a point, a line, etc., the top and bottom are shown in the frontal plane; the terms "above" and "below" can also describe directions in this plane. The horizontal view can help to determine if a point is "in front of" or "in back of" a

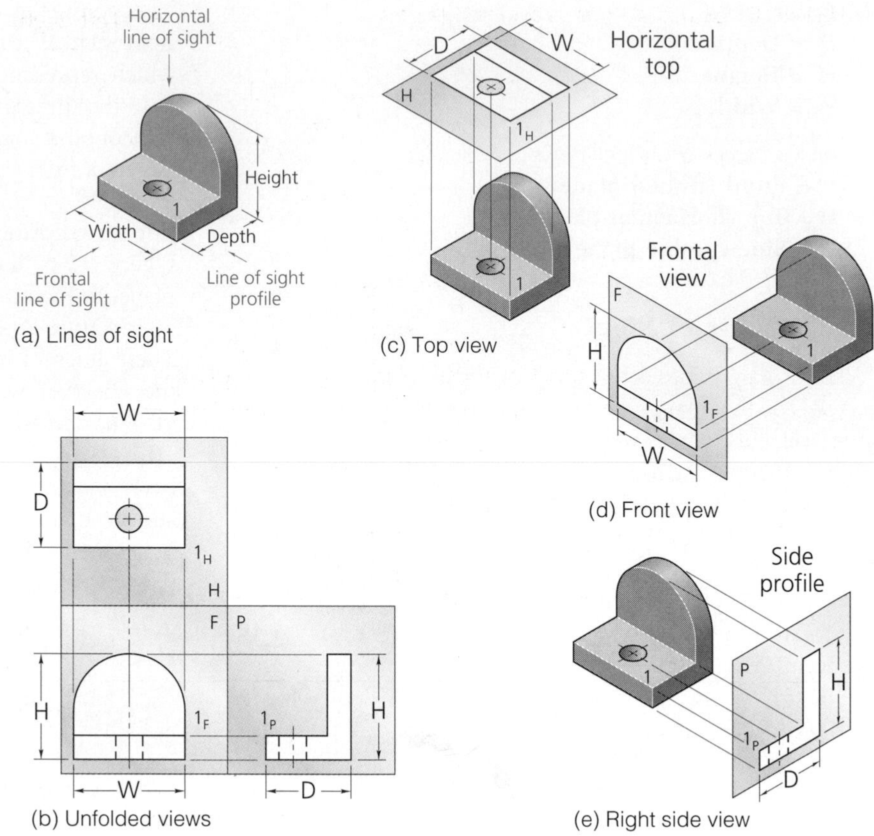

FIGURE 10.7 Line of Sight

particular starting point or fold line. To locate a point to the right or left of a fold line or an established point, the frontal or horizontal plane can be used. In the profile plane, the top, bottom, front, and back can be determined. In Figure 10.8(b) and (c) a part is shown in each of the six standard views (and pictorially enclosed in a glass box). The six standard views are shown in first-angle and third-angle projection.

10.4 FIRST- AND THIRD-ANGLE PROJECTION

Two types of orthographic projection are employed in industry throughout the world: **first-angle** and **third-angle projections.** The six principal views of a part, or the glass box, have been presented in the type of orthographic projection known as *third-angle orthographic projection.* This form of projection is used throughout the United States and Canada and is the primary form of projection in all of American industry. In third-angle projection, the line of sight goes through the image plane to the part. To obtain views of the part, you must assume that the part is projected back (along the lines of sight) to the image plane. Projection lines serve to show this projection from the part to where they intersect the image plane. Figure 10.8(c) illustrates third-angle projection and the normal procedure for unfolding the glass box.

First-angle orthographic projection is common in most countries apart from the United States and Canada [Fig. 10.8(b)]. In this form of projection, the part is assumed to be in front of the image plane. Each view is formed by projecting through the part and onto the image plane. Figure 10.9 compares first- and third-angle projection.

In Figure 10.10(a), the four quadrants and their corresponding angles of projection are shown. A simple part is placed in the first quadrant in Figure 10.10(b). This is the quadrant used in first-angle projection. In Figure 10.10(c), the same part is placed in the third quadrant, as would be appropriate for third-angle projection. The glass box is added and the quadrants removed in Figure 10.10(e). Here, the part resides inside the glass box and is ready for projection. Figure 10.10(f) illustrates how the top, front,

FIGURE 10.8 **Standard Views and Projection**

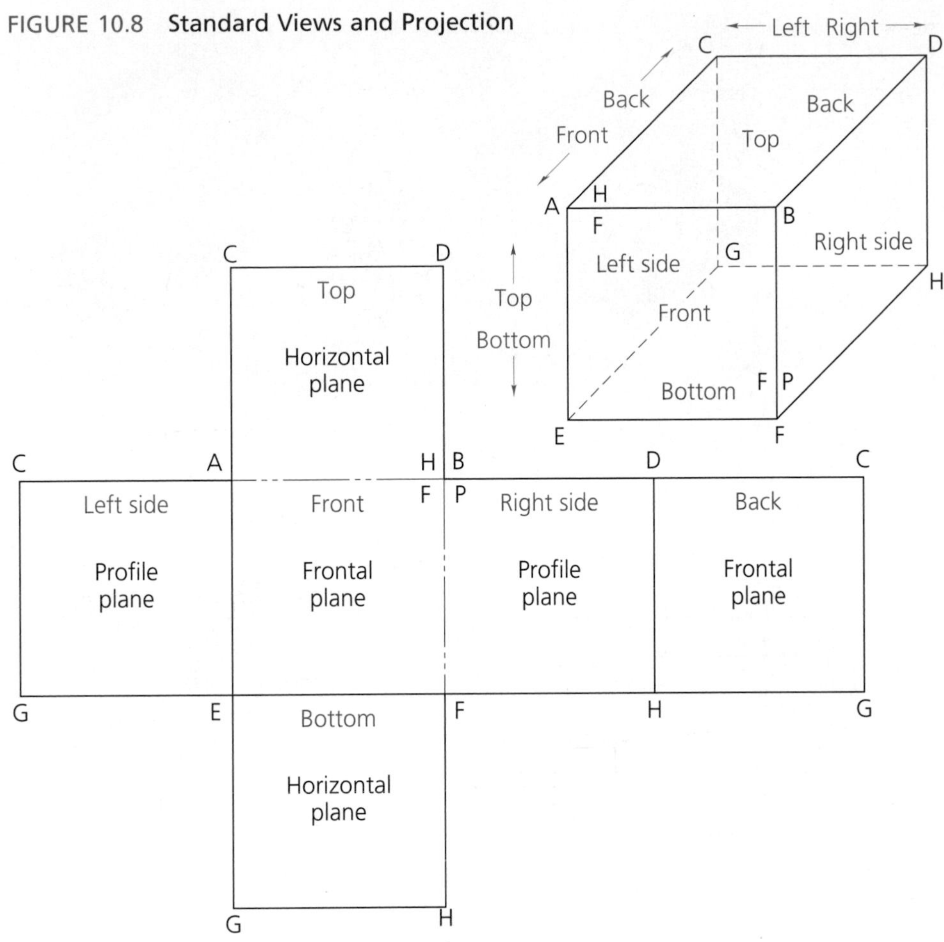

(a) Six standard views

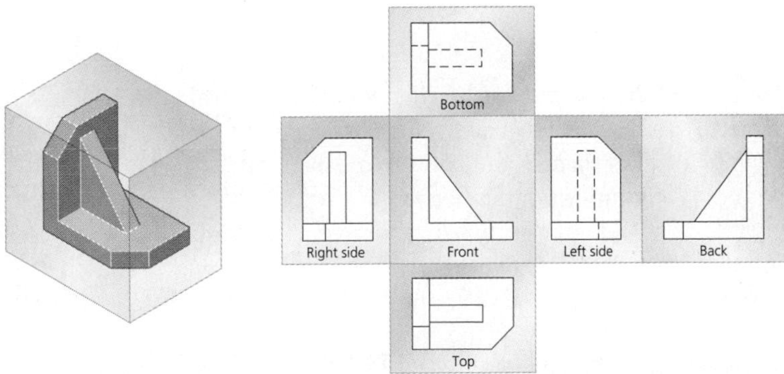

(b) First-angle projection

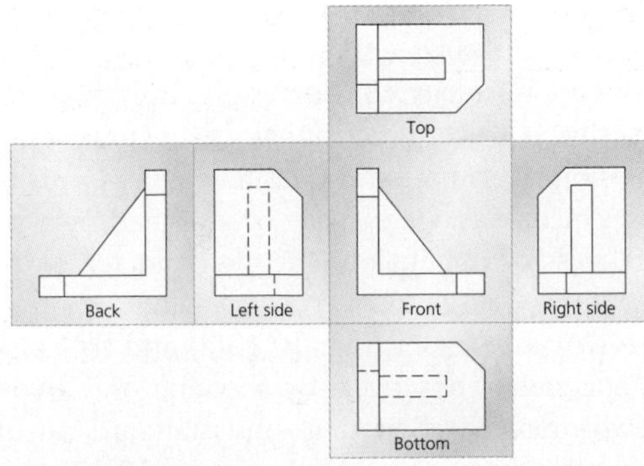

(c) Third-angle projection

and side views are projected onto the glass box. The **six standard views** are established by the six directions of sight [Fig. 10.10(g)]: top, front, right side, left side, rear, and bottom. We have begun to unfold the glass box (with its corresponding projections of each of the six sides) in Figure 10.10(h). The unfolded position of the glass box is shown in Figure 10.10(i). This is the true projection of all six sides

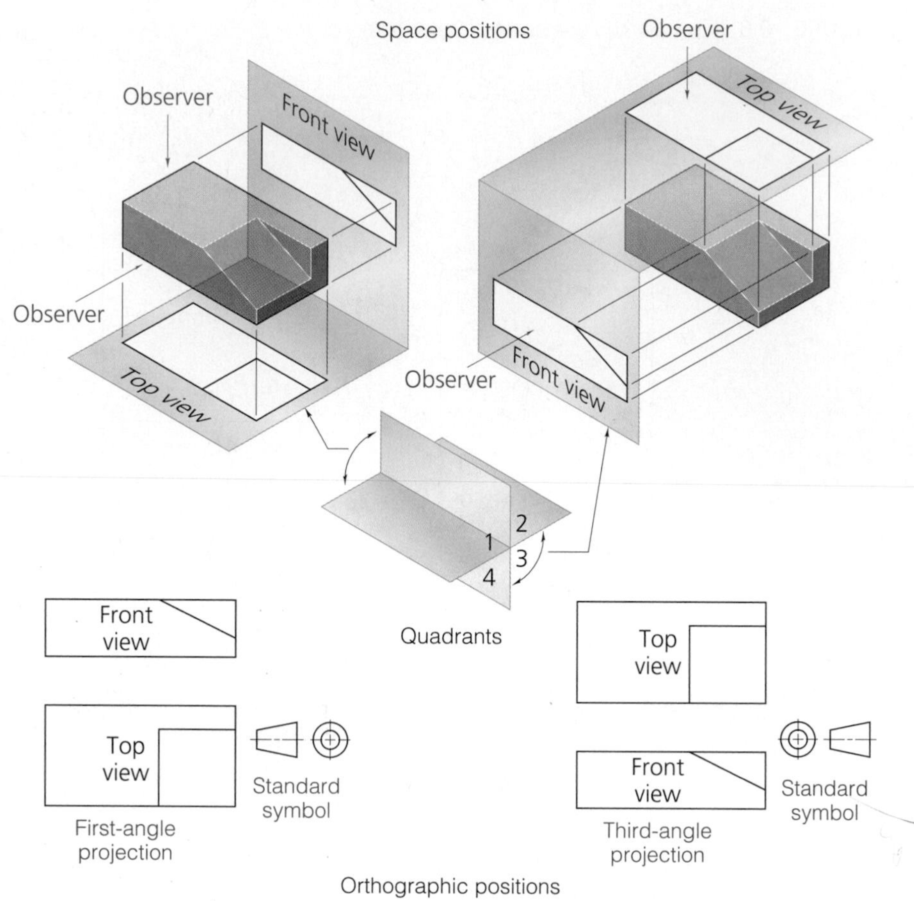

FIGURE 10.9 First- and Third-Angle Projection

using third-angle projection. The first-angle projection of this same part is shown in Figure 10.10(j). The part's left side view is drawn on the right side of the part. The top view is placed below the front view; the bottom view is placed above the front view.

The internationally recognized **ISO projection symbols** for first- and third-angle projections are shown on drawings as in Figure 10.9. Identifying symbols are required on drawings so that they can be understood and interchanged internationally. The symbol is normally placed to the left of the title block, as in Figure 10.11. This text uses third-angle projection exclusively.

10.5 MULTIVIEW DRAWINGS

Multiview drawings represent the shape of a part through two or more views. These views, together with the necessary notes and dimensions, are sufficient for fabrication of the part without further information concerning its shape. Consideration is given to the choice and number of views so that all surfaces are shown in their true shape and with a minimum of confusion.

Four basic types of drawings are found in engineering work; one-, two-, three-, and multiple-view. The choice of how many views are needed is determined by the shape and complexity of the part. One view can be sufficient to describe many types of parts. You must draw as many views as are necessary to describe the part completely. The four types of drawings are:

One-view drawings [Fig. 10.12(a) and (b)] Two adjacent views are normally considered the minimum requirement to describe a three-dimensional part. However, the third dimension of some parts (washers, shafts, bushings, spacers, sheet metal parts, etc.) may be specified by a note giving the thickness or dimensions for the diameter.

Two-view drawings [Fig. 10.13(a) and (b)] Many parts may be adequately described by showing only two views. These views must be aligned in any standard position that will clearly illustrate the part. In Figure 10.13(a), the side view was necessary to describe and dimension the part.

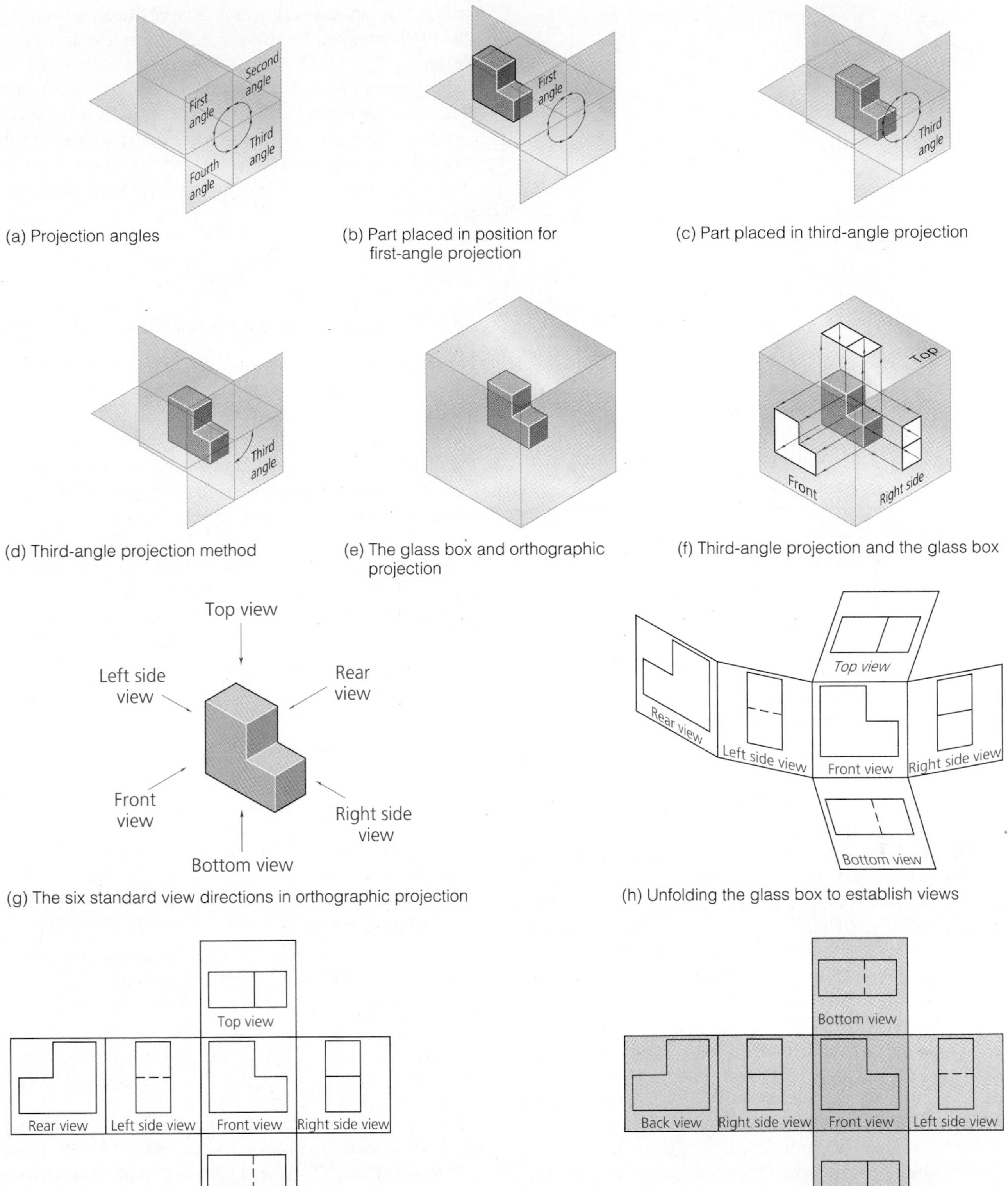

(a) Projection angles

(b) Part placed in position for first-angle projection

(c) Part placed in third-angle projection

(d) Third-angle projection method

(e) The glass box and orthographic projection

(f) Third-angle projection and the glass box

(g) The six standard view directions in orthographic projection

(h) Unfolding the glass box to establish views

(i) Third-angle projection and the six standard views

(j) First-angle projection and the six standard views

FIGURE 10.10 Projection Theory

Three-view drawings [Fig. 10.14(a) and (b)] Most drawings consist of front, top, and side views arranged in their standard positions. Any three adjacent views that best suit the shape of the part may be drawn. Each view of the part shows features that could not be graphically described in any of the other views. The holes show in the top and the front views, and the slot and angled surfaces show in the right side view.

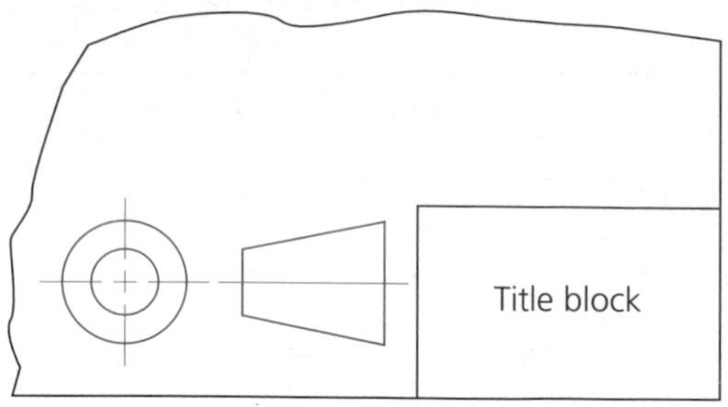

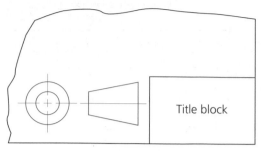

(a) Third-angle projection symbols

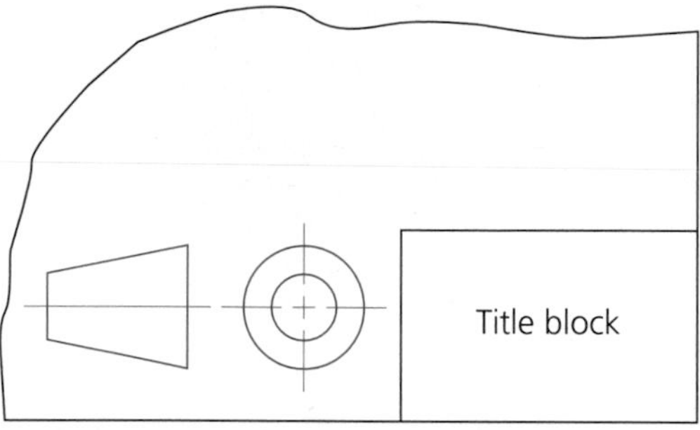

(b) First-angle projection symbols

FIGURE 10.11 **Projection Symbols**

Multiple-view and auxiliary-view drawings (Fig. 10.15) When a part cannot be defined graphically with one, two, or three views, a multiple-view drawing may be required. The part shown here required four views to describe its configuration properly.

10.5.1 Choice and Orientation of Views on a Drawing

The first step in any drawing is deciding which views of the part should be drawn and dimensioned. Because dimensioning is not covered in this chapter, it will be somewhat difficult to estimate the space and view needs of a part. Alternate positions of views may be made to conserve space or to position dimensions, but they must be properly oriented to each other. For example, the right or left side might be placed adjacent to, and in alignment, with the top view. The rear view is sometimes placed in alignment with, and to the right of, the right side view. Under certain conditions, it may be impractical to place views in the normal aligned positions or even on the same sheet. Before starting the drawing, you must analyze the configuration of the part and its view requirements. The proper decisions at this stage will reduce drawing time, provide a clearer and more concise arrangement of views, and reduce the cost of the final drawing.

A part is normally shown in a **natural** or **assembled position.** The minimum number of views necessary to describe the part is established first. Views are selected that will show the fewest hidden lines and yet convey maximum clarity. In general, since the part will be mounted or sit on a surface, the top view is obvious. The choice of top view may also be determined by the machining process and its complexity.

The front view should normally be the longest orientation of the part. In Figure 10.16, the part requires three views. It could not have been adequately described without all three views. The top view choice is obvious. The front view is the longest orientation, and the right side view is necessary to describe the V-shaped cut.

10.5.2 Relationship of Views on a Drawing

The *relationship of views* on a drawing is determined by the choice of part orientation. In Figure 10.17(a), the six standard view directions of the part are labeled. In Figure 10.17(b), the views are laid out using third-angle projection. The placement and orientation of the top view determine that the front view will be the longest orientation, or principal shape, of the part. In Figure 10.17(c), the same part is shown slightly differently, but not incorrectly. Here, the part has been turned so that the front view will not show the part's longest orientation. In fact, the side views show the longest orientation [Fig. 10.17(d)]. Although this orientation is not incorrect, it is less acceptable than Figure 10.17(b). The longest orientation should be the front view so that the predominant dimension will be the width.

10.5.3 Spacing Views

After the number of views is determined, the next step is to establish the paper format size based on the part's size, the scale to be used, and the detailing requirements. Remember, the drawing must have space for views, dimensions, and notes.

A simple method to determine roughly the sheet size is to add the dimensions of the part—width plus depth (if a side view is required), which gives the total width of the views. Add extra space for separation of the views and for a margin at each border. The height requirements of the drawing can be determined by adding the height of the part to its depth. Then add some space for the separation of the views and for the margin at the top and bottom borders. The drawing format—A, B, C, D, E, or larger—is determined by these dimensions and company/school practice.

In Figure 10.18, the part has been laid out on the sheet using the preceding formula. The height, the depth, the distance between the lower border and the front view (A), the space between the front and top views (B), and the space between the top view and the border (C) were added together to establish the vertical requirements of the drawing. The width, the depth, the space between the left border and the front view (D), the space between the front and the right side views (B), and the space between the right side

FIGURE 10.12 One-View Drawings

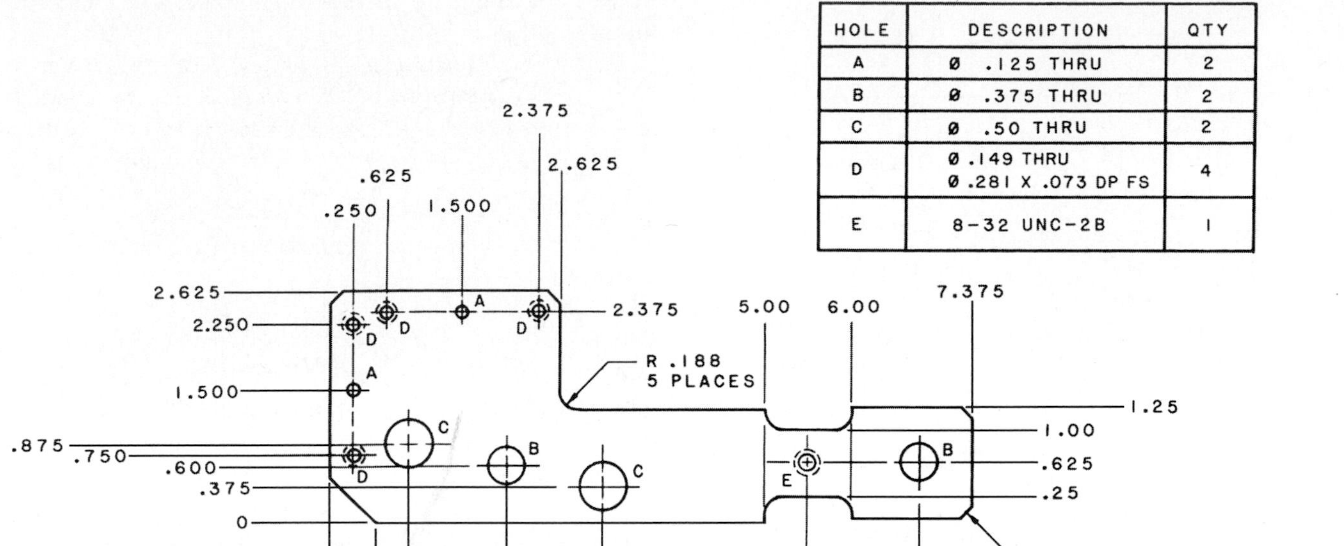

HOLE	DESCRIPTION	QTY
A	Ø .125 THRU	2
B	Ø .375 THRU	2
C	Ø .50 THRU	2
D	Ø .149 THRU Ø .281 X .073 DP FS	4
E	8-32 UNC-2B	1

(a) One-view detail of the Connector

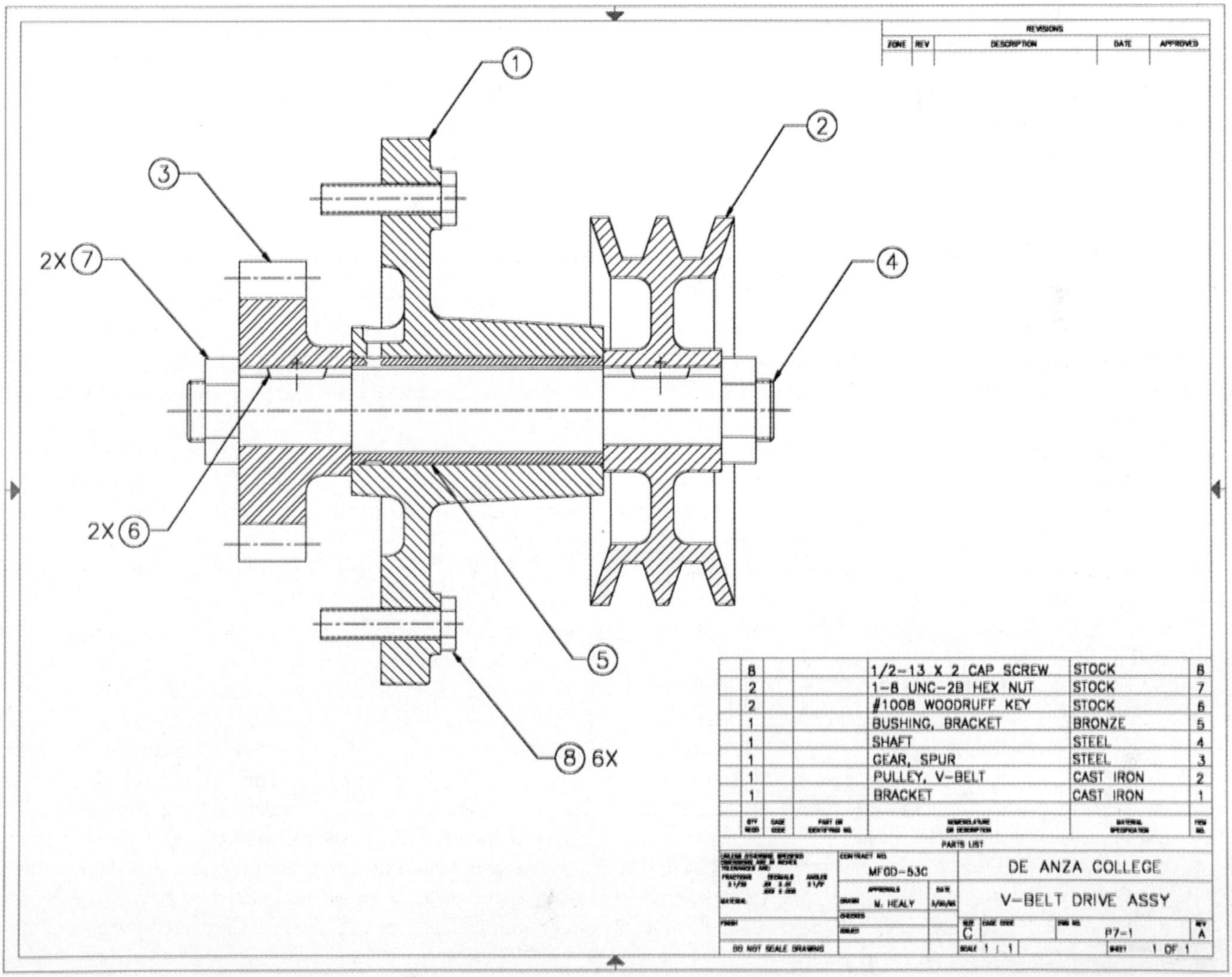

1
2
3
4
5
2X 6
2X 7
8 6X

QTY			DESCRIPTION	MATERIAL	ITEM NO.
8			1/2-13 X 2 CAP SCREW	STOCK	8
2			1-8 UNC-2B HEX NUT	STOCK	7
2			#1008 WOODRUFF KEY	STOCK	6
1			BUSHING, BRACKET	BRONZE	5
1			SHAFT	STEEL	4
1			GEAR, SPUR	STEEL	3
1			PULLEY, V-BELT	CAST IRON	2
1			BRACKET	CAST IRON	1

PARTS LIST

MFGD-53C
M. HEALY
DE ANZA COLLEGE
V-BELT DRIVE ASSY
C
P7-1
A
SCALE 1 : 1
1 OF 1
DO NOT SCALE DRAWING

(b) One-view assembly drawing of V-Belt Drive drawn with a CAD system

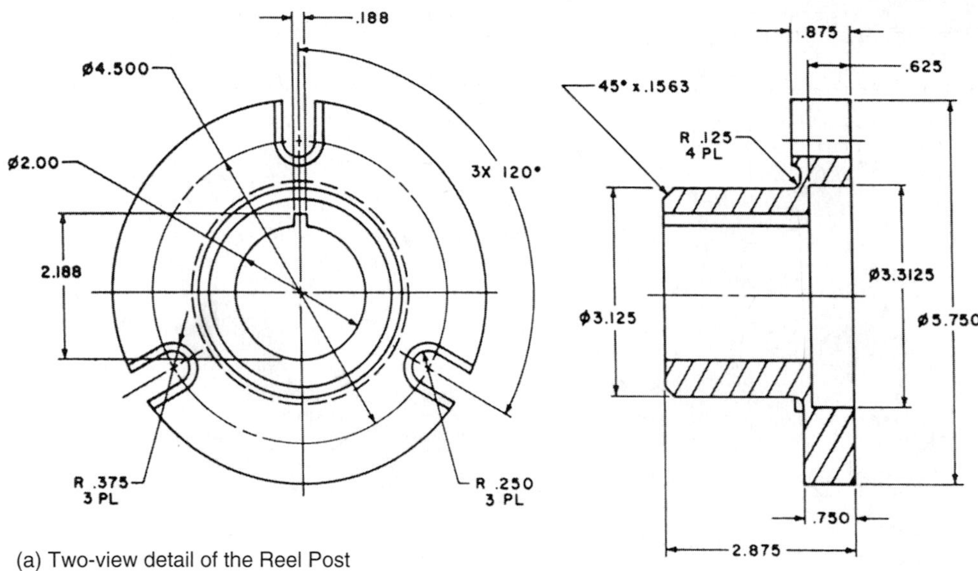

(a) Two-view detail of the Reel Post

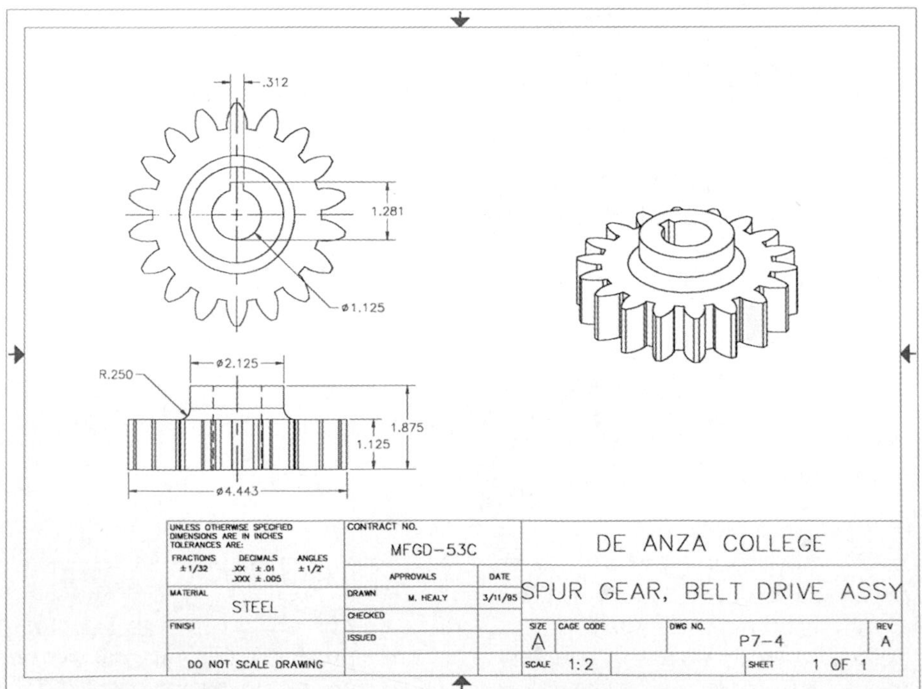

(b) Two-view detail and model of Gear

FIGURE 10.13 Two-View Drawings

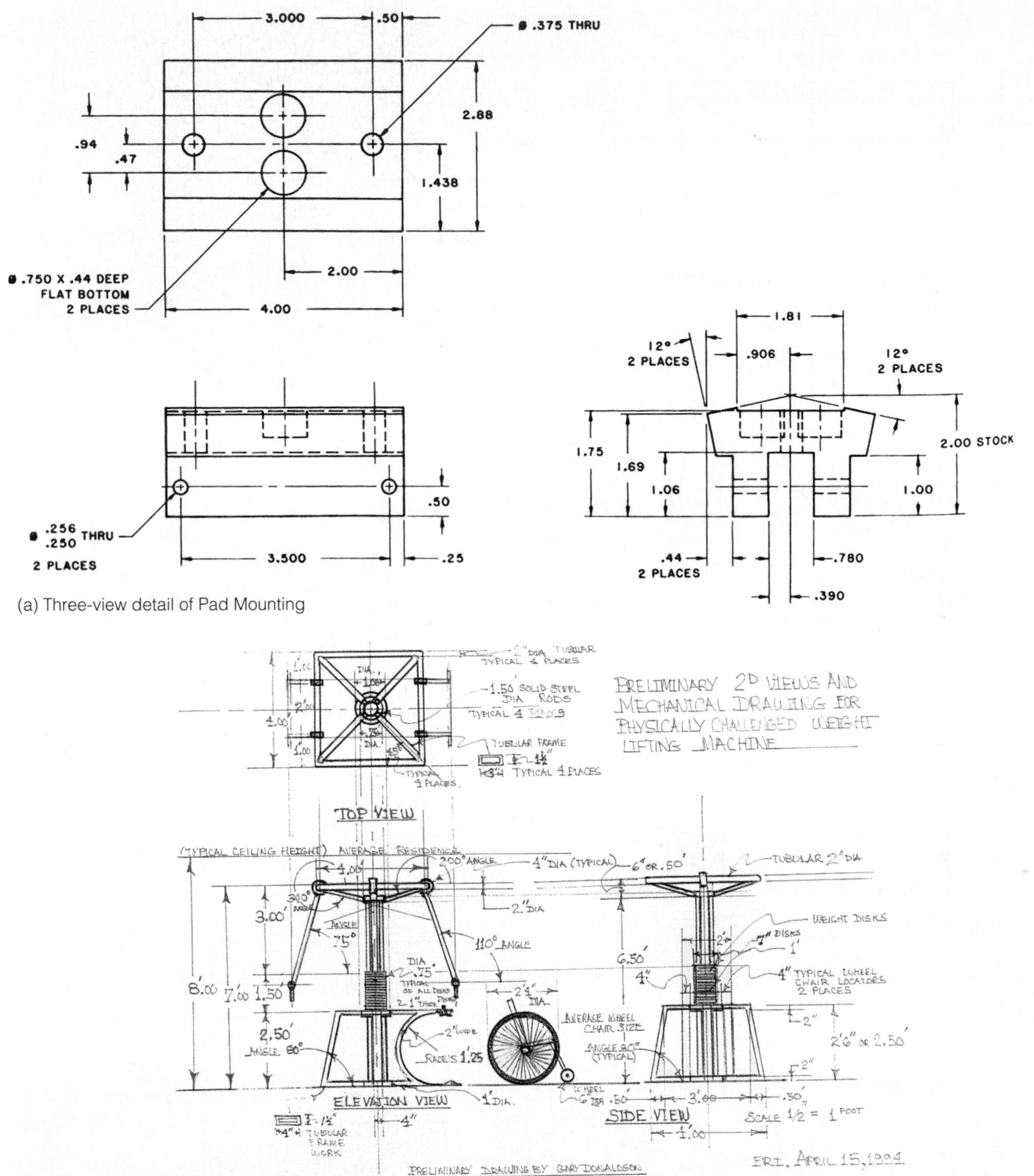

(a) Three-view detail of Pad Mounting

(b) Three-view assembly design drawing of physically challenged weight machine

FIGURE 10.14 Three-View Drawings

view and the right border (E) were added to establish the horizontal requirements. Remember, dimensions A, B, C, D, and E were determined by the space required for dimensioning.

How much space is needed between the views is usually determined by the number of dimensions that will be placed in this area. In Figure 10.19, the shaded portion of the drawing shows the space between the top and front views and between the front and side views. Some texts suggest that these areas always be equal. However, this will not always be the case. If a number of dimensions must be placed between the top and front views, this area should be greater than that between the front and side views (unless, of course, a number of dimensions are also needed there).

The drawing is laid out by *blocking in* the views with

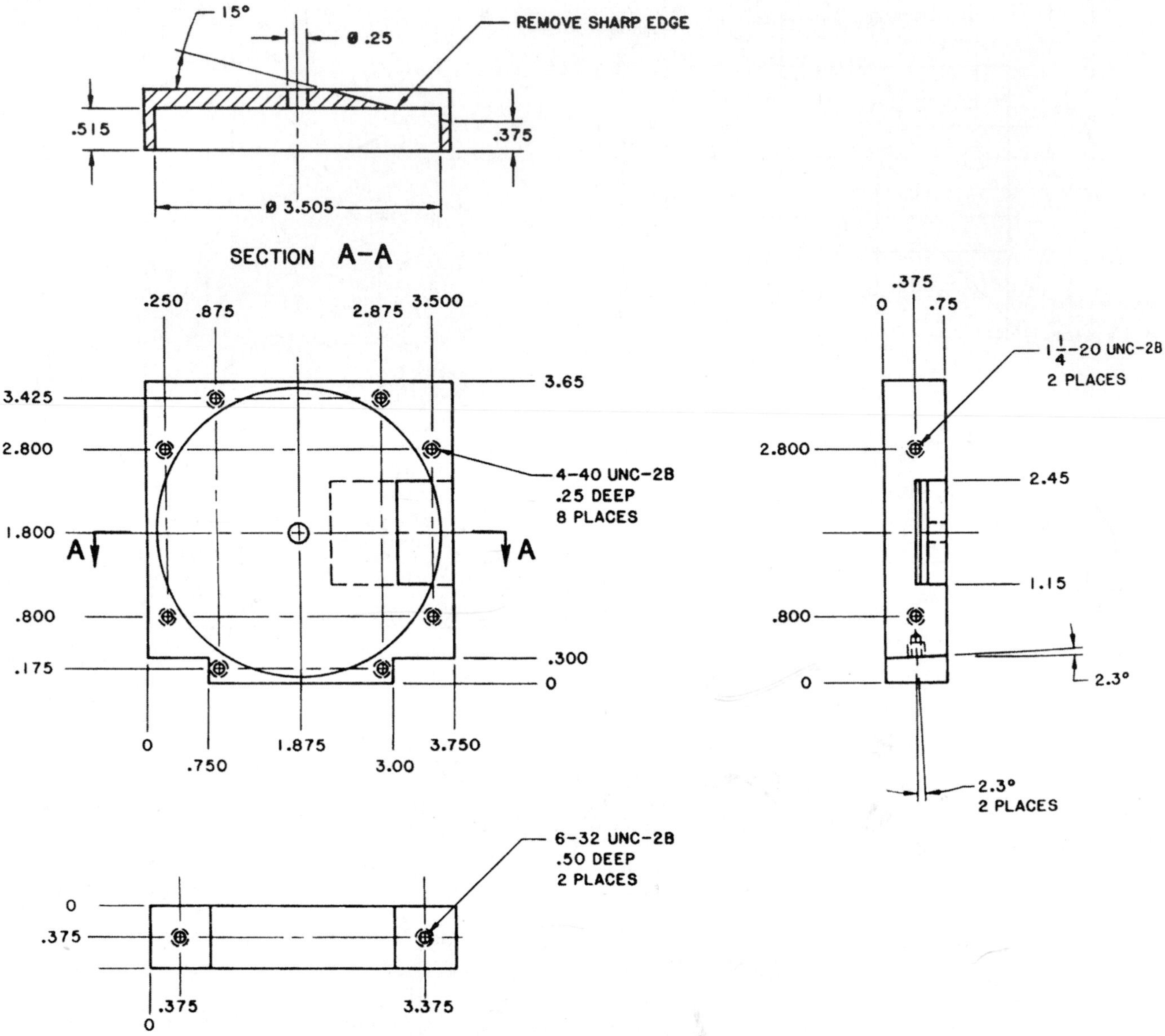

15°
⌀ .25
REMOVE SHARP EDGE
.515
.375
⌀ 3.505

SECTION A–A

.250 .875 2.875 3.500
3.425
2.800
1.800
.800
.175
3.65
4-40 UNC-2B
.25 DEEP
8 PLACES
A A
.300
0
0 .750 1.875 3.00 3.750

.375
0 .75
1 1/4-20 UNC-2B
2 PLACES
2.800
2.45
1.15
.800
0
2.3°
2.3°
2 PLACES

6-32 UNC-2B
.50 DEEP
2 PLACES
0
.375
.375
0
3.375

FIGURE 10.15 Top, Front, Back, and Side Views of the Interface Bracket

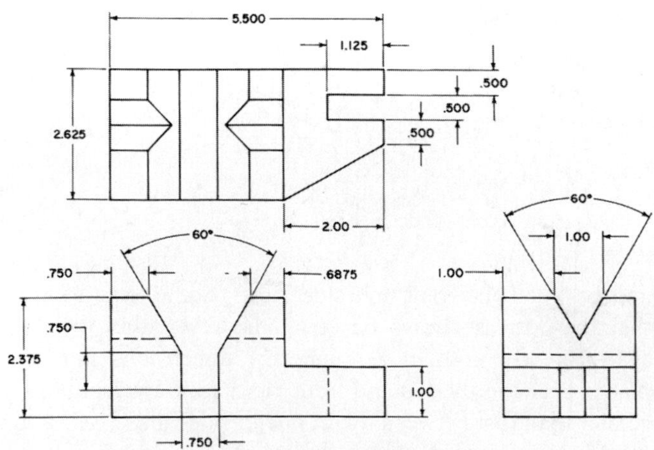

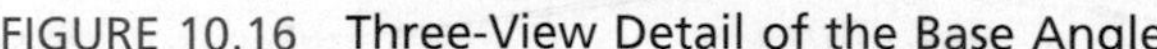

FIGURE 10.16 Three-View Detail of the Base Angle

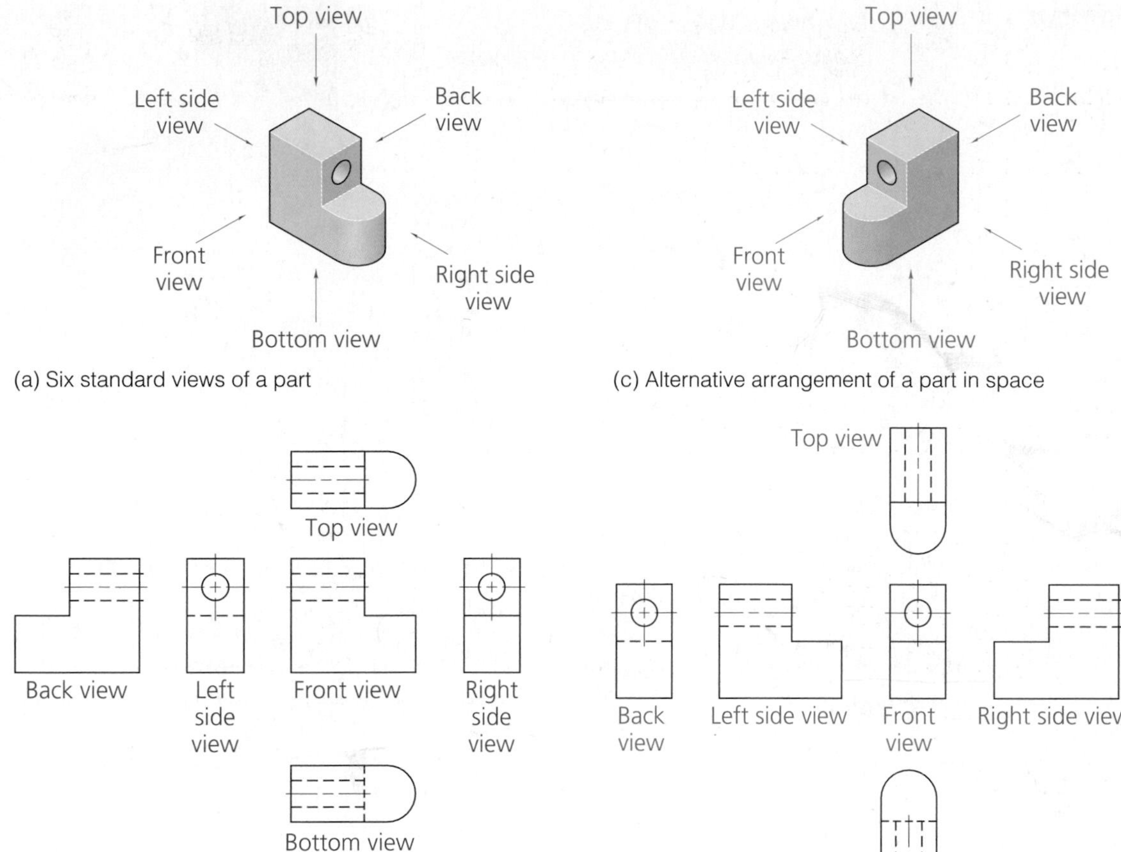

(a) Six standard views of a part

(c) Alternative arrangement of a part in space

(b) Six standard views of a part using third-angle projection

(d) Alternative arrangement views of a part

FIGURE 10.17 Views of a Part

construction lines. At this stage of the drawing, changes are easily made in the spacing of the views and the general layout. After the construction lines are drawn, the circles and radii are darkened. Each part requires careful individual consideration. There are no hard-and-fast rules for drawing layouts. After some experience, you will understand intuitively a part's space requirements and adapt the drawing accordingly.

10.5.4 Related and Adjacent Views

Regardless of whether the drawing to be constructed is to have two, three, or more views, the basics of construction and projection are the same. Two adjoining orthographic views aligned by projection lines are considered **adjacent views.** Two views adjacent to the same intermediate view are called **related views.** Each view shares one dimension with a related

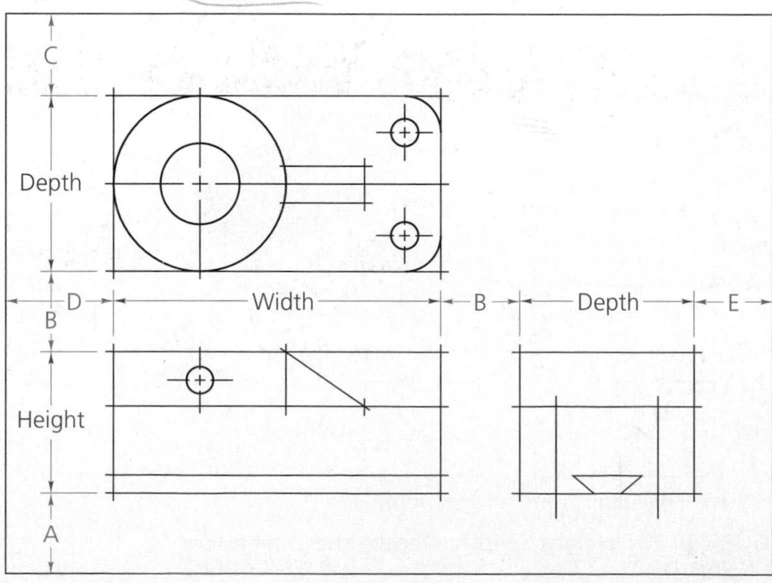

FIGURE 10.18 Laying Out a Drawing

FIGURE 10.19 Spacing Views on a Drawing

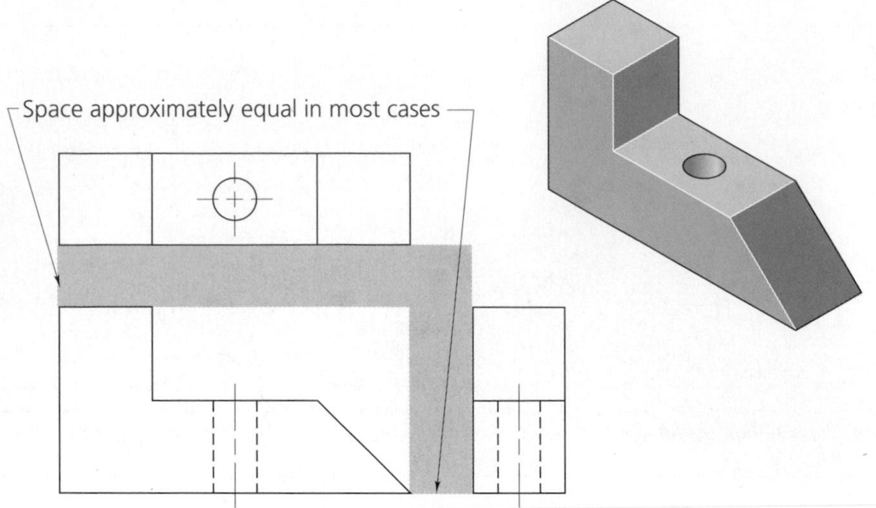

view and another dimension with an adjacent view (Fig. 10.20). The top and front views share one dimension—the width. The front and side views share the height dimension. The top and front views are therefore adjacent views, as are the front and side views. The top and side views share the depth dimension and are considered related views.

10.5.5 Drawing Order

Whether the project is a one-, two-, three-, or multiview project, the same sequence of construction will generally be applied. The order in which you do your work determines the efficiency and quality of the finished drawing. Figure 10.21 provides a series of steps in the construction of a drawing.

1. Figure 10.21(a) shows a pictorial view of the part. Based on the part's overall dimensions, establish the sheet size and format via the technique previously described. The scale and dimensioning requirements also have to be determined at this time. The number of views depends on the part's configuration and complexity and the dimensioning requirements. Sketching the possible view requirements and alternatives helps establish a well-planned drawing that requires fewer alterations at a later stage.
2. Based on the part's overall dimensions, lay out the principal dimensions to establish the three views. Use the scale to measure and establish the dimensions with small construction lines, as shown in Figure 10.21(b). Since dimensions are shared with adjacent views, it is necessary to scale only once for each of the three major dimensions. The width can be established in the top view and projected to the front view. The height can be established in the front view and projected to the side. Because the front view can be used for both the adjacent views—side and top—some designers prefer to draw the front view's outline first.
3. Using construction lines, connect the measured points to establish the outline of the part [Fig. 10.21(c)]. Since unneeded construction lines require erasing before darkening, draw only those construction lines that are necessary.
4. At this step [Fig. 10.21(d)], you need to use your scale to measure all secondary details of the part and establish them on the drawing. Measure from the existing principal lines. This step is also done with construction lines.
5. Draw all secondary features of the part [Fig. 10.21(e)]. To avoid more measuring, project features to adjacent views where possible.
6. Establish the centerlines and curved features of the part using construction lines [Fig. 10.21(f)]. The part's fillets and circles require centerlines for their construction. All curved features are drawn with the aid of a template or compass. On projects where the primary shape of the part is curved or where there are prominent circular features, this would be step 3 or 4. Do not darken the drawing yet. Check the drawing thoroughly before going on to the next step. Mistakes caught at this stage of the project, where there are no finalized (darkened) lines, are easily corrected.
7. It is easier to match a straight line to a curve than a curve to a straight line, so circles, arcs, and fillets are the first features darkened on a drawing [Fig. 10.21(g)].

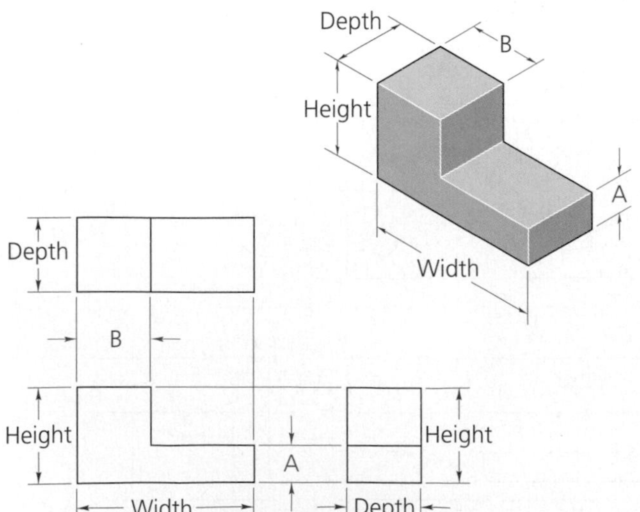

FIGURE 10.20 Height, Width, Depth, and Dimensions of a Part

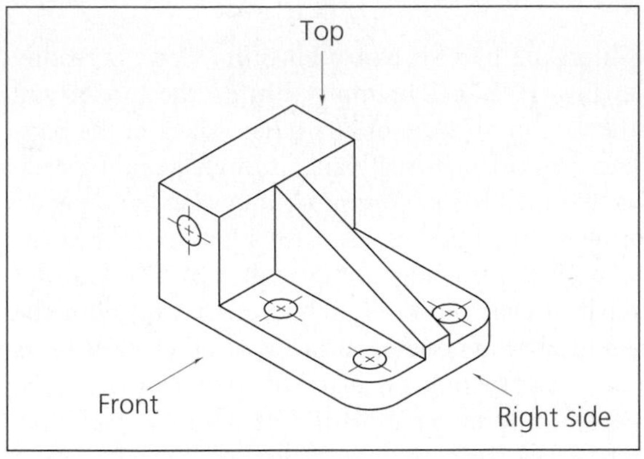

(a) Isometric view of a part

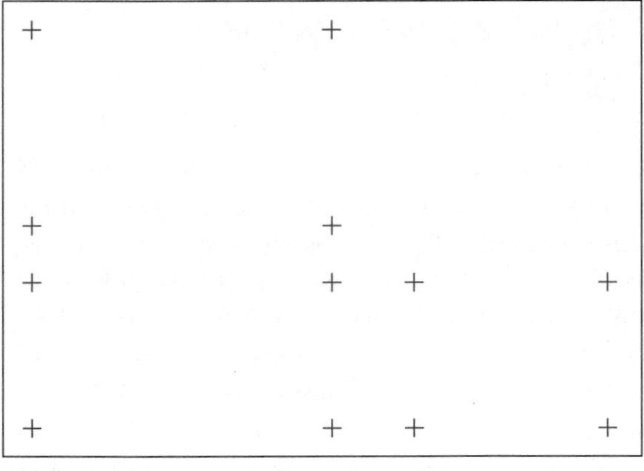

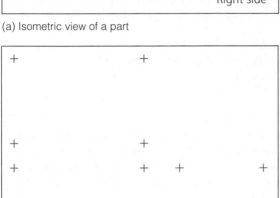

(b) Establish the overall dimensions of the part using a scale and space appropriately

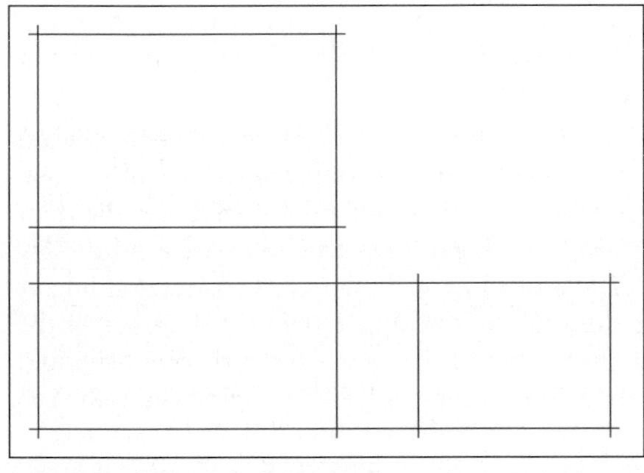

(c) Block-in the part using construction lines

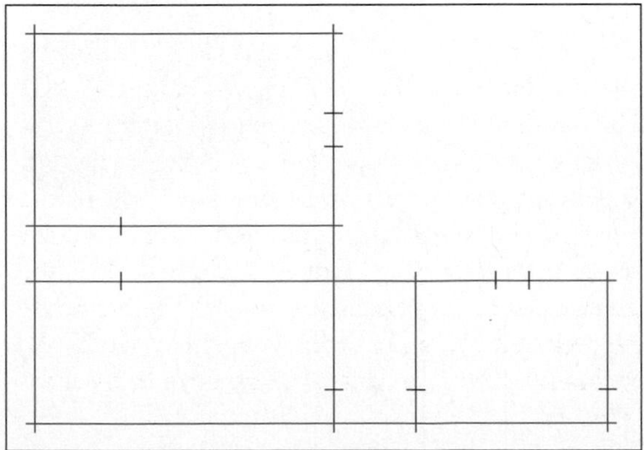

(d) Establish all the major features of the part

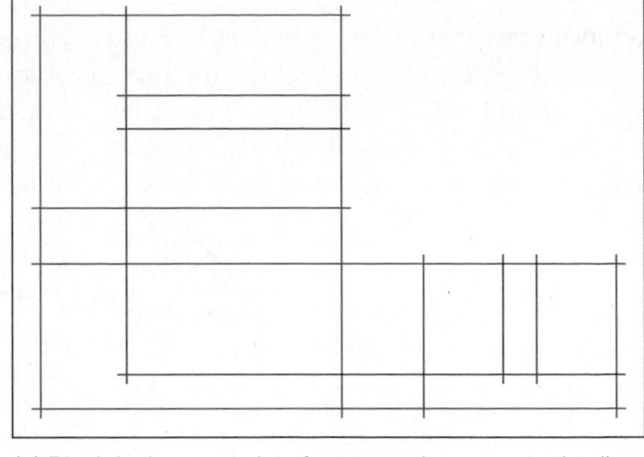

(e) Block-in the secondary features using construction lines

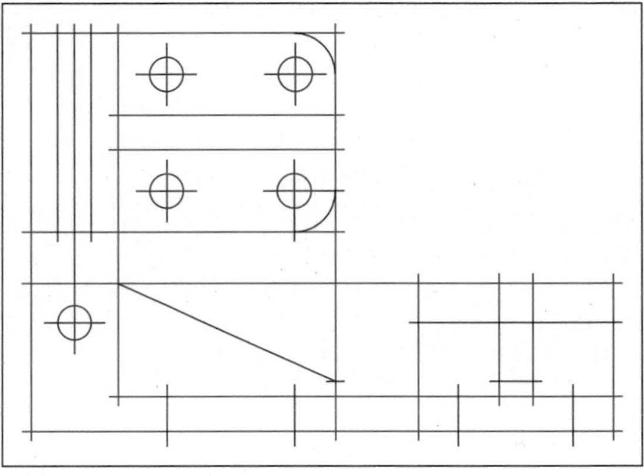

(f) Establish all holes and draw circles with construction lines using a compass or template

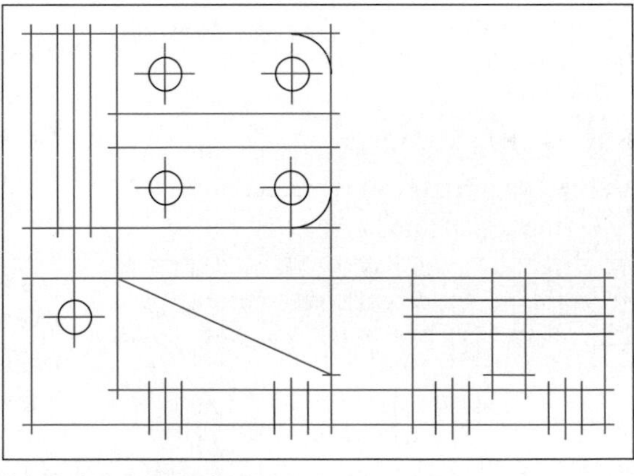

(g) Darken arcs and circles

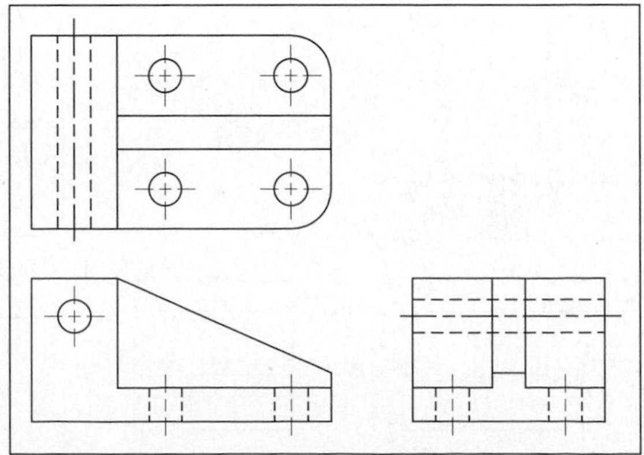

(h) Darken drawing and remove construction lines

FIGURE 10.21 Steps in the Construction of a Drawing

8. The remaining lines can now be darkened [Fig. 10.21(h)]. Care should be exercised in matching the line thickness of the curves and the straight lines. Erase all construction lines still showing after all lines are darkened. (You could also erase extra constructions *before* darkening in the drawing. Try both ways to see which works best for you.)

After the drawing is complete, check it thoroughly. Fill in the title block as a last step. Since dimensioning is not discussed here, that step has *not* been included in the description.

10.5.6 Alternative Selection of Views for a Drawing

Before discussing the construction of a drawing with three or more views, it is important to understand the selection of views. A part must be analyzed carefully before starting the drawing. During this step, the proper view selection and the number of views must be determined.

10.5.7 Models for View Description and Reading a Drawing

Learning to visualize a part's views can be aided by the use of models. Plastic, metal, wood, clay, or soap models enable you to position the part so that each of its views is readily observable (Fig. 10.22). By simply turning the model you can view the top, front, side, or any other aspect of the part.

Sketching the part pictorially aids in understanding each of its views. Normally, isometric or oblique sketching paper, with preprinted grid lines, is used to "block out" the part before it is drawn in orthographic projection (see Chapter 9). The sketch-modeling process helps you clearly define the part. Sometimes hidden edges, surfaces, or other parts of its geometry are discovered or clarified. Even with CAD, sketching is an important part of the design process.

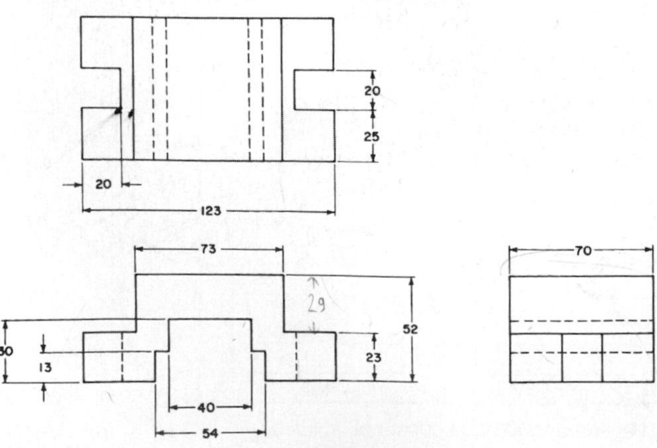

FIGURE 10.22 Three-View Detail of the Clamp

10.6 VIEW PROJECTION METHODS

The four separate ways to project the third view of a part are the **miter method**, the **radius method**, the **divider method**, and the **scale method.** The miter method helps in learning how to project the third view and in understanding the relationship of the top and side views. The miter method, along with the radius method, becomes less useful when the shape of the part is not simple or uncomplicated. Almost all industry drawings are completed by using the scale and the dividers to establish depth dimensions in the third view or simply by reading (understanding) the third view.

10.6.1 Miter Lines for Transferring Depth Dimensions

The **miter line method** is a simple and straightforward procedure for establishing the depth dimensions of a three-dimensional part. After the front and top views (or the front and side views) are drawn, construction of the third view can begin. The **miter line** is drawn as a construction line. A 45° line is drawn from the upper right-hand corner of the front view of the part, which is the intersection of the fold lines (Fig. 10.23). The upper edge line of the part, in the top

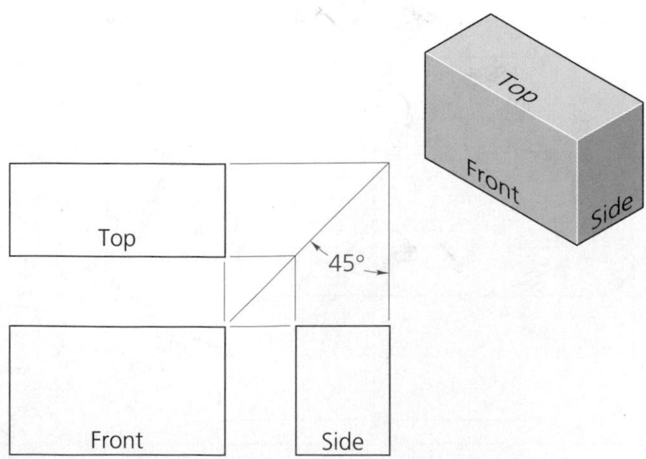

FIGURE 10.23 Establishing the Depth of a Part Using the Miter Line Method

Focus On . . .

EVINRUDE

Who would have imagined that the son of an immigrant farmer, with only a third-grade education, would be responsible for the hours of pleasure experienced by people who fish and boat? Ole Evinrude was born in Norway and came to America with his parents to farm in Wisconsin. He wasn't a very good farmer, preferring to channel his energies into work on mechanical devices. At sixteen, he built his first project, a sailboat. He used this project to secure a job as a machinist in Madison. After several jobs in Chicago and Pittsburgh, he settled in Milwaukee, working as a pattern maker. In his spare time, he "tinkered" with his idea of constructing a standard engine for the increasingly popular horseless carriage. The U.S. government became interested in this concept and contracted with him to produce fifty engines. As a result, he opened his own company.

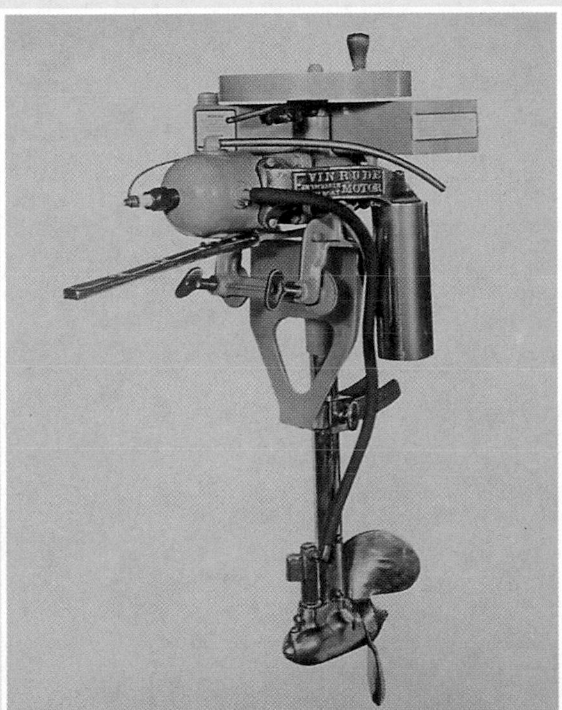

Evinrude's first motor.

The idea for the outboard motor was the result of being embarrassed during a summer picnic. His future wife asked him to row across the lake to get ice cream. On the return trip, the wind became so gusty that he was unable to row fast enough to keep the ice cream from melting. Ole was a large, strong man and was embarrassed over his inability to control the boat. The following Monday he began work on his outboard motor.

Evinrude introduced his 1.5-hp motor in 1907. It has remained essentially unchanged to this day. It has a horizontal cylinder with a vertical crankshaft, employing power direction changes with gears in a submerged lower unit. Ole was only thirty-two when he formed Evinrude Motor Company to produce the outboard motors.

The company was sold in 1914. Later, another company, Evinrude Light Twin Outboard (ELTO), produced the first practical twin-cylinder outboard. In it, many heavy engine parts were replaced with aluminum. Also, exhaust gases were passed through the propeller hub.

Evinrude died in 1934. A few years ago his original 1909 outboard motor was dedicated as a National Historic Mechanical Engineering Landmark. It was the first consumer product to be so recognized. Another Wisconsinite, Harry Armenius Miller of Menomonie, is credited with inventing the first motorboat and motorcycle, although he never patented them.

No doubt Evinrude spent many hours sketching his ideas. To manufacture those motors, many working and assembly drawings were also produced. Evinrude had the genius to take an idea in his mind and turn it into a valuable product. This is not so different from what we try to do today.

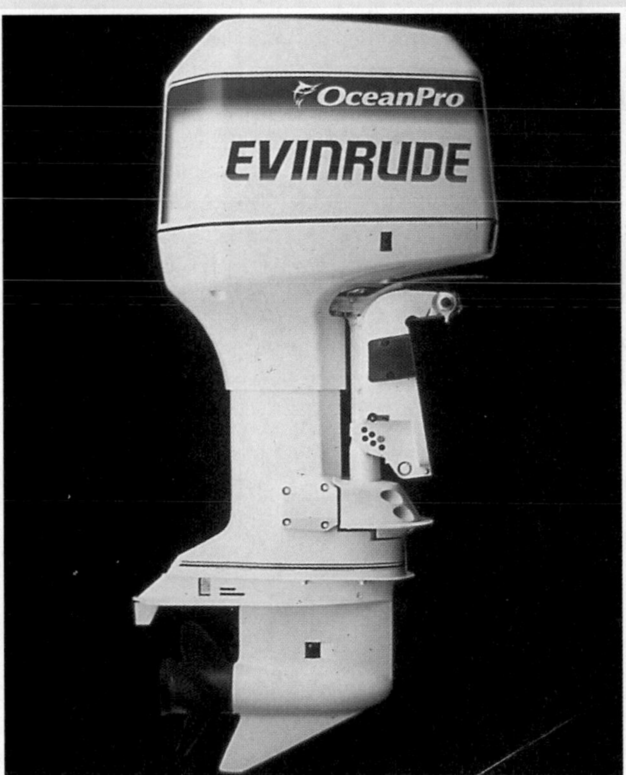

A modern outboard motor.

view, is then extended until it intersects the miter line. The intersection point helps establish the outside edge of the side view by drawing a vertical construction line through it. Since it is adjacent to the side view, the height of the part is projected from the front view. Other depth dimensions can now be extended to the miter line from the top view and

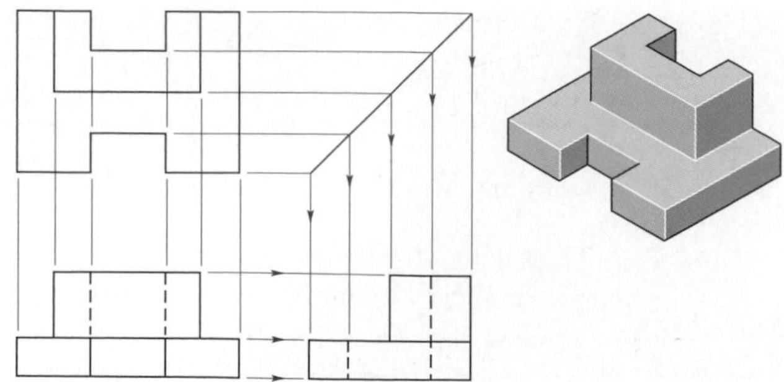

FIGURE 10.24 Miter Line Method of Projecting the Depth of the Third View

then to the side view. The drawing of the part in Figure 10.24 illustrates how each of the depth dimensions has been extended from the top view to the miter line and projected downward to establish the right side view. Height dimensions are projected directly from the front view. Miter lines and projection lines are erased after the view is completed.

10.6.2 Radius Method for Determining Depth

The **radius method** is shown in Figure 10.25. The upper right-hand corner of the front view is used to swing arcs R1 and R2 (90°) so as to establish the depth of the side view. In this method, as in the miter line method, the spacing between the front and top views and the front and side views is the same. Each feature in the top view is transferred to the side view via radii. Of course, the process could be reversed to transfer features from the side view to the top view, as is the case when the side view is drawn first. All radius lines and construction lines must be erased after the view is completed.

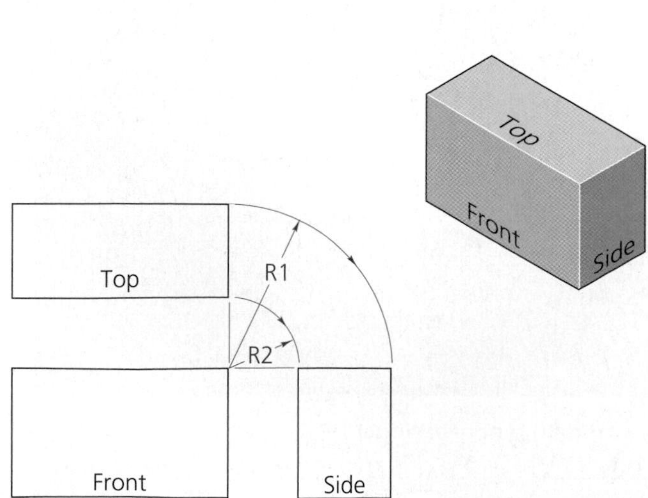

FIGURE 10.25 Radius Method of Projecting the Depth of the Third View

10.6.3 Divider Method for Establishing the Depth Dimension

Since the **divider method** (Fig. 10.26) is quick and accurate, it is used for descriptive geometry problems and for engineering drawings. This method allows the placement of the third view at any distance from its adjacent projection. In other words, the front and side view spacing need not be the same as the spacing between the front and top views. Since the spacing between the views is determined by the part's complexity and the dimensions required to detail the part, this will most likely be the case for most projects.

Dividers are used to establish all depth dimensions in the third view. Unlike the miter and radius methods, this method does not require that you erase construction lines after transferring the depth dimensions. In general, the miter and radius methods are limited to instructional drawings when learning to draw. A combination of dividers and scale measurements is the normal procedure to draw the third view. If the front and side views were drawn first, the "third" view could be the top view.

10.6.4 Scale Method for Transferring Depth Dimensions

The **scale method** to establish the depth dimension is common in industry. The scale is used to measure the depth dimension of the part in the top or side view (whichever view was constructed first). Depth dimensions then help establish the third view. You could utilize the dimensions of the part to construct each view (with the scale) without transferring dimensions. Though this method is acceptable,

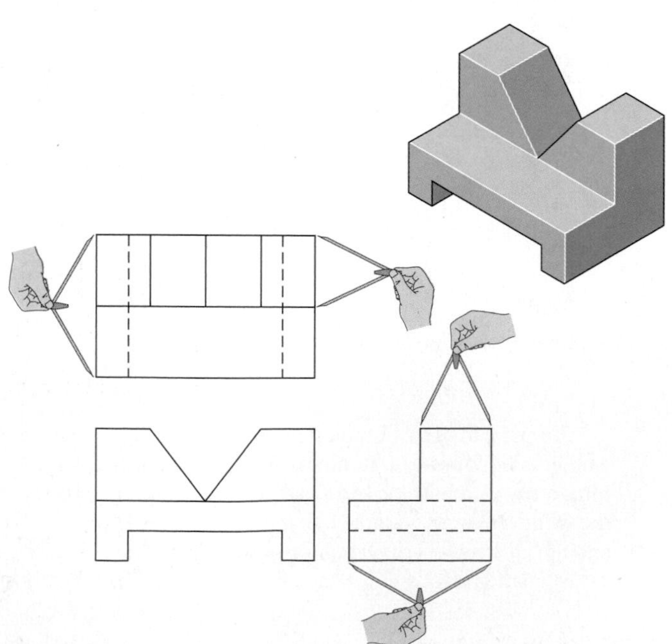

FIGURE 10.26 Transferring the Depth Dimension Using Dividers

it does require the repetitious use of the scale and takes longer. Measurements established once can normally be projected from adjacent views or transferred by dividers from related views.

Which method to employ depends on the configuration of the part and the views required. A minimum amount of scaling in each view will increase efficiency and speed.

10.6.5 Precedence of Lines on a Drawing

Views of a part will show its edges, surfaces, centerlines, and other features. A surface in one view will show as an edge in its adjacent view and as a surface in its related view. Since each view has so many features, they will at times interfere with one another. In other words, some features will coincide. Because showing all features in every view would only confuse the drawing, an order of importance, or **precedence of lines,** has been established for engineering drawings. The most important lines are drawn and the less important are left off the drawing. Figure 10.27 shows the proper precedence of lines on a drawing.

All outside edges of a part (boundary lines), in a particular view, will be drawn as **visible lines** and have precedence over all other lines. Visible edges are solid lines and always have precedence over hidden lines (dashed). **Dashed lines** represent hidden edge lines of the part and, therefore, have precedence over **centerlines** (which do not really exist as aspects of the part's geometry; they represent the center of curved features, e.g., circles and arcs). **Dimension lines** and **extension lines** should be positioned so as to avoid coinciding with visible and hidden lines.

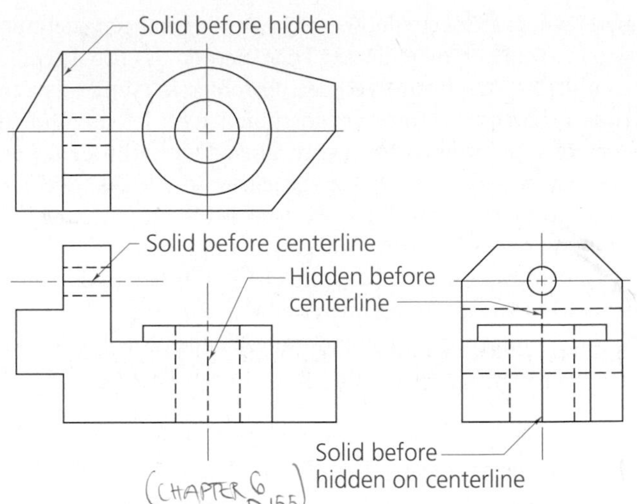

FIGURE 10.27 Precedence of Lines on a Drawing

Order of Precedence of Lines on a Drawing

1. Visible lines (solid)
2. Hidden lines (dashed)
3. Cutting-plane lines or centerlines (depending on importance)
4. Break lines (solid)
5. Extension lines and dimension lines (solid, thin)
6. Section lines (crosshatch)

10.6.6 Interpreting Multiview Drawings

Labeling a part's features with numbers or letters may help develop understanding and visualization of three-dimensional parts. This may also help in constructing views of complicated shapes. In Figure 10.28, each edge line of the

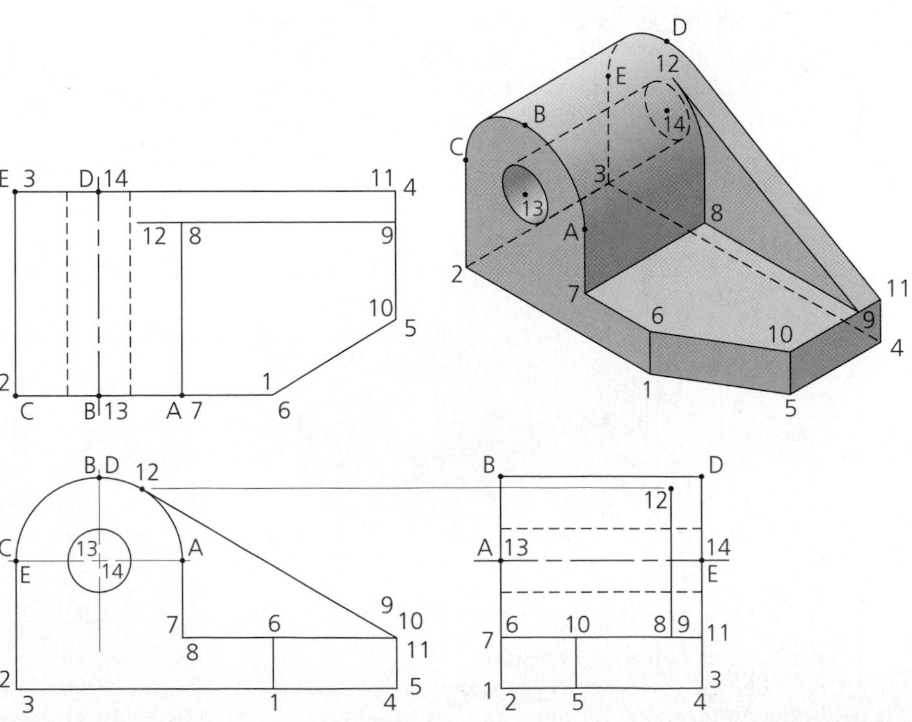

FIGURE 10.28 Labeling Points on a Part to Establish Features in Views

part, where it meets another edge line, has been identified with a number or a letter. This method is also used for completing descriptive geometry problems. Notice that the ends of curved features are identified with letters, and the ends of straight-line features are labeled with numbers. Each line can be seen in every view as either *true length, foreshortened,* or a *point.* Most lines, except for the angled lines 1-5, 6-10, and 9-12, will show as two numbered ends in two views and as a point view (coincident ends) in another view. Line 13-14 is the centerline for the hole and for the curved surface. Projecting views (and individual features) of the part becomes a matter of locating points from view to view.

10.6.7 Projection Lines for Views

Projection lines are thin, lightly drawn construction lines that "project" features between adjacent views. Such lines are erased after the views are complete and before darkening. The lines eliminate the need to measure and scale every aspect of a view. Elements that are already established in one view can easily be extended (projected) to the adjacent view. As an example, in Figure 10.29 the front view has been drawn first. Since the front view is adjacent to both the top and side views, it can be used to establish those views by projection. The top view is constructed with projectors extended from the front view to establish its width dimensions. The depth dimensions for the top view are constructed with scale measurements. Since it shares all height and elevation dimensions, the side view can be projected from the front view. The depth dimensions must be established by one of the four methods described previously.

Most parts are too complicated to draw only one view at a time. Edges and features in one view may need to be drawn in the adjacent view first and then located by projection. A majority of the time, you will construct aspects of each view that are easily identified and then project those features to the adjacent view, working back and forth until the drawing is complete.

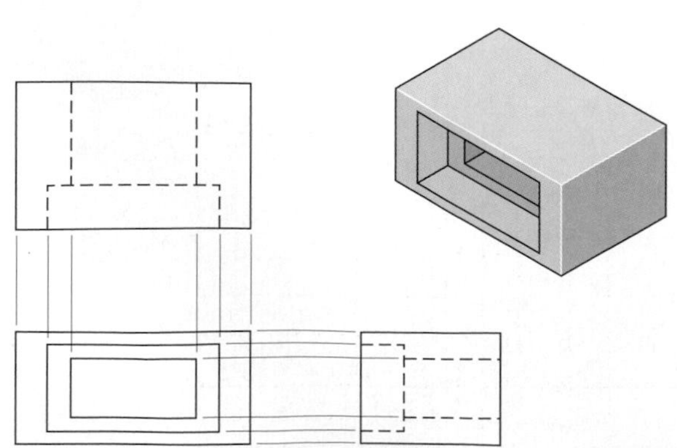

FIGURE 10.29 Projecting Hidden Features of a Part

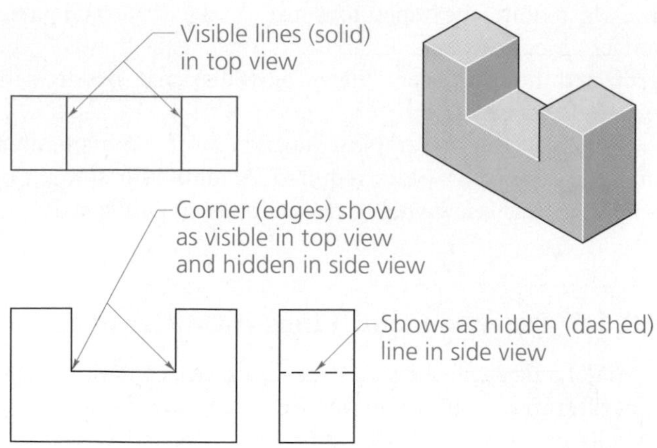

FIGURE 10.30 Solid (Visible) and Dashed (Hidden) Lines of a Part

10.6.8 Hidden Lines in Views

Since every feature of a part is seen in each view as an edge or a surface, many aspects of the part may be viewed as "*hidden*" features (Fig. 10.29). Features that lie behind other features of a part are still represented. To show the part's features, both hidden and visible, different line symbols are required. All features (edge lines, surfaces, and intersecting surfaces) that cannot be seen directly as visible lines in a particular view will be drawn with **hidden lines.**

In Figure 10.30, the use of visible (solid) and hidden (dashed) lines is shown. Visible lines in the top view of this part show as visible edges and corners in the front view and as hidden lines in the side view. When constructing dashed and solid lines, the following drafting conventions for spacing must be maintained.

Spacing Conventions for Constructing Dashed and Solid Lines

- Do not leave a gap between a hidden (dashed) line and a visible (solid) line that meet (Fig. 10.31).
- When a hidden line crosses a solid line, leave a gap (Fig. 10.32).
- When a hidden line continues as a visible line after crossing a visible line, leave a gap (Fig. 10.33).

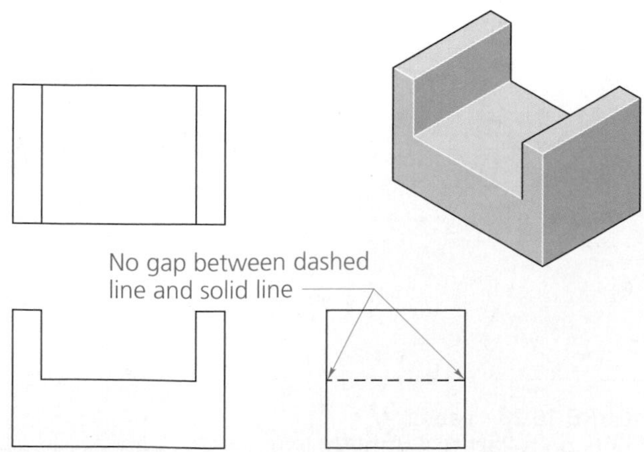

FIGURE 10.31 Drawing Dashed (Hidden) Lines

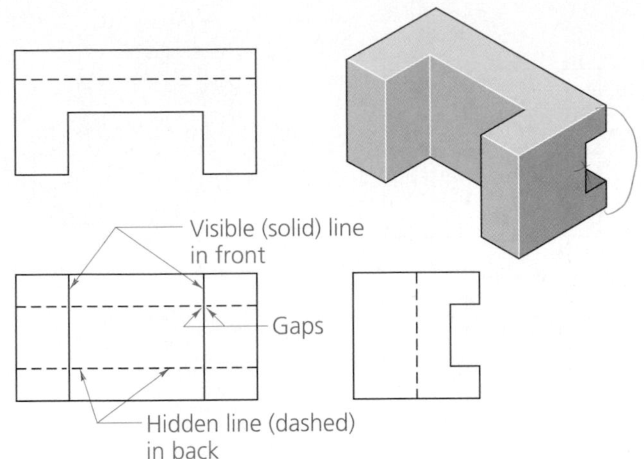

FIGURE 10.32 Visible and Hidden Lines on a Drawing

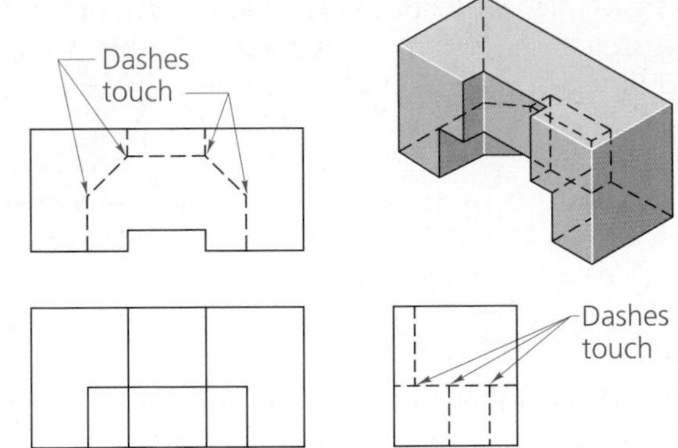

FIGURE 10.34 Dashed Lines and Drawing Conventions

- Hidden lines that meet other hidden lines should not have gaps between them. In other words, the dashes will touch (Fig. 10.34). Hidden lines that establish corners always touch.
- When a hidden line (or arc) meets a visible line (or arc) and is tangent to that line, leave a gap.
- When hidden lines cross, draw the one that lies in front of the other as continuous and through a space (between dashes) in the one behind it.

10.6.9 Curved Lines in Views

All curved features of a part are shown in each view. In most cases, a curved feature shows as a curved line or surface in only one view and as an edge line (straight) in its adjacent projection. The most common type of **curved feature** is the circle. Arcs (and fillets) also occur widely on parts. Circles, arcs, and fillets are really one end of a curved surface. **Curved surfaces** make up much of a typical machined part. A hole is really a cylindrical surface. Connected arcs and fillets are also portions of cylinders. Holes are formed by drills and other rotating tools. Parts that are made up of curved surfaces such as spheres, cylinders, and conical shapes are normally machined on lathes or other turning devices.

Since an internal curved surface (hole) and an external curved surface (normally a cylinder) are both curved surfaces, they are drawn the same way. In Figure 10.35, the part has both internal and external curved surfaces. The holes and the cylinder both show as curves in the top view and as straight edge lines in the front and side views. The hole shows as hidden features in these views and the cylindrical surface as visible lines. The outside arcs of the part also show as visible edge lines in the front and side views. The part in Figure 10.36 shows holes, arcs, and cylindrical surfaces. Here the miter line method is used to project the third view

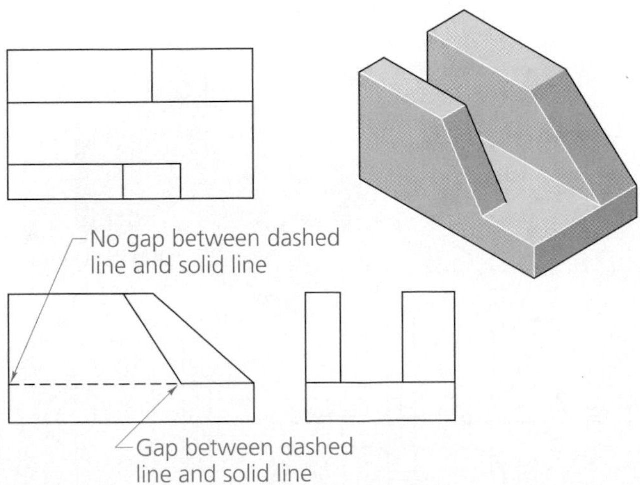

FIGURE 10.33 Drawing Dashed Lines

10.6.10 Use of Centerlines in Views

Curved features are normally established, located in space, and dimensioned with the aid of a centerline. Except for outside arcs, **centerlines** are required in all views of curved features (Figures 10.35 and 10.36). Except for fillets and

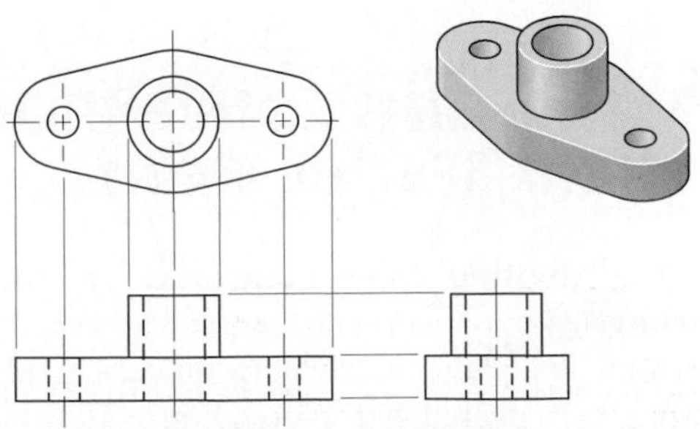

FIGURE 10.35 Curved Features in Views

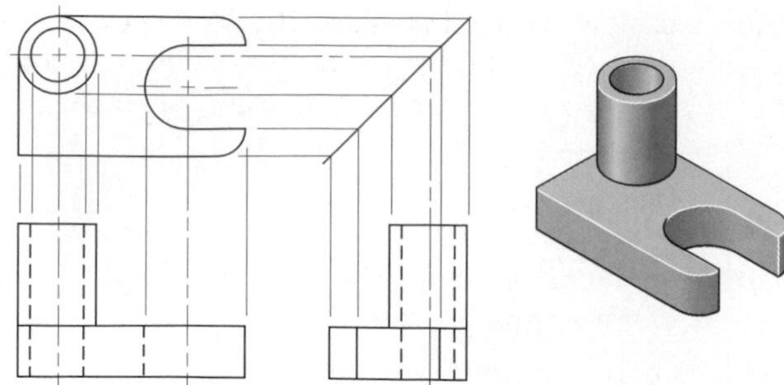

FIGURE 10.36 Miter Line Method for Projecting Curved Features

rounds, all curves require centerlines to establish their curved features. Centerlines for the end view of curved features are drawn as perpendicular crossing lines with short dashes at the center and as single centerlines (long dash, short dash) in adjacent views. Centerlines do not really exist as a feature of the part—they are not edge or surface lines. Therefore, they are drawn to extend slightly beyond the boundaries of the part or curved feature. They do *not* take precedence over visible or hidden lines.

Centerlines also appear on drawings where the part is *symmetrical about a centerline.* Cones, spheres, and other curved shapes require centerlines. When looking into the curve's end view, centerlines establish the center point of the curved feature; when shown in adjacent views, they represent the axis line of the curved surface.

You May Complete Exercises 10.1 Through 10.4 at This Time

10.6.11 Parallel Lines on Parts

When lines are *parallel* in all three views, they will show as parallel in all views of the part. If the lines are shown from an end view, they appear as points (point view). *Parallelism* can easily be seen in the pictorial view of the part. In Figure 10.37 the part has an angled surface that does not show as a true shape in any of the three principal views. This *oblique surface* is shown by edge lines 1-2 and 3-4 (or you could say lines 2-4 and 1-3). The top, front, and right side views show that each of these edge lines is parallel to the other in every view (including the pictorial view of the part).

10.7 DRAFTING CONVENTIONS AND SPECIAL VIEWS

A variety of **drafting conventions** and procedures and **design conventions** and procedures have been devised to draw projects concisely, clearly, and quickly. A number of conventions are covered here, including partial views, enlarged views, and revolved views.

The need for complete views with all hidden lines shown

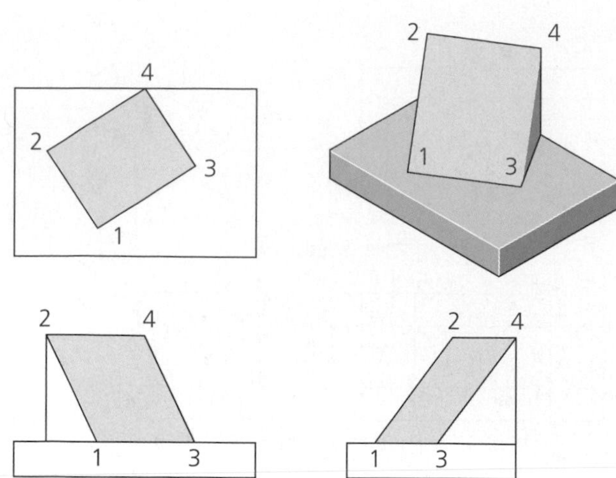

FIGURE 10.37 Parallel Lines on Parts

would take too much costly time and create drawings that were less usable than those with only the necessary lines shown. **Partial views** are one convention for solving this problem. Complicated, cluttered portions of drawings need to be shown in larger, clearer representations; therefore the use of **enlarged views** was established. **Rotated (revolved) views** came into practice to describe portions of a part that were projected as oblique surfaces and actually confused the drawing rather than clarifying it. Each of these methods was developed and standardized over a number of years.

10.7.1 Partial Views

As long as the geometry of a part is adequately described in another view, a partial view may be used. A **partial view** is a view where the dominant features, shape, and outline of the part are shown without the extra clutter of unneeded hidden lines. In Figure 10.38, the part has different shapes on each end. Since the top view would be very similar to the front view, it has been eliminated. And since the right and the left side views show only the visible lines of the corresponding end, they are partial views. These views do not show the hidden features of the opposite end, which

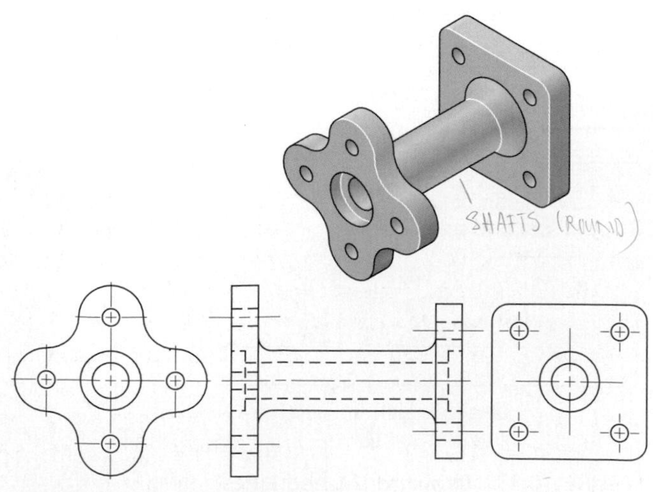

FIGURE 10.38 Partial Views

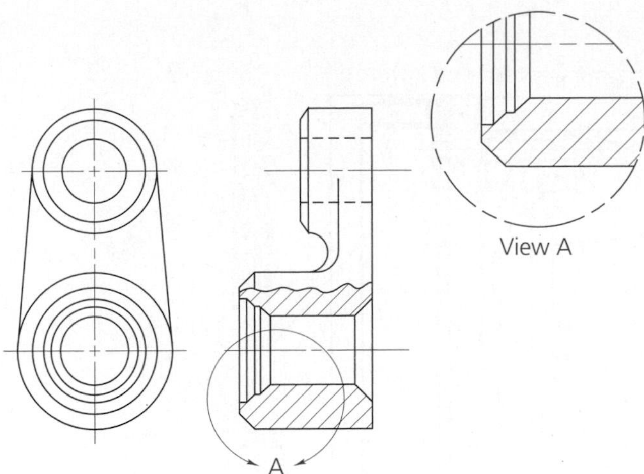

FIGURE 10.39 Enlarged Views

would add nothing to the drawing.

Hidden features on a partial view should include only those directly behind the visible shapes. In Figure 10.38, the cylinder's outside diameter (OD) lies directly behind the counterbored hole on each base plate. Therefore, since visible lines take precedence over hidden lines, this feature does not show on the drawing. The two side views have no hidden lines. On parts where the hidden feature will not appear in another view, the feature must be included on the partial view.

10.7.2 Enlarged Views

Enlarged views increase the size of a crowded or complicated area of a part. Many times this procedure is necessary to provide sufficient space for dimensions. In Figure 10.39, VIEW A is the enlarged portion of the part. The interior and exterior chamfers are now clearly visible. The area to be enlarged is circled with a phantom line, and the **view-letter designation** is positioned as in Figure 10.39. The enlarged view is identified on the drawing by placing the view-letter designation under the view (in the case of Fig. 10.39, VIEW A).

10.7.3 Revolved Views

Rotated (revolved) views are utilized where a true projection of the part would only confuse the reader. Figure 10.40a shows an example of a part that is better described with a rotated view. The detail of this part requires two views to describe its geometry and place dimensions adequately. If a *true projection* had been used, the front view would have been confusing and complicated. The clevis portion of the arm was rotated parallel to the front view and projected as a normal (true shape) view. This procedure saved considerable drawing time and is less misleading. The Gravity Probe Tilt Stand assembly shown in Figure 10.40b shows how the probe was rotated vertically in the right side view instead of using a true projection from the front view, where the probe is tilted.

10.7.4 Surfaces and Edges on Multiple-View Drawings

To understand orthographic projection, you must begin to see parts as simple shapes, edges, lines, and points. Surfaces are created by combining lines. The surfaces can be combinations of straight lines or straight and curved lines. Surfaces, or *areas* as they are sometimes called, show **true shape/size (TS)** when they are parallel to the plane of projection and show as **edges (EV)** when they are perpendicular to the plane of projection. A plane that appears true shape/size in a view is called a **normal surface.** The view is a normal view of a plane. The adjacent projection (view) of the plane shows as an edge (edge view).

Curved surfaces show as curved edges in views where they are perpendicular to the viewing plane, and as plane shapes with straight sides in views where they are parallel to the viewing plane. When three surfaces come together, they meet at a corner (point). Most parts can be defined by establishing their corners (points in space). Figure 10.41 provides examples of each condition. The pictorial view in the upper right provides a 3D model of the part. The part is composed of planar surfaces and curved surfaces. The hole shows as circular only in the side view. It appears as an edge in the front and top views. Notice that the circular surface of the projected hole shows as a rectangle in the front and top views. The same is true of the vertical curved surface on which the hole appears. All planar surfaces of the part show as true shape or as edges in their adjacent views.

10.7.5 Reading a Drawing

We have already said that a drawing is "*read,*" not scaled. This does not mean that you read it aloud. "*Reading*" is what a designer or engineer does mentally to understand and then interpret the drawing. Here are the mental steps required to read a drawing.

1. Study the total drawing by scanning all views and dimensions.
2. Visualize the shape of the part by orientating yourself as the observer for each view.
3. Reduce the part to simple geometric shapes, e.g., planes, circles, surfaces, and other common features.
4. Study each view and feature as it corresponds to its adjacent and related projection. The depth, for instance, can be studied in the top view and related side view. Adjacent views can be studied to establish the true shape of a surface and its edge view projection.
5. If necessary, sketch a simple 3D pictorial of the part to clarify the general configuration and details.

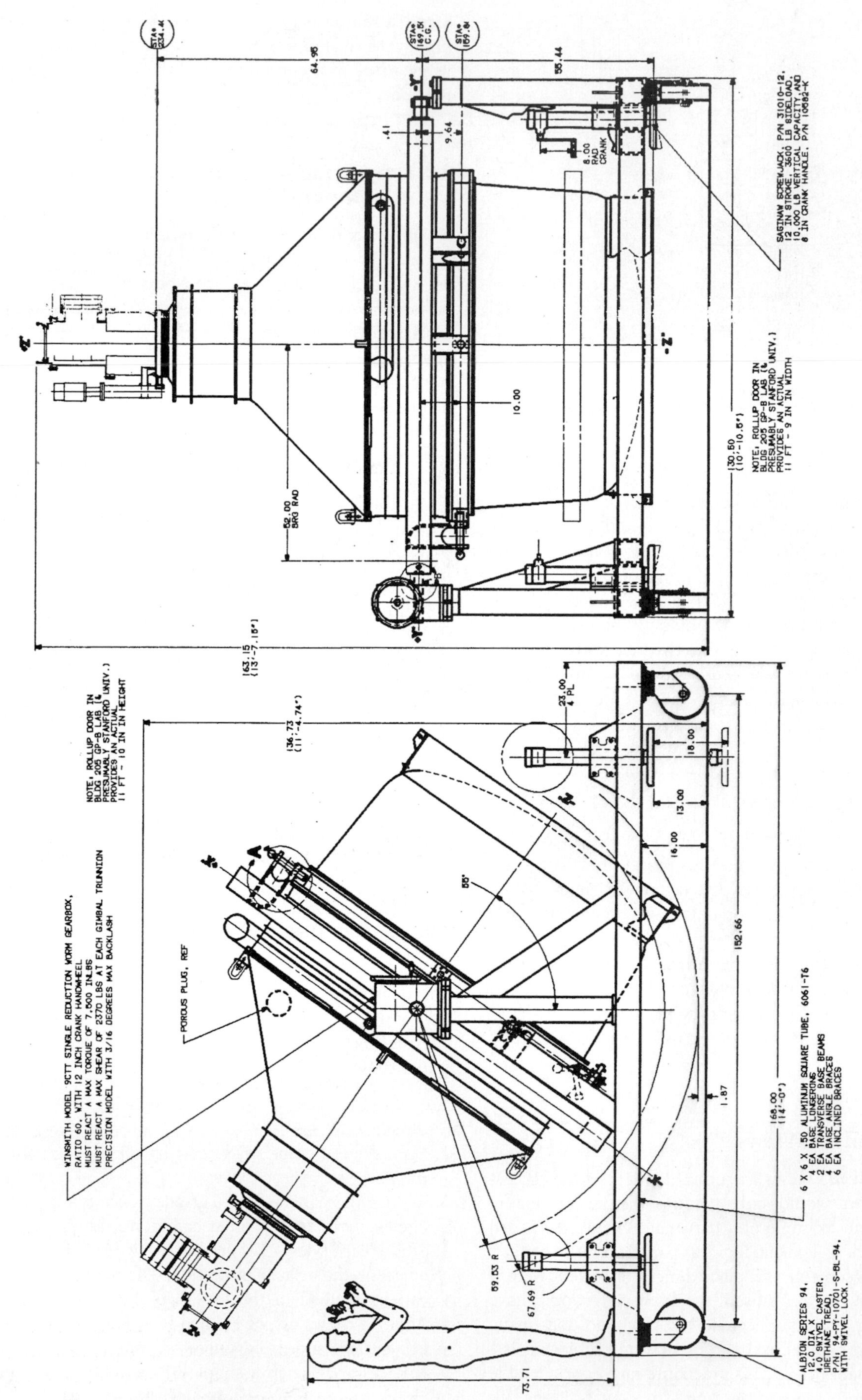

FIGURE 10.40a Rotated/Revolved Views

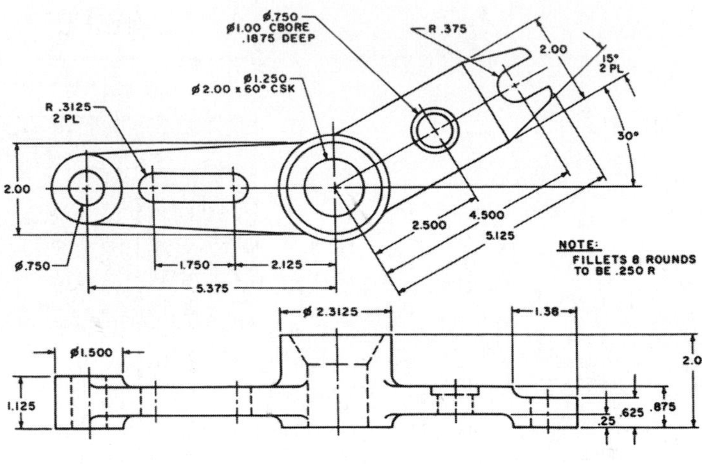

(b) Drawing of angle frame

FIGURE 10.40b Rotated/Revolved Views—*Continued*

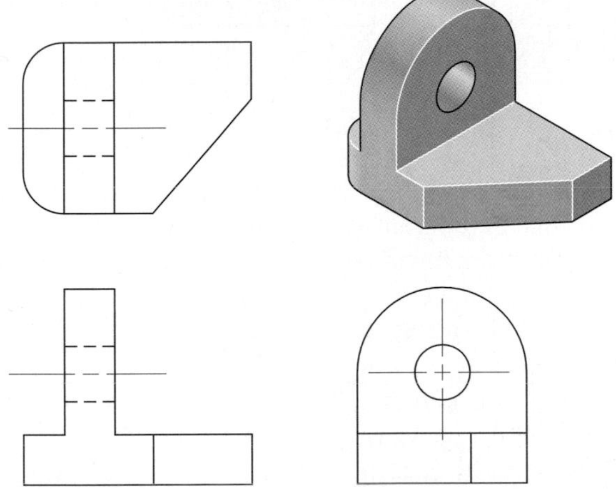

FIGURE 10.41 Surfaces on a Part

6. Note each hole, tangent area, curved feature, and other special contour that distinguishes the part.

Assuming that the pictorial view of the part (right side orientation) in Figure 10.42 is not provided, read the part.

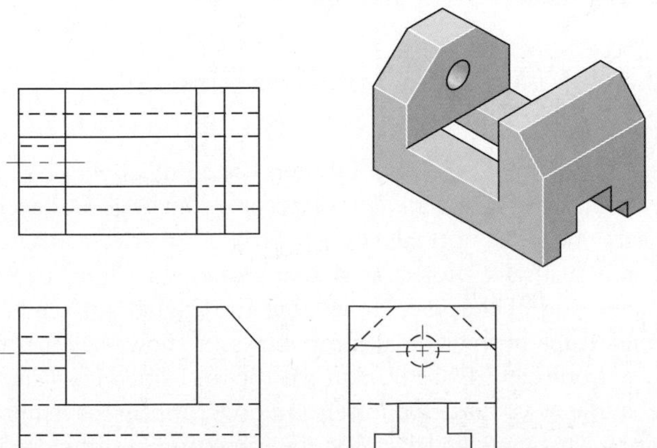

FIGURE 10.42 Three Views and Pictorial Illustration of the Guide

Notice that three views were required to represent the part's geometry adequately. Most of the part's features can be seen in the front and side views. The top view adds little to our understanding of the drawing but does show that the slot extends through the part. The front view shows the angled cut (its edge view). This is the only surface that is not normal and, therefore, does not appear true shape on the drawing in any view. The hole is described in the side view. Since the hole is hidden, only the portion of the part on the far side is penetrated. The side view also shows that the slot extends the entire length of the part. A pictorial sketch would help in reading this project.

10.8 Visualization and Shape Description

To read a drawing, the reader needs some skill at **visualization.** *Visualization is the process of converting a 2D drawing into a 3D image and being able to understand the part as it exists in three-dimensional space.* This skill is not innate for everyone, but can be developed, in most cases, through the study of a variety of drawings, parts, and models.

Upon entering an engineering field that requires the use of drawings, you must be able to understand both the 3D and the 2D illustrations of a part and its representative drawing. Visualizing is a skill that will be necessary for both situations.

10.8.1 Areas on Adjacent and Related Views of a Drawing

Visualization helps in examining a part by comparing surfaces and edges on adjacent and related views. When studying adjacent areas, remember that *adjacent areas cannot lie in the same plane.* If they did, they would not exist; they would not have a boundary between them.

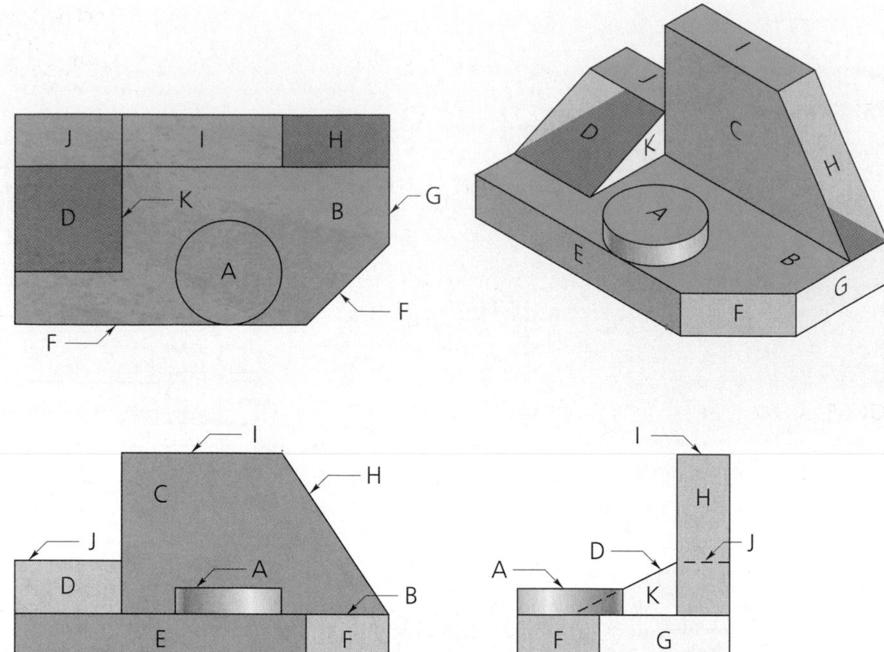

FIGURE 10.43 Related Surfaces and Edges

Adjacent areas can be studied in Figure 10.43. The three principal views are labeled in each projection and on the pictorial view. In each view, a surface or an edge is labeled.

- Surface A is shown true shape in the top view and as an edge in the front and side projections.
- Surface B is also true shape in the top view and, therefore, an edge view in the front and side views of the drawing.
- Surface C is true shape in the front view. Can you find it in the top and side views? It will show as an edge view in each. If you cannot find it in the top and side projections, the pictorial view will locate surface C. Remember, if a surface is true shape in the top view, it shows as an edge in the other two views (front and side).
- Surface D is an angled surface. Its slant angle can be seen in the side view, where it shows as an edge. The front and top projections of surface D are not true shape.
- Surface E is along the front of the part and is true shape in the front view. It shows as an edge in the top view and the side view.
- Surface F is at an angle and does not show in any view as true length. The top view shows this surface as an edge view, and its angle to the part can be measured from the edge view of surface E. The side and front views of surface F show as foreshortened (not true shape).
- Surface G forms the right side of the part and shows as an edge in the top view and as true shape in the front and side views.
- Surface H is an inclined surface, and its slant angle can be measured in the front view as the angle it makes with surface B. Surface H is an edge in this view and is shown foreshortened in the other two projections.
- Surface I is the top, or highest, surface on the part and shows as an edge in the front view, true shape in the top view, and as an edge in the side view. If a surface appears as an edge in the front view, it will also be an edge in the side projection; it will be true shape only in the top view.
- Surface J is parallel to surface I. Therefore, it also is true shape in the top view and an edge in the other two projections.
- Surface K is true shape in the side view and an edge in the top and front views. Surfaces G and K are the only labeled surfaces that are true shape in the side view.

In addition to seeing the true shape and the edge views of a surface, it is important to develop a sense of how each surface relates to another surface. Surface C, for instance, is parallel to surface E and perpendicular to surfaces I and B. Surface D is at an angle to surface B and surface C. Surface G is parallel to surface K and perpendicular to surfaces B and E. Being aware of *parallelism, perpendicularity,* and *angularity* are important aspects of visualizing a 3D part and reading its 2D representation—its drawing.

10.8.2 Visualizing Similar Shapes of Surfaces

Here is a simple rule of projection: *In an adjacent view, an area will project as a similar shape or as an edge.* Adjacent projections of a normal surface project as edges. Related views of a surface project as similar shapes. In Figure 10.44, the drawing of the part shows that the angled surface is a *similar shape* in the side and top views. It shows as an edge in the front view. Even though the top and side views show the surface as distorted, their outlines appear as similar shapes. The angled surface has the same number of sides in each view where it does not appear as an edge. Thus, the preceding rule has a corollary: *The area shapes will have the*

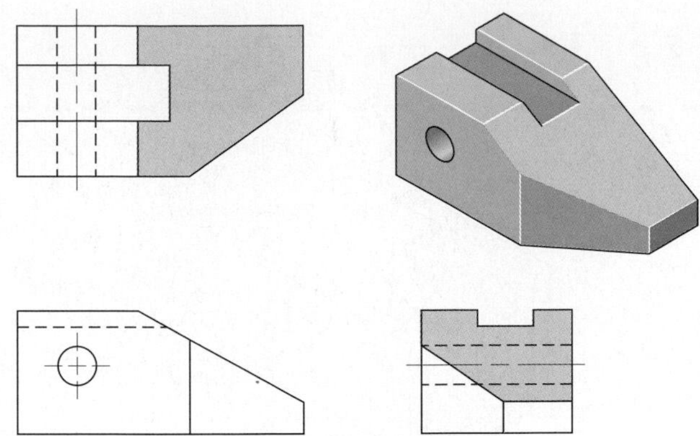

FIGURE 10.44 Angled Surfaces and Edge Views

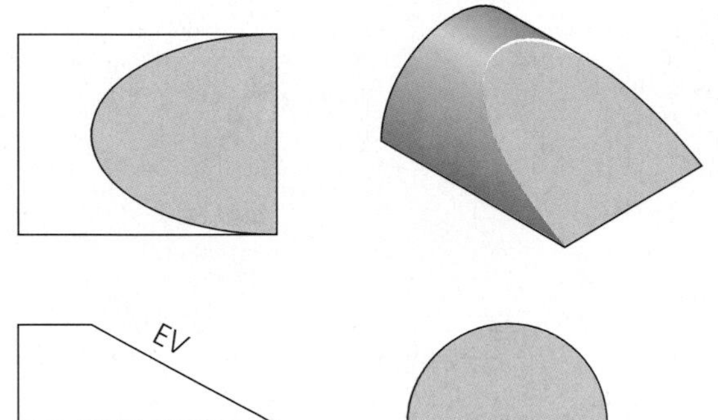

FIGURE 10.45 Elliptical Surface

same number of sides, and the sides of the areas are connected in the same sequence.

Curved shapes may distort in related views, but they also maintain similar shapes, as in Figure 10.45. The top and side views show similar-shaped views of the angled surface. The front view shows the surface as an edge (EV).

10.8.3 True Shape or Normal Surfaces of a Part

Much has already been said about normal views and true shapes of surfaces. *Surfaces that are parallel to a plane of projection are normal surfaces.* In other words, they will show as **true shape,** and each line, arc, circle, or other form that lies on this surface, or is parallel to it, will be true shape and **true length/size.** Figure 10.46 demonstrates this rule. The true-shape surfaces (normal surfaces) are labeled in each of the three views of the part. The surfaces that are not normal to the projection plane are **inclined surfaces** and do not project as true shape in any given view on this drawing.

10.8.4 Edge Views and Edge Lines of a Surface

A surface projects as an edge in a view where the plane of projection is perpendicular to the surface. A line that shows

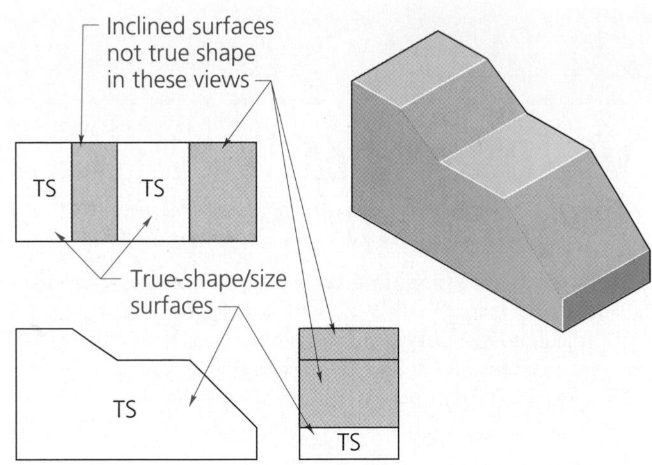

FIGURE 10.46 Inclined Surfaces and True-Shape Surfaces

as a **point view** is a normal edge; that is, it is perpendicular to the projection plane.

Edge lines are always shown on views where the surfaces they represent are perpendicular to the adjacent view. In Figure 10.47, the front view of the part shows two perpendicular surfaces that will project as edge lines in the top view. The surface that is at a slight angle and blends with its mating surfaces is not represented with an edge line in the top view. The same convention applies in the right side view and the left side view.

10.8.5 Angles on Multiview Drawings

In Figure 10.48, the part has two **angled surfaces.** The **true angle** of these surfaces is shown in the side view of the part, where they show as edge lines that lie normal to the view. Angles can be measured only in views where they are in a normal plane. The front and top views show the angled surfaces as if they were rectangular and true shape; their inclination cannot be read in these views. Without the side view, the part's configuration could not be determined.

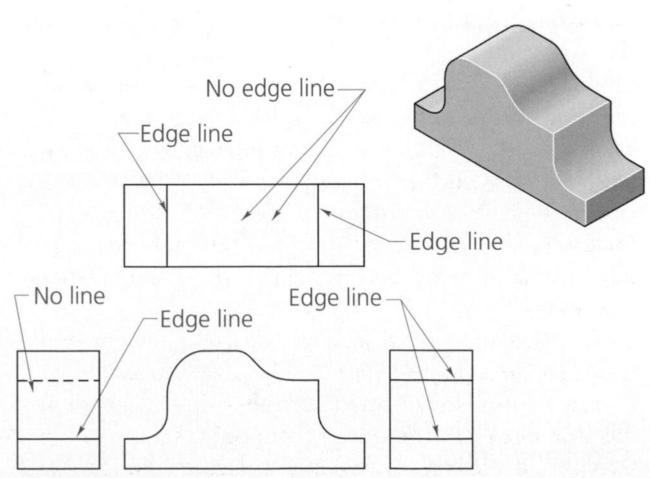

FIGURE 10.47 Curved Surfaces and Edge Lines

Applying Parametric Design . . .

VIEWS FROM PARAMETRIC MODELS

Views created by a CAD/CAM system are exactly like views constructed manually by a designer on paper. The same rules of projection are applied, the only difference is that you merely command the system to create the views as needed (see Fig. A). The original 3D part database must be completed before views are established. The first view established is the general view showing the parametric model (Fig. B).

A wide variety of views can be derived automatically from the parametric model. One of the most common is projection views. The system automatically creates projection views by looking to the left, to the right, above, and below the picked view location (see Fig. C) to determine the orientation of a projection view (see Fig. D). When conflicting view orientations are found by the system, you are prompted to select the view to be the parent view. A view will then be constructed from the selected view.

At the time they are created, projection, auxiliary, detailed, and revolved views have the same representation and explosion offsets, if any, as their parent views. From that time onward, each view can be simplified and restored and have its explosion distance modified without affecting the parent view. The only exceptions are detailed views, which will always be displayed with the same explosion distances and geometry as their parent views.

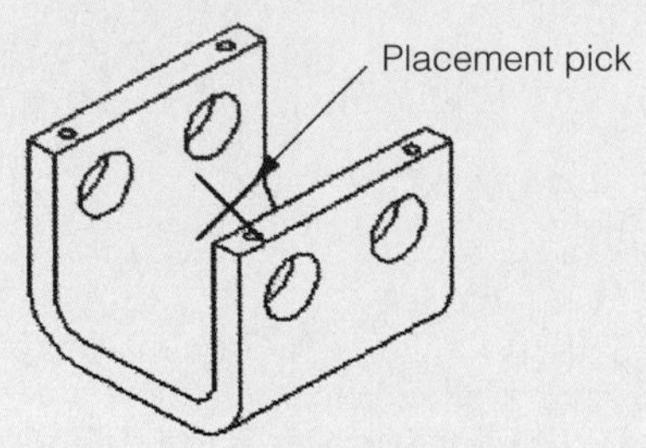

FIGURE B The General View (Default Orientation—First View Added to a Drawing)

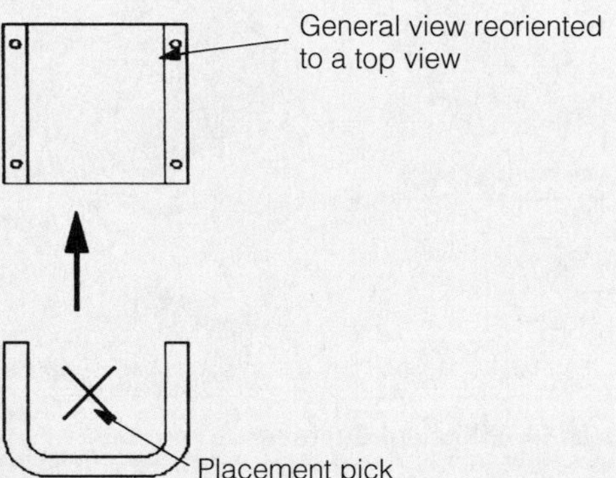

FIGURE C Projecting the Front View

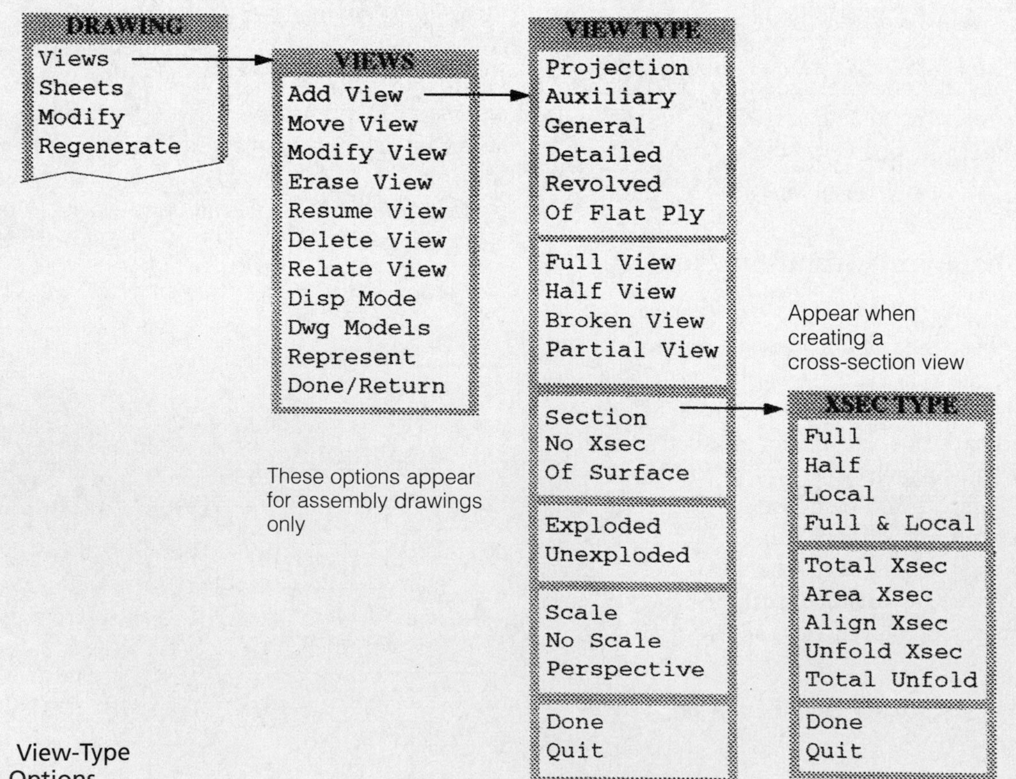

FIGURE A View-Type Command Options

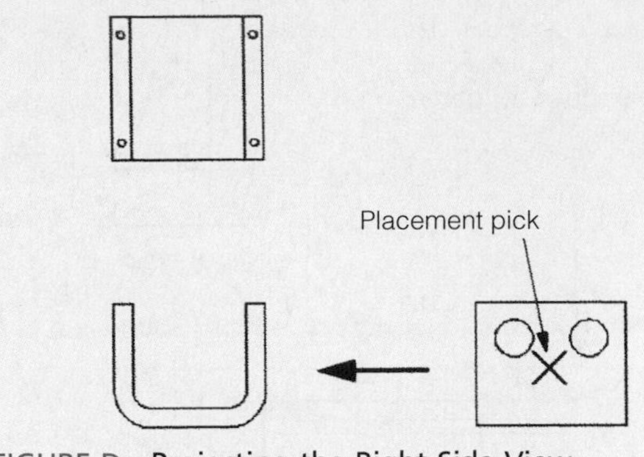

FIGURE D Projecting the Right Side View

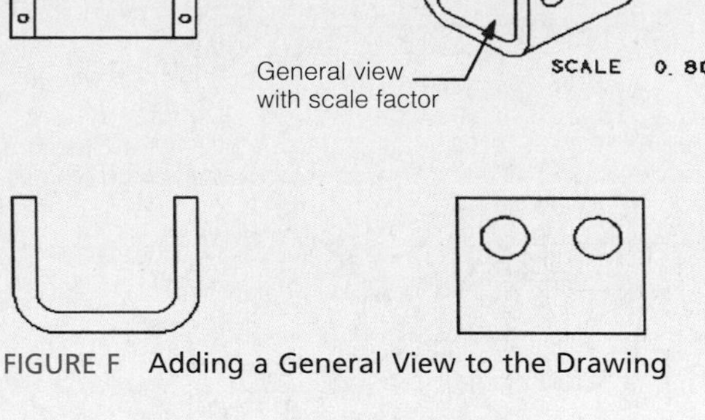

FIGURE F Adding a General View to the Drawing

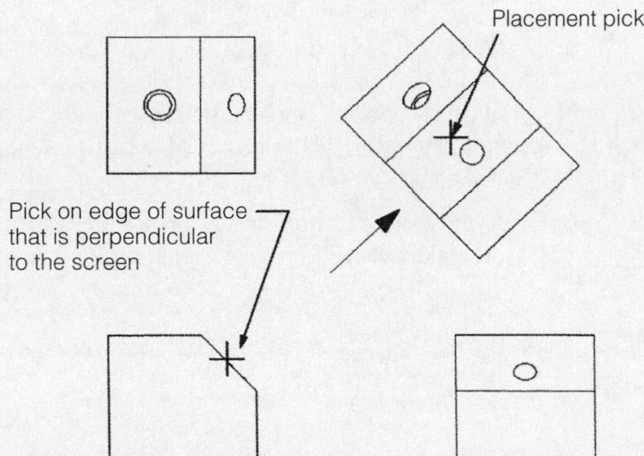

FIGURE E Projecting an Auxiliary View

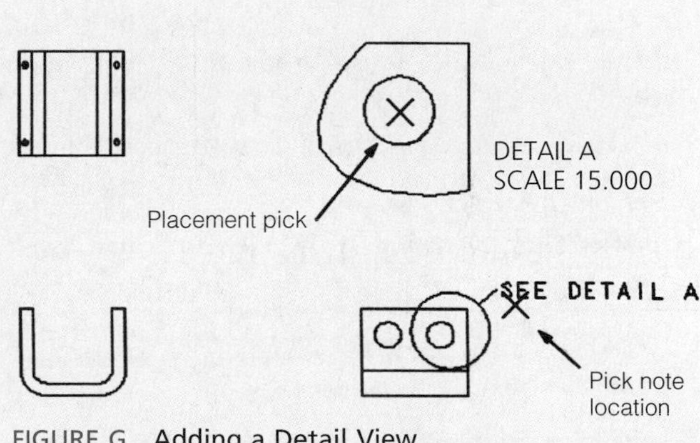

FIGURE G Adding a Detail View

Available View Types

Auxiliary Develops one view from another view by projecting the geometry at right angles to a selected surface or along an axis. The surface selected from the parent view must be perpendicular to the plane of the screen (Fig. E).

Projection Develops one view from another view by projecting the geometry along a horizontal or vertical direction of viewing (orthographic projection). The projection type is specified by you in the drawing setup file, and may be based on third-angle (default) rules or first-angle rules (see Fig. F).

General Creates a view with no particular orientation or relationship to other views in the drawing. The model will first be oriented in the default view orientation established by you (Fig. F).

Detailed Details a portion of the model appearing in another view. Its orientation is the same as the view from which it is created, but its scale may be different so that the portion of the model being detailed can be visualized better (Fig. G).

Revolved Creates a planar-area cross section from an existing view; the section is revolved 90° around the cutting-plane projection and offset along its length. A revolved view may be full or partial, exploded or unexploded (Fig. H).

View Options That Affect How Much of the Model Is Visible in the View

Full View Shows the model in its entirety.

Half View Removes a portion of the model from the view on one side of a cutting plane.

Broken View Removes a portion of the model from between two selected points, and closes the remaining two portions together within a specified distance.

Partial View Displays a portion of the model in a view within a closed boundary. The geometry appearing within the boundary is displayed; the geometry outside of it is removed (Fig. I).

Options That Determine If the View Is of a Single Surface or Has a Cross Section

Section Displays an existing cross section of the view if the view orientation is such that the cross-section plane is parallel to the screen.

Continues

(Continued)

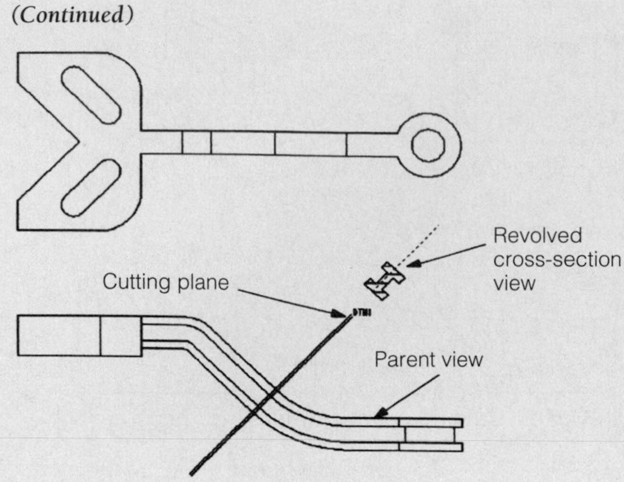

FIGURE H A Revolved-Area Cross-Section View

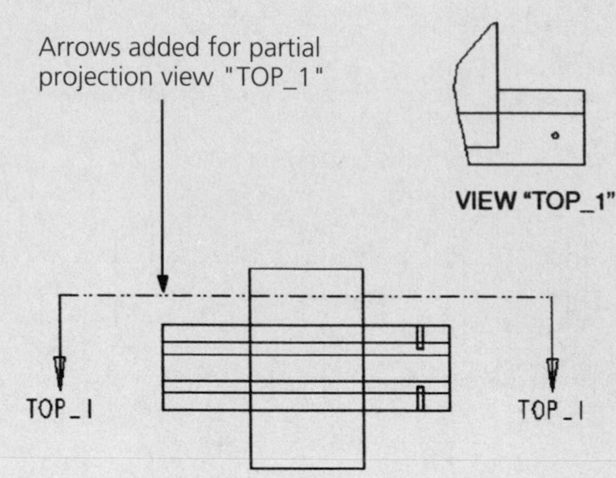

FIGURE I Partial View

No Xsec Indicates that no cross section is to be displayed in the view.

Of Surface Displays a selected surface of a model in the view. The single surface view can be of any view type except detailed.

Options That Determine If the View Is Scaled

Scale Allows you to create a view with an individual scale shown under it. When the view is being created, the system will prompt you for the scale value. This value can be modified later. General and detailed views can be scaled.

No Scale A view will be scaled automatically using a predefined scale value that will appear in the lower left corner of the screen as "SCALE."

Perspective Creates a perspective general view.

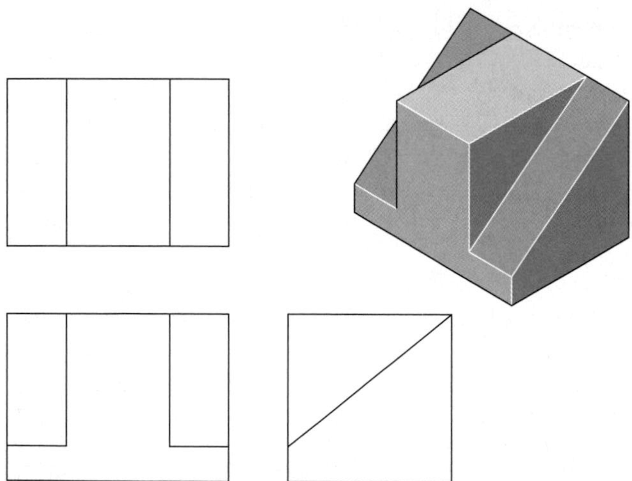

FIGURE 10.48 Inclined Surfaces on Parts

10.8.6 Inclined Surfaces of a Part

An **inclined surface** shows as an edge in one view and as foreshortened in the adjacent view. The edge view of the inclined surface shows the *true angle* of the surface. Figure 10.49 has three inclined surfaces. The angles that surfaces A and C make with the horizontal plane is shown in the front view, where each appears as an edge line. The true angle of surface B can be measured in the side view, where it appears as an edge line. The other views of surface B show as *foreshortened.* The amount of foreshortening depends on the *angle of the inclination:* The greater the angle of incline to a view, the more the surface is foreshortened.

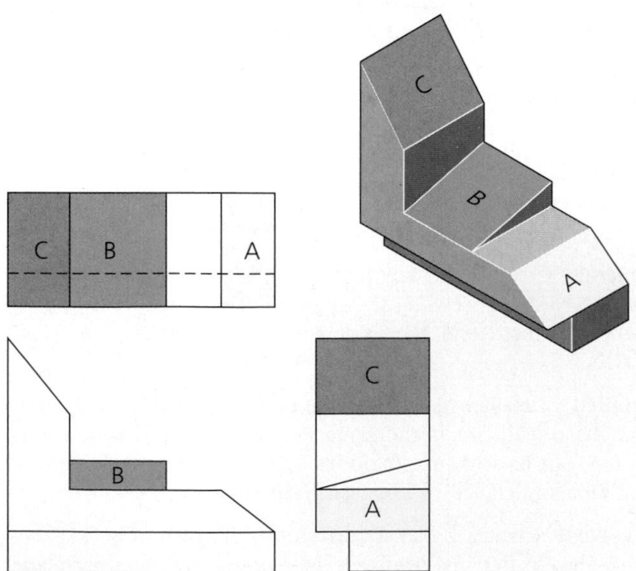

FIGURE 10.49 Inclined Surfaces in Adjacent and Related Views

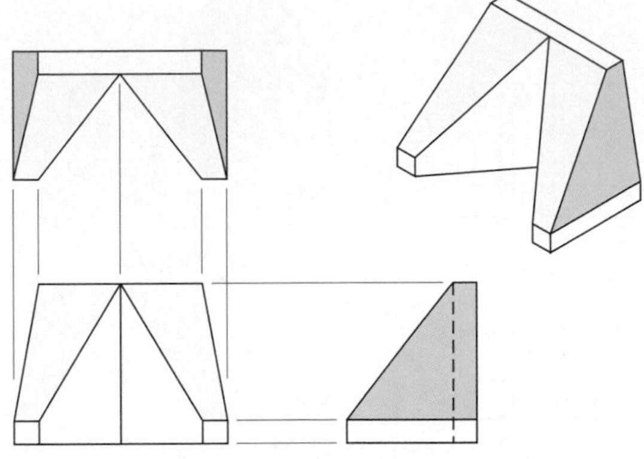

FIGURE 10.50 Inclined Surfaces

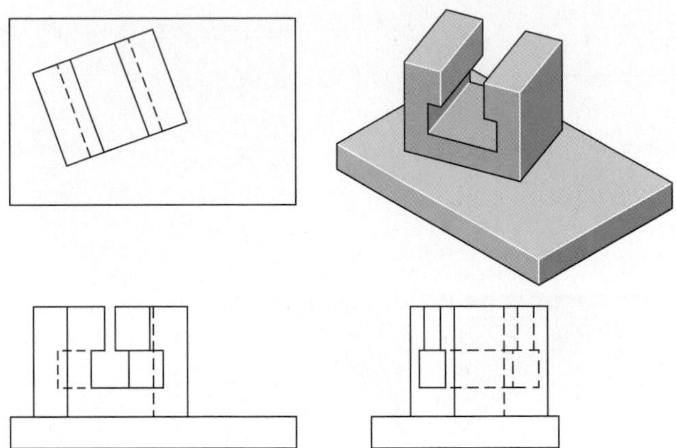

FIGURE 10.52 Distorted View of Surfaces

The part shown in Figure 10.50 has a number of angled surfaces, each represented by different shading. Each view shows the angle of two surfaces. The V-shaped cut in the top view shows two edge lines of surfaces that appear foreshortened in the front (and side) view. The angled surface on the front of the part is seen in the side view as an edge line making a true angle with the part's base. The front view shows the edge lines of the two angled sides of the part.

10.8.7 Edge Views of Inclined Surfaces

As was stated in the last section, the **edge view** of an inclined surface shows in a view where it forms a true angle in a normal plane. The adjacent and related views of the inclined surface always appear foreshortened (they never appear as true shape or larger than the plane itself). This is seen in Figure 10.51. The part has two angled surfaces: one inclined to the horizontal projection plane (top view), the other inclined to the frontal projection plane (front view). The first inclined surface appears as an edge in the front view, and its true angle with the horizontal plane (its base) can be measured here. The second inclined surface shows as an edge line in the side view (hidden line) and as foreshortened in the top and front views. The angle it makes with the frontal plane (and the horizontal-base plane) can be measured in only the side view.

Since many of the surfaces of the part in Figure 10.52 are at an angle to the standard projection planes, it is an example of a drawing that does not adequately describe its features. When this happens, an auxiliary view showing the angled surface as true shape is necessary. The surfaces are at an angle to the frontal projection plane, the front view, and the profile projection plane, side view. Nowhere do the vertical surfaces of the part's upper portion show as true shape.

10.8.8 Oblique Surfaces

Oblique surfaces are inclined to all three principal planes of projection, which makes each view of the surface appear foreshortened (distorted). Since the oblique plane cannot appear as an edge line, each view of it always displays the same number of sides and has a similar shape. Figure 10.53 is an example of a part with an oblique surface. Since it is three-sided, each view of the surface will have three sides and each view shows the plane distorted.

The true shape of an oblique plane cannot be seen in any of the principal projection planes. To establish a true-shape view of an oblique surface, a secondary auxiliary view must be projected (auxiliary views are discussed in Chapter 12).

In Figure 10.53, the oblique surface is labeled and shaded. The surface is formed by the removal of the front corner of the part. In Figure 10.54, the part has two oblique surfaces. The intersecting line formed by the two oblique surfaces shows as true length in the side view. This line is inclined to the base of the part; but since it shows as true length in one of the three principal planes of projection, it is not an oblique line. *An oblique line is inclined to all three principal planes of projection.*

10.8.9 Curved and Cylindrical Surfaces

Curved features, such as **cylindrical**, **conical**, and **spherical** shapes, are displayed on drawings as shown in Figures 10.55, 10.56, and 10.57. Cylindrical shapes, as in Figure

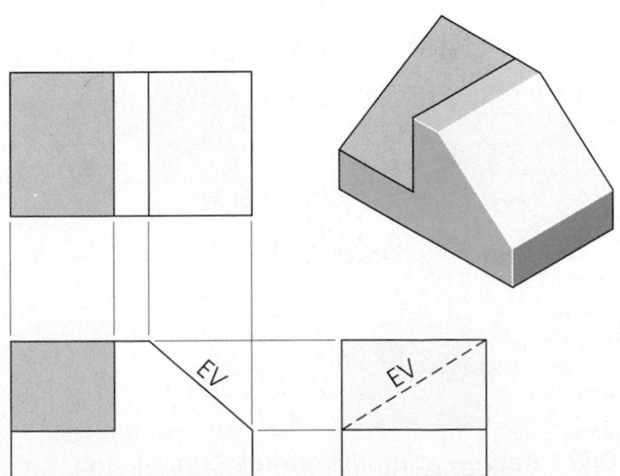

FIGURE 10.51 Edge Views and Inclined Surfaces

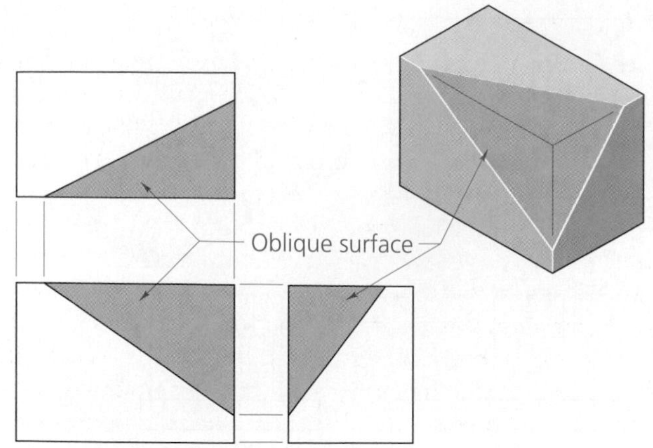

FIGURE 10.53 Oblique Surfaces in Related and Adjacent Views

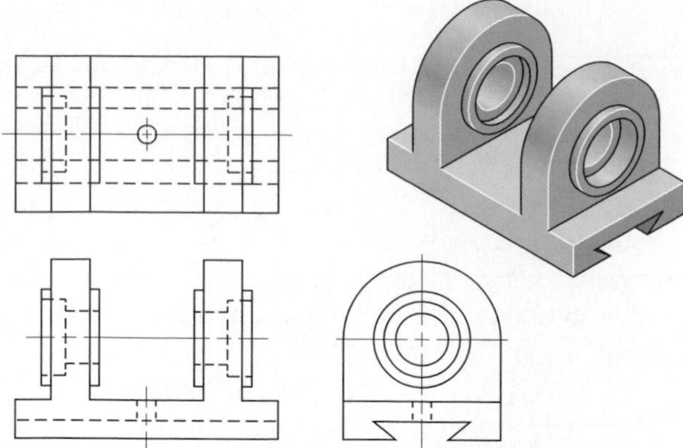

FIGURE 10.56 Curved Surfaces on Drawings

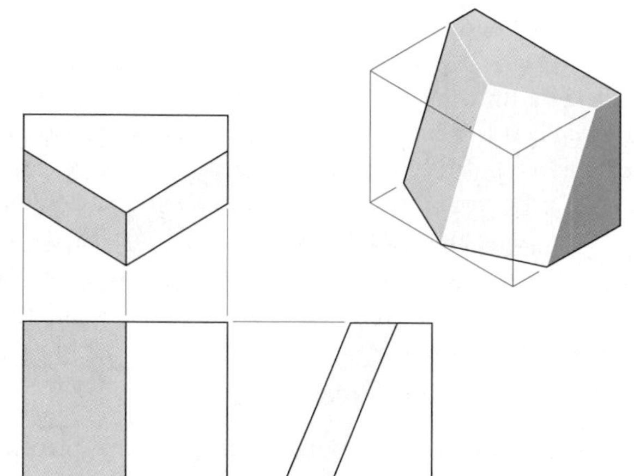

FIGURE 10.54 Oblique Surfaces

10.55, show as true-shape curves in views that are perpendicular to their surface. The front view of this part shows the true-shape/size curve of the cylindrical surface. The side and top views are parallel to the curved surface. Therefore, in these views, the cylindrical shape appears as a rectangle.

In Figure 10.56, the part has a number of cylindrical surfaces. The side view of the part shows the true shape and size of the curves, whereas the top and front views display only the edges of the curved surfaces. Without the side view, the drawing could not have been accurately read; the curved features would not have been apparent. For parts with curved features, always provide at least one view where the curve appears true shape.

Figure 10.57 displays the three types of curved surfaces. The **cylindrical surface** shows as a circle in one view and as a rectangle in the other two views. The **conical surface** appears as a circle in one view also, but its other two views show the surface as a triangle. The **spherical surface** shows as a circle in all three views, as would a ball when viewed from any direction.

In both Figures 10.56 and 10.57, the pictorial view of the part provided in the upper right of the illustration is a CAD-modeled true 3D wireframe model of the part, as are many of the examples in the text. Wireframe models are displayed with all edge lines. True visibility is difficult to establish without some experience.

You May Complete Exercises 10.5 Through 10.8 at This Time

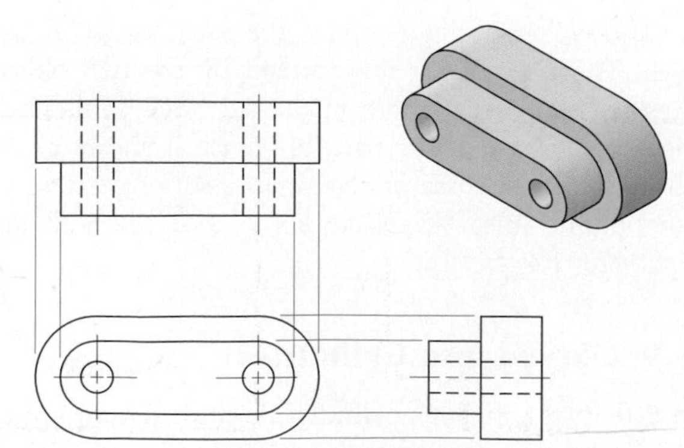

FIGURE 10.55 Cylindrical Features

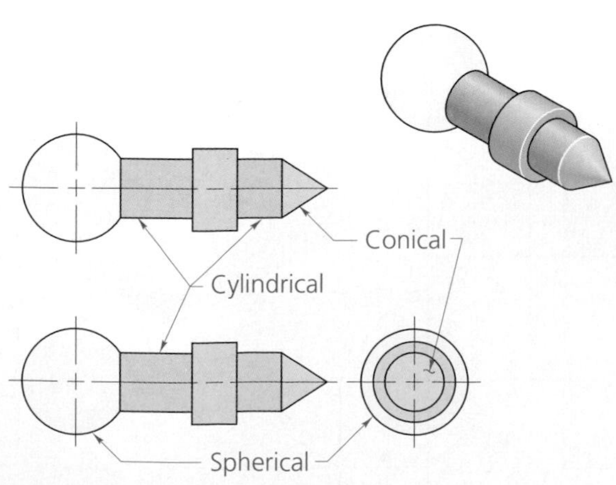

FIGURE 10.57 Representing Cylindrical, Conical, and Spherical Features

10.8.10 Intersection of Curved Surfaces

Where two cylindrical surfaces meet, a line of intersection must be determined. With a 3D CAD system, the line of intersection is determined automatically with either an "intersection of surfaces" or "union of solids" command. The system displays the surfaces and calculates their common line (intersection line). When the line of intersection is derived manually, it must be plotted or represented according to established drafting conventions. Three conditions are possible:

- The two curved surfaces have the same diameter.
- The two curved surfaces have different diameters.
- One of the two curved surfaces is so small that it would be a waste of time to plot the line of intersection.

In Figure 10.58, the small-diameter cylindrical surface, which intersects the vertical cylinder, does not show a distinct-enough line of intersection. Therefore, it is accepted conventional practice to show the intersection as a straight line or to use an ellipse template and show a small curved intersection line. The right side of the intersecting cylinders shows a cylindrical surface large enough to be plotted. The miter line method can be used, or transferring the points with dividers will suffice. Points are established on the curve of the cylinder in the top view, either randomly or evenly spaced, as shown here. The points are projected to the side view first. The side and the top views of each point are then projected to the front view as shown. *The intersection of related projection lines locates a point on the line of intersection.* The points are connected with an irregular curve.

10.8.11 Plotting Elliptical Curves

Elliptical shapes are created by the intersection of planes and curved surfaces. In Figure 10.59, the curve is formed by the intersection of the curved surface and a flat plane surface (not shown). The resulting shape is a surface that is elliptical on one end and a straight line on the other. This inclined surface does not appear as true shape in any of the given three principal planes of projection. To establish the line of intersection in the top view (curved edge), the side view of the cylindrical surface has a series of points located along it. The greater the number of points, the greater the accuracy of the plotted curve. Each point on the curve is projected to the front view. The points are then transferred to the top view via the miter line method or with the aid of dividers. The intersection of related projection lines and transferred distances establishes points along the line of intersection. Connecting the points with a smooth curve completes the view.

10.8.12 Space Curves

Irregular-shaped surfaces (**space curves**) must be plotted (Figure 10.60). The curved surface of this part was cut by an inclined plane (not shown). The true shape of the inclined surface does not appear in any of the three views. To plot the resulting intersection, establish a number of points along the curve in the top view, where the curve's edge line is shown. The more points that are plotted, the greater the accuracy of the curve. Each point is projected to the front view. The points are then projected to the side view from the front view. Lastly, the points are transferred to the side view from the top view. The resulting series of points in the side view is connected using an irregular curve to establish a smooth curve.

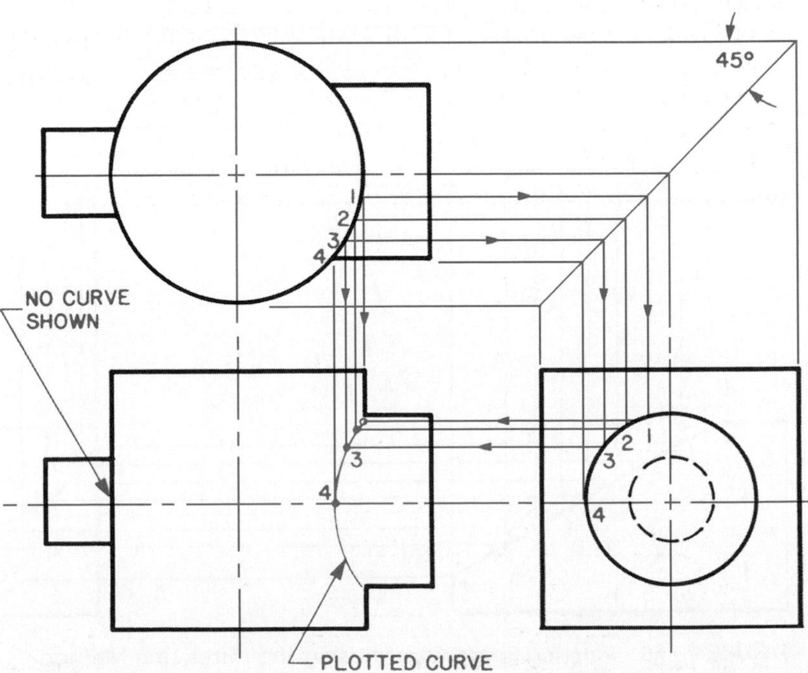

FIGURE 10.58 Intersection of Dissimilar-Size Cylinders

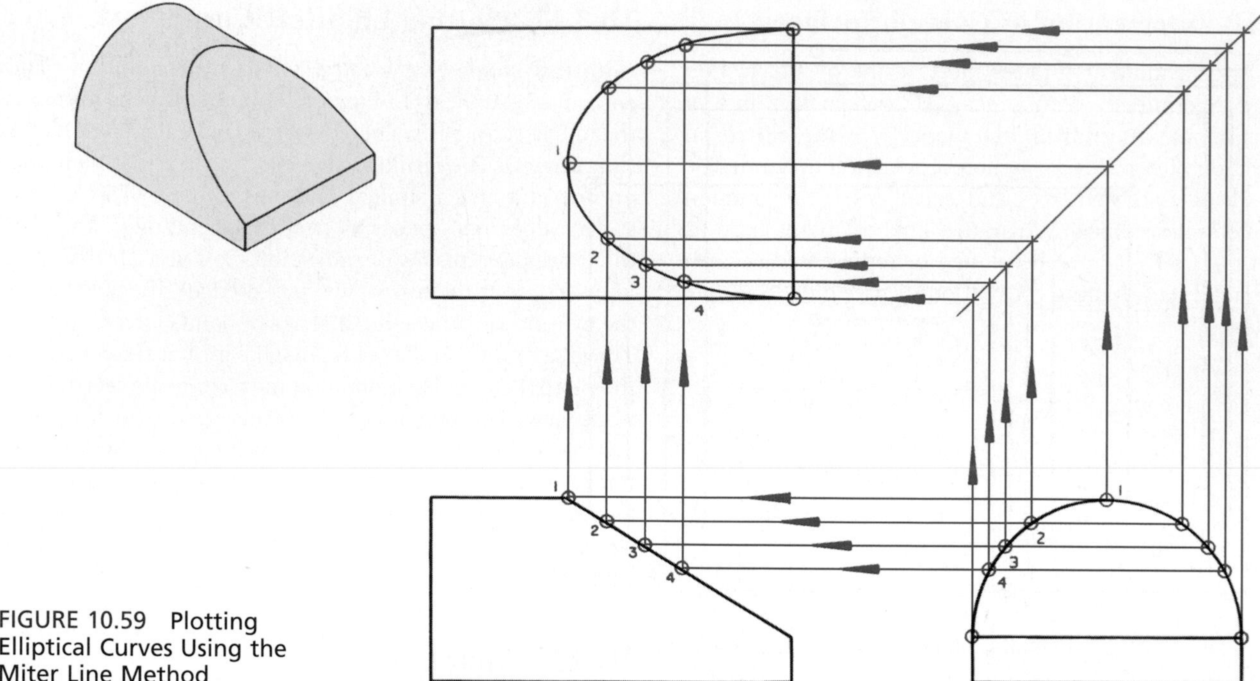

FIGURE 10.59 Plotting Elliptical Curves Using the Miter Line Method

10.8.13 Hole Representation

The part in Figure 10.61 has a number of curved features, including a through-hole and a counterbored hole. The diameter of the hole (.8125) is given for the two holes that are aligned. The counterbored hole has a diameter of .5625 for the thru-hole and a counterbore diameter of .875 to a depth of .250. A machinist reading this drawing would be able to choose the proper equipment to accomplish these machined features. In most cases, the type of hole is no longer noted. The machinist determines whether to use a drill, a reamer, or a boring tool. The decision depends on the hole size, the material of the part, and the tolerance requirements. *A hole is always defined by its diameter, never by its*

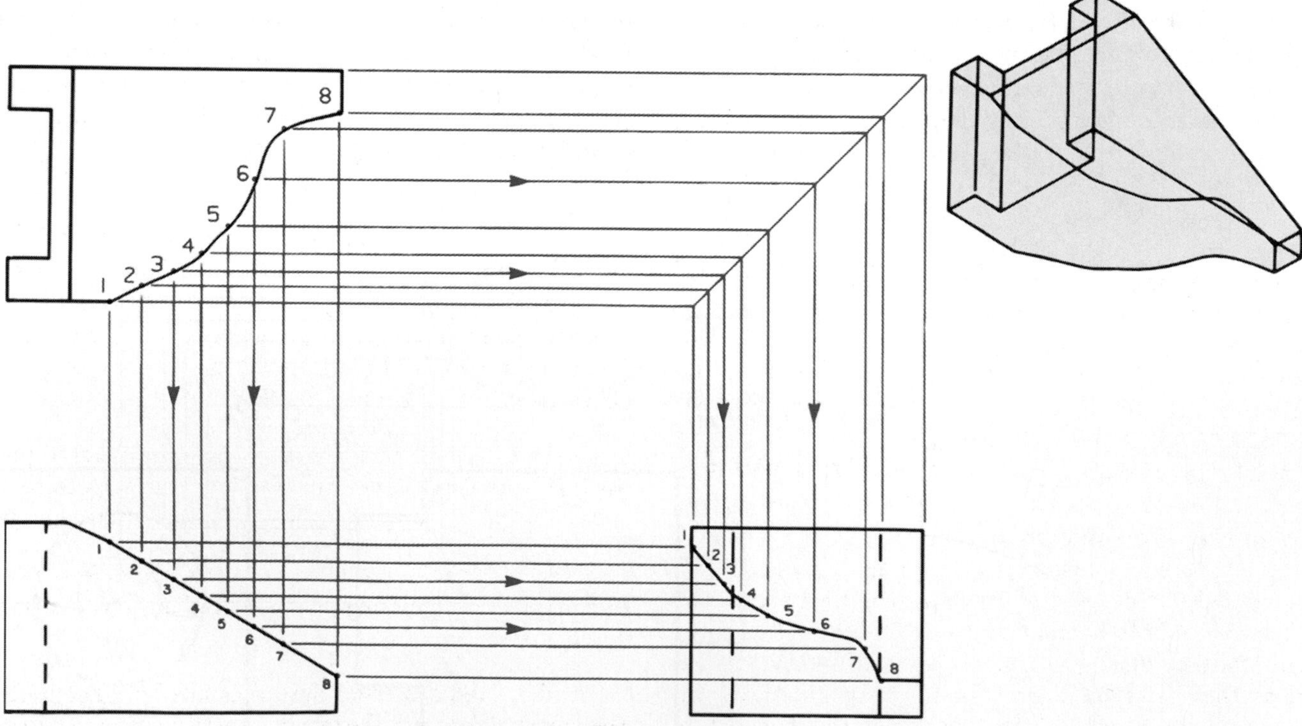

FIGURE 10.60 Plotting Space Curves Using the Miter Line Method

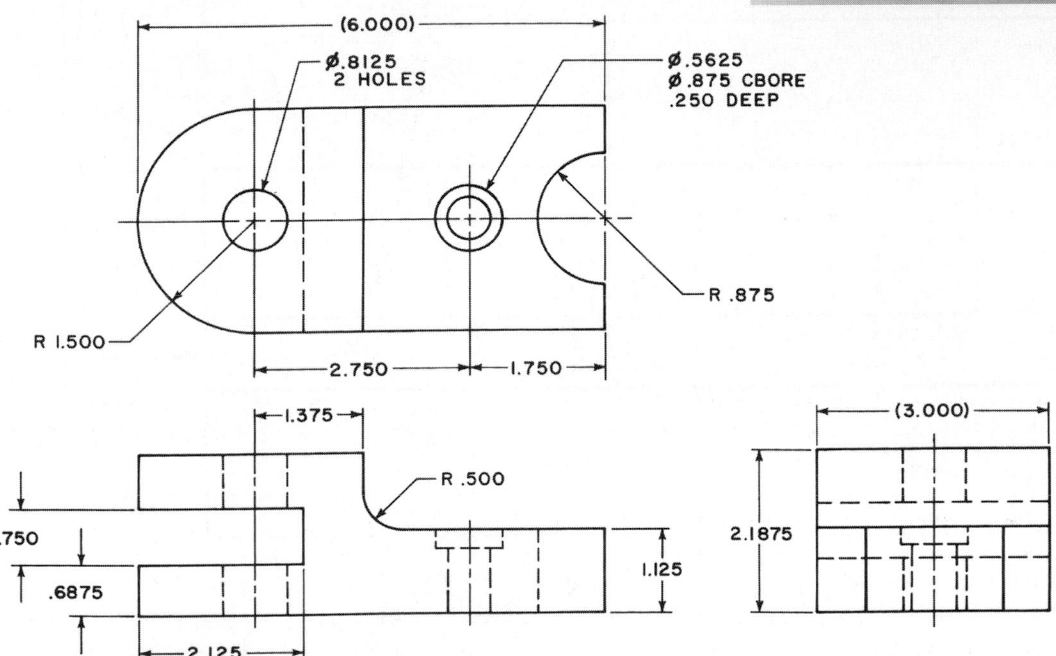

FIGURE 10.61 Detail of Breaker

radius. Drills, reamers, bores, and other hole machining tools are described by their diameter, not their radius value.

Figure 10.62 provides a detailed demonstration of how holes should and should not be represented on drawings. Since each situation and type of hole will be encountered repeatedly, this illustration should be studied carefully. The simplest hole callout provides the diameter symbol and the diameter value as in the **DRILL OR REAM** callout. Unless the depth is given, the hole depth is understood to be through the part. When holes will completely penetrate the part, they are sometimes noted on drawings with the word **THRU** (instead of "through"). Notice the difference between the **CORRECT REPRESENTATION** and the **INCORRECT REPRESENTATION** for each type of hole.

A hole that does not go through the part is called a **blind hole.** In Figure 10.62 it is shown in the depth view as two lines that represent the edges of the hole diameter, plus a centerline. A centerline is required for both blind holes and through-holes in every view in which they are shown. The bottom of the hole is a conical point. The conical shape is formed by the drill tip and, for convenience, is drawn at 30°. The depth of the blind hole is represented by the end of the cylindrical portion of the hole. The depth value is noted in the dimension under the diameter

Holes are either blind holes or through-holes. In Figure 10.62, five are depicted as thru-holes. If they were blind holes, the drill depth would be stated under the diameter callout in the dimension. The following hole types are found on machined parts throughout industry.

Common Hole Types on Machined Parts

Spotface A hole that has been drilled to the required depth and whose upper part is enlarged. The depth of the spotface is sometimes not noted. The spotface depth is drawn, depending on the part, at .0625 (1.5 mm) to .125 (3 mm). Spotfacing cleans up the surface around the hole so that a bolt head or other item may rest flush with the surface.

Counterbore Similar to a spotface, except the enlarged hole has a specific depth. The counterbore depth is specified in the callout dimension under the counterbore diameter.

Countersink A hole that has been enlarged conically to a specified diameter and depth The conical angle is drawn at 90° for simplicity.

Counterdrill A countersink and a counterbore combined. The transition between the two diameters is a conical surface formed by the angle of the Moors tip. Countrdrills are

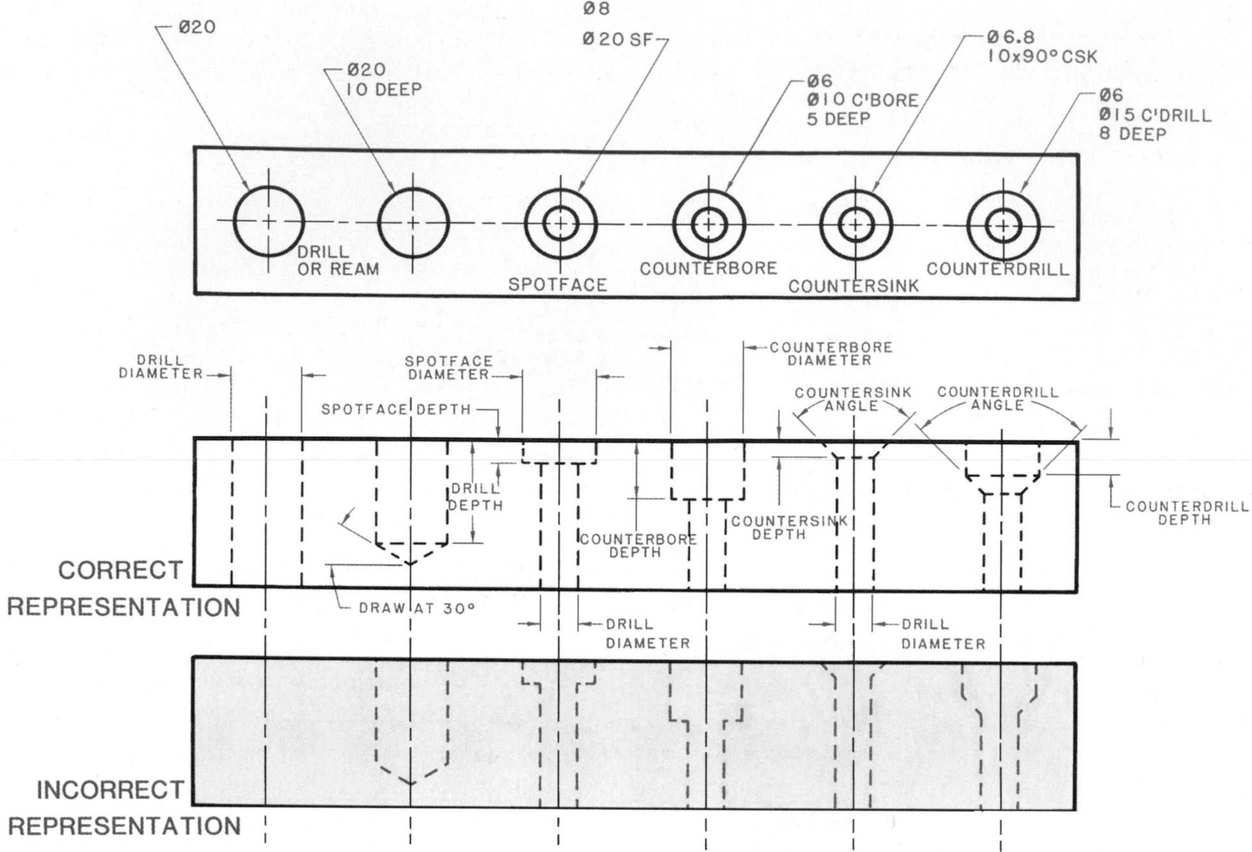

FIGURE 10.62 **Types and Representation of Holes on Drawings**

specified by their diameter and depth. The angle of the counterdrill is shown in the adjacent view.

10.8.14 Fillets and Rounds

Castings are rough parts that are usually machined along one or more of their surfaces. A casting will have curved intersections between mating surfaces. Castings cannot be formed accurately without these curved corners. Perfectly sharp corners are not possible with the casting process. Drawings of machined castings require the representation of these surfaces and their intersections. Two rough interior surfaces intersect and form a rounded corner called a **fillet.** Two rough exterior surfaces meet and form a corner called a **round.** The part in Figure 10.63 has a variety of rounds and fillets.

When two intersecting surfaces meet and one is machined, the corner becomes a sharp edge. If both surfaces are machined, the corner is also shown as a sharp edge. Rounds will show only when both of the mating exterior surfaces are unmachined (rough or cast surfaces). The material removed during machining is determined by the part's casting dimensions and the machining dimensions. Sometimes separate drawings are used. A **casting drawing** is done for the foundry, and a machine drawing is completed for the machine shop (see Chapter 14).

As a design requirement, fillets and rounds serve to reduce the possibility of failure of a joint. Sharp points are possible points of fracture. Most fillets are determined by the foundry to meet the design requirements, the methods of casting, and the thickness of the part. In many cases, the selection of the fillet diameter is left to the pattern maker.

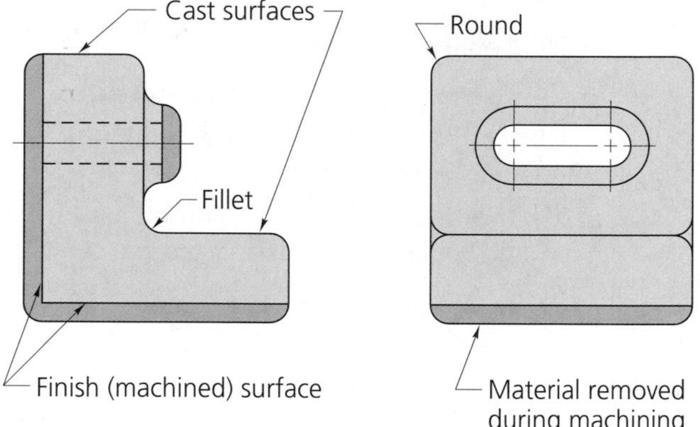

FIGURE 10.63 **Fillets, Rounds, and Castings**

10.8.15 Tangent Surfaces

When a curved and a plane surface are tangent, a *point of tangency* may be required. In Figure 10.64, the cylindrical surfaces are connected by plane surfaces along the sides of the part. Since the cylindrical ends are different diameters, the tangent points of the cylinders and the planes will not fall along the centerline in the front view. The back surface is flush with the two diameters; tangent points A therefore fall

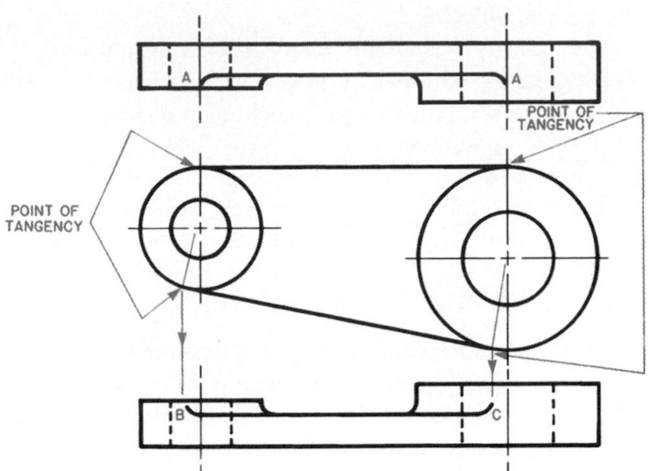

FIGURE 10.64 Runouts and Points of Tangency on Drawings

along the centerline. Because the circles are staggered and of different diameters, the front view of the tangent points does not fall along the centerline. Tangent points B and C are determined by drawing construction lines perpendicular to the front edge and through the center of each cylindrical surface in the view where the diameter shows true shape (top view here). The intersection of this line and each circle's circumference determines the points of tangency (B and C).

10.8.16 Runouts and Edge Representation

After the point of tangency between a plane surface and a cylindrical surface has been determined, the runout can be drawn. **Runouts** are curves at the point of tangency. If the part is a casting, the runout will be a fillet at the tangent point, as in Figure 10.64. Points B and C are the points of tangency of the surface intersections, but they are also the transition points of the cast surfaces. Therefore, the fillet must be drawn as shown. The radius of the fillet establishes the runout; it is normally constructed with a template. Only 45° (one-eighth) of the curve need be drawn for most situations.

You May Complete Exercises 10.9 Through 10.12 at This Time

10.9 OPPOSITE-HAND PARTS

There are many industrial applications for parts that are the exact opposite of one another. These are called **opposite-hand parts** or **right-hand** and **left-hand parts.** In most cases, only one drawing is needed to describe both parts. To visualize a right-hand and a left-hand part, take an existing drawing (one from the text will do) and hold it up to a mirror. The reflection in the mirror shows the opposite hand of the part. If a right-hand part was used, the mirror shows the left-hand projection. Of course, to see a simple example of right-hand and left-hand parts, just look at your own hands.

Examples of industrial applications of right-hand and left-hand parts are numerous. A car has many opposite-hand parts, both in the engine and on the body of the automobile. When viewing parts, care must be taken not to confuse right-hand and left-hand parts with parts that are the same but just happen to be installed on both sides of an assembly. For instance, a car's fenders and doors are obviously right-hand and left-hand parts. But headlights, wheels, hubcaps, and headrests are not.

Right-hand and left-hand parts are required in many circumstances. If a project requires a right-hand and a left-hand part, it is accepted practice to draw only one of the parts and to note on the drawing:

NOTE: RIGHT-HAND AND LEFT-HAND PART REQUIRED.
RH PART SHOWN.

In general, if there are any differences between the two parts, it is normal practice to draw both. If the differences are minor, such as a hole size or the addition of a hole, then these differences can sometimes be established with a note or with a callout. The following example for the diameter dimension for a hole shows this situation:

.500 DIA THRU
LH PART ONLY

When both left-hand and right-hand parts must be drawn, you can save time and energy by tracing the completed side (or making a copy on an office copier), turning it over, and using it to draw the opposite side. A light table allows you to see through the paper to view the reversed drawing that is to be traced.

10.9.1 2D and 3D CAD Mirroring Commands for Opposite-Hand Parts

A CAD system will eliminate the need to draw the opposite-hand part. The **MIRROR** command displays the mirror-image view of the part (or selected geometry of a part). Even a 2D system can project the opposite hand of one view of the part. The choice of mirrored views depends on the complexity of the part. The view with the most complex geometry should be mirrored.

A 3D CAD system will have the advantage of projecting a true 3D model of the part's opposite hand, as shown in Figure 10.65. In this illustration, the right-hand and left-hand projections of the part are shown. The part has been mirrored about a plane (shown as a line in the lower illustration and as a plane in the 3D projection). After one hand of the part has been modeled on the system, it is a simple matter to give one command to establish the opposite-hand part.

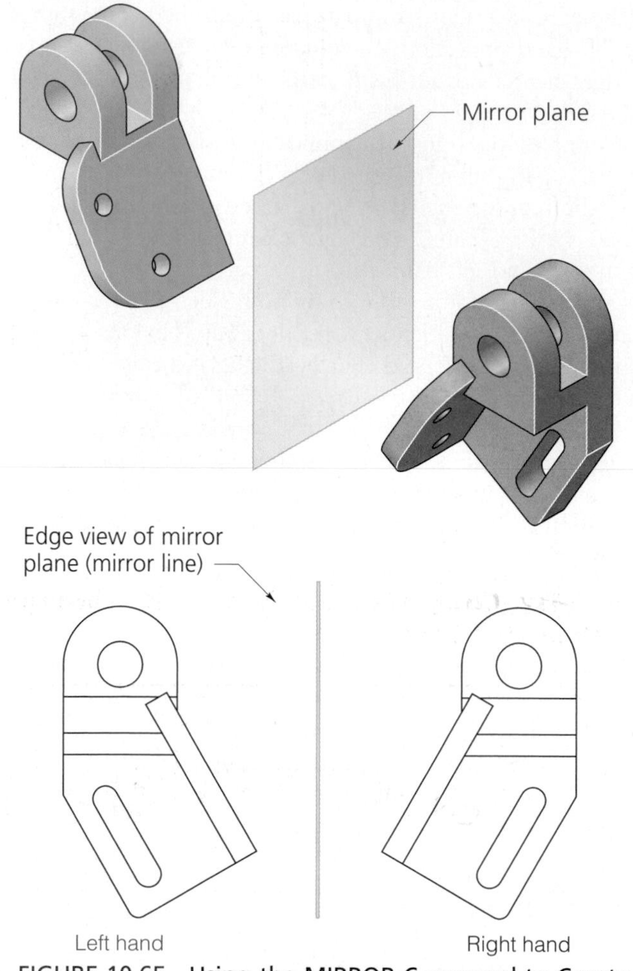

FIGURE 10.65 Using the MIRROR Command to Create Opposite-Hand Parts

If using AutoCAD, the **MIRROR** command is given as follows:

```
Command: MIRROR
Select objects: use a window (or select each object)
Pick first corner: Pick first corner of window
Pick second corner: Pick second point of window (enclose the whole part)
Select objects: <RETURN>
First point of mirror line: Pick point on mirror line
Second point: Pick any point above or below—near mirror line
Delete old objects? <N> <RETURN>
```

Because of the speed and simplicity of creating the opposite-hand part, a CAD system for generating the second drawing of the part is a practical alternative to just noting the need for an opposite-hand part on the drawing.

10.10 VIEW CONSTRUCTION USING CAD

Views are constructed on a 2D CAD system in much the same way as with manually drawn projects, so all of the preceding descriptions for constructing views are valid. 3D CAD systems, on the other hand, create true three-dimensional models of the part. Because of this, the construction process is very different.

In general, every 3D system requires one or more standard views (or **VIEWPORTS**) when modeling. Since the part can be rotated in 3D space, you need to display only one "view" (the top, normally). As the construction progresses, the model geometry is rotated into other orientations to model the complete part. Afterward, you can request the system to display additional views of the part for dimensioning. In Figure 10.66, the 3D system is displaying the completed model in three standard views and in a rotated view.

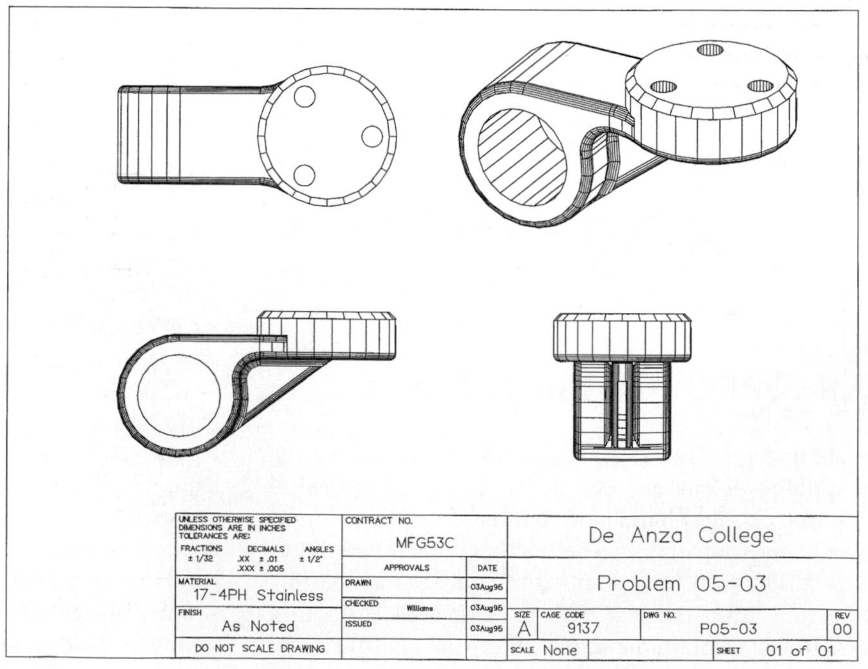

UNLESS OTHERWISE SPECIFIED DIMENSIONS ARE IN INCHES TOLERANCES ARE:
FRACTIONS ± 1/32
DECIMALS .XX ± .01 .XXX ± .005
ANGLES ± 1/2°
MATERIAL
17-4PH Stainless
FINISH
As Noted
DO NOT SCALE DRAWING
CONTRACT NO.
MFG53C
APPROVALS
DATE
DRAWN
03Aug95
CHECKED
Williams
03Aug95
ISSUED
03Aug95
De Anza College
Problem 05-03
SIZE
A
CAGE CODE
9137
DWG NO.
P05-03
REV
00
SCALE None
SHEET 01 of 01

FIGURE 10.66 Views on a CAD System

It is not the purpose of this text to explain in detail the process of 3D modeling, but you should understand the differences in establishing views via this procedure. Most CAD systems have six or seven standard views, along with an infinite number of user-defined views. Six of the predefined views are the same as the six principal views. The seventh (when available) is a standard isometric (or rotated) view. Figure 10.67 shows the seven views: (1) top, (2) front, (3) right side, (4) bottom, (5) left side, (6) back/rear, and (7) isometric.

A part was modeled and is shown in a rotated 3D position in Figure 10.68(a). Since you need to show the model in accepted standard orthographic views to place the dimensions, a number of views must be established. The top is displayed in Figure 10.68(b). The front view is then displayed in Figure 10.68(c), and the drawing's right side view is defined in (d).

Regardless of the design method (manual, 2D CAD, or 3D CAD), knowledge and understanding of orthographic projection to create multiview drawings is essential.

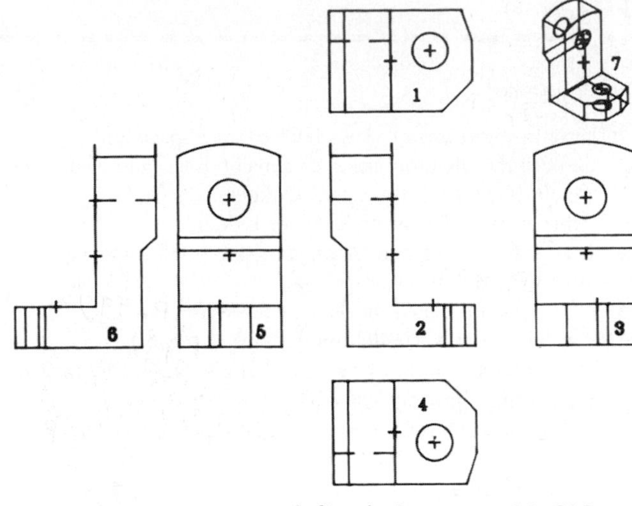

FIGURE 10.67 Seven Predefined Views on a 3D CAD System

You May Complete Exercises 10.13 Through 10.16 at This Time

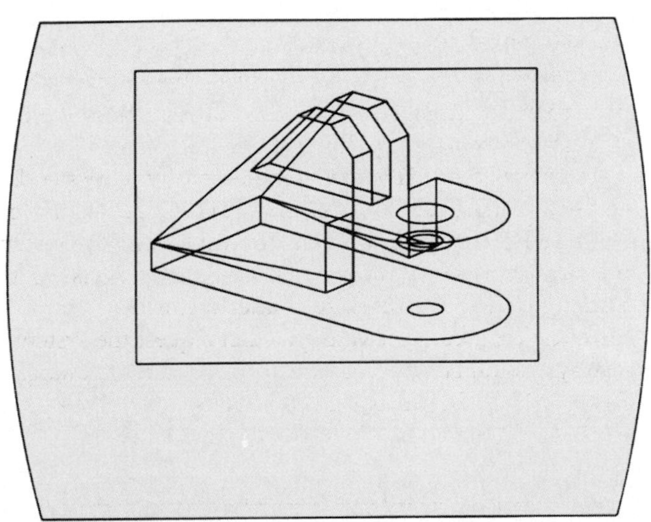

(a) 3D model of part

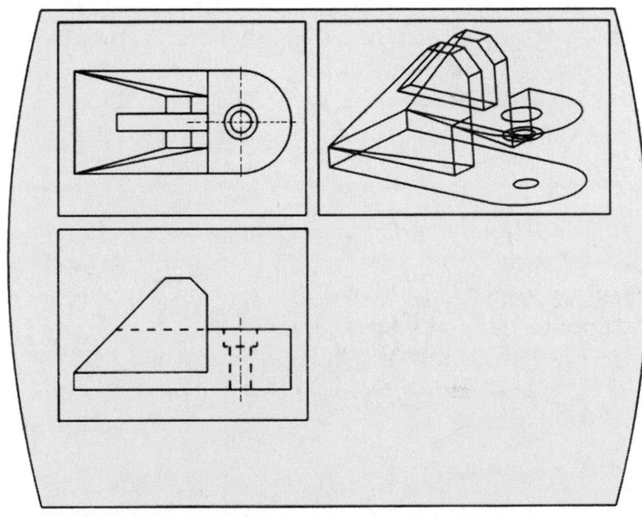

(c) Front view displayed with top and 3D view

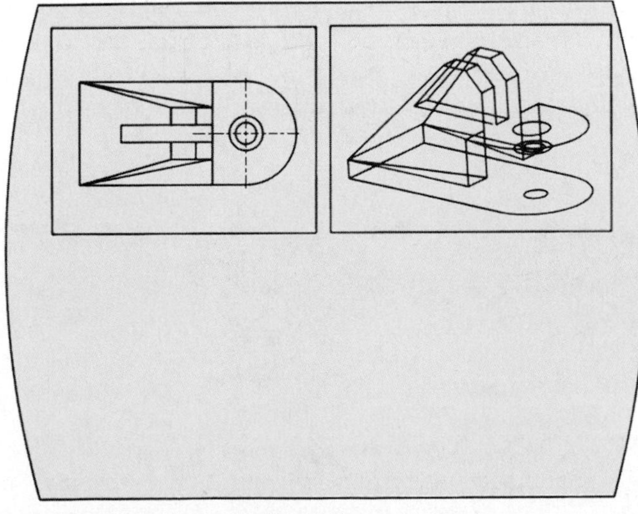

(b) Top view of part displayed along with 3D view

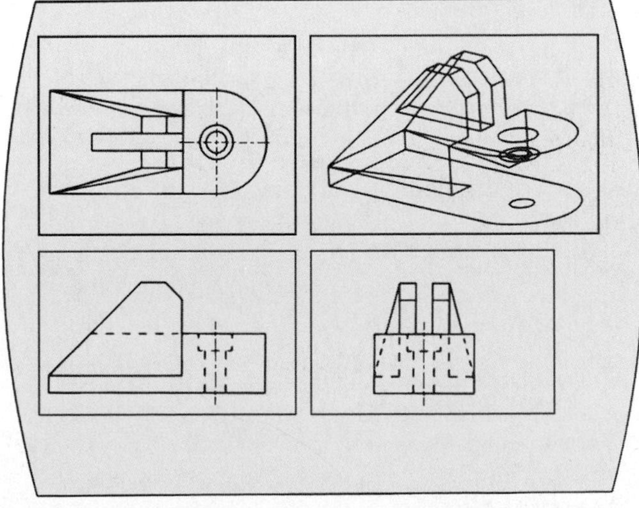

(d) Right side view displayed with top, front, and 3D view

FIGURE 10.68 Orthographic Views

QUIZ

True or False

1. Partial projections of views help to save space and paper.
2. Centerlines, phantom lines, dimension lines, and leader lines are all drawn with the same thickness.
3. Centerlines take precedence over hidden lines.
4. The glass box method of projection is used for most drawings.
5. Adjacent and related views are the same.
6. Parallel lines are parallel in all views.
7. Most foreign countries use third-angle projection for their engineering drawings.
8. All orthographic projection is right-angle projection.

Fill in the Blanks

9. __________ view drawings are normally limited to thin, flat, or __________ round parts.
10. When the object is relatively simple, a __________ line is used to project the third view.
11. Dimensions can be transferred from the top to the side view using __________ lines, the __________ method, or __________.
12. __________ are considered to be a series of __________ in space having __________ but not __________.
13. __________ are used to show round features of a part on drawings.
14. **MIRROR** commands are useful in creating __________ __________ and __________ __________ parts.
15. __________ lines always take precedence over hidden lines.
16. A __________ is a specific location in space.

Answer the Following

17. What is a fold line, and how is it used?
18. What are the six standard views? How do they relate to the use of 3D CAD?
19. What is the difference between the glass box method and the natural method?
20. What is the image plane for projection?
21. Describe adjacent and related views.
22. Explain the difference between first- and third-angle projection.
23. What determines the spacing and choice of views for a drawing?
24. Describe the ISO projection symbol and its use.

EXERCISES

Exercises may be assigned as sketching, instrument, or CAD projects. Transfer the given information to an "A"-size sheet of .25 in. grid paper. Complete all views and ***solve for proper visibility, including centerlines, object lines, and hidden lines.*** Exercises that are not assigned by the instructor can be sketched in the text to provide practice and enhance understanding of the preceding instructional material.

After Reading the Chapter Through Section 10.6.10, You May Complete the Following Exercises

Exercise 10.1 Through Exercise 10.4 Complete each of the given views and the third view, if required.

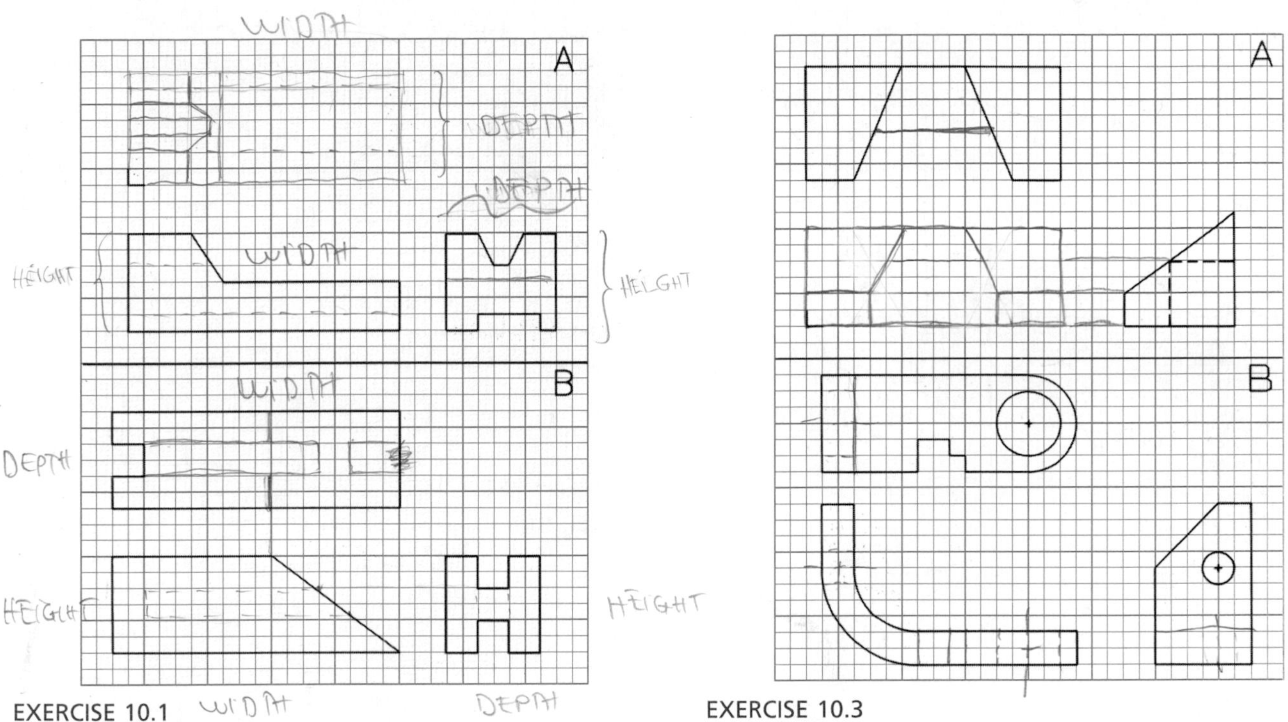

EXERCISE 10.1

EXERCISE 10.3

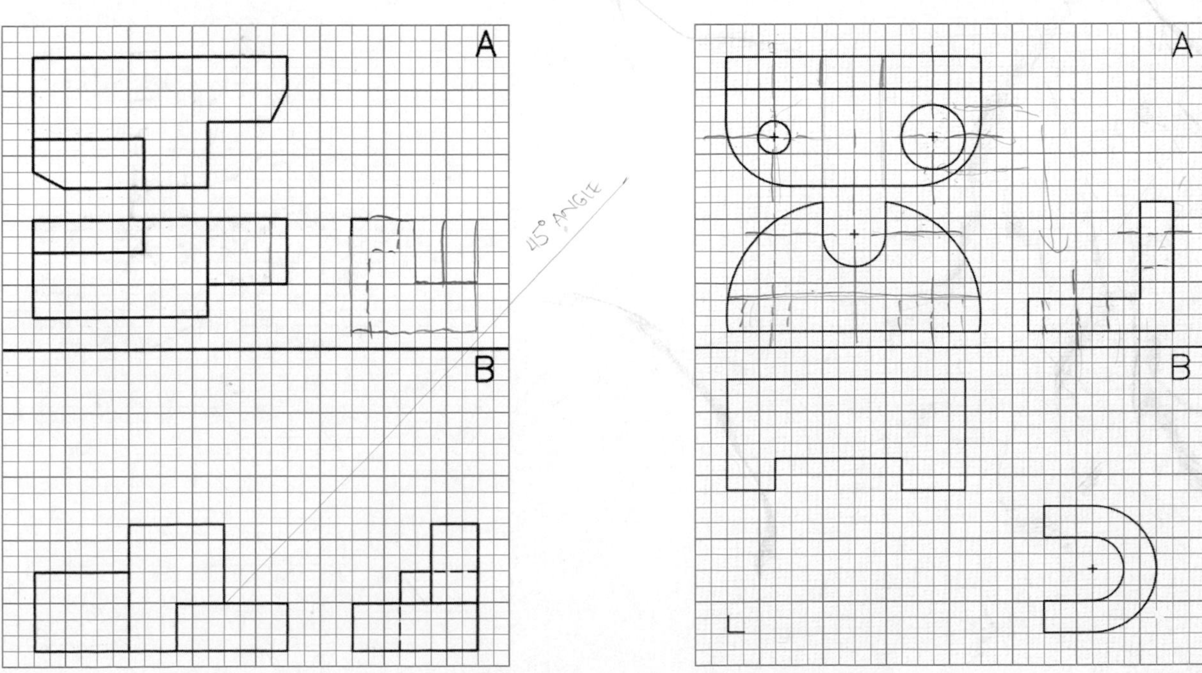

EXERCISE 10.2

EXERCISE 10.4

After Reading the Chapter Through Section 10.8.9, You May Complete the Following Exercises

Exercise 10.5 Through Exercise 10.8 Complete each of the given views and the third view, if required.

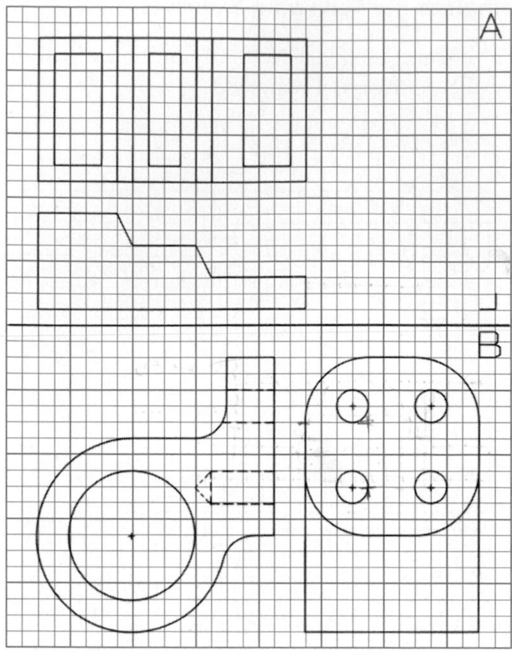

EXERCISE 10.5

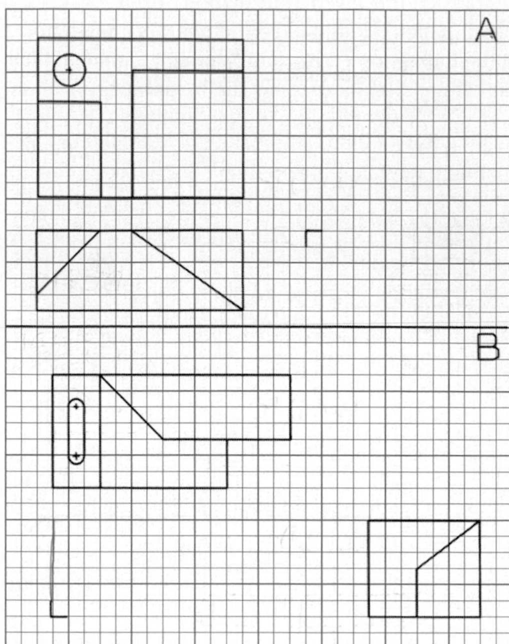

EXERCISE 10.7

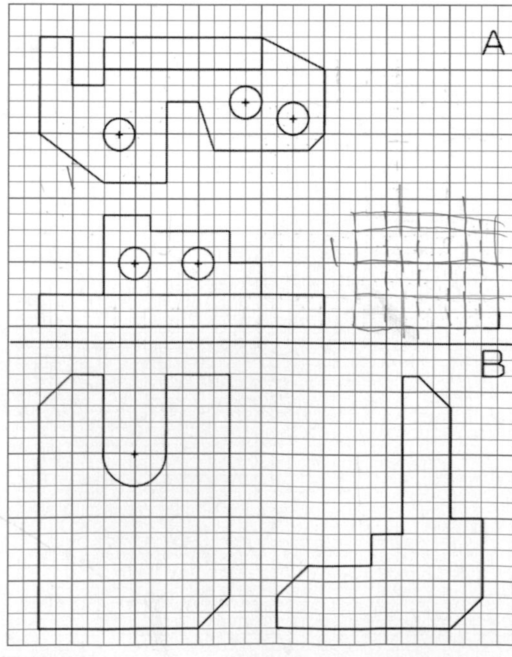

EXERCISE 10.6

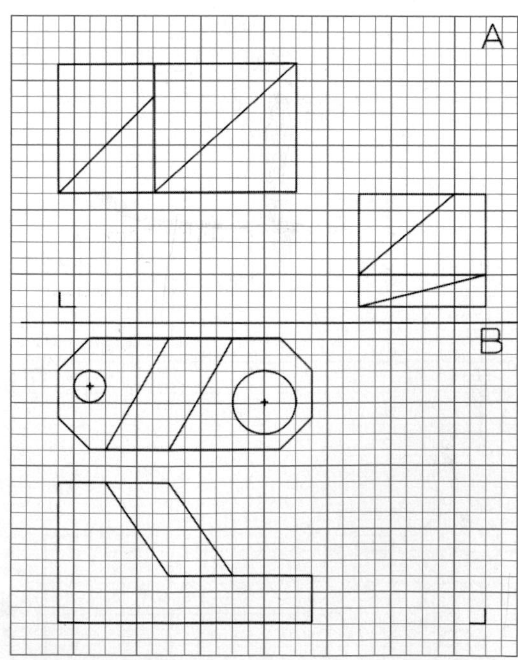

EXERCISE 10.8

After Reading the Chapter Through Section 10.8.16, You May Complete the Following Exercises

Exercise 10.9 Through Exercise 10.12 Complete each of the given views and the third view, if required.

EXERCISE 10.9

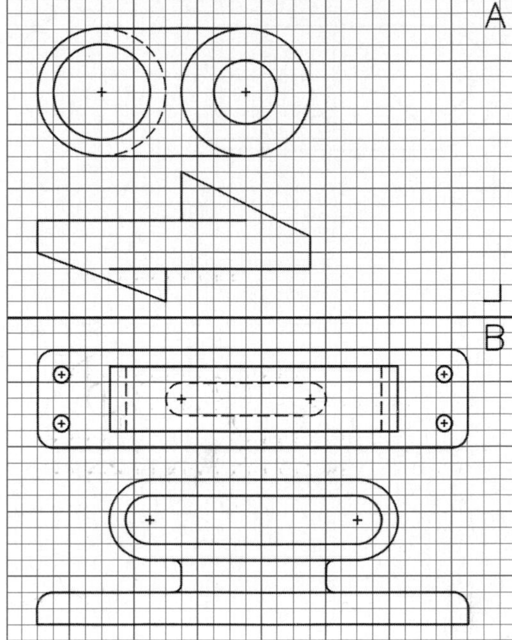

EXERCISE 10.11

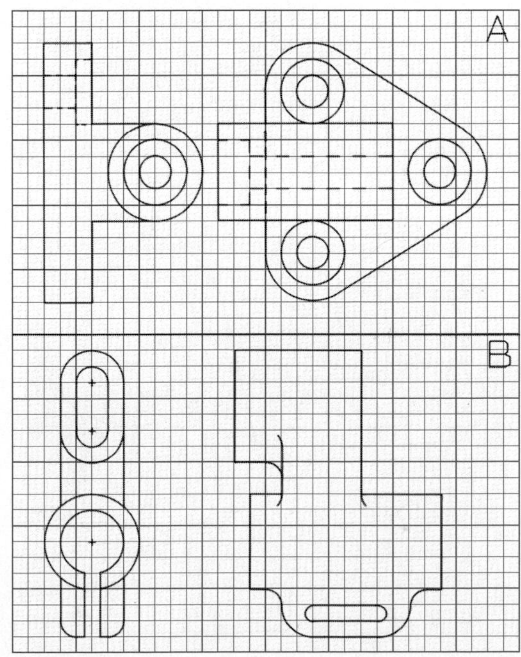

EXERCISE 10.10

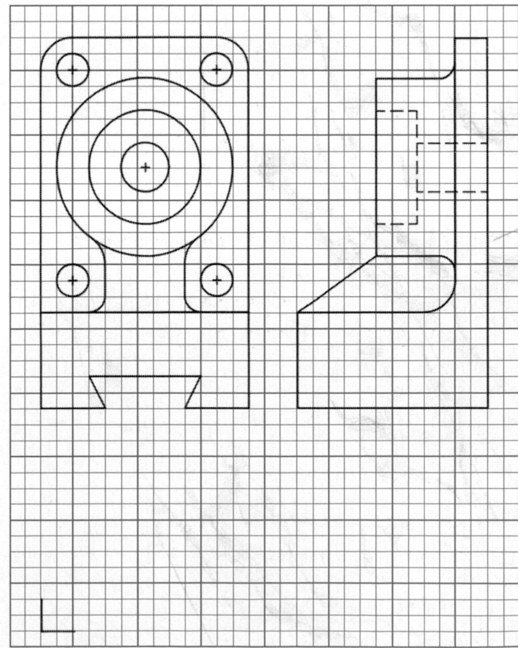

EXERCISE 10.12

After Reading the Chapter Through Section 10.10, You May Complete the Following Exercises

Exercise 10.13 Through Exercise 10.16 Complete each of the given views and the third view, if required.

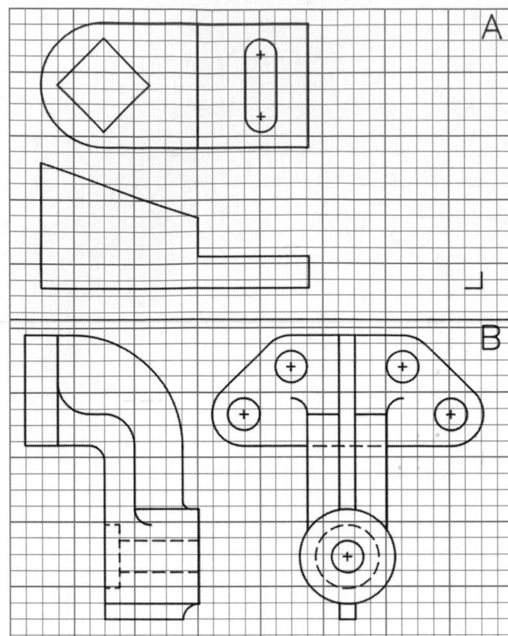

EXERCISE 10.13

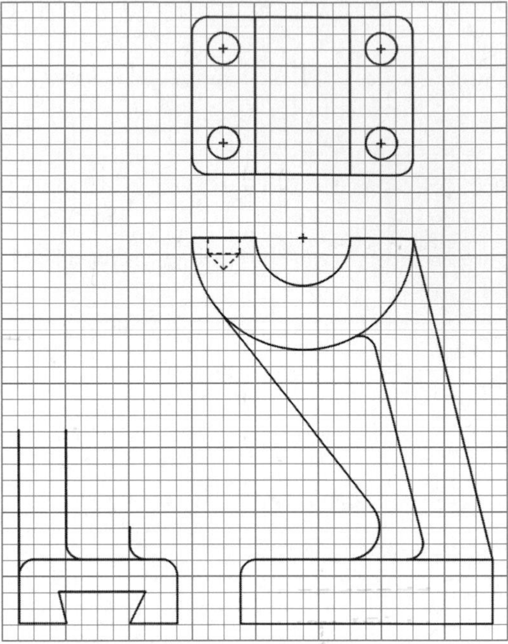

EXERCISE 10.15

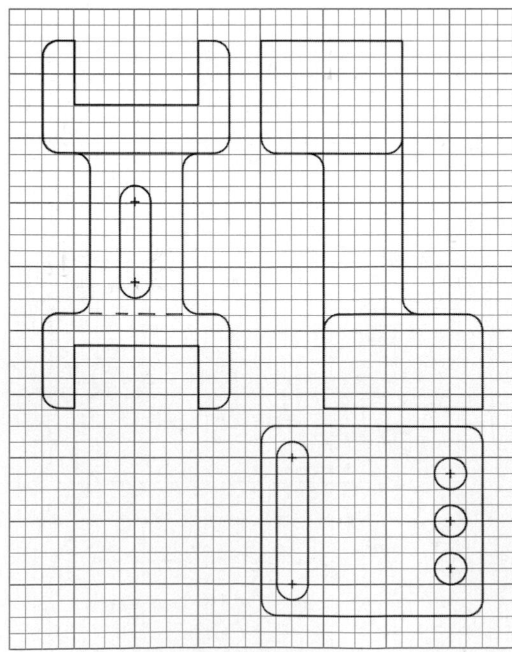

EXERCISE 10.14

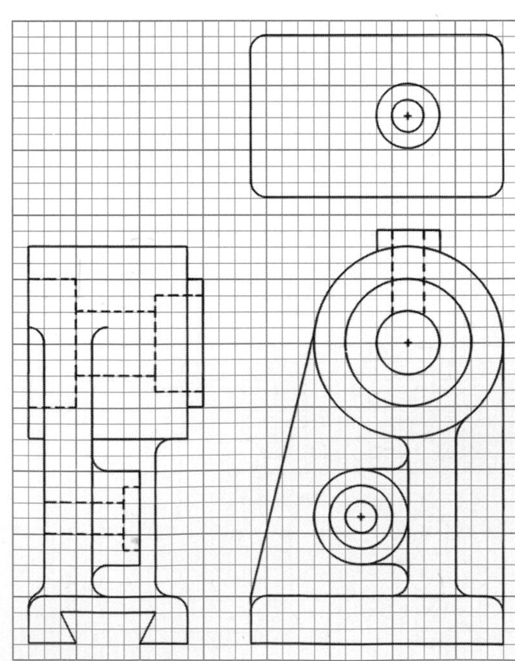

EXERCISE 10.16

PROBLEMS

Problems 10.1(A) Through (K) Complete each of the problems on an "A"- or "B"-size sheet, as required. Use one of the three scales provided in the lower left corner of the page. Use dividers to take measurements from the drawing and set off on one of the scales to establish the parts dimensions. Round off dimensions where necessary. Solve for the missing view in each problem. All projects will have three views.

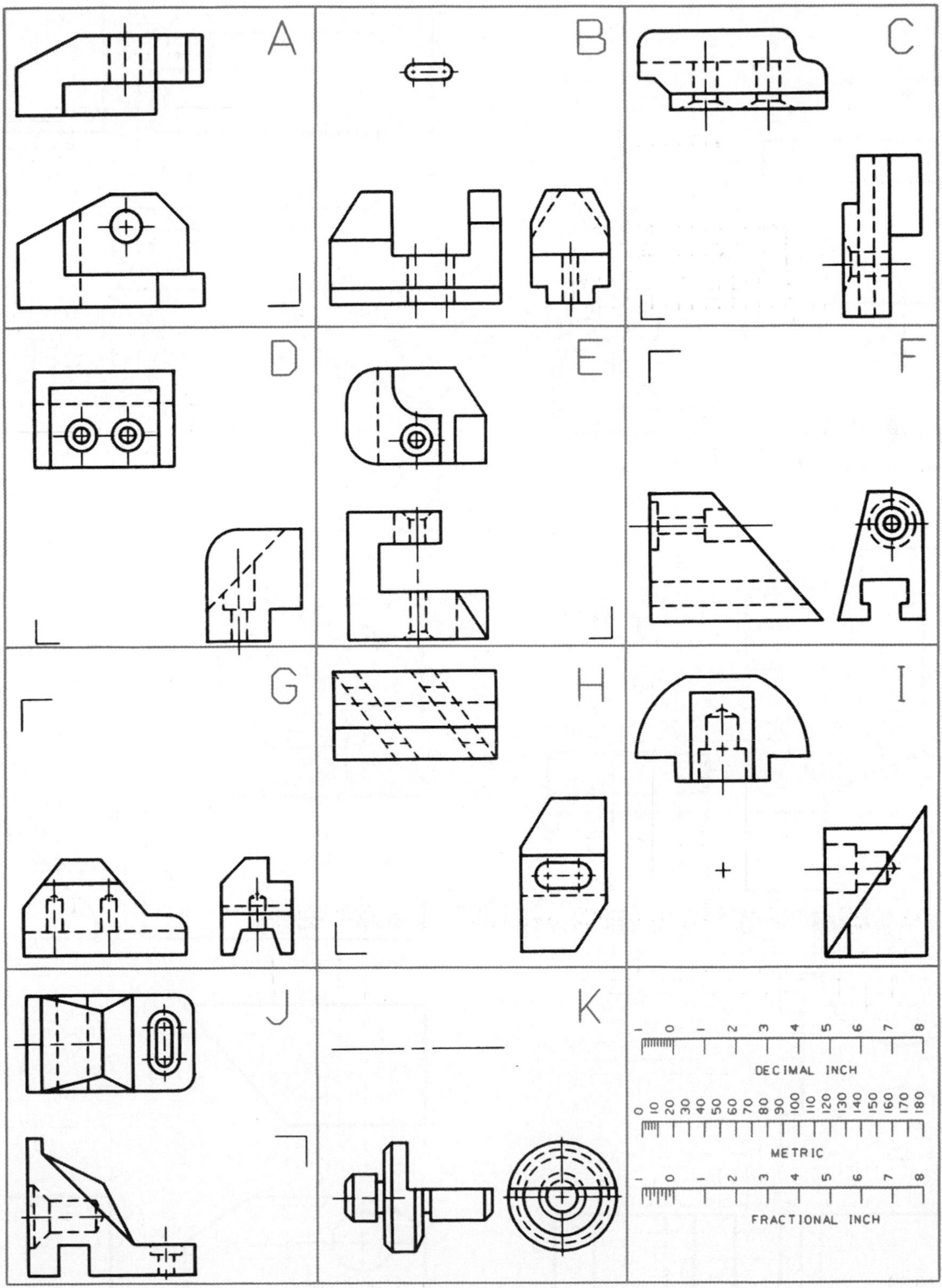

Problems 10.2(A) Through (G) Use the same directions as for Problem 10.1. In these problems some of *the given views are incomplete,* though the outline of each of the three views is given. Complete the views as needed.

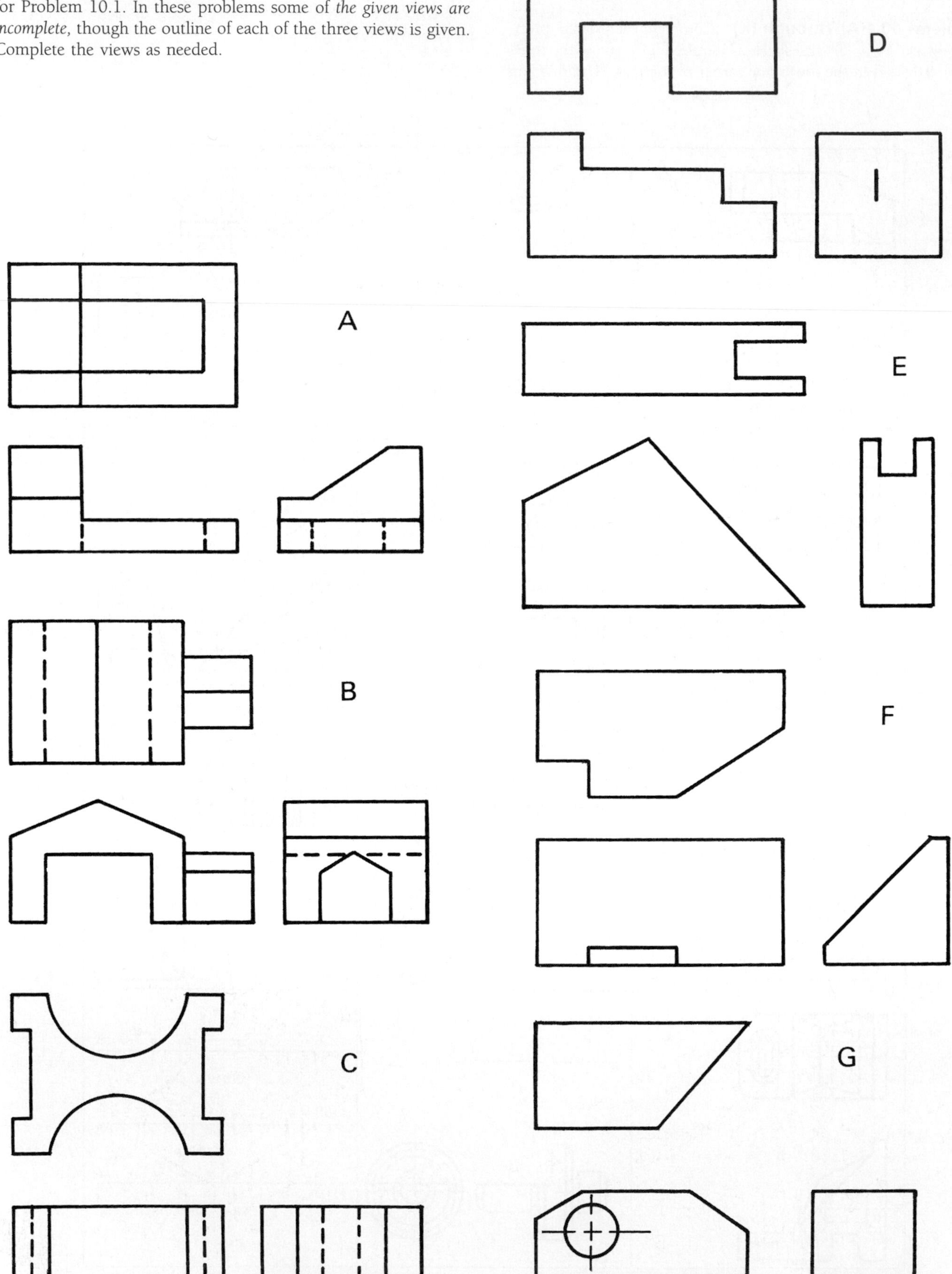

Problems 10.3 Through 10.8 Draw enough views to describe the part graphically. These projects can be used later for dimensioning projects after completing Chapter 15. Because of this, leave sufficient spacing between views to accommodate dimensions and notes.

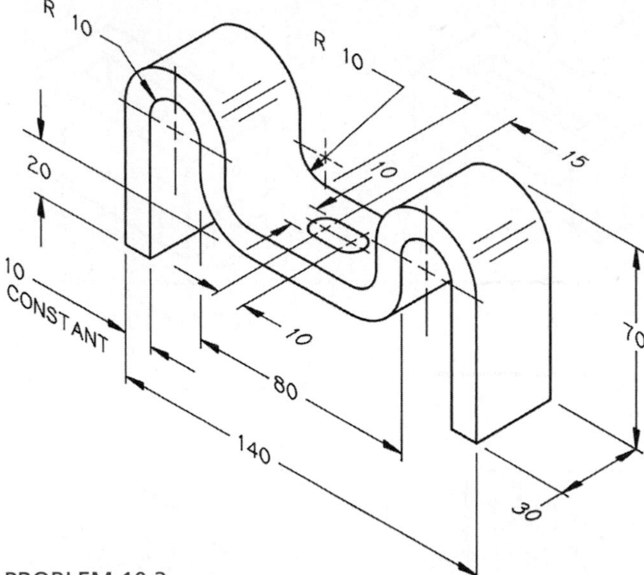

PROBLEM 10.3

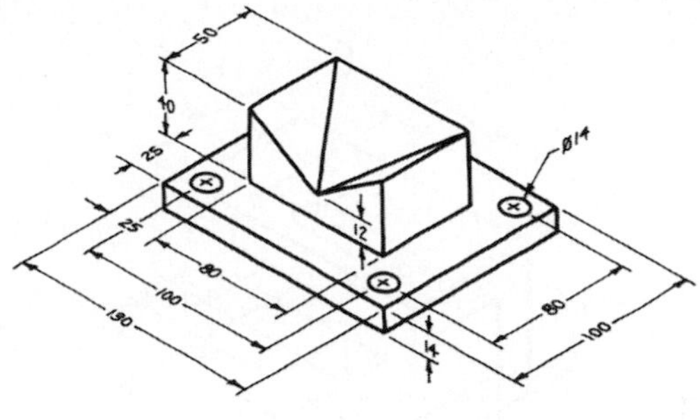

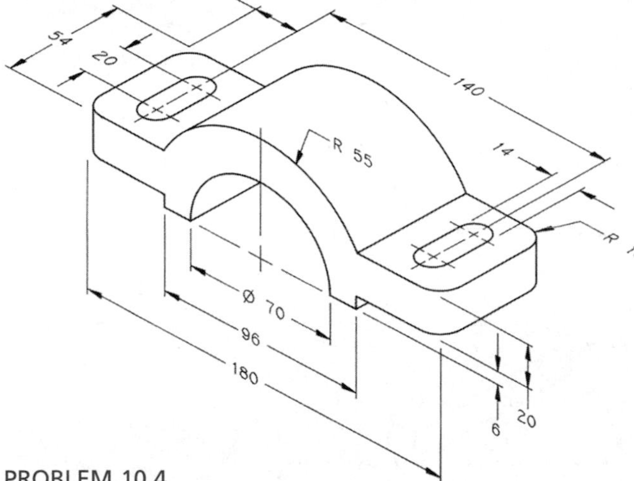

PROBLEM 10.4

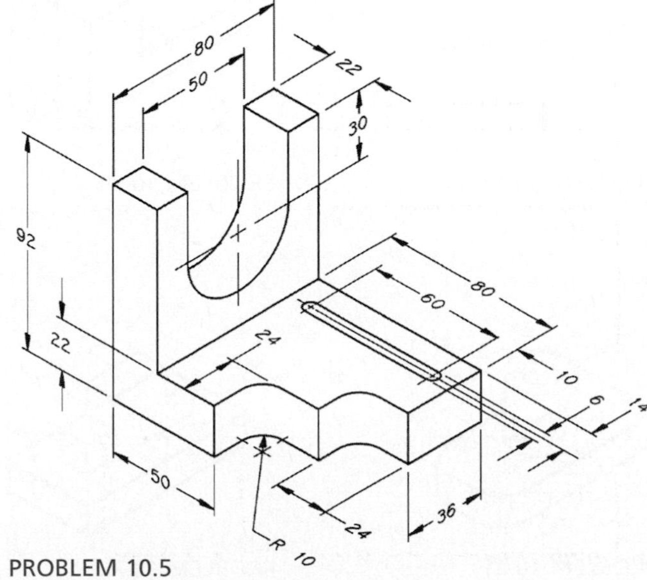

PROBLEM 10.5

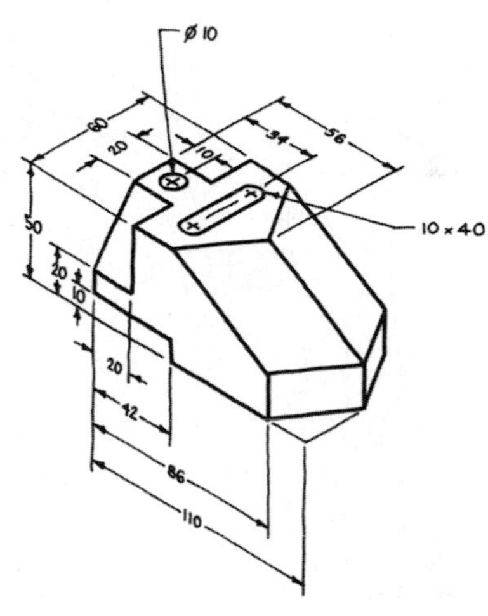

PROBLEM 10.7

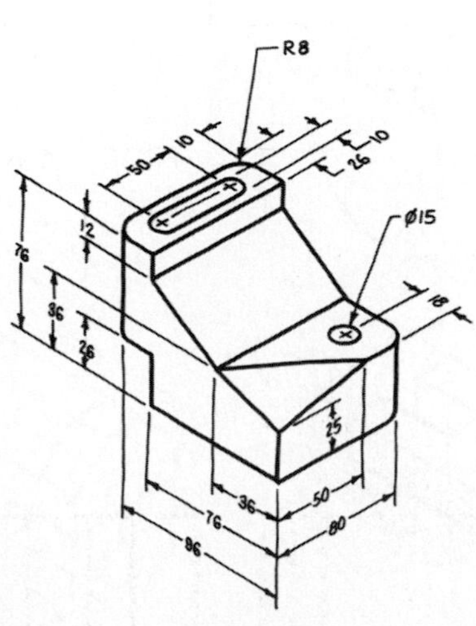

PROBLEM 10.8

PROBLEM 10.6

Problems 10.9 Through 10.26 Draw three views for each of the given problems. Use an "A"-size sheet for each project. Establish all dimensions through grid squares equal to 1.00 in. or 20 mm, as assigned by the instructor.

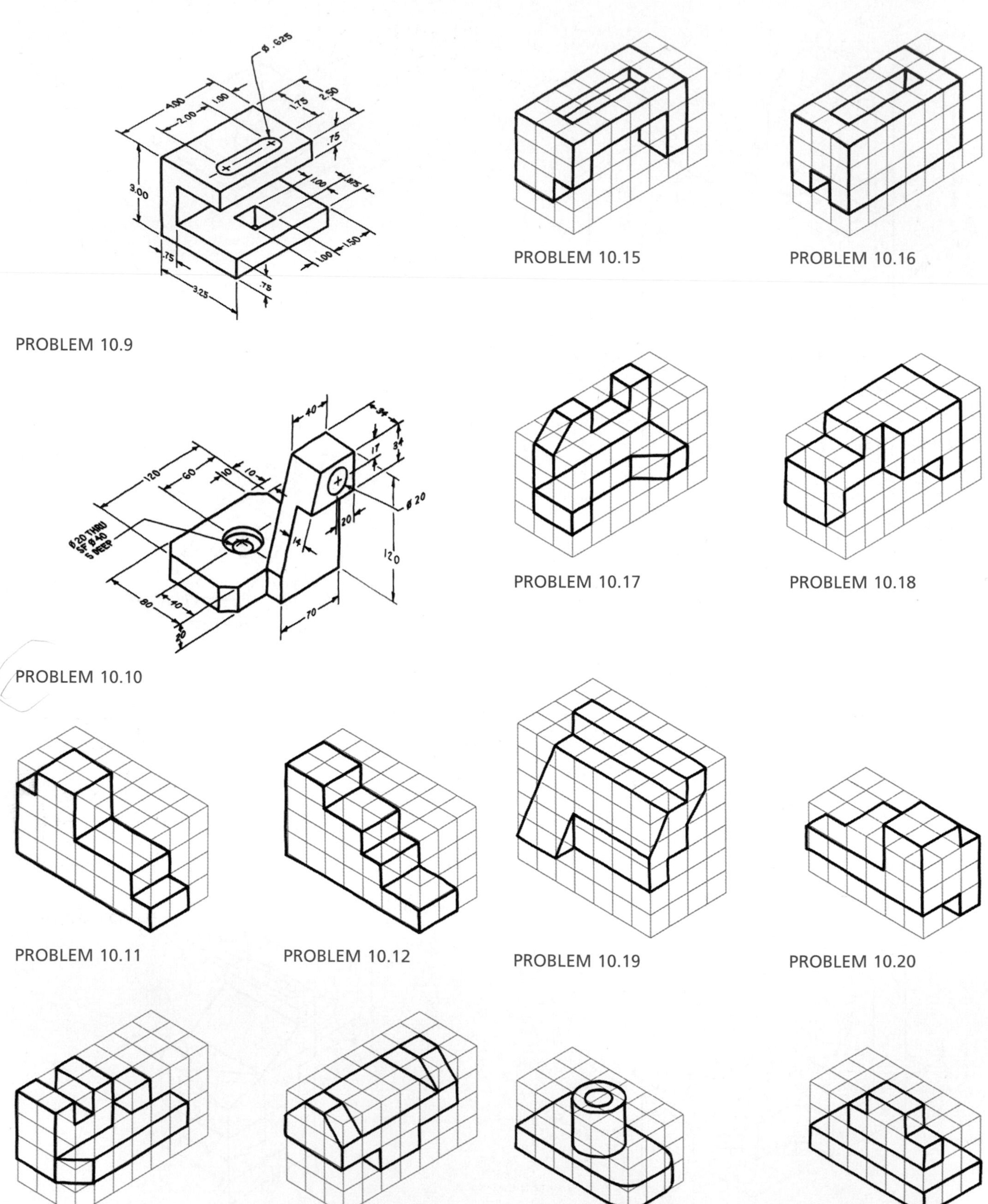

PROBLEM 10.9

PROBLEM 10.15

PROBLEM 10.16

PROBLEM 10.10

PROBLEM 10.17

PROBLEM 10.18

PROBLEM 10.11

PROBLEM 10.12

PROBLEM 10.19

PROBLEM 10.20

PROBLEM 10.13

PROBLEM 10.14

PROBLEM 10.21

PROBLEM 10.22

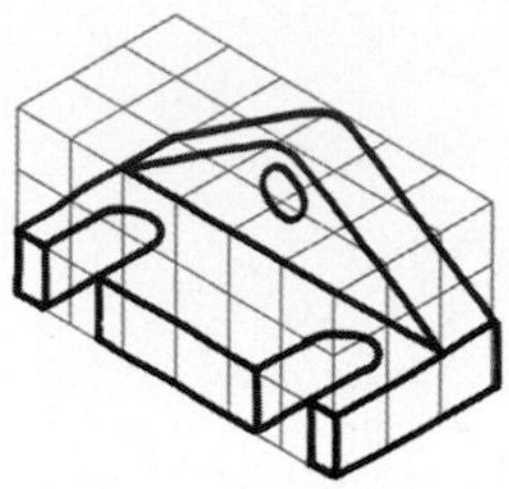
PROBLEM 10.23

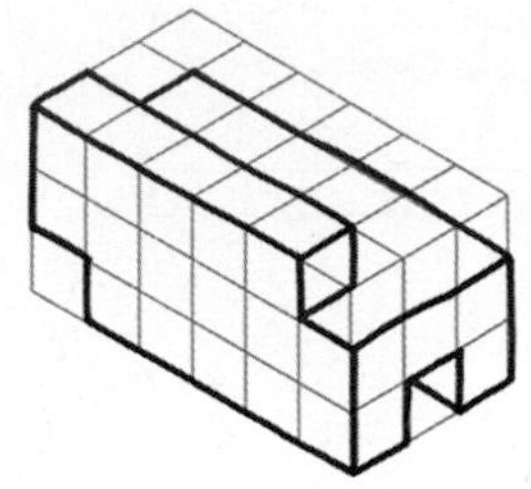
PROBLEM 10.24

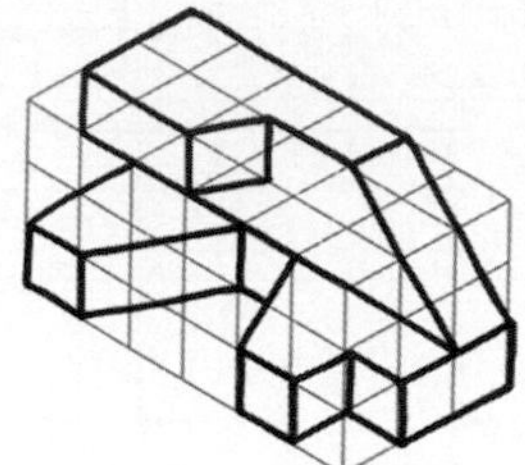
PROBLEM 10.25

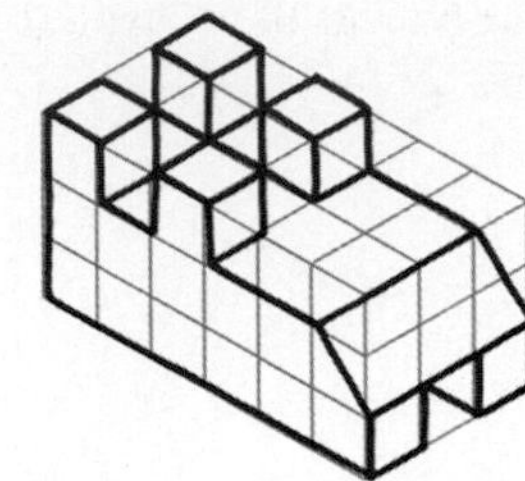
PROBLEM 10.26

Problems 10.27 Through 10.39 Draw, but do not dimension, each problem assigned by the instructor. Do not section any of the parts.

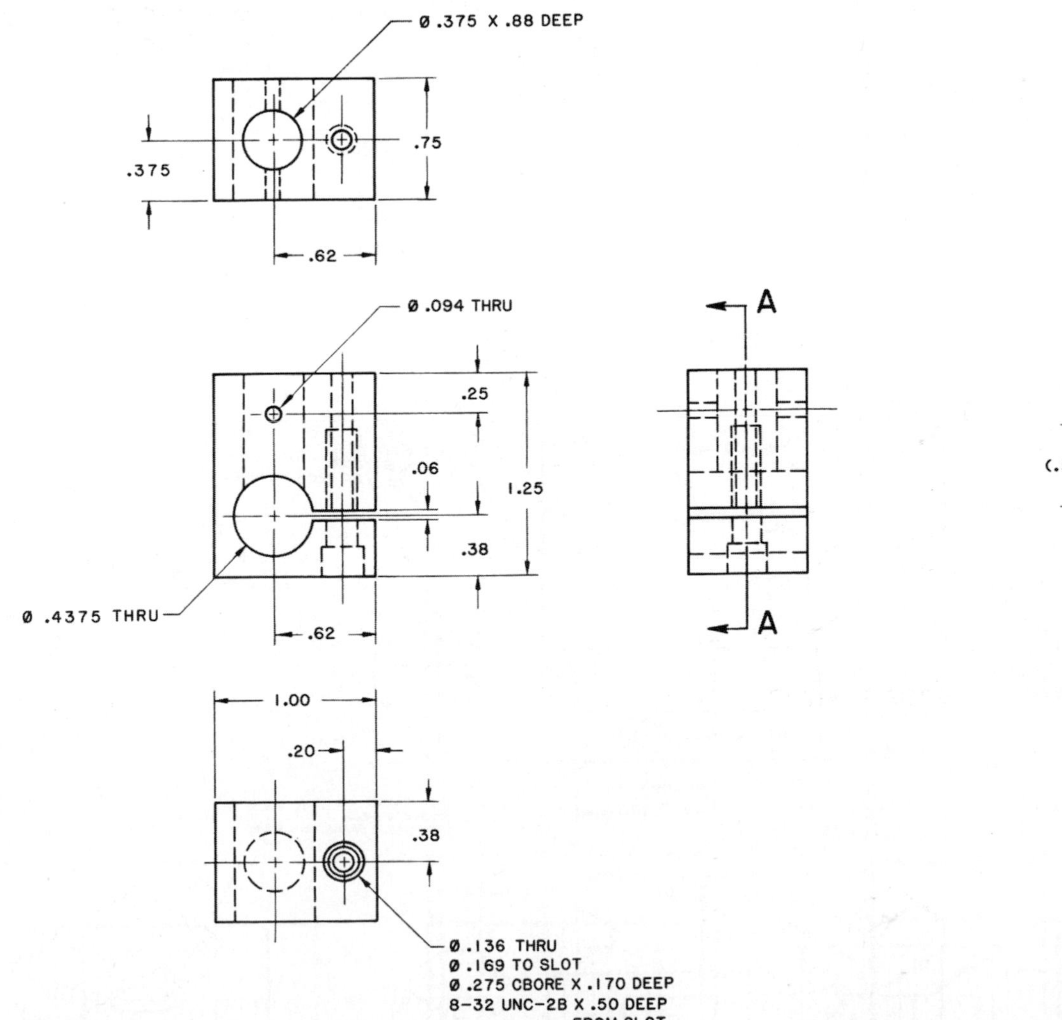

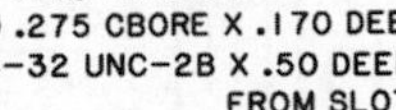

PROBLEM 10.27

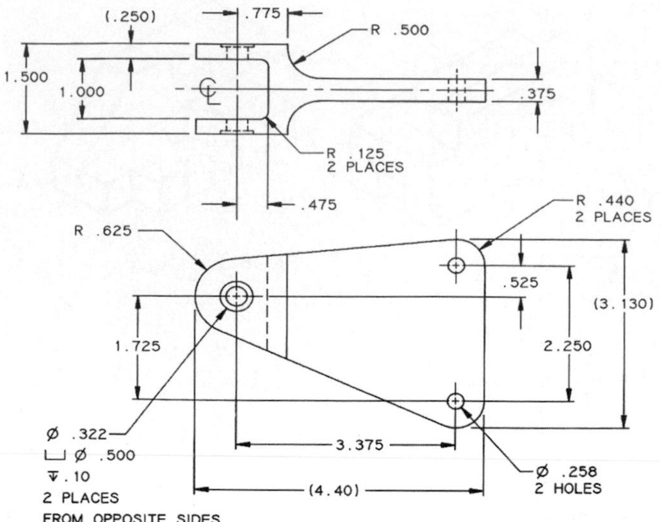

PROBLEM 10.28

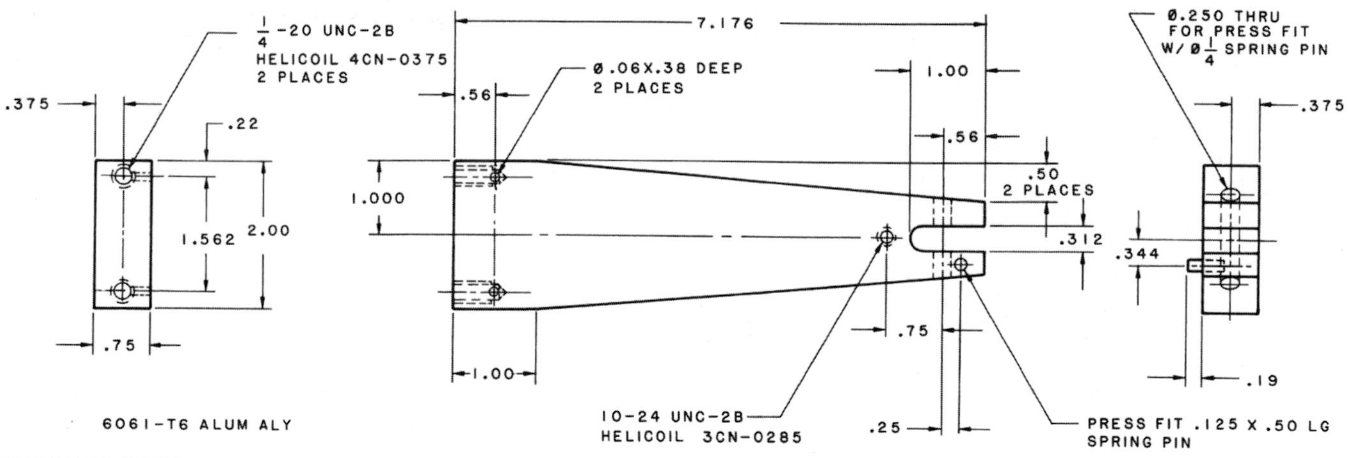

PROBLEM 10.29

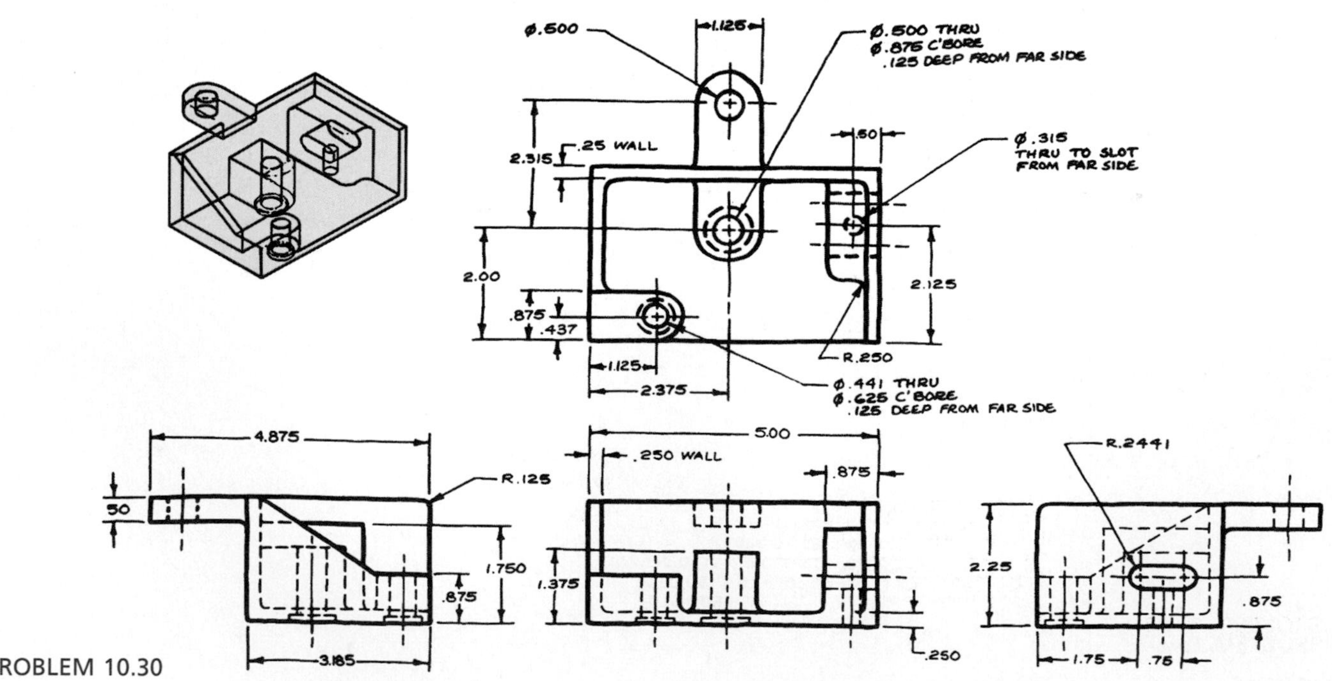

PROBLEM 10.30

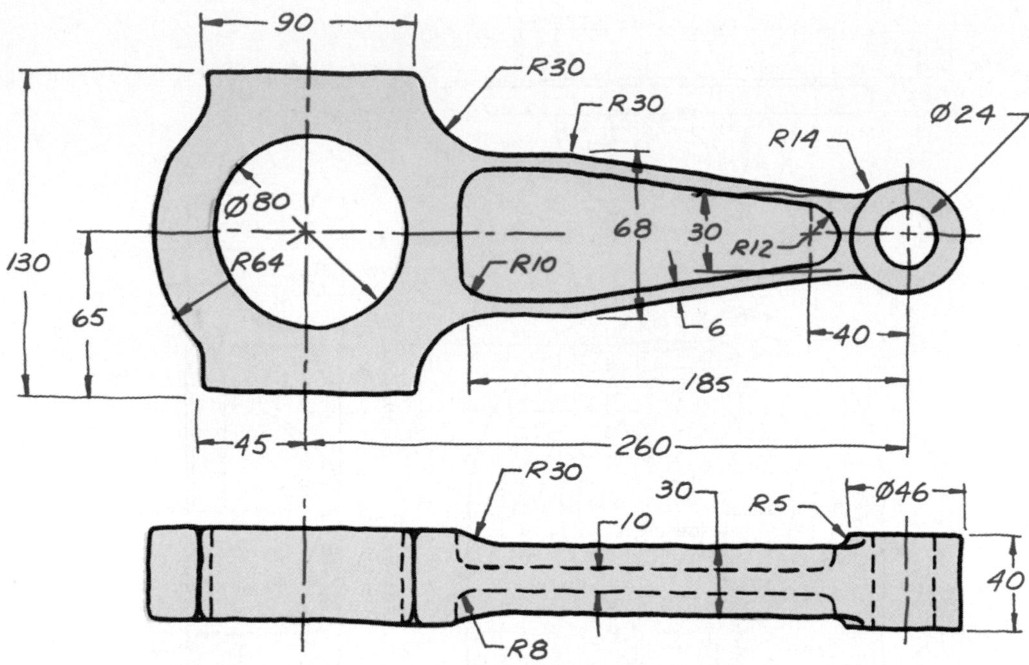

PROBLEM 10.31

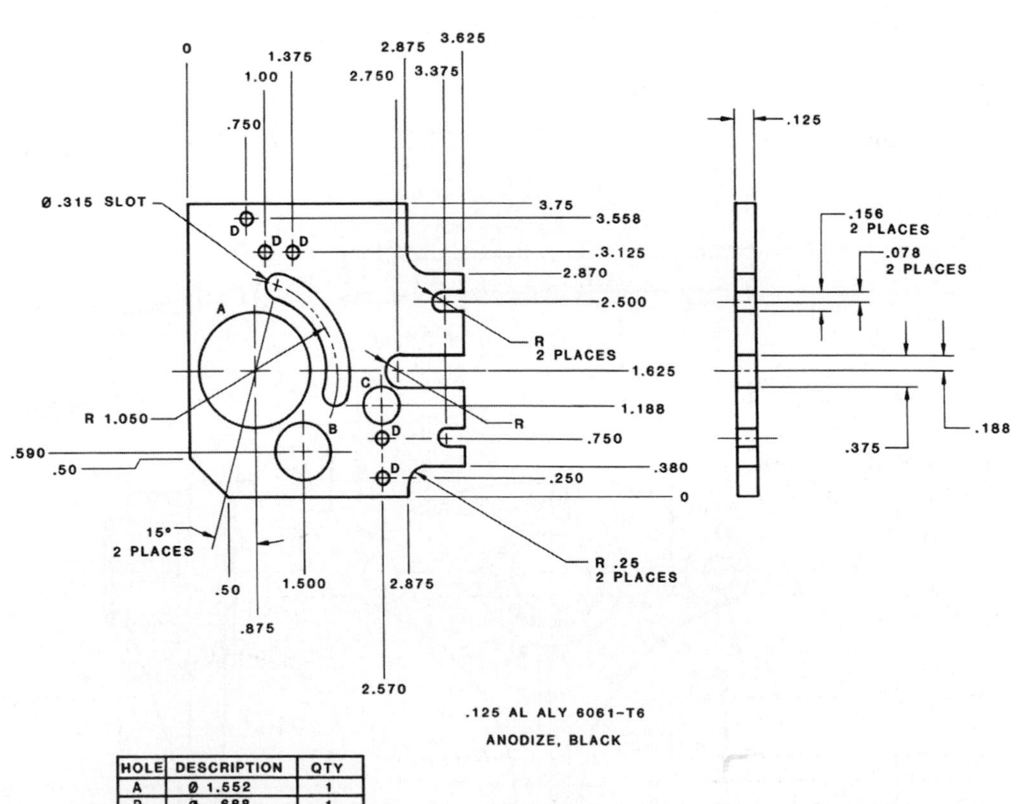

HOLE	DESCRIPTION	QTY
A	Ø 1.552	1
B	Ø .688	1
C	Ø .500	1
D	Ø .149	5

PROBLEM 10.32

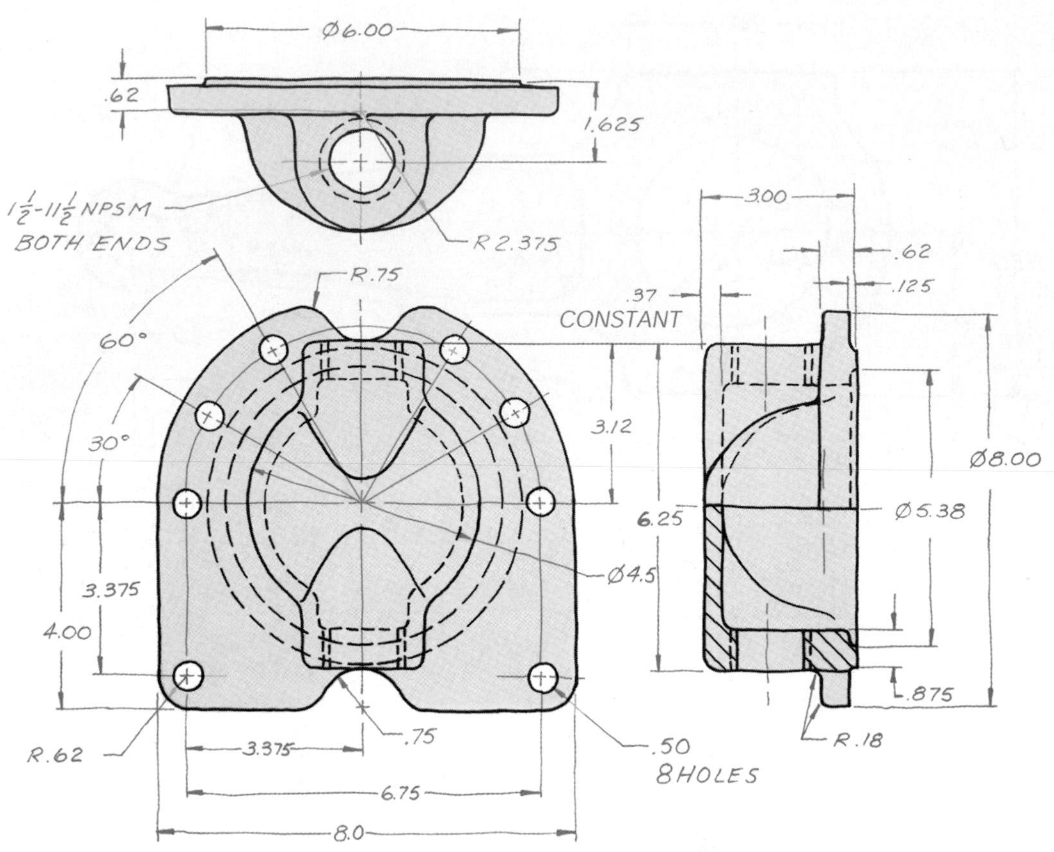

PROBLEM 10.33

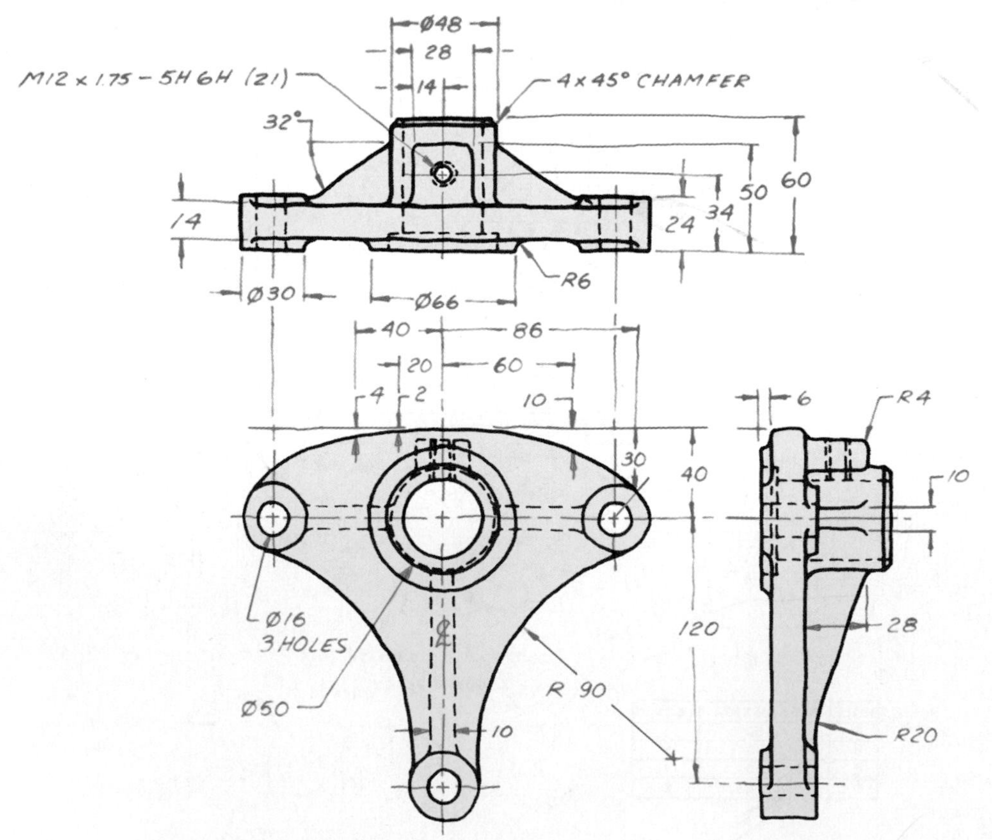

PROBLEM 10.34

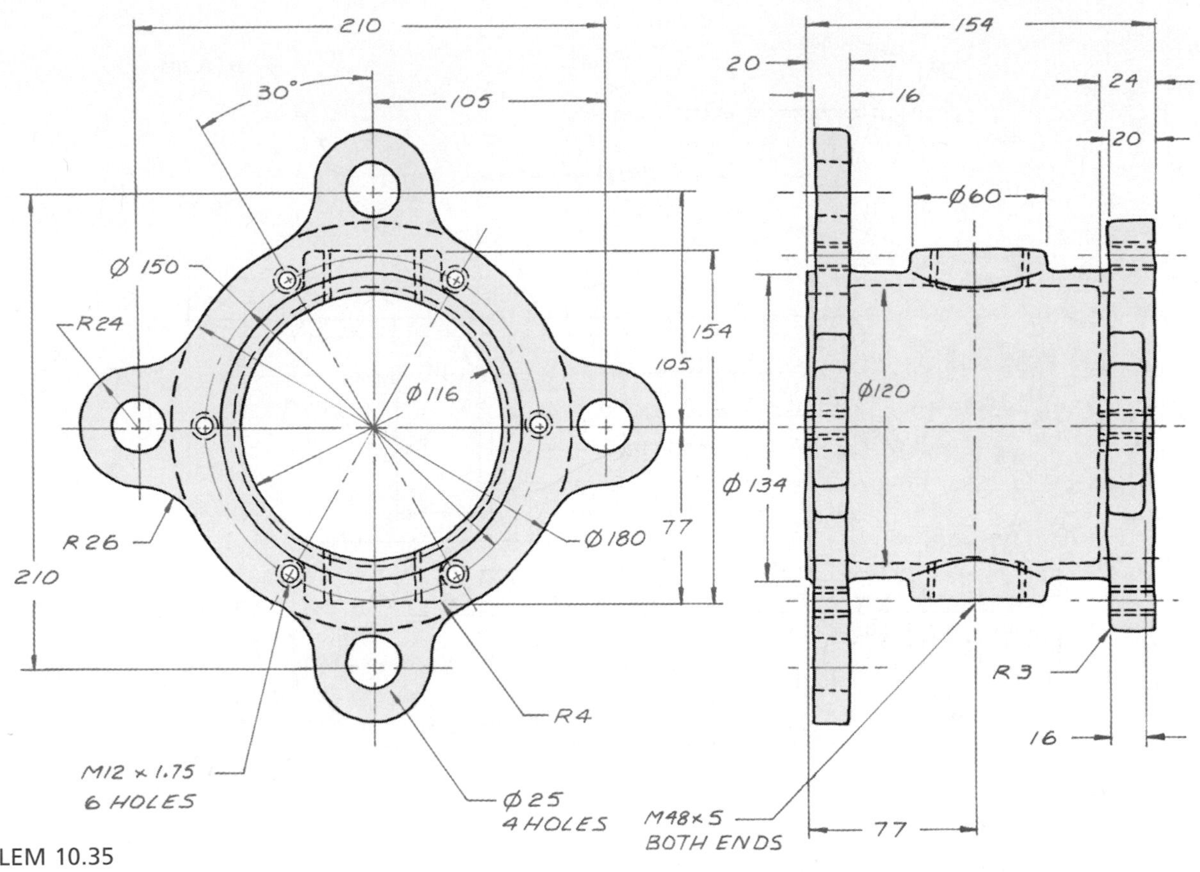

PROBLEM 10.35

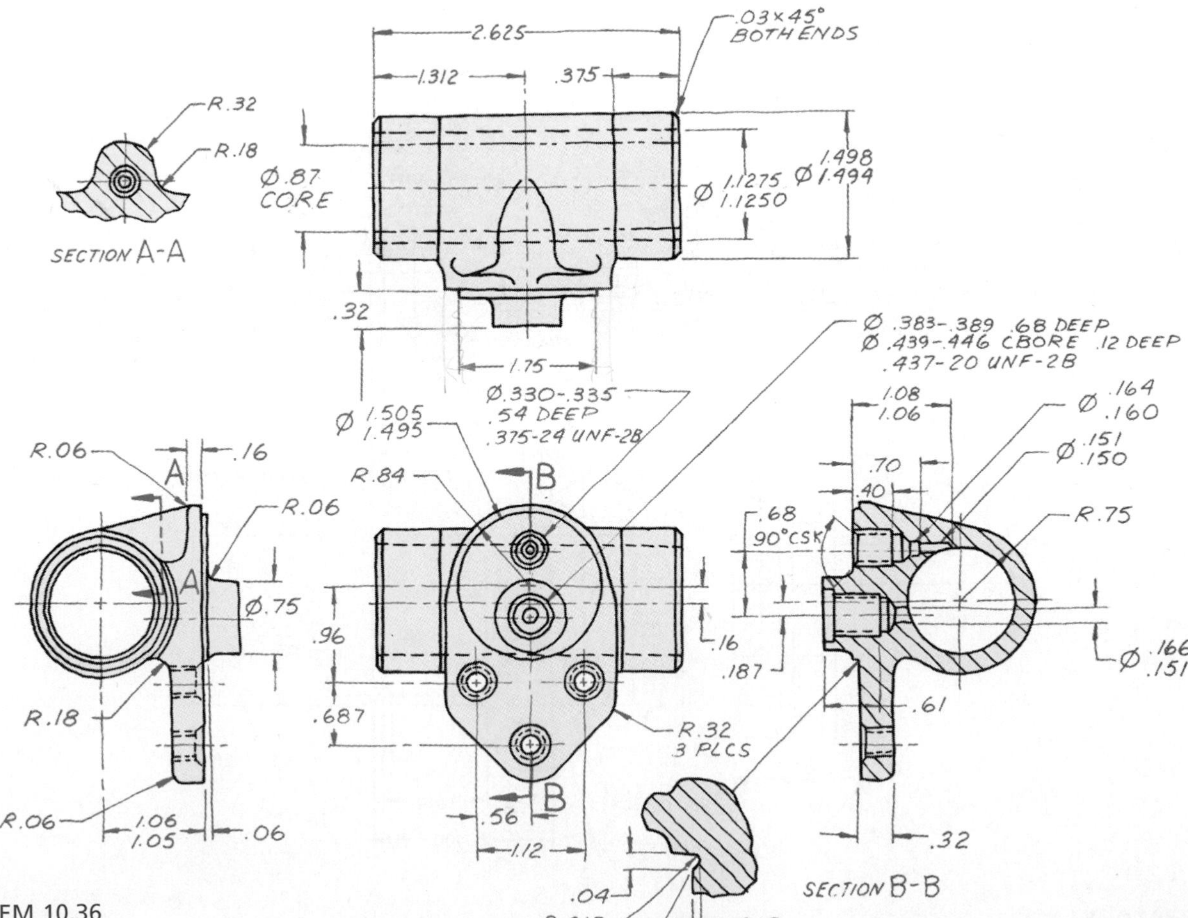

PROBLEM 10.36

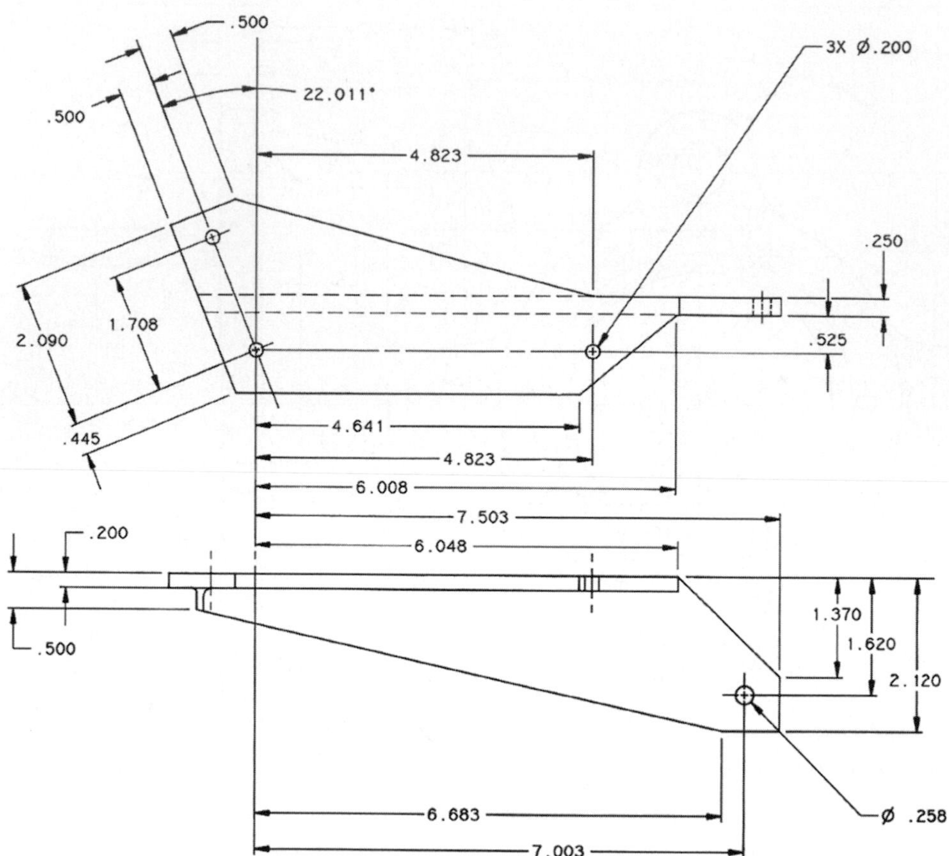

PROBLEM 10.37

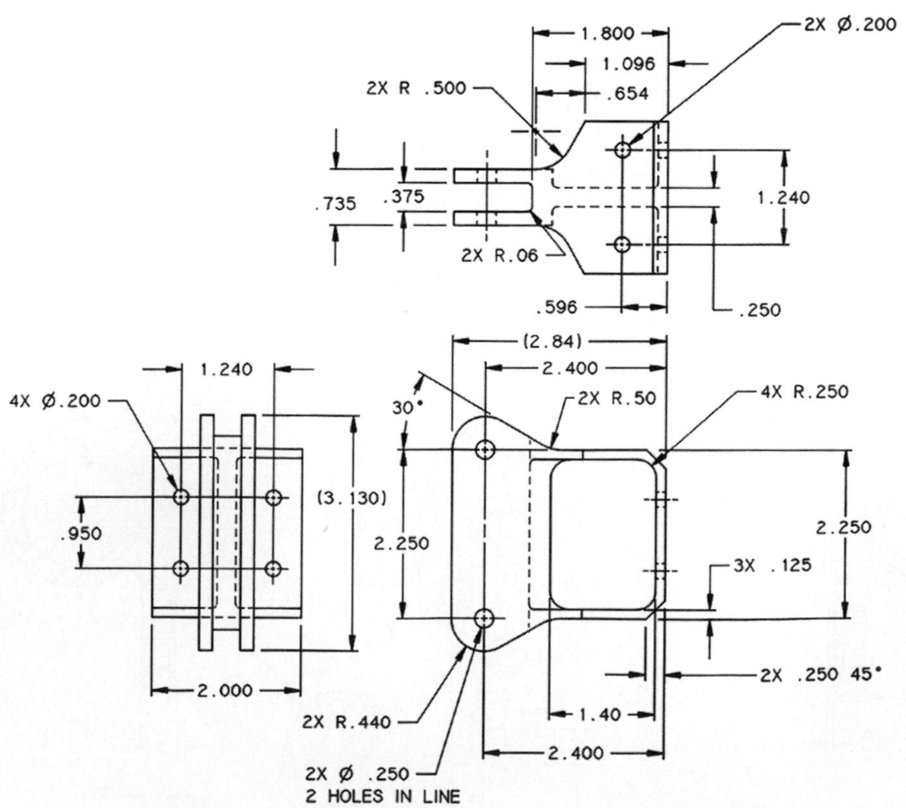

PROBLEM 10.38

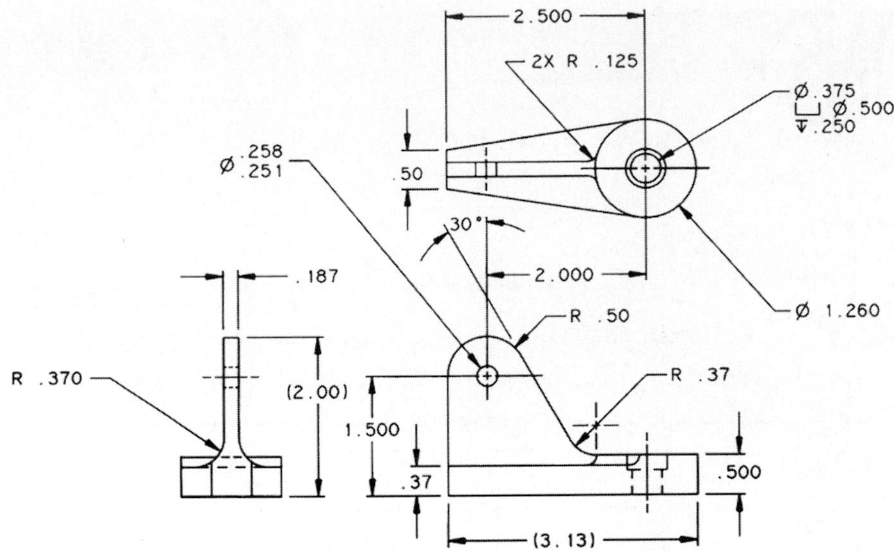

PROBLEM 10.39

SECTIONS

Chapter 11

LEARNING OBJECTIVES

Upon completion of this chapter you will be able to:

1. Identify the need for sectional views in order to clarify interior features of a part.
2. Apply standard drafting conventions and line types to illustrate interior features.
3. Identify cutting planes and resulting views.
4. Differentiate between and produce full, half, offset, aligned, removed, revolved, broken-out, and assembly sections.
5. Integrate standard sectioning methods into the CAD environment.

11.1 INTRODUCTION

Designers and drafters use **sectional views,** also called **sections,** to clarify and dimension the internal construction of a part. The spring in Figure 11.1(a) is shown as a removed pictorial section in Figure 11.1(b). Sections are needed for interior features that cannot be described clearly by hidden lines in conventional views. For example, the valve in Figure 11.2(a) has a portion of its exterior body removed to allow a view of the disk, seating, and stem. Figure 11.2(b) shows the same valve with its front removed (full section), allowing a view of all the interior parts. Without removing portions of the valve body it is impossible to describe accurately the internal features of the valve.

This chapter presents different types of sections, and discusses their variations when applied to mechanical parts and assemblies. Sections make use of a number of **drafting conventions**—standard, accepted ways of showing part features on a drawing.

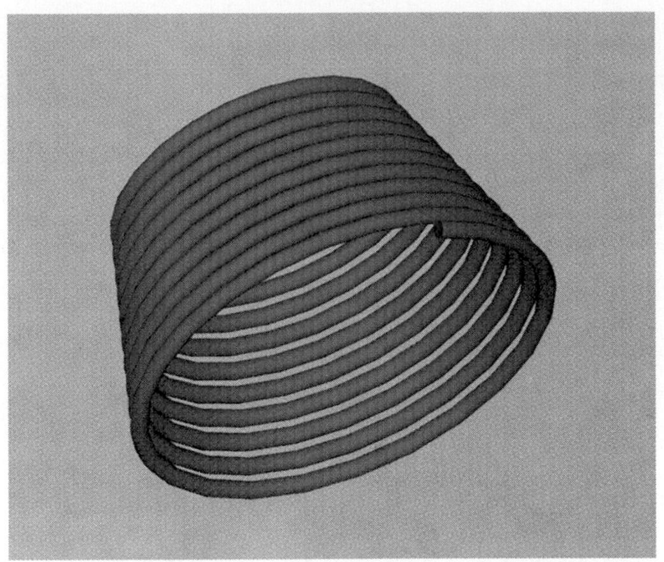

(a) Parametric model of a spring

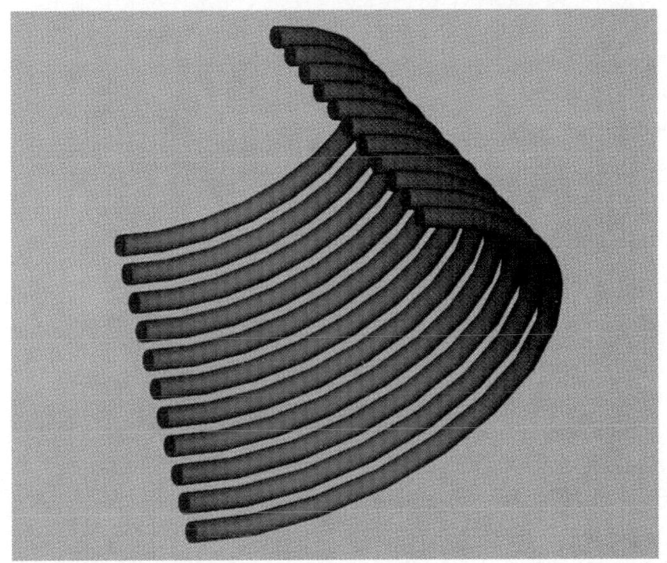

(b) Removed pictorial section of a spring

FIGURE 11.1 **Spring**

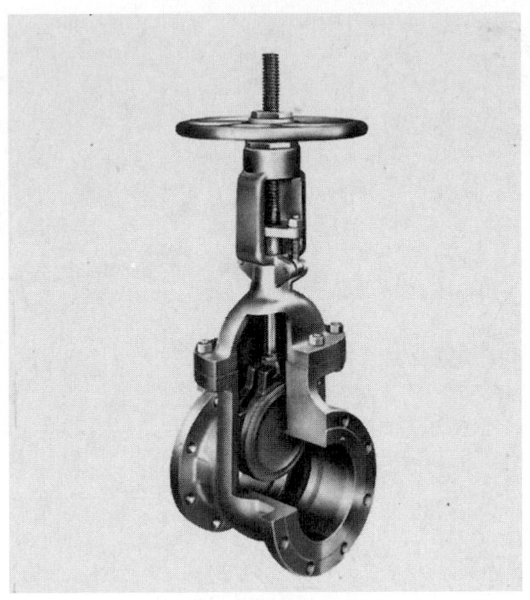

(a) Sectioned gate valve

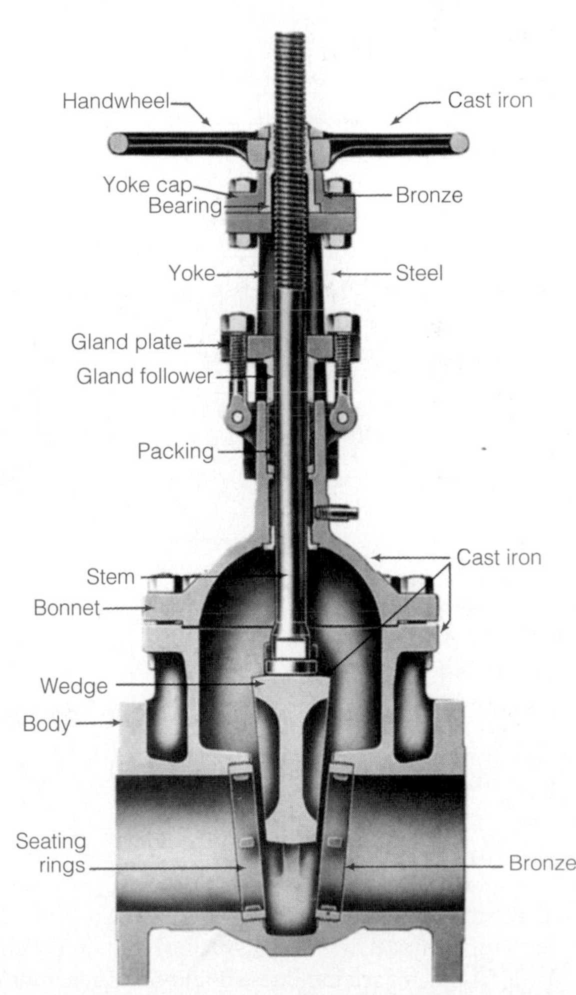

(b) Front section of gate valve showing the stem and disk

FIGURE 11.2 **Valve**

11.2 SECTIONS

A sectional view is obtained by passing an imaginary **cutting plane** through the part, perpendicular to the **line of sight,** as in Figure 11.3 (**SECTION A–A**). The line of sight is the direction in which the part is viewed (Fig. 11.4). The portion of the part between the cutting plane and the observer is "removed." The part's exposed solid surfaces are indicated by **section lines,** which are uniformly spaced angular lines drawn in proportion to the size of the drawing.

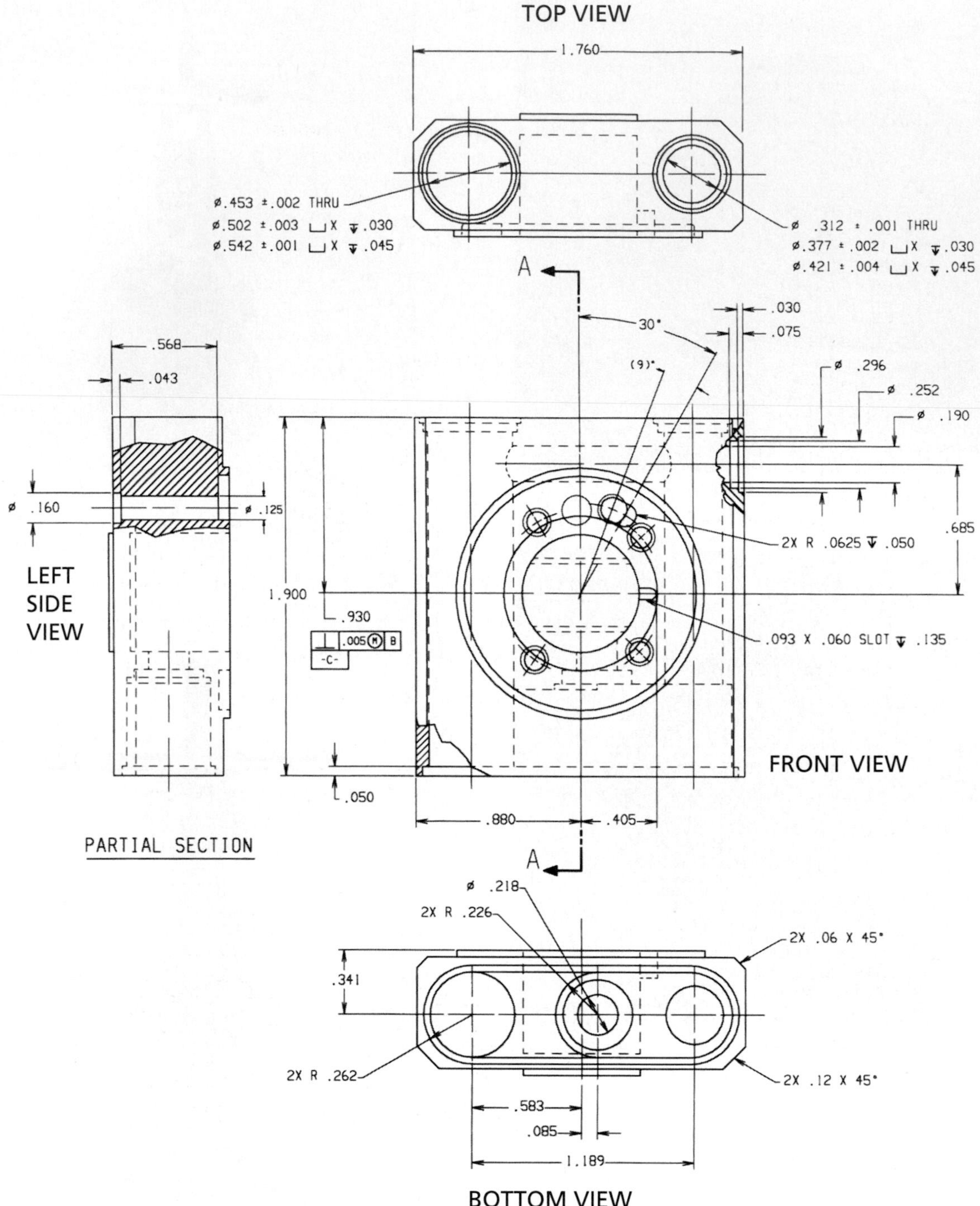

FIGURE 11.3 **Detail of a Mechanical Part with Three Sections**

In all section views on a drawing, section lines for the same part are identical in angle, spacing, and uniformity (Fig. 11.4). Spacing of section lines should be as generous as possible and yet preserve the unity of the sectioned area. In other words, section lines should be constructed so they are spaced clearly, are pleasing to look at, and will reduce and enlarge without distorting.

There are many different types of section views. Figure 11.3 shows a drawing of a complex part containing a full section (**SECTION A–A**), a partial section (left side), and a

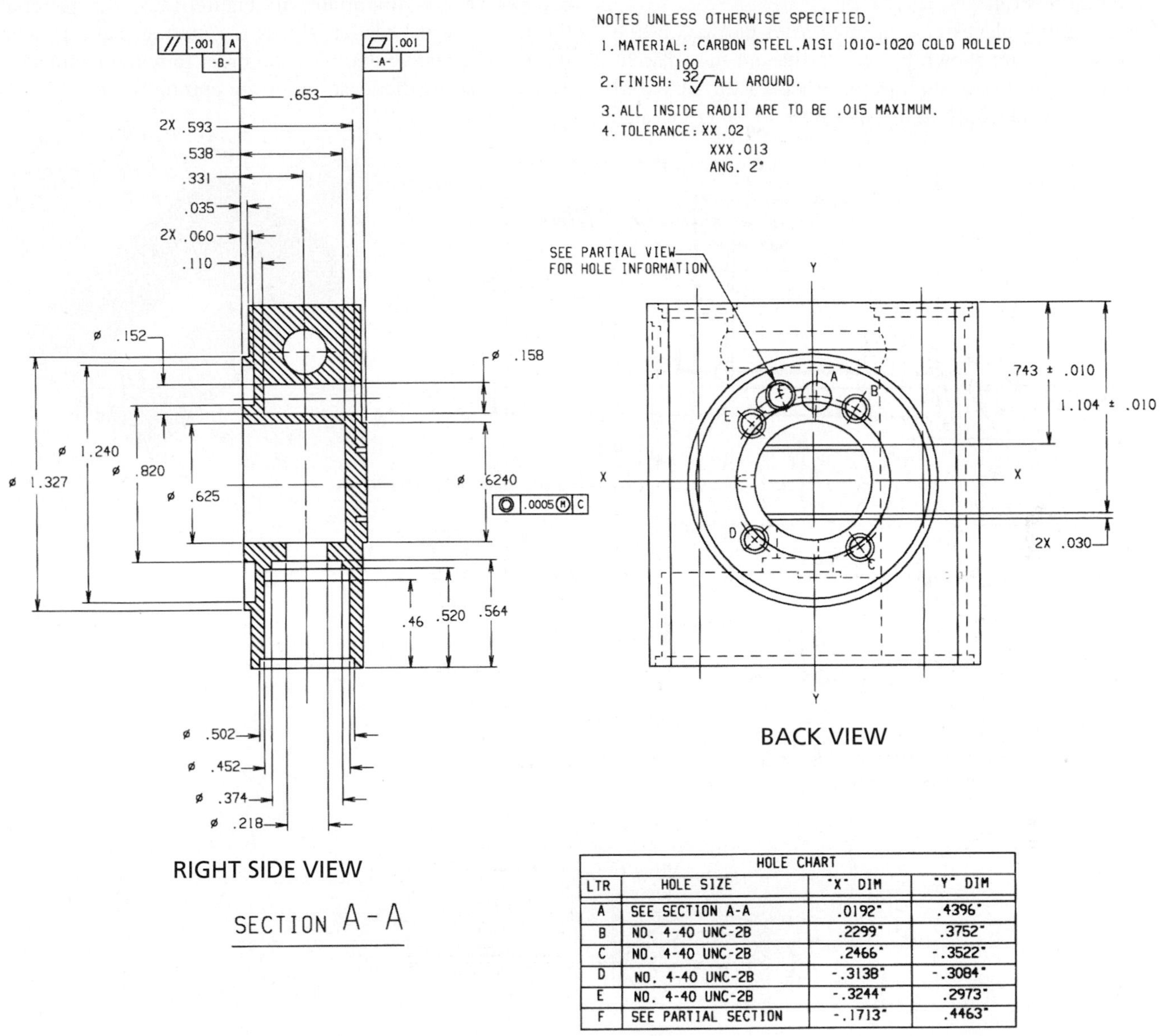

HOLE CHART			
LTR	HOLE SIZE	"X" DIM	"Y" DIM
A	SEE SECTION A-A	.0192"	.4396"
B	NO. 4-40 UNC-2B	.2299"	.3752"
C	NO. 4-40 UNC-2B	.2466"	-.3522"
D	NO. 4-40 UNC-2B	-.3138"	-.3084"
E	NO. 4-40 UNC-2B	-.3244"	.2973"
F	SEE PARTIAL SECTION	-.1713"	.4463"

FIGURE 11.3 Detail of a Mechanical Part with Three Sections—*Continued*

broken-out section (left corner of front view). These types of sections are covered in detail later in the chapter.

Sections are rotated 90° out of the plane of principal or auxiliary views from which they are taken, following the customary rules of projection rotation. A heavy line across or near the principal view indicates the plane of projection, with arrows to indicate the viewing direction, or line of sight (Fig. 11.4). This line, called a *cutting plane line,* represents the edge of the imaginary cutting plane. The sections in Figure 11.4 are also views (front and right side). When the plane of projection passes through the view, it is called the cutting plane, and the resulting adjacent view is called a section. Each cutting plane, and corresponding view, has view identification letters assigned to it, such as **SECTION A–A** in Figure 11.4.

When cutting planes pass through solid portions of the part, these areas are shown by section lines in the adjacent section view. When the cutting plane passes through void areas (open spaces), such as a slot, a hole, or other cutouts, the area is left blank (without section lines) in the adjacent section view (Fig. 11.4).

Since cutting planes are positioned to reveal interior details most effectively, selecting the proper location for the cutting plane is important. In Figure 11.5, the pictorial illustration of the section shows the cutting plane passing through the middle of the part in order to reveal its interior. This is typically the location for the cutting plane.

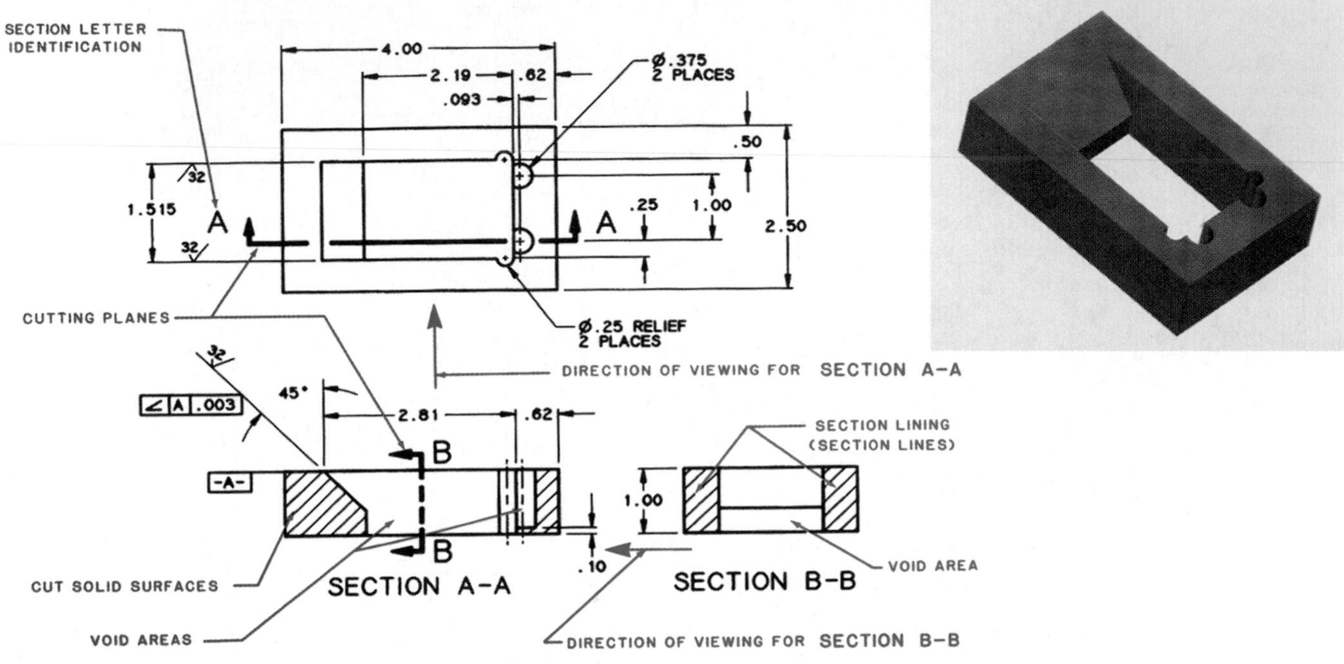

FIGURE 11.4 Three-View Drawing Using Sections as the Front and Side Views

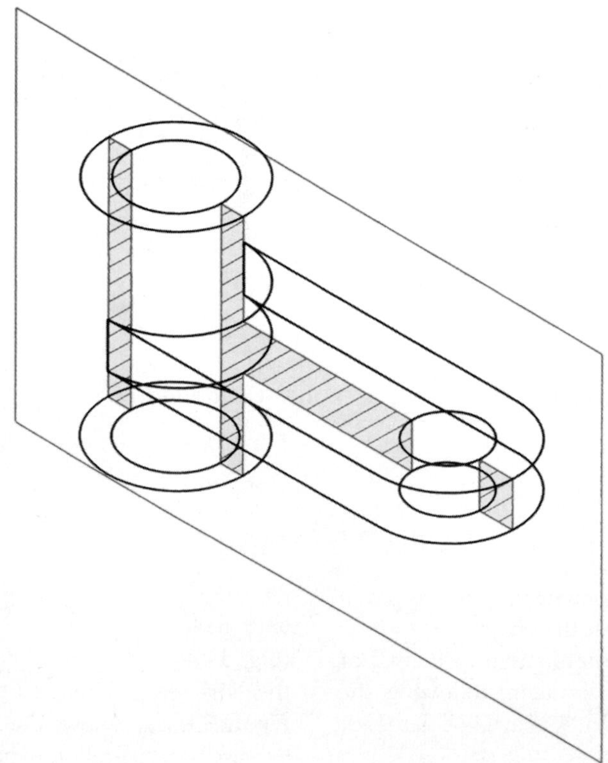

FIGURE 11.5 Sectioned 3D Part

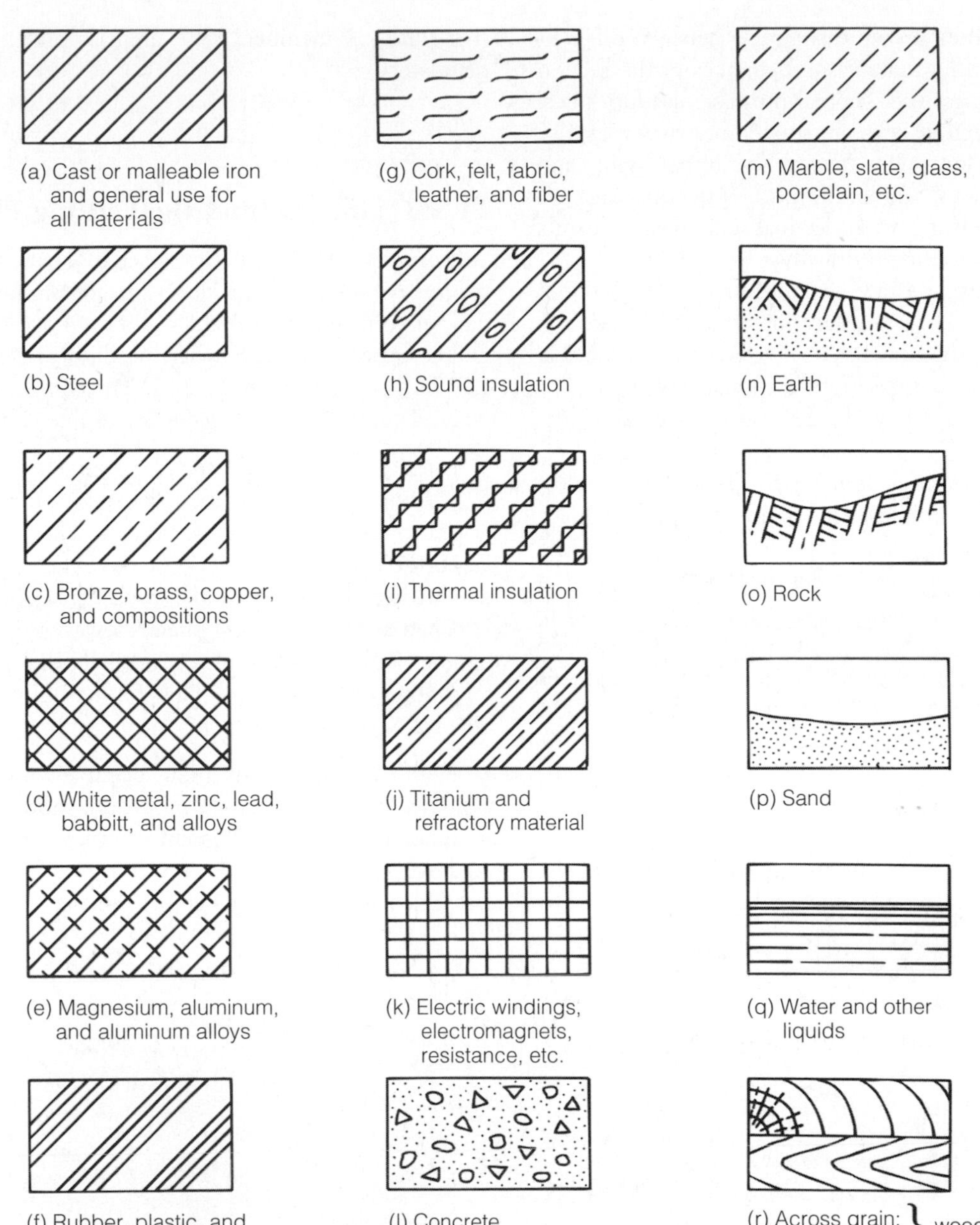

FIGURE 11.6 **Section Symbols for Material Specification**

11.2.1 Section Material Specification

Sometimes you must distinguish between materials of a part through the use of symbolic section lining. **Symbolic section lining** is sometimes found on assembly drawings, such as illustrations for parts catalogs, display assemblies, promotional illustrations, and when it is desirable to distinguish between different materials.

Since it may not reduce and enlarge well, symbolic section lining is not recommended for drawings that will be microfilmed or put onto microfiche. Thus, the most common practice is to use the general-purpose symbol for all materials

11.2.2 General-Purpose Section Lines

Figure 11.6(a) shows the lining symbol for cast iron, which is also considered the general-purpose symbol. **General-**

purpose section lines do not distinguish between different materials; they identify the cut solid surfaces of the section view. Most drawings use general-purpose section lines. General-purpose section lines are single lines drawn at 45°, slanting from the lower left toward the upper right, and spaced evenly at about .10 in. (2.5 mm). Some drawings use $\frac{1}{8}$ in. (.125 in.) spacing with decimal-inch measurements and 2.5 to 3 mm spacing on drawings with SI units.

Since they are easy to draw, general-purpose section lines are constructed quickly. The exact material specification is given elsewhere on the drawing in note form or in the title block. An exception is made for parts made of wood, for which it is necessary to show the direction of the grain [Fig. 11.6(r)].

Figure 11.7 shows measurements for the construction of general-purpose section lines. This figure includes examples of incorrect construction. Section lines should be thin (0.25 to 0.30 mm), sharp, and black. And they should not be too close [Fig. 11.7(d)], or they may merge and blotch during reduction and reproduction. Section lines must be spaced consistently and be of consistent weight [Fig. 11.7(b) and (e)], and they must end at visible object lines [Fig. 11.7(f)]. When the shape or position of a section area is such that the section lines would be parallel or perpendicular to a prominent visible line bounding the sectioned area [Fig. 11.7(g)], a different angle should be chosen.

To avoid drawing section lines perpendicular or parallel to object lines, the angle of the section lines can be changed (Fig. 11.8). Remember, a 45° angle is preferred, but is not mandatory.

11.2.3 Lines Behind the Cutting Plane

Sections describe the interior space of a part. *Hidden features that are behind the cutting planes are almost always omitted.* In half sections, however, hidden lines are occasionally shown on the unsectioned half when needed for dimensioning or for clarity (see Section 11.3.2). The following rules apply when determining the precedence of lines on a section.

Line Precedence on a Section

1. **Visible object lines** take precedence over hidden lines and centerlines.
2. **Hidden lines** take precedence over centerlines.
3. **Cutting-plane lines** take precedence over centerlines when locating a cutting plane. However, the cutting-plane line can be omitted entirely if it falls along a centerline of symmetry for the part. This will be discussed in Section 11.2.5.

Figure 11.9 illustrates a few examples of line representation in sections. The correct procedure shows all visible lines as solid [Fig. 11.9(a)]. Remember, even though the section "removes" a portion of the part in front of the cutting plane, the object lines on and behind the plane are still visible.

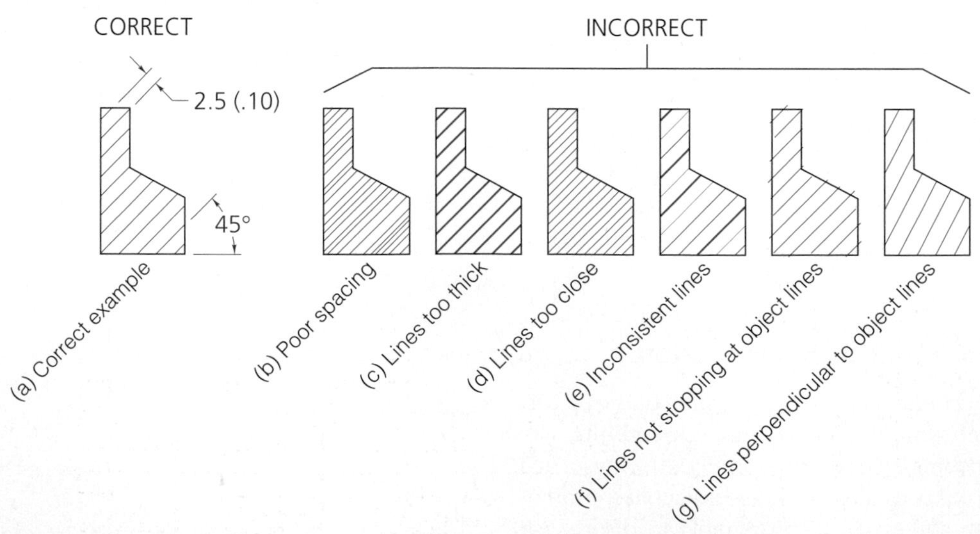

FIGURE 11.7 Section Lining

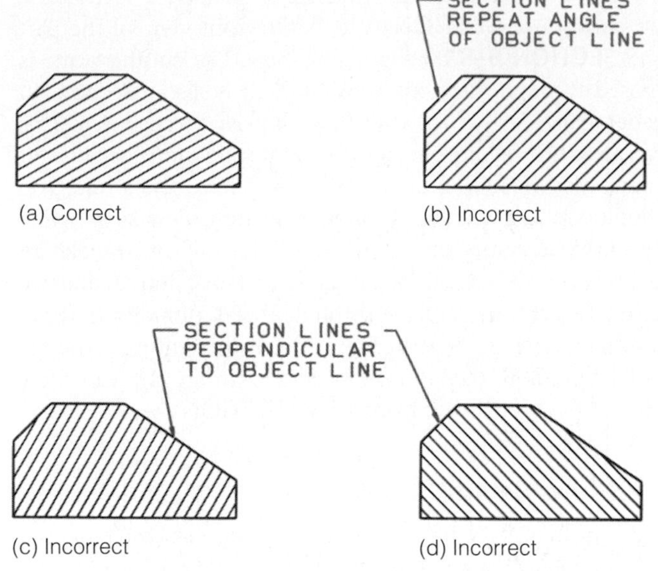

FIGURE 11.8 Section Line Direction

Figure 11.9(b) neglects to show the back portion of the hole's edges (void area), which should be shown with solid lines. Figure 11.9(c) shows a hidden line running through the section, a practice that should be avoided because it complicates the drawing and does not add any clarity to the part definition. Visible lines behind the cutting plane are always shown in the sectional view, whereas hidden lines are not. In some cases, it is acceptable to show hidden lines in sections, but only if the part could not be properly defined otherwise.

Figure 11.9(d) shows incorrectly dashed interior lines representing the outline of the hole and the slot (void areas). The outline of a part should never be described with dashed lines. This type of line symbol is reserved for hidden lines, not visible lines.

Section lines on the same part must run in the same direction, not opposing directions (on assemblies, mating parts that are sectioned have section lines with differing angles). Figure 11.9(e) shows the incorrect procedure for section lines on the same part that are separated by a void area.

Dimensions or other labeling should not be placed within sectioned areas of the drawing. When this is unavoidable, the section lines are omitted behind the label (see Chapter 15).

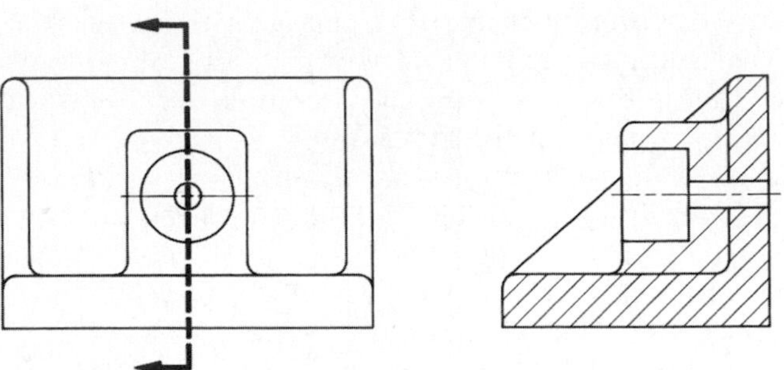

FIGURE 11.10 Double-Spaced Section Lines

Some features on a part are shown with **double-spaced section lines,** as in Figure 11.10. Here, the cutting plane passes through distinct features of the part. To show the part's features clearly, the section lining is drawn at the same angle, but the spacing is doubled.

11.2.4 Sections as Views

The section view should appear on the same drawing sheet with the cutting-plane view. Section views are projected directly from, and perpendicular to, the cutting plane, in conformity with the standard arrangement of views. If, because of space limitations, this arrangement of views is impractical, the views should be clearly labeled as to type.

The section view is placed in direct projection with the principal view from which it is taken, behind and normal to the cutting plane. The view should not be rotated or shown on a different sheet than the cutting plane unless necessary due to the size of the view or the drawing space available. If rotation is necessary, specify the angle and the direction of rotation below the section label, as in Figure 11.11, where only the section view is shown. Here, **SECTION A–A** has been rotated counterclockwise (**CCW**) out of its normal position **13°**. In some cases, the section will be enlarged, as in this figure (**SCALE: 2/1**). In Figure 11.11 the section identification label is center-justified and displayed as follows:

SECTION A–A
ROTATED 13° CCW
SCALE: 2/1

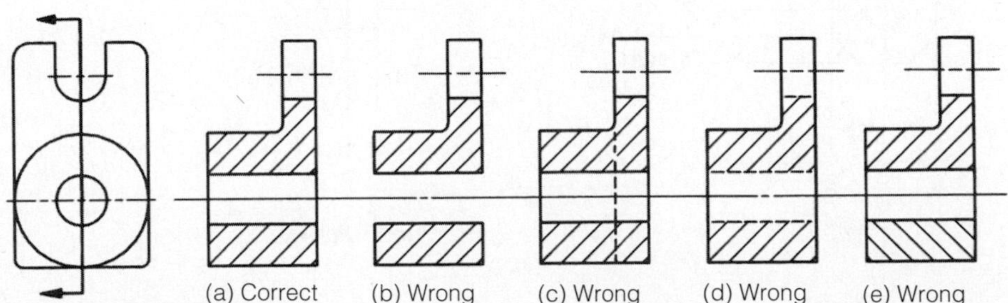

FIGURE 11.9 Hidden Lines in Sections

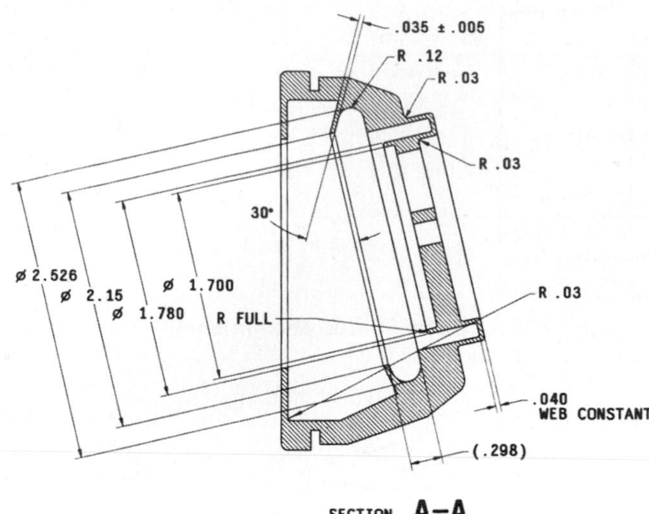

ROTATED 13° CCW
SCALE: 2/1

FIGURE 11.11 Rotated Sections

Figure 11.4 illustrated the practice of making a section the principal view. **SECTION A–A** is the front view of the part and **SECTION B–B** the right side view. The cutting plane is passed through the front view—which is also a section. In general, *avoid constructing a section through a section view.* This can lead to confusion and misinterpretation because it sometimes involves multiple plane rotations. (As a rule, you should draw a section through a section view only when necessary to clarify the intent of the drawing or to make an assembly sequence understandable.) The preferred practice is to pass the cutting plane through an exterior view and not through a section view. In Figure 11.4, the cutting plane for **SECTION B–B** could have been drawn in the top view instead of through the front view (**SECTION A–A**).

11.2.5 Cutting Planes

The cutting-plane line is shown on the view where the **cutting plane** appears as an edge (Figs. 11.4 and 11.12). The ends of the cutting-plane line are turned 90° and terminated with large arrowheads to show the direction of sight, as was shown in Figure 11.4. The cutting-plane arrows point away from the viewer and away from the section view. Figure 11.12 shows the proper direction of the cutting-plane arrows. Figure 11.13(a) shows the incorrect direction for arrows and in (b) the correct direction.

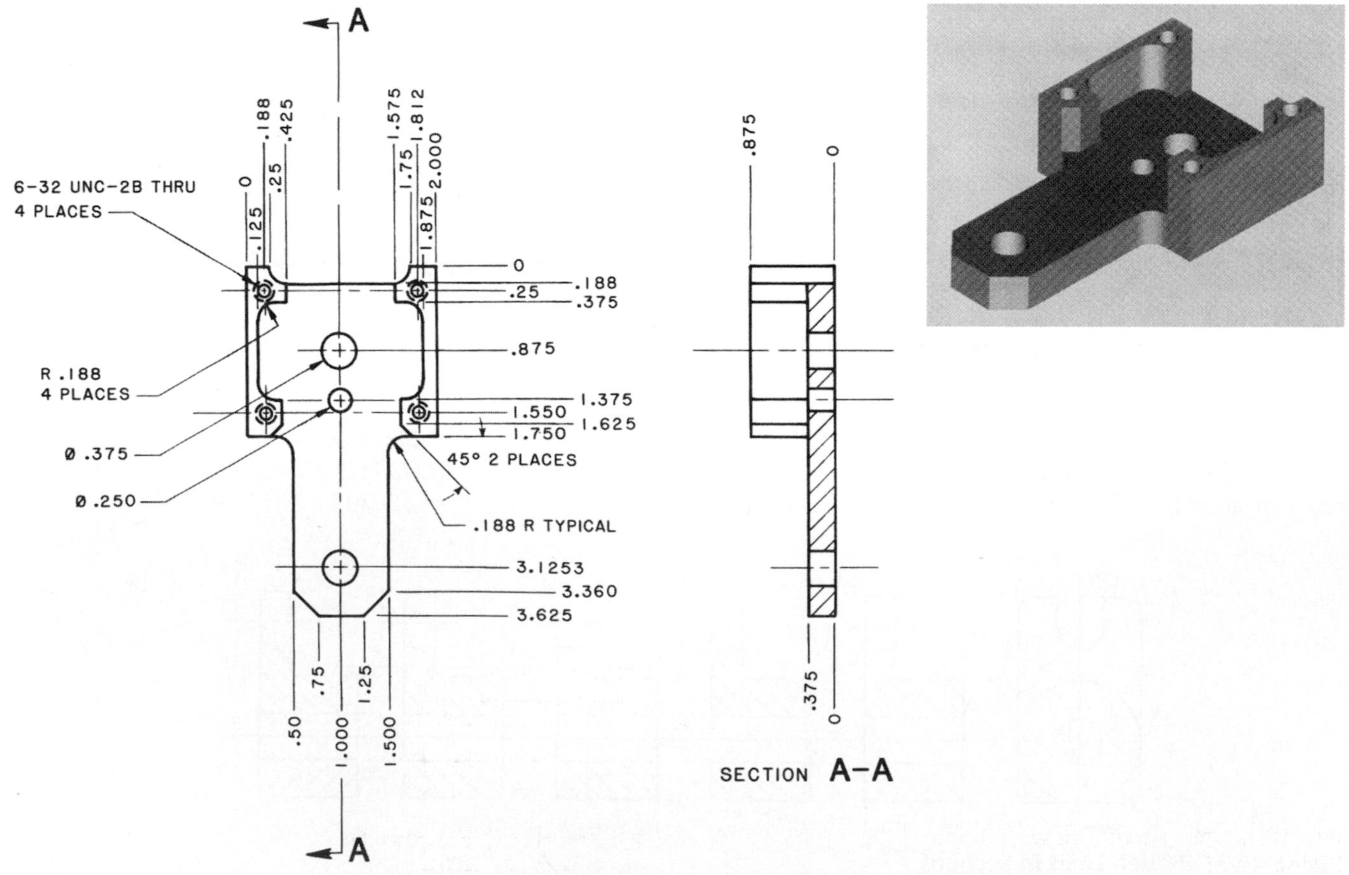

FIGURE 11.12 Section with Correct Direction of the Cutting-Plane Arrows

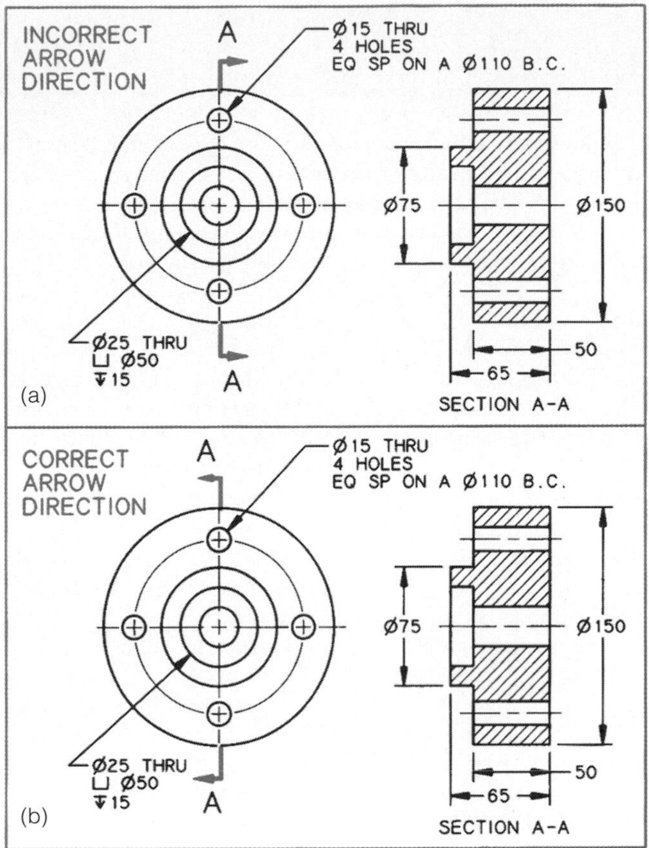

FIGURE 11.13 Arrow Direction on Sections

In simple sections, or when the location of the section is obvious, the cutting-plane line is omitted. The cutting-plane line and all identifying letters may be omitted only when the location of the cutting plane coincides with a centerline of symmetry (Fig. 11.14) or, as mentioned, when the location is obvious. Figure 11.14 is an industry example of a welded pipe fabrication. The pipe and flange are separate pieces that are to be joined by welding. The front view is a full section assembly. The pieces have section lines drawn at different angles so as to differentiate between the pipe and the flange.

Figure 11.15 shows the accepted sizes and line types for constructing cutting-plane lines. The first two examples in this figure follow the accepted ANSI standard. However, some companies use a solid line (third example) or just a portion of the cutting-plane line—the bent ends and the arrows (Fig. 11.12). The cutting-plane line is always shown when the cutting plane is bent or offset or when the resulting section is not symmetrical. Cutting-plane lines are drawn 0.7 to 0.9 mm thick. Border lines and cutting-plane lines will be the thickest lines on your drawing.

11.2.6 Section Identification and Multiple Sections

To identify the cutting plane with its sectioned view, capital letters (A, B, C, etc.) are placed adjacent to or behind the

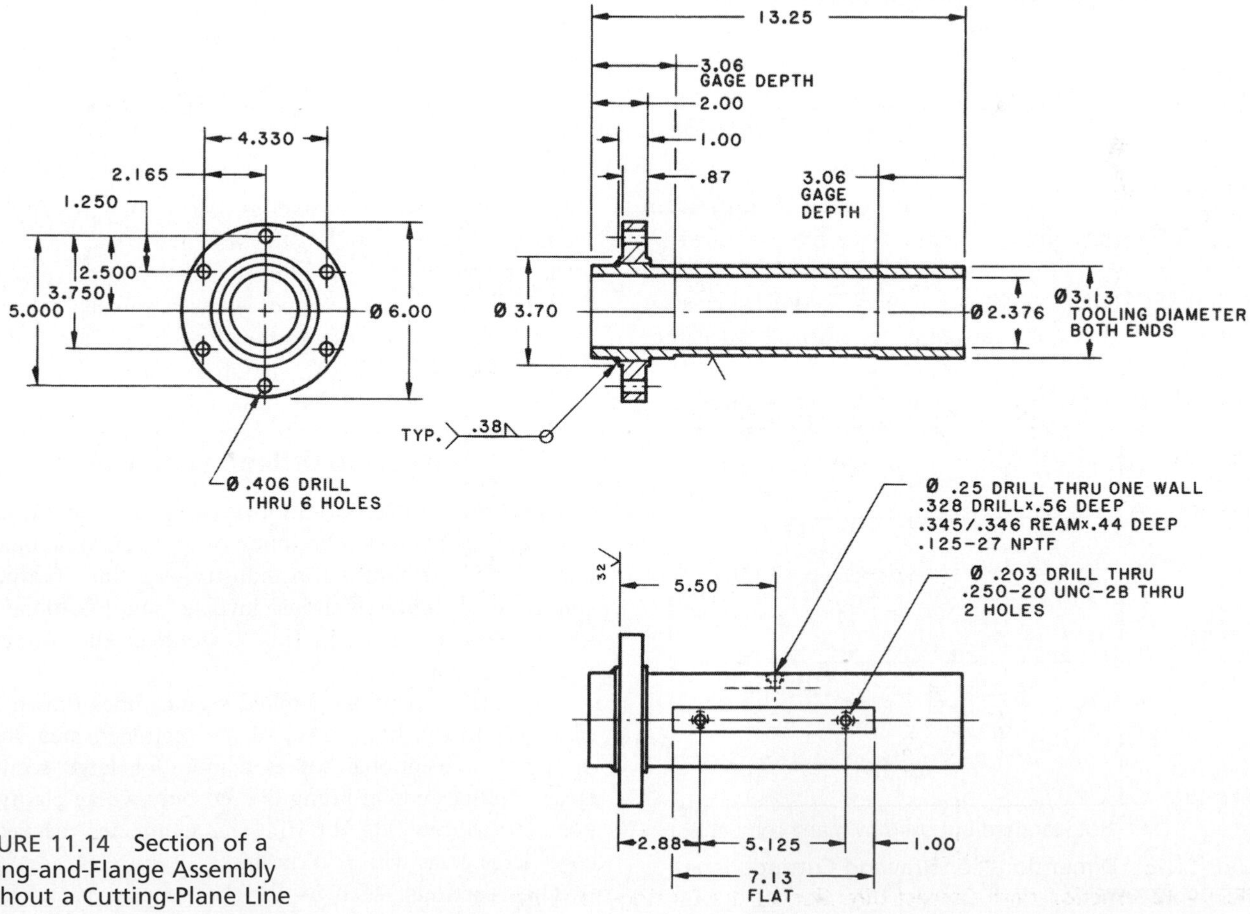

FIGURE 11.14 Section of a Piping-and-Flange Assembly Without a Cutting-Plane Line

Focus On . . .

ULTRASOUND

What do submarines, bats, whales, fish finders, and modern hospital technology have in common? They all depend on information gained via ultrasonic waves.

Ultrasonic waves are vibrations similar to the sound waves that are audible to humans. They are measured by intensity, length, velocity, wave period, and frequency. The number of vibrations per unit time is the frequency of that wave. Waves with a frequency greater than 20,000 Hz are ultrasonic waves.

A fish finder.

Ultrasonic waves are generated by passing an electric current through quartz or certain other materials. As an echo strikes the quartz, an electric current is produced, which in turn is used to produce a picture. This property of quartz is called *piezoelectricity*. The generating and receiving device is a *transducer*. In medical equipment, the transducer passes over the part of the body that is being examined. Since each tissue varies in density, these waves are reflected differently, producing different images. These images are displayed on a screen or recorded. Internal organs such as the heart and heart valves can be viewed in a static image or, by moving the transducer to different views, can be viewed in sequences in real time.

Recently, tiny ultrasonic transducers have been developed that can produce images from inside blood vessels and ducts. The transducer is rotated 360° to create a series of 2D cross sections. Computers are used to combine these 2D section images into a 3D image.

The sections produced with ultrasound equipment for medical applications are not unlike the sectional drawings in mechanical drawing. Both types of sections show internal details. It doesn't really matter whether they are the internal features of a part or of an organ. The concepts are the same. Mechanical engineers also use ultrasound waves to check for internal defects, such as cracks and small holes (voids). Sectional views in medicine and in graphics are intended to show internal features that would not otherwise be visible. Sectional views are valuable for visualization regardless of the application.

arrowheads. These letters are called **section identification letters.** The corresponding section views are identified by the same letters, for example, **SECTION A–A**, **SECTION B–B**, and **SECTION C-C**. If two or more sections appear on the same sheet, they are arranged in alphabetical order from left to right and/or top to bottom (Fig. 11.4). This applies to the cutting plane as well as the sectional view.

Section letters are applied in alphabetical order, excluding I, O, and Q. Once all alphabet letters have been exhausted, use double letters for additional sections, for example, AA–AA, AB–AB, AC–AC, etc., in alphabetical order.

(All dimensions are approximate only)

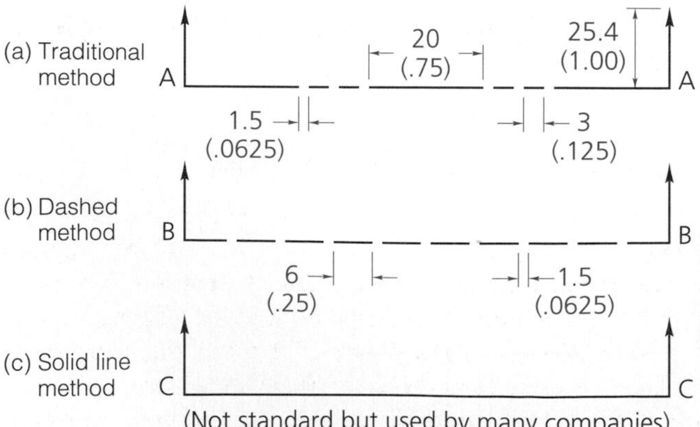

FIGURE 11.15 Dimensions for Drawing Cutting-Plane Lines and Arrows

11.2.7 Conventional Representation

Conventional representation, or accepted practice, is any recognized practice of description or representation of a part that has been established in industry over time. Ordinarily, conventional representations involve simplifications that speed the drawing task. This is done in the interest of drawing economy and clarity.

For **outline sections,** limited section lines drawn adjacent only to the boundaries of the sectioned area are the preferred conventional representation for large sectioned areas. Outline section lining is used only where clarity will not be sacrificed (Fig. 11.16). This eliminates the need to cover large areas with section lines.

Thin sections, such as for sheet metal, packing, and

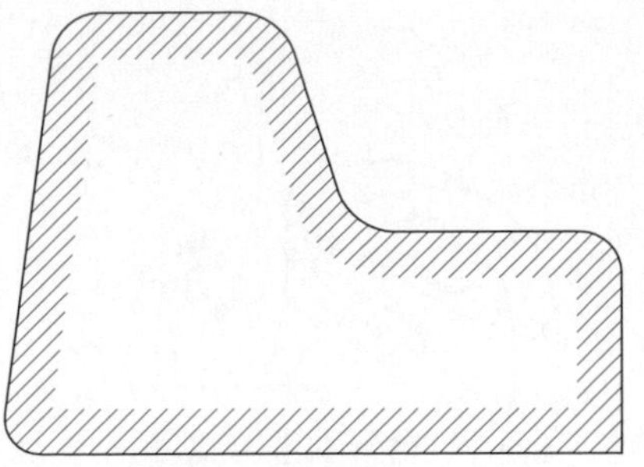

FIGURE 11.16 Outline Section Lining

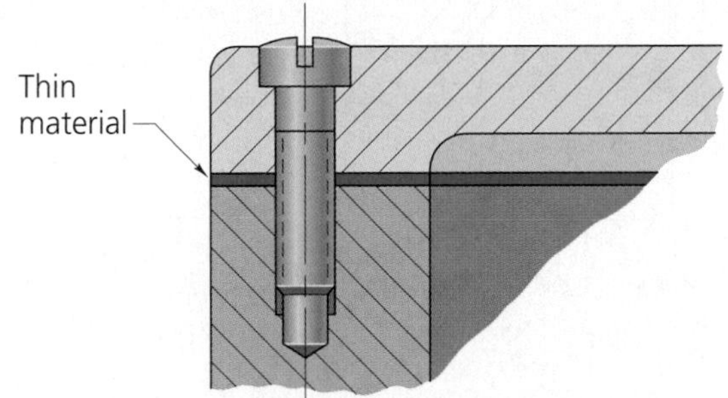

FIGURE 11.17 Thin Materials in Sections

gaskets, are drawn solid (filled). When drawing two or more thicknesses or layers, leave a narrow space between them to maintain their separate identities. Figure 11.17 illustrates the use of the solid sectioning symbol on thin materials such as gaskets. This figure shows three parts and a gasket. The screw is not sectioned because solid standard parts are not sectioned. The top cover has section lining at 45° angling in one direction, and the lower part has section lining in the opposite direction, per section standard conventions.

11.3 TYPES OF SECTIONS

Many types of sections are used on technical drawings, including the following.

- Full sections
- Half sections
- Offset sections
- Aligned sections
- Removed sections
- Revolved sections
- Broken-out sections
- Assembly sections
- Auxiliary sections (covered in Chapter 12)

A drawing may contain one or more of these types of sections, as in Figure 11.3. Each of these section types is covered in the following discussion, except auxiliary views, which, as noted, are covered in Chapter 12.

11.3.1 Full Sections

When the cutting plane extends through the entire part, in a straight line, usually on the centerline of symmetry, a full section results (Fig. 11.18). **Full sections,** because the entire orthographic view is sectioned, are the most common type of section view. The part in Figure 11.18 shows four different aspects of the sectioning process. Figure 11.18(a) gives a pictorial view of the part. In Figure 11.18(b), a cutting plane is passed through the part and the sectioned area is shown. In Figure 11.18(c), the line of sight is displayed and the part split along the cutting plane. Figure 11.18(d) presents three views of the part: a front view, a left side view, and a full right side section view.

The part in Figure 11.19 has a right side view along with a full right side section view. The portion of the part between the observer and the cutting plane is assumed to be removed, exposing the cut surface and the visible background lines of the remaining portion. (This is an actual industry drawing.)

Figure 11.20 contrasts a full section view and a half section view. The front view is a normal external view. Note that the outline of each is the same.

11.3.2 Half Sections

The view of a symmetrical or cylindrical part that represents both the interior and the exterior features by showing one-fourth in section and the other three-fourths as an external view is known as a **half section**, because the half of the orthographic view is sectioned (Fig. 11.21). Figure 11.22 is a half section obtained by passing two cutting planes at right angles to each other. The intersection line of the two cutting planes is coincident with each axis of symmetry of the part. One-fourth of the part is "removed," and the interior is exposed. Figure 11.22(b) shows the part placed in the front and the top views, with the front view showing the half section. When the cutting planes are coincident with the centerline, the cutting-plane line, arrows, and section letters may be omitted. The line that separates the sectioned half from the nonsectioned half is a centerline and not a visible solid line.

You May Complete Exercises 11.1 Through 11.4 at This Time

11.3.3 Offset Sections

To include features of a part not located in a straight line, the cutting plane may be stepped, or offset, at right angles to pass through these features. **Offset sections** reduce the number of required sections for a complicated part. An offset section (Fig. 11.23) is drawn as if the offsets were in one plane, and *the offsets are not indicated in the sectioned view.* In Figure 11.23 the front view shows the section as if it had a straight cutting plane. No extra lines are introduced into the view to show where the section changes direction.

FIGURE 11.18 **Full Section**

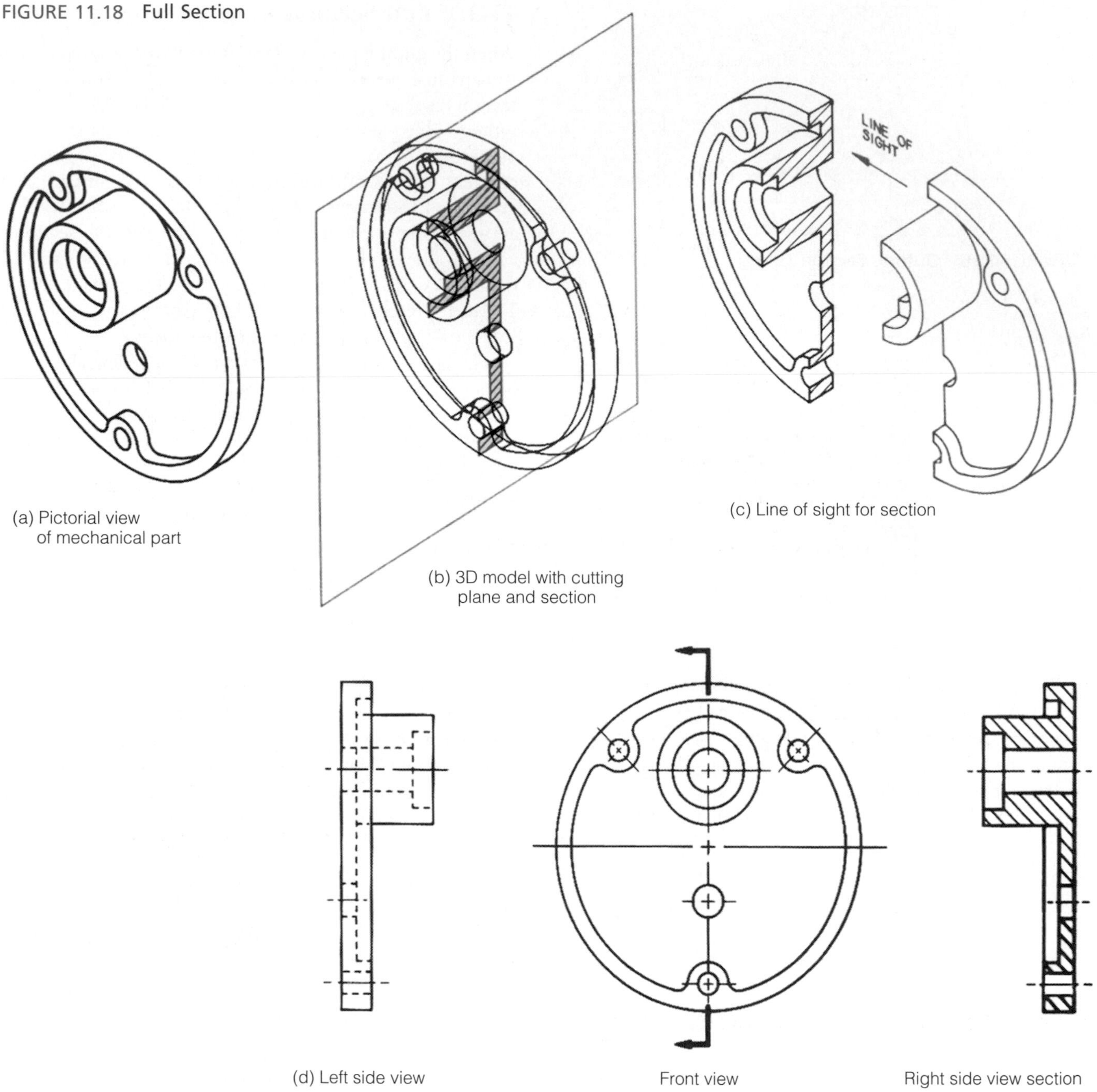

(a) Pictorial view of mechanical part

(b) 3D model with cutting plane and section

(c) Line of sight for section

(d) Left side view

Front view

Right side view section

The part in Figure 11.24 has important features at three separate positions in the top view. The cutting plane is offset twice, once to pass through the hole and again to pass through the counterbored hole near the back of the part. Observe that no line is shown at the offset in the cutting-plane line in the section view [Fig. 11.24(d)]. When changes in viewing direction are not obvious, you can place reference letters at each turning point of the cutting plane.

11.3.4 Aligned Sections

If the true projection of a part results in foreshortening or requires unnecessary drawing time, inclined elements such as lugs, ribs, spokes, and arms are rotated into a plane perpendicular to the line of sight of the section. Cutting-plane lines are normally omitted for rotated features. This type of section is called an **aligned section** (Fig. 11.25).

Aligned sections are the recommended conventional practice in industry. This convention speeds the construction of the view, even though it is not a true projection. The true projection is completed only if it is important to establish clearance between features of a part or in an assembly of parts. Holes, slots, and similar features spaced around a bolt circle or a cylindrical flange may also be rotated to their true distance from the center axis and then projected to the adjacent section view.

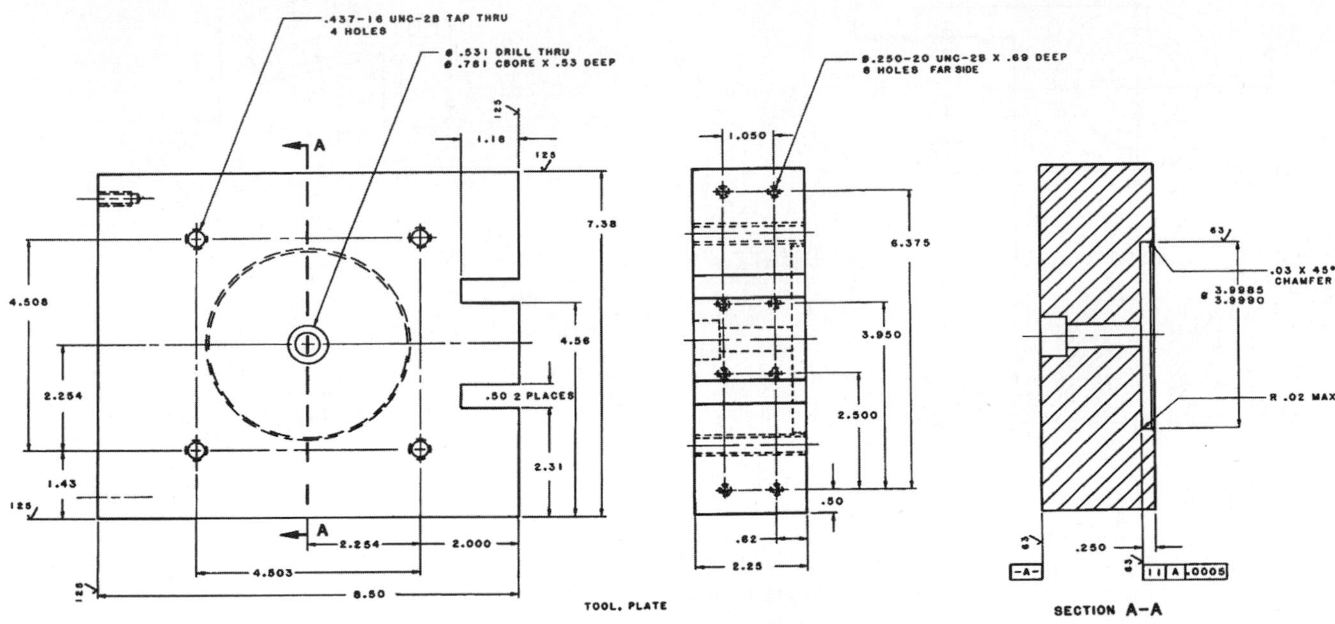

FIGURE 11.19 Detail with Both an External Right Side View and a Full Right Side Section

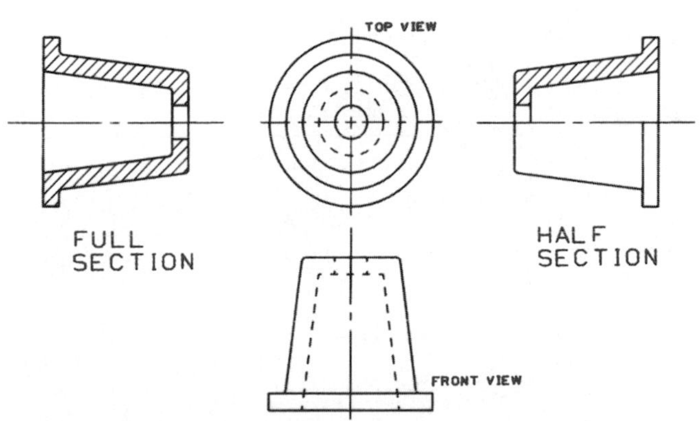

FIGURE 11.20 Full Section, Half Section, and External Views

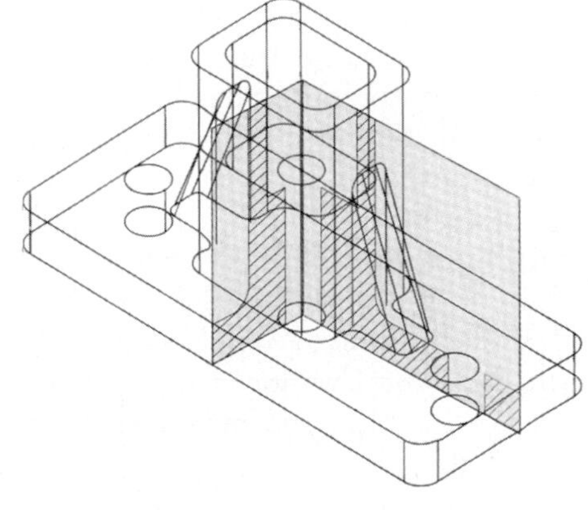

(a) Pictorial illustration of a half section

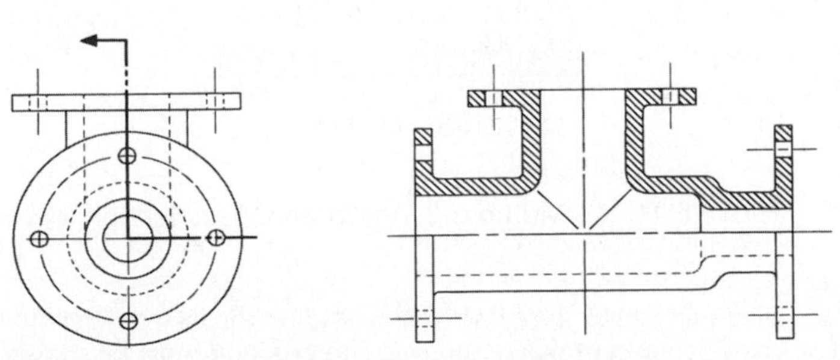

FIGURE 11.21 Half Section

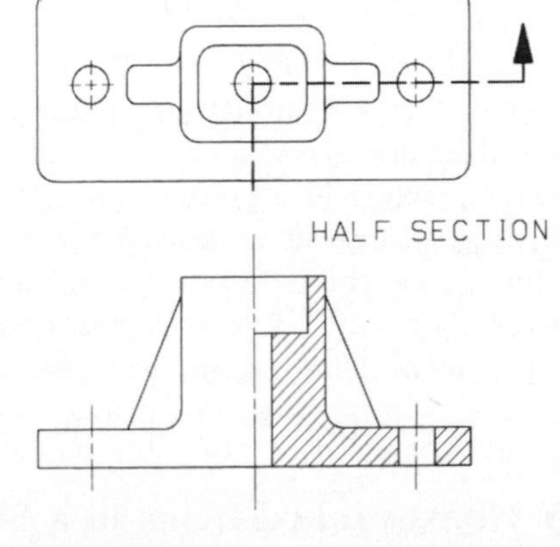

(b) Top view and front half section of a part

FIGURE 11.22 Half Sections

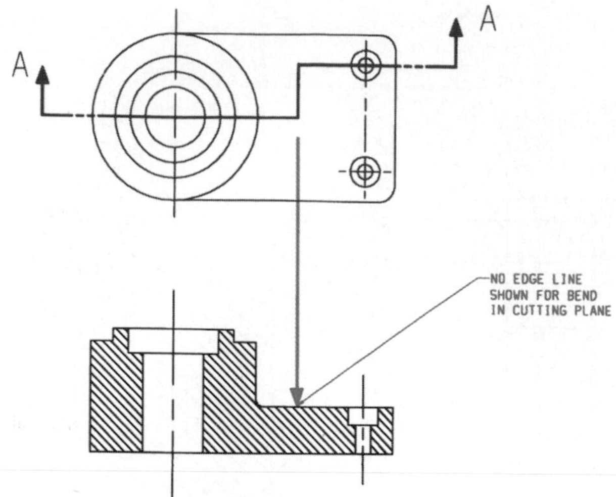

FIGURE 11.23 Offset Section

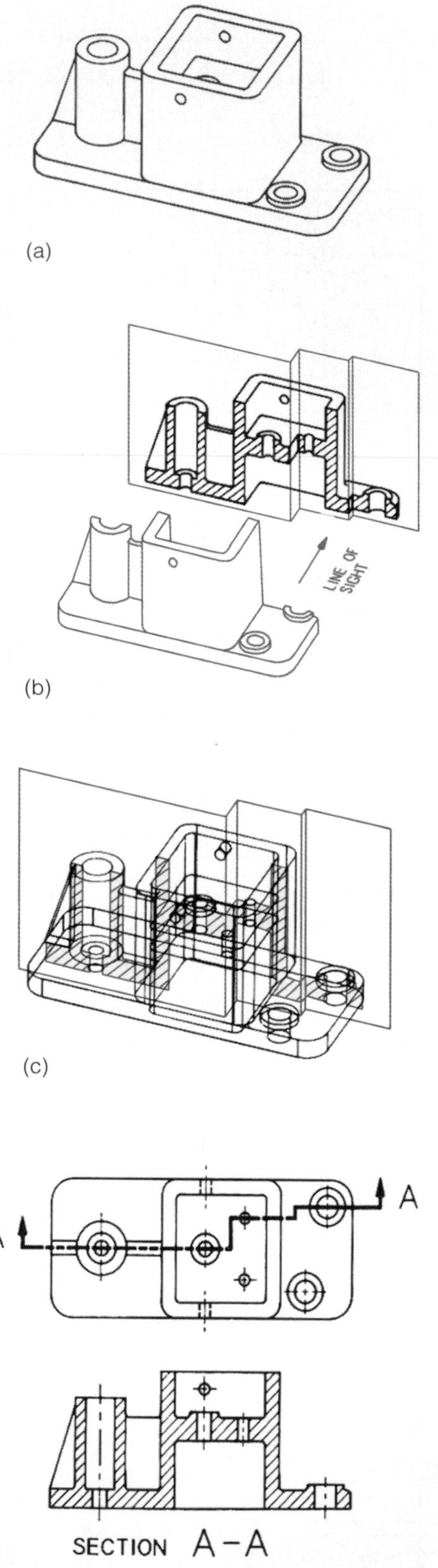

FIGURE 11.24 Multiple Bends in an Offset Section

In aligned sections, features of a symmetrical part that would be foreshortened in a strict interpretation are rotated into the plane of the paper. This preserves the feeling of symmetry, is easier to draw, and is more easily interpreted by the machinist. In Figure 11.25, the unrecommended, foreshortened, true projected view of the part is provided to contrast the two methods. The true projected view of the spokes is hard to construct and does not add to the drawing's clarity. In this figure, the spokes of the wheel have been rotated to project as true shape in the right side view. In Figure 11.26, the right side view is an aligned section. Both spokes and the keyseat are drawn as if they were cut by the cutting plane.

Another example of an aligned section is provided in Figure 11.27. Figure 11.27(a) shows the true front view projection of a part; Figure 11.27(b) shows the rib as rotated. It is now easier to complete a full section of the part. Compare the two views for clarity and simplicity: Figure 11.27(a) is a less clear and more complex projection than Figure 11.27(b).

When the features of a part lend themselves to an angular change of less than 90° in the direction of the cutting plane, the section view is drawn as if the cutting plane and feature were rotated into the plane of the paper. In some cases, the cutting plane is bent to pass through a desired feature, as in the industry drawing in Figure 11.28. In Figure 11.29, the cutting plane is drawn through the portion to be rotated.

Figure 11.29 also shows an alternative way of sectioning a rib (also see Section 11.3.5). Here, the cutting plane passes through the rib. Instead of leaving the rib area without section lines, as is common practice, the area was **double sectioned** by extending every other section line from the surrounding area. This method was also used in Figure 11.10.

11.3.5 Nonsectioned Items in a Section View

When the cutting plane lies along the longitudinal axis of shafts, bolts, nuts, rods, rivets, keys, pins, screws, ball or roller bearings, gear teeth, ribs, or spokes, sectioning is not required except where internal construction must be shown. This convention is needed mainly on assembly sections

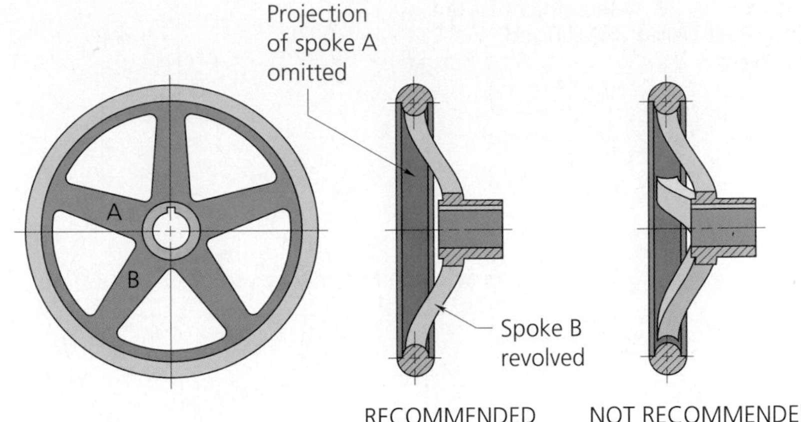

FIGURE 11.25 Spokes in Section

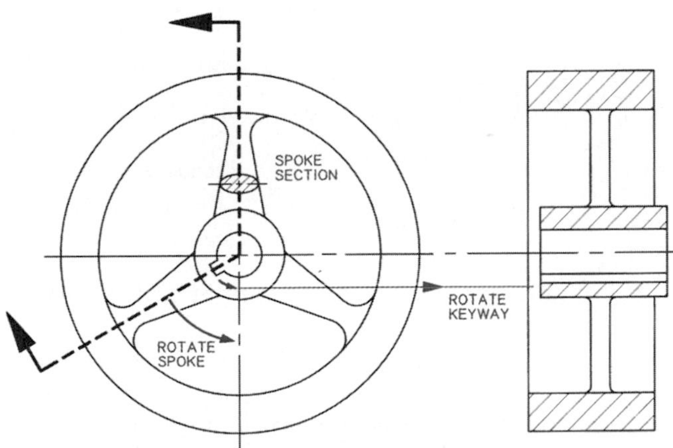

FIGURE 11.26 Conventional Layout for Aligned and Rotated Sections

where more than one part is sectioned and a number of standard hardware items, such as bolts, screws, and dowels, are found.

For shafts and other machine parts detailed as separate parts, it is normal practice to use **broken-out sections** for any internal construction that needs to be displayed. Sections through nuts, bolts, shafts, pins, and other solid machine elements that have no internal construction are not shown sectioned, even though the cutting plane passes through these features. These items are more easily recognized by their exterior (Fig. 11.30). Figure 11.31 shows an example of a sectioned assembly. The shaft in this figure is also unsectioned.

When a cutting plane passes through a rib (Fig. 11.32), leave the rib portion of the section without section lining. Because ribs fall into the category of a thin solid shape, they are usually represented without section lining or are sometimes double sectioned.

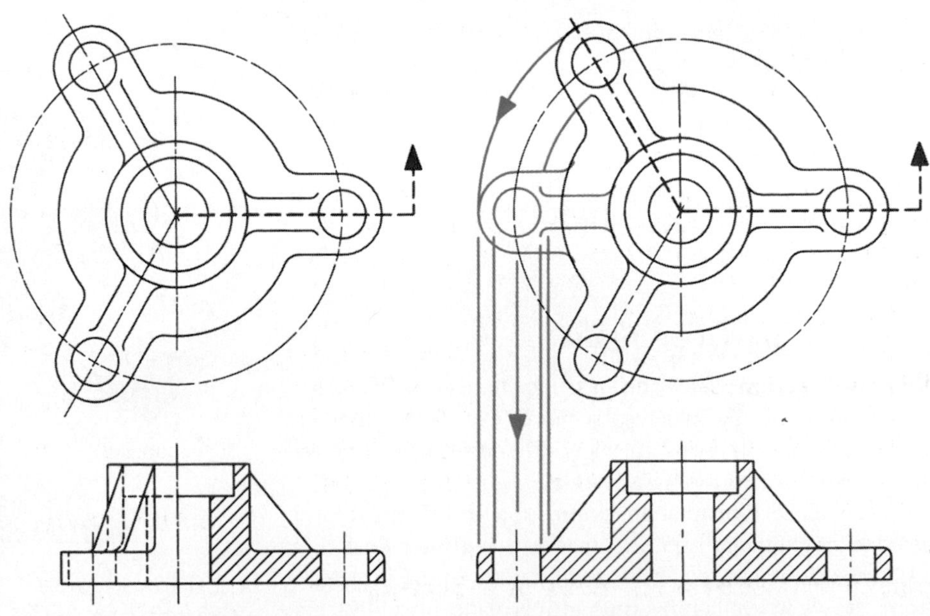

(a) Half section with true front projection of the part

(b) Full section with aligned (rotated) frontal projection

FIGURE 11.27 Full and Half Sections

FIGURE 11.28 Mechanical Detail of a Part Using an Aligned Section

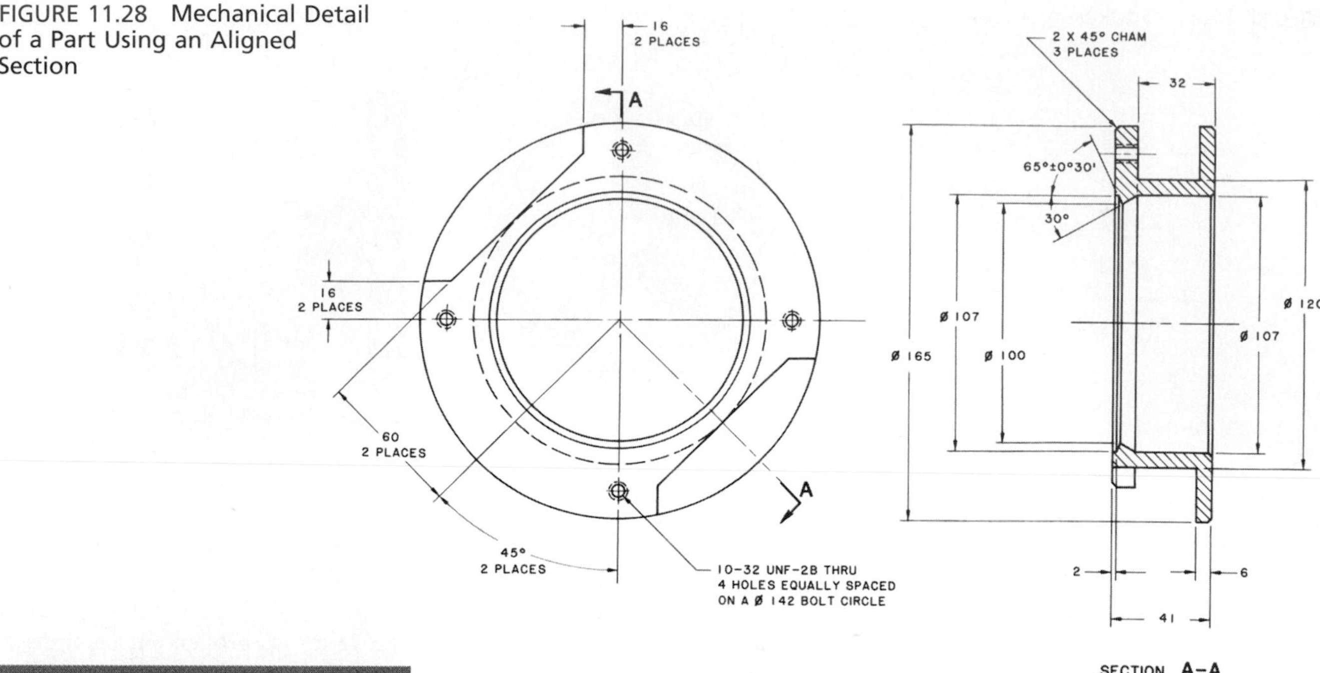

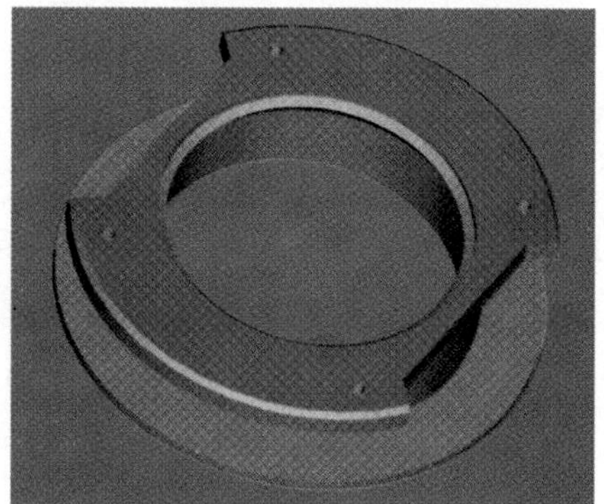

Sectioning ribs gives the appearance of more mass than actually exists, as in the incorrect example of Figure 11.32. Ribs are not sectioned when the cutting plane passes through them "flatwise," but are shown as visible edges. However, ribs are sectioned when the cutting plane passes perpendicular to them.

11.3.6 Removed Sections

Removed sections show the special or transitional details of a part. They are like revolved sections, except that they are placed outside the principal view. In some cases, removed sections are drawn to a larger scale.

Removed sections that are symmetrical may be placed on centerlines extended from the imaginary cutting planes (Fig. 11.33). A removed section is usually not a direct projection from the view containing the cutting-plane line; it is displaced from its normal projection position. In this case, formal identification is necessary. Figure 11.34 shows a detailed mechanical part from industry. **SECTION A–A** is a removed section drawn at **2:1** scale.

If it is impractical to place a removed section on the same sheet with the regular views, you must clearly identify the sheet number and the drawing zone location of the cutting-plane line. Where the cutting plane is shown, place a note that refers to the sheet and the zone where the removed section or section title is, along with a leader pointing to the

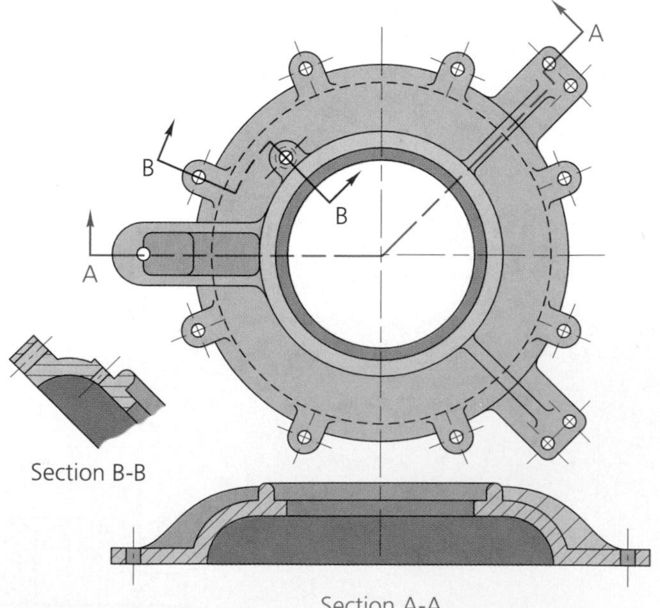

FIGURE 11.29 Aligned Section Through a Rib. An alternative method of sectioning a rib with double-spaced section lines is also shown.

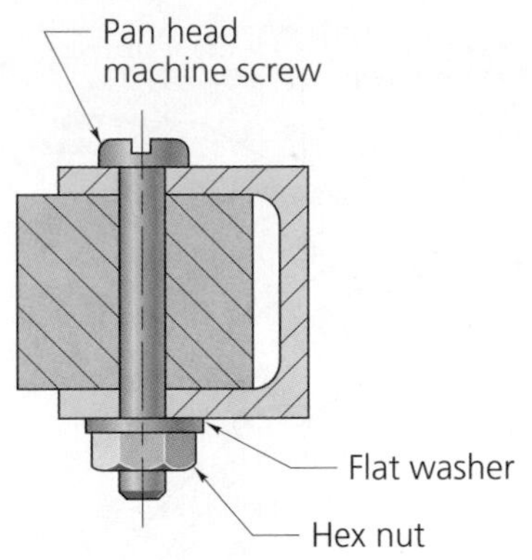

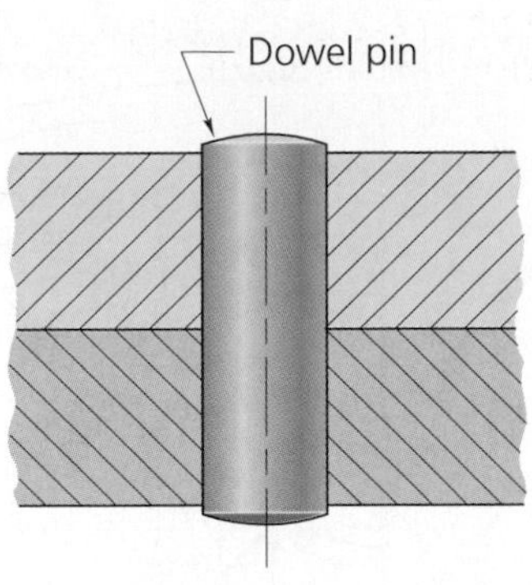

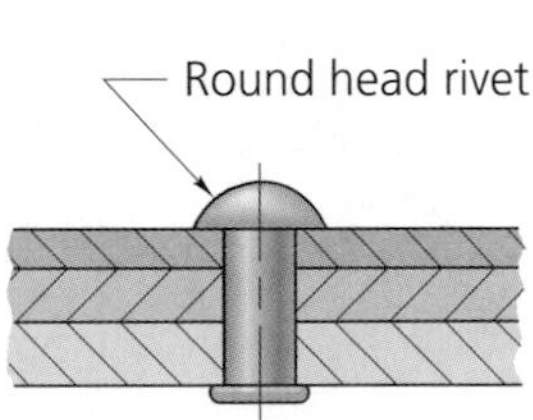

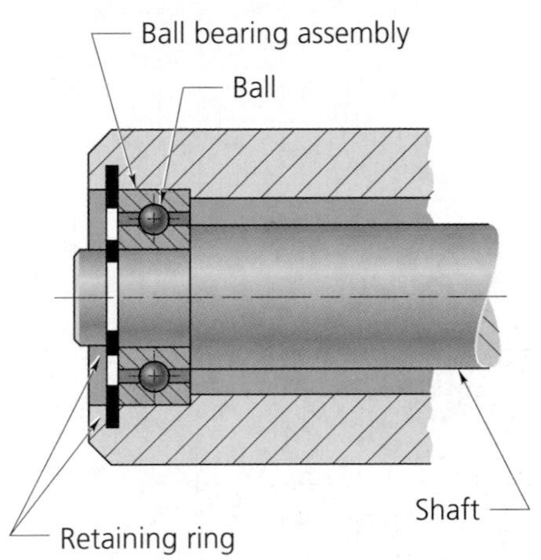

FIGURE 11.30 Solids in Section

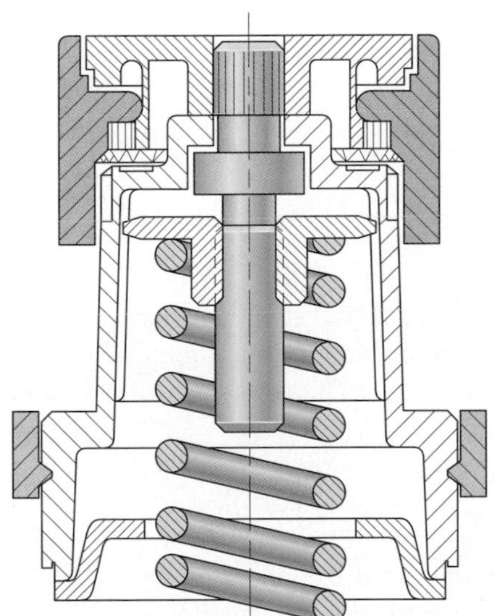

FIGURE 11.31 Assembly and Solid Threaded Part in Section

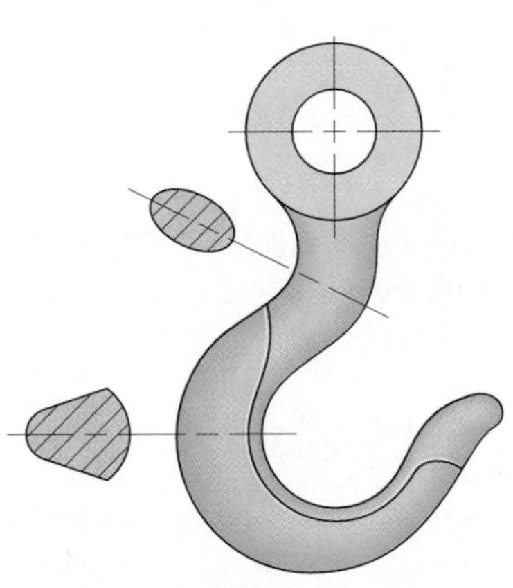

FIGURE 11.33 Removed Sections

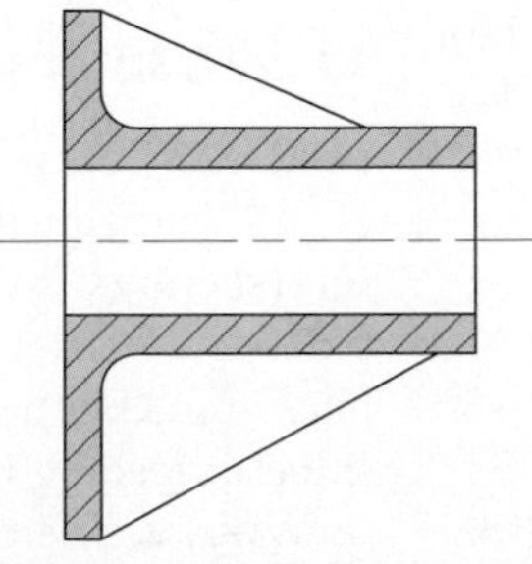

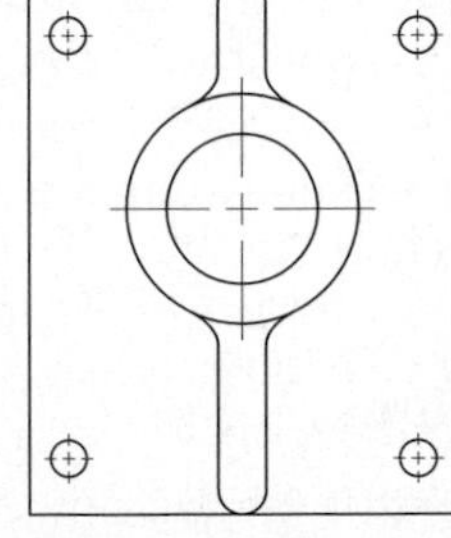

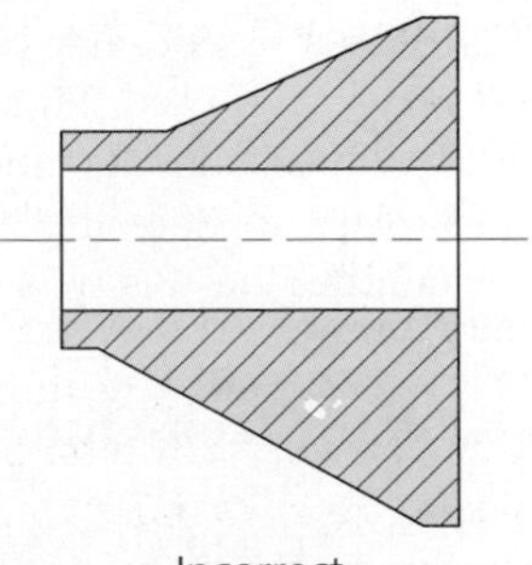

FIGURE 11.32 Ribs in Sectional Views

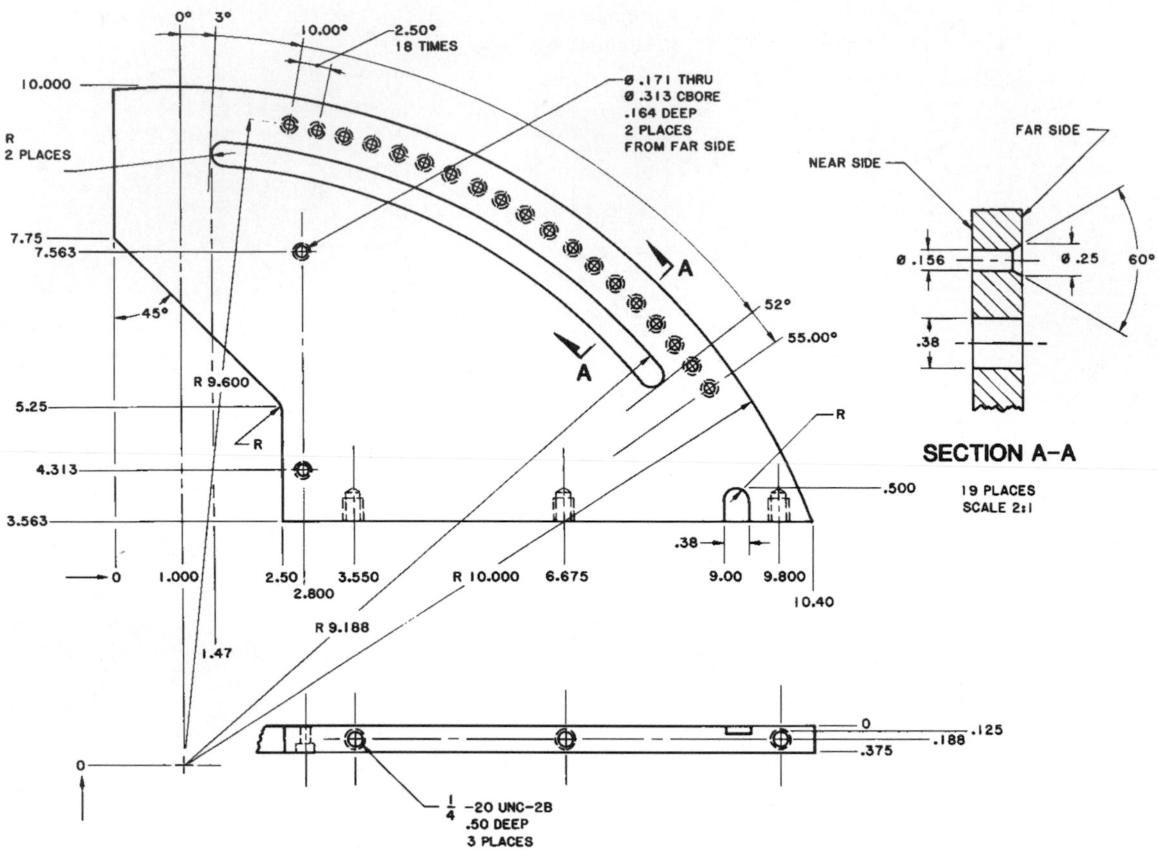

FIGURE 11.34 Detail of a Mechanical Part with a Removed Section

cutting plane. Figure 11.35 is an example of a part detail that employs a removed section (SECTION B–B) to display interior features that would be difficult to dimension with only an exterior view.

11.3.7 Revolved Sections

A **revolved section** is constructed by passing a cutting plane perpendicular to the axis of an elongated symmetrical feature such as a spoke, a beam, or an arm, and then revolving it in place through 90° into the plane of the drawing (Fig. 11.36). Visible lines extending on each side of the revolved section may be left in, or they may be removed and break lines used. Figure 11.37 involves both methods. The spoke sections do not have the visible lines removed and broken, as does the wheel section. Cutting planes are not indicated on this type of section.

11.3.8 Broken-Out Sections

When it is necessary to show only a portion of the part in section, the sectioned area is limited by a freehand **break line,** and the section is called a **broken-out section** (Fig. 11.38). A cutting-plane line is not indicated for this type of section. Broken-out sections are sometimes referred to as **partial sections** (see Fig. 11.3).

One of the most important reasons for showing sections on a drawing is to display complicated interior features that require dimensioning. Figures 11.39 and 11.40 show industry drawings that make use of broken-out sections to display and dimension normally hidden features.

11.3.9 Intersections in Section

If the exact shape of the curve of an intersection is slight or of no consequence, you may simplify sections through **intersections** by ignoring the true projection. Conventional practice does not require the true projection when the true lines of intersection are time-consuming to draw or are of no value in reading the drawing.

When a difference in proportions exists, the true projection should be shown. When the cutting plane is perpen-

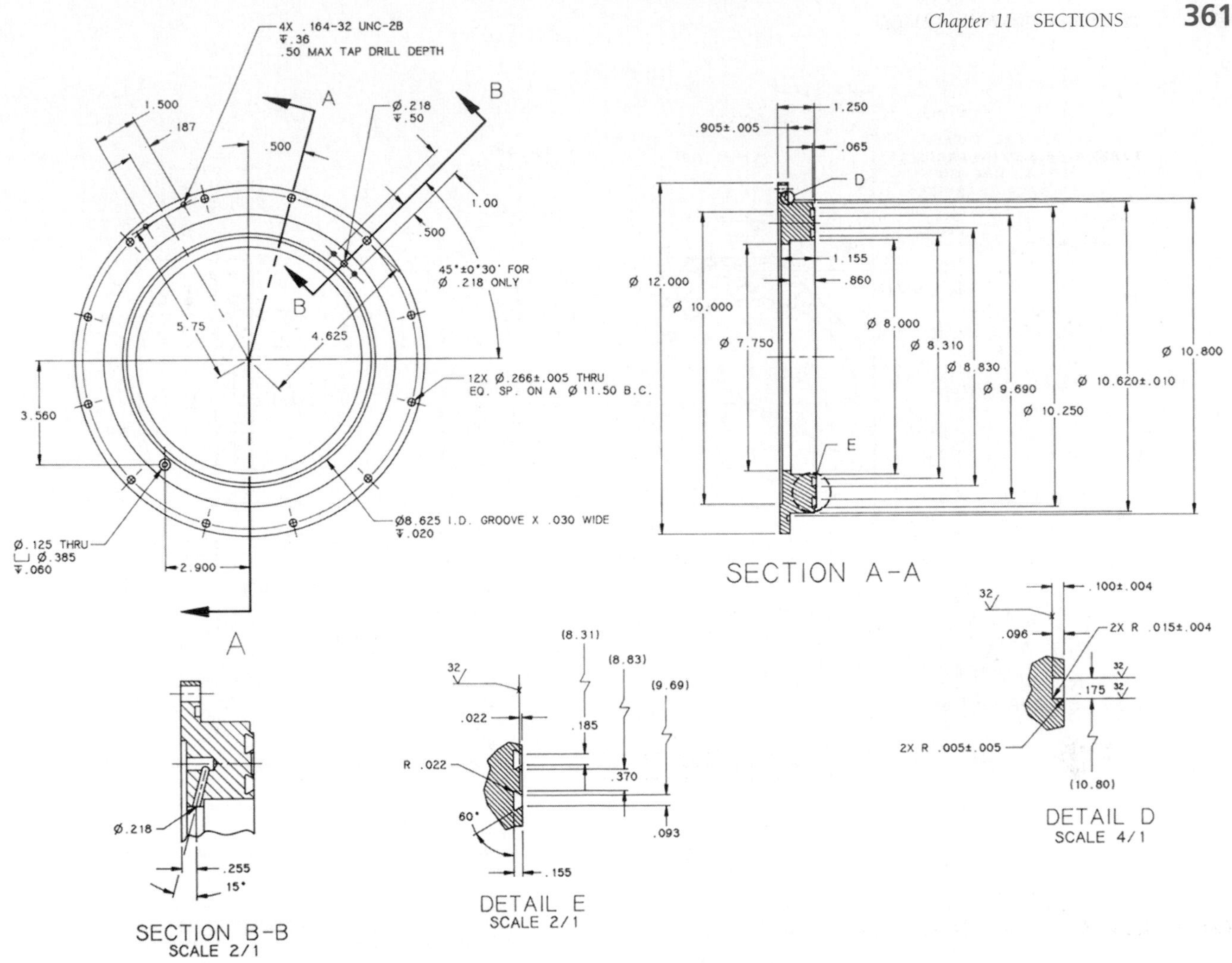

4X .164-32 UNC-2B
↧.36
.50 MAX TAP DRILL DEPTH

Ø.218
↧.50

45°±0°30' FOR
Ø .218 ONLY

12X Ø.266±.005 THRU
EQ. SP. ON A Ø 11.50 B.C.

Ø8.625 I.D. GROOVE X .030 WIDE
↧.020

Ø.125 THRU
⌴ Ø.385
↧.060

SECTION A-A

SECTION B-B
SCALE 2/1

DETAIL E
SCALE 2/1

DETAIL D
SCALE 4/1

FIGURE 11.35 Removed Sections on Detail Drawing

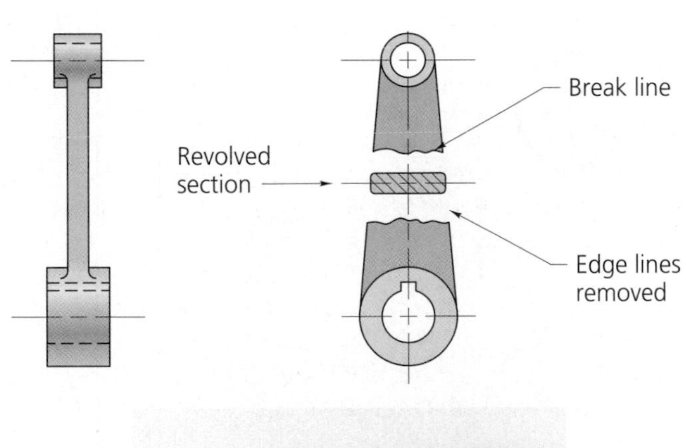

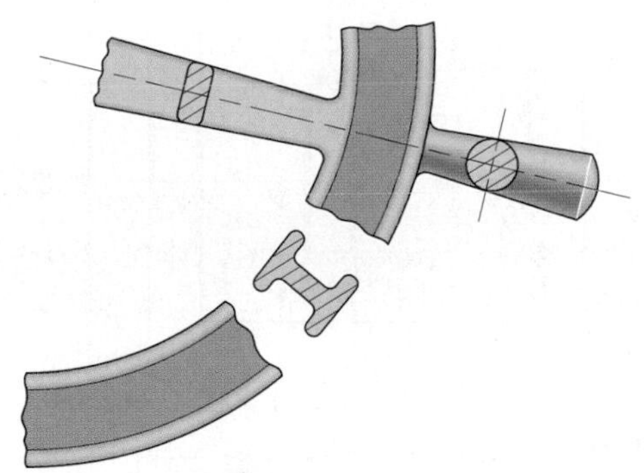

FIGURE 11.37 Revolved Sections on a Handwheel

FIGURE 11.36 Revolved Section of an Arm

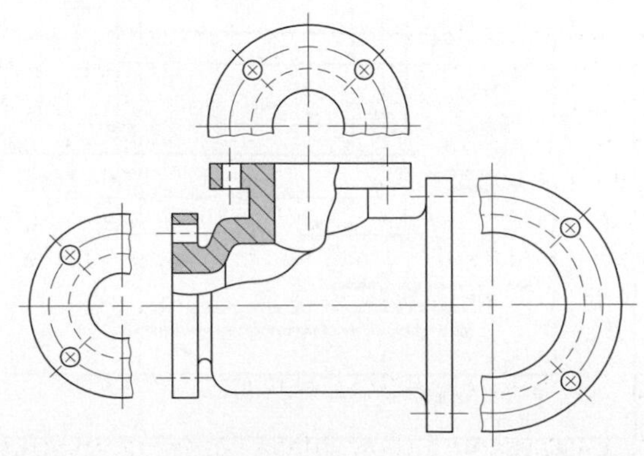

FIGURE 11.38 Broken-Out Section of a Pipe Fitting

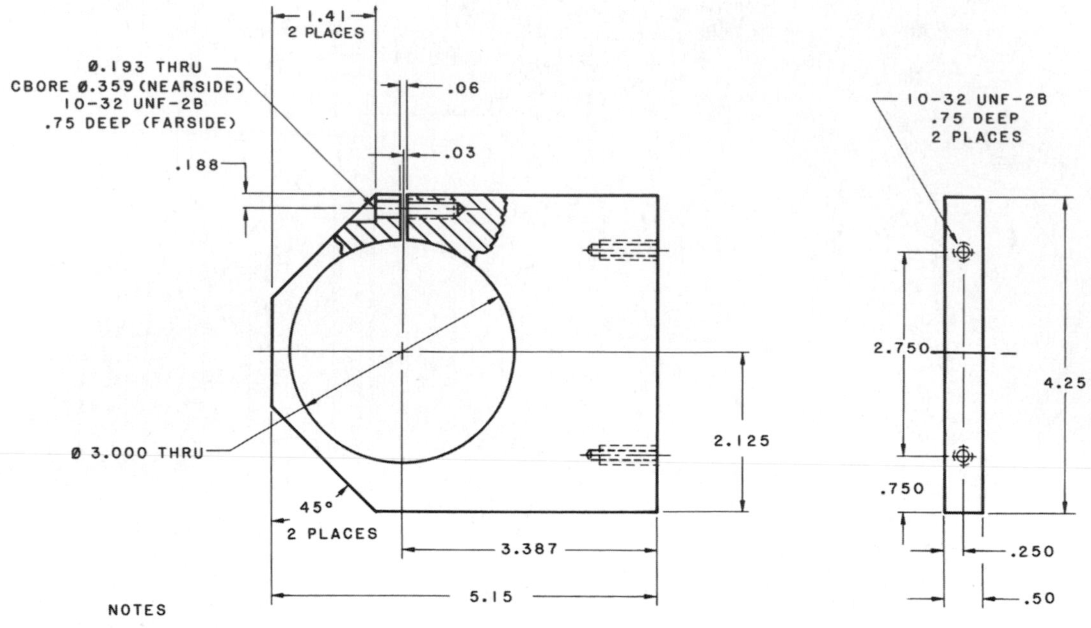

FIGURE 11.39 Broken-Out Section

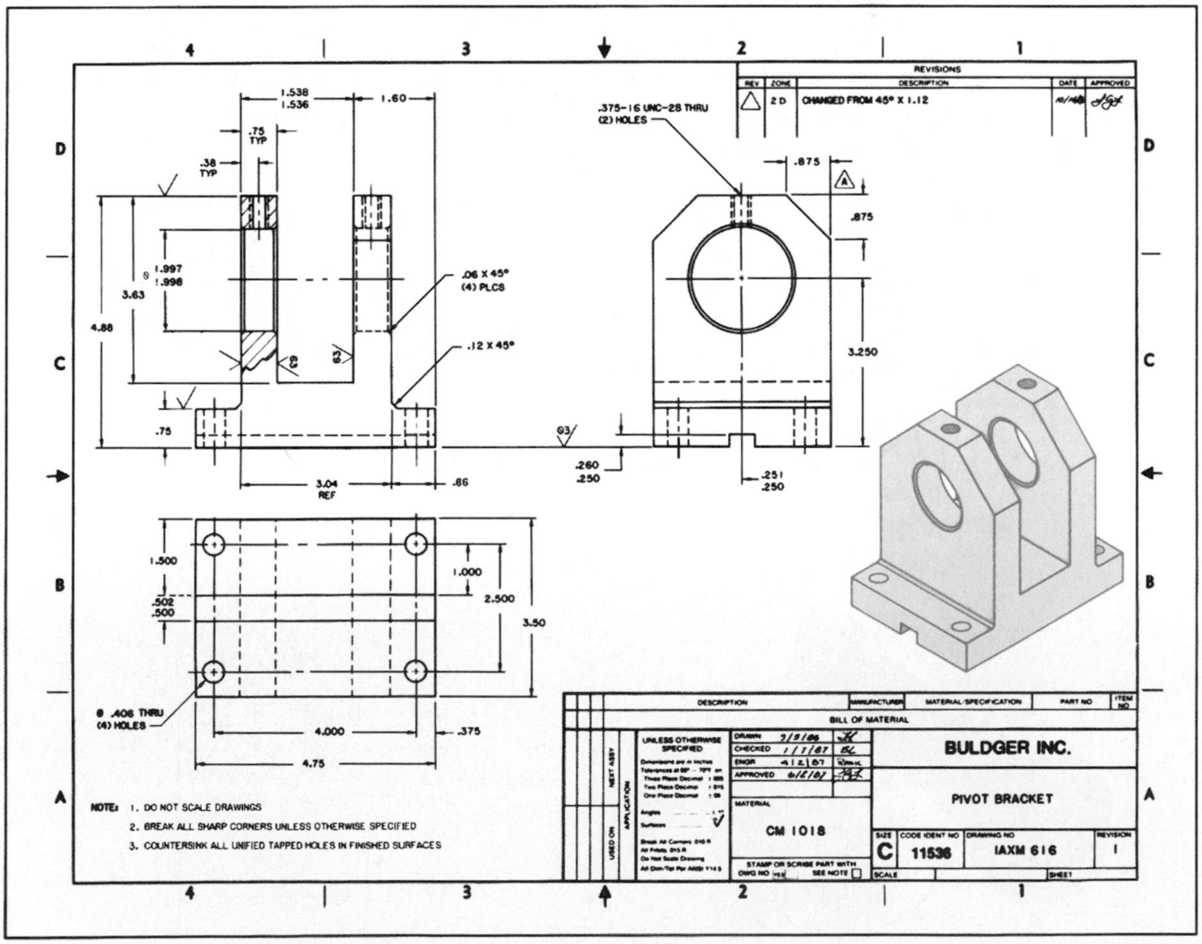

NOTE: 1. DO NOT SCALE DRAWINGS
2. BREAK ALL SHARP CORNERS UNLESS OTHERWISE SPECIFIED
3. COUNTERSINK ALL UNIFIED TAPPED HOLES IN FINISHED SURFACES

BULDGER INC.

PIVOT BRACKET

FIGURE 11.40 Mechanical Part with a Broken-Out Section

Applying Parametric Design . . .

SECTIONING PARAMETRIC MODELS

Cross-sectional views are slices through a part or an assembly and are valuable for opening up the part or assembly to display features and detailing in draw mode. Part cross sections may also be used to calculate cross-sectional mass properties. Each cross section has its own unique name within the part or assembly, allowing any number of cross sections to be created and then retrieved for use in drawing. A variety of ANSI-standard section lining materials can be generated automatically (see Fig. A). You have can create a variety of cross-section types:

- Standard planar cross sections of models (part or assemblies)
- Offset cross sections of models (part or assemblies)

Planar cross sections are created along a datum plane (Fig. B). The datum may be created during the creation of the cross section using the **Make Datum** options, or an existing plane may be selected. DTM5 (Fig. C) was used to create the removed section in the next example (Fig. D). The socket-head cap shoulder screw (Fig. E) is sectioned along DTM3 (Fig. F) and shown as shaded. The section can also be created for use in a drawing, in Draw Mode (Fig. G).

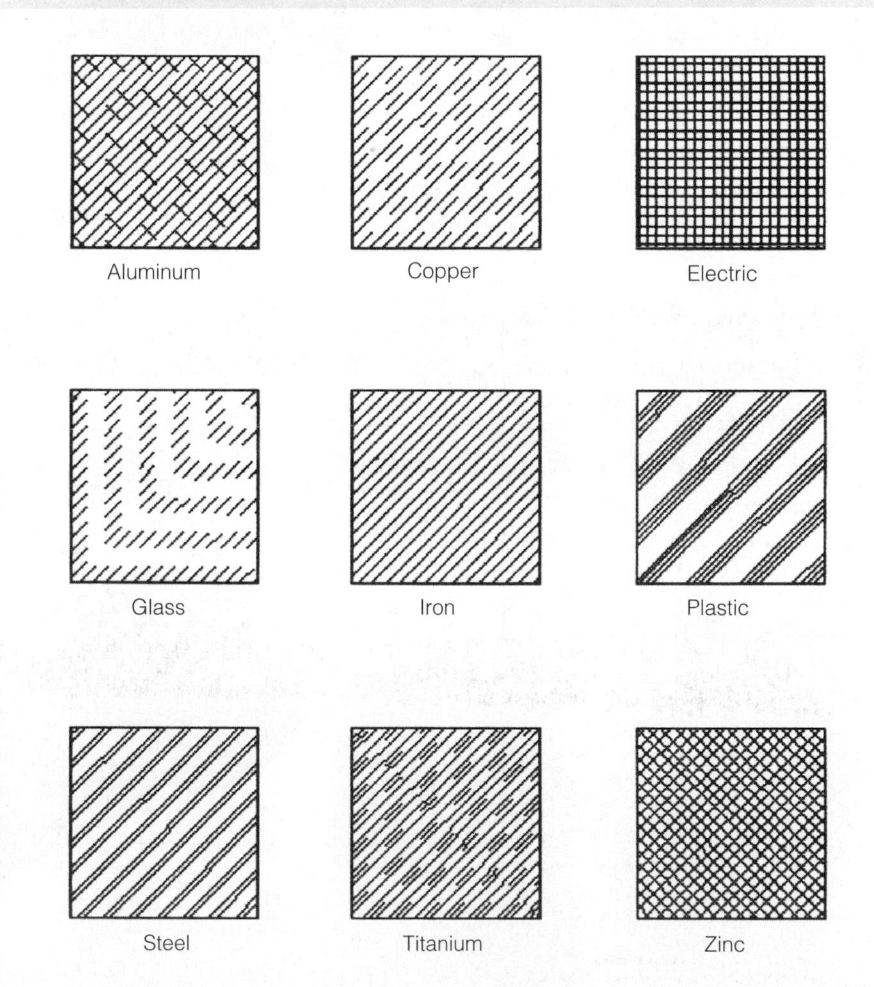

FIGURE A Material Lining Symbols

(Continued)

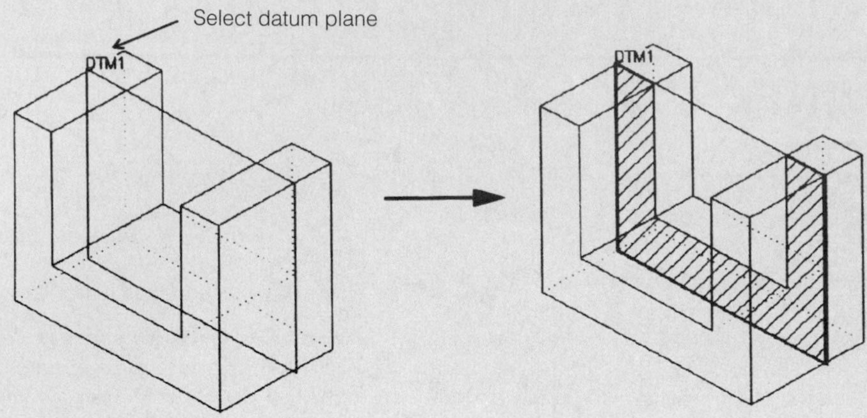

FIGURE B Selecting a Datum Plane for Cross Section

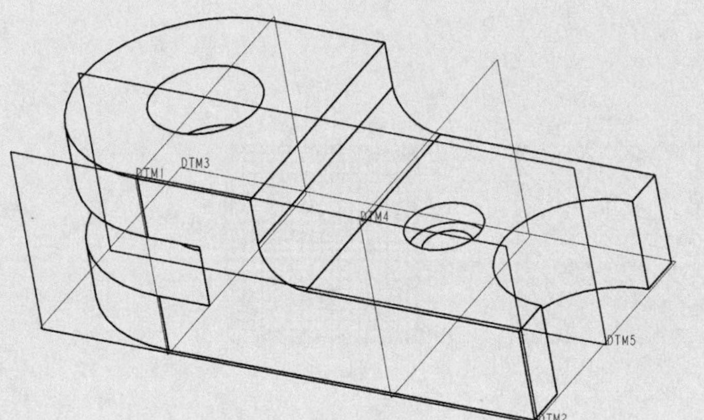

FIGURE C Part with Datum Planes Displayed

FIGURE D Sectioned Part with Front Removed

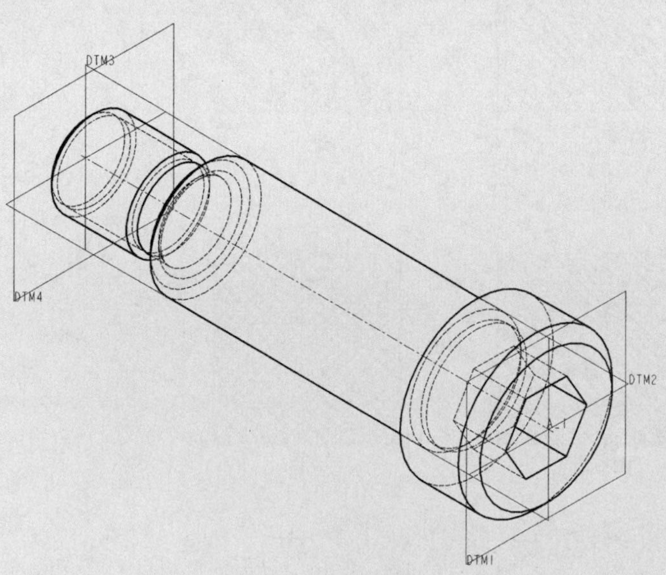

FIGURE E Socket-Head Cap Shoulder Screw

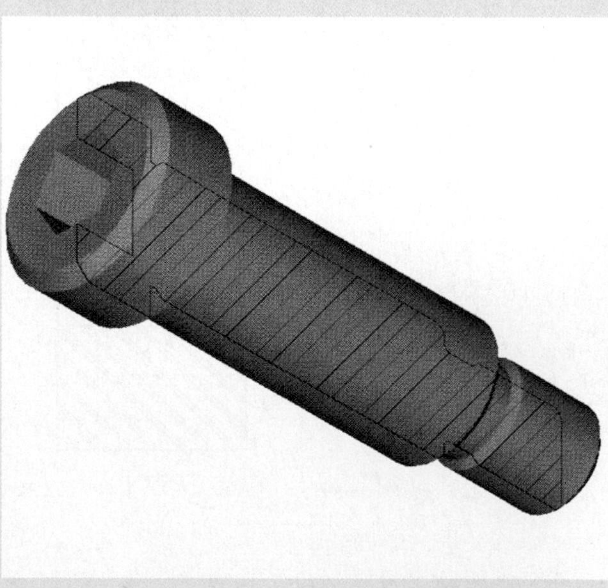

FIGURE F Sectioned and Shaded Model of Screw

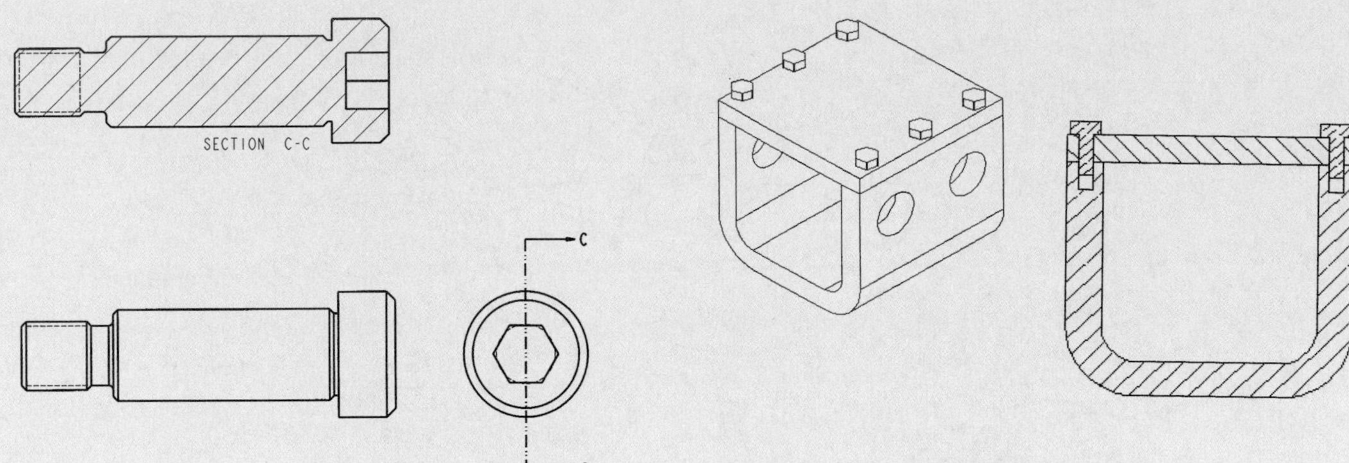

FIGURE G Drawing of Screw with a Sectioned View

FIGURE H Assembly and Section

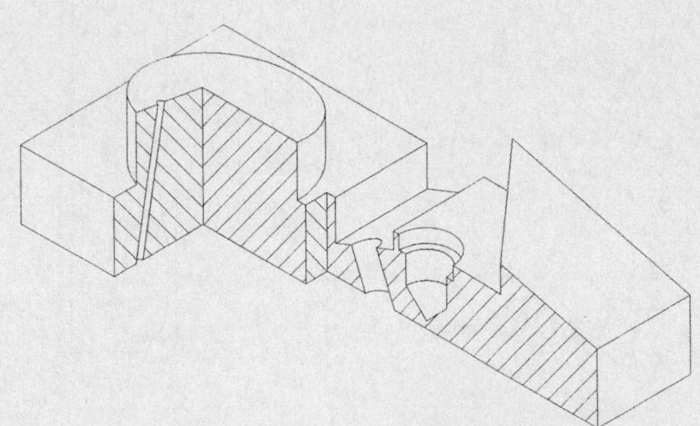

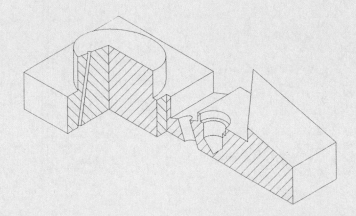

FIGURE I Offset Section

To Create a Planar Cross Section of a Part:

1. Choose **X-section** from the PART menu and **Create** from the XSEC ENTER menu.
2. Choose **Planar** from the XSEC CREATE menu, then **Done.**
3. Enter a name for the cross section, and then select (or make) the datum along which the section is to be generated.

To Create a Planar Cross Section of an Assembly (Fig. H):

1. Choose **Set Up** from the ASSEMBLY menu and **X-section** from the ASSEM SETUP menu, then Create from the XSEC ENTER menu.
2. Choose **Planar** from the XSEC CREATE menu, then **Done.**
3. Enter a name for the cross section.
4. Select or create the **assembly** datum along which the section is to be generated.

An **offset cross section** (Fig. I) is created by extruding a 2D section perpendicular to the sketching plane, just like creating an extruded cut but without removing any material. This type of cross section is valuable for opening up the part to display several features with a single cross section (Fig. J).

Restrictions on the Offset Cross Section:

- The sketched section must be an open section.
- The first and last segments of the open section must be straight lines. The cutting-plane arrows displayed in a drawing will be perpendicular to these end segments.
- Circular and spline cross-section geometry will create unmodifiable horizontal crosshatching.
- In drawing, cross-section edges will always appear wherever the plane of the cross section is not parallel or perpendicular to the screen (Fig. K).

To Create an Offset Cross Section:

1. Choose **X-section** from the PART or ASSEM SETUP menu and **Create** from the XSEC ENTER menu.
2. Choose **Offset** and **One Side** or **Both Sides** from the XSEC CREATE menu, and then **Done.**
3. Enter a name for the cross section.
4. Answer the prompts for entering Sketcher. The sketching plane can be created using the **Make Datum** option.
5. Sketch the cross section and dimension it to the model. Choose **Done** when the section has been regenerated successfully.

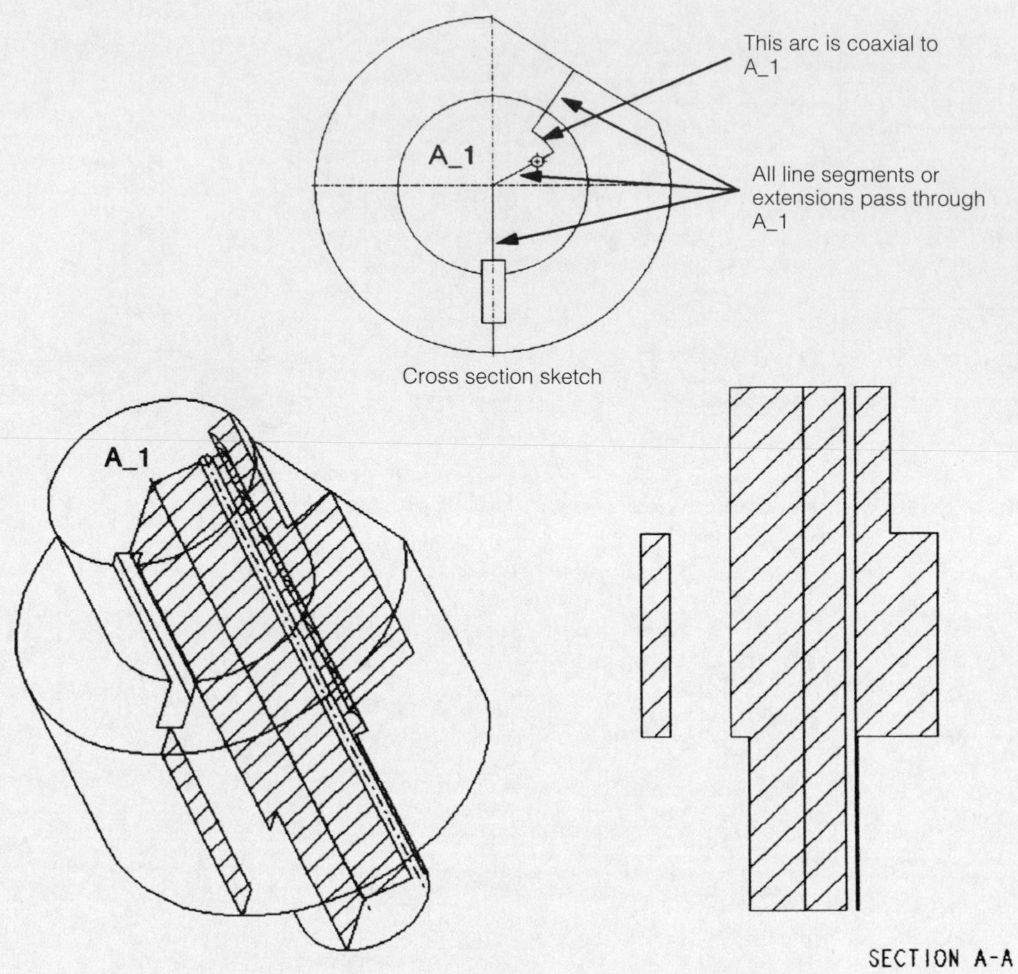

FIGURE J Aligned Offset Cross Section

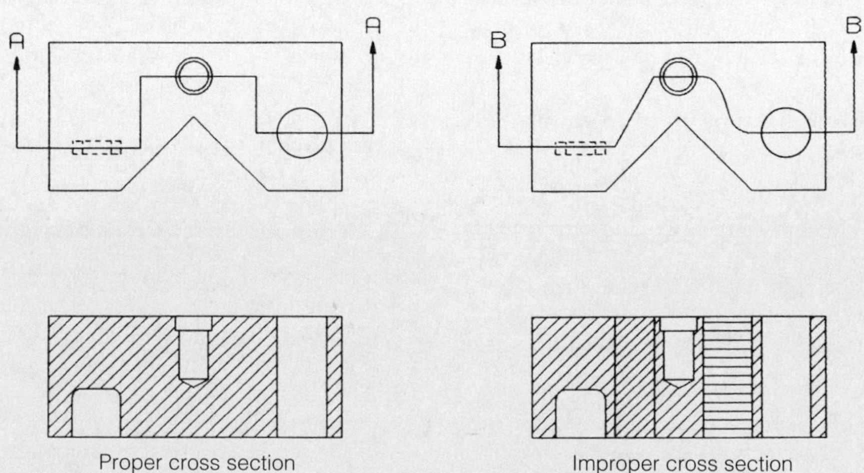

FIGURE K Correct and Incorrect Representations of a Cross Section

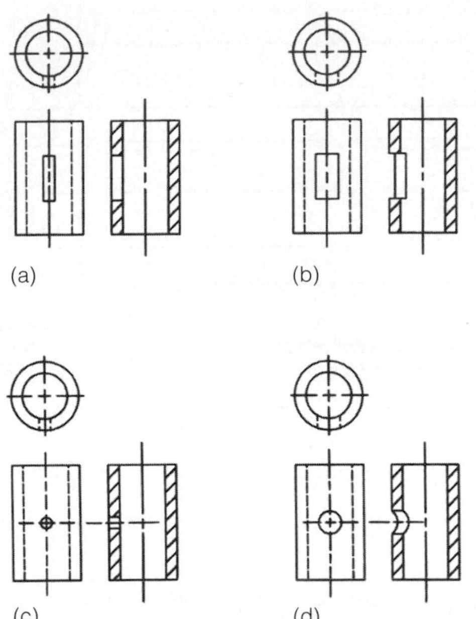

FIGURE 11.41 Intersections in Section. (a) and (c) show a small intersection; (b) and (d) show more pronounced intersecting features, which are projected true.

dicular or cuts across these features, the section view is section lined in the usual manner.

When a section is drawn through an intersection in which the true projection of the intersection is small, the true line of intersection is disregarded [Fig. 11.41(a) and (c)]. More pronounced intersecting features are projected true [Fig. 11.41(b)] or approximated by arcs [Fig. 11.41(d)].

11.3.10 Breaks and Sectioning

Conventional breaks shorten a view of an elongated part (Fig. 11.42) and in broken-out sections. The type of break representation is determined by the material and the shape of the part. Solid and tubular rounds are shown in Figure 11.42(a) and (b), respectively. The break can be drawn with the aid of an ellipse template or constructed manually. In industry, because they are time-consuming and therefore costly, such representations are never constructed via precise methods.

Tubular shapes are sectioned as shown in Figure 11.42(c). Break lines for Figure 11.42(c) and (d) are drawn freehand. The break for wood is also drawn freehand, but is jagged, not smooth, as shown in Figure 11.42(e).

You May Complete Exercises 11.5 Through 11.8 at This Time

11.4 ASSEMBLY DRAWINGS AND SECTIONING

Assembly sections show two or more mating parts in section (Figs. 11.43 and 11.44). General-purpose section lines are normally used on assembly drawings. When several adjacent parts are shown in a section view, the parts are sectioned as shown in the industrial example in Figure 11.43. Here the fixture has its two major parts sectioned with the general-purpose sectioning symbol. Because the piece to be machined is not really a portion of this fixture, it is shown in phantom lines and is not sectioned.

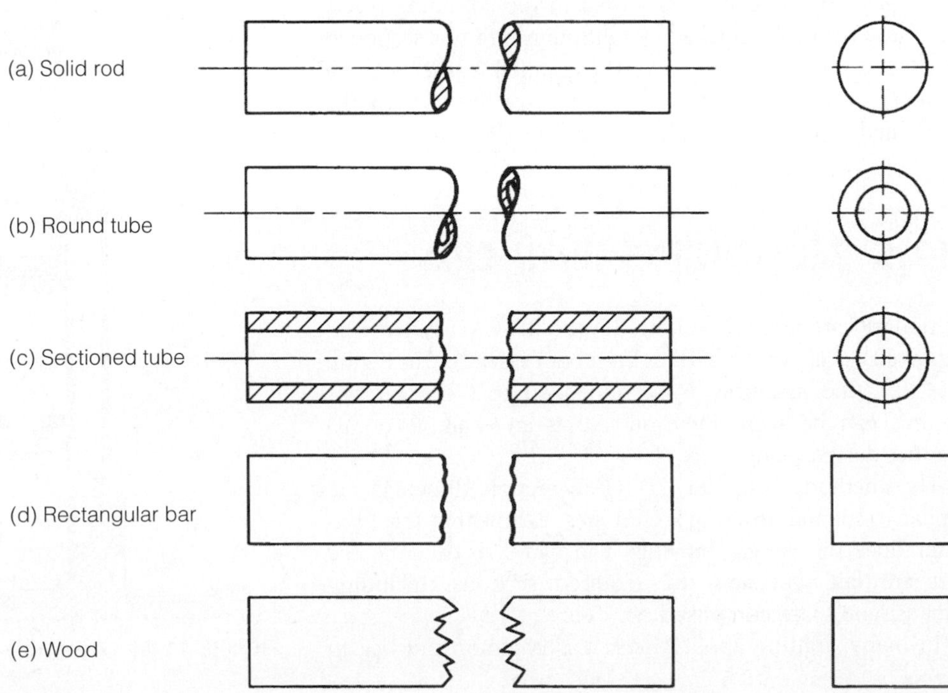

FIGURE 11.42 Conventional Representation of Breaks in Elongated Parts

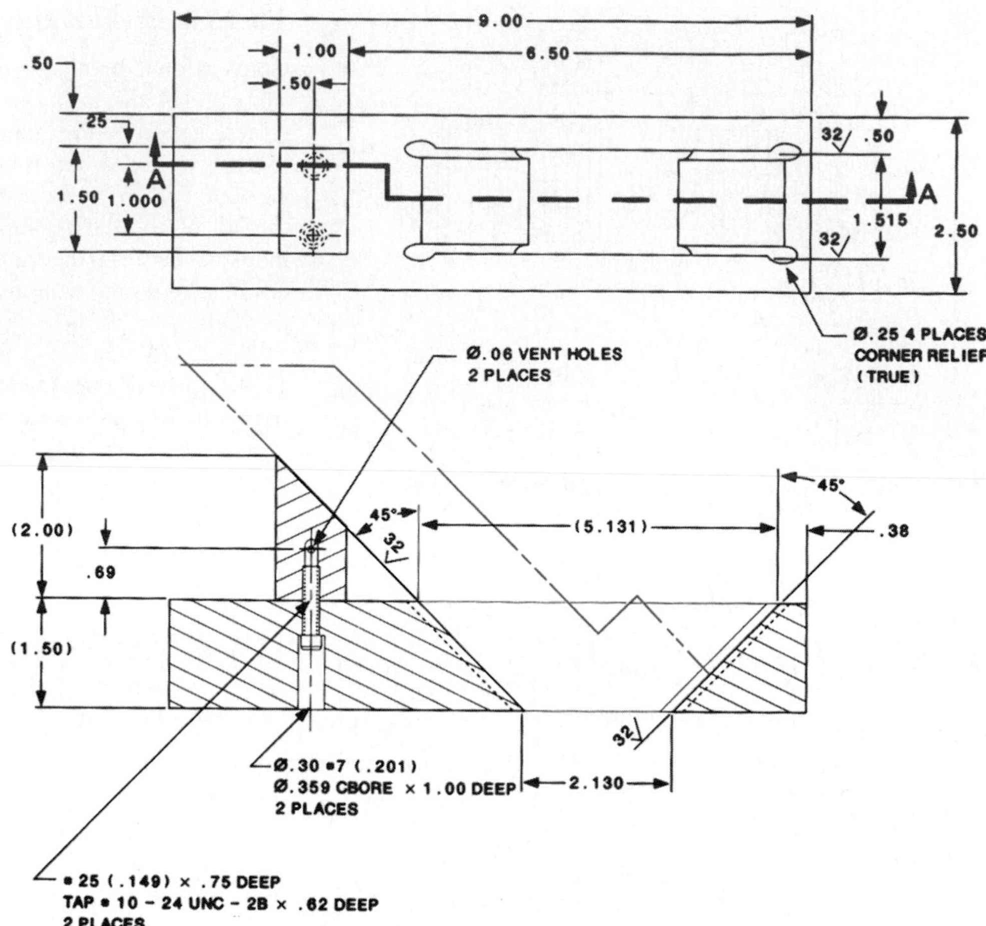

FIGURE 11.43 Assembly of Fixture with a Full Front Section View

Figure 11.44 shows the jack assembly as a front section. Each individual piece of the assembly has section lines running in different directions than in the adjoining piece. The threaded pieces and other solid items are not sectioned per the sectioning conventions explained earlier in the chapter. Symbolic section lines are also used in this example. (Sectioned assemblies are also covered in Chapter 23.)

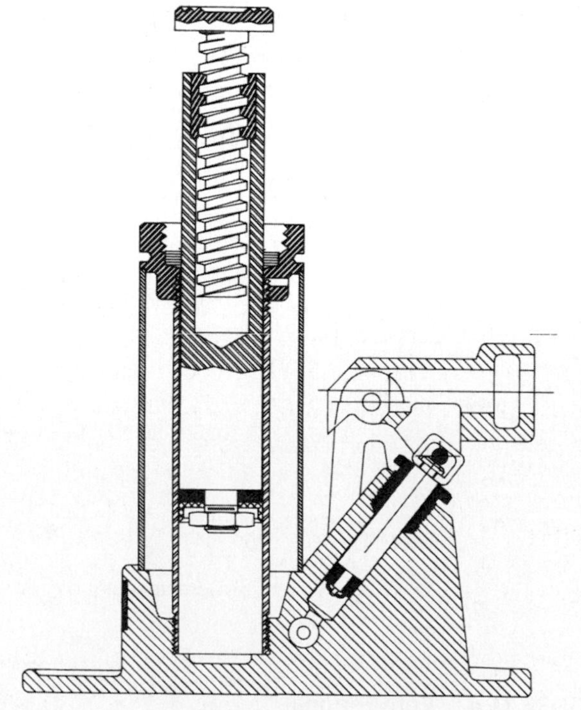

FIGURE 11.44 Assembly Section

11.5 SECTIONING WITH CAD

Sectioning can be done on both 3D and 2D CAD systems. In Figure 11.45(a) we see a 3D solid model assembly. In Figure 11.45(b), the assembly is sectioned so that the interior features can be seen. Figure 11.46 is an example of 3D product design using CAD.

The methods used for 2D CAD section drawings are similar to manual drafting techniques, except that the computer does the actual drawing. The views to describe the part are laid out and the required sections, including dimensioning, are completed.

In many drafting applications, it is common practice to

(a) Solid model of an assembly

FIGURE 11.46 An Assembly Shown on a CAD System

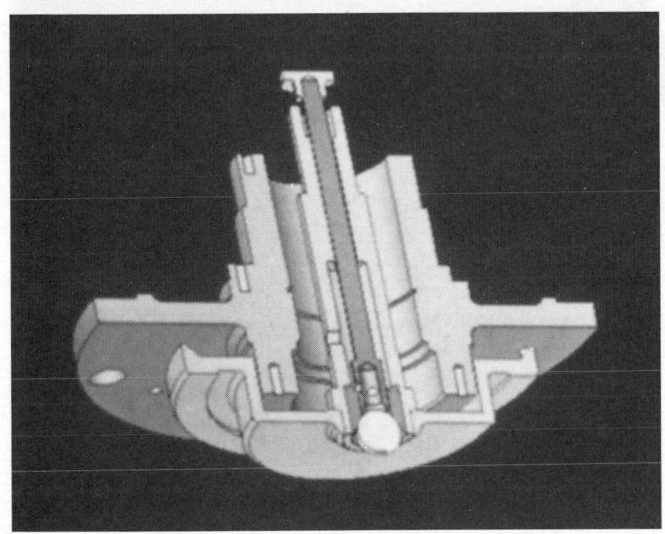

(b) Sectioned solid model of an assembly

FIGURE 11.45 Solid Modeling and Sections

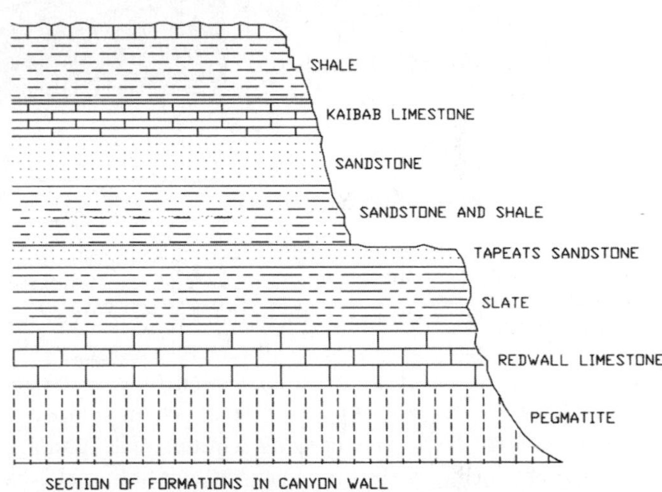

FIGURE 11.47 Section Formations in Canyon Wall Using Hatch Patterns to Represent the Types of Rock and Mineral Layers of Stratification

fill an area with a pattern. The pattern can help differentiate between components of a 3D part, can define an area of a part that has been sectioned, or can identify the material that composes a part (Fig. 11.47). Filling an area with a pattern is called crosshatching, hatching, or pattern filling, and it can be accomplished using a **HATCH** command.

CAD systems provide a library of standard ANSI hatch patterns. You can hatch with one of these standard patterns, with a custom pattern from your own library, or with a simple pattern defined during the command. On most systems the screen or tablet menu normally has a variety of hatch patterns available for immediate insertion (Fig. 11.48). For example, AutoCAD has more than forty predefined patterns that can be identified through the **HATCH** command (Fig. 11.48). AutoCAD's pulldown menus and dialog boxes will graphically display the hatch patterns and allow you to select visually the hatch pattern for your application. Hatch patterns can be modified before insertion.

11.5.1 Hatch Patterns on CAD Systems

Each hatch pattern is composed of one or more hatch lines or figures at specified angles and spacing. The pattern you insert is repeated or clipped, as necessary, to fill exactly the area being hatched.

Hatching generates line entities for the chosen pattern and adds them to the drawing. Hatched areas are blocks or groups. This means that the CAD system treats the group of section lines as a unit. Therefore, if you have hatched an area but then decide you do not like the hatching, you can select any individual line of the pattern with the **ERASE** command and the hatching will be removed.

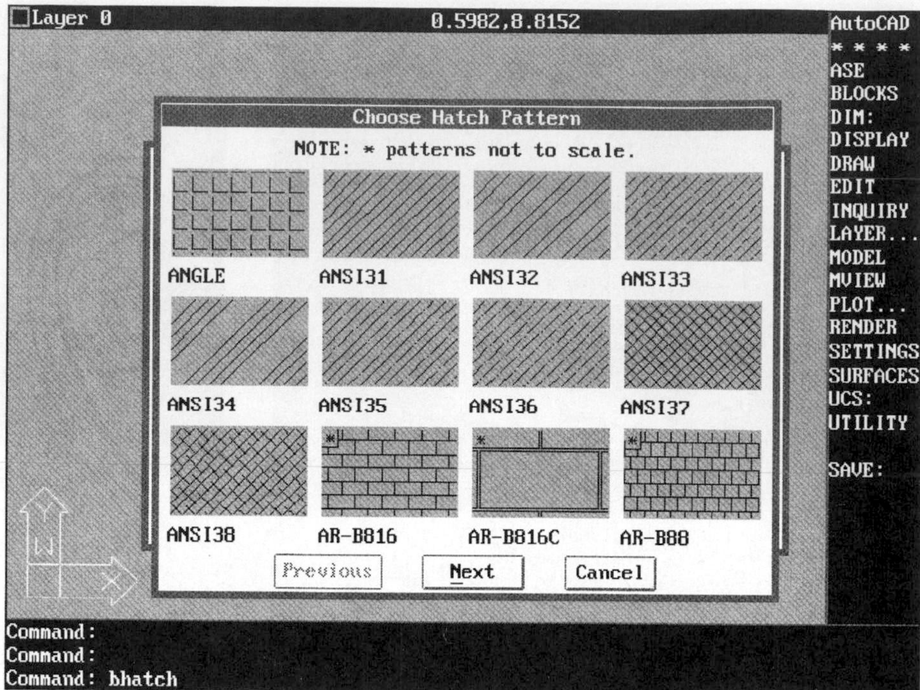

FIGURE 11.48 AutoCAD Hatch Pattern Dialog Box

11.5.2 Defining the Boundary Using CAD

Hatching fills in an area of the drawing enclosed by a boundary made from lines, arcs, circles, splines, polylines, or other geometric entities. When hatching an area, the entities that define the boundary must be selected (normally in sequence). The entities forming the hatching boundary should intersect. If your system requires that the endpoints of the entities meet, overhanging entities will produce incorrect hatching and hatching may spill out of the selected boundary area. Some systems allow for entities to cross, and some even hatch areas not completely enclosed by boundaries, although on most systems you must define a closed nonintersecting envelope of geometry.

Figure 11.49 illustrates the hatching of a section of a part using AutoCAD. After the hatching command is given, the boundaries of the area to be hatched are successively indicated by picking each entity, in this case D1 through D5. The following command illustrates the procedure. Enter the **HATCH** command from the **DRAW** pull-down menu and use the following steps:

`Command:` **HATCH**
`Pattern (? or name/U, style):` Pick the desired hatch pattern (ANS131 was used here)
`Scale for Pattern:` Press the *Enter* key to accept full scale
`Angle for Pattern <a>:` Select angle, or use default by pressing the *Enter* key (ANS131 uses 45°)
`Select Objects:` **D1 D2 D3 D4 D5** (select the outline border)

Hatching patterns are varied by specifying the angle of the hatching and the spacing, as in Figure 11.50. Figure 11.51 shows two concentric circles: The outer circle was picked first, and then the inner circle was picked. The resulting hatch filled a doughnut-shaped area on the part. Because default values were used, the pattern was a series of lines with a predetermined angle and spacing. The system inserted hatch-

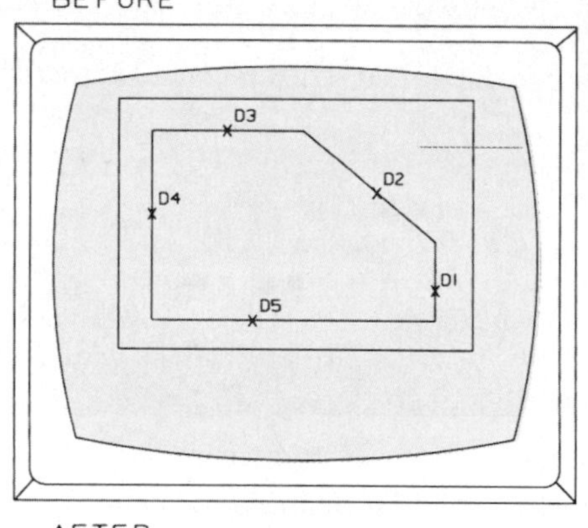

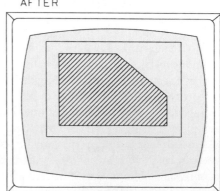

FIGURE 11.49 Defining Hatch Boundary

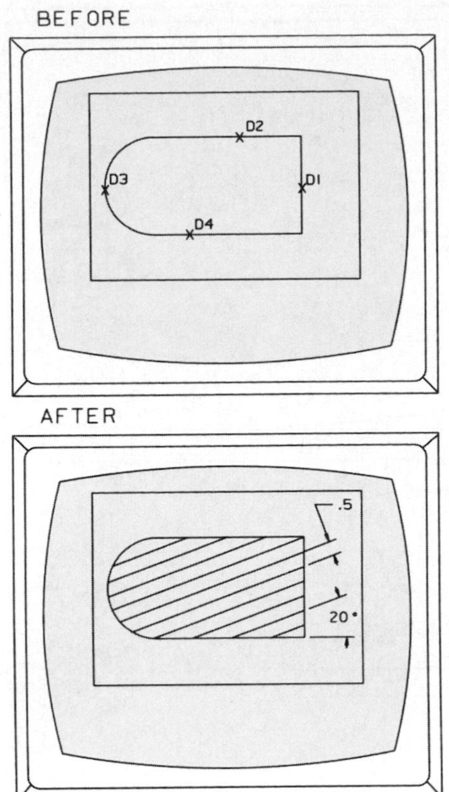

FIGURE 11.50 Altering Hatching Default Settings

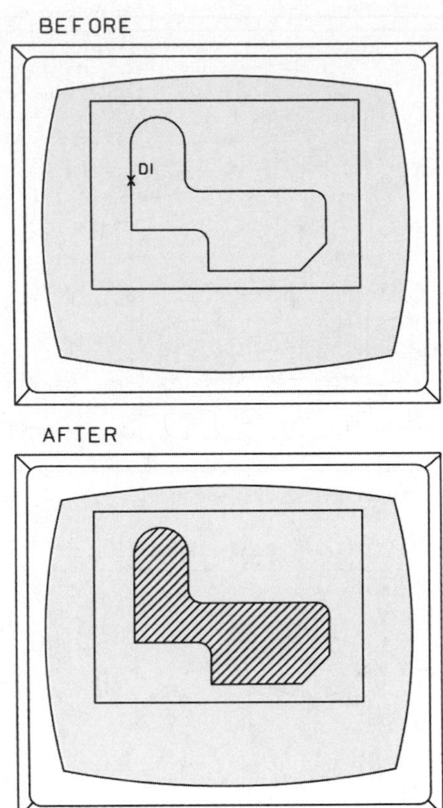

FIGURE 11.52 Using CHAIN Modifier on Personal Designer CAD Software

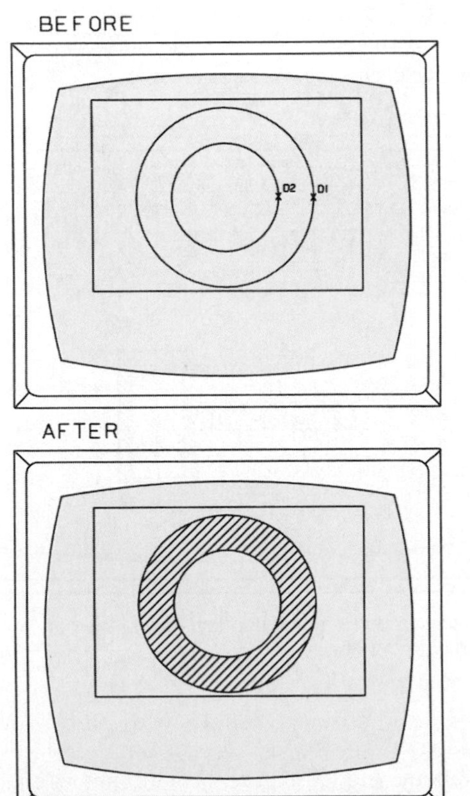

FIGURE 11.51 Hatching Interior and Exterior Areas

ing inward, starting at the boundary of the first (outer) circle. When an internal entity is encountered, the hatching turns off until another entity is encountered (each item must be picked in the command). AutoCAD has an option called **OUTERMOST,** which hatches from an outside boundary to the first interior boundary it encounters.

Some systems (though not AutoCAD) have a **CHAIN** capability. **CHAIN** is normally used with a command to select a series of connected entities quickly. The **CHAIN** modifier ties all entities that touch into a single, temporary unit. The area to be hatched is identified by entering the **CHAIN** modifier and then simply selecting one entity on the boundary. The area enclosed (linked) by the chain is then quickly hatched (Fig. 11.52).

By creating a boundary with a string or a **polyline,** you can hatch an area by simply picking the entity. The system uses the polyline or string as the outer boundary for the hatch pattern.

11.5.3 Sectioning with 3D CAD

Because the section can be an actual 3D slice through the part at a selected level or along a defined plane, the 3D process is different. In Figure 11.53(a), a 3D model of the part is shown in two orientations. Unlike a 2D section, which is confined to its views on the drawing, the 3D model

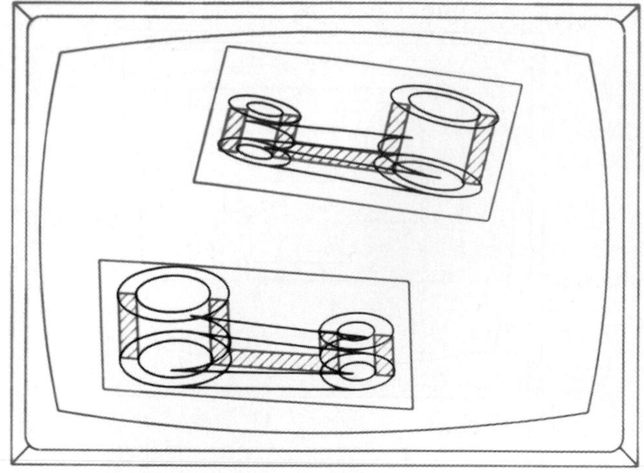
(a) Two-view orientations of 3D model

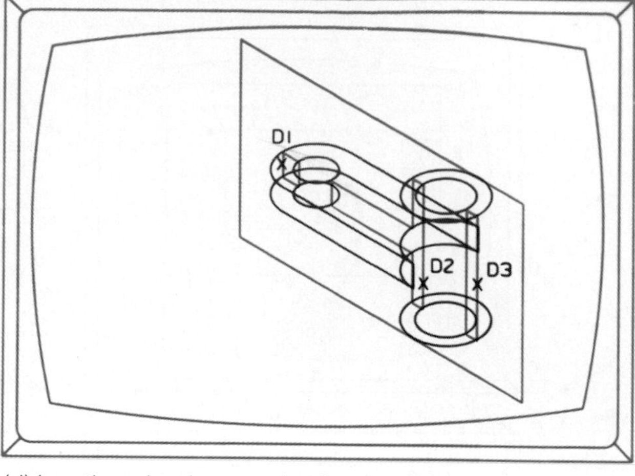

(d) Inserting a hatch pattern in 3D

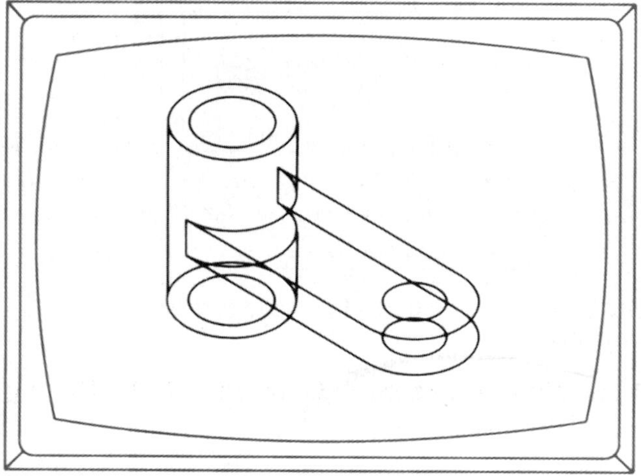
(b) Wireframe model

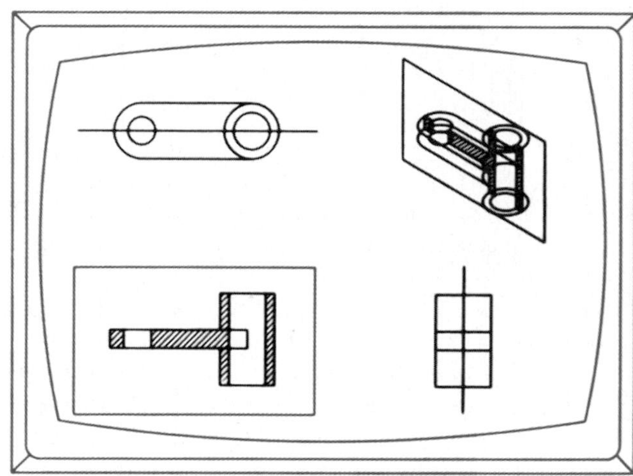
(e) Cut-plane, orthographic section views

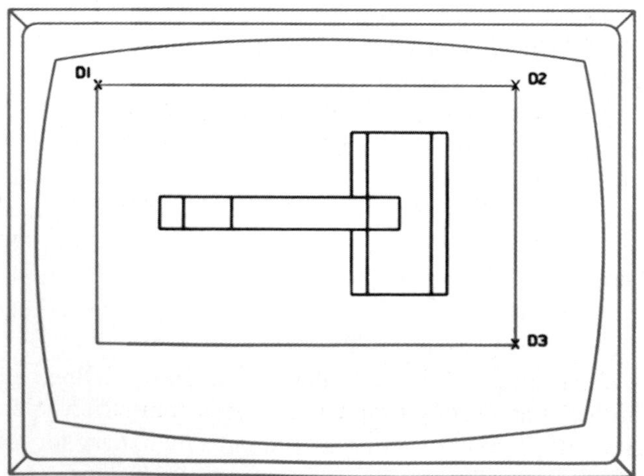

(c) Intersecting the model with a plane

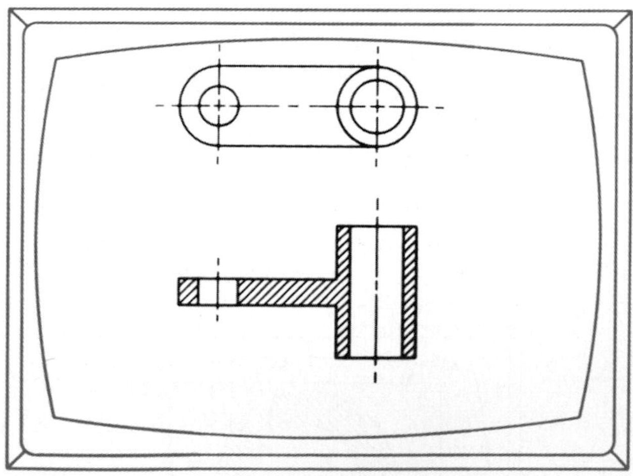
(f) Displaying front section and top view of the part with correct visibility

FIGURE 11.53 **Creating Sections with a 3D CAD System**

can be displayed in multiple viewports, rotated, and viewed from any angle.

In Figure 11.53(b), a rotated view of the 3D part is shown as a wireframe model. Figure 11.53(c) shows the part in a front view; a plane has been established lengthwise along its center. A **CUT PLANE** (or **INTERSECT SURFACE**) com-

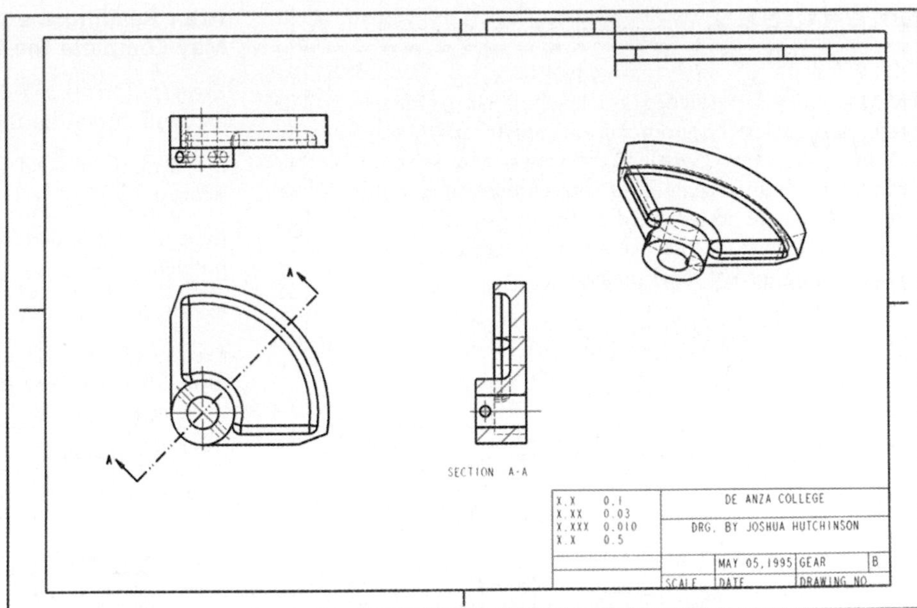

FIGURE 11.54 Part Displayed in Drawing with Section View

mand is used to section the model by selecting the plane (**D1**, **D2**, and **D3**) and then identifying the surfaces to be intersected. The rotated model is shown in Figure 11.53(d). Here, the cut lines are shown along with the plane used in the command. Figure 11.53(e) shows the section and the hatch pattern in the three standard views and in a rotated pictorial view. In Figure 11.53(f), the part is placed in the standard top view and front view orientations, the cutting plane is removed, and the drawing displayed according to ANSI projection standards. Centerlines are also added. The result looks basically the same when using 2D or 3D CAD or when drawn manually. However, with 3D CAD the section and model can be rotated to other positions. (The part in Figure 11.53 was designed and sectioned using Computervision's Personal Designer System.)

Figure 11.54 shows a part created as a parametric model, displayed in appropiate views and sectioned using a system command.

You May Complete Exercises 11.9 Through 11.12 at This Time

QUIZ

True or False

1. Sections describe the exterior of a part so that fewer views are required.
2. Sections and views are always rotated 90° as projections from existing views.
3. It is conventional practice to show all hidden lines that fall behind the cutting plane.
4. The cutting-plane arrows are always pointing in the direction of sight.
5. Section lines should be drawn thick, black, and close together so as to be readily seen and identified.
6. Material-specific hatching symbols are used on all drawings.
7. The placement of dimensions within sectioned areas is a common and accepted practice.
8. Intersections in sections always show the true projection of the elements.

Fill in the Blanks

9. A section is an ________ cut taken through an ________ .
10. Section lining on assembly drawings should be drawn at ________ angles for each ________ .
11. A ________ taken through an existing ________ view should be avoided.
12. Section lettering for identification of sections and views should be used in ________ ________ .
13. Thin sections are always shown ________ .
14. ________ , ________ , ________ , and ________ are usually not shown sectioned.
15. The ________ symbol is used on most sectional drawings.
16. On simple parts or where the section location is obvious, it is common practice to ________ the ________ ________ ________ .

Answer the Following

17. What is the difference between a removed section and a revolved section?
18. When is a broken-out section likely to be used?
19. What are hatch patterns, and how are they used with a CAD system?
20. Describe the difference between a full section, a half section, and an external view.
21. What is an offset section, and when is it used?
22. What type of part features are rotated in aligned sections?
23. What is a cutting plane?
24. Name and describe three conventional practices used on sections.

EXERCISES

Exercises may be assigned as sketching, instrument, or CAD projects. Transfer the given information to an "A"-size sheet of .25 in. grid paper. Complete all views, and solve for proper visibility, including centerlines, object lines, and hidden lines. Exercises that are not assigned by the instructor can be sketched in the text to provide practice and to enhance understanding of the preceding instructional material.

After Reading the Chapter Through Section 11.3.2 You May Complete the Following Exercises

Exercises 11.1(A) and (B) Draw the two views of the part, and do a full section for the front view.

Exercises 11.2(A) and (B) Draw three views of the part. Construct a full front section.

Exercises 11.3(A) and (B) Section the appropriate views for each problem.

Exercise 11.4(A) Draw a full left side section.

Exercise 11.4(B) Draw the two views. Construct a half section for the left side view.

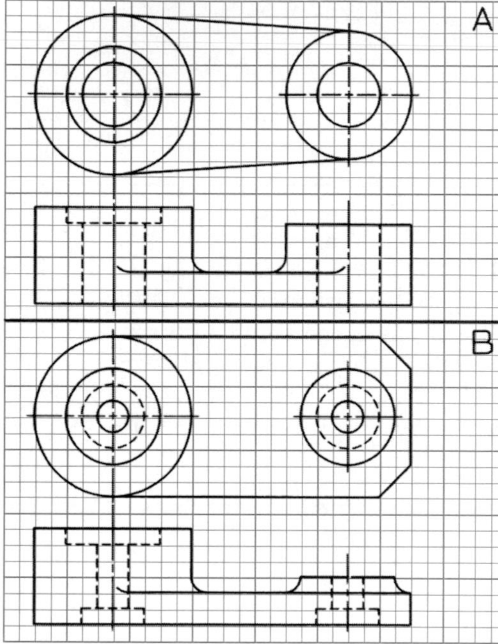

EXERCISE 11.1

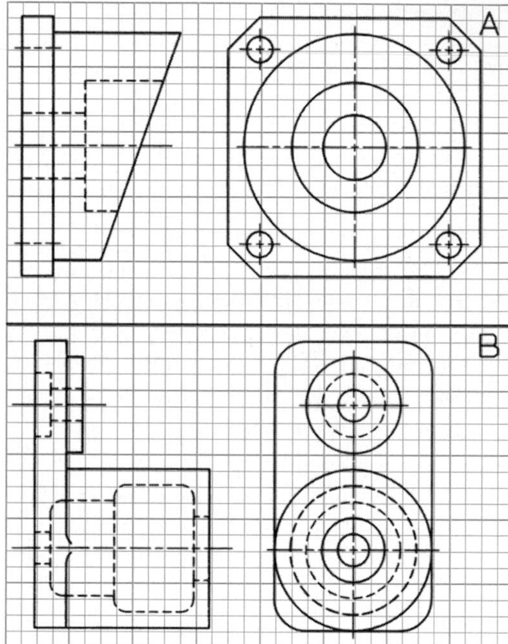

EXERCISE 11.3

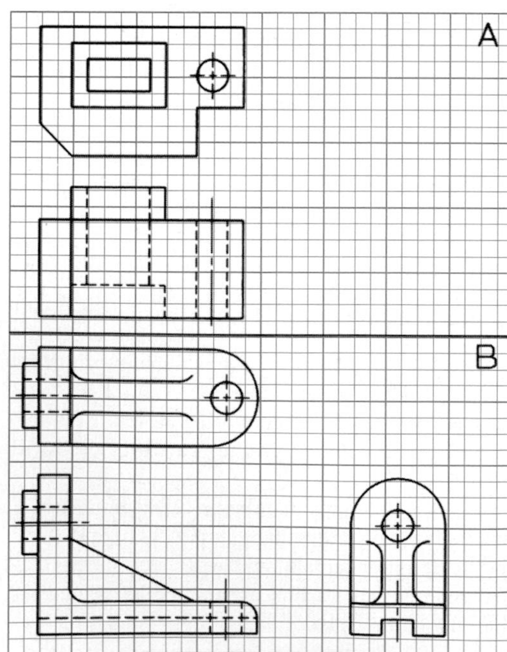

EXERCISE 11.2

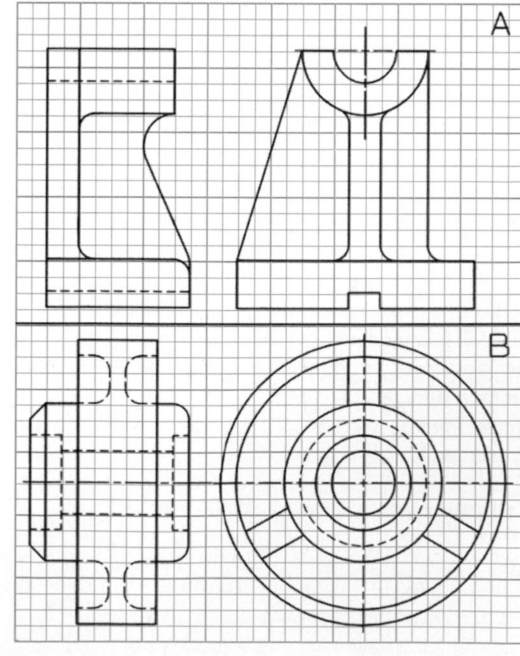

EXERCISE 11.4

After Reading the Chapter Through Section 11.3.10 You May Complete the Following Exercises

Exercises 11.5(A) and (B) Construct a full left side section view for each part.

Exercises 11.6(A) and (B) Draw half sections of the parts.

Exercises 11.7(A) and (B) Draw full sections of the parts.

Exercises 11.8(A) and (B) Draw half sections of the parts.

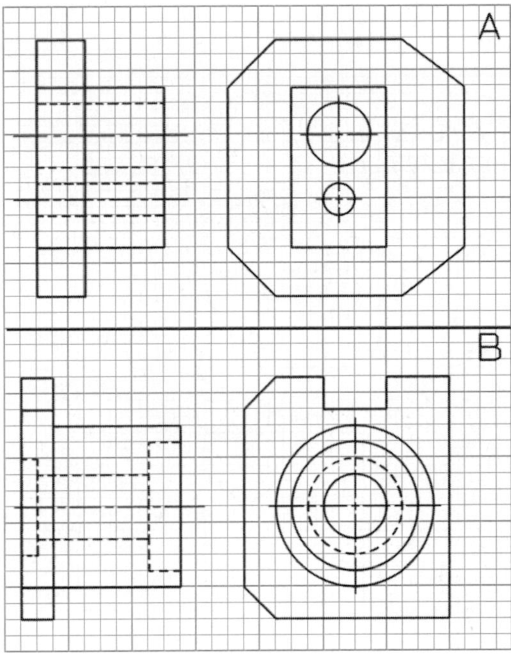

EXERCISE 11.5

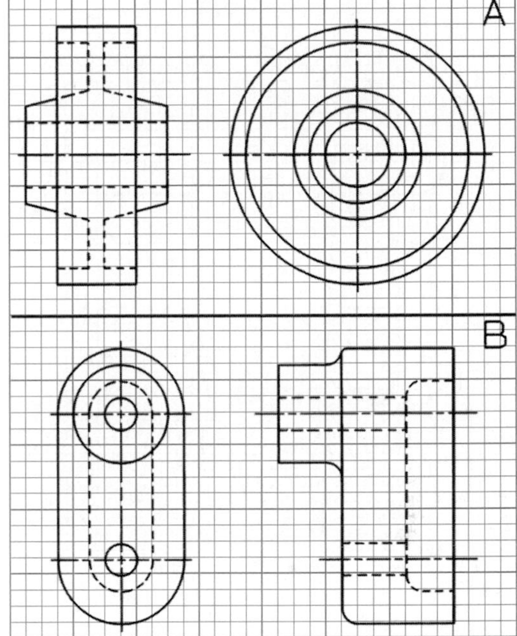

EXERCISE 11.7

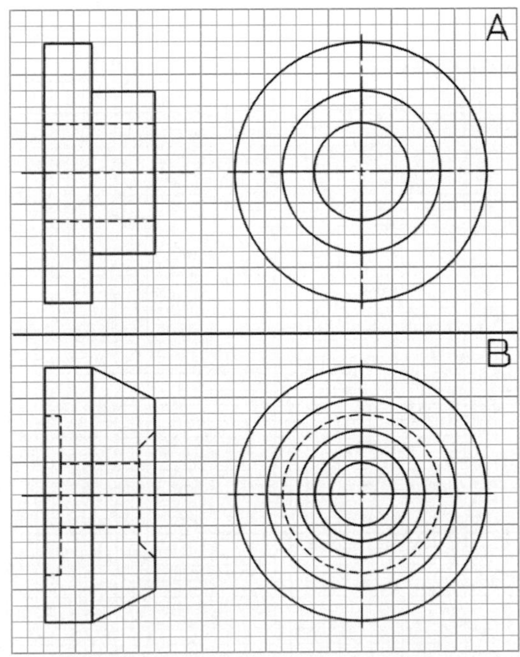

EXERCISE 11.6

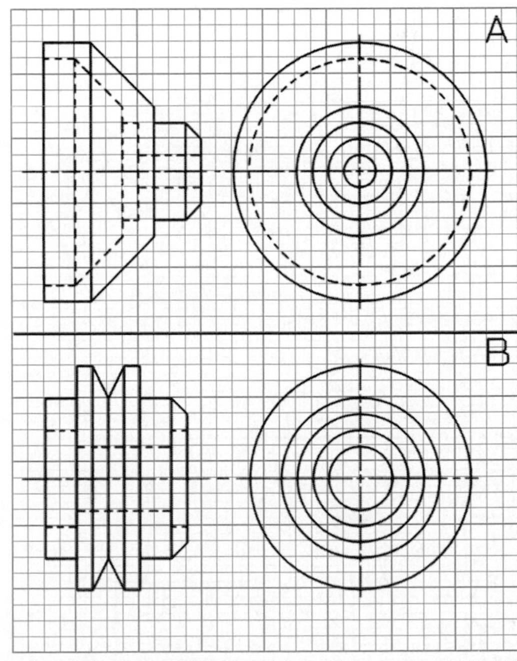

EXERCISE 11.8

After Reading the Chapter Through Section 11.5.3 You May Complete the Following Exercises

Exercise 11.9 Section the right side view of the part.

Exercise 11.10 Section the whole part in the right side view, and construct a partial (broken-out) section, as required, for the hub in the front view (left). The right side view is an aligned view.

Exercise 11.11 Draw an offset section of the part. Pass the cutting plane through the two holes and the slot.

Exercise 11.12 Draw a complete full section of the assembly.

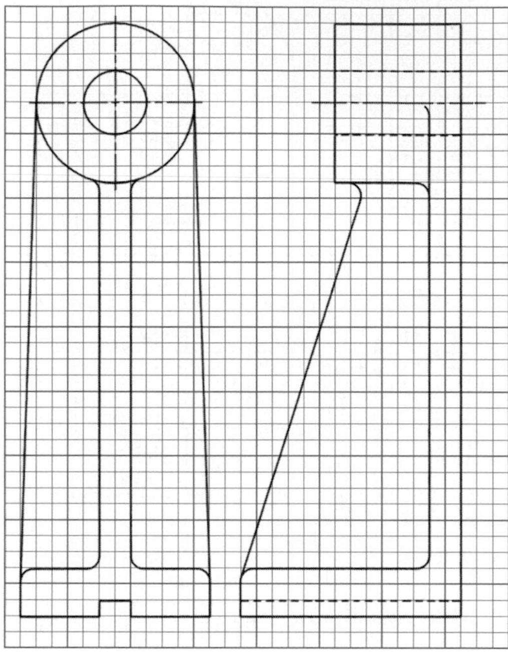

EXERCISE 11.9

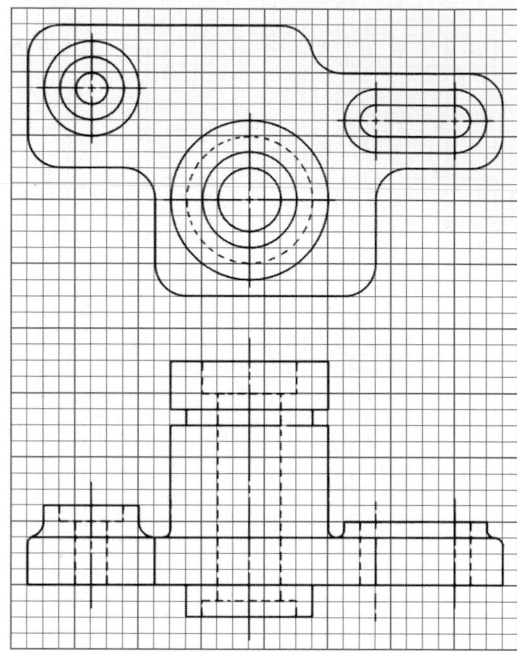

EXERCISE 11.11

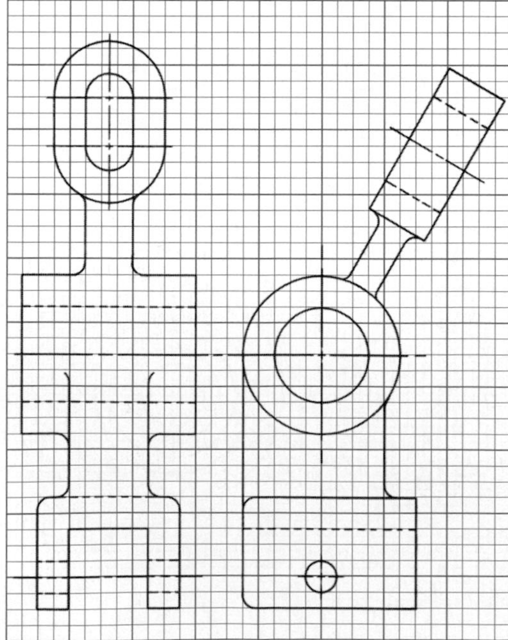

EXERCISE 11.10

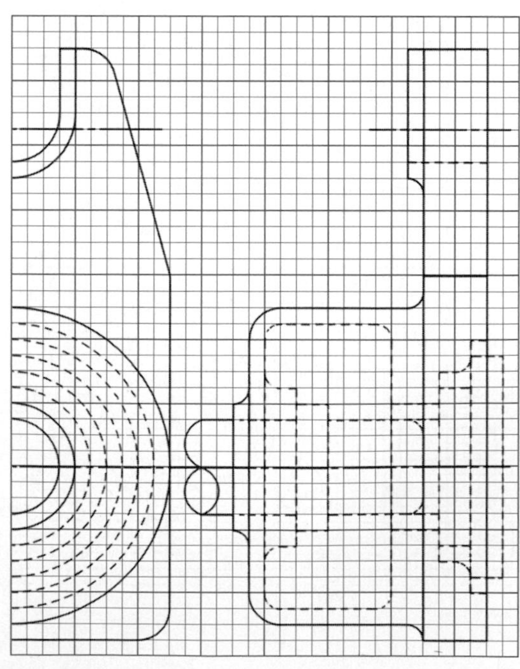

EXERCISE 11.12

PROBLEMS

To use these same projects for dimensioning after covering Chapter 15, allow enough space between views and select an appropriate-size sheet of paper when completing these problems. Complete all views, and solve for proper visibility, including centerlines, object lines, and hidden lines. Do *not* dimension any of the following problems until you complete Chapter 15 or are requested to do so by your instructor.

Problems 11.1(A) Through (K) Using the scales provided, draw and section the appropriate views. Problems can be either metric, fraction-inch, or decimal-inch units. One, two, or three views may be required for a particular problem.

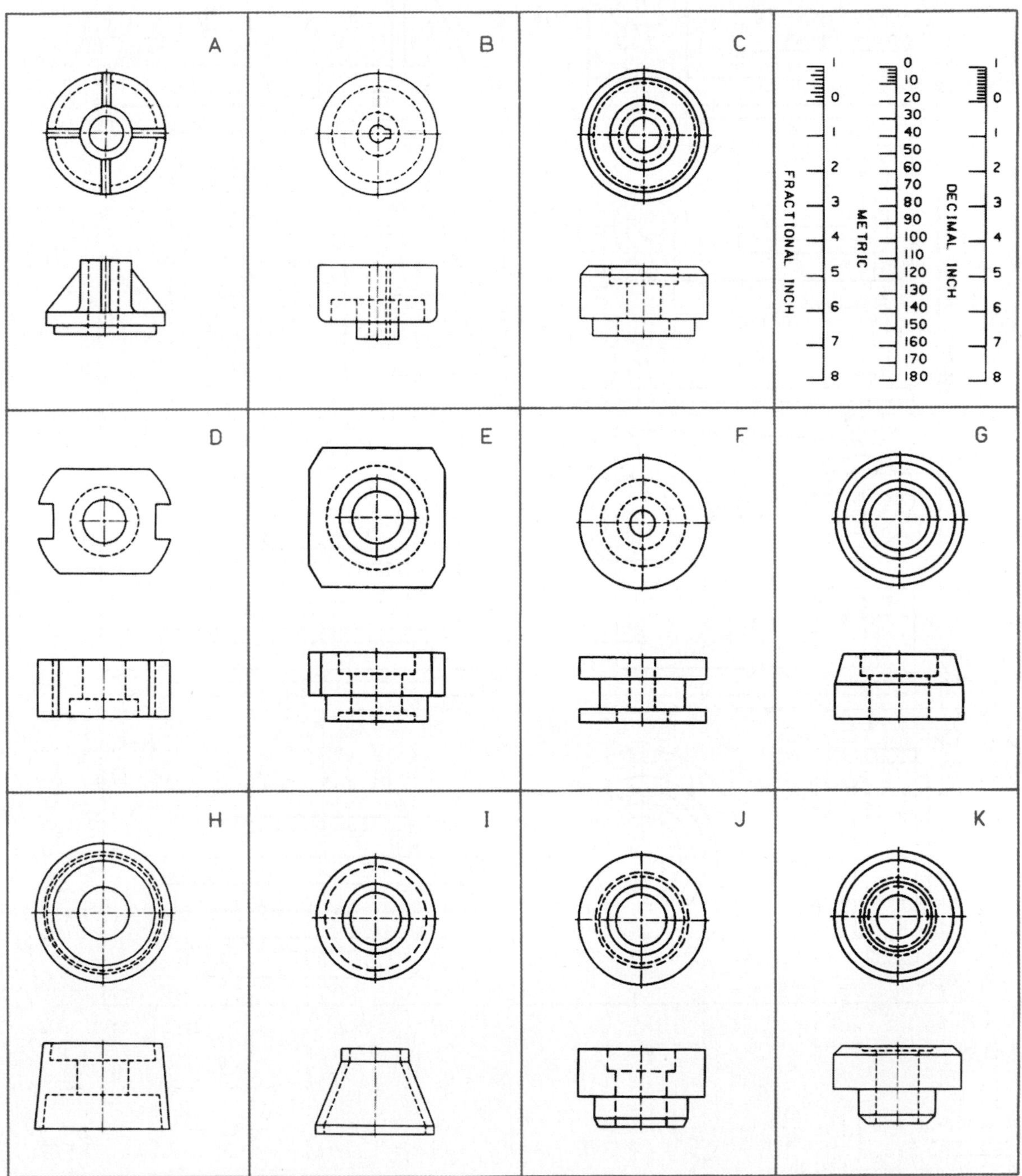

PROBLEM 11.1

Problems 11.2(A) Through (H) Same as Problem 11.1.

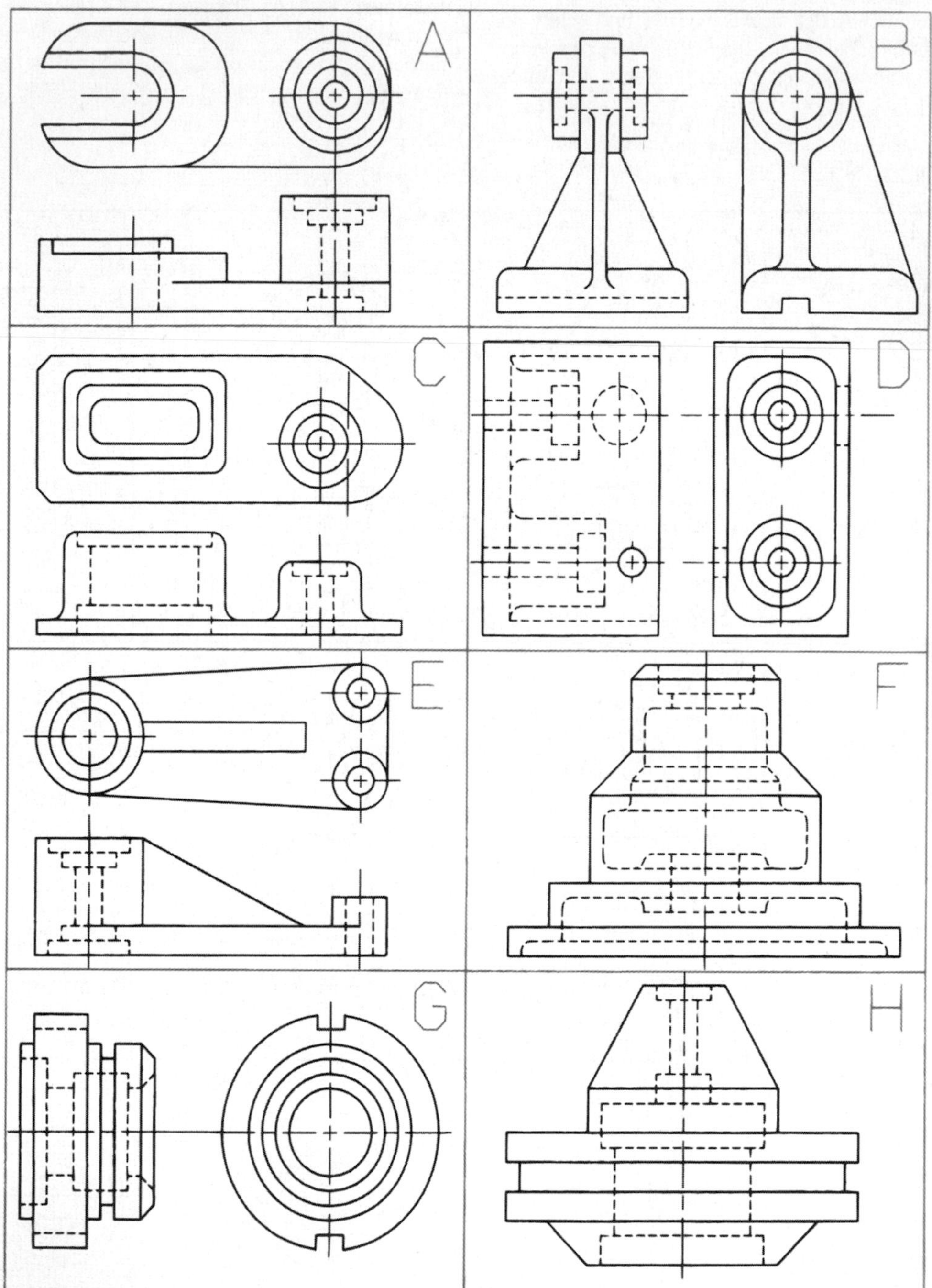

PROBLEM 11.2

Problems 11.3 Through 11.18 Establish the views and sections required to describe the parts properly. Do not dimension the parts. Use half sections, broken-out sections, aligned sections, and revolved sections where useful to describe the part. Complete all views, and add centerlines, hidden lines, and correct visibility for each problem.

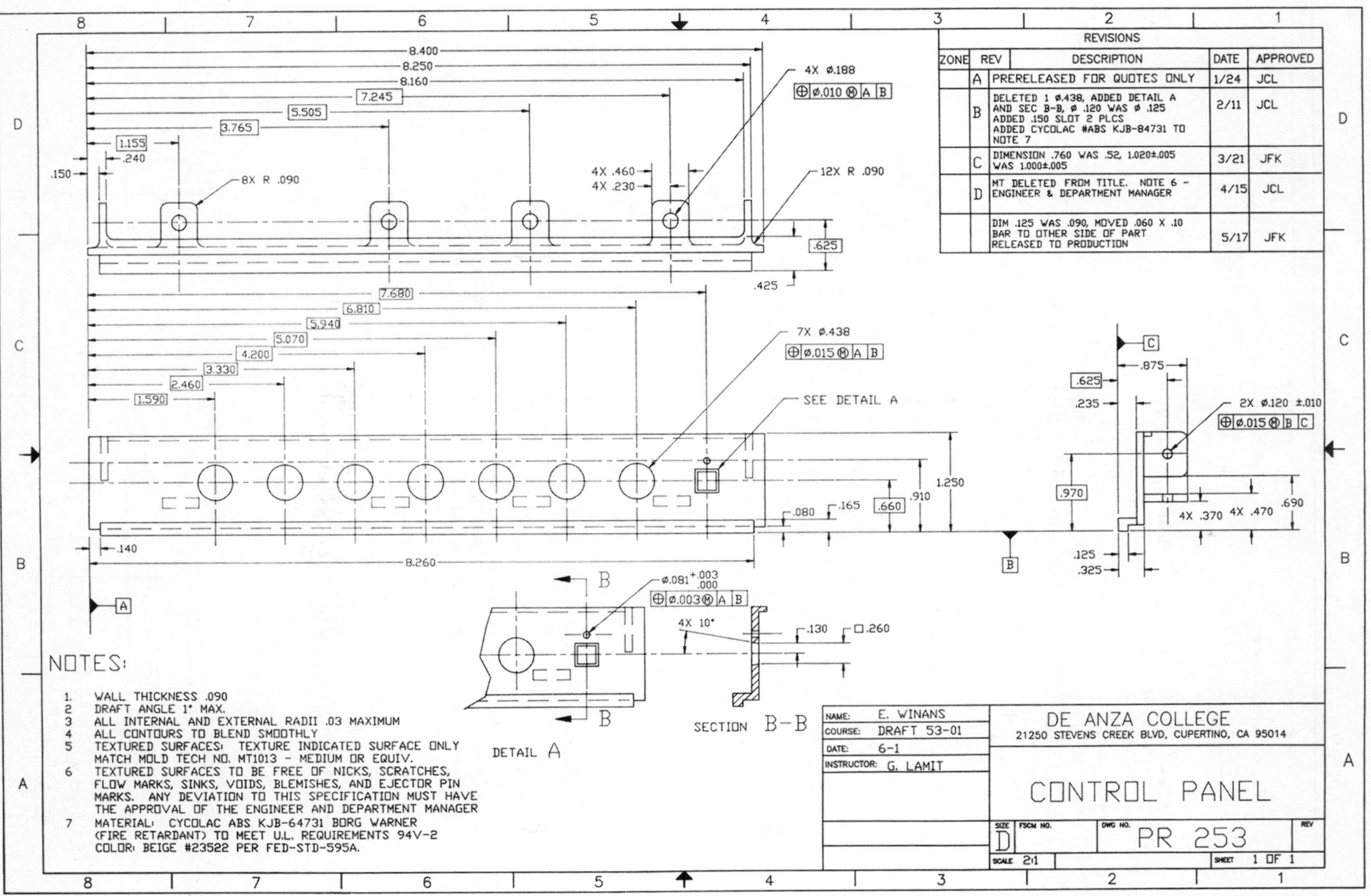
REVISIONS
ZONE | REV | DESCRIPTION | DATE | APPROVED
A | PRERELEASED FOR QUOTES ONLY | 1/24 | JCL
B | DELETED 1 Ø.438, ADDED DETAIL A AND SEC B-B, Ø .120 WAS Ø .125 ADDED .150 SLOT 2 PLCS ADDED CYCOLAC #ABS KJB-84731 TO NOTE 7 | 2/11 | JCL
C | DIMENSION .760 WAS .52, 1.020±.005 WAS 1.000±.005 | 3/21 | JFK
D | MT DELETED FROM TITLE. NOTE 6 - ENGINEER & DEPARTMENT MANAGER | 4/15 | JCL
DIM .125 WAS .090, MOVED .060 X .10 BAR TO OTHER SIDE OF PART RELEASED TO PRODUCTION | 5/17 | JFK
4X Ø.188
8X R .090
12X R .090
7X Ø.438
SEE DETAIL A
2X Ø.120 ±.010
DETAIL A
SECTION B-B
NOTES:
1. WALL THICKNESS .090
2 DRAFT ANGLE 1° MAX.
3 ALL INTERNAL AND EXTERNAL RADII .03 MAXIMUM
4 ALL CONTOURS TO BLEND SMOOTHLY
5 TEXTURED SURFACES: TEXTURE INDICATED SURFACE ONLY MATCH MOLD TECH NO. MT1013 - MEDIUM OR EQUIV.
6 TEXTURED SURFACES TO BE FREE OF NICKS, SCRATCHES, FLOW MARKS, SINKS, VOIDS, BLEMISHES, AND EJECTOR PIN MARKS. ANY DEVIATION TO THIS SPECIFICATION MUST HAVE THE APPROVAL OF THE ENGINEER AND DEPARTMENT MANAGER
7 MATERIAL: CYCOLAC ABS KJB-64731 BORG WARNER (FIRE RETARDANT) TO MEET U.L. REQUIREMENTS 94V-2 COLOR: BEIGE #23522 PER FED-STD-595A.
NAME: E. WINANS
COURSE: DRAFT 53-01
DATE: 6-1
INSTRUCTOR: G. LAMIT
DE ANZA COLLEGE
21250 STEVENS CREEK BLVD, CUPERTINO, CA 95014
CONTROL PANEL
SIZE D
DWG NO. PR 253
SCALE 2:1
SHEET 1 OF 1

PROBLEM 11.3

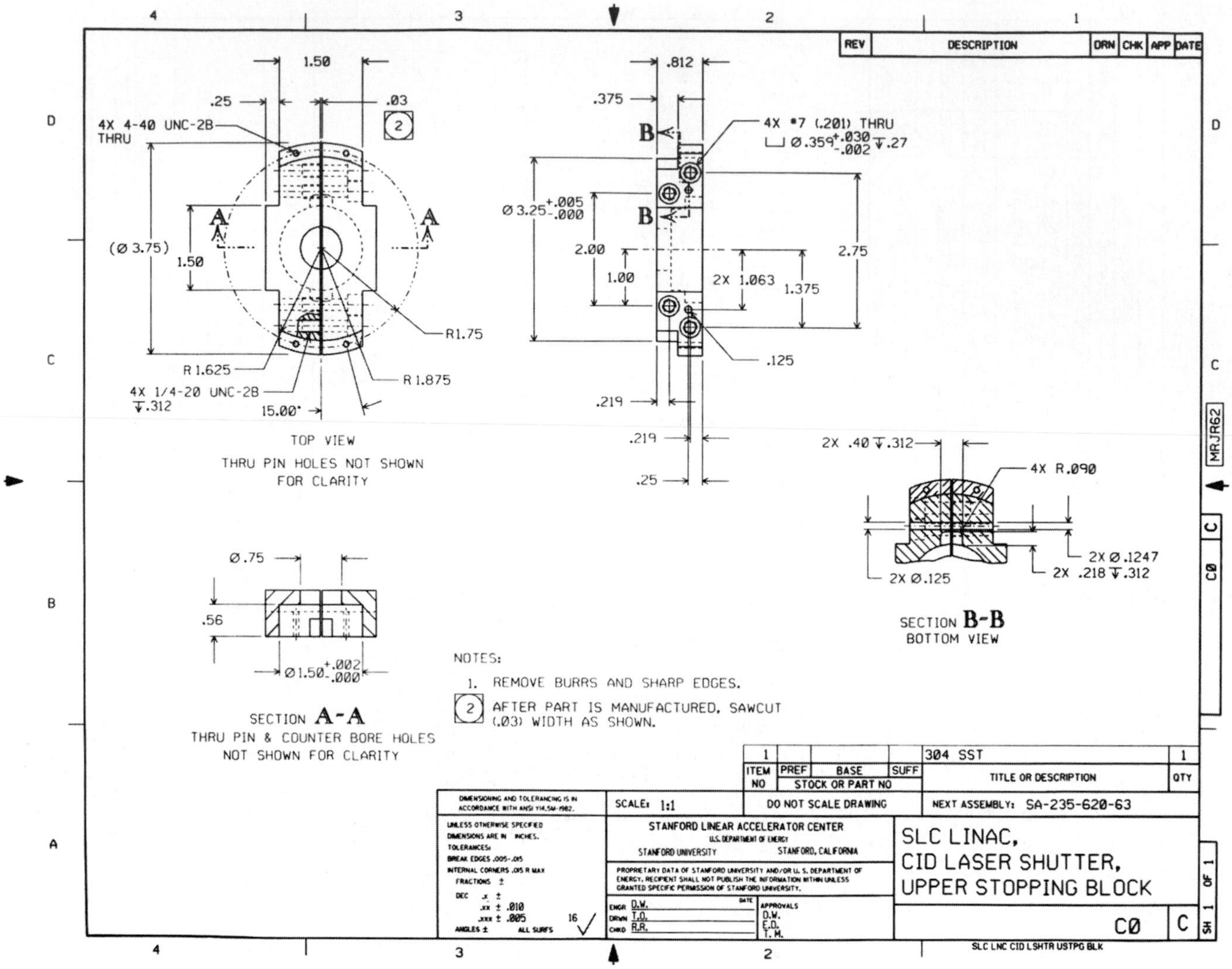

TOP VIEW
THRU PIN HOLES NOT SHOWN FOR CLARITY

SECTION **A-A**
THRU PIN & COUNTER BORE HOLES NOT SHOWN FOR CLARITY

SECTION **B-B**
BOTTOM VIEW

NOTES:

1. REMOVE BURRS AND SHARP EDGES.
2. AFTER PART IS MANUFACTURED, SAWCUT (.03) WIDTH AS SHOWN.

ITEM NO	PREF	BASE	SUFF	TITLE OR DESCRIPTION	QTY
1				304 SST	1

DIMENSIONING AND TOLERANCING IS IN ACCORDANCE WITH ANSI Y14.5M-1982.
SCALE: 1:1 DO NOT SCALE DRAWING NEXT ASSEMBLY: SA-235-620-63
STANFORD LINEAR ACCELERATOR CENTER, U.S. DEPARTMENT OF ENERGY, STANFORD UNIVERSITY, STANFORD, CALIFORNIA
SLC LINAC, CID LASER SHUTTER, UPPER STOPPING BLOCK
C0 C SH 1 OF 1
SLC LNC CID LSHTR USTPG BLK

PROBLEM 11.4

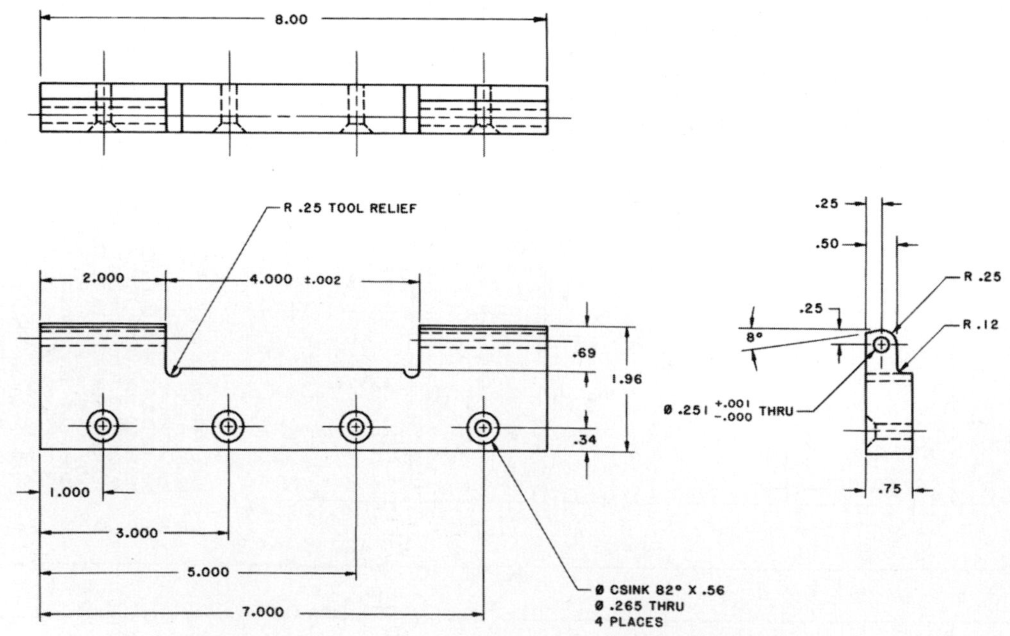

PROBLEM 11.5

PROBLEM 11.6

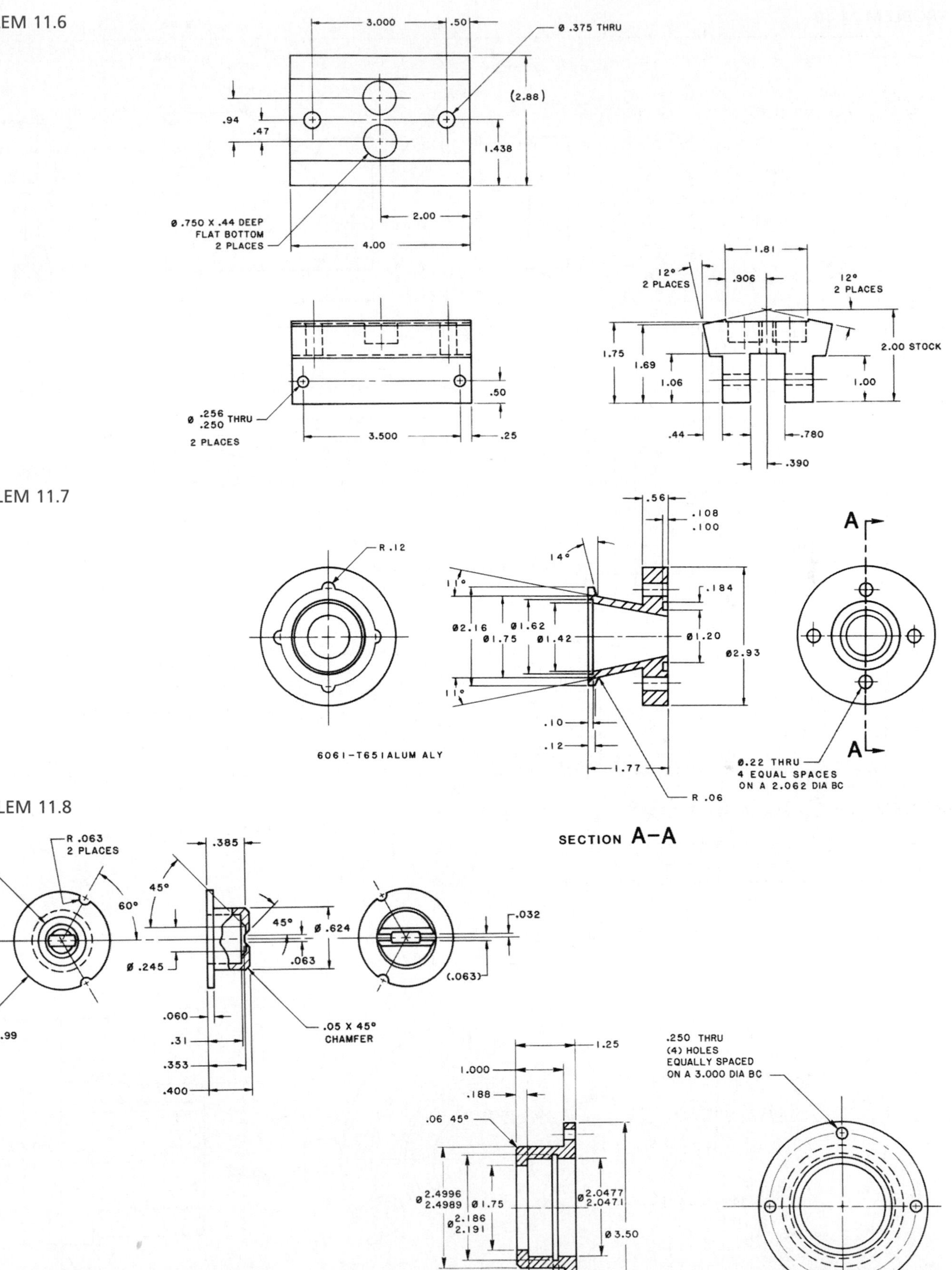

PROBLEM 11.7

PROBLEM 11.8

PROBLEM 11.9

PROBLEM 11.10

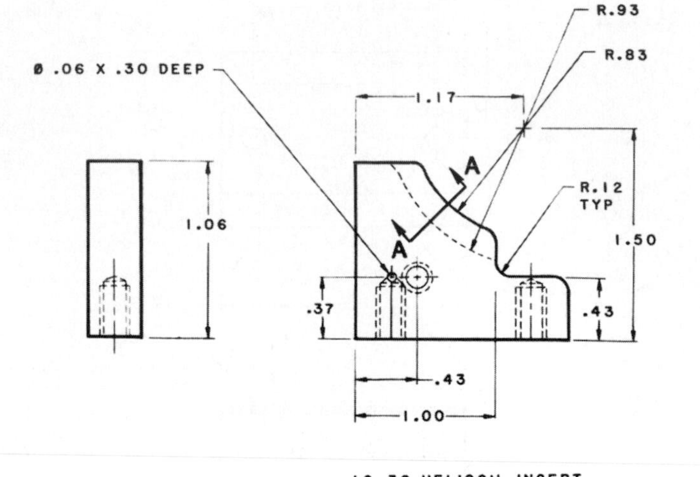

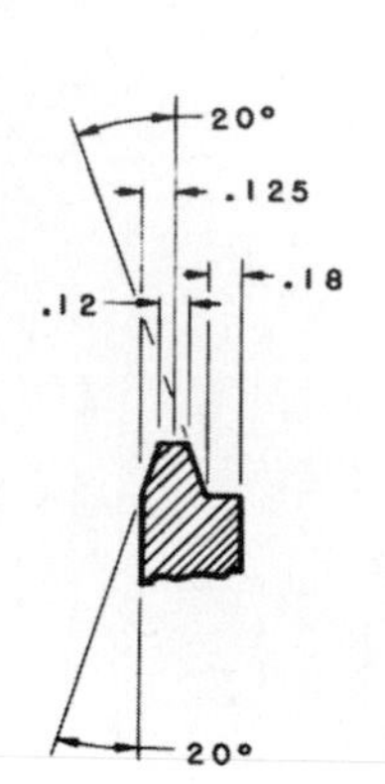

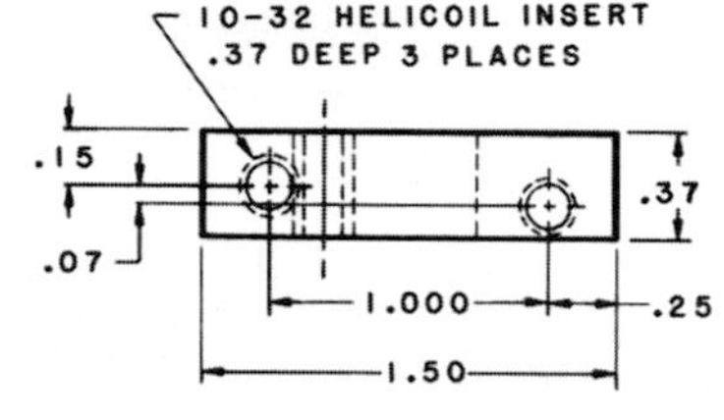

SECTION A–A

RULON

TOP ROW FOOT JIG

PROBLEM 11.11

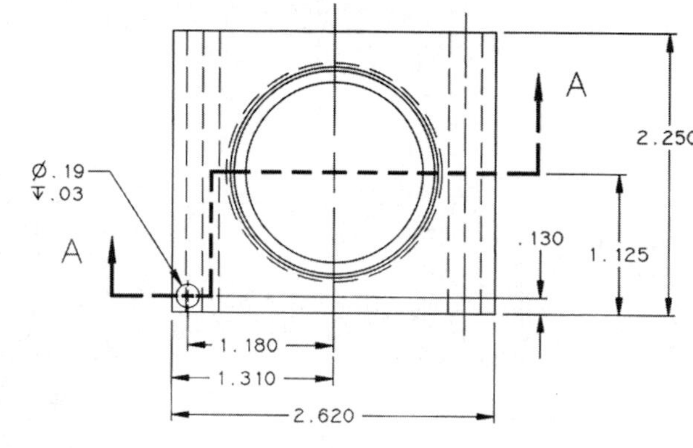

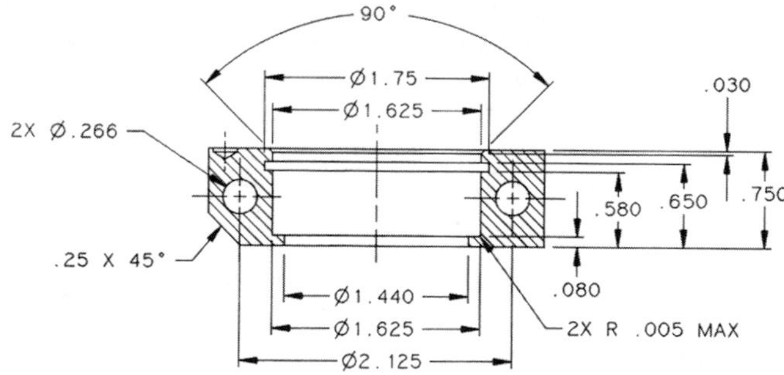

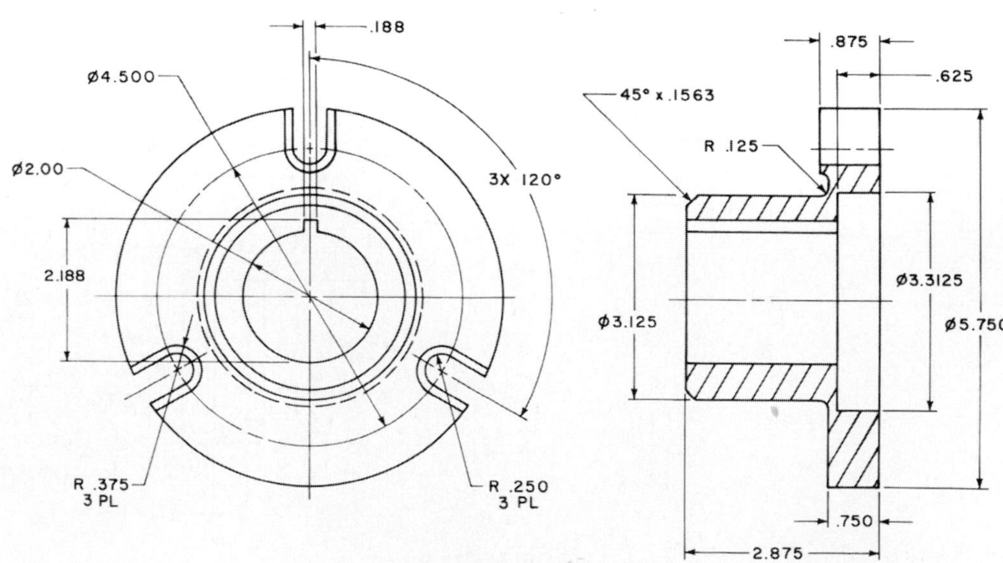

PROBLEM 11.12

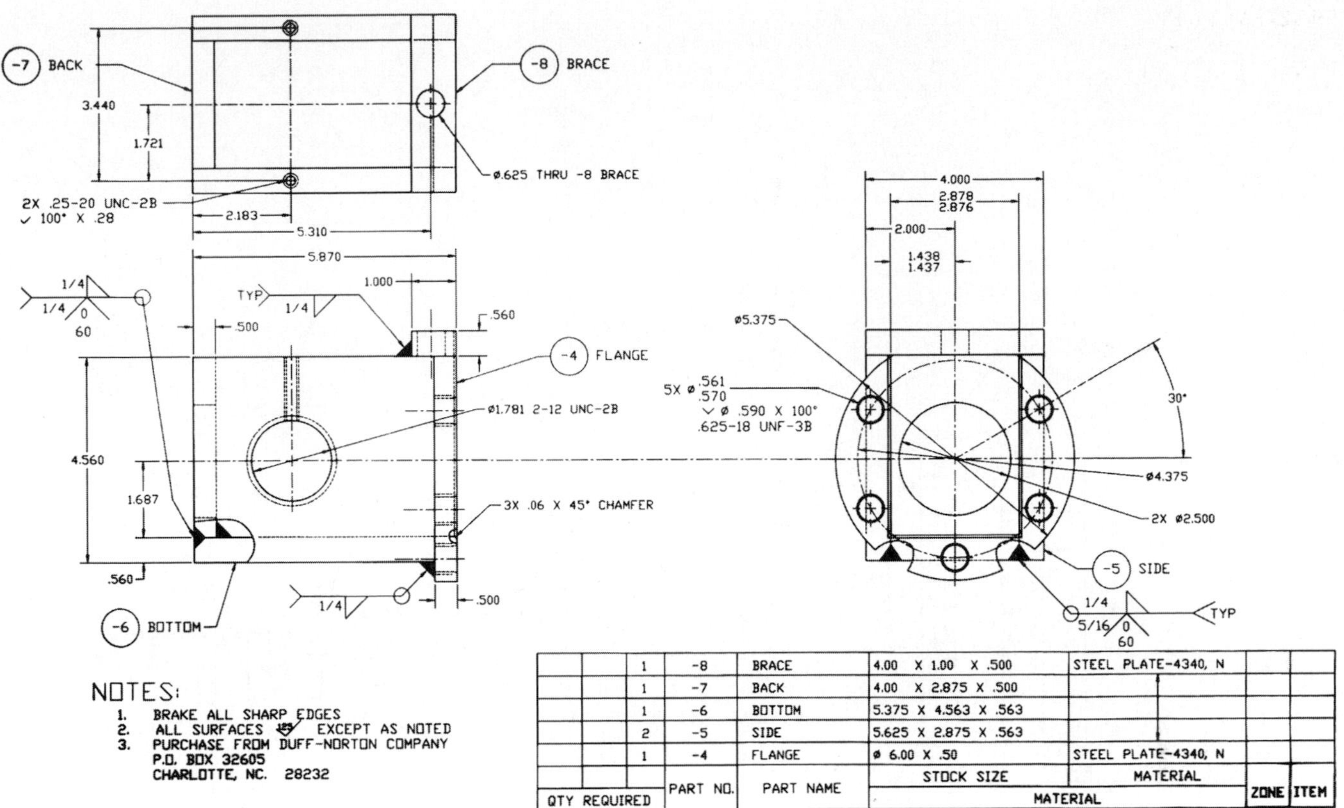

		1	-8	BRACE	4.00 X 1.00 X .500	STEEL PLATE-4340, N		
		1	-7	BACK	4.00 X 2.875 X .500			
		1	-6	BOTTOM	5.375 X 4.563 X .563			
		2	-5	SIDE	5.625 X 2.875 X .563			
		1	-4	FLANGE	ø 6.00 X .50	STEEL PLATE-4340, N		
QTY REQUIRED			PART NO.	PART NAME	STOCK SIZE	MATERIAL	ZONE	ITEM
					MATERIAL			

PROBLEM 11.13

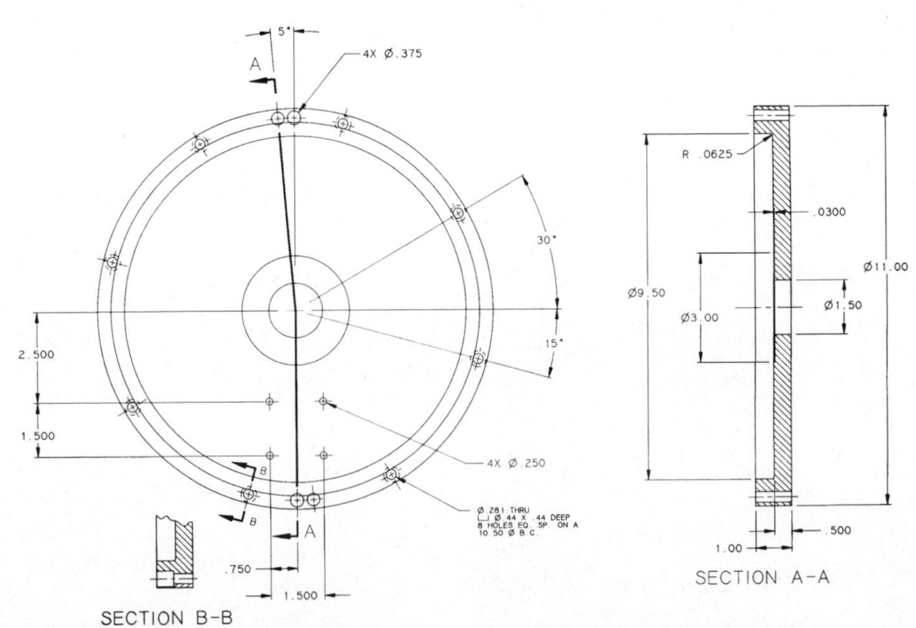

PROBLEM 11.14

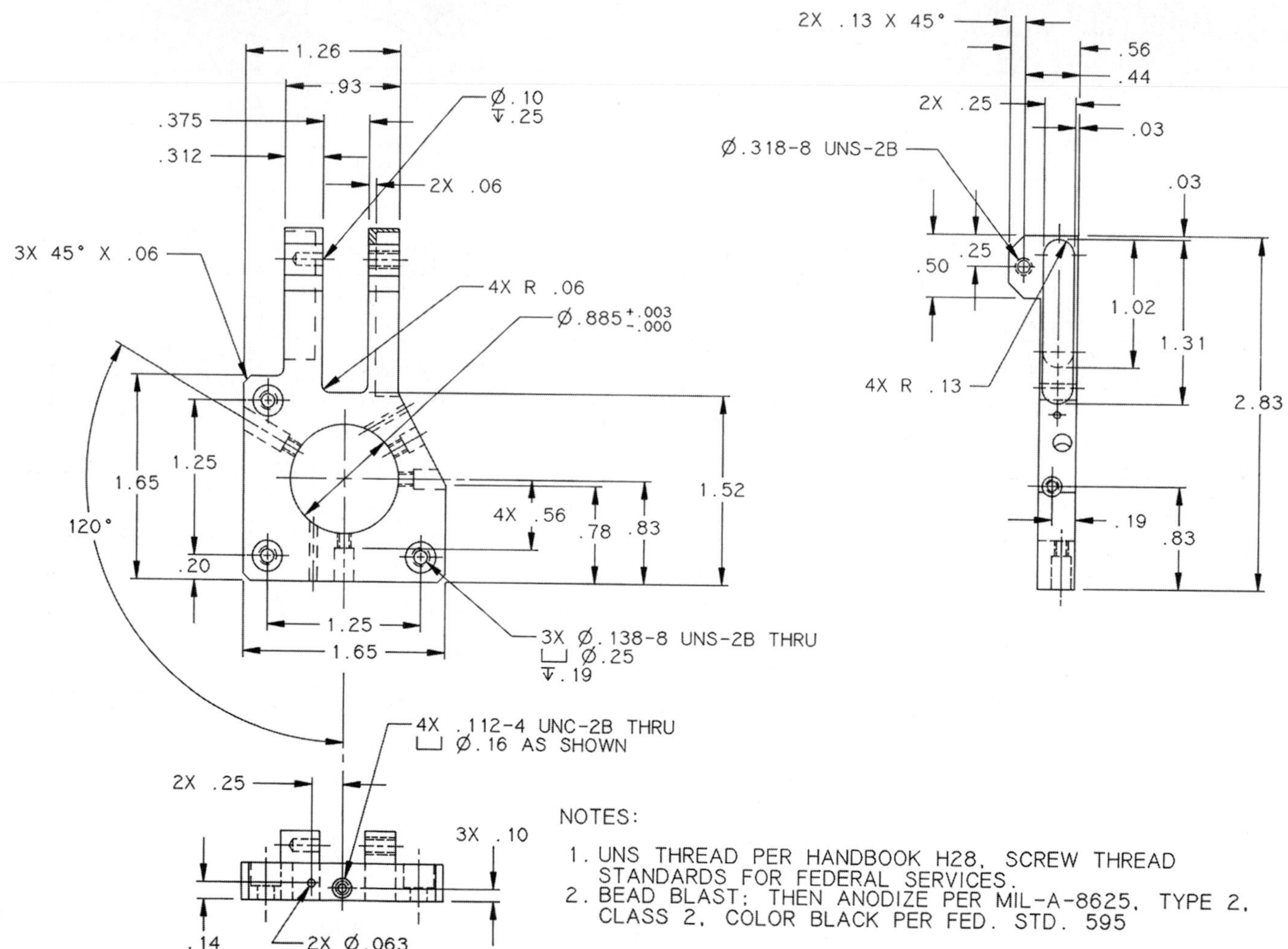
1.26
.93
.375
.312
Ø.10
↧.25
2X .06
3X 45° X .06
4X R .06
Ø.885 +.003 −.000
1.25
1.65
120°
.20
4X .56
.78
.83
1.52
1.25
1.65
3X Ø.138-8 UNS-2B THRU
⌴ Ø.25
↧.19
4X .112-4 UNC-2B THRU
⌴ Ø.16 AS SHOWN
2X .25
3X .10
.14
2X Ø.063
2X .13 X 45°
.56
.44
2X .25
.03
Ø.318-8 UNS-2B
.03
.25
.50
1.02
1.31
2.83
4X R .13
.19
.83
NOTES:
1. UNS THREAD PER HANDBOOK H28, SCREW THREAD STANDARDS FOR FEDERAL SERVICES.
2. BEAD BLAST; THEN ANODIZE PER MIL-A-8625, TYPE 2, CLASS 2, COLOR BLACK PER FED. STD. 595

PROBLEM 11.15

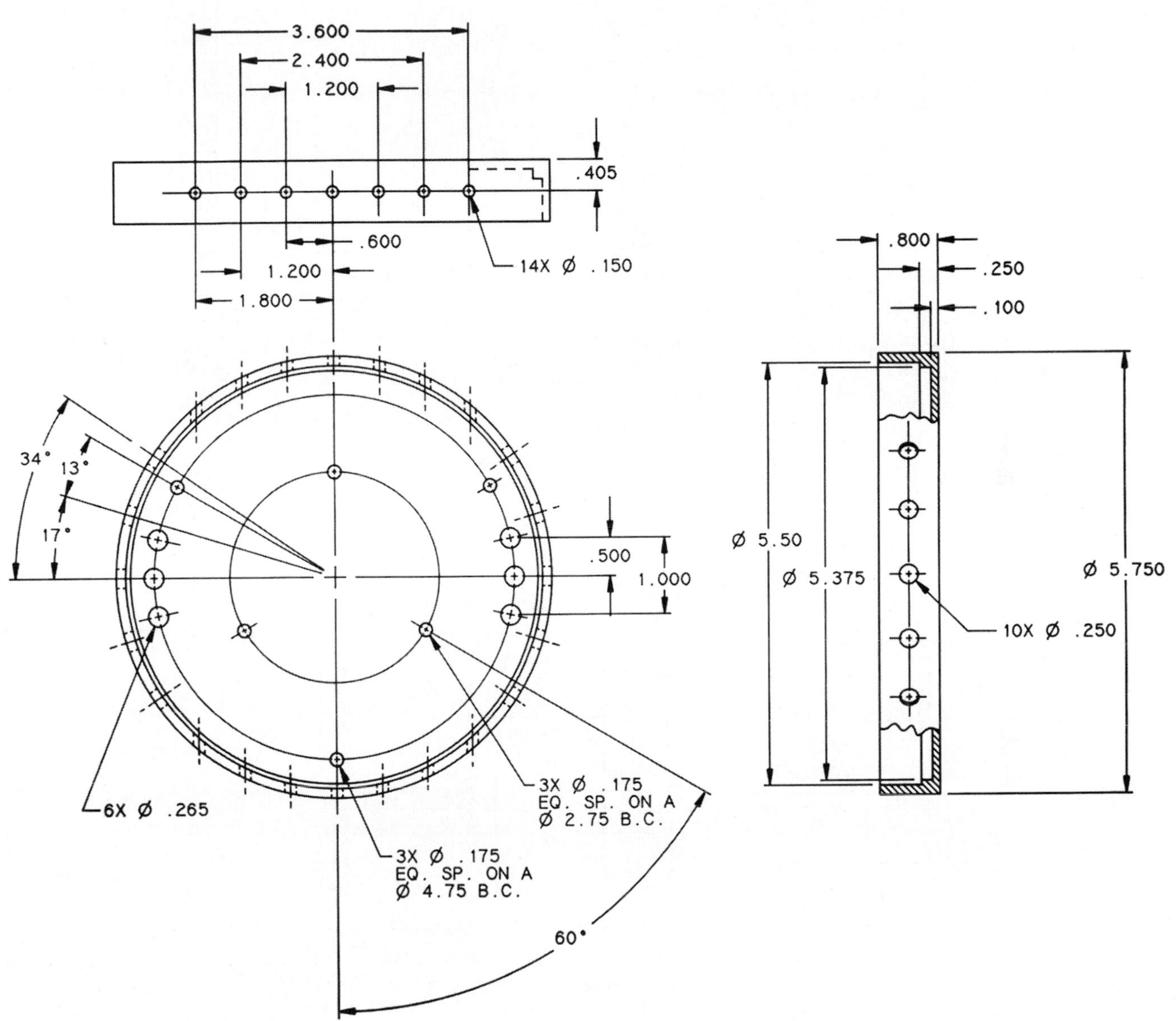

PROBLEM 11.16

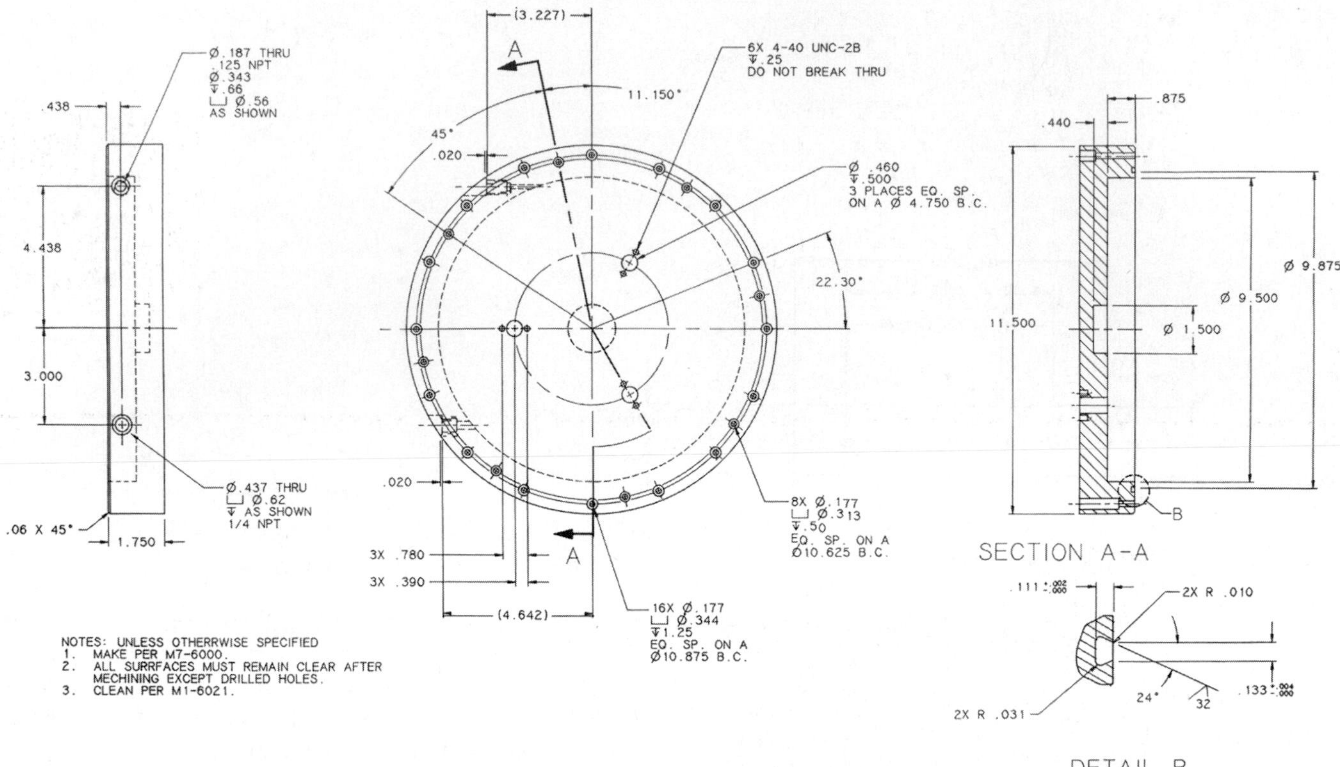

PROBLEM 11.17

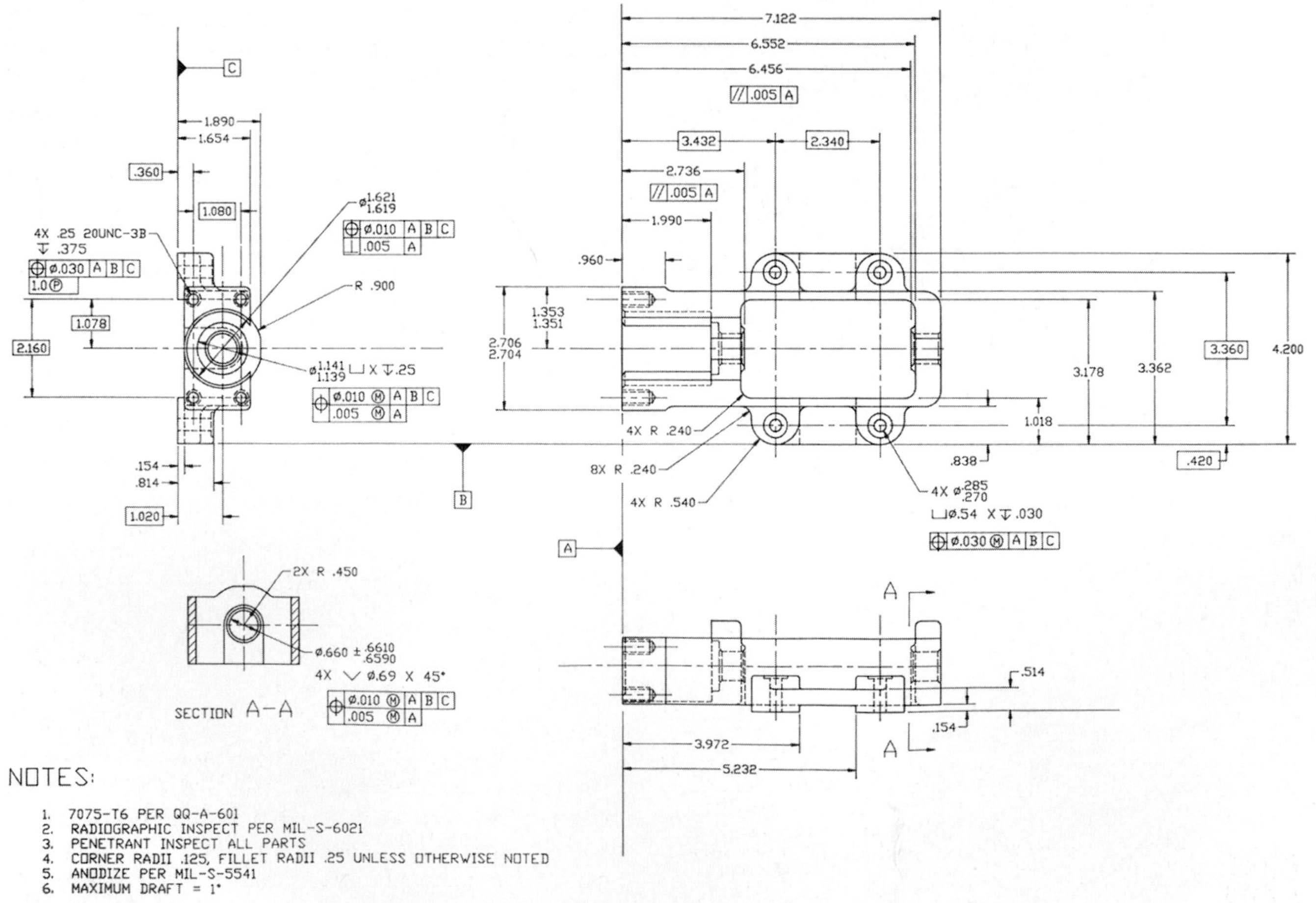

SECTION A-A

NOTES:

1. 7075-T6 PER QQ-A-601
2. RADIOGRAPHIC INSPECT PER MIL-S-6021
3. PENETRANT INSPECT ALL PARTS
4. CORNER RADII .125, FILLET RADII .25 UNLESS OTHERWISE NOTED
5. ANODIZE PER MIL-S-5541
6. MAXIMUM DRAFT = 1°

PROBLEM 11.18

AUXILIARY VIEWS

Chapter 12

LEARNING OBJECTIVES

Upon completion of this chapter you will be able to:

1. Identify the need for auxiliary views in order to show the actual shape, size, and relationship of an angled part feature.
2. Differentiate between and be able to produce primary and secondary auxiliary views using the fold line method and the reference plane method.
3. Solve for the true shape of an angled surface using an auxiliary view.
4. Produce partial, broken, half, and sectional auxiliary views.
5. Discern two- and three-dimensional CAD capabilities to generate auxiliary projections.

12.1 INTRODUCTION

Auxiliary views show the true shape/size of a feature or the relationship of part features that are not parallel to any of the principal planes of projection. The basic method of multiview drawing, described in Chapter 10, is adequate to draw parts composed of horizontal and vertical surfaces and for parts with simple inclined features. However, many parts have inclined surfaces and features that cannot be adequately displayed and described through principal views alone. To provide a clear description of these features, it is necessary to draw a view that will show them true shape/size.

The anchor in Figure 12.1 has an inclined surface that cannot be seen in its true shape in a principal view. The detail of the part uses a front view, a left side view, and an auxiliary view to show the inclined surface and the hole's true shape/size. The shaded image pictures the angled surface and the hole.

Besides showing features true size, auxiliary views are used to dimension features that are distorted in principal views and to solve graphically a variety of engineering problems. *Auxiliary views enable you to check the interference between two parts or clearances between pieces of an assembly.* In these cases, the view may or may not display the true shape of an inclined surface, depending on the part's features and the view direction selected.

12.1.1 Selection and Alignment of Views

The proper selection of views, view orientation, and view alignment is determined by a part's features and its natural or assembled position. Normally, the front view is the primary view, and the top view is obvious based on the position of the part in space or when assembled. The choice of additional views is determined by the part's features and the minimum number of views necessary to describe the part and show its dimensions. The detail of the anchor in Figure 12.1 required three views: front, left side, and auxiliary; the top view was not needed. The detail of the

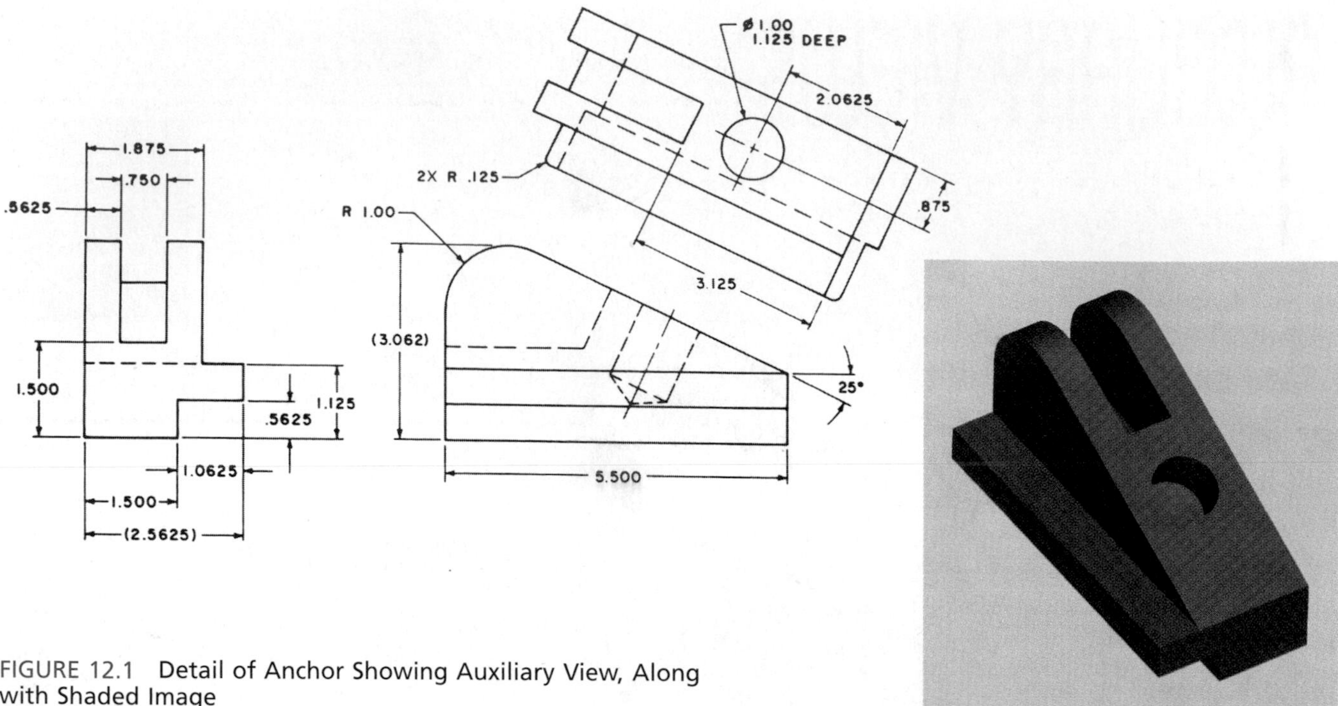

FIGURE 12.1 Detail of Anchor Showing Auxiliary View, Along with Shaded Image

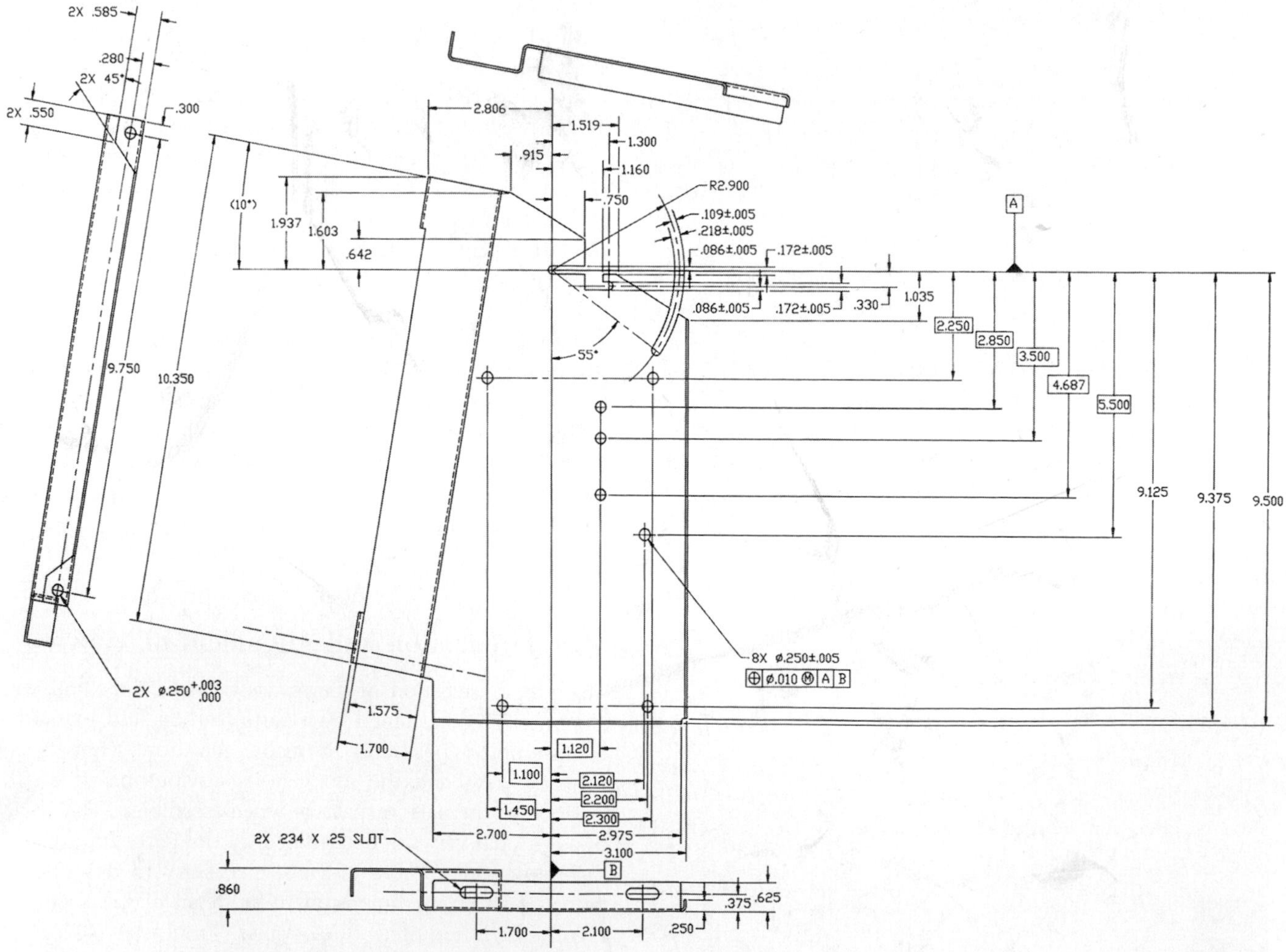

FIGURE 12.2 Bracket Detail with Two Auxiliary Views

Focus On . . .

HAND TOOLS AND DEVICES

There is evidence that hand tools and other devices were used by primates nearly a million years ago. It could be assumed that hand tools, after evolving with mankind for a million years or so, would now be specifically adapted for human use. In fact, this is not the case. Until recently, human biomechanical factors have been mostly ignored in the design of hand tools.

The human hand and wrist are complex structures of bones, nerves, ligaments, tendons, and arteries. Movement of the wrist occurs in two planes. The hand is flexed up and down in the first plane. Side-to-side movement, or ulnar deviation, occurs in the second plane. Continued use of tools that call for motions along these planes can injure the hand and wrist.

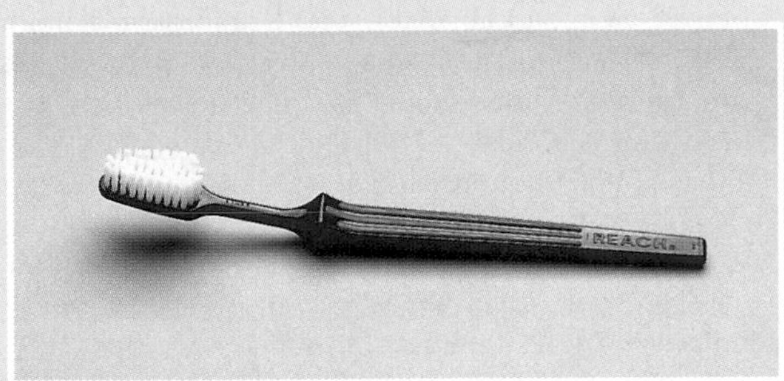

Ergonomically designed toothbrush.

Recent studies have shown how to design tools that avoid these types of motion. Using x-rays of the wrist and computer-generated wireframe auxiliary models, designers are able to configure tools that require a relatively straight wrist motion. For example, by bending or rotating the handle of a pair of pliers or a hammer about 19°, grip strength is increased while fatigue is reduced. This bent-handle design is now found in softball bats and is approved for regulation play. Golf clubs and fishing rods also incorporate this technology into their designs.

The most common hand-held device is probably the toothbrush. The only major development since it was introduced in 1780 was nylon bristles, which replaced hog hair in the 1930s.

Johnson and Johnson, Inc., designed a new toothbrush based on human-factor and time-motion research data. Prototypes were developed with different handle shapes and bristle head rotations. These prototypes were tested, and the optimal features found from the testing were incorporated into the final design. The result was the Reach toothbrush, which has a small, bilevel bristle head in an angled, countered handle for easier handling, better gum stimulation, and better plaque removal.

The new toothbrush is one example of design with human factors. Future tool designs will require these research studies to produce hand tools specifically adapted for human use. Without auxiliary views, projections, and models, none of this would have been possible.

bracket in Figure 12.2 shows the front view, the bottom view, and two auxiliary views.

As with all multiview drawings, auxiliary views are aligned with the views from which they are projected. In many cases, a centerline or a projection line continues between adjacent views to indicate the proper alignment (Fig. 12.3).

12.2 AUXILIARY VIEWS

Any view that lies in a projection plane other than the horizontal (top), frontal (front), or profile (side) plane (or a plane parallel to one of these three—bottom, back, opposite side) is an **auxiliary view.** This type of projection is essential if the part to be drawn is complex and has a variety of lines or surfaces that are not parallel to one of the three principal planes.

Auxiliary views are classified by the view from which they are projected. **Primary auxiliary views** are projected from one of the principal views. A primary auxiliary view is perpendicular to one of the three principal planes and inclined to the other two. **Secondary auxiliary views** are projected from a primary auxiliary view and are inclined to

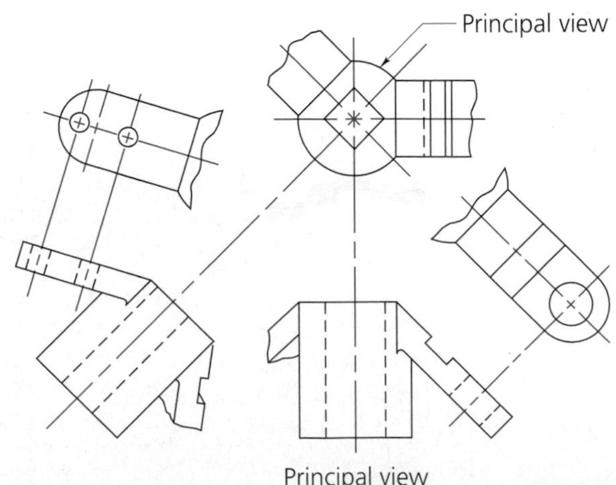

FIGURE 12.3 **Principal and Auxiliary Views of a Part**

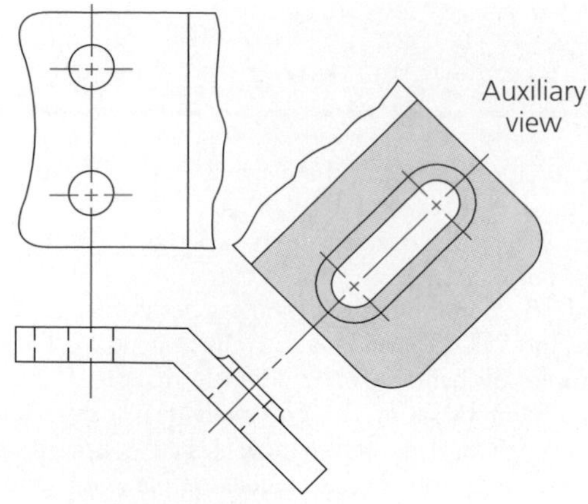

FIGURE 12.4 Full Front View, Partial Top View, and Partial Auxiliary View of a Simple Part

all three principal planes of projection. **Successive auxiliary views** are projected from secondary auxiliary views.

In most cases, only **partial auxiliary views** are constructed, as in Figure 12.4, where only the features that appear true shape are drawn. Features that appear distorted are left off the view or are shown partially and cut off using break lines. In Figure 12.4, the top view is also a partial view.

12.2.1 Primary Auxiliary Views

A **primary auxiliary view** is one that is adjacent to and aligned with one of the principal views. A primary auxiliary view is identified as **front-adjacent, top-adjacent,** or **side-adjacent** to indicate the principal view with which it is aligned (and projected from). In industry, auxiliary views show aspects of a mechanical part or portions of a system such as piping configurations or structural bracing that cannot be adequately represented in the three principal views. The machined block shown in Figure 12.5 required auxiliary views to clarify the shape of the angled surfaces and the positions of the holes and the slots. For this part, the three principal views (top, front, side) do not provide true-shape/size views of each surface. It is necessary to project three primary auxiliary views to describe the angled surfaces in detail.

Primary auxiliary views are divided into three types, depending on the principal view from which they are projected. Primary auxiliary views projected from the top (top-adjacent) view are **horizontal auxiliary views.** Primary auxiliary views projected from the front (front-adjacent) view are **frontal auxiliary views.** Primary auxiliary views projected from the side (side-adjacent) view are **profile auxiliary views.** These three types are represented in Figure 12.5. Here, auxiliary view A is projected from the top (horizontal) view, auxiliary view B is projected from the front (frontal) view, and auxiliary view C is projected from the side (profile) view. The auxiliary projections in this figure are partial views, showing only the inclined surfaces as true shape. This is normal industry practice, since the projection of the total part not only would add little to an understanding of the part's configuration, but might actually confuse the view. For the same reason, hidden lines that fall behind the true-shape surface in an auxiliary view can normally be eliminated for the same reason.

Each primary auxiliary view, besides being projected from one of the three principal views, will have one dimension in common with at least one other principal view. The height dimension (H) in the front view is used to establish the limits of auxiliary view A. The depth (D) of the part can be found in the top view (and side view) and establishes dimension D in auxiliary view B. Dimension A in auxiliary view C is taken from the view where the width of the slot is drawn true size (the front view).

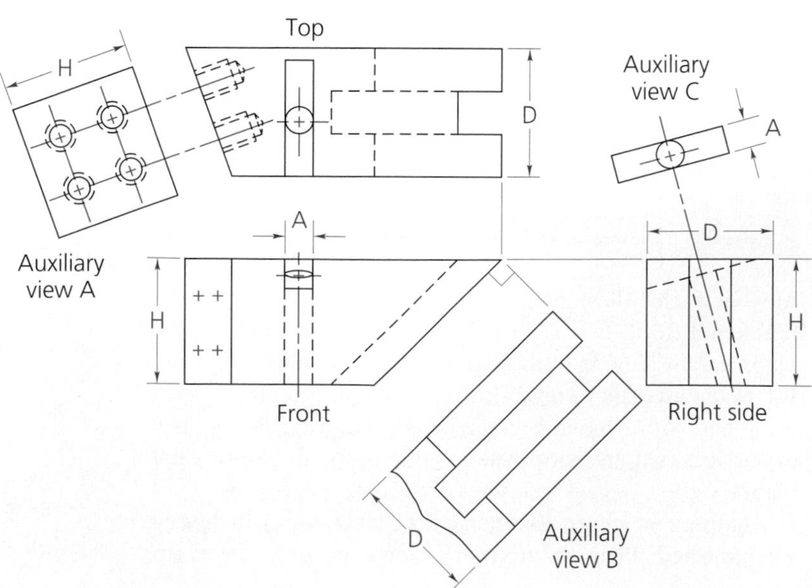

FIGURE 12.5 Auxiliary Views

FIGURE 12.6 Auxiliary View Projection from the Front View

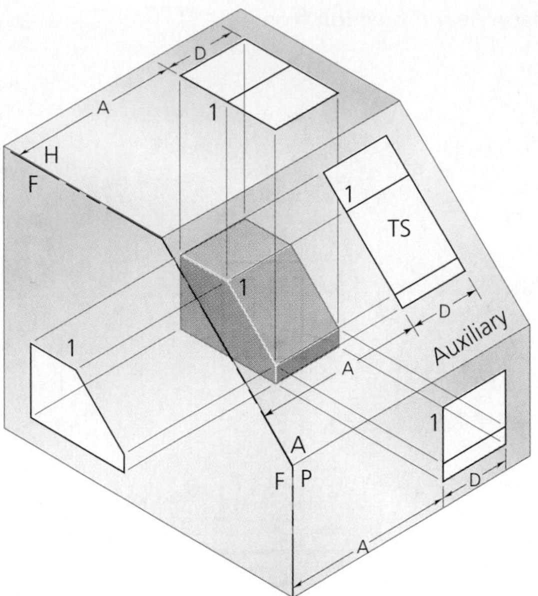

(a) Glass box method

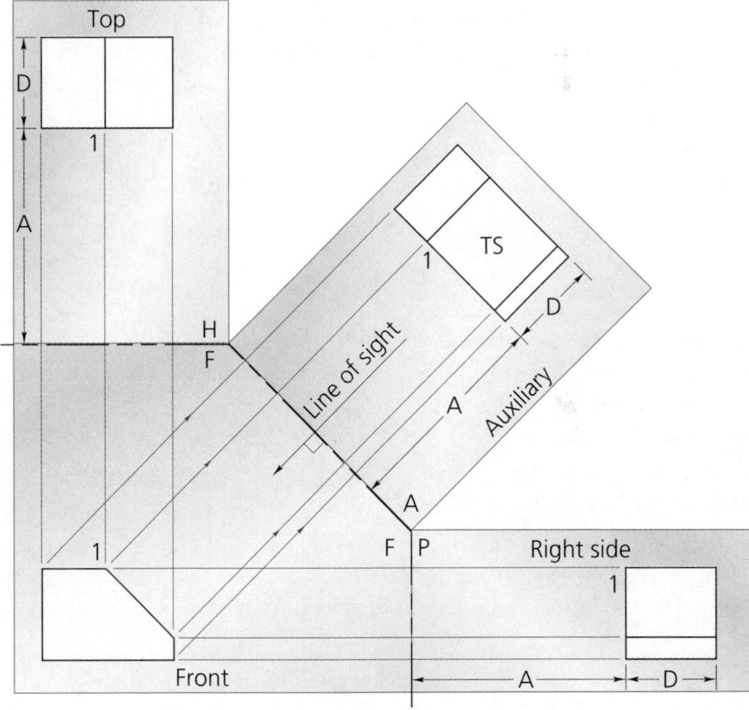

(b) Fold line method

12.2.2 Frontal Auxiliary Views (Fold Line Method)

The true shape of an inclined plane that appears as an edge in the front view must be projected from that view. The **glass box method** is pictorially illustrated in Figure 12.6(a). The following steps (using the fold line method) describe the projection of the frontal auxiliary view shown in Figure 12.6(b).

1. The line of sight for a frontal auxiliary view is perpendicular to the inclined surface, which appears as an edge in the frontal view.
2. Fold line F/A is established perpendicular to the line of sight and parallel to the inclined surface (edge view).
3. Projectors are drawn from all points in the front view perpendicular to the fold line. (Hidden lines were omitted in this example.)

FIGURE 12.7 Auxiliary View Projection from the Top View

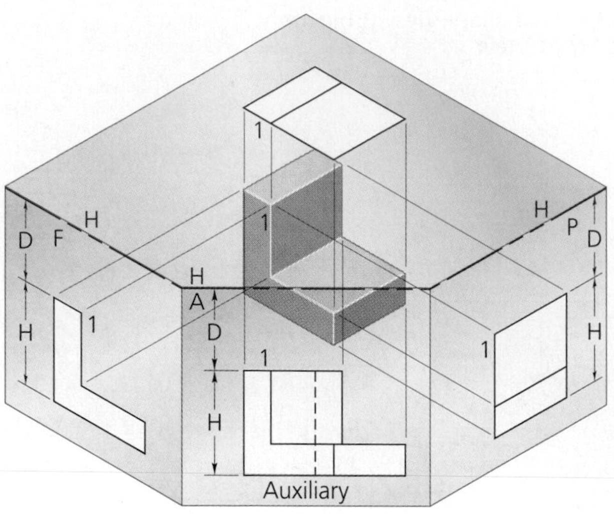

(a) Glass box method

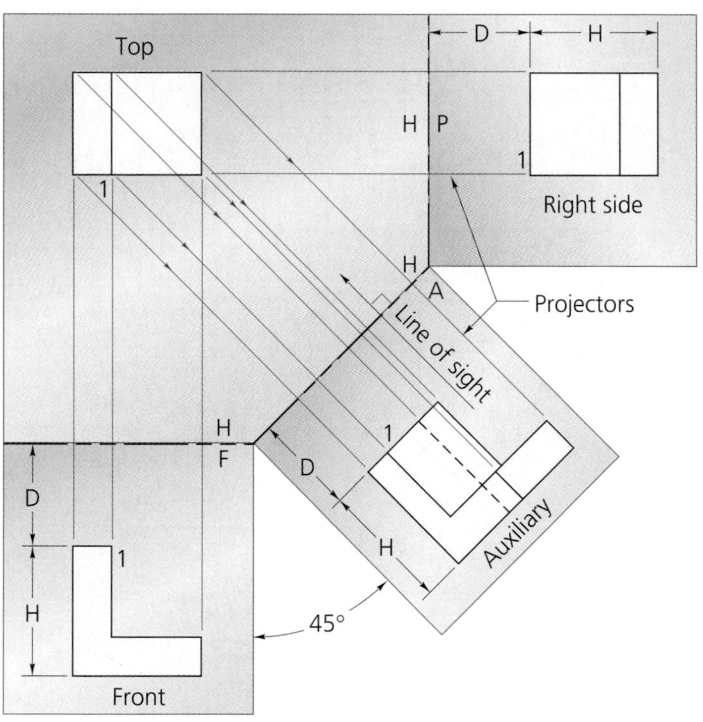

(b) Fold line method

4. Measurements are taken (using dividers for speed and accuracy) from fold line H/F or P/F to establish the front face of the part in the auxiliary view. Dimension *A* is transferred from the top or side view to establish the distance from the F/A fold line to the front face of the part in the auxiliary view. The depth dimension (*D*) of the part is then transferred.

12.2.3 Horizontal Auxiliary Views (Fold Line Method)

The second type of primary auxiliary view is the **horizontal auxiliary view.** In this case, the auxiliary view is taken perpendicular to the horizontal plane and is inclined to the other two principal planes. The glass box method is shown pictorially in Figure 12.7(a). In this example, the auxiliary view is projected at a required viewing angle, and is *not* being used to solve for the true shape of an inclined surface, as was the case in Figure 12.6. Because of this, the view does not show the true shape of a surface but instead provides a different viewing angle. The following steps describe the process of projecting a horizontal auxiliary view using the fold line method shown in Figure 12.7(b).

1. Establish a line of sight at a required angle of viewing. (45° was used here.)

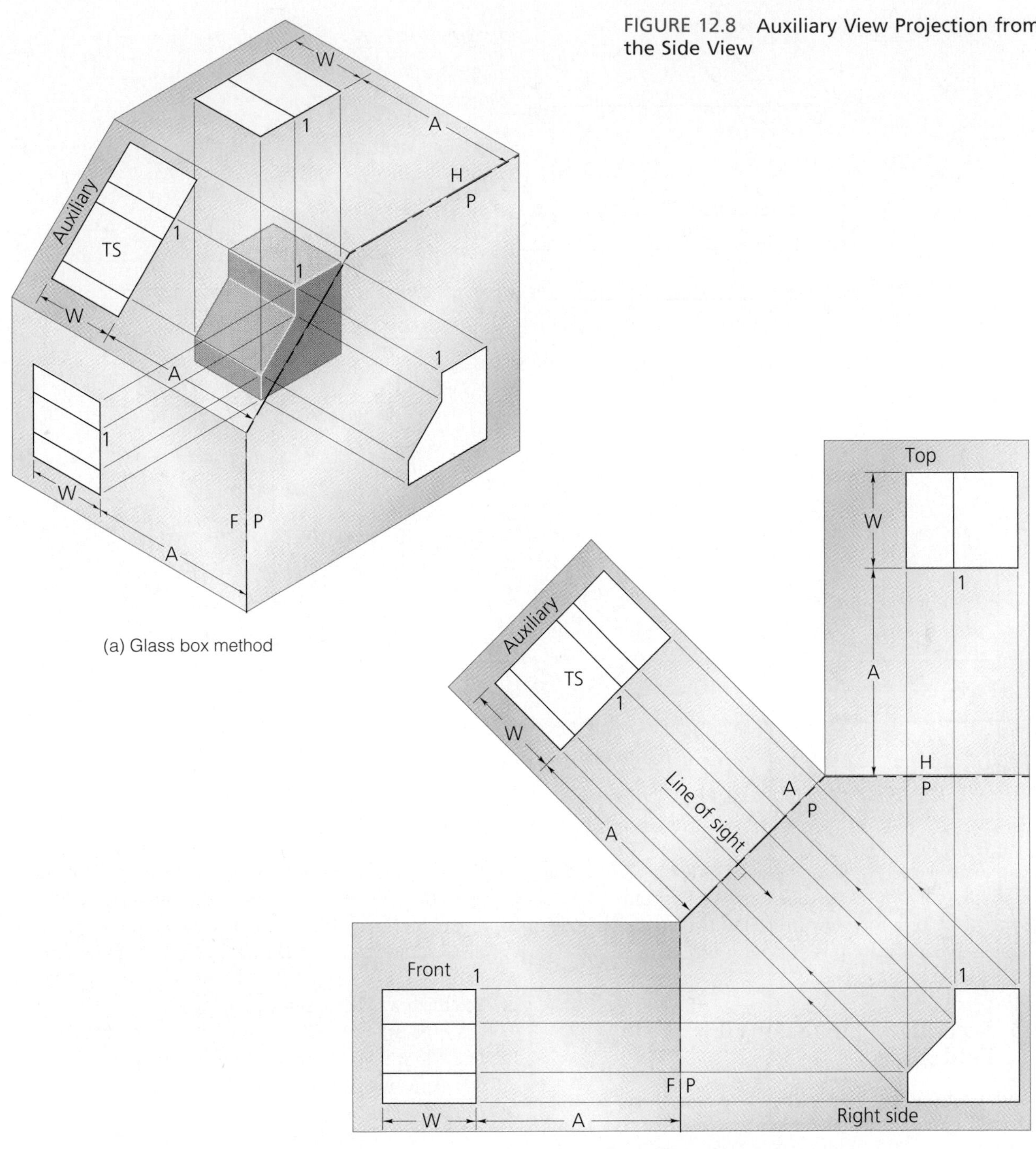

FIGURE 12.8 Auxiliary View Projection from the Side View

(a) Glass box method

(b) Fold line method

2. Draw fold line H/A perpendicular to the line of sight.
3. From each point in the top (horizontal) view, extend a projector parallel to the line of sight and perpendicular to the fold line. (In this example, hidden lines are shown.)
4. Transfer dimension *D* from the side or front view to establish the distance from the H/A fold line to the top of the part. Then transfer the height dimension (*H*) to locate the bottom of the part. Determine visibility, and the view is completed.

12.2.4 Profile Auxiliary Views (Fold Line Method)

The third type of primary auxiliary view is the **profile auxiliary view.** In Figure 12.8 one surface of the part is inclined to the front and top views, and appears as an edge in the side view. By projecting an auxiliary view with a line of sight perpendicular to the edge view of the inclined surface, the true shape of the surface will be seen in the

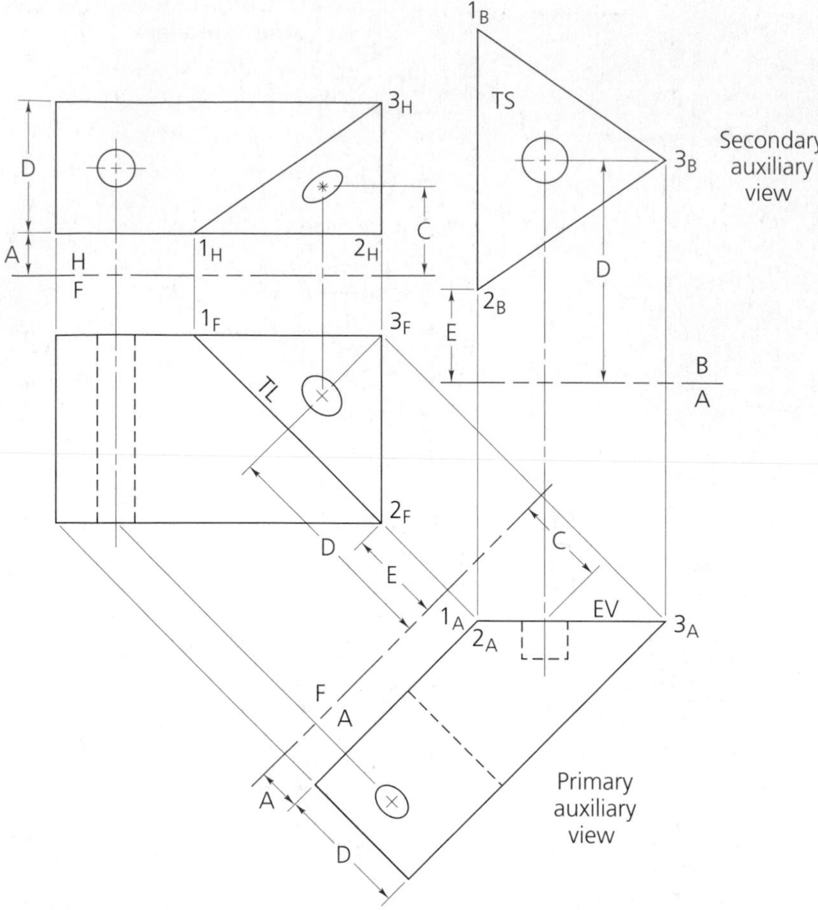

FIGURE 12.9 Secondary Auxiliary Views

profile auxiliary view. The same basic steps are used to draw profile auxiliary views as in Sections 12.3.1 and 12.3.2. Notice the need for a top view projected from the right side view. This is the alternate position for a top view.

12.2.5 Secondary Auxiliary Views Using Fold Lines

A **secondary auxiliary view** is one that is adjacent to and aligned with (projected from) a primary auxiliary view. In Figure 12.9, the part has one surface that is inclined to all three principal planes of projection. Therefore, it is not possible to solve for the true shape of the surface in a primary auxiliary view. This type of surface is normally referred to as an **oblique surface** (not to be confused with oblique projection). Since all consecutive views of a part are at right angles, secondary auxiliary views are perpendicular to primary auxiliary views. Views projected from a secondary auxiliary view are called **successive auxiliary views.** The following steps were used to draw the part in Figure 12.9.

1. Establish the line of sight parallel to true-length (TL) line 1-2 in the front view.
2. Draw fold line F/A perpendicular to the line of sight and at a convenient distance from the front view.
3. Complete the primary auxiliary view by transferring dimensions *A*, *C*, and *D* from the front view, and draw the part.
4. Establish a line of sight perpendicular to the edge view (EV) of surface 1_A-2_A-3_A in the primary auxiliary view.
5. Draw fold line A/B perpendicular to the line of sight and at a convenient distance from auxiliary view A.
6. Complete the secondary auxiliary view by transferring dimensions from the front view. Draw only plane 1-2-3, which will show true shape. Dimensions *D* and *E* establish points 3 and 2.

12.2.6 Adjacent Views

Each view and its preceding view and following view are considered **adjacent views.** An adjacent view is any view that is aligned with another view by means of a direct projection. The primary auxiliary view of the part in Figure 12.9 is projected from its adjacent principal view (the front view). Secondary auxiliary views are taken from their adjacent primary auxiliary view. Therefore the secondary auxiliary view is adjacent to the primary auxiliary view.

12.3 AUXILIARY VIEWS USING THE REFERENCE PLANE METHOD

In drawing the auxiliary view, dimensions in one direction are projected into the auxiliary view from the adjacent view. The dimensions in the other direction are transferred to the auxiliary view by measurement. To aid in the transfer of these measurements, a **reference plane** can be used instead of a fold line. The reference plane is placed perpendicular to the inclined surface that is being drawn and represented in this view by its edge, which shows as a line. All measurements are transferred from the edge view of the reference plane.

The reference line (edge) appears in the view where the inclined surface is shown as foreshortened. It will not appear in the view where the surface to be drawn is seen as an edge. In Figure 12.10, the reference plane shows as a plane surface in the front view and as an edge in the top view and the auxiliary view. Any convenient parallel position can serve to establish the reference plane. It could have been passed through the center of the part (as seen from the top) or the back plane instead of the front plane as done here.

12.3.1 Drawing an Auxiliary View

To draw the auxiliary view in Figure 12.10 using the reference plane method, first locate the reference plane for the auxiliary view so that it is parallel to the edge view of the inclined surface being drawn. Here, the plane was passed so that it coincided with the front surface of the part and shows as a reference line (edge) in the top and auxiliary views. The reference line is positioned at a distance away from the edge view of the inclined surface that is equal to the depth of the part plus the space desired between the views.

Spacing of the views can also be accomplished as when drawing standard normal views, as discussed in Chapter 10. The thickness (depth dimension 2.500 in. in Fig. 12.10) plus the space required between views determine the amount of space needed for the auxiliary view.

Place the auxiliary view (the reference line-edge) so there is sufficient space for dimensions and notes. *Do not put the auxiliary view too close to the view from which it is projected.* Since each part will have a different shape and different dimensioning requirements, it is impossible to specify a distance that could be applied to every part. You will learn through practice and experience the amount of room necessary for the view to be properly positioned.

After the extents of the view are projected (perpendicularly) from the adjacent view (the front view in Fig. 12.10), measurements for establishing the thickness of the auxiliary view are taken from the existing view (here 2.500). Measurements that can be taken perpendicular to the reference line are then transferred to the auxiliary view. At the same time, all dimensions that are parallel to the reference line are projected to the auxiliary view. This procedure (projection lines and transfer distances) is exactly the same as for the fold line method. The line of projection for each point is always perpendicular to the reference line. All features can be established in the auxiliary view by projecting one point at a time.

Note that the fold line or the reference line, depending on which method is employed, is always erased after the projection of the auxiliary view is completed. Finished drawings have only views of the part (Fig. 12.11).

12.3.2 Secondary Auxiliary Views

Secondary auxiliary views derived via the fold line method have already been presented. For typical industry drawings that require the detailing of an oblique surface, either the

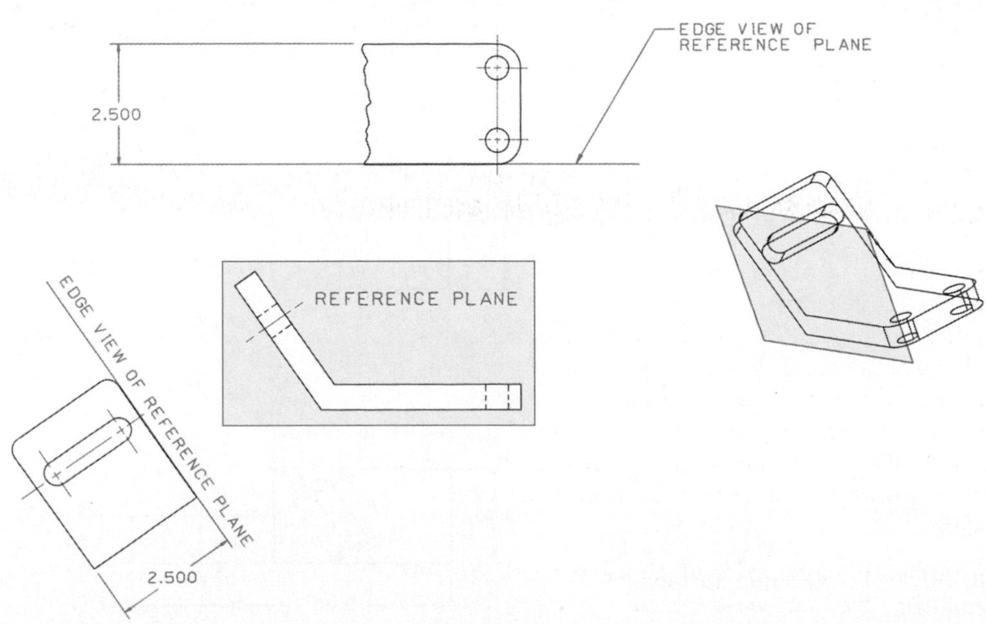

FIGURE 12.10 Auxiliary View Projection Using the Reference Plane Method

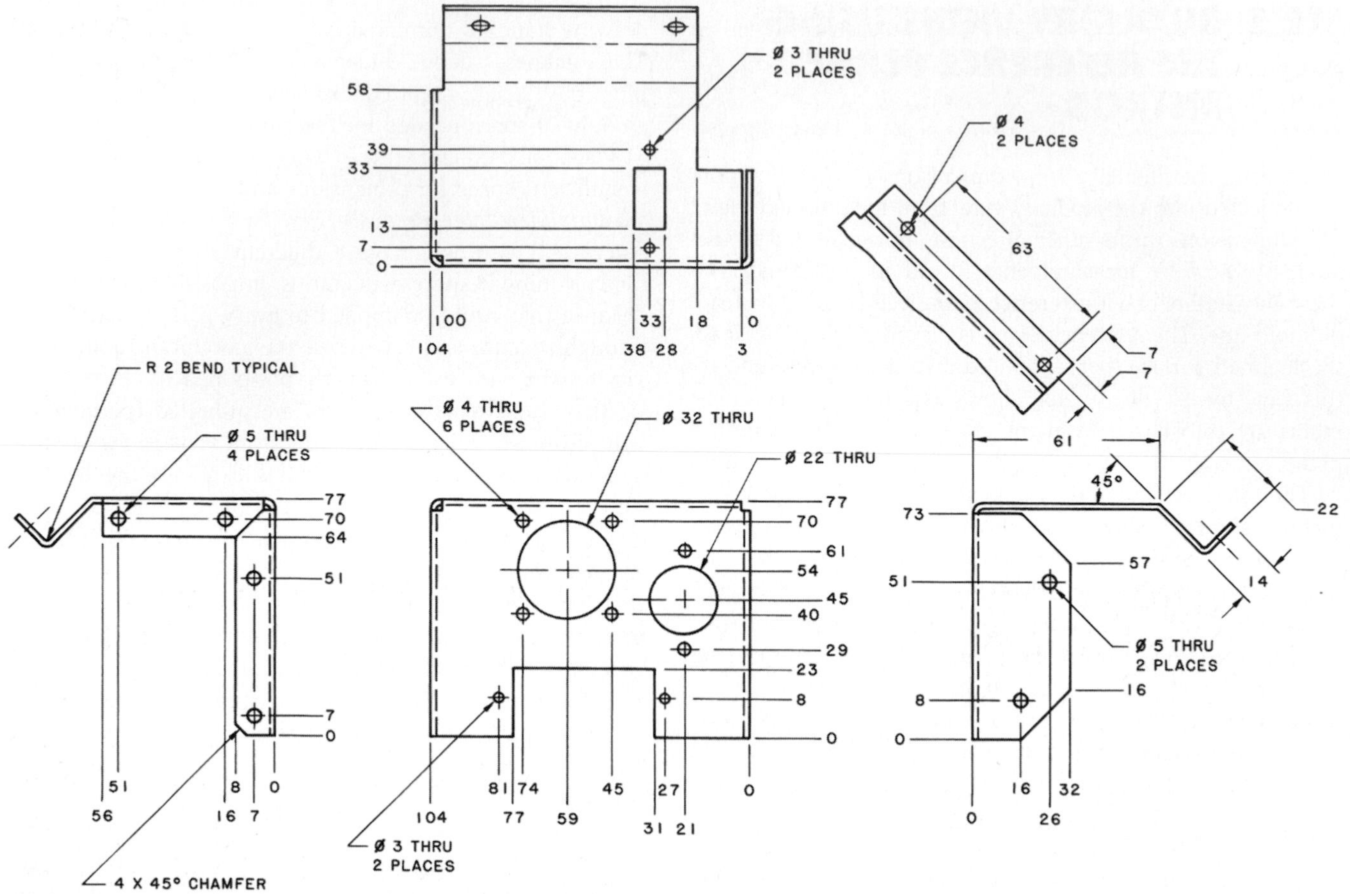

FIGURE 12.11 Electronic Bracket Mount Detail

fold line or the reference plane method can be implemented, with equally good results. The fold line method works best for complicated parts that require the whole part to be projected from view to view. In Figure 12.12, the part has an oblique surface with a hole centered on it. This surface and the hole do not show as true shape in any of the principal

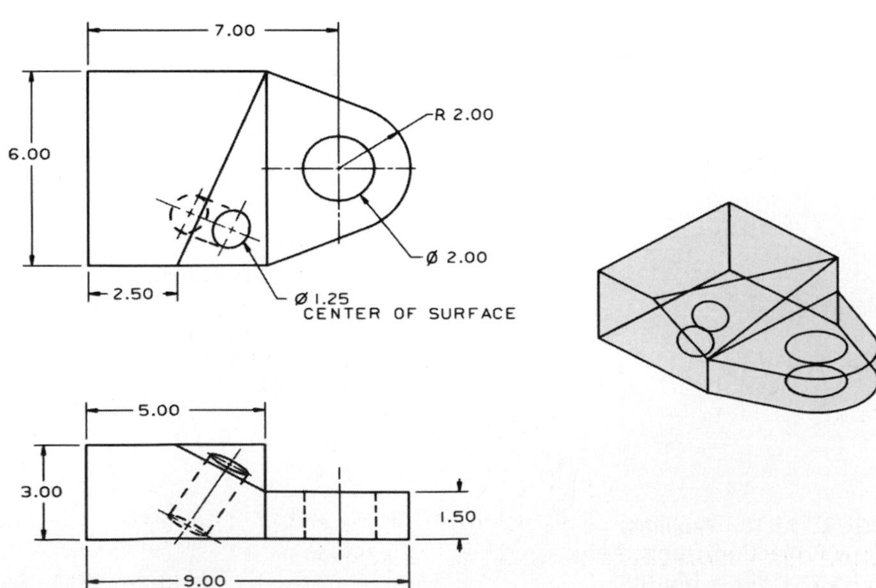

FIGURE 12.12 Oblique Surface on a Part

views. This is an example of a part where a primary view and a secondary auxiliary view will be required in order to display and detail the part properly.

The part in Figure 12.13 has a surface that is oblique. This surface also has a slot positioned on it. To solve for the true-shape view of the surface, a primary auxiliary view showing the surface as an edge was projected first. By projecting a view perpendicular to the edge view, a true-shape secondary auxiliary view was then established. Note that fold lines and reference planes are not shown. The primary auxiliary view shows the true angle that the inclined surface makes with the base of the part.

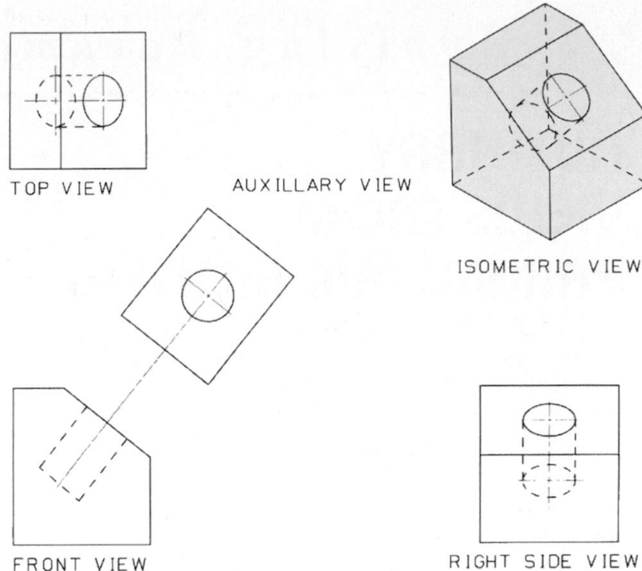

FIGURE 12.14 Front-Adjacent Auxiliary View

12.4 AUXILIARY VIEW CONVENTIONS

Auxiliary views are aligned with the views from which they are projected. A centerline or projection line (Fig. 12.13) may continue between the adjacent views to indicate this alignment. In Figure 12.14 the centerline of the hole has been extended from the front view to the auxiliary view to show alignment.

In many cases, hidden lines in auxiliary views are not shown, unless they would help clarify the view. Hidden lines are shown only when they do not complicate the auxiliary view or where they are necessary to describe the part adequately.

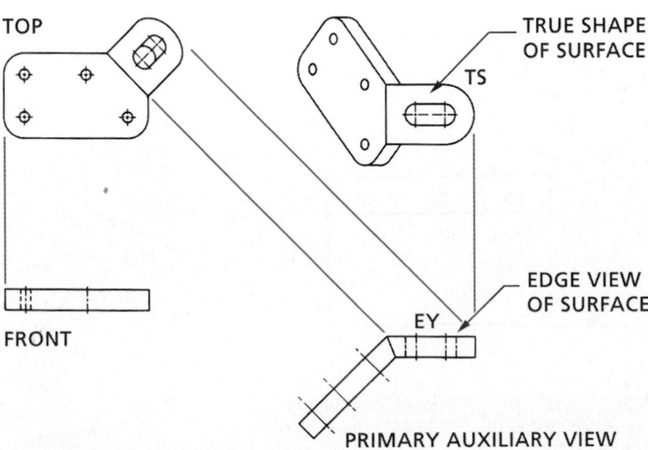

FIGURE 12.13 True Shape of an Oblique Surface by Auxiliary View

In general, the complete auxiliary view need not be drawn. Showing only the true-shape surface is normally all that is required (Fig. 12.15). The complete view may be necessary to show clearances or other information, especially when the auxiliary projection was not drawn to show the true shape of a surface.

You May Now Complete Exercises 12.1 Through 12.4

12.4.1 Partial Auxiliary Views

Partial auxiliary views (or partial principal views) may show only pertinent features not described by true projection in the principal or other views (Fig. 12.15). They are used instead of complete views to simplify the drawing. In

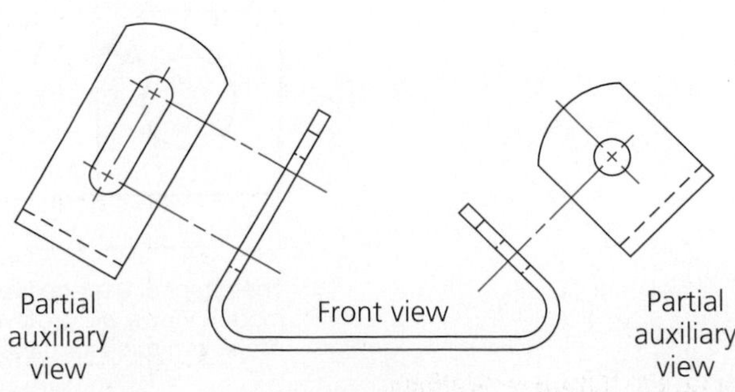

FIGURE 12.15 Front View and Two Auxiliary Views

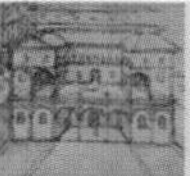

Applying Parametric Design . . .

AUXILIARY VIEWS FROM PARAMETRIC MODELS

Auxiliary views are created by making a projection of the model perpendicular to a selected edge (see Fig. A). They normally serve to describe the true size and shape of a planar

Point you picked for the view origin
Auxiliary view origin at the intersection of a projection ray of the main view origin and normal from the point you picked onto the ray
Point you picked on the main view becomes its origin
Point you picked for projection view origin
Projection view origin lies on the projection ray of the main view origin
Effects of model changes
This distance is fixed whenever you update the model
The effect of user-defined origin is noticeable after you update the model. Views will grow relative to their new origins in compliance with projection rules for projection views.

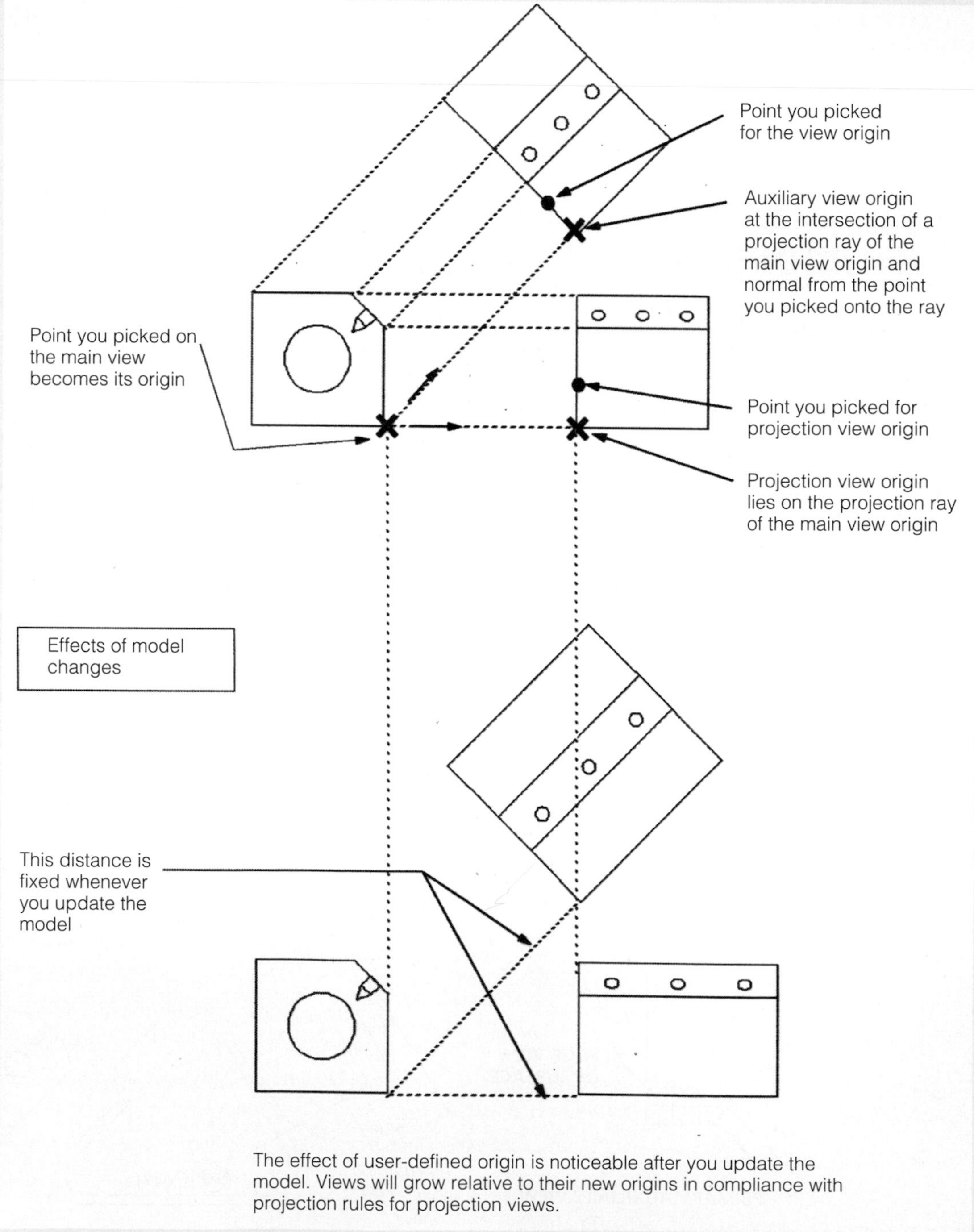

FIGURE A User-Defined Auxiliary View Origin

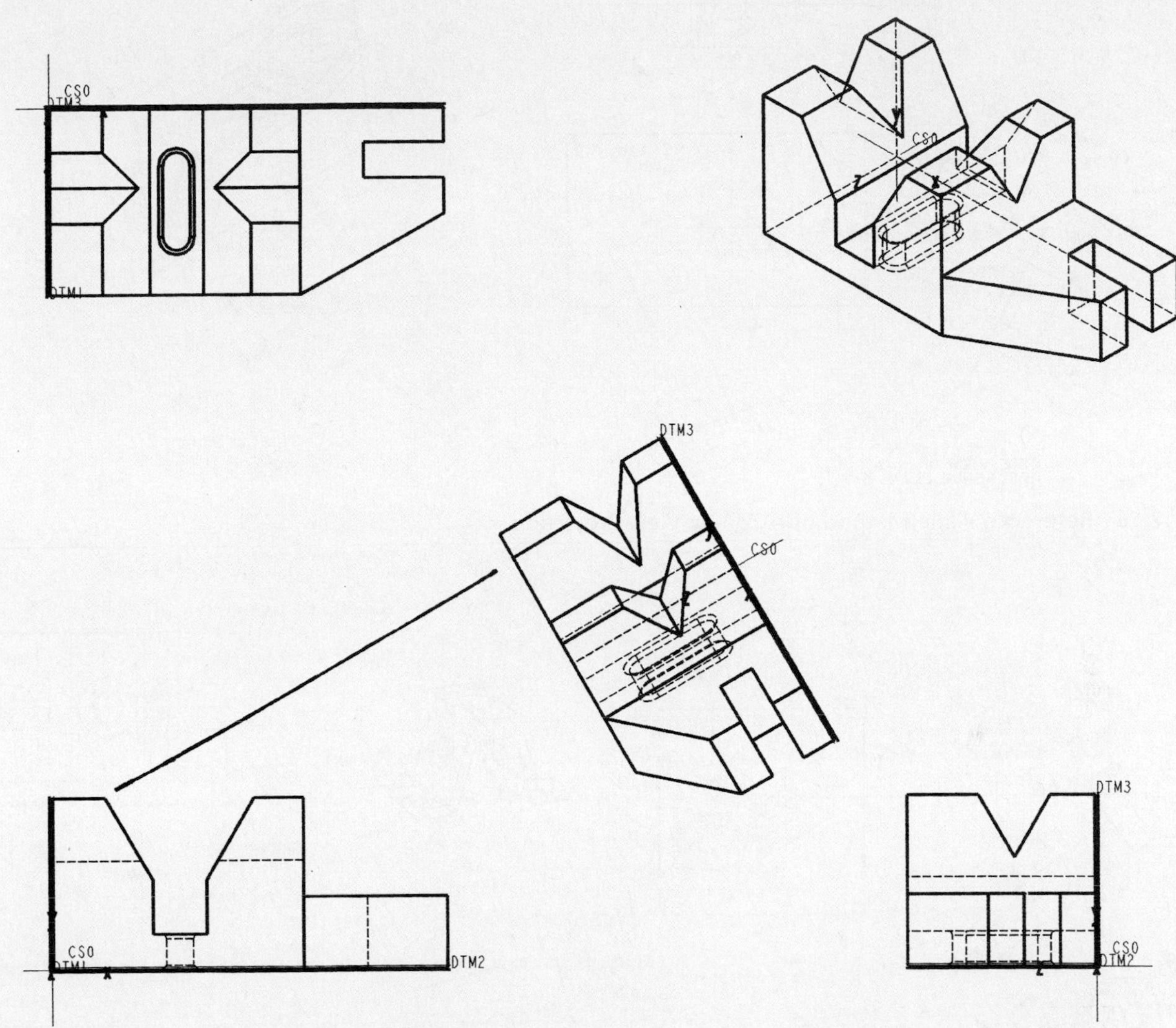

FIGURE B Auxiliary View of Model Surface

surface on a part (see Fig. B). An auxiliary view can be created from any other type of view. Auxiliary views may have arrows created for them that point back at the view(s) from which they were created. To add an auxiliary view to a drawing, use the following command options.

1. Choose **Auxiliary** and other available options from the VIEW TYPE menu.
2. Choose **Done** to accept the options, or **Quit** to quit the creation of a new view.
3. Pick the location of the new view on the drawing.
4. Pick an edge of, or axis through, the surface of the model in the view from which the auxiliary view will be developed. If the edge selected is from a view that has a pictorial (isometric-trimetric) orientation, the new view will be oriented as the base feature section was; otherwise, the view will be oriented with the selected surface parallel to the plane of the drawing.

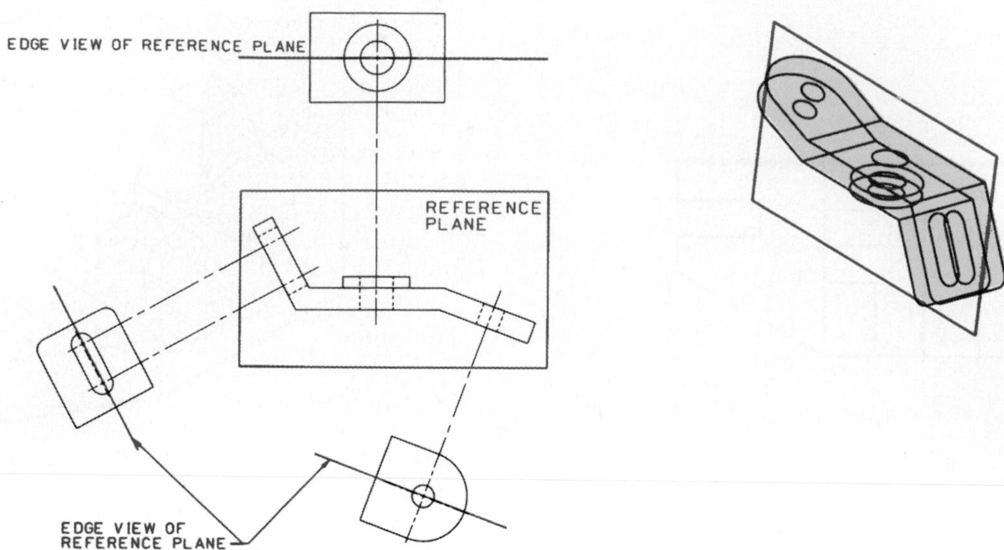

FIGURE 12.16 Reference Plane Method of Auxiliary View Projection

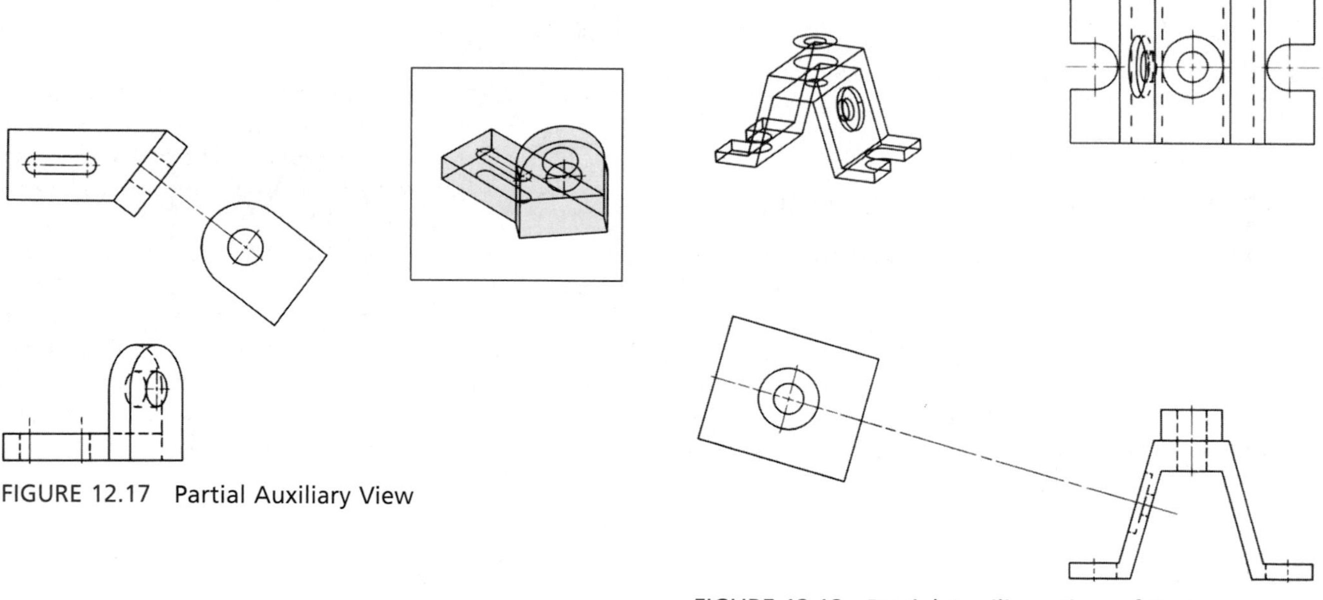

FIGURE 12.17 Partial Auxiliary View

FIGURE 12.18 Partial Auxiliary View of Part

Figure 12.16, the top view of the part is only partially shown; in fact, only the front view of this example is complete. Partial top and auxiliary views were all that was required to define the part's configuration adequately. In this figure, the reference plane was passed through the center of the part, rather than along one of the edges. This method is frequently used where the part to be drawn is symmetrical about its centerline. Passing the reference plane down the centerline of a part makes it easy to transfer the dimensions.

Reference planes are not shown in Figures 12.17 and 12.18. In both cases, the auxiliary view is a partial auxiliary view. Features that would have appeared distorted (not true shape) and all hidden lines have been left off.

12.4.2 Broken and Half Auxiliary Views

In some situations, a portion of the auxiliary view must be shown, as in Figure 12.19. Here, the base is partially shown (*broken*) in the auxiliary view. This is a form of partial auxiliary view. In Figure 12.20, a **half top view** and a **half auxiliary view** are shown. The part is symmetrical about its centerline; therefore, little is gained by drawing a complete top view. The same can be said of the auxiliary views. In this example, one of the auxiliary views is shown as a full view to

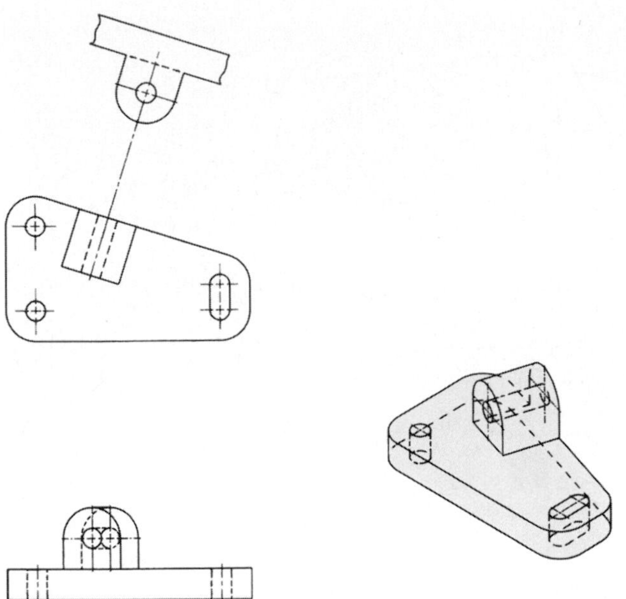

FIGURE 12.19 Broken Partial Auxiliary View

indicate the difference between the types. The only complete view in this example is the front view. The centerline dividing the part is always shown on half views.

12.4.3 Auxiliary Views of Curved Features

Circular and **curved features** are true size/shape in views where the line of sight is perpendicular to the edge view of the surface on which they lie. In the adjacent projection the plane appears as an edge and parallel to the fold line. The length of the edge view line is equal to the circle's diameter.

When a circular plane is oblique, it appears as an ellipse. An elliptical view of a circular plane along with each adjacent auxiliary view is plotted by locating a series of points along the outline of the circle in a true-size view. These points are located in each adjacent view by projection and by transferring distances to establish each individual point. The series of points is connected with a template or an irregular curve.

To locate a given circle on a plane, a true-shape view of the plane must be found. A typical problem in industry is centering a hole on a given surface. In Figure 12.21, plane 1-2-3-4 is given and a hole/circle of a specific size is to be drilled/drawn in the exact center of an oblique plane. Primary and secondary auxiliary views will be required. The following steps were used to complete the problem.

1. Line 1_H-3_H and line 2_H-4_H are horizontal lines (true length in the horizontal view). Therefore, a true-length line need not be constructed to find the edge view. Draw H/A perpendicular to the horizontal lines, and project auxiliary view A. Plane 1_A-2_A-3_A-4_A is an edge in this view [Fig. 12.21(a)].
2. Draw A/B parallel to the edge view of plane 1_A-2_A-3_A-4_A, and project auxiliary view B. This view shows the true size of the plane [Fig. 12.21(a)].
3. Locate the exact center of plane 1_B-2_B-3_B-4_B, and draw the given circle [Fig. 12.21(a)].
4. To project the centered circle back to all previous views, a series of points needs to be located along its circumference. A simple method to locate points on the circle is to divide the circle evenly by drawing lines from the corners of the plane [Fig. 12.21(b)].
5. Locate each point in auxiliary view A by projection where they fall on the edge of plane 1_A-2_A-3_A-4_A. Use dimensions D1, D2, and D3 to locate each point in the horizontal view by transferring them along their respective projection lines. Axes A (major diameter) and B (minor diameter) could also be used to locate and draw each view of the circle [Fig. 12.21(b)].

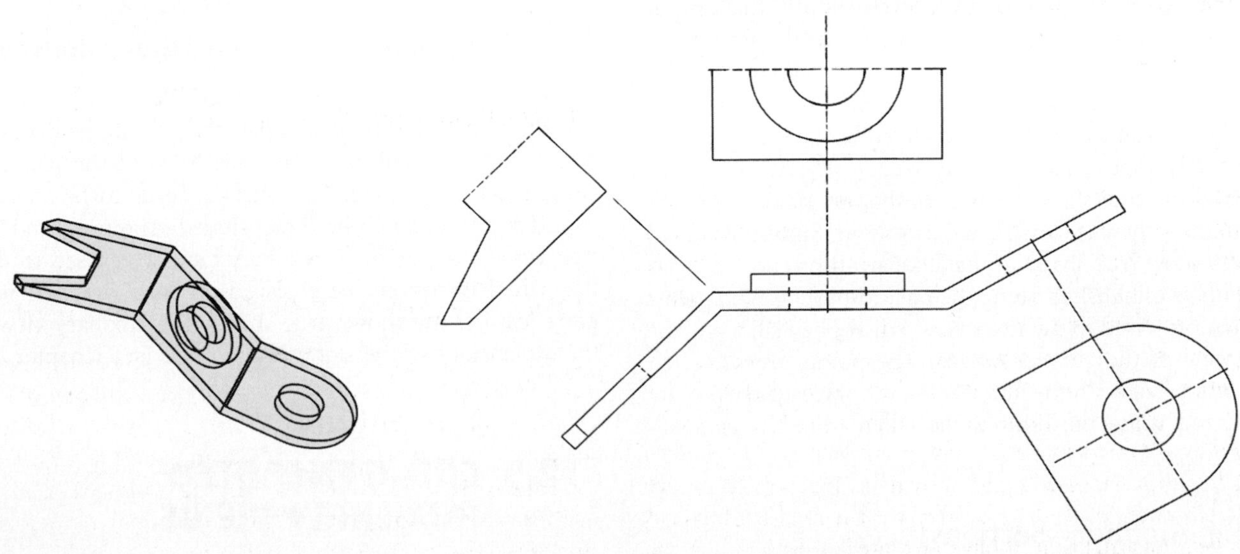

FIGURE 12.20 Half Views

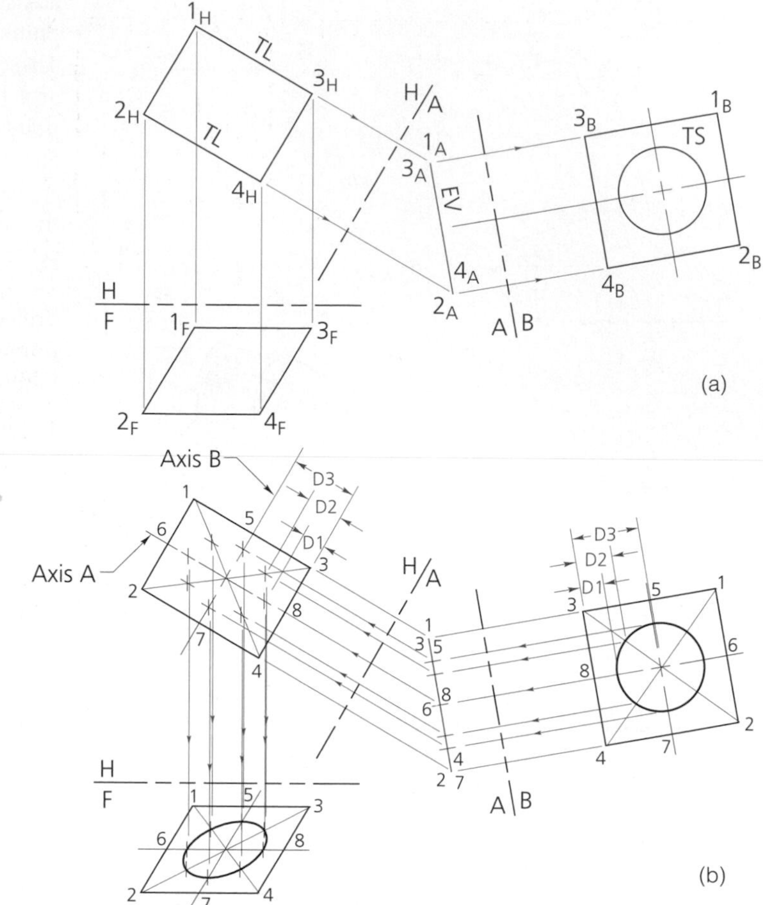

FIGURE 12.21 Reverse Construction for Plotting Curves on Views

6. Obtain the frontal view of the circle by projection and by transferring distances from auxiliary view A (from H/A to each point on the edge view).
7. Then connect the points with a smooth curve using an irregular curve.

In Figure 12.22, the part has curved features that appear oblique in the top view, show as an edge in the front view, and are true shape in the auxiliary projection. In this situation, *reverse construction* of the curved features is required if the features are to be projected back to the top view (where they appear distorted—*not true shape*). After the front view and the true-shape features of the top view are drawn, the auxiliary view is constructed as shown. Since the curved features show true shape in the auxiliary projection, a series of points is established along the curved outline. The points are then projected to the front view, where they fall along the edge view of the curved surface. The points are projected to the top view from the front view. Measurements are transferred using the dimensions taken from the auxiliary projection.

12.4.4 Auxiliary Sections

Auxiliary views that are sections are called **auxiliary sections.** In Figure 12.23 the part has a section passed through the ribs. This feature cannot be adequately defined and detailed through the top, front, or partial side view. A section was cut perpendicular through the ribs and projected as an auxiliary section view. Section lining is drawn at a different angle than that of the lines of the part features.

12.4.5 Auxiliary Views and Dimensioning

The primary reason for projecting auxiliary views is to show and dimension the shape of a part that cannot be defined in one of the principal views. In Figure 12.24 the part has a surface that is inclined. This surface needs to be shown as true shape in order to be dimensioned. The front and right side views along with an auxiliary view were used to detail the part. Dimensions were placed on each view where the part's features are shown true shape. The auxiliary view has the dimensions of the slot and the holes (see Chapter 15).

12.5 CAD-GENERATED AUXILIARY VIEWS

Two-dimensional CAD systems can rotate an axis in 2D for easier projection of an auxiliary view, but they still require

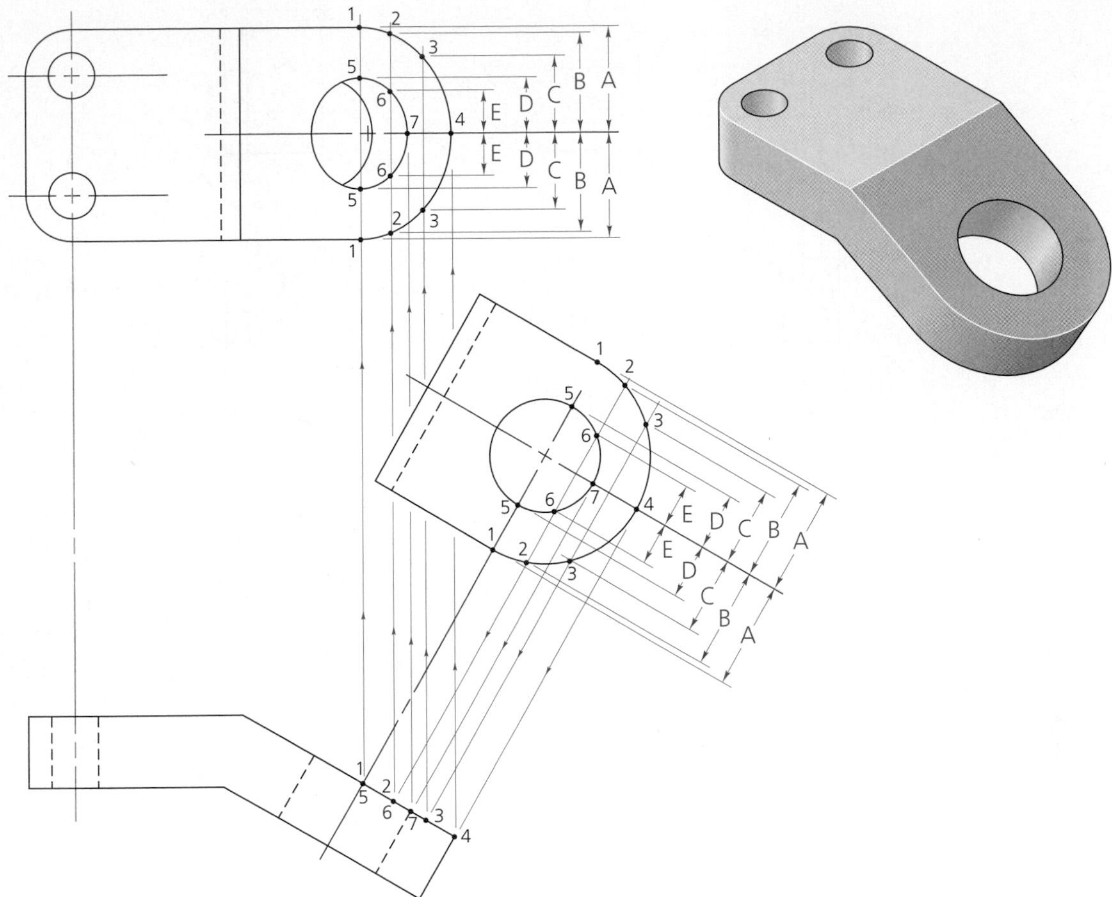

FIGURE 12.22 Projecting Curved Features into Principal Views

similar techniques for mastering and projecting auxiliary views as those previously described for manual drafting. Since a 3D system builds a database containing the complete part (not just 2D views), you can automatically display standard views as well as auxiliary views.

In Figure 12.25 the part has been modeled on a 3D CAD system. After modeling, the part's views, including a complete auxiliary view, were displayed. In Figure 12.26 the two ears of the part are at an angle to the front and top principal planes. An auxiliary view is needed to describe the part's features properly. The part had already been modeled and displayed in the top, front, and right side views as shown. A

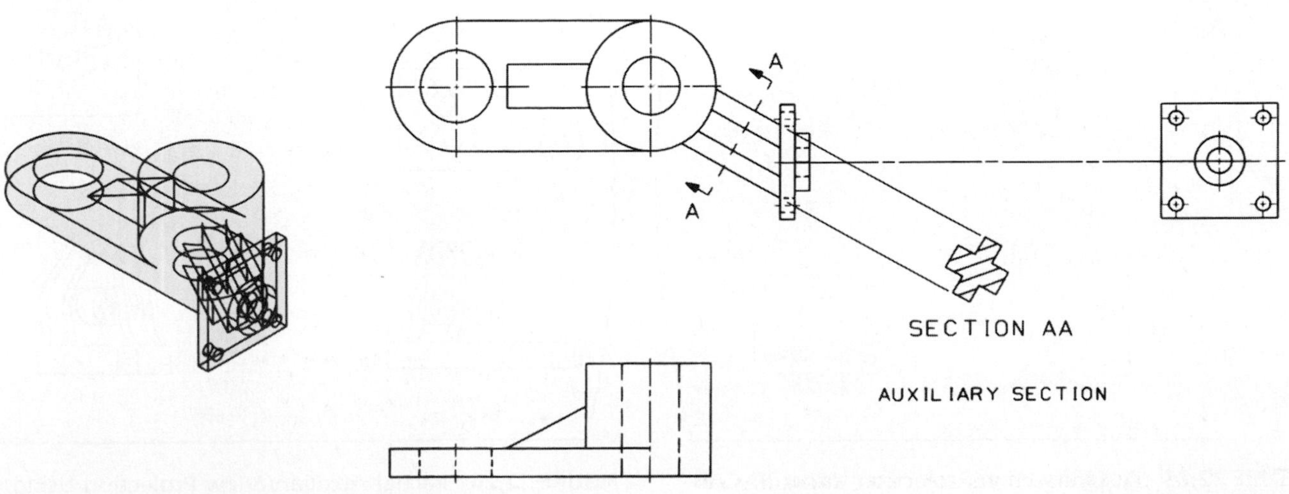

FIGURE 12.23 Auxiliary Section View

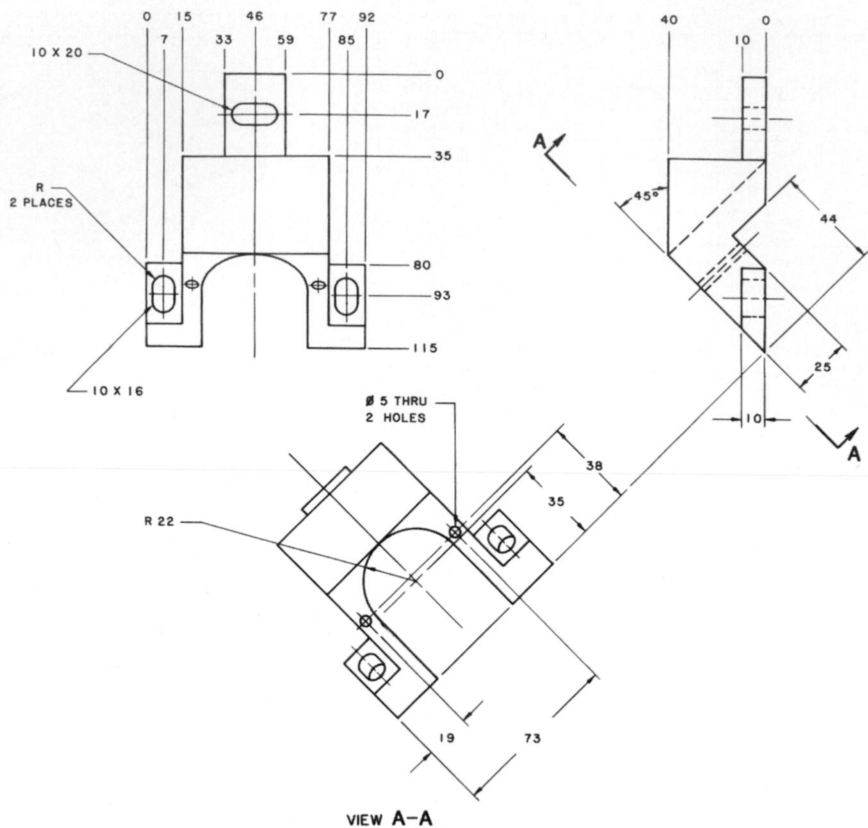

FIGURE 12.24 Auxiliary View and Dimensioning

partial view was established by folding only the inclined surfaces. All other edges of the part are not displayed in the auxiliary view. In each of these cases, the auxiliary view was generated for the sole purpose of establishing the circular features of the part that did not show as true shape in a principal view. Figure 12.27 was created on AutoCAD as a solid 3D part, displayed in appropiate views and in a drawing format placed about the drawing. The auxiliary view was created automatically by establishing a **user coordinate system** (**UCS**), selecting the new UCS, and requesting a view of that surface.

You May Now Complete Exercises 12.5 Through 12.8

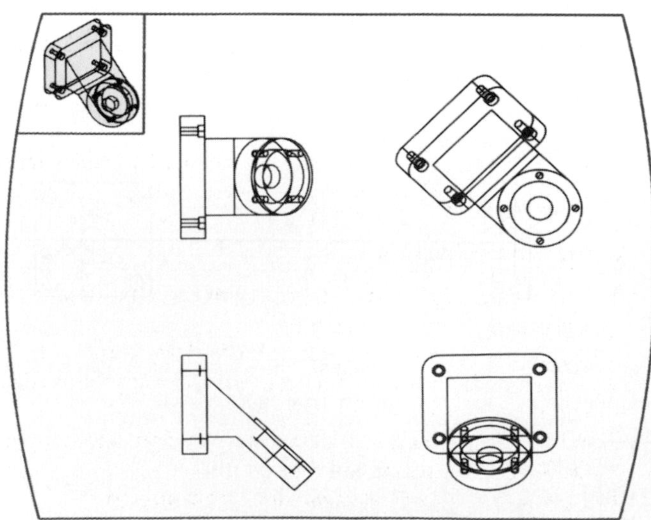

FIGURE 12.25 Auxiliary View Projection Using 3D CAD

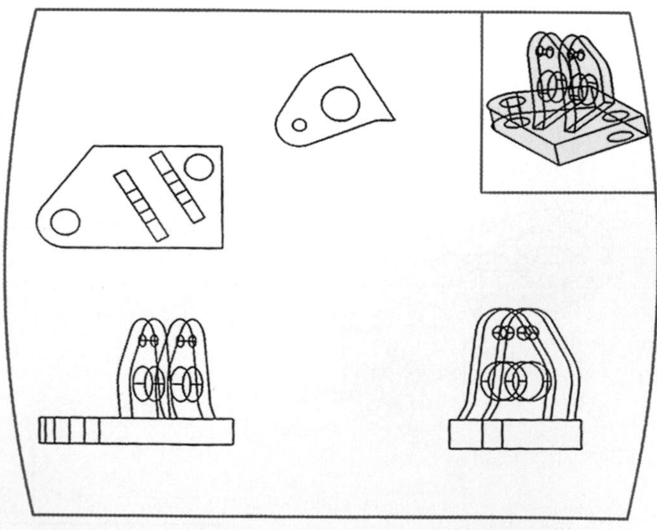

FIGURE 12.26 Partial Auxiliary View Projection Using 3D CAD

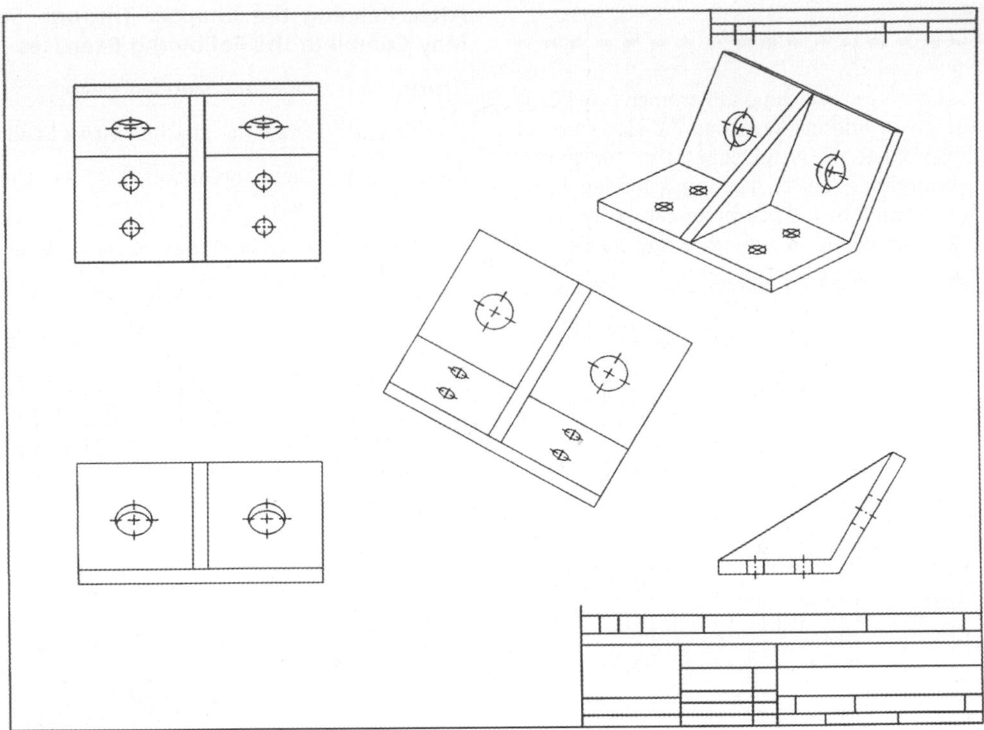

FIGURE 12.27 Angle Bracket Modeled on AutoCAD Using Solids and Displayed on a Drawing Format with Top, Front, Right Side, Auxiliary, and Pictorial Views

QUIZ

True or False

1. Most auxiliary views are only partial projections.
2. Oblique, inclined, and otherwise-distorted geometry is always shown on a view.
3. The top, front, and side views are always shown on a drawing when an auxiliary view is required to display inclined features for a part.
4. On a 2D CAD system, views can be generated automatically from existing geometry.
5. Auxiliary views may reduce the need for principal views of the part.
6. Auxiliary views are normally used for projecting a view to show the true shape of a surface that is inclined or oblique in the principal views.
7. A reference plane is always placed so that it is perpendicular to the inclined surface that is to be projected to an auxiliary view.
8. Auxiliary views are used only to display the true shape of a feature.

Fill in the Blanks

9. A __________ auxiliary view is projected from one of the standard principal views.
10. A reference plane or a fold line can be established on a part to aid in the __________ of an __________ view.
11. __________ __________ views are projected from the front views.
12. The __________ __________ is normally passed through a prominent feature of the part so as to make projection of auxiliary views easier and quicker.
13. CAD systems enable the drafter to __________ views from existing projections of a 3D part.
14. An auxiliary view can be __________ from an adjacent view when using a 3D CAD system
15. Half auxiliary views are normally used where the part is __________ about a __________ .
16. A __________ __________ view is adjacent and aligned with a secondary view.

Answer the Following

17. What is the edge view of a plane, and how is it used in the projection of a true-shape view?
18. What is the primary purpose of an auxiliary view?
19. Compare the fold line method with the reference plane method.
20. Why are partial auxiliary views more common than complete auxiliary projections?
21. How does 3D CAD affect auxiliary view projection?
22. What is a fold line, and how is it used?
23. What are half sections, and why are they used?
24. What is a broken auxiliary view?

EXERCISES

Exercises may be assigned as sketching, instrument, or CAD projects. Transfer the given information to an "A"-size sheet of .25 in. grid paper. Complete all views, and solve for proper visibility, including centerlines, object lines, and hidden lines. Exercises that are not assigned by the instructor can be sketched in the text to provide practice and to enhance understanding of the preceding instructional material.

After Reading the Chapter Through Section 12.4 You May Complete the Following Exercises

Exercise 12.1 Draw the required views.

Exercise 12.2 Draw the required views as shown.

Exercise 12.3 Draw the required views. Complete a full top view.

Exercise 12.4 Draw the three views as shown.

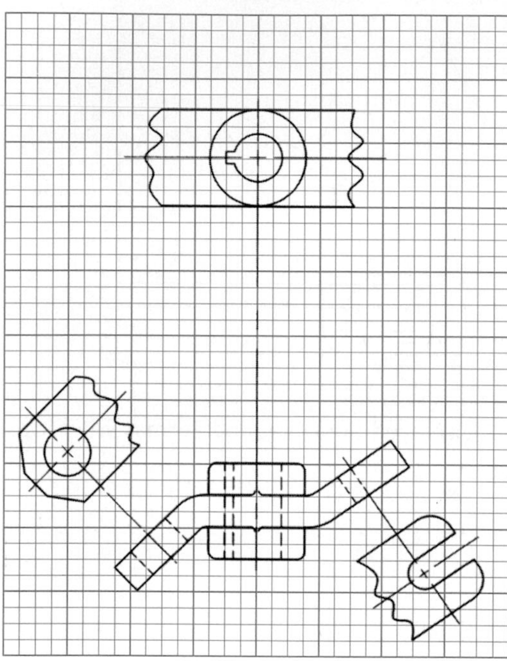

EXERCISE 12.1

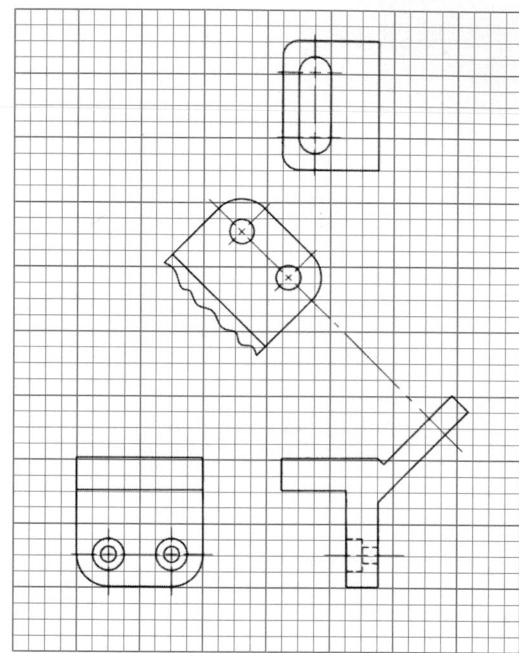

EXERCISE 12.3

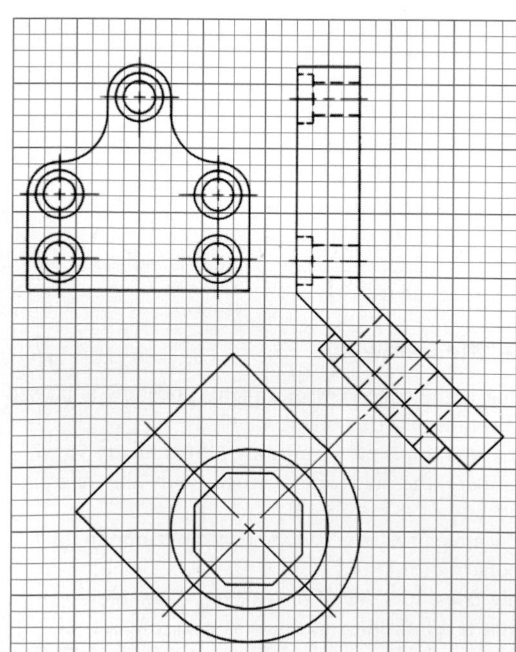

EXERCISE 12.2

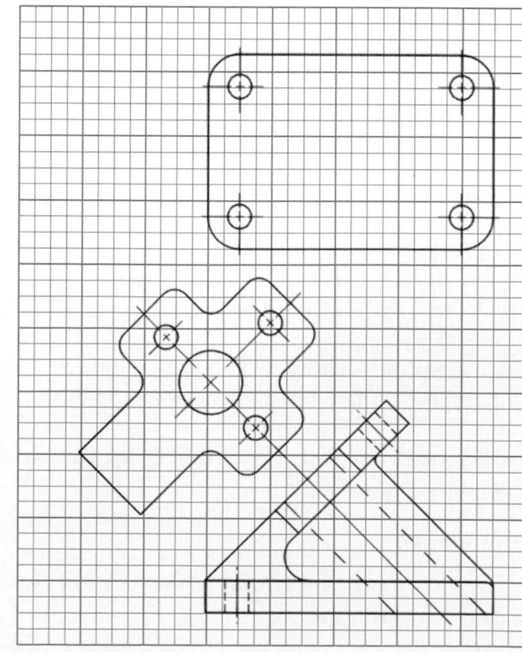

EXERCISE 12.4

After Reading the Chapter Through Section 12.5 You May Complete the Following Exercises

Exercise 12.5 Complete the required views and the auxiliary section.

Exercise 12.6 Draw the required views.

Exercise 12.7 Complete the required views and draw a full front view.

Exercise 12.8 Draw the required views. Project a secondary auxiliary view showing surface A or B as true shape/size.

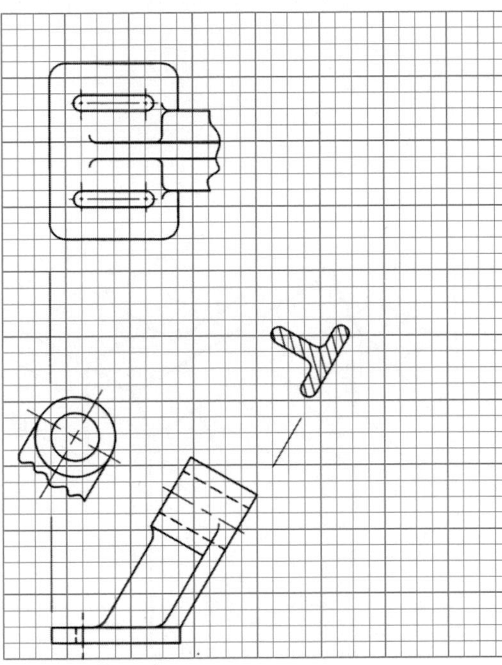

EXERCISE 12.5

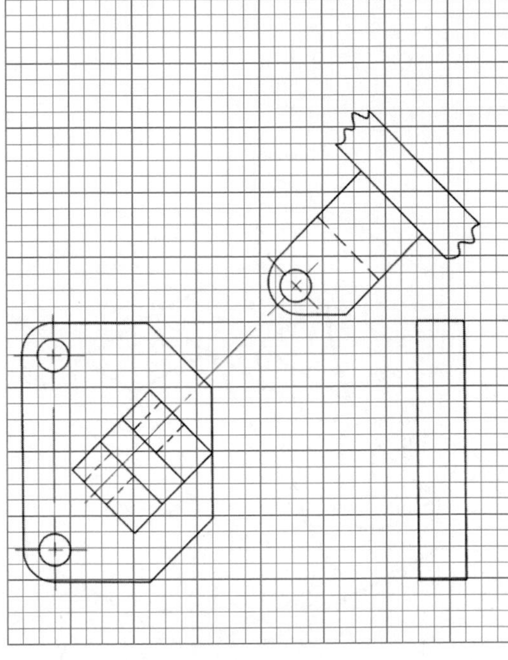

EXERCISE 12.7

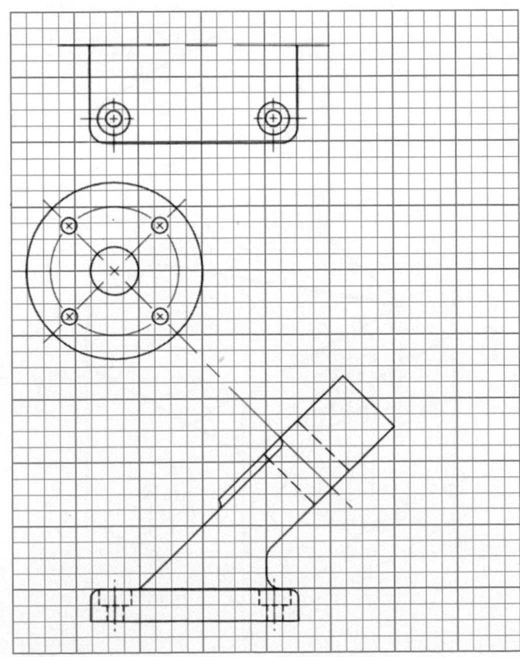

EXERCISE 12.6

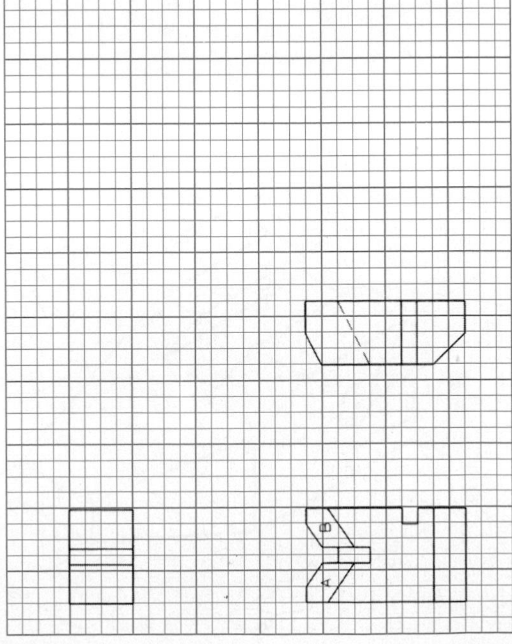

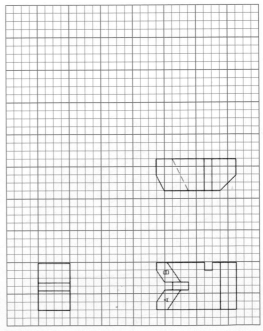

EXERCISE 12.8

PROBLEMS

Problems may be assigned as sketching, instrument, or CAD projects. Use these projects for problems when completing Chapter 15 on dimensioning. Complete all views, and solve for proper visibility, including centerlines, object lines, and hidden lines. When laying out these projects, leave sufficient room for dimensioning. Your instructor may assign projects to be dimensioned as problems for Chapter 15.

Problem 12.1 Draw the appropriate views of the part in order to describe each of its surfaces completely. Dimension after completing Chapter 15.

Problem 12.2 Draw the top, front, and auxiliary views of the part.

Problem 12.3 Draw the right side, top, and auxiliary views of the part in order to show each surface as true shape. Dimension after completing Chapter 15.

Problem 12.4 Draw the top, front, and auxiliary projections of the part.

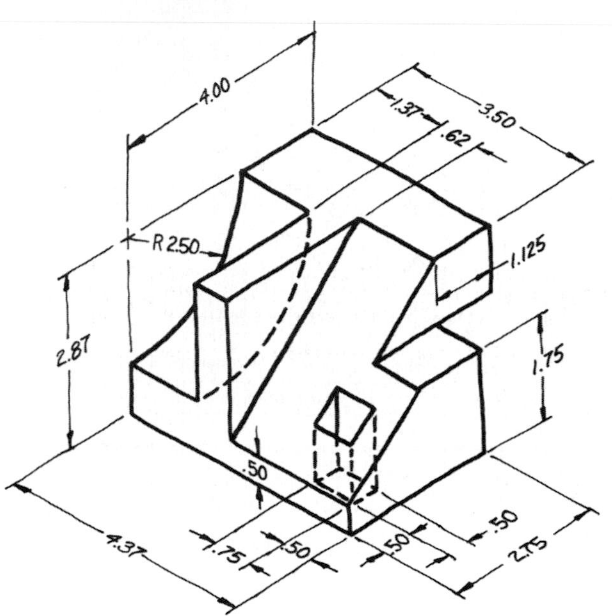

PROBLEM 12.1

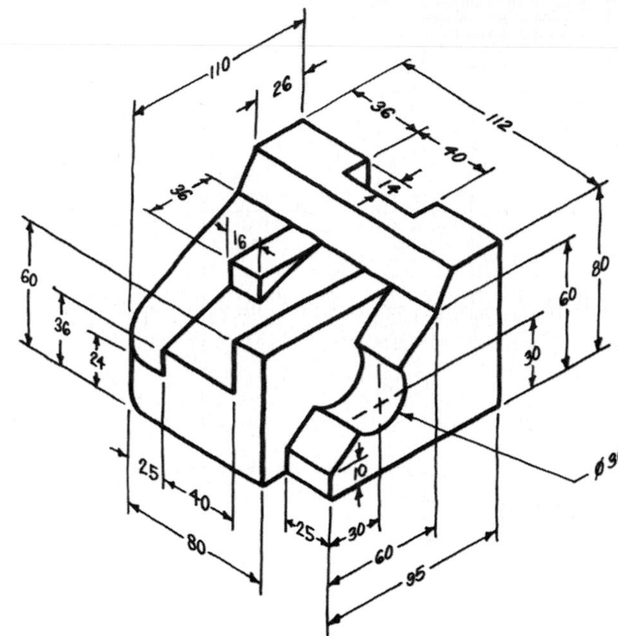

PROBLEM 12.3

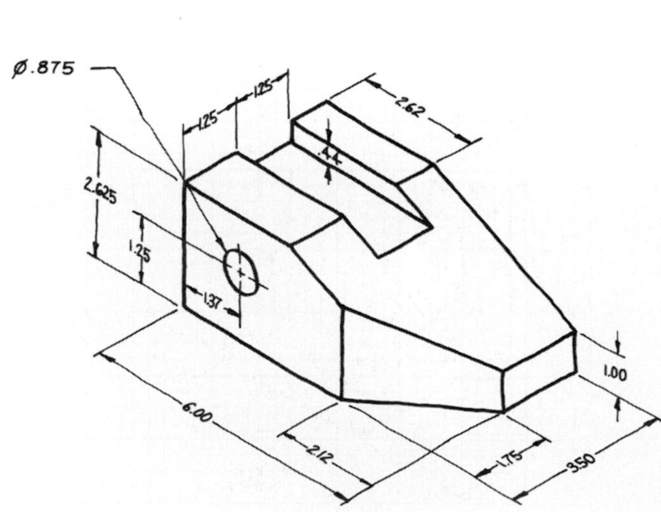

PROBLEM 12.2

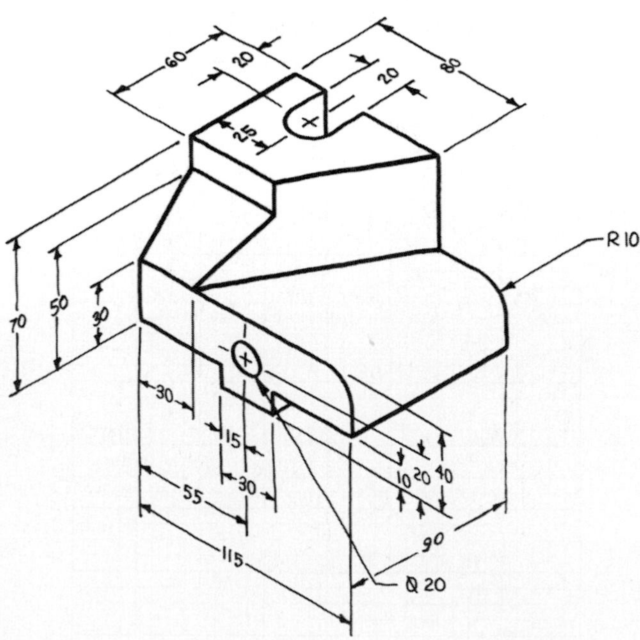

PROBLEM 12.4

Problem 12.5 Draw the front and right side views of the part. Project a true-shape view of the inclined surface. Position a 1.00 in. diameter hole near the middle of the surface, and show in all views. The hole is to be .25 in. deep with a flat bottom. Dimension after completing Chapter 15.

Problem 12.6 Draw the top, front, and side views and an auxiliary view projected from the top of the part. Center a 20 mm hole on the auxiliary surface. The hole is 15 mm deep with a flat bottom. Dimension after completing Chapter 15.

Problem 12.7 Draw the appropriate views needed to describe the part completely. Dimension after completing Chapter 15.

Problem 12.8 Draw the top and front views and any auxiliary views needed to display the triangular surface's true shape.

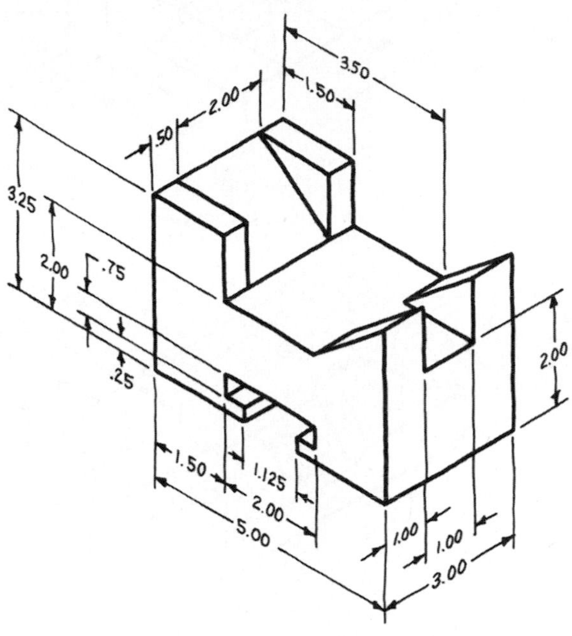

PROBLEM 12.5

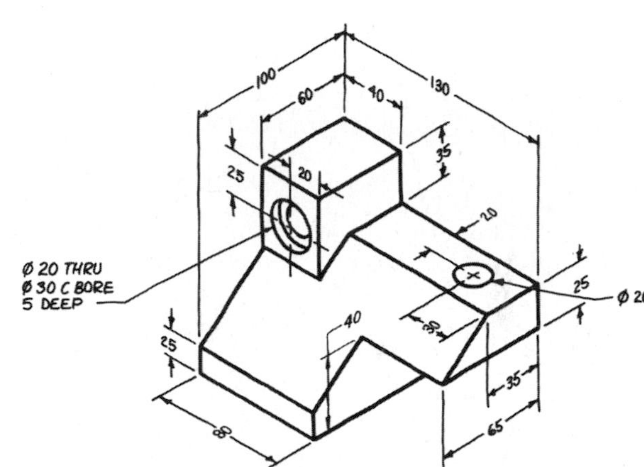

PROBLEM 12.7

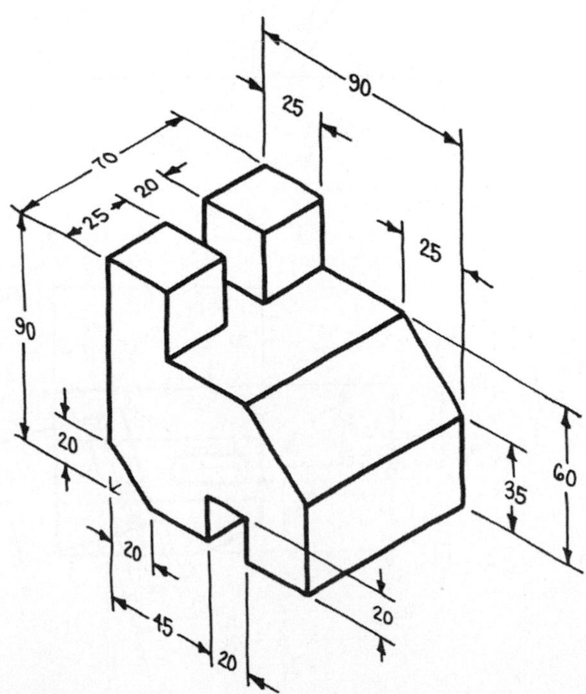

PROBLEM 12.6

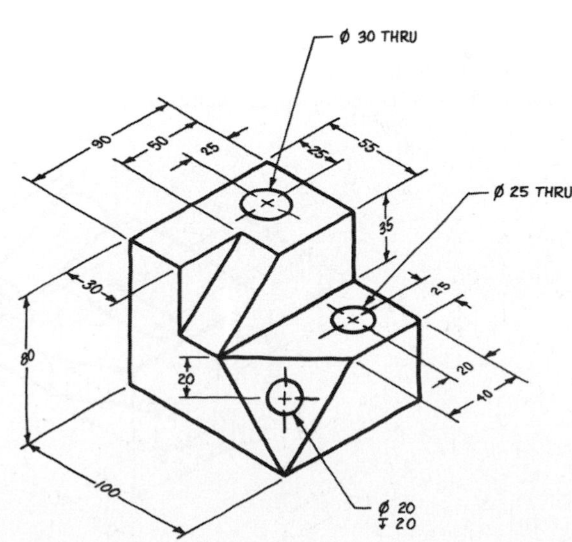

PROBLEM 12.8

Problem 12.9 Draw the views necessary to describe the part completely. The auxiliary projection should be a complete view. Dimension after completing Chapter 15.

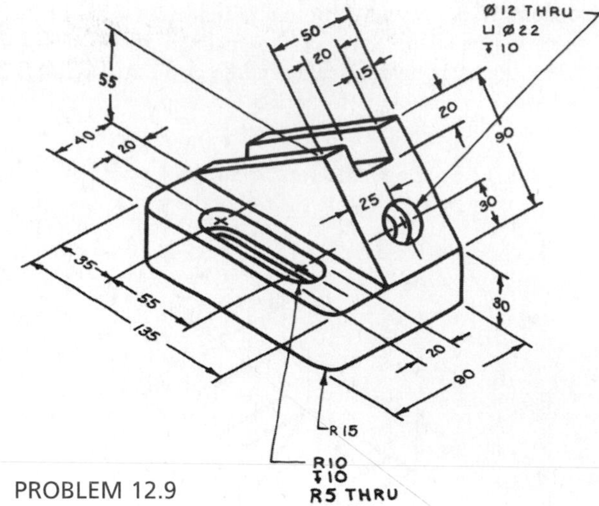

PROBLEM 12.9

Problem 12.10 Draw the views required to detail the part. Dimension after completing Chapter 15.

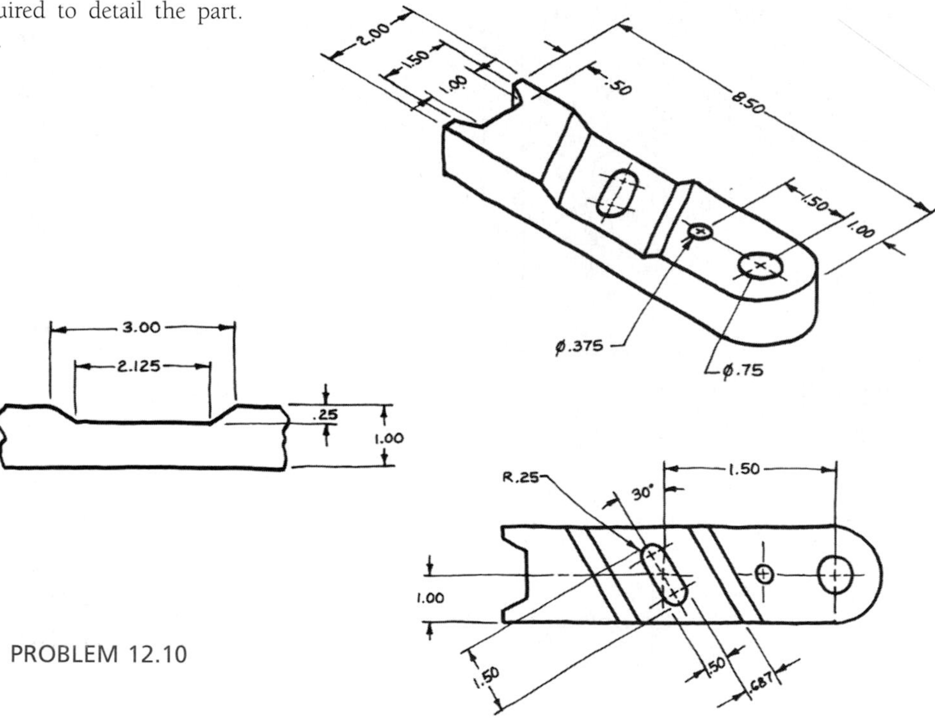

PROBLEM 12.10

Problem 12.11 Model the part in 3D, display the appropriate views, and dimension as required after completing Chapter 15.

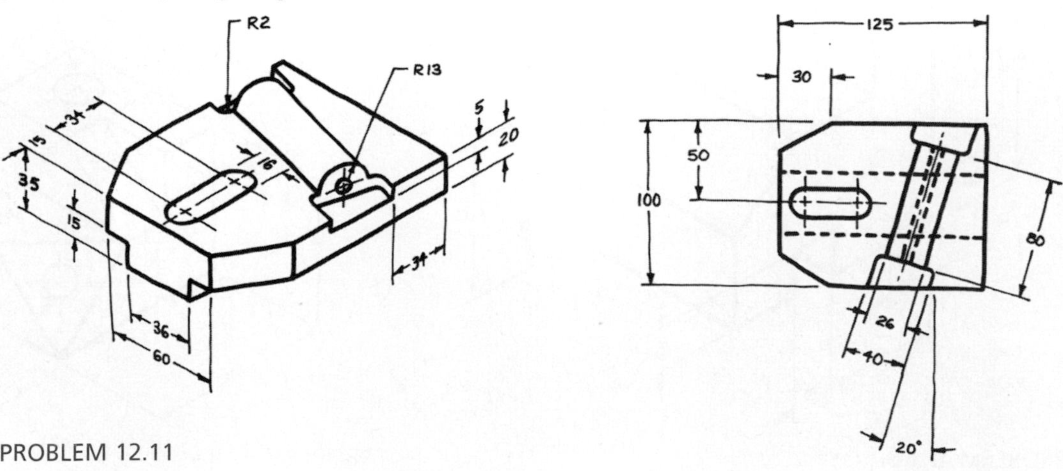

PROBLEM 12.11

Problem 12.12 Create a solid model of the part. Display the views required for dimensioning. Dimension the part as needed after completing Chapter 15.

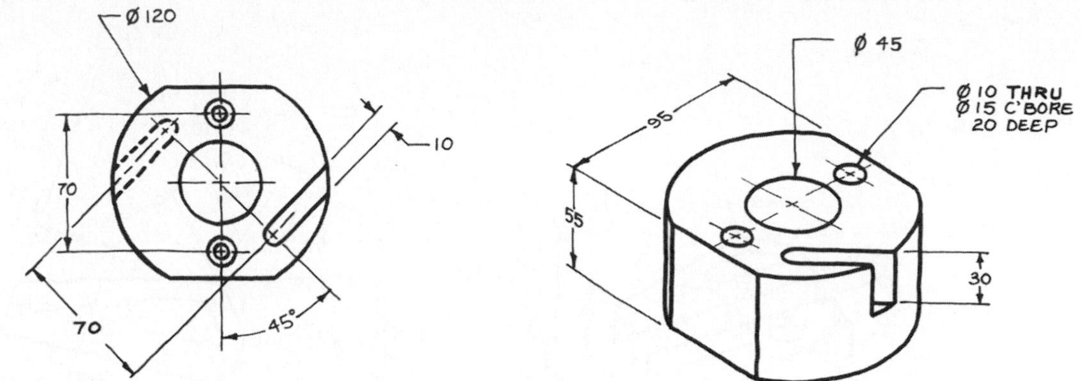

PROBLEM 12.12

Problem 12.13 Model the bracket on a 3D CAD system, and then display the proper views required for dimensioning.

NOTE:
ALL FILLETS AND ROUNDS TO BE .062 UNLESS OTHERWISE NOTED

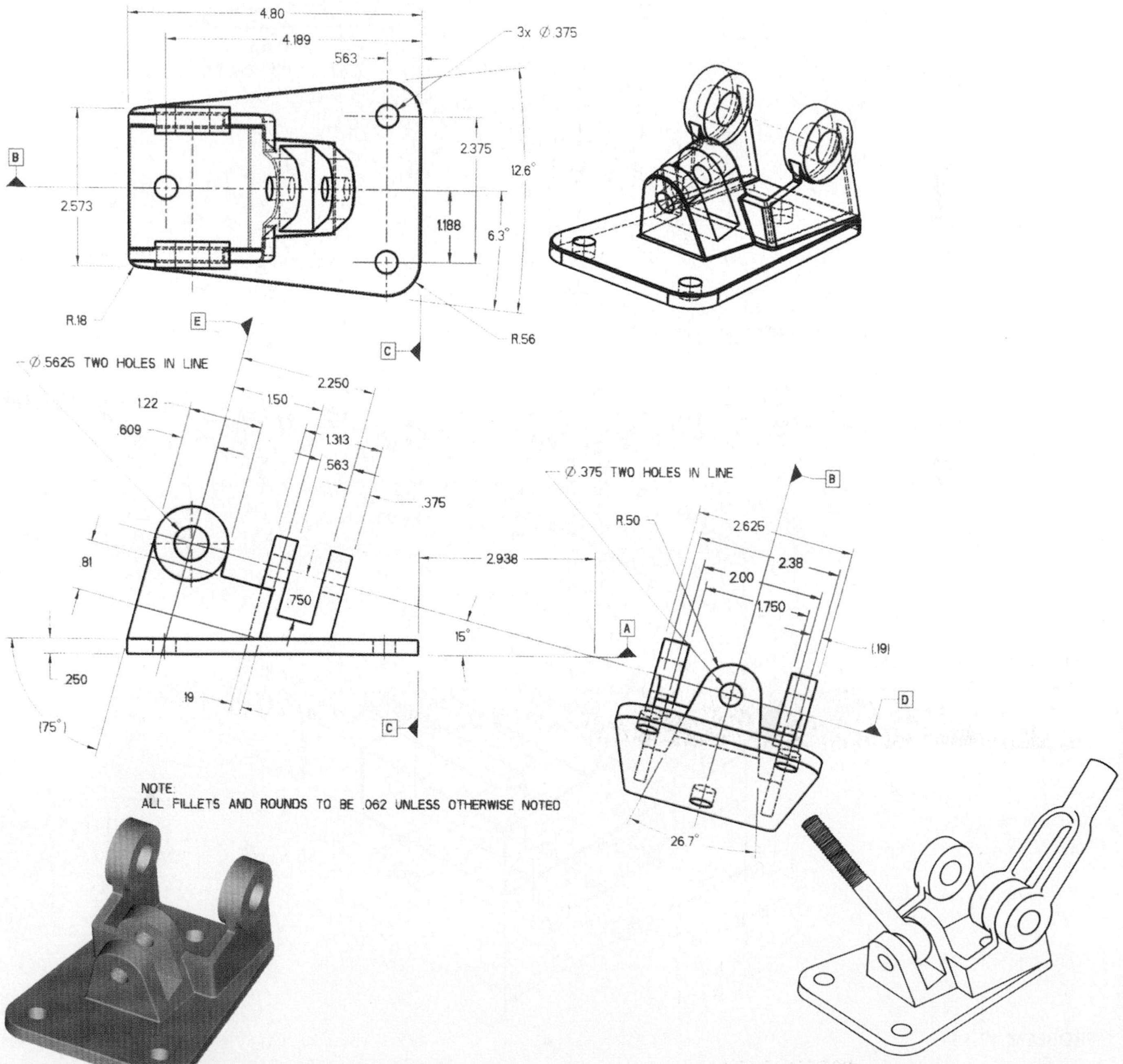

PROBLEM 12.13

Problem 12.14 Model the part, and show all required views. Dimension after completing Chapter 15.

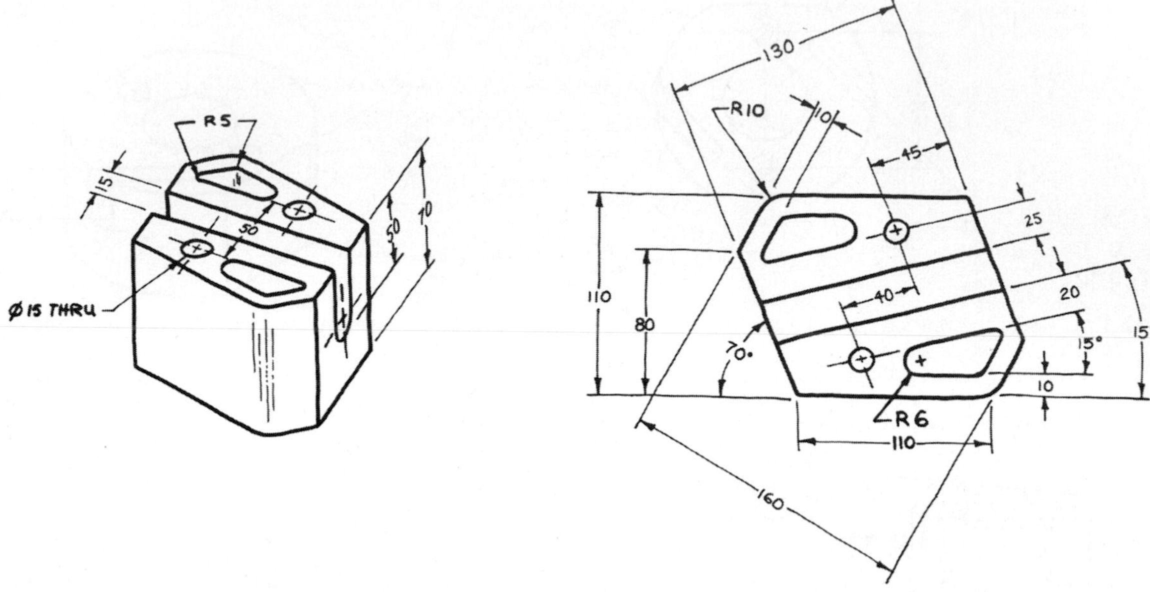

PROBLEM 12.14

Problem 12.15 Create a 3D model, and display a minimum number of views to detail the part. Dimension after completing Chapter 15.

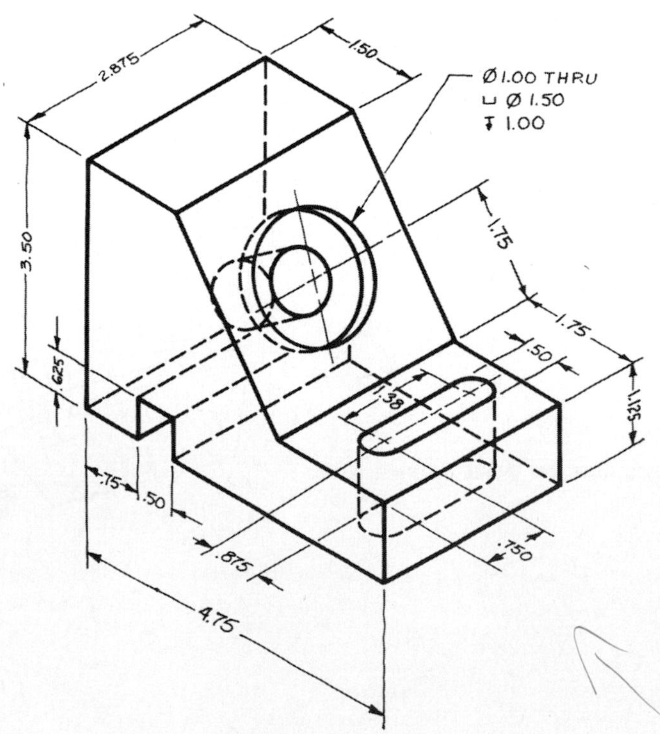

PROBLEM 12.15

Problem 12.16 Draw or model the microwave fitting. Lay out the views required to describe the part completely. Dimension after completing Chapter 15.

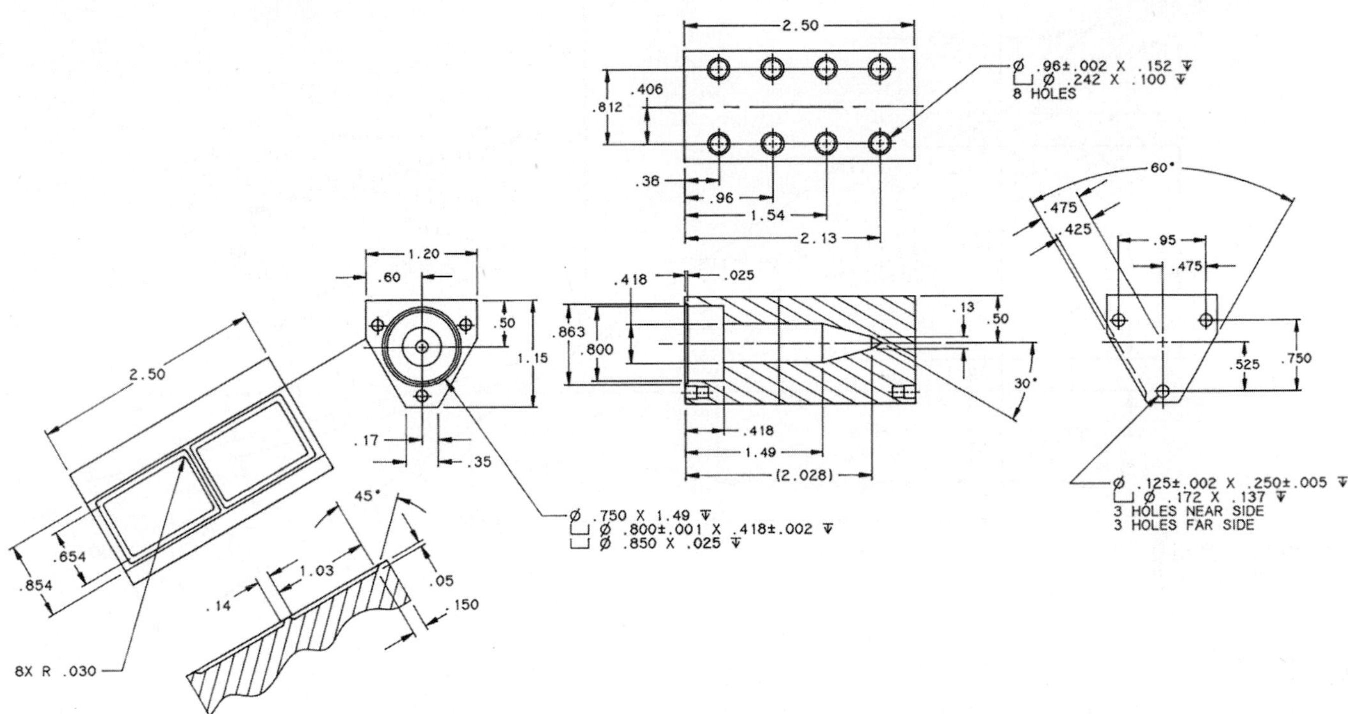

PROBLEM 12.16

Problem 12.17 Model the wind tunnel bracket in 3D, and display the required views in full. Dimension after completing Chapter 15.

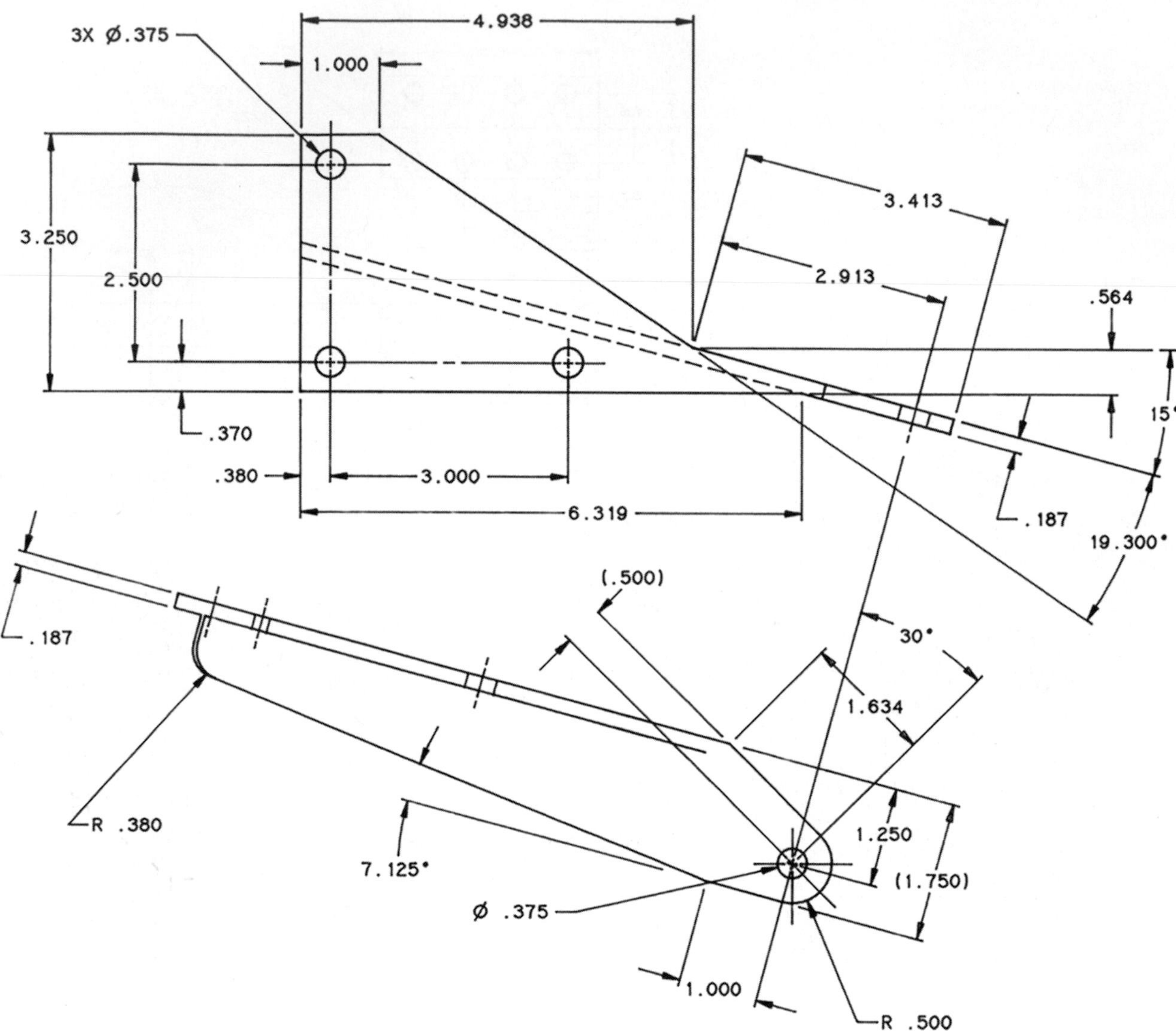

PROBLEM 12.17

Problem 12.18 Draw the views required to describe the casting. Use a .125 radius for all fillets and rounds unless sizes are called out on the drawing. Dimension after completing Chapter 15.

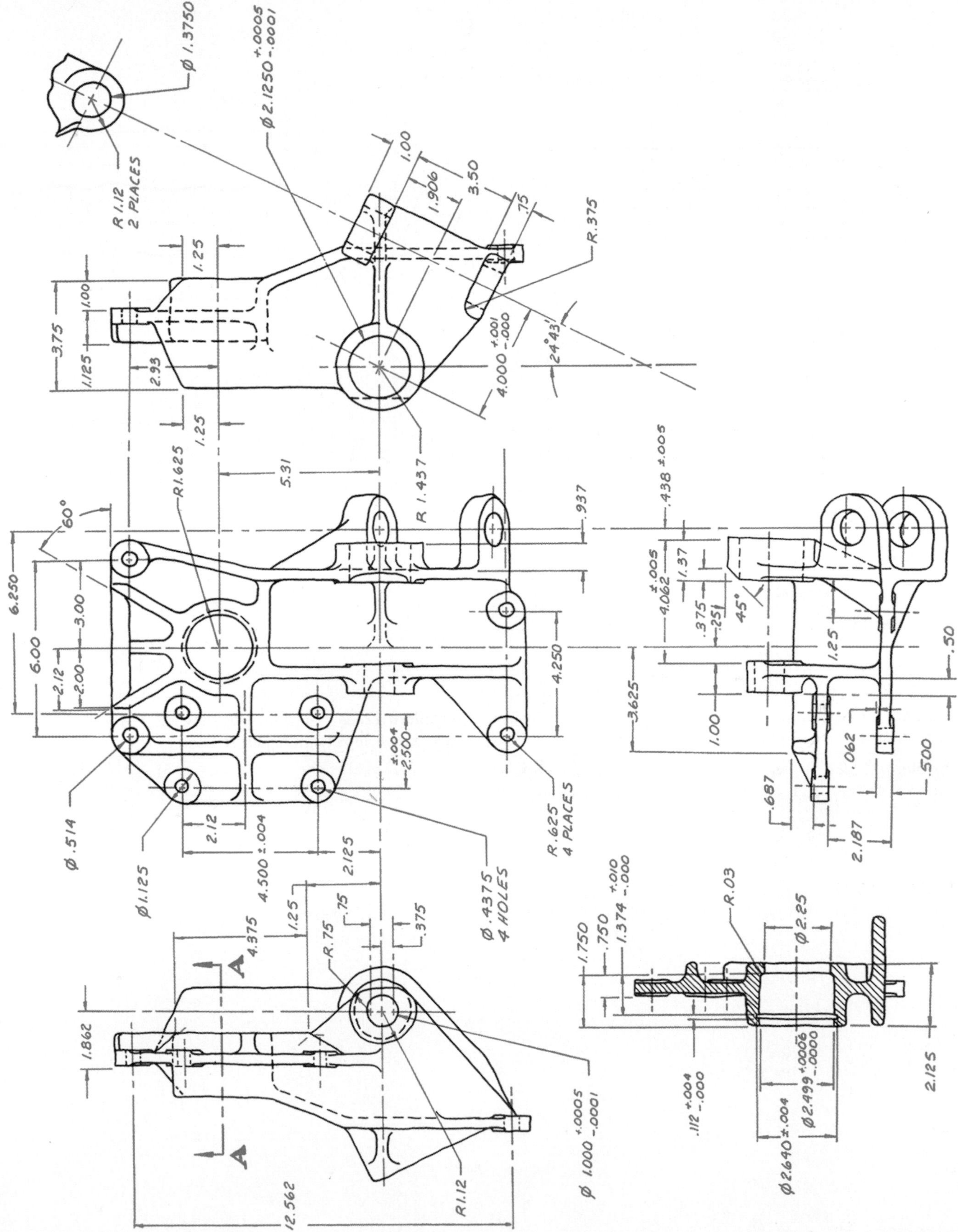

PROBLEM 12.18

Problem 12.19 Draw the detail of the bracket. Dimension after completing Chapter 15.

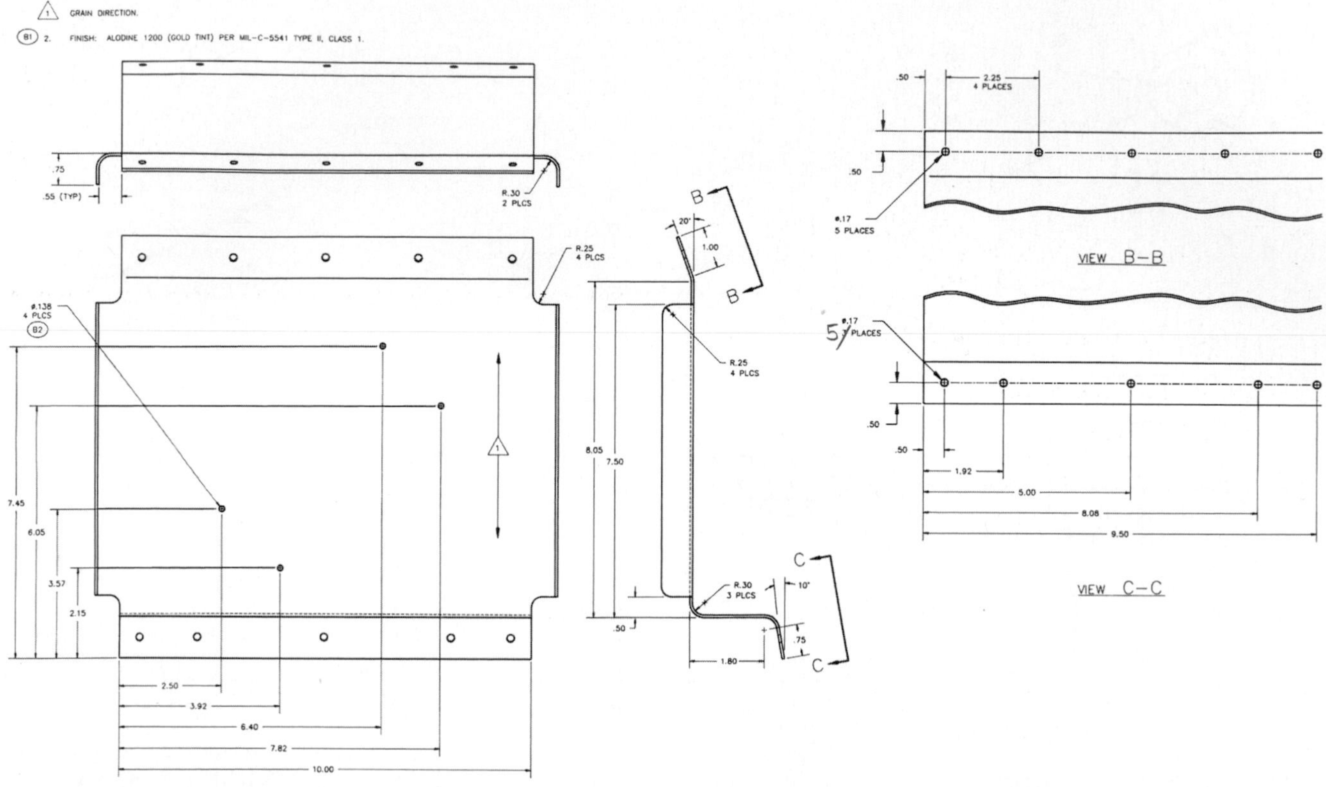

PROBLEM 12.19

Problem 12.20 Draw the part shown in Figure 12.2. Dimension after completing Chapter 15.

Problem 12.21 Draw the electronic component bracket shown in Figure 12.11. Dimension after completing Chapter 15.

Problem 12.22 Draw the part shown in Figure 12.24. Dimension after completing Chapter 15.

PICTORIALS: 3D REPRESENTATIONS AND 3D MODELING

Chapter 13

LEARNING OBJECTIVES

Upon completion of this chapter you will be able to:

1. Understand the difference between 3D representations and 3D modeling.
2. Recognize pictorial drawings as single-plane projections representing 3D shapes.
3. Understand the ways in which pictorial drawings may be most useful.
4. Understand and apply the functions of hidden lines, centerlines, and techniques for dimensioning on pictorials.
5. Become familiar with drafting conventions for illustrating certain part features pictorially.
6. Understand the basic capabilities and methodology of 3D modeling.
7. Recognize the three-dimensional modeling capabilities of CAD as applied to pictorials.
8. Define and be able to produce axonometric, oblique, and perspective drawings.

13.1 INTRODUCTION

Pictorial drawing is the oldest written method of communication known, but the character of pictorial drawing has continually changed with the advance of civilization. In this chapter, the types of pictorials commonly employed by engineers, designers, and illustrators are described. Pictorial drawings (whether manual or CAD) are single-plane projections. In other words, they present three primary surfaces to the viewer at the same time. Pictorials created on 3D CAD systems are actual to-scale **models** of a part, a structure, or some other object. The part in Figure 13.1(a) is a 3D shaded model of the flange bracket detail shown in Figure 13.1(b). The shaded pictorial was generated from the part database and displayed as a pictorial via a rendering program. The part was modeled and detailed with AutoCAD. A manual technical illustration is shown in Figure 13.2. Here, the exploded assembly pictorial was drawn by hand and inked with technical pens.

(a) Shaded image of a 3D model

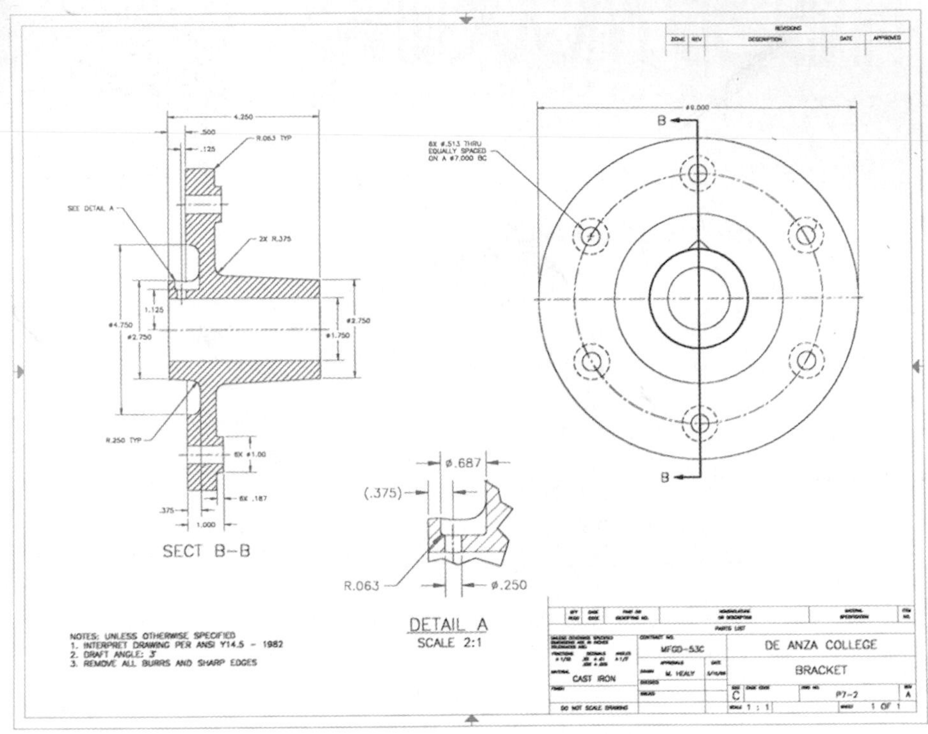

(b) Detail drawing generated from the 3D model

FIGURE 13.1 Bracket

Pictorials are useful in design, construction or production, erection or assembly, service or repairs, and sales. Pictorial sketching (Figure 13.3) was discussed in Chapter 9, where the use of pictorials was limited to the initial stages of the design process. Engineers and designers use pictorial sketches to refine and communicate 3D designs before they are formally drawn or modeled.

The choice of pictorial drawing is dependent on its intended application. Pictorials are used in a variety of ways throughout industry and business.

Uses of Pictorial Drawings

- To *explain* complicated engineering drawings to people who are not trained or who lack the time to read the conventional multiview drawings
- As a *supplement* to the engineering detail [Fig. 13.1(a)]
- To *train* new shop employees with the aid of illustrated training manuals
- To *speed up* and clarify the *assembly* of a machine
- For *ordering* new parts, as in parts catalogs and service manuals (Fig.13.2)

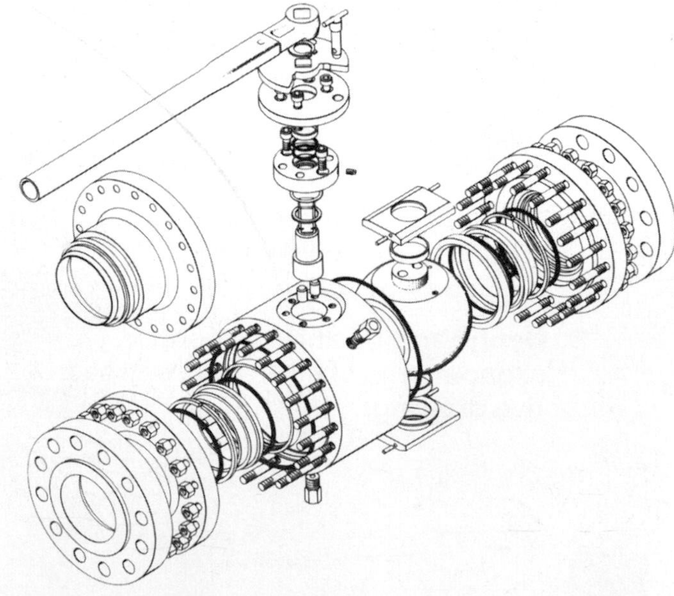

FIGURE 13.2 Technical Illustration of a Ball Valve from a Sales Catalog

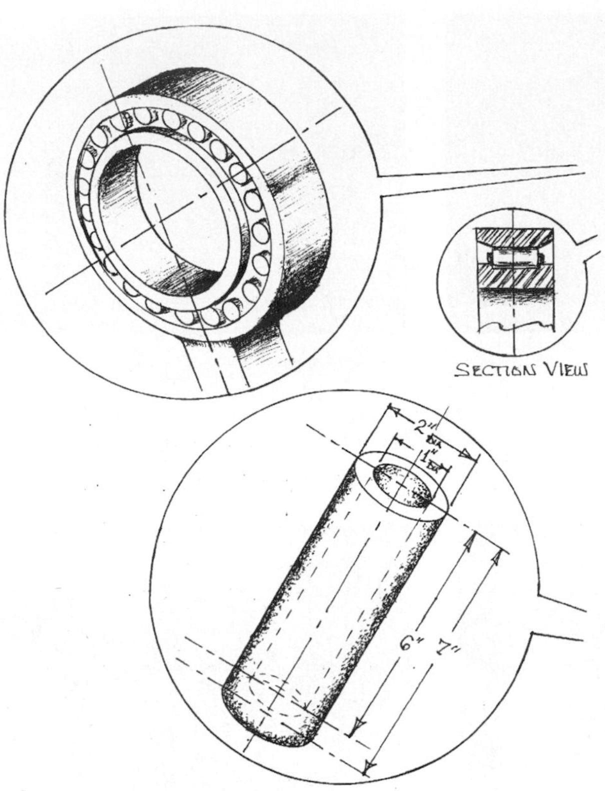

FIGURE 13.3 Pictorial Sketch

FIGURE 13.4 Space Station Solar Panels and Support System

- As design *sketches* to clarify a concept or process (Fig. 13.3)
- To *transmit ideas* from person to person, from shop to shop, or from sales to purchasing
- To *display* futuristic *designs* or concepts (Fig. 13.4)
- As an *educational aid* in developing visualization.
- To *present new* product *designs* (Fig.13.5)
- To *render* a product, project, or display [Fig. 13.6(a)–(c)]
- To *help* the designer or engineer *work out problems in 3D space,* such as clearances, intersections, interferences, and routing [Fig. 13.7(a)–(e)]
- To *design and modify complex subassemblies and assemblies* [Fig. 13.8(a) and (b)]

FIGURE 13.5 Research and Development Illustration of a New Product

(a) Sauna

(b) Yacht interior

(c) Sunroom

FIGURE 13.6 Room Interiors

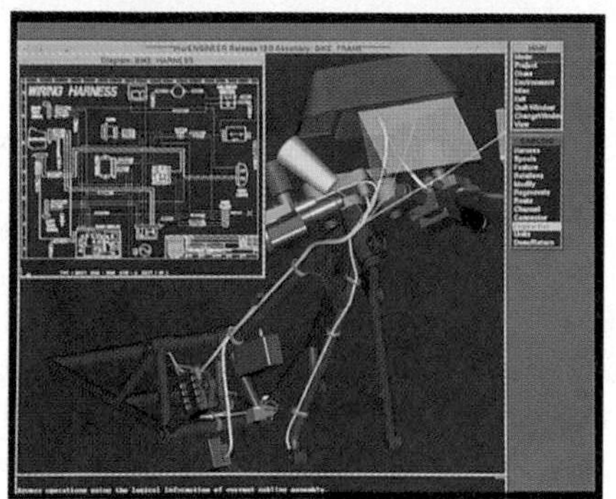
(a) Pro/CABLING

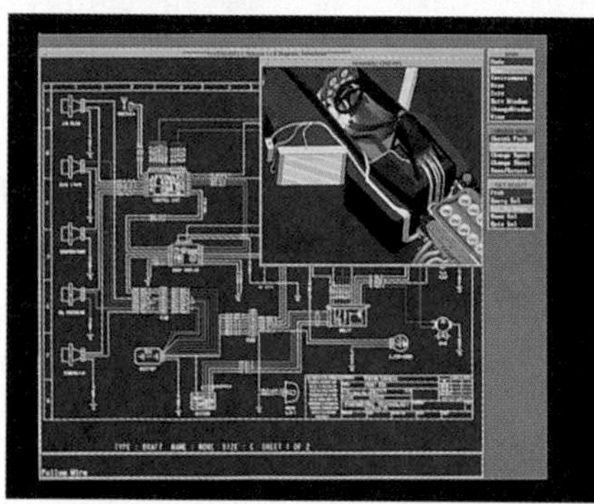
(b) Pro/ECAD

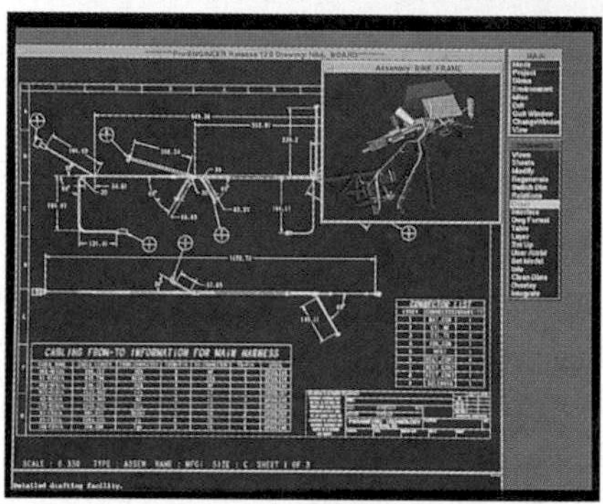
(c) Pro/HARNESS

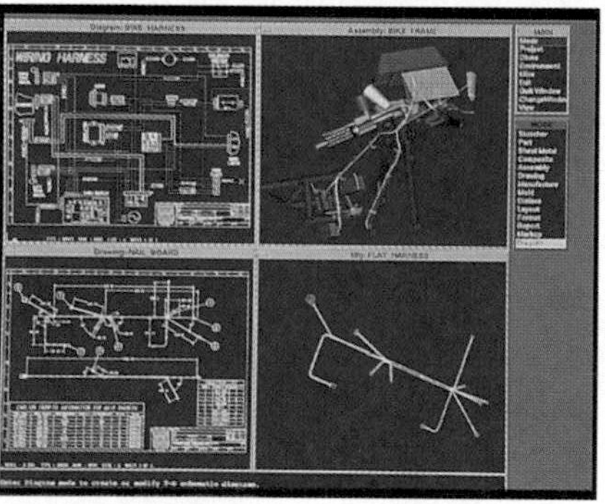
(d) Pro/HARNESS

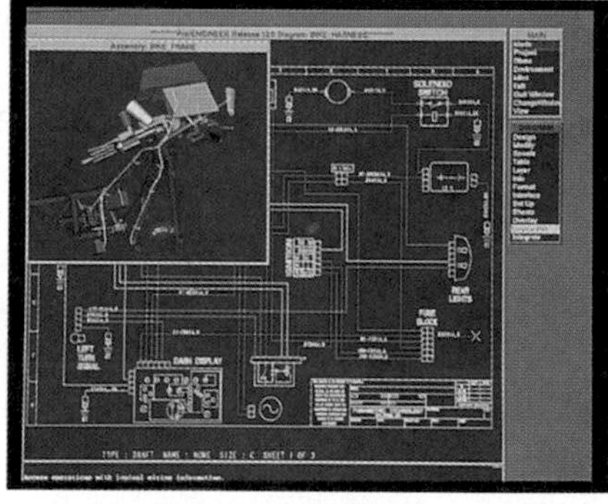
(e) Pro/HARNESS

FIGURE 13.7 Using Pictorials to Enhance 3D Design

13.2 TYPES OF PICTORIAL DRAWING

Pictorials can be divided into three general projection methods: axonometric, oblique, and perspective. These differ from each other in the fundamental scheme of projection (Fig. 13.9). Axonometric projection is a form of orthographic projection. Each of the three projection methods is subdivided by varying some of the relationships between point of sight, plane of projection, and the object. In Figures 13.10, 13.11, and 13.12, the same assembly has been displayed by each of the projection types and their accompanying versions. The four versions of axonometric projection are illustrated in Figure 13.10: isometric projection, isometric drawing, dimetric projection, and trimetric projection. The three versions of oblique projection are illustrated in Figure 13.11: cavalier, cabinet, and general. The three versions of perspective projection are illustrated in Figure 13.12: one-point, two-point, and three-point.

The view of a part is normally selected so that it will give the greatest information possible, unless its natural position or its relationship to other parts must take precedence.

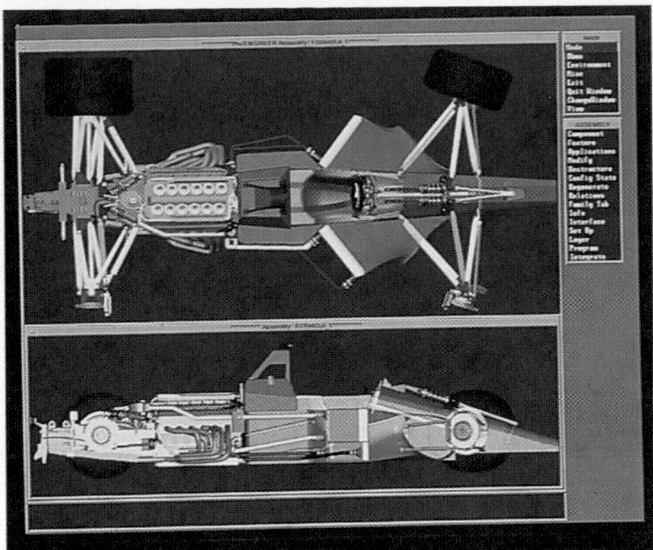

(a) Two views of Indy car

(b) Internal view of Indy car

FIGURE 13.8 Indy Car Design

13.3 AXONOMETRIC PROJECTION

A projected view in which the lines of sight are perpendicular to the plane of projection but in which the three faces of a rectangular object are all inclined to the plane of projection is called an **axonometric projection.** The projections of the three principal axes may make any angle with each other except 90°. Three types of axonometric projection are used: isometric, dimetric, and trimetric. Isometric is the most common.

An **isometric projection** is a pictorial drawing in which the three principal faces and the three principal axes of the object are inclined equally to the plane of projection. The plane of projection is called the *isometric plane*. The three axes on the drawing also make equal angles with each other [Fig. 13.13(a)], but may be placed in a variety of positions. A true orthographic projection of an object on the isometric plane is an isometric projection. The scales on all three axes are equal and foreshortened in the ratio of approximately 0.8 to 1.0. The term *axes* refers to the projections of the principal axes, unless otherwise stated.

A **dimetric projection** [Fig. 13.13(b)] is drawn with two axes making equal angles and the third axis at any selected angle. A **trimetric projection** uses three different scales (one for each axis) and has three different angles for the axes [Fig. 13.13(c)]. Trimetric projection is the most lifelike method, but it is also the most time-consuming and difficult to draw.

Since most pictorials are drawn with isometric projection methods, the following discussion will concentrate on this type. Dimetric projection and trimetric projection are completed with the same general layout procedures as isometric projection. Therefore, the following techniques will apply for all three types.

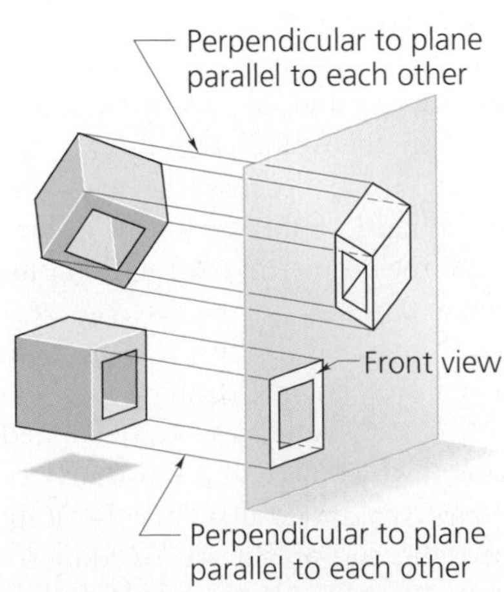

(a) Axonometric

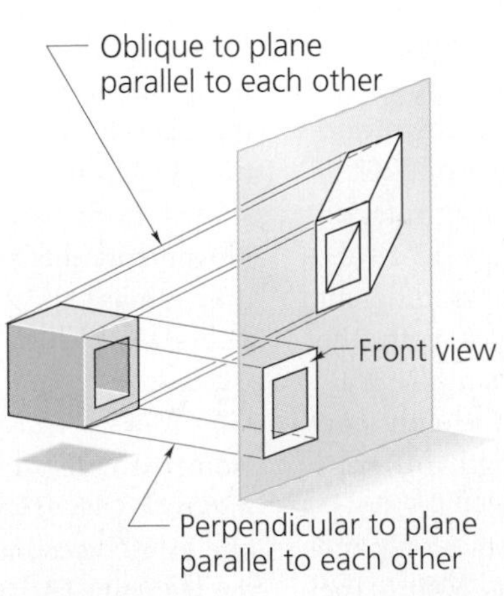

(b) Oblique

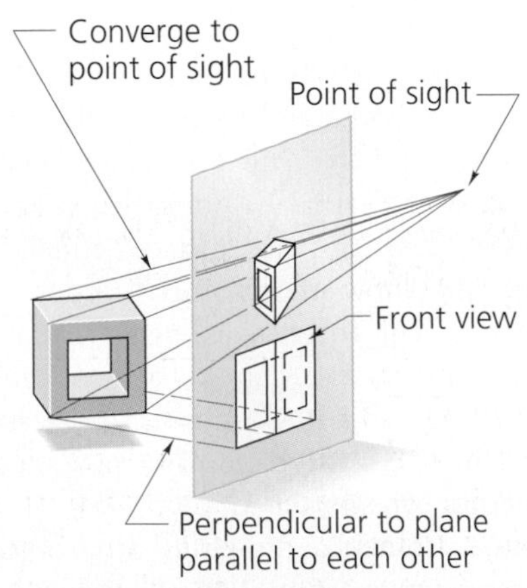

(c) Perspective

FIGURE 13.9 Kinds of Projection

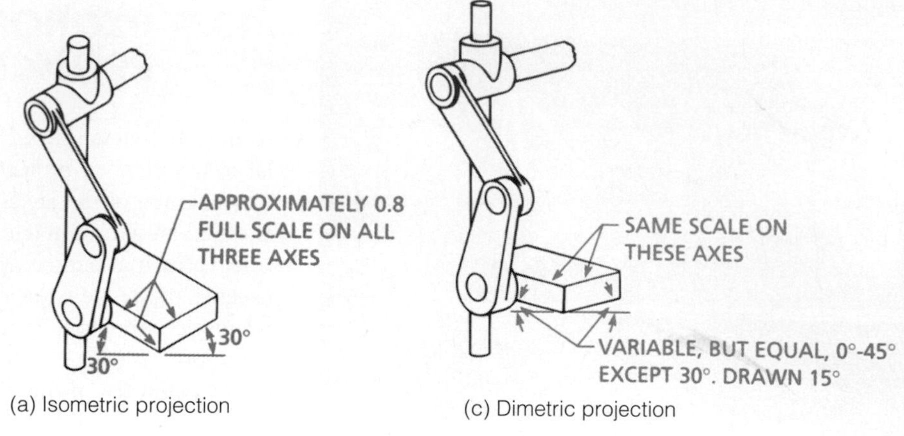

(a) Isometric projection

(c) Dimetric projection

FULL SCALE ON
ALL THREE AXES
30°
30°

(b) Isometric drawing

DIFFERENT SCALE
ON EACH AXIS
DRAWN 30°
DRAWN
15°
VARIABLE, BUT NOT EQUAL. SUM OF
THESE TWO ANGLES LESS THAN 90°,
BUT NEITHER ANGLE IS 0°.

(d) Trimetric projection

FIGURE 13.10 Types of Axonometric Projection

13.3.1 Isometric Drawings

For **isometric drawing,** the distances on each axis are measured true length, with any standard scale, thus making a drawing larger than isometric projection (which is normally 81% of the original in size). Isometric drawing is the form in which the isometric technique is most commonly used. Isometric projection and isometric drawing are both based on the assumption that a cube representing the projection axes will be rotated until its front face is 45° to the horizontal plane and then tipped forward or downward at an angle of 35°16′. The axes make equal angles of 120° to one another [Fig. 13.14(a) and (b)]. The resulting rotation displays all three primary surfaces equally. Figure 13.14(d), (e), and (f) show the isometric cube in three different orientations. All three axes make equal angles with the projection plane and can be drawn easily using 30°/60° triangles [Fig. 13.14(c)]. The three faces of the cube are identical in size and shape. The projected lengths of each edge are not foreshortened.

Because isometric drawings are constructed along the three axes (one vertical and the other two at 30° to the horizontal to the right and left), each dimension is measured true length (not foreshortened) along an axis. *All lines in isometric drawings that are on or parallel to the three axes are drawn true length.* Lines not on or parallel to the axes are constructed with *offset dimensions.*

The orientation of the axis determines which faces of the part are visible. Figure 13.14 shows three of many alternatives for placing the axes. The most typical orientation is Figure 13.14(d), where the cube is viewed so that the top, front, and side of the object are visible. In Figure 13.14(e), the axes have been turned on their side, and in (f), the bottom, front, and side are visible because the axes are shown from beneath the isometric cube. A variety of arrangements are possible for the isometric axes as long as they remain at 120° to one another.

13.3.2 Isometric Construction

Isometric construction using the box method is illustrated in Figure 13.15. The three axes are drawn first: one vertical, one at 30° receding to the right, and one at 30° receding to the left [Fig. 13.15(b)]. The edges of the box are constructed from the height, width, and depth dimensions transferred from the multiview drawing of the part [Fig. 13.15(a)].

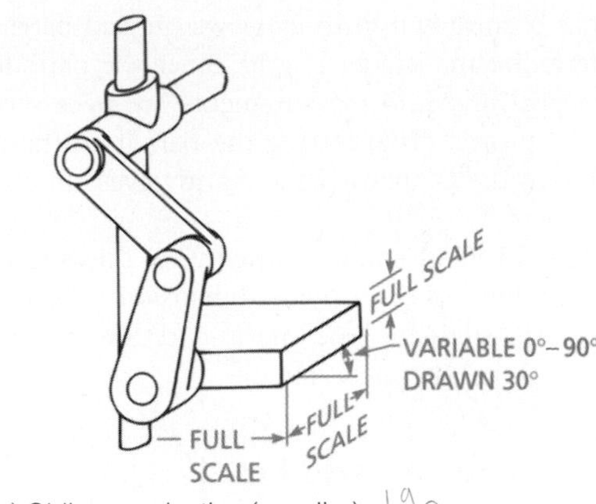

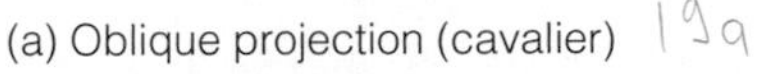
(a) Oblique projection (cavalier)

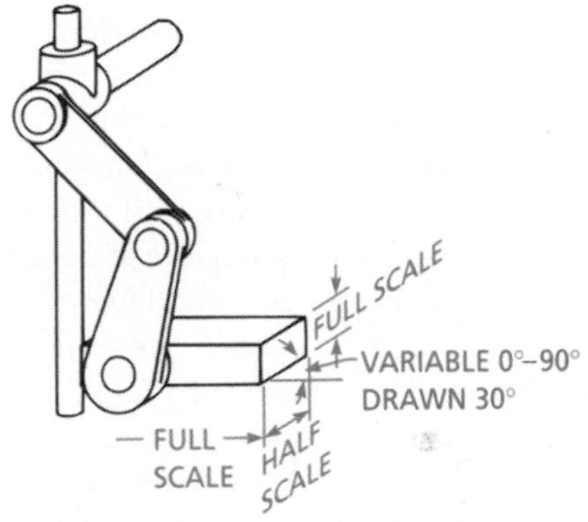

(b) Oblique projection (cabinet)

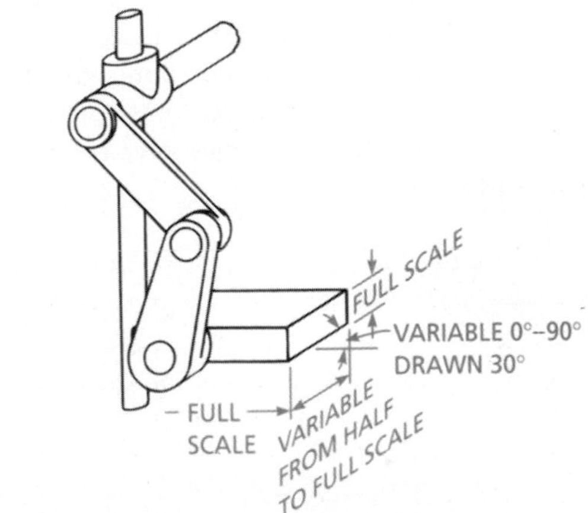

(c) Oblique projection (general)

FIGURE 13.11 Types of Oblique Projection

Remember, in an isometric drawing the dimensions are not foreshortened. Therefore, if the distance is on or parallel to one of the axes, each measurement is full scale from the multiview projection (or directly from the part). Dimensions can be marked off with a scale or transferred with dividers.

All lines on isometric drawings that are parallel to or on one of the three axes are true length. This type of line is called an **isometric line.** Lines that are not parallel to or on an axis, called **nonisometric lines,** will not show true length

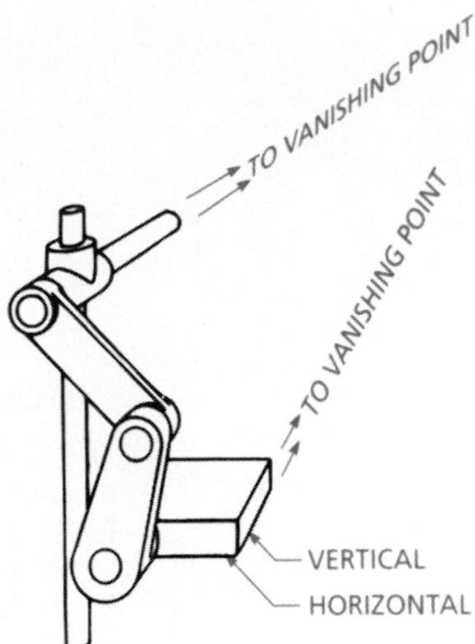

(a) Perspective (one-point)

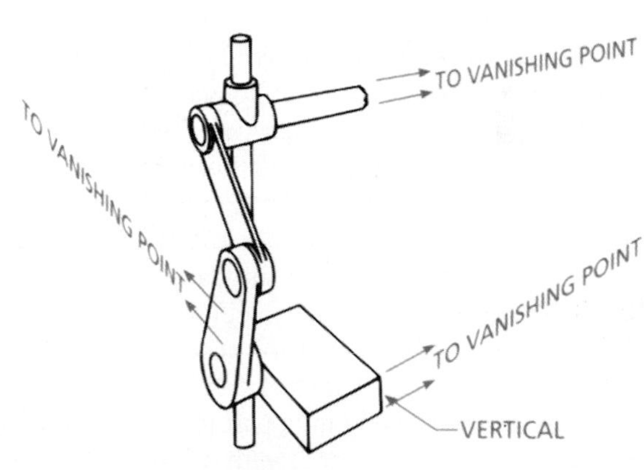

(b) Perspective (two-point)

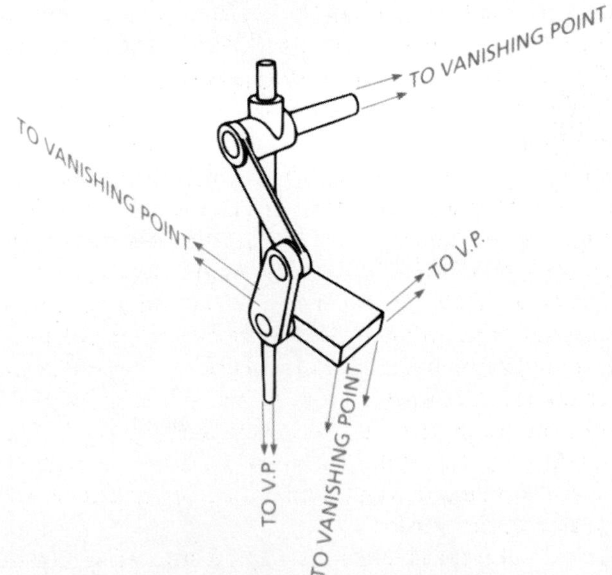

(c) Perspective (three-point)

FIGURE 13.12 Types of Perspective Projection

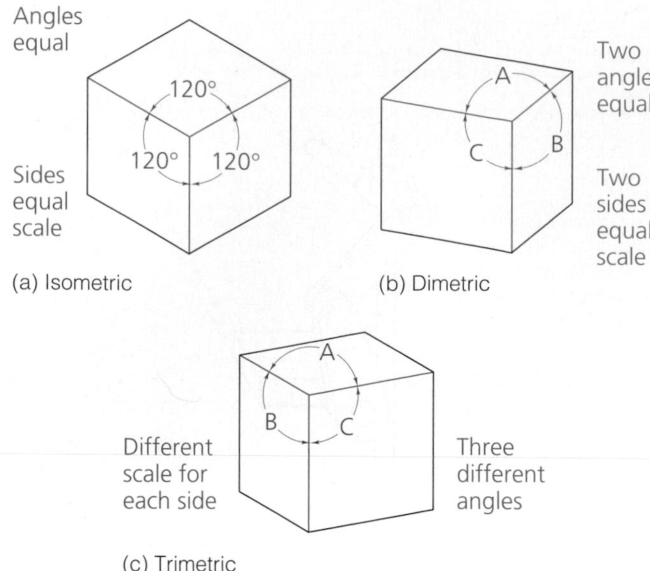

FIGURE 13.13 Axonometric Axes

on the isometric drawing. *Nonisometric lines must be established from their endpoints, located along isometric lines.*

After the part is boxed in, the remainder of the drawing is completed. Dimensions A, B, C, and D are taken from the multiview drawing of the part in Figure 13.15(a) and transferred to the isometric box [Figure 13.15(c)]. This establishes the steplike features of the part. The remaining features are created in the same manner [Fig. 13.15(d)]. After the part is complete, all axes and construction lines are erased and the object lines darkened [Fig. 13.15(e)].

The procedure of "blocking in" a part is similar to carving a model out of some soft material with a knife. One aid in this process is isometric grids (Fig. 13.16). In the figure, the part has been drawn in three views on grid paper and then transferred to the isometric grid. Since the part's features all fall on grid lines, no measurements are necessary to complete the project. Transferring the part from the three-view drawing to the isometric drawing involves simply counting grid lines.

Figure 13.17(a) shows a three-view drawing of an integrated circuit, complete with dimensions. Figure 13.17(b) provides the steps for blocking in and drawing an isometric pictorial of the integrated circuit.

13.3.3 Nonisometric Lines

The two lines that make the V-shaped feature in Figure 13.18 are not parallel to one of the three axes. Therefore, these lines are **nonisometric lines.** Nonisometric lines cannot be scaled, but their endpoints are easily located through the box method and offset dimensions. Depending on their orientation, nonisometric lines may become longer or shorter on the isometric drawing. In this figure, the nonisometric lines are at the same angle, but slanting from different directions. In the isometric view [Figure 13.18(d)], the two lines now make different angles. Also, one is longer than the original line and the other is shorter. This distortion is typical of nonisometric lines.

In Figure 13.18, using the part's overall dimensions, the isometric box is drawn first in (b). Using dimensions transferred from Figure 13.18(a), the primary features are then "carved" [Figure 13.138(c).] Nonisometric lines are established by locating their endpoints using offset dimensions [Fig. 13.18(d)]. The angled (nonisometric lines) features are established using offset dimensions I and J. In Figure 13.18(e), construction lines have been removed and the part darkened.

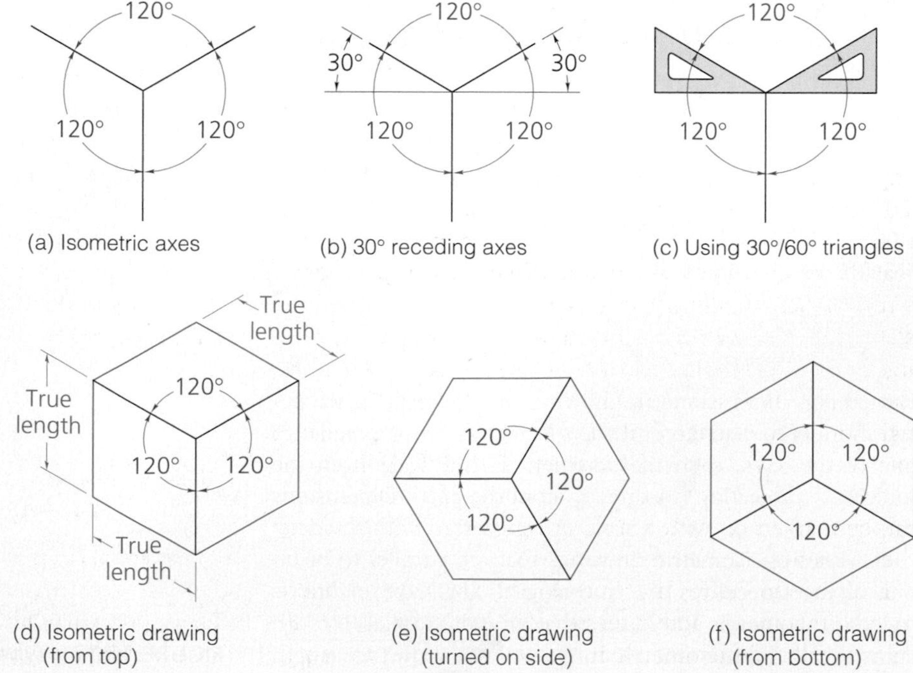

FIGURE 13.14 Isometric Axes

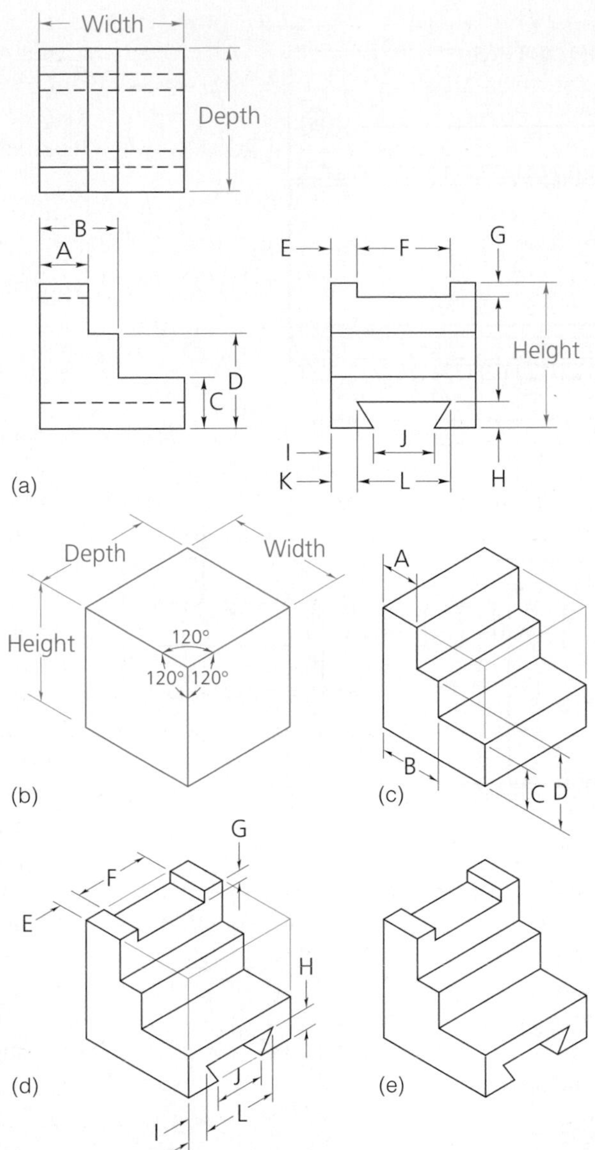

FIGURE 13.15 Isometric Construction Using the Box Method

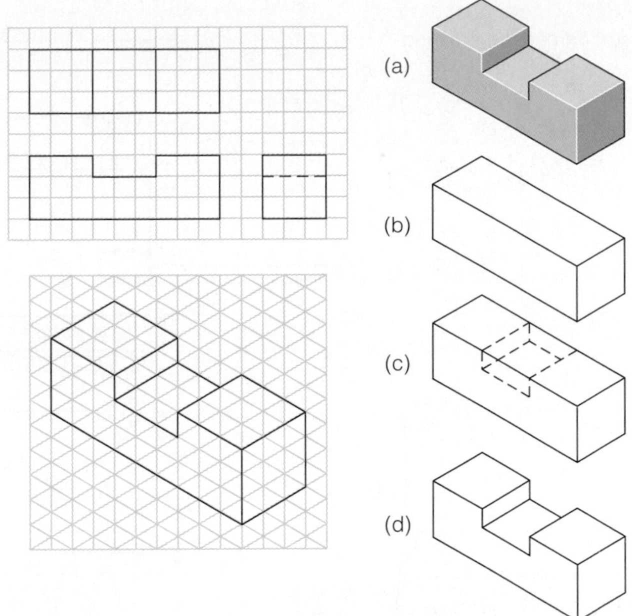

FIGURE 13.16 Box Construction and Grids for Isometric Drawings

13.3.4 Isometric Angles

The three major axes along an isometric box (or cube) are at 120° angles to one another. In reality, all lines of a cube are at 90° or are parallel to each other. Because of the distortion created by the isometric view of the box, few angles appear as true angles. Angles, as with nonisometric lines, must be established by means of offset dimensions. Angles appear larger or smaller than true size on isometric drawings in relation to their position in the view. The lines that make an angle are nonisometric lines. Angles cannot be measured from the multiview drawing and transferred directly to the isometric view. Instead, they must be drawn by locating their endpoints along isometric lines using offset dimensions, as when drawing nonisometric lines.

The block in Figure 13.19 has an angled surface. To draw the part in isometric, it is necessary to use dimensions A, B, and C. These dimensions can be taken along true-length lines. Points 1, 2, 3, and 4 are established in the isometric view using these dimensions. The angle is not true size (it is smaller than the original) in the isometric view. The steps in this figure were the same ones used to draw a part containing nonisometric lines with the box method and offset dimensions. Remember, **offset dimensions** are always taken parallel to one of the three axes or along isometric lines.

13.3.5 Irregular Objects on Isometric Drawings

Any shape can be drawn isometrically with the box method and offset dimensions. In Figure 13.20, a pyramid has been drawn this way. Given the three-view drawing of the part in Figure 13.20(a), the isometric drawing is started as in the previous examples. The isometric box is drawn with the part's three primary dimensions [Fig. 13.20(b)]. Using offset dimensions A and B, the base is established first (points 1, 2, and 3). Point O is located with offset dimensions C and D [Figure 13.20(c)].

13.3.6 Circles and Arcs on Isometric Drawings

All circles and circular arcs on isometric drawings appear elliptical. A variety of methods are available for isometric ellipse construction: template, trammel, four-center, and point plotting, to name a few. A template should be used for

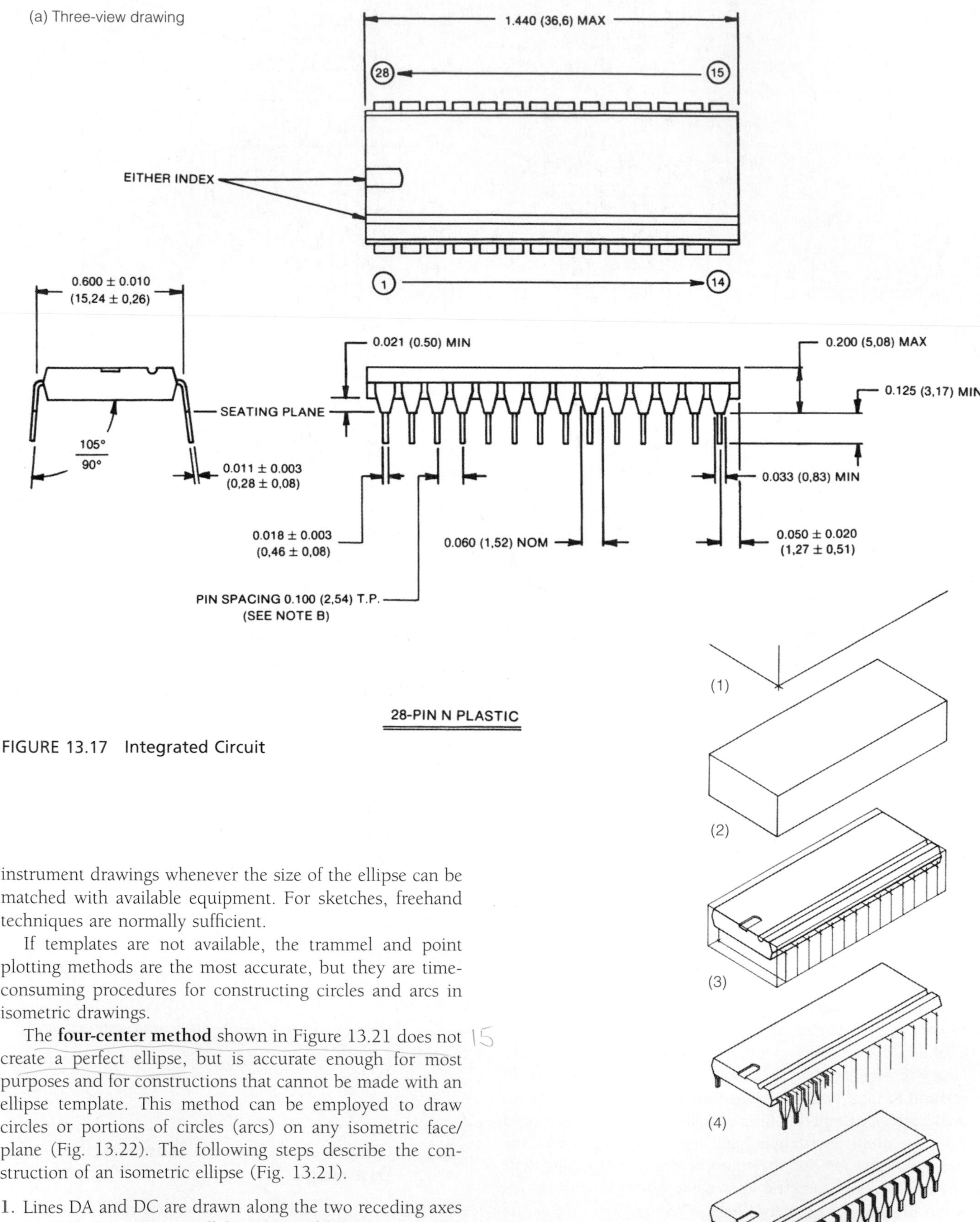

FIGURE 13.17 Integrated Circuit

instrument drawings whenever the size of the ellipse can be matched with available equipment. For sketches, freehand techniques are normally sufficient.

If templates are not available, the trammel and point plotting methods are the most accurate, but they are time-consuming procedures for constructing circles and arcs in isometric drawings.

The **four-center method** shown in Figure 13.21 does not create a perfect ellipse, but is accurate enough for most purposes and for constructions that cannot be made with an ellipse template. This method can be employed to draw circles or portions of circles (arcs) on any isometric face/plane (Fig. 13.22). The following steps describe the construction of an isometric ellipse (Fig. 13.21).

1. Lines DA and DC are drawn along the two receding axes (at 30°). Line AB is parallel to DC, and line CB is parallel to AD. Each of the lines will be the same length as the diameter of the circle [Fig. 13.21(a)].

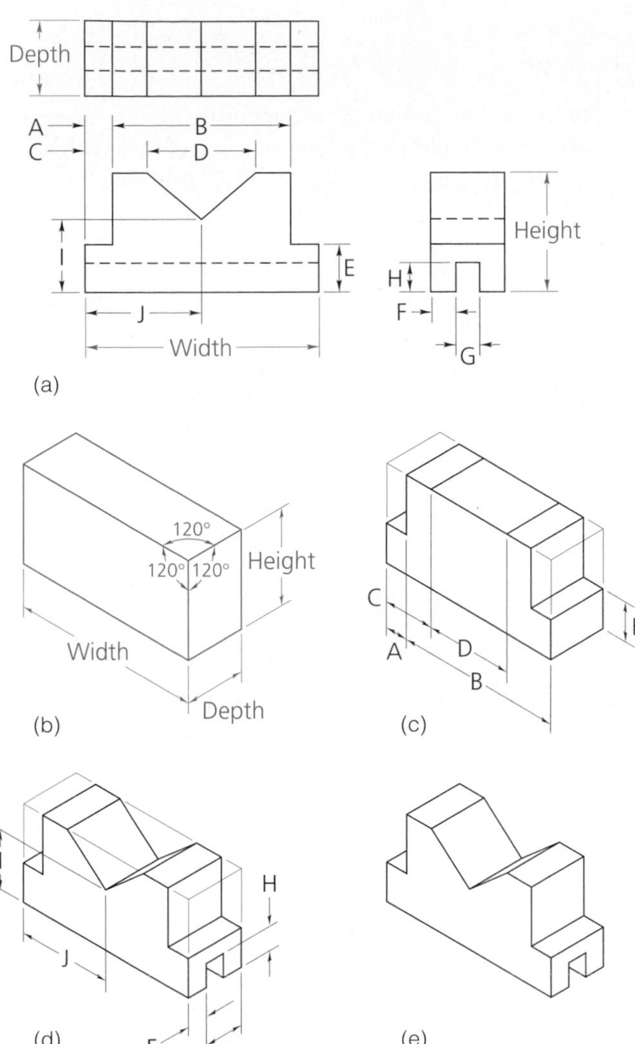

FIGURE 13.18 Nonisometric Lines in an Isometric Drawing

2. Construction lines are drawn from point D perpendicular to line AB at its midpoint and perpendicular to line CB at its V midpoint [Fig. 13.21(b)].
3. Step 2 is repeated for point B and lines DA and DC [Fig. 13.21(c)].
4. The intersection of the construction lines is used to draw R1. The radius is equal to the distance from the intersection of the construction lines to one of the numbered points (1, 2, 3, or 4). The radius will thus be tangent to two edge lines (AB and AD or CB and CD) [Fig. 13.21(d)].
5. Points D and B are used to draw arc R2. Arc R2 originates at the intersection of the construction lines for both sides of the ellipse (B or D). Radius R2 will be tangent to two sides each (BA and BC or DA and DC) [Fig. 13.21(e)].
6. Lastly, all construction lines are erased and the ellipse is darkened [Fig. 13.21(f)].

Portions of circles (arcs) are sometimes required for parts that have fillets and rounds. The same procedure for construction is used for these cases. In Figure 13.23, the round has been constructed as a portion of an isometric ellipse. In Figure 13.23(a) the round is shown as a true shape. The ellipse is boxed in using two times the radius as each side for construction lines in Figure 13.23(b), and the radius of the bend is located to establish the tangent points in (c). Since just one-quarter of the circle (one-quarter ellipse) is being drawn, only one radius is necessary [Fig. 13.23(d)]. Unless the ellipse is an odd size or very large, a template is normally used for this construction, as shown in Figure 13.23(e). When using a template to construct the ellipse, care must be taken. The major axis of the ellipse will be at 30° unless the curve falls in the top or bottom face of the part.

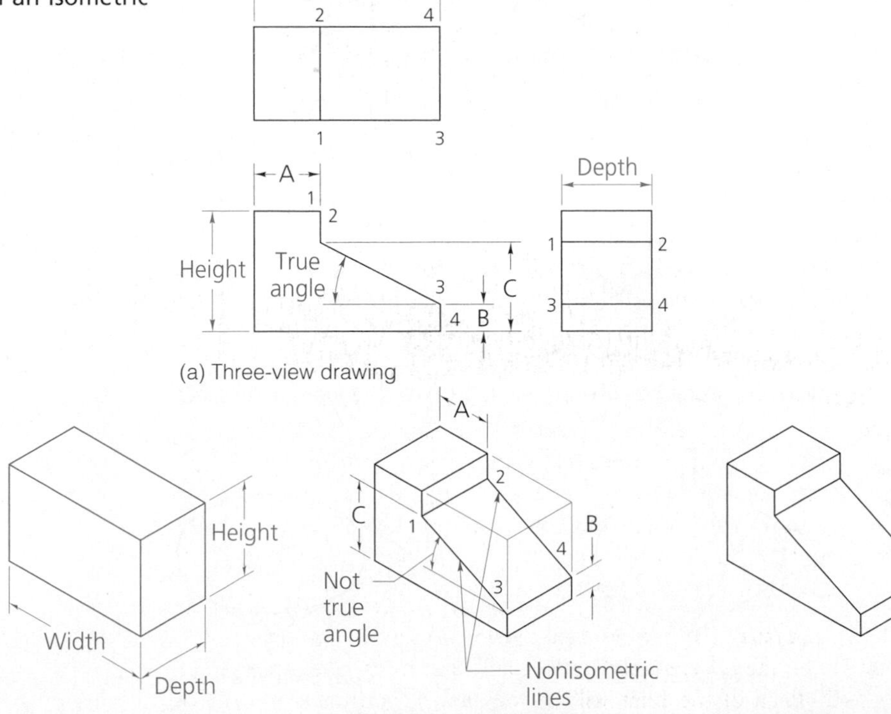

FIGURE 13.19 Offset Dimensions for Isometric Construction

13.3.7 Using Offset Dimensions for Ellipse Construction

The **offset dimension method** locates a series of points along the curve of an ellipse. This method is more accurate than the four-center method, but is time-consuming and the quality of the finished curve is dependent on the designer's skill with an irregular curve. Two versions of this method are given here. The first method (Fig. 13.24) divides the circle

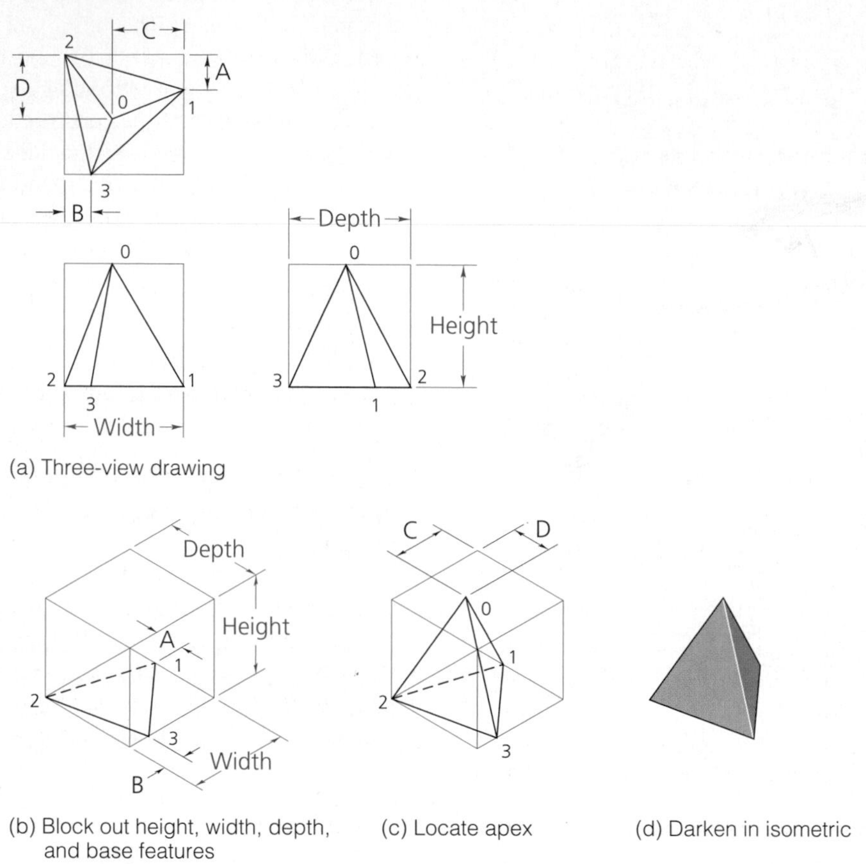

FIGURE 13.20 Construction of Irregular Objects in an Isometric Drawing

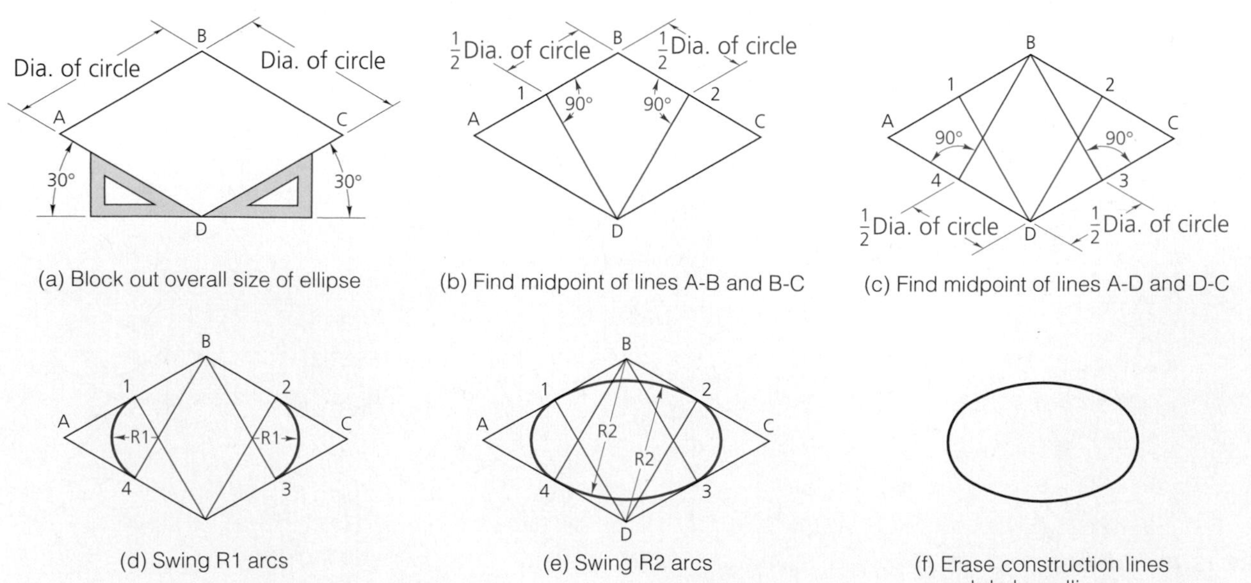

FIGURE 13.21 Drawing a Four-Center Ellipse

evenly by drawing equally spaced construction lines emanating from the center of the circle to where they intersect the circle's circumference. The circle is drawn first, along with its centerline, in Figure 13.24(a); then the circle is boxed in [Fig. 13.24(b)]. Equally spaced construction lines are drawn from the center of the circle to the circle's circumference [Fig. 13.24(c)]. The number of equally spaced lines drawn is dependent on the accuracy desired: the more points established on the circumference, the more accurate the ellipse. Here, a 30° spacing was used to establish twelve evenly spaced points along the circumference (points 1–12). The box shape is drawn isometrically in Figure 13.24(d), and each of the points is transferred from (c) using offset dimensions. Dimensions *D* and *C* establish point 1. Dimensions *A* and *B* establish point 2. Points 3 and 12 are located at the tangent points of the circle and the box, and are established on the isometric view at the intersection of the box and the centerline. To complete the ellipse, each of the four quadrants can be drawn by the same method [Fig. 13.24(e)]. Actually, since quadrants 1 and 3 are the same as are quadrants 2 and 4, only two quadrants need to be established; the opposite side can be mirrored. The darkened, finished ellipse is shown in Figure 13.24(f).

The second method (Fig. 13.25) is similar, but the points are arbitrarily fixed along the circumference of the circle and offset dimensions are taken as shown in Figure 13.25(c). The steps of Figure 13.25(a), (b), (d), (e), and (f) are the same as the first method. The points should be located on the circumference and of sufficient number so that a smooth curve can be established.

Circles, arcs, or curves that do not lie in isometric planes must be plotted with offset dimensions. This procedure requires that a series of points be established along the curved outline. Offset dimensions for each point are transferred to the isometric drawing and marked off along isometric lines.

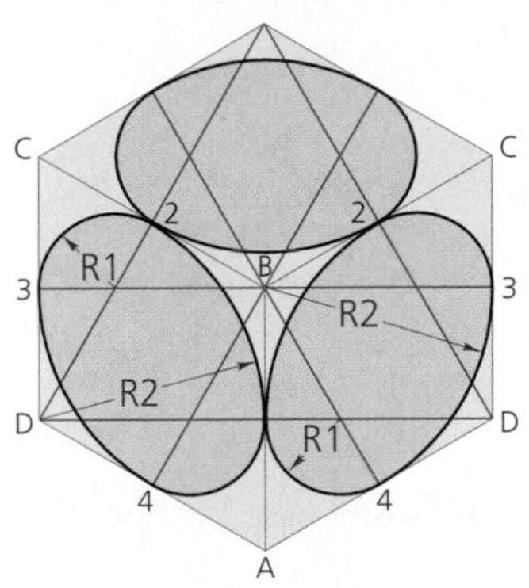

FIGURE 13.22 Four-Center Ellipses on the Surfaces of an Isometric Cube

13.3.8 Curves on Isometric Drawings

A space curve can be constructed isometrically using offset dimensions and box construction. The methods are not much different from those employed to draw space curves on multiview drawings with orthographic projection. The difference is in the use of receding axes drawn at 30°. Otherwise, all measurements are marked off the same for both types of drawings. The offset method can be used for any shape. Points are located along the curve and their positions transferred to the pictorial with dividers or a scale. A sufficient number of points are established to lay out the curve accurately. After the points are located on the pictorial, a light curve is drawn freehand through the points, and an

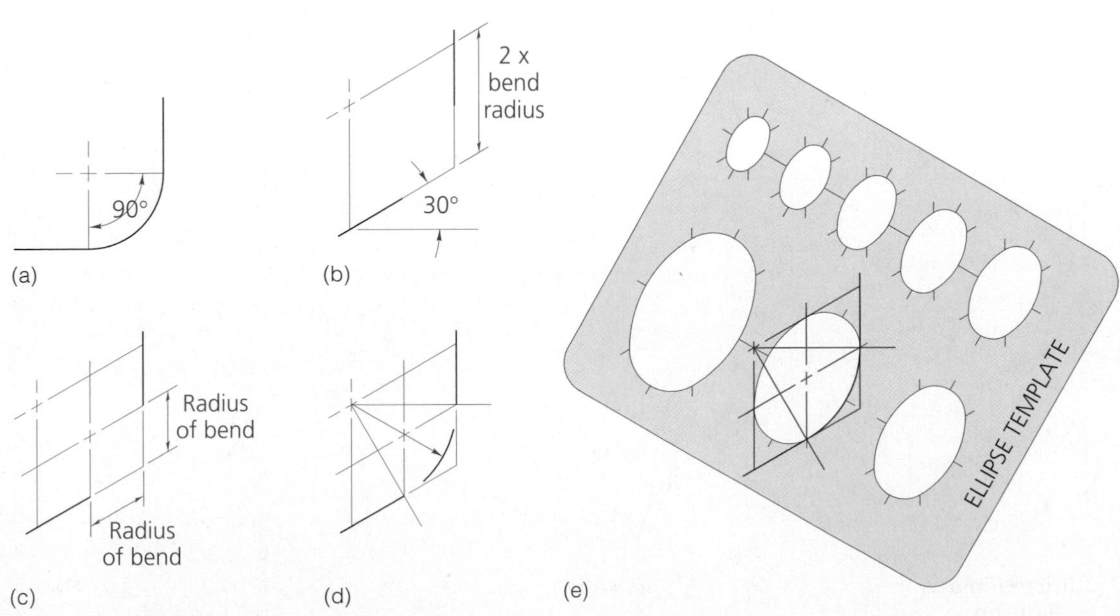

FIGURE 13.23 Construction of Arcs in Isometric Drawings

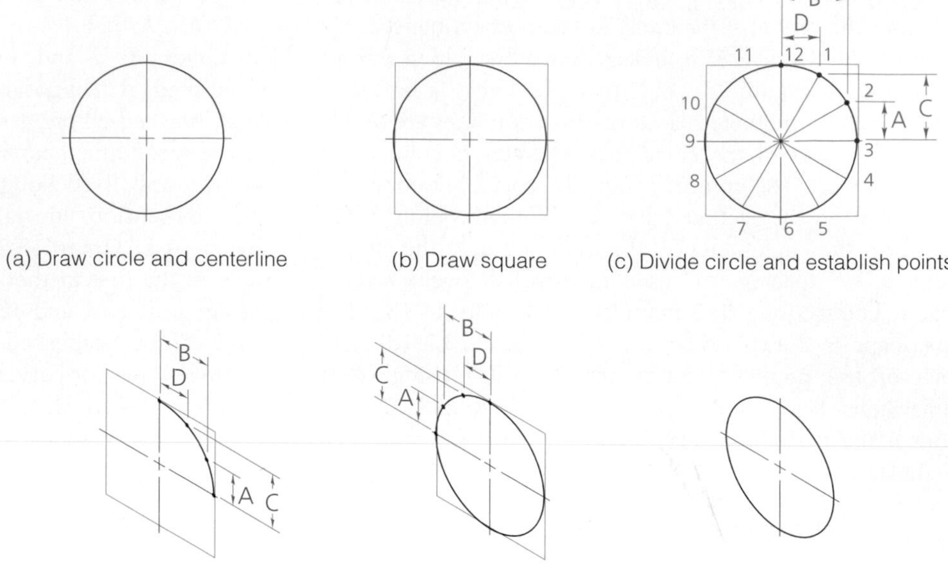

(a) Draw circle and centerline (b) Draw square (c) Divide circle and establish points (d) Locate points along curve (e) Locate remaining points (f) Darken ellipse

FIGURE 13.24 Construction of True Ellipse Using Offset Dimensions

irregular curve is used to draw the curve with the appropriate line thickness.

In Figure 13.26(a), the top and the front views of the part are drawn first. Points are then established along the curve in the top view. Offset dimensions A through M are located from the edges of the part. The height, width, and depth are used to box in the part in the isometric drawing [Fig. 13.26(b)]. Using offset dimensions A through M, each of the points 1 through 7 is located from the edges of the part [Fig. 13.26(c)]. All point dimensions are taken parallel to their corresponding axis (edge). Point 1 is located by dimensions A and G; point 2 by dimensions B and H; point 3 by dimensions C and I. Vertical lines are drawn from points 1 through 7 to establish the part's thickness [Fig. 13.26(c)]. To complete the pictorial construction, lines are erased and the outline is darkened [Fig. 13.26(d)].

13.3.9 Hidden Lines on Isometric Drawings

Hidden lines are omitted on most pictorial illustrations unless required for clarifying interior features. When an

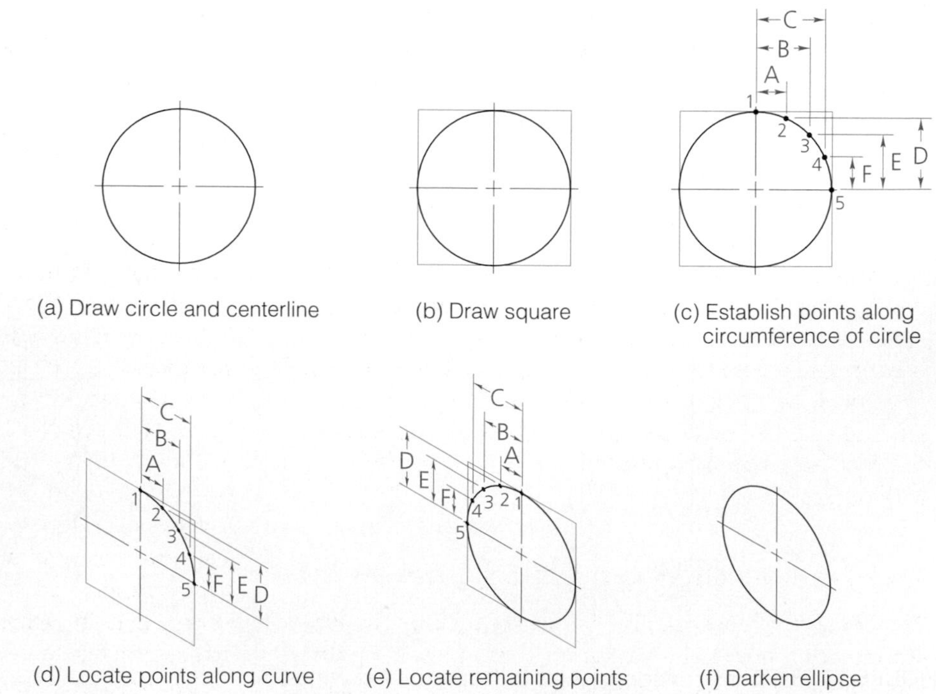

(a) Draw circle and centerline (b) Draw square (c) Establish points along circumference of circle (d) Locate points along curve (e) Locate remaining points (f) Darken ellipse

FIGURE 13.25 True Ellipse Construction by Plotting Points

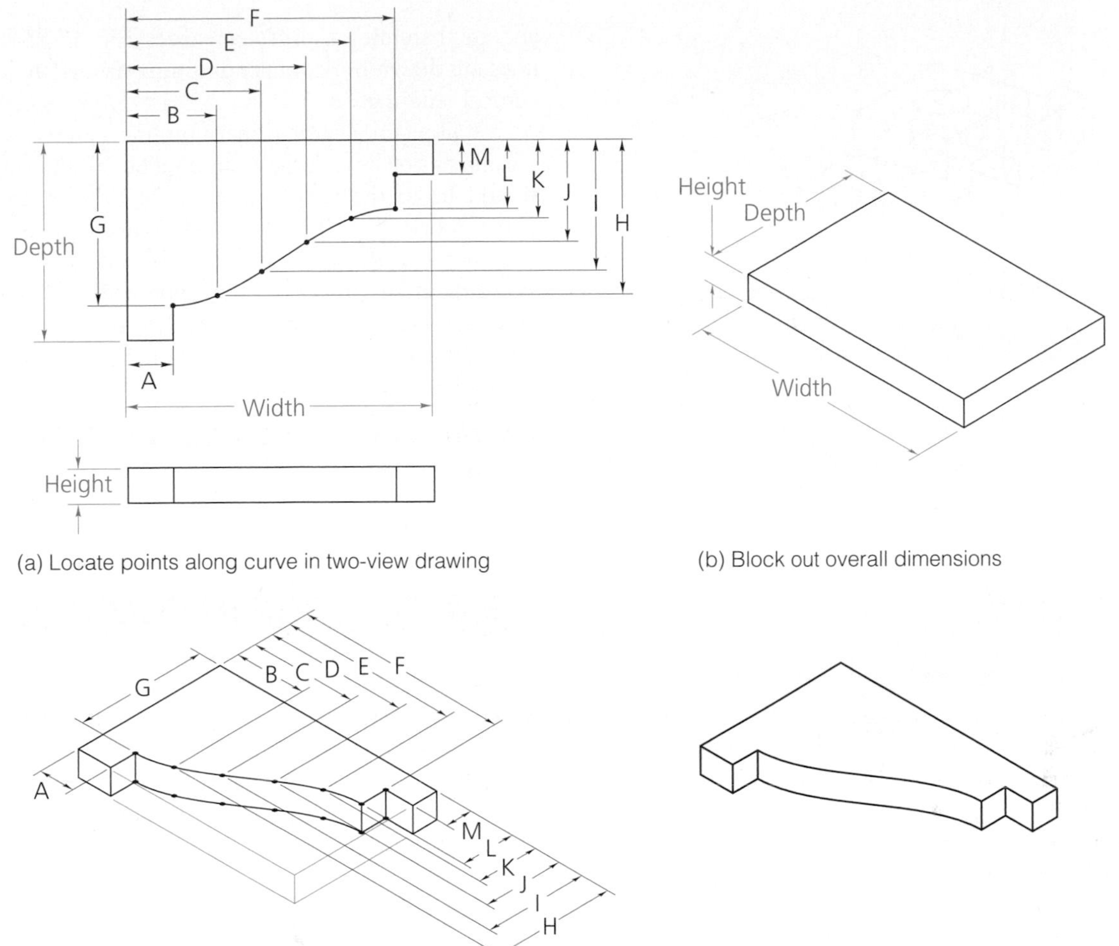

(a) Locate points along curve in two-view drawing

(b) Block out overall dimensions

(c) Locate points

(d) Erase construction lines and darken lines

FIGURE 13.26 **Space Curves in Isometric Drawing**

illustration requires hidden lines, a sectioned pictorial should be considered. In Figure 13.27, three variations of a pictorial drawing are shown. In Figure 13.27(a), the part is shown with all hidden lines; in (b), only visible lines are shown. This would normally be the case for most pictorials. In the last variation (c), the part is shown as it would appear on a CAD display modeled in 3D as a wireframe model. Here, the part has all edges shown.

When using a CAD system with wireframe modeling, you must correctly visualize the part and which sides are shown at any given moment. In Figure 13.27 we are looking at the top, front, and right side or the bottom, front, and left side. Since the examples in (a) and (b) show the first possibility, it is hard to see that the second viewing direction is also valid when viewing (c). Most CAD systems have a hidden line removal capability (**HIDE** command) that eliminates the problem of determining the correct viewing direction of a wireframe model.

13.3.10 Centerlines on Isometric Drawings

Centerlines that are needed to locate and identify circular or symmetrical aspects of a part are found on isometric drawings. Many pictorials do not show centerlines so that the part looks more realistic. If dimensions are required on the drawing (Fig.13.28), centerlines are included.

During the construction of a pictorial, centerlines identifying the origin of a part's symmetrical or curved features are as necessary as any other construction line. In most cases, they may be erased after the pictorial is constructed and before it is darkened in with pencil or inked.

13.3.11 Dimensioning Isometric Pictorials

Dimensions on isometric drawings can be either aligned or unidirectional. Aligned dimensions look pictorially correct but are harder to draw. Unidirectional dimensions and notes are easier to add to the illustration and are often either typeset or labeled mechanically.

In Figure 13.28, the part's dimensions are shown by both methods. Figure 13.23(a) was drawn with aligned dimensions. Guidelines for the lettering are drawn parallel to the feature being dimensioned and in the same isometric plane. The arrowheads for aligned dimensions are drawn with their backs parallel to the extension line, as shown in the enlargement in Figure 13.28(c). With a 3D CAD system, you can automatically insert dimensions pictorially.

Unidirectional dimensions are positioned horizontally

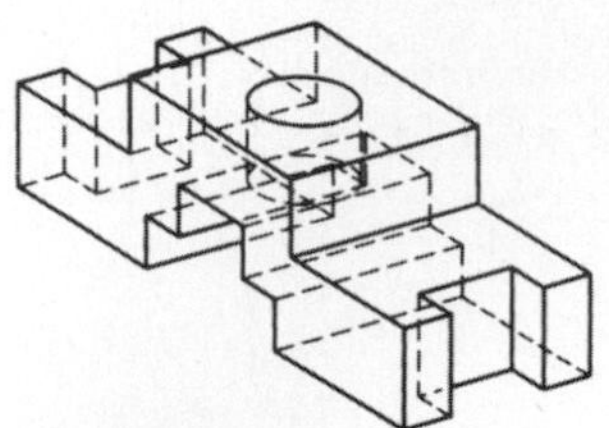

(a) Part with hidden lines

(b) Part with hidden lines removed

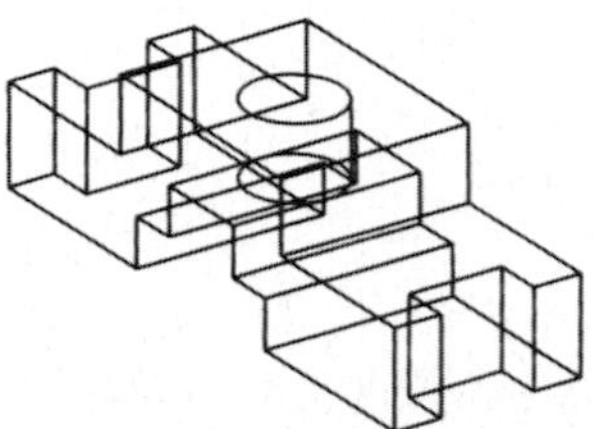

(c) Wireframe model of part on 3D CAD system

FIGURE 13.27 Hidden Lines in an Isometric Drawing

and are therefore easiest to construct [Fig. 13.28(b)]. Guidelines are drawn horizontally and dimensions are added with vertical lettering.

For all pictorials, the dimension line, extension lines, and the dimension text (unless unidirectional lettering is used) should lie in the same plane as the line or feature being dimensioned [Fig. 13.28(a)]. Arrowheads should be long and narrow, with a ratio of 3:1, and should lie in the plane of the dimension and extension lines [Fig. 13.28(a)]. For unidirectional dimensioning, the lettering should be made with vertical letters and should read from the bottom of the sheet [Fig. 13.28(b)].

You May Complete Exercises 13.1 Through 13.4 at This Time

13.4 OBLIQUE PROJECTION

A projected view in which the lines of sight are parallel to each other but inclined to the plane of projection is called an **oblique projection** (Fig. 13.11). For practical purposes, the principal face is placed parallel to the plane of projection, thus making it and parallel faces show in true shape. In all forms of oblique projection, the receding axis may be drawn

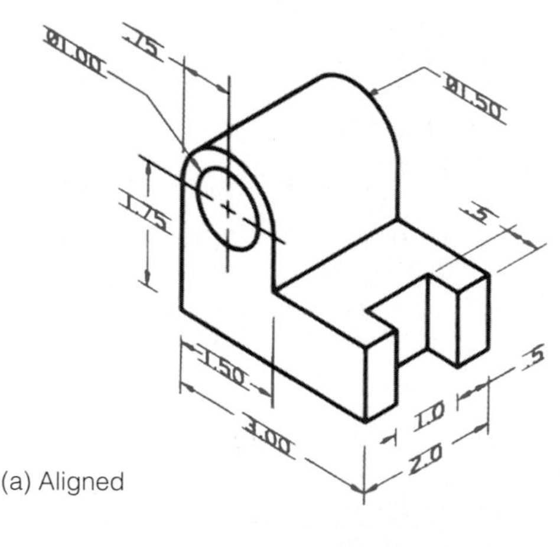

(a) Aligned

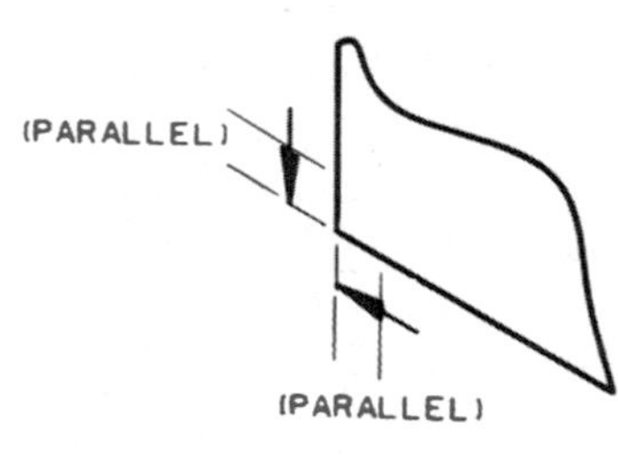

(c) Arrowhead construction

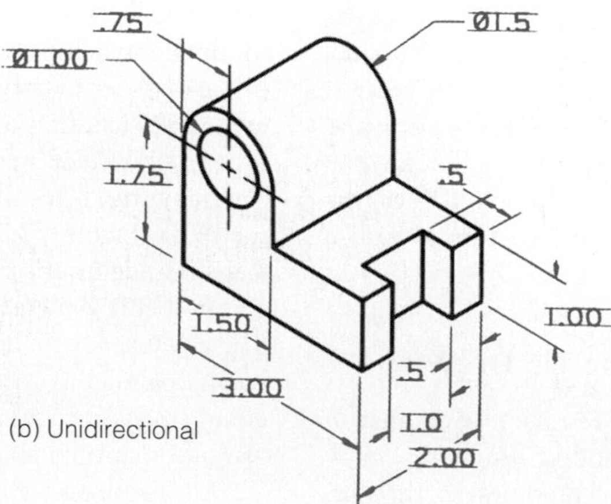

(b) Unidirectional

FIGURE 13.28 Dimensioning Isometric Drawings

Focus On . . .

PICTORIALS

Pictorial drawings help the viewer to visualize a part better and gain a better understanding of its components and features. These drawings help bridge the gap between photograph and part.

Engineering drawings contain a wealth of information about a product: its size, shape, location of features, construction materials, and assembly specifications. However, engineering drawings (multiview projections) are not always easy to read for a nontechnical person untrained in those projection techniques. A more realistic-looking 3D drawing (technical illustration) is produced for situations in which engineering drawings are not the most appropriate presentation, such as in marketing meetings and in maintenance documentation.

Early tries at technical illustration by the Egyptians and Greeks didn't really show all three dimensions in one view. Around 1500 A.D., pictorial drawings that showed all three dimensions in one view evolved. Leonardo da Vinci was the most famous of this group of inventors/illustrators. His artistic ability and scientific foresight provided the means for true technical illustration. Techniques were further refined during the Industrial Revolution. After 1940, technical illustration became popular design and development tools.

Today, technical illustrators produce pictorial drawings that aid in product development, assembly, marketing, illustration, repair, and maintenance. It is a fact that technical illustrations accelerate production, improve communications during development, and reduce product cost. Even people with limited technical knowledge can understand complex assemblies and interrelationships of parts and features. Indeed, pictorials prove to us "a picture is worth a thousand words."

The solid models on advanced CAD stations today are an extension of this same principle. Not only do these parts look three dimensional, they are 3D mathematically. The advanced renderings of parts on these sophisticated systems makes the parts look very real on the computer screen—in fact, they look almost as good as photographs. The 3D database can be used to make renderings and illustrations and to generate a tool path to machine the part. Improved visualization is one of the key factors driving the increasing popularity of these systems.

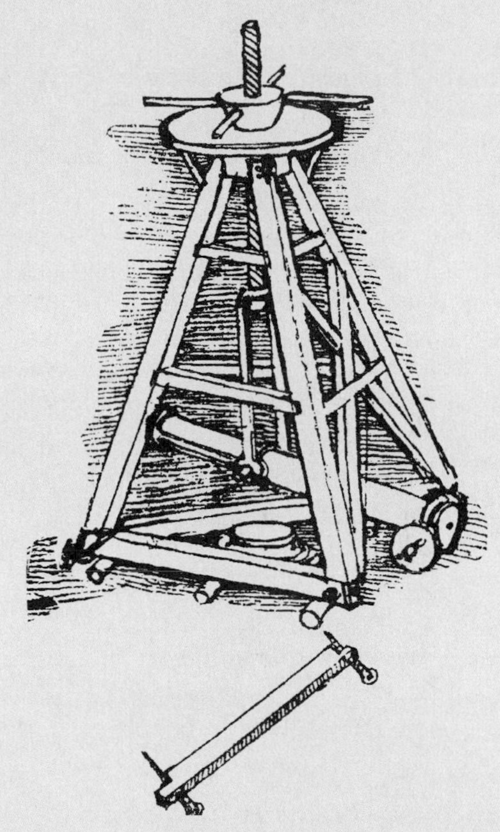

One of Leonardo da Vinci's mechanical sketches.

However, the lesson learned by humankind long ago is that we really need to be able to "see" a part to understand it. Leonardo da Vinci was a master of this long before the computer age.

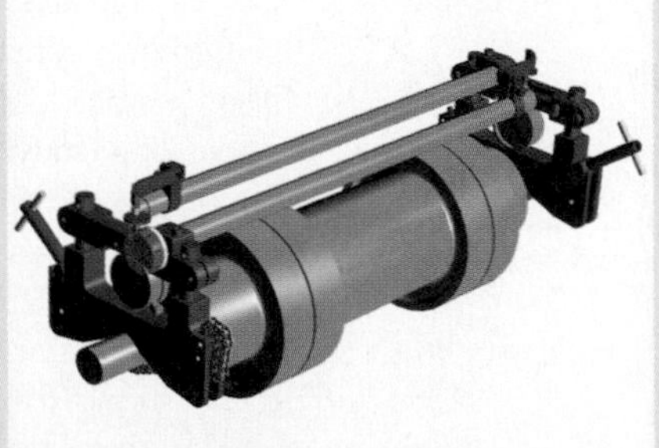

3D solid models.

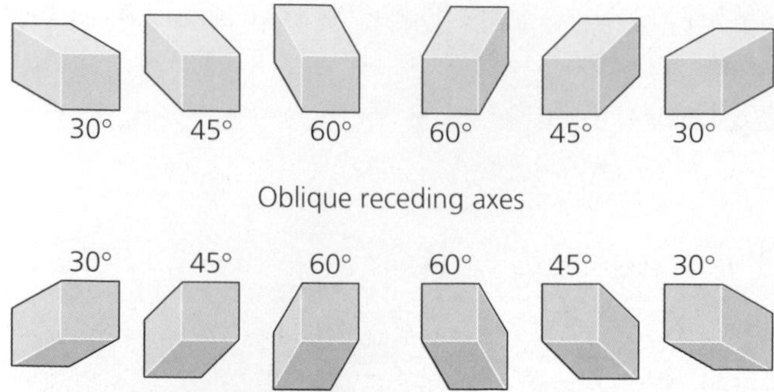

FIGURE 13.29 Axis Choice for Oblique Projection

in any direction (Fig. 13.29). By changing the axis angle and the choice of front face, any orientation required to exhibit the part properly and clearly can be attained.

Oblique drawings are similar to isometric drawings. However, they are produced from parallel projectors that are not perpendicular to the projection plane. The primary difference lies in the use of only one receding axis and the ability to draw one surface as true shape and size in the front plane.

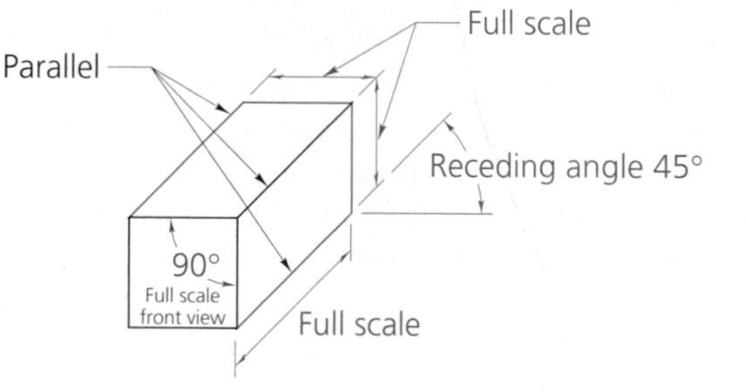

(a) Cavalier projection

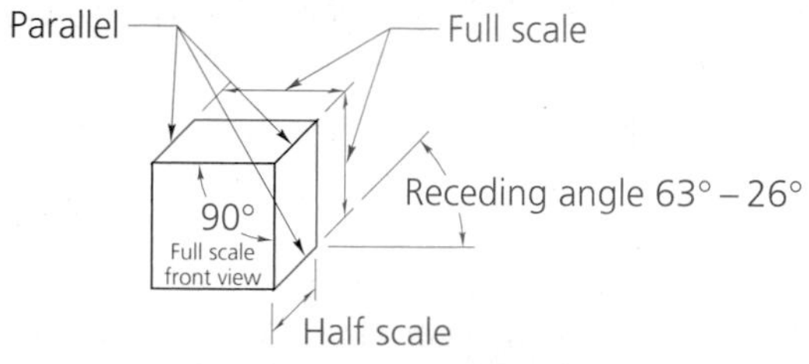

(b) Cabinet projection

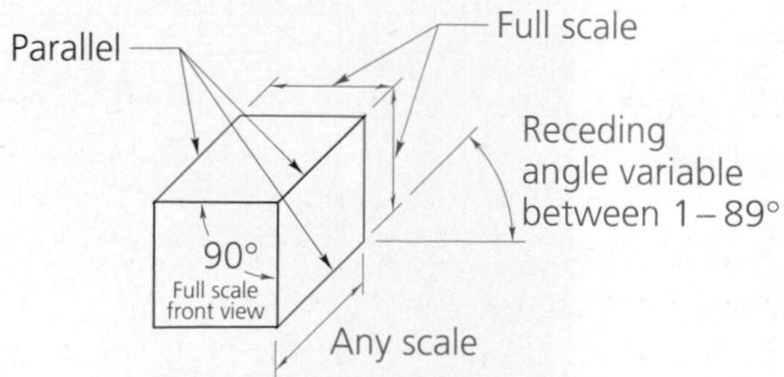

(c) General oblique

FIGURE 13.30 Types of Oblique Projection

There are three versions of oblique projection, differing only in the comparative scales used along the receding axis and the angle of the receding axis (Fig. 13.30). An oblique projection on which the lines of sight make an angle of 45° with the plane of projection is called a **cavalier projection** [Fig. 13.30(a)]. The front is drawn full scale and true shape, as with all forms of oblique projection. The same scale is used on all axes; therefore, the receding faces are drawn full scale (but not true shape). An oblique projection in which the lines of sight make an angle of between 63° and 26° with the plane of projection is called a **cabinet projection** [Fig. 13.30(b)]. *The scale on the receding axis is one-half of the scale on the other axes.*

An oblique projection in which the lines of sight make any angle other than 45° or 63° to 26° is called a **general oblique.** The scale on the receding axis should be something between full scale and one-half scale of the horizontal and vertical axes, as shown in Figure 13.30(c). The choice of the receding angle (1° to 89°) is determined by the shape of the object and the most descriptive view orientation.

The distortion often noticeable in oblique projection may be decreased by reducing the scale on the receding axis. Cylinders and cones should have their axes on the receding axis to reduce distortion and to make it possible to draw circles with a compass or template.

Oblique projection is most commonly used for objects that have a series of circles, curves, or irregular outlines in the same or parallel planes. By placing curved outlines in the front face, they can be drawn true shape and full scale without distortion. A standard circle template or a compass can be used in the construction. In other words, the front face of an oblique projection is exactly the same as the front view of a part drawn in a multiview projection.

13.4.1 Oblique Construction

Objects that are drawn with oblique projection should be oriented so the surface with curved lines lies in the front plane bounded by the axes that are at 90°. Since all surfaces that lie on the front plane or that are parallel to it are drawn true shape and size, this orientation lessens drawing time. Circles and arcs are therefore true projections.

Oblique construction is started the same as a multiview or an isometric drawing—by blocking in the overall dimensions. The drawing is started by establishing the width and the height of the front and the rear face. Next, the depth of each face is established, and then the part's edges are constructed. Circular features are then located and their dimensions blocked in. Finally, the part is darkened. Figure 13.31 shows four steps in this process.

The front face of the part in Figure 13.31 (with all curved features) is drawn true shape and size, and all measurements on this front face are true length. The measurements are

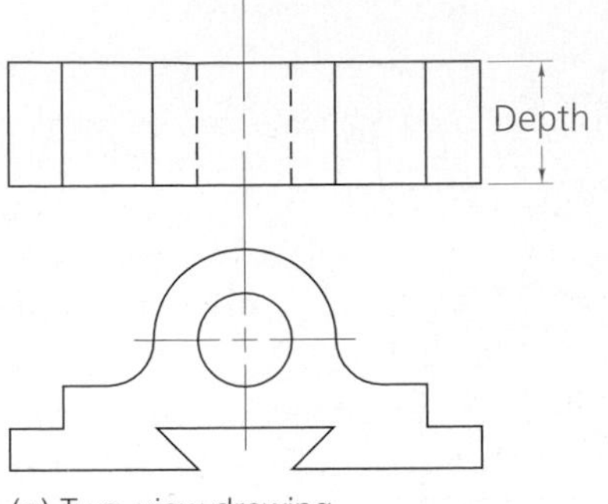

(a) Two–view drawing

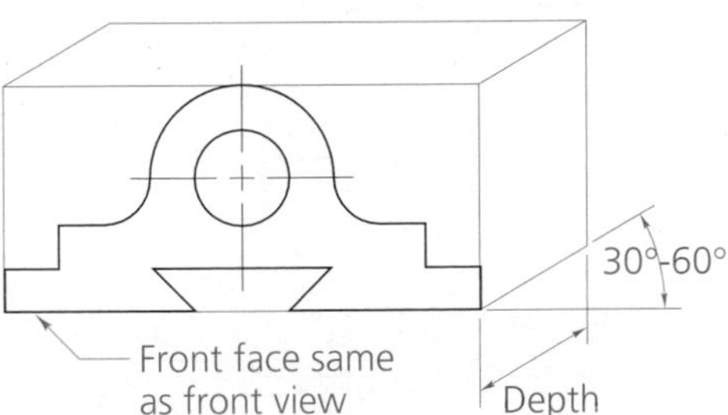

(b) Draw front face and establish receding angle

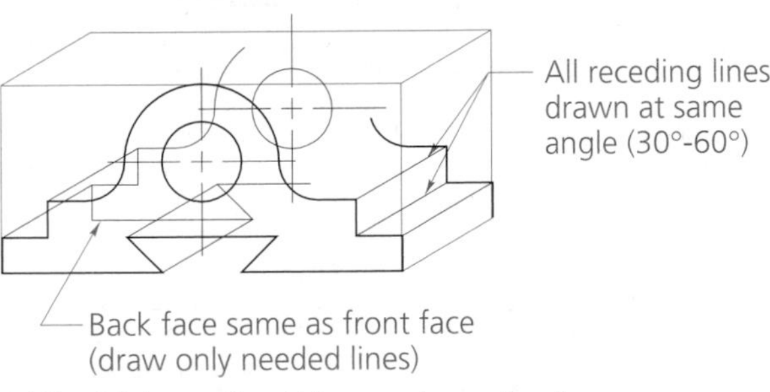

(c) Establish rear (back) face and receding lines

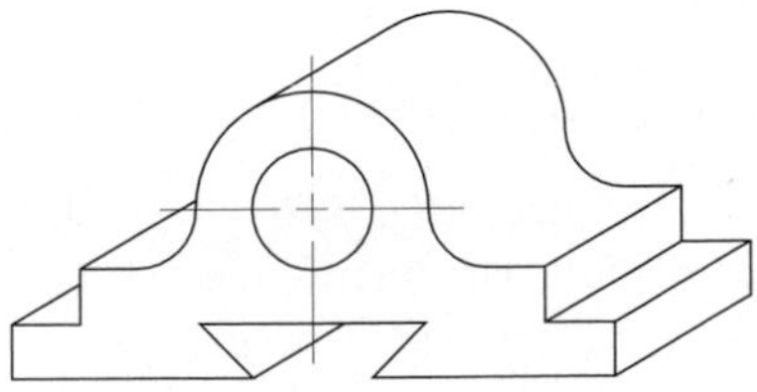
(d) Erase construction lines and darken

FIGURE 13.31 **Step-by-Step Construction of Oblique Drawing**

taken from the front view in (a) and transferred to (b). The angle for the receding axis is then determined. (The most common angle for the receding axis is 45°.) After the angle is determined, the rear face of the part is blocked in. The features of the rear face can then be drawn, as in Figure 13.31(c). Because the front and the rear faces are parallel and therefore identical, only the portions of the rear face that show along the receding face need to be drawn. The receding edge lines are drawn parallel to the receding axis between the part's corners and tangent to the curved feature on the top edge [Fig. 13.31(c)]; the part is completed by darkening in the visible edges [Fig. 13.31(d)].

13.4.2 Using Offset Measurements for Oblique Drawings

When the object to be drawn is placed so that the curved features do not fall in the front face or two or more faces have curved features, offset measurements must be used to establish the curves. After the feature's points are plotted, an irregular curve is employed to draw the curve. The curved features are divided vertically and horizontally with construction lines [Fig. 13.32(a)]. The intersection of vertical construction lines with related horizontal construction lines establishes points on the curved feature.

The oblique projection is started by establishing a front face. The choice of front face in this example was made solely on the need to demonstrate this procedure. The construction lines are transferred to the oblique view and the points plotted in Figure 13.32(b). A smooth curve is drawn through the points using an irregular curve. Since the opposite portion can be mirrored, only half of each hole needs to be plotted.

The projection is completed by drawing the end lines parallel to the axes and tangent to the curves in Figure 13.32(c), and darkening in the lines in (d). If a cabinet drawing is involved, the depth dimensions are halved and the same procedure used in its construction.

The construction process for oblique projection with slanted, inclined lines and inclined planes is similar to that for isometric drawings. Their endpoints are located along lines that are parallel to one of the axes.

13.5 PERSPECTIVE PROJECTION

A pictorial drawing made by the intersection of the picture plane with lines of sight converging from points on the object to the point of sight that is located at a finite distance from the picture plane is called a **perspective.** Perspective drawings are pictorials that appear similar to photographs. The use of perspective projection gives the illustration a photolike realism. The observer is stationed at a fixed position relative to the object being drawn, as with a photograph.

Perspective projection provides illustrations that approximate how a particular object looks to the human eye or as a camera would record the object on film. Since a perspective drawing approximates how an object really looks, it is not dimensionally correct and cannot be scaled. The only lines that can be scaled are those lines on the object that actually lie in the picture plane. Technical illustrations for advertisements, sales catalogs, technical manuals, and architectural renderings make extensive use of this form of pictorial

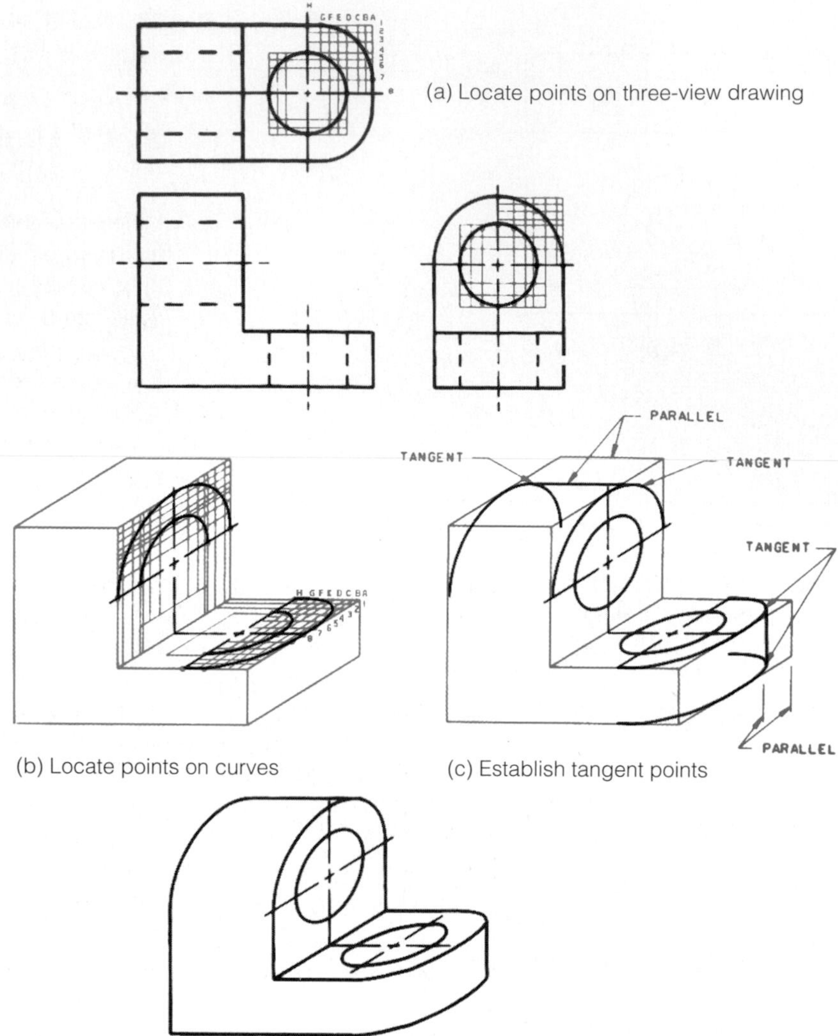

(a) Locate points on three-view drawing

(b) Locate points on curves

(c) Establish tangent points

(d) Erase construction lines and darken lines

FIGURE 13.32 Offset Dimensions for Curves Not in or Parallel to the Front Face of the Part

projection. All lines in perspective drawings converge at one, two, or three points on the horizon (*vanishing points*) and, therefore, are not parallel, as in oblique and axonometric projection.

There are three basic categories in perspective projection: parallel, angular, and oblique (Fig. 13.33). A perspective in which two of the principal axes of the object are parallel to the picture plane and the third is perpendicular to the plane is called **parallel,** or **one-point, perspective** [Fig. 13.33(a)]. A perspective in which one axis of the object (usually the vertical axis) is parallel to the picture plane and the other two axes are inclined to it is called an **angular,** or **two-point, perspective** [Fig. 13.33(b)]. A perspective in which all three principal axes of the object are oblique to the plane or projection is called an **oblique,** or **three-point, perspective** [Fig. 13.33(c)].

13.5.1 Perspective Pictorial Drawing Terminology

The following terms are used with perspective drawings (Fig. 13.34):

Station point (SP) The assumed position of the observer.

Picture plane (PP) A vertical plane that is 90° to the line of sight from the station point (SP). The picture plane is usually placed between the object and the station point.

Horizon line (HL) The line of intersection made by a horizontal plane located at eye level and the picture plane. The horizon line is raised or lowered as the observer is raised or lowered. The horizon line remains in a horizontal position.

Ground line (GL) The intersection of the ground surface plane and the object or structure contacting the ground surface.

Vanishing point (VP) A point located in space where the ground line appears to intersect with the horizon line. The number of vanishing points depends on the type of perspective. There will be either one, two, or three vanishing points (in this figure there are two, VPL and VPR).

Height line (HL) A vertical line in the plane of sight that falls on the line of sight on which measurements of height

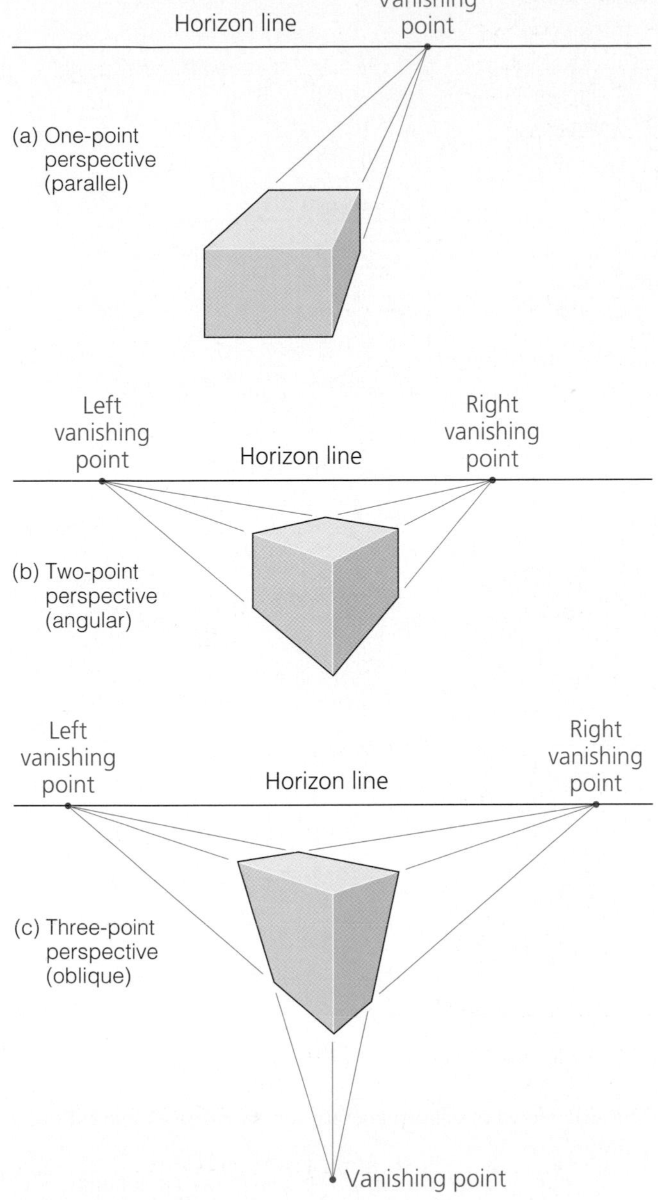

FIGURE 13.33 Types of Perspective

correspond to the height in the elevation (distance 1-2 in Fig. 13.34). It is drawn perpendicular to the edge view of the picture plane.

13.5.2 Locating the Horizon Line

The horizon line is usually located on eye level with the observer in the horizontal plane. The use of a higher horizon line will change the perspective appearance. Figure 13.35 shows three possible positions of the horizon line. The ground line remained the same for each projection, but the horizon line (VP 1 H, VP 2 H, VP 3 H) was adjusted to see the part from the bottom, the front, and the top, respectively.

13.5.3 Locating the Station Point in Perspective

To avoid undue distortion in perspective, the station point should be located so that the cone of rays has its apex at the point of sight and includes the entire object. This should have an angle at the apex not greater than 30°, shown as the angle of vision in Figure 13.34. When the object is close to the horizon, a greater angle may be used. Pleasing results are usually obtained if the point of sight is located centrally in front of the object and at a height that will show the desired amount of the horizontal surfaces.

13.5.4 One-Point Perspectives

The **one-point (parallel) perspectives** use a frontal plane that is parallel to the front face of the part (Fig. 13.36). The frontal plane is perpendicular to the line of sight. Parallel perspective pictorial drawings are employed most commonly to illustrate interior views of rooms or other spatial conditions. On solid objects, one-point perspectives more nearly resemble oblique pictorial drawings. The frontal surface of the pictorial box is perpendicular to the lines of sight (axis of vision) and shows height and width in true distance. The depth lines of the object converge toward a common vanishing point (CV). The top, front, and side faces are drawn first with full-scale dimensions. Height dimensions are taken from the side view for the front face.

After the top view and the front face of the part are drawn, the station point and the common vanishing point are established. Visual rays are projected from each point of the part to the station point. The intersection of a visual ray and the picture plane establishes points along the picture plane that are then projected to the front view. The intersection of these points and rays extending from the front view to the CV establishes the depth features of the part. This same procedure was used in drawing Figure 13.37. Here, the CV was placed to the right of the part, not centered as in the previous example.

Since the curves are drawn without distortion in the front plane, parts with curved features on one surface are easily drawn with this form of perspective (Fig. 13.38). Receding curves are located in the perspective view (front) by establishing the intersection of each curve's center point with the picture plane, points 1^1, 2^1, and 3^1.

13.5.5 Two-Point Perspectives

The **two-point perspective** is also called an **angular perspective.** In Figure 13.39, the top view shows the width and depth of the part. The height is either projected to the height line (common to the line of sight) or measured directly (to scale) on this line. There are two height lines on this example because two mating parts are drawn. Each has the same top view (except for visibility). The height line for the top piece goes from the TOP LINE to point 1. The bottom piece has a height line from the GROUND LINE to point 1.

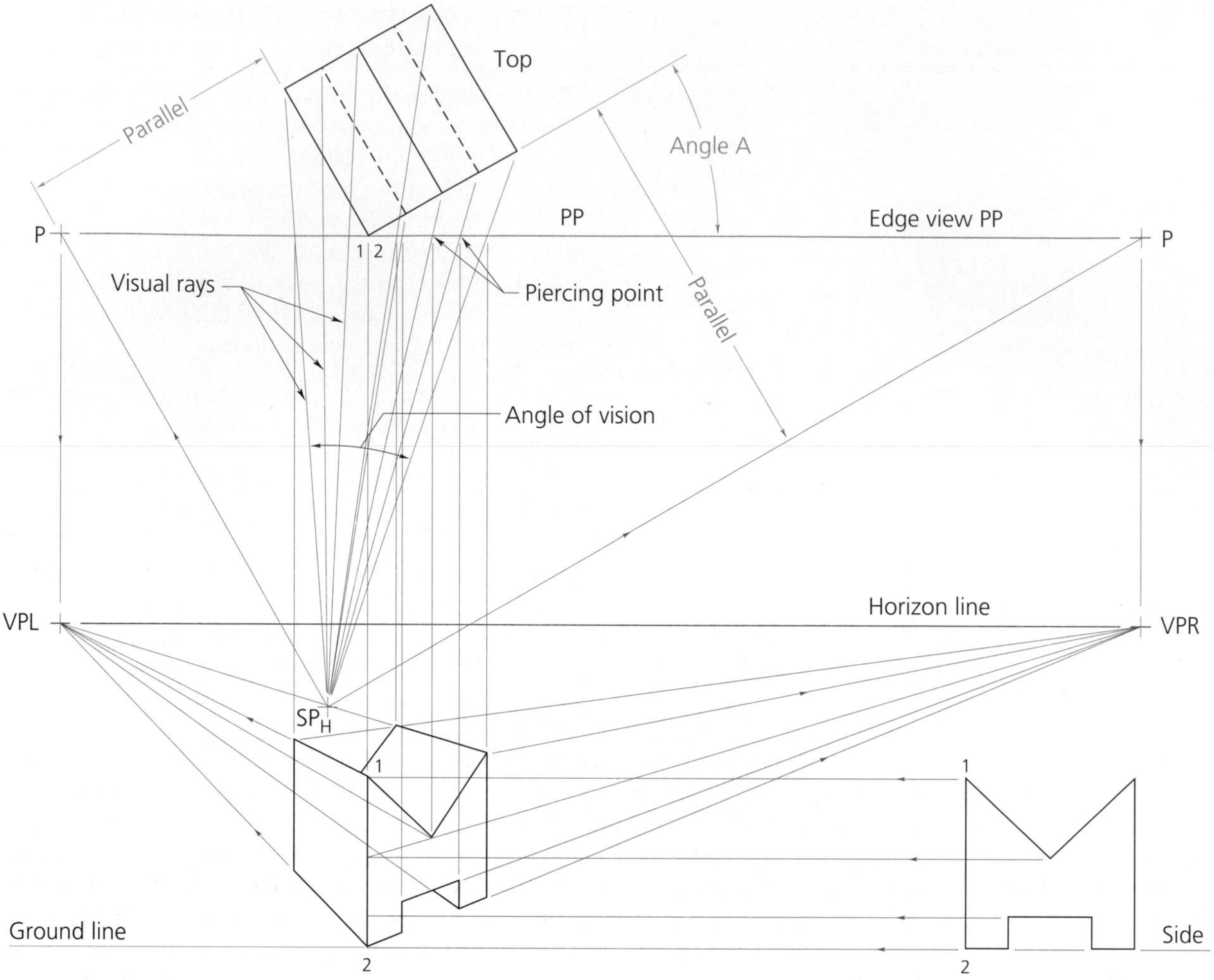

FIGURE 13.34 Angular Perspective Projection

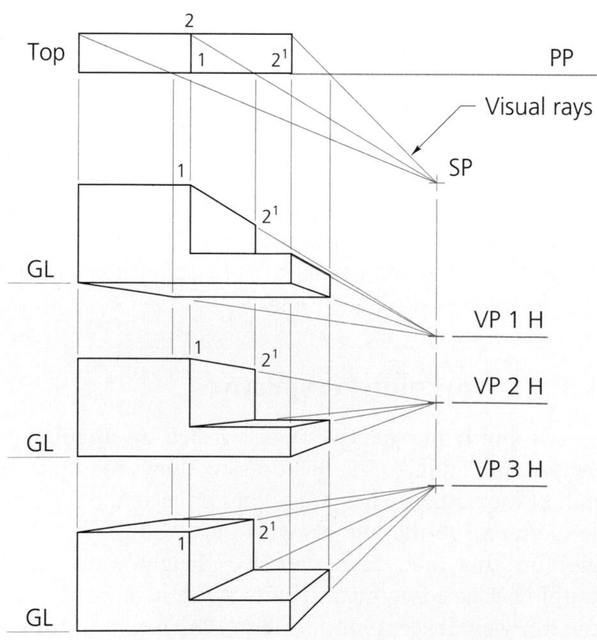

FIGURE 13.35 Variations in the Placement of the Horizon Line

The side views of each piece are reversed (and have different visibility).

The part is angled in the top view so that it makes 30° with the picture plane (PP). Lines are drawn from the SP parallel to the part's edge in this view. The angle formed by the SP and the two vanishing points in the top view will be 90° (angle A-SP-B). The intersection of each line and the PP determines the right and left vanishing points, which are then projected to the front view on the horizon line.

All lines on the drawing are determined by projection from location points on the height lines, with lines extended to the proper vanishing points. Lines to the left of the plan view go toward the left vanishing point (VPL). Lines to the right on the plan view are drawn toward the right vanishing point (VPR). Projection from these points must follow the direction of the planes in the plan view of the part. If these lines change planes in following the contour or details of the part, the direction must also change from that point toward the vanishing point for that plane.

A line from the station point toward the outer points, both left and right, should make an angle with the height line (line of sight) of 15° or less. In other words the angle

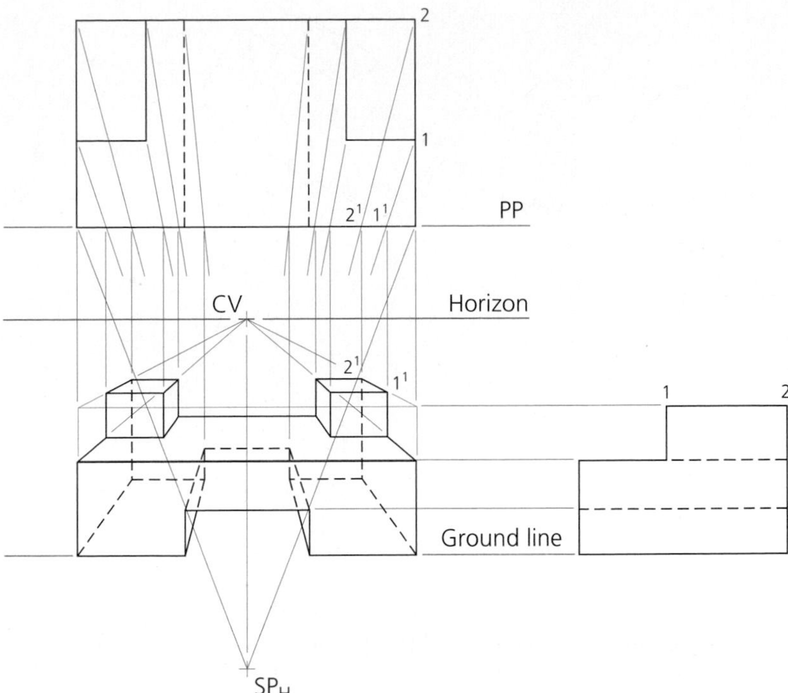

FIGURE 13.36 **One-Point Perspective Projection**

made by the visual rays should not exceed 30° in most cases. In Figure 13.39 a slightly larger angle was used. A larger angle is likely to create excessive distortion. The horizon line should be located at some distance from the picture plane to avoid overlapping of the plan view and the perspective pictorial drawing. This was *not* done in Figure 13.34 and, therefore, the construction there overlaps. Figure 13.39 is easier to read because the construction lines of the two views do not overlap.

The vertical dimensions of the part are measured to scale or projected from the side view directly. The scale of the plan view and of the elevation should be the same, to avoid distortion on the pictorial drawing.

Increasing the distance between the plan view of the part and the edge view of the picture plane decreases the size of the perspective and gives an appearance of distance from the part. However, increasing this distance does not compensate for a change in height and can cause distortion. The plan view should touch the edge view of the picture plane (Fig. 13.39).

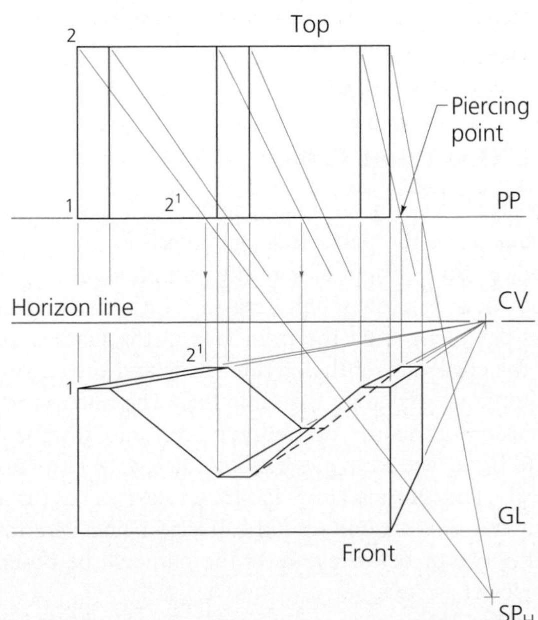

FIGURE 13.37 **Parallel Perspective Projection**

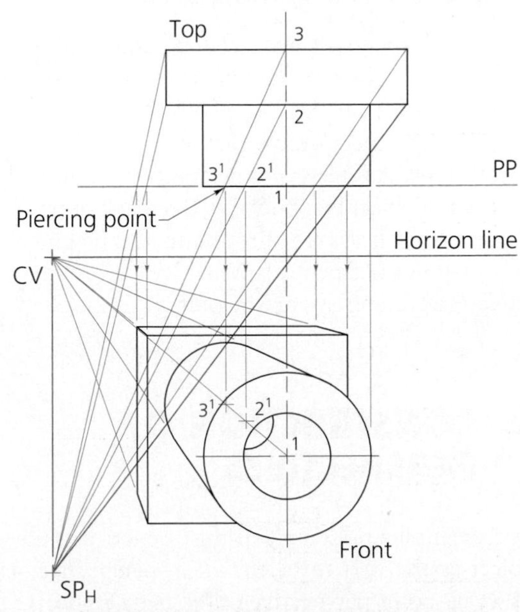

FIGURE 13.38 **Circles in Parallel Perspective Projection**

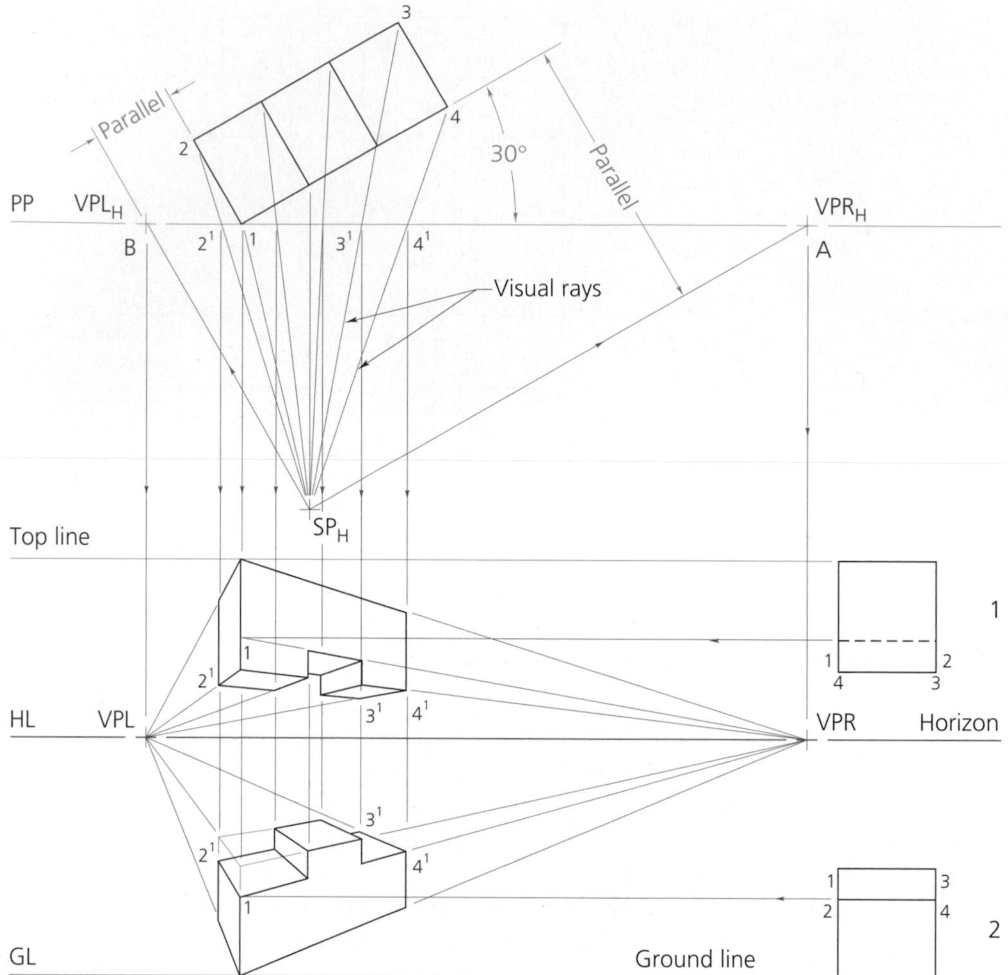

FIGURE 13.39 Two-Point Perspective Projection

13.5.6 Three-Point Perspectives

Three-point perspectives are called **oblique perspectives** [Figure 13.33(c)]. They are useful in situations where the object would not appear excessively distorted, as for very tall buildings. Oblique perspective pictorial drawings aid perception very little. A three-point perspective requires that all three axes of the object be oblique to the plane of projection. Height cannot be measured directly on the height line, as with the two-point perspective. When creating a three-point perspective, grid underlays are helpful.

13.6 CONSTRUCTION OF PERSPECTIVES

The three examples presented in this section use the same basic object as the part to be drawn in perspective. Figure 13.40 is a one-point perspective of the part, Figure 13.41 is a two-point perspective of the same part, and Figure 13.42 is a two-point perspective of the same basic shape but with curved features.

13.6.1 One-Point Construction

The construction of a one-point perspective starts with the determination of the part's scale and position in space. The top surface and the right side of the part should be viewed. The top view is drawn first [Fig. 13.40(a)]. The picture plane is passed through the front face of the part. In other words, the edge view of the picture plane and the edge view of the front face are along the same line. The horizon line is drawn according to the desired eye level and whether the part is to be viewed from eye level, below eye level, or above eye level. The ground line is drawn last. The distance between the ground line and the horizon line determines how far above or below eye level the part will be observed by the viewer.

The front view is drawn second [Fig. 13.40(b)]. The distance between the picture plane line in the top view and

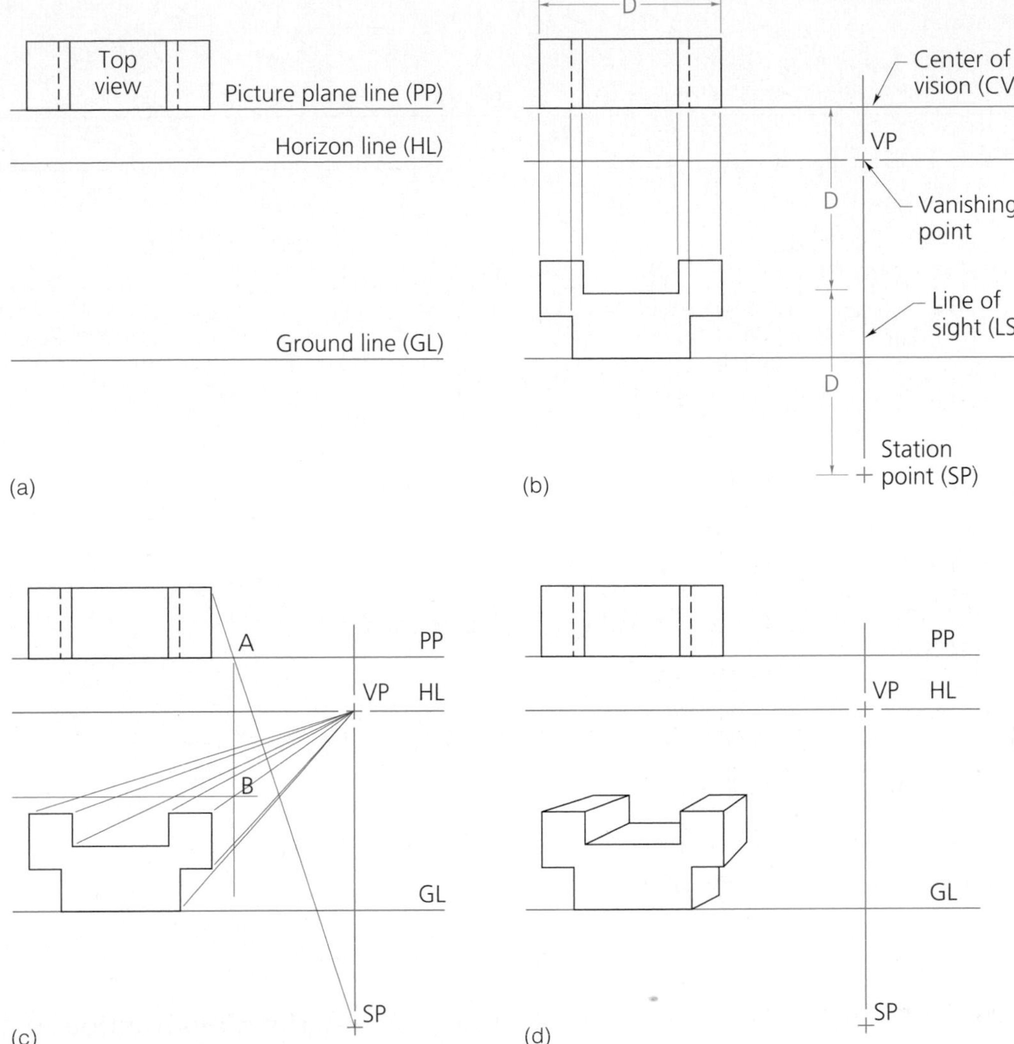

FIGURE 13.40 Constructing a One-Point Perspective

the station point is drawn two times (or more) the width of the part (dimension *D* in this figure). The location of the vertical line (line of sight) will be determined by which side the part is to recede to and how much of the part's side needs to be shown. Here, the vertical line is drawn on the right of the part, so the perspective recedes to the right. Dimension *D* establishes this distance. The line of sight is to the right of the part at a distance equal to dimension *D*. The farther to the side this line is drawn, the more the right side will show. The front view is then drawn using the width dimensions projected from the top view and completing the front face's features. The vanishing point is at the intersection of the line of sight (vertical line) and the horizon line.

Lines are then drawn from every point on the front view to the vanishing point (VP) in Figure 13.40(c). A line drawn from the station point to the back corner of the part in the top view intersects the picture plane (PP) to establish point A. A line is then drawn vertically from point A to the receding lines, which extend from the front view toward the VP. This will establish point B and the back vertical edge of the part. A horizontal line is then drawn from point B to the left to establish the back edge. All other features are drawn by the same procedure to establish points along the picture plane and to project to the front view [Fig. 13.40(d)].

13.6.2 Two-Point Construction

Figure 13.41 shows a two-point perspective of the same part as in Figure 13.40. Note the differences and similarities of the procedure and the finished illustration. Two-point perspectives require more work and the end result is more realistic.

Start by drawing the picture plane line (PP), as shown. The top view is then drawn with one of its corners touching the picture plane line. This will also establish the center of vision (CV). The front face is drawn at an angle of 30° to the PP, as shown. Other angles can be used. To show enough detail, the side with the most features should be at the

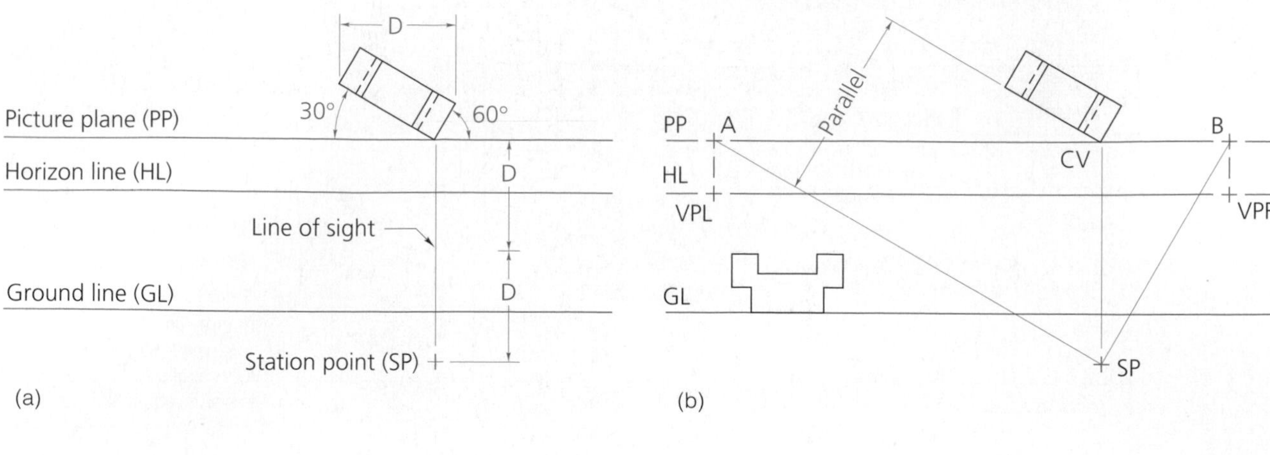

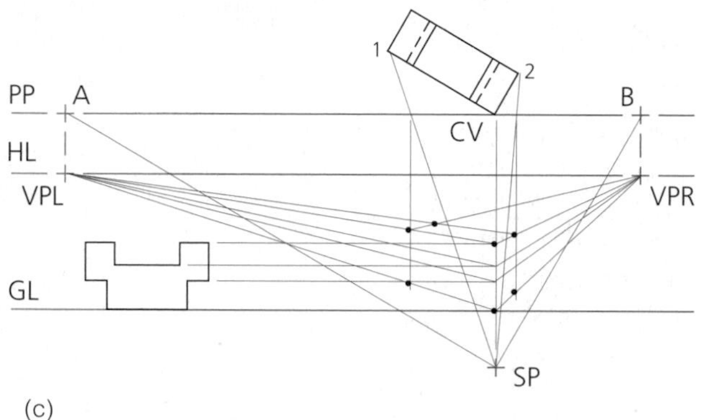

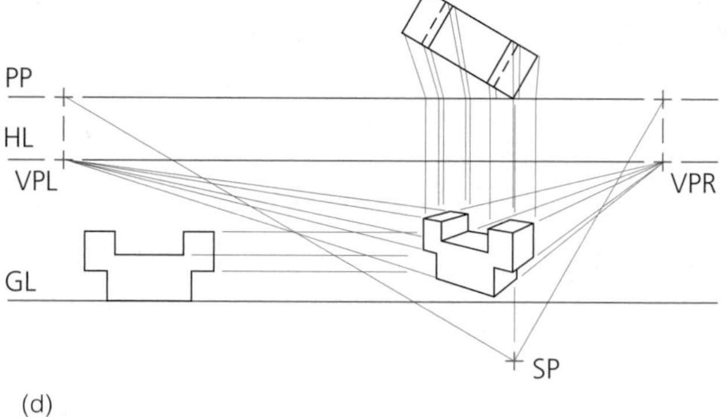

FIGURE 13.41 Constructing a Two-Point Perspective

smaller angle to the PP. The line of sight is drawn as a vertical line extending from the intersection of the part's front corner (the one touching the PP) in Figure 13.41(a). The horizon line, the ground line, and the station point are established as in Figure 13.40. Draw lines SP-A and SP-B from the station point parallel to the edges of the part to where they intersect the PP and establish points A and B [Fig. 13.41(b)]. Vanishing point left (VPL) and vanishing point right (VPR) are drawn by dropping vertical lines from points A and B to the horizon line.

The right or left side view is then drawn with its base on the ground line, as in Figure 13.41(c). Height lines are established in the perspective view by projecting each vertical dimension from the side view to the line of sight. The intersection of each line projected from the side view to the line of sight establishes points. Draw a line from each point to the VPL and the VPR. Draw lines from the SP to the corners of the top view at points 1 and 2. The intersection of these projectors and the PP establishes the outside limits of the perspective view when they are drawn vertically until they intersect their corresponding receding projectors. The part's outside dimensions have now been determined. By repeating the previous two steps, every feature of the part is established by projection. The perspective is then darkened, as in Figure 13.41(d).

13.6.3 Two-Point Construction of Curved Features

In Figure 13.42 the part has been constructed using the same procedure as in Figures 13.40 and 13.41. The parts are identical except that the cutout is now curved instead of rectangular. To draw a perspective of a part with curved features, points are established along the curve (Fig. 13.42). After the part's general shape is established, the points along each curve are projected and located by the same procedure

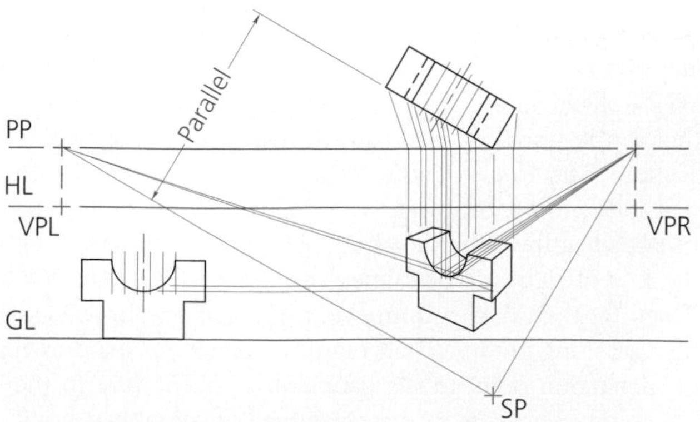

FIGURE 13.42 Constructing a Two-Point Perspective with Curved Features

as for locating an endpoint of a line or any straight feature. After a sufficient number of points is established along the curve in the perspective view, the curve can be drawn with the aid of an irregular curve.

13.7 TECHNICAL ILLUSTRATION

Various procedures and accepted drafting conventions for representing certain features are incorporated into pictorial illustrations. Pictorial sections and cutaways, breaks, fillet and round representation, and thread representation increase the lifelike qualities of an illustration. Shading and shadows are also added to pictorials to give a more lifelike representation of the part or system, as in Figure 13.43, where the degreaser system was pictorially sketched. Pictorial assemblies incorporate exploded views (Fig. 13.44) when it is necessary to show how a device fits together. CAD systems allow the user to create lifelike images in 2D (Fig. 13.45) and 3D images like the exploded view of the headset in Figure 13.46. These new and exciting possibilities include the ablity to display the part or system in any number of orientations and to add movement and animation to the engineering field.

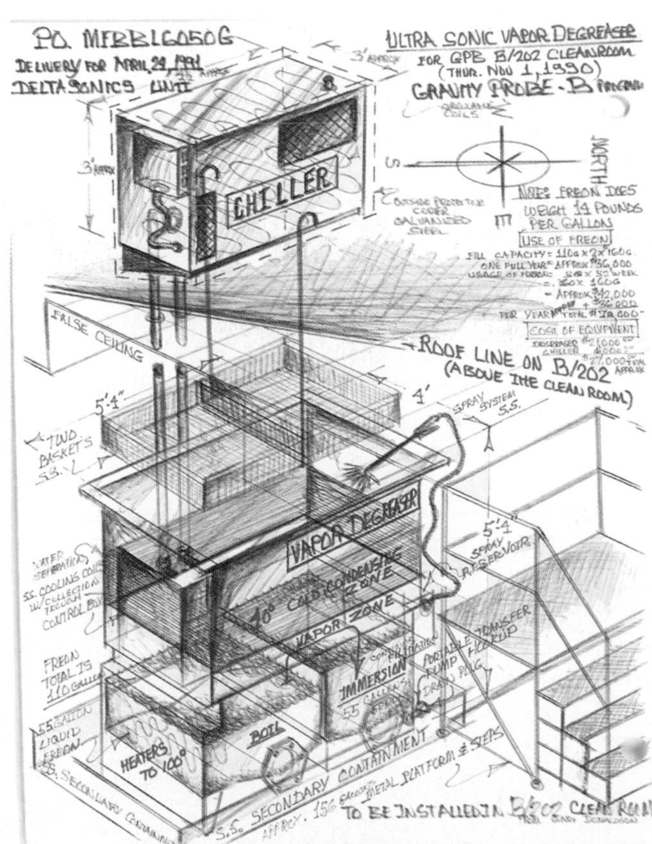

FIGURE 13.43 Pictorial Sketch of Vapor Degreaser

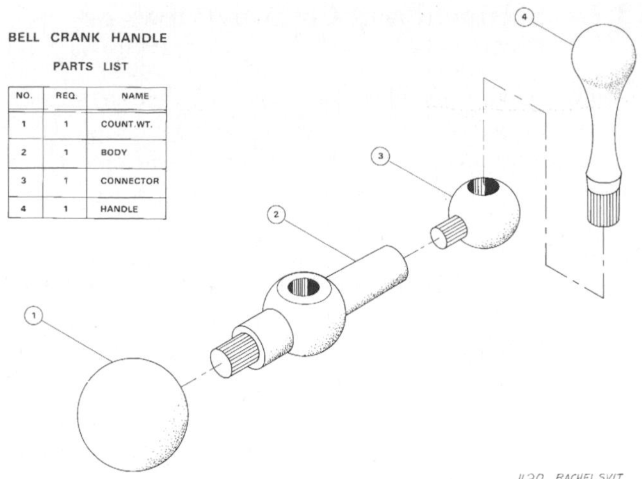

NO.	REQ.	NAME
1	1	COUNT.WT.
2	1	BODY
3	1	CONNECTOR
4	1	HANDLE

FIGURE 13.44 Bell Crank Handle

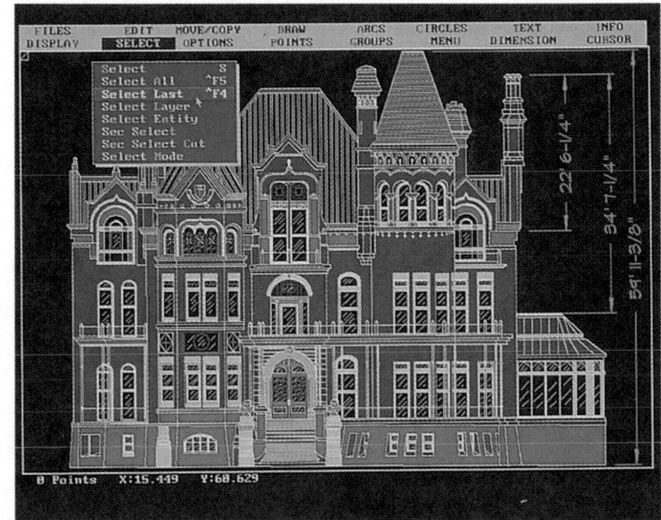

FIGURE 13.45 2D Illustration of a House

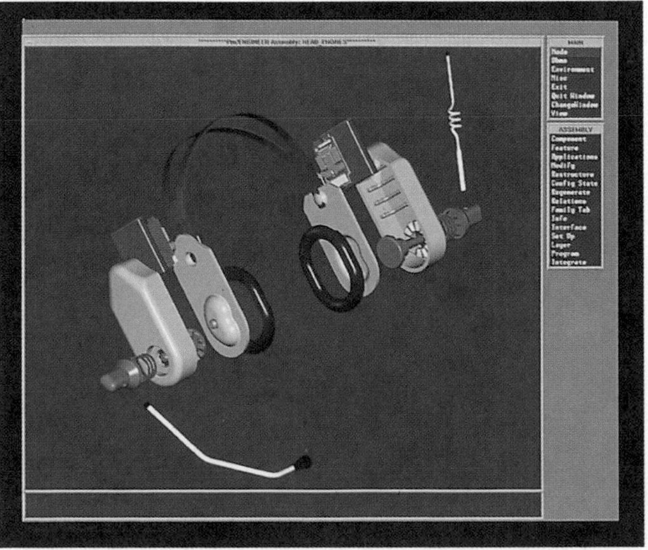

FIGURE 13.46 Exploded Shaded Assembly of a Headset

13.7.1 Sectional and Cutaway Views on Pictorials

Sectioned pictorials allow the viewing of the interior of a part or an assembly. When possible, section-cutting planes are passed through centerlines and parallel to one of the principal faces of the part. Figure 13.47 shows a half section (a) and a full section (b) of a part. Section lines in a half section should be drawn so that they would appear to coincide if the planes were folded together [Fig. 13.47(a)]. With a full section, all of the crosshatching should be drawn in the same direction—at the same angle and with the same spacing.

In assemblies, individual pieces are differentiated by appropriate symbols and by changing the direction of the section lining. When a section plane passes through a shaft, bolt, key, pin, or solid round item, it is desirable to run the section around that item and to show the entire bolt or shaft in the pictorial. Except for such cases, the section lines should indicate exactly what material has been cut. Figure 13.48(a) shows the first step in the creation of a section of a pictorial assembly. Each of the parts is blocked out. The assembly is then completed [Fig. 13.48(b)].

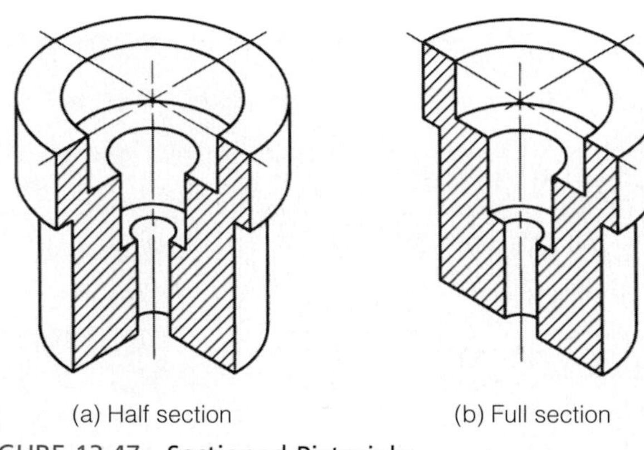

(a) Half section (b) Full section

FIGURE 13.47 Sectioned Pictorials

13.7.2 Pictorials and Break Lines

When the length of a part is beyond the size of the drawing format, and there are no features that require displaying and dimensioning, you may shorten the drawing with **break lines.** Position the break at a place on the part that does not interfere with the part features and the required dimensions. Freehand breaks are acceptable for most situations. Figure 13.49 gives the preferred and the acceptable methods for showing breaks.

13.7.3 Fillets and Rounds on Pictorials

Fillets and **rounds** usually can be highlighted or can be shown as straight or curved lines representing the filleted and rounded edges of a part, as in Figure 13.50. Highlighting and shading are drawn freehand. When a CAD system is used to generate a 3D model (Fig. 13.51), the model can display fillets and rounds in a variety of ways, including: as a wireframe with hidden lines and tangent curves shown [Fig. 13.51(a)]; as an edge representation with only the visible lines and tangent curves [Fig.13.51(b)]; as a solid

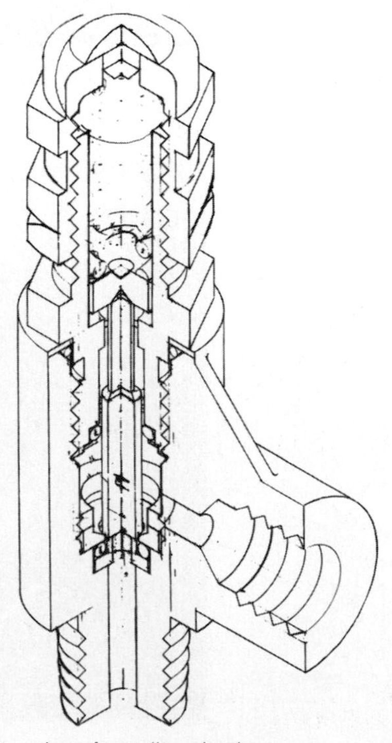

(a) Construction of needle valve in an isometric drawing using a half section

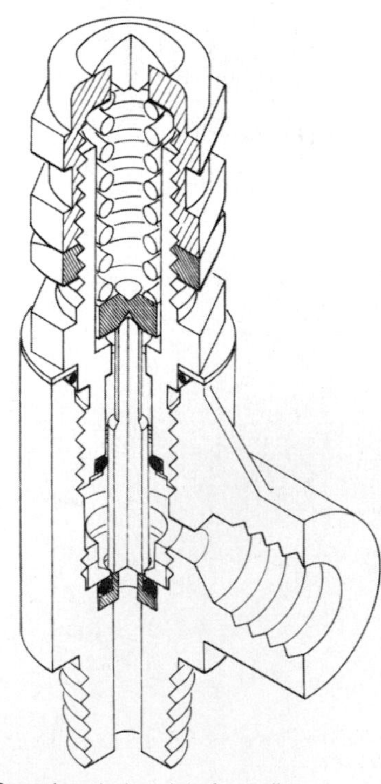

(b) Completed pictorial of needle valve

FIGURE 13.48 Pictorial Construction

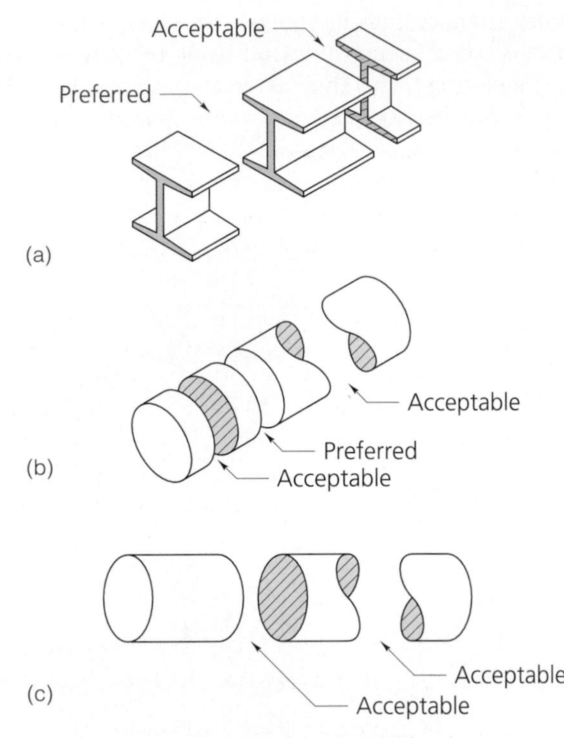

FIGURE 13.49 Break Lines for Pictorials

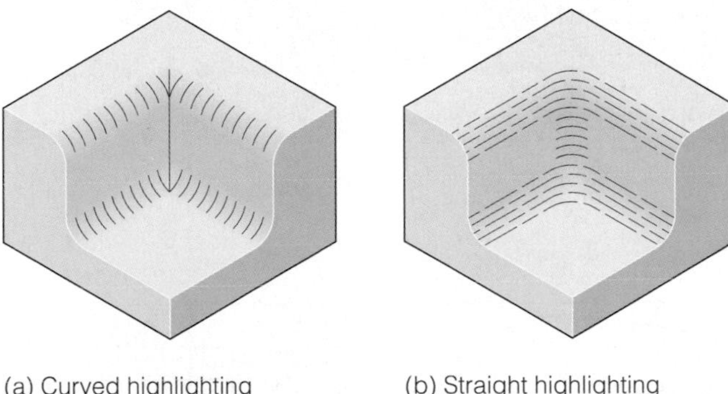

(a) Curved highlighting (b) Straight highlighting

FIGURE 13.50 Fillets and Rounds in Pictorials

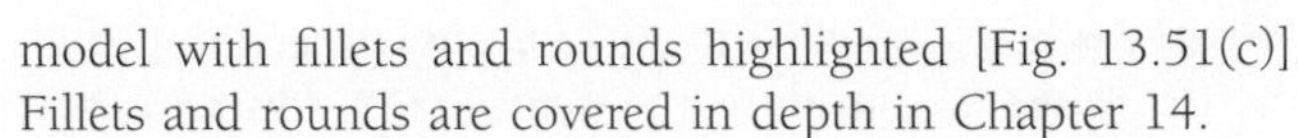

model with fillets and rounds highlighted [Fig. 13.51(c)]. Fillets and rounds are covered in depth in Chapter 14.

13.7.4 Pictorial Thread Representation

Threads may be represented by a series of ellipses or circles uniformly spaced along the centerline of the thread. Shading increases the effectiveness of the thread appearance. In Figure 13.52, the exploded assembly has both internal and

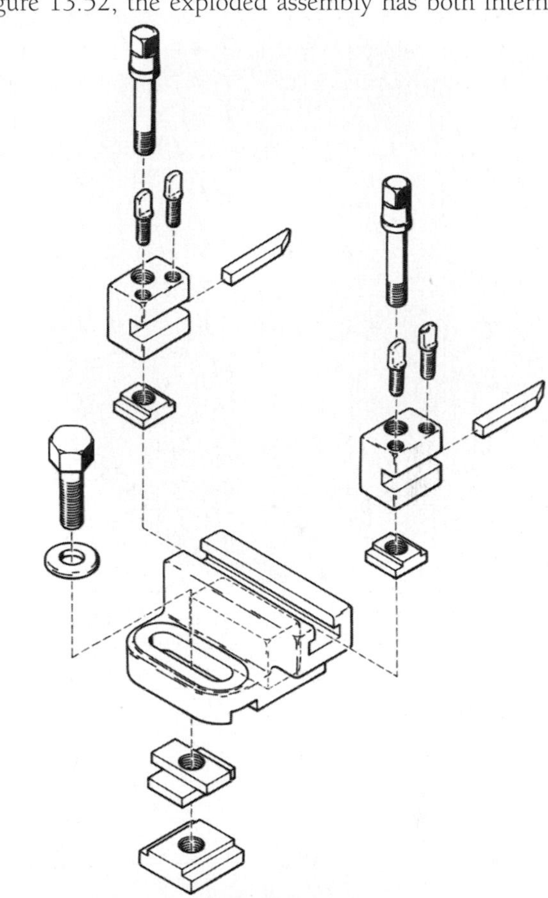

FIGURE 13.52 Exploded Assembly

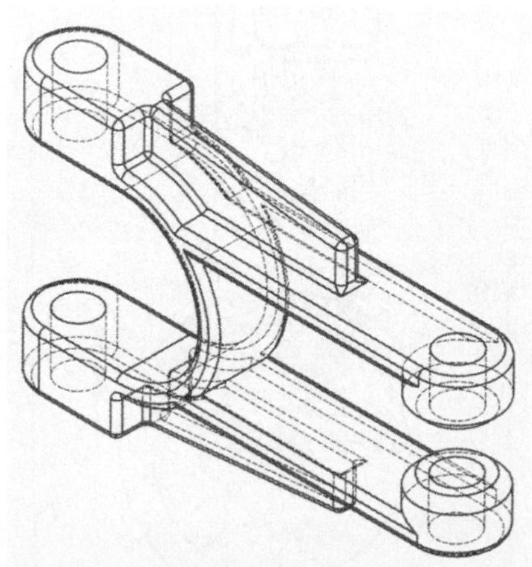

(a) With hidden lines and tangent curves (rounds and fillets)

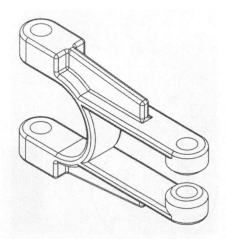

(b) With tangent curves (rounds and fillets) and without hidden lines

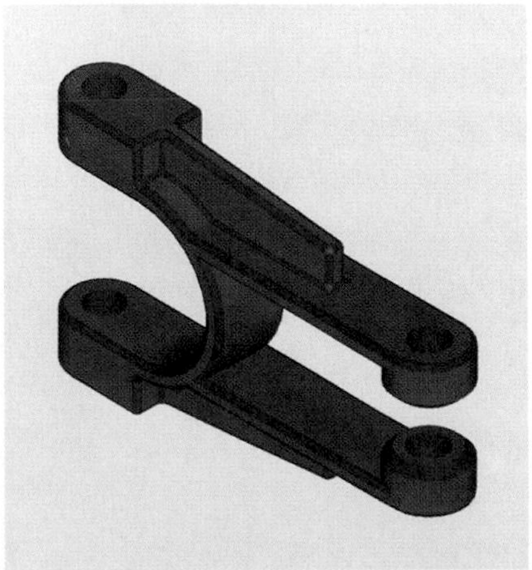

(c) Shaded image with rounds and fillets highlighted

FIGURE 13.51 3D Model

external threads. Threads should be evenly spaced, but it is not necessary to reproduce the actual *pitch* (distance between crests of the threads) or the exact number of threads. The solid model of the part in Figure 13.53 has a buttress thread incorporated into its design. The thread was generated with a *helical sweep* command using the actual thread profile dimensions. The threads created a very large file (database) and therefore required more time to regenerate

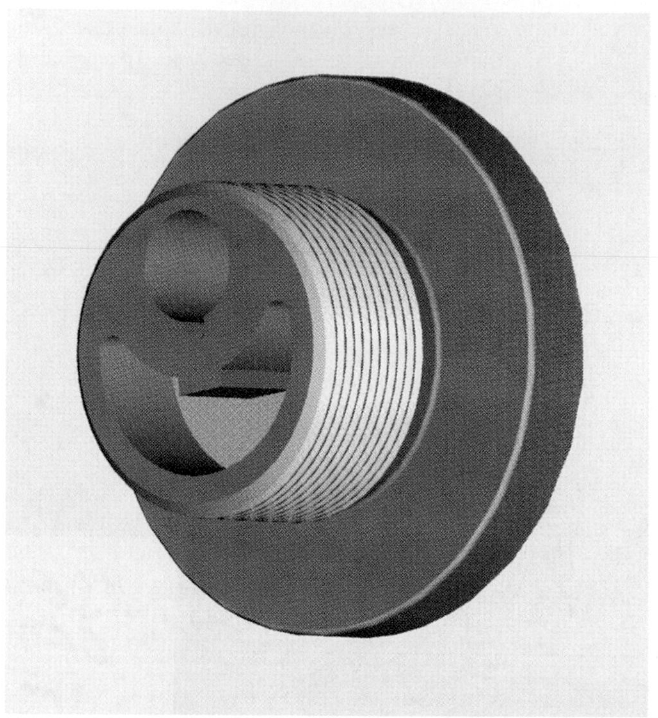

(a) Shaded image

(b) Closeup view of threads (shaded image)

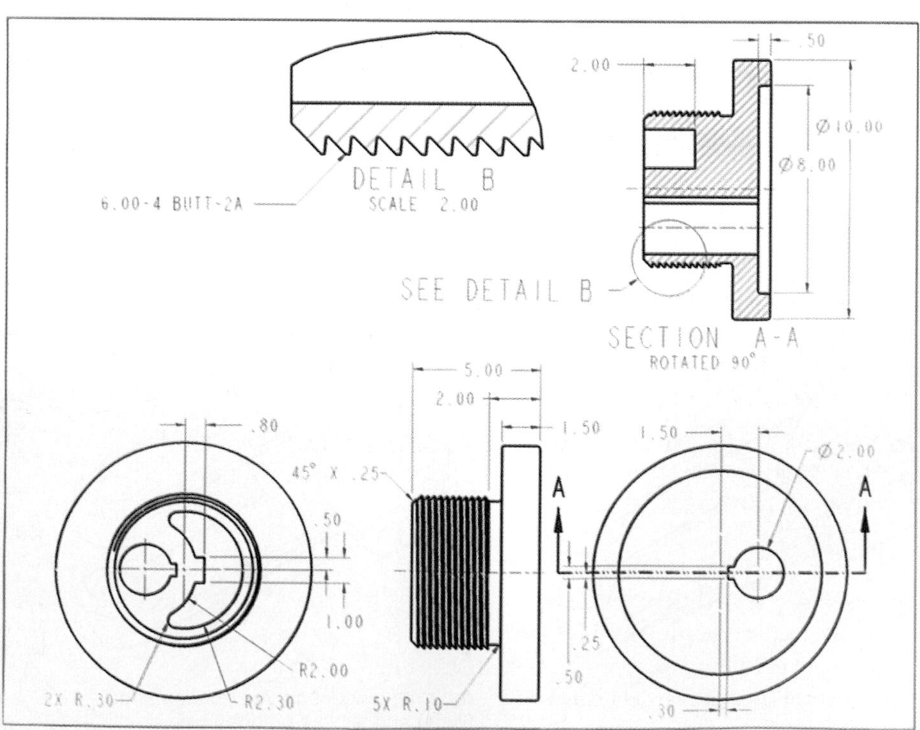

(c) Detail drawing

FIGURE 13.53 3D Part with Buttress Threads

FIGURE 13.54 Exploded Pictorial

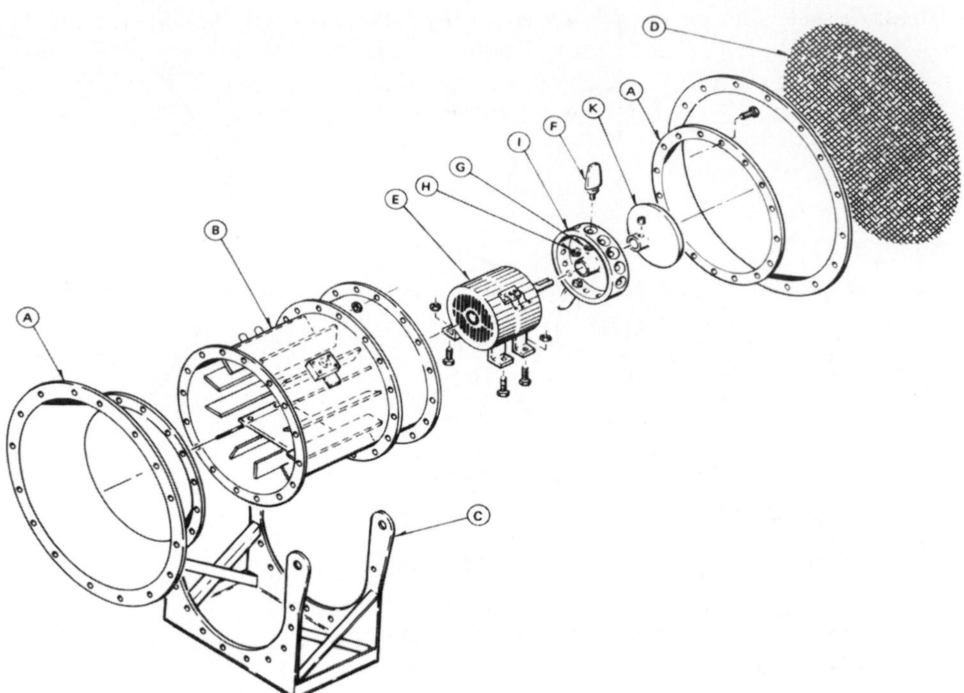

while the part was in the design stage (25 minutes of laser plotting time). Normally the threads on a 3D solid model will be displayed as cosmetic threads (see Chapter 17).

13.7.5 Exploded Assembly Pictorials

A pictorial drawing showing the various parts of an assembly—separated but in proper position and alignment for reassembly—is called an **exploded assembly** (Fig. 13.54). Exploded pictorials are used extensively in service manuals and as an aid in assembling or erecting a machine or structure. Any type of pictorial drawing may serve this purpose, and the shading may be as simple or as complete as desired. In Figure 13.55 the exploded assembly is drawn isometrically. Highlighting and shading have been added to provide a realistic illustration of the pieces.

Each piece in an exploded assembly should be connected to its mating part by a centerline, as shown in Figures 13.54 and 13.55. If there is insufficient room to extend the exploded pieces out from each other in one line, the piece can be moved, as in Figure 13.52, where the bolt and washer have been brought forward and up. The *jogged centerline* still connects related pieces.

You May Complete Exercises 13.5 Through 13.8 at This Time

13.7.6 Pictorial Drawing Using CAD

The designer seated at a 2D CAD station gets no more feeling of three-dimensional definition from a single view on the screen than he or she would from a drawing on paper. However, the designer can visualize the three-dimensional part better when the features are seen in the view that indicates depth, even if in an artificial way. Creating a drawing with *perspective, isometric,* or *oblique* views helps to indicate depth to the designer.

Two-dimensional pictures can be made to look more realistic with **isometric views** of three-dimensional objects,

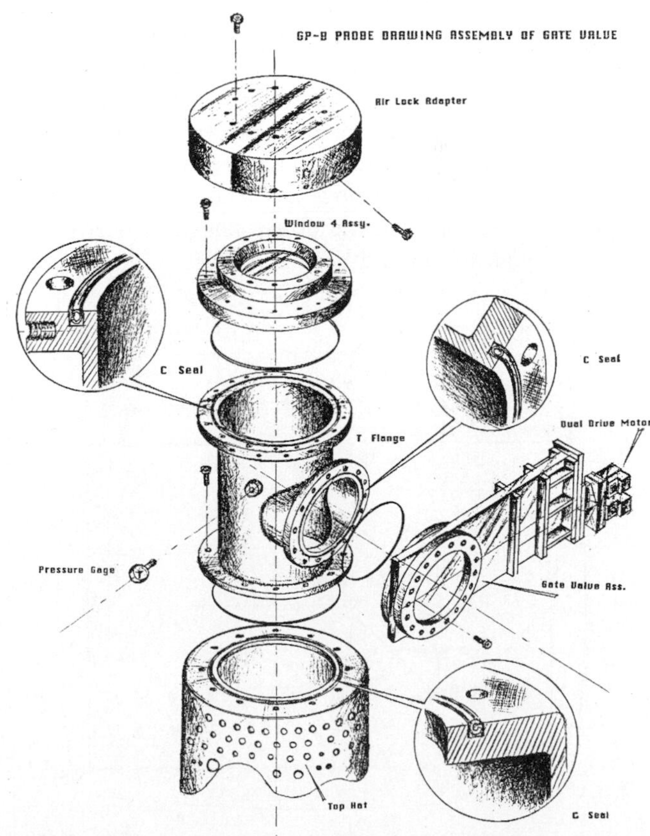

FIGURE 13.55 Exploded Sketch of Gravity Probe Assembly

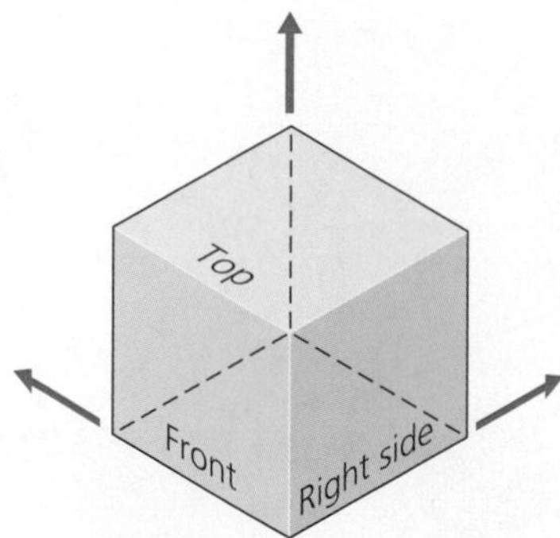

FIGURE 13.56 Isometric Axes

such as the cube shown in Figure 13.56. **Oblique views** also can create illustrations that simulate the third dimension (Figure 13.57).

The **perspective** capability is different from parallel orthographic projection in that it uses depth information. Perspective drawings can be constructed on CAD systems, but normally the perspective is generated from an existing view of a 3D modeled part. The size of the part is drawn in proportion to its distance from the viewer. The perspective projection of the part shown in Figure 13.58 demonstrates this scaling. The **PERSPECTIVE** command temporarily distorts the part so that it can be viewed in perspective. This option is limited to three-dimensional systems with modeling capabilities. Some systems automatically set the perspective parameters to give the part a certain amount of distortion. The location of the station point can be specified, or the default can be used. The default location assumes that the part is in the center of the screen. The distance between the station point and the picture plane can also be specified.

Some CAD systems still offer the choice of drawing in isometric. Isometric drawings are simulations, not true 3D drawings—once drawn, the object cannot be viewed from another angle or in perspective, hidden lines cannot be removed.

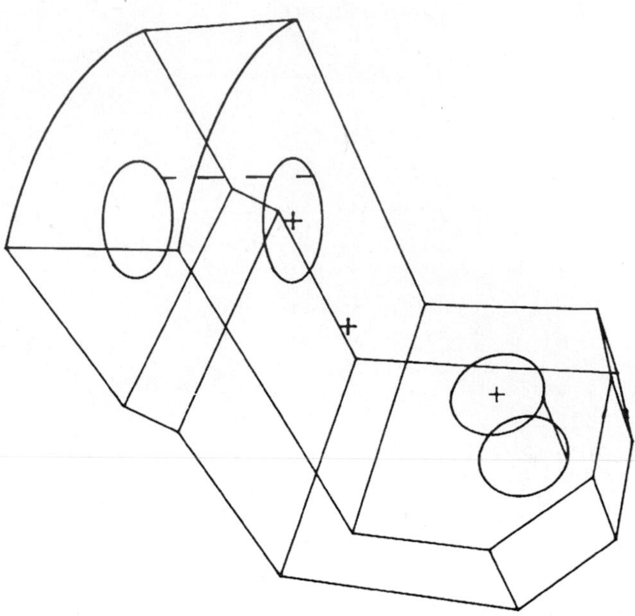

FIGURE 13.58 3D Model Displayed in Perspective

To construct a drawing in isometric via AutoCAD, an isometric plane, which utilizes the **SNAP** and **GRID** commands, can be activated. The isometric **SNAP** grid has three major axes. Assuming that rotation has not also been applied to the Snap grid, the axes are vertical, 30°, and 150° (Fig. 13.59).

ORTHO mode and keyboard pointing with the cursor movement keys can only deal with two of the three axes at a time. Therefore, AutoCAD assumes you are drawing on one of three isometric planes (left, top, or right), each of which has an associated pair of axes. The meaning of **ORTHO** mode and the action of the cursor movement keys are then modified to follow the current pair of axes.

You can set the **SNAP** to isometric by means of the **SNAP STYLE ISOMETRIC** command sequence. The current isometric plane also determines the orientation of the isometric

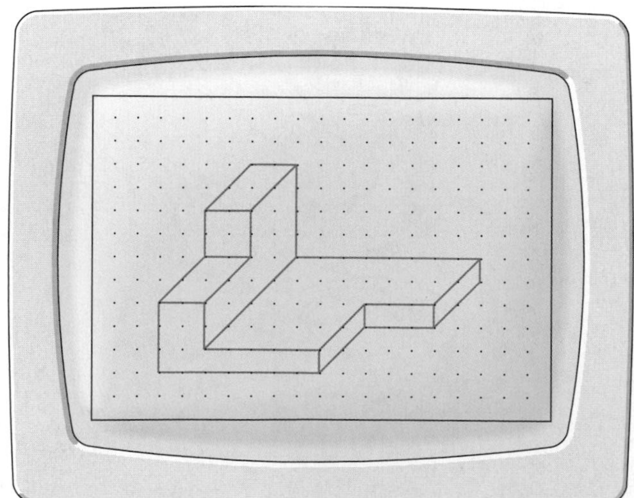

FIGURE 13.57 Oblique Drawing

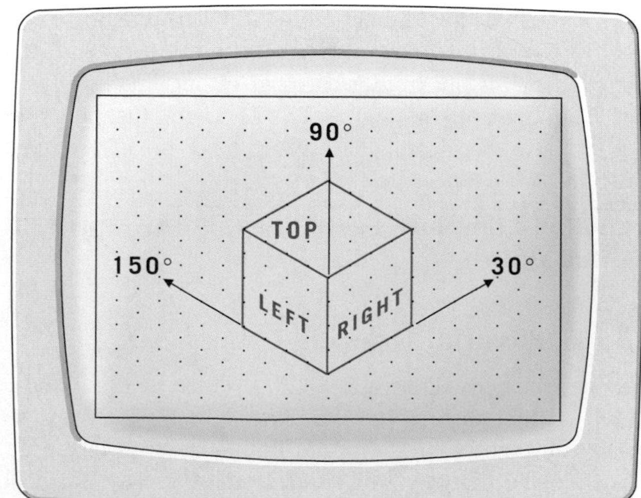

FIGURE 13.59 AutoCAD Isoplane Axes

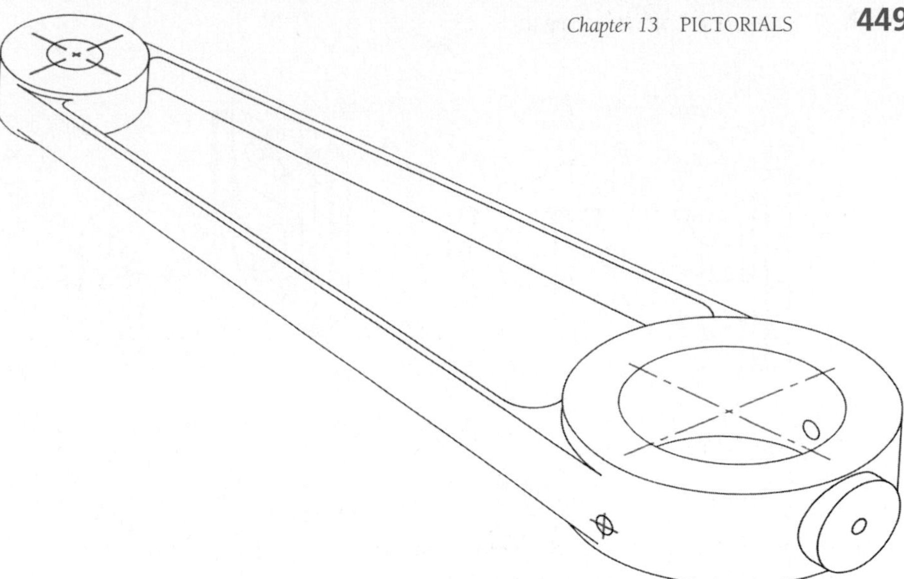

FIGURE 13.60 Isometric Drawing Created on AutoCAD

circles drawn via the **ELLIPSE** command. Figure 13.60 required the **ELLIPSE** command to represent the holes in the part. The **ISOPLANE** command selects the current isometric plane and thus the current pair of axes:

```
Command: ISOPLANE
Left/Top/Right/(toggle):
```

LEFT This option selects the left-hand plane, defined by the 90° and 150° axis pair. When **SNAP** mode is on, the up and the down cursor keys move you along the 90° axis, and the left and the right cursor keys move you along the 150° axis.

TOP The **TOP** isometric plane is the top face of the cube; it uses the 30° and 150° axis pair. When **SNAP** mode is on, the up and the down cursor keys move you along the 90° axis, and the left and the right cursor keys move you along the 150° axis.

RIGHT Responding to the prompt with **RIGHT** selects the right-hand plane, defined by the 90° and 30° axis pair. On this plane, the up and the down cursor keys move you along the 90° axis, and the left and the right cursor keys move you along the 30° axis.

The **ISOPLANE** command and the Isoplane toggle key are but two of the four methods available for setting the current isometric plane. The **SETVAR** command and **AutoLisp** are the other methods. The current isometric plane is maintained in the system variable **SNAPISOPAIR.**

While perspective, isometric, and oblique views are useful for depicting three-dimensional objects more realistically in a two-dimensional view, many CAD systems offer the capability to employ solid models. Here, the illustration of depth can be added through the use of color and shading. Figure 13.61 shows a solid model created on AutoCAD. The addition of color and shading enable the viewer to see the

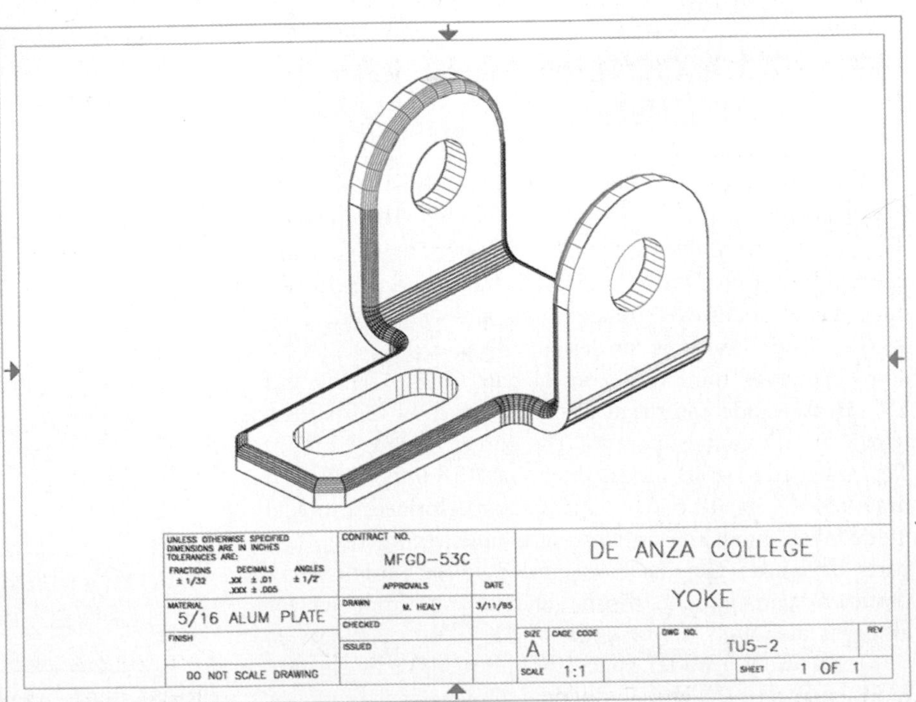

FIGURE 13.61 Part Created on AutoCAD Using Solids

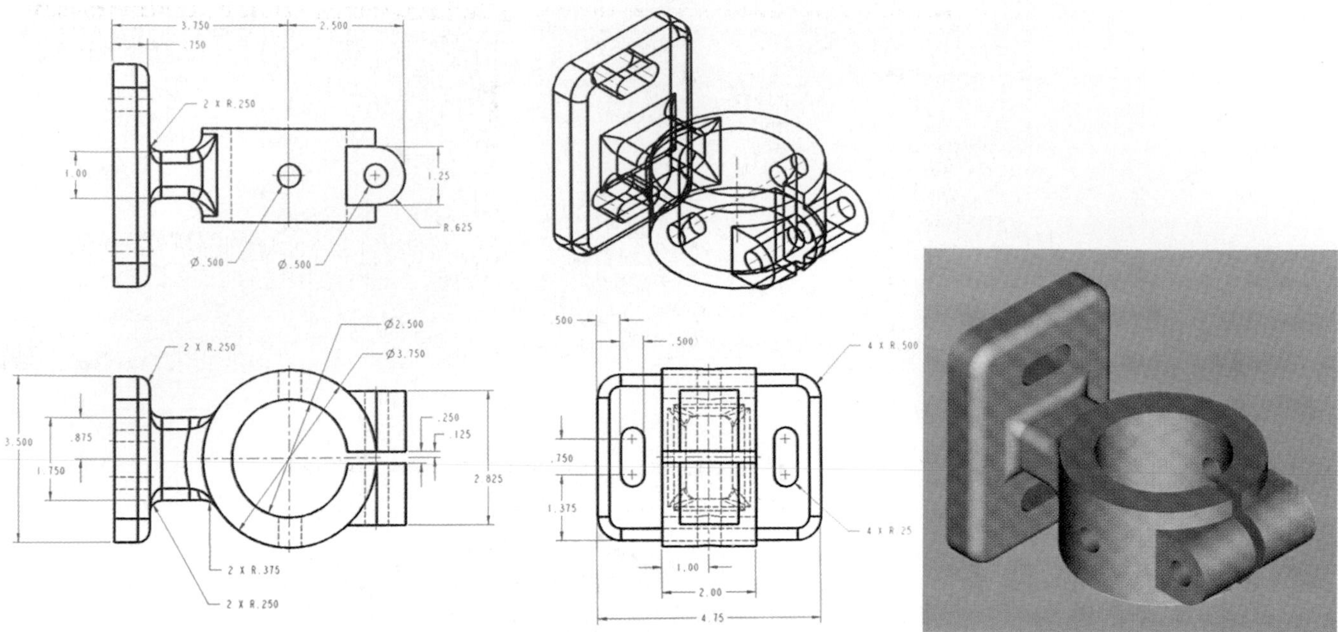

(a) Detail of part

(b) Shaded image of model

FIGURE 13.62 Parametric Model

part's curved geometry. The settings used in this figure did not produce a smooth, high-quality plot. In Figure 13.62, on the other hand, the model is displayed with high-quality graphics. Here the part was detailed [Fig.13.62(a)] and displayed [Fig. 13.62(b)] via CAD with high-quality graphics and a laser color plotter.

13.8 3D MODELING AND 2D DRAWING

CAD systems with three-dimensional capabilities have been designed so their use is as natural as possible. This includes recognizing the different thought processes involved and normally associated with design and drafting. Typically, two operational modes exist: model mode and draw mode (Fig. 13.63). **Model mode** is for designing a part [Fig. 13.64(a)] and generating numerical control data [Fig.13.64(b) and (c)]. **Draw mode** can create detail drawings of the part by using the 3D model in views. The part in Figure 13.65(a) was designed as a 3D model [Fig. 13.65(b)] and detailed in draw mode [Fig. 13.65(c)]. Operations performed in model mode create model descriptions and model geometry of the parts designed. The database created in this mode for a particular part model is distinct and separate from that for all other models.

Model mode (**model space** for AutoCAD) can create a representation of a real-world three-dimensional object. A designer in model mode is creating an actual three-dimensional layout of model geometry. Draw mode (**paper space** for AutoCAD) creates drawing representations of the model by modifying or editing the model's geometry to change its visual appearance. Draw mode uses the model's database for information representing the model's geometry.

A designer in draw mode accesses the model database to create two-dimensional drawings from that database. Detail drawings with dimensions, text, and notes are created in draw mode. Drawing items can also be inserted in draw mode (draw entities) and are separate from the model items. One way to understand this more clearly is to imagine the model as being created within a transparent three-dimensional box in which the model's geometry exists physically in three-dimensional space. In contrast, a drawing created from the model in draw mode shows the model's projection on the sides of the box (Fig. 13.66).

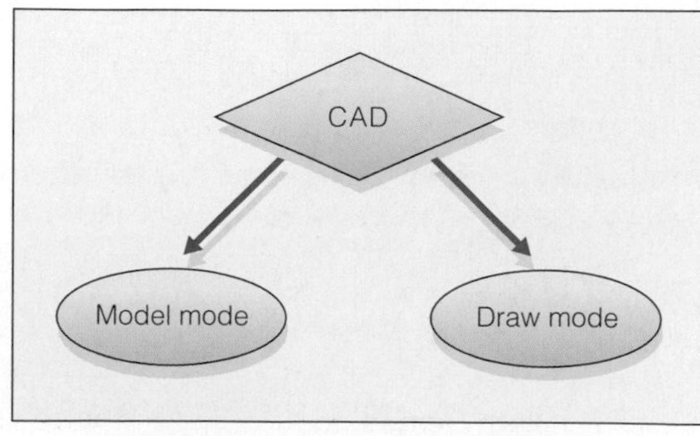

FIGURE 13.63 Model Mode and Draw Mode

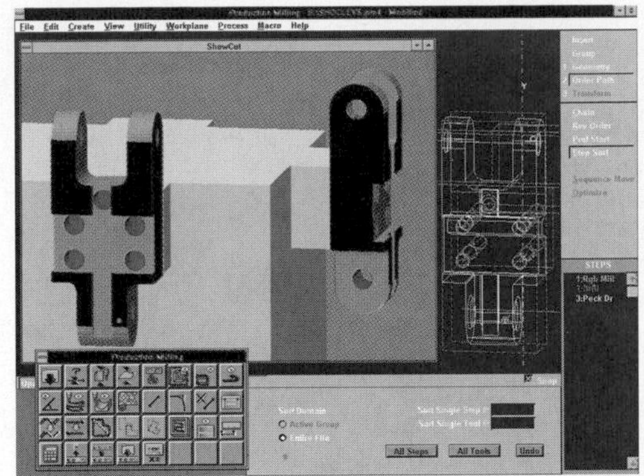

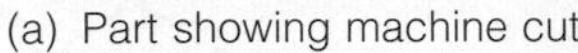

(a) Part showing machine cut

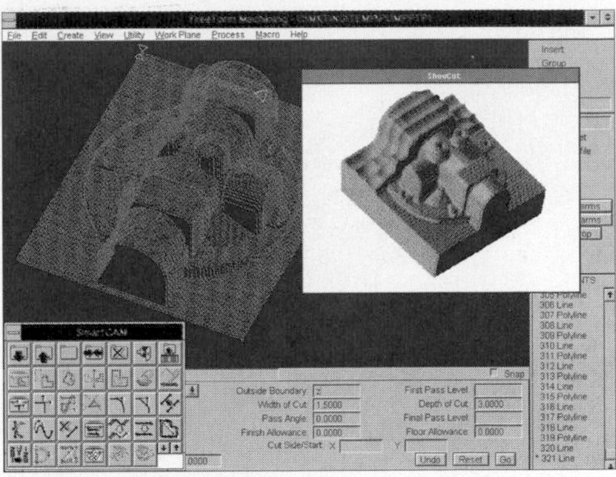

(b) Freeform machining

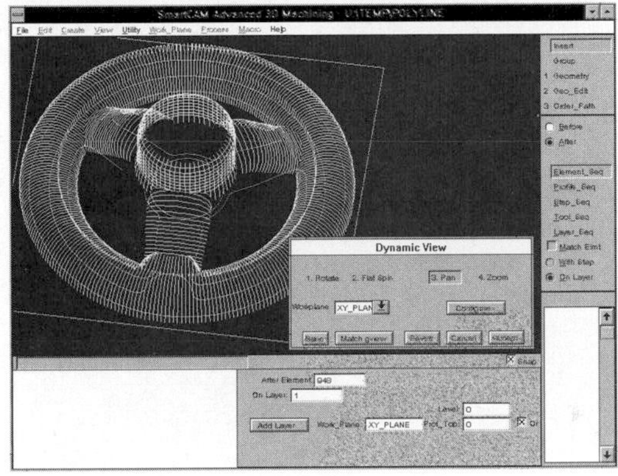

(c) Advanced 3D machining

FIGURE 13.64 3D Machining Using CAM Program

When draw mode is used to edit the model's visual appearance, the changes made are only pictorial, similar to air-brushing a photograph. In model mode, in contrast, the changes are made to the model and are reflected in all views. Changes made in draw mode allow the detailer to manipulate the model for drafting purposes. For example, solid lines could be changed into dashed lines to show that they are hidden or to indicate where a hole might be located. Lines can be erased temporarily for visual clarity or to prevent certain lines from being plotted (as hard copy) twice if they are normally seen one behind the other in a particular view. In this way the model's database retains its integrity while different views of the model are altered as needed for detailing purposes.

A large number of drawings can be created in draw mode and associated with a specific mode (Fig. 13.67). These drawings can be created at any size. It is important to realize that a drawing is a collection of views that depict the part. A view shows the part at a particular orientation (e.g., top, front, right). Three-dimensional CAD provides the capability to define any number of views for a drawing (Fig. 13.68). These views can be scaled at any display size. Additionally, a view will be defined by a border or frame whose size can also be redefined.

Annotation can be added to the drawing to enhance it. Annotation includes dimensions, text, and graphic items. Drawing items—lines, points, arcs, circles—look the same as model items, except that they are always associated with the drawing and never affect the model itself (and are never added to the model's database). The model's geometry is transferred pictorially to draw mode and the designer can alter it, but only the appearance is altered. In addition, the transferred geometry can be manipulated in any number of ways. For example, it can be scaled larger or smaller in size, sectioned, or manipulated into a particular view or set of views simultaneously. Two-dimensional geometry can be added (or deleted) for purposes of presentation. The geometry of the model can be hidden selectively to stimulate normal viewing. Pictorial views can also be generated from the 3D database. Pictorial illustrations for presentations, manuals, and other traditional uses are all generated automatically from the 3D database, not drawn individually with dimensions taken from a detail of the part.

13.8.1 Coordinate Systems

Model mode and draw mode have distinct spatial coordinate systems associated with them. Model space is the **three-dimensional coordinate system** in which model geometry is constructed. Model space is considered to be a real-world space existing in the three directions (axes). Those axes are X (horizontal, or left–right, equating to width), Y (vertical, or up–down, equating to height), and Z (back and forth, which

(a) 3D part shown as a shaded image

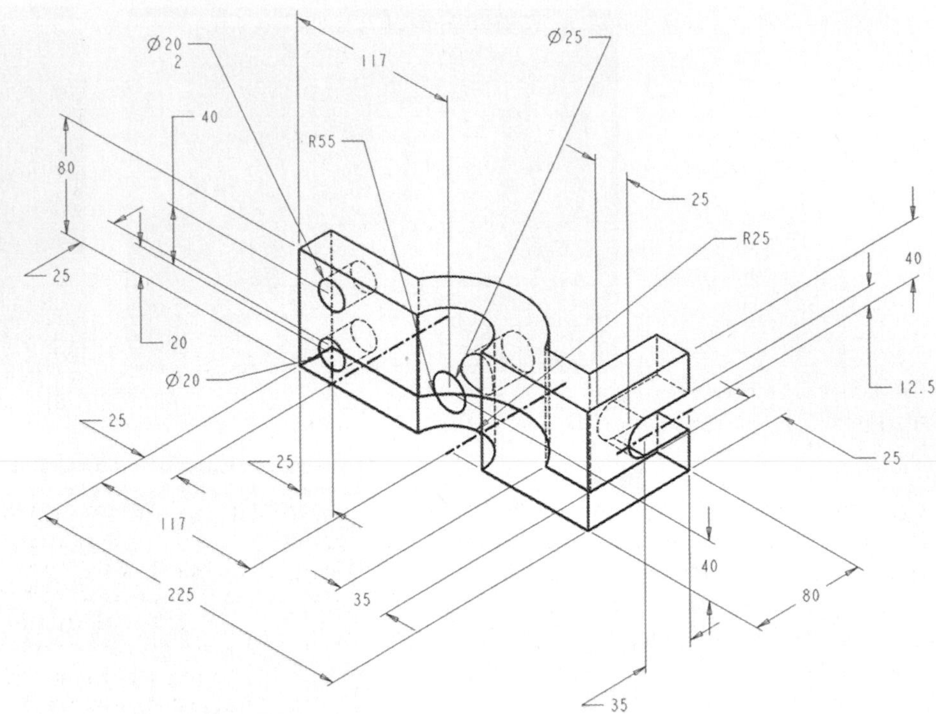

(b) Rotated view of part with dimensions displayed

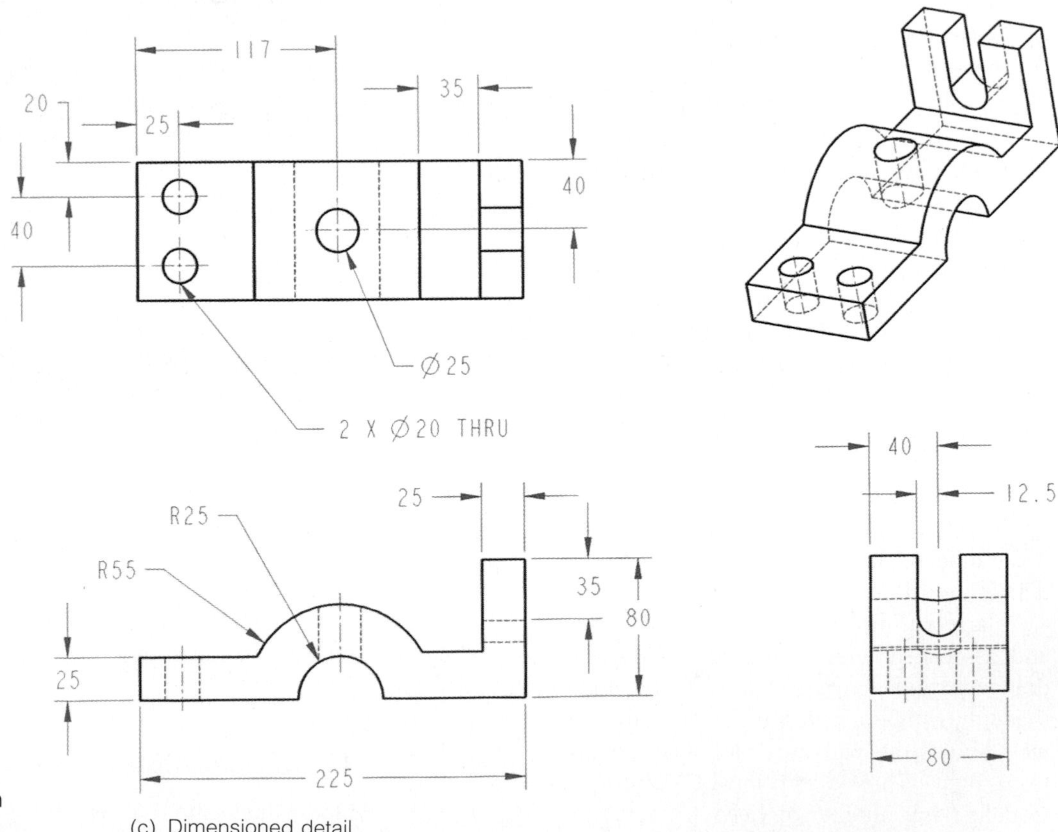

FIGURE 13.65 3D Design and Documentation

(c) Dimensioned detail

means in and out from the screen, equating to depth, as shown in Fig. 13.69). The location of the origin or all three axes is defined by the designer.

Drawing space is a **two-dimensional coordinate system** associated with draw mode. Drawing space is considered to be a flat, two-dimensional coordinate system existing in two

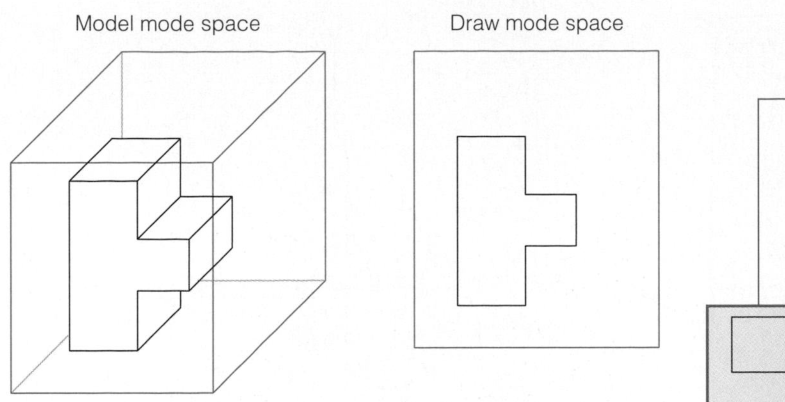

FIGURE 13.66 **Model Mode Space vs. Draw Mode Space**

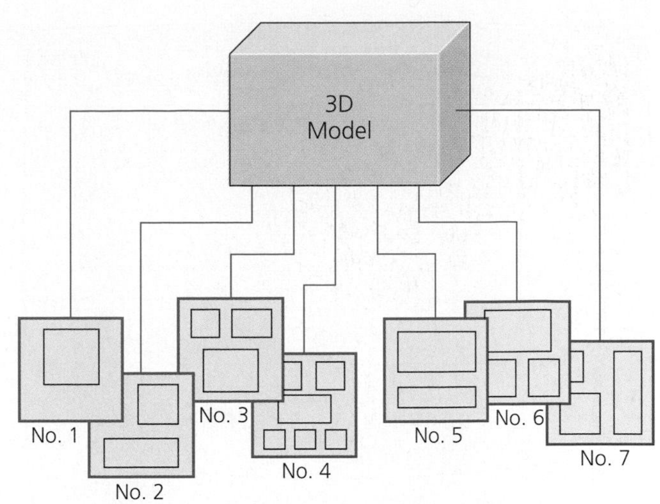

FIGURE 13.67 **Using the 3D Database to Generate Drawings. Any number of drawings can be created automatically from the original 3D model. The drawings are associative to the part geometry: Any change on the model will also update the drawings. On parametric systems, the model, the assembly, and the drawings are linked and associative: Any change made on the assembly updates the drawings and the model of the part, and any change on the drawings will update the part model and the assembly.**

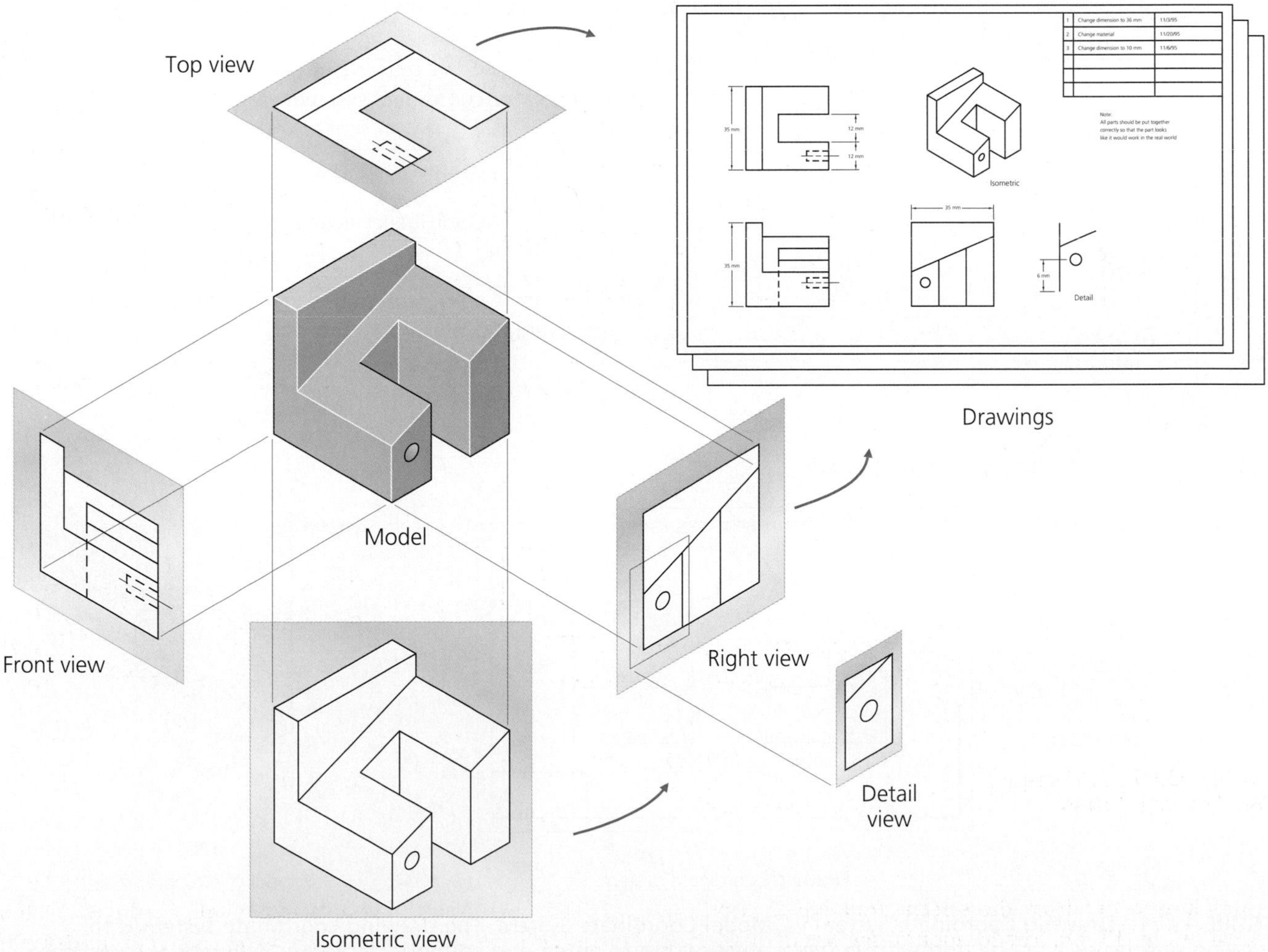

directions, whose axes are X and Y (Fig. 13.70). The *illusion* of depth, or replicating the Z axis, can be created on a two-dimensional coordinate system. Figure 13.71 illustrates the difference between model space and drawing space and their associated coordinate systems. The origin, or the intersection of the X and Y axes, is located at the lower left corner of the drawing.

FIGURE 13.68 **The Model Is Used to Generate the Views of the Drawing**

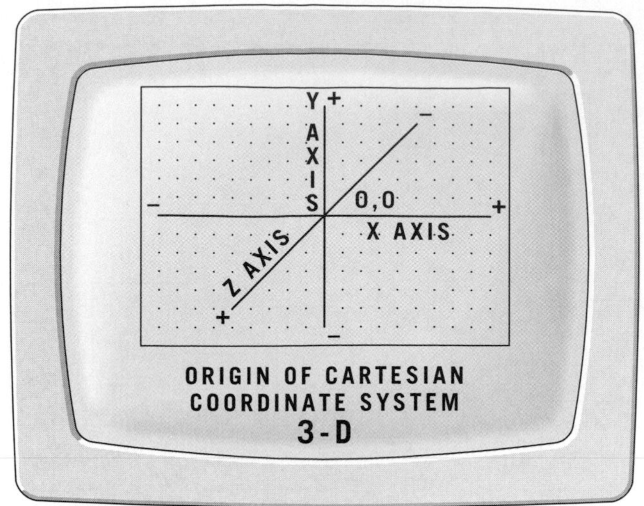

FIGURE 13.69 The Center of the Screen Is the Origin on Most CAD Systems. The Z axis comes out toward the viewer. This is the vertical axis, and when looking into it you are seeing the top view of the part (plan view).

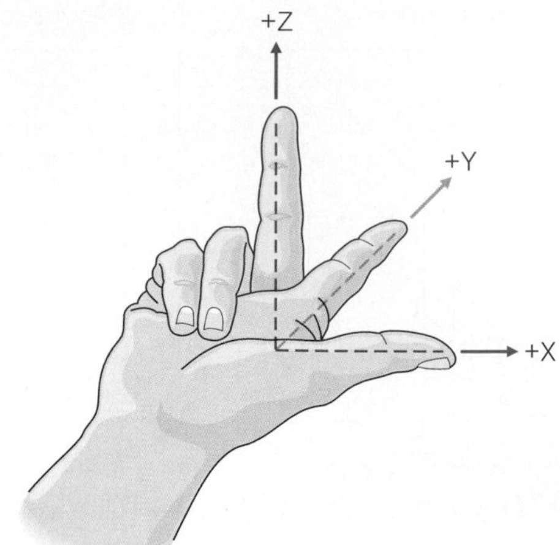

FIGURE 13.72 Right-Hand Rule. The middle finger represents the vertical (Z) axis, the thumb the X axis, and the pointing finger the Y axis. Use your right hand to help visualize the coordinate system in space (for the top—plan view) and when applying it to one of the standard orthographic views or an auxiliary surface.

13.8.2 Cartesian, Cylindrical, and Spherical Coordinate Systems

Coordinate systems are always displayed with X, Y, and Z axes. This can be visualized by using your right hand as shown in Figure 13.72 (the right-hand rule). The thumb is the X axis, the pointing finger is the Y axis, and the middle finger is the Z axis.

When referencing a coordinate system to make other features, the coordinate system can be interpreted as follows (Fig. 13.73):

Cartesian Coordinate values are interpreted as X, Y, and Z.

Cylindrical Coordinate values are interpreted as radius (r), theta (θ), and Z.

Spherical Coordinate values are interpreted as radius (r), theta (θ), and phi (ϕ).

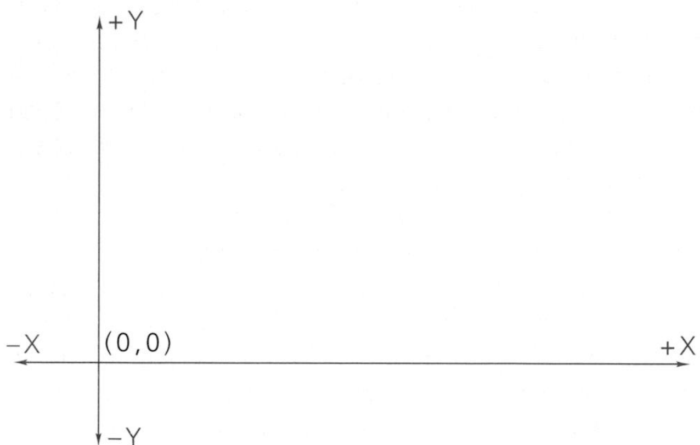

FIGURE 13.70 Cartesian Coordinate System

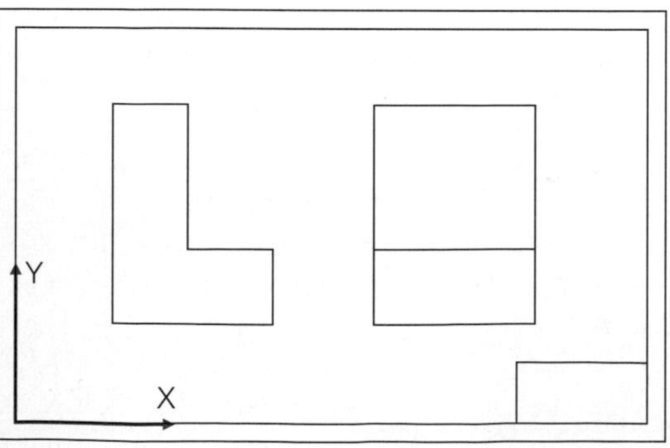

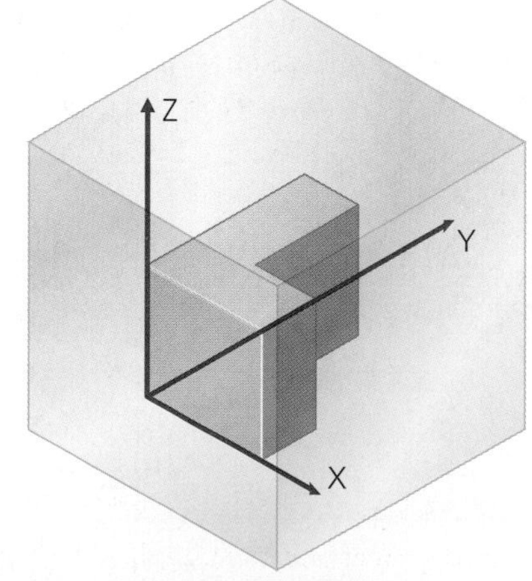

FIGURE 13.71 Drawing Coordinate System vs. Model Coordinate System. The drawing coordinate system is for drawing entities such as the border, title block, revision block, notes, and cosmetic geometry. The model coordinate system is for establishing the part's features in space.

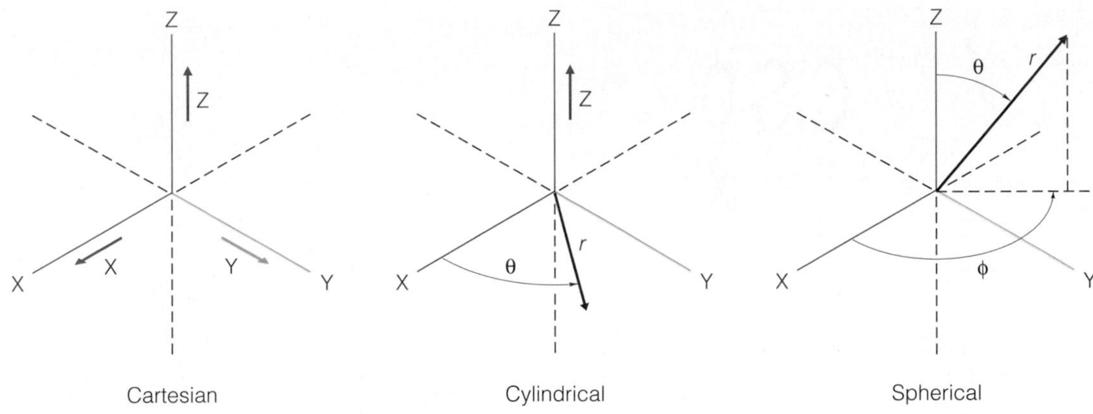

FIGURE 13.73 **Cartesian, Cylindrical, and Spherical Coordinate Systems**

13.8.3 Modeling with Coordinate Systems

On most CAD systems, coordinate systems are reference features that can be added to parts and assemblies for the following purposes:

- Calculating mass properties
- Assembling components
- Placing constraints for finite element meshing
- Providing manufacturing operation reference for tool paths
- Locating other features (coordinate systems, datum planes, planes and axes, imported geometry, etc.)

The following example creates a coordinate system [Fig. 13.74(a)] as base feature for Pro/Engineer:

1. Choose **Create** from the FEAT menu, then **Datum.**
2. Choose **Coord Sys** from the DATUM menu.
3. The coordinate system named CS0 will be created.

13.8.4 Datum Planes and Coordinate Systems

Three orthogonal **datum planes** can be created as the base feature, prior to adding any solid feature. This is helpful when the first solid feature is to be a sphere, a toroid, or sculptured surfaces; these tend not to have the planar surfaces needed to reorient the model or to specify sketching planes.

To create a default datum plane on Pro/ENGINEER use the following commands [Fig. 13.74(b)]:

1. Choose **Feature** from the PART menu.
2. Choose **Create** from the FEAT menu, then **Datum.** Then choose **Plane.**
3. The MENUDTM OPT pick **Default**.

Default creates three orthogonal datum planes intersecting at the default origin (X0,Y0,Z0). Three datum planes, with the names DTM1, DTM2, DTM3, appear in the center of the screen at right angles to one another [Fig. 13.74(b)]. The coordinate system and datum planes are then used to model the part geometry [Fig. 13.74(c) and (d)]. The drawing is created from the model, as shown in Figure 13.74(e), and then displayed pictorially as a shaded image [Figure 13.74(f)].

13.8.5 Construction Planes

The concepts and application of **construction planes** is another CAD feature that provides a real breakthrough for the designer. The use of construction planes makes the construction of model geometry easier and faster. Instead of employing datum planes to create geometry, many systems use construction planes. On AutoCAD, the default coordinate system is called the **world coordinate system (WCS)** and user-defined construction planes are referred to as the **user coordinate system (UCS).**

A construction plane is a planar surface that can be selected from the model's geometry. A construction plane can be predefined because it is associated with a specific view; e.g., for a FRONT view the construction plane is FRONT [(Fig. 13.75(a)]. A designer can also define a construction plane from preexisting geometry in any view that shows the model in three dimensions. This is called an **auxiliary construction plane** (or user coordinate system) [Fig. 13.75(b)]. You can think of an auxiliary construction plane as a secondary coordinate system. Once a construction plane is defined and selected, the following types of activities can take place.

- All digitizes (picks) are projected directly onto the construction plane.
- A coordinate system is set up when a construction plane is defined by the designer. The origin of the coordinate system is the same as the origin of the construction plane. Geometry can be created and/or located via this coordinate system; the coordinate system will be "local."
- Construction planes can be used to insert geometry or text, directly on the plane or parallel to it.

Construction planes serve as design aids. Along with the default top view (plan view) coordinate system (world coordinate system), an unlimited number of user construc-

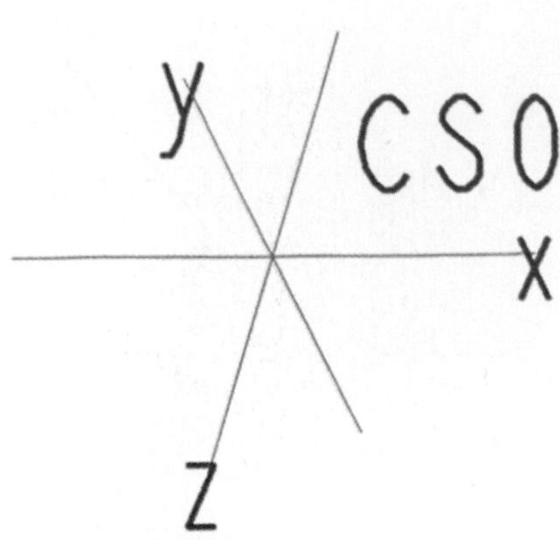

(a) CS0 (coordinate system zero)

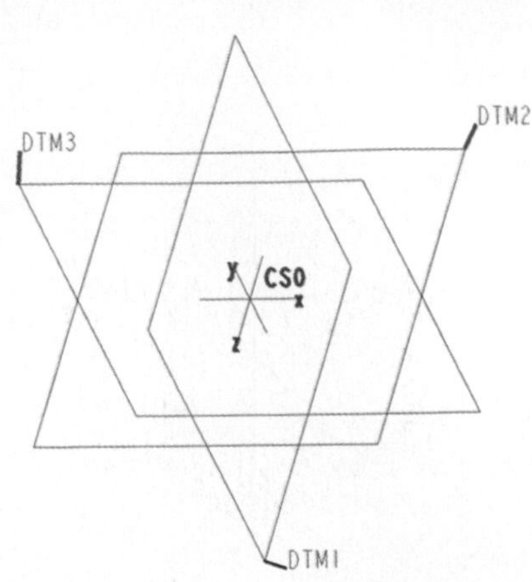

(b) DTM1, DTM2, and DTM3 default datum systems, with the coordinate system as the origin and the three datum planes intersecting at (0,0,0).

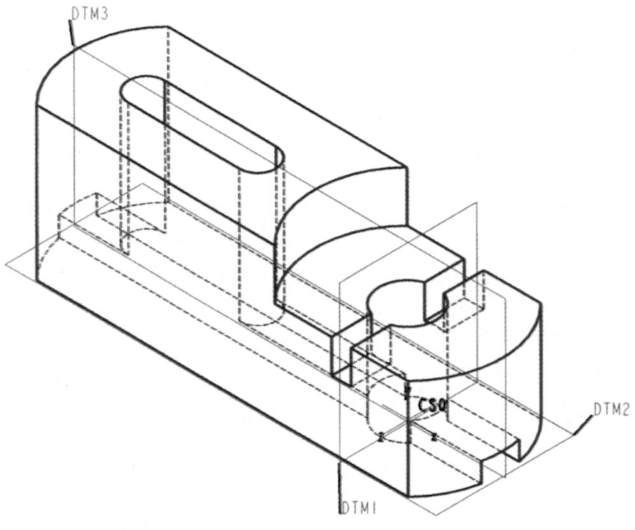

(c) Part geometry established using the datum planes and the coordinate system

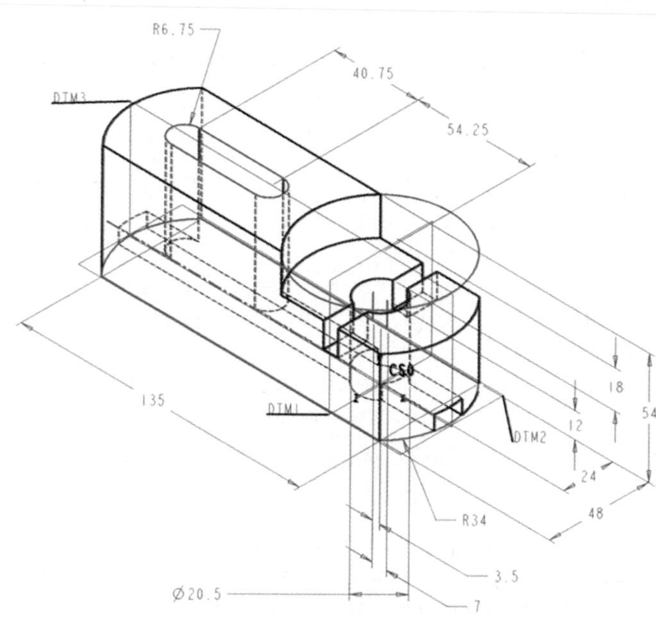

(d) Parametric model

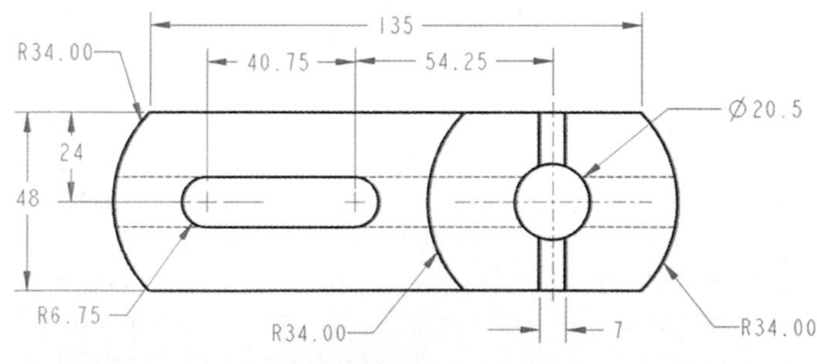

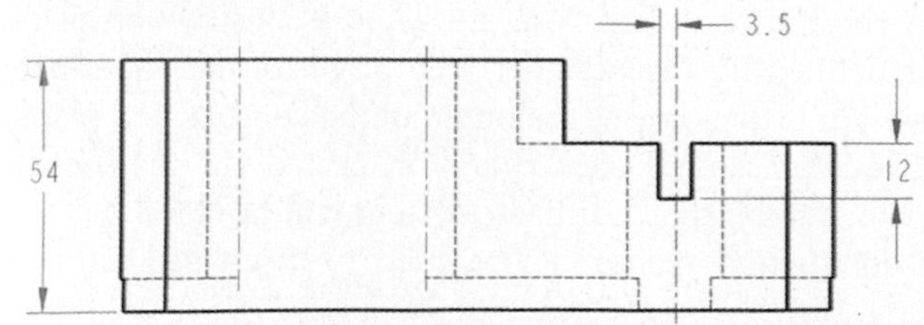

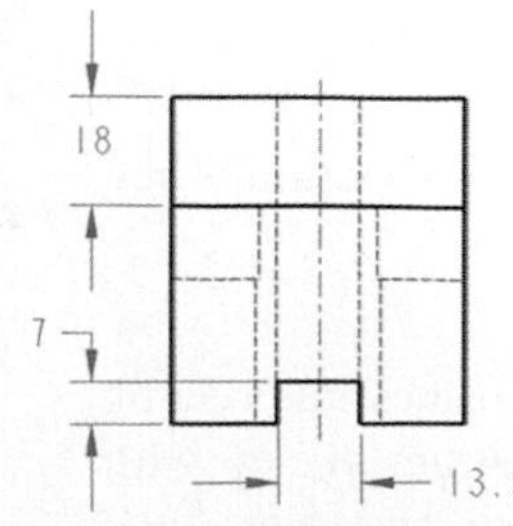

(e) Model used in **DRAW** mode

(f) Shaded model

FIGURE 13.74 **Creating a Part**

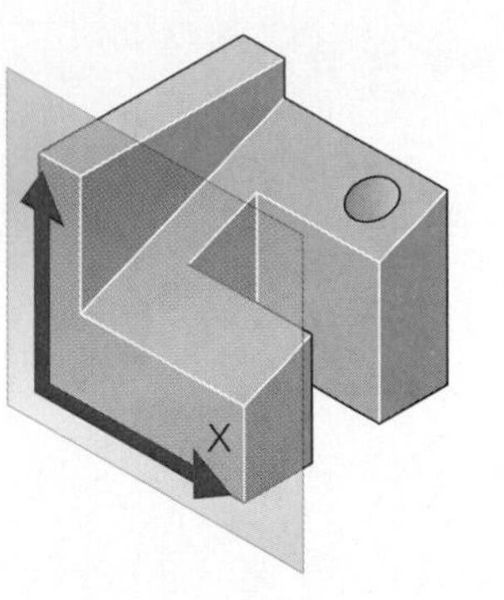

(a) Construction plane parallel to the front side

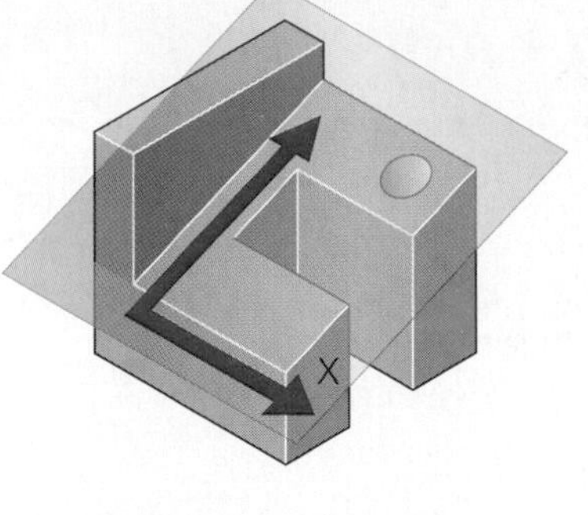

(b) Construction plane parallel to the part's inclined surface

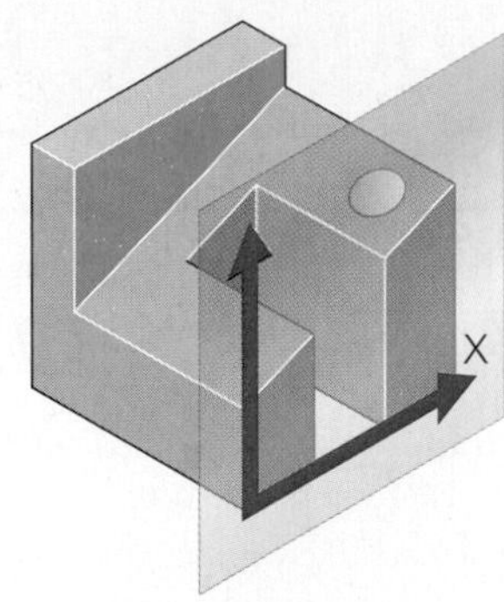

(c) Construction plane parallel to the right side view

FIGURE 13.75 Using Construction Planes

tion planes can be activated or created. If multiple views are selected by the designer, each orthographic view will have an equivalent construction plane associated with it. For example, a front view has a construction plane on, and therefore parallel to, the front surface [Fig. 13.75(a)]. A right side view has a construction plane parallel and on its surface [Fig. 13.75(c)]. The inclined construction plane is shown on and parallel to the inclined surface in Figure 13.75(b). These types of construction planes allow geometry items to be projected directly onto them, and facilitate a two-dimensional approach to model construction. Figure 13.76 shows a three-dimensional model and a variety of construction plane coordinate systems that could be established to model the part.

The power of construction planes can be seen in a three-dimensional approach to part construction. For example, if the designer were constructing model geometry from one view along with the dynamics capabilities, designer-defined construction planes would be useful. Assume that the model was displayed in some rotated view. The designer wants to add some circles to one side or face of the model and the particular side is not directly parallel to the screen. Only the side or plane of the model to which the circles will be added would need to be defined. Once the side or construction plane is defined and selected, explicit coordinates can be specified or the location of the circles can be digitized, and the circles are added, displayed elliptically, as they should be.

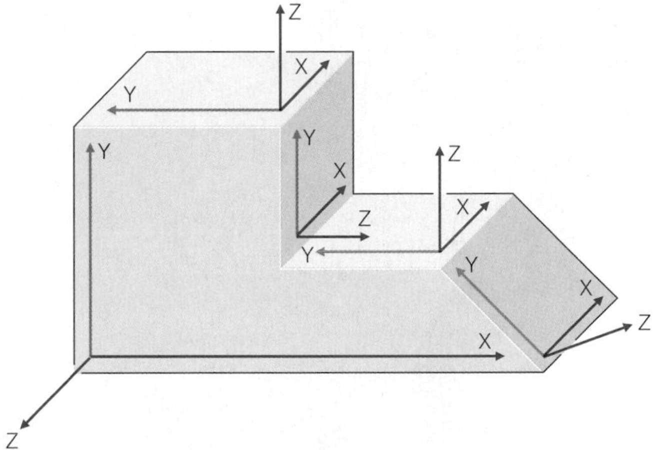

FIGURE 13.76 Auxiliary Coordinate Systems (User Coordinate System on AutoCAD). With commands, these can be placed on any surface of the part or oriented in space. The coordinate systems are construction planes and serve to place geometry and construct the 3D model.

13.9 CAD PICTORIAL ILLUSTRATIONS

After a part is modeled [Fig. 13.77(a)], it can be rotated, enlarged, or zoomed into a desired pictorial position and type (rotated or perspective). This capability eliminates the need to redraw the part as an isometric, oblique, or perspective drawing. In Figure 13.77(b), the model of the valve housing has had all hidden lines removed via a **HIDE** (hidden line removal) command. The model is now visually correct. The 3D model is used to create a drawing showing correct visibility, including all hidden lines, and centerlines, as shown in Figure 13.77(c). Note that the inclusion of a pictorial view (upper right corner) on the detail drawing enhances the understanding of the part's geometry, especially for nontechnical personnel. In this figure the dimensions are not included. The last illustration of this part shows a shaded image [Fig. 13.77(d)], which can be used for any of the traditional pictorial applications—display, manuals, catalogs, etc.

After the CAD illustrator displays the desired pictorial views, the 3D model can be embellished as required. Shading, color, or other artistic qualities help to prepare the final output as an illustration for technical manuals, advertisements, training manuals, sales literature, or design pre-

Applying Parametric Design . . .

PICTORIALS FOR PARAMETRIC MODELS

Pictorial illustrations are generated directly from the 3D model database. There is no need to recreate a part model via isometric, oblique, or perspective projection. The model can be displayed and oriented in any position automatically. You may select and orient the part to provide the required view orientation to display the part from underneath or from any side or position. Perspective projections are completely automated with a simple selection from a menu. The model can be spun around, reoriented, and even clipped to show the interior features. When assemblies are illustrated, you have the choice of displaying all components, and subassemblies, or any combinations of the design (see Fig. A).

Images of your parametric model are displayed with a wide variety of choices. The model can be displayed with any combination of hidden lines, coordinate systems, centerlines, or datum turned on or off, as required (see Figs. B and C). Each combination of selections can then be printed or plotted at the desired size and with the user-defined color settings.

Master state:

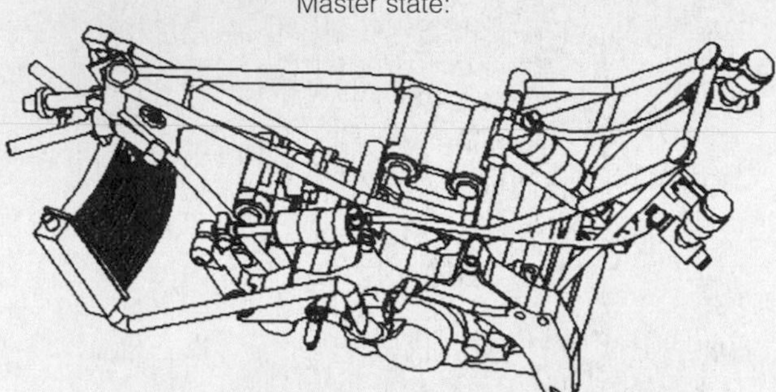

Config state that excludes all parts except those relating to the engine:

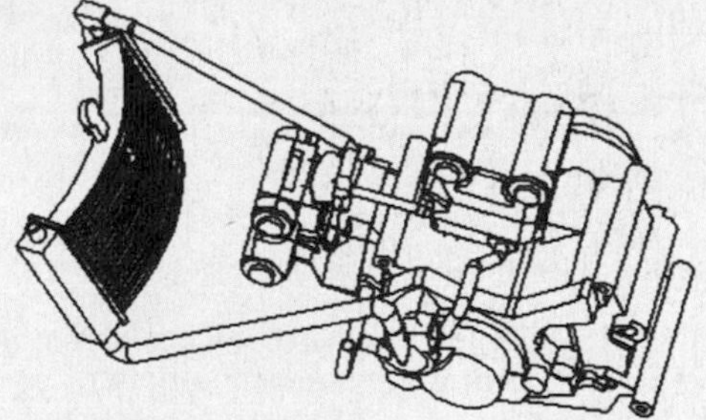

Config state that excludes all parts except those relating to the frame:

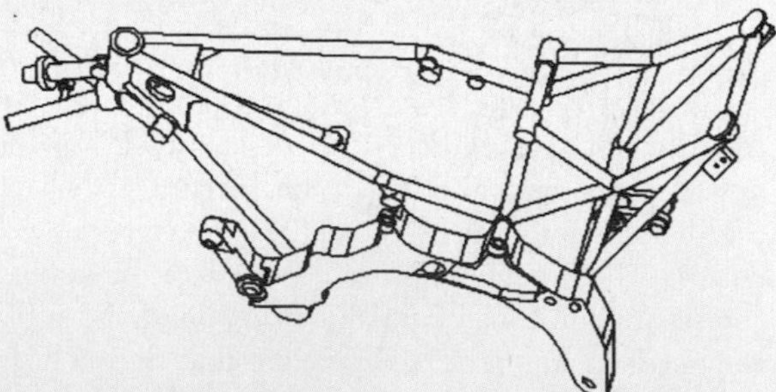

Config state that excludes all parts except those relating to hydraulics:

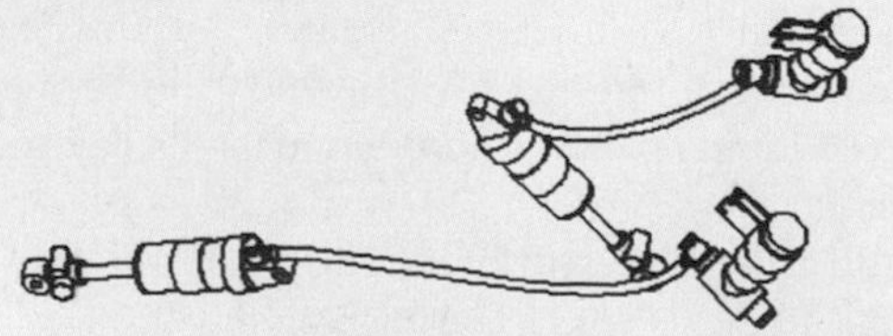

FIGURE A Excluding Parts, and Subassemblies, from an Assembly Illustration

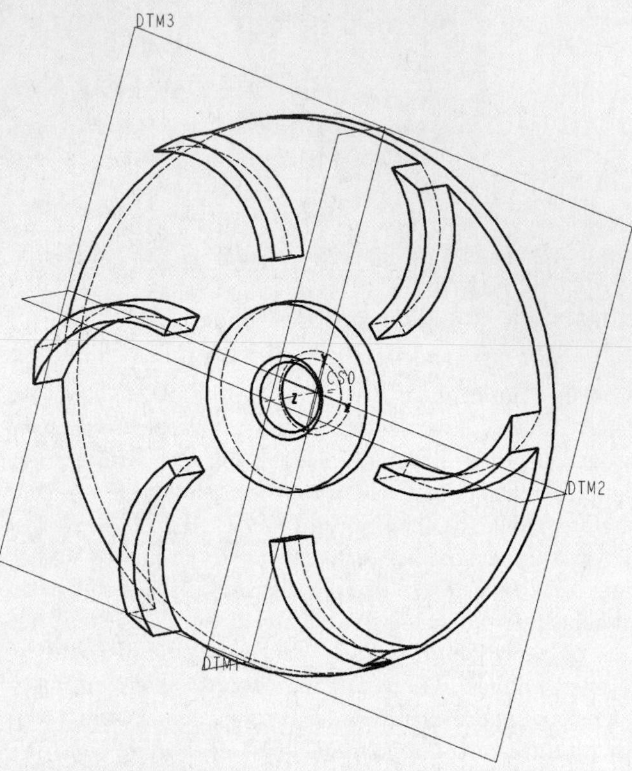

FIGURE B Flywheel with Hidden Lines, Datums, and Coordinate System Displayed

FIGURE C Flywheel with Only Visible Edges Displayed

FIGURE D Shaded Flywheel

Shaded images can be generated automatically from the parametric model (see Fig. D). The quality and choice of shading can be selected from a menu and applied to your model (see Fig. E). If a color plotter or printer is available, you can shade your model in any desired color and highlight.

FIGURE E Shaded Flywheel with Different Display Settings

sentations. The airplane in Figure 13.78 was modeled as a solid and then displayed pictorially.

While perspective, isometric, and rotated views are useful in depicting 3D objects more realistically, most CAD systems offer the capability to use solid models (Figure 13.79). Here, a cutaway view of a helicopter is displayed. Depth is shown through color, shading, and perspective projection. Wireframe, surface, and solid models can all be displayed pictorially via simple commands. Most CAD systems offer the option of an automated perspective command, with a variety of options for displaying the model (Figure 13.79). There are many rendering programs available for capturing high-quality images of your part model. The shaded image of the part in Figure 13.80(a) shows a view orientation and

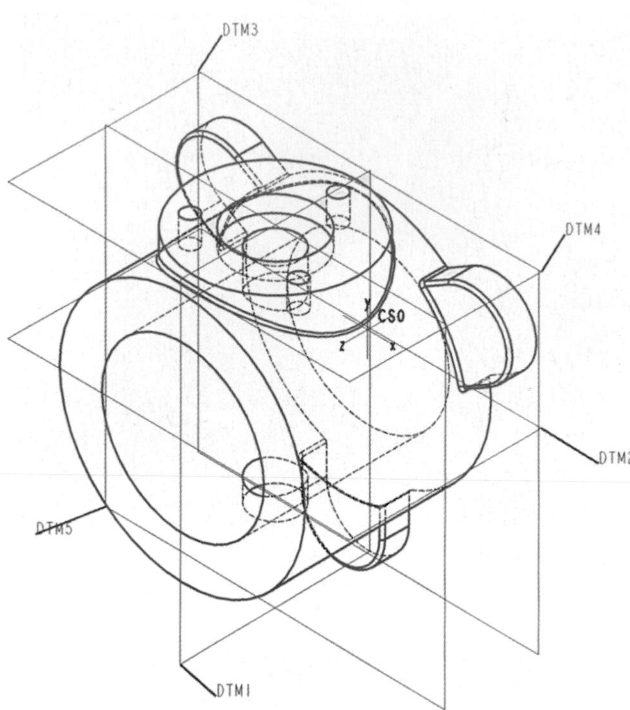

(a) Part modeled with datum features and coordinate system

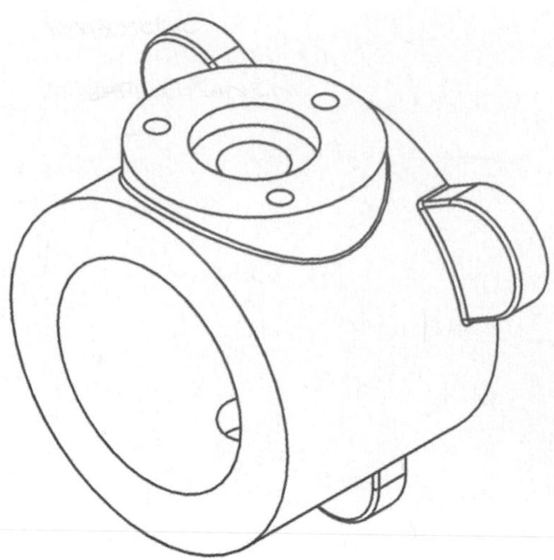

(b) Part shown with hidden lines removed

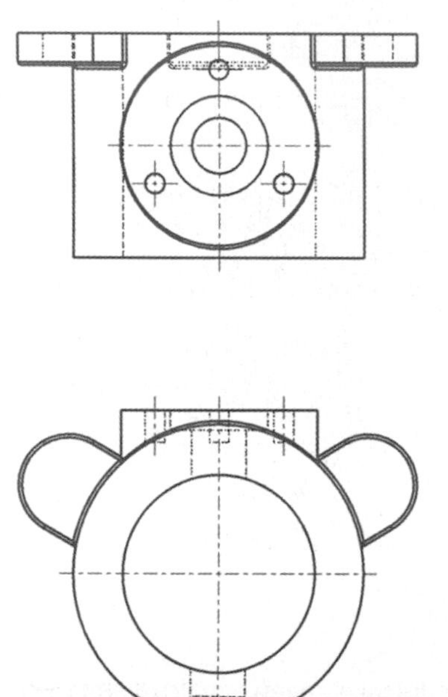

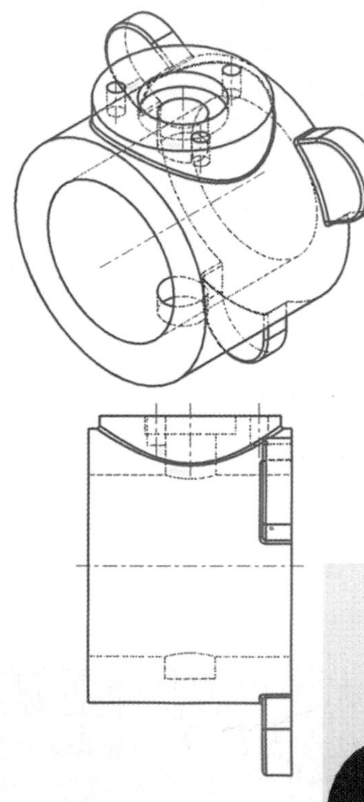

(c) Four views of the part, with hidden lines shown

(d) Shaded image of the part

FIGURE 13.77 Valve Housing

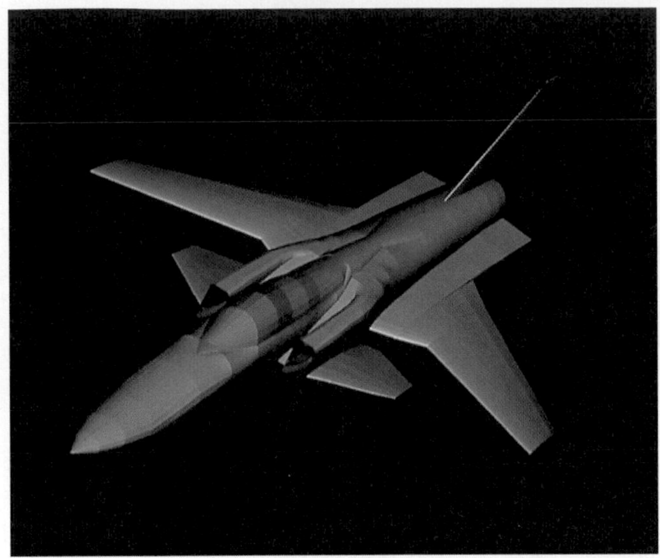

FIGURE 13.78 Shaded Image of Plane Design

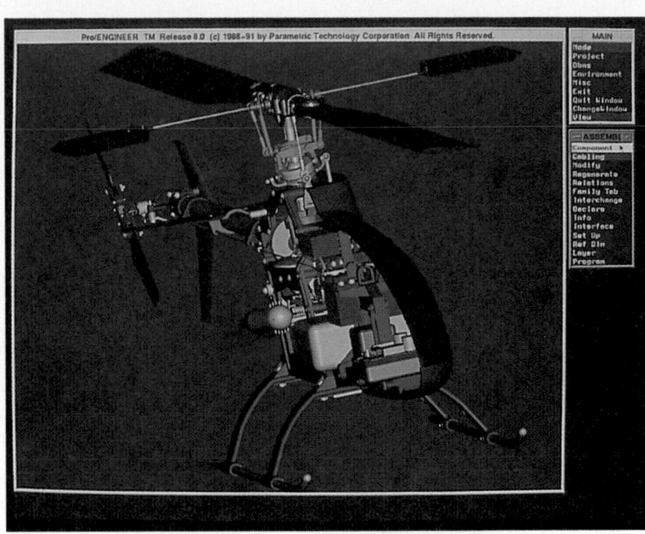

FIGURE 13.79 Perspective Image of Helicopter

a color selection. Figure 13.80(b) shows another orientation and color mix. In Figure 13.81(a) we see a 3D view of a part with hidden lines displayed. The part can be shaded and the background color altered as required [Figure 13.81(b)]. Note that the dark background reduces the contrast around the slot. In Figure 13.81(c) the slot and holes have been recolored so the part stands out better from the dark background.

Assemblies also lend themselves to color and shading. The valve assembly in Figure 13.82 shows as a shaded model (a), as an exploded shaded image (b), with the arm as transparent (c), and with all parts except the valve desk as transparent (d). Figure 13.83 shows a pulley assembly (transparent) with the belt (a) and as an exploded assembly (b). Exploded pictorial assemblies and transparent plotting allow the designer to create high-quality visual aids with a CAD system and a rendering package.

Besides standard color and shading capabilities, a variety

(a) Shaded pictorial of model using the default orientation

(b) New orientation and color mix for shaded model

FIGURE 13.80 Shaded Images

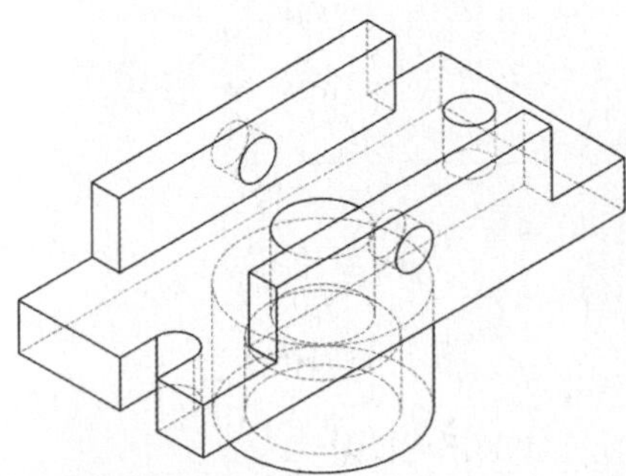

(a) 3D image with hidden lines displayed

(b) Shaded color image with dark holes and slot

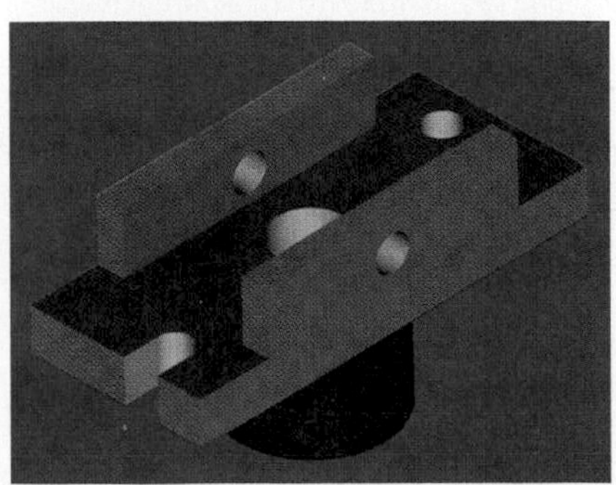

(c) Shaded image with light-colored holes and slot

FIGURE 13.81 Model Displays

(a) Shaded image of assembly

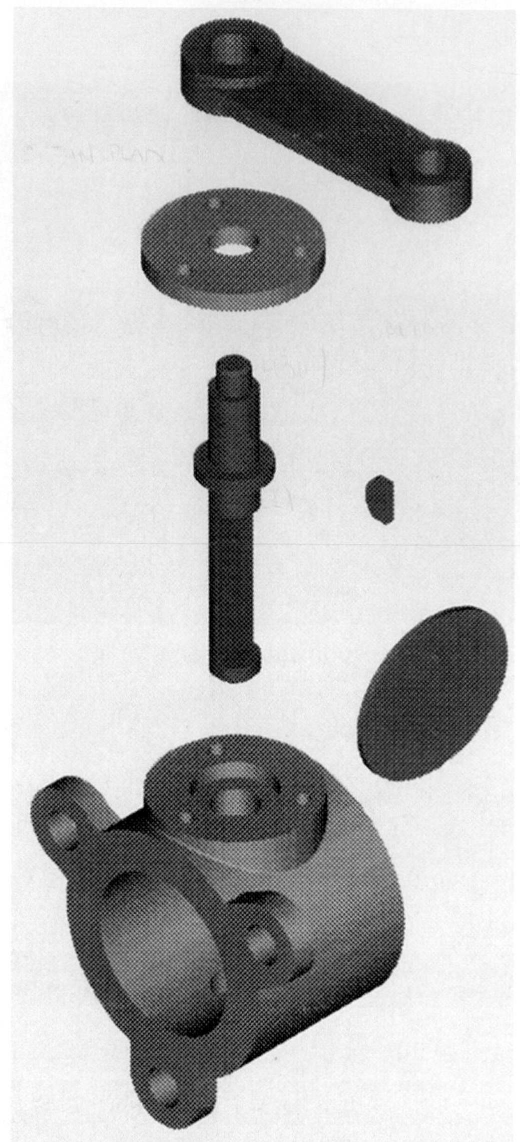

(b) Exploded shaded image of assembly

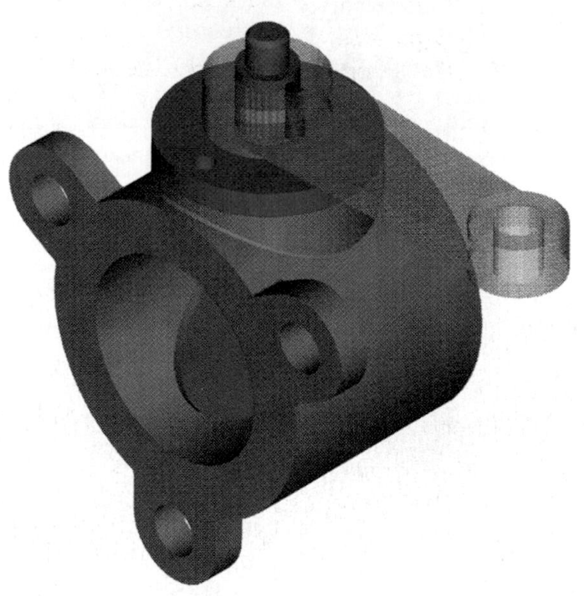

(c) Shaded image with transparent handle

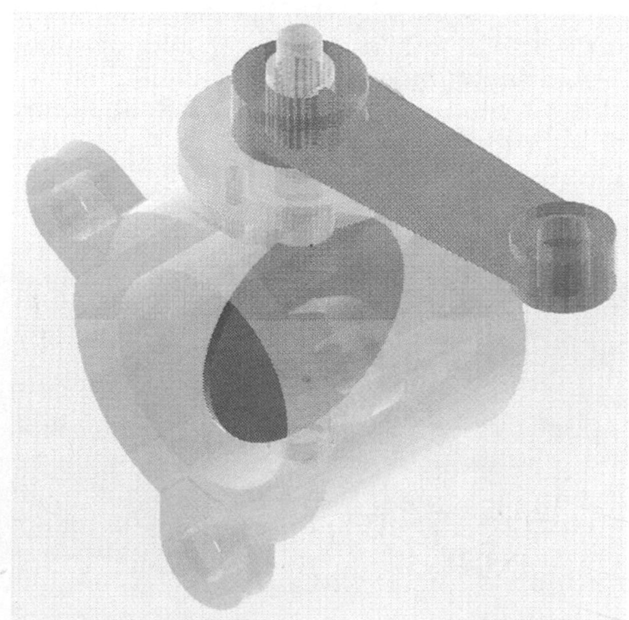

(d) Transparent model

FIGURE 13.82 **Shaded Assembly**

(a) Shaded assembly

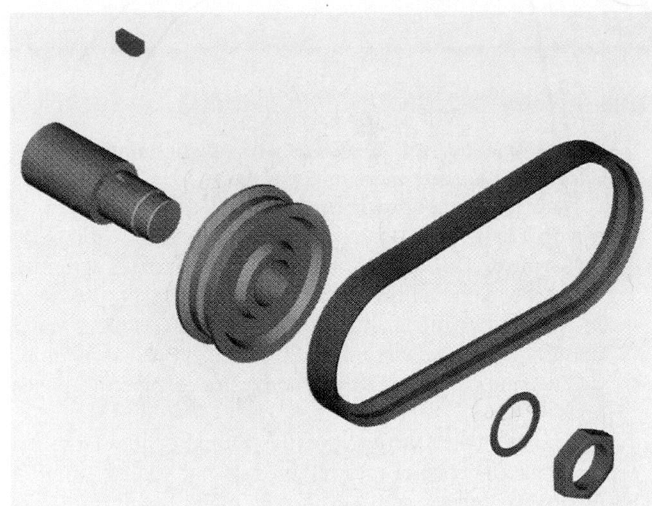

(b) Exploded assembly

FIGURE 13.83 **Pulley and Belt Assembly**

of programs are available that create lifelike images of a design, such as the illustrations in Figure 13.84(a)–(f), which were created and rendered with AUTODESK products. The choices of color and view are limited only by your imagination, your hardware and software, and the plotter.

Regardless of the method used or the CAD system available, pictorials are found increasingly in engineering and design work. The need to describe in detail to nontechnical personnel the workings and assembly of products and machinery and a project's construction requirements will become even more important in the future. Therefore, the use of color, shading, rendering, and other pictorial capabilities will increasingly find there way into engineering and design.

(a) Building

(b) Pleiades

(c) Buildings

(d) Buildings and background

(e) Interior view

(f) Interior design

FIGURE 13.84 **Architectural Images Using Rendering Program**

QUIZ

True or False

1. Curves that do not lie in isometric planes must be constructed with offset measurements.
2. A general oblique drawing is constructed using 45° for the receding axis.
3. An isometric drawing is constructed using true-length measurements along all three axis lines.
4. A cavalier drawing is always foreshortened.
5. Centerlines are included on all pictorials.
6. Cabinet and cavalier drawings are types of perspective projections.
7. The point of sight for a perspective should be located so that the angle the cone of rays makes does not exceed 45°.
8. A trimetric projection uses different angles for all three axes.

Fill in the Blanks

9. A ________ view shows the interior of the part or assembly.
10. ________ dimensioning is found on most pictorial drawings.
11. ________ projection approximates how a part will look to the human eye.
12. In true isometric projection, all ________ make equal ________ with the projection plane.
13. ________ lines are not parallel to or on one of the isometric axes.
14. A ________ is a planar surface that can be placed on the model's geometry or is available as a default at the part's origin.
15. The ________ method of ellipse construction does not create an ellipse.
16. ________ features should be oriented so they lie in the ________ face of the object when ________ projection is used on a drawing.

Answer the Following

17. What is the difference between an isometric drawing and an isometric projection?
18. In what situation would an oblique drawing be used instead of an isometric drawing?
19. What are the three types of oblique projection? Describe each, and explain how they differ.
20. How does 3D CAD eliminate the need to construct traditional 2D pictorial drawings?
21. Give four uses of pictorial drawings.
22. Describe the three types of perspective projection, and explain their differences.
23. What are offset measurements, and when are they used in the construction of a pictorial drawing?
24. What is the difference between model mode and draw mode (model space and paper space for AutoCAD)?

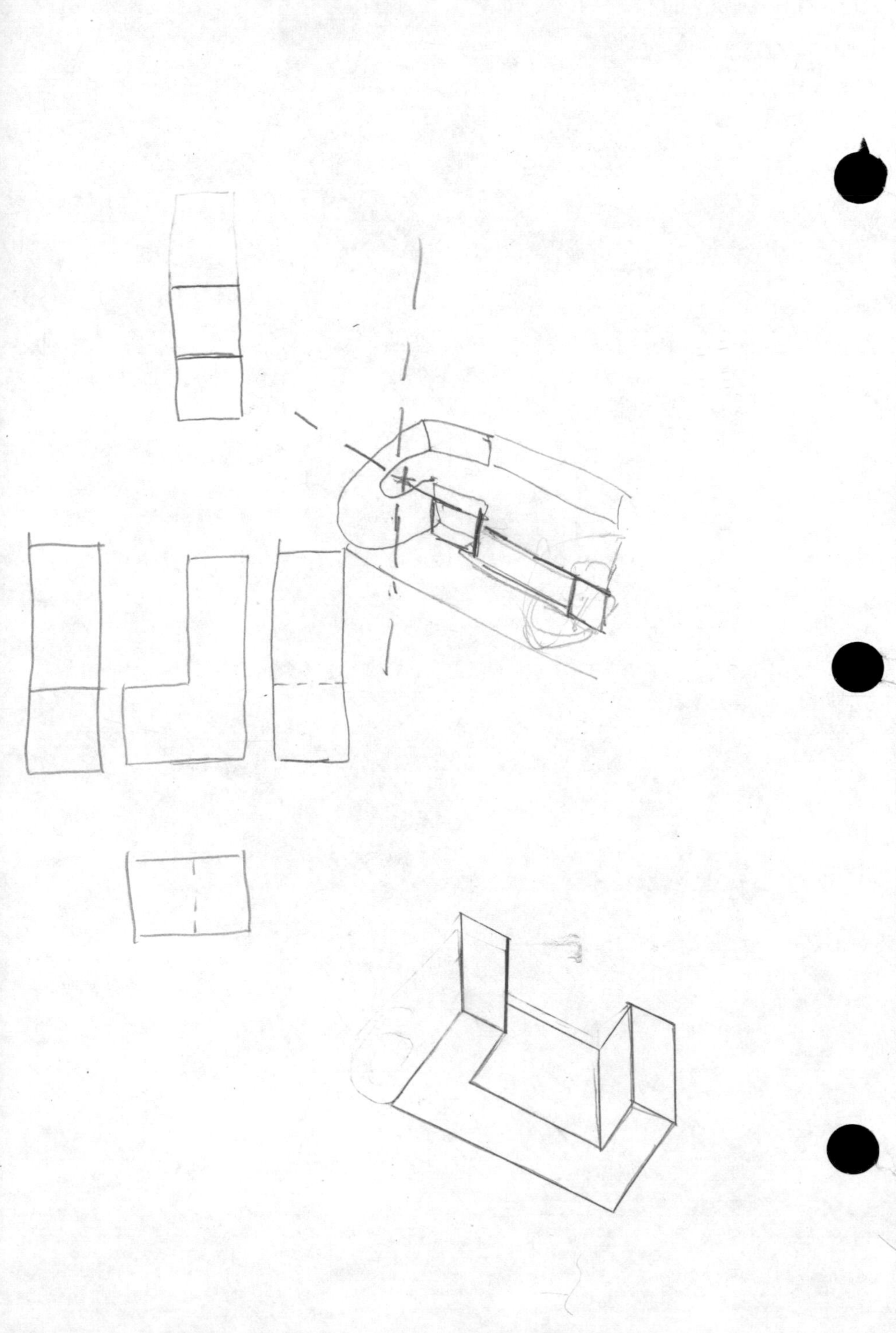

EXERCISES

Exercises may be assigned as sketching, instrument, or CAD projects. Transfer the given information to an "A"-size sheet of .25 in. grid paper. Exercises that are not assigned by the instructor can be sketched in the text to provide practice and to enhance understanding of the preceding instructional material.

After Reading the Chapter Through Section 13.3.11 You May Complete the Following Exercises

Exercise 13.1 Using the part provided in Exercise 10.5B draw an isometric pictorial.

Exercise 13.2 Using the part provided in Exercise 10.9A draw an isometric pictorial.

Exercise 13.3 Using the part given in Exercise 10.10B draw an isometric pictorial.

Exercise 13.4 Using the part provided in Exercise 10.3A draw an isometric pictorial.

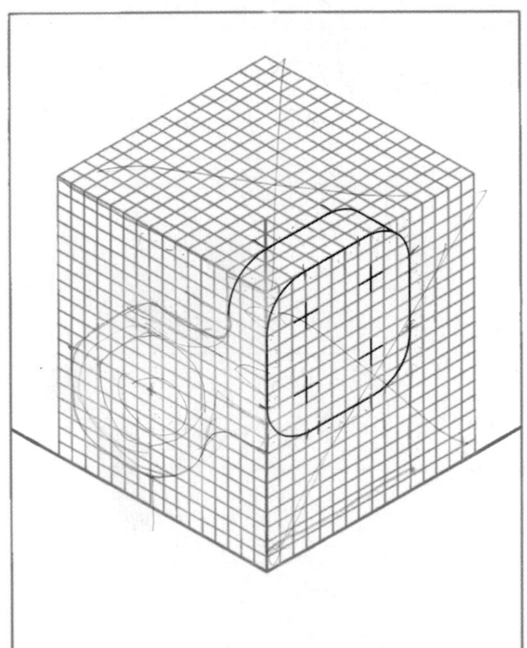

EXERCISE 13.1

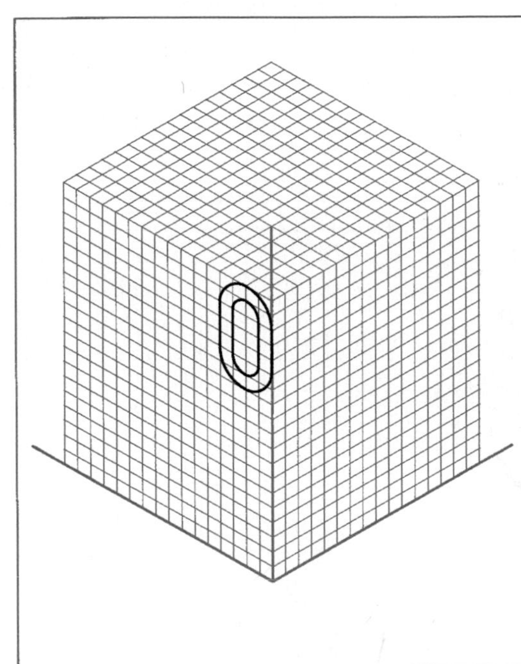

EXERCISE 13.3

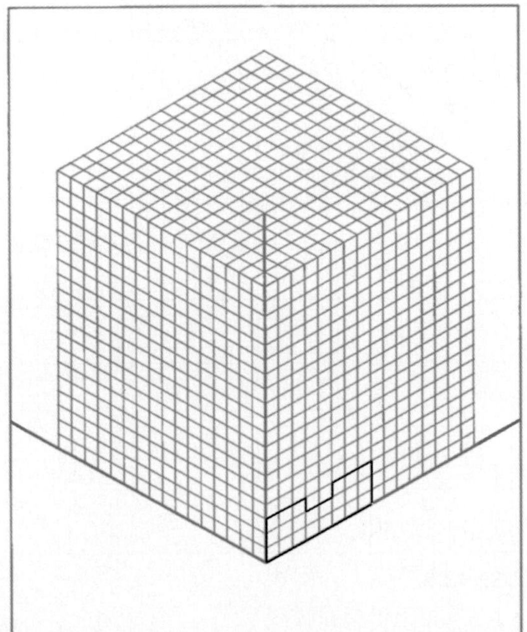

EXERCISE 13.2

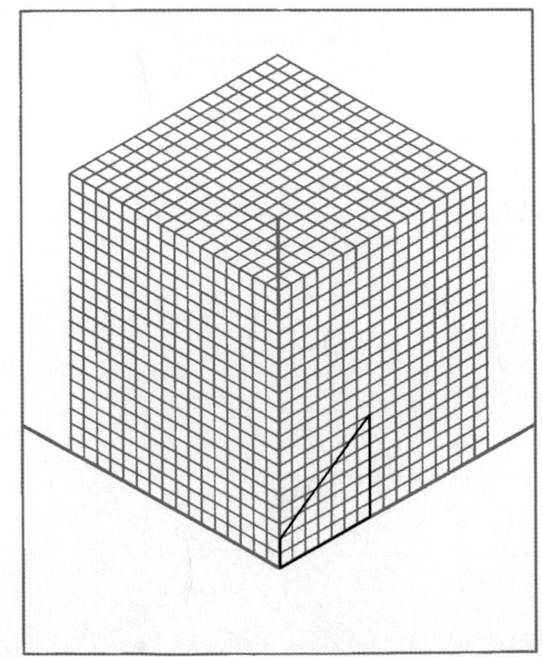

EXERCISE 13.4

After Reading the Chapter Through Section 13.7.5 You May Complete the Following Exercises

Exercise 13.5 Using the part given in Exercise 10.13B complete an oblique pictorial.

Exercise 13.6 Using the part given in Exercise 10.11B draw an oblique pictorial.

Exercise 13.7 Using the part provided in Exercise 10.4B draw an oblique pictorial.

Exercise 13.8 Using the part provided in Exercise 10.1A draw a one-point perspective pictorial.

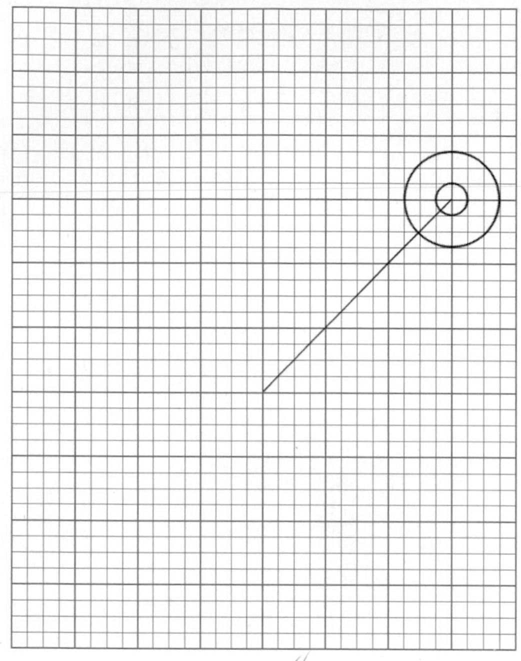

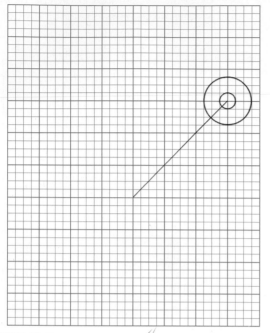

EXERCISE 13.5

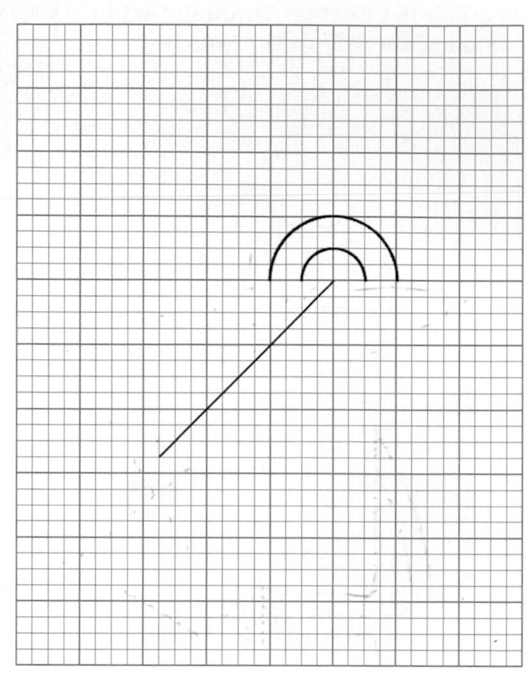

EXERCISE 13.7

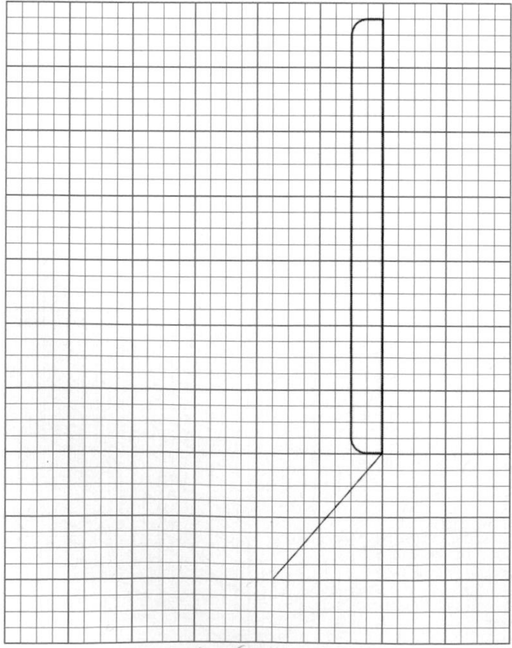

EXERCISE 13.6

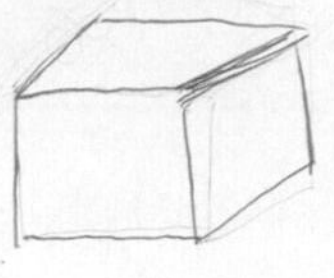

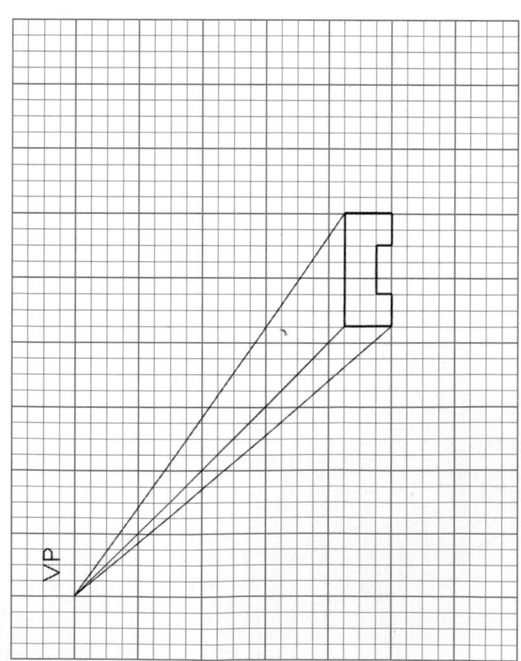

EXERCISE 13.8

PROBLEMS

Problems 13.1(A) Through (K) These problems can be assigned as any of the three major types of pictorial projection or as 3D CAD models. Unless assigned as a specific type of projection, the problems could be used to test students' understanding of the suitability of projection types for a particular problem. The instructor can allow the student to determine the projection method based on the part's features and pictorial requirements as described by the instructor.

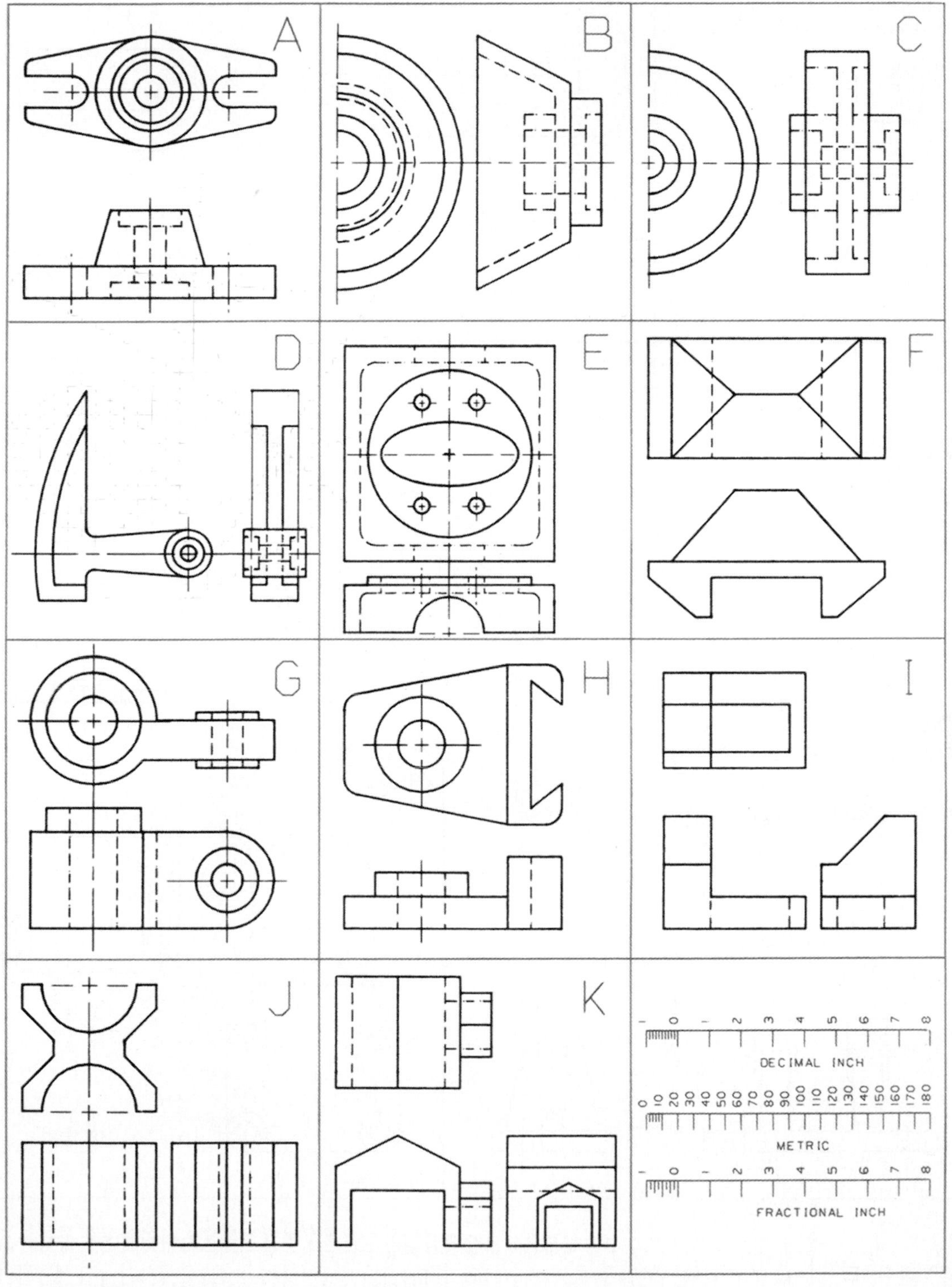

Problems 13.2 through 13.4 were created in metric units, and the scale provided is to be used when taking the part from the text and transferring it to the drawing board (or computer). The decimal scale can also be used if the problem as assigned will be done in decimal-inch units.

Problems 13.2(A) Through (H) These problems are meant for isometric projection but can be drawn as any type of pictorial projection, as assigned.

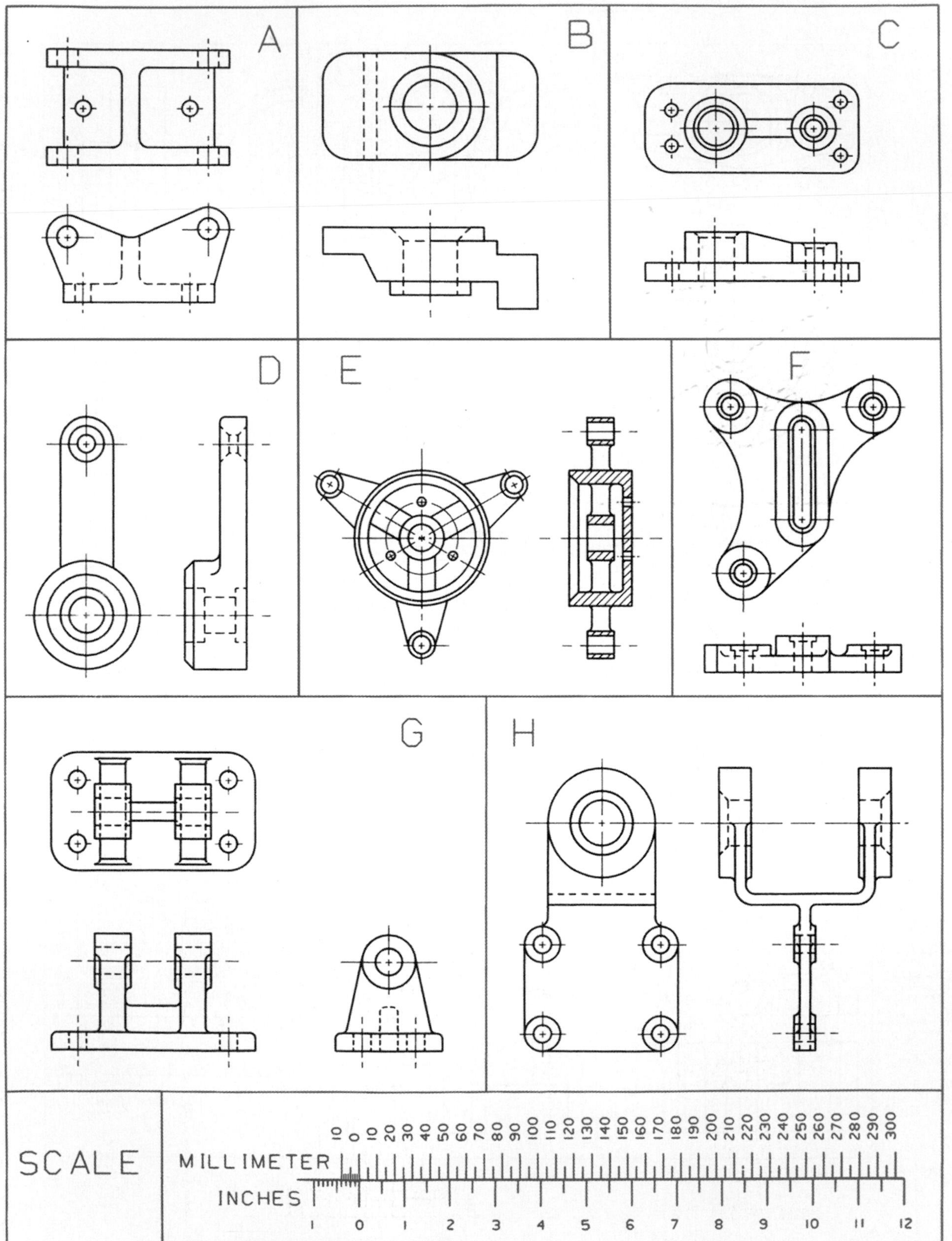

Problems 13.3(A) Through (F) These problems are designed as oblique projects, although the instructor can assign other methods of projection.

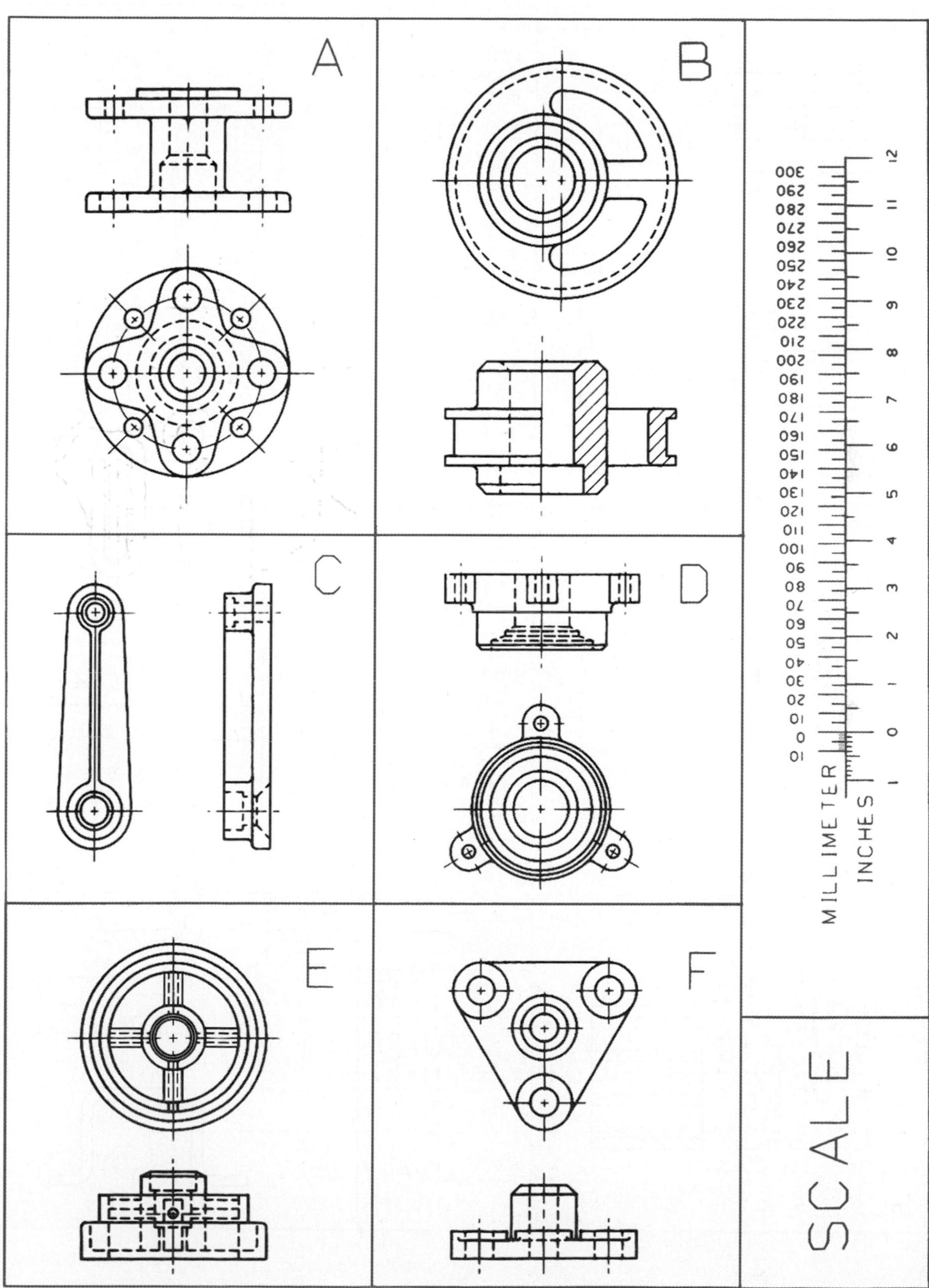

Problems 13.4(A) Through (F) These problems can be used for any method of pictorial projection but were intended as perspective projection projects.

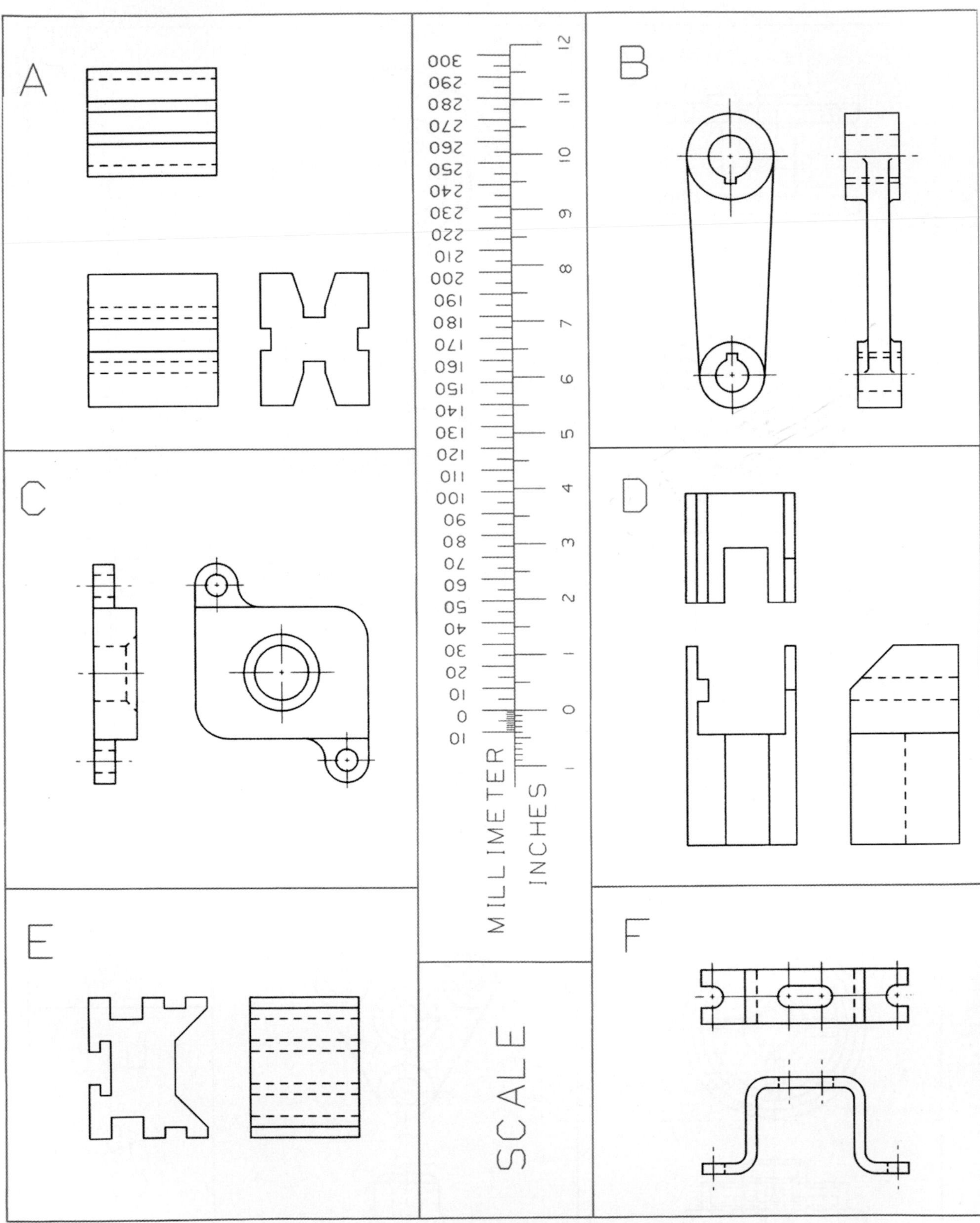

Problem 13.5 Model the wrench in 3D. Display and plot the part as a shaded model (a), as a 3D model with hidden lines (b), as a dimensioned pictorial (c), and as a detail (d).

(a)

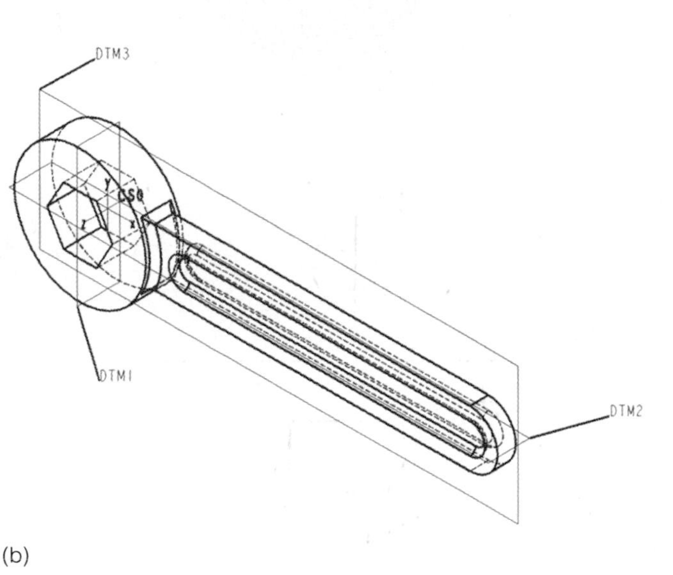

(b)

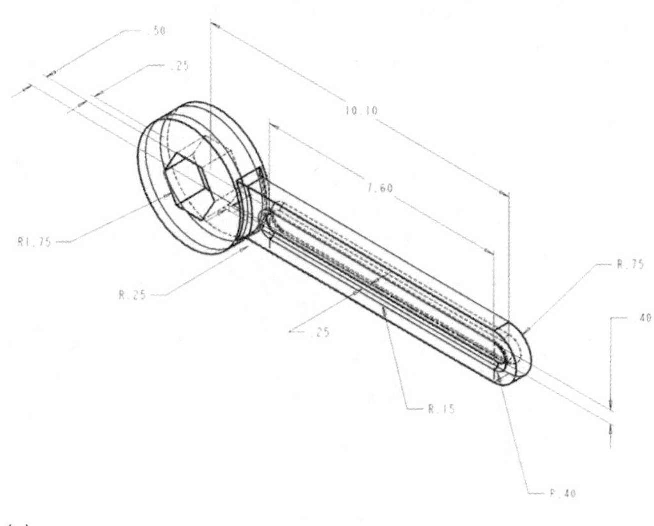

(c)

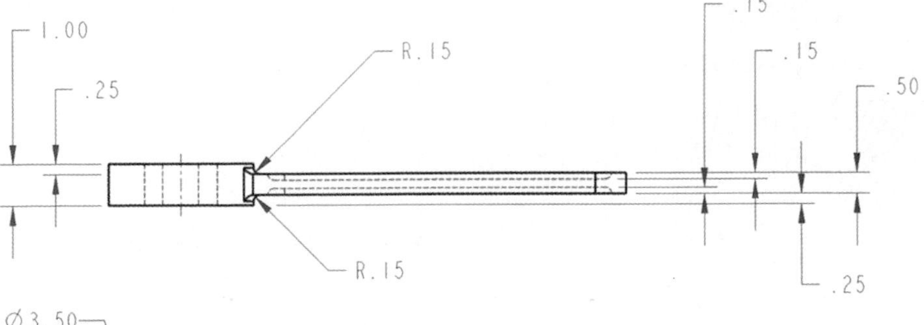

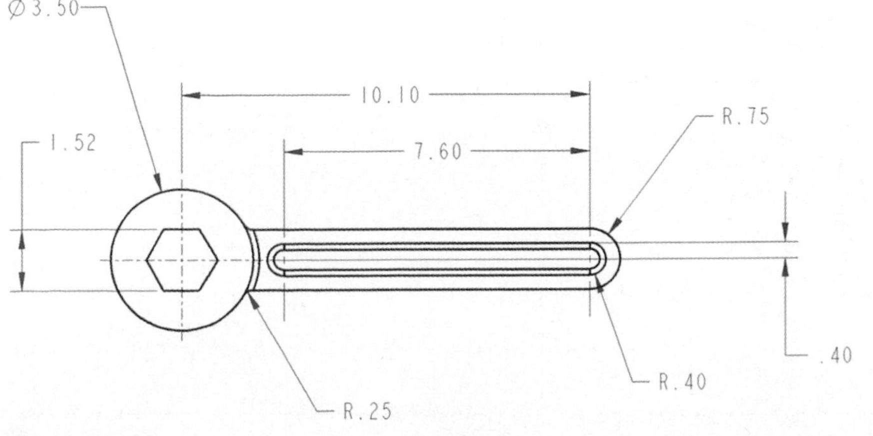

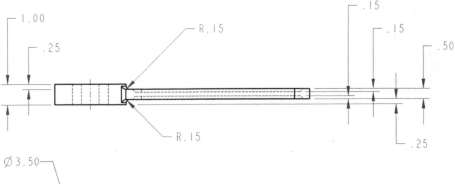

(d)

PROBLEM 13.5

Problem 13.6 Model the part in 3D. Display and plot the part as a shaded model (a), as a dimensioned pictorial (b), and as a dimensioned detail (c).

(a)

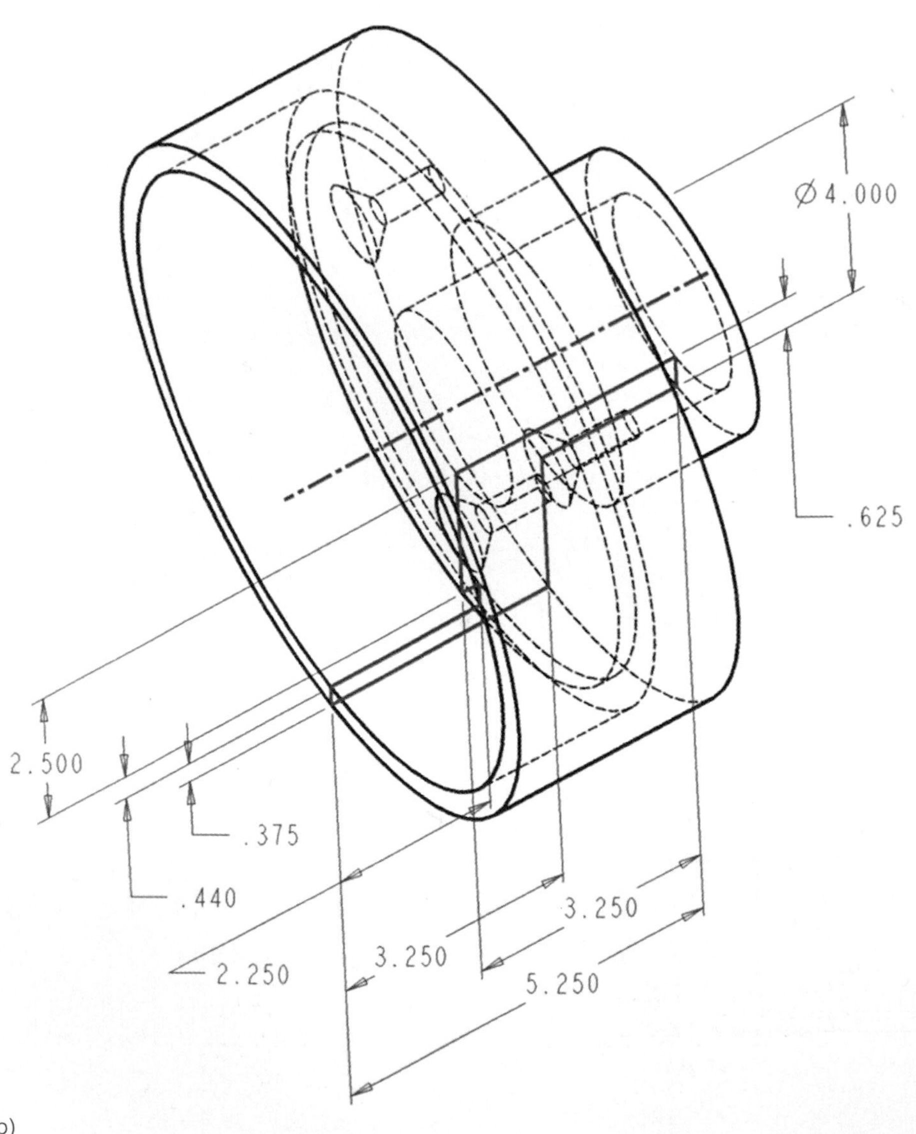

(b)

PROBLEM 13.6

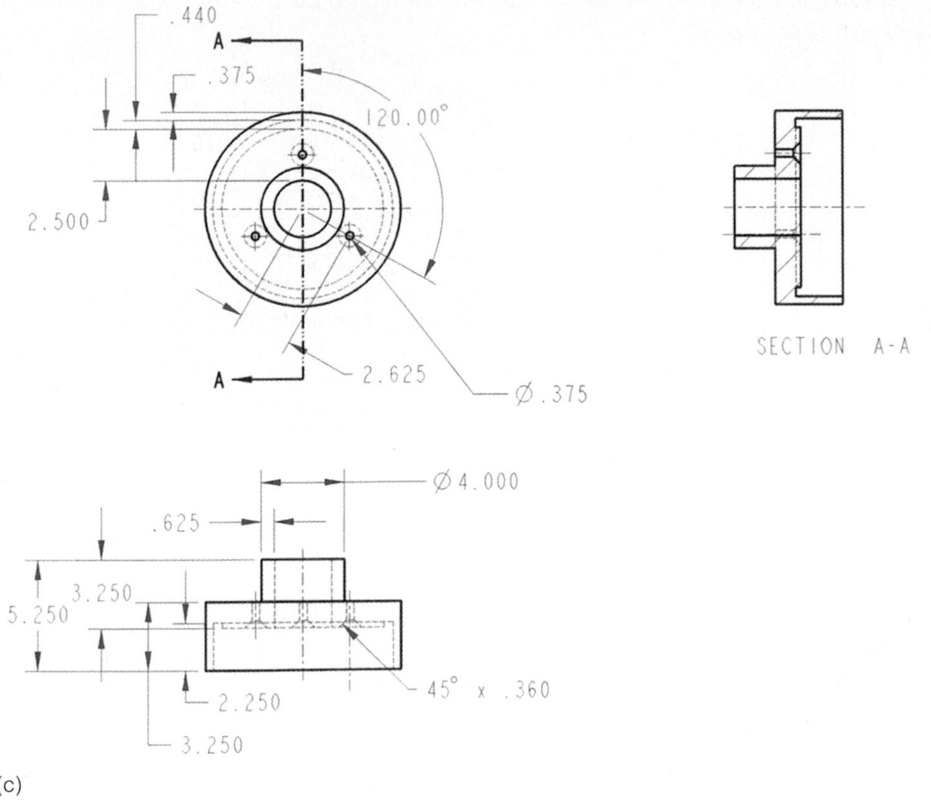

(c)

Problem 13.7 Model the part in 3D. Display and plot the part as a shaded model (a) and as a dimensioned pictorial (b).

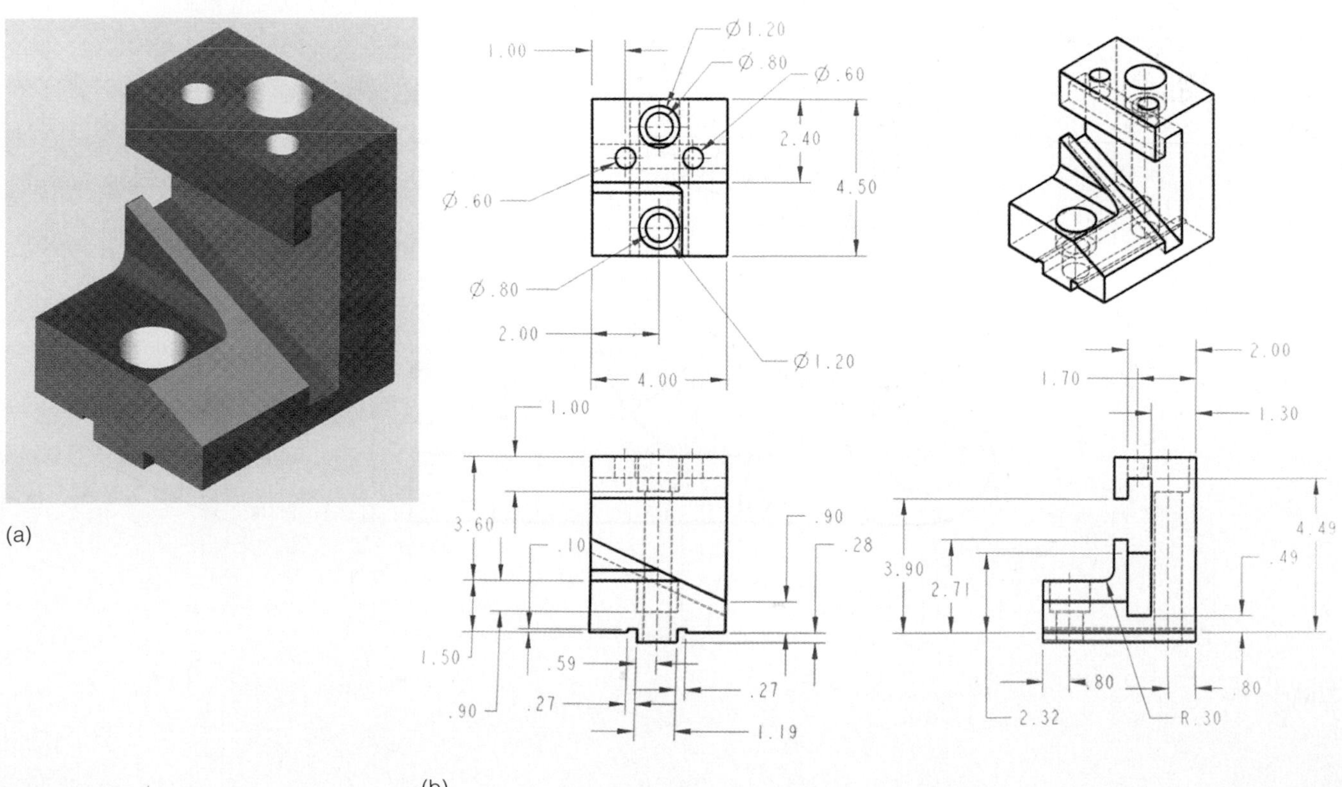

(a)

(b)

PROBLEM 13.7

Problem 13.8 Model the part in 3D. Display and plot the part as a shaded model (a), as a 3D model with hidden lines (b), as a 3D model with without hidden lines (c), and as a dimensioned detail (d).

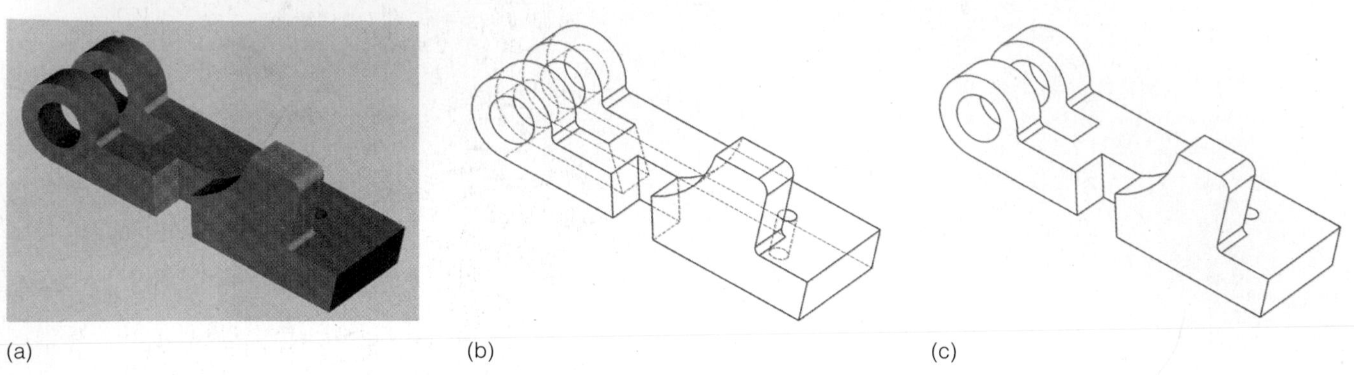

(a) (b) (c)

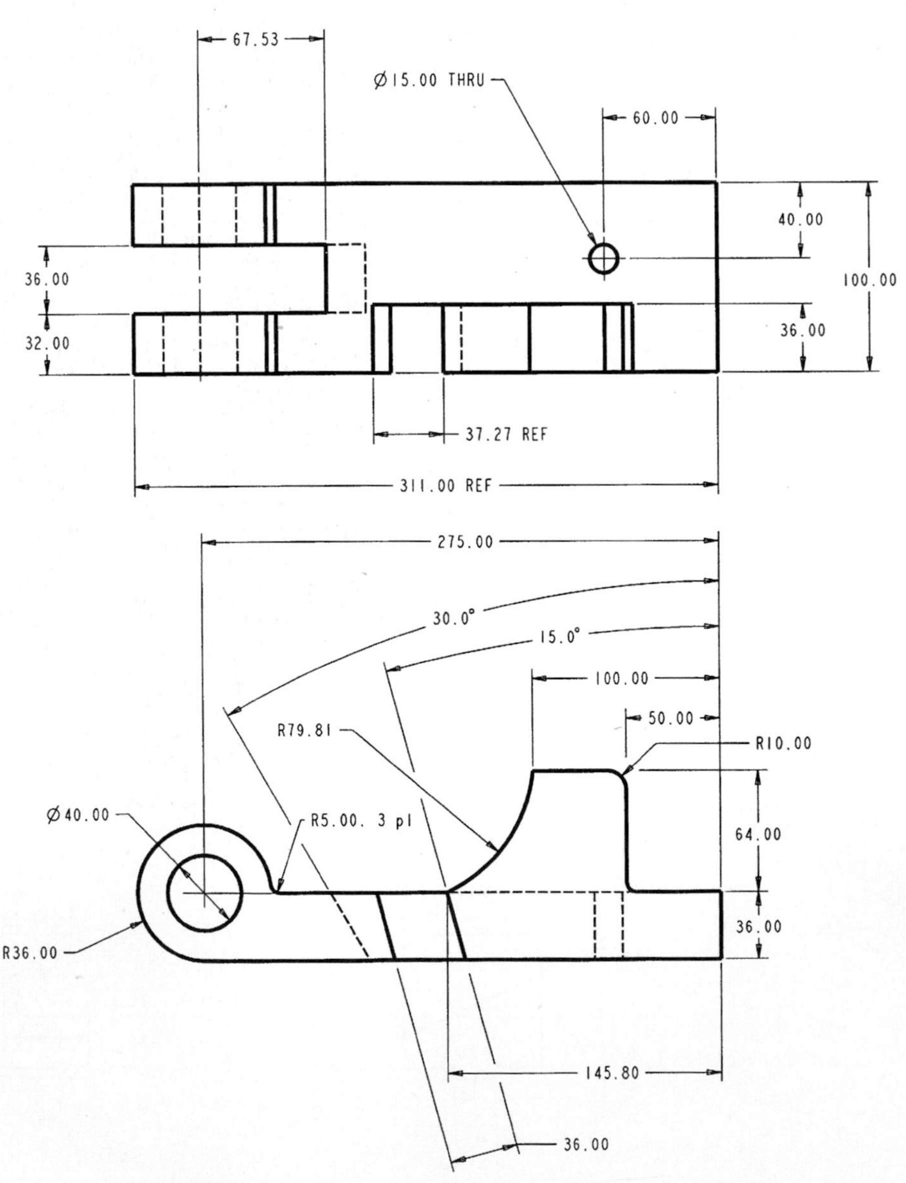

(d)

PROBLEM 13.8

Problems 13.9 and 13.10 Model the part in 3D. Display and plot the part as a shaded model with two separate orientations and colors, as a dimensioned detail showing the bend dimensions, and as a flat pattern detail with dimensions. These projects should be completed *after* Chapter 28 is covered.

Instructor may also assign any appropriate problems or figures found in the text as pictorial drawing projects, either manual or CAD.

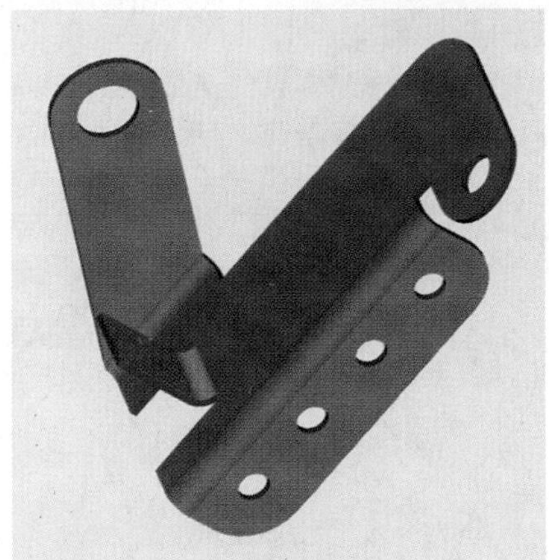

(a)

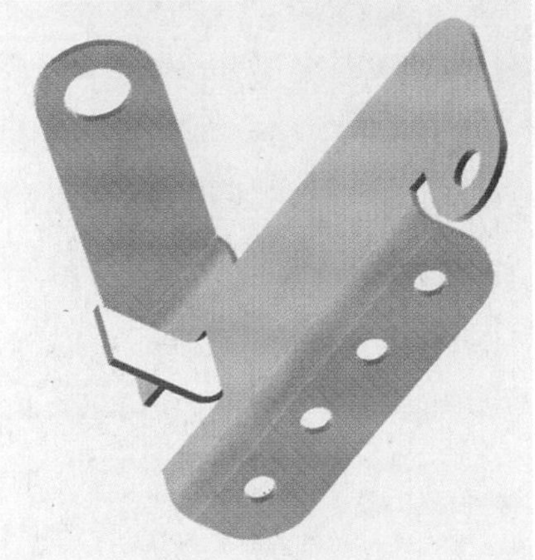

(b)

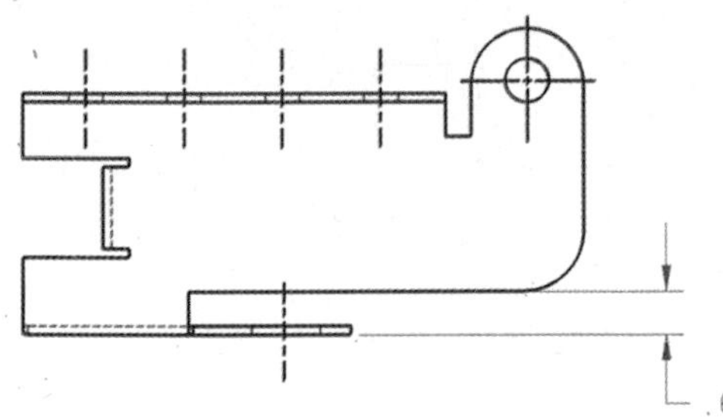

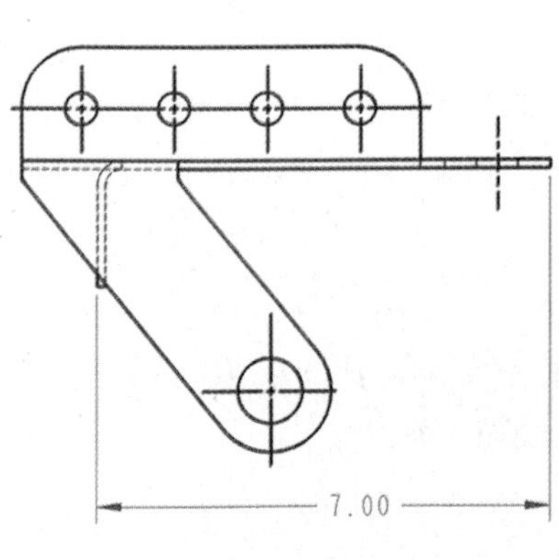

(c)

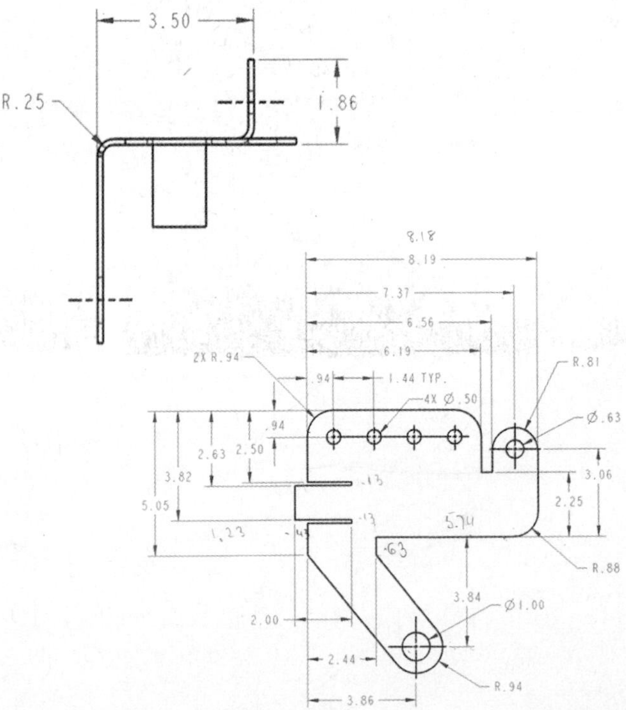

(d)

PROBLEM 13.9

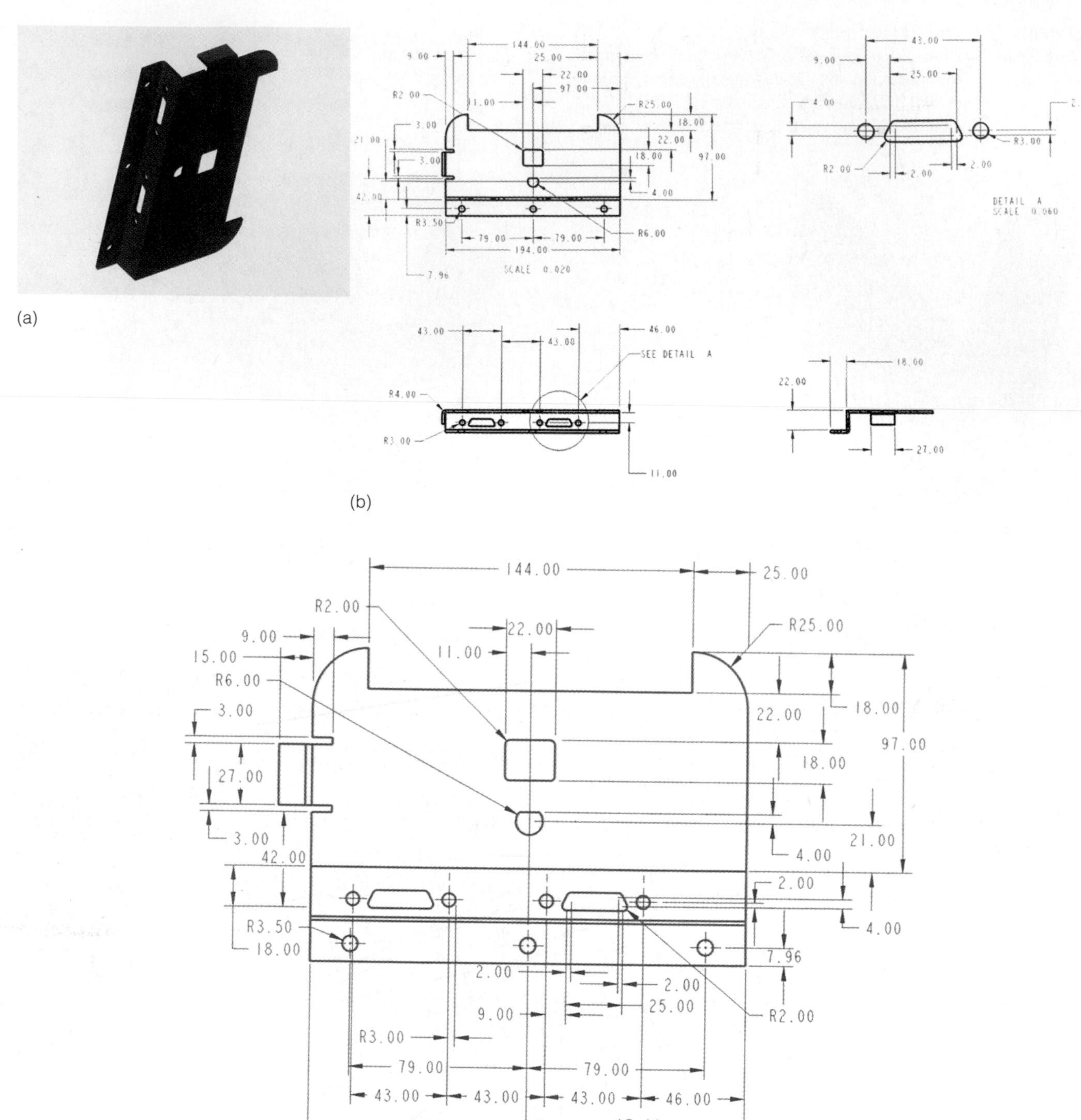

PROBLEM 13.10

PROCESSES AND DOCUMENTATION

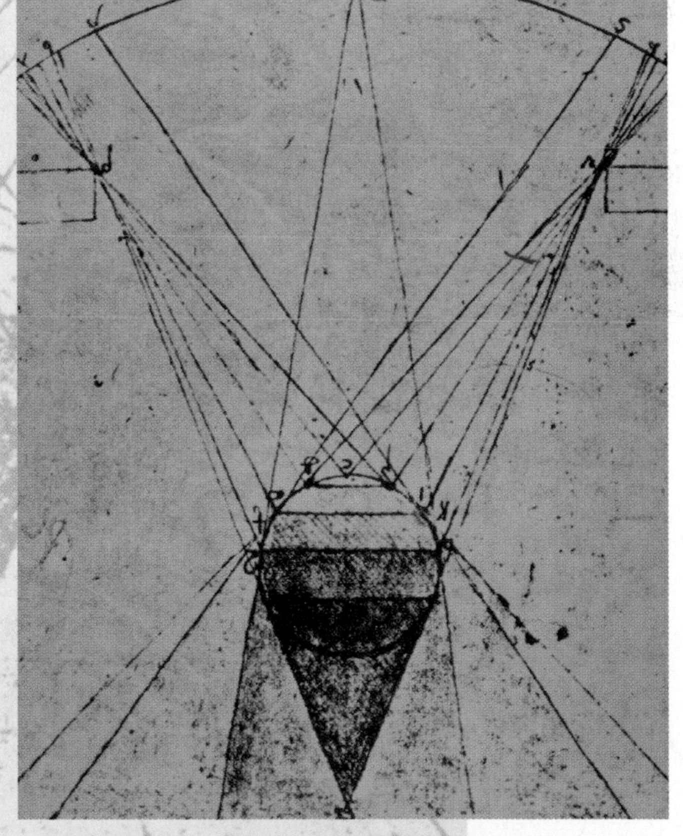

MANUFACTURING PROCESSES

Chapter 14

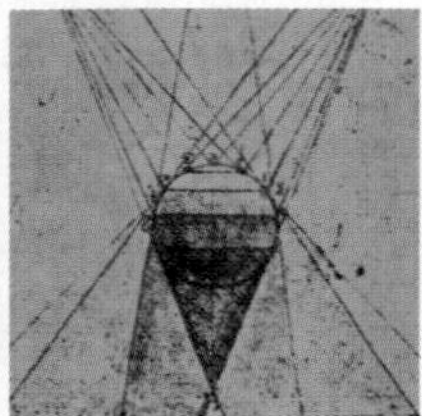

LEARNING OBJECTIVES

Upon completion of this chapter you will be able to:

1. Identify specific stages in the manufacturing process.
2. Demonstrate an understanding of materials used in the manufacturing process.
3. Develop an understanding of design-for-manufacturability (DFM) concepts.
4. Identify the basic types of machine tool operations.
5. Describe the processes involved in materials forming.
6. Understand the differences among finishing techniques.
7. Describe the process of automated and computer-aided manufacturing.
8. Define robotics and describe its role in the manufacturing process.

14.1 INTRODUCTION

The purpose of any engineering drawing or design database is to provide the information necessary to manufacture a part or system. To design and manufacture a part properly, engineers and designers must understand manufacturing. This chapter describes basic manufacturing and production processes.

When a 3D CAD/CAM system is being employed, the part design might be completely described in the database. When this is the case, the need for engineering drawings may be lessened or entirely eliminated. Regardless of the method of manufacture, the part must be produced from the information provided to the manufacturing facility by the engineering/design department. Figure 14.1 shows a series of steps in the design and manufacture of a connecting rod. Of course, the last step is the actual machining of the part, but the manufacturing methods for producing the part must be known and understood at the beginning of the project, not after the part has been designed and documented. Because the manufacturing process will influence and determine many aspects of the design's configuration, the aspiring designer or engineer must be familiar with the traditional machine tool capabilities and the advanced automated processes and methods.

The engineering drawing shows the specific size and geometric shape of the part. It also provides related information about material specifications, finish requirements, and required treatments, along with the revisions and releases made to the document. The drawing in Figure 14.2 shows the revisions in the upper right-hand corner. The notes, in the lower left-hand corner, provide manufacturing with information about the part. Here, the corners are to be ground to BREAK ALL SHARP CORNERS, and the finish (surface texture) is established for the part.

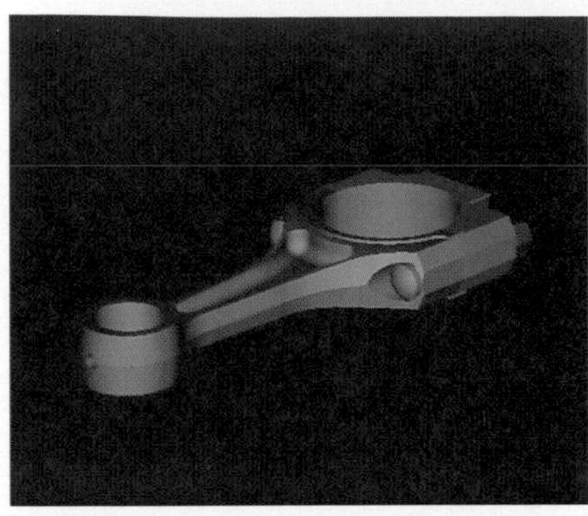

(a) Via interactive commands, the ICEM Solid Modeler assists the design engineer in creating a connecting rod. The engineer constructs shaded, color images in true 3D perspective by combining fourteen geometric primitives

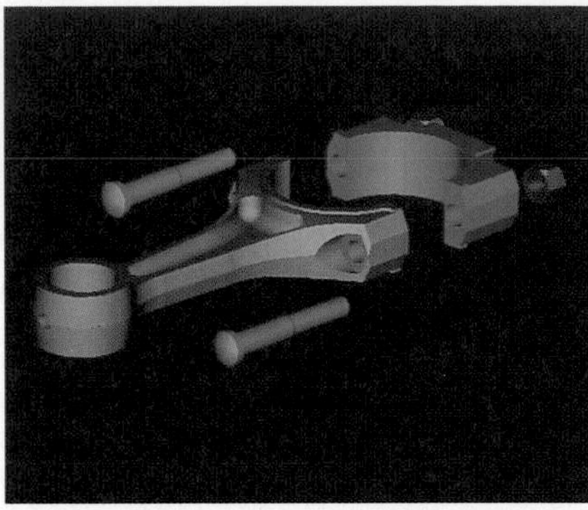

(b) Once the geometric model is created, the ICEM Solid Modeler can "explode" the connecting rod into its component parts, rotate them for viewing at different angles, create cross sections, and check for interference fits

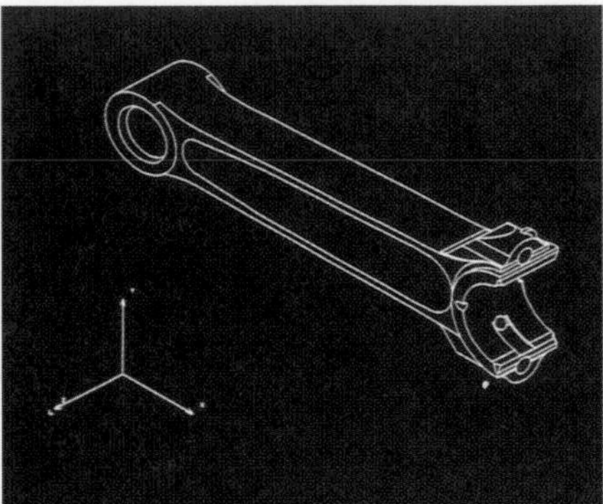

(c) The ICEM Solid Modeler creates a wireframe model automatically from the solid geometry. Hidden lines are also removed automatically

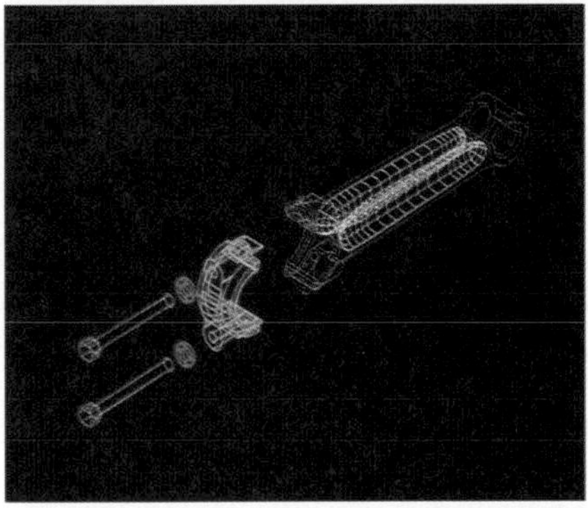

(d) The ICEM Solid Modeler can create an "exploded"-view wireframe model. Weights, volumes, surface areas, moments of intertia, and radii of gyration can also be calculated automatically

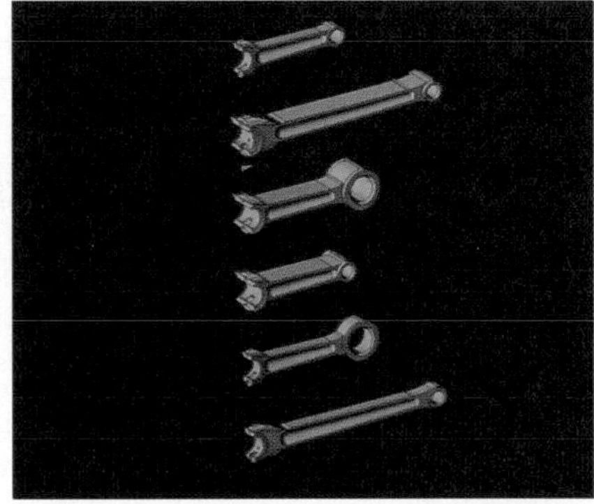

(e) The ICEM Solid Modeler gives the design engineer parametric modeling capability. This allows automatic generation of families of parts

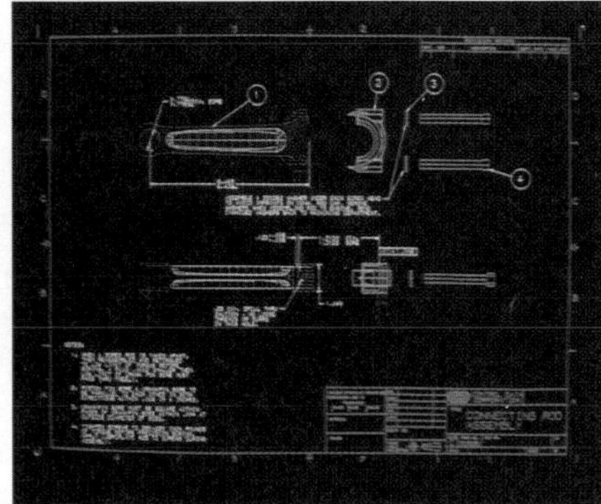

(f) The ICEM Engineering Data Library provides the design engineer with comprehensive, automatic, and security-controlled progression of product documentation

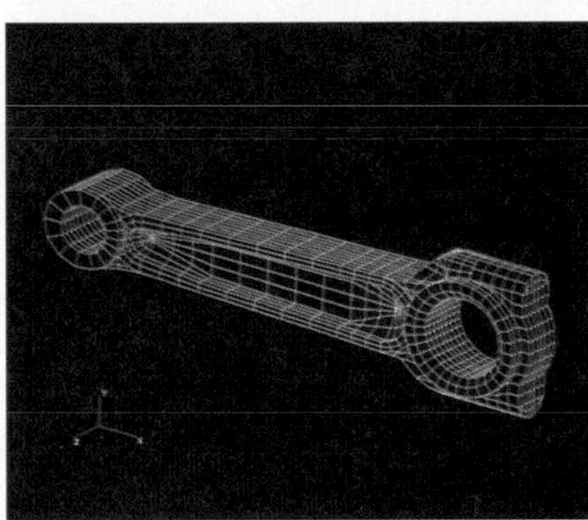

(g) The ICEM utilizes Control Data's UNISTRUC II system or Patran-G for automatic mesh generation for finite-element models

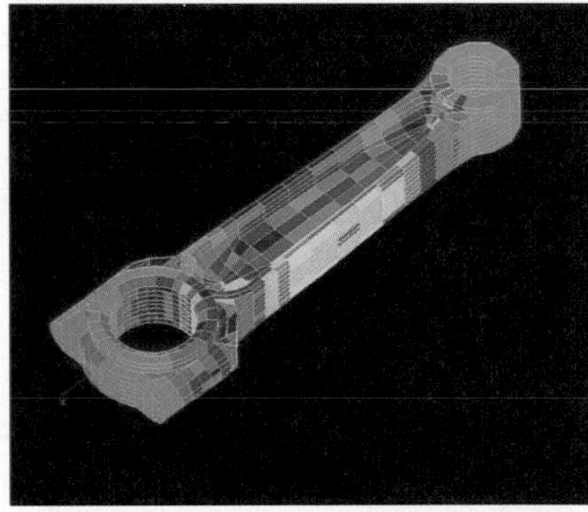

(h) ICEM provides a wide variety of mesh controls. Color schemes depict stress levels at the centroids of each element

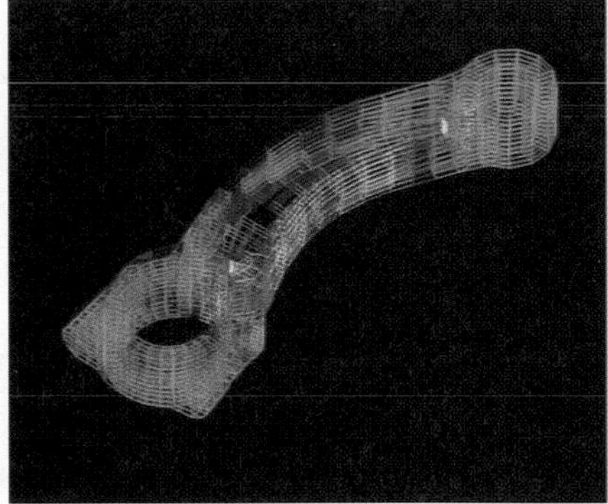

(i) Magnified deformation of connecting rod also shows stress data

(Continues)

FIGURE 14.1 CAD/CAM Design and Manufacture of a Part

14.2 MANUFACTURING

Manufacturing is the process of coordinating workers, machines, tools, and materials to create a product. The primary purpose of manufacturing is to produce quality parts from raw materials and to assemble related parts in creating assemblies. Manufacturing steps include:

1. Selecting materials and manufacturing methods

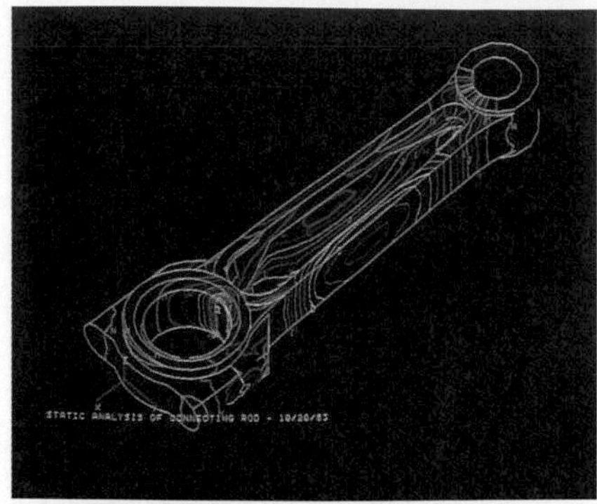

(j) Colored lines depict uniform stress lines in the connecting rod

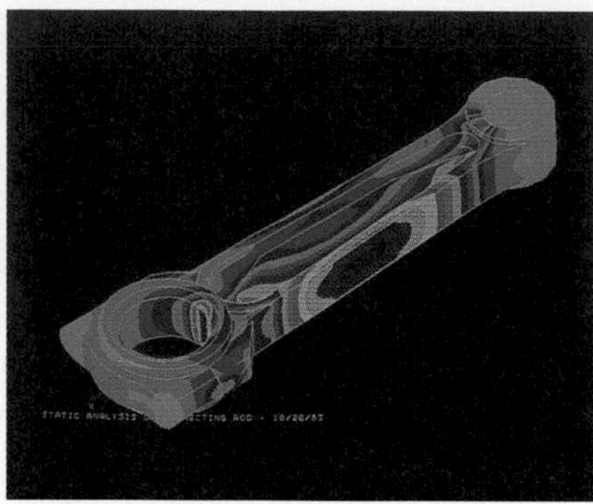

(k) Colored regions indicate ranges of stress or deformations

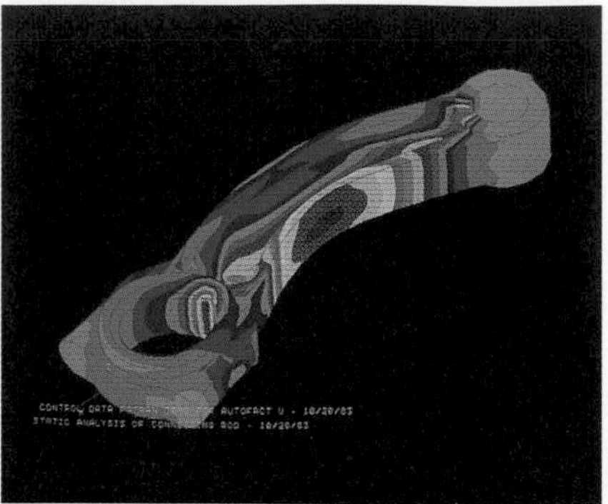

(l) Colored regions are contoured to display accurately stress of connecting rod in motion

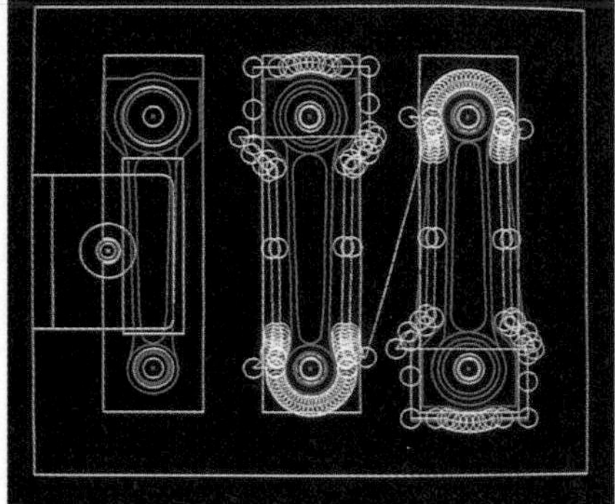

(m) Design engineers can preview cutter paths for CNC machining of the part. Changes can be input before machining so that time to part is reduced

(n) The ICEM NC capability generates control tapes directly from design geometry. The NC output is used for machining the actual part

(o) The ICEM assists design engineers in creating CNC machining codes for complex surfaces of dies, molds, and finished parts

FIGURE 14.1 CAD/CAM Design and Manufacture of a Part—*Continued*

2. Determining assembly requirements
3. Production control
4. Determining planning and tooling requirements
5. Production and manufacture of the product
6. Inspection and quality control

Many companies have separate areas for product development, tooling and manufacturing, and facilities. **Product development** is where the conceptual work is done in the development of a product. Producing and manufacturing a product requires new machines, tools, dies, jigs, and fixtures. Thus, **tool design** is very important for a successful product. *Facility design* covers building and plant upgrading, maintenance design, and new additions.

If you understand the cost, mechanical capabilities, and limitations of basic processes, you can design the part with the manufacturing process in mind. This increases **manufacturability** and reduces the cost of the item. The final product is what is manufactured and produced for sale. The drawing or the CAD database is the starting point for the design-through-manufacture sequence.

14.2.1 Manufacturing Processes and Manufacturability

The primary goal of all manufacturing is to produce a product cost-effectively, quickly, and at the required level of accuracy. Although manufacturing engineers decide the way to produce the part, designers have major input.

Once the engineering drawing has been received by manufacturing, it is reviewed to ensure that all information necessary to make the part is provided. During this review, manufacturing engineers decide on tooling, machines, inspection, and time to produce the part. New concepts, including the integration of manufacturing decisions into the beginning stages of design, are being implemented throughout industry today. This is called **design for manufacturability** (DFM). DFM is a company design philosophy. Since the way a product is designed determines 70–90% of the total ongoing cost of the product, it makes sense to design for quality and manufacturability. **Concurrent engineering** is the effort to get design, engineering, manufacturing, and production to work in parallel rather than in sequence. The following considerations are important for a successful product, but they *must* be considered during design, when changes can be implemented most readily:

1. Material specification
2. Size and configuration
3. Production run (how many parts are needed), which greatly influences the production method
4. Tolerances specified for the part
5. Machine and tooling operations

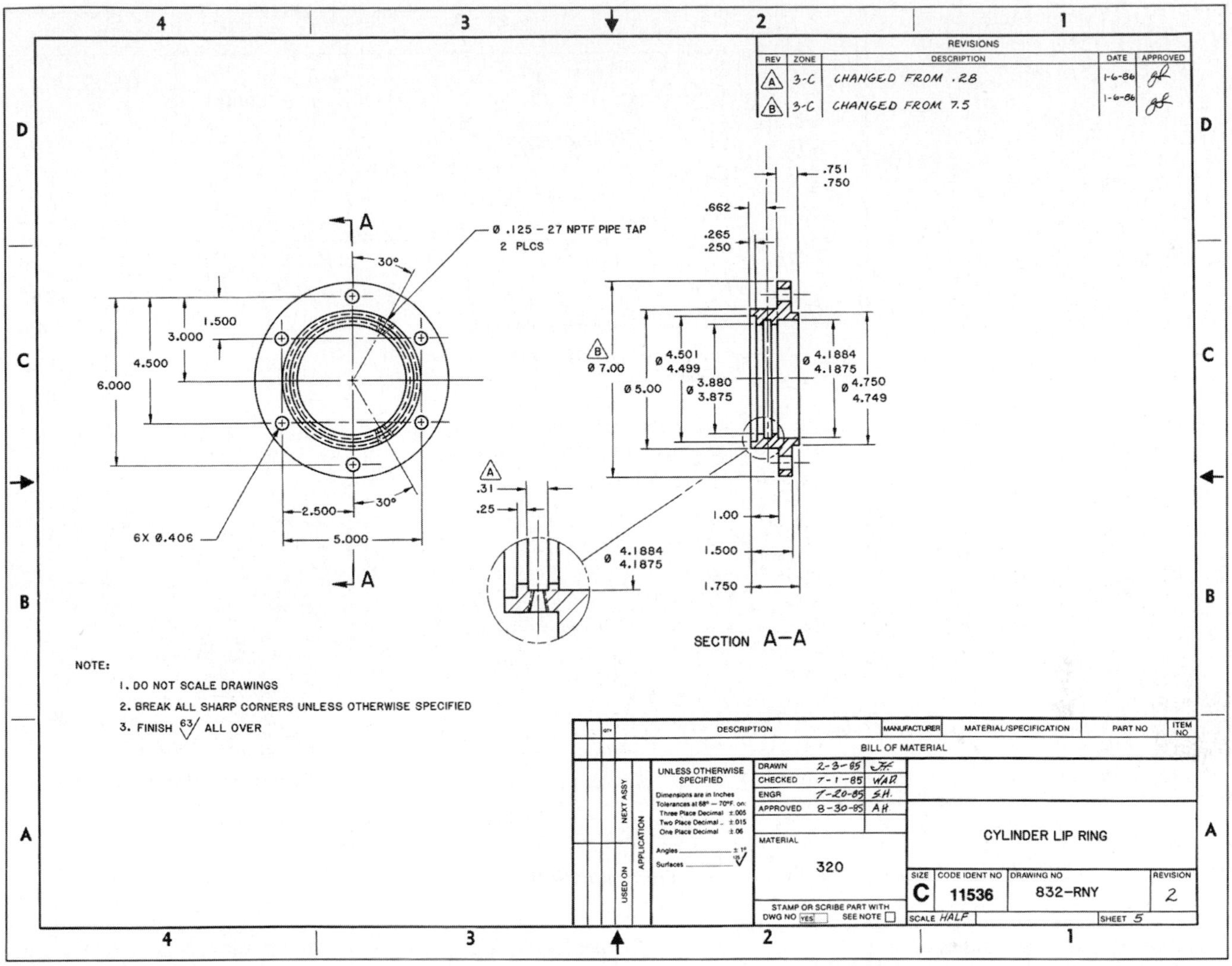

FIGURE 14.2 Cylinder Lap Ring Detail Drawing

The part (Fig. 14.3) is manufactured from a **stock piece** or other raw material. A variety of standard **stock forms** are available. **Bar stock** comes in square, round, and hexagonal shapes (Fig. 14.4). Figure 14.5 shows the available types of **structural shapes.** If a stock form is not used, then the part must be cast, extruded, or formed through other processes.

FIGURE 14.3 6061 Aluminum Outer Support Ring for Electronic Control Cables

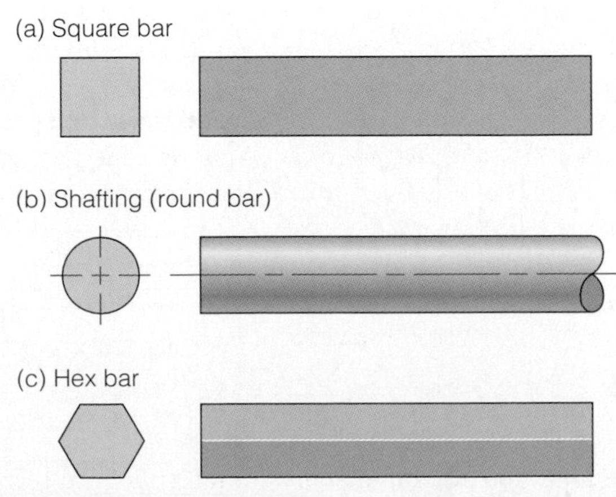

FIGURE 14.4 Stock Forms

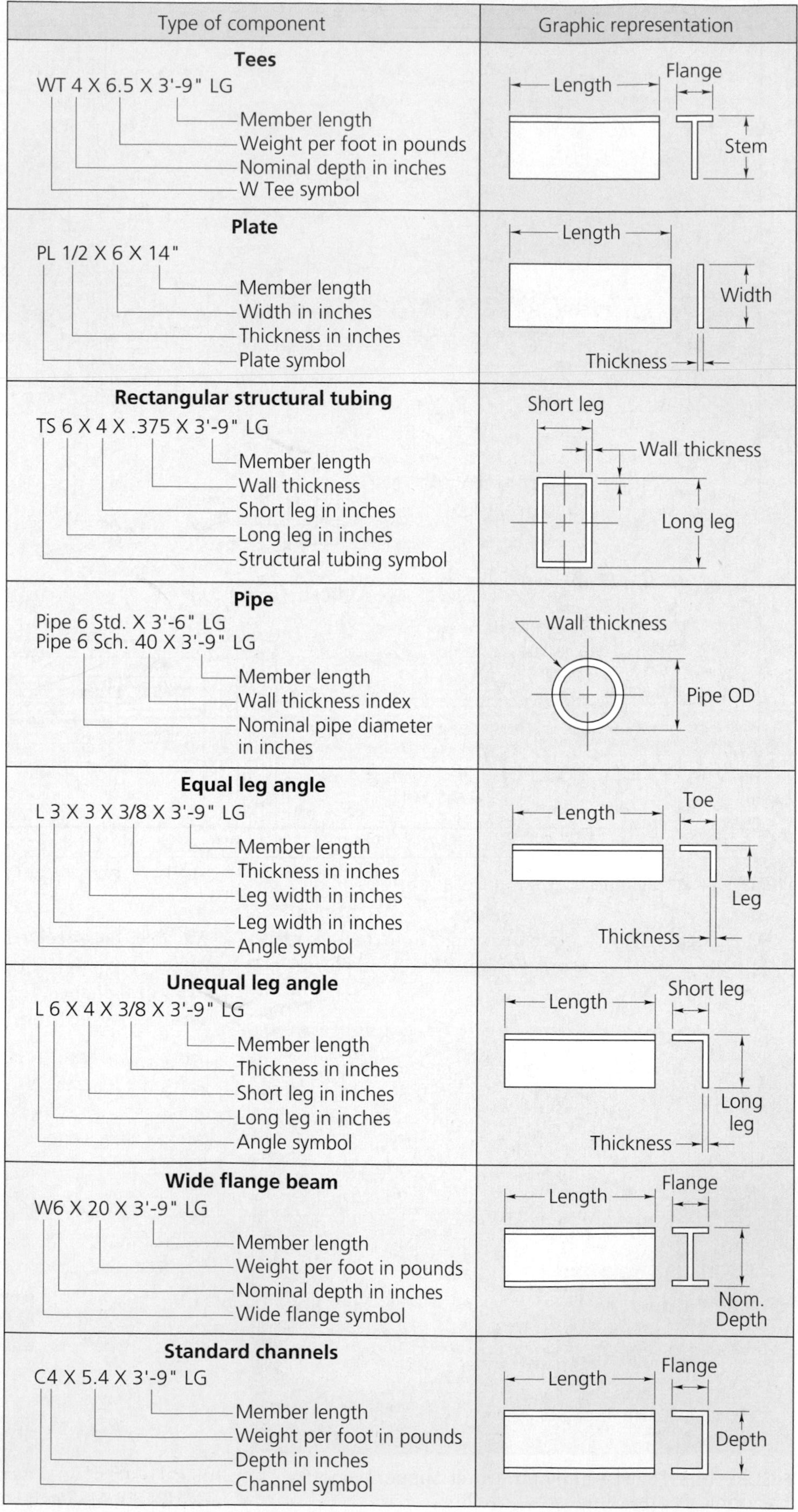

FIGURE 14.5 Structural Stock Forms

There are five basic families of processes:

1. **Molding** or **casting** into the proper configuration
2. Forming by **bending** into the required shape
3. **Cutting** or **sawing** into the proper size and shape
4. Pounding or **forging** into shape
5. **Fabrication** via a fastening method: *welding, riveting, bolting, screwing, adhering,* or *nailing* parts formed by any of the preceding processes

14.3 MACHINE TOOL OPERATIONS

Machine tools are machines that cut metal or form new material. Some machines are dedicated to one operation; others can perform many types of cutting or drilling operations. Figure 14.6 shows manufacturing plants equipped with a wide variety of traditional and computer-controlled machine tools. Five basic processes are performed on machine tools:

- **Drilling** (drilling, reaming, counterboring, countersinking, spotfacing)
- **Turning** (lathe work)
- **Planing** and **shaping**
- **Milling**
- **Grinding**

(a) Aerospace manufacturing facility

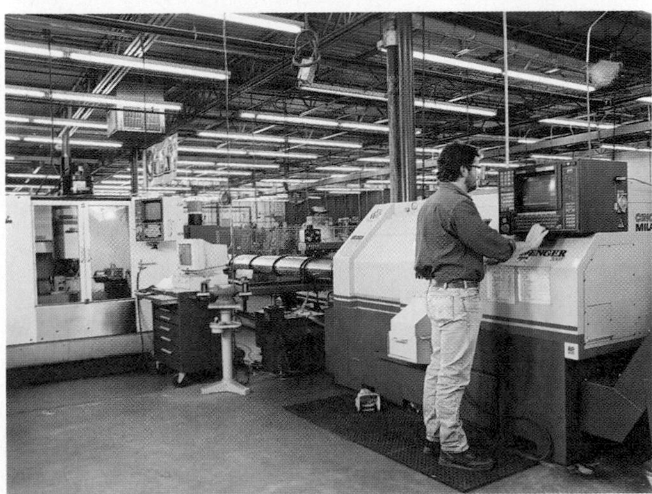

(b) CNC machine on factory floor

FIGURE 14.6 Manufacturing Facilities

14.3.1 Drilling

Drilling is one of the most common of the basic machine tool operations. It includes drilling holes from under $\frac{1}{64}$ in. (0.4 mm) to more than 2 in. (50 mm). Machined holes include: counterboring, countersinking, spotfacing, spot or center drilling, and reaming (Fig. 14.7). In industrial drilling, the **drill bit** [Fig. 14.7(a)] is a cutting tool held by a chuck and rotated by a large motor. The rotating tool is fed into the part at a controlled rate. The **turning speed** and **feed rate** of the drill are determined by the material and by the size of the hole.

Almost every machined part has drilled holes (Fig. 14.8). The type of process required is determined by the tolerance of the hole. Drilling [Fig. 14.7(a)] is also used to create rough holes before the boring, reaming, counterboring, countersinking, or tapping operations are performed. **Reamers** [Fig. 14.7(c)], **counterbores** [Fig. 14.7(d)], **center drills** and **countersinks** [Fig. 14.7(f)] are used after a hole has been drilled.

A tap drill is used when the hole will have a **thread** applied to it with a tapping tool. The tap drill must be the proper size to produce the minor diameter of the internal thread. (Threads are covered in Chapter 17.)

14.3.2 Reamers

When a hole must be precise, a **reamer** is used [Fig. 14.7(c)]. Reamers are required because twist drills make holes that are not accurately sized, are not precisely round, and have poor finishes. An undersized drill removes most of the material, then the reamer finishes the hole. Reamers are made of tungsten carbide (tool) steel. Many types of reamers are available.

14.3.3 Counterboring

A drilled hole must be made before any **counterboring** [Fig. 14.7(d)]. A counterbored hole is deeper than a spotfaced hole and has a specific dimension to its recessed depth. Counterboring enables socket-head and fillister screws to be seated with their heads flush or below the surface of the part.

14.3.4 Spotfacing

Spotfacing [Fig. 14.7(e)] is basically the same as counterboring, but it is done to no more than $\frac{1}{8}$ inch (3 mm) deep.

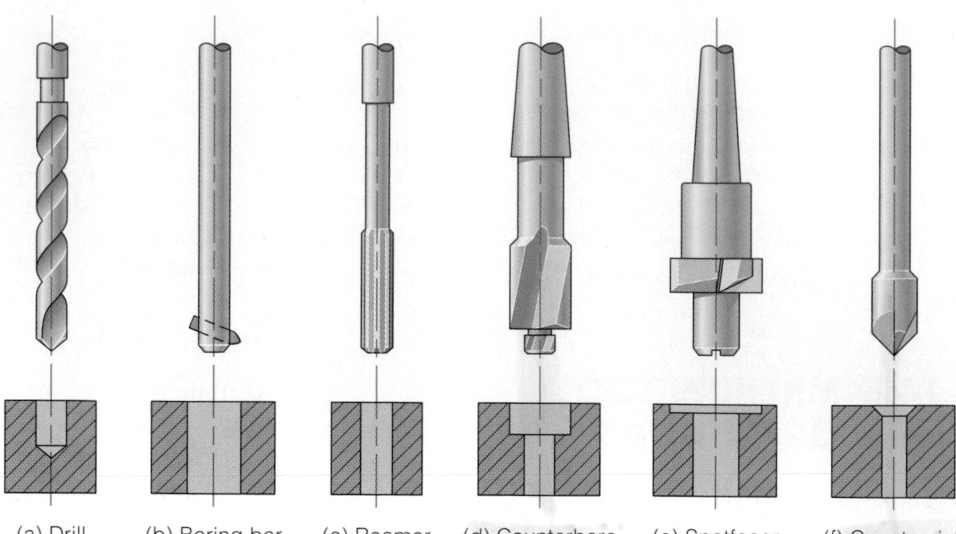

FIGURE 14.7 Machined Holes

This process is good for cleaning up the area around the hole, especially if the part is made of a cast material. The spotface provides a smooth bearing surface for **fasteners** (nuts, bolts, screws, rivets).

14.3.5 Countersinking

Countersinking creates a small **chamfer,** or bevel, at the edge of a hole [Fig. 14.7(f)]. A hole is drilled before countersinking. Countersinking makes it easier to insert dowel pins, bolts, taps, and reamers into the hole. For flathead bolts, chamfers are usually 82°.

14.3.6 Center Drilling

Center drilling is required when the part is to be held between centers for machining on a lathe. Center drilling also can create an accurately located starting hole for a twist drill.

FIGURE 14.8 Inside and Outside Windows on Gravity Probe Telescope

14.3.7 Taps and Dies

Taps and **dies** are employed to machine internal and external threads. External threads on shafts are cut by a die; internal threads are cut by a tapping tool.

14.3.8 Broaching

Broaches are used to create odd-shaped holes or openings. A broaching machine can cut special features like keyseats and can form square, hexagonal, or odd-shaped holes after a drilled hole has been created. A *broach* is a long tool with a series of teeth or cutting edges that increase in size progressively so that each tooth removes only a small portion of the material as it is pulled or pushed through the part.

14.3.9 Boring

Boring is a machining process for producing a wide range of precise-tolerance holes, and it requires a milling machine, a lathe, or a special boring machine by which accuracy can be closely controlled. Boring can create a wide range of hole diameters that require precise tolerances or geometry [Fig. 14.7(b)].

The part in Figure 14.9 is an example of an industrial part that required multiple holes, counterbores, and slots. Study each of the "callouts" on the drawing. Notice that each hole is dimensioned to the center point, and the notes call out the required hole diameters and, where appropriate, the depths. A number of drilled holes, counterbored holes, and taps are required for the part. Note that *the process required for a particular hole is not specified in the note, only the size and type*. Manufacturing determines the proper tool and machine needed to manufacture the part economically.

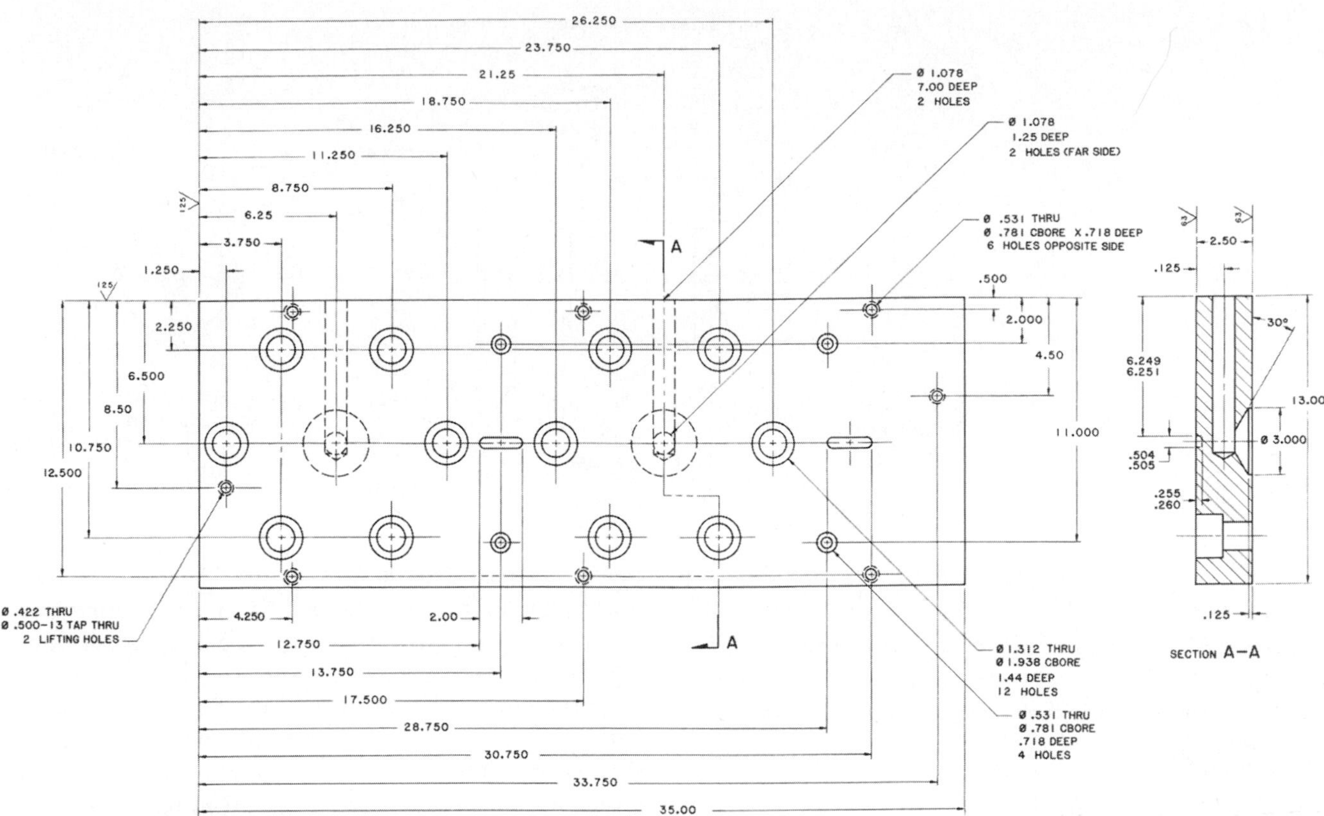

FIGURE 14.9 Detail Drawing

14.3.10 Turning Operations

Turning operations use the **CNC turning center** (Fig. 14.10), the **engine lathe** (Fig. 14.11), the **turret lathe,** and a variety of **boring machines.** A *lathe* is a machine that rotates the part rapidly while a stationary cutting tool performs the operation. The **vertical boring mill** is employed for turning large parts that need round cuts and for facing and contouring. Figure 14.12 shows an industrial detail of a pivot pin. This part was turned on a lathe.

The most common and versatile type of machine tool (found in every machine tool area) is the engine lathe. The engine lathe handles cylindrical part operations that include: cutting threads, facing, tapering, parting, turning, and knurling (Fig. 14.13). A part is usually held in a lathe by a

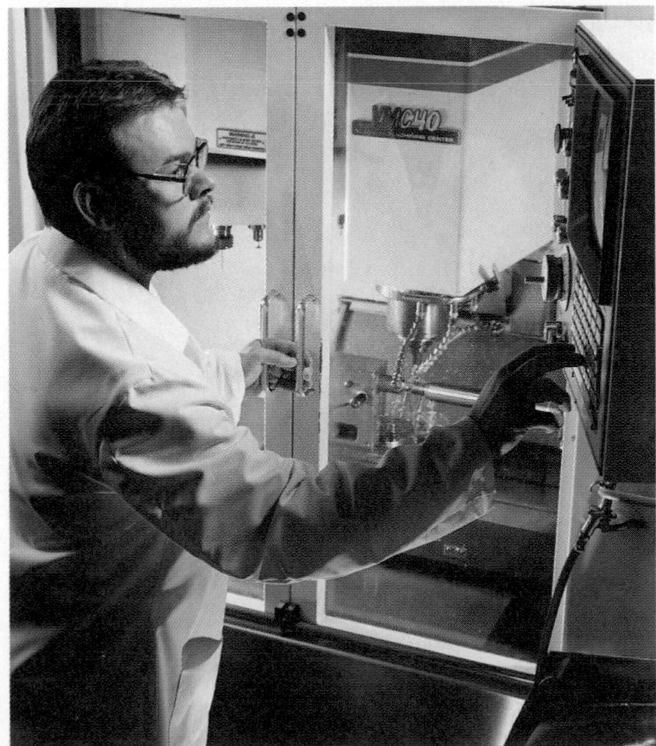

FIGURE 14.10 CNC Turning Center

FIGURE 14.11 Lathe Machining

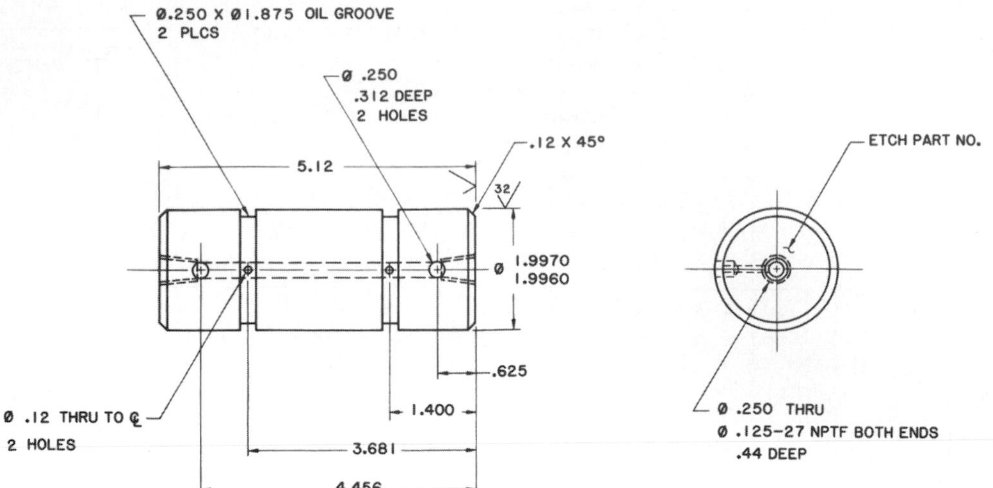

FIGURE 14.12 Pivot Pin Detail Drawing

chuck. The chuck is connected to the powered end of the machine (Fig. 14.11). Collets, face plates, drive plates, and other devices can also hold and drive the workpiece in the lathe.

A lathe can be used for drilling, reaming, boring, counterboring, facing, threading, knurling, and polishing. Drilling, reaming, boring, and counterboring are done on the face of the part as it turns. Boring and reaming on a lathe can be accomplished along the **Z** axis, in line with the center of the tail stock. The **tail stock** supports the part on one end, and the **tool post** fastens the tool holder securely. The tool post can be moved to the right or the left and rotated at an angle.

Computer numerically controlled (CNC) engine lathes are also available. All of the functions are controlled by a computer (and program). Therefore, manual controls are limited on this type of machine. The **turret lathe** has a rotating multisided turret on which a variety of cutting tools can be mounted. This allows the rapid changing of tools for low-volume vs. high-volume production. CNC turning centers help to perform turning operations on small, highly toleranced parts (Fig. 14.14).

Turning uses a lathe to reduce the outside diameter of a part. In this situation, the tool bit will travel parallel to the **Z** axis. **Facing** decreases the length of the part or flange and creates a flat surface (Fig. 14.13). **Threading** is done on an engine lathe with a single-point tool (a slow process). Drilling and reaming can be done on a lathe, but the hole location is limited to the center of the lathe's **Z** axis, in line with the tailstock center. **Knurling** (Fig. 14.13) is a pattern formed into the surface of a part, either for appearance or to provide a gripping surface. The pattern is either straight or diamond shaped.

The cylinder rod in Figure 14.15 is an example of a part produced on a lathe. Dimensions A, B, and C are given in three different sizes. This part is made from 1420 cold roll steel (CRS) and requires a tapped hole in the large end. Chamfering, facing, parting, drilling, and threading are required to complete the part.

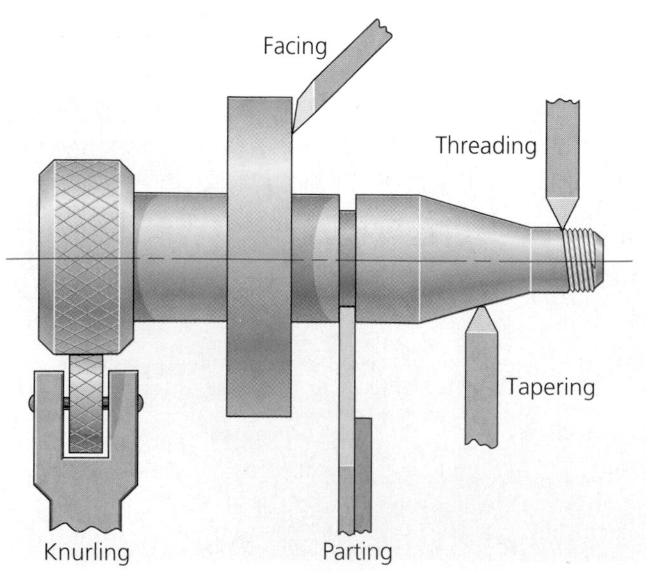

FIGURE 14.13 Lathe Processes

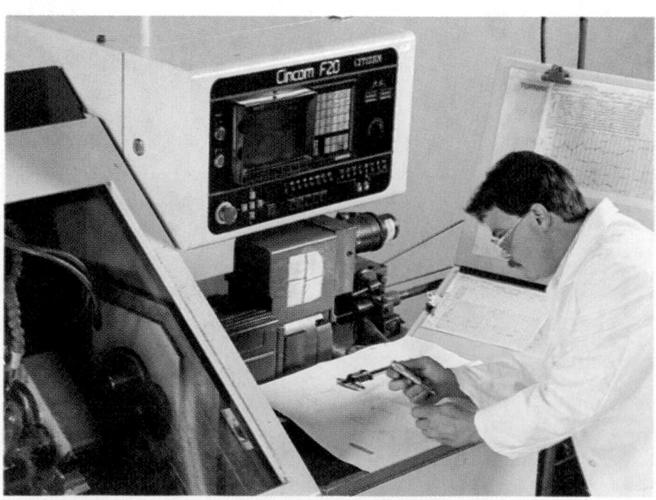

FIGURE 14.14 CNC Machine

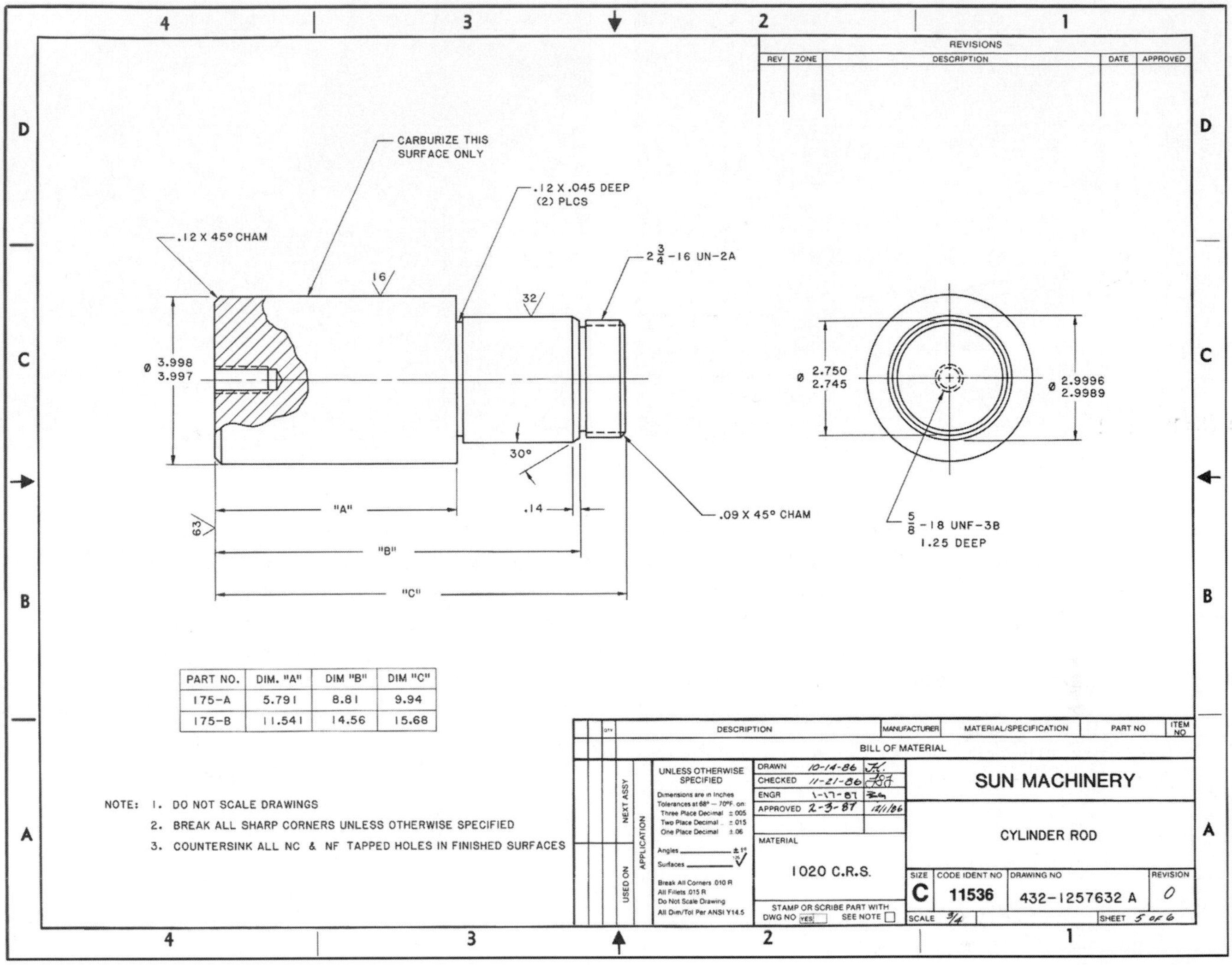

CARBURIZE THIS SURFACE ONLY

.12 X .045 DEEP (2) PLCS

.12 X 45° CHAM

$2\frac{3}{4}$-16 UN-2A

⌀ 3.998 3.997

⌀ 2.750 2.745

⌀ 2.9996 2.9989

30°

.14

.09 X 45° CHAM

$\frac{5}{8}$-18 UNF-3B 1.25 DEEP

"A" "B" "C"

PART NO.	DIM. "A"	DIM "B"	DIM "C"
175-A	5.791	8.81	9.94
175-B	11.541	14.56	15.68

NOTE: 1. DO NOT SCALE DRAWINGS
2. BREAK ALL SHARP CORNERS UNLESS OTHERWISE SPECIFIED
3. COUNTERSINK ALL NC & NF TAPPED HOLES IN FINISHED SURFACES

REVISIONS: REV | ZONE | DESCRIPTION | DATE | APPROVED

BILL OF MATERIAL: QTY | DESCRIPTION | MANUFACTURER | MATERIAL/SPECIFICATION | PART NO | ITEM NO

UNLESS OTHERWISE SPECIFIED

DRAWN 10-14-86 | CHECKED 11-21-86 | ENGR 1-17-87 | APPROVED 2-3-87

MATERIAL 1020 C.R.S.

SUN MACHINERY

CYLINDER ROD

SIZE C | CODE IDENT NO 11536 | DRAWING NO 432-1257632 A | REVISION 0

SCALE 3/4 | SHEET 5 OF 6

FIGURE 14.15 Cylinder Rod

14.3.11 Milling Machines and Milling Cutters

A **milling machine** is one of the most important and accurate machines in manufacturing. The typical milling machine has a table on which the part is securely fastened. Cutting is done by a rotary milling cutter with single or multiple cutting edges. One or more cutters are on each machine. Drilling, boring, reaming, slotting, facing, pocketing, and other types of cuts are made with this machine.

Milling machines are divided into two categories: vertical and horizontal. The classification depends on the orientation of the **spindle.** Figure 14.16 shows a vertical milling machine. The table is a flat surface with a variety of tee slots to insert clamping mechanisms that hold the part in place. Milling machines can also cut irregular surfaces, gears, slots, and keyways. Figure 14.17 shows a horizontal-spindle milling machine. This is also referred to as a **slitting saw.** Cutters are held in place by **collet adapters, arbors,** and quick-change **holders.**

FIGURE 14.16 Vertical Mill

FIGURE 14.17 Horizontal Mill

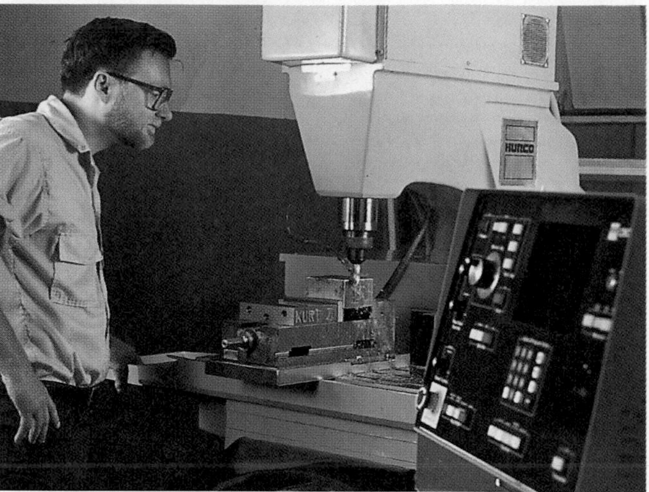

FIGURE 14.18 Part Being Machined on a Vertical Mill

Cutters fall into four basic categories:

- End mills
- Shell mills
- Face mills
- Plane milling cutters, including side mills

End mills are versatile cutters used for many types of machining work, especially where close tolerances must be maintained. An end mill is shown milling parts in Figure 14.18. End mills are also employed for pocketing parts. **Shell mills** are intended for simple facing or cutting steps that can't be done by a face mill. **Face mills** are used for facing flat surfaces and are found primarily on horizontal milling machines. Face mills either come with inserted teeth or are slab types.

14.3.12 Grinding

Grinding is also a cutting process except that the cutters are grinding wheels made from irregular-shaped abrasive grit. This abrasive grit cuts or grinds a part. The basic purpose of a grinding wheel is to provide a fine-finished surface and to maintain accurate size control.

Edges and corners can be removed from a part with stones and sandpaper or hand grinders. As an example, the note on the pull link detail in Figure 14.19 requires that the

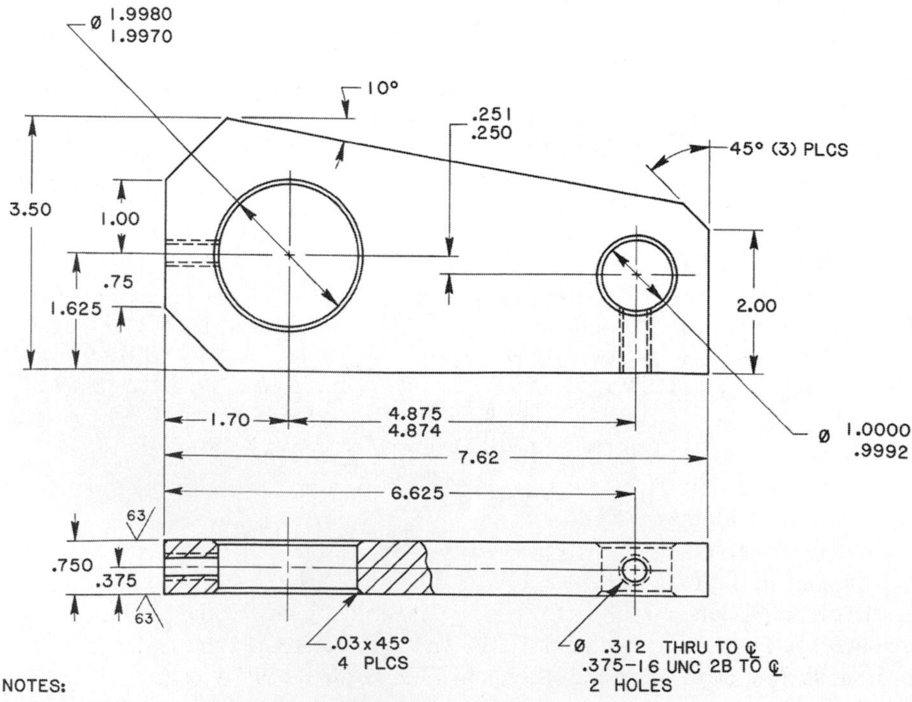

FIGURE 14.19 Pull Link Detail

Focus On . . .

COMPUTERS IN MANUFACTURING

Computer numerically controlled (CNC) machines have transformed manufacturing methods and techniques during the past twenty years. Today, they are integral parts of flexible manufacturing systems (FMS) that can machine one part, a thousand parts, or several different kinds of parts. Changes to the computer program controlling the system modify what part the system machines by redefining the sequence of events needed to complete the machining steps.

Numerical control (NC) began in 1947 with John Parsons' experiments on producing aircraft components with three-axis curvature data to control machine tools. The U.S. Air Force awarded Parsons a contract in 1949 to build the first NC machine. The Massachusetts Institute of Technology took over the development contract in 1951 and produced the first machine in 1952. Refined industrial machines followed in 1955.

Coordinate measuring machine (CMM).

Flexible manufacturing system (FMS).

Early NC machines used either punched tape or punched cards to send commands to the machine. Most machines used punched tape and tape readers. The tape was fragile and broke easily in industrial settings; and if 1000 parts were to be made, the reader read the tape 1000 times. Because of the need to make NC more efficient, computer control was developed. The part programmer employs English-like commands to write the program, and the computer translates the commands into machine code.

Distributed numerical control (DNC) allows control of a system of CNC machines via a networked computer. By planning a network of computer control effectively, it is possible to control an entire factory. FMS systems are networked into the computer control scheme.

Numerical control was developed to increase productivity, increase quality, increase accuracy, reduce labor costs, and do jobs that were considered impossible or impractical. CNC machines require a large initial investment and have higher per-hour operating costs than traditional machines tools, but the other advantages outweigh these disadvantages.

NC, CNC, and DNC machines will play increasingly important roles in automated and flexible manufacturing in the future. Today, stand-alone or networked CNC machines are found widely in both large and small production shops. Because of the great advances in and great advantages of this technology, the "factory of the future" will rely on these machines to be the backbone of the machining processes.

machinist **Break all sharp corners unless otherwise specified.**

Grinding machines are divided into surface types: cylindrical, internal, and centerless. Vertical-spindle surface grinders machine flat surfaces. Single-purpose abrasive machines, such as abrasive cutoff machines and snagging grinders, are common. Figure 14.20 shows a pedestal grinder. Figure 14.21 shows CNC OD and ID grinding equipment. This system monitors the diameter being ground as linear probes maintain accurate linear dimensions.

FIGURE 14.20 Pedestal Grinder

FIGURE 14.21 CNC OD and ID Grinding Equipment

14.3.13 Saws

Many types of **sawing machines** are found on the shop floor. The power saw is a band-saw cutoff machine with a continuous band-saw blade. This type of saw can cut bar stock to length. On thin material, it can also cut irregular shapes, make beveled cuts on tubing or solid stock, or make slots or slits.

14.3.14 Shapers and Planers

Shapers and **planers** are limited to straight-line cuts. A shaper can handle relatively small parts; a planer is for parts weighing up to several thousand pounds. Planers and

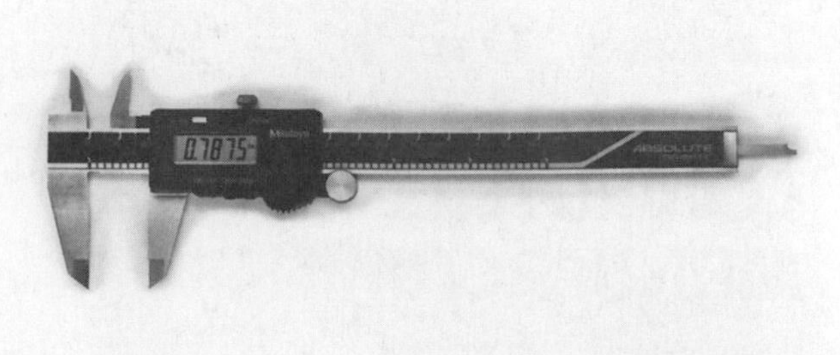

FIGURE 14.22 Digital Vernier Calipers

shapers make facing cuts (both top and side), slotting, step cuts, and dovetails (both male and female). Both machines are capable of creating finished surfaces. Multiple pieces can be machined at the same time with a planer. The planer can machine large iron castings or steel weldments that weigh hundreds of pounds. Shapers come in both horizontal and vertical types. Vertical shapers are sometimes called **slotters.**

14.3.15 Hand-Held Measuring Devices

A variety of measuring tools are used in manufacturing, including the **pocket steel ruler**, inside and outside **calipers**, micrometers, and vernier or dial calipers. **Vernier calipers** (Fig. 14.22) measure both the inside and the outside of a part. They have a beam or bar marked in inches and hundredths or in centimeters and millimeters.

The **micrometer**, also referred to as the micrometer caliper, is available in inside and outside versions. The micrometer is the most accurate of the precision hand-held measuring instruments. Digital versions of vernier calipers (Fig. 14.22) and micrometers are available in a variety of sizes.

FIGURE 14.23 Measuring a Part

14.4 SURFACE TEXTURE SPECIFICATION

A variety of standards have been developed by the American National Standards Institute (ANSI) and American Society of Mechanical Engineers (ASME) for specifying **surface textures.** The **surface roughness measurement** is important in machining. The finer the finish, the more expensive the machine process required. Processes such as milling, shaping, and turning can produce precise surface textures ranging from 125 to 32 μin. Only a lathe can produce 8 μin. on a production basis. Grinding operations produce surface textures ranging from 64 to 4 μin. The Greek letter μ (microinch, μin; micrometer, μm) is used on the drawing.

Surface texture is specified as part of the design specifications. The surface texture value is used along with the **surface texture symbol** [Fig. 14.24(a)]. The surface texture symbol designates the waviness, lay, and classification of roughness. **Roughness** is the irregularity on the surface of the part. It is *not* the distance between the peaks and valleys of the roughness, but the average amount of irregularity above and below an assumed centerline. **Waviness** is the irregularity from the centerline. The **waviness height** is the peak-to-valley height of the roughness.

Roughness is caused by the machining action during the production process. The roughness height is designated above the V portion of the surface texture symbol [Fig. 14.24(b)]. The symbol is constructed with the measure-

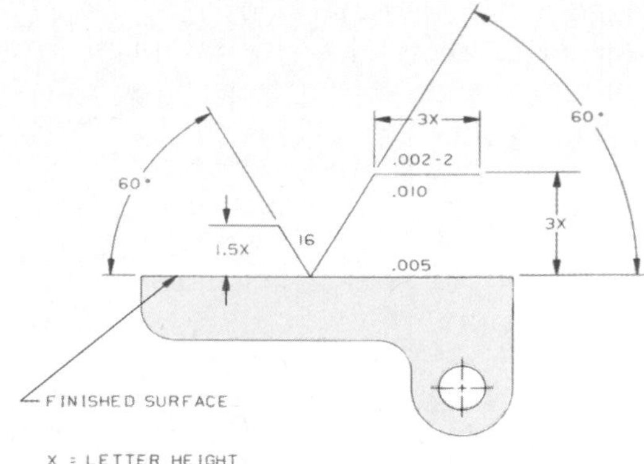

(a) Surface texture symbol specification

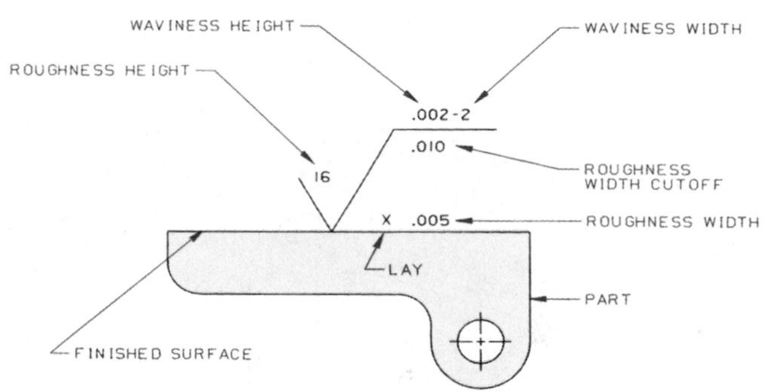

(b) Surface texture symbol description

Symbol	Purpose	Intent
X.X	Basic symbol: roughness average specified	Where roughness height only is indicated, the surface maybe produced by any method.
	Removal of material required to produce part	Material removal by machining is required. The horizontal bar indicates that the material removal is required to produce the surface, and material must be provided for that purpose.
X.X	Removal of material required to achieve surface	Material removal allowance.The number indicates the amount of stock to be removed by machining (mm or inches). Tolerances may be added to the basic value shown or by note.
	No material removal permitted	Material removal prohibited. The circle indicates that the surface must be produced by processes such as casting, forging, hot or cold finishing, etc. without subsequent material removal.
	Special surface characteristics indicated	Surface texture symbol. Used when any surface characteristics are specified above the horizontal line or to the right of the symbol. Surface may be produced by any method except when the bar or circle is specified.

FIGURE 14.24 Surface Texture

(c) Surface texture symbol variations

FIGURE 14.25
Surface Texture Concepts

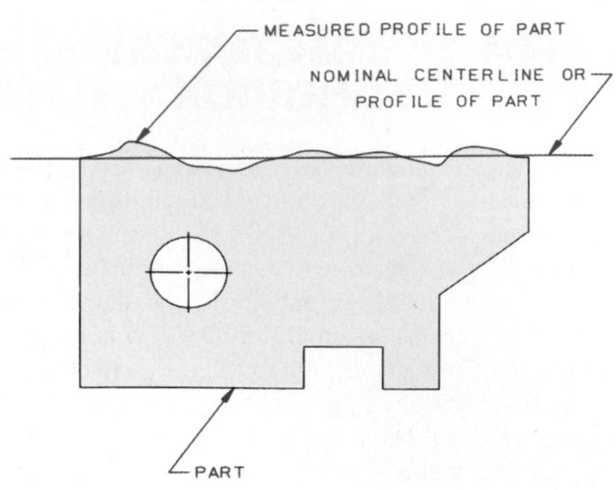

(a) Nominal center and measured profile of a part's surface

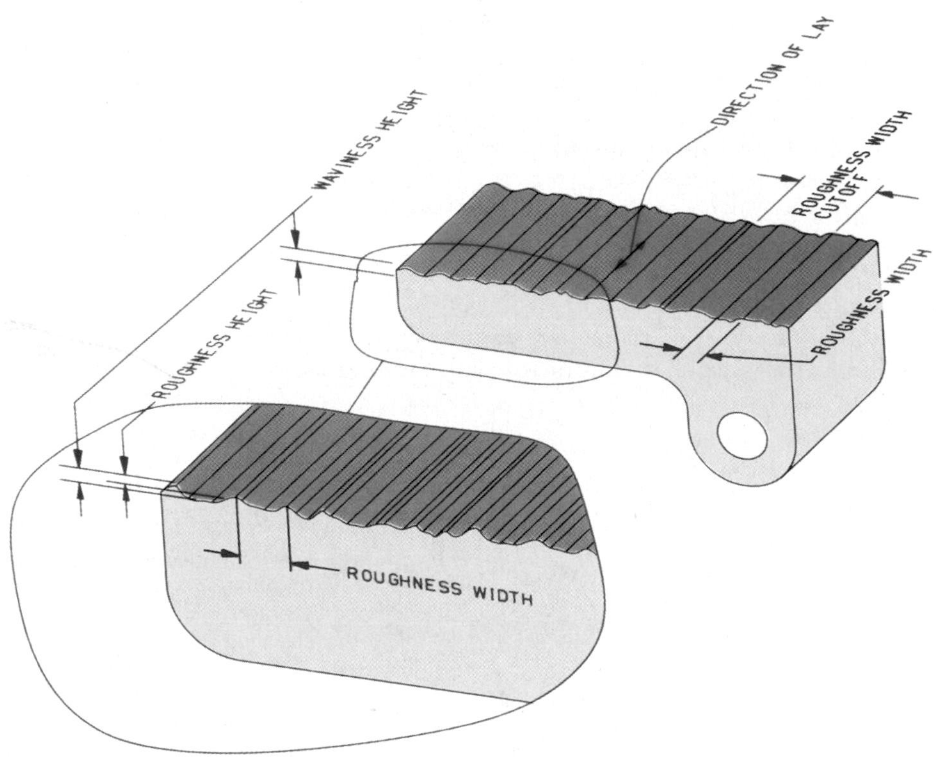

(b) Surface texture terminology

ments provided. Figure 14.24(b) defines each of the portions of this symbol and what they mean. *The symbol provides information on the waviness height, the waviness width, roughness height, and width.* The surface texture symbol variations are shown in Figure 14.24(c).

Figure 14.25(a) shows a part with an exaggerated measured profile. The **nominal centerline** or **profile of the part** helps establish the surface roughness deviation. A profilometer measures the **smoothness** of a surface texture roughness in microinches or micrometers. Surface texture is the deviation from the nominal center line or nominal surface that forms the pattern of the surface, and includes flaws, lay, waviness, and roughness. The direction of lay, roughness width, and roughness height are shown in Figure 14.25(b).

The centerline or nominal surface line [Fig. 14.25(a)] is a line about which the roughness is measured and is parallel to the direction to the profile, within the limits of the roughness width cutoff. The roughness consists of the finer irregularities in the surface texture, including those that result from action in the production process. These include transverse feed marks and other irregularities. **Roughness height** is an average deviation, expressed in microinches or micrometers, measured normal to the centerline. **Roughness width** is the distance parallel to the nominal surface between

Lay symbol	Meaning	Direction of tool marks
=	Lay is parallel to the line that represents the surface to which the symbol is applied	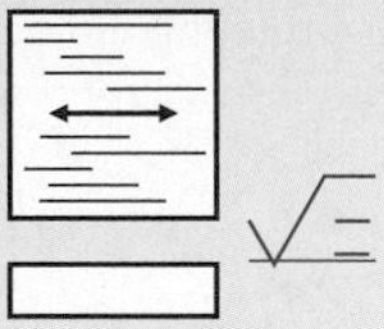
⊥	Lay is perpendicular to the line that represents the surface to which the symbol is applied	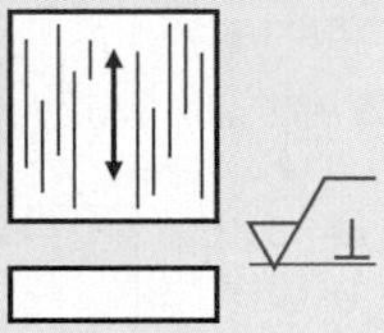
X	Lay is angular in both directions to the line representing the surface to which the symbol is applied	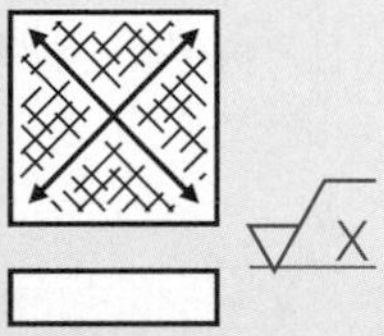
M	Lay is multidirectional	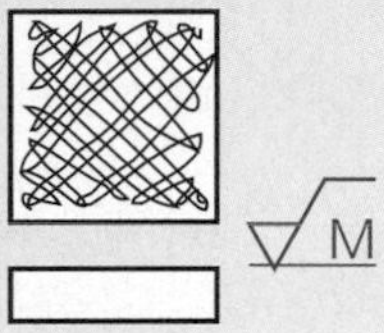
C	Lay is circular relative to the center of the surface to which the symbol is applied	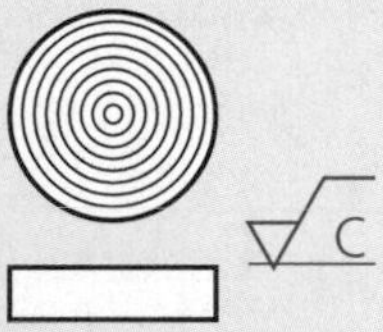
R	Lay is radial relative to the center of the surface to which the symbol is applied	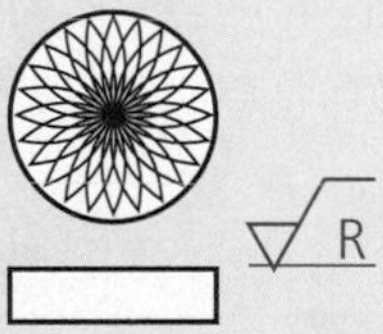
P	Lay is nondirectional, or protuberant in nature	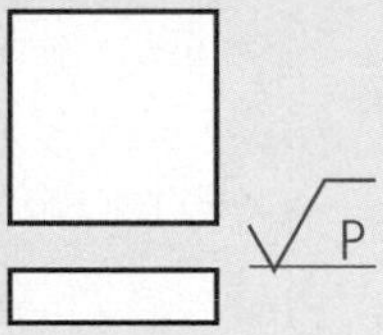

FIGURE 14.26 Lay Symbols

successive peaks or ridges on the part. *Nominal surface* is the surface contour shape that is usually shown and dimensioned by the designer. The **roughness width cutoff** is the distance over the surface on which the roughness measurement is made.

Waviness is caused by vibration of the machine during the machining process, heat treatment, or other processes applied to the part. The **waviness width** is rated as a measurement of spacing of successive wave peaks or wave valleys. The **lay** is the direction of surface pattern. Lay symbols are shown in Figure 14.26. **Flaws** are the irregularities, including cracks, blowholes, checks, ridges, and scratches.

Figure 14.27(a) shows how to specify the removal of material via machining by varying the surface texture symbol: optional, required, prohibited, and removal allowance. The preferred series of roughness height values are shown in Figure 14.27(b); the surface roughness produced by common production methods is shown in Figure 14.27(c).

14.5 PRODUCTION PROCESSES

Production processes include casting, forging, bending, rolling, press work, injection molding, dies, EDM, ECM, blow molding, and variations of other hot and cold processes.

Designing for automated production helps ensure a more efficient and cost-effective production process. *Design for manufacturability* ensures that the right process is chosen, existing factory resources are utilized, setup times are minimized, and tolerances are specified correctly. These procedures reduce labor costs and break down barriers between different areas (islands) of information in the company.

14.5.1 Casting

Casting is the process of forming parts to approximate rough sizes by introducing liquid material into a formed cavity called a mold, allowing the material to solidify by cooling, then removing the mold, leaving the solid shaped part. Casting methods available include sand casting, mold casting, die casting (Fig. 14.28), and investment casting. **Molding** and **die casting** is similar to casting except that the material involved is not in liquid form but is softened to a plastic state and forced into the mold under high pressure.

Everyday items, from toys to electronic components, are cast. One common type of casting is **sand casting.** Figure 14.29 shows a sand-cast part before machining. Casting is divided into two basic processes, **gravity** and **pressure.** Sand-casting molds are formed by patterns. **Patterns** look like the cast part and are used to create a shape in the mold cavity. The wood pattern in Figure 14.30(a) is inserted into sand to create the proper configuration of the part (front). Figure 14.30(b) shows another example of a wood pattern. Here, the pattern is designed to shape six identical parts.

A designer prepares a combination casting and machining drawing. Some companies require separate drawings, however. The **casting detail** (Fig. 14.31) is used by the pattern maker, and the **machining drawing** is used by the machinist. The notes establish the heat treatment requirements and the size of the fillets and rounds. The **draft angle** is the angle of the **taper** of the part that makes it easier to withdraw the pattern from the mold. After the material hardens, the sand is removed from the casting (destroying the mold). In Figure 14.31 the draft angle is specified as 3° maximum per side.

Tooling points on three **datum planes** (that are perpendicular to one another) locate dimensions on the casting. The planes are established by the tooling points on the casting.

Since it is not possible to cast sharp corners and angles accurately, the internal angles on a casting are filled with a material to eliminate sharp corners. Contoured surfaces that fill the sharp inside corners are **fillets** (Fig. 14.32). **Rounds** are the exterior corners that have been smoothed out to remove their sharp edges. In Figure 14.31, the notes state that fillets are to be R .25 maximum and rounds R .12 maximum.

Aluminum, magnesium, zinc, copper, bronze, brass, iron, and steel are all used to make castings. Designing a casting requires an understanding of how much the material will shrink during the cooling process. The dimensions shown on the casting drawing must reflect the **shrinkage allowance.**

Centrifugal casting involves feeding the molten material into a rotating mold. The rotation forces the molten material

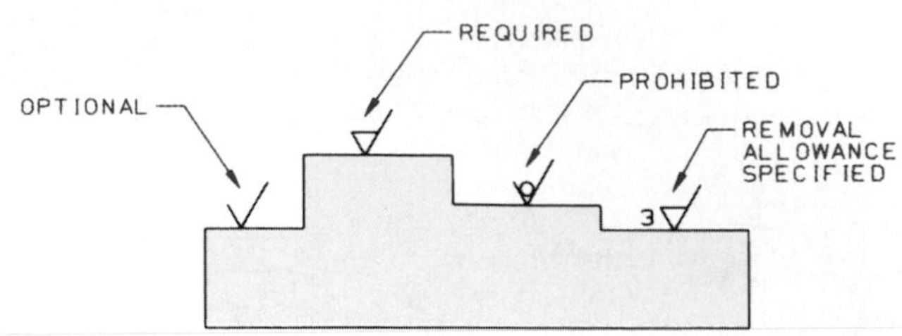

(a) Surface texture symbols

Roughness height rating		Surface description	Process
Micrometers	Microinches		
25.2	1000	Very rough	Saw and torch cutting, forging or sand casting.
12.5	500	Rough machining	Heavy cuts and coarse feeds in turning, milling and boring.
6.3	250	Course	Very course surface grind, rapid feeds in turning, planning, milling, boring and filing.
3.2	125	Medium	Machine operations with sharp tools, high speeds, fine feeds and light cuts.
1.6	63	Good machine finish	Sharp tools, high speeds, extra fine feeds and cuts.
0.8	32	High grade machine finish	Extremely fine feeds and cuts on lathe, mill and shapers required. Easily produced by centerless, cylindrical and surface grinding.
0.4	16	High quality machine finish	Very smooth reaming or fine cylindrical or surface grinding, or course hone or lapping of surface.
0.2	8	Very fine machine finish	Fine honing and lapping of surface.
0.05 0.1	2-4	Extremely smooth machine finish	Extra fine honing and lapping of surface.

FIGURE 14.27 Surface Texture

(b) Description of roughness height values on symbols

to fill the cavity or mold. Permanent molds are used for this process. **Die casting** is a permanent mold process that uses pressure to force the molten material into a metal die. **Injection molding** is also a type of permanent mold casting. Figure 14.33 shows an injection-molded part before and after machining. Injection molds are very similar to die-casting molds. There are many other types of molding processes, including blow molding, compression molding, transfer molding, layup molding, pressure molding, and vacuum molding.

14.5.2 Extruding

Materials-forming processes employ pressure to change the shape or the size of the material. This category of processes includes extruding, forging, stamping, punching, rolling, bending, and shearing.

Extrusion is a metal-working process for producing long, straight, semifinished products having constant cross sections (Fig. 14.34), such as bars, tubes, solid and hollow sections, wire, and strips. The metal is squeezed from a

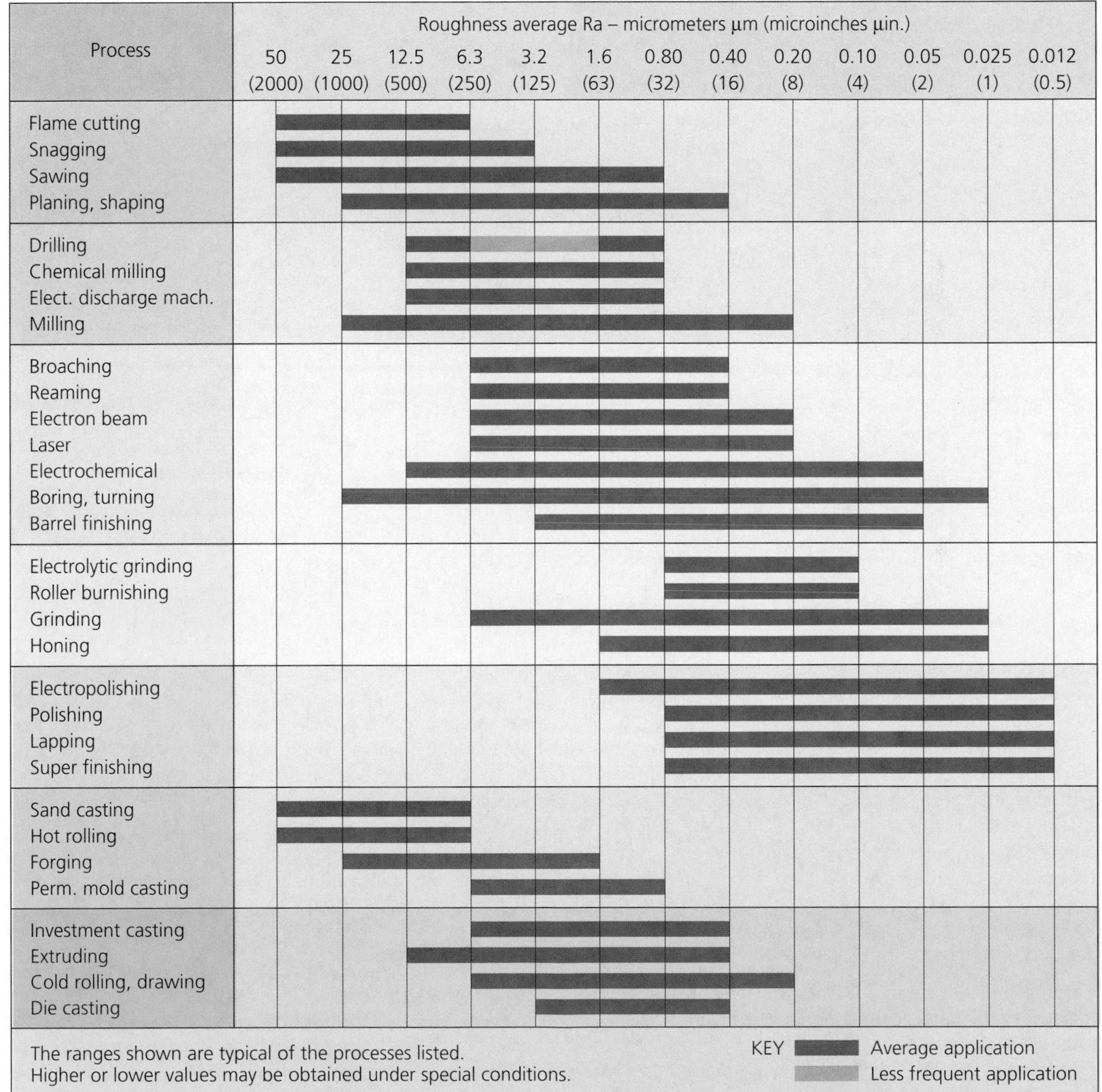

Process
Roughness average Ra – micrometers μm (microinches μin.)
50 (2000)
25 (1000)
12.5 (500)
6.3 (250)
3.2 (125)
1.6 (63)
0.80 (32)
0.40 (16)
0.20 (8)
0.10 (4)
0.05 (2)
0.025 (1)
0.012 (0.5)
Flame cutting
Snagging
Sawing
Planing, shaping
Drilling
Chemical milling
Elect. discharge mach.
Milling
Broaching
Reaming
Electron beam
Laser
Electrochemical
Boring, turning
Barrel finishing
Electrolytic grinding
Roller burnishing
Grinding
Honing
Electropolishing
Polishing
Lapping
Super finishing
Sand casting
Hot rolling
Forging
Perm. mold casting
Investment casting
Extruding
Cold rolling, drawing
Die casting
The ranges shown are typical of the processes listed.
Higher or lower values may be obtained under special conditions.
KEY
Average application
Less frequent application

(c) Surface roughness produced by common production methods

FIGURE 14.27 Surface Texture—*Continued*

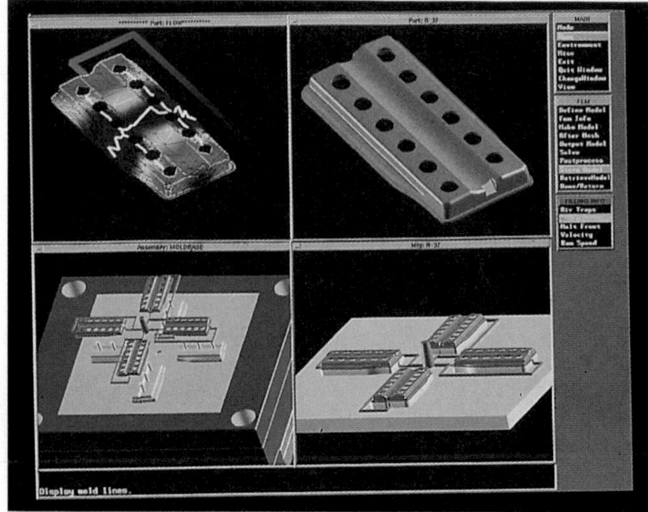

FIGURE 14.28 Die Casting

(a) Wood pattern and cast part

FIGURE 14.29 Sand-Cast Part Before Machining

(b) Wood pattern designed for casting multiple parts

FIGURE 14.30 Casting Patterns

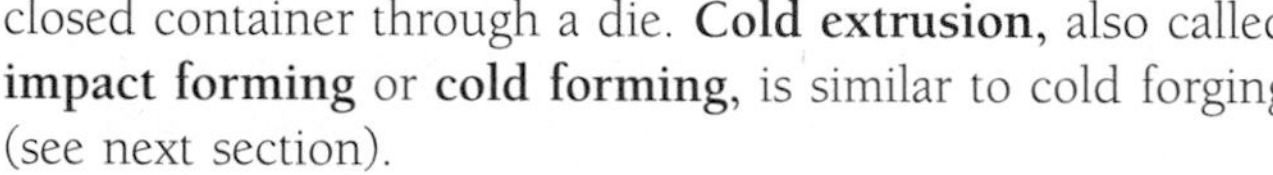

closed container through a die. **Cold extrusion,** also called **impact forming** or **cold forming,** is similar to cold forging (see next section).

Hot extrusion is a way to make long and irregular-shaped parts. The billets and slugs are heated above their critical temperature, placed on a press, and squeezed through a die into the required shape. Figure 14.34(a) shows aluminum extrusions designed to fit together in an interlocking assembly [Fig. 14.34(b)].

In **drop forging,** the hot metal is forced into dies by means of drop hammers. The material itself is very hot, but not molten, and is forced into the die by pounding. This pounding force pushes the metal into the shape of the cavity of the die, but does not create a very accurate part. Tolerances are large for this process, and the dies are expensive; however, forging produces stronger parts than many manufacturing processes. Low-carbon and low-alloy steels and aluminum alloys are the most common materials.

14.5.3 Forging

Forging utilizes impact and pressure to form parts. Types include smith forging, upset forging, and drop forging. A forging is a metal part shaped to its desired form by hammering, pressing, or upsetting. The metal is usually heated to an elevated temperature. Forging without heat is known as **cold forging.** A forging drawing is shown in Figure 14.35.

14.5.4 Stamping

In **stamping,** a punch and a die are used to cut or form sheet material. The assembled tool is called a die, as is the cutting part of the tool. **Progressive dies** require that several operations take place in sequential order. Stamping includes cutting, parting, blanking, punching, piercing, perforating, trimming, slitting, shaving, forming, bending, coining, embossing, and drawing.

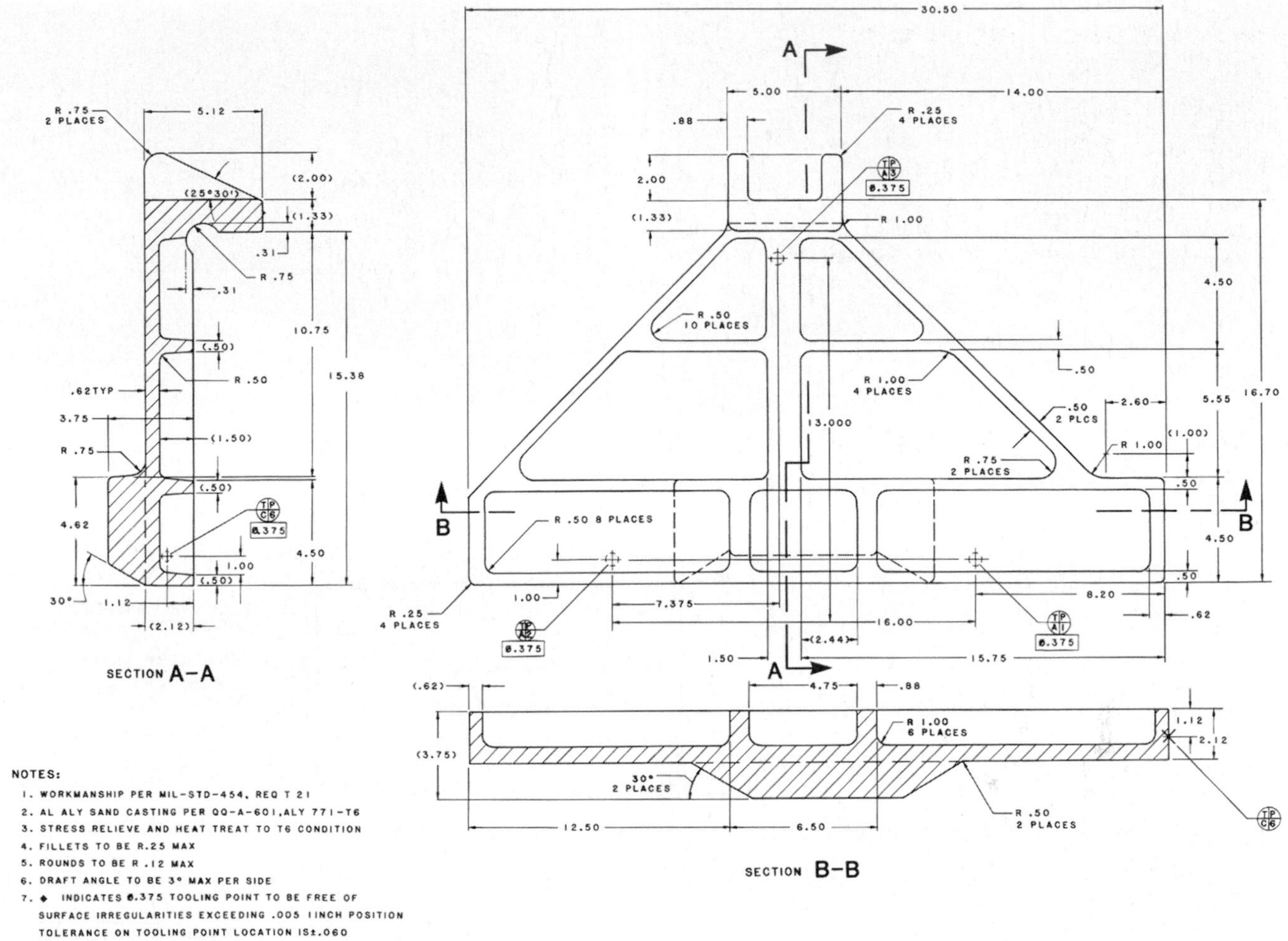

SECTION A–A
SECTION B–B
NOTES:
1. WORKMANSHIP PER MIL-STD-454, REQ T 21
2. AL ALY SAND CASTING PER QQ-A-601,ALY 771-T6
3. STRESS RELIEVE AND HEAT TREAT TO T6 CONDITION
4. FILLETS TO BE R.25 MAX
5. ROUNDS TO BE R .12 MAX
6. DRAFT ANGLE TO BE 3° MAX PER SIDE
7. ◆ INDICATES ⌀.375 TOOLING POINT TO BE FREE OF SURFACE IRREGULARITIES EXCEEDING .005 INCH POSITION TOLERANCE ON TOOLING POINT LOCATION IS±.060

FIGURE 14.31 Casting Detail for Adapter

The part in Figure 14.36 was made by a progressive stamp that uses dies to cut or form the metal sheets into the desired form. Dies are assemblies that include a housing and the cutter.

14.5.5 Punching

Punching operations include shearing, cutting off, and blanking. **Shearing** is done along a straight line on a part. **Cutting** is performed on a part so as to produce an edge other than a straight edge. **Blanking** produces parts with a

Round
Fillet
Round
Round
Fillet
Round

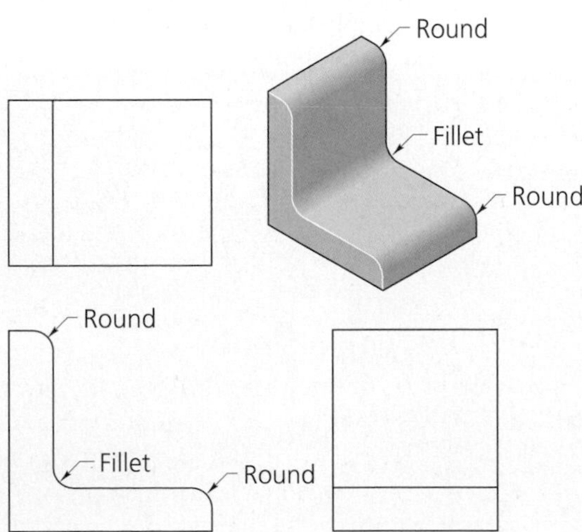

FIGURE 14.32 Fillets and Rounds

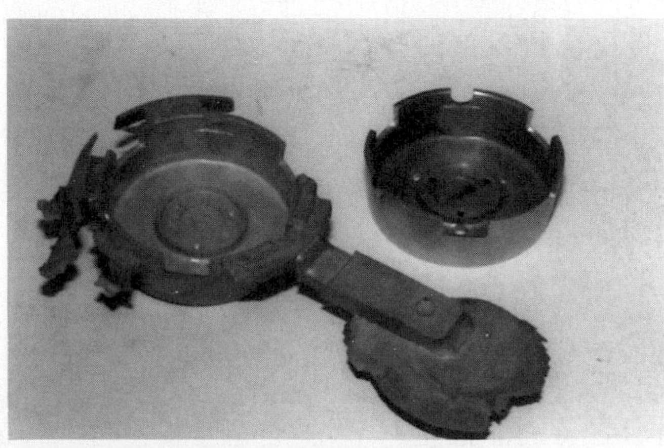

FIGURE 14.33 Injection Mold and Part

(a) Extruded shapes

(b) Assembled extrusions

FIGURE 14.34 Extrusions

FIGURE 14.35 Forging Drawing

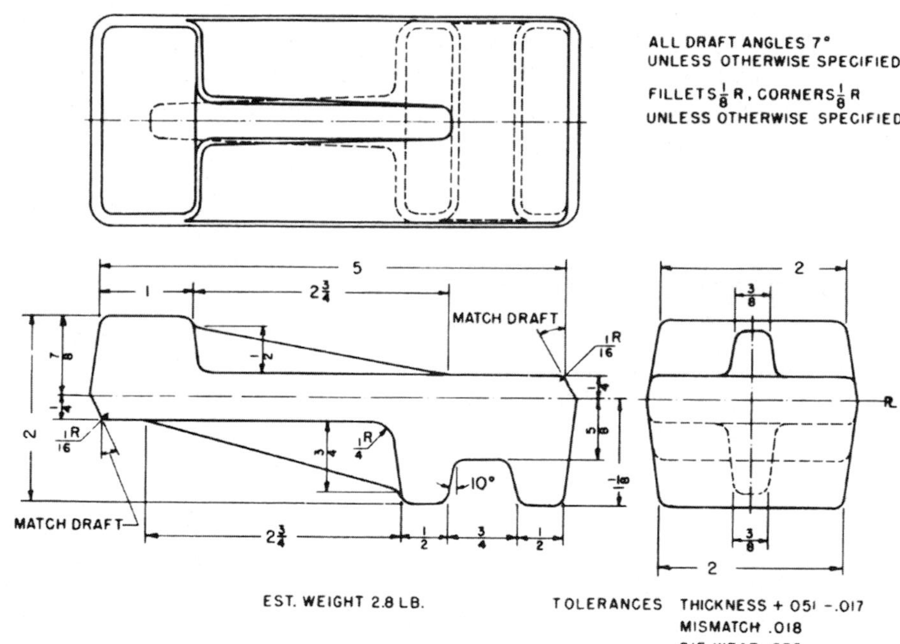

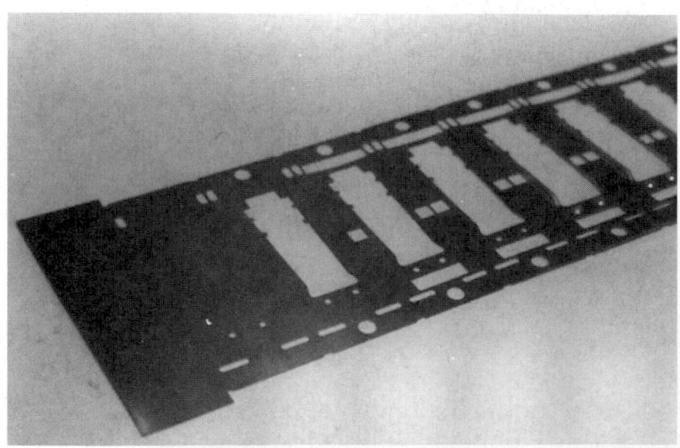

(a) Stamped part

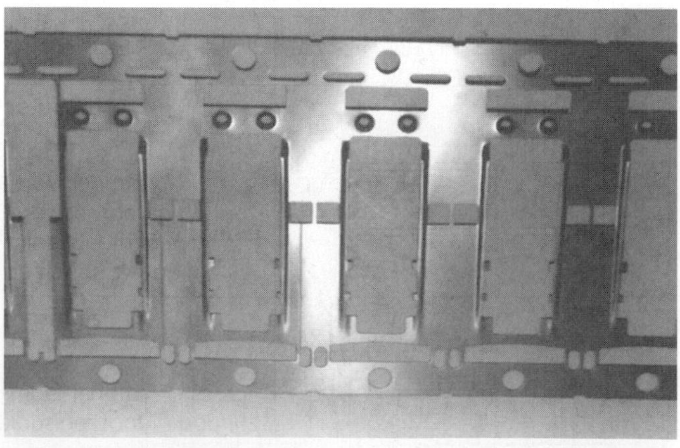

(b) Progressive stamping

FIGURE 14.36 Stamps

punch and a die. Holes are also produced in thin sheets of material by punching. **Piercing** is similar to punching, except that no scrap is produced. **Perforating** is a stamping operation performed on sheets to produce a hole pattern or decoration.

14.5.6 Electrical Discharge Machining and Electrochemical Machining (ECM)

Electrical discharge machining (EDM) is machining by removing small particles of metal via an electric spark. The material is vaporized by exposing the metal to sparks from a shaped electrode. The electrical discharge machine is a vertical-spindle milling machine with a rectangular tank on the worktable. The table can be moved along the **X** and **Y** axes, or it can be numerically controlled. Originally, EDM was used as a rough method for removing metal. EDM has been refined to do precision work in the electronics, aerospace, and tool-making industries.

Electrochemical machining (ECM) has many of the same machining capabilities as EDM, but will machine a part much faster. ECM requires more electricity and is more expensive. This process uses electrolyte fluid and electric current to ionize and remove metal from the part.

14.6 HEAT TREATMENT

Heat treatment is the process of applying heat to a material to change the material's properties but not its shape or size (Fig. 14.37). Heat treatment can increase a part's strength and hardness, improve its ductility, change the grain size and chemical composition, and improve its machinability. Heat treatment also is used to relieve stresses, harden a part, and modify the electrical and magnetic properties of the material.

FIGURE 14.37 Heat Treatment of Gear Blanks

Heating metal to just above its upper critical temperature for a specified period of time followed by controlled slow cooling in the furnace is called **annealing.** This results in a fully softened, stress-free part. Heating the metal to just below the lower critical temperature and then cooling it by a predetermined method is called **process annealing.** Process annealing is often used on metals that have been work-hardened. Process annealing softens the metal for further cold work.

Heating metal to above its lower critical temperature and then **quenching** it in water, oil, or air is called **hardening.** The resulting hardness is tested with the Rockwell Hardness Test. The **Rockwell Hardness Number** refers to the hardness of the steel. Although there are many different hardness scales, for steel the higher the number the harder it is.

Tempering, also called **drawing,** involves reheating hardened steel to a predetermined temperature below its lower critical temperature and then cooling it at a specified rate. Tempering removes brittleness and toughens the steel (**tempered martensite**).

Heating steel to just below the upper critical temperature and then cooling the material in air is called **normalizing.** This improves the grain structure and removes the stresses. **Lower critical temperature** is the lowest temperature at which steel may be quenched to harden it. **Upper critical temperature** is the highest temperature at which steel can be quenched to attain the finest grain structure and the maximum hardness (martensite). In a drawing, heat treatment requirements are typically listed in notes or in the title block.

Heat treatment is normally applied after the part has been machined, welded, or forged. To avoid problems during machining and heat treatment, consider doing the following during the design stage: Balance the areas of mass, avoid sharp corners and internal recesses, and keep hubs of gears, pulleys, and cutters a consistent thickness.

14.7 AUTOMATED MANUFACTURING PROCESSES

Automated manufacturing techniques are used throughout industry. The role of CAM in a CAD/CAM environment includes helping firms achieve the benefits of **computer-integrated manufacturing (CIM)**. The CIM concept encompasses manufacturing and computer-based automation applications. CIM can be thought of as a system whose primary inputs are product requirements, and whose outputs are finished products. CIM comprises a combination of software and hardware for product design, for production planning/control, and for production processes.

CAD/CAM is the CIM integrator for computer-based

Applying Parametric Design . . .

PARAMETRIC MODELS AND MACHINING

Pro/MANUFACTURING (Fig. A) is a module for Pro/ENGINEER that provides the tools to simulate numerical control manufacturing processes. Information created can be updated quickly should the engineering design model change. Capabilities from Pro/MANUFACTURING include NC programs in the form of ASCII CL data files, tool lists, operation reports, and in-process geometry.

Pro/MANUFACTURING will create the data necessary to drive an NC machine tool to machine a part. It lets the manufacturing engineer follow a logical sequence of steps to progress into NC machine data.

The **design model** (Fig. B), representing the finished product, becomes the basis for all manufacturing operations (features, surfaces, and edges are selected on the design model as references for each manufacturing operation). Referencing the geometry of the design model sets up a parametric relationship between the design model and the workpiece. Because of this relationship, when the design model is changed, all associated manufacturing operations are updated to reflect the change. Multiple-part machining is possible through such capabilities as nesting the part in the workpiece (Fig. C).

FIGURE A Pro/MANUFACTURING

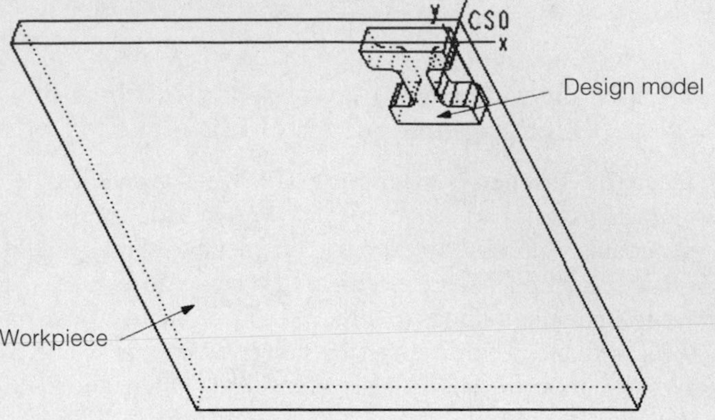

FIGURE B Design Model and Workpiece

The **workpiece** (Fig. D) represents the raw stock that is going to be machined by the manufacturing operations. It can be any form of raw stock: bar stock, casting, etc. It can easily be created by copying the design model and modifying the dimensions or deleting or suppressing features to represent the real workpiece.

A regular **manufacturing model** consists of a design model (also called *reference part,* since it is a reference for creating NC sequences) and a workpiece assembled together. As the manufacturing process is developed, the material removal simulation can be performed on the workpiece (Fig. E). Generally, at the end of the manufacturing process the workpiece geometry should be coincident with the geometry of the design model. However, material removal is an optional step. The Pro/MANUFACTURING process consists of the following steps.

1. Set Up the Process Environment.

The setup may contain the following components:

- Operation name
- Workcell (machine tool)

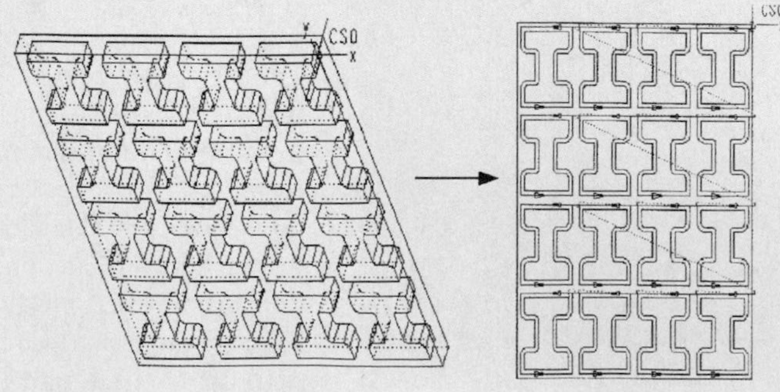

FIGURE C Nesting the Design Model in the Workpiece of Multiple-Part Machining

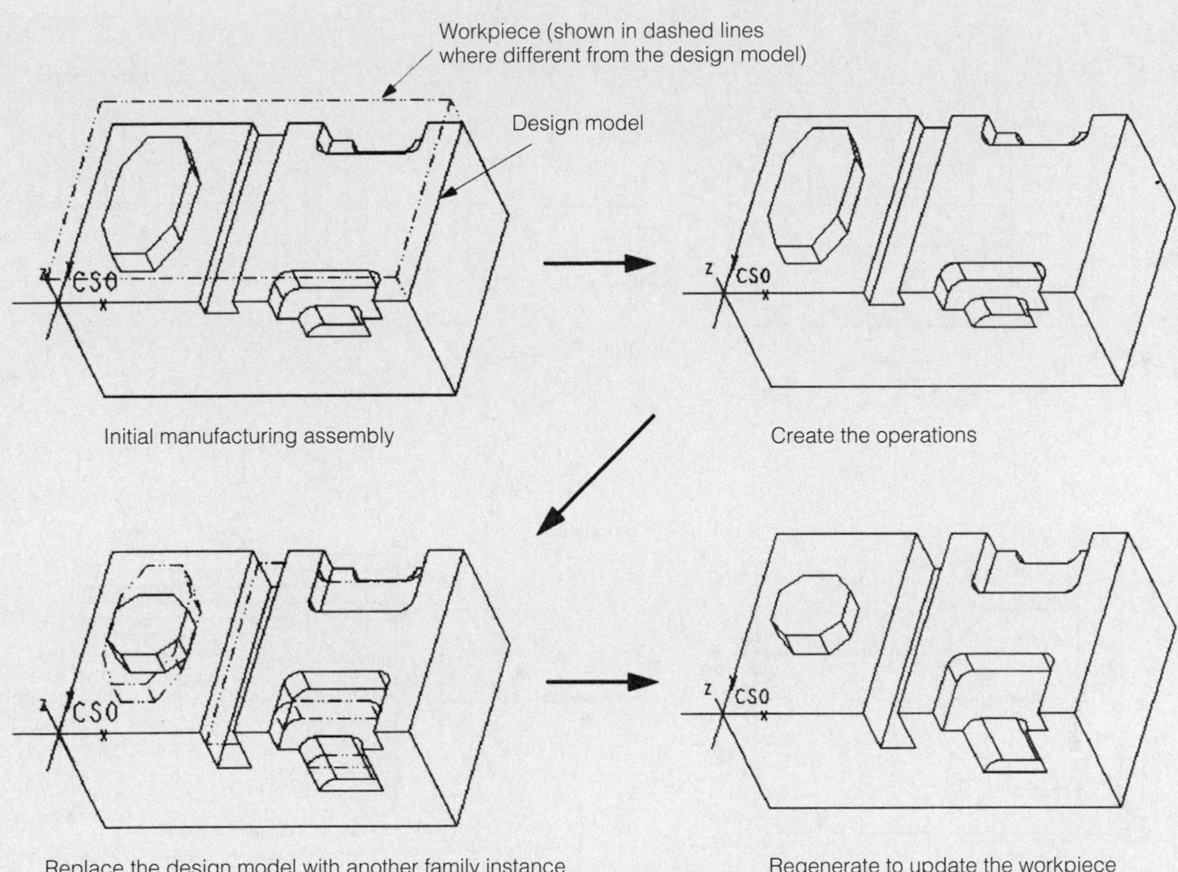

FIGURE D Workpiece and Manufacturing Assembly

- Fixture configuration
- Site parameters
- Tool to be used
- Coordinate system for CL output
- Retract plan, if applicable, i.e., the plane to which the tool is retracted after a cut

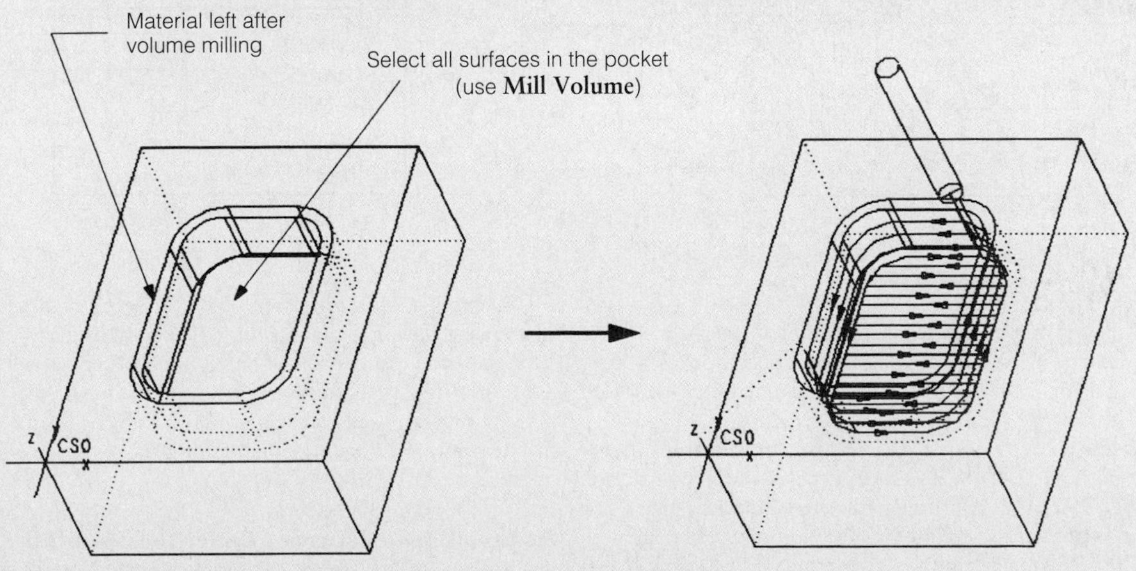

FIGURE E Volume Milling, Material Removal, and Cutter Path Generation *(Continued)*

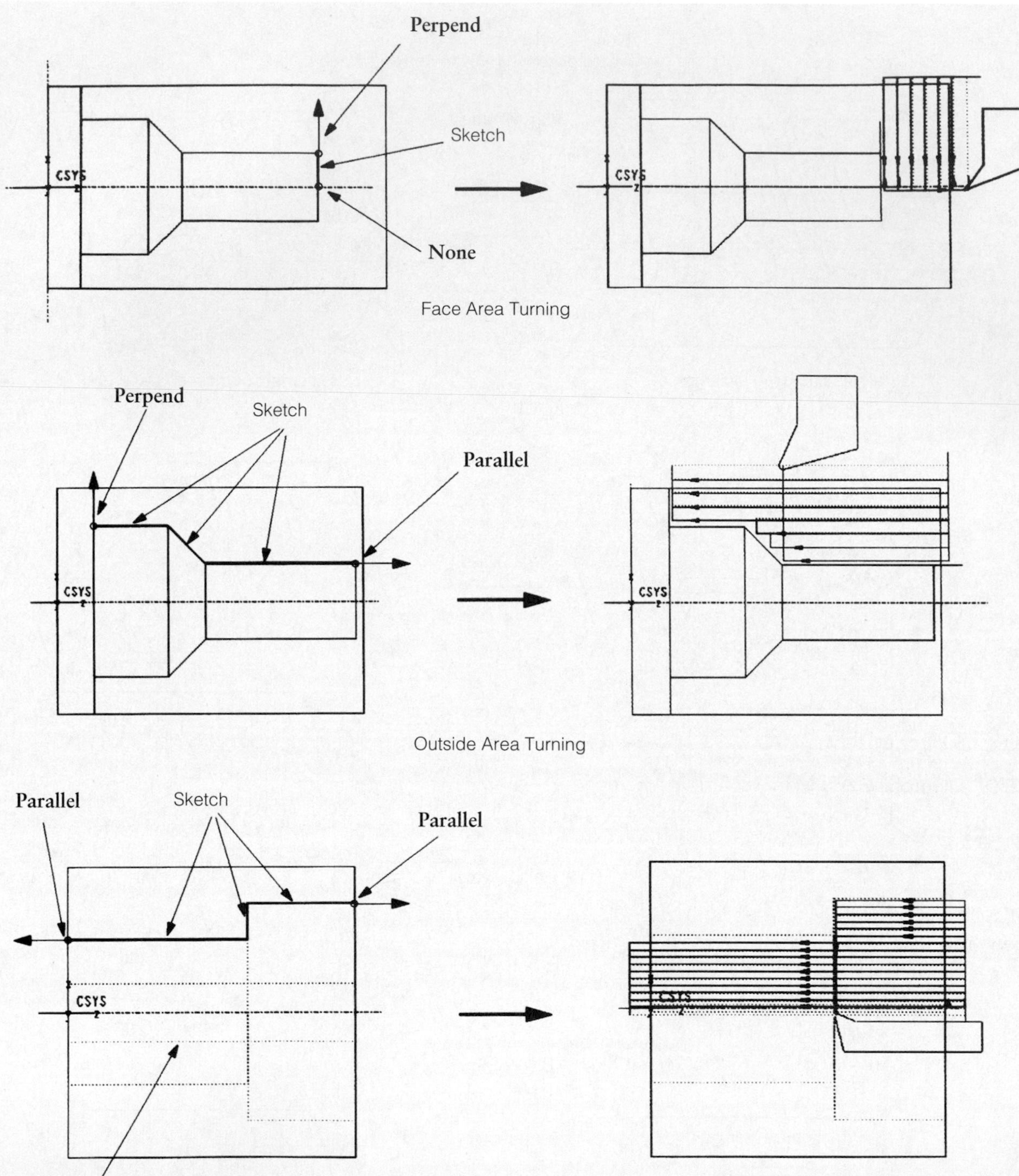

FIGURE F Turning Operations

You have to define an operation name and a workcell before you can start creating NC sequences. Other setup components are either optional or can be specified when creating the NC sequence.

A **workcell** is a workpiece (or assembly) feature that specifies a machine tool via its name, type, set of parameters, and associated tools. The workcell type determines the types of NC sequences that can be created with it [four-axis lathe allows you to perform two- and four-axis turning (Fig. F) and hole making].

Fixtures are parts or assemblies that help orient and hold the workpiece during a manufacturing operation. They can be created and saved in Part or Assembly mode, and retrieved into the Manufacturing mode during fixture setup. Creating the fixture in Assembly mode is advantageous, since fixtures can be created as needed during the intermediate process steps by referencing the workpiece.

2. Create NC Sequences Under the Specified Setup. Each NC sequence is a series of tool motions with the addition of specific postprocessor words that are not motion-related but

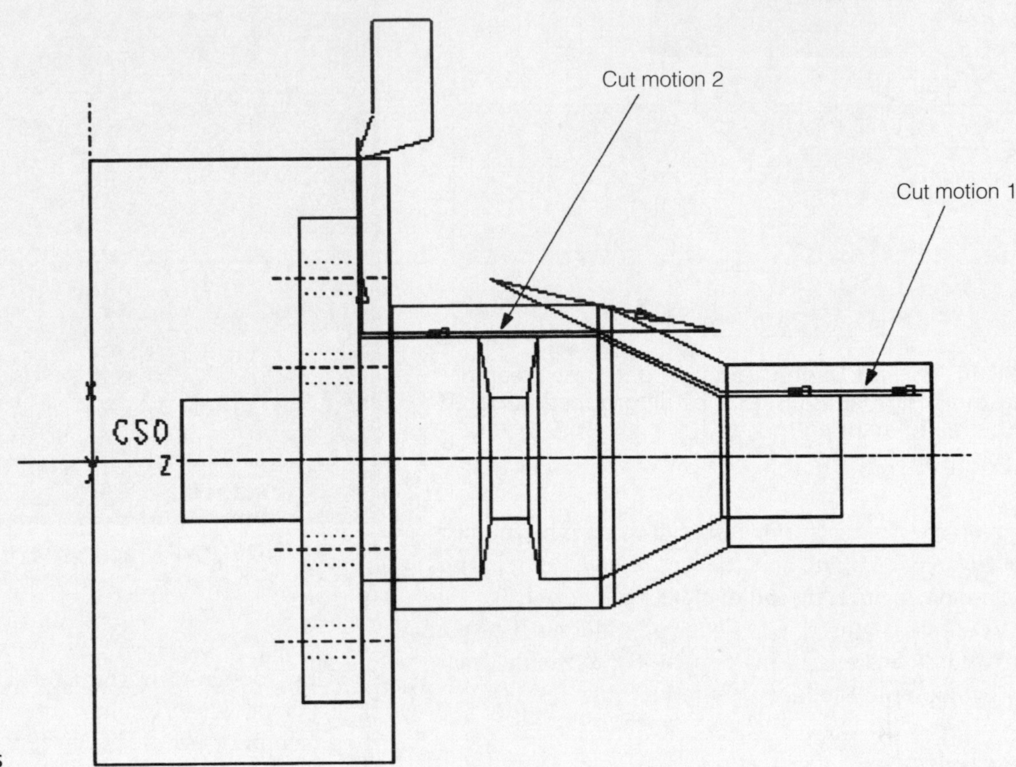

FIGURE G Cut Motions

are required for the correct NC output. **Tool motions** are generated automatically by the system, based on the NC sequence type (e.g., volume milling, outside turning), cut geometry, and manufacturing parameters (Fig. G).

For each completed NC sequence, you can create a material removal feature, either by making the system remove material automatically (where applicable) or by manually constructing a regular feature on the workpiece (slot, hole, etc.).

The **interactive path control** controls the motion of the tool when creating or redefining NC sequences (Fig. H). You can use it if you are not satisfied with the tool path generated automatically by the system. Pro/MANUFACTURING provides two forms of interactive path control:

Cut Motion—Generate the cut motions, i.e., the path followed by the tool while actually cutting work material

Build Path—Finalize the tool path by specifying which cut motions to follow, defining approach and exit motions, and inserting CL commands

Cut motions depend on the type of the NC sequence. Generally, cut motions are generated automatically by the system, based on the cut geometry and the manufacturing parameters. The **Cut Motion** option in the NC SEQUENCE menu provides low-level control over cut motions.

For most NC sequences, you can either accept the cut motions generated automatically by the system or generate your own. For trajectory milling, profile turning (see Fig. H), and 2D contouring (wire EDM, laser, etc.), you have to apply interactive cut motion control. Automatic cut motions are described in appropriate NC sequence sections.

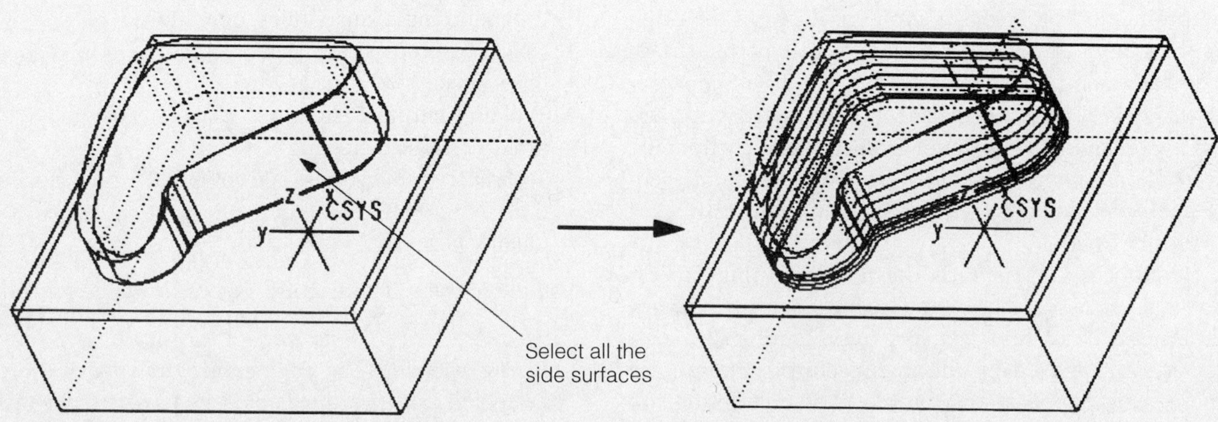

FIGURE H Profile Cutting and Path Generation

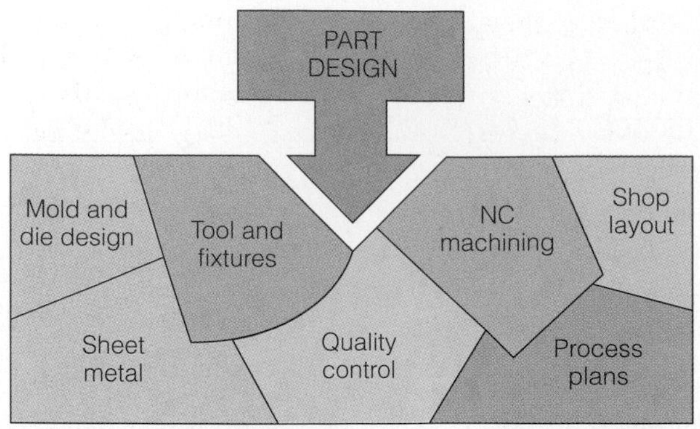

FIGURE 14.38 Part Design. The part database created during the design phase is used by all groups associated with the manufacturing process.

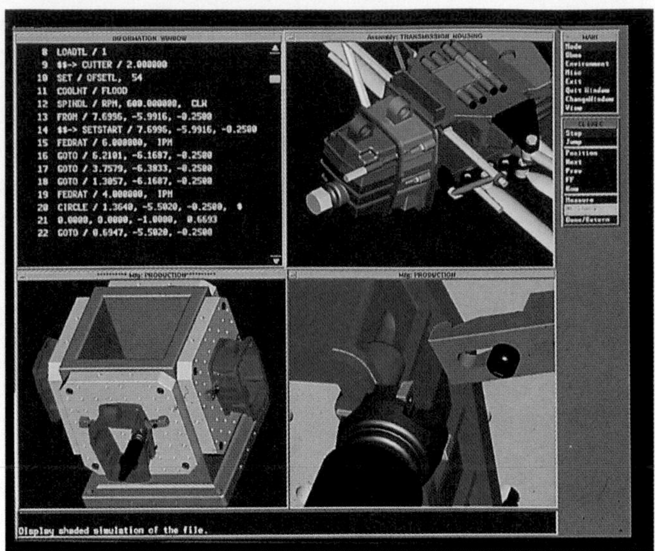

FIGURE 14.39 On-Screen Setup of Part Machining

applications in manufacturing, especially computer numerical control programming and robotics. CAD/CAM depends on a common engineering and manufacturing database. This database allows engineering to define a product model (part design) and the manufacturing department to use that same model definition to produce the product (Fig. 14.38).

14.7.1 Computer-Aided Manufacturing (CAM)

Computer-aided design uses a computer to help create or modify a design. *Computer-aided manufacturing (CAM) uses a computer to manage and control the operations of a manufacturing facility.* CAM includes computer numerical control (CNC) for machining operations, tool and fixture design and setup, and integration of industrial robots into the manufacturing process. The integration of computer-aided design and computer-aided manufacturing eliminates duplication of effort by the engineering/design and manufacturing or production departments. An engineering drawing created on a graphics terminal defines the product geometry, which otherwise must be manually derived from the drawing by the manufacturing department before the product is produced.

The production process is computerized, from the original graphics input through to the manufacture of the part on a numerically controlled machine (Fig. 14.39). Shop production drawings have been entirely eliminated with this process. By obtaining the product geometry directly from the engineering data, the programmer can extract accurate geometric data, replicating the engineer's definition of the part to be manufactured.

As mentioned, CAM speeds the manufacturing process because it uses the database initially created in the design-and-drafting cycle. This database, representing the part (model) design, is used by the manufacturing group. The system serves all applications, promotes standardization to enhance management control, accumulates (rather than randomly collecting) manufacturing information, and reduces redundancy and error.

Many design-through-manufacture processes require skilled labor, which is, and probably will continue to be, in short supply. One of the major goals of the CAD/CAM system is to transfer the experience and skills of a few individuals to the database. This provides less experienced personnel with access to technical information. Design for manufacturability usually simplifies the part design and the manufacturing requirements for production of the part, thereby reducing the level of skilled labor required to produce the product.

Using a CAD/CAM system, the engineer or designer applies the CAD features to create a model of the part. Then, using the information stored in the database, the manufacturing engineer applies the CAM capabilities. A CAD system may have a variety of specialized CAM capabilities, including the following:

- Group technology
- Process planning
- Shop layout
- Programming of machining operations
- CNC postprocessing
- Sheet metal applications
- Tool and fixture design
- Mold design and testing
- Technical publications and manufacturing documentation
- Quality control

Computer-aided manufacturing goes through, the following steps:

1. *Process planning:* The engineering drawing of the part to be tooled must be interpreted in terms of the manufacturing processes to be employed. This step should be given thought and consideration *before* part programming is begun.

2. *Part programming:* Part programmers plan the process for the portions of the job to be accomplished by computer numerical control. They are knowledgeable about the machining process, and they have been trained to program for computer numerical control. They are responsible for planning the sequence of machining steps to be performed by CNC and to document these in a special format. There are two ways to program for CNC: manual part programming and computer-assisted part programming.

   In **manual part programming,** the machining instructions are prepared on a form called a *part program manuscript.* This is a listing of the relative cutter positions that must be followed to machine the part. In **computer-assisted part programming,** much of the computational work required in manual part programming is transferred to the computer. This is especially advantageous for complex part geometries and jobs with many machining steps. In computer-assisted part programming, the computer interprets the list of part programming instructions, performs the necessary calculations to convert this into a detailed set of machine tool motion commands, and develops a chosen transfer medium containing the CNC data for the specific CNC machine.
3. *Verification:* The program is checked by plotting the tool movements on paper. In this way, errors in the program can be discovered. The test of the part program is making a trial part on the machine tool. A foam or plastic material is sometimes used for this test. CAD systems with CAD/CAM capabilities allow verification of toolpaths and cutter motion on the display
4. *Transfer media preparation:* Originally, punched tape was the medium for transferring a part program from the computer to an NC machine. Disks, minidisks, and direct computer networks are now the preferred transfer media.
5. *Production:* Production involves ordering the rough parts, specifying and preparing the tooling and any special fixturing that may be required, and setting up the CNC machine. The machine tool operator's function during production is to load the data into the machine and to establish the starting position of the cutting tool relative to the rough part. The CNC system then machines the part according to the programmed instructions. When the part is completed, the operator removes it from the machine and loads the next part. In more automated operations, a programmable robot performs these tasks in conjunction with computer control instead of an operator.

14.7.2 Numerical Control

Numerical control (NC) can be defined as a form of programmable automation in which the process is controlled by numbers, letters, and symbols. In NC, the numbers form a program of instructions designed for a particular part or job. When the job changes, the program of instructions is changed. This capability to change the program for each new job gives NC its flexibility. It is much easier to write new programs than to make major changes in the production equipment.

Programming an NC machine requires a good working knowledge of machine tools, tool design, print reading, and manufacturing processes. Figure 14.40 shows a part dimensioned for ease of NC programming. Each hole and edge has a dimension taken from the **X0,Y0,Z0** position of the piece, which in this case is in the lower right-hand corner. The **X0,Y0,Z0** position is established according to the machine and the part configuration and machining requirements.

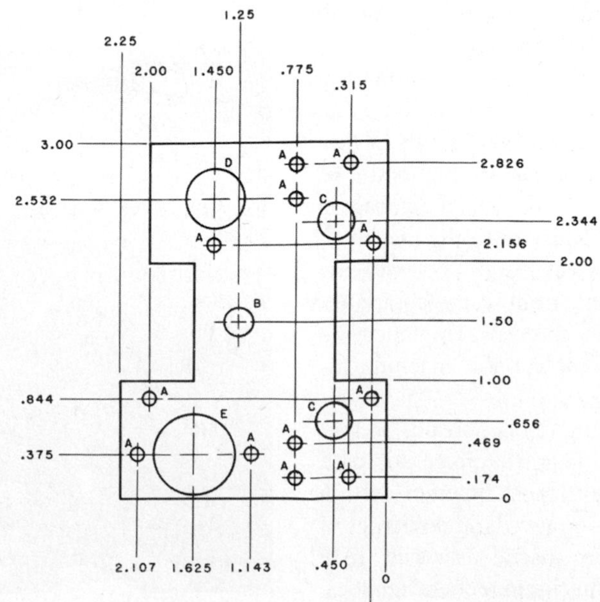

HOLE	DESCRIPTION	QTY
A	.125 DIA	12
B	.250 DIA	1
C	.312 DIA	2
D	.500 DIA	1
E	.688 DIA	1

FIGURE 14.40 Connector Plate Dimensioned for NC Programming

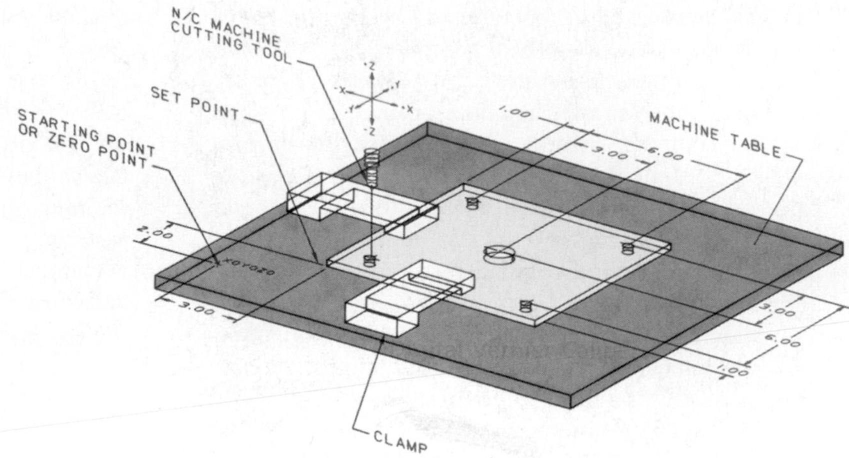

FIGURE 14.41 CNC Part Setup

Figure 14.41 shows the machining table, the part, and the clamps holding the part. The starting point is **X0,Y0,Z0.** Note the 3D coordinate system shown at the top of the cutting tool.

The two major types of NC machines in use today are point-to-point and continuous-path machines. The movement of the tool in reference to the workpiece establishes the difference between the two. **Point-to-point** machines operate on a series of programmed coordinates to locate the position of the tool. When the tool finishes at one point, it continues to the next point (position). This type of control is typical of drilling and punching machines. Milling machines require continuous control of tool position and therefore use a **continuous path.** Complicated operations, including contouring, angle surfaces, fillets, and radii, can be programmed by the continuous-path method. The **toolpath** can be displayed on the CAD/CAM system, thereby verifying the cutter's movement without running an actual part on the machine. The toolpath is the trace of the movement of the tip of a cutting tool used to guide or control machining equipment.

Computer numerical control (CNC) is eliminating the older form of programming. When the program is complete, repetitive productions are accomplished by controls having memory of the part in the computer system. Figure 14.42 shows a CNC turning center. In CNC, the design database is passed directly form the CAD/CAM system to the machine's computer. The description of the part developed with the computer-aided design system is the input to the computer-aided manufacturing system, which in turn commands the machine tool postprocessor to complete the machine instructions.

The programmer defines cutting tools, creates a tool library, and retrieves these tools later to create toolpath information. CAM packages support most types of cutting tools; therefore, the programmer can describe many types of cutting tools (flat, ball, tapered) in general use. The CAM system allows for definition of machining characteristics, such as retract and clearance plane, cutting depth, feed rate (rate of travel), and spindle speed (rate of spindle rotation). Figure 14.43 shows a sequence of design, analysis, simulation, and manufacturing for a spindle. The menu shown in Figure 14.43(a) helps manage the engineering data needed to model and test the part. The solid model of Figure 14.43(b) assists the designer in creating, analyzing, and visually displaying the part. In Figure 14.43(c), **cutter paths** for CNC machining are defined and modified by the part programmer. In Figure 14.43(d), output from the postprocessor is then utilized for machining the actual part. As a last step, the finished assembly can be displayed and reviewed, as shown in Figure 14.43(e).

14.7.3 Machining Operations

A variety of machining operations are possible, from simple two-axis point-to-point functions to complex multiaxis machining. These operations may include drilling, punching, milling, turning, profiling, pocketing, surface machining,

FIGURE 14.42 CNC Machining

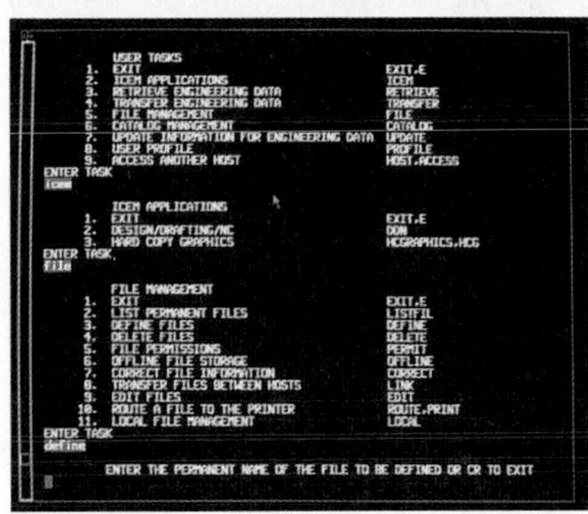

(a) Task menu from Control Data's ICEM engineering library

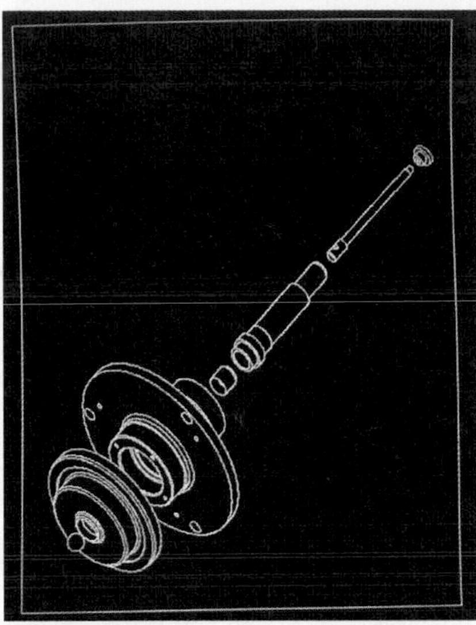

(b) The solid model can be rotated, exploded, and viewed from any angle

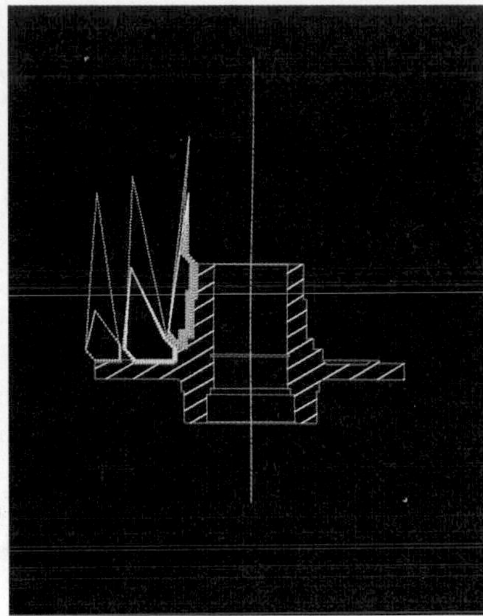

(c) Cutter paths for numerical control machining can be defined and modified at the CAD terminal

(d) Numerical output can be utilized for CNC machining of the actual part

(e) Finished assembly review

FIGURE 14.43 On-Screen Programming

and flame cutting. The types of parts that may be produced on CNC equipment from output generated by CAD/CAM systems include:

- Irregular or uniquely machined parts [Fig.14.44(a)]
- 2D parts created by point-to-point operations
- Parts produced by turning operations
- $2\frac{1}{2}$D parts, which may require pocketing and profiling operations (Fig. 14.44(b)]
- 3D parts produced by using all of the CNC operations provided on the CAD/CAM system [Fig. 14.44(c) and (d)]

Pocketing involves completely removing material within a bounded area (Fig. 14.45). Machine pocket programs provide automatic pocketing on a CAD system by generating a toolpath to remove the material contained within a closed boundary. Capabilities include multiple-base **rough cutting** [Fig.14.45(a)], **multiple-side cutting** [Fig.14.45(b)], a designer-specified final **finishing pass**, and **islands** defined within a pocket [Fig. 14.45(c)].

Profiling is the automatic generation of a continuously contoured toolpath around a boundary (Figs. 14.46 and 14.47). The cutting tool moves outside or inside a profile. Capabilities include multiple-base rough cutting, multiple-side rough cutting, and a designer-specified final finishing pass.

14.7.4 Toolpath Simulation and Verification

CAD/CAM systems provide accurate and realistic verification of both 2D and 3D toolpaths without cutting metal. The programmer can simulate and visually verify the toolpath on

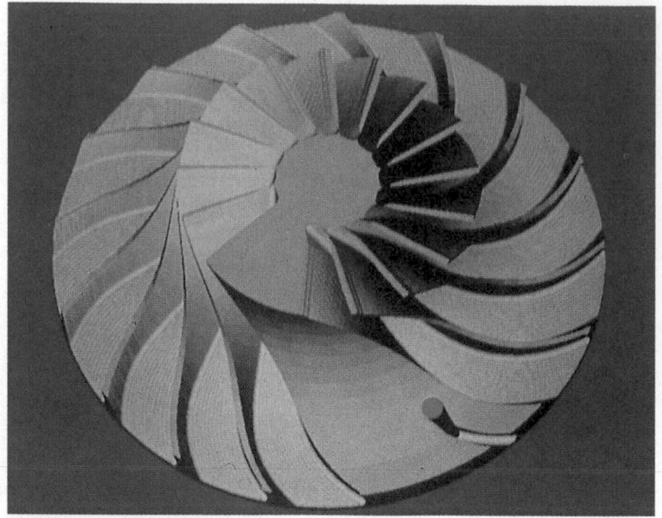

(a) Complex surfaces for a turbine blade

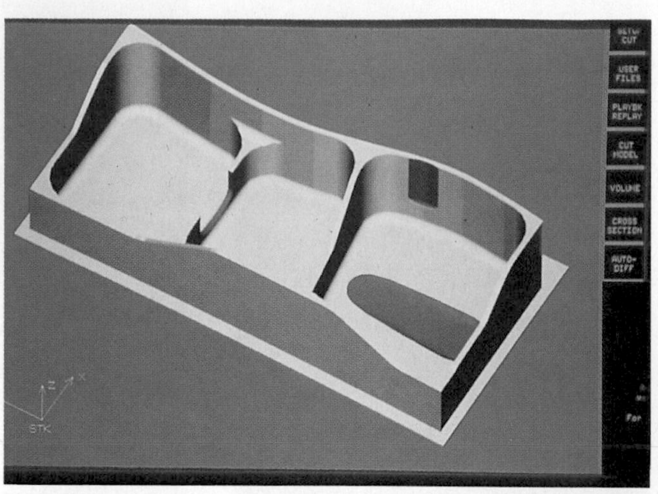

(b) Pocketing

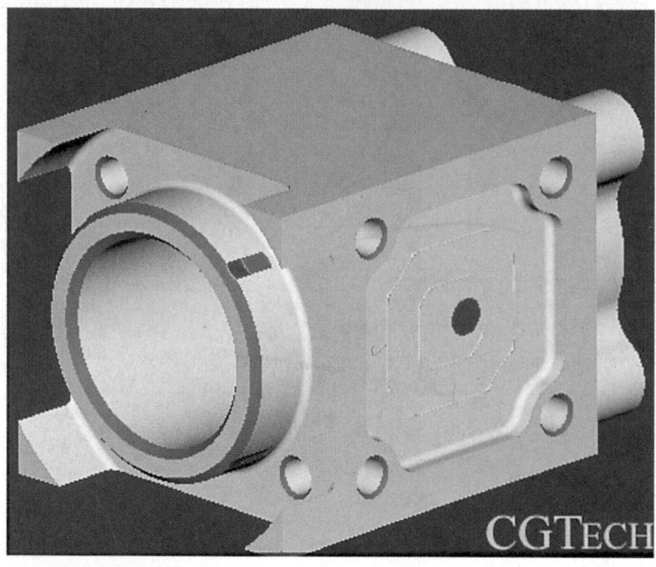

(c) Multiaxis machined part

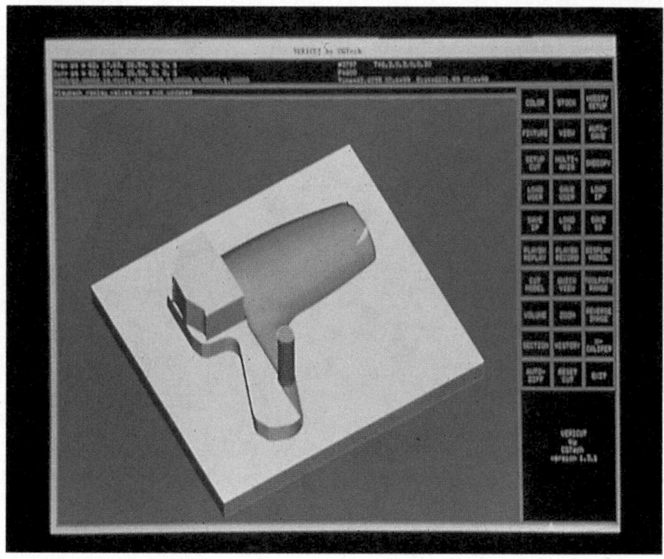

(d) Toolpath generation on a complex surface

FIGURE 14.44 Machined Parts

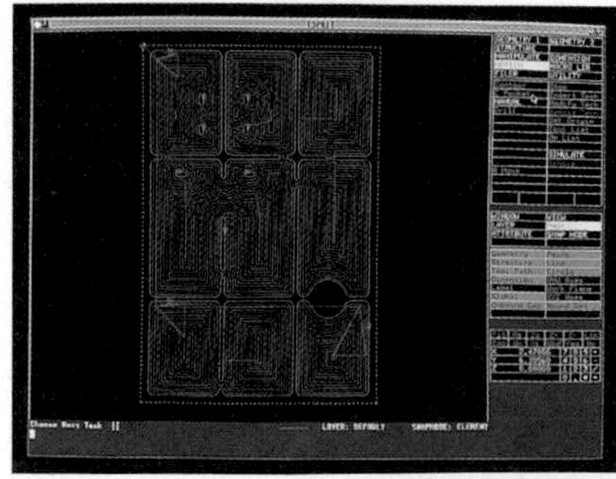

(a) Pocketing

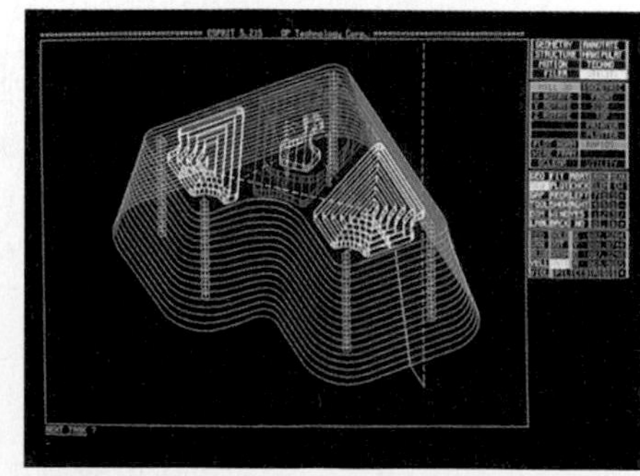

(b) Complex-surface machining

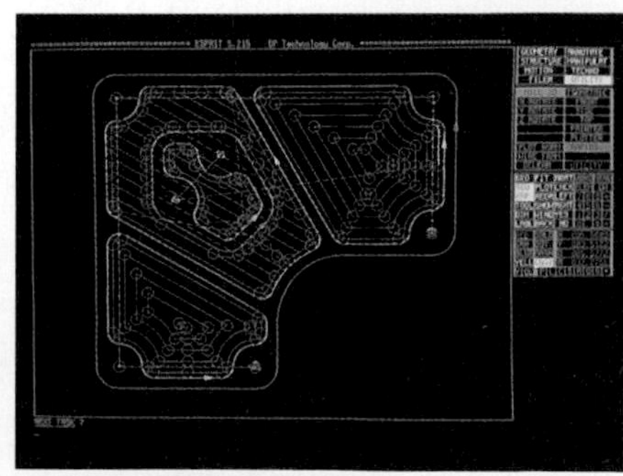

(c) Pocketing and islands

FIGURE 14.45 Toolpath Generation

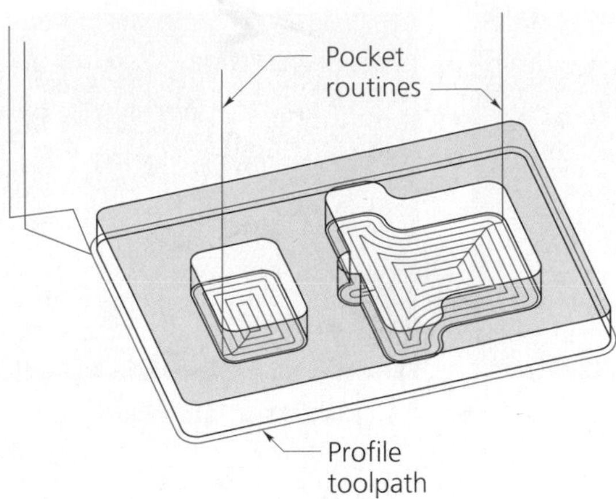

FIGURE 14.46 Toolpath Generation. A variety of toolpaths can be created, including profiling and pocketing.

the display (Fig. 14.48). The toolpath seen on the display may show the tool and holder actually moving along the part, from any viewing angle. This permits the designer to check for toolpath correctness and clearance of tools, parts, and fixtures. Once toolpaths are created, they may be edited and assembled into sets, machining statements may be added, and then toolpaths may be output to a specific machine. Toolpaths may also be transformed into a programming language, such as APT or COMPACT.

14.7.5 Tools, Fixtures, and Mold Design

In general, a tool is a piece of equipment that helps create a finished part. It may be anything that must be designed and/or made in order to manufacture the part. CAD systems may support the design and manufacture of the following tools.

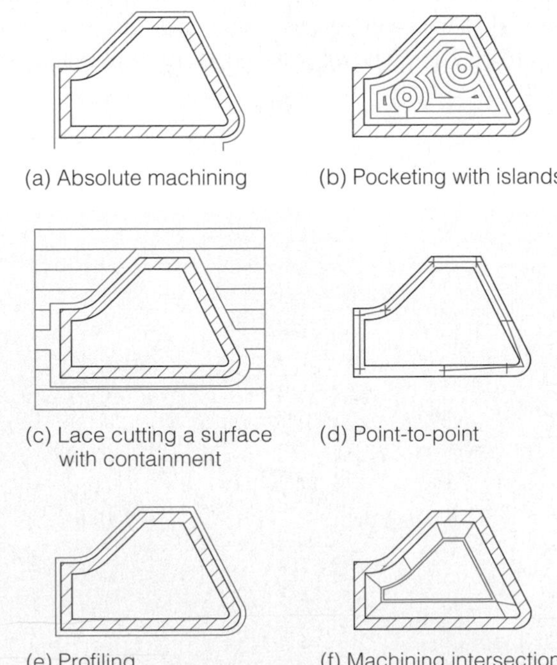

(a) Absolute machining (b) Pocketing with islands (c) Lace cutting a surface with containment (d) Point-to-point (e) Profiling (f) Machining intersections of surfaces

FIGURE 14.47 Toolpaths. Six examples of toolpath generation are shown.

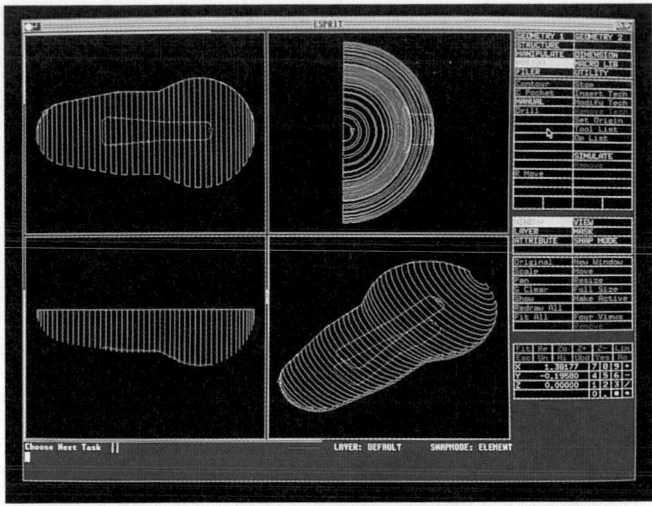

(a) Displaying a toolpath

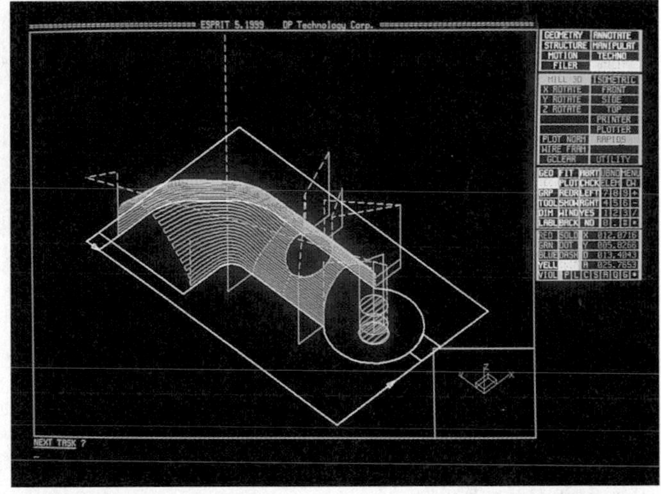

(b) Surface machining

FIGURE 14.48 On-Screen Toolpath Generation

Molds Used to form a variety of parts for consumer, industrial, and medical applications

Dies Used to forge, cast, extrude, and stamp materials while in various physical states (solid through fluid)

Tooling The individual component of mold or die; might include a cavity, nest, core, punch, bushing, slide, or sleeve

Figure 14.49(a) shows an example of mold design on a CAD system. The mold for the part being machined in (b) is shown complete in (c). Figure 14.50 shows a shoe designed and displayed on a CRT using a mesh model [(a)]. The mold was also designed on the system [(b)] and is being machined in (c).

Fixtures function to hold and locate parts of assemblies

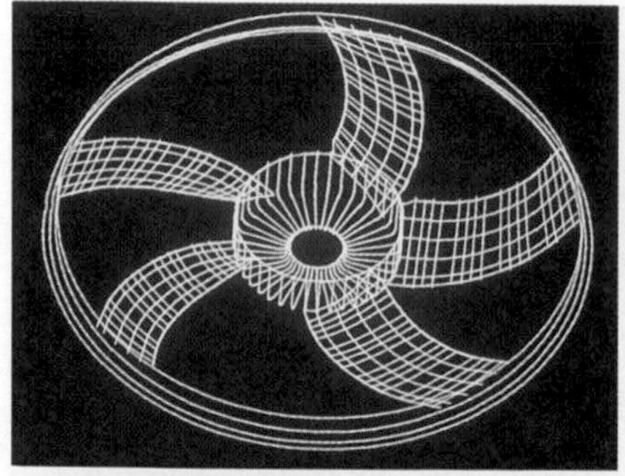

(a) Computer design of part

(b) Mold being machined

(c) Finished part and mold

FIGURE 14.49 Mold Design

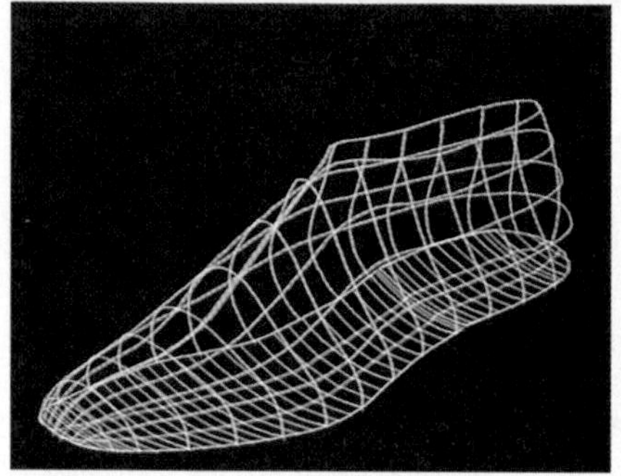

(a) Mesh model of a shoe design

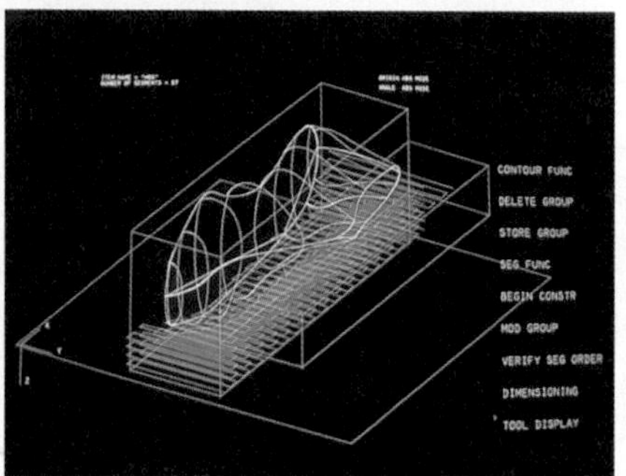

(b) Shoe mold design

(c) CNC machining of a shoe mold

FIGURE 14.50 Shoe Mold

during machining or other manufacturing operations (Fig. 14.51). The accuracy of the product being produced determines the precision with which a fixture is designed. To design and manufacture a finished part efficiently, product design engineers must work with tool and fixture designers as well as manufacturing engineers. CAD promotes this interaction by providing a common database for the product design and the associated tool/fixture design, manufacture, and production. When designing a tool or fixture, the manufacturing engineer retrieves the part design from the database to determine how the tool or fixture should be built to produce the finished product.

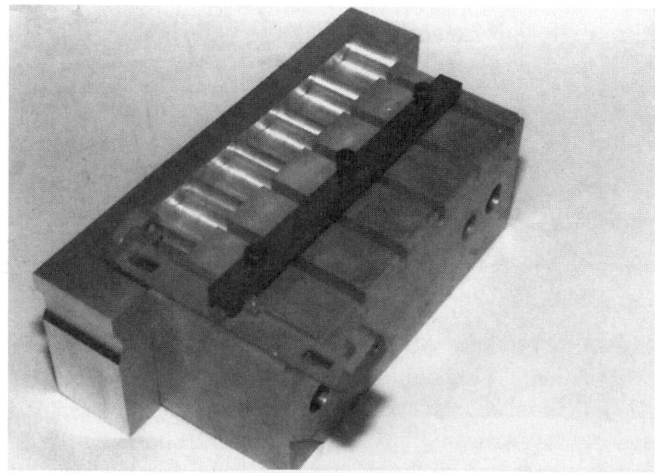

(a) Fixture for machining multiple parts

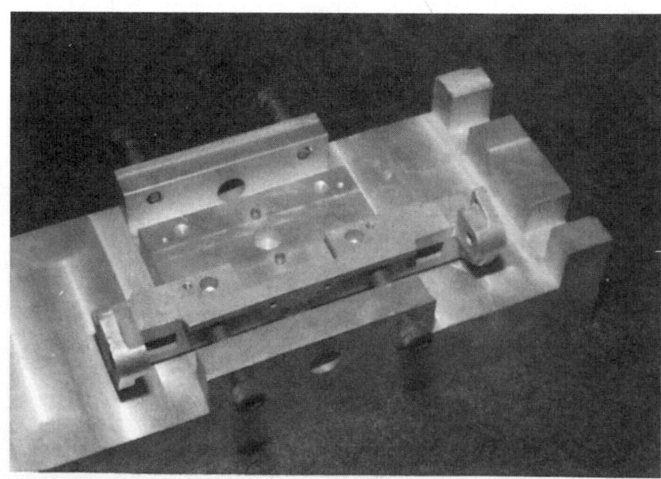

(b) Fixture for machining two parts

FIGURE 14.51 Fixtures

To determine the materials needed to produce a tool/fixture designed on the system, CAD can output a bill of materials for the purchasing department automatically. This lists quantities and associated information needed to manufacture the product(s). Process planners can then access the database to create process instructions and plans.

14.8 ROBOTICS

Robotics is the integration of computer-controlled robots into the manufacturing process. Industrial robots (Fig. 14.52) are used to move, manipulate, position, weld, machine, and do a variety of other manufacturing processes. A **robot** is a reprogrammable, multifunction manipulator designed to move material, parts (including the workpiece), tools, or specialized devices through variable, programmed motions for the performance of a variety of tasks. Robotics includes the control and synchronization of the equipment with which the robot works, a capability that can eliminate the need for humans to work in hazardous environments. Robots are controlled by a microprocessor and are composed of a separate, stand-alone computer station, the robot mechanism itself, and an electrical-hydraulic power unit.

The part workpiece being placed by the robot can be visualized on the screen via simulation (Fig. 14.53). To take fullest advantage of robotic control and movement of the workpiece during manufacturing, the designer needs to design the part with robotic manufacturing methods in mind—not after the fact. A 3D CAD database for the part allows this type of robotic programming before manufacturing begins. DFM includes part design, with robotic manu-

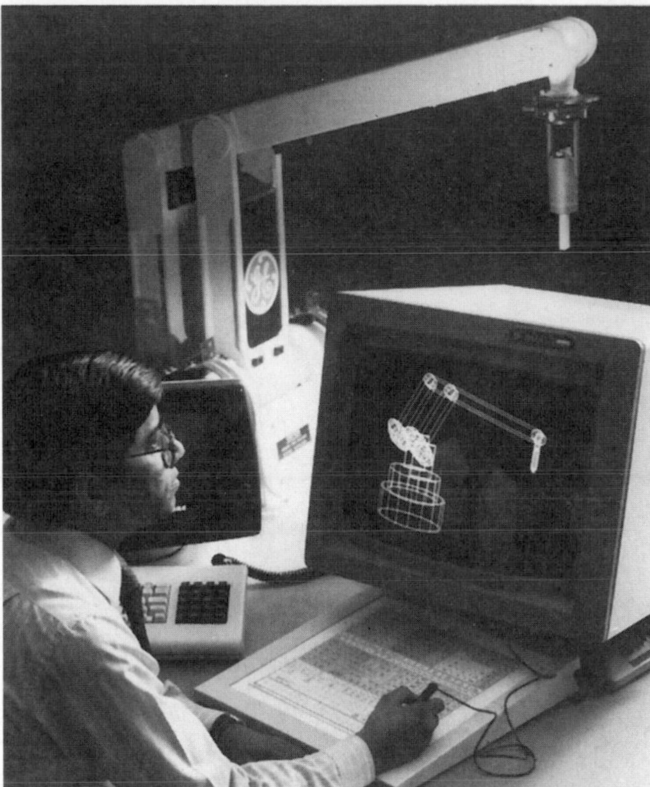

FIGURE 14.53 Robot Simulation. Robotics simulation program enables automation engineers to put a robot through its paces on the computer screen rather than via trial-and-error on the factory floor. You can design a factory workcell, simulate a robot's movements and performance in it, and then modify both the robot's movements and the surrounding machinery for optimal efficiency. This can be accomplished at the computer terminal, without employing any robotic hardware, material-handling devices, part-presentation equipment, or robot grippers.

(a) Cincinnati Milicron robot

(b) Control panel, gripper, and arm of robot

FIGURE 14.52 Industrial Robots

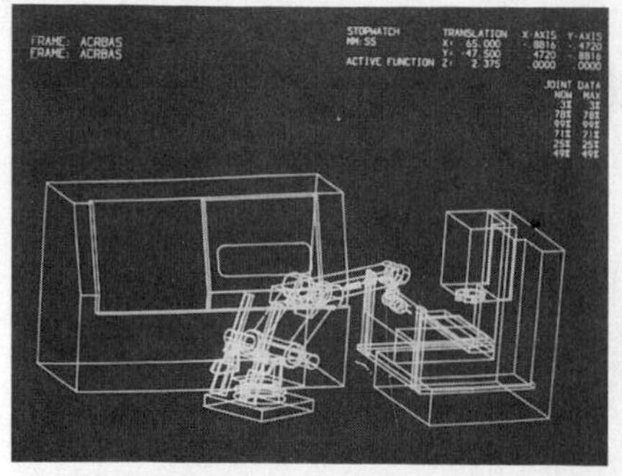
(a) Robot and related machinery workcell evaluation simulation shown on a display

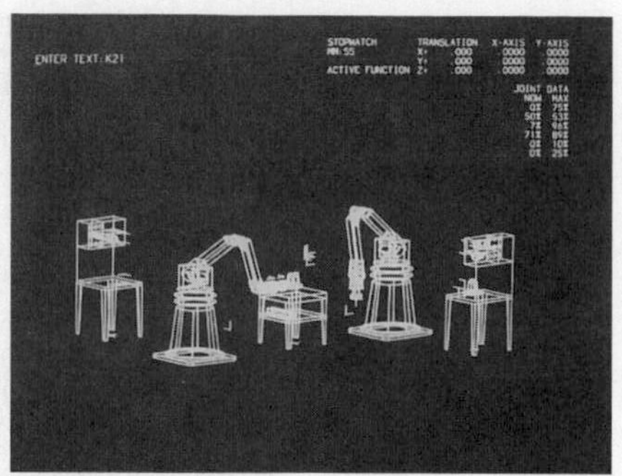
(b) Robotic workcell library

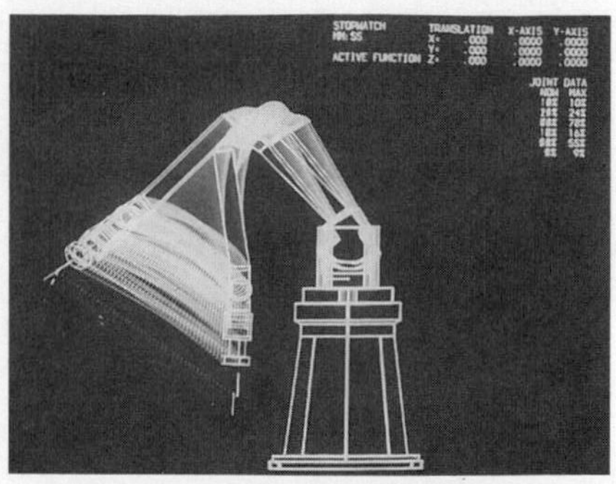
(c) Robot simulation of arm movement

FIGURE 14.54 Robotics

facturing techniques designed into the part at the earliest stages of the project.

14.8.1 CAD/CAM Robotic Applications

The integration of CAD/CAM and robotics results in increased productivity for robotic implementation activities. CAD/CAM robotic applications include robotic workcell design, robotic workcell programming, and robotic workcell simulation.

The **robotic workcell** contains all the physical equipment needed to create a functioning robot application [Fig. 14.54(a)]. Besides the robot, a workcell can have special fixturing, automated machines (CNC machines, coordinate measuring machines, or visual-inspection equipment), materials-handling devices, part-presentation equipment, and robot grippers.

The equipment in the workcell must be arranged so that the **robot work envelope** includes all required device areas. The work envelope is controlled by the size of the robot. Libraries of workcell components can be stored on the CAD/CAM system and recalled when needed [Fig. 14.54(b)]. For example, a **robot library** could contain commercial robots along with their work envelopes.

CAD/CAM workcell design has many benefits. First, the design activity is more productive, plus design time and costs are reduced. Second, CAD/CAM for workcell layout allows more alternatives to be considered, resulting in an optimal layout. Third, the lead time to design and lay out the cell is reduced. Fourth, quality of the designed components and the overall cell quality are increased.

With **graphic robotic simulation,** CAD systems can simulate the programmed robot path. Simulation checks whether or not the robot can position its end-effector to the specified positions and orientations. If the robot's end-effector cannot assume the desired position and required orientation, revision of the path or workcell may be necessary. Also, the robot's **degrees of freedom** [Fig. 14.54(c)] may not be sufficient to accomplish a given task. The degrees of freedom are the total area and movement capability of the robot. Simulation creates the actual robot trajectory using end-effector positions available from graphic robotic programming.

QUIZ

True or False

1. Patterns are made smaller than the real size of the part to allow for expansion of the metal (expansion allowance).
2. The surface texture symbol designates the classification of roughness, waviness, and lay.
3. Roughness is the distance between ridges or peaks on a surface.
4. Robots can be programmed and their movement verified without touching the actual robot hardware.
5. NC is a form of programmable automation controlled by numbers, letters, or symbols.
6. Pocketing is the process of removing material from the outer boundaries of a part.
7. A true CAD/CAM system can create a common database that is then used to derive part geometry for all areas of manufacturing and design.
8. Reamers are used to produce precise holes.

Fill in the Blanks

9. ______, ______, and ______ are done on a drill press.
10. ______, ______, ______, ______, and ______ are the five basic types of machining processes.
11. A ______ is used to allow the cast part to be removed from the form more easily.
12. ______ is the process of pouring molten metal into a mold.
13. Machining a continuous toolpath about a part is called ______.
14. The creation of a common ______ enables the part geometry to be used by many departments.
15. Toolpaths can be ______ and ______ on the display.
16. ______ is basically the same process as counterboring.

Answer the Following

17. Describe the difference between drilling, reaming, and boring.
18. From your own experience, name five metal parts that have been cast.
19. Drilling is used before what types of basic tooling operations?
20. What are robots, and how are they being used in industry? What type of tasks are they doing, and why?
21. What part does CAD play in the total CAM process? How does the use of a common database effect the design-through-manufacturing process?
22. How can a CAD system aid in verification? Discuss its uses and effects on CAM in general. Describe CNC, tooling design, and robotics in your evaluation.
23. What is a robotic workcell, and how can a CAD system help its overall efficiency?
24. What are profiling and pocketing?

PROBLEMS

For each of the following problems, draw (or model) the part. Display the part using the minimum number of views necessary to describe the design graphically. Leave sufficient space for dimensioning. After completing Chapter 15, dimension each of these projects as assigned by your instructor.

On a separate sheet of paper, list the operations required for manufacturing each of the parts—drilling, reaming, boring, threading, milling machine operations (including profiling, pocketing, etc.), and lathe operations (including facing and parting, etc.). List the material and whether the part is to be made from a stock piece or to be cast, forged, stamped, or created via some other process.

Problem 14.1 Draw or model the detail of the cylinder lip ring shown in Figure 14.2.

Problem 14.2 Redraw the plate in Figure 14.9.

Problem 14.3 Draw or model the pivot pin in Figure 14.12.

Problem 14.4 Draw or model the cylinder rod shown in Figure 14.15.

Problem 14.5 Draw or model the link shown in Figure 14.19.

Problem 14.6 Draw or model the adapter shown in Figure 14.31.

Problem 14.7 Redraw the detail of the part in Figure 14.35. Use decimal inches and the latest ANSI standards.

Problem 14.8 Draw the plate in Figure 14.40.

DIMENSIONING (ANSI Y14.5 1994)

ASME

Chapter 15

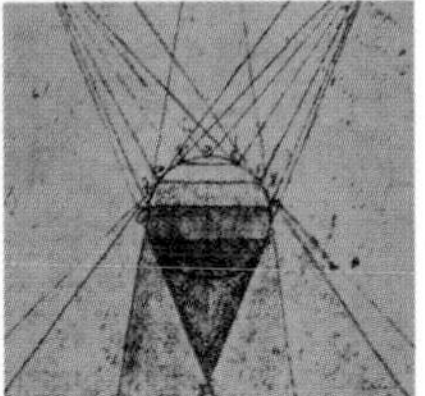

LEARNING OBJECTIVES

Upon completion of this chapter you will be able to:

1. Analyze part features in terms of integral geometric shapes to facilitate concise dimensioning within prescribed tolerances.
2. Apply ANSI standards for dimensions and tolerances.
3. Apply angular, callout, overall, limited length, and area dimensions.
4. Dimension and recognize standard symbols for curved features.
5. Define and dimension chamfers, threads, center drills, tapers, knurling, and keyways.
6. Recognize finish marks, general symbols and notes, and ANSI basic surface texture symbols.
7. Apply rectangular continuous coordinate dimensioning and polar coordinate dimensioning.
8. Understand the associative dimensioning capabilities of CAD.

15.1 INTRODUCTION

The ability to analyze a part by recognizing that it is composed of simple geometric shapes enables you to understand what dimensions are required to manufacture that part. Complete or portions of prisms, cylinders, cones, and spheres, alone or in combination, will be common in all design of mechanical parts. Partly for ease of manufacture and partly because of design requirements, these shapes are used throughout engineering design. To dimension, break the mechanical system into these simple shapes. After all, the only real purpose of an engineering drawing is to convey information correctly so that the part can be manufactured correctly from the drawing.

Engineering drawings use dimensions and notes to convey this information. Regardless of whether the part is drawn and dimensioned manually or with a CAD system (Fig. 15.1), knowledge of the methods and practices of dimensioning and tolerancing is essential. The multiview projections of a part graphically represent its shape (*shape description*). However, the drawing must also contain information that specifies size and other requirements.

Drawings are *annotated* with dimensions and notes. Dimensions must be provided between points, lines, or surfaces that are functionally related or to control relationships of other parts. Manufacturing personnel should not have to compute dimensions or guess intent. Each dimension on a drawing has a **tolerance,** implied or specified. The general tolerance given in the title block is called a **general tolerance** or **sheet tolerance** (see Fig. 15.77). Specific tolerances are provided with each appropriate dimension. Together, the views, dimensions, and notes describe the complete shape and size of the part (Fig. 15.2). If any of these are incorrect, the part will be fabricated incorrectly. Therefore, accuracy of views and dimensions is of utmost importance. (Tolerances are discussed in more detail in Chapter 16.)

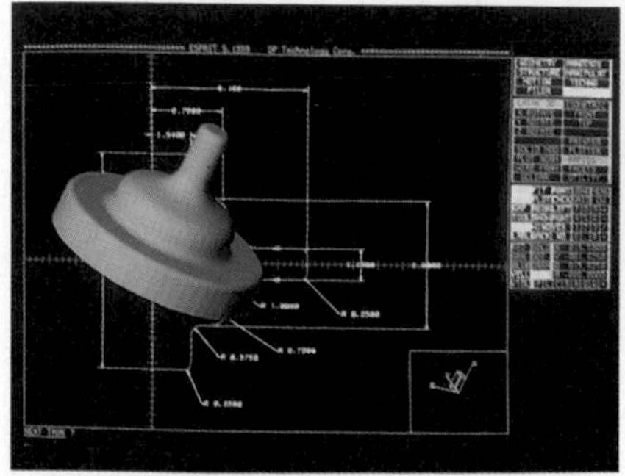

(a) Solid model dimensioning with a CAD system

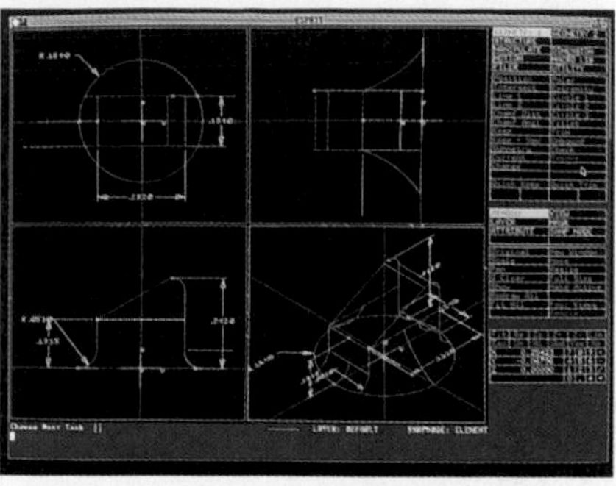

(b) Multiview drawing dimensioning with a CAD system

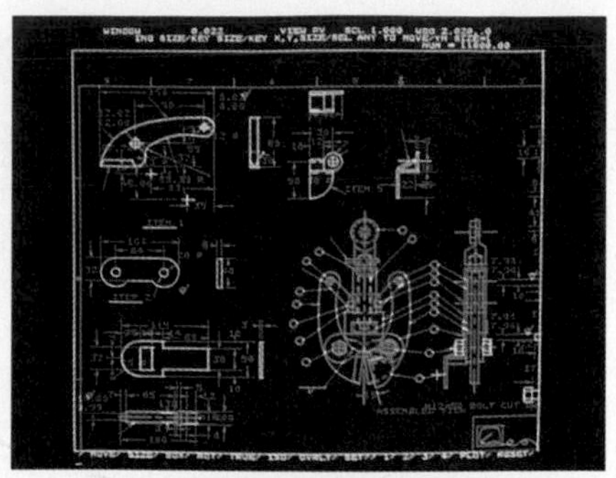

(c) Dimensioning showing assembly and detail drawing of a mechanical part

FIGURE 15.1 Part Design Using CAD

15.2 DIMENSIONING STANDARDS

Uniform practices for stating and interpreting dimensioning and tolerancing requirements were established in **ANSI Y14.5M.** Engineering firms typically have a copy of these standards. This chapter uses both the International System of Units (SI) (metric) and U.S. customary units because SI units are expected someday to replace U.S. customary units on engineering drawings. Figure 15.2 shows a part dimensioned in SI units; Figure 15.3 shows a part dimensioned in U.S. decimal-inch units. Either type of unit can be used, with equal results.

Some of the industry example drawings and problems in the text were completed before 1982 and, therefore, conform to earlier standards. Study them carefully. You will be in contact with older standards in your career since some companies continue to use older practices rather than face the expense of converting to the new standards. *Your instructor will help you to use the most recent standard to complete the exercises in this text. Many instructors have a complete copy of the current ANSI standards in a reference area.*

All drawings must be clear, be laid out well, and contain the required dimensions, text notes, finishes, etc. The advantage of a CAD database over manual drawing is that checker changes and corrections are easily incorporated into the drawing and a new "original" drawing can be plotted. The manual method requires the original drawing to be erased and corrected and requires more time. Another advantage of creating a CAD database for a part is that manufacturing can call up the part and verify the geometry,

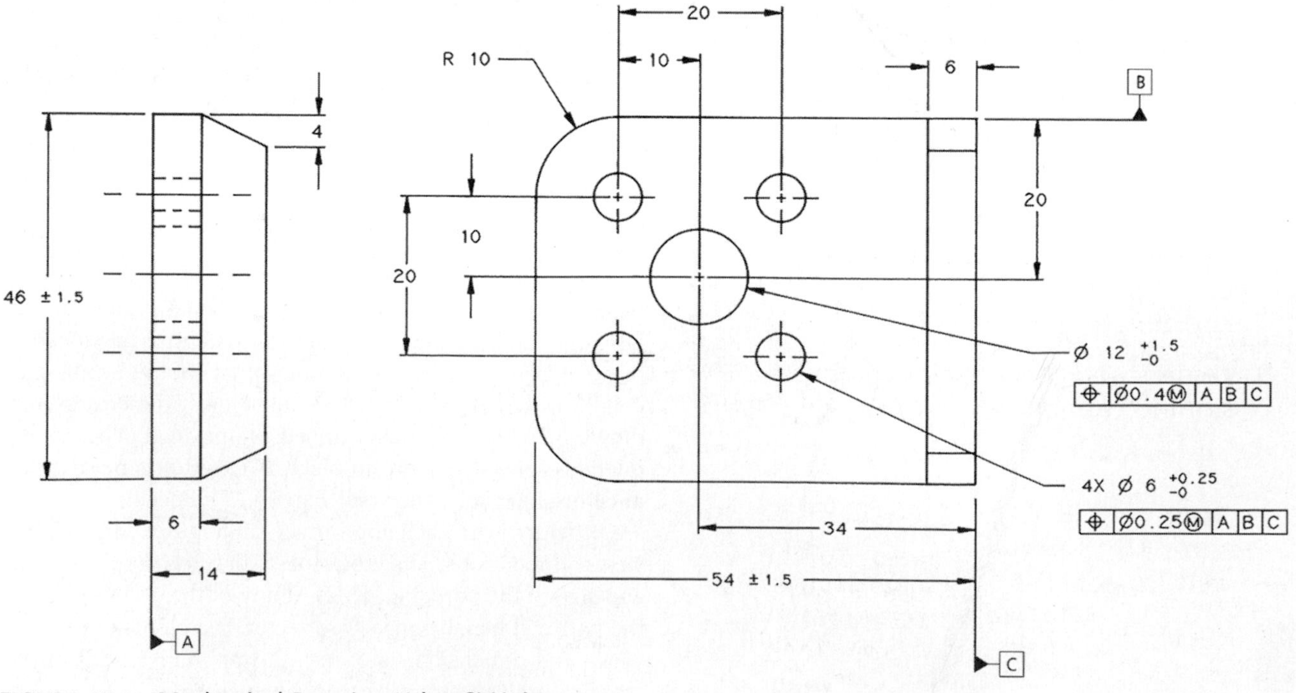

FIGURE 15.2 Mechanical Drawing Using SI Units

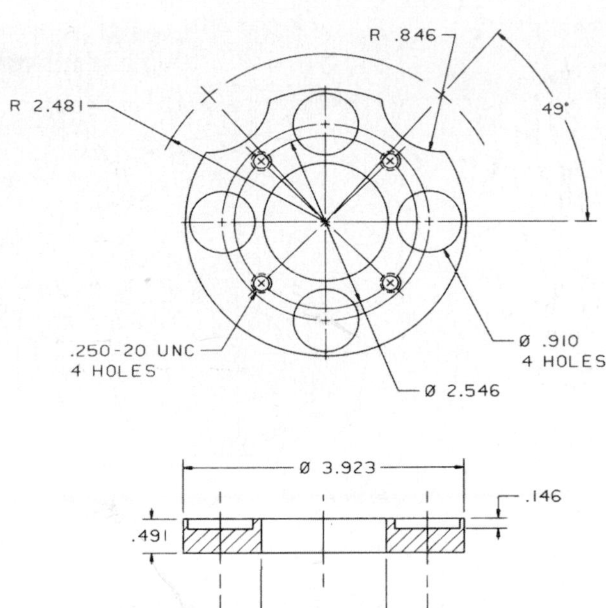

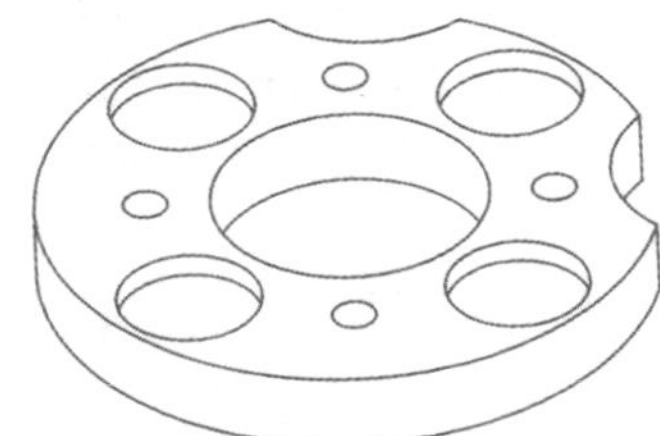

FIGURE 15.3 Mechanical Drawing Using U.S. Decimal Units

ask the system for clarification of a feature, request dimensions not included on the plotted drawing, and even create part programs for CNC machining from the database.

15.2.1 Dimensioning Terms

The following terms are used throughout this chapter.

Dimension A numeric value expressed in appropriate units of measure and indicated on a drawing and in other documents, along with lines, symbols, and notes, to define size or geometric characteristic, or both, of a part or part feature. *Examples:* 12.875 (in.), 25 (mm)

Reference dimension A dimension, usually without tolerance, used for information only. It is considered auxiliary information and does not govern production or inspection operations. A reference dimension either repeats a dimension or size already given or is derived from other values shown on the drawing or related drawings. Reference dimensions are enclosed within parentheses. *Examples:* (23.50), (50)

Datum An exact point, axis, or plane derived from the true geometric counterpart of a specified datum feature. A datum is the origin from which the location or geometric characteristics of features of a part are established.

Feature The general term for a physical portion of a part. *Examples:* a surface, a hole, a slot

Datum feature A geometric feature of a part used to establish a datum. *Examples:* a point, a line, a surface, a hole

Actual size The measured size of the feature.

Limits of size The specified maximum and minimum limits of a feature.

Tolerance The total amount by which a specific dimension is permitted to vary. The tolerance is the difference between the maximum and minimum limits.

15.2.2 Units of Measurement

The SI linear unit commonly shown on engineering drawings is the millimeter. The U.S. customary linear unit on engineering drawings is the decimal-inch. On drawings where all dimensions are either in millimeters or in inches, individual identification of linear units is not required. However, the drawing must contain a note stating:

UNLESS OTHERWISE SPECIFIED, ALL DIMENSIONS ARE IN MILLIMETERS (or INCHES).

Dimensions are shown to as many decimal places as accuracy requires. The inch or millimeter symbol is omitted unless the dimension might be misunderstood or where feet and inches are used on construction drawings. With U.S. customary units, fractions and decimals are not mixed on the same drawing. If inch dimensions are shown on a millimeter-dimensioned drawing, the abbreviation "in." must follow the inch values. If millimeter dimensions are shown on an inch-dimensioned drawing, the symbol "mm" must follow the millimeter values.

Angular dimensions are expressed either in decimal parts of a degree or in degrees, minutes, seconds (° = degrees, ′ = minutes, ″ = seconds). If degrees are indicated alone, the numerical value is followed by the symbol °.

15.3 Types of Dimensioning

Decimal dimensioning is used on U.S. drawings, except where certain commercial commodities are identified by standardized nominal designations, such as pipe, steel, and lumber sizes.

Metric Dimensioning (Figs. 15.2 and 15.4):

1. If the dimension is less than 1 mm, a zero precedes the decimal point. *Example:* 0.75
2. If the dimension is a whole number, neither the decimal point nor a zero is shown. *Example:* 12

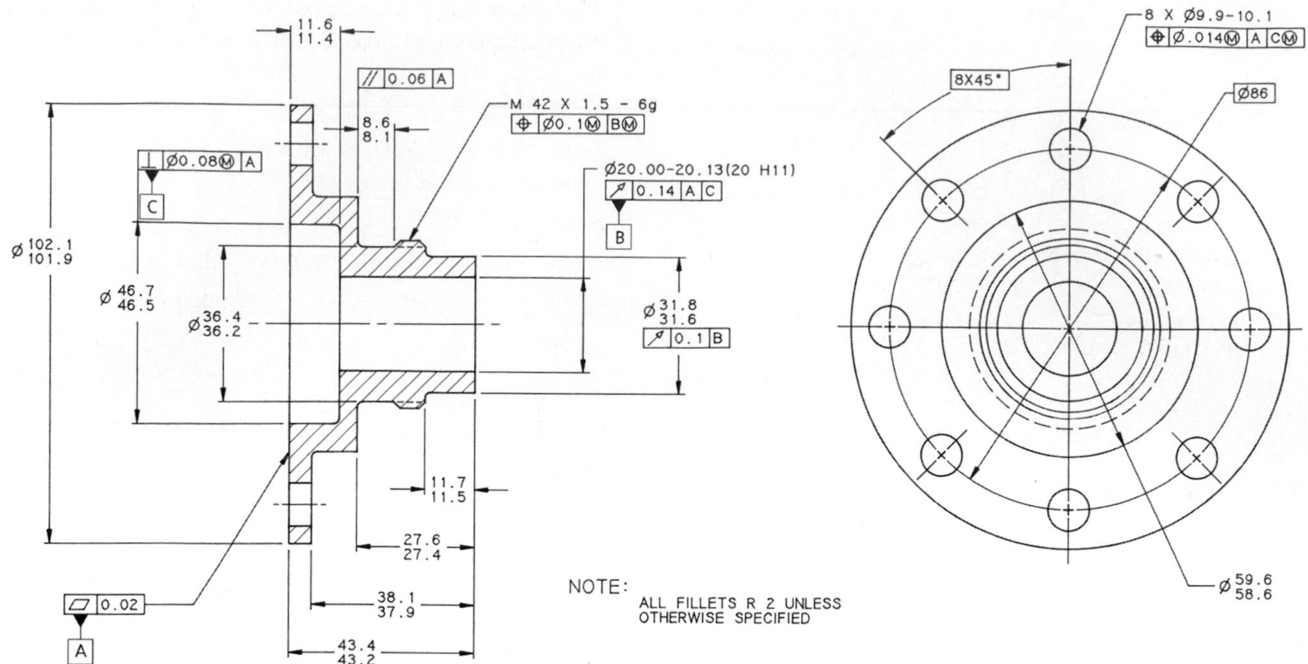

FIGURE 15.4 Geometric Tolerancing and Dimensioning Employed to Dimension a Mechanical Part

3. If the dimension exceeds a whole number by a decimal fraction of 1 mm, the last digit to the right of the decimal point is not followed by a zero. *Example:* **1.5**
4. Neither commas nor spaces are used to separate digits into groups in specifying millimeter dimensions on drawings. *Example:* **2500**

Decimal-Inch Dimensioning (Figs. 15.3 and 15.5):

1. A zero is not used before the decimal point for values less than 1 in. *Example:* **.375**
2. A tolerance is expressed to the same number of decimal places as its dimension. Zeros are added to the right of

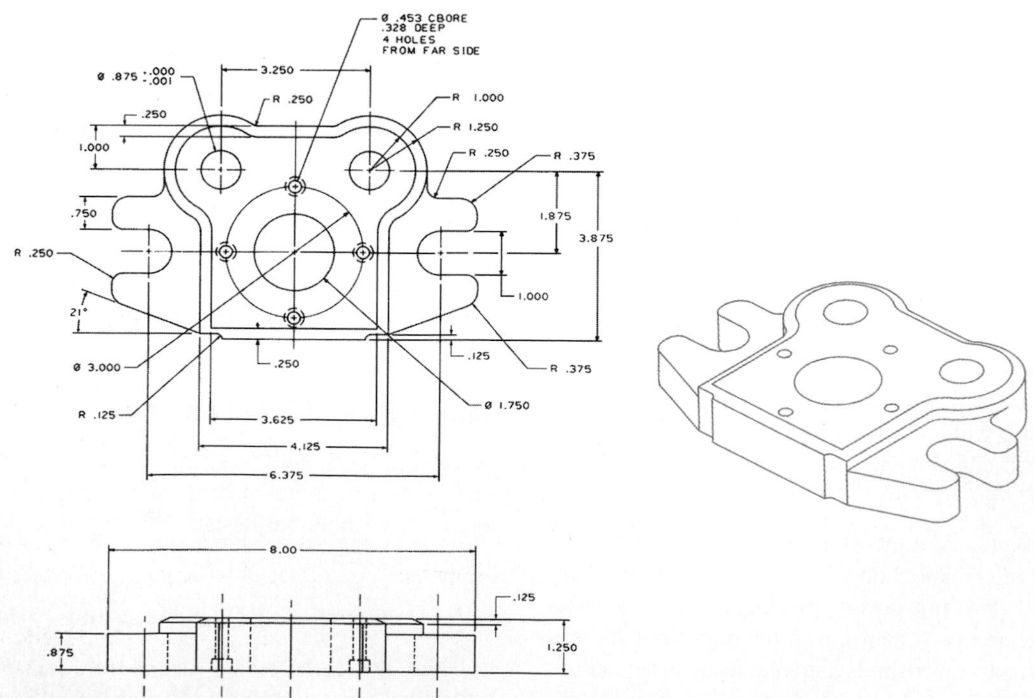

FIGURE 15.5 Mechanical Part Designed and Dimensioned in U.S. Standard Decimal Units

the decimal point where necessary for both the dimension and the tolerance.

Example: **1.001**
1.000

Decimal Points (SI and U.S. units):

1. Decimal points must be uniform, dense, and large enough to be clearly visible and to meet the reproduction requirements of ANSI Y14.2M. Decimal points are placed in line with the bottom of the associated digits. *Example:* **.875**
2. When a dimension is 1 unit, always add a decimal and a zero. *Example:* **1.0**

15.3.1 Dual Dimensioning

Because many parts designed in the United States are manufactured or traded in foreign countries, some drawings employ **dual dimensioning,** that is, U.S. customary units and metric units. The top measurement, or the first measurement when placed on the same line, is always the unit of measurement used to design the part. *Example:* $\frac{1.00}{25.4}$

15.3.2 Dimensioning Numerals

Whole numbers in the inch system are normally shown to at least one decimal place (e.g., **1.0** or **2.0**). This practice prevents dimensions from being "lost" on the drawing, which is common when the number 1 is not accompanied by a decimal point and a zero.

Common-fraction dimensions are seldom used, except on construction drawings. Before the decimal-inch was adopted as a standard, common fractions were employed for subdivisions of an inch. Some companies still use this system. Older drawings and sheet metal drawings also show common fractions.

Using decimals has many advantages. Decimals reduce arithmetic computation time. For example, it can take as much as five times longer to add a series of fractions than a series of decimals. Many decimal measurements must be rounded before they are used.

15.3.3 Rounding Decimal-Inch Measurements

ANSI has a standard method to round decimals. A decimal-inch value may be rounded off to a lesser number of places by the following procedure:

1. If the last digit to be dropped is less than 5, there is no change in the preceding digits.

Examples

.47244	rounds to	.4724
.1562	rounds to	.156
.20312	rounds to	.2031
.35433	rounds to	.3543

2. If the last digit to be dropped is greater than 5, the preceding digit is increased by 1.

Examples

.23437	rounds to	.2344
.55118	rounds to	.5512
.03937	rounds to	.0394
.6406	rounds to	.641

3. If the last digit to be dropped is 5 followed by a zero, round the preceding digit to the nearest even number.

Examples

.98425	rounds to	.9842
.59055	rounds to	.5906
.19685	rounds to	.1968
.4375	rounds to	.438

If precise calculation is required, values should be calculated to two places beyond the desired number of places; rounding should be based on the last two significant digits.

15.3.4 Drawing Scale

Drawings should be drawn to a scale so that they are easy to read and interpret. Scales are constant within a given project for which multiple drawings are needed. Scales are stated in the title block: 1:1 (full scale), 1:2 (half scale), 5:1, 10:1, and so on.

In some cases, such as when a portion of the drawing is enlarged, more than one scale is used on a drawing. In Figure 15.6, **DETAIL B** is **4/1**. The predominant scale is shown in the scale area within the title block.

15.4 DIMENSIONS

Dimensions involve standard elements: dimension lines, extension lines, leaders, arrowheads, and dimension values. The types of dimensions include vertical, horizontal, and aligned linear dimensions, angular dimensions, and callout dimensions using leaders for notes (Fig. 15.7). Figure 15.8 shows typical dimensions with examples in both decimal-inches and millimeters. When a dimension is small, the arrowheads and dimension line can go outside the extension lines, with the value inside. Another method allows the dimension value as well to be placed outside the extension lines.

Any drawing is only as good as its dimensioning. Accurate drawing and correct placement of all dimensioning elements is essential for the engineering drawing to transfer information correctly. *Dimension to get the part made correctly.*

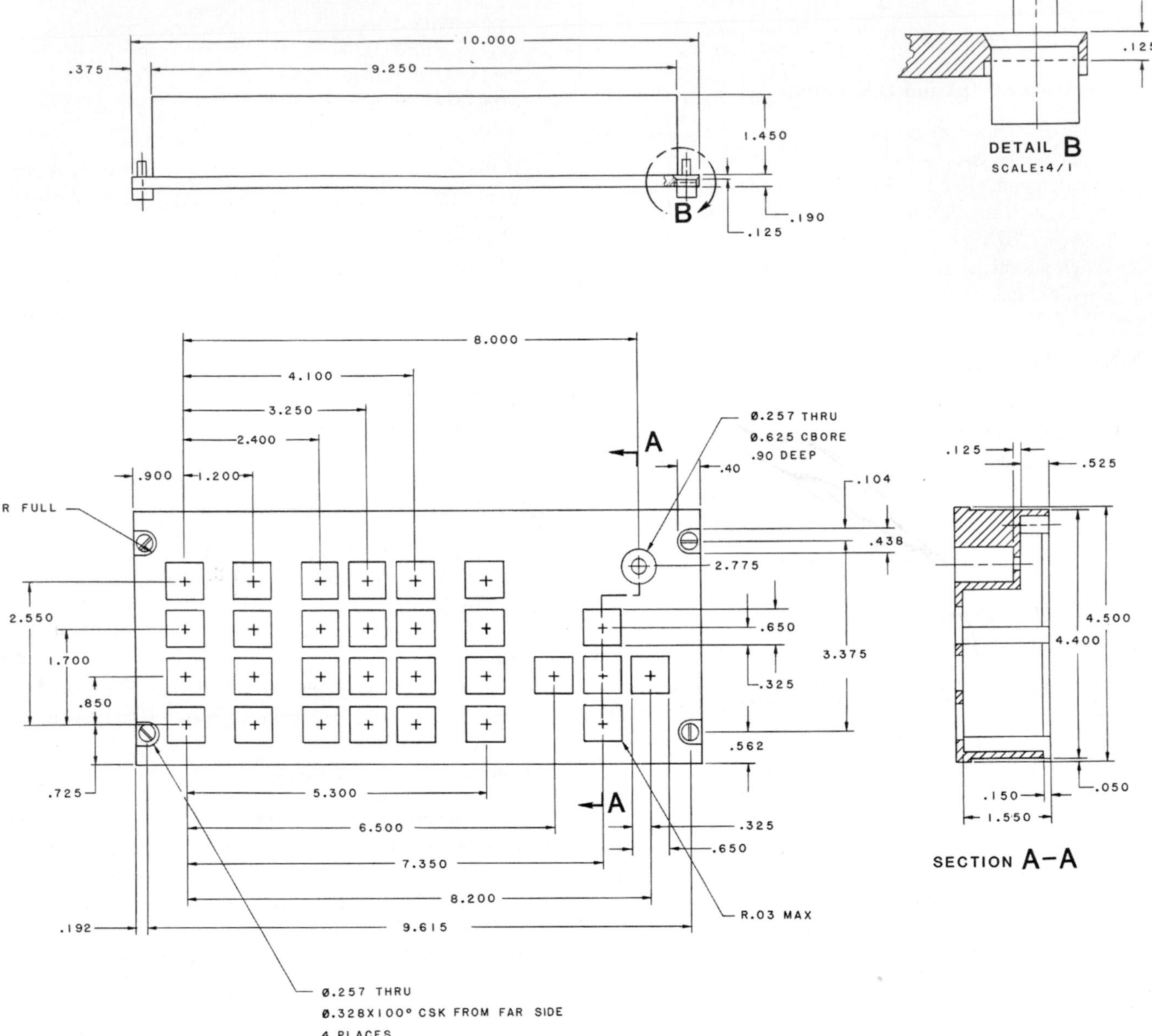

FIGURE 15.6 Panel Detail

15.4.1 Dimension Lines

A **dimension line**, with its arrowheads, shows the direction and extent of a dimension. Numerals indicate the number of units of a measurement. Preferably, dimension lines are broken to insert these numerals, as shown in Figure 15.7. If horizontal dimension lines are not broken, the numerals are placed above and parallel to the dimension lines. *Do not use centerlines, phantom lines, object lines that represent the outline of a part, or a continuation of any of these lines for dimension lines.* A dimension line is used as an extension line only where a simplified method of coordinate dimensioning is employed to define curved outlines.

Avoid crossing dimension lines. Where this is unavoidable, break the dimension lines at the crossing point. The largest dimension always goes on the outside, farthest from the part's outline (Fig. 15.9). Figure 15.9 illustrates a number of rules:

- Cross a dimension line only if it is unavoidable.
- Do not place dimensions within the part outline unless there is no other place to show the dimension properly.
- Place larger dimensions farthest from the part's outline.

Dimensions are usually placed outside the outline of the part. If directness of application makes it desirable or if

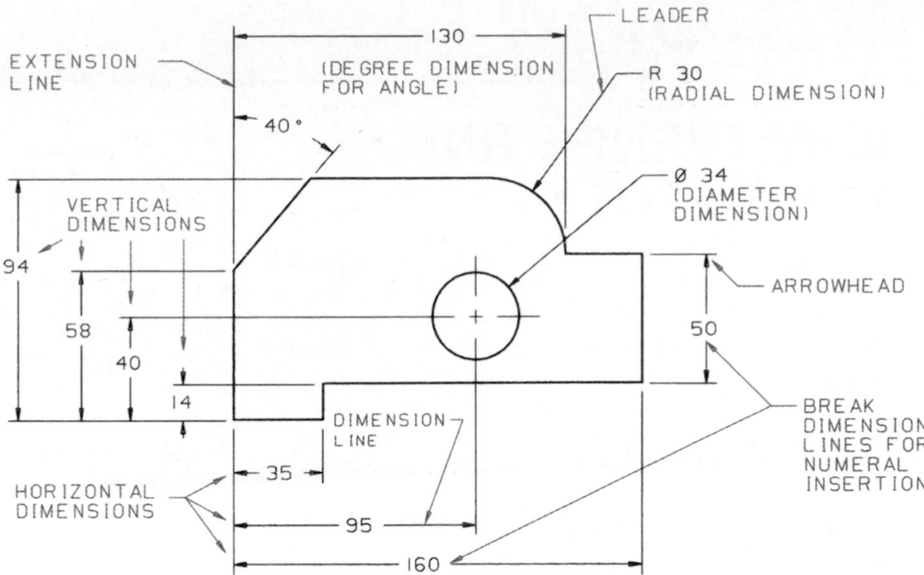

FIGURE 15.7 Dimension Elements

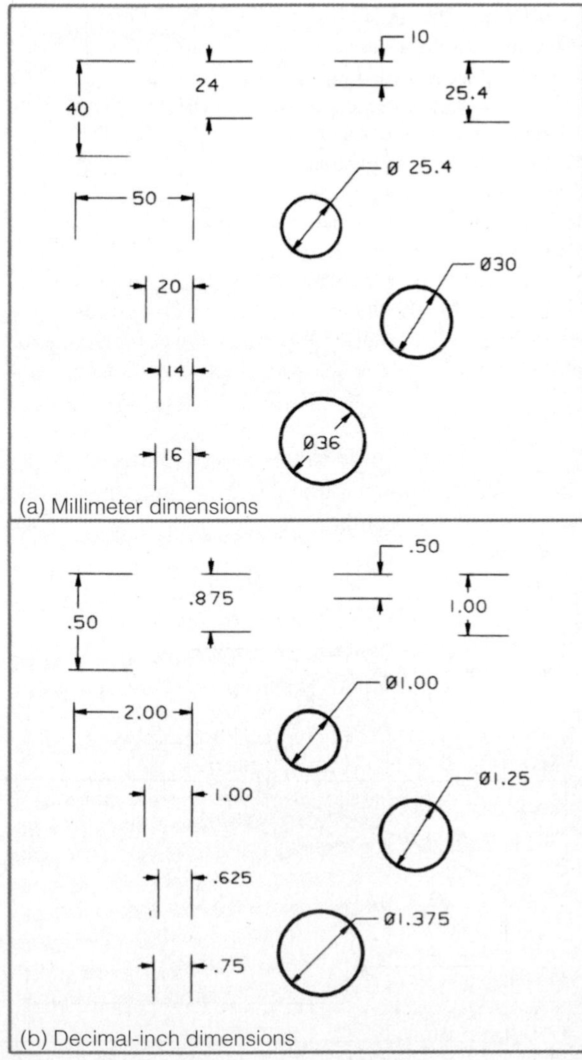

(a) Millimeter dimensions

(b) Decimal-inch dimensions

FIGURE 15.8 Dimensions

extension lines or leader lines would be excessively long, dimensions may be placed within the outline of a view. On large, complex drawings, dimensions are sometimes placed within the outline of the part, even when this contradicts the dimensioning rules. If it is necessary to place a dimensioning inside a part's outline that is sectioned, break the section lines around the dimension (Fig. 15.10).

15.4.2 Extension Lines

Extension lines indicate the extension of a surface or point to a location outside the part outline. Extension lines start with a short visible gap from the outline of the part and extend beyond the outermost related dimension line. Extension lines are drawn perpendicular to dimension lines. If space is limited, extension lines may be drawn at an oblique

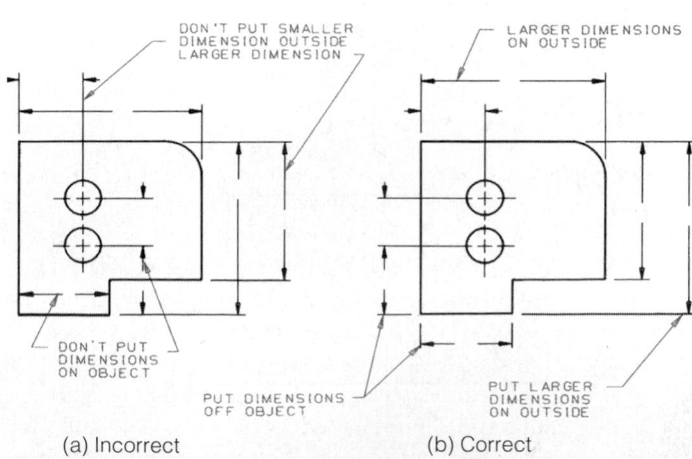

(a) Incorrect (b) Correct

FIGURE 15.9 Dimension and Extension Lines

Focus On . . .

WHY CHANGE ANSI STANDARDS?

Ever since you began your study of technical or engineering drawing, you have been learning how to produce drawings according to standards that have been established by the American National Standards Institute (ANSI). You may not have realized that these established standards change and evolve to match the needs of the ever-changing technology involved in manufacturing and production. At first it might seem odd to you that an established standard could or should change. After all, the very purpose of a standard seems to oppose the idea of changing it. However, standards exist to assist manufacturers and to make the production of parts and assemblies more efficient. If you think carefully about the quick evolution of modern technology and the new worldwide marketing and manufacturing environment, it seems reasonable to expect standards to change.

In 1935 the American Standards Association (the predecessor to ANSI) published the first recognized standard for engineering drawings in the United States—"American Drawing and Drafting Room Practices." The document was eighteen pages long, and the entire subject of tolerancing was covered in two paragraphs. It was clear in that era that the assembly-line manufacturing process created largely by Henry Ford for his Model T replaced forever the old "fit and file to size" craftsman-type manufacturing process. This mass assembly process created a pressing need for different shops to be able to produce the same parts. The exchange of drawings for those parts became critical, and a group was formed to create a standard way to communicate manufacturing and engineering details graphically. It took years for the group to publish the standards

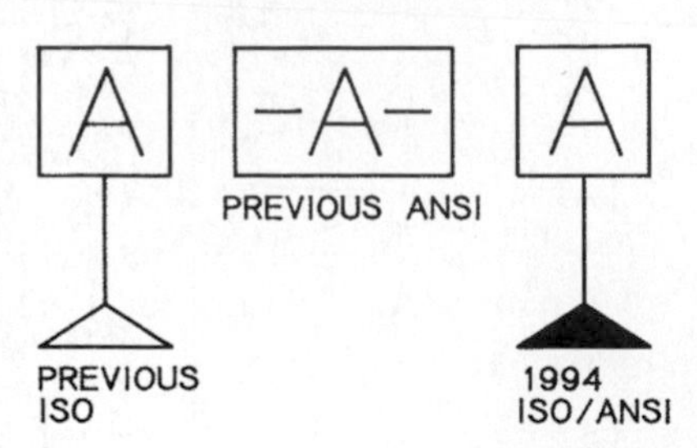

Datum identifying symbols.

document. Whose standard is best is, and will continue to be, a difficult question for any group of individuals charged with creating a standard.

World War II provided the motivation to continue to improve engineering drawings and mass production techniques. Scrap rates were too high, and assemblies were hampered by the limitations of the plus/minus tolerance system. It became apparent that geometry and not just variation in size controlled many assemblies. How many times have you drilled a hole with a hand drill and realized that the hole was the correct size but it was of no use to the assembly because the axis of the hole wasn't perpendicular to the right plane? The U.S. Army published an Ordinance Manual on Dimensioning and Tolerancing in 1945 that used symbols to specify form and position tolerances. Unfortunately, the American Standards Association's "American Standard Drawing and Drafting Room Practice," second edition, published in 1946, lacked a comprehensive section on tolerancing. To make matters worse, the Society of Automotive Engineers published its own standards in 1946 and in 1952. After the war, there were *three different*

angle to illustrate clearly where they apply. If oblique lines are involved, the dimension lines are shown in the direction in which they apply (Fig. 15.11).

FIGURE 15.10 Dimensions on Section Lining

Extension lines should not cross dimension lines. To minimize such crossings, the shortest dimension line is shown nearest the outline of the part (Fig. 15.12). If

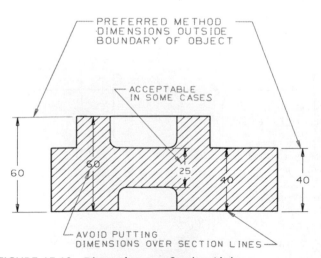

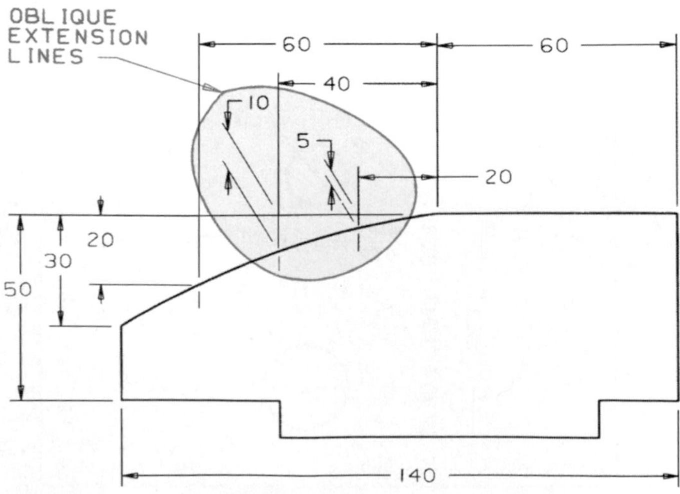

FIGURE 15.11 Oblique Dimensions

Parallelism orientation tolerancing standards.

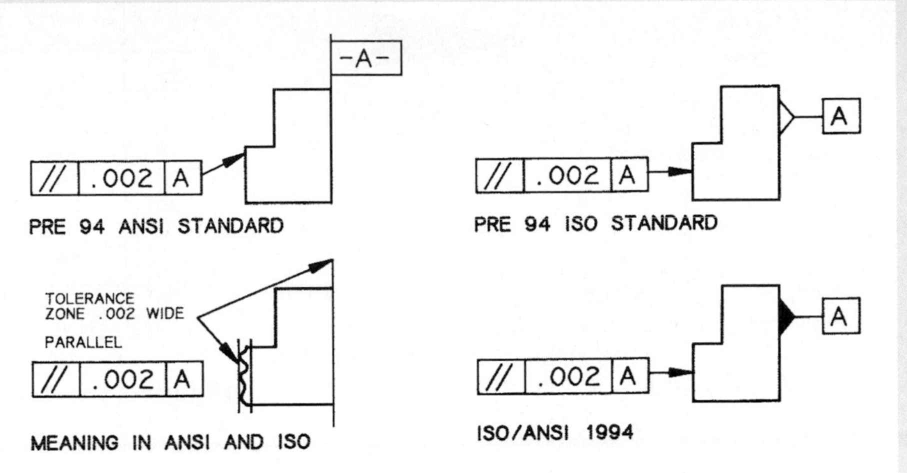

standards for tolerancing engineering drawings. It wasn't until 1966, after years of debate, that ANSI published the first unified standard on tolerancing and dimensioning—ANSI Y14.5. The standard was updated in 1973 and 1982 to replace notes with symbols for all tolerancing, and the current version was published in 1994. If all that seems a bit complicated, remember that the rest of the world has been developing their own standards and formed the International Organization for Standardization (ISO).

Evolving technology and the need to compete in world-class manufacturing seem to be driving the next round of ANSI standard revisions. CAD and CAM have become key components in manufacturing since the last ANSI Y14.5 revision. Producing a part with a CNC machine becomes easier when the part is dimensioned with that production technique in mind. The use of decimals has replaced fractions for that same reason. Unfortunately, anyone who has used a CAD system will tell you that keeping to ANSI standards has never seemed to worry the makers of CAD systems very much. The outcome of that dilemma has not been resolved. However, competing in world-class manufacturing is very important to all American manufacturers. Parts for any one assembly will more than likely be produced in a variety of shops across the world. To be part of that network, it seems that ANSI standards and ISO standards must be compatible so that engineering drawings convey the same information worldwide. Conveying information quickly and correctly is a must to compete effectively in today's world-class manufacturing environment.

The men and women charged with making ANSI and ISO standards have a difficult and complex job. Each document they produce must contain compromises. As technology and the world environment change, standards must evolve with them. As the world economy becomes more unified, more world-unified standards will certainly follow. The ability to change and adapt seems more important than ever to our continued success.

extension lines must cross other extension lines, dimension lines, or lines depicting features, they are not broken. However, an extension line is broken where it crosses arrowheads or dimension lines close to arrowheads (Fig. 15.12). Note that most CAD systems will not break the extension line for any reason. As a design engineer using a

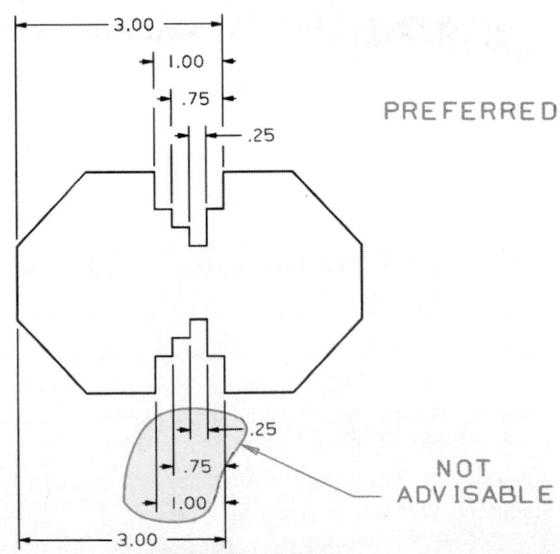

FIGURE 15.12 **Breaks in Extension Lines**

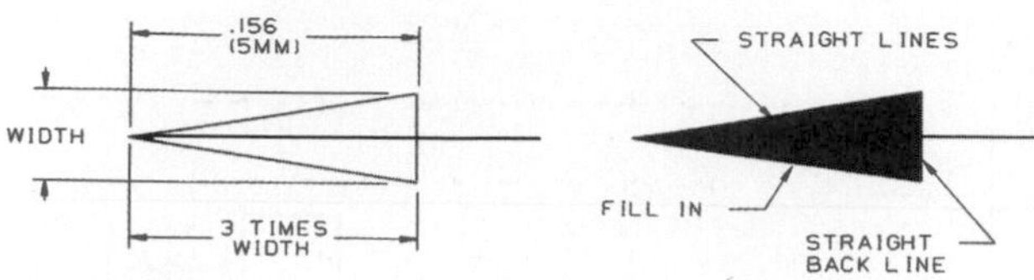

FIGURE 15.13 Arrowheads

CAD system, you will be limited by the capabilities of the system. However, many systems today have sophisticated features that have enhanced abilities to model complex geometries and surfaces.

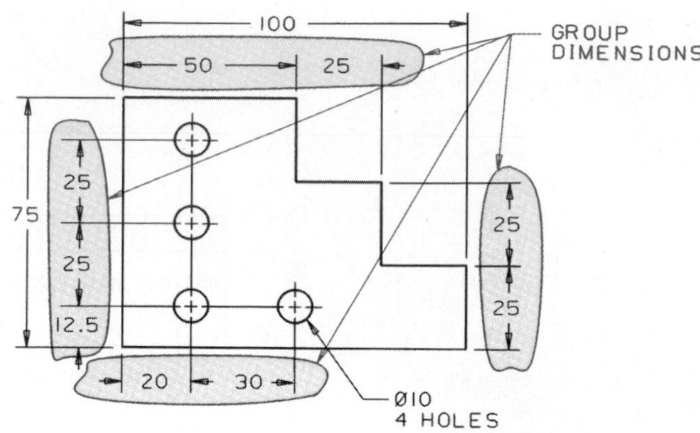

FIGURE 15.14 Grouping Dimensions

15.4.3 Drawing Dimension Arrowheads

The thickness of dimension, leader, or extension lines is normally 0.3 to 0.35 mm. They are the thinnest lines on the drawing (along with section lines) and must be drawn crisp and black. For all lines except construction lines, the thickness may change, but the darkness remains the same.

The arrowhead for dimensions is shown in Figure 15.13. The sides and back of the arrowhead are straight, not curved. An arrowhead is about three times as long as it is wide, with a length approximately equal to the height of the lettering on the drawing. Arrowheads are drawn completely filled. Other types of line terminators used throughout industry include open arrowheads, dots, and slashes. Keep arrowheads consistent and uniform. Avoid large arrowheads that stand out when reading the drawing. With time and practice, your freehand arrowheads will become easy to construct and well formed.

CAD systems provide arrowheads in a variety of sizes, shapes, and types, all of which can be inserted automatically. With a CAD system, you do not actually construct dimensions and arrowheads, but the proper selection of dimensions and their placement is still your responsibility.

15.4.4 Drawing Dimension and Extension Lines

Dimension lines are aligned and grouped for uniform appearance (Fig. 15.14). If there are several parallel dimension lines, the numerals should be staggered for easier reading (Fig. 15.15). Figures 15.15 and 15.16 show staggered spacing for horizontal dimensions; Figure 15.17 shows staggered vertical dimensions.

The minimum distance from the first dimension line to the part outline should be .375 in. (10 mm). The minimum spacing between parallel dimension lines should be .25 in. (6 mm) (Fig. 15.18). In general, .50 in. (12 mm) from the part and .375 in. to .50 in. (10 to 12 mm) between dimensions is suggested for large drawings and those that

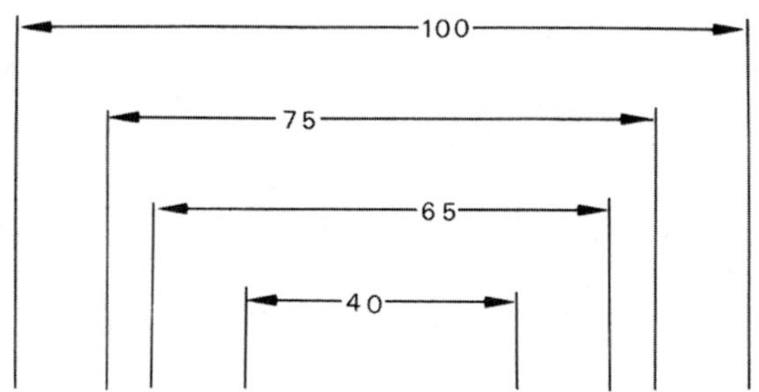

FIGURE 15.15 Staggered Dimensions

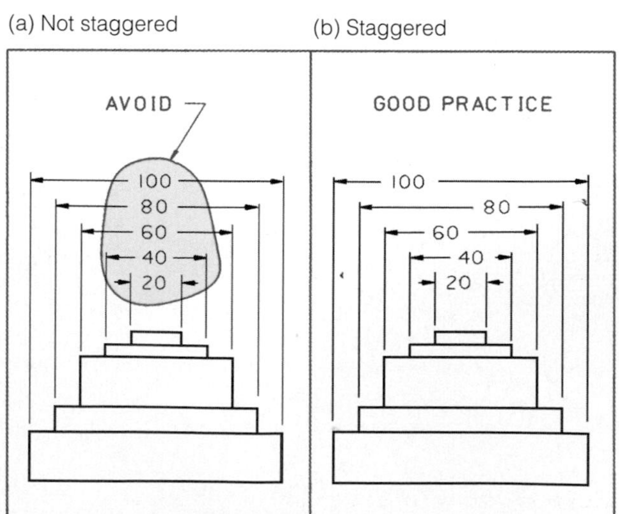

FIGURE 15.16 Horizontal Dimensions

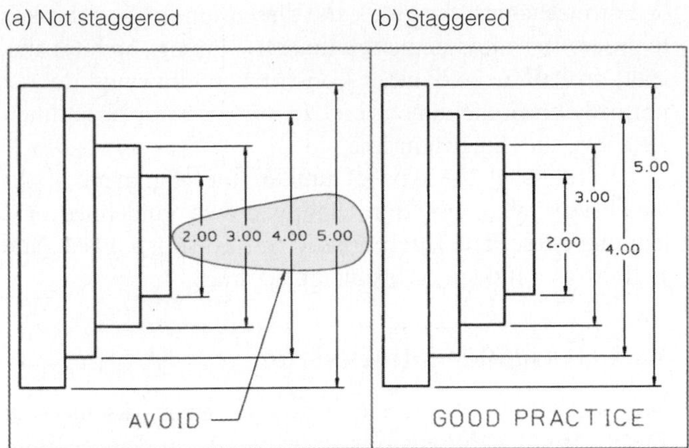

FIGURE 15.17 Vertical Dimensions

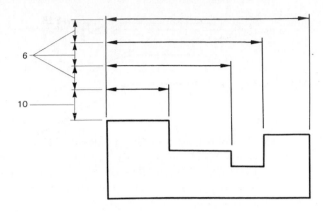

FIGURE 15.18 Setup and Spacing of Dimensions

need to be greatly reduced. These spacings are intended as a guide when dimensioning, not as a rule. If the drawing meets the reproduction requirements of the accepted industry or military reproduction specification, these spacing requirements are not mandatory.

Extension lines should start about .06 in. (1.3 mm) from the part and end approximately .12 in. (2.5 mm) beyond the dimension line and arrowhead (Fig. 15.19). *Centerlines can be used as extension lines but not as dimension lines.*

All holes are dimensioned to their centerlines in two directions, except when the holes are arrayed in a circular pattern (as with a bolt circle). If a point is to be located only by extension lines, the extension lines (from the surfaces) pass through the point (Fig. 15.20).

Extension lines are not drawn to hidden lines on hidden features of the part. However, dimensioning to hidden features is acceptable in some circumstances (when a feature cannot be seen in another view). Another way to avoid dimensioning to hidden lines is to make use of a broken-out section for the hidden features. *Whenever possible, dimension to a visible feature.*

Remember: for almost every dimensioning rule, there is an exception. The rules apply in probably 90% of the situations that you will encounter.

15.4.5 Lettering Dimensions

The preferred heights for lettering dimensions are shown in Figure 15.21. Dimension heights are standardized for each drawing size and reduction requirement. If reduction is not required, .125 inch (3 mm) height for lettering is acceptable.

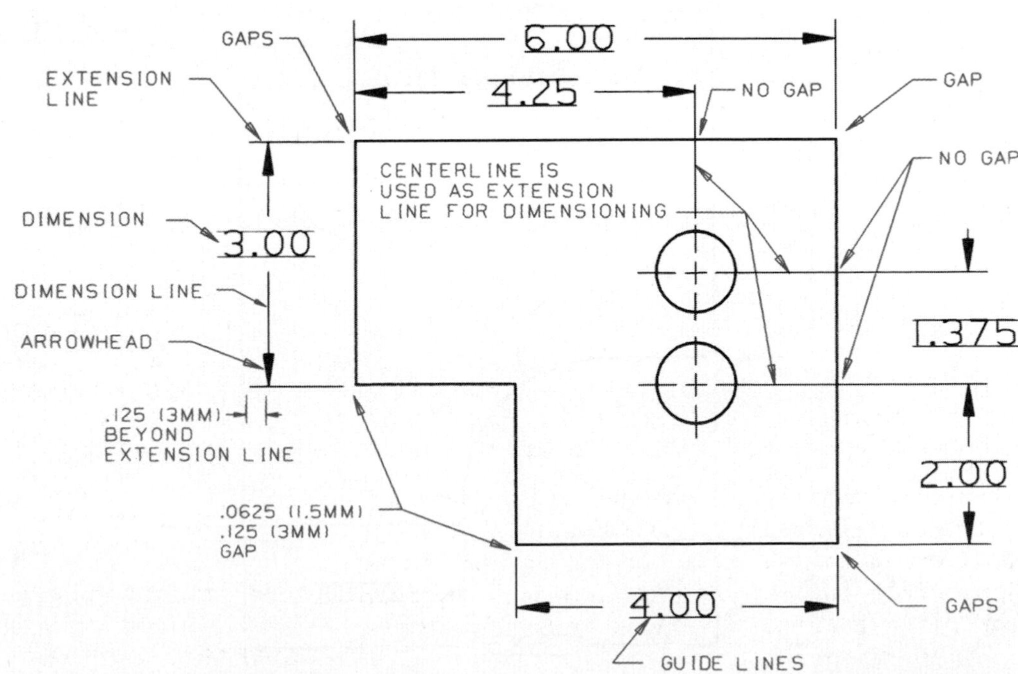

FIGURE 15.19 Gaps and Placement of Extension Lines

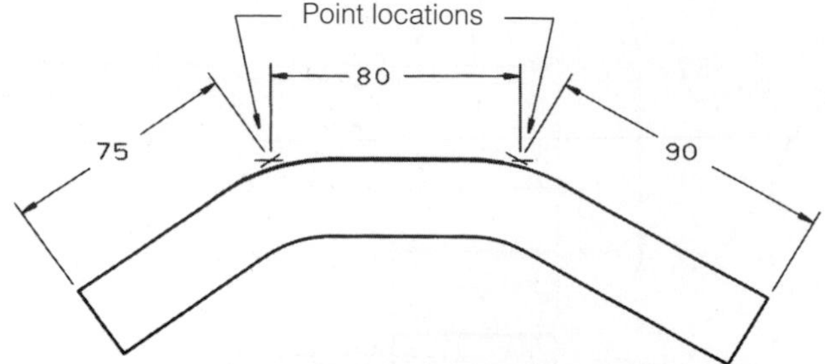

FIGURE 15.20 Point Locations Using Extension Lines

Follow the spacing of lettering in dimensions in Figure 15.21 to complete projects in this text.

Numerals that are placed parallel to dimension lines are called **aligned dimensions** [Fig. 15.22(a)]. Horizontal dimensions are readable from the bottom, vertical dimensions from the right side of the drawing. Point-to-point dimensions of angled edges have the dimensions aligned (parallel) to the edge itself. Aligned dimensions are *not* accepted ANSI practice.

Unidirectional dimensioning [Fig. 15.22(b)] places the dimension text parallel to the bottom of the drawing. This system is preferred, since the drawing can be read and lettered without being turned (Fig. 15.23); that is, it is readable from the bottom of the drawing.

For mechanical drawings, the dimension lines are broken to insert the measurement numerals. Piping, architecture, civil, structural, and other construction drawings do not normally break the dimension line, but instead place numerals above the dimension line.

Regardless of the type of unit or the alignment of the dimension value, use thin, lightly drawn guidelines or a lettering guide. The lettering itself must be crisp, black, and as thick as a hidden or visible object line.

15.4.6 Angular Dimensions

Size and location dimensions may be linear distances or angles. **Angular dimensions** are expressed in degrees, minutes, and seconds or as decimal equivalents of degrees, as in Figure 15.24. For angles of less than 1°, precede the minute mark by 0° (e.g., **0°40′**). For both unidirectional and aligned dimensioning, angular dimensions are placed to be read horizontally between guidelines, with no dash between degrees and minutes.

Angular dimensions should be avoided by locating the endpoints of inclined lines and planes. Because it is easier, quicker, and more reliable, coordinate dimensioning of angled features increases the accuracy during manufacturing.

The dimension line for an angle is drawn as an arc from

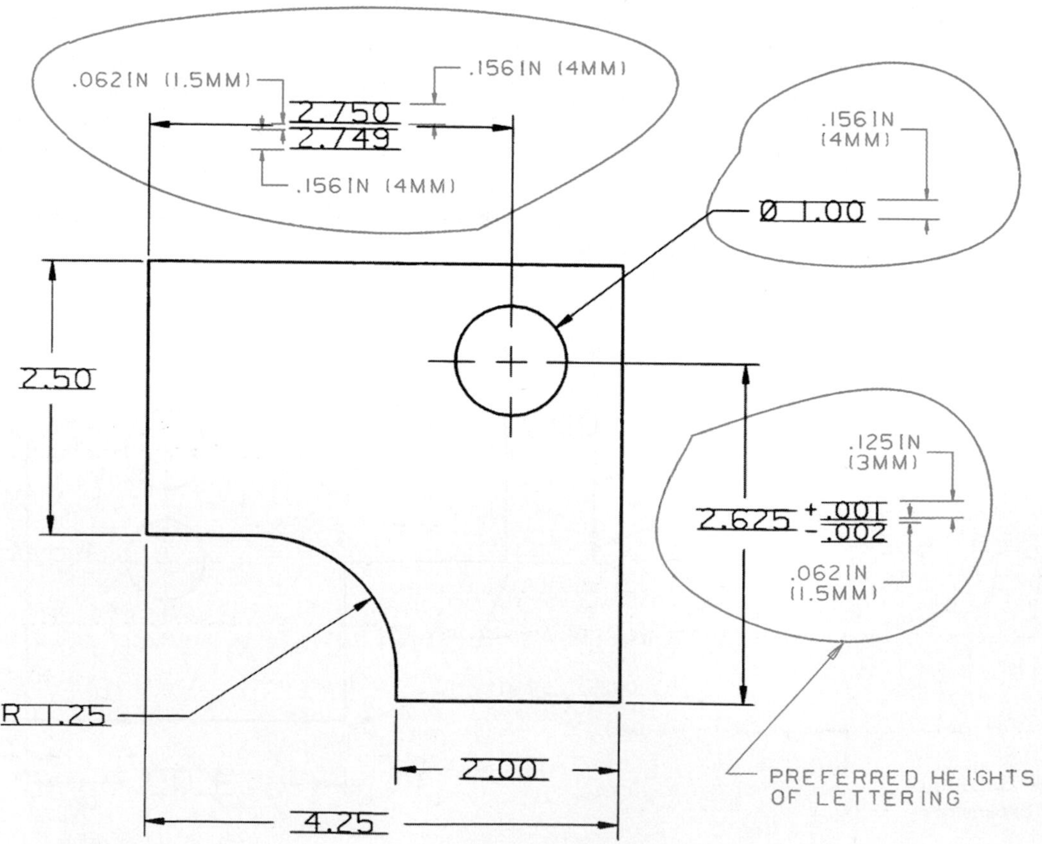

FIGURE 15.21 Preferred Lettering Height for Dimensions

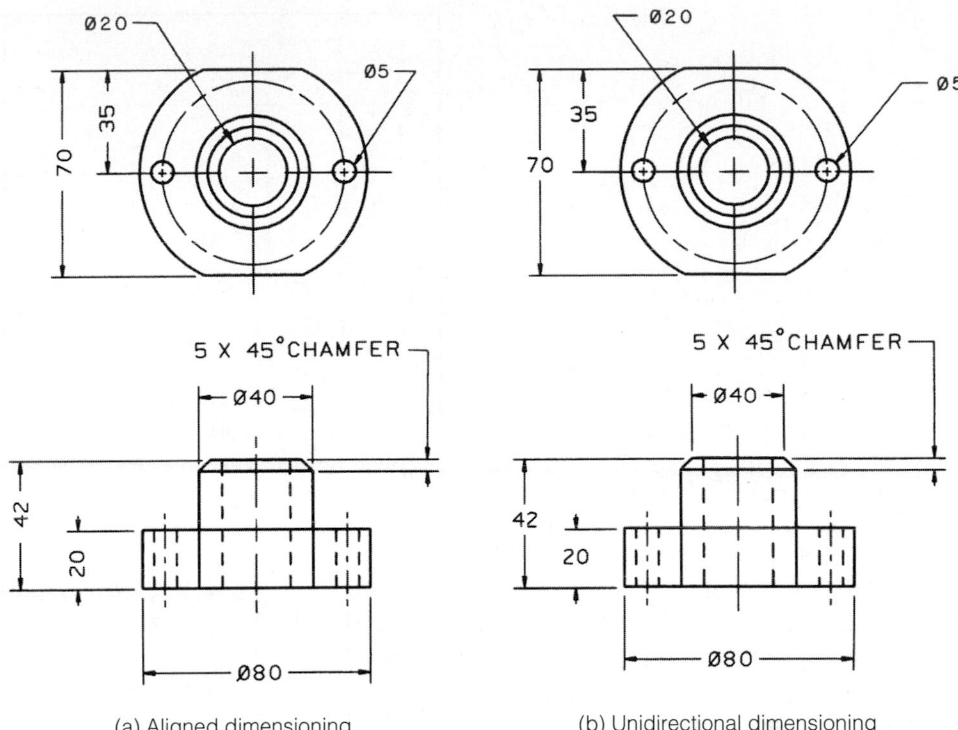

FIGURE 15.22 **Dimensioning Methods**

a center at the intersection of the sides of the angle. A variety of methods are employed to dimension angles (Fig. 15.24). The arrowheads terminate at the extensions of the two sides, inside or outside the extension lines. The dimension line is an arc with its center at the vertex of the angle being measured, and the angular dimension is placed inside or outside the two controlling extension lines.

Angles are used only where other forms of linear dimensions are unsuitable. In Figure 15.25, two methods of dimensioning a part are illustrated. One method [Fig. 15.25(a)] involves angle dimensions, and the other [Fig. 15.25(b)] the offset method. Because it is easier for the machinist to locate the features of the part with linear measurements, the offset method is preferred. Figure 15.26 shows another example of these methods. Here the parts are different and lend themselves to different dimensioning styles: (a) uses the offset method to locate the holes; (b) has a slot angled to the base. Because the features in Figure 15.26(b) would be difficult to locate with offset dimensions, an angle dimension works best. The features of part (b) are related to the angled surface and, therefore, are located in relation to it when establishing dimensions.

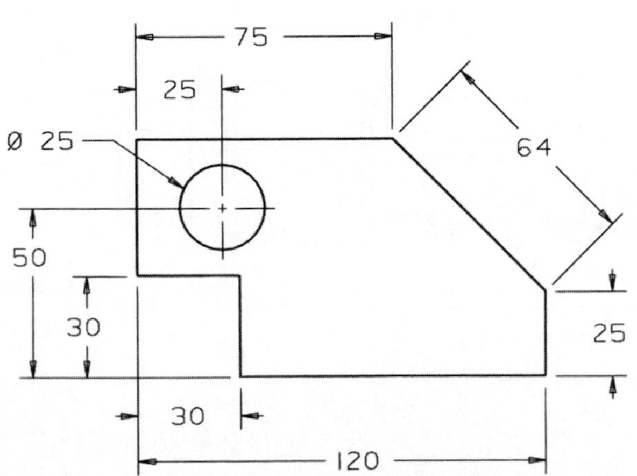

FIGURE 15.23 **Unidirectional Dimensions**

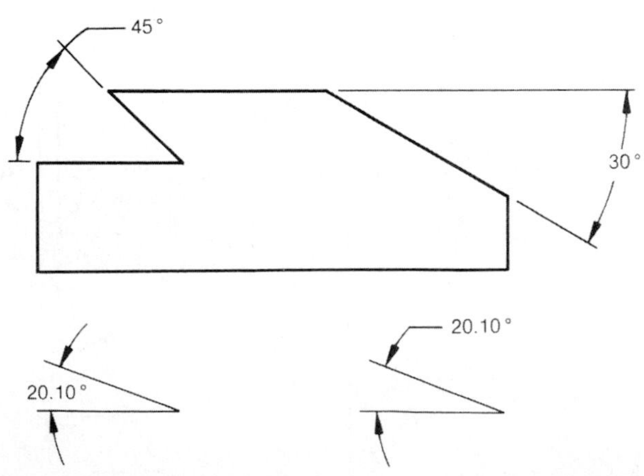

FIGURE 15.24 **Dimensioning Angles**

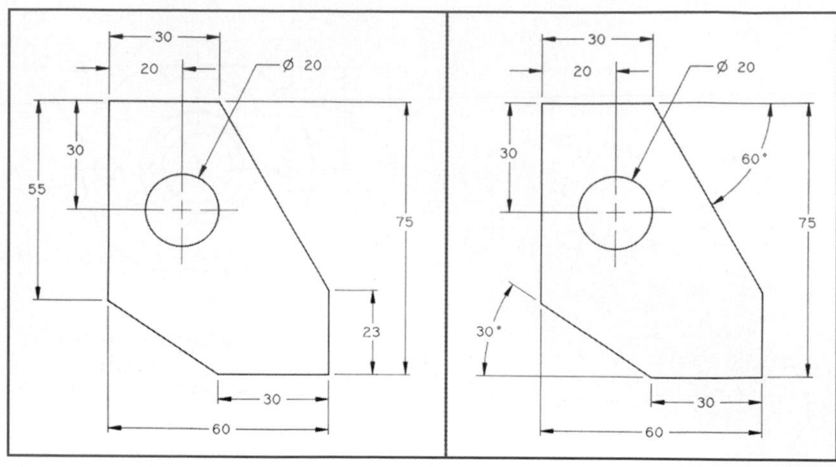

FIGURE 15.25 Dimensioning

(a) Offset (square) dimensioning (b) Angular dimensioning

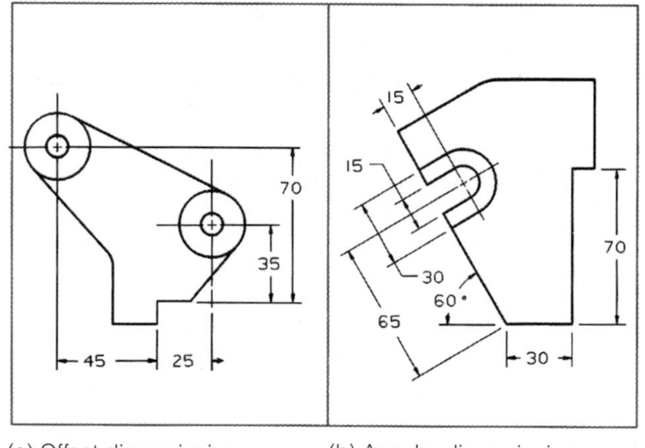

(a) Offset dimensioning (b) Angular dimensioning

FIGURE 15.26 Dimensioning

15.4.7 Callout Dimensions and Notes Using Leaders

A **leader** directs a dimension, note, or symbol to the intended feature on the drawing (Fig. 15.27). Leaders can point to a curved feature of a part or reference a portion or surface. Most leaders are drawn at 45° to 60° to the horizontal (30° to the vertical) (Fig. 15.28). Leaders terminate in arrowheads. The dimension figure for a callout is placed at the end or the head of a short [6 mm (.25 in.)] horizontal line.

Figure 15.29 shows the three most common uses of a leader: to call out a hole diameter, to call out a radius, and to reference a surface or part with a note. When a leader serves to dimension a circle or arc, it must point to or from (or through) the center of the circle or radius. The arrowhead

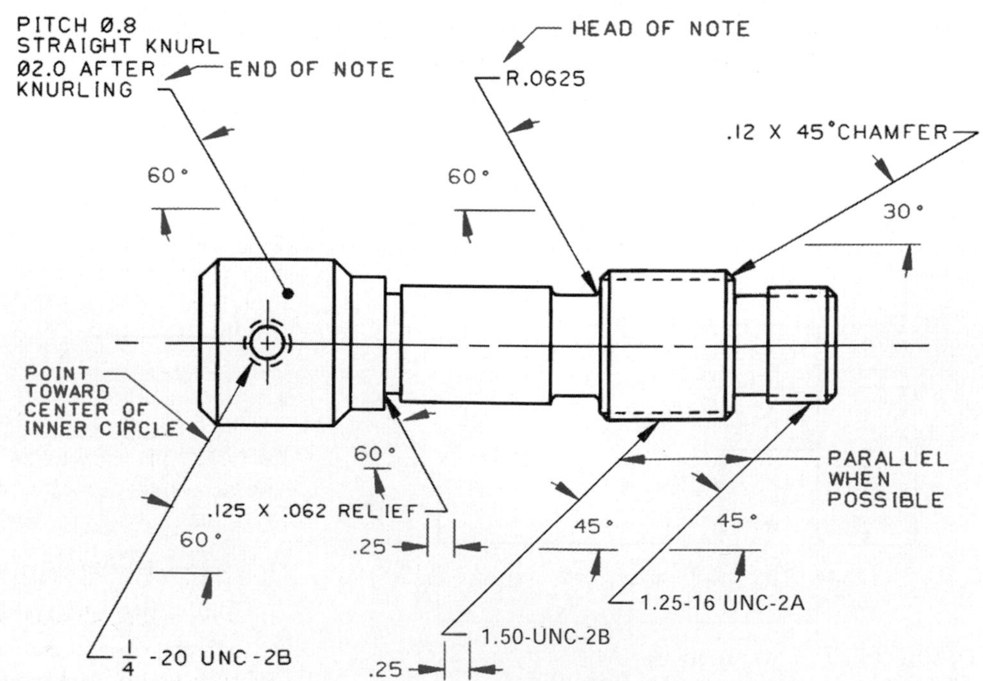

FIGURE 15.27 Leaders on Drawings

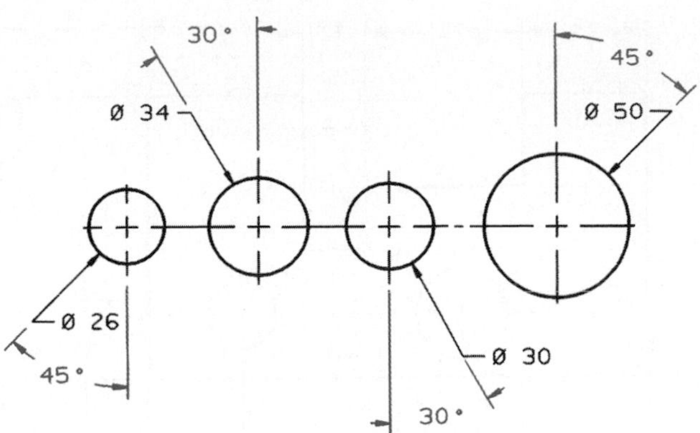

FIGURE 15.28 Leaders for Hole Callouts

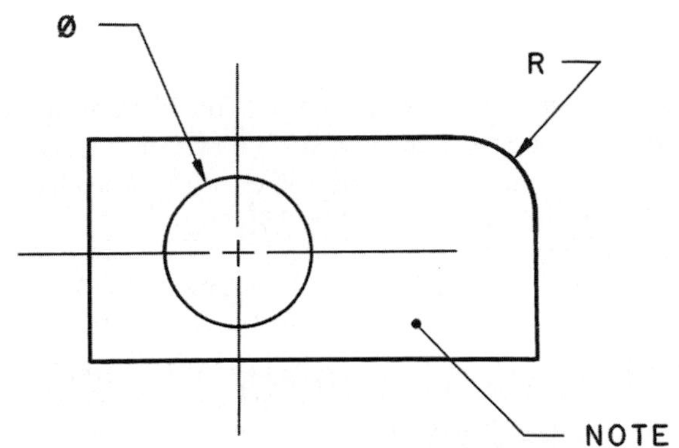

FIGURE 15.29 Three Common Uses of Leaders

points toward the center of the curve (Fig. 15.30). Therefore, *all leaders for radii and diameters are radial.* The arrowhead for a leader terminates at the circumference of the arc or diameter.

The crossing of dimension lines and extension lines by

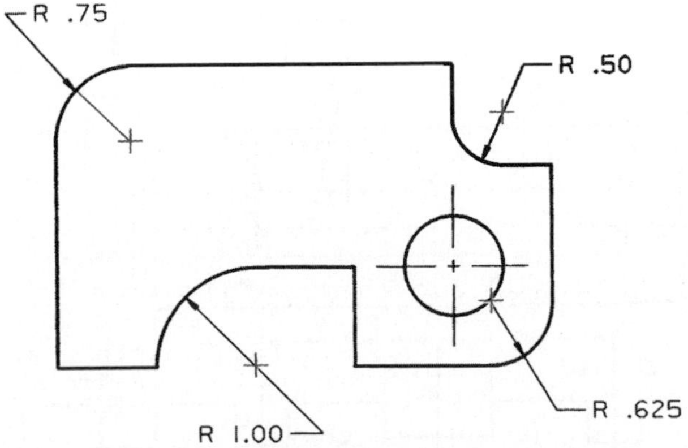

FIGURE 15.30 Dimensioning Fillets and Arcs with Callouts

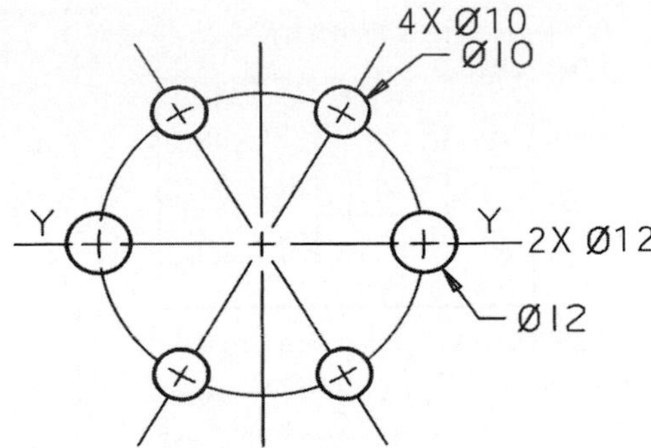

FIGURE 15.31 Minimizing Leaders on Drawings

leaders should be kept to a minimum. The leader line is drawn at a different angle than object lines of the part or section lines on the drawing.

Leaders and their accompanying notes and callouts are kept outside dimension lines and away from the part being dimensioned. Leaders are placed on the drawing after the part is dimensioned. Although leaders can cross object, dimension, and extension lines, *they should never cross other leader lines.*

Leader-directed dimensions are specified individually, for simplicity (Fig. 15.30). If too many leaders impair the legibility of the drawing, letters or symbols are used to identify the features (Fig. 15.31).

15.4.8 Reference, Overall, and Not-to-Scale Dimensions

Reference dimensions are not used for manufacturing or inspection. To identify a reference dimension or reference data on drawings, *enclose the dimension or data within parentheses.*

If an overall dimension is specified, one intermediate dimension is omitted or identified as a reference dimension (Fig. 15.32). When the intermediate dimension is more important than the overall dimension, the overall dimension is identified as a reference dimension.

To indicate that a feature is **not to scale,** the dimension should be underlined with a straight thick line (e.g., **101** in Fig. 15.33), or **NTS** (not to scale) should be added to the dimension.

Only the dimensions required for manufacturing the part are on the drawing. In Figure 15.34, the overdimensioned part is shown on the top of the figure and the correctly dimensioned part below it. Note that the correctly dimensioned example has fewer dimensions and an uncluttered look. The placement of ℄ on the part's centerline means the part is *symmetrical about its centerline.*

15.4.9 Indicating Limited Length or Area

To indicate that a limited length or a limited area of a surface is to receive additional treatment or consideration within limits specified on the drawing, the extent of those limits is

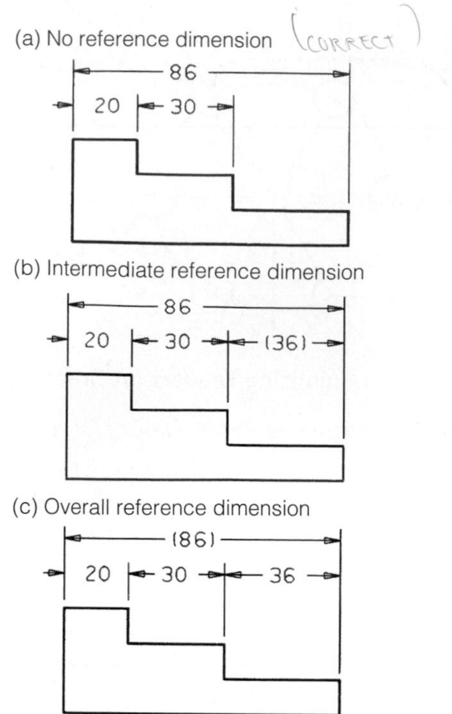

FIGURE 15.32 Overall and Reference Dimensions

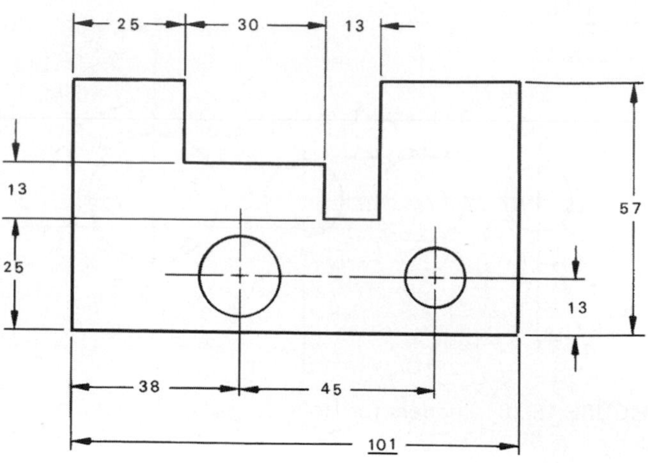

FIGURE 15.33 Not-to-Scale (NTS) Dimensions

indicated by a **chain line** (Fig. 15.35). In an appropriate view or section, a chain line is drawn parallel to the surface profile at a short distance from it. Dimensions are added for length and location [Fig. 15.35 (a)]. For a surface of revolution, such as a shaft, the indication is shown on one side only [Fig. 15.35 (a)].

As long as the chain line clearly indicates the location extent of the *limited length,* dimensions may be omitted [Fig. 15.35(b)]. When the *limited area* is shown on a direct view of the surface, the area is section-lined within the chain line boundary and dimensioned [Fig. 15.35(c)].

15.5 DIMENSIONING CURVED FEATURES

Included in this section are methods of noting and dimensioning curved features, such as radii, diameters, slots, counterdrills, countersinks, spotfaces, and counterbores. ANSI symbology is also covered.

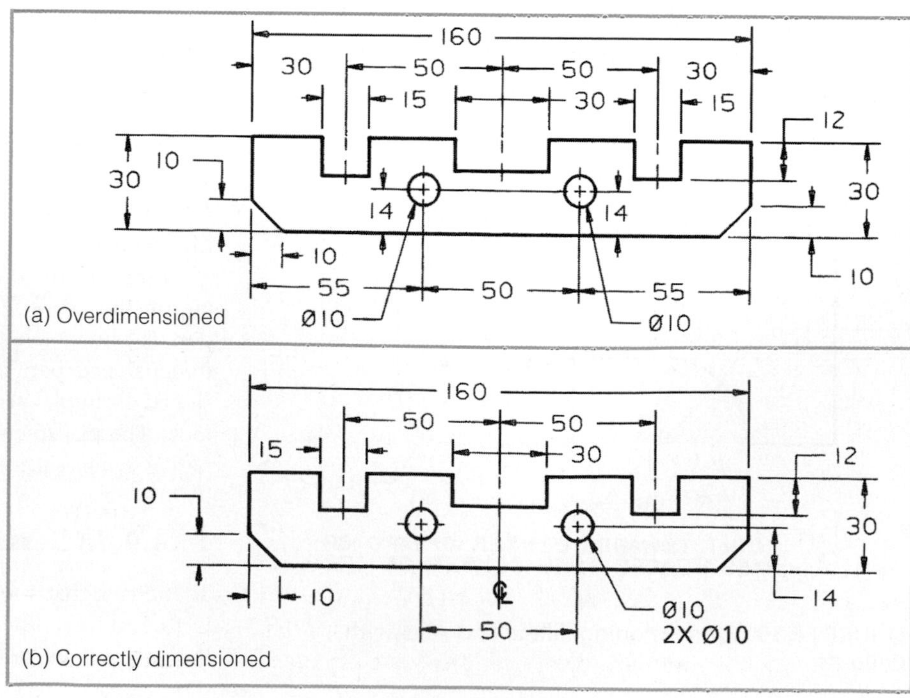

FIGURE 15.34 Overdimensioning a Part

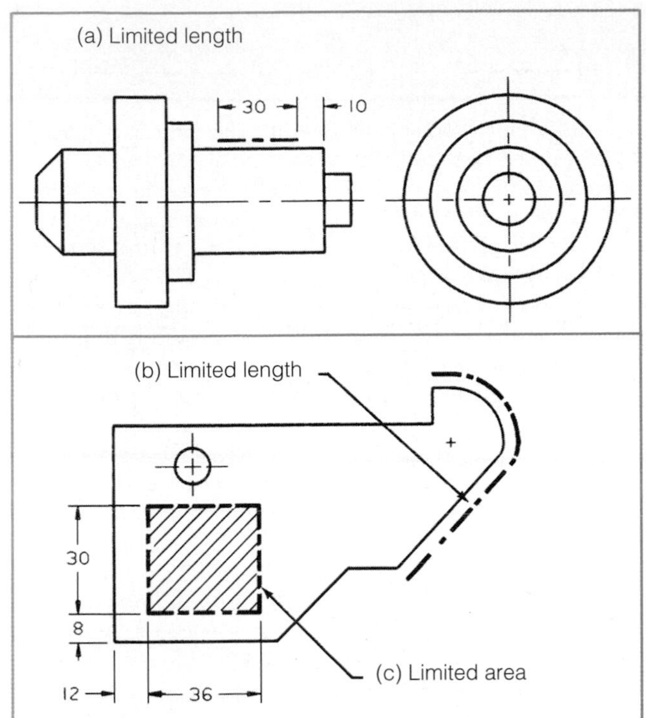

FIGURE 15.35 **Limited-Length and Limited-Area Indicators**

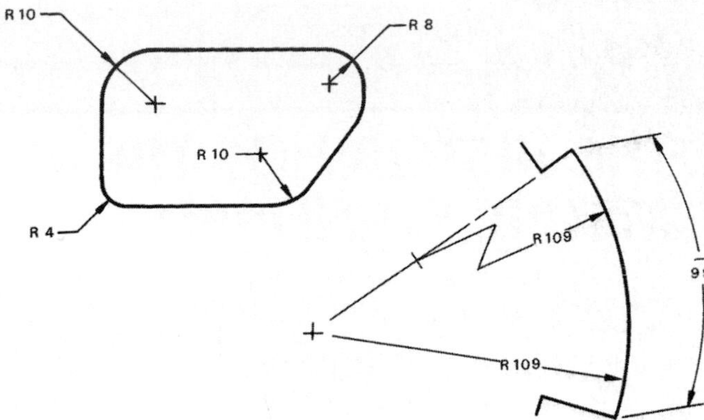

FIGURE 15.36 **Dimensioning Radii and Arcs**

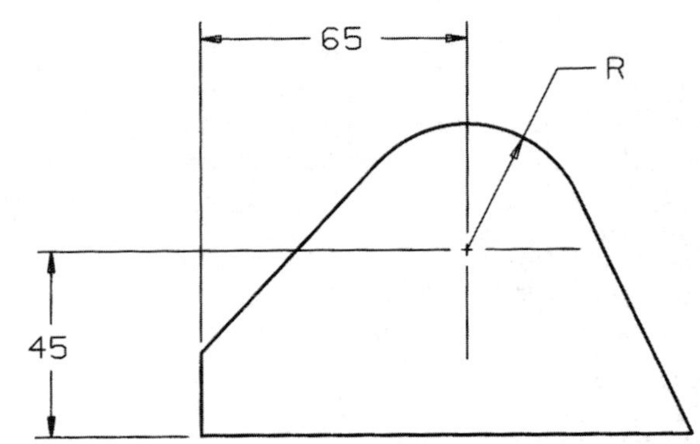

FIGURE 15.37 **Radius with a Located Center**

15.5.1 Radius Dimensioning

Radius dimensions help to call out slots, curves, arcs, rounds, and fillets. Each radius value on a radius dimension is preceded by the appropriate radius symbol, R (Fig. 15.36). A radius dimension line has one arrowhead, which points to the arc from the center. An arrowhead is not used at the radius center. The dimension line for any radius is an angular line extending radially through, from, or toward the center of the feature. Do not use horizontal or vertical lines when dimensioning arcs. Figure 15.36 illustrates the following:

- If the location of the center is important and space permits, draw a dimension line from the radius center, with the arrowhead touching the arc. Place the dimension between the arrowhead and the center.
- When space is limited, extend the dimension line through the radius center.
- When it is inconvenient to place the arrowhead between the radius center and the arc, place it outside the arc, with a leader.
- If the center of a radius is not located dimensionally, no center is indicated.

To locate the center of a radius, draw a small cross at the center. Extension lines and dimension lines can be used to locate the center of an arc (Fig. 15.37). If the location of the center is unimportant, the drawing must show clearly that the arc location is controlled by other dimensioned features, such as tangent surfaces (Fig. 15.38). The center of a fillet or round is not located by dimensions.

Sometimes the center of an arc is moved on a drawing because there is a break or the center lies outside the drawing paper (Figs. 15.36 and 15.39). The new position is on a centerline of the arc, and the newly located "false"

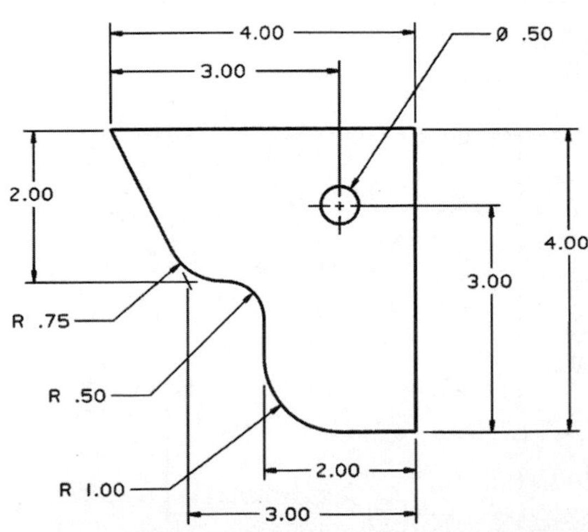

FIGURE 15.38 **Radii with Unlocated Centers**

Focus On . . .

THE HISTORY OF THE METRIC STANDARD

The metric system is a "standard" system of weights and measures based on the meter, a unit of length, and the kilogram, a unit of mass. But what does "standard" mean?

Noah was told to build his ark 300 cubits long. A cubit was the measured distance from the elbow to the extended finger. Some people have longer arms and fingers than others, so this was an interesting standard unit of length. On average, a cubit is about 18 inches, which means that Noah built an ark about 450 feet long (as big as an ocean liner)!

If you study the history of measurement, you will discover that standards were loosely defined and crudely measured. Many variations were found within a country. Charlemagne, emperor of the Holy Roman Empire from 800–814, used his foot as the standard length measurement. In Europe, the measure used was shorter than the English foot. The Chinese used a measure that was longer. King Henry stated that a yard was the distance from his nose to the outstretched middle finger of his right hand. An inch was the width of three barley corns laying side by side.

It was obvious to many that a "standard" system of measurement was desperately needed. In the 1790s Thomas Jefferson proposed a plan to Congress for the adoption of a standard system. Louis XVI of France tried to persuade the United States and Great Britain to cooperate in setting a standard. Although Great Britain and the United States did not join his effort, many other countries did. The end result of that project was the metric system. The standard was organized when a committee from the French Academy made its report to the National Assembly. It was adopted into French law and, even though other countries adopted it, use of the system spread slowly.

Originally, the meter was one ten-millionth part of the distance from the North Pole to the Equator, passing through Paris. Later, they discovered the measurement was slightly short, so they defined it again. This time it was the distance between two marks on a platinum/iridium bar. The bar became known as the International Prototype Meter and was placed in the Bureau of Archives in Paris. A meter was later redefined as 1,650,763.73 wavelengths of the orange-red line of krypton 86. The International Bureau of Weights and Measures was formed in 1875 (Paris). The copies of the standards owned by the United States are housed in the National Institute of Standards and Technology, NIST, in Washington D.C. (formerly the National Bureau of Standards).

The metric system has been universally accepted—except in the United States and parts of the British Commonwealth. Its use was legalized in the United States in 1866. In 1975, the U.S. Congress passed a bill allowing for voluntary conversion to the metric system. A special board, the U.S. Metric Board, was formed to implement this program.

The use of the metric system in the United States has increased consistently over the years. The automobile industry has been one proponent of this conversion. With cars assembled from parts manufactured all over the world, it seems very reasonable to agree on one standard measurement. How-

center leads to a *staggered dimension.* The portion of the dimension line touching the arc is a radial line drawn from the true center, whereas the staggered dimension is drawn parallel to the first radial line. When the radius dimension line is foreshortened and the center is located by coordinate dimensions, the dimension line locating the center is foreshortened as well.

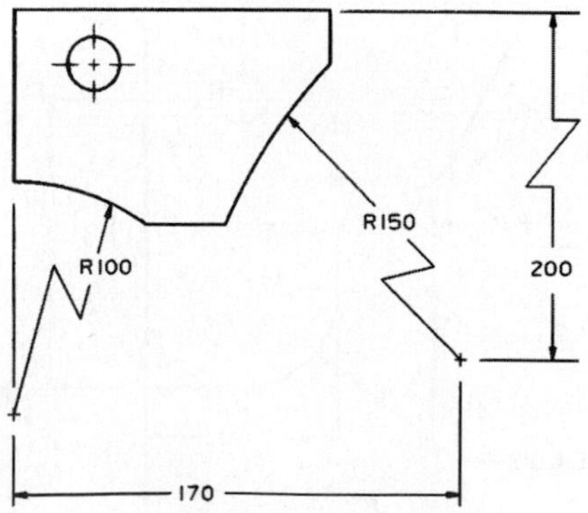

FIGURE 15.39 Foreshortened Radii Dimensions

When a radius is dimensioned in a view that does not show the true shape of the radius, **TRUE R** is added before the radius dimension. A true-shape view of the radius is shown and dimensioned whenever possible.

Instead of dimensioning each radius when a part has a number of radii of the same dimension, a note such as the following may be used:

ALL RADII .75 UNLESS OTHERWISE NOTED

A **spherical surface** for a solid part is dimensioned with a radius dimension preceded by the symbol **SR** (Fig. 15.40).

15.5.2 Detailing Chords, Arcs, and Rounded Ends

An angle measurement is the most common way to dimension arcs and chords (Fig. 15.41). The arc dimension with the arc symbol and the chord dimension are used in

The cubit, an ancient unit of measure.

ever, there is an investment in the "English" system in the United States. The "English" system is now called the U.S. Customary System. New computer numerically controlled (CNC) machines can be used to cut a millimeter or an inch because of the way their motors are controlled. It seems reasonable to expect metric units to replace U.S. customary units in the United States and become the universal "standard." When is another question.

applications such as nipple placement on large pressure vessels in piping design.

Overall dimensions are required for parts having rounded ends (Fig. 15.42). For the fully rounded ends of Figure 15.42(a), the radii are indicated but not dimensioned. For parts with partially rounded ends, the radii are dimensioned [Fig. 15.42(b)]. If corners are rounded, dimensions define the edges, and the arcs are tangent to the edge lines (Fig. 15.43). Radii dimensions use leaders to point to the arc. *The*

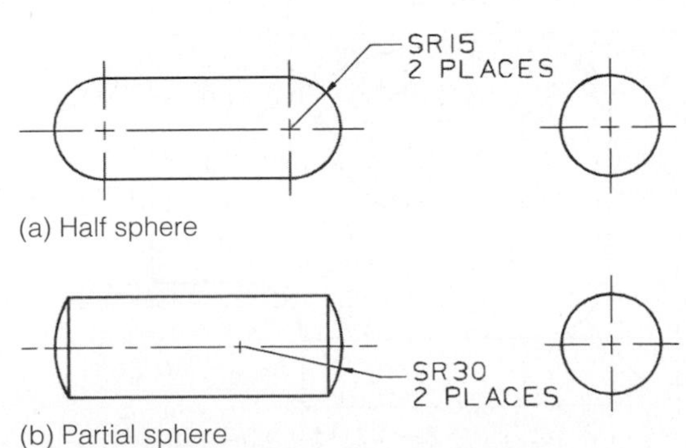

FIGURE 15.40 Spherical Radius Dimensions

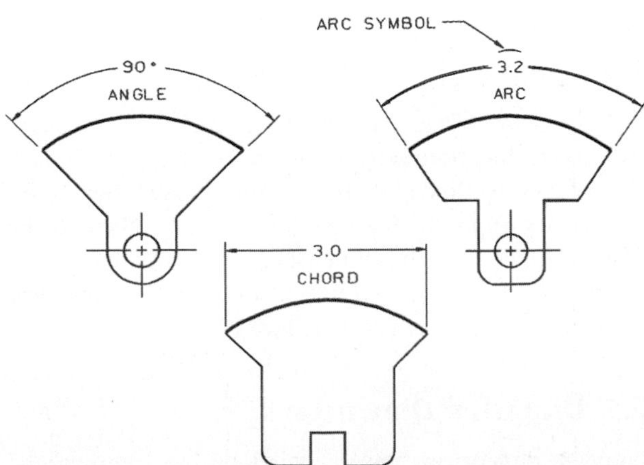

FIGURE 15.41 Dimensioning Angles, Arcs, and Chords

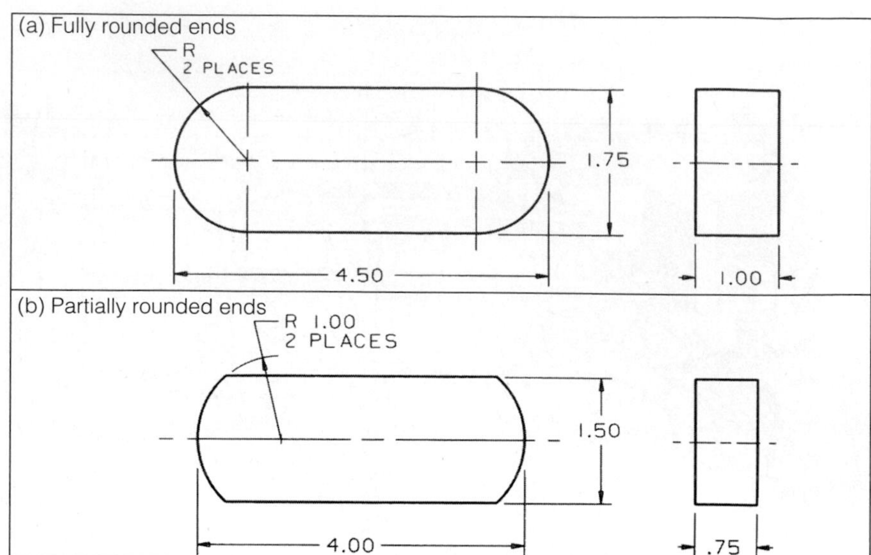

FIGURE 15.42 Dimensioning Rounded Ends

leader "aims" at the center point of the arc. It is acceptable to cross one extension or one dimension line.

A curved outline composed of two or more arcs is dimensioned by giving the radii of all arcs and locating the necessary centers with coordinate dimensions (Fig. 15.44). Other radii are located on the basis of their points of tangency.

Regardless of the arc requirements, the dimensions for a part are shown in a view that best displays the features. In Figure 15.45, the dimensions for the part's angles and radii are dimensioned in the only view that shows them accurately; the true shape is shown in the front view.

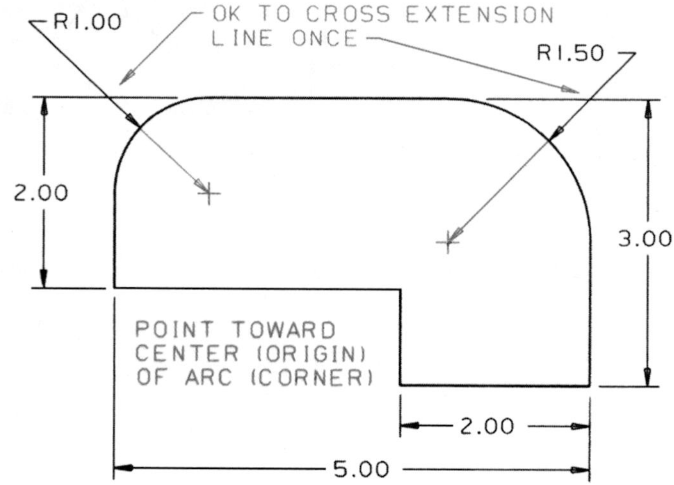

FIGURE 15.43 Dimensioning Rounded Corners

15.5.3 Irregular Outlines

Irregular outlines are dimensioned in Figures 15.46 and 15.47. Circular or noncircular objects are dimensioned through rectangular coordinates or an offset method. Coordinates are dimensioned from base or datum lines. If many coordinates are required to define an outline, the vertical and horizontal coordinate dimensions can be given in a table.

15.5.4 Symmetrical Outlines

When only part of a symmetrical outline can be conveniently shown, the **symmetrical outline** is dimensioned on one side of its *centerline of symmetry* (Fig. 15.47). Symmetry is indicated by applying symbols for part symmetry to the centerline. Notice that the dimension in Figure 15.47 uses *dimension lines as extension lines.* This is one of the few situations where this practice is allowed.

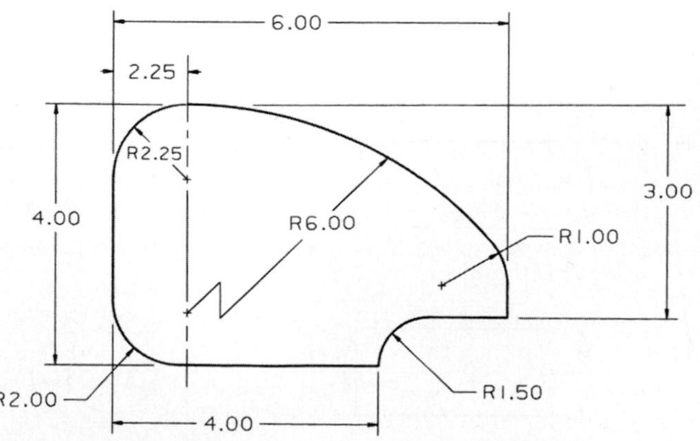

FIGURE 15.44 Dimensioning Circular Arc Outlines

15.5.5 Diameter Dimensions

All diameter dimensions are preceded by the international symbol for diameter: a circle drawn the same size as the

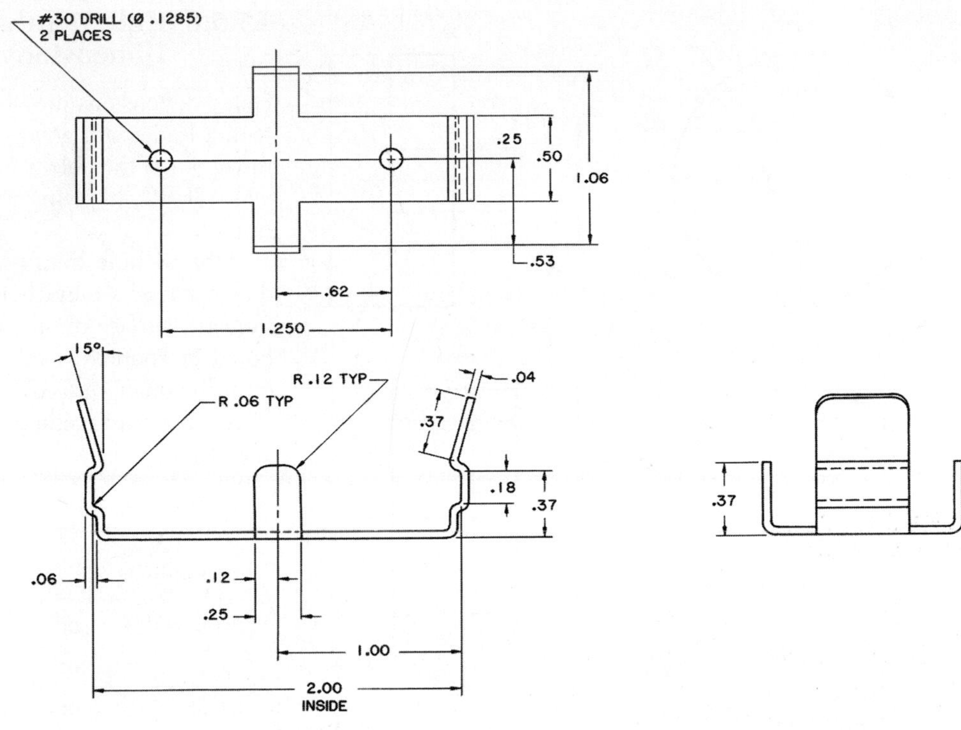

FIGURE 15.45 Detail of CRT Holder

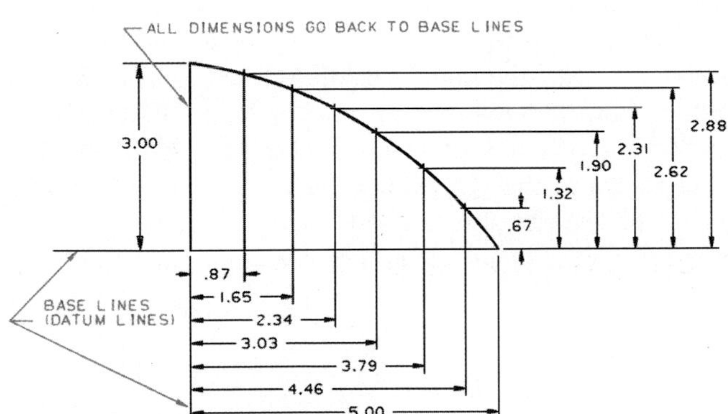

FIGURE 15.46 Coordinate Dimensioning of Curved Outlines

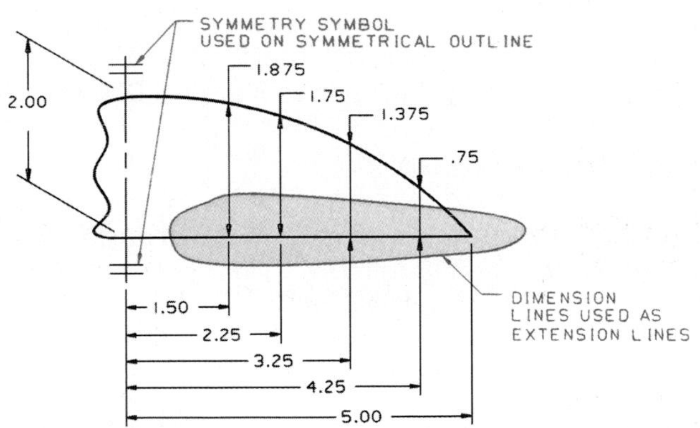

FIGURE 15.47 Dimensioning Symmetrical Outlines Using Dimension Lines as Extension Lines

numerals, with a 60° slanted line passing through its center (Ø). On some older U.S. standard unit drawings, the size of the diameter is called out with the abbreviation **DIA** after the numerals (e.g., **.375 DIA**). Some of the drawings in this text reflect this older practice.

The diameter symbol precedes all diameter values (Fig. 15.48). When the diameters of a number of concentric cylindrical features are specified, the diameter is dimensioned in a longitudinal view (Fig. 15.48).

When a hole cannot be adequately called out where it shows as a circle, the hole is dimensioned in a side view or a section view. The depth of the hole, if not included in a note, can be dimensioned in the longitudinal view. The dimensions of a very large hole are shown by drawing the dimension line at an angle through the diameter [Figure 15.48 (lower left)]. For aligned dimensions placed inside the circular form, the area within the section should be avoided when the dimension runs through the diameter.

Holes should be called out with a leader and a note. The leader points toward the center of the circle. *Solid round shapes* are dimensioned on the noncircular view.

Figure 15.49 shows an alternative way to dimension a

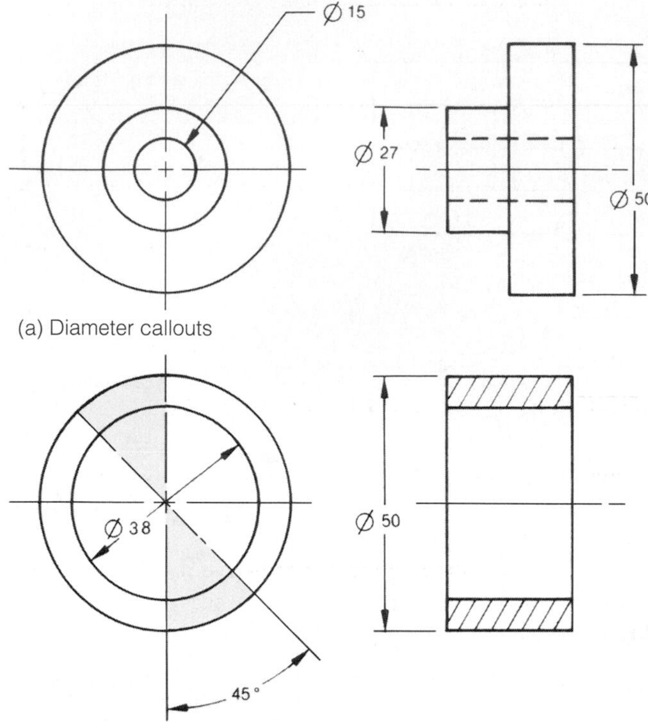

(b) Diameter dimensions and area to avoid

FIGURE 15.48 Dimensioning Diameters

cylindrical part. The first method [Fig. 15.49(a)] shows two views of the part, with standard dimensioning callouts for the hole diameters. The second method, (b), gives only the longitudinal edge view of the part and uses the **DIA** callout for all diameter dimensions.

You May Complete Exercises 15.1 Through 15.4 at This Time

15.5.6 Hole Depths and Diameter Dimensions

Holes dimensions are shown by pointing to the diameter with a leader and giving a note containing size and type. If the depth of the hole is not obvious or not dimensioned, the word **THRU**, implying drill through, follows the size specification.

A **blind hole** does not go through the part. The depth dimension of a blind hole is the depth of the full diameter from the surface of the part. If a blind hole is also counterbored or counterdrilled, the depth dimension is still taken from the outer surface.

A number of methods are used to call out hole diameter and depth:

Fraction-Inch		Decimal-Inch		Decimal-Inch (symbology)
$\frac{1}{2}$ DIA THRU	or	.50 DIA THRU	or	∅ .50 THRU
$\frac{1}{2}$ DIA	or	.50 DIA		∅ .50
$\frac{3}{4}$ DEEP	or	.750 DEEP	or	↧ .750

15.5.7 Dimensioning Slotted Holes

Figure 15.50 shows three methods for dimensioning slots. In Figure 15.50(a) the slot's centerlines are located between centers. A dimension from the edge of the part or other controlling feature is given as well. The slot width is given as an **R** (radius) pointing to the end of the slot arc. The **R** is accompanied by the note **2 PLACES**. ANSI calls for **R** for a radius; however, many companies still use **RAD**. Figure 15.50(b) shows a leader and a note stating the outside dimensions of the slot (**20 × 60**). An **R** callout is also included. The slot also can be located from the part's edges [Fig. 15.50(c)], or its centerlines can be located from two

(a) Two-view drawing with circular view

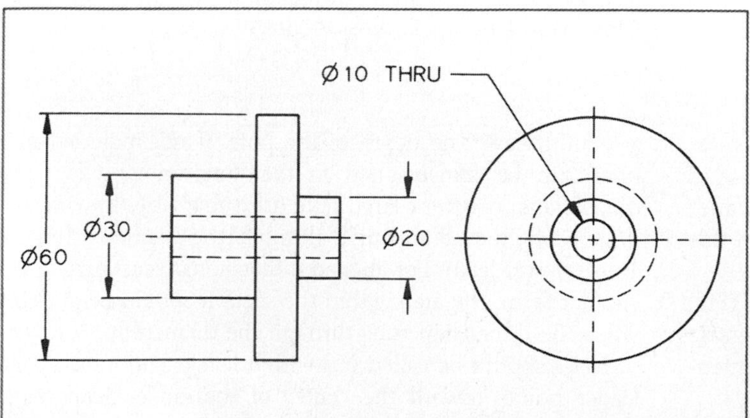

(b) One-view drawing without circular view

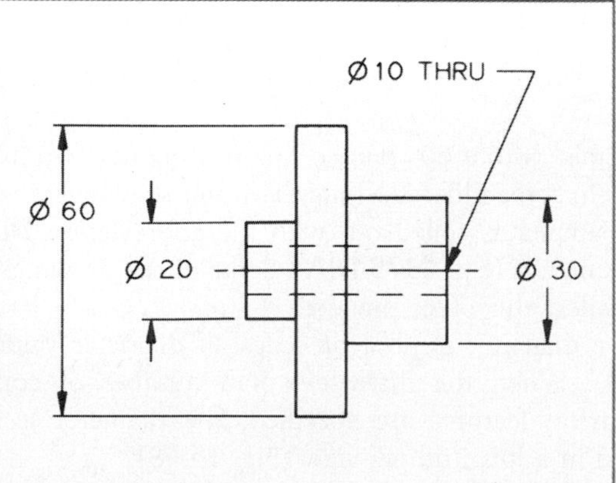

FIGURE 15.49 Dimensioning Diameters on Drawings Without Circular Views

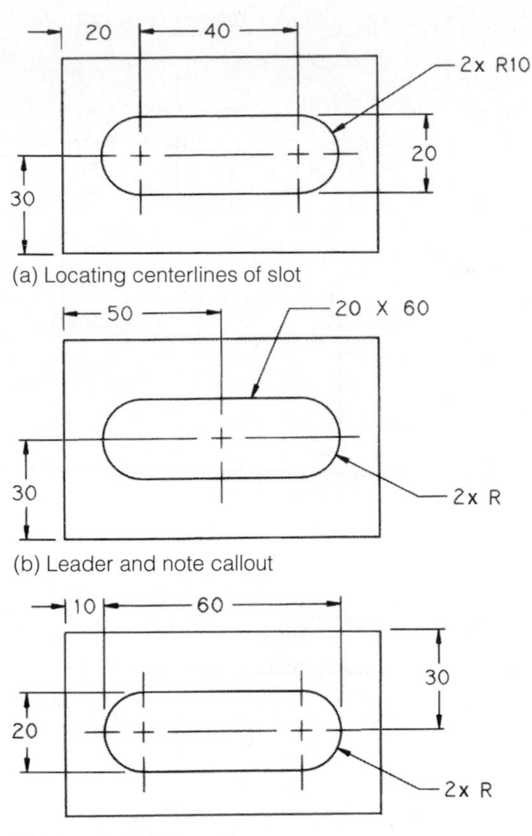

FIGURE 15.50 Dimensioning Slots

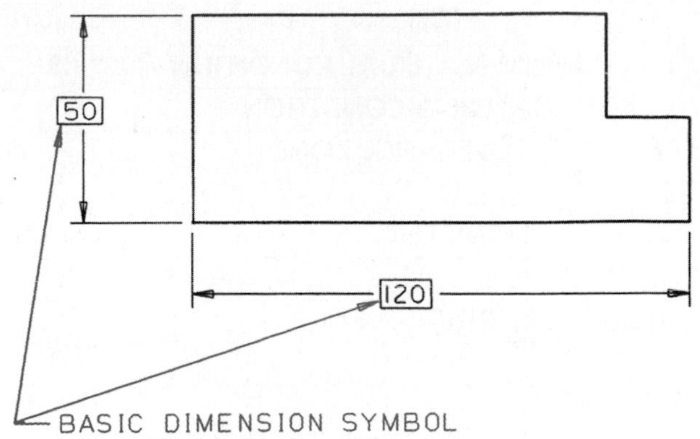

FIGURE 15.52 Basic Dimensioning Symbol

controlling edges. Figure 15.50(c) shows the dimensions of the slot on the view; an **R** callout is also given.

The choice of methods for dimensioning slots is determined by the design and the required slot tolerance. If something fits into the slot, accurate tolerance and dimensions are required. The methods in Figure 15.50(a) and (c) are recommended when accuracy is important. The method in Figure 15.50(a) is good for milled slots; the method in Figure 15.50(c) is good for punched forms.

15.6 Dimensioning Features with Symbols

Geometric characteristics and other dimensional requirements can be established via standard **symbols** instead of traditional terms and abbreviations. These symbols must conform to ANSI Y14.2M (for symbols denoting geometric characteristics see Fig. 15.51, and for symbols identifying a basic dimension see Fig. 15.52). *A basic dimension is a numerical value describing the theoretically exact size, profile orientation, or location of a feature or datum target.* Basic dimensions are the basis from which permissible variations are established by tolerances on other dimensions or in notes.

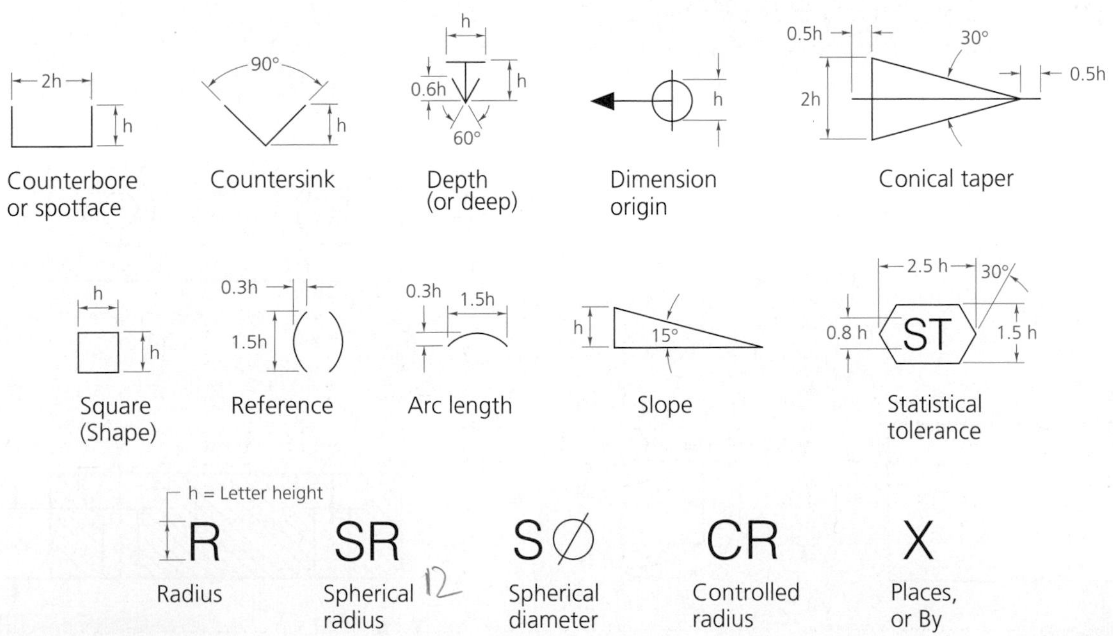

FIGURE 15.51 Form and Proportion of Dimensioning Symbols

Term	Symbol
AT MAXIMUM MATERIAL CONDITION	Ⓜ
AT LEAST MATERIAL CONDITION	Ⓛ
PROJECTED TOLERANCE ZONE	Ⓟ
DIAMETER	∅
SPHERICAL DIAMETER	S∅
RADIUS	R
SPHERICAL RADIUS	SR
REFERENCE	( )
ARC LENGTH	⌒

FIGURE 15.53 Modifying Symbols for Dimensions

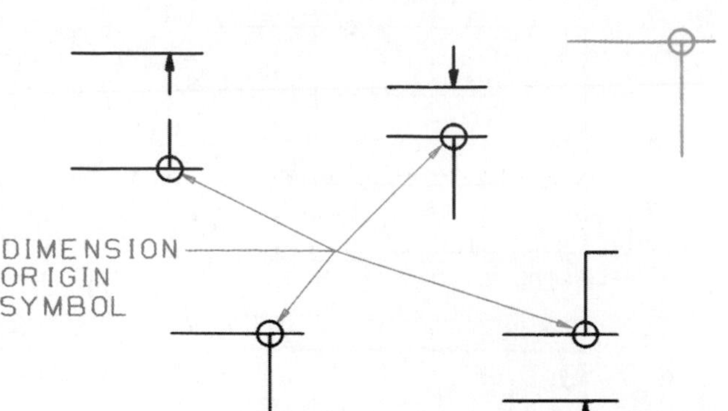

FIGURE 15.55 Dimension Origin Symbol

The symbols for indicating diameter, spherical diameter, radius, and spherical radius are shown in Figure 15.53. Symbols precede the value of a dimension or tolerance given as diameter or radius. Reference dimensions (or reference data) are enclosed within parentheses. Symbology designates a variety of geometric features and dimensions, including the following.

- The symbol to indicate a linear dimension is an arc length measured on a curved outline (Fig. 15.53). The symbol is placed above the dimension (Fig. 15.41).
- To indicate a single dimension applied to a square shape, the "square" symbol precedes the dimension (Fig. 15.54).
- The symbol to indicate a toleranced dimension between two features originates from one of these features (Fig. 15.55).
- The depth of a hole (Fig. 15.56), a counterbore (Fig. 15.57), a spotface (Fig. 15.58), a countersink (Fig. 15.59), or a counterdrill (Fig. 15.59) can be given symbolically. To indicate where a dimension applies to the depth of a feature, the depth symbol precedes the dimension.

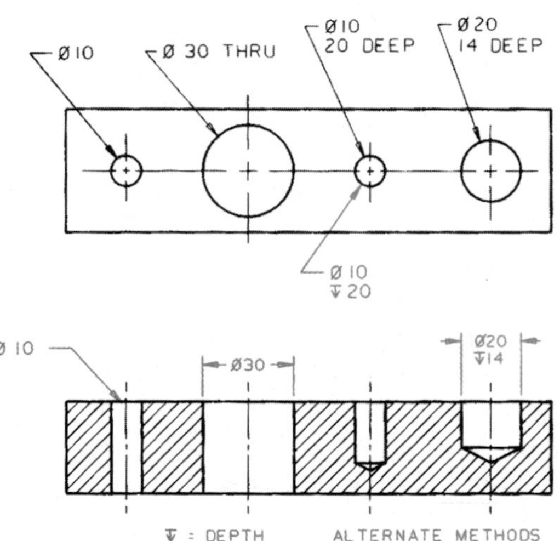

FIGURE 15.56 Using Symbols to Dimension Holes

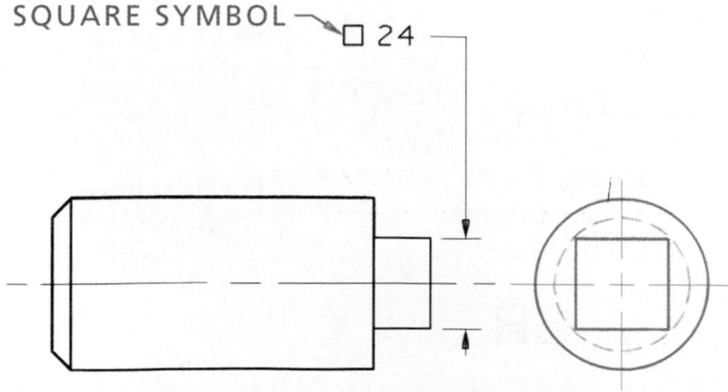

FIGURE 15.54 Square Dimensioning Symbol

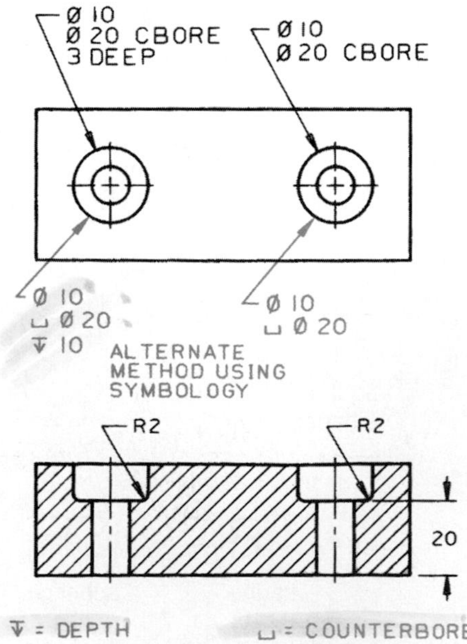

FIGURE 15.57 Dimensioning Counterbores

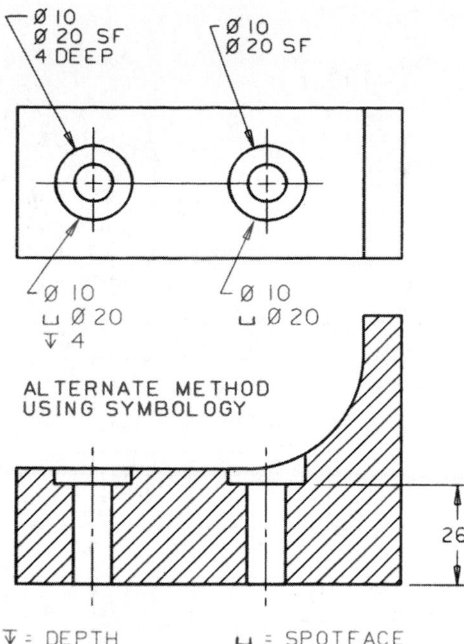

FIGURE 15.58 Dimensioning Spotfaces

15.6.1 Countersunk and Counterdrilled Holes

Countersinking (CSK) ensures that flathead screws are flush with the surface of the part (Fig. 15.59). The diameter and included angle of the countersink are specified. The flathead screw requires a conical seat, usually specified by the included angle and the diameter at the large end.

For **counterdrilled holes (CDRILL)**, the diameter and depth of the counterdrill are given. Specifying the included angle of the counterdrill is optional (Fig. 15.59, lower right). The depth dimension is the depth of the full diameter of the counterdrill measured from the outer surface of the part. Symbology can also be used on these features. A counter-

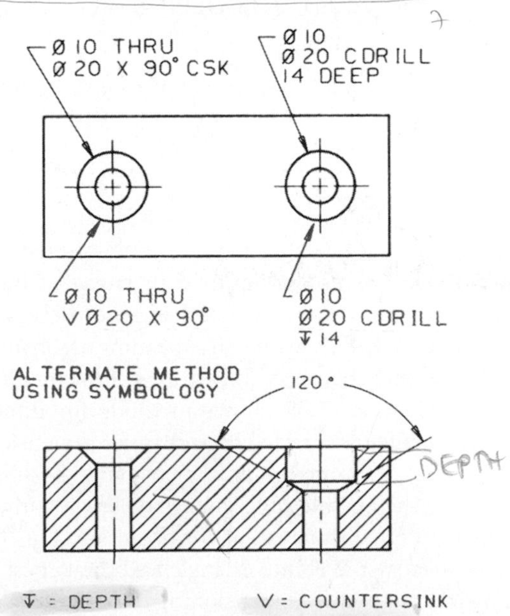

FIGURE 15.59 Dimensioning Countersinks and Counterdrills

drilled hole differs from a counterbored hole in that the bottom of the counterdrilled hole is conical. Counterdrilled holes are created with a step drill or with two drills of different diameters.

15.6.2 Spotfaced Holes

A **spotface (SF)** (Fig. 15.58) is a method of cleaning up and squaring a rough surface, such as on a cast metal part. Material is removed so a screw head will seat flush against the surface. Its depth is usually not dimensioned.

The diameter of the spotfaced area is specified by the diameter symbol and a value. When a depth is required, either the depth or the remaining thickness of material may be specified. A spotface sometimes is specified by a note. If no depth or remaining thickness of material is specified, the spotfacing is the minimum depth necessary to clean up the surface. Figure 15.58 shows both methods for calling out the spotface.

15.6.3 Counterbored Holes

Counterbored holes are used extensively for socket-head screws so that the head of the screw is flush with or below the surface of the part. A **counterbore (CBORE)** is an enlarged hole, piloted from a smaller hole to maintain concentricity. Counterbored holes are machined to a square seat at a specified depth (Fig. 15.57). The depth is called out within the hole note as the distance from the upper surface (beginning surface) to the bottom of the counterbore. Either the symbol for the counterbore or the note **CBORE** is used. The depth symbol or the note **DEEP** can also be used. When the thickness of the remaining material has significance, it, rather than the depth, is dimensioned (Fig. 15.57). Figure 15.60 shows a simple mechanical part dimensioned with symbols.

You May Complete Exercises 15.5 Through 15.8 at This Time

15.7 DIMENSIONING SPECIAL FEATURES

Chamfers, threads, centerdrills, tapers, knurling, keyways, and other *geometric features* require specific, standardized dimensioning. These dimensions are based on the method used to machine them or on a standard purchased part mated with the feature.

15.7.1 Threads

Thread callouts are found in almost every mechanical drawing. Figure 15.4 shows a part designed with metric units. The callout **M 42 × 1.5 - 6g** specifies a metric thread.

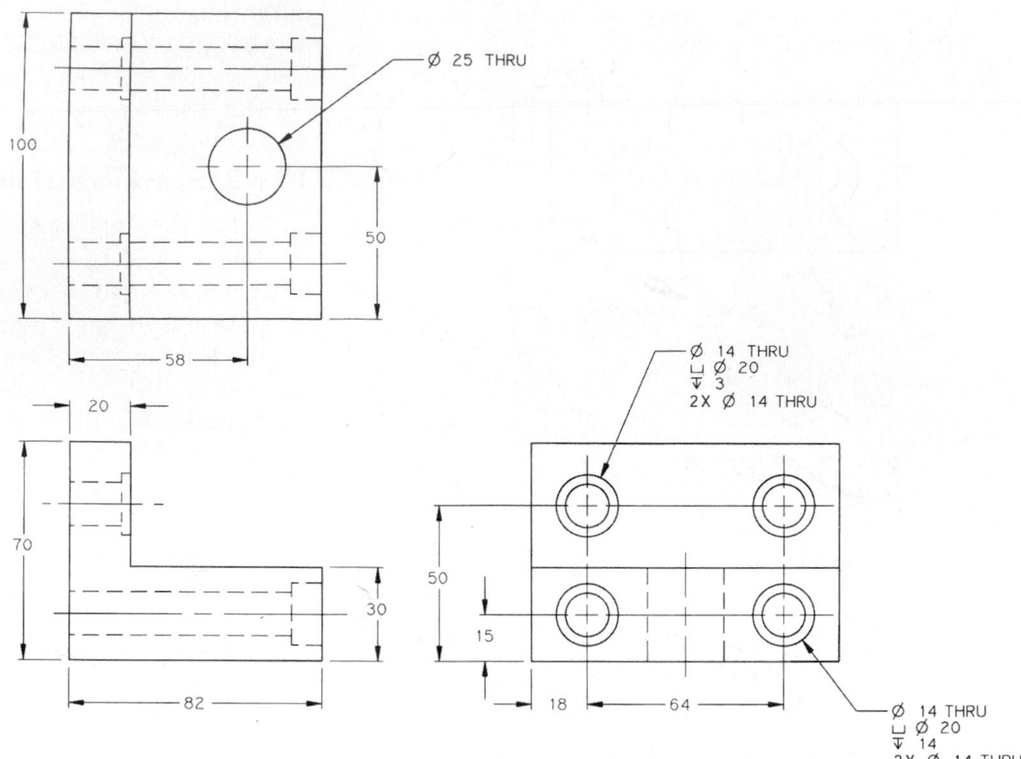

FIGURE 15.60 Part Dimensioned Using Dimensioning Symbols

Figure 15.3 shows an example of a unified thread callout on a decimal-inch drawing (**.250-20 UNC**).

Nonmetric threads are classified according to the number of threads applied to a specific diameter. Unified (**UN**) thread is the standard type of thread for the United States. To specify screw threads, the nominal major diameter is given first, followed by the number of threads per inch and the series designation. Finally, the class of fit between male and female threads is given, followed by an **A** for male threads or a **B** for female threads. For tapped holes, the complete note contains the tap drill diameter and the depth of the hole, followed by the thread specification and the length of the tapped threads. All threads are assumed to be right hand unless left hand is specified by **LH** following the class. A few examples of screw thread notations follow.

Decimal-Inch

- **.190-32 UNF-2A** or **#10-32 UNF-2A**
- **.250-20 UNC-2B** or **$\frac{1}{4}$-20 UNC-2B**
- **2.000-16 UN-2A**
- **2.500-10 UNS-2B**

Metric

- **M6 × 1-4h6h**
- **M16 × L4 -P2-4h6h**

The thread type and size are given on the drawing, and the machinist chooses the correct drill diameter. Specifying the drill and tapping requirements requires the diameter and the depth. In this case, the tap drill size, its depth, the thread specification, and the depth of threads are provided, as in the examples that follow.

∅.312 1.25 DEEP
.375-16 UNC-2B, .88 DEEP or **$\frac{3}{8}$-16 UNC-2B**
3 HOLES

∅ .422 1.25 DEEP
.500-13 UNC-2B LH, 1.12 DEEP or **$\frac{1}{2}$-13 UNC-2B LH**
2 HOLES

More information on methods of specifying and dimensioning screw threads is found in ANSI Y14.6.

15.7.2 Chamfers

Manual and automated assembly techniques both benefit from tapered features to help the parts engage. **Chamfers** are specified by dimensions or notes. It is not necessary to use the word **CHAMFER** when the meaning is obvious. If the chamfer is other than 45°, dimensions show the direction of the slope. Figure 15.61 shows methods for dimensioning external chamfers. You can show chamfer dimensions by the chamfer angle and one leg, by dimensioning both legs, or by pointing to the chamfer and giving the angle and one leg as a callout. Internal dimensions for chamfers (Fig. 15.62) are dimensioned by the included angle and the largest diameter. The metric method of dimensioning chamfers is also shown on this figure. For inch-unit drawings, the angle is sometimes given second and the leg first, for example, **.25 × 45°**.

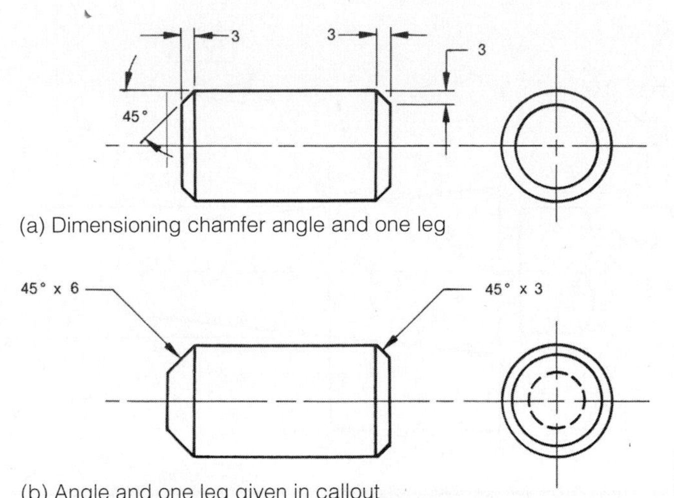

(a) Dimensioning chamfer angle and one leg

(b) Angle and one leg given in callout

FIGURE 15.61 **Dimensioning Chamfers**

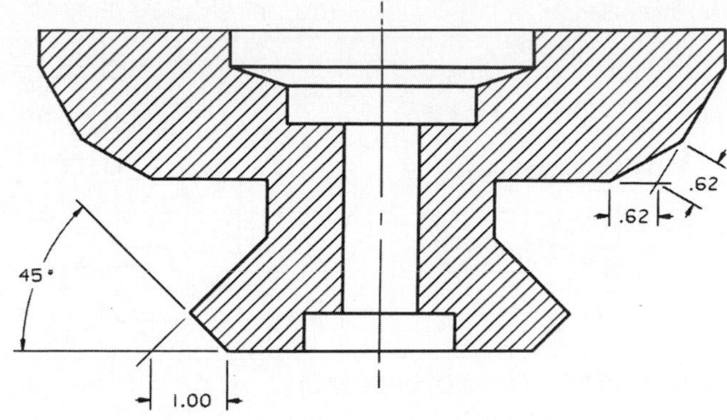

FIGURE 15.63 **Dimensioning Chamfers Between Surfaces Not at 90°**

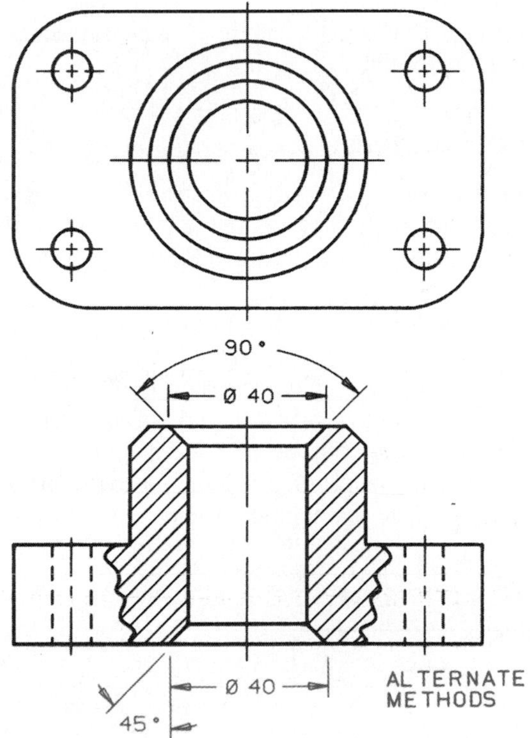

FIGURE 15.62 **Internal Chamfers**

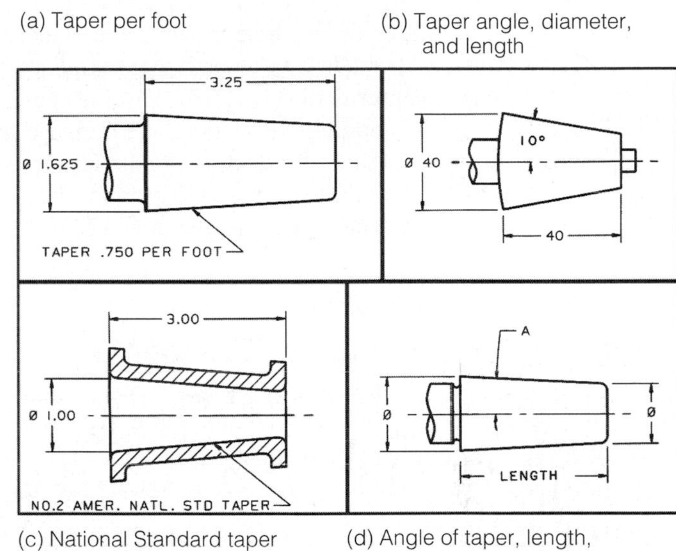

(a) Taper per foot

(b) Taper angle, diameter, and length

(c) National Standard taper

(d) Angle of taper, length, and diameter at both ends

FIGURE 15.64 **Dimensioning Tapers**

This method is being replaced by ANSI Y14.5M. If chamfers are required for surfaces intersecting at other than right angles, the methods shown in Figure 15.63 apply.

15.7.3 Taper Dimensioning

Tapers are used on machines to align and hold machined parts that require simple and speedy assembly and disassembly. A round taper has a uniform increase in the diameter on a round part for a given length measured parallel to the axis of the workpiece (conical). Internal or external tapers are noted by taper per foot (TPF), taper per inch (TPI), or degrees. TPF or TPI refers to the difference in diameters within 1 foot or 1 inch [(Fig. 15.64(a)]. The difference is measured in inches. The *angles of taper* refer to the inclined angles with the part's centerline (axis) [Figure 15.64(b)].

In Figure 15.64(a), the taper per foot, the length of the part, and the large diameter are given. In Figure 15.64(b), the diameter, the length, and the angle are given. In Figure 15.64(c), the length, the diameter, and the note **NO. 2 AMER. NATL. STD TAPER** are given. In the last example [Fig. 15.64(d)], the two diameters, the length, and the angle are given.

In Figure 15.65(a), the internal taper is designated through a note (**TAPER 1.75:12 ON DIA FIT TO GAGE**), the gage diameter (**1.00 GAGE**), locating dimension (**1.50**), angle (**4°10′**), and the part length (**3.50**). Figure 15.65(b) uses the same method on an external taper. Figure 15.66 expresses the taper ratio (**10:1**) and gives the gage location and gage diameter.

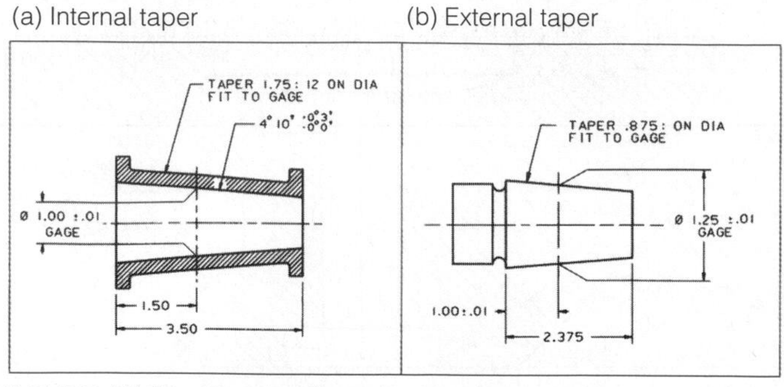

FIGURE 15.65 Taper Dimensioning

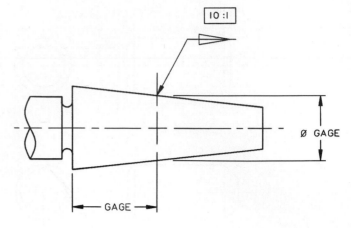

FIGURE 15.66 Dimensioning a Taper with a Ratio

15.7.4 Center Drill Dimensioning

When a part is held and turned between the centers of a lathe, a *center hole* is required on each end of the cylindrical workpiece. The center hole has a 60° angle that conforms to the center and a smaller drilled hole to clear the center's point. The center hole is made with a combination drill and countersink called a **center drill** (Fig. 15.67). In this figure, the A dimension is the workpiece diameter, the B dimension is the body diameter of the center drill, the C dimension is for the diameter of the drilled center hole, and the D dimension is the depth. The drill tip is drawn at 120°.

15.7.5 Keys and Keyseats

A **key** as a demountable machinery part. When assembled into keyseats, a key provides a positive means for transmitting torque between a shaft and a hub. A **keyseat** is an axially located rectangular groove in a shaft or hub. Keyseats are dimensioned by width, depth, location, and, if required, length (Fig. 15.68). The depth is dimensioned from the opposite side of the shaft or hole.

15.7.6 Knurling

A **knurl** is a machined rough geometrical surface on a round metal part. Knurling improves the grip or helps press-fit the knurled part into a hole in a mating part. Knurling is also done for appearance.

Knurling is specified in terms of type, pitch, and diameter before and after knurling. When diameter control is not required, the diameter after knurling is omitted. If only a portion of a feature is to be knurled, axial dimensioning is necessary. Knurling can be either diamond patterned or straight patterned and fine, medium, or coarse. Knurling is specified by a note that includes the type of knurl required,

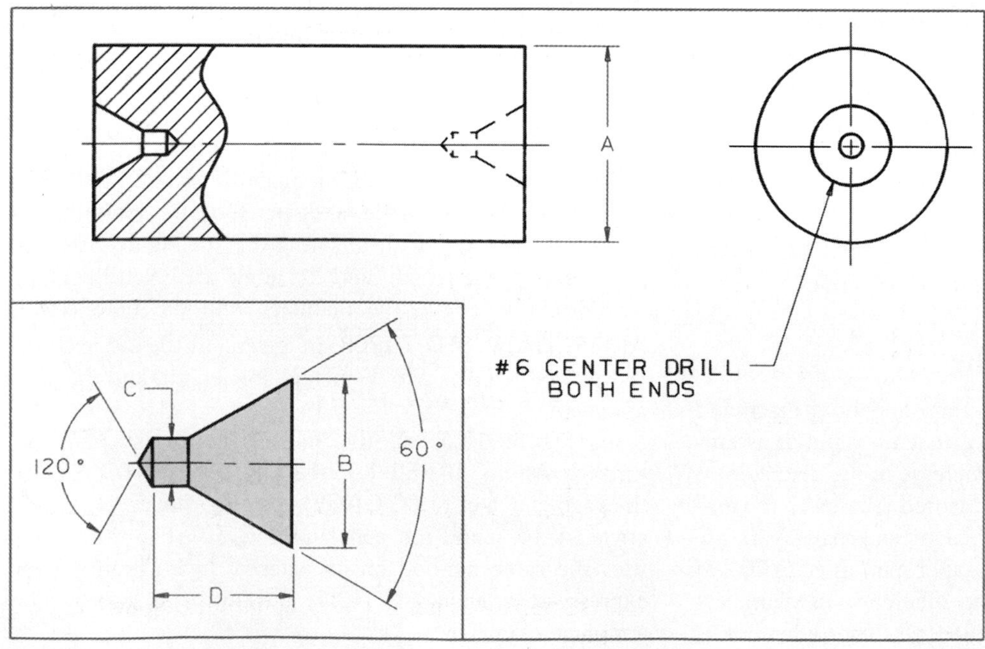

FIGURE 15.67 Center Holes and Center Drills

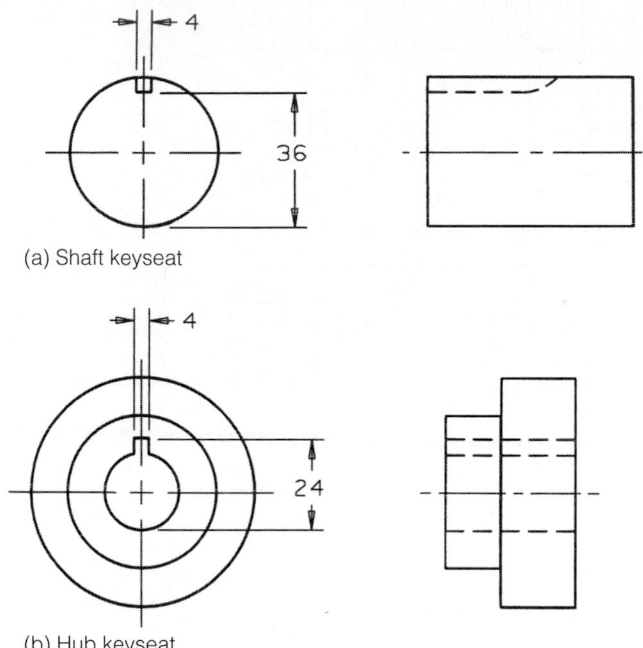

FIGURE 15.68 Dimensioning Keyseats

the pitch, the toleranced diameter of the feature prior to knurling, and the minimum acceptable diameter after knurling (Fig. 15.69).

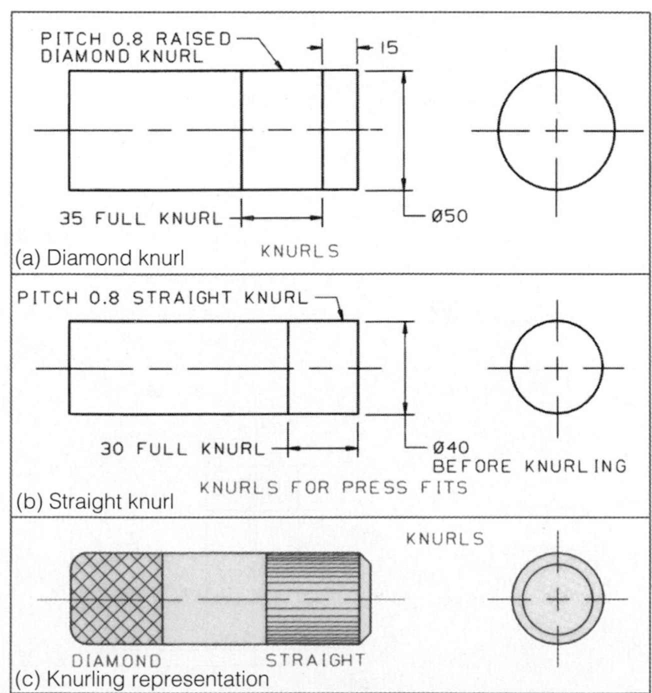

FIGURE 15.69 Dimensioning Knurling

15.8 LOCATING FEATURES ON A DRAWING

The location of holes, slots, and machined features on a part is very important. During dimensioning, *consider how the part is to be machined.* Understanding the detailing and dimensioning process begins with analyzing the part geometrically.

If a CAD system was used for the design of the part, the engineer need only call up the 3D design and place it in the views necessary to describe the part with dimensions and notes.

15.8.1 Geometric Analysis of a Part

Figure 15.70 shows simple geometric shapes and the dimensions required to describe the shapes. The machinist should have all necessary dimensions. *A drawing is never "scaled" to find a location or size that should have been described by a dimension.*

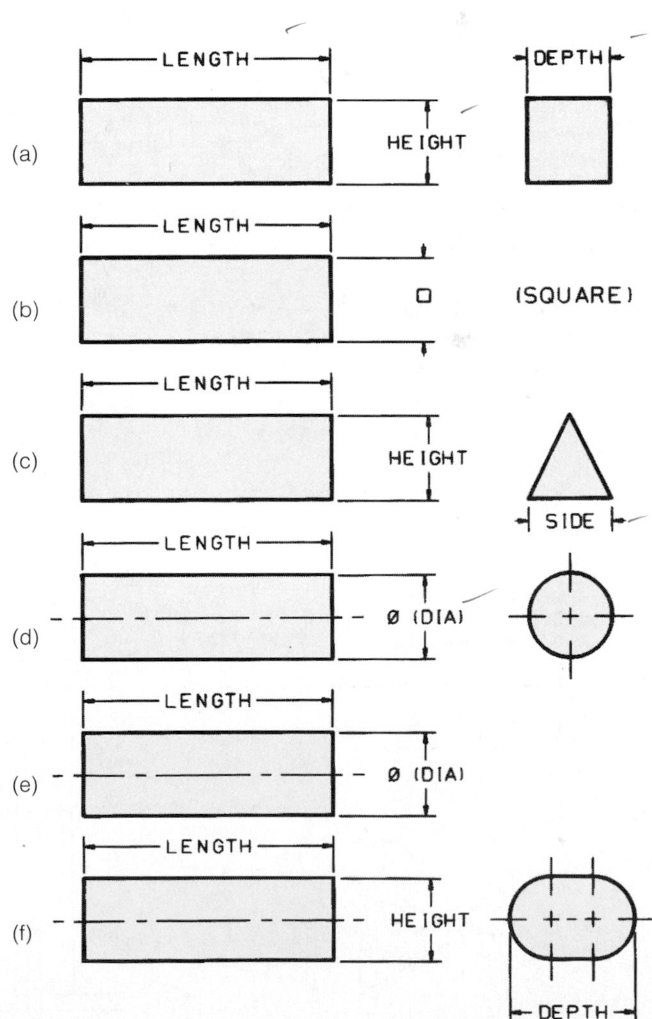

FIGURE 15.70 Dimensions for Common Geometric Shapes

In Figure 15.71, a simple clamp is shown in three views with appropriate dimensioning. It is composed entirely of rectangular prisms. Each of these prisms must be sufficiently dimensioned so a machinist can make the part. *The three most important dimensions are also required: height, width, and depth.* The 20 × 20 cutout in the top view, in Figure 15.71, is an example of a negative area. When a mating part must fit into the area, the negative area must be dimensioned.

The part in Figure 15.72 is composed entirely of cylindrical shapes. In fact, only the ends are flat planar surfaces. Notes that the holes are removed negative cylinders.

Size dimensions for a part are given to establish the shape itself. The diameter of the cylinder is a size dimension. **Location dimensions** position a geometric shape in space. In Figure 15.73, the .34 dimension establishing the location of the hole in the front view is an example of a location dimension. The location of a shape and the shape's size are

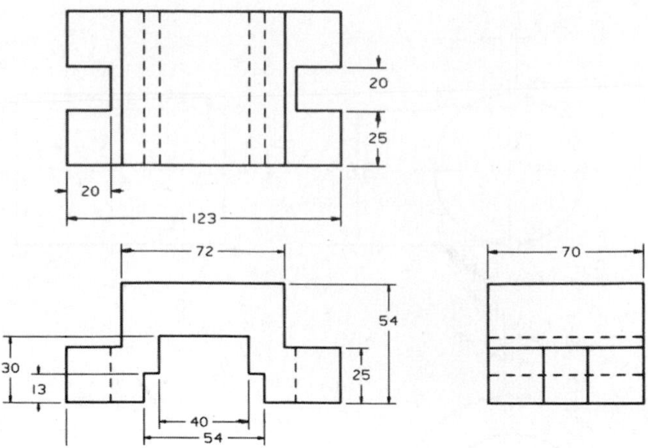

FIGURE 15.71 Dimensioned Clamp

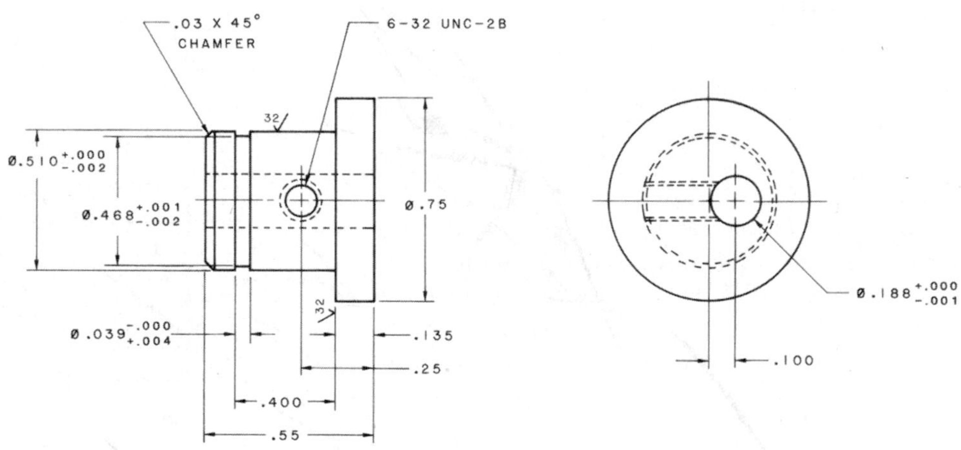

FIGURE 15.72 Cap Detail

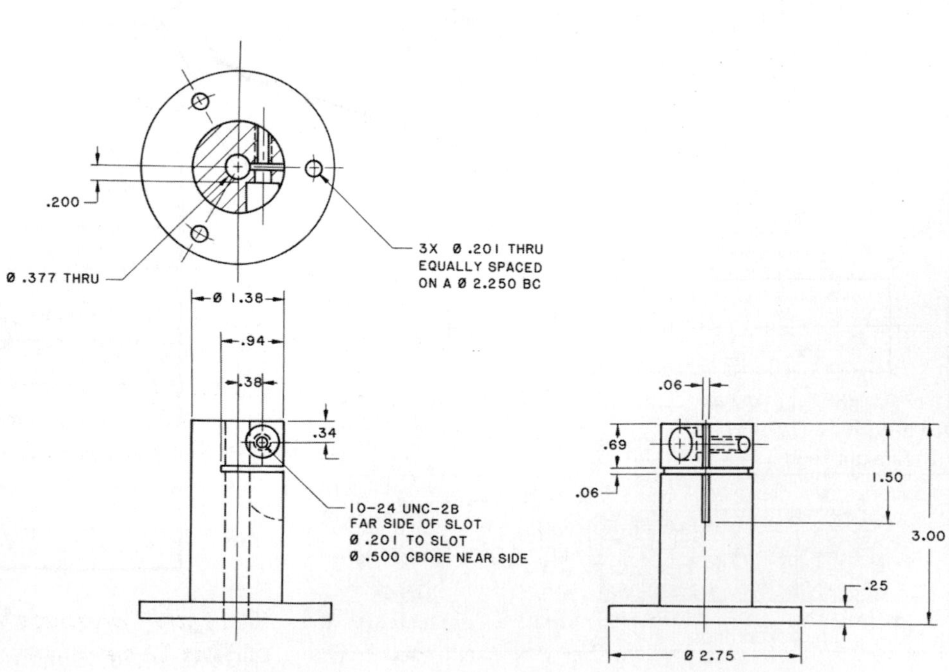

FIGURE 15.73 Pedestal Detail

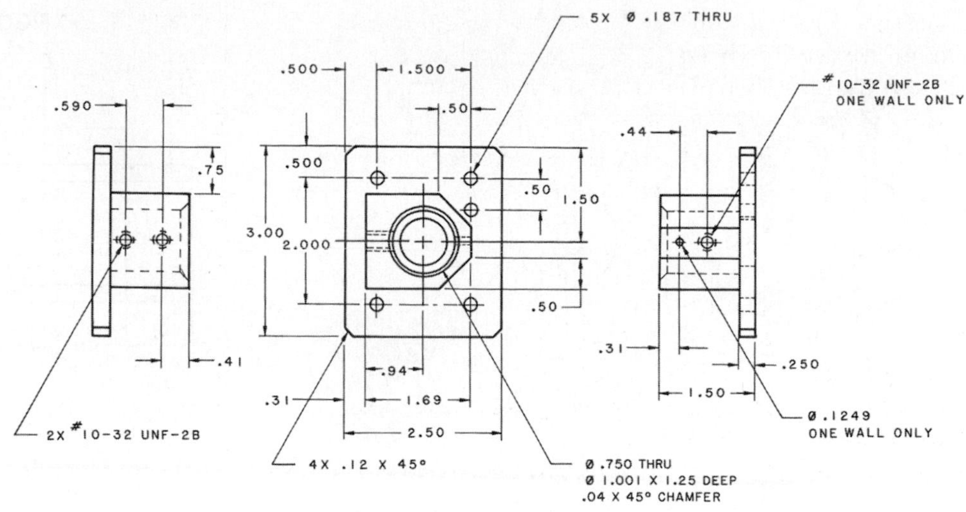

6061-T6 ALUM ALY BLACK ANODIZE

FIGURE 15.74 **Base Mounting Detail**

equally important. Size and location dimensions must be complete to avoid misunderstandings. On the other hand, it is important not to overdimension, that is, to give two dimensions that locate the same feature. The details of locating holes about a center and locating holes on a part are given in section 15.8.5. The details covering datum dimensions are given in section 15.10.1.

15.8.2 Mating Parts and Dimensions

In Figure 15.74, the part has features that obviously relate to a mating piece. The base of the part attaches to a mating part using the .187 clearance holes. A .750 diameter chamfered hole runs through the part. A shaft or other cylindrical item is to be inserted here during assembly and will be held in place by one or more screws entering the side of the part. In most cases, the part to be detailed will be accompanied by a description and/or an illustration of the assembly. *From the assembly drawing, the use, location, orientation in space, and mating pieces are readily identified.*

The assembly of the slide plate in Figure 15.75(a) was designed on a 3D CAD system. Each piece is shown separately in Figure 15.75(b), (c), and (d). An assembly is provided in Figure 15.75(e). Because the slide must fit into the slot in the base, the slide and base have **related dimensions.** The slide's bottom portion is mated with the top of the base. The mating dimension for the slide is slightly smaller than that for the base because it must fit inside the slot. The designer establishes the *clearance fit*.

When dimensioning parts that must mate with other parts in an assembly, the related surfaces on each part should be dimensioned. Mating dimensions are also necessary to establish hole patterns used to secure one part to another.

15.8.3 Finish Marks and Machined Surfaces

Rough stock shapes, castings, and forgings have rough and unmachined surface textures. **Machined surfaces** are established on the drawing through finish marks. A **finish mark** is a symbol that tells the machinist the machining requirements for a surface. Machined surfaces must be established from a rough surface, in any direction (top, front, side). Many features on a casting or forging must be machined, because these processes produce a part with every required geometric shape, but the surfaces are rough. All other machined surfaces or holes are established from that first machined surface. The symbol can be the traditional finish mark [Figure 15.76(a)], the general symbol [Figure 15.76(b)], or the ANSI-recognized **basic surface texture symbol** [Figure 15.76(c)].

The placements and measurements for constructing the three types of symbols are shown in Figure 15.76. Symbol templates are available for quick, easy, and accurate insertion of symbols on a drawing.

The general symbol establishes the surface to be machined without providing any details as to the quality or type of surface. The basic surface texture symbol, on the other hand, establishes a surface to be machined or how it can be altered to provide specifications for the lay, roughness, and waviness of a surface. This symbol is used whenever there is a need to control the surface irregularities of a part (Fig. 15.77).

You May Complete Exercises 15.9 Through 15.12 at This Time

FIGURE 15.75 Mechanical Assembly

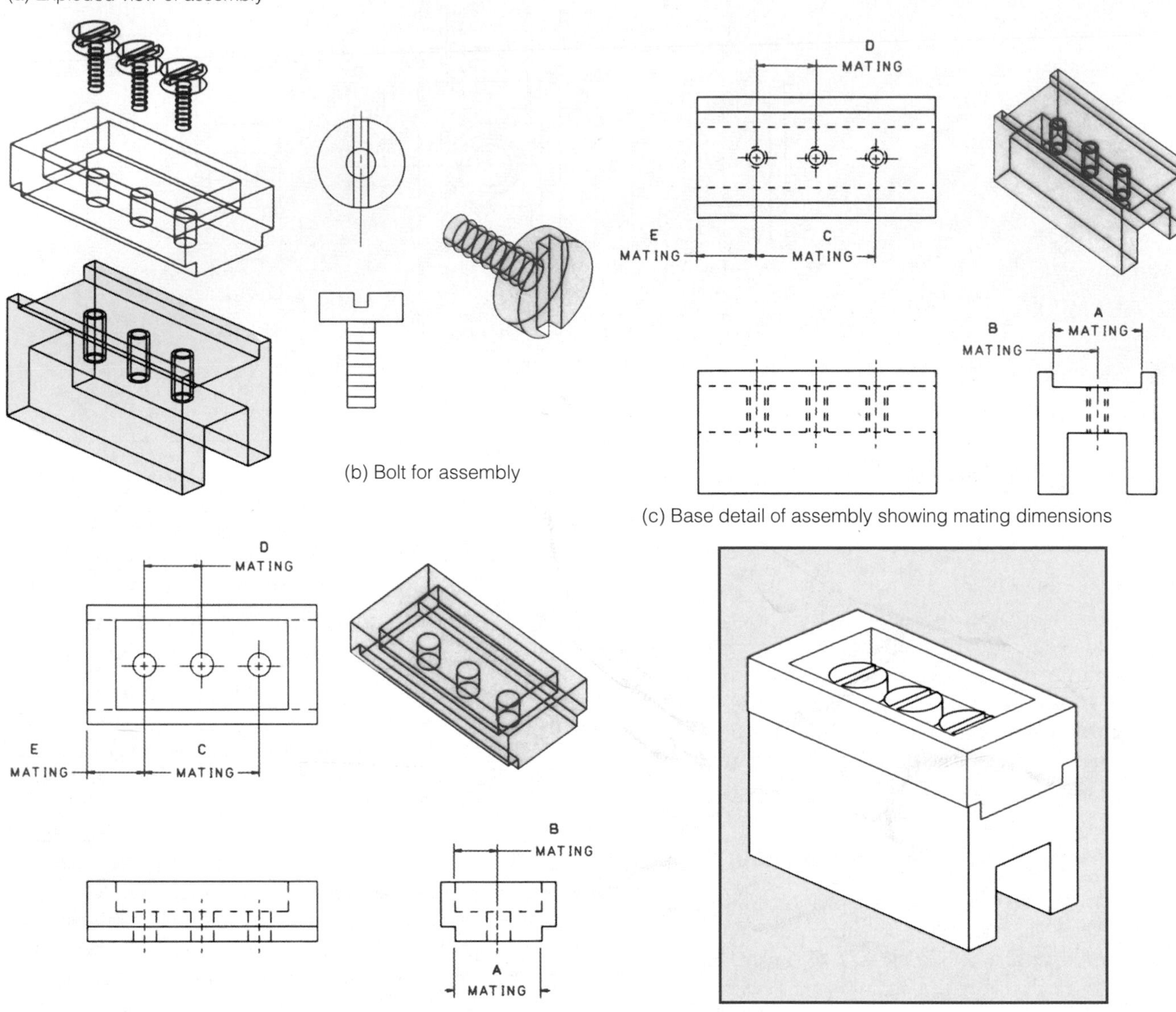

(a) Exploded view of assembly

(b) Bolt for assembly

(c) Base detail of assembly showing mating dimensions

(d) Slide plate of assembly showing mating dimensions

(e) Assembly created by inserting parts together

15.8.4 Locating Holes and Features on a View

Because machined surfaces are used to establish machined features such as holes and slots, it is important to locate them by dimensions from prominent features or surfaces (Fig. 15.78). The bracket arm is a cast part and has a number of machined surfaces and holes. Because the central hole is obviously the most important, all machined holes and slots are located from it. In the front view, the bottom surface was used to locate each of the height dimensions.

A general rule for dimensioning is to dimension from a rough surface to a finished surface once in each direction and between rough surfaces for all other nonmachined surfaces in each direction. Dimensions are given between all other machined surfaces and the first finished surface in each direction. Features such as holes and slots are dimensioned between each other and back to the prominent finished surface in each direction.

When the true shape of a feature or surface does not appear in one of the six standard views, an auxiliary view of that surface and feature should be projected to locate it properly (Fig. 15.79).

15.8.5 Locating Holes on a Part

Size dimensions for a part's features are established first, followed by the location of features such as holes. Holes are located from a machined surface. In most cases, holes are established in patterns and dimensioned accordingly. Figure 15.80 shows a detail of a connector. Because the part is thin (.25), only one view is needed. Each of the holes is located from the lower left corner. The 0,0 position (origin) is used to establish control surfaces from which all dimensions are taken. This part has dimensions without dimension lines. This is called **rectangular coordinate dimensioning with-**

FIGURE 15.76 Finish Marks

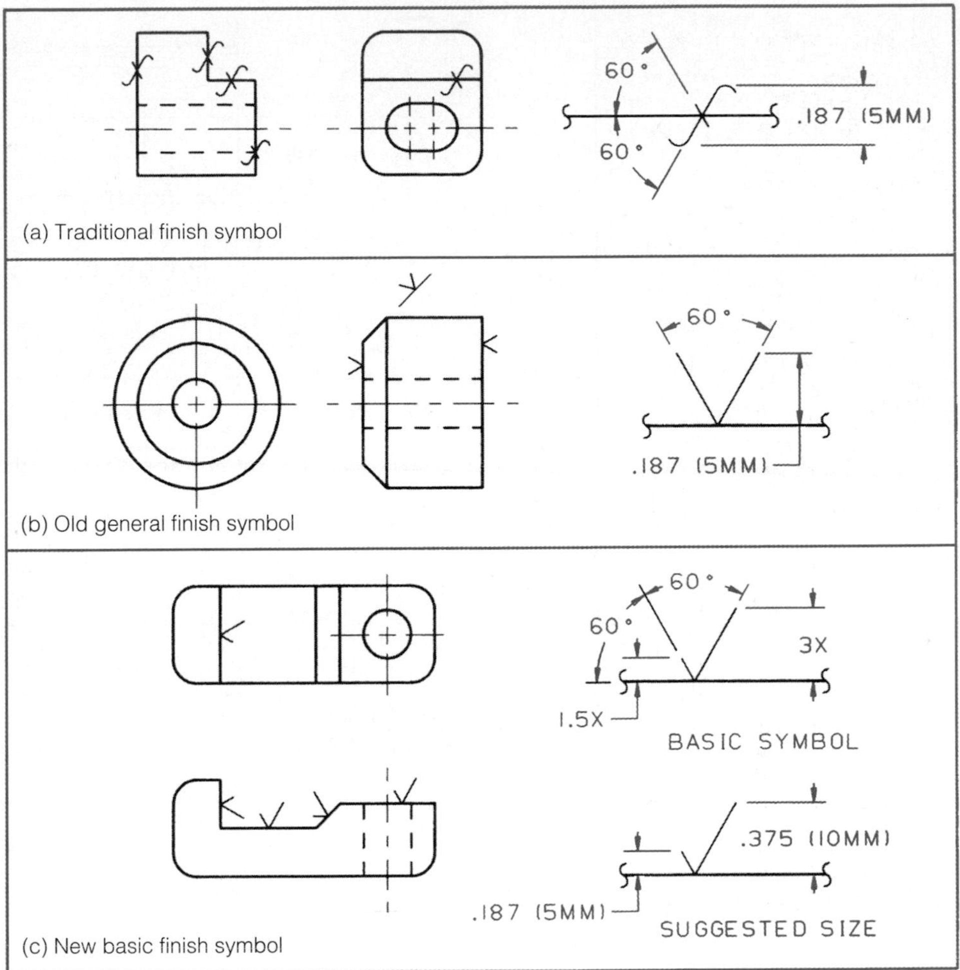

(a) Traditional finish symbol

(b) Old general finish symbol

(c) New basic finish symbol

out dimension lines.

Features that lie about a common center, such as slots and holes (Fig. 15.81), can be dimensioned with angular dimensions, (a), or with a note such as "equally spaced," (b). **Offset dimensioning** takes each locating dimension along the axis of the part from its centerline. This method is preferred because it is easier to set up a machine to locate the holes for machining with rectangular coordinates.

Because each of the holes dimensioned in Figures 15.81 and 15.82 is taken from the center of the part, they are all **dimensioned from a finished surface.** Whenever possible, location dimensions to machined features are taken from a finished surface (Fig. 15.2).

Hole patterns, a set of holes related to another mating part, are established by locating the center hole (if there is one), or by locating the same hole in both directions, in which case dimensions between the holes are given.

15.9 NOTES ON DRAWINGS

Notes can be either **local notes,** as in the callout of a hole, or **general notes** (Fig. 15.45). General notes are placed outside the geometry and beyond dimensions. Notes are one of the last items to be placed on a drawing.

General notes are located, according to ANSI standards, in the upper left-hand corner or the lower left-hand corner of the drawing, as in Figure 15.77, where the following note appears:

NOTE:
ALL FILLETS AND ROUNDS
TO BE R .250 UNLESS
OTHERWISE SPECIFIED

Drawings completed to older ANSI standards have notes above the title block on the right side of the drawing. Some of the examples in the text reflect this older standard, as will many drawings encountered on the job. Many companies apply their own in-house standards that may deviate from accepted ANSI standards.

Here is an example of typical general notes:

NOTES:
1. MATL: .093 THK. ALUMINUM-5052.
2. FINISH: CLEAR ANODIZE–FRONT & REAR PANELS BRUSHED.
3. OPTIONAL RELIEF FOR BREAK.
4. MIN. BEND RAD. TYP. (4) PLACES.
5. SILK-SCREEN PER DWG. 18014-201

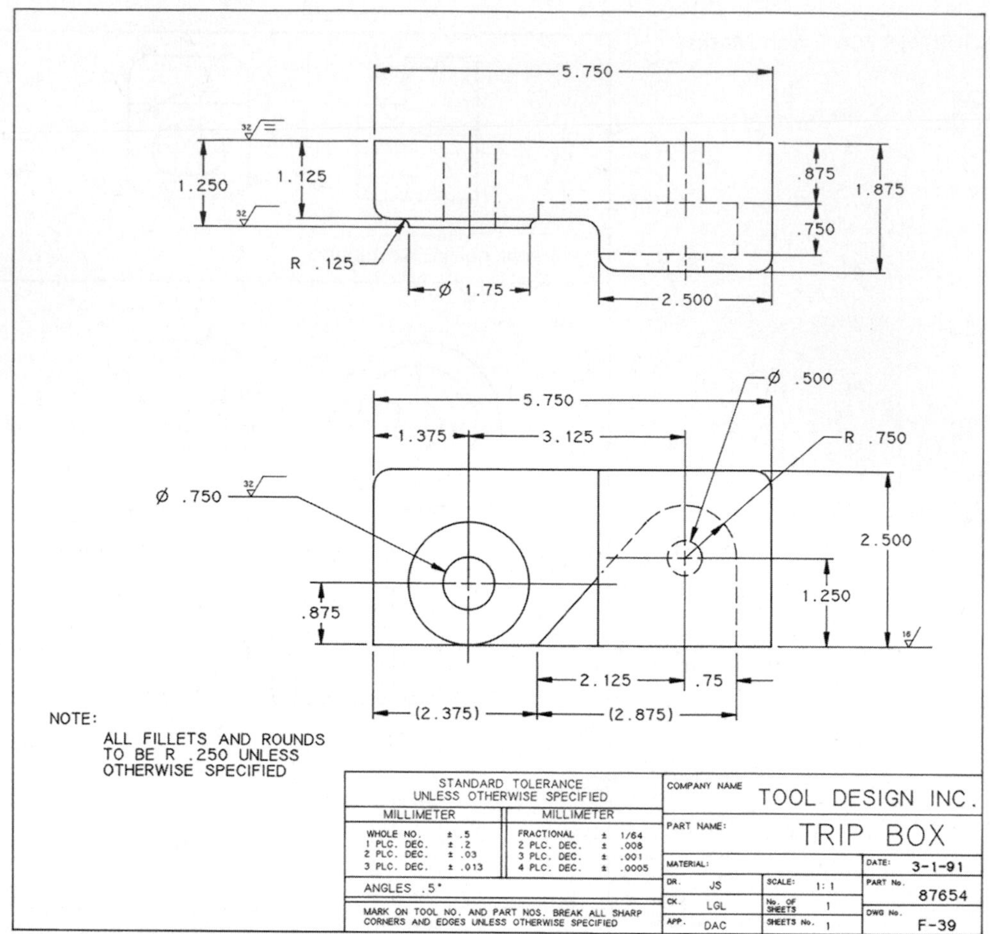

FIGURE 15.77 Finish Marks Used on Mechanical Detail

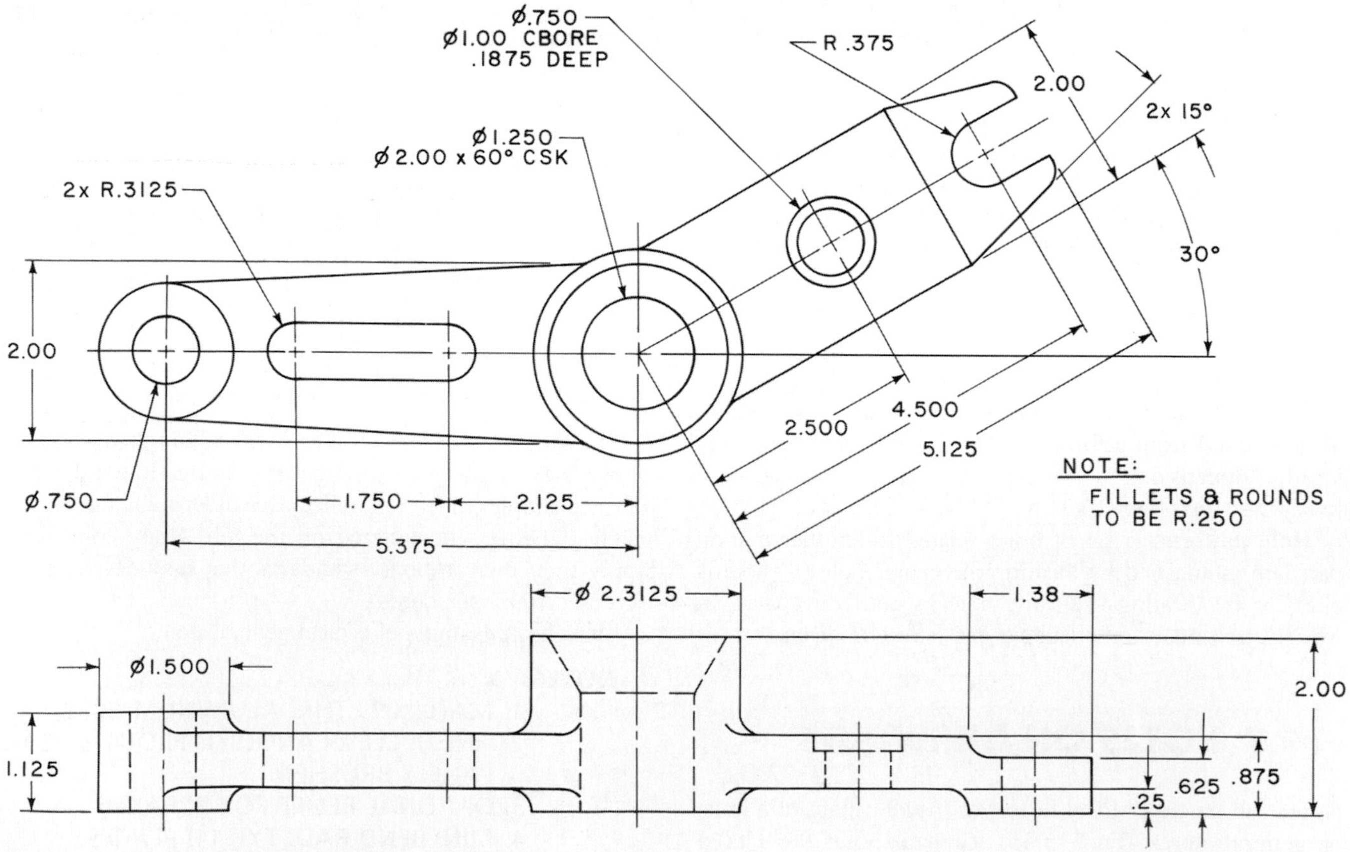

Ø.750
Ø1.00 CBORE
.1875 DEEP
R .375
2.00
2x 15°
Ø1.250
Ø2.00 x 60° CSK
2x R.3125
30°
2.00
4.500
2.500
5.125
Ø.750
1.750
2.125
5.375
NOTE:
FILLETS & ROUNDS TO BE R.250
Ø 2.3125
1.38
Ø1.500
2.00
1.125
.625
.875
.25

FIGURE 15.78 Dimensioning Machined Features

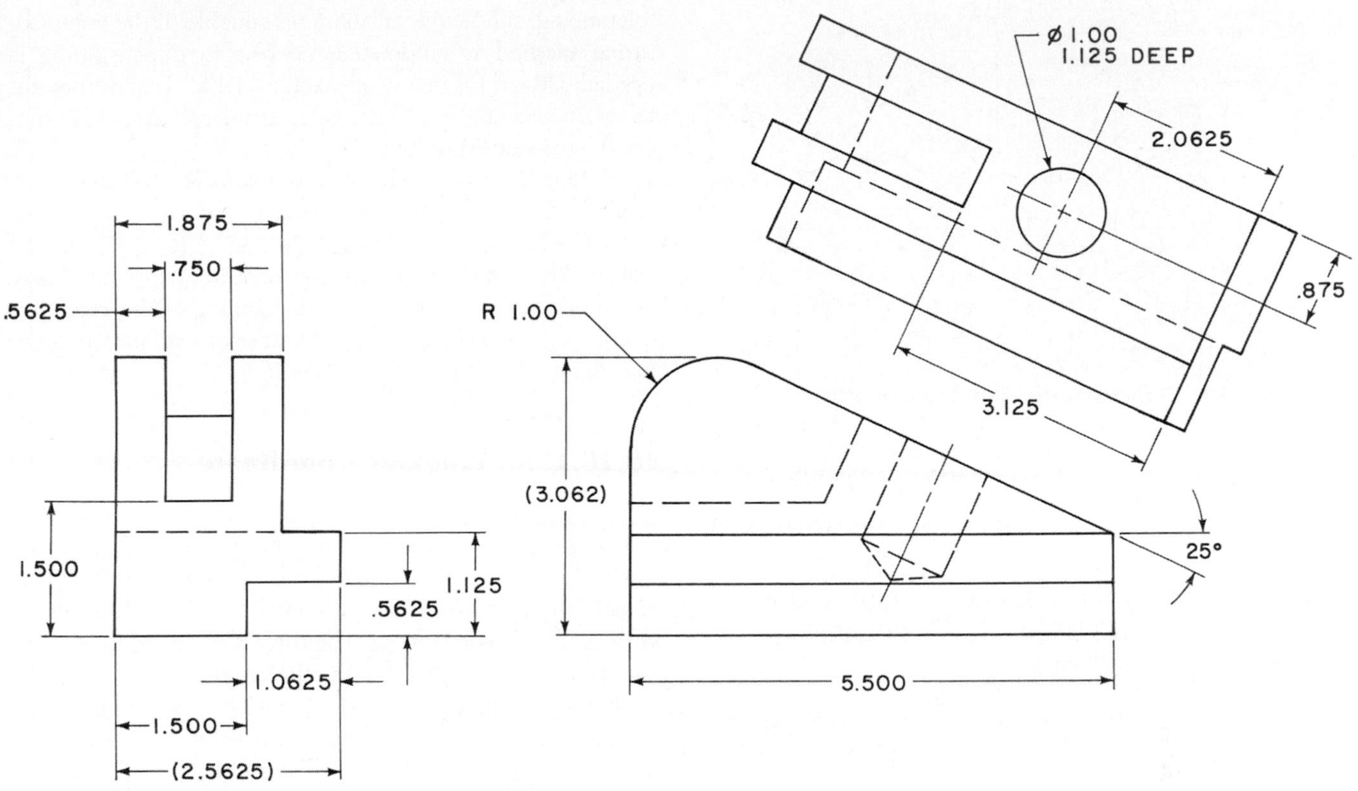

FIGURE 15.79 Anchor Detail

A variety of abbreviations appear in notes. Abbreviations should conform to ANSI Y1.1. See Appendix B for common abbreviations on drawings. Keep your use of abbreviations to a minimum.

Notes are lettered in uppercase except when they are long and detailed; here it is acceptable to use upper- and lowercase. This is the only place on mechanical drawings where lowercase lettering is permitted. The width of notes should be limited to the width of the parts list or of the revision block on the drawing.

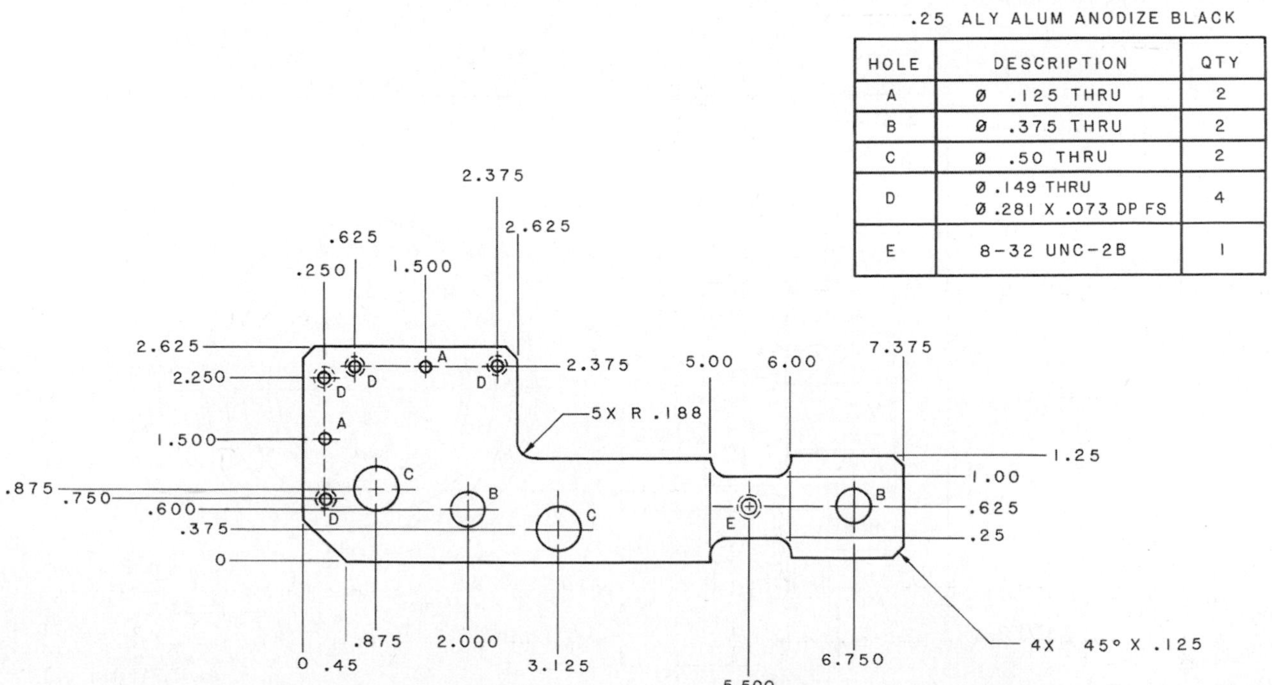

FIGURE 15.80 Dimensioned Part

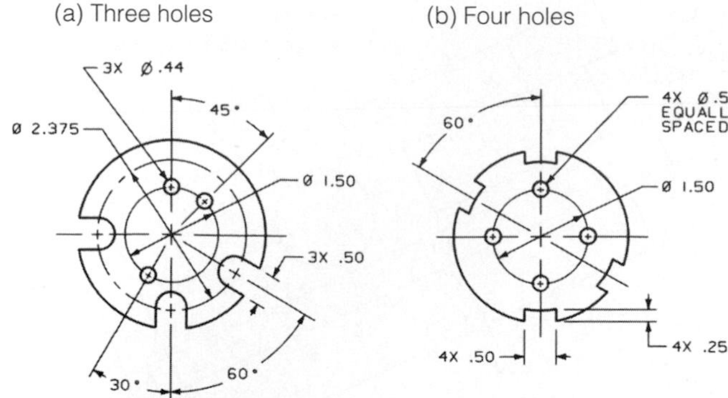

FIGURE 15.81 Dimensioning Repetitive Features

Notes that apply to a view can be placed under the view. **Local notes** are placed away from the view outline (Fig. 15.83):

6-32 UNC-2B	4-40 UNC-2B	.250-20 UNC-2B
.50 DEEP	.25 DEEP	2 PLACES
2 PLACES	8 PLACES	

If a drawing is large and complicated, local notes are allowed within the view. However, avoid this practice whenever possible.

15.10 LOCATION OF FEATURES AND DIMENSIONING METHODS

To design a part, you must know its manufacturing method. If the part to be manufactured does not require close tolerancing, simple dimensioning is suitable. If the manufacturing method is automated, coordinate dimensioning is needed. Design for manufacturability (DFM) is an important factor in creating clear, precise, manufacturable, and successful parts and products.

Rectangular coordinate dimensions locate features accurately with respect to one another and, as a group or individually, from a datum or origin (Fig. 15.82). The features that establish the datum must be identified clearly on the drawing. Coordinate dimensioning is the most frequent method of dimensioning because of automation in the machine tool and manufacturing areas.

15.10.1 Rectangular Coordinate Dimensioning

Rectangular coordinate dimensioning locates features by dimensioning from two or three *mutually perpendicular planes*. The cylindrical part in Figure 15.84 is dimensioned with geometric tolerancing. The three mutually perpendicular planes are established from the center and the bottom. This type of dimensioning either establishes **datum lines** (**X**, **Y**, and **Z** coordinate lines from which all dimensions are taken) or uses the centerlines of a symmetrical or circular shape. In Figure 15.85(a), the **X** and **Y** coordinates serve as datum lines. Here, all dimensions are positioned rectangularly from the datum lines/baselines. The part is located in quadrant I so that all values for dimensions are positive. In Figure 15.85(b), the circular part and its hole pattern are dimensioned from the center of the piece. All dimensions are drawn perpendicular to the part's center.

The four quadrants of the rectangular coordinate system are shown in Figure 15.86. The rectangular coordinate system has two perpendicular axes, **X** and **Y**. The plane

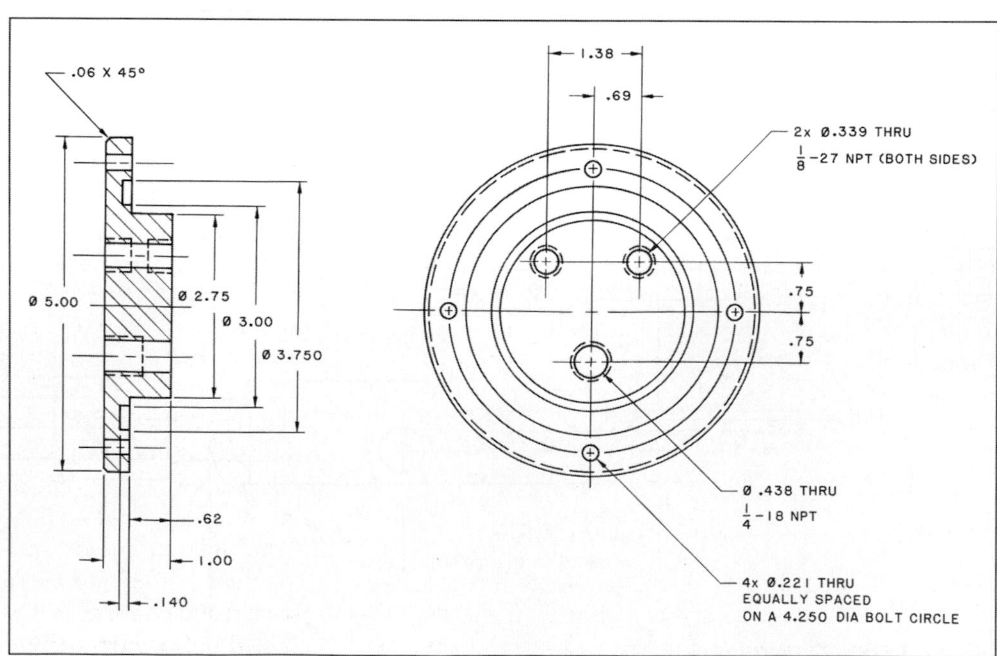

FIGURE 15.82 Square Dimensioning Holes

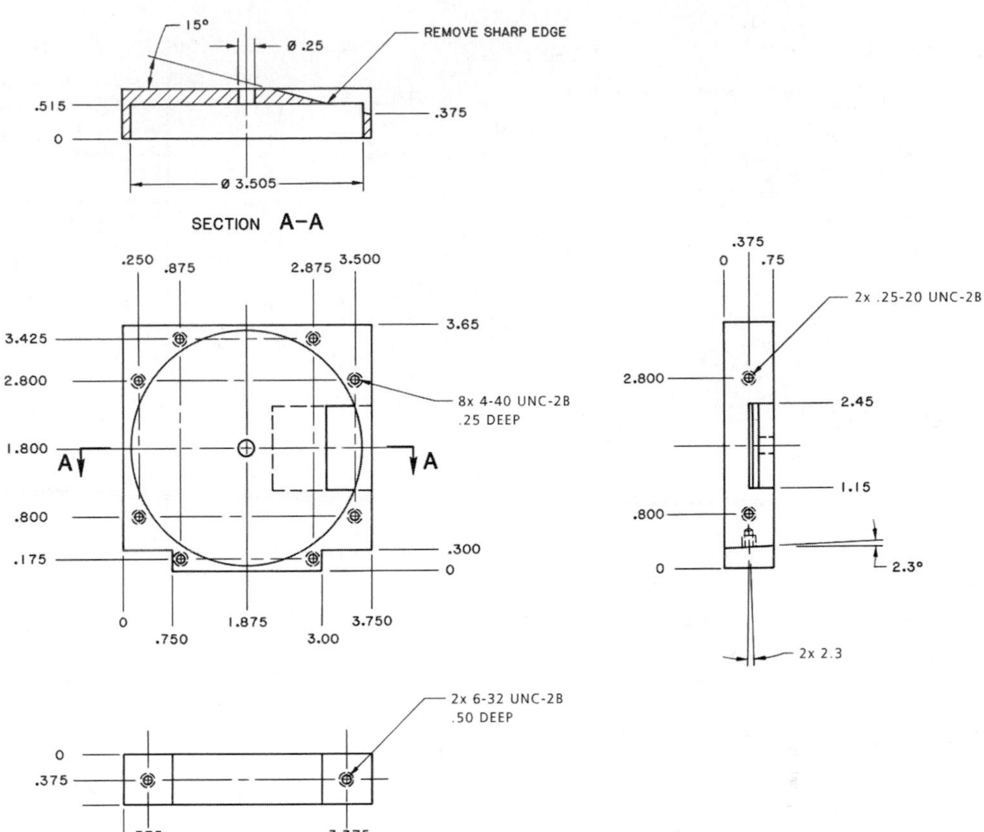

FIGURE 15.83 Part Detailed Using Dimensions Without Dimension Lines

formed by the **X** and **Y** axes establishes the origin of the **Z** axis (Fig. 15.87). The intersection of the three axes is the origin, which has a numerical value of zero (**X0,Y0,Z0**). The three reference planes can locate the part, as in Figure 15.88. The **X** and **Y** axes may also be established from the part, as in Figure 15.89.

Figures 15.90 and 15.91 use the rectangular coordinate method for dimensioning. Holes and curved features are dimensioned by locating center points from datum lines/baselines, indicated by zero coordinates. Dimensions are established so as to have values that can be entered easily when programming the part during CNC machining. This part also uses a hole chart. All holes are through the workpiece, so **X** and **Y** dimensions are required.

The parts in Figures 15.90 and 15.91 are dimensioned from datum lines. The dimension lines are eliminated, and only measurements and extension lines are shown. This is called **rectangular coordinate dimensioning without dimension lines** (ordinate method). **Ordinate dimensioning** is one of the easiest and clearest ways to dimension a part. Dimensions are shown on extension lines without dimension lines or arrowheads. The base (datum) lines are indicated as zero coordinates, or labeled as **X**, **Y**, and **Z**.

15.10.2 Polar Coordinate Dimensioning

When **polar coordinate dimensioning** is used to locate features, a linear and an angular dimension specify a distance from a fixed point at an angular direction from two or three mutually perpendicular planes. The fixed point is the intersection of these planes (Fig. 15.92). The holes are established with a radial value (**R2 .62**) and angles for each hole. The 0,0 position is in the lower left; the radial value and the angles are established from a location hole.

If a CAD system is used to detail the part, polar coordinates should be given in decimal units and in decimal degrees.

15.10.3 Datums and Tolerances

Datum points, lines, or **surfaces** are features that are assumed to be exact. They are baselines or references for locating other features of the part. A feature selected as a datum must be easily accessible and clearly identified. In many cases, datums are established as the far left surface and bottom surface in a view (Figs. 15.90 and 15.91). An artificial datum like a construction hole or a line edge is sometimes machined in a part for manufacturing and checking only. In Figure 15.93, the part is symmetrical about its vertical centerline. In this example, all dimensions are established from the center hole. The lower left corner of the part is a large curve, which makes it inappropriate for establishing dimensions.

A datum surface must be more accurate than any location measured from that datum. It may be necessary to specify **form tolerances** for the datum surface to ensure that locations can be established accurately. Mating parts use the same feature surface. When parts must match or mate, the related hole centers serve as the datum.

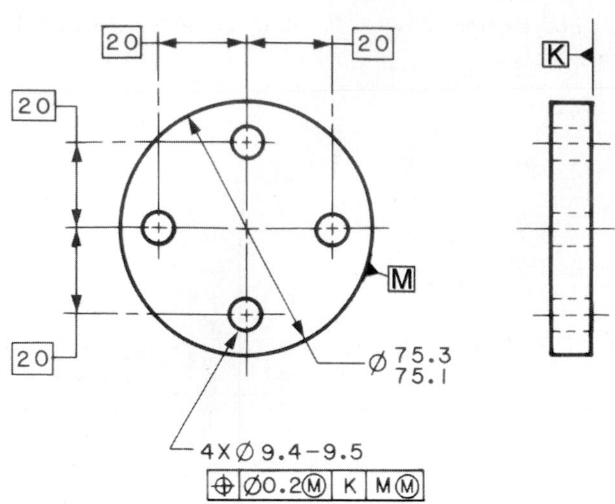

(a) X and Y coordinates used as datums

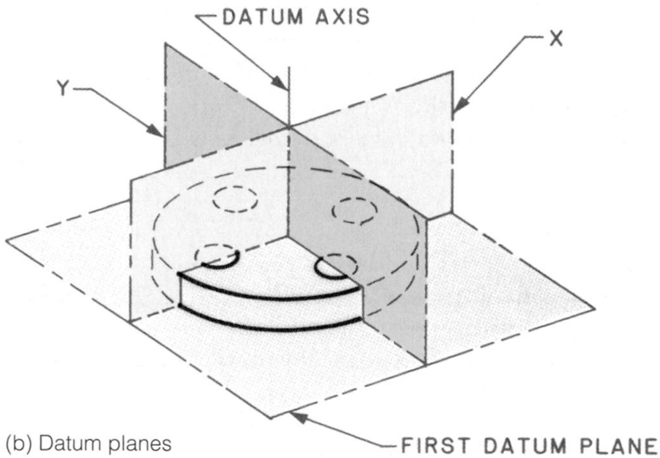

(b) Datum planes

FIGURE 15.84 Part with Cylindrical Datum Feature

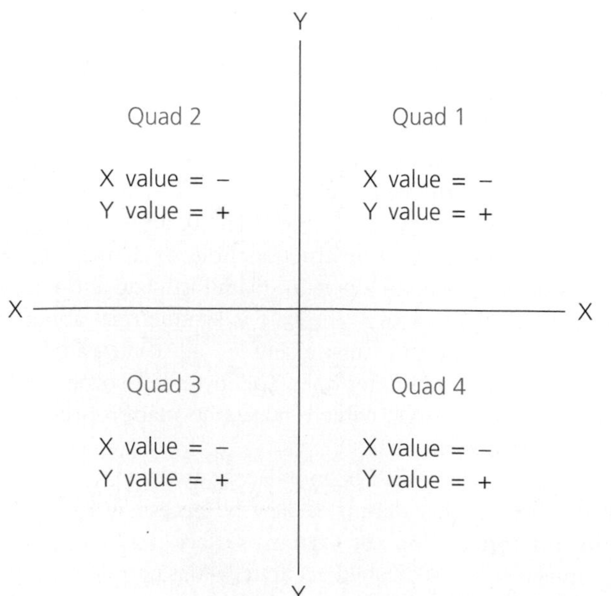

FIGURE 15.86 Quadrants

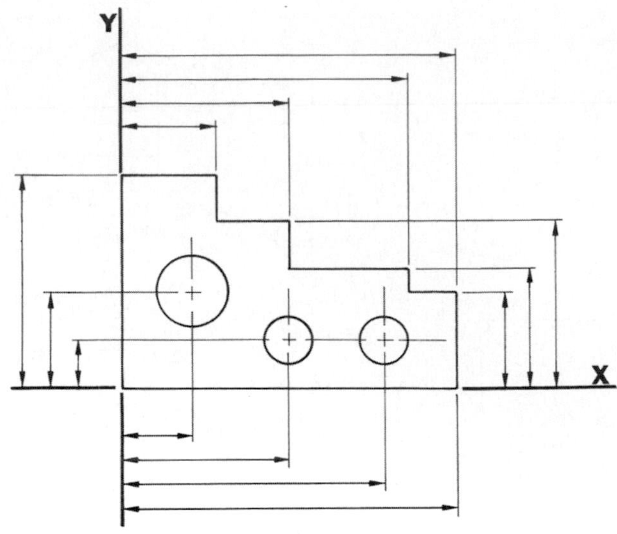

(a) Datum line dimensioning

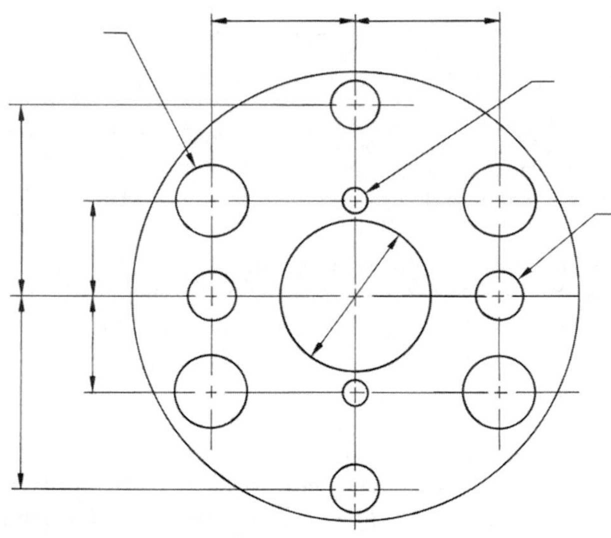
(b) Rectangular coordinate dimensioning

FIGURE 15.85 Dimensioning Methods

Dimensioning from a common base or datum reduces the overall accumulation of the tolerance. But the tolerance on the distance between any two features, located with respect to a datum and not with respect to one another, is equal to the sum of their tolerances. Therefore, if it is important to control two features closely, the dimension is given directly from a datum or a baseline.

15.10.4 Hole Charts and Tabular Dimensioning

Tabular dimensioning is a type of rectangular coordinate dimensioning in which dimensions from mutually perpendicular datums are listed in a table on the drawing (Fig. 15.94). This method is good for parts that require locating a large number of similarly shaped features, such as multiple

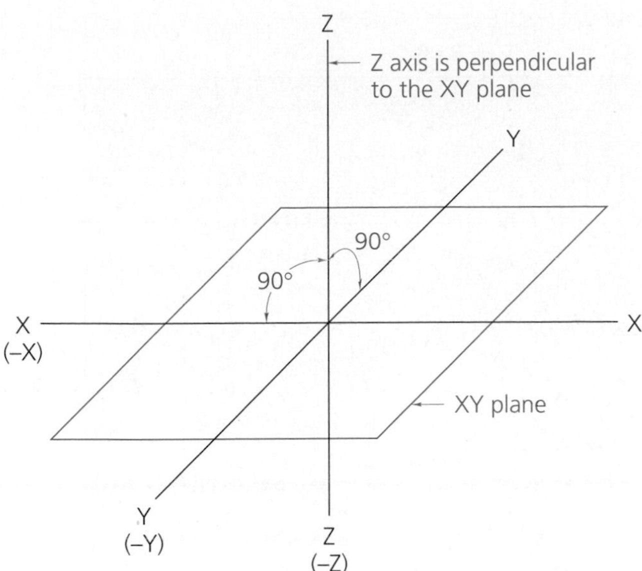

FIGURE 15.87 X, Y, Z Axes

holes, slots, or hole patterns. The information is listed in tables. For automated tooling and programming CNC machines, providing **X, Y** dimensions and **Z** depths is the best method. Hole sizes are also given on a hole chart.

For complicated parts, or a parts with a multitude of holes in one or more surfaces, **hole charts** simplify the drawing. In hole charts, the surface of hole entry and each hole are identified on the drawing. In Figure 15.94, the hole chart lists the **X** and **Y** position of each hole with the depth (**Z**).

The surfaces of hole entry are identified with the names of the principal views. The order of these views for hole charts is:

1. Top
2. Front
3. Right
4. Left
5. Bottom
6. Rear
7. Auxiliary (if used)

The hole chart shows the surface of entry of each hole, the symbol number that identifies each hole, and the number of times each hole is used in this surface. It also gives the complete specification for each hole. Identical holes in a surface are shown by a single symbol number or letter. Hole charts are used for sheet metal details and drilling drawings for printed circuit boards. On parts with very complex hole patterns, the locating dimensions for the holes are shown in the chart as the **X** and **Y** positions in each view; this is called **rectangular dimensioning in tabular form** (Fig. 15.94).

In **X** and **Y** coordinate dimensioning, each hole has a separate identifying symbol. You should group holes by giving diameters the same size and the same letter symbols or by numbering them consecutively. All holes are listed in the hole chart. Holes are normally listed alphabetically, starting from the largest with the letter A. In another method of labeling holes for tabular dimensioning, each hole is numbered consecutively from number 1, without regard to size.

When the hole is completely through the part, **THRU** is

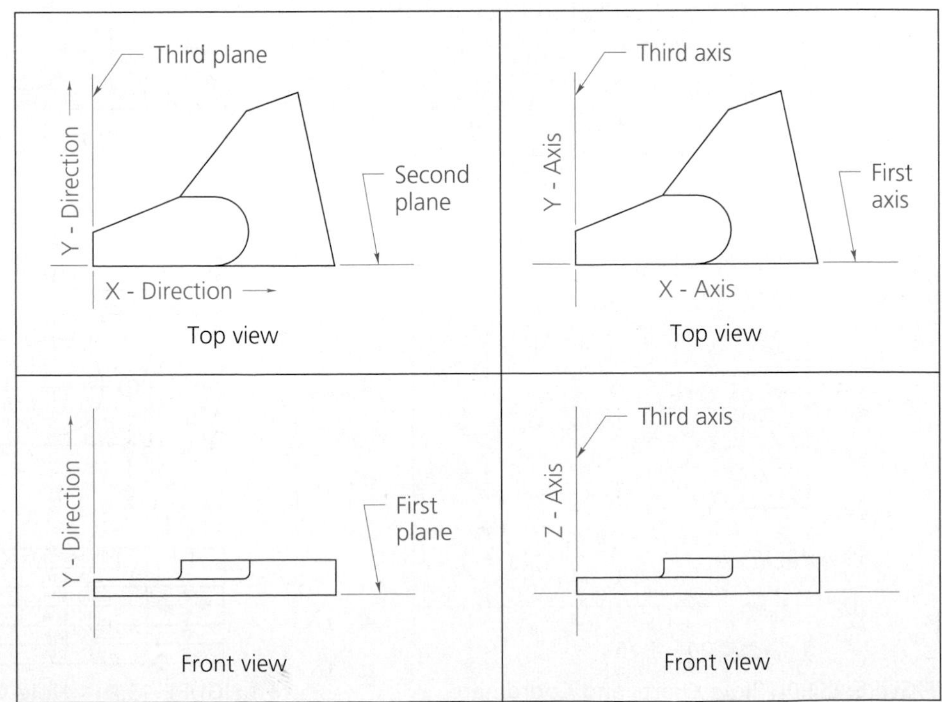

(a) Reference planes (b) Reference axes

FIGURE 15.88 Reference Surfaces

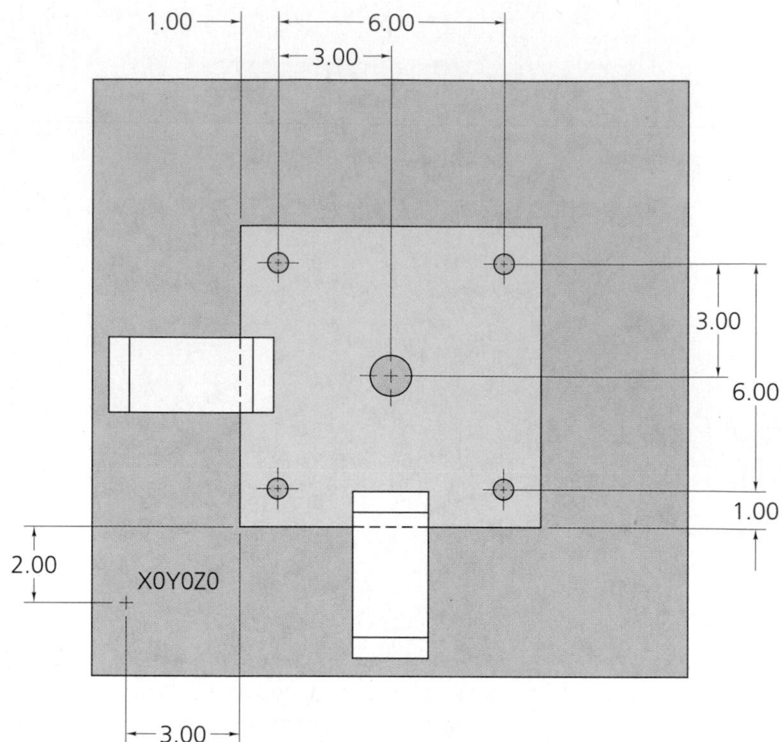

FIGURE 15.89 **0,0,0 Position Established from the Workpiece. Worktable and clamps shown with part.**

used as the **Z** dimension. If more than one surface is to have holes called out, **X** and **Y** axes are established for each surface or view. The depth is specified for each hole, and the view is noted in the hole chart.

Tabular dimensioning is also found in many catalogs, where a standard part has varying dimensions for size and length. Bolts, screws, keys, pipe fittings, valves, and other

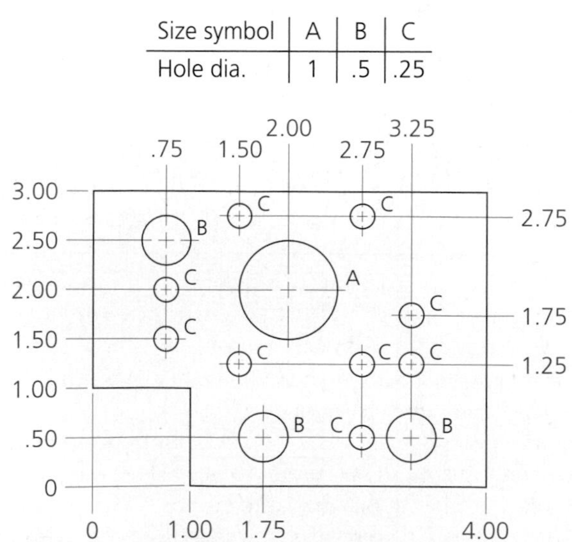

Size symbol	A	B	C
Hole dia.	1	.5	.25

FIGURE 15.90 Hole Charts and Coordinate Dimensioning

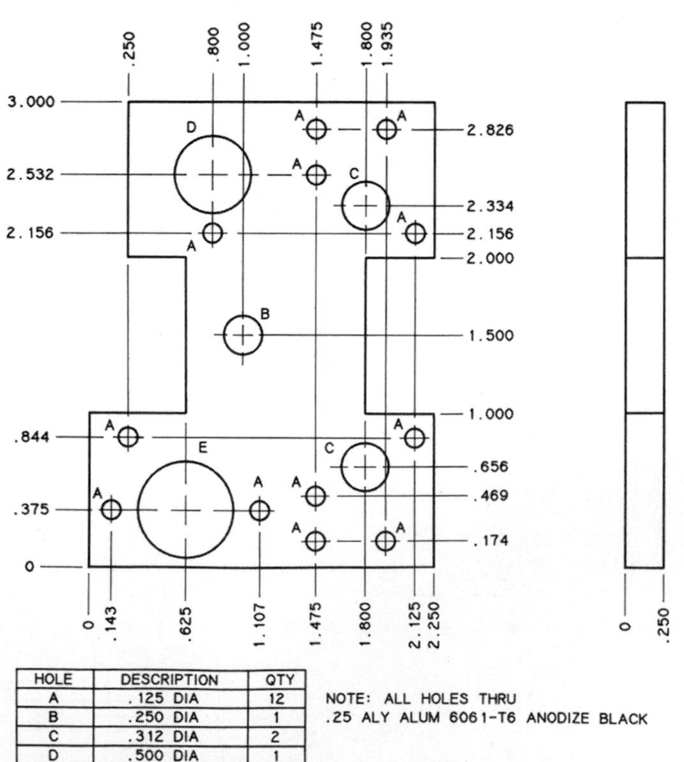

HOLE	DESCRIPTION	QTY
A	.125 DIA	12
B	.250 DIA	1
C	.312 DIA	2
D	.500 DIA	1
E	.625 DIA	1

FIGURE 15.91 Hole Charts and Coordinate Dimensioning

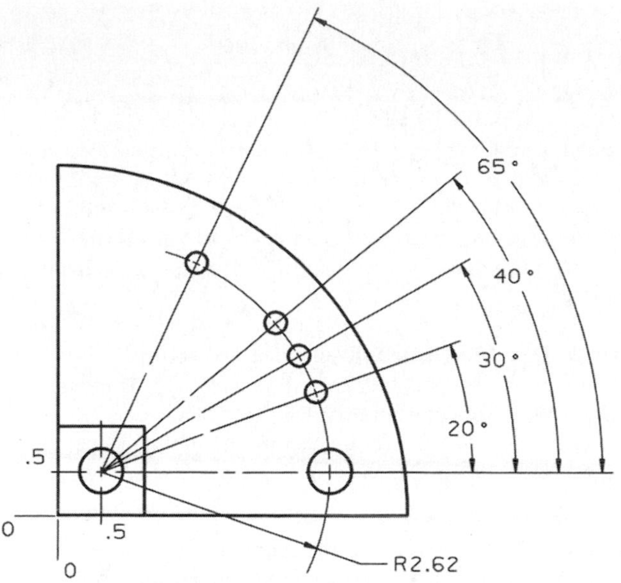

FIGURE 15.92 Polar Coordinate Dimensioning

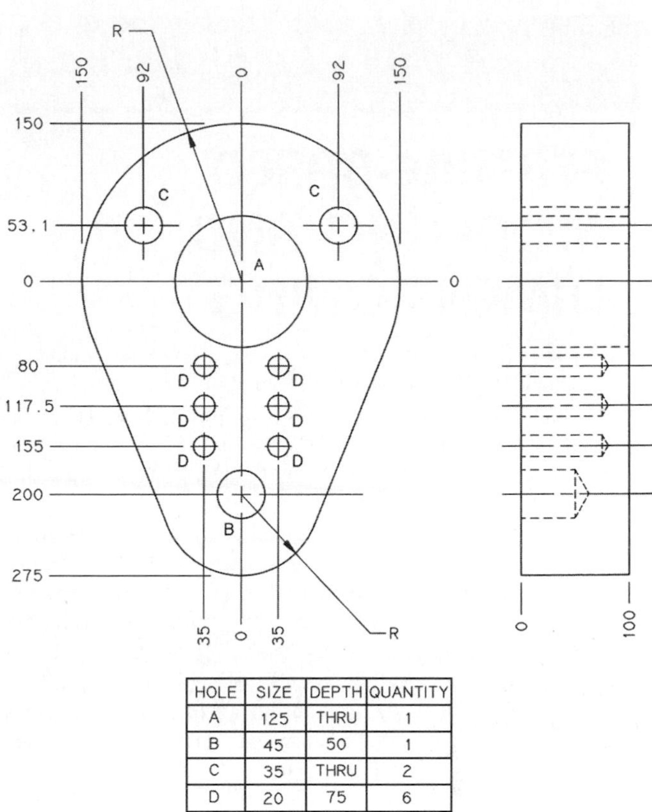

HOLE	SIZE	DEPTH	QUANTITY
A	125	THRU	1
B	45	50	1
C	35	THRU	2
D	20	75	6

FIGURE 15.93 0,0 Position Established at Center of Part

HOLE	FROM	X	Y	−Z
A1	X,Y	90	44	10
B1	"	26	150	30
B2	"		150	30
B3	"	26	26	30
C1	"	64	100	40
C2	"	40	76	40

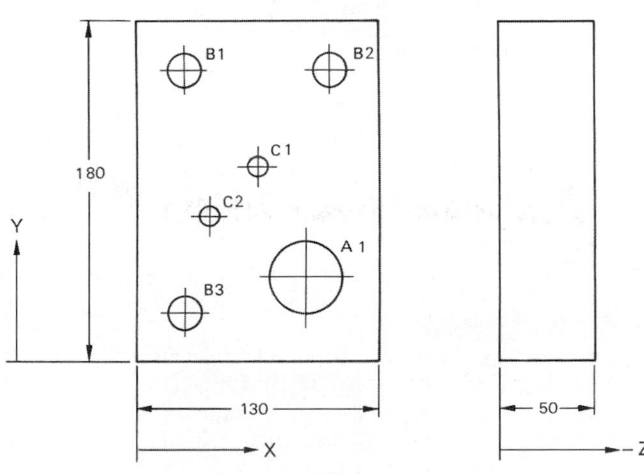

HOLE	DESC	QTY
A	Ø 40	1
B	Ø 20	3
C	Ø 10	2

FIGURE 15.94 Rectangular Coordinate Dimensioning in Tabular Form

standard items have dimensions in tabular form (see Appendix C).

15.10.5 Repetitive Features or Dimensions

Repetitive features (Fig. 15.95) or dimensions are specified with an **×** following a numeral to indicate the "number of times" or "places" that a feature is required. Features like holes and slots, which are repeated in a series or pattern, are specified by giving the required number of features and an **×** followed by the size dimension of the feature. A space is placed between the **×** and the dimension (Fig. 15.95).

If it is difficult to distinguish between the dimension and the number of spaces, one space is dimensioned and identified as a reference (**1.00** in Figure 15.95). *Reference dimensions* are enclosed in parentheses.

The part in Figure 15.96 has repetitive features (holes) that are not equally spaced. Angle dimensions in degrees locate each hole from the vertical or horizontal centerline. A note gives the size and number of holes.

Equal spacing of features in a series or pattern may be specified by giving the required number of spaces and an **×**, followed by the applicable dimension (Figs. 15.97 and 15.98). A space is inserted between the **×** and the dimension. In Figure 15.97 the part has five holes, each with a diameter of 14 mm, equally spaced at 15°. The dimension

Applying Parametric Design . . .

FEATURE-BASED MODELING AND DIMENSIONING

Models can be dimensioned automatically in Draw mode (Fig. A). Pro/ENGINEER displays **dimensions** in a view based on how the part was modeled (Fig. B). The dimension type is selected before the options for showing the dimensions on the drawing. Linear dimensions (Fig. C) and ordinate dimensions (Fig. D) are two of the options.

After a part's features are sketched (Fig. E), aligned, and dimensioned, you modify the dimension values to be the exact sizes required on the design (Fig. F). The dimensioning scheme, the controlling features, the parent–child relationships, and the datums (Fig. G) used to define and control the part features are determined as you design and model on the system. When detailing, you simply ask the system to display views needed to describe the part (Fig. H) and then to display the dimensions for modeling the part. These are the same dimensions as in the part design. You cannot underdimension or overdimension the part because the system displays exactly what is required to model the part. Pro/ENGINEER will not duplicate dimensions on a drawing. If a dimension is shown in one view, it will not be shown in another view. The dimension, however, can be switched to the other view through detailing options.

How to Display Dimensions on a Drawing

1. Choose **Show** from the DETAIL menu and **Dimension** orientation **Ref Dim** from the DETAIL ITEM menu (Fig. I).
2. Choose the dimension type from the LIN ORD menu.
3. Choose one of the following options from the SHOW ITEM menu:

> **Show All** Shows all the dimensions for an object. If an assembly drawing, shows assembly dimensions and also previously erased component dimensions; if a part, shows all feature dimensions.

> **By View** Shows all the dimensions associated with a selected view. Select the view(s) you would like dimensioned.

> **By Feature** Shows all the dimensions associated with a particular feature in the appropriate views. Selects feature to

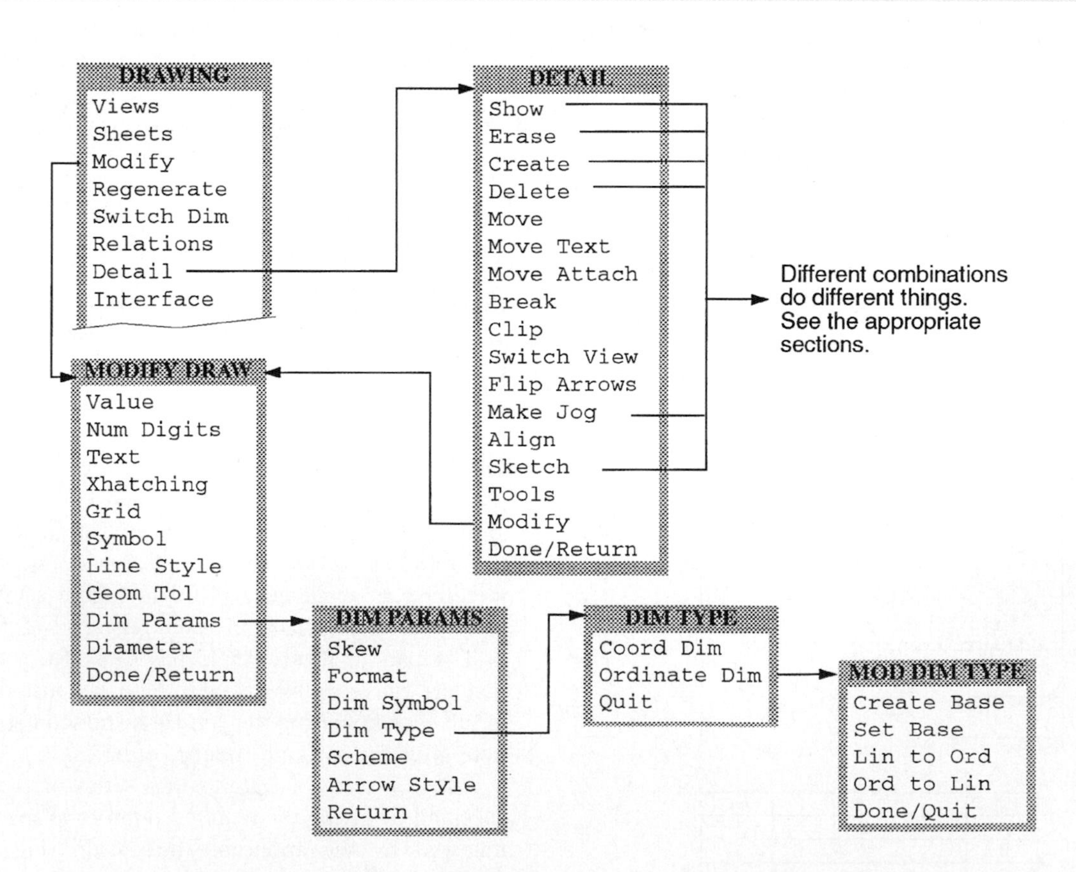

FIGURE A Menu Structure for Dimensioning

FIGURE B Dimensioned Part

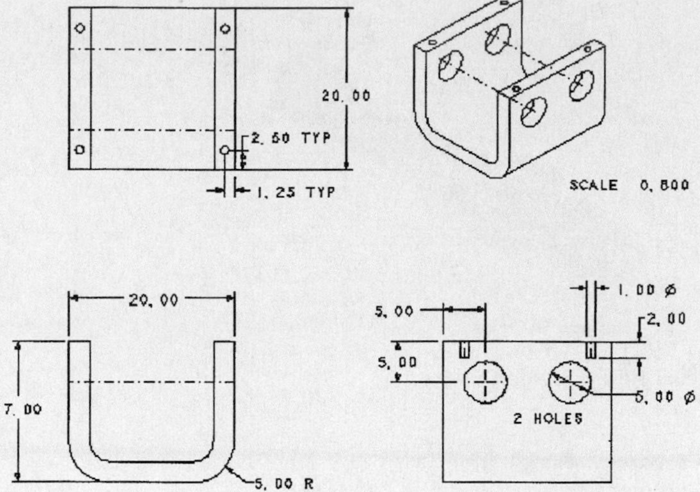

FIGURE C Linear Dimensioning

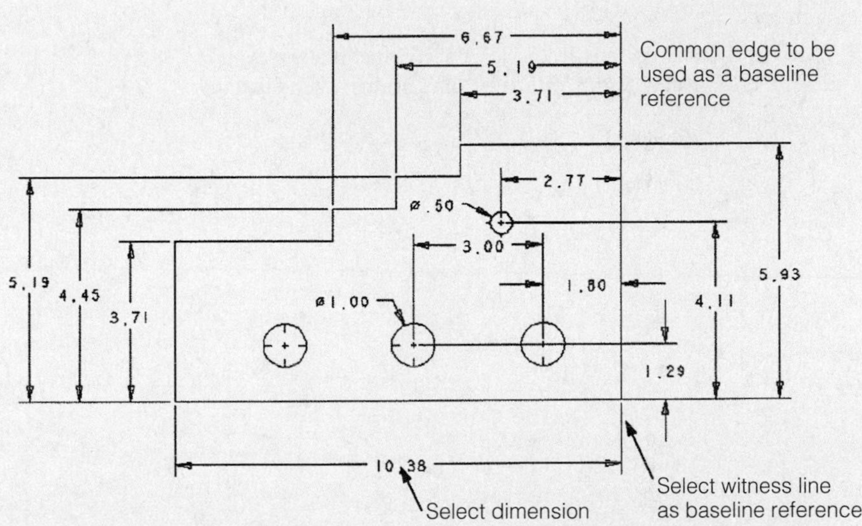

FIGURE D Ordinate Dimensioning

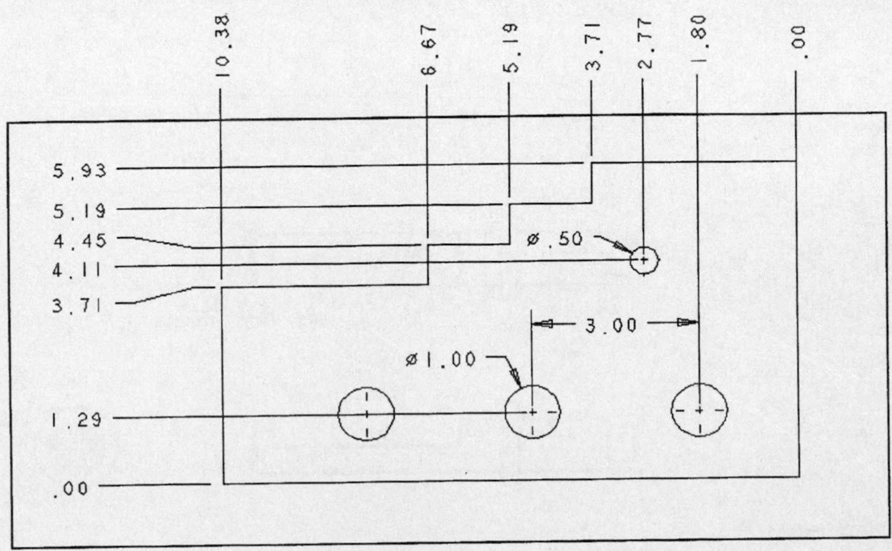

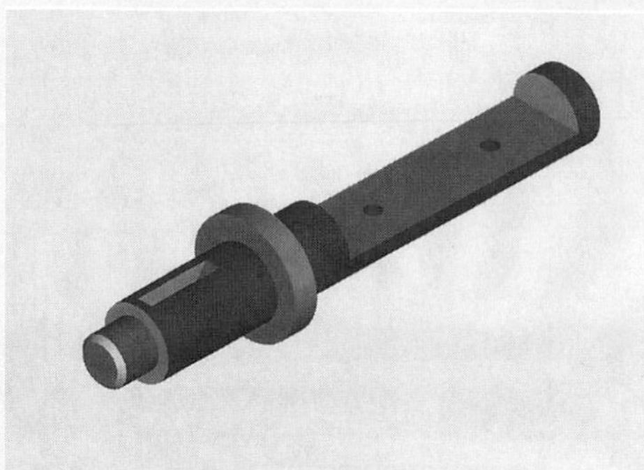

FIGURE E Shaded Shaft

be dimensioned. In models with a lot of features and dimensions, this is the easiest way to work.

> **Feat & View** Shows all dimensions for a single feature in a single view. Select a feature in the view where the dimensions are to be displayed.

The **Clean Dims** options in the DRAWING menu allows you to distribute standard and ordinate dimensions with equidistant spacing along witness lines, displaying them in a more orderly and readable fashion (Fig. J).

To Clean Up the Dimension Display:

1. Select **Clean Dims** from the DRAWING menu.
2. Enter the offset value for the first dimension line (the one closest to the model).
3. Enter the distance between all other dimensions.
4. Select the view to be cleaned up by picking on the model.
5. Dimensions pertaining to the selected view are displayed with the specified spacing. In the event that the new display of dimensions is unsatisfactory, Pro/ENGINEER will ask if you would like to move the dimensions back to their previous display.
6. Select another view, to clean dimensions with the same offsets, or press the middle mouse button to quit the process.

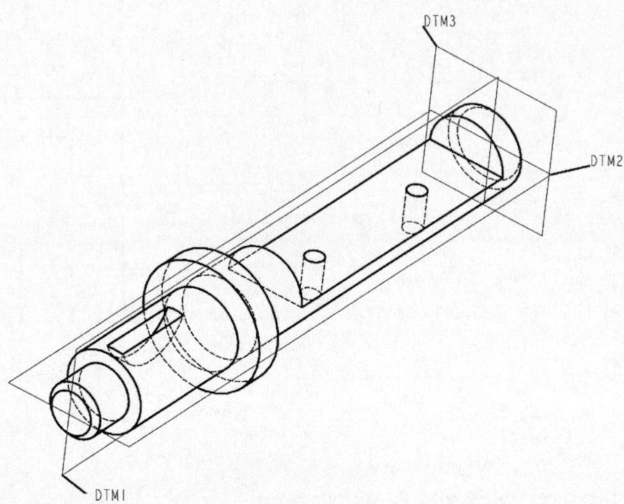

FIGURE G Datums Used to Create, Align, and Dimension the Shaft

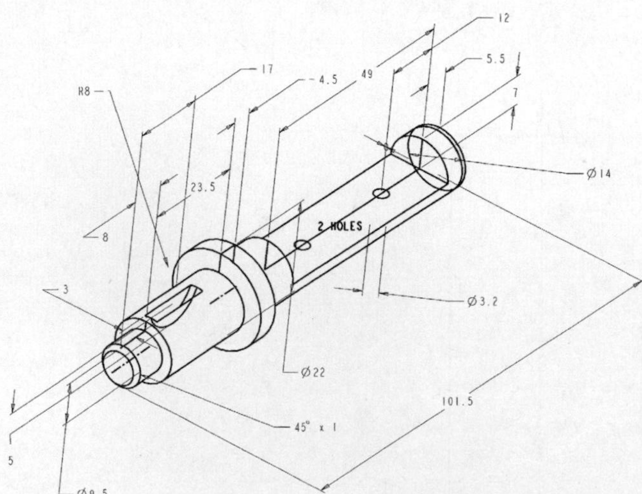

FIGURE F Pictorial View of Shaft with Dimensions Displayed

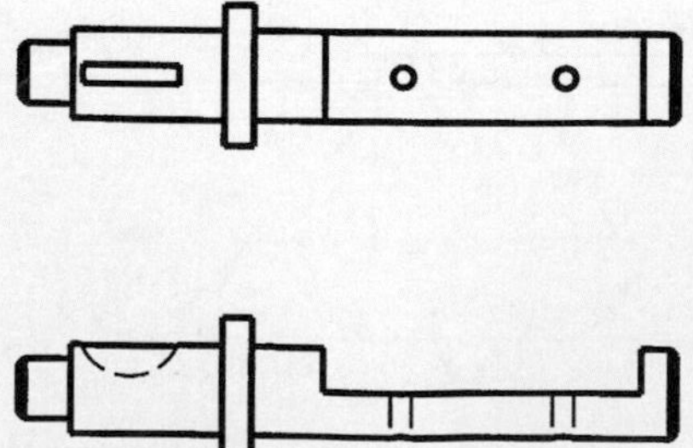

FIGURE H Views of the Shaft Displayed on a Drawing

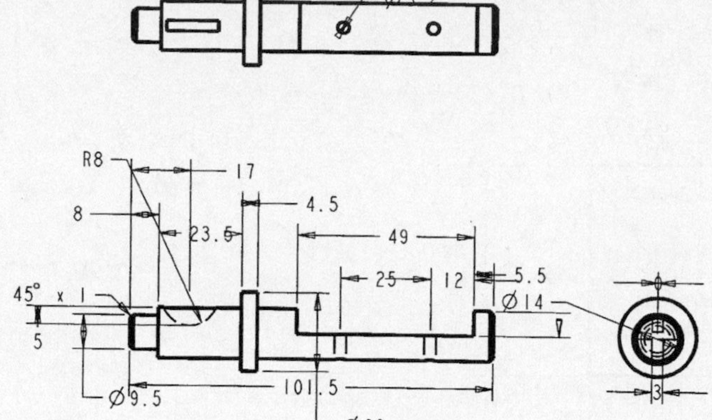

FIGURE I Dimensions Displayed with **Show**

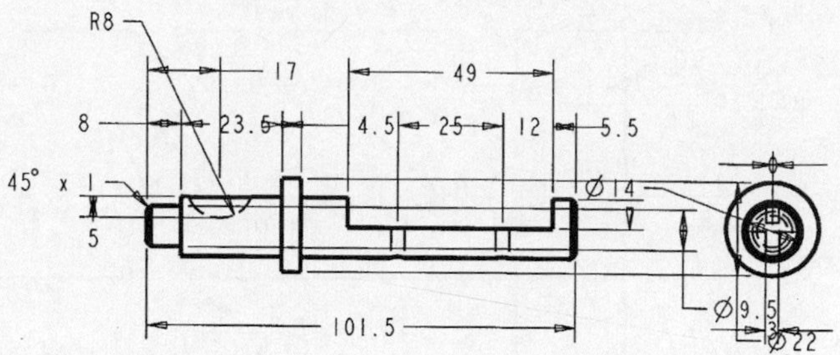

FIGURE J Dimensions After the **Clean Dim** Command

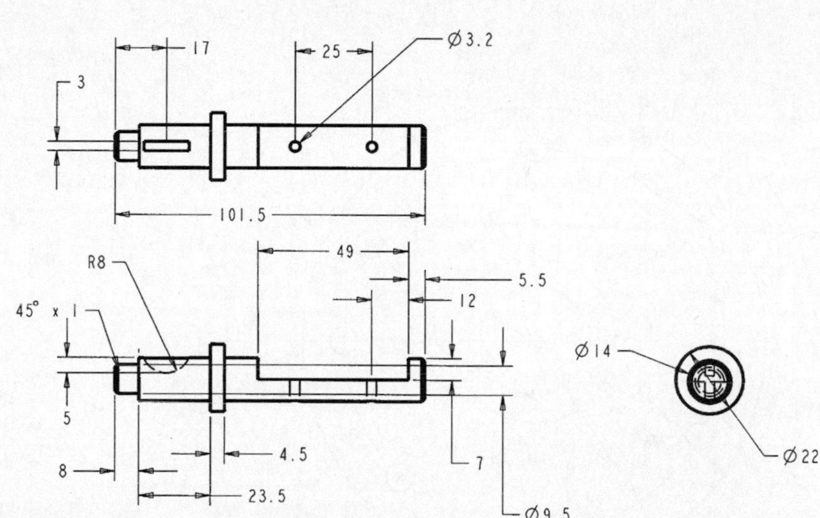

FIGURE K Repositioned Dimensions Using **Move, Move Attach, Move Text,** and **Flip Arrows**

The cleaned dimensions are usually not in the best positions for each dimension and note. After cleaning, the next step normally is to move and reposition the dimensions to create an ANSI-standard drawing with correct dimensioning standards (Fig. K).

Dimensions can be removed from the display by erasing them. **Erasing dimensions** does not delete them from the model (regular dimensions cannot be deleted, but reference dimensions can). Dimensions that have been erased can be redisplayed with the option **Show.**

To Erase a Dimension from the Drawing:

1. Choose **Erase** from the DETAIL menu and **Dimension** or **Ref Dim** from the lower portion of the ERASE ITEM menu.
2. Choose one of the following options from the ERASE ITEM menu.

> **By Feature** Erases all the dimensions associated with a particular feature. Select the feature.

> **By View** Erases all the dimensions associated with a selected view. Select the view(s).

> **Erase All** Erases all the dimensions in the drawing.

> **One Item** Erases the dimension selected.

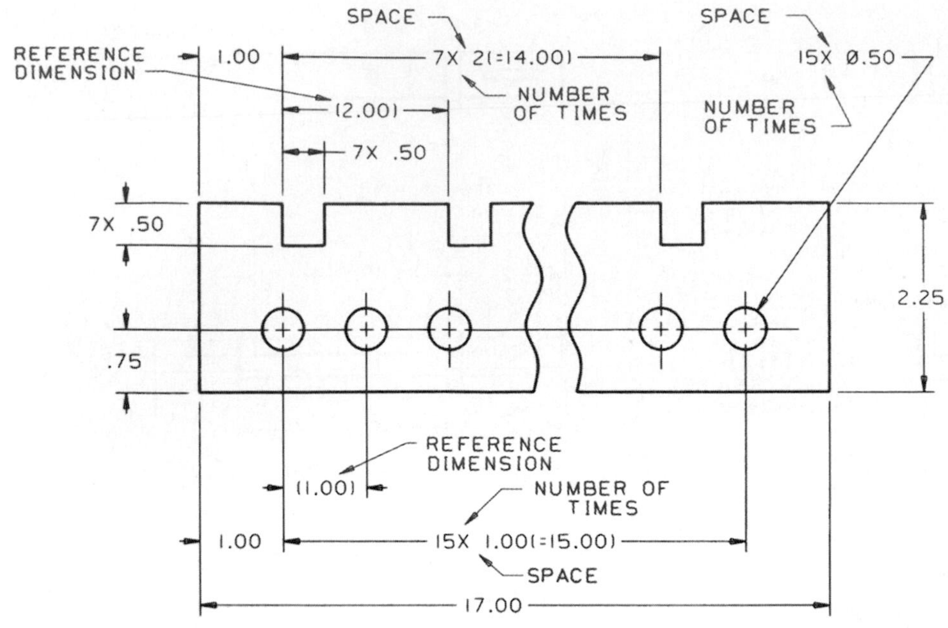

FIGURE 15.95 Repetitive Feature Dimensioning

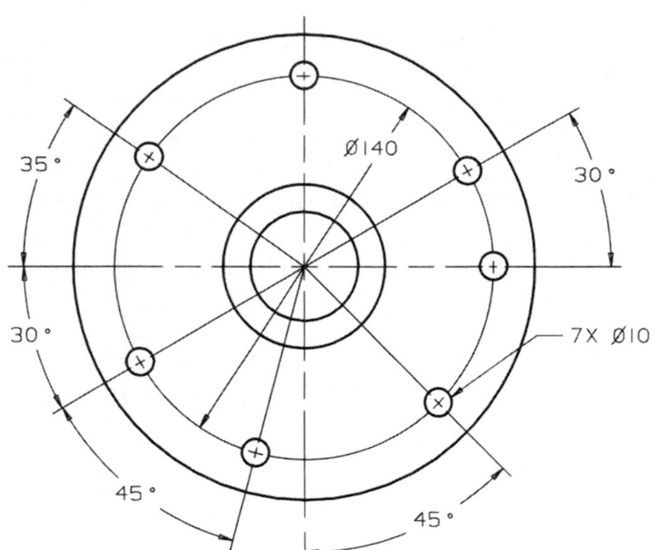

FIGURE 15.96 Dimensioning Repetitive Holes on a Common Center

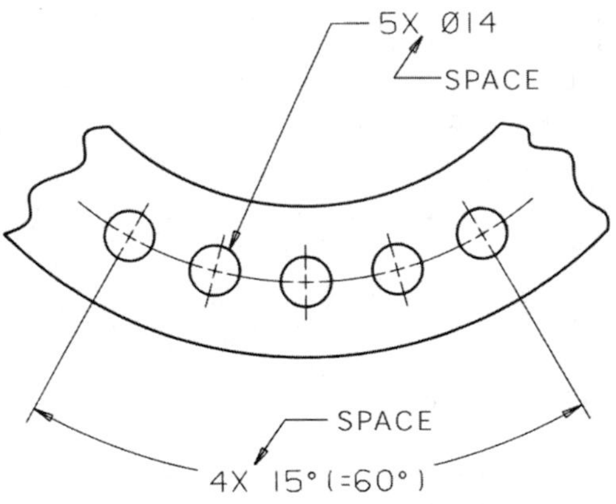

FIGURE 15.97 Repetitive Dimensions

for spacing the holes gives the number of spaces (**4**), the degrees between each hole (**15**), and the total degrees (**60**).

The notation **×** may also be used to indicate "by" between coordinate dimensions. An example is when dimensioning a chamfer: **50 × 45°** or **.250 × 30°**. *The* **×** *is preceded and followed by a space.* If both these practices ("by" and "number of features") are used on the same drawing, ensure that each usage is clear by providing proper spaces.

You May Complete Exercises 15.13 Through 15.16 at This Time

15.11 DIMENSIONING WITH A CAD SYSTEM

One of the most important aspects of the introduction of the computer into the design process is that the modeled 3D part is associative to the dimensions, which means that the engineer or designer inserts the dimensions with regard to placement but the system puts the proper dimension value on the drawing based on the size and location when the geometry was created.

The elements that make up the geometry of the part are established mathematically. Therefore, it is impossible to put the wrong-size dimension value on the drawing. Others utilizing the same database can verify (**LIST**) each feature as to size and location. This is impossible when a manual

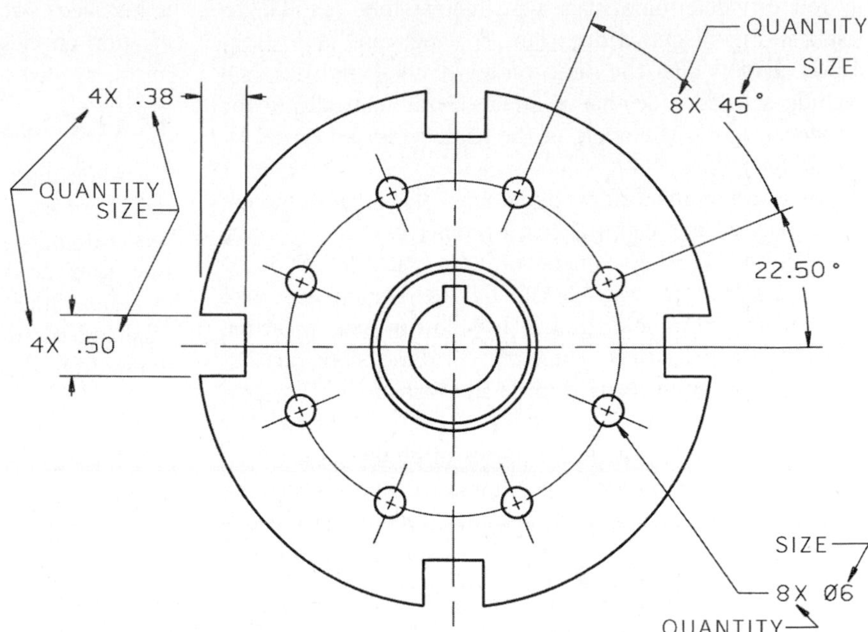

FIGURE 15.98 Repetitive Features and Dimensioning

drawing is produced. If a CAD-generated part is dimensioned insufficiently, manufacturing can activate the part and request the information from the system via an **ID, LIST,** or **MEASURE** command (AutoCAD).

In most engineering applications, a precise drawing plotted to scale is not sufficient to convey all of the desired information. Annotations must be added to show the lengths of features, the distances between features, or the angles between features. Until all CAD databases can be transmitted to the machine tool area for postprocessing and for driving a numerical control machine, dimensioning will be required. The machine tool area and the manufacturing department will be able to use the graphically created database directly to machine and manufacture the part. Many companies already follow this method, and a fully integrated CAD/CAM system is the goal of most manufacturers. Until this technology is in place throughout industry, the designer or engineer will need to define the drawing with dimensions based on the most recent ANSI standards. Many CAD systems provide ANSI standards for geometric tolerancing and dimensioning, though the quality of dimensioning packages differs widely between systems. The designer must still determine the proper dimensioning requirements and decide on their placement on the drawing.

Dimensioning in CAD involves adding annotations to a drawing. Dimensioning also refers to the annotations themselves. CAD systems provide a variety of dimensioning options. The commands and procedures for dimensioning differ among systems. All systems provide quick and easy insertion of dimensions, but you still need to know why certain things are dimensioned and where to place the dimensions. CAD systems automate the process, but the knowledge of ANSI or other standard dimensioning and tolerancing specifications must be mastered along with how to enter the commands for a specific system.

The designer selects dimension options that include decimal or fractional representation, U.S. or SI units of measure, bilateral or unilateral tolerances, feature control symbols, and datums. Dimensions are easily inserted on a drawing by identifying the two locations to be measured and dimensioned. A third location places the dimensioning text and associated values. The system automatically inserts extension lines, dimension lines, leader lines, dimension arrowheads, and dimensioning text at the location indicated. Linear, rotated, diameter, radial, angular, and ordinate dimensioning are available. A variety of arrowhead lengths and types can also be selected (Fig. 15.99). Dimension text, notes, and labels are easily inserted on detail drawings.

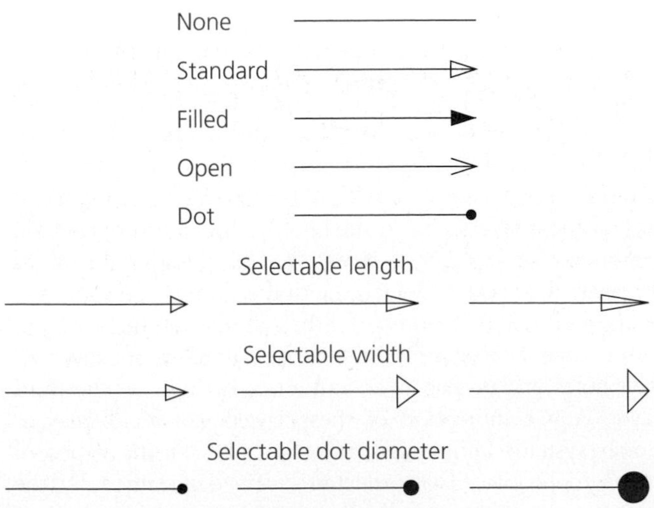

FIGURE 15.99 Arrowhead Variations

You can determine what type of text font (**STYLE**) to select and its height, width, slant, spacing, case, and justification. **Labels** offer the same variety of characteristics, and include a leader line that is attached automatically to the associated label. The angle of the leader line can be set by the designer.

Dimensioning is a drawing activity rather than a modeling activity when creating the part geometry; in other words, it is 2D, not 3D. The geometry of the part can be 3D or 2D depending on the system's capabilities. Dimensions, like text, are for information only. They do not exist as actual part entities or features. Therefore, all dimensions are 2D. The same procedure is used to detail a part on a 2D system as on a 3D system.

Before proceeding with the details of dimensioning with CAD, a few terms, system capabilities, and options must be explained. Each system has certain differences that determine exactly where dimensions can be placed. Sometimes it is necessary to work around these limitations.

15.11.1 Dimension Line

A **dimension line** is a line with arrows at each end, drawn at the angle at which the dimension has been measured. The dimension text is situated along this line, usually dividing it into two lines. Usually, the dimension line is inside the measured area. Sometimes, however, it does not fit. If it doesn't, two short lines are drawn outside the measured area, with the arrows pointing inward. The option for arrows inside or arrows outside is available on most CAD systems. The dimension line is established on the drawing by selecting the distance away from the part, normally the third selection in the command. The first two selections locate the feature ends or two positions to be dimensioned. For angular dimensioning, the dimension line is actually an arc.

15.11.2 Extension Lines

If the dimension line is drawn outside the part being measured, straight **extension lines,** sometimes called *witness lines,* are drawn from a feature of the part, perpendicular to the dimension line. Extension lines are used only in linear and angular dimensioning. When not needed, one or both of them can be left off via a suppression capability available on most systems.

15.11.3 Dimension Text

Dimension text is a **text string** that specifies the actual measurement. Most CAD systems provide methods to use the measurement computed automatically by the system, supply different text, or suppress the text entirely. If you utilize the default text, the system can be instructed to append plus or minus tolerances to it automatically.

The dimension text is drawn in the currently selected text font (style). The default text format is governed by the default units. Defaults are embedded in the software when it is installed. Defaults can be changed before or during part creation on most systems.

15.11.4 Leaders

For some dimensioning, notes, and other annotations, the text is not placed next to the part it describes. In such cases, it is customary to place the text nearby and to draw a **leader line** from the text to the part. For instance, when diameter or radius dimensioning is desired, but the arc or circle is too small for the dimension text to fit inside, a leader can be drawn from the text to the arc or circle.

15.11.5 Center Mark and Centerline

A **center mark** is a small cross marking the center of a circle or arc. **Centerlines** are broken lines crossing at the center and intersecting the circumference of the circle or arc at its quadrant points. A center mark and centerlines are needed for all circular dimensions. CAD systems know where the center of each circle or arc is located. Inserting a point or center mark at the origin of an arc or circle involves telling the system to put it at the center of the selected arc, fillet, or circle. For many systems, drawing a centerline involves one command that inserts two perpendicular centerlines, with their short dashes crossing at the center of the curved entity.

15.11.6 Dimensions and Scaling

An engineer can change the CRT display size of the part for dimensioning purposes. For example, if the part is increased in size for visual clarification, dimensions inserted by the designer will reflect the true size of the part and not the new CRT display scale. In other words, the display size may be set at 2 to 1 but the dimensions will always be 1 to 1. By zooming in on a portion of a drawing, it is easier to place dimensions, especially in complicated or cluttered portions of a complex part.

15.11.7 Layer Separation of Dimensions on CAD Systems

A **layering scheme** is a means to separate logical groups or types of entities. Each part created on the CAD system has multiple layers associated with it. Direct access is available to any of these layers and to the specific entity or information contained on it. These layers should be thought of as transparent sheets on which the drafter places specific types of information. Any number of these layers can be displayed at one time. For example, text can be placed on one layer, all bolt holes on another layer, and all centerlines on the third layer. Any combination of these layers can be displayed. Some systems can assign automatically specific types of items to be placed on selected layers determined by the engineer. *Dimensions should always be assigned a layer of their own.* Figure 15.100 shows an example of placing dimensions

(a) Part feature layer

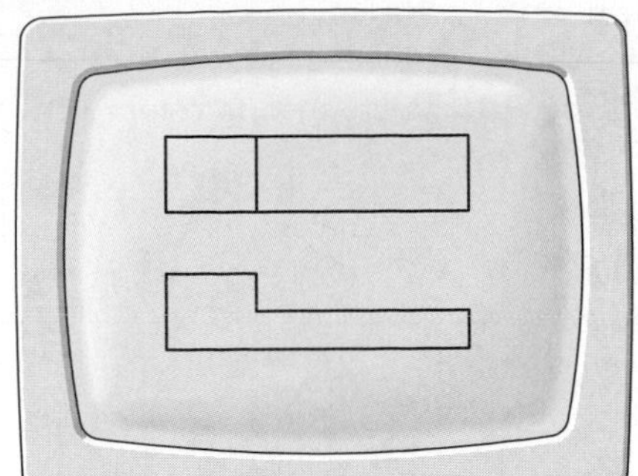

(b) Dimension layer

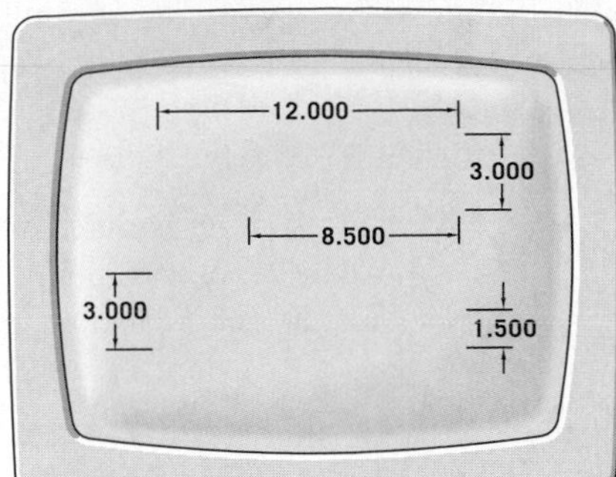

(c) All layers shown

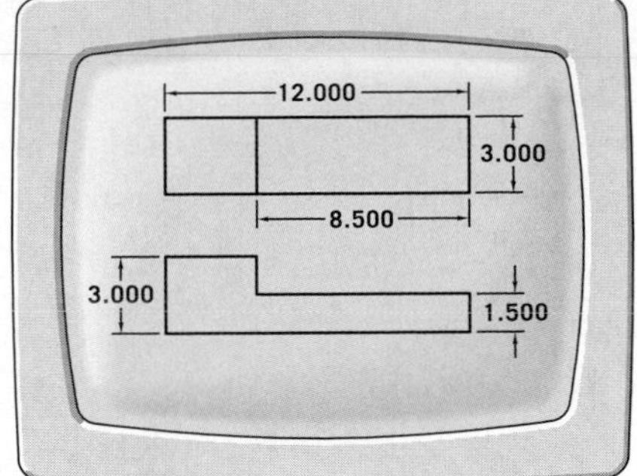

FIGURE 15.100 **Dimensioning and Layers**

on a separate layer from the geometry of the part. The dimensions or the geometry can be viewed separately [(a) and (b)] or together [(c)].

15.11.8 Color and Linetype

CAD systems with color capabilities provide a palette of colors. *Colors* make it easy to identify and distinguish different kinds of information on the drawing. Many engineers associate a certain color with a specific layer. Layers, entities, or information such as dimensions or notes can all be color coded.

With layers, components of a drawing are easily grouped. A layer or a set of layers holds the items related to a particular aspect of the drawing. Visibility, color, and linetype are easily controlled. Most companies develop a *standard layering scheme,* with assigned layers for construction lines, dimensions, and the part itself, each with its own associated color and *linetype* (font). The following tables show possible layering schemes:

Font, Color, Pen Size, and Layer Scheme

Layer	Color Number	Use	Linetype (Font)	Pen Size (mm)
1	4 (Yellow)	Part geometry	Continuous	0.7
5	7 (Magenta)	Hidden geometry	Dashed	0.5
10	6 (Gray)	Dimensions	Continuous	0.35
15	3 (Cyan)	Centerlines	Centerline	0.35
20	8 (Red)	Labels	Continuous	0.5
30	12 (Blue)	Border and title block	Continuous	0.9

A layering scheme makes it easy to keep track of where different information resides. Layering can also serve to sort graphic information temporarily. For example, layers can help separate geometry in a congested area of the part. By turning off the display of unnecessary information, such as text and dimensions, computer processing takes less time. Placing geometry on one layer and dimensions on another allows for viewing of the model (part) with or without dimensions.

Industry Layering Scheme

Layer Number	Contents
0	Layer Index/Table of Contents
1-50	Construction Geometry and Drawing Formats [contains all construction items used in the design of your part(s), e.g., lines, points, arcs, and the different types of drawing formats you may use]
51-120	Manufacturing (contains manufacturing information, e.g., NC and tool path information, jigs, fixtures, and tooling)
121-145	Dimensions, Text, Labels (contains all dimension information, text, and labels)
146-175	Illustrations [contains technical illustrations using the part(s) as its source—may be presented in 3D view with hidden lines removed]
176-200	Analysis (Engineering), FEM, Physical Properties (contains different kinds of analytical information concerning the part's structure, content, and properties)
201-254	Construction Aids, Miscellaneous Information (contains construction items that help design and dimension a part, as well as any miscellaneous information connected with the part design)

15.12 DIMENSIONING COMMANDS

When dimensioning a drawing, the **DIMENSION** command (**DIM** in AutoCAD) is entered from the keyboard or picked from a screen or from a dimensioning toolbar. All systems provide screen or tablet menus for quick and efficient dimensioning. Figure 15.101 shows a tablet menu with areas for selecting dimension parameters, changing existing dimensions, adding text, suppressing extension lines, altering the arrows and leader style or location, and specifying the type of dimension and its tolerance. Most systems also have screen menus devoted entirely to dimensioning commands. Selecting standards as defaults, inserting dimen-

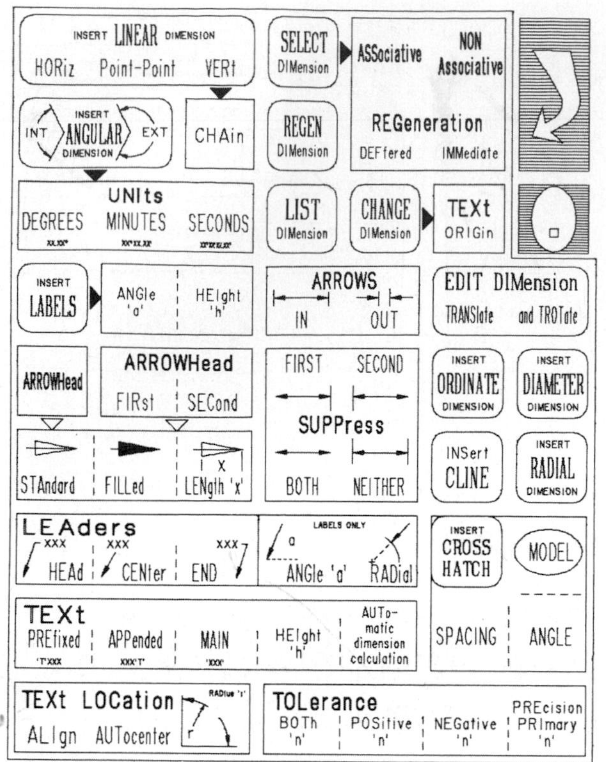

FIGURE 15.101 Dimensioning Menu

sions, and changing existing dimensions can be accomplished with pull-down menus, dialog boxes, and other dynamic menu capabilities.

Dimensioning commands can be grouped into four general categories:

- Linear dimensioning (vertical, horizontal, point-to-point, ordinate)
- Angular dimensioning
- Diameter dimensioning
- Radius dimensioning

15.12.1 Linear Dimensioning Commands

The following gives a general overview of linear dimension capabilities.

Horizontal generates a horizontal dimension line (Fig. 15.102). After the dimension command is entered, the drafter selects the endpoints of the horizontal distance to be dimensioned (**D1** and **D2**) and then the location of the dimension line and text (**D3**). In AutoCAD R13, linear dimensioning is used for both horizontal and vertical lines.

Vertical generates a vertical dimension line (Fig. 15.103) The first, second, and third selections accomplish the same results as in horizontal dimensioning.

(a) Before

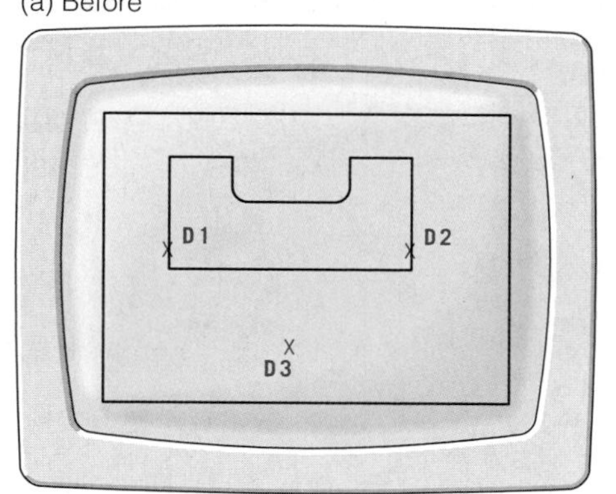

(b) After

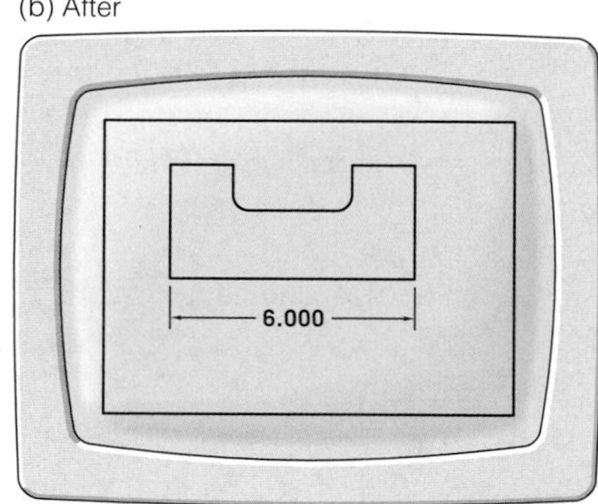

FIGURE 15.102 Placing a Horizontal Dimension

(a) Before

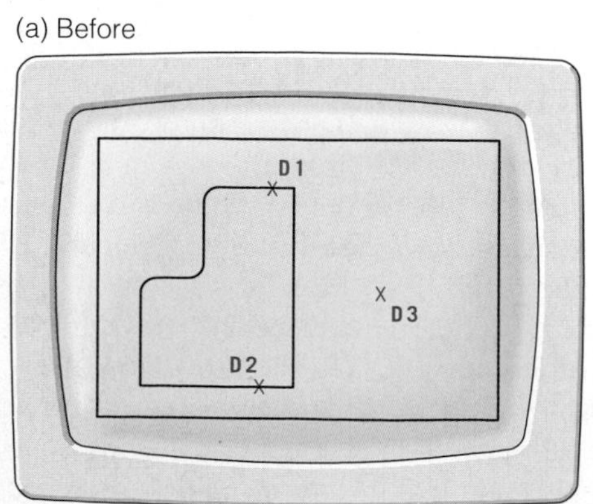

(b) After

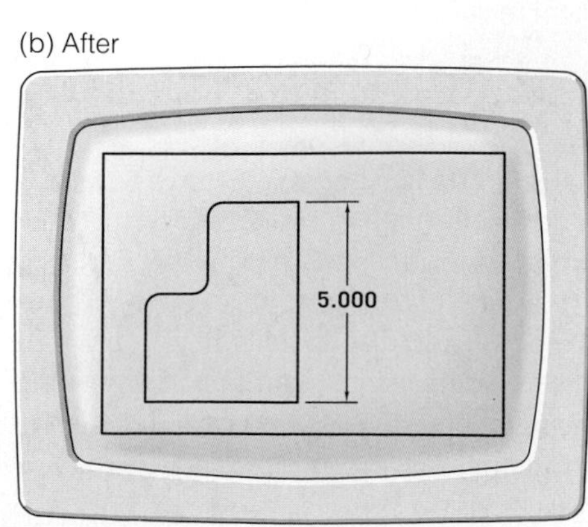

FIGURE 15.103 Placing a Vertical Dimension

(a) Before

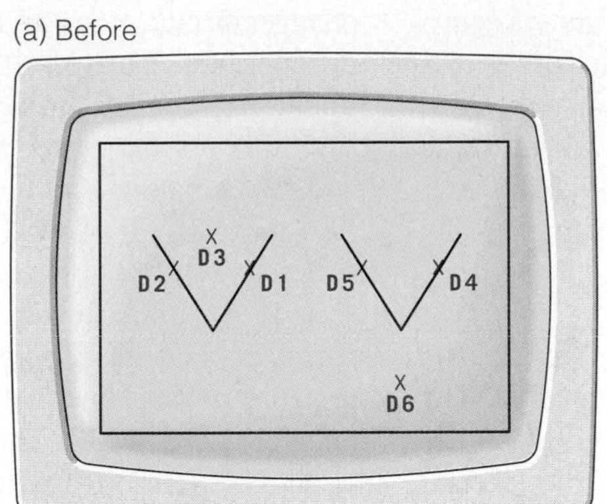

(b) After

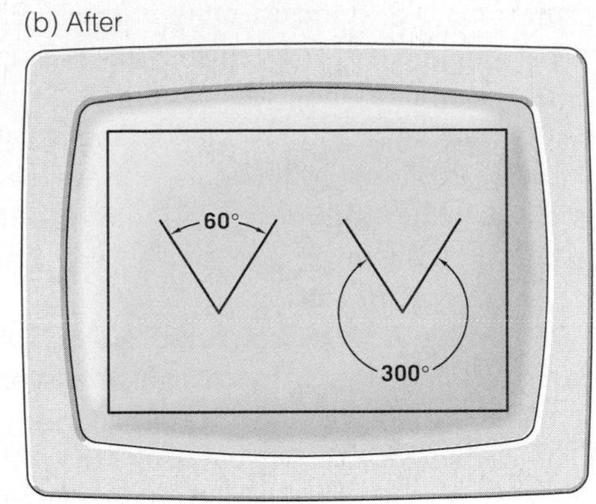

FIGURE 15.104 Placing Angle Dimensions

Aligned (or rotated) generates a linear dimension, with the dimension line drawn parallel to an angled linear entity or surface edge or rotated to a specific angle.

Ordinate allows the selection of two perpendicular datum lines or surface edges, and generates dimensions using rectangular coordinate dimensions without dimension lines.

15.12.2 Angular Dimensioning

Angular dimensioning generates an arc to show the angle between two nonparallel lines. The angle can be either inside or outside; Figure 15.104 shows examples of both inside (60°) and outside (300°) angular dimensioning. In both cases, the engineer enters the command, identifies the two lines to be measured, and places the dimension with the third selected location.

15.12.3 Diameter and Radius Dimensioning

When dimensioning the diameter of a circle, only two selections are required. After the command is entered, the designer identifies the circle to be dimensioned, then locates the dimension and the end of the leader with the second selection (Fig. 15.105).

Radius dimensioning is the same as **diameter dimensioning,** except the system measures and then dimensions the radius of an arc (Fig. 15.105). Remember, circles are dimensioned by giving a diameter dimension, not a radius dimension. Radius dimensions are to be provided for fillets, arcs, and slots.

15.13 CAD AND DIMENSION STANDARDS

Some CAD systems are designed to use dimensions that adhere to American National Standards Institute (ANSI) standards. Some systems provide the option to choose Japanese Industrial Standards (JIS) or the International Organization for Standardization (ISO) standards, which differ somewhat from the ANSI conventions. The selection of a drafting standard and unit of measurement should be made *before* the project is started, though many CAD systems allow you to reset standards, units, tolerances, etc., and to update the entire project automatically. AutoCAD uses SETVAR and the UNITS command to establish defaults for a project.

15.13.1 U.S. versus Metric Units

You can choose either SI or U.S. customary units of measurement for your design. Both of these standards can have particular units specified for dimensions: inches, feet, yards,

(a) Before

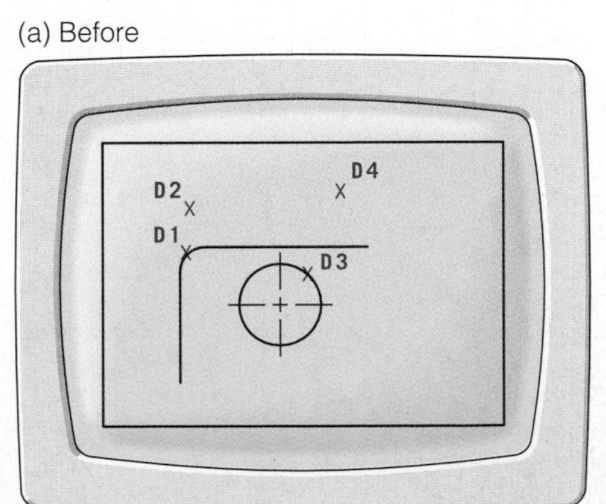

(b) After

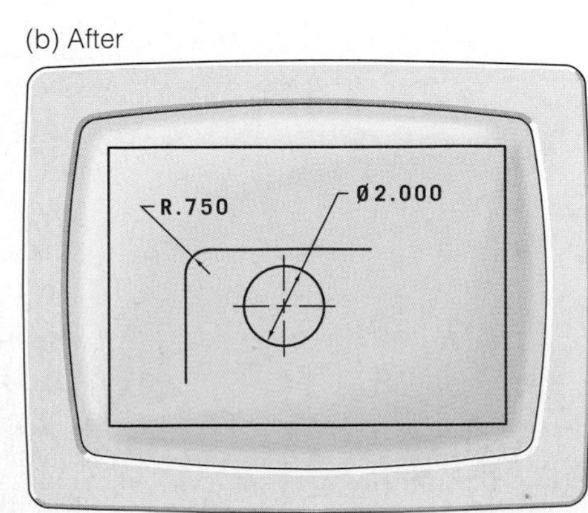

FIGURE 15.105 Placing Radius and Diameter Dimensions

or miles for U.S. standard units of measurements, or centimeters, millimeters, or kilometers for SI (metric) units.

Some systems allow the automatic placement of U.S. units on one layer and SI units on another. In addition, the option for dual dimensioning may be available. The designer dimensions the part once, and the system automatically places the specified primary unit together with the secondary unit in one dimension.

Designs created in one unit of measurement can be converted to other units by changing the setup units (**UNITS** command in **DDIM**) and then updating the file with the **UPDATE** command when using an AutoCAD system. **UPDATE** is reached through the **DIM** command. This capability makes dual dimensioning obsolete. There are several powerful features in AutoCAD R13 for modifying the style of the dimensions. **MODIFY** can update a particular dimension only if that is desired.

15.14 MECHANICAL DESIGN AND DIMENSIONING WITH CAD

Mechanical-design CAD programs can add dimensional information, notes, and labels to your drawings. You also can manipulate drawings of the model for aesthetic reasons or for visual clarification. These manipulation features include choosing a variety of line patterns, removing hidden lines, defining any type or number of views, inserting dual dimensions, defining standards, sectioning, and crosshatching. Dimensional information is associative.

15.14.1 Associativity

Associativity means that if the geometry is changed or modified in the model, its dimensions will be updated automatically to reflect those changes on detail drawings. Associativity also refers to the ability to carry out design change specifications all the way to the manufacture of the product; e.g., changes to the database could automatically update CNC files and quality-control features as well as inventory and other items attached to the database. Both 2D and 3D systems can be associative. But a 3D system is associative in all of its 3D views, whereas a 2D system is associative in only one view at a time.

It is not unusual for design changes to be made after a part is dimensioned. If the model has modifications, existing dimensions are updated automatically by the system to reflect those changes. The design in Figure 15.106(a) is the original dimensioned part. After design modifications to the part, the dimensions were automatically updated by the system [Fig. 15.106(b)].

15.15 PREPARING THE DRAWING: 2D AND 3D EXAMPLES

Figure 15.107 shows the step-by-step procedures for detailing the one-view drawing of a hold-down plate. The series starts with the part geometry already created [Fig. 15.107(a)]. This could have been done on a 2D or 3D system. The **ZOOM WINDOW** command can enlarge the area where a dimension is to be inserted on the part. Figure 15.107(b) shows the before-and-after sequence of the command for drawing a horizontal dimension on the lower portion of the part. Not all of the part's dimensioning is described in detail; only one example of each of the basic types is shown.

A vertical dimension is inserted between the center of the hole and the bottom of the plate [Fig. 15.107(c)]. Normally, you would have had to tell the system to lock onto the endpoint of the line and the center of the circle. Figure 15.107(d) shows an alternative to an angle dimension. Here, a **rotated (aligned)** linear dimension is inserted to measure

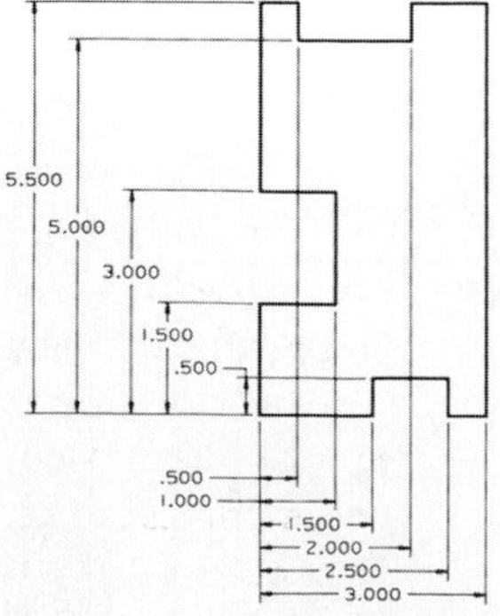

(a) The original part geometry that was created and later dimensioned

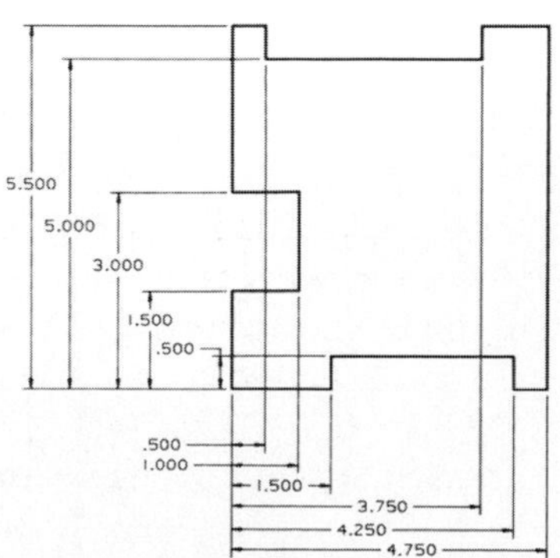

(b) The original part after design modifications. The dimensions were updated automatically when modifications were made to the design.

FIGURE 15.106 Associativity

FIGURE 15.107
Dimensioning a One-View Drawing

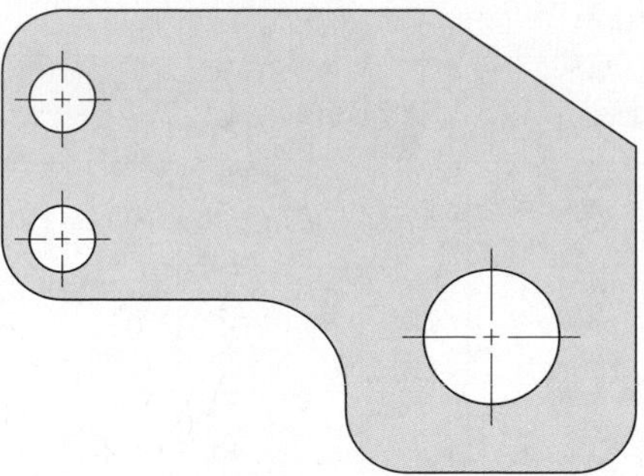

(a) Single-view drawing of a hold-down piece

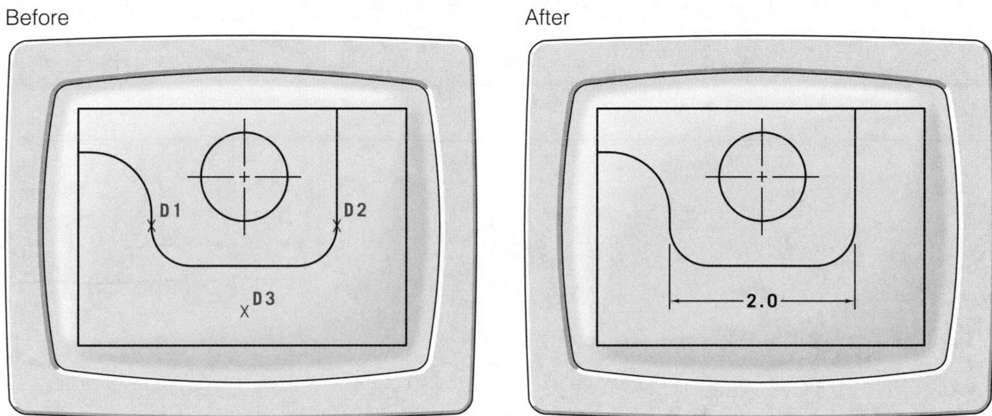

(b) Placing a horizontal dimension via the **ZOOM** command to enlarge the area to be dimensioned and then placing the dimension

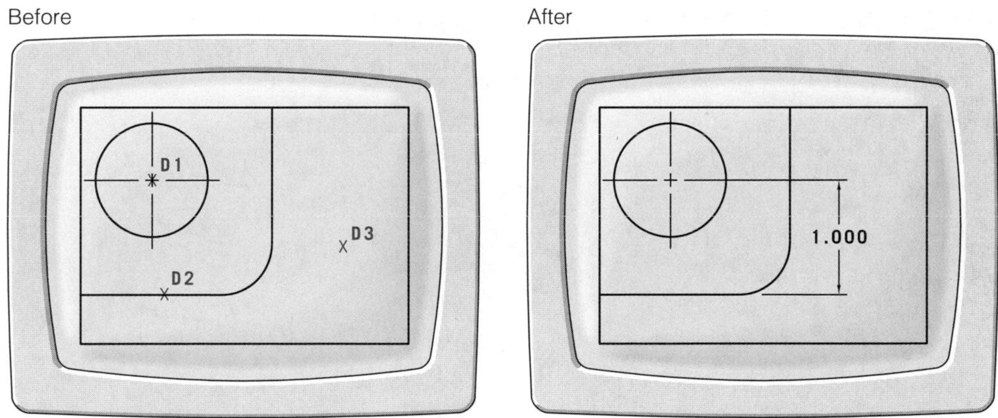

(c) Dimensioning the vertical distance between the hole and the hold-down plate's lower edge

the distance of the angled cut. The **DIMENSION ANGLE** command is used [Fig. 15.107(e)] to show the angle of the cut, instead of an aligned measurement. The diameter of the two small holes is dimensioned next [Fig. 15.107(f)]. The large fillet is then dimensioned with a radius [Fig. 15.107(g)]. Last, the notes are added with a text insertion command [Fig. 15.107(h)]. Figure 15.107(i) shows the completed part with all dimensions placed on the drawing. Figure 15.107 was created with Personal Designer.

Computervision software was used to create the breaker shown as a 3D model in Figure 15.108(a). The engineer activates the part file and places it in appropriate views [Fig. 15.108(b)]. The engineer then changes the appearance of the model to conform to standard drafting conventions. For example, the hidden lines are changed to dashed lines and the centerlines are added. Last, the part is dimensioned [Fig. 15.108(c)].

Remember, regardless of the method used to draw the part, manual or CAD, the standards and rules of dimensioning apply to every drawing.

FIGURE 15.107 Dimensioning a One-View Drawing—*Continued*

Before

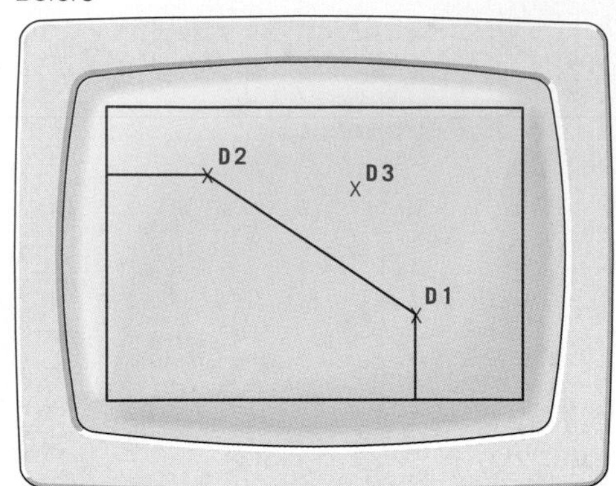

After

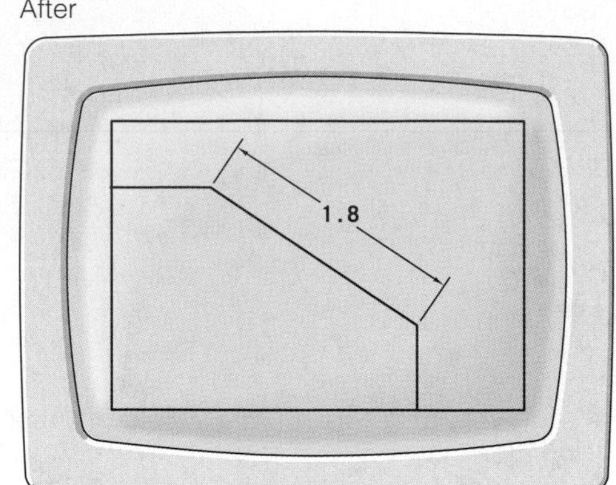

(d) Dimensioning the angled cut with the **POINT TO POINT** linear dimensioning command

Before

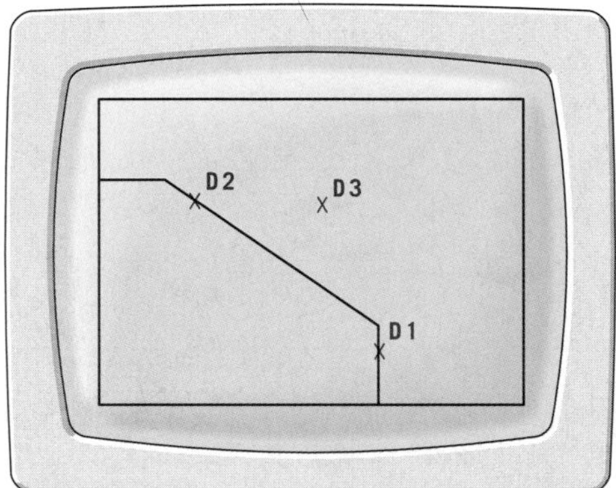

After

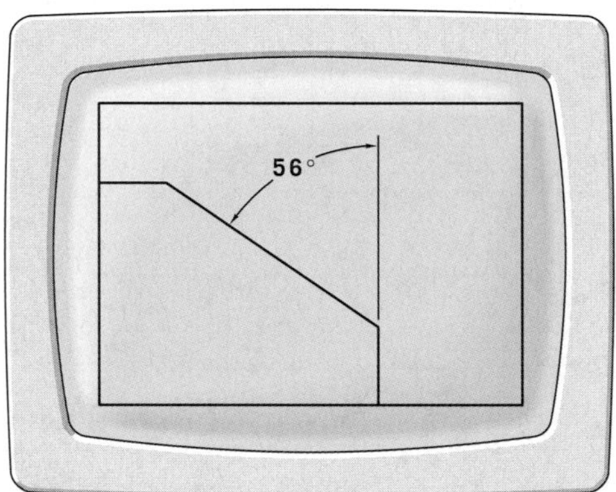

(e) Dimensioning the angled cut using the **DIMENSION ANGLE** command

Before

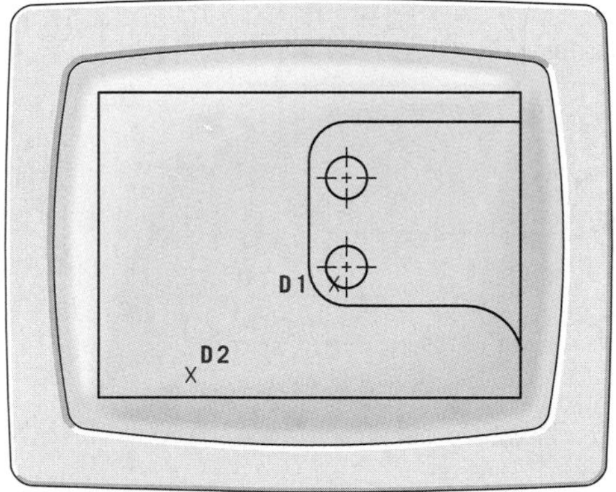

After

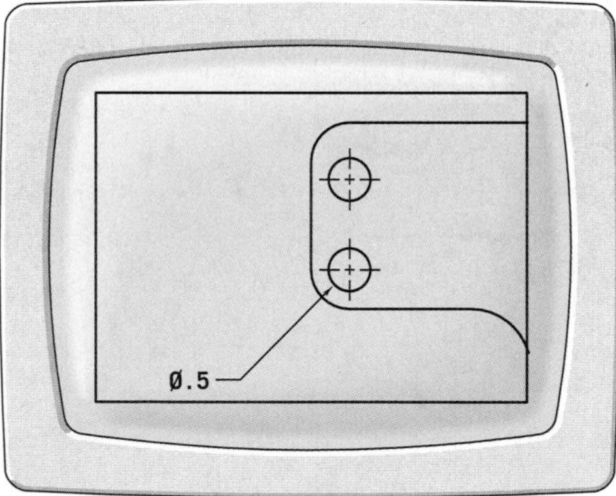

(f) Dimensioning the small holes

15.16 BASIC DIMENSIONING RULES AND DRAWING CHECKLIST

The following list is provided as a guide to dimensioning any drawing and to check a drawing after it is dimensioned. This list is by no means exhaustive.

1. Give the dimensions that will be used to fabricate the part in the shop or in CNC programming.
2. Make all figures totally legible—a misread dimension can result in an error in fabrication.
3. To help legibility, do not crowd dimensions around the part. Allow space for the dimensions in their proper location by planning for dimensions at the layout stage of the project.

FIGURE 15.107
Dimensioning a One-View Drawing—*Continued*

Before

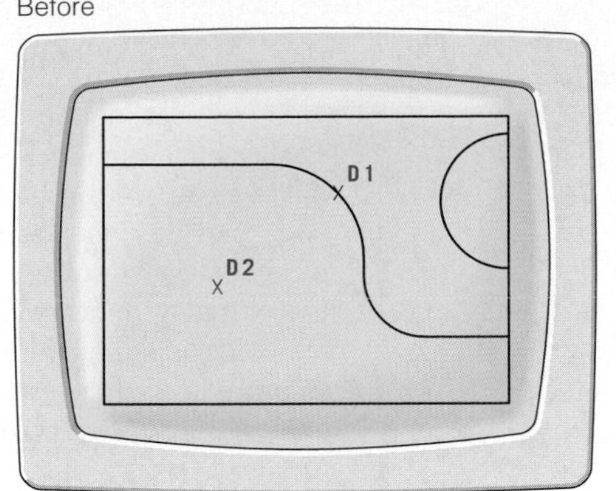

After

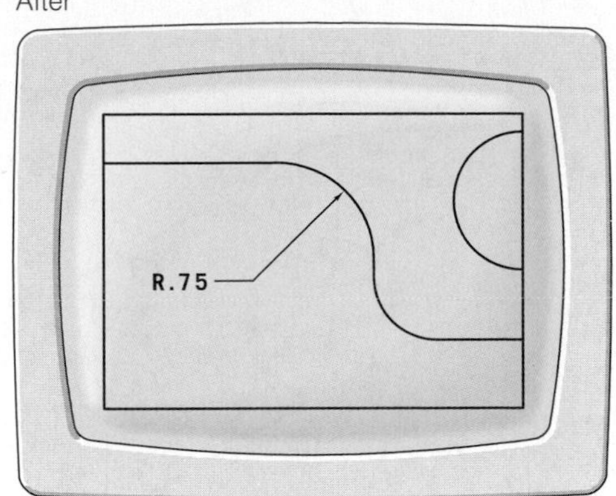

(g) Dimensioning the large radius

Before

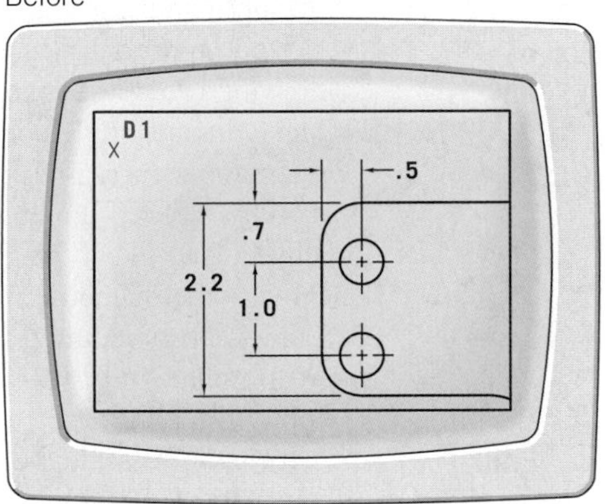

After

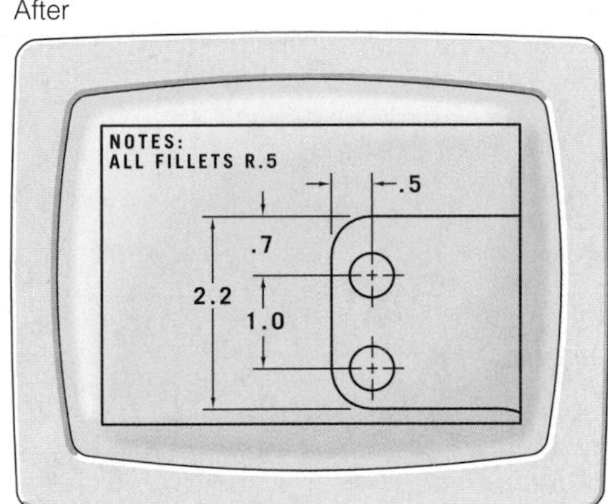

(h) Inserting notes

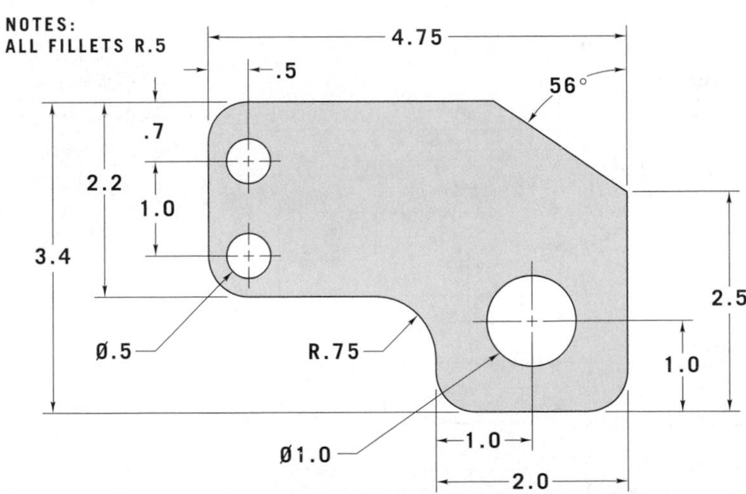

(i) Completed detail of the hold-down plate

4. Do not dimension on the part unless it is absolutely unavoidable. Use extension lines, and whenever possible keep figures off the views. Place dimensions outside a view.
5. Use proper lettering technique (with guidelines) for all lettering.
6. Dimension the views that show the characteristic shape and prominent features of each portion of the part.
7. Place numbers for dimension values so that they can be read from the bottom of the drawing (aligned), unless the drawing is for one of the construction engineering fields.

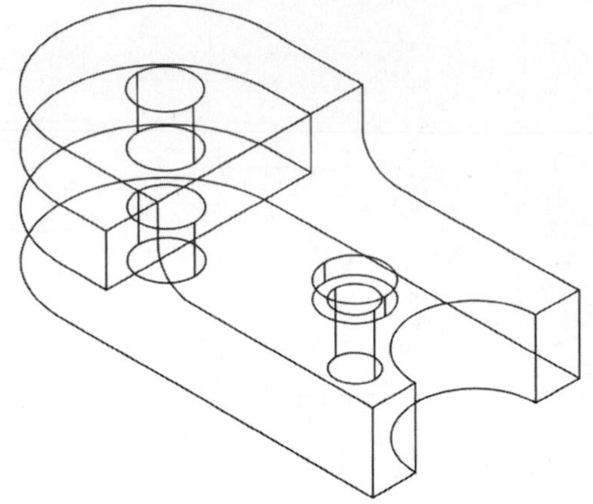

(a) 3D wireframe of the breaker

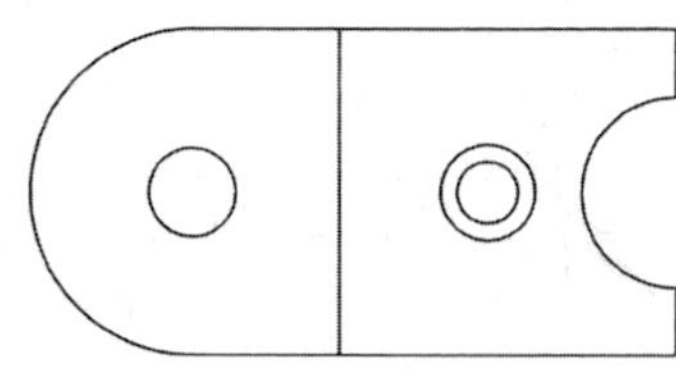

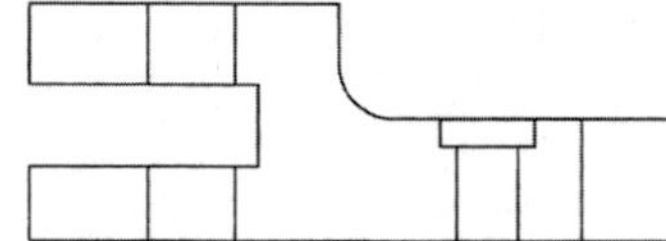

(b) Front and top views

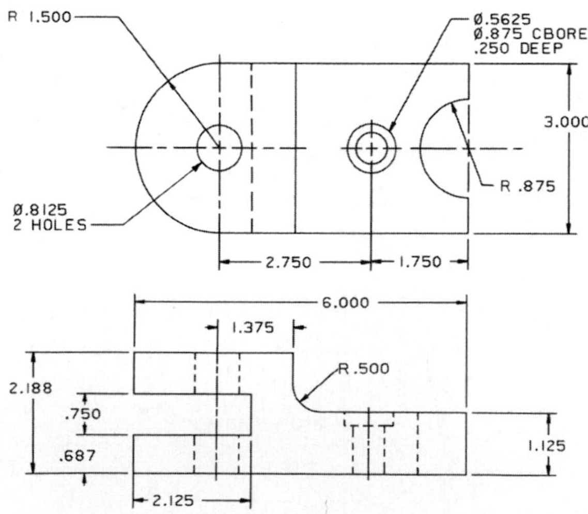

(c) Completed detail

FIGURE 15.108 **Dimensioning a 3D Part**

8. Do not use a part line as a dimension line. Object lines are used as extension lines only if unavoidable.
9. Locate dimension lines so they do not cross extension lines, by placing the largest dimensions outside of smaller dimensions.
10. Never cross two dimension lines.
11. Place parallel dimensions equally spaced and the numerals staggered, to avoid confusion on the drawing.
12. Give locating dimensions to the centers of circles that represent holes, cylindrical features, bosses, and slots.
13. Group related dimensions on the view where the contour of a feature is prominent.
14. Arrange a series of dimensions in a continuous line, i.e., chain dimensions.
15. Dimension from a machined (finished) surface, a centerline, or a datum (base) line that is easily established during manufacturing.
16. Do not repeat dimensions of the same feature on a drawing (double dimension).
17. Make dimensioning complete so that it is not necessary for manufacturing or inspection to add or subtract to obtain a needed dimension to scale the drawing manually.
18. Provide the diameter of a circle, never the radius.
19. Dimension as required by the production method. Parts with radial ends will have diameters and center-to-center dimensions.
20. Dimension to limit the tolerance buildup and to maintain ease of manufacture.
21. Dimension so that mating parts will fit in the worst case of tolerance buildup on the part.
22. When all dimensions are in inches, generally omit the inch symbol, except for construction drawings.
23. Provide the radius of an arc, and place the abbreviation R before the dimension.
24. If possible, avoid dimensioning to a hidden line.
25. Avoid dimensioning on sectioned areas of the part.
26. Use a note to establish repetitious features of a part, e.g., fillets with the same radius value.

QUIZ

True or False

1. Dimensioning is not as important as a graphically correct drawing.
2. Holes should be called out with a note giving the radius of the hole and its depth.
3. Center drills are used to hold a workpiece between centers on a lathe.
4. Dual dimensioning is used on most drawings in the United States.
5. Simplified methods for showing threads should be used on metric drawings only.
6. The diameter symbol always follows the size dimension.
7. Symbols can be used when calling out counterbores, spotfaces, and counterdrills.
8. Leaders are always drawn radially from a curved feature when placing a local note.

Fill in the Blanks

9. Fractions are used on ________, ________, and ________ drawings in the United States.
10. The ability of the system to update dimensions automatically after design changes have been made is called ________
11. Angles can be called out as ________ angles, or ________, and ________.
12. SR is used to define ________ and ________.
13. Counterbores can be specified by the symbol or ________
14. ________ dimensions are enclosed within parentheses.
15. Chamfers can be specified by ________ or ________.
16. There are two types of knurling: ________ and ________ patterned.

Answer the Following

17. Describe the difference between the dimensioning process of a 3D CAD system and that of a 2D CAD system.
18. What are the four types of linear dimensions? Describe the process of placing each on a part.
19. Describe four methods for calling out a taper.
20. Describe the process of geometric breakdown of a part.
21. Why are mating parts and mating dimensions important when dimensioning a part?
22. What is the difference between a radial and a diameter dimension, and when should each be used?
23. What is a finish mark, and why is it important when dimensioning a part?
24. Describe what notes are used for on a drawing. What is a local note, and what is a general note?

PROBLEMS

Your instructor can assign any of the figures presented in this chapter as problems. For every problem, redraw the part and dimension using the most recent ANSI Y14.5M standards. Other industry drawings and problems at the end of each chapter throughout the text can also be assigned by the instructor.

EXERCISES

Exercises may be assigned as sketching, instrument, or digitizing projects. Transfer the given information to an "A"-size sheet of .25 in. grid paper. Complete all views and solve for proper visibility, including centerlines, object lines, and hidden lines. Exercises that are not assigned by the instructor can be sketched in the text to provide practice and to enhance understanding of the preceding instructional material. Complete the views, and add hidden lines where required.

After Reading the Chapter Through Section 15.5.5 You May Complete the Following Four Exercises

Exercise 15.1 Dimension the .25 in. thick one-view part completely.
Exercise 15.2 Dimension the .125 in. thick aluminum plate completely.
Exercise 15.3 Dimension the two-view part as needed.
Exercise 15.4 Show the proper placement of all dimensions on appropriate views.

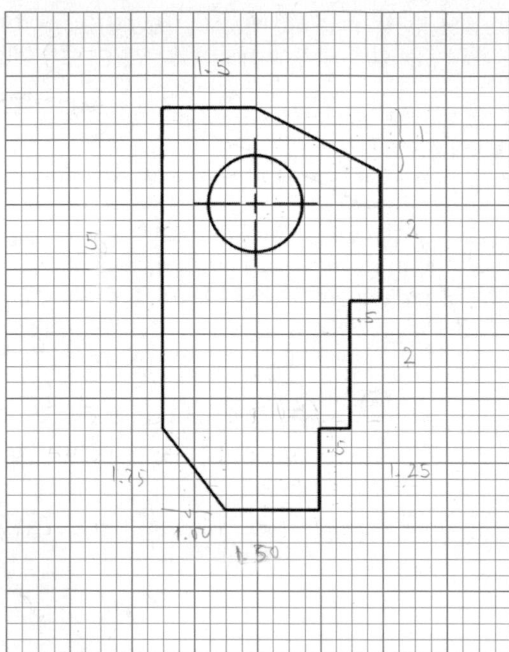

EXERCISE 15.1

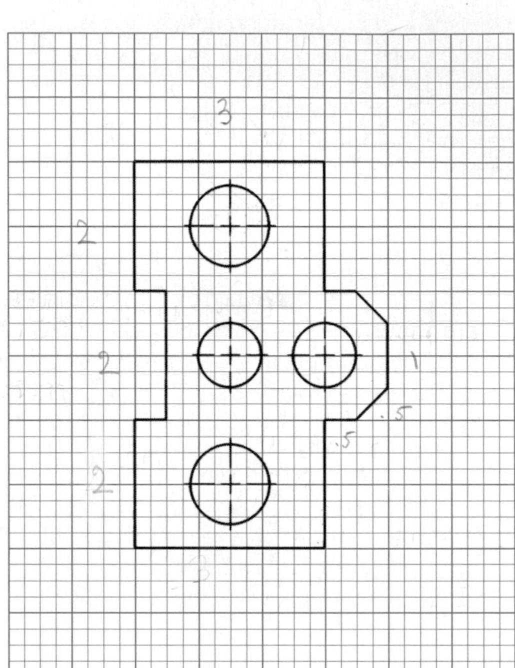

EXERCISE 15.2

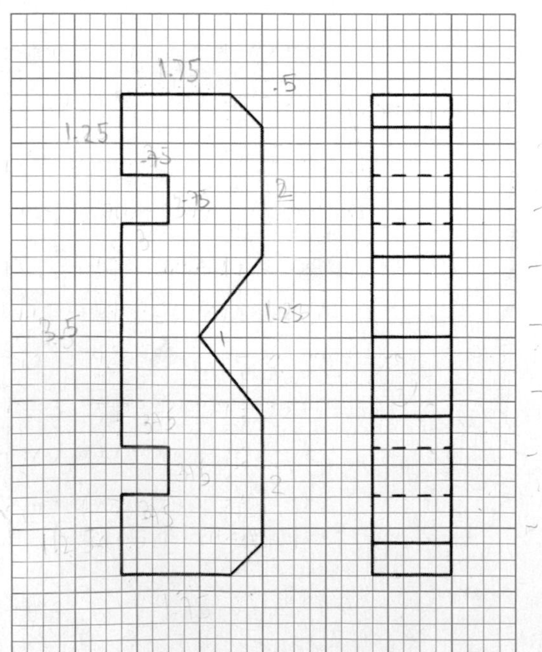

EXERCISE 15.3

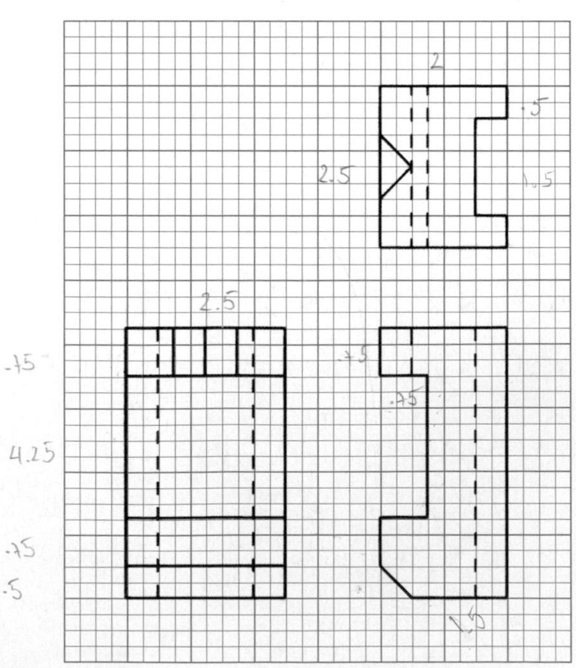

EXERCISE 15.4

After Reading the Chapter Through Section 15.6.3 You May Complete the Following Four Exercises

Exercise 15.5 Completely dimension the part as required. Use symbology to call out the spotfaced holes. Place finish marks on the machined faces, and dimension accordingly.

Exercise 15.6 Dimension the part completely. The bottom surface is machined.

Exercise 15.7 Dimension the two-view part.

Exercise 15.8 Dimension the three views of the part. The bottom surface, the left side surface, and the boss are the only finished surfaces. Add appropriate fillets and rounds for the cast surfaces (top and around the boss). Place basic finish marks on machined surfaces.

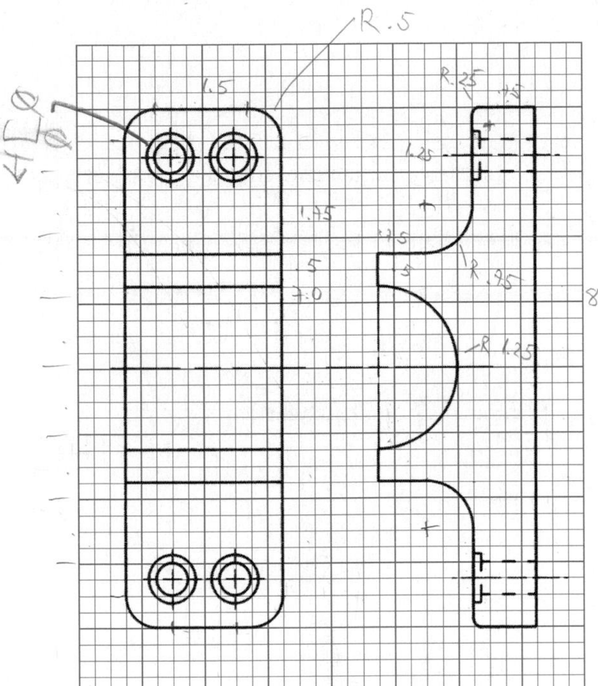

EXERCISE 15.5

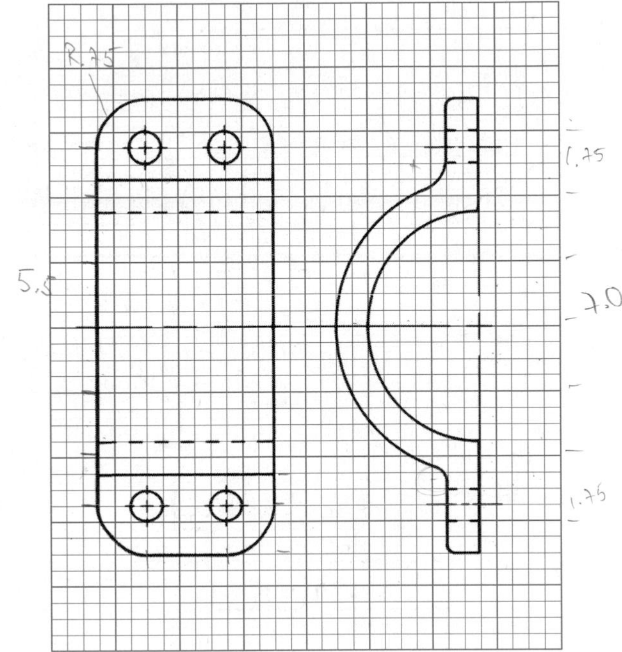

EXERCISE 15.6

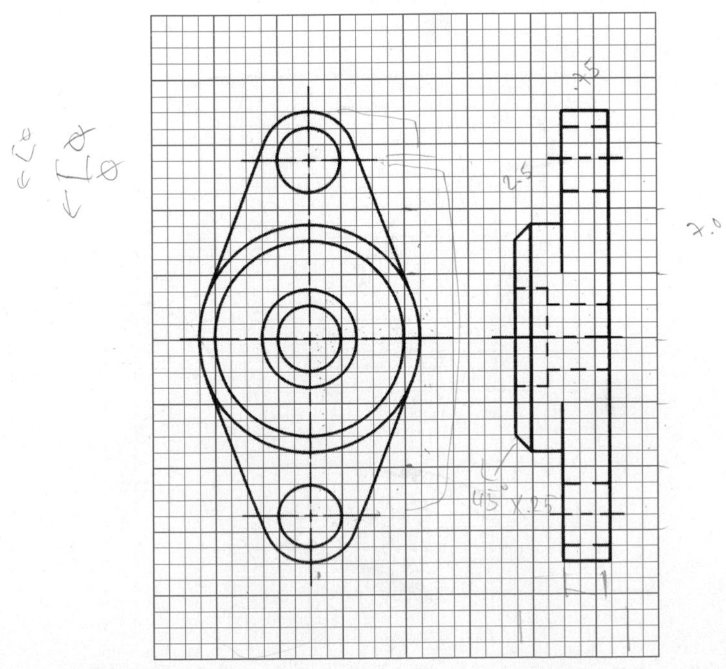

EXERCISE 15.7

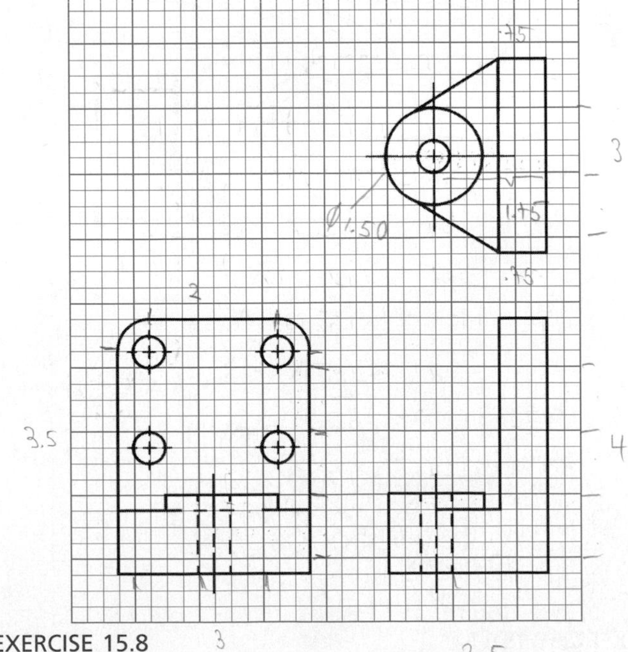

EXERCISE 15.8

After Reading the Chapter Through Section 15.8.3 You May Complete the Following Four Exercises

Exercise 15.9 Dimension the cast part completely. Add appropriate fillets and rounds to cast surfaces. Place finish marks on machine surfaces. The left surface and bottom surface are machined, along with the upper **U**-shaped surface. All other surfaces are cast.

Exercise 15.10 Because of space limitations, dimension only the hole pattern and holes (call out the bolt circle), the slots, and the chamfer. Make sure all views are visually correct.

Exercise 15.11 Dimension the part completely. Complete the views for proper visibility. Call out the knurling with a note. The small hole goes through to the center hole only.

Exercise 15.12 Because of limited space, dimension only the hole pattern, the slot, and the counterdrilled holes. Use symbology to call out the holes.

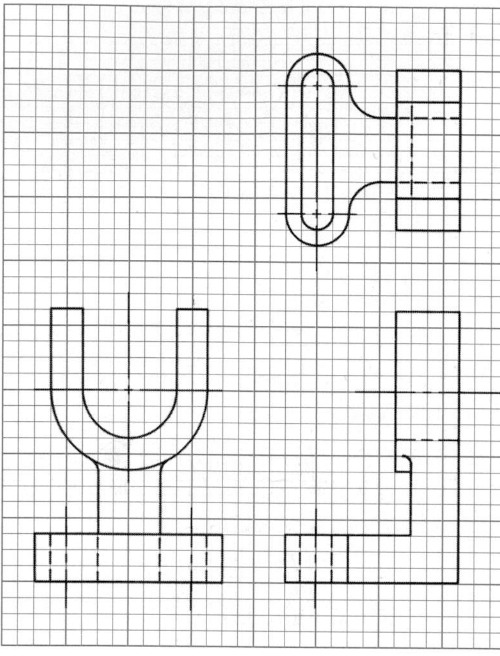

EXERCISE 15.9

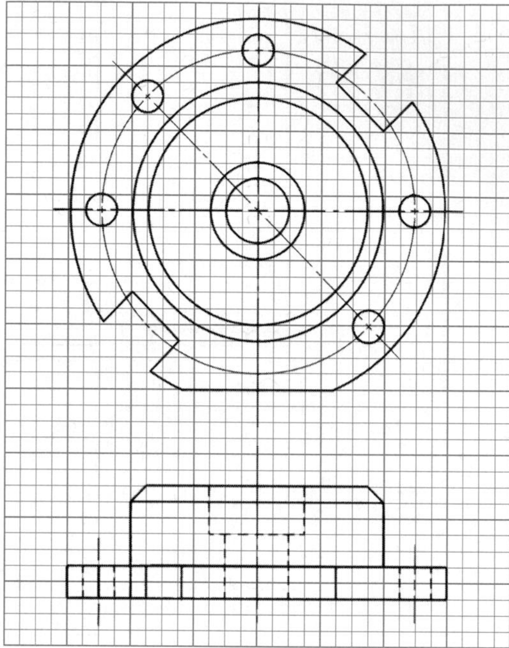

EXERCISE 15.10

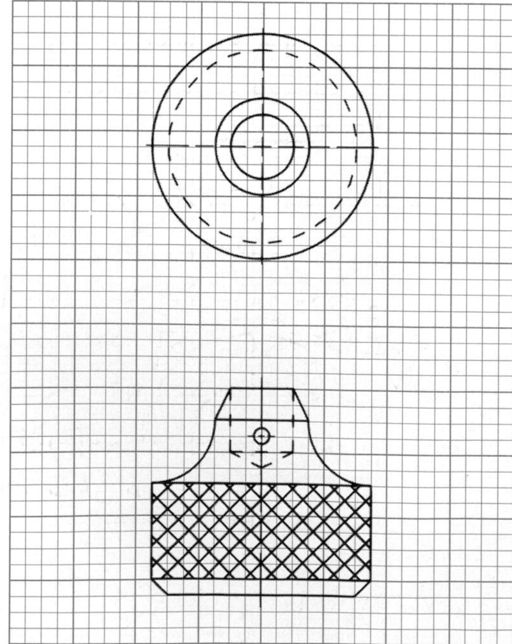

EXERCISE 15.11

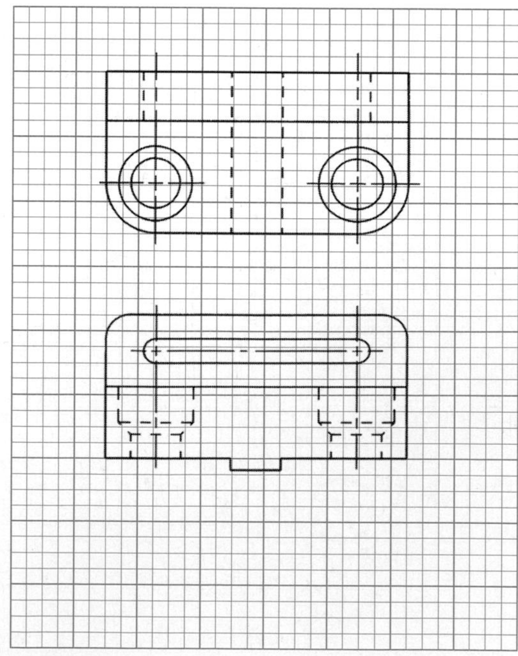

EXERCISE 15.12

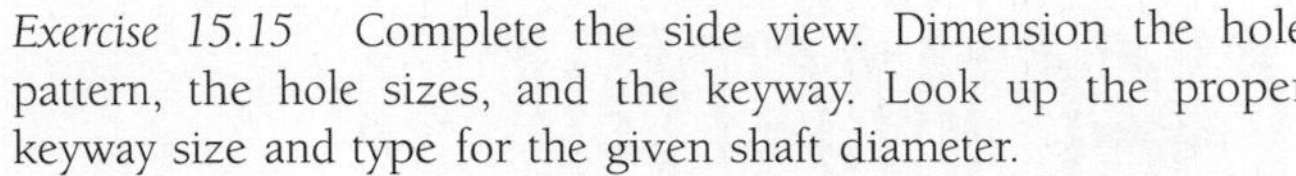

After Reading the Chapter Through Section 15.10.5 You May Complete the Following Four Exercises

Exercise 15.13 Dimension the taper with a callout. Because of space limitations, dimension only the lateral length dimensions, not the diameter dimensions of the rest of the part.
Exercise 15.14 Place a #4 center hole for a center drill on both ends of the workpiece. Dimension the whole part, and call out the center drill with a note. Complete the views.

Exercise 15.15 Complete the side view. Dimension the hole pattern, the hole sizes, and the keyway. Look up the proper keyway size and type for the given shaft diameter.
Exercise 15.16 Complete the side view of the part. Dimension the holes with a callout using symbology. Call out the keyway based on the shaft diameter. Dimension only one "ear" of the part.

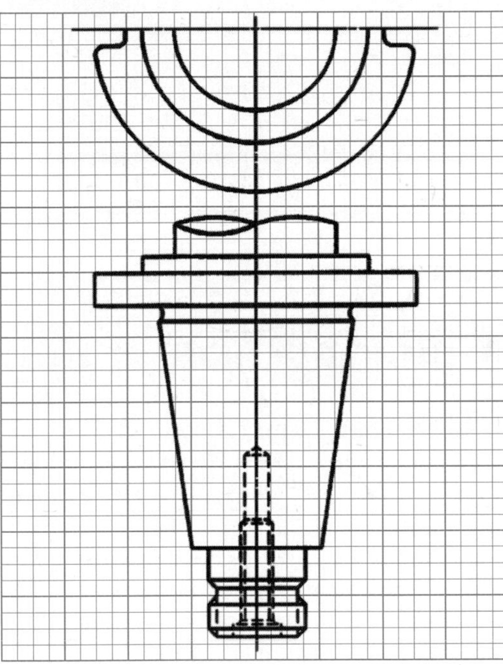

EXERCISE 15.13

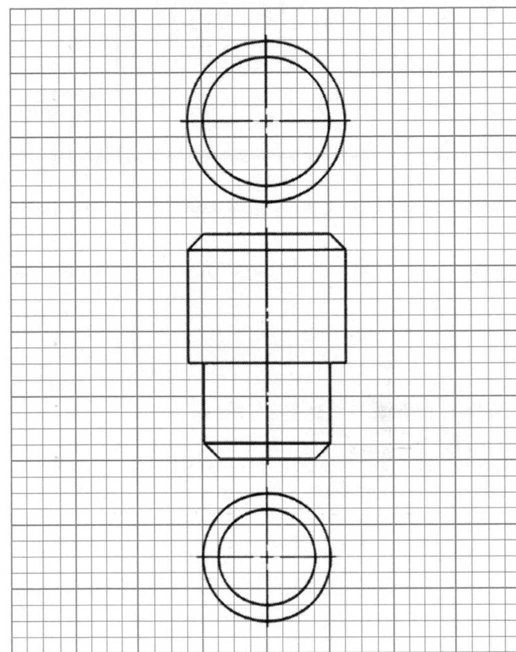

EXERCISE 15.14

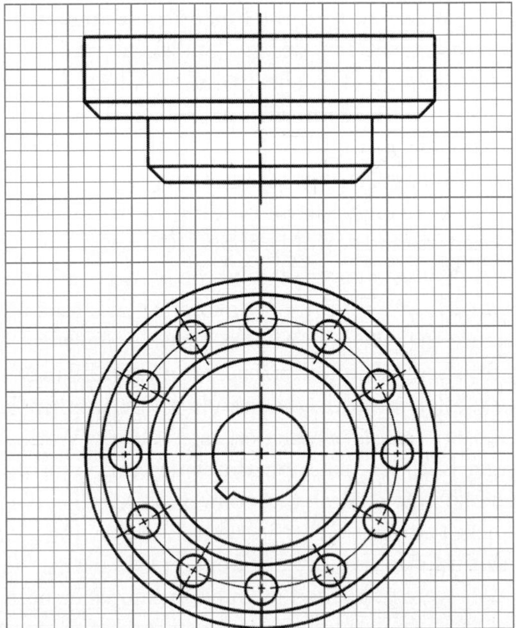

EXERCISE 15.15

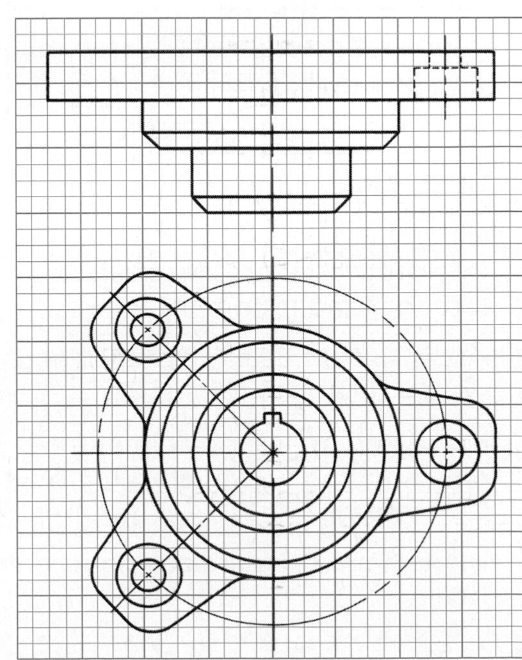

EXERCISE 15.16

GEOMETRIC DIMENSIONING & TOLERANCING (ANSI Y14.5 1994)

Chapter 16

LEARNING OBJECTIVES

Upon completion of this chapter you will be able to:

1. Differentiate between precision and accuracy, and understand tolerancing terms and techniques.
2. Recognize ISO and ANSI interpretations of angle of projection and limits of size.
3. Understand the use of general and geometric tolerancing rules, symbology, and modifiers.
4. Identify feature control frames.
5. Understand datums and datum systems.
6. Interpret form, profile, orientation, location, and runout tolerances.
7. Apply fixed, floating fastener, and system tolerance formulas.
8. Know how to use guidelines for dimensioning and tolerancing on a CAD system.
9. Understand standardized limits and fits.

16.1 INTRODUCTION

Features of manufactured parts vary in size, form, orientation, or location. Such variation is expected, and, as long as it is understood and controlled, the part will perform as designed. You may have tried to assemble some consumer product and found that holes did not line up between parts or that a hole for a bolt was not drilled perpendicular to the surface. Assembly was no doubt frustrating and the resulting product may not have performed up to expectations without modifications. *Geometric dimensioning and tolerancing (GD&T) is a symbolic system of tolerancing to control the size, form, profile, orientation, location, and runout of a part according to geometry.* Cost-effective designs provide the largest allowable **tolerances** consistent with the function and interchangeability requirements of the design. Statistical process control (SPC) often requires the effective use of GD&T to control process variations and improve product quality.

Even though technical drawings have been employed to communicate engineering information for over 6000 years, the concept of tolerancing, or holding variations within limits, has been around for only about 100 years. At one time, part variations were controlled by the worker rather than by engineering. It was not until the evolution of interchangeable manufacture that the goal of *exact* size gave way to holding parts within *limits.* The *Taylor concept,* introduced in 1905 and still in use today, introduced methods of limit-gaging for holes and shafts. Increased production rates during World War II from larger factories that tapped a wider variety of suppliers created a high rate of scrap that sometimes hampered wartime requirements. Inadequacies in technical drawings for conveying this information became apparent. In 1945, the Gladman papers were published in Great Britain, and these issues of inadequacies in drawings were discussed at the first American, British, Canadian Conference on the Unification of Engineering Standards.

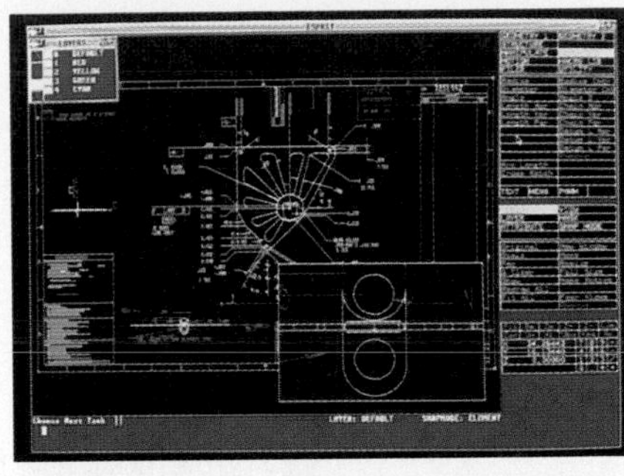

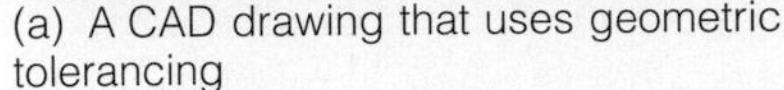

(a) A CAD drawing that uses geometric tolerancing

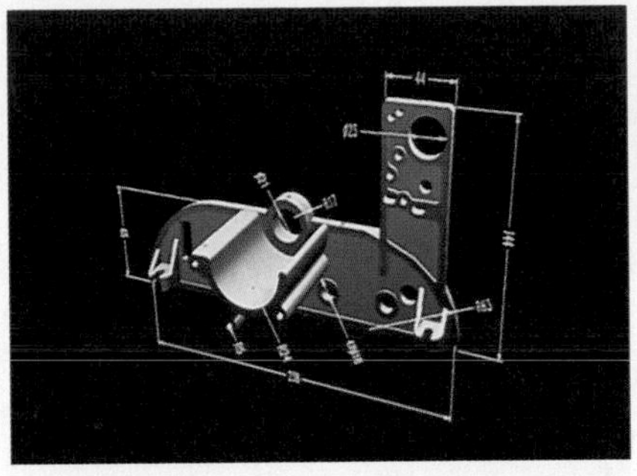

(b) Solid model showing part sizes

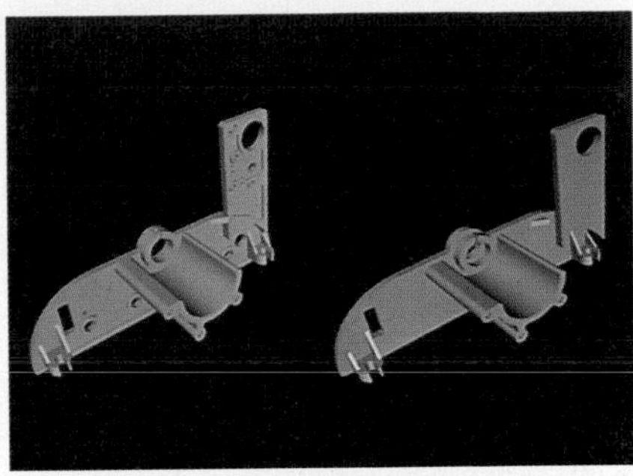

(c) Solid model family of parts

FIGURE 16.1 Geometric Tolerancing on a CAD System

Unfortunately, geometric tolerancing was put into practice only partially in the 1950s and 1960s. In 1972, the International Organization for Standardization (ISO) established a separate subcommittee to develop dimensioning and tolerancing standards. During the 1970s and 1980s, geometric dimensioning and tolerancing was employed extensively in industry and by the military. ANSI and ISO developed standards to ensure universal interpretation of tolerance requirements on drawings. The drawing in Figure 16.1 shows GD&T applied to a particular part. As product cycle times decrease and demands for quality grow in the increasingly competitive global marketplace of the 1990s, GD&T will play a more and more important role in meeting those demands.

16.1.1 Terms Used in Geometric Dimensioning and Tolerancing

The following terms are used throughout the chapter.

Actual size The measured size.

Basic dimension The theoretically exact size, profile, orientation, or location of a feature or datum target. It is the basis from which permissible variations are established by tolerances on other dimensions, in notes, or in feature control frames.

Basic size The size to which limits or deviations are assigned. This is the same for both members of a fit.

Clearance fit The relationship between assembled parts when clearance occurs under all tolerance conditions.

Datum The origin from which the location or geometric characteristics of features of a part are established.

Datum feature A geometric feature of a part that is used to establish a datum.

Datum target A specified point, line, or area on a part used to establish a datum.

Deviation The difference between the actual size and the corresponding basic size.

Interference fit The relationship between assembled parts when interference occurs under all tolerance conditions.

Lower deviation The difference between the minimum limit of size and the corresponding basic size.

Upper deviation The difference between the maximum limit of size and the corresponding basic size.

Feature A physical portion of a part, such as a surface, a hole, or a slot.

Feature of size A cylindrical or spherical surface, or a set of two parallel surfaces, each of which is associated with a size dimension.

Least material condition (LMC) The condition in which a feature of size contains the least amount of material within stated limits of size, for example, the maximum hole diameter or the minimum shaft diameter.

Limits of size The specified maximum and minimum sizes.

Maximum material condition (MMC) The condition in which a feature of size contains the maximum amount of material within the stated limits of size, for example, the minimum hole diameter or the maximum shaft diameter.

Regardless of feature size (RFS) The geometric tolerance or datum reference applies at any increment of size of the feature within its size tolerance.

Tolerance The total amount by which a specific dimension is permitted to vary; the difference between the maximum and minimum limits.

Tolerance, bilateral A tolerance in which variation is permitted in both directions from the specified dimension.

Tolerance, geometric A tolerance used to control form, profile, orientation, location, or runout.

Tolerance, unilateral A tolerance in which variation is permitted in one direction from the specified dimension.

Tolerance zone An area representing the tolerance and its position in relation to the basic size.

Transition fit The relationship between assembled parts when either a clearance fit or an interference fit results.

True position The theoretically exact location of a feature established by basic dimensions.

Virtual condition The boundary generated by the collective effects of the specified MMC limit of size of a feature and any applicable geometric tolerances.

16.2 STANDARDS AND SPECIFICATIONS

ANSI and ISO standards exist to ensure the universal interpretation of tolerance requirements. However, some companies tailor these standards to meet their particular product requirements. Also, there is not complete agreement between ANSI and ISO standards at this time. To avoid misinterpretation, a note such as "Interpret Drawing in Accordance with ANSI Y14.5M-1982" should appear on the drawing. The note should state the standard, the revision, and the revision date.

Recall that ANSI-standard drawings in the United States use third-angle projection [Fig. 16.2(a)] and that ISO drawings involve first-angle projection [Fig. 16.2(b)]. Although view placement is different, the views that result are the same. However, limits of size are defined differently for the two standards. This book concentrates on ANSI-standard tolerancing techniques, although this chapter also describes ISO techniques.

16.3 SYMBOLOGY

Geometric dimensioning and tolerancing is a **symbolic system** for controlling economically the function, interchangeability, size, form, profile, orientation, position, and runout of features or parts and for establishing datums and other necessary tolerancing practices. This section describes the symbols for specifying geometric characteristics and other dimensional requirements on engineering drawings.

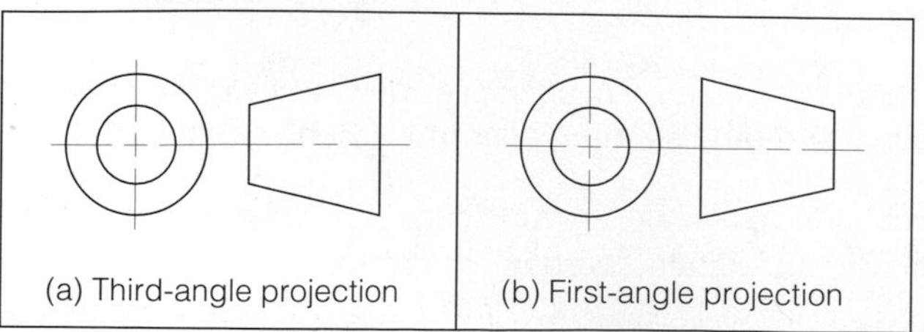

FIGURE 16.2 ANSI and ISO Orthographic Projection Symbols

Symbols should be of sufficient clarity to meet the legibility and reproducibility requirements of ANSI Yl4.5M.

Symbols are always preferred to notes because they take less space, overcome language barriers, and are less subject to interpretation. These are the very reasons that GDT uses a symbolic language to communicate specifications. Most individual symbols not only represent an entire standardized engineering concept, but are variously combined in a **feature control frame** to form complete engineering, production, and inspection quality specifications. The form and proportion of geometric tolerancing symbols are shown in Figure 16.3. The geometric characteristic symbols and the modifying symbols are further categorized in Figure 16.4.

Situations may arise where the desired geometric requirement cannot be conveyed completely by symbology. In such cases, a note can describe the requirement, either separately or supplementing a geometric tolerance.

16.3.1 Geometric Characteristic Symbols

Following are the symbols denoting geometric characteristics.

Basic dimension symbols A basic dimension is identified by enclosing the dimension in a rectangle. See Figures 16.3 and 16.4.

Datum feature symbol This consists of a frame containing the datum-identifying letter preceded and followed by a dash.

Letters of the alphabet All letters except I, O, and Q can be used to identify datums. Each datum feature requiring identification is assigned a different letter. When datum features requiring identification on a drawing exceed single alpha lettering, the double alpha series is employed—AA through AZ, BA through BZ, etc.

Datum target symbol This is a circle divided horizontally into two halves. The lower half contains a letter identifying the associated datum, followed by the target number, assigned sequentially starting with 1, for each datum. If the datum target is an area, the area size may be entered in the upper half of the symbol; otherwise, the upper half is left blank. A radial line attached to the symbol is directed to a target point (indicated by an "X"), target line, or target area.

Material condition symbol The symbols for maximum material condition and least material condition are shown in Figures 16.3 and 16.4. If no material condition symbol is present, then regardless of feature size is assumed.

Projected tolerance zone symbol See Figures 16.3 and 16.4.

Diameter and radius symbols The symbols for diameter, spherical diameter, radius, and spherical radius are shown in Figure 16.3. These symbols precede the value of a dimension or tolerance given as a diameter or radius.

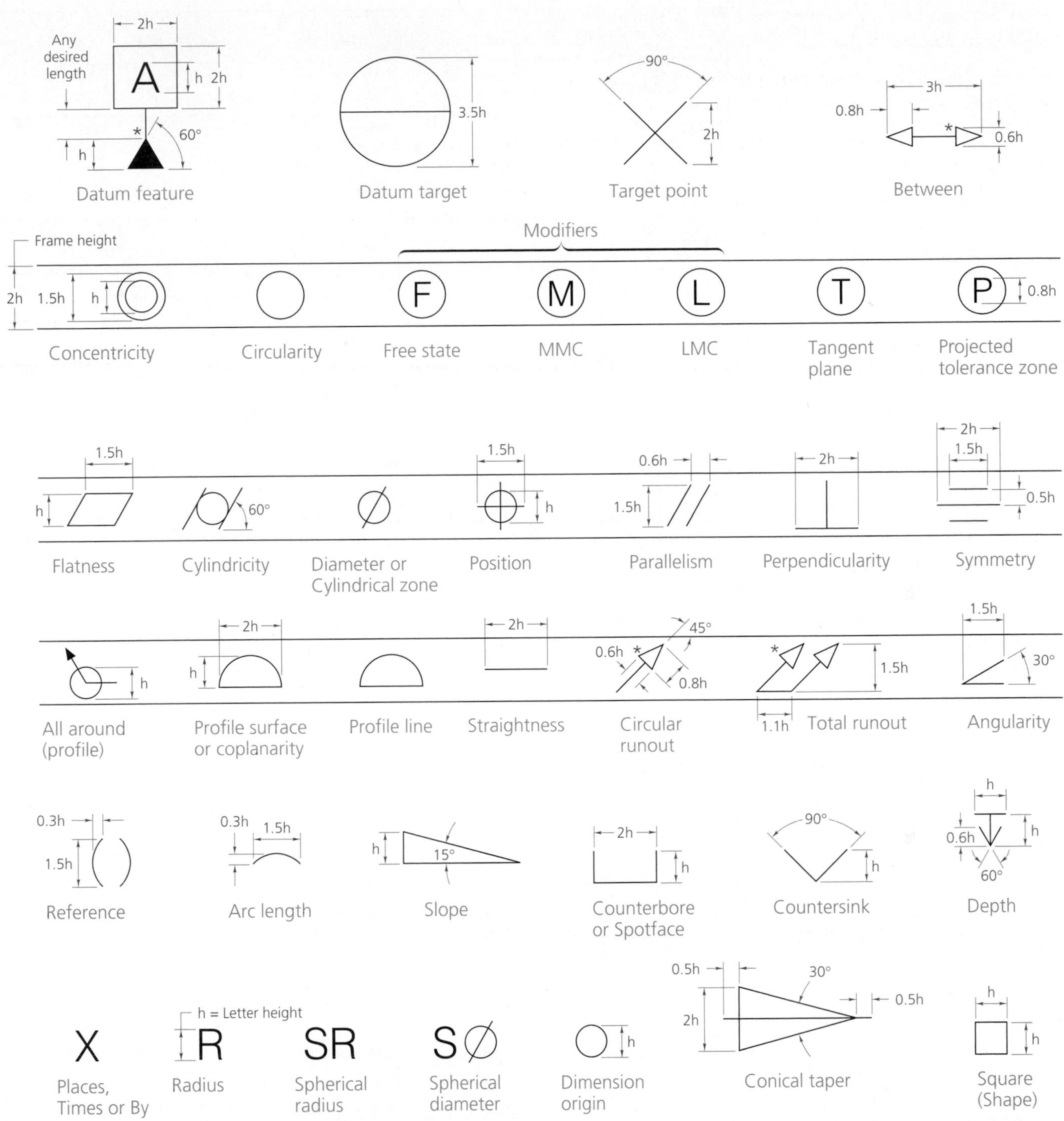

FIGURE 16.3 Geometric Tolerancing Symbols (Sizes)—*Continues*

Reference symbol A reference dimension or reference data is identified by enclosing the dimension or data within parentheses.

Arc length symbol The symbol that indicates that a linear dimension is an arc length measured on a curved outline is shown in Figures 16.3 and 16.4. This symbol is placed above the dimension.

Counterbore or spotface symbol This symbol precedes the dimension of the counterbore or spotface. See Figure 16.3.

Countersink symbol This symbol precedes the dimensions of the countersink. See Figure 16.3.

Depth symbol The symbol for indicating that a dimension applies to the depth of a feature precedes that dimension (Fig. 16.3).

Symbol for:	ASME Y14.5M	ISO
Straightness	—	—
Flatness	▱	▱
Circularity	○	○
Cylindricity	⌭	⌭
Profile of a line	⌒	⌒
Profile of a surface	⌓	⌓
All around		(proposed)
Angularity	∠	∠
Perpendicularity	⊥	⊥
Parallelism	//	//
Position	⌖	⌖
Concentricity (concentricity and coaxiality in ISO)	◎	◎
Symmetry	⌯	⌯
Circular runout	↗	↗
Total runout	⌰	⌰
At maximum material condition	Ⓜ	Ⓜ
At least material condition	Ⓛ	Ⓛ
Regardless of feature size	None	None
Projected tolerance zone	Ⓟ	Ⓟ
Tangent plane	Ⓣ	Ⓣ (proposed)
Free state	Ⓕ	Ⓕ
Diameter	∅	∅
Basic dimension (theoretically exact dimension in ISO)	50	50
Reference dimension (auxiliary dimension in ISO)	(50)	(50)
Datum feature	A	or A

FIGURE 16.3 Geometric Tolerancing Symbols (Sizes)—*Continued*

Symbol for:	ASME Y14.5M	ISO
Dimension origin	⌖→	⌖→
Feature control frame	⌖ | Ø 0.5 Ⓜ | A | B | C	⌖ | Ø 0.5 Ⓜ | A | B | C
Conical taper	⌲	⌲
Slope	⌳	⌳
Counterbore/spotface	⌴	⌴ (proposed)
Countersink	⌵	⌵ (proposed)
Depth/deep	↧	↧ (proposed)
Square	□	□
Dimension not to scale	<u>15</u>	<u>15</u>
Number of places	8X	8X
Arc length	⌒105	⌒105
Radius	R	R
Spherical radius	SR	SR
Spherical diameter	SØ	SØ
Controlled radius	CR	None
Between	*◄—►	None
Statistical tolerance	⟨ST⟩	None
Datum target	Ø6/A1 or A1 —Ø6	Ø6/A1 or A1 —Ø6
Target point	X	X

*May be filled or not filled

FIGURE 16.3 Geometric Tolerancing Symbols (Sizes)—*Continued*

Square symbol The symbol that indicates that a single dimension applies to a square shape precedes that dimension (Fig. 16.4).

Dimension origin symbol This symbol, a small circle placed at the origin, indicates that a toleranced dimension between two features originates from one of those features.

Taper and slope symbols Symbols specifying taper and slope for conical and flat tapers are shown in Figure 16.3.

16.3.2 Modifiers

Modifiers stipulate whether a tolerance is to apply regardless of size or only at a specific size (see Fig. 16.5). If no modifier is present, then regardless of feature size is assumed. The following rules for modifiers are based on the size of features and the geometry involved.

- Modifiers may be used only for features and/or datums that have a size tolerance. The MMC modifier may be

Feature	Tolerance Type	Symbol	Characteristic
Individual (single)	Form (shape)	—	Straightness
		▱	Flatness
		○	Circularity
		/○/	Cylindricity
Individual or related	Profile (contour)	⌒	Profile of a line
		⌓	Profile of a surface
Related	Orientation (attitude)	∠	Angularity
		⊥	Perpendicularity
		//	Parallelism
	Location	⌖	Position
		◎	Concentricity
	Runout	↗	Circular runout
		⌰	Total runout
Modifying symbols		Ⓜ	Maximum material condition-MMC
		Ⓛ	Least material condition
Additional symbols		Ⓟ	Projected tolerance zone
		∅	Diameter (face of dwg.)
		S∅	Spherical diameter
		R	Radius
		SR	Spherical radius
		( )	Reference
		⌒	Arc length

FIGURE 16.4 **Categories of Geometric Tolerancing Symbols**

used in conjunction with the straightness of a feature axis based on the cross-sectional size, flatness (by special note on features of size), datums of size with profile tolerances, and all datums and features of size or orientation and position tolerances.

- The RFS symbol is no longer used in the United States. In all countries, unless otherwise specified, all tolerances automatically apply RFS.
- Position, except in the case of a single-plane surface, requires a modifier for all features and datums (Fig. 16.6).
- Circularity, cylindricity, runout, concentricity, straightness

Modifying Symbols		
Symbol	Abbreviation	Meaning
Ⓜ	MMC	Maximum material condition
Ⓛ	LMC	Least material condition

FIGURE 16.5 **Modifying Symbols**

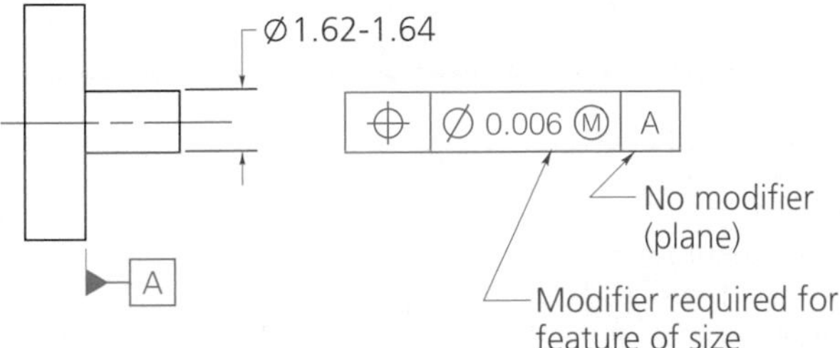

FIGURE 16.6 **Single-Plane Surface, No Modifier**

of element lines, and profile of a feature may not use the MMC modifier. The exception is for datums of size used in conjunction with profile. A special note is required to incorporate the MMC modifier in conjunction with flatness:

(PERFECT FORM AT MMC NOT REQUIRED)

16.4 FEATURE CONTROL FRAME

Geometric tolerances are placed in a **feature control frame,** which contains a geometric characteristic symbol, the tolerance, modifiers, and datums (Fig. 16.7). The feature control frame consists of at least the first two compartments shown in Figure 16.8, but may contain three or more compartments. The *first compartment* contains the geometric characteristic symbol (one of the thirteen from Fig. 16.3). The *second compartment* may contain a zone shape symbol, such as the diameter symbol indicating the diameter of a cylindrical zone; the tolerance, in inches or millimeters; and a modifier. The *third compartment* usually contains datums. This compartment may have **separators** to order the datums.

Feature control frames are not repeated or referenced on a technical drawing. **Datum identification symbols,**

may be repeated where it is essential to ensure the correct meaning.

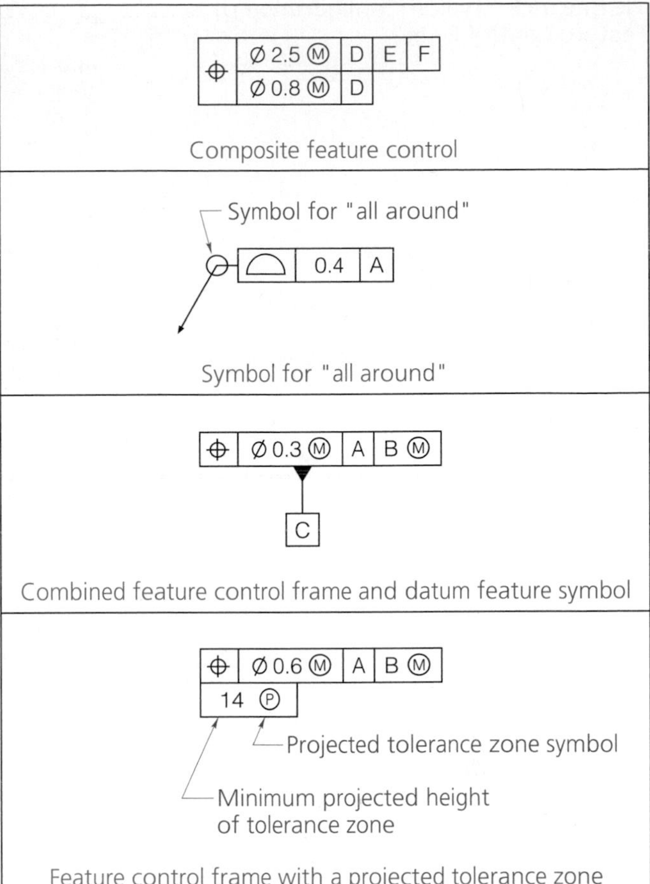

FIGURE 16.7 **Feature Control Frames**

16.4.1 Maximum Material Condition (MMC)

In the **maximum material condition (MMC),** a feature or datum feature is at the tolerance limit, meaning the part will contain the most material (*weigh the most*). For an external feature, such as a pin or shaft, MMC is the maximum limit (Fig. 16.9). For an internal feature, such as a hole, MMC is the minimum limit (Fig. 16.10). Remember that a part weighs the most when the hole in it is the smallest size in the range. Figure 16.11 shows the MMC and the least material condition (LMC) in both an external and an internal feature. The tightest fit between the two results when both features are at MMC; the loosest fit results when both features are at LMC.

If the MMC modifying symbol appears in a feature control frame (Fig. 16.12), the specified tolerance applies only at MMC. In Figure 16.12, the perpendicularity tolerance is .004 when the feature is at MMC (.512). As the feature deviates from MMC, additional perpendicularity tolerance equal to the deviation is allowed. This is called the *bonus tolerance* (Fig. 16.13). In other words, as the male diameter decreases, the increase in perpendicularity results in the same fit to the mating part. The modifying symbol for MMC, specified in the feature control frame for the feature, datum, or both, works the same way for all geometric tolerances.

FIGURE 16.8 Typical Configuration of a Feature Control Frame

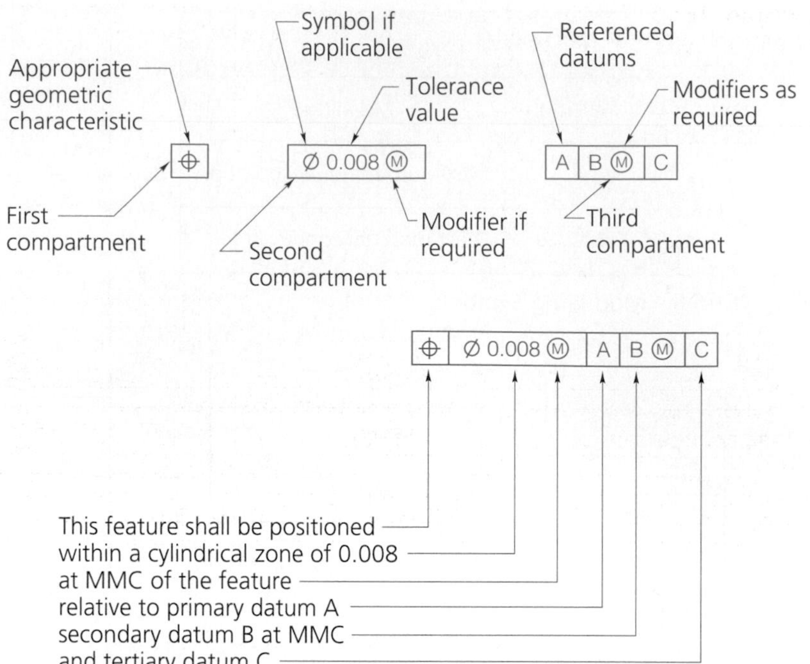

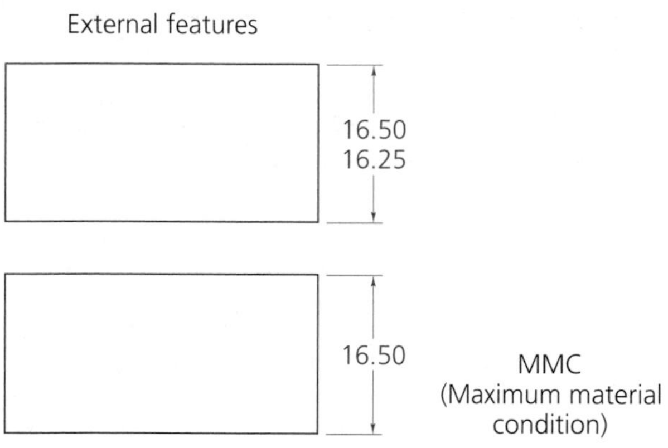

FIGURE 16.9 MMC of an External Feature

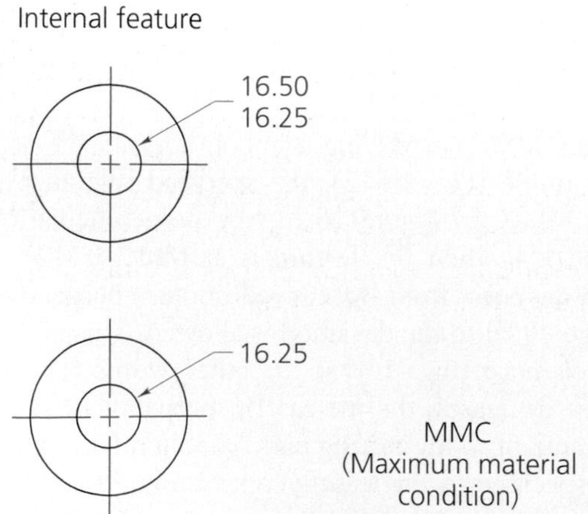

FIGURE 16.10 MMC of an Internal Feature

16.4.2 Least Material Condition (LMC)

In the **least material condition (LMC),** a feature or datum feature is at the tolerance limit, meaning the part will contain the least material (*weigh the least*). For an external feature, such as a pin, LMC is the minimum limit (Fig. 16.14). For an Internal feature, such as a hole, LMC is the maximum limit (Fig. 16.15). The modifying symbol for LMC, specified in the feature control frame for the feature, datum, or both, works the same way for all geometric tolerances. Table 16.1 shows the result of using Figure 16.11 as though LMC, rather than MMC, were specified in the feature control frame. LMC is generally employed where minimum bearing areas, minimum wall thickness, or alignment of parts is the main concern, not fit.

16.4.3 Regardless of Feature Size (RFS)

The newest ANSI standard no longer uses the RFS modifier symbol. In the ISO standard, RFS applies to every geometric tolerance unless MMC or LMC is specified. For positional tolerance, MMC or LMC must be specified for all features and datums of size.

If no modifier is placed after the feature tolerance in the second compartment, the tolerance must be met at all sizes.

16.4.4 Virtual Condition

The **virtual condition** (Fig. 16.16) is the condition resulting from the worst-case effect of the size and geometric tolerance applied to the feature. The free assembly of components is

FIGURE 16.11 MMC and LMC Limits for External and Internal Features

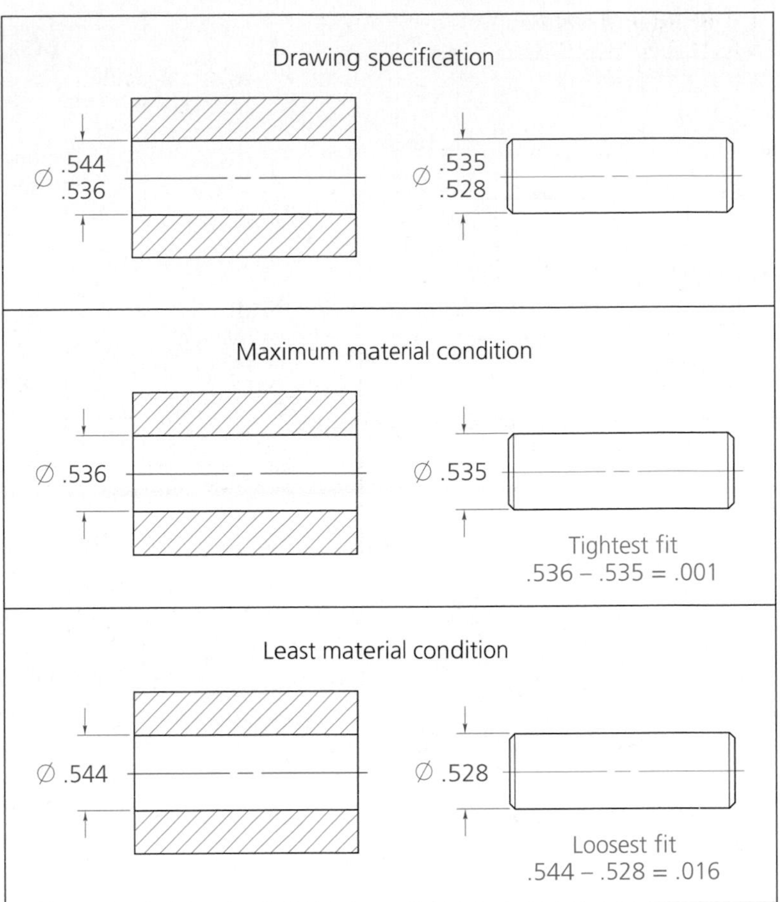

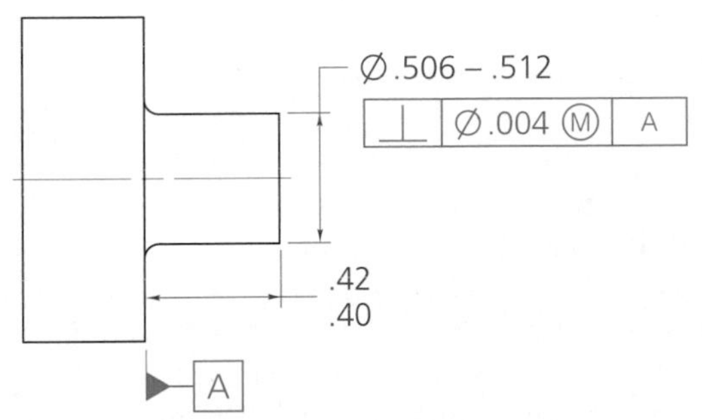

FIGURE 16.12 Perpendicularity When the Feature Is at MMC

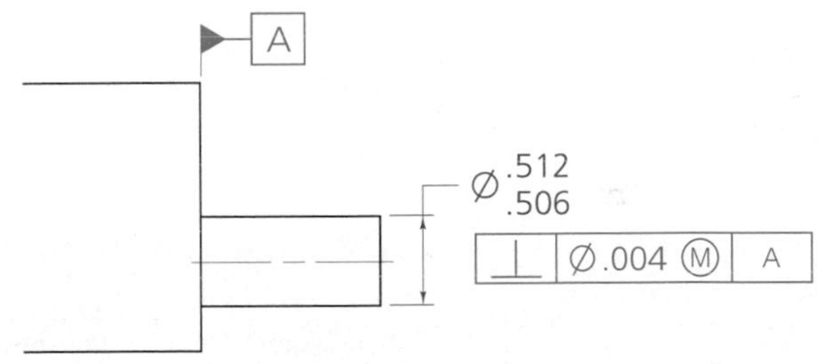

MMC size	Actual size	Tolerance allowed	Virtual (fit) condition
.512	.512	.004	.516
.512	.511	.005	.516
.512	.510	.006	.516
.512	.509	.007	.516
.512	.508	.008	.516
.512	.507	.009	.516
.512	.506	.010	.516

FIGURE 16.13 Bonus Tolerance Addition to Geometric Tolerance at MMC

dependent on the combined effect of the actual sizes of the part features and the errors of form, orientation, location, or runout—for example, the axis is out of straight, the size of a shaft is virtually increased, or the size of a hole is virtually decreased. The formulas for determining the virtual condition are as follows.

External Feature:

Virtual condition = MMC size + geometric tolerance

Internal Feature:

Virtual condition = MMC size – geometric tolerance

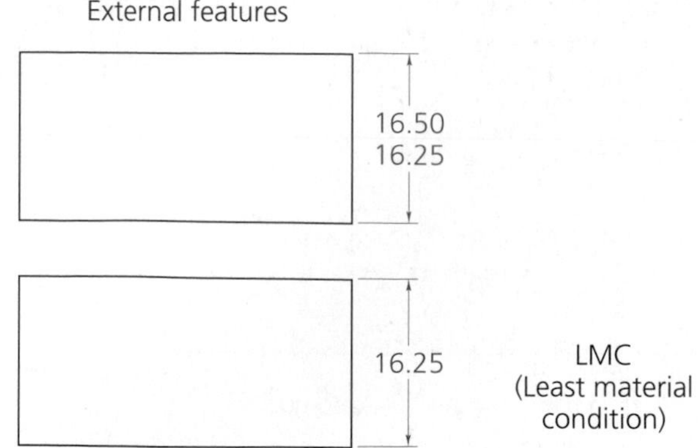

FIGURE 16.14 LMC of an External Feature

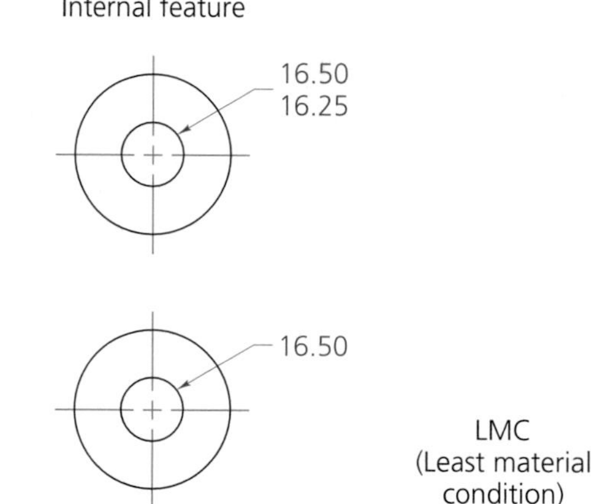

FIGURE 16.15 LMC of an Internal Feature

TABLE 16.1 Bonus Tolerance Addition to Geometric Tolerance at LMC

LMC Size	Actual Size	Tolerance Allowed	Minimum Bearing Area
.506	.506	.004	.502
.506	.507	.005	.502
.506	.508	.006	.502
.506	.509	.007	.502
.506	.510	.008	.502
.506	.511	.009	.502
.506	.512	.010	.502

16.4.5 Angular Surfaces

If an **angular surface** is defined by the combination of a linear dimension and an angle, the surface must lie within a tolerance zone represented by two nonparallel planes (Fig. 16.17). The tolerance zone will be wider as the distance from the apex of the angle increases.

16.5 DATUMS AND DATUM SYSTEMS

Datums are theoretically exact geometric references derived from the datum feature. Figure 16.18 shows the primary datum plane established on a surface by three area contact positions. Datums are not assumed to exist on the part itself, but are simulated by the more precisely made manufacturing or inspection equipment or a computerized mathematical model. A datum plane, for example, could be *simulated* from the datum feature by a surface plate (Fig. 16.19).

Datums are points, lines, and planes. Datums provide repeatable part and feature orientation for manufacturing and inspection consistent with the expected mating characteristics or orientation at assembly. Datums should be established from "hard" features on the part, such as one or two specific diameter(s) on a shaft (Fig. 16.20).

16.5.1 Applicability of Datums

A **datum** is a theoretically exact point, axis, or plane derived from the true geometric counterpart of a specified datum feature. A datum is the origin from which the location or geometric characteristics of features of a part are established. A **datum target** is a specified point, line, or area on a part used to establish a datum. Tolerances, as they relate to datums, are described according to the feature they locate.

16.5.2 Part and Feature Direction and Orientation

If a drawing contains two or mor<e features, it is incomplete if one or more datums are not specified. Without datums, reliable engineering interchangeability is difficult or impossible; setup criteria for manufacturing and inspection is then arbitrary. Without datums, the design is compromised and the manufactured part or assembly may not function as intended.

16.5.3 Datum Reference Frame

Locations and measurements are taken relative to three mutually perpendicular planes, collectively called a **datum reference frame** (Fig. 16.21). In inspection, a surface plate and two angle plates perpendicular to it can simulate the datum reference frame. In manufacturing, the bed of the machine and clamps or other devices, along with the direction of machine movement, provide location relative to three mutually perpendicular planes.

16.5.4 Datum Features

Datum features are selected to ensure the orientation of the part and its associated features for interchangeability and to ensure functional relationships. If a functional datum feature is undesirable from a manufacturing or inspection standpoint, a nonfunctional feature with a precise toleranced relationship to the functional feature may be used, provided all design requirements are met.

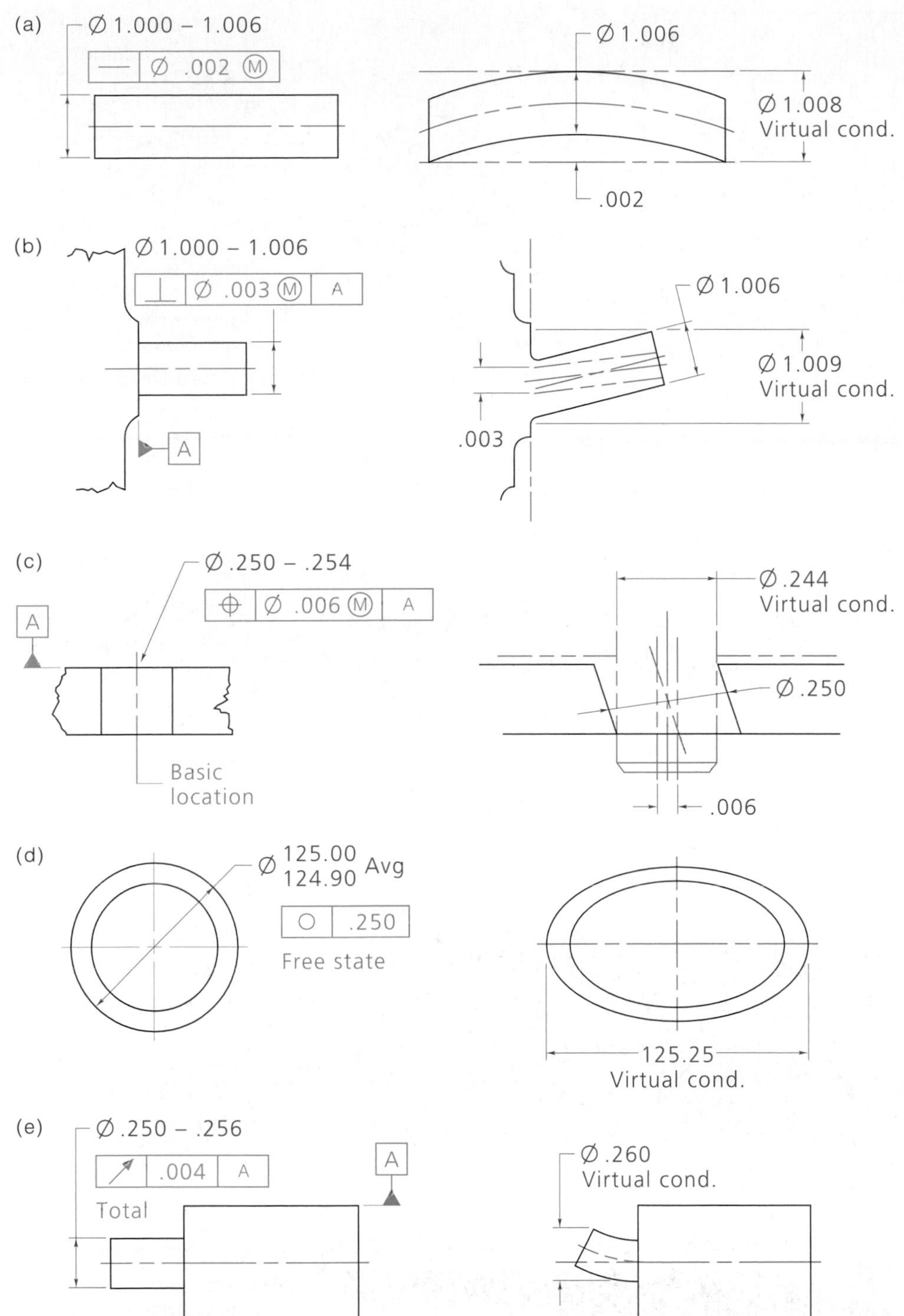

FIGURE 16.16 Examples of Virtual Condition

16.5.5 Datum Precedence

The sequence of datums specified in the feature control frame determines the order in which the datum features contact the datum reference frames (Fig. 16.22):

1. The part primary datum feature is aligned with the primary datum.
2. While in full contact with the primary datum, the secondary datum feature is aligned with the secondary datum.
3. While in full contact with the primary datum and aligned to the secondary datum, the tertiary datum feature is pushed into contact with the tertiary datum.

The **primary datum** is established by full contact with of a minimum of three noncollinear points on the part (recall that three noncollinear points define a plane). The **secondary datum** is perpendicular to the primary datum and is established by contacting a minimum of two points on the part (two points establish a line). The **tertiary datum** is perpendicular to the primary and the secondary datums

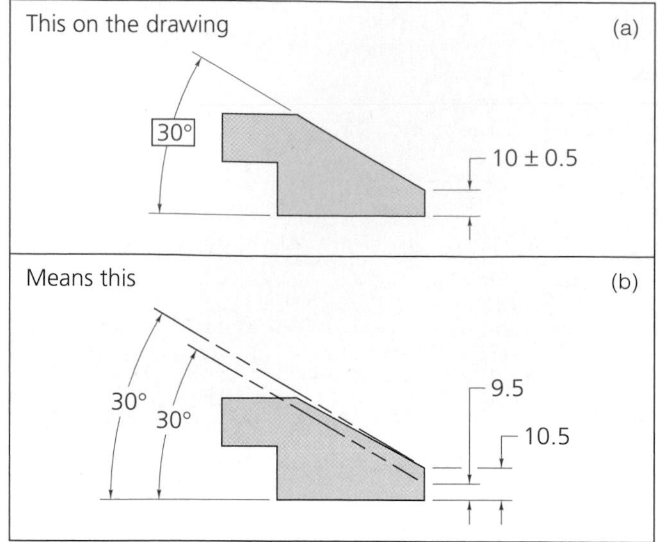

FIGURE 16.17 Tolerancing an Angular Surface Using Linear and Angular Dimensioning

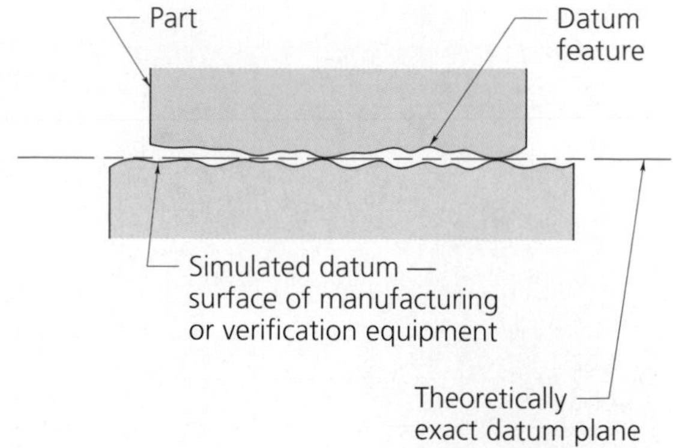

FIGURE 16.19 Theoretical and Simulated Datum and Datum Plane

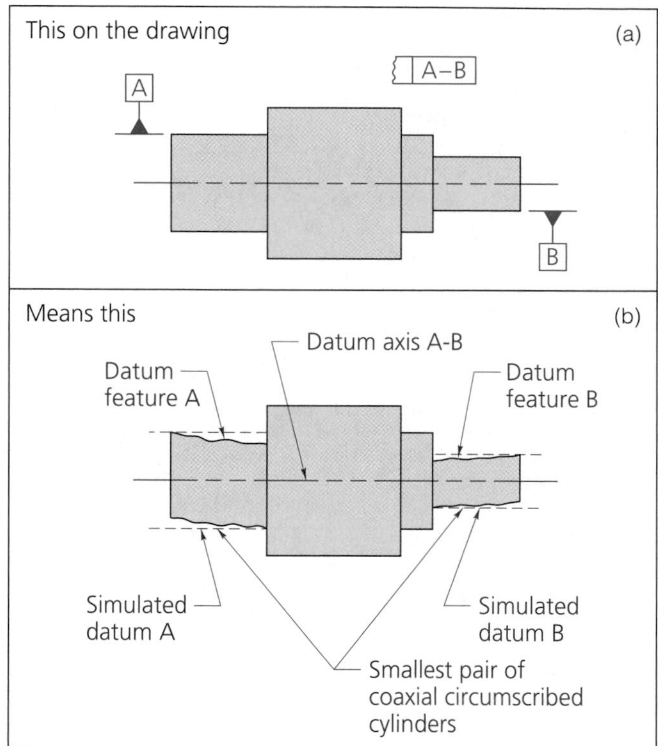

FIGURE 16.20 Coaxial Datum Features

and, therefore, needs only one point of contact on the part to establish it. In Figure 16.22, notice that the three directions of measurement, **X, Y,** and **Z,** are established on the part, as are their origin datums. Precise and repeatable measurements may now be made as the part is oriented and locked in position. Datums are specified on the drawing to ensure the intended datum reference frame.

16.5.6 Datum Targets

Datum targets are specific points (Fig. 16.23), lines (Fig. 16.24), or areas (Fig. 16.25) that are used when an entire surface may not be suitable as a datum feature. For example, the rough surfaces of castings and forgings are difficult to use. If a limited portion of a feature is not a point, line, or

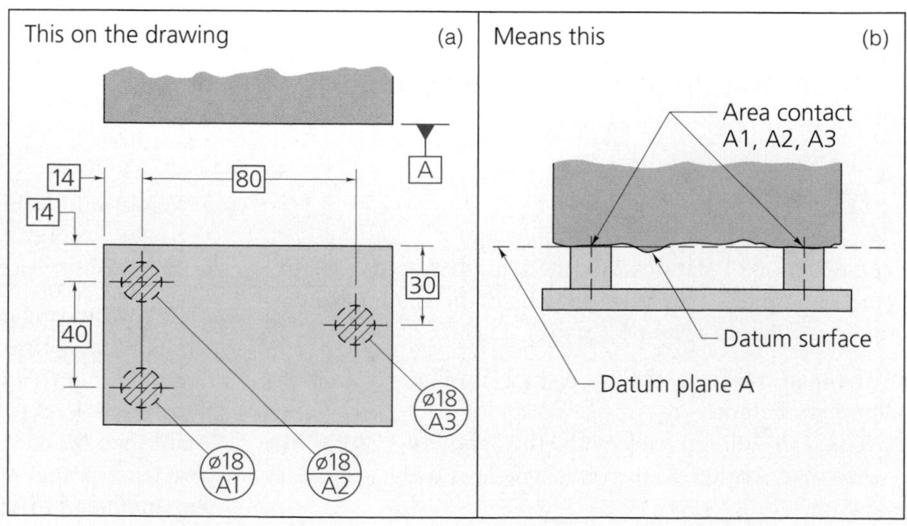

FIGURE 16.18 The Primary Datum Established by Three Area Contact Positions

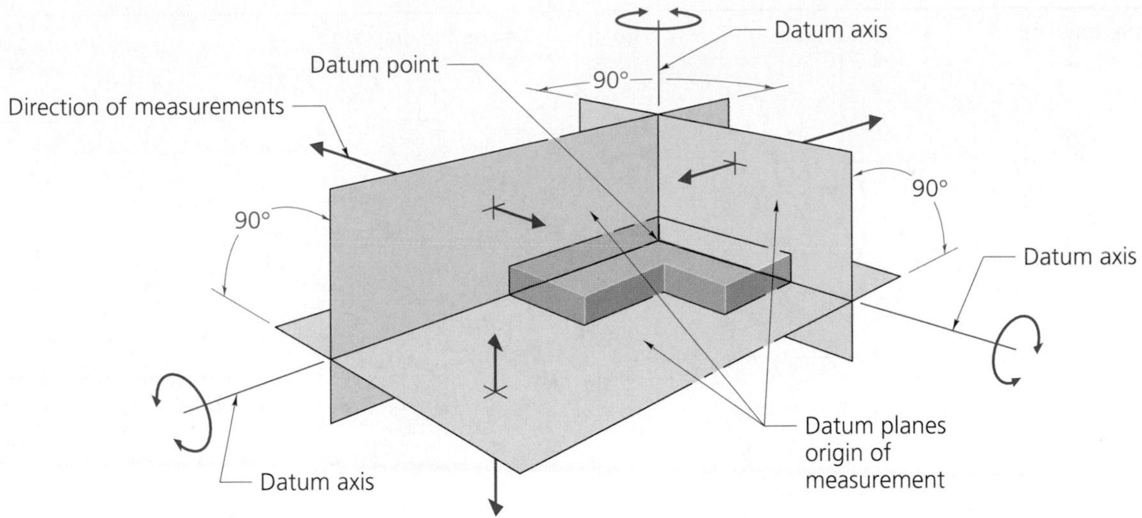

FIGURE 16.21 Datum Reference Frame

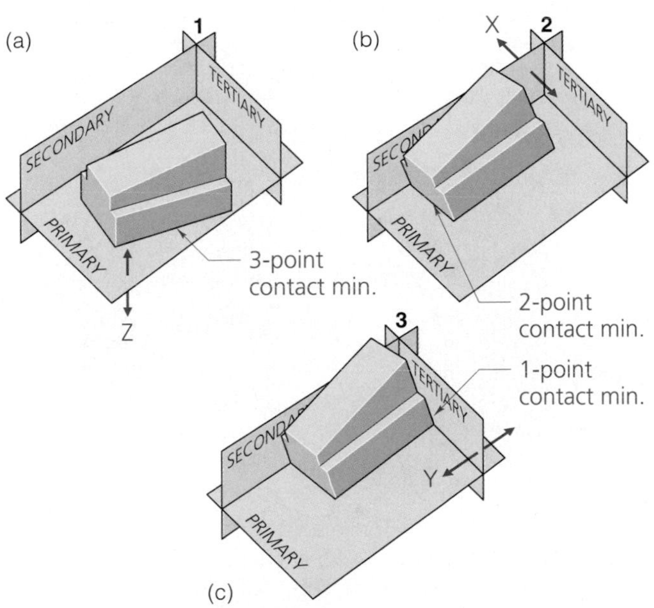

FIGURE 16.22 Datum Reference Frame—Datum Precedence

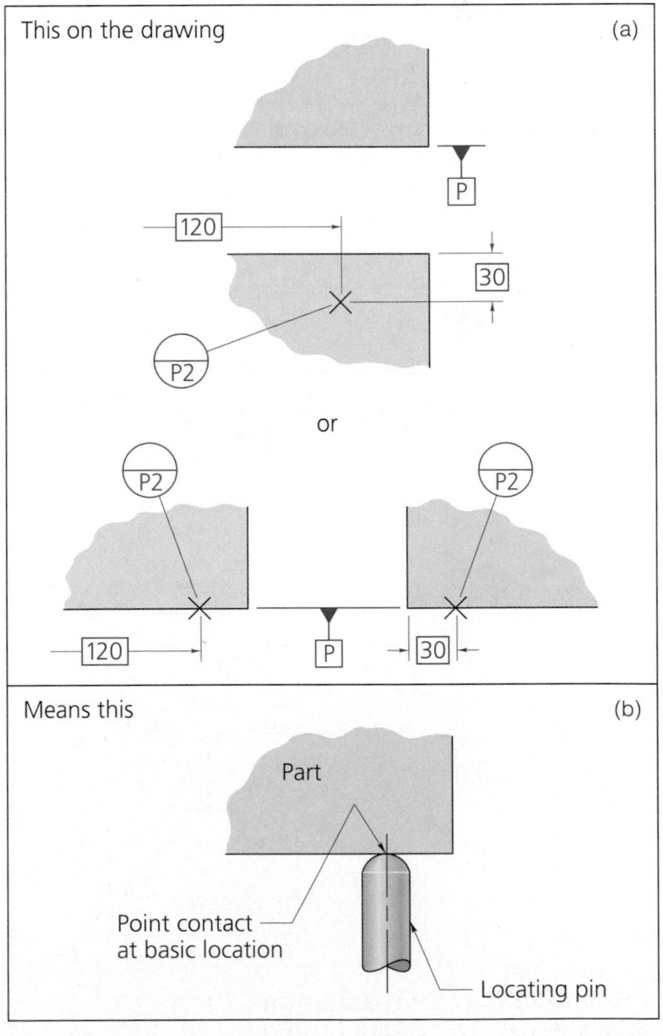

FIGURE 16.23 Datum Target Point

local flat area (a portion of a cylindrical surface, for example), then partial datums (Fig. 16.26) may be employed instead of targets.

In Figure 16.27 datum targets **A1**, **A2**, and **A3** establish the primary datum; datum targets **B1** and **B2** establish a secondary plane perpendicular to the primary plane; and **C1** establishes the tertiary plane perpendicular to the primary and secondary planes. The datum target identification symbol is shown in Figure 16.28.

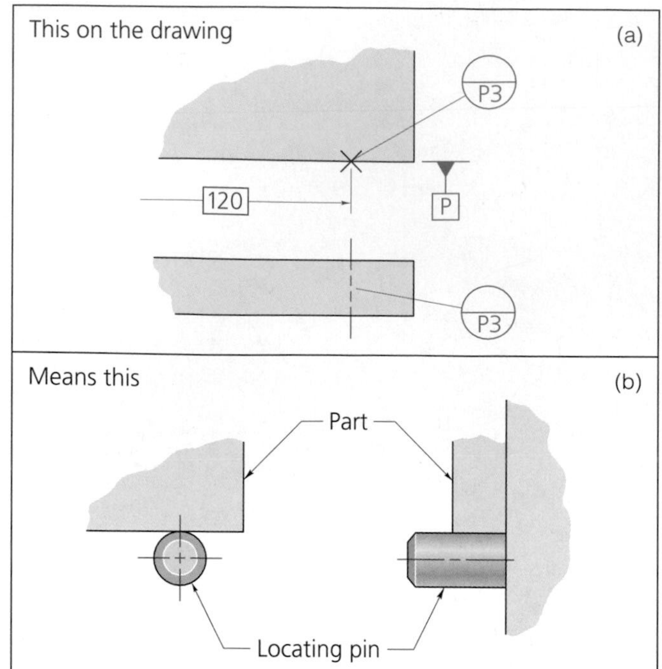

FIGURE 16.24 Datum Target Line

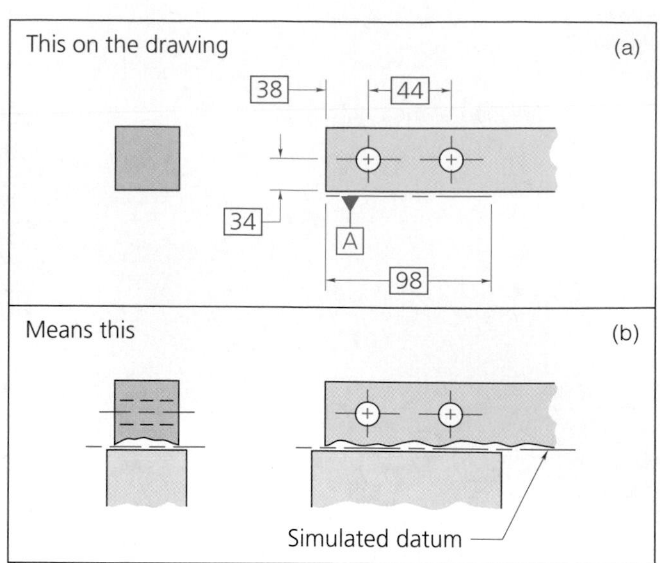

FIGURE 16.26 Partial Datums

16.5.7 Datum Target Depiction

Datum target points are depicted by a dense 90° "cross" (**X**) at 45° to the centerline (Fig. 16.29), at twice the letter height. The leader line from the datum target symbol does not terminate in an arrowhead. A solid leader line indicates that the target is on the near side; a dashed leader line indicates that the target is on the far side. The three mutually

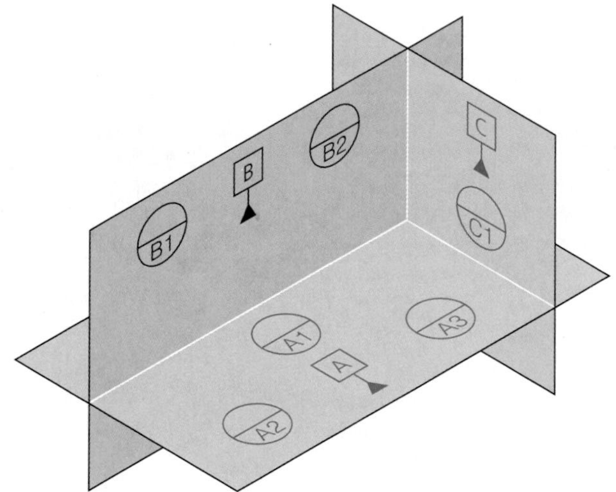

FIGURE 16.27 Datum Targets Used to Establish a Datum Reference Plane

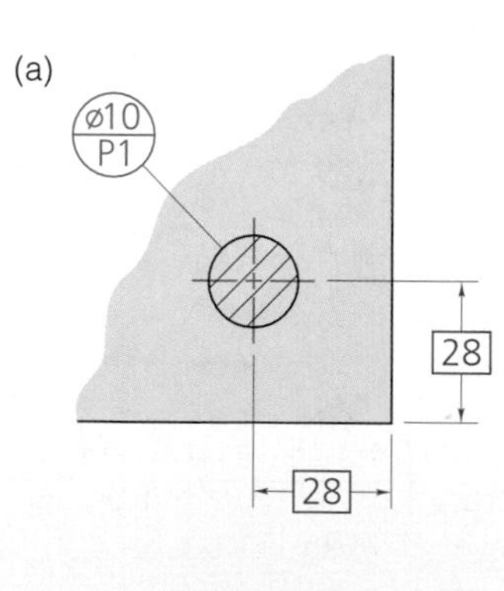

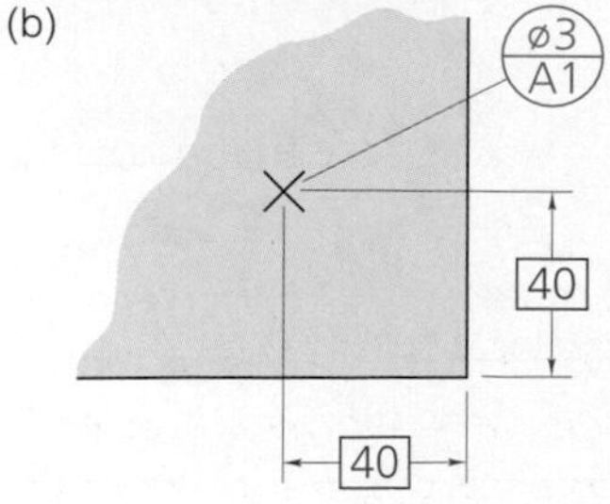

FIGURE 16.25 Datum Target Area

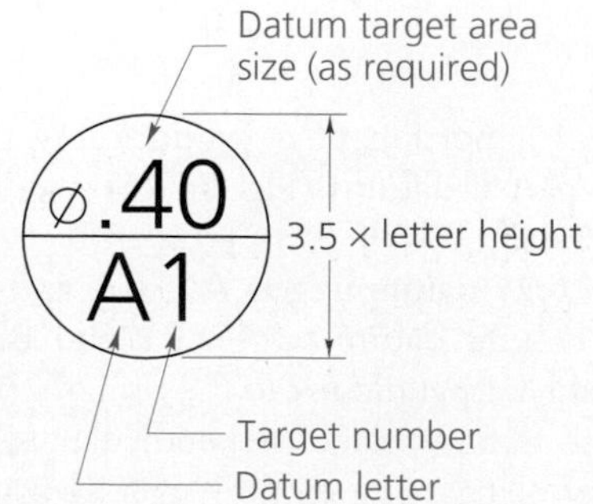

FIGURE 16.28 Datum Target Identification Symbol

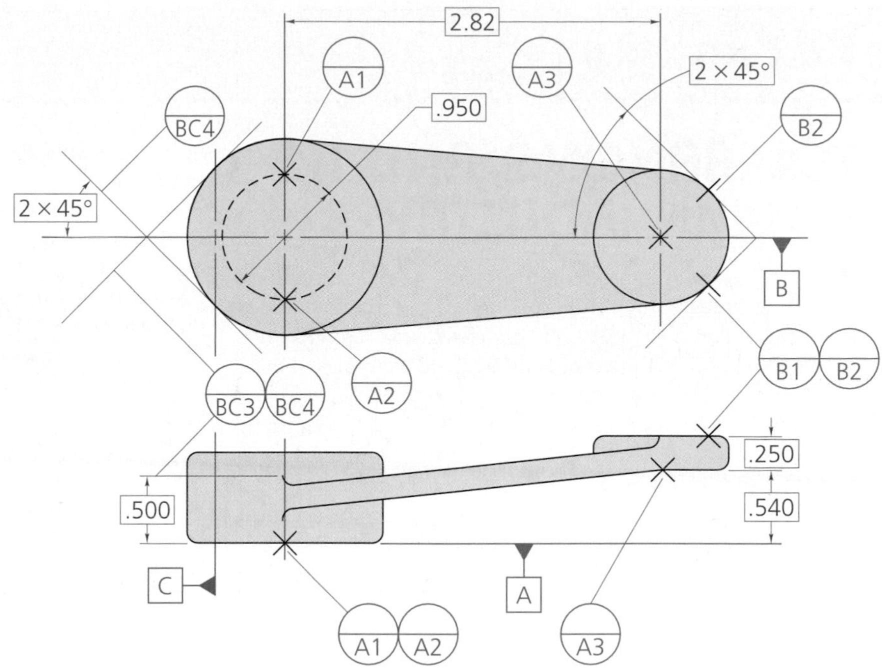

FIGURE 16.29 Datum Targets Showing "Step" and "Equalizing Dimensions"

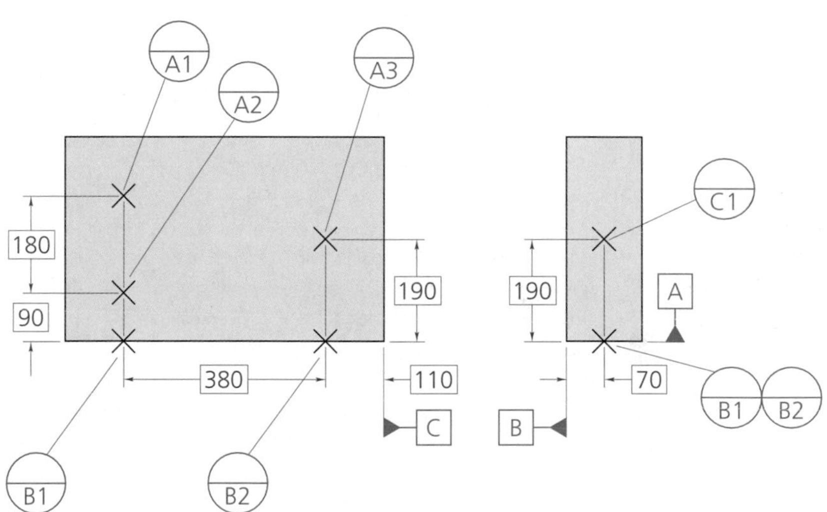

FIGURE 16.30 Dimensioning Datum Targets

perpendicular planes from which to measure **X**, **Y**, and **Z** distances are locked in place and repeatable for each individual part. Datum targets may also be located on the drawing by dimensions (Fig. 16.30).

16.6 GEOMETRIC TOLERANCE OF FORM, PROFILE, ORIENTATION, LOCATION, AND RUNOUT

Geometric tolerances of form, profile, orientation, location, and runout are described in this section.

16.6.1 Form Tolerances

Form tolerances are applicable to individual features or elements of single features. Such tolerances do not use datums because they are related to a perfect counterpart of themselves. These "pure form" tolerances are: straightness, flatness, circularity, and cylindricity.

16.6.2 Straightness of Element Lines

The **straightness** tolerance specifies variation from a straight line. Each element line on the surface must be straight within the specified straightness tolerance. For element control, the leader from the feature control frame must be directed to the outline of the part where the element to be controlled appears as a straight line [Fig. 16.31(b)]. For a

Focus On . . .

TOLERANCING AND ITS ROLE IN INDUSTRY

Mass production of interchangeable parts played an important role in the Industrial Revolution. Much of the technology that we enjoy today also relies on interchangeable components. Automobiles and computer circuits are good examples of mass production and the importance of size control.

While it is impossible to make any part exactly the same size as another part, it is possible to keep component dimensions to a specific range of sizes. Geometrical relationships can also be specified. These dimension restrictions are specified with *tolerances*. Component function determines the degree of tolerance. This process ensures that parts made in one location are interchangeable with parts made in another location.

For example, Eagle Engine Manufacturing produces V-8 engines for top fuel dragsters. The Eagle engine can produce 3000 hp and is designed to allow for different configurations. Cylinders are interchangeable, and the head accommodates one to three spark plugs per cylinder. This means the engine can be configured for a dragster or a tractor. Specific parts for the engine were designed on a CAD system with tolerance capabilities to sixteen decimal places. The design was easily modified to fit another configuration with its tolerance specifications.

Producing components to specific tolerances makes it possible to mass-produce goods and modify existing components to fit different needs. This system gives the manufacturer flexibility, allowing the part to change quickly with market trends and technological advances. This kind of flexibility is essential in the competitive world of today and tomorrow.

rectangular part, the view in which the leader is shown determines the direction of the indicator movement zone. In this case, each element on the surface is to be straight within the specified tolerance, and the feature must meet the size tolerance.

16.6.3 Straightness of an Axis

If straightness of an axis is specified, the leader from the feature control frame must be directed to the size dimension [Fig. 16.31(c)], and a diameter symbol (∅) must precede the tolerance in the feature control frame. An exception is made if the zone is not cylindrical.

16.6.4 Flatness

Flatness means that a surface has all elements in one plane. Flatness must be within the size tolerance, but has no orientation requirement. Therefore, it may be tilted in the size zone. A **flatness tolerance** specifies a tolerance zone defined by two parallel planes within which the surface must lie [Fig. 16.31(d)]. When a flatness tolerance is specified, the feature control frame is attached to a leader directed to the surface or to an extension line of the surface. It is placed in a view where the surface elements to be controlled are represented by a line. If the considered surface is associated with a size dimension, the flatness must be less than the size tolerance.

16.6.5 Circularity

A **circularity tolerance** specifies a tolerance zone bounded by two concentric circles within which each circular element of the surface must lie, and applies independently at any plane described in the list in Figure 16.31(e). The circularity tolerance must be less than the size tolerance, except for those parts subject to three-state variation.

16.6.6 Cylindricity

Cylindricity is a surface of revolution in which all points of the surface are equidistant from a common axis. A **cylindricity tolerance** specifies a tolerance zone bounded by two concentric cylinders within which the surface must lie [Fig. 16.31(f)]. In the case of cylindricity, unlike that of circularity, the tolerance applies simultaneously to the entire surface. The leader from the feature control frame may be directed to either view. The cylindricity tolerance must be less than the size tolerance.

16.7 PROFILE TOLERANCES

A **profile** is an outline of a 2D part in a given plane. Profiles are formed by projecting a 3D figure onto a plane or by taking cross sections through the figure. The elements of a profile are straight lines, arcs, and other curved lines. If the drawing specifies individual tolerances for the elements or points of a profile, these elements or points must be verified individually. With profile tolerancing, the true profile may be defined by basic radii, basic angular dimensions, basic coordinate dimensions, formulas, or undimensioned drawings.

The **profile tolerance** specifies a uniform boundary along the true profile within which the elements of the surface must lie. It is used to control form or combinations of size,

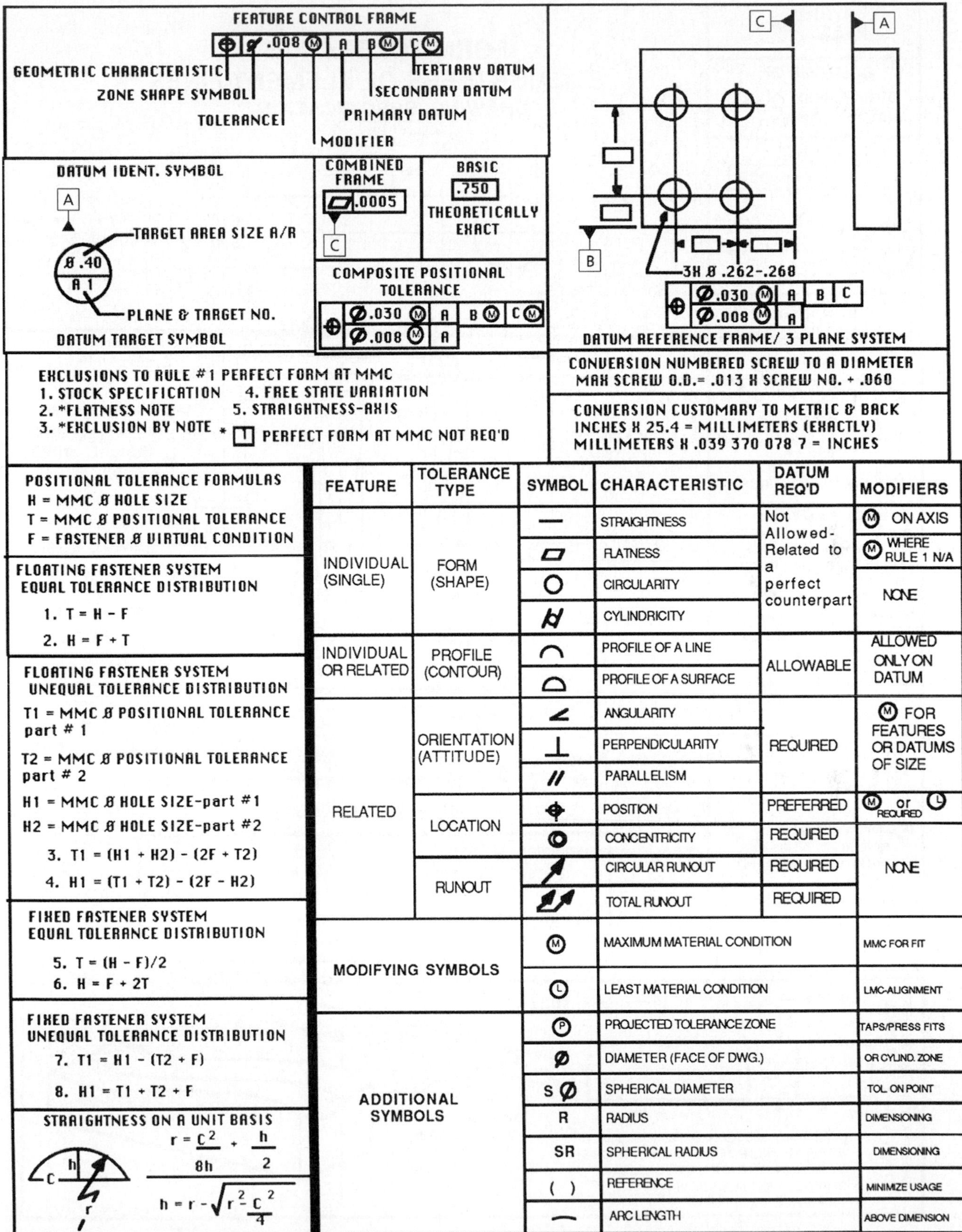

FEATURE CONTROL FRAME

⊕ | Ø .008 Ⓜ | A | B Ⓜ | C Ⓜ

GEOMETRIC CHARACTERISTIC
ZONE SHAPE SYMBOL
TOLERANCE
MODIFIER
PRIMARY DATUM
SECONDARY DATUM
TERTIARY DATUM

DATUM IDENT. SYMBOL

A

TARGET AREA SIZE A/R

Ø .40

A 1

PLANE & TARGET NO.

DATUM TARGET SYMBOL

COMBINED FRAME

▱ .0005

C

BASIC

.750

THEORETICALLY EXACT

COMPOSITE POSITIONAL TOLERANCE

⊕ | Ø.030 Ⓜ | A | B Ⓜ | C Ⓜ
  | Ø.008 Ⓜ | A

C A B

3X Ø .262-.268

⊕ | Ø.030 Ⓜ | A | B | C
  | Ø.008 Ⓜ | A

DATUM REFERENCE FRAME/ 3 PLANE SYSTEM

EXCLUSIONS TO RULE #1 PERFECT FORM AT MMC
1. STOCK SPECIFICATION
2. *FLATNESS NOTE
3. *EXCLUSION BY NOTE
4. FREE STATE VARIATION
5. STRAIGHTNESS-AXIS

* Ⓘ PERFECT FORM AT MMC NOT REQ'D

CONVERSION NUMBERED SCREW TO A DIAMETER
MAX SCREW O.D.= .013 X SCREW NO. + .060

CONVERSION CUSTOMARY TO METRIC & BACK
INCHES X 25.4 = MILLIMETERS (EXACTLY)
MILLIMETERS X .039 370 078 7 = INCHES

POSITIONAL TOLERANCE FORMULAS
H = MMC Ø HOLE SIZE
T = MMC Ø POSITIONAL TOLERANCE
F = FASTENER Ø VIRTUAL CONDITION

FLOATING FASTENER SYSTEM
EQUAL TOLERANCE DISTRIBUTION
1. T = H − F
2. H = F + T

FLOATING FASTENER SYSTEM
UNEQUAL TOLERANCE DISTRIBUTION
T1 = MMC Ø POSITIONAL TOLERANCE part # 1
T2 = MMC Ø POSITIONAL TOLERANCE part # 2
H1 = MMC Ø HOLE SIZE-part #1
H2 = MMC Ø HOLE SIZE-part #2
3. T1 = (H1 + H2) − (2F + T2)
4. H1 = (T1 + T2) − (2F − H2)

FIXED FASTENER SYSTEM
EQUAL TOLERANCE DISTRIBUTION
5. T = (H − F)/2
6. H = F + 2T

FIXED FASTENER SYSTEM
UNEQUAL TOLERANCE DISTRIBUTION
7. T1 = H1 − (T2 + F)
8. H1 = T1 + T2 + F

STRAIGHTNESS ON A UNIT BASIS

$$r = \frac{C^2}{8h} + \frac{h}{2}$$

$$h = r - \sqrt{r^2 - \frac{C^2}{4}}$$

FEATURE	TOLERANCE TYPE	SYMBOL	CHARACTERISTIC	DATUM REQ'D	MODIFIERS
INDIVIDUAL (SINGLE)	FORM (SHAPE)	—	STRAIGHTNESS	Not Allowed-Related to a perfect counterpart	Ⓜ ON AXIS
		▱	FLATNESS		Ⓜ WHERE RULE 1 N/A
		○	CIRCULARITY		NONE
		⌭	CYLINDRICITY		
INDIVIDUAL OR RELATED	PROFILE (CONTOUR)	⌒	PROFILE OF A LINE	ALLOWABLE	ALLOWED ONLY ON DATUM
		⌓	PROFILE OF A SURFACE		
RELATED	ORIENTATION (ATTITUDE)	∠	ANGULARITY	REQUIRED	Ⓜ FOR FEATURES OR DATUMS OF SIZE
		⊥	PERPENDICULARITY		
		//	PARALLELISM		
	LOCATION	⌖	POSITION	PREFERRED	Ⓜ or Ⓛ REQUIRED
		◎	CONCENTRICITY	REQUIRED	NONE
	RUNOUT	↗	CIRCULAR RUNOUT	REQUIRED	
		⌰	TOTAL RUNOUT	REQUIRED	
MODIFYING SYMBOLS		Ⓜ	MAXIMUM MATERIAL CONDITION		MMC FOR FIT
		Ⓛ	LEAST MATERIAL CONDITION		LMC-ALIGNMENT
ADDITIONAL SYMBOLS		Ⓟ	PROJECTED TOLERANCE ZONE		TAPS/PRESS FITS
		Ø	DIAMETER (FACE OF DWG.)		OR CYLIND. ZONE
		S Ø	SPHERICAL DIAMETER		TOL. ON POINT
		R	RADIUS		DIMENSIONING
		SR	SPHERICAL RADIUS		DIMENSIONING
		( )	REFERENCE		MINIMIZE USAGE
		⌒	ARC LENGTH		ABOVE DIMENSION

(a) Cover

FIGURE 16.31 Summary Fact Data Sheets

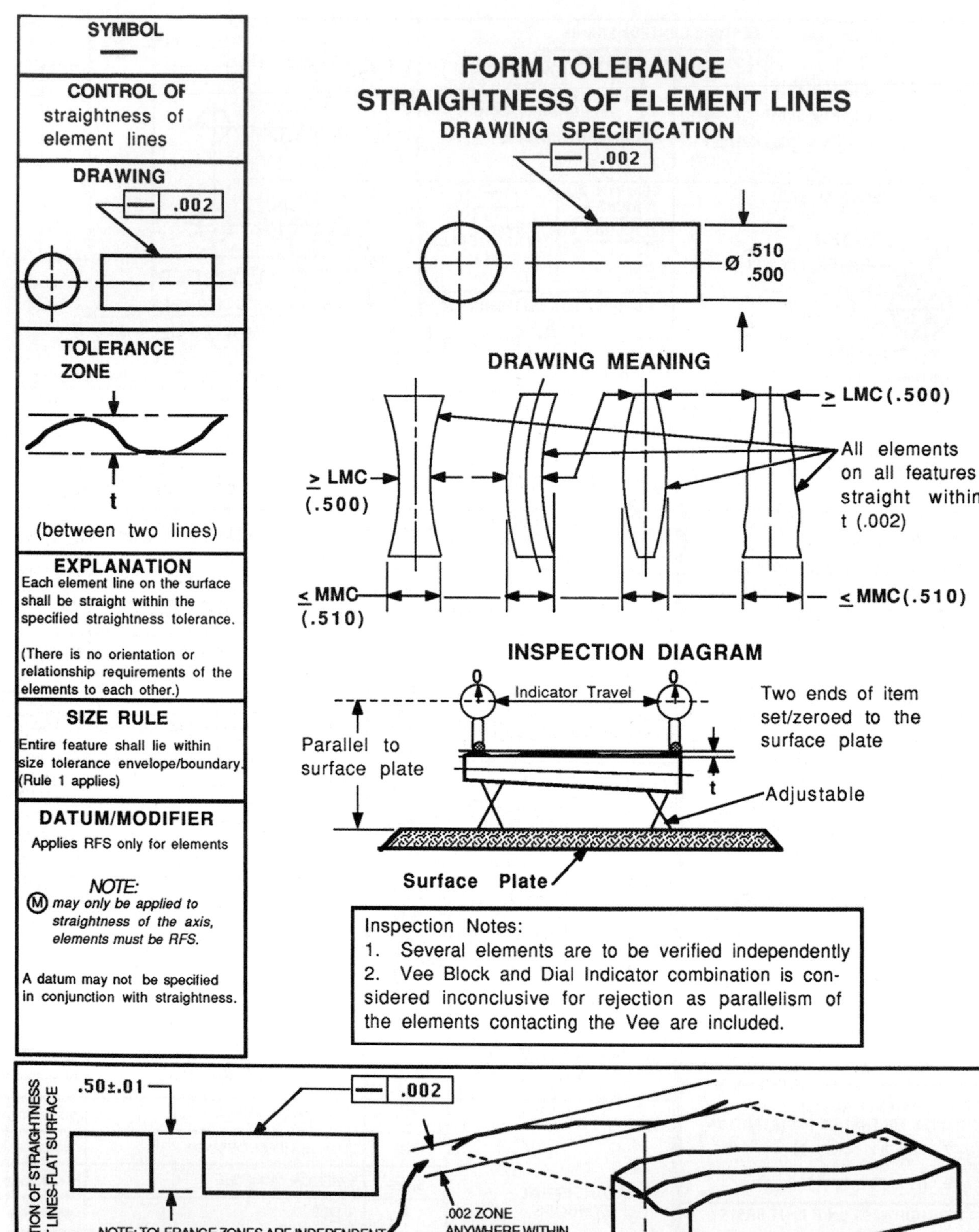

(b) Straightness of element lines

FIGURE 16.31 Summary Fact Data Sheets—*Continued*

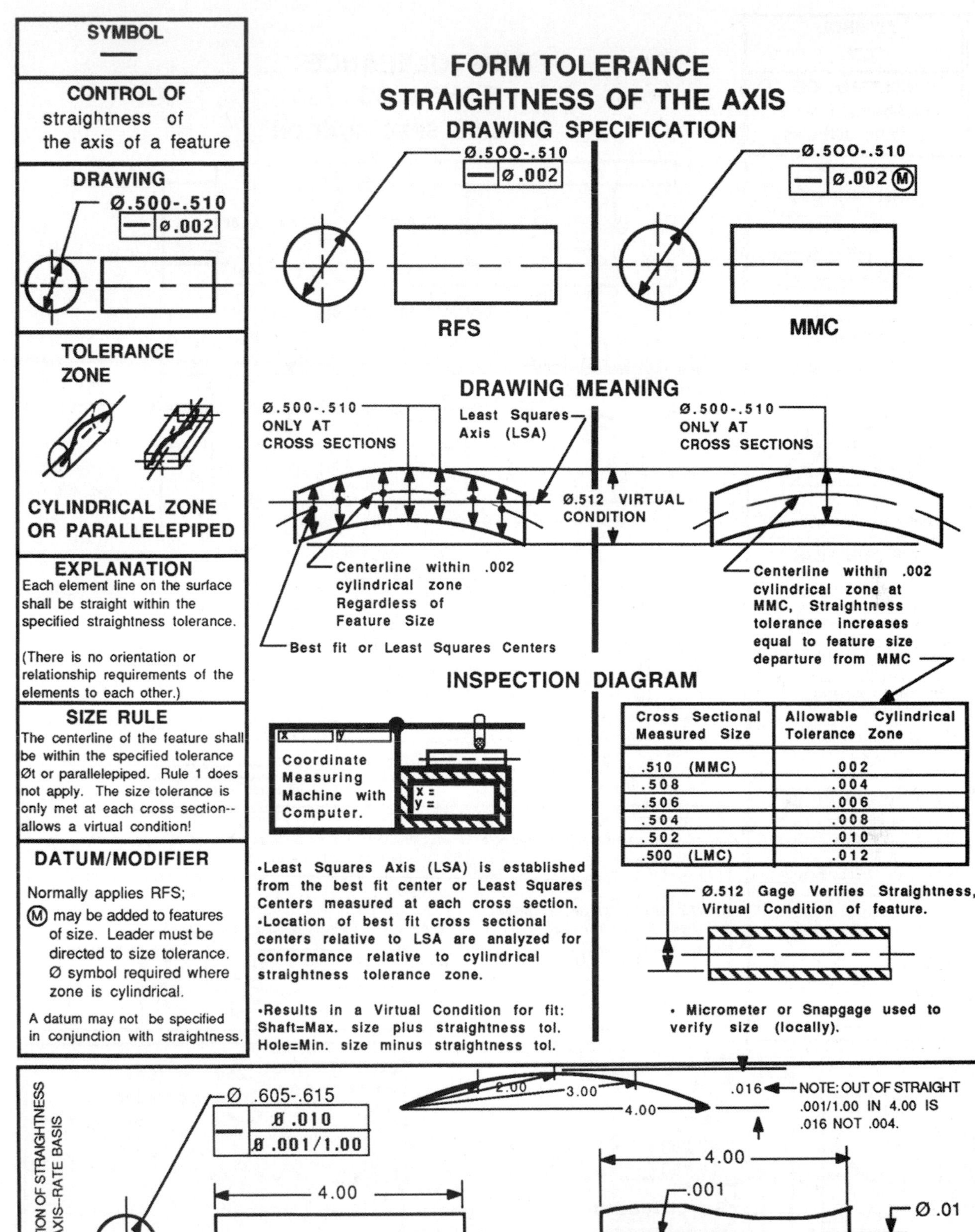

Cross Sectional Measured Size	Allowable Cylindrical Tolerance Zone
.510 (MMC)	.002
.508	.004
.506	.006
.504	.008
.502	.010
.500 (LMC)	.012

(c) Straightness of the axis

FIGURE 16.31 Summary Fact Data Sheets—*Continues*

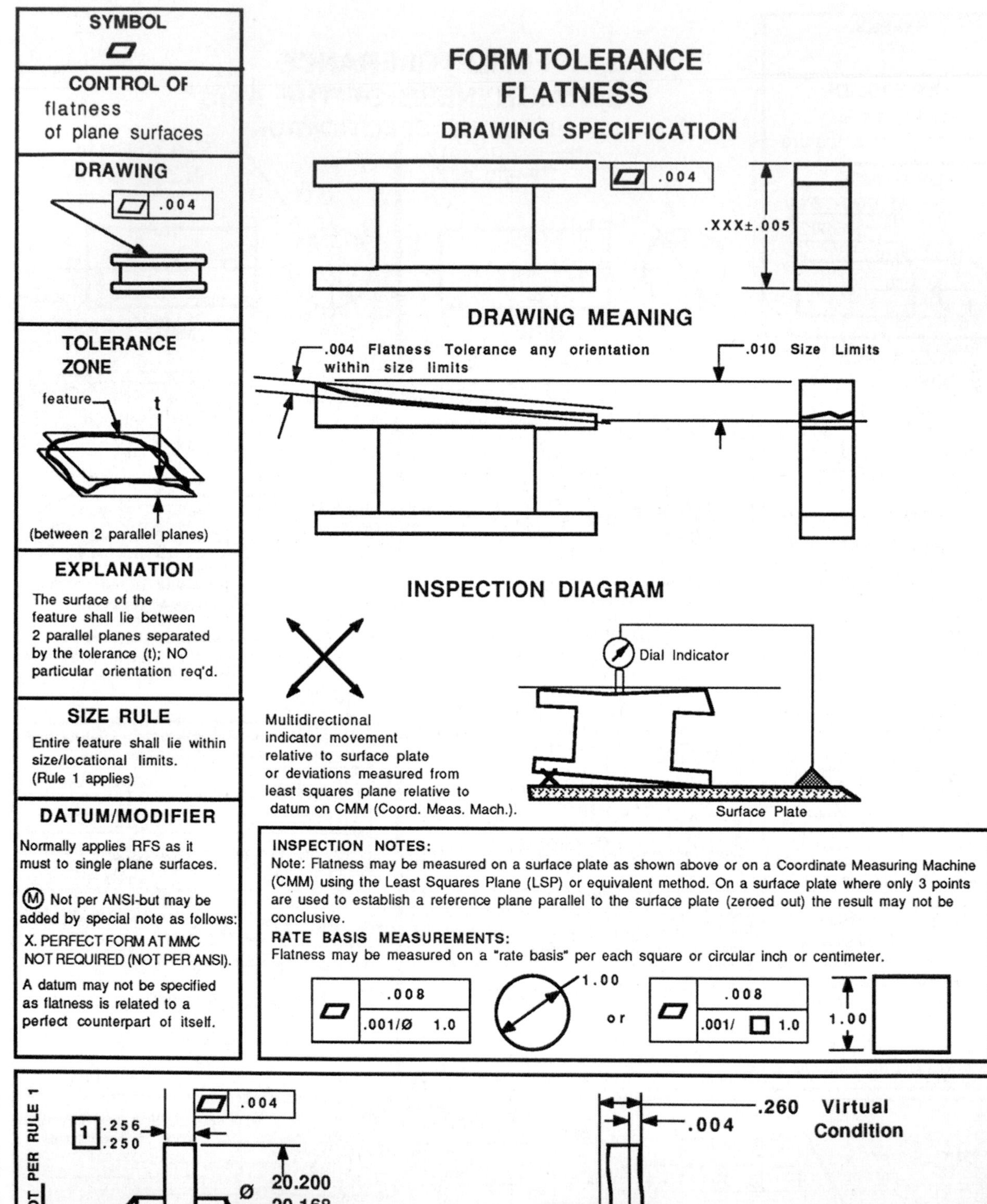

INSPECTION NOTES:
Note: Flatness may be measured on a surface plate as shown above or on a Coordinate Measuring Machine (CMM) using the Least Squares Plane (LSP) or equivalent method. On a surface plate where only 3 points are used to establish a reference plane parallel to the surface plate (zeroed out) the result may not be conclusive.

RATE BASIS MEASUREMENTS:
Flatness may be measured on a "rate basis" per each square or circular inch or centimeter.

.008 / .001/Ø 1.0 — 1.00 — or — .008 / .001/ □ 1.0 — 1.00

FLATNESS-NOT PER RULE 1

.256 / .250 — .004 — Ø 20.200 / 20.168 — Specification

.260 Virtual Condition — .004 — .256 / .250 (local) — Meaning

1 PERFECT FORM AT MMC NOT REQUIRED..

(d) Flatness

FIGURE 16.31 Summary Fact Data Sheets—*Continued*

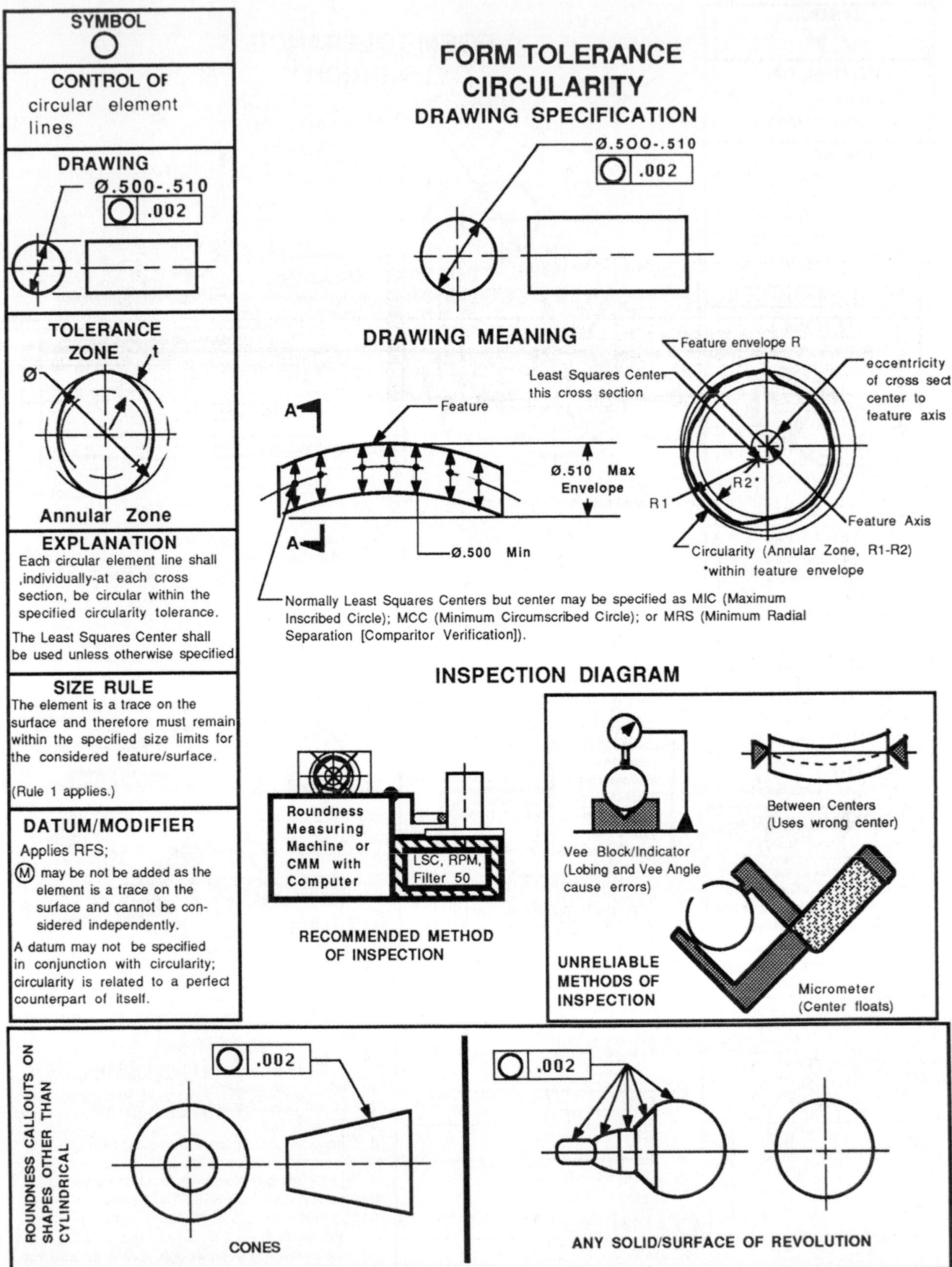

(e) Circularity

FIGURE 16.31 Summary Fact Data Sheets—*Continues*

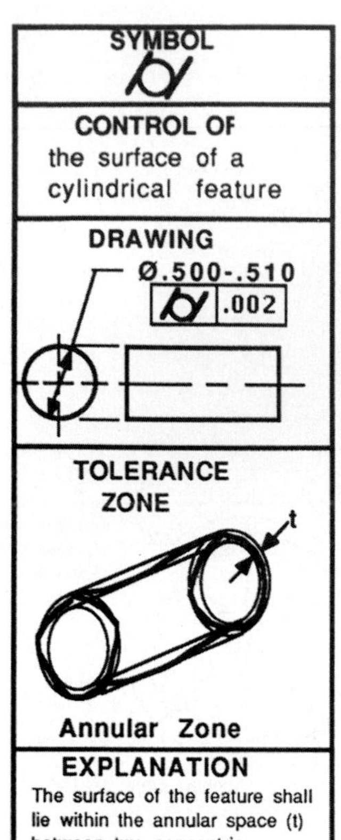

SYMBOL
CONTROL OF
the surface of a cylindrical feature
DRAWING
Ø.500-.510
.002
TOLERANCE ZONE
t
Annular Zone

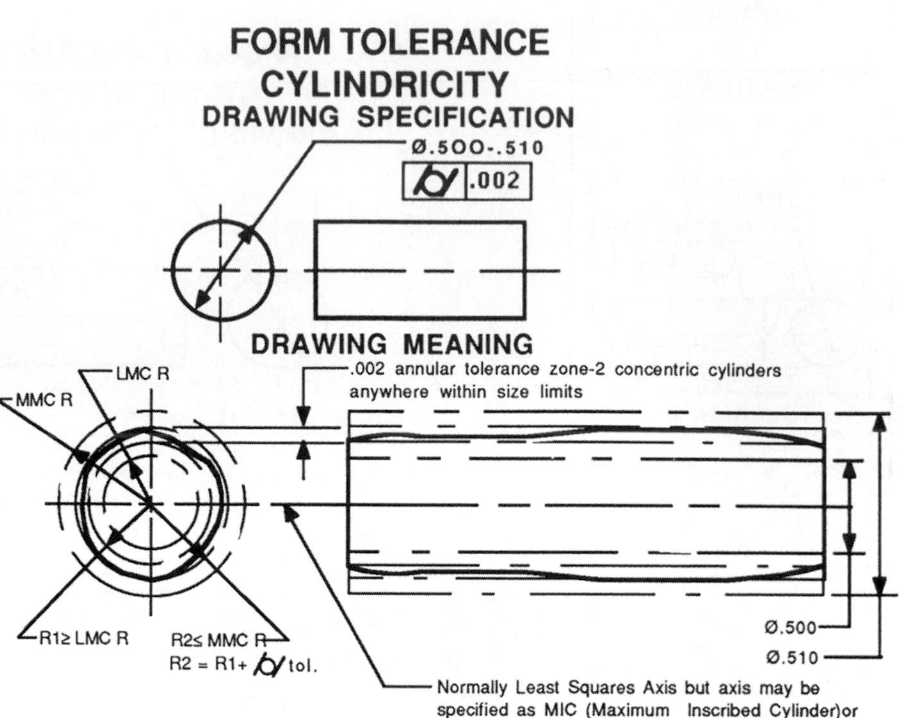

EXPLANATION

The surface of the feature shall lie within the annular space (t) between two concentric cylinders

The Least Squares Axis shall be used unless otherwise specified

SIZE RULE

The cylindricity tolerance for *rigid parts must be within the specified size limits for the considered feature/surface. (Rule 1 applies.)

*Parts in the free state excepted.

DATUM/MODIFIER

Applies RFS;

Ⓜ may be not be added as this tolerance is a refinement of the surface shape and cannot be considered independently.

A datum may not be specified in conjunction with cylindricity; cylindricity is related to a perfect counterpart of itself.

INSPECTION DIAGRAM

RECOMMENDED METHOD OF INSPECTION

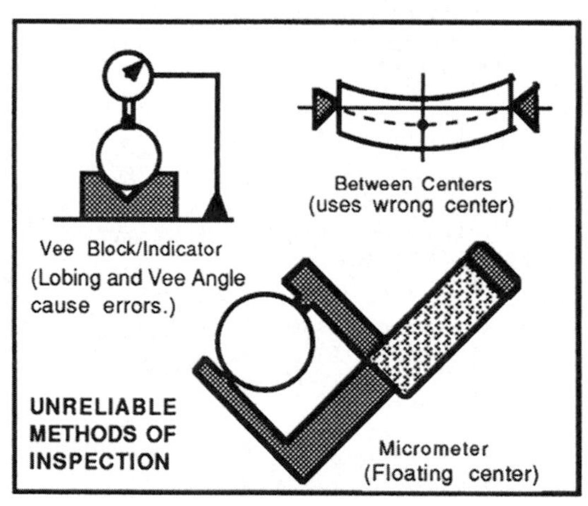

CYLINDRICITY ON A PART SUBJECT TO FREE STATE VARIATION.

SPECIFICATION

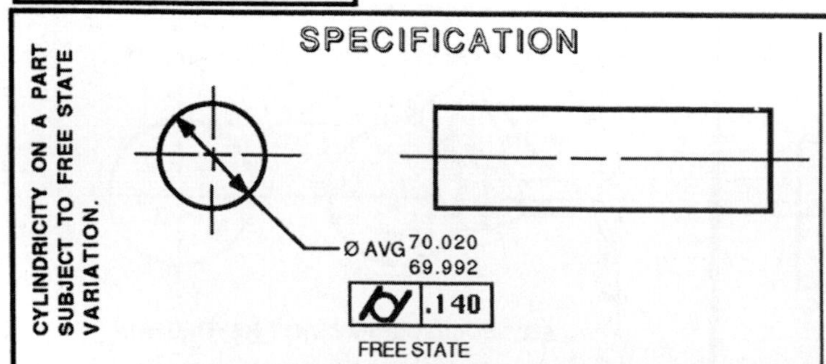

MEANING

1. Find the Least Squares Centers (LSC) at several cross sections.
2. Find the Least Squares Axis (LSA) from the LSC's.
3. Determine conformance by taking radii on the surface relative to the LSA.
4. The Cylindricity tolerance must be larger than the AVG DIA. for FREE STATE parts.
5. Max width of part is 70.020 + .140. Min width is 69.992 - .140. This is true mathematically even though .140 is a radial value.

(f) Cylindricity

FIGURE 16.31 Summary Fact Data Sheets—*Continued*

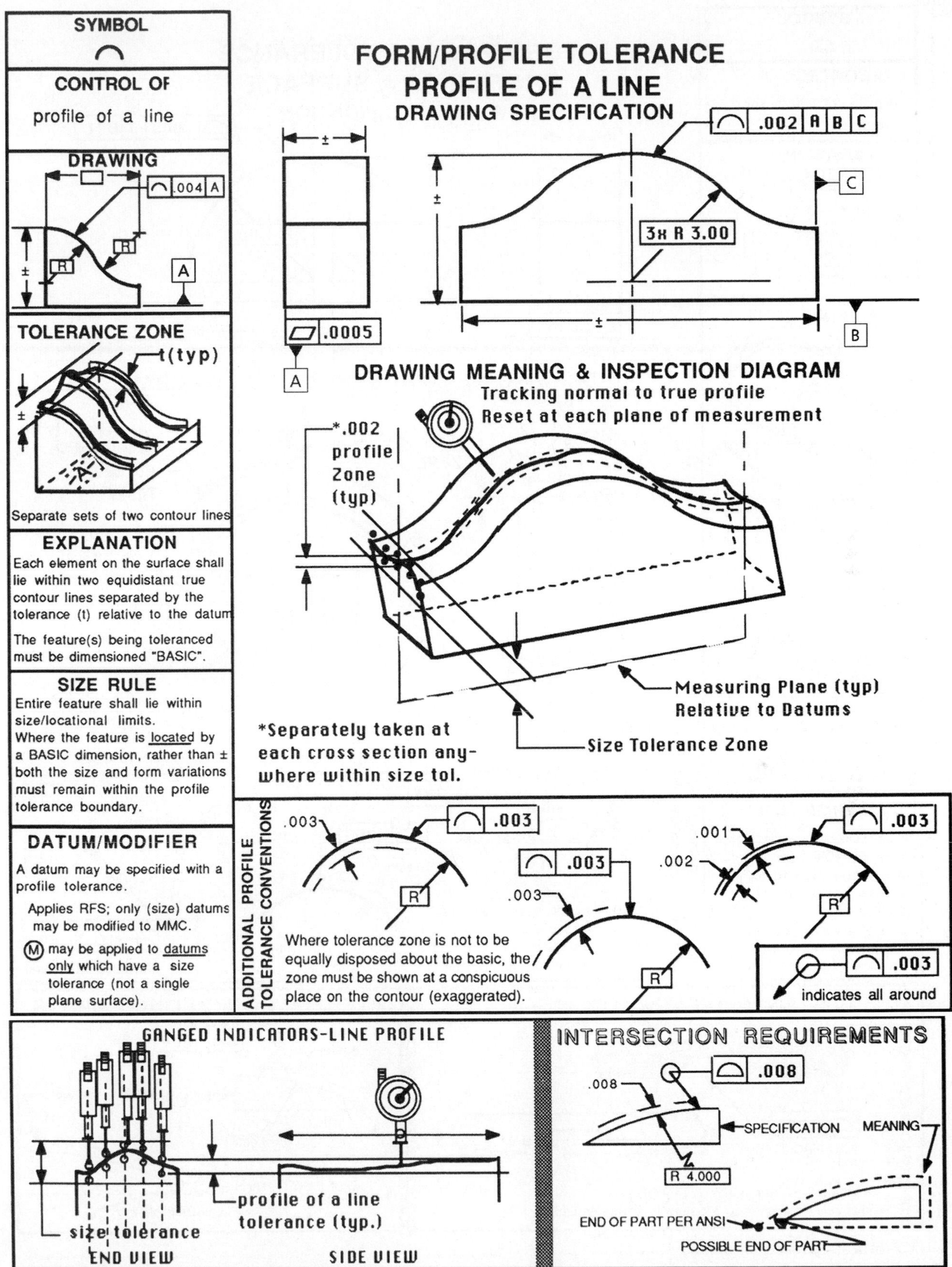

(g) Profile of a line

FIGURE 16.31 Summary Fact Data Sheets—*Continues*

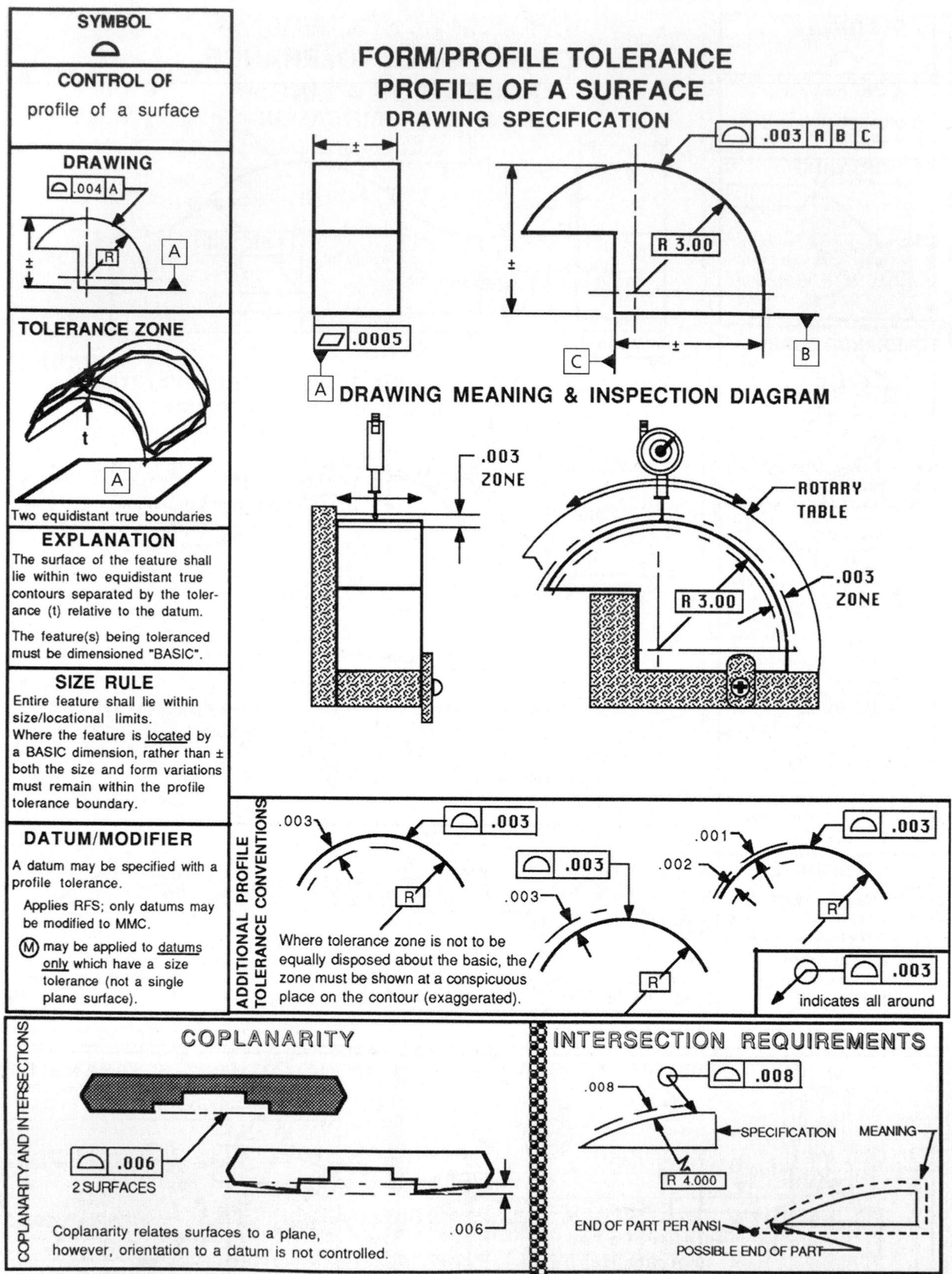

(h) Profile of a surface

FIGURE 16.31 Summary Fact Data Sheets—*Continues*

ORIENTATION TOLERANCE ANGULARITY

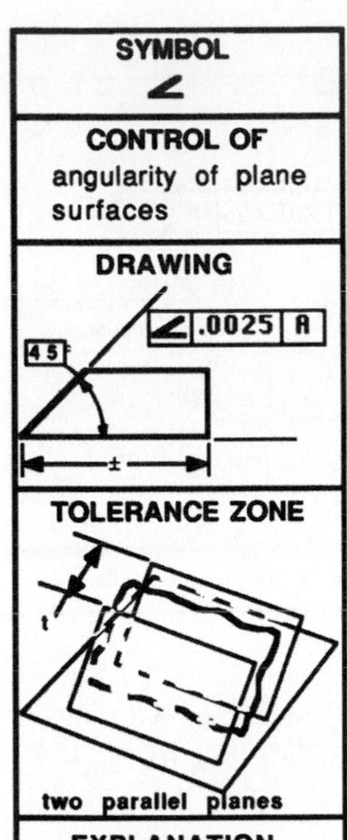

SYMBOL
CONTROL OF
angularity of plane surfaces
DRAWING
.0025 A
45
TOLERANCE ZONE
t
two parallel planes

DRAWING SPECIFICATION

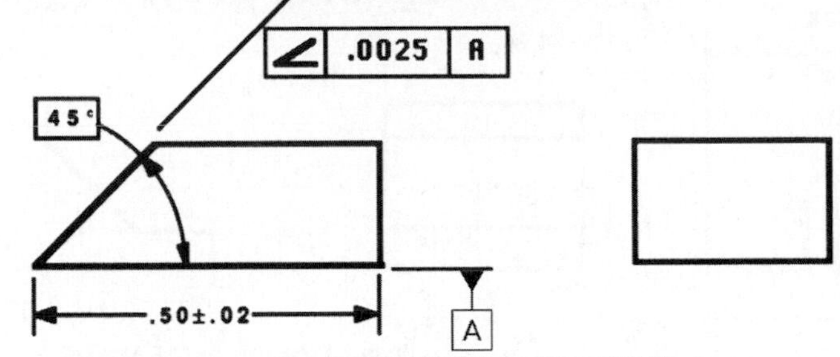

DRAWING MEANING

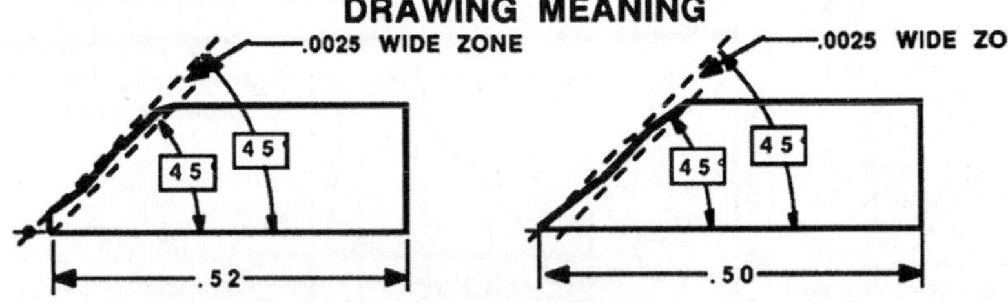

NOTE: LENGTH IS MEASURED INDEPENDENT OF THE ANGLE.

EXPLANATION

The surface of the feature shall lie between 2 parallel planes separated by the tolerance (t) which are at the basic angle to the datum.

SIZE RULE

The end of the part is measured to the end of the physical feature; not the zone intersection.

DATUM/MODIFIER

Normally applies RFS as it must to single plane surfaces.

Ⓜ may be applied to datums or features which have a size tolerance (not a single plane surface).

A datum must be specified with angularity even though it may be obvious.

INSPECTION DIAGRAM

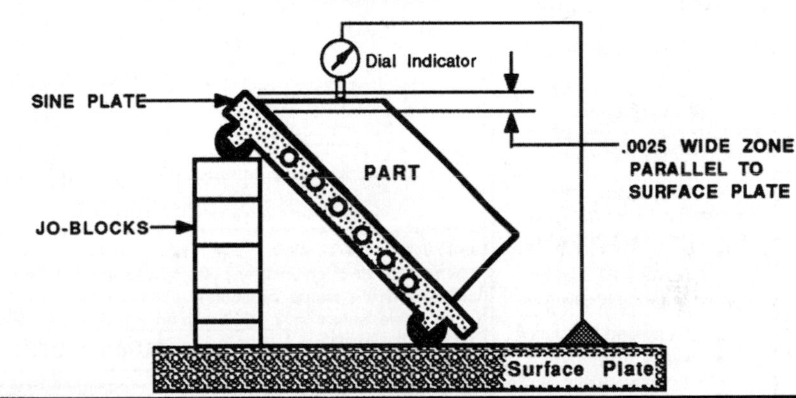

INSPECTION AT MMC

Where features or datums (or both) of size are specified angular at MMC the angularity tolerance increases as the feature or datum (or both) depart from MMC by a like amount. (e.g. A male feature .502 ±.002 with an actual size of .502; and a male datum of .754±.004 with an actual size of .754 which are

∠ .005 Ⓜ A Ⓜ may be .002+.004+.005 out of angularity (.011).

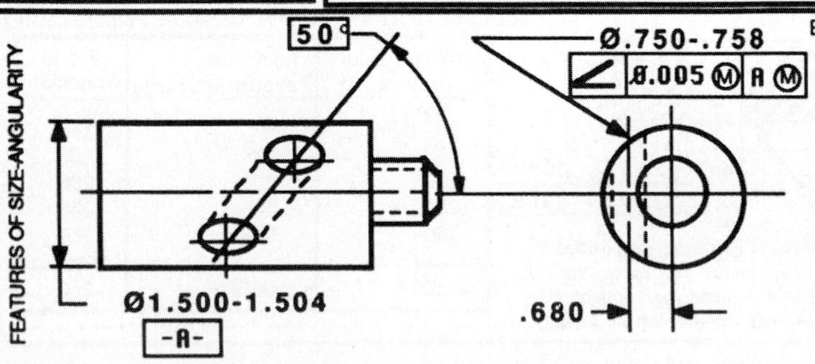

Examples of feature/datum sizes vs. allowable Angularity

Actual Datum Diameter	Actual Feature Diameter	Allowable Angularity
1.504 (MMC)	.750 (MMC)	.005
1.503	.751	.007
1.502	.752	.009
1.501	.753	.011
1.500	.754	.013
1.500	.755	.014
1.500	.756	.015
1.500	.757	.016
1.500	.758	.017
1.502	.750 (MMC)	.007

(i) Angularity

FIGURE 16.31 Summary Fact Data Sheets—*Continues*

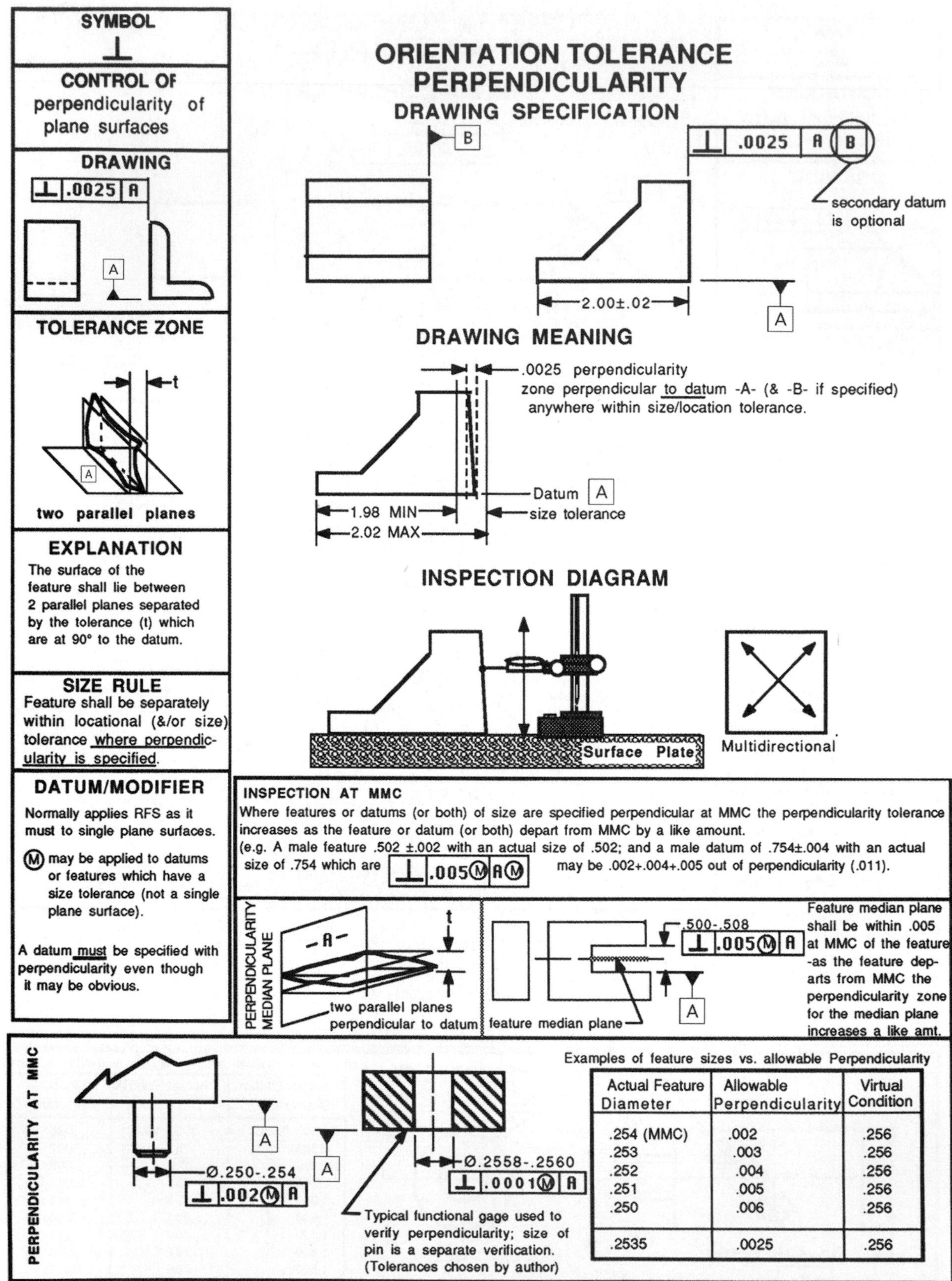

Actual Feature Diameter	Allowable Perpendicularity	Virtual Condition
.254 (MMC)	.002	.256
.253	.003	.256
.252	.004	.256
.251	.005	.256
.250	.006	.256
.2535	.0025	.256

(j) Perpendicularity

FIGURE 16.31 Summary Fact Data Sheets—*Continued*

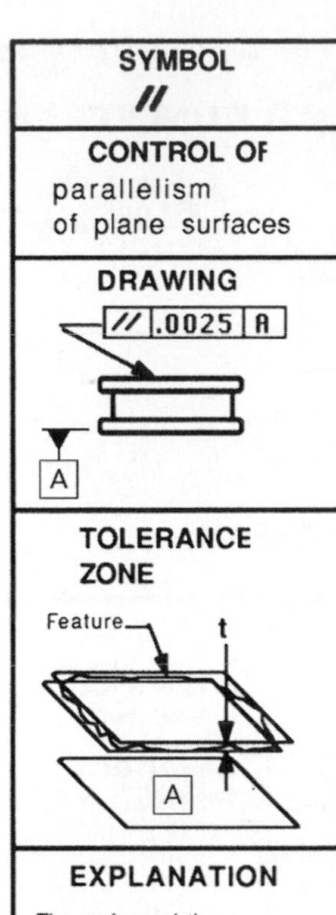

SYMBOL
//
CONTROL OF
parallelism
of plane surfaces
DRAWING
// .0025 A
A
TOLERANCE ZONE
Feature
t
A

ORIENTATION TOLERANCE PARALELLISM

DRAWING SPECIFICATION

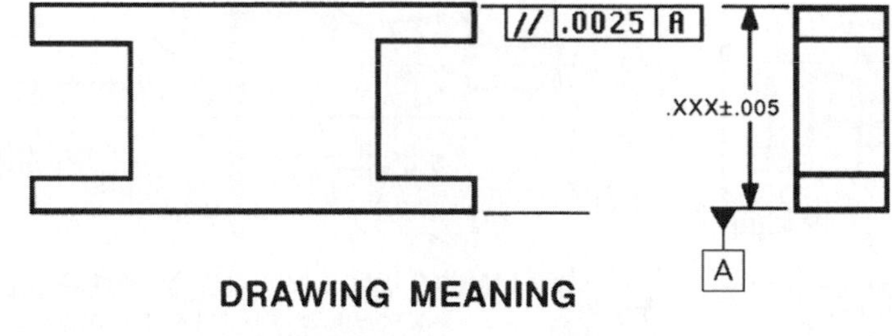

DRAWING MEANING

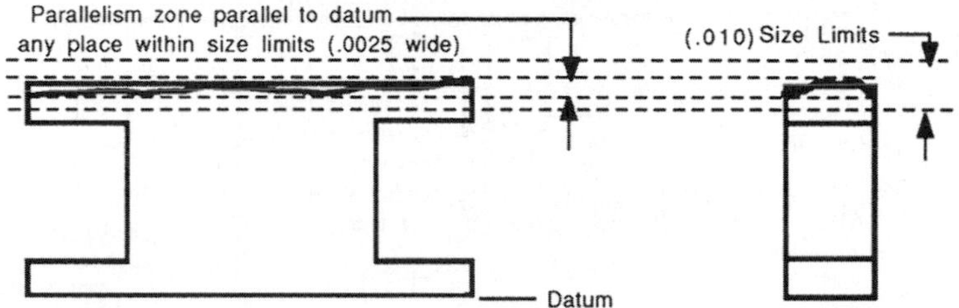

Parallelism zone parallel to datum any place within size limits (.0025 wide)
(.010) Size Limits

INSPECTION DIAGRAM

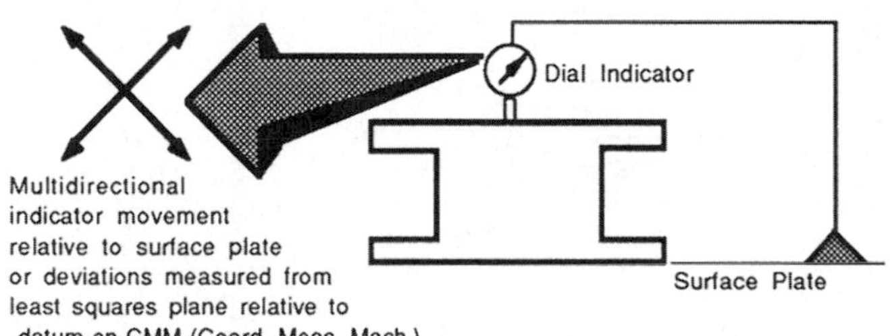

Dial Indicator
Multidirectional indicator movement relative to surface plate or deviations measured from least squares plane relative to datum on CMM (Coord. Meas. Mach.).

EXPLANATION

The surface of the feature shall lie between 2 parallel planes separated by the tolerance (t) which are parallel to the datum.

SIZE RULE

F

Entire feature shall lie within size/locational limits. (Rule 1 applies)

DATUM/MODIFIER

Normally applies RFS as it must to single plane surfaces.

Ⓜ may be applied to datums or features which have a size tolerance (not a single plane surface).

A datum must be specified with parallelism even though it may be obvious.

INSPECTION NOTES:

Note: Parallelism must be relative to a datum (point, line, or plane) therefore (unlike the dictionary definition) curved equidistant lines are NOT considered parallel.

INSPECTION AT MMC

Where features or datums (or both) of size are specified parallel at MMC the parallelism tolerance increases as the feature or datum (or both) depart from MMC by a like amount. (e.g. A male feature .502 ±.002 with an actual size of .502; and a male datum of .754±.004 with an actual size of .754 which are | // | .005 Ⓜ | A Ⓜ | may be .002+.004+.005 out of parallel (.011).

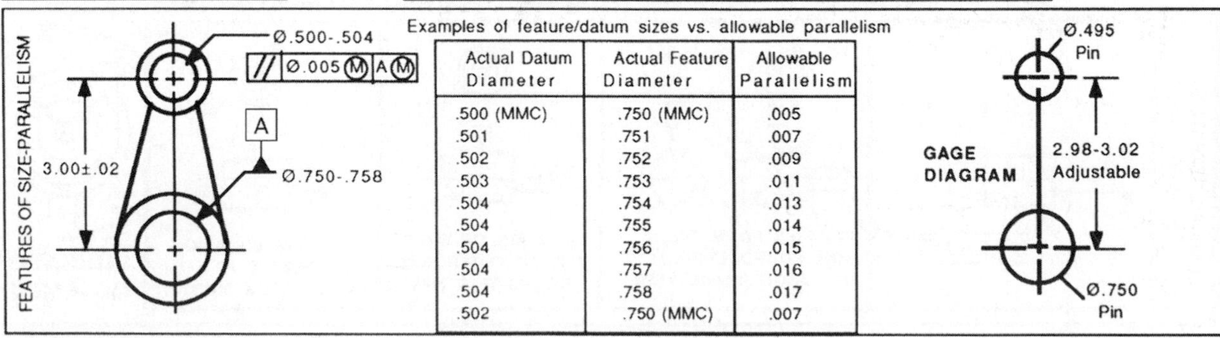

GAGE DIAGRAM

Examples of feature/datum sizes vs. allowable parallelism

Actual Datum Diameter	Actual Feature Diameter	Allowable Parallelism
.500 (MMC)	.750 (MMC)	.005
.501	.751	.007
.502	.752	.009
.503	.753	.011
.504	.754	.013
.504	.755	.014
.504	.756	.015
.504	.757	.016
.504	.758	.017
.502	.750 (MMC)	.007

(k) Parallelism

FIGURE 16.31 Summary Fact Data Sheets—*Continues*

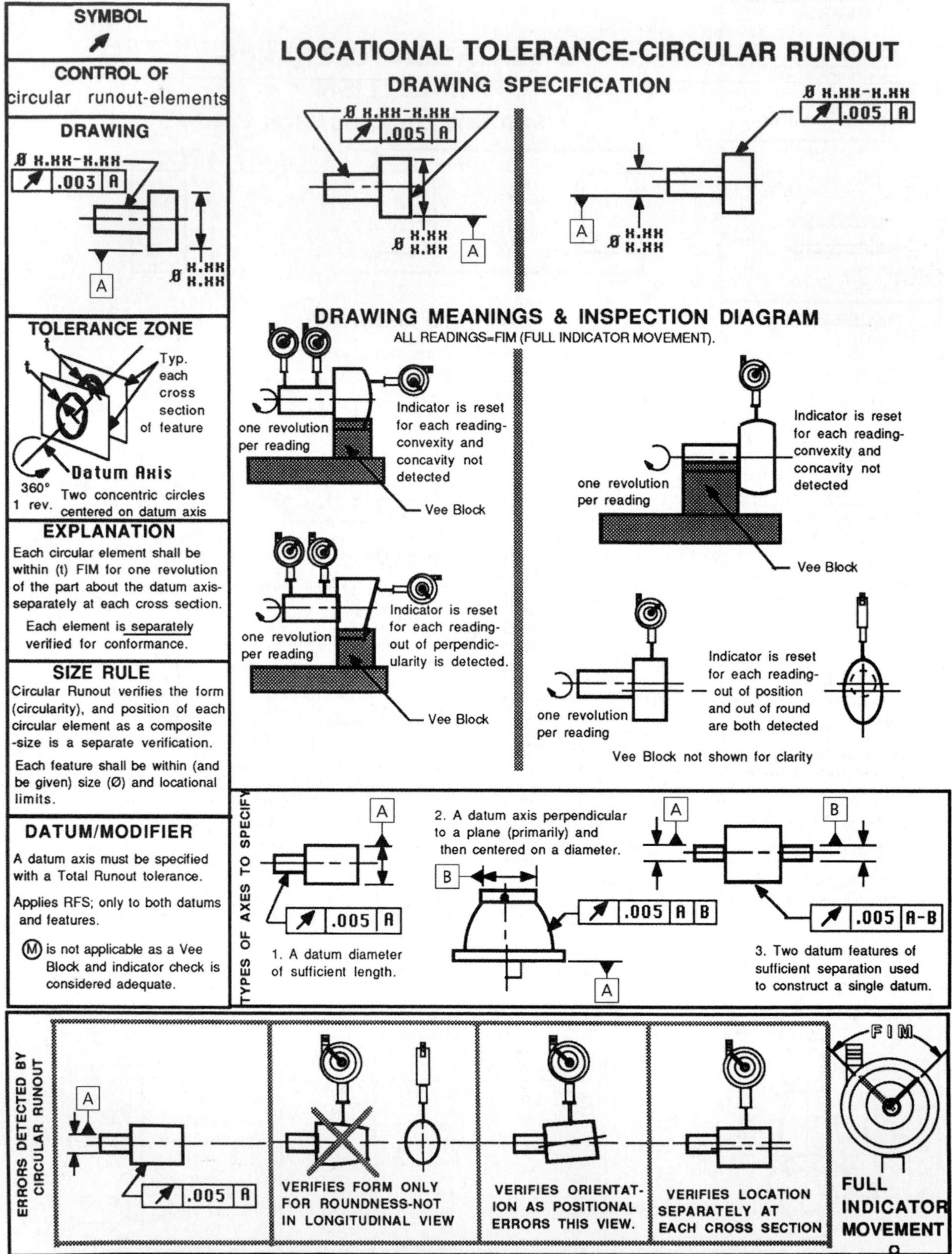
SYMBOL
CONTROL OF
circular runout-elements
DRAWING
Ø X.XX-X.XX
.003 A
A
Ø X.XX X.XX
TOLERANCE ZONE
Typ. each cross section of feature
Datum Axis
360° 1 rev.
Two concentric circles centered on datum axis
EXPLANATION
Each circular element shall be within (t) FIM for one revolution of the part about the datum axis-separately at each cross section.
Each element is separately verified for conformance.
SIZE RULE
Circular Runout verifies the form (circularity), and position of each circular element as a composite -size is a separate verification.
Each feature shall be within (and be given) size (Ø) and locational limits.
DATUM/MODIFIER
A datum axis must be specified with a Total Runout tolerance.
Applies RFS; only to both datums and features.
Ⓜ is not applicable as a Vee Block and indicator check is considered adequate.
LOCATIONAL TOLERANCE-CIRCULAR RUNOUT
DRAWING SPECIFICATION
Ø X.XX-X.XX
.005 A
Ø X.XX X.XX
A
DRAWING MEANINGS & INSPECTION DIAGRAM
ALL READINGS=FIM (FULL INDICATOR MOVEMENT).
one revolution per reading
Indicator is reset for each reading-convexity and concavity not detected
Vee Block
Indicator is reset for each reading-out of perpendicularity is detected.
Indicator is reset for each reading-out of position and out of round are both detected
Vee Block not shown for clarity
TYPES OF AXES TO SPECIFY
1. A datum diameter of sufficient length.
2. A datum axis perpendicular to a plane (primarily) and then centered on a diameter.
3. Two datum features of sufficient separation used to construct a single datum.
.005 A
.005 A B
.005 A-B
B
ERRORS DETECTED BY CIRCULAR RUNOUT
VERIFIES FORM ONLY FOR ROUNDNESS-NOT IN LONGITUDINAL VIEW
VERIFIES ORIENTATION AS POSITIONAL ERRORS THIS VIEW.
VERIFIES LOCATION SEPARATELY AT EACH CROSS SECTION
FIM
FULL INDICATOR MOVEMENT

(l) Circular runout

FIGURE 16.31 Summary Fact Data Sheets—*Continued*

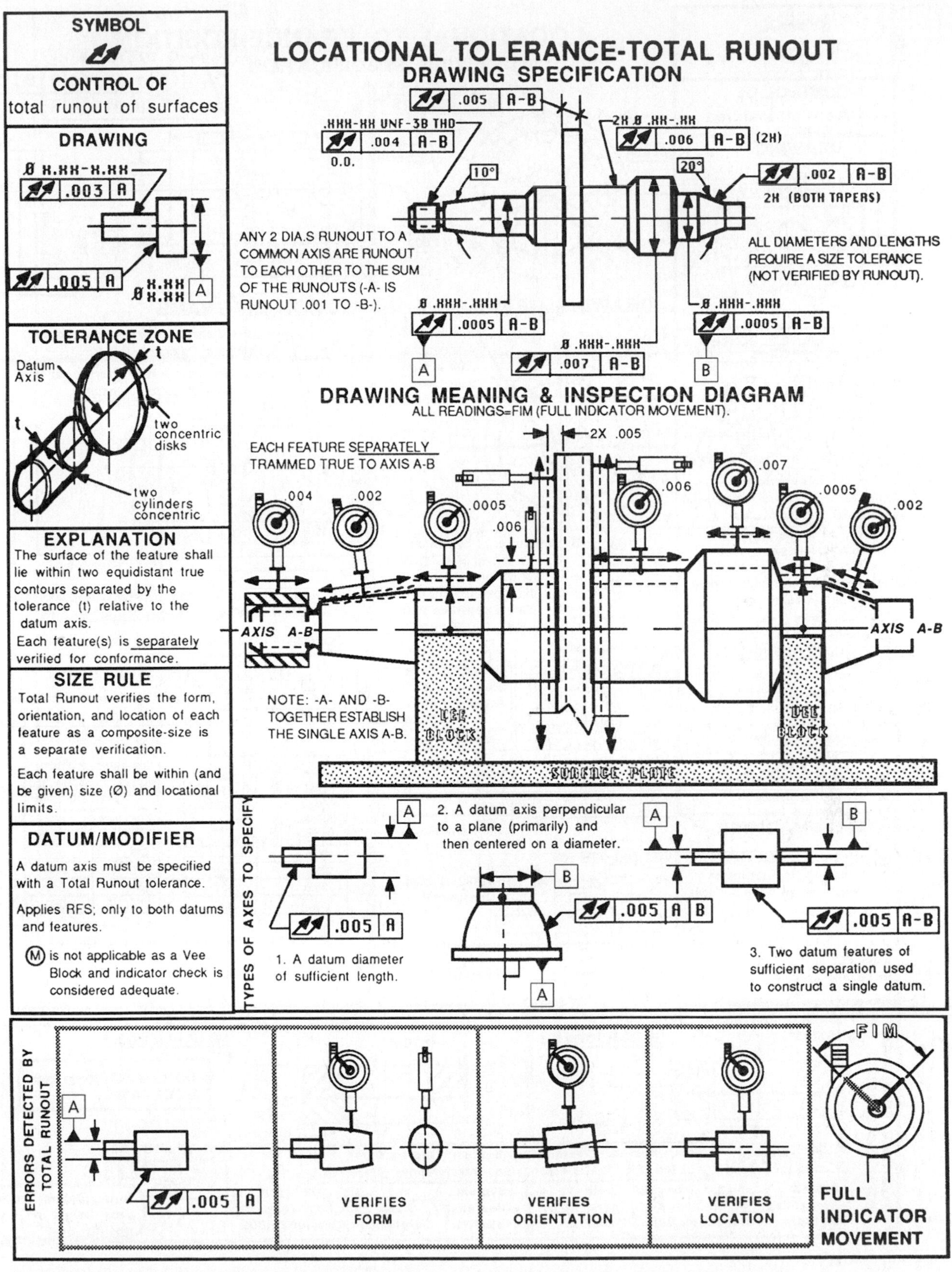

SYMBOL
CONTROL OF
total runout of surfaces
DRAWING
.003 A
.005 A
A
TOLERANCE ZONE
Datum Axis
t
two concentric disks
two cylinders concentric
EXPLANATION
The surface of the feature shall lie within two equidistant true contours separated by the tolerance (t) relative to the datum axis.
Each feature(s) is separately verified for conformance.
SIZE RULE
Total Runout verifies the form, orientation, and location of each feature as a composite-size is a separate verification.
Each feature shall be within (and be given) size (Ø) and locational limits.
DATUM/MODIFIER
A datum axis must be specified with a Total Runout tolerance.
Applies RFS; only to both datums and features.
Ⓜ is not applicable as a Vee Block and indicator check is considered adequate.
LOCATIONAL TOLERANCE-TOTAL RUNOUT
DRAWING SPECIFICATION
.005 A-B
.004 A-B
O.D.
.006 A-B (2X)
10°
20°
.002 A-B
2X (BOTH TAPERS)
ANY 2 DIA.S RUNOUT TO A COMMON AXIS ARE RUNOUT TO EACH OTHER TO THE SUM OF THE RUNOUTS (-A- IS RUNOUT .001 TO -B-).
ALL DIAMETERS AND LENGTHS REQUIRE A SIZE TOLERANCE (NOT VERIFIED BY RUNOUT).
.0005 A-B
.007 A-B
.0005 A-B
A
B
DRAWING MEANING & INSPECTION DIAGRAM
ALL READINGS=FIM (FULL INDICATOR MOVEMENT).
2X .005
EACH FEATURE SEPARATELY TRAMMED TRUE TO AXIS A-B
.004
.002
.0005
.006
.006
.007
.0005
.002
AXIS A-B
AXIS A-B
NOTE: -A- AND -B- TOGETHER ESTABLISH THE SINGLE AXIS A-B.
VEE BLOCK
VEE BLOCK
SURFACE PLATE
TYPES OF AXES TO SPECIFY
A
.005 A
1. A datum diameter of sufficient length.
2. A datum axis perpendicular to a plane (primarily) and then centered on a diameter.
A
B
.005 A B
A
B
.005 A-B
3. Two datum features of sufficient separation used to construct a single datum.
ERRORS DETECTED BY TOTAL RUNOUT
A
.005 A
VERIFIES FORM
VERIFIES ORIENTATION
VERIFIES LOCATION
FIM
FULL INDICATOR MOVEMENT

(m) Total runout

FIGURE 16.31 Summary Fact Data Sheets—*Continues*

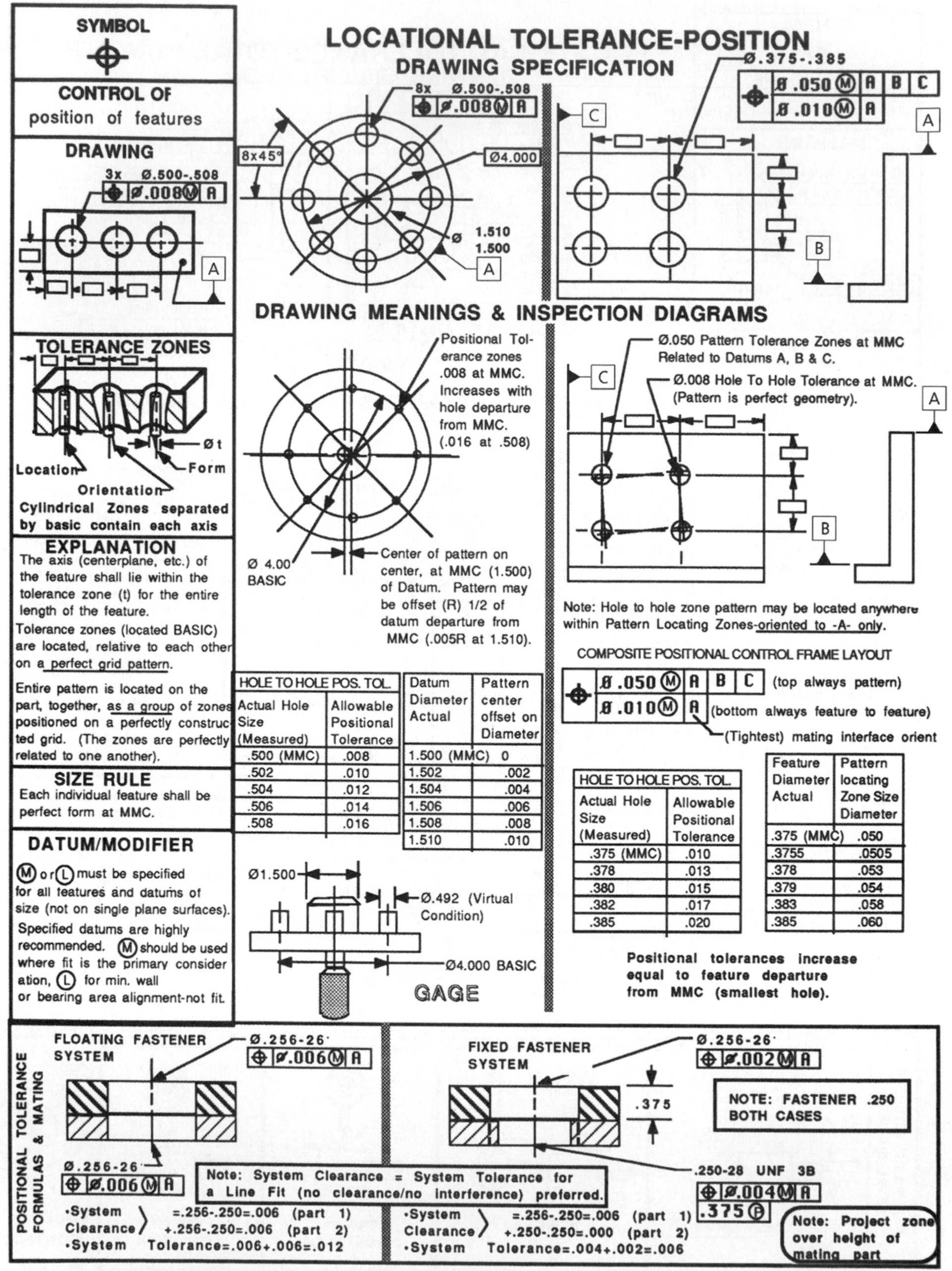
SYMBOL
CONTROL OF
position of features
DRAWING
3x Ø.500-.508
Ø.008 M A
A
TOLERANCE ZONES
Øt
Location
Form
Orientation
Cylindrical Zones separated by basic contain each axis
EXPLANATION
The axis (centerplane, etc.) of the feature shall lie within the tolerance zone (t) for the entire length of the feature.
Tolerance zones (located BASIC) are located, relative to each other on a perfect grid pattern.
Entire pattern is located on the part, together, as a group of zones positioned on a perfectly constructed grid. (The zones are perfectly related to one another).
SIZE RULE
Each individual feature shall be perfect form at MMC.
DATUM/MODIFIER
M or L must be specified for all features and datums of size (not on single plane surfaces).
Specified datums are highly recommended. M should be used where fit is the primary consideration, L for min. wall or bearing area alignment-not fit.
LOCATIONAL TOLERANCE-POSITION
DRAWING SPECIFICATION
8x Ø.500-.508
Ø.008 M A
8x45°
Ø4.000
Ø 1.510
1.500
A
Ø.375-.385
Ø.050 M A B C
Ø.010 M A
C
A
B
DRAWING MEANINGS & INSPECTION DIAGRAMS
Positional Tolerance zones .008 at MMC. Increases with hole departure from MMC. (.016 at .508)
Ø 4.00 BASIC
Center of pattern on center, at MMC (1.500) of Datum. Pattern may be offset (R) 1/2 of datum departure from MMC (.005R at 1.510).
Ø.050 Pattern Tolerance Zones at MMC Related to Datums A, B & C.
Ø.008 Hole To Hole Tolerance at MMC. (Pattern is perfect geometry).
C
A
B
Note: Hole to hole zone pattern may be located anywhere within Pattern Locating Zones-oriented to -A- only.
COMPOSITE POSITIONAL CONTROL FRAME LAYOUT
Ø.050 M A B C (top always pattern)
Ø.010 M A (bottom always feature to feature)
(Tightest) mating interface orient
Ø1.500
Ø.492 (Virtual Condition)
Ø4.000 BASIC
GAGE
Positional tolerances increase equal to feature departure from MMC (smallest hole).
POSITIONAL TOLERANCE FORMULAS & MATING
FLOATING FASTENER SYSTEM
Ø.256-26
Ø.006 M A
Ø.256-26
Ø.006 M A
Note: System Clearance = System Tolerance for a Line Fit (no clearance/no interference) preferred.
•System Clearance =.256-.250=.006 (part 1) +.256-.250=.006 (part 2)
•System Tolerance=.006+.006=.012
FIXED FASTENER SYSTEM
Ø.256-26
Ø.002 M A
.375
NOTE: FASTENER .250 BOTH CASES
.250-28 UNF 3B
Ø.004 M A
.375 P
•System Clearance =.256-.250=.006 (part 1) +.250-.250=.000 (part 2)
•System Tolerance=.004+.002=.006
Note: Project zone over height of mating part

HOLE TO HOLE POS. TOL. Actual Hole Size (Measured)	Allowable Positional Tolerance
.500 (MMC)	.008
.502	.010
.504	.012
.506	.014
.508	.016

Datum Diameter Actual	Pattern center offset on Diameter
1.500 (MMC)	0
1.502	.002
1.504	.004
1.506	.006
1.508	.008
1.510	.010

HOLE TO HOLE POS. TOL. Actual Hole Size (Measured)	Allowable Positional Tolerance
.375 (MMC)	.010
.378	.013
.380	.015
.382	.017
.385	.020

Feature Diameter Actual	Pattern locating Zone Size Diameter
.375 (MMC)	.050
.3755	.0505
.378	.053
.379	.054
.383	.058
.385	.060

(n) position

FIGURE 16.31 Summary Fact Data Sheets—*Continued*

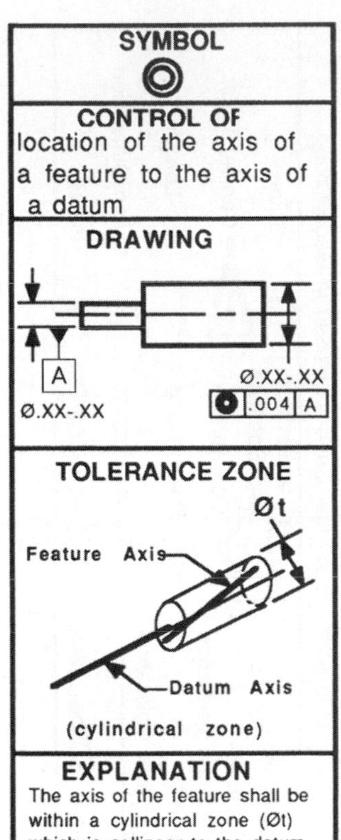

SYMBOL
CONTROL OF
location of the axis of a feature to the axis of a datum
DRAWING
A
Ø.XX-.XX
Ø.XX-.XX
.004 A
TOLERANCE ZONE
Øt
Feature Axis
Datum Axis
(cylindrical zone)

EXPLANATION

The axis of the feature shall be within a cylindrical zone (Øt) which is collinear to the datum axis.

The Least Squares Axes shall be used unless otherwise specified.

SIZE RULE

The feature (and datum) must be within the specified size limits. (Rule 1 applies to each.)

DATUM/MODIFIER

Always applies RFS;

Ⓜ may be not be added as only the axis of the feature and the datum are involved and these are not subject to variations of size.

A datum (axis) must be specified in conjunction with concentricity; this is required even where the datum would be obvious.

LOCATIONAL TOLERANCE CONCENTRICITY

DRAWING SPECIFICATION

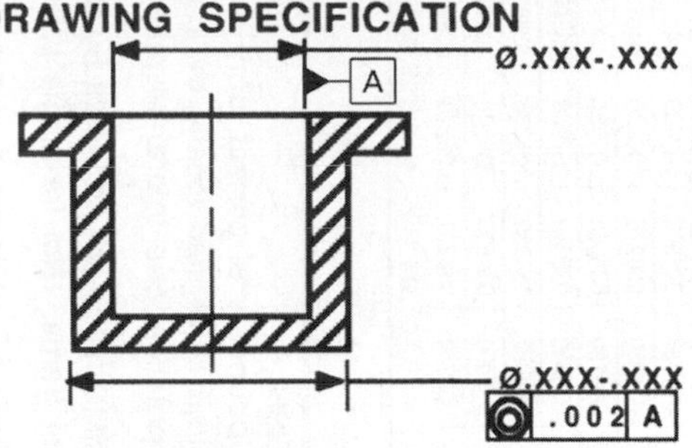

DRAWING MEANING

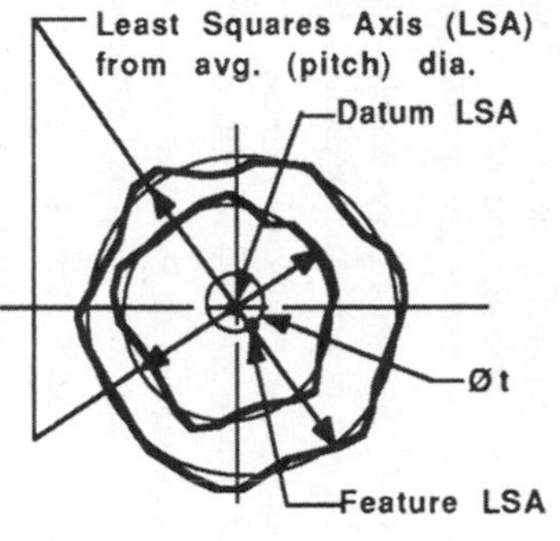

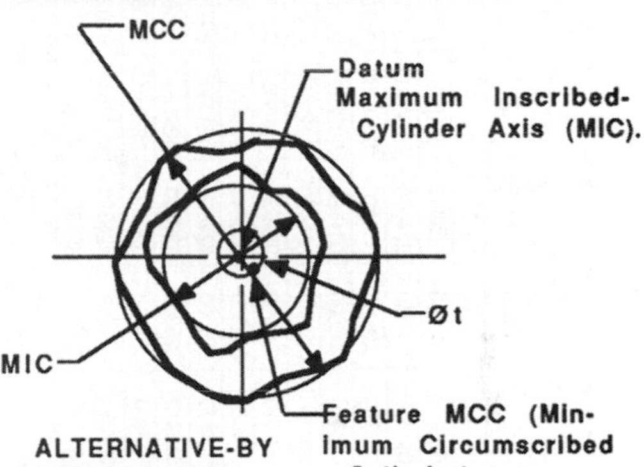

ALTERNATIVE-BY SPECIFICATION

INSPECTION DIAGRAM

LSA FOUND FROM LEAST SQUARES CENTERS AT VARIOUS CROSS SECTIONS.

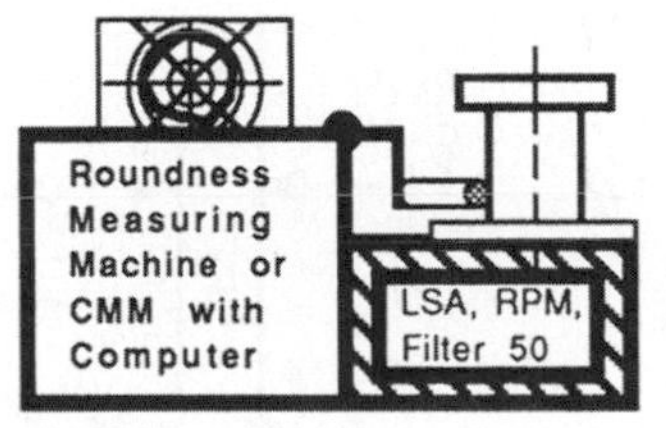

RECOMMENDED METHOD OF INSPECTION

1. THE ALTERNATIVE METHOD OF INSPECTION FINDS THE AXIS OF A MALE FEATURE WITH A COMPARITOR, ADJUSTABLE RING (COLLETT) (OR BY CMM) AND THE INTERNAL BY USING AN EXPANDING MANDREL, FIT PIN, COMPARITOR (OR BY CMM OR ROUNDNESS MEASURING MACHINE).

2. THIS METHOD IS INVOKED BY DIRECT SPECIFICATION ON THE DRAWING SUCH AS: "X." DETERMINE AXIS BY MIC (MAXIMUM INSCRIBED CYLINDER) METHOD.

ALTERNATIVE METHOD OF INSPECTION

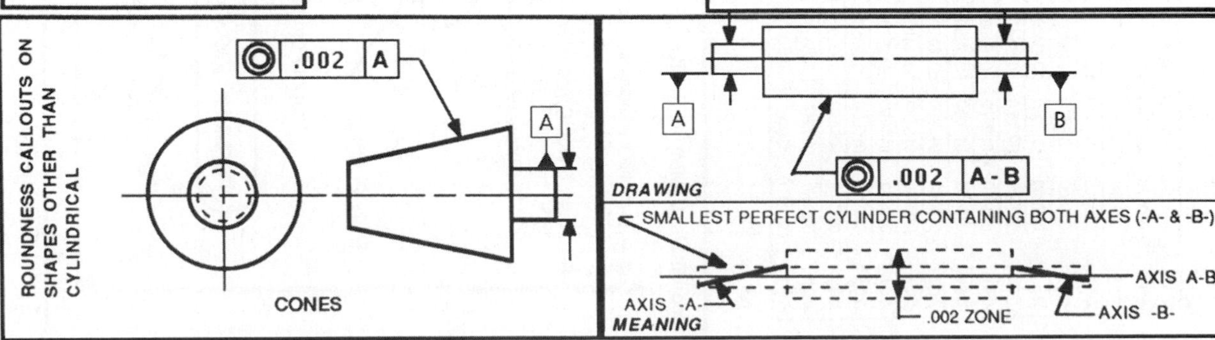

(o) Concentricity

FIGURE 16.31 Summary Fact Data Sheets—*Continues*

.020	.040200	.040450	.040790	.041230	.041760	.042380	.043080	.043860	.044720	.045650	.046650	.047710	.048830	.050000	.051220	.052500	.053810	.055170	.056570
.019	.038210	.038470	.038830	.039290	.039850	.040500	.041230	.042050	.042940	.043910	.044940	.046040	.047200	.048410	.049680	.050990	.052350	.053740	.055170
.018	.036220	.036500	.036880	.037360	.037950	.038630	.039400	.040250	.041180	.042190	.043270	.044410	.045610	.046860	.048170	.049520	.050910	.052350	.053810
.017	.034230	.034530	.034930	.035440	.036060	.036770	.037580	.038470	.039450	.040500	.041620	.042800	.044050	.045340	.046690	.048080	.049520	.050990	.052500
.016	.032250	.032560	.032980	.033530	.034180	.034930	.035780	.036720	.037740	.038830	.040000	.041230	.042520	.043860	.045250	.046690	.048170	.049680	.051220
.015	.030270	.030590	.031050	.031620	.032310	.033110	.034000	.034990	.036060	.037200	.038420	.039700	.041040	.042430	.043860	.045340	.046860	.048410	.050000
.014	.028280	.028640	.029120	.029730	.030460	.031300	.032250	.033290	.034410	.035610	.036880	.038210	.039600	.041040	.042520	.044050	.045610	.047200	.048830
.013	.026310	.026680	.027200	.027860	.028640	.029530	.030530	.031620	.032800	.034060	.035380	.036770	.038210	.039700	.041230	.042800	.044410	.046040	.047710
.012	.024330	.024740	.025300	.026000	.026830	.027780	.028840	.030000	.031240	.032560	.033940	.035380	.036880	.038420	.040000	.041620	.043270	.044940	.046650
.011	.022360	.022800	.023410	.024170	.025060	.026080	.027200	.028430	.029730	.031110	.032560	.034060	.035610	.037200	.038830	.040500	.042190	.043910	.045650
.010	.020400	.020880	.021540	.022360	.023320	.024410	.025610	.026910	.028280	.029730	.031240	.032800	.034410	.036060	.037740	.039450	.041180	.042940	.044720
.009	.018440	.018970	.019700	.020590	.021630	.022800	.024080	.025460	.026910	.028430	.030000	.031620	.033290	.034990	.036720	.038470	.040250	.042050	.043860
.008	.016490	.017090	.017890	.018870	.020000	.021260	.022630	.024080	.025610	.027200	.028840	.030530	.032250	.034000	.035780	.037580	.039400	.041230	.043080
.007	.014560	.015230	.016120	.017200	.018440	.019800	.021260	.022800	.024410	.026080	.027780	.029530	.031300	.033110	.034930	.036770	.038630	.040500	.042380
.006	.012650	.013420	.014420	.015620	.016970	.018440	.020000	.021630	.023320	.025060	.026830	.028640	.030460	.032310	.034180	.036060	.037950	.039850	.041760
.005	.010770	.011660	.012810	.014140	.015620	.017200	.018870	.020590	.022360	.024170	.026000	.027860	.029730	.031620	.033530	.035440	.037360	.039290	.041230
.004	.008940	.010000	.011310	.012810	.014420	.016120	.017890	.019700	.021540	.023410	.025300	.027200	.029120	.031050	.032980	.034930	.036880	.038830	.040790
.003	.007210	.008490	.010000	.011660	.013420	.015230	.017090	.018970	.020880	.022800	.024740	.026680	.028640	.030590	.032560	.034530	.036500	.038470	.040450
.002	.005660	.007210	.008940	.010770	.012650	.014560	.016490	.018440	.020400	.022360	.024330	.026310	.028280	.030270	.032250	.034230	.036220	.038210	.040200
.001	.002	.003	.004	.005	.006	.007	.008	.009	.010	.011	.012	.013	.014	.015	.016	.017	.018	.019	.020

Coordinate (CMM) to Positional Zone Conversion (Chart Above).

Actual Measurement

Basic Dwg. Dimension

X Difference

Y Difference

True Position

Actual Positional Ø = Z

Basic Dwg. Dimension

Actual Measurement

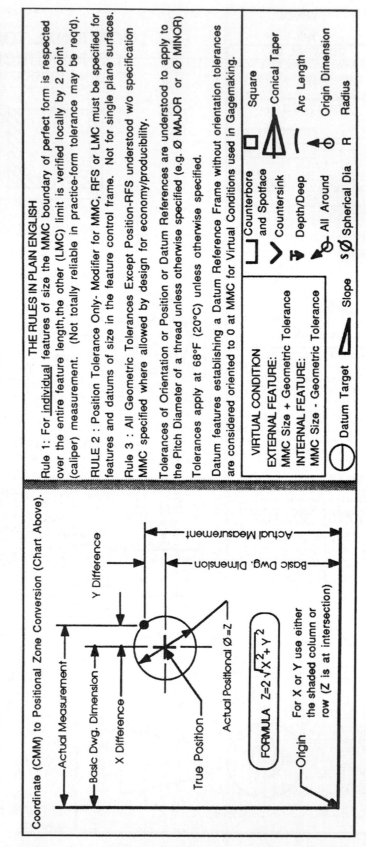

FORMULA $Z=2\sqrt{X^2+Y^2}$

Origin

For X or Y use either the shaded column or row (Z is at intersection)

THE RULES IN PLAIN ENGLISH

Rule 1: For individual features of size the MMC boundary of perfect form is respected over the entire feature length, the other (LMC) limit is verified locally by 2 point (caliper) measurement. (Not totally reliable in practice-form tolerance may be req'd).

RULE 2 : Position Tolerance Only- Modifier for MMC, RFS or LMC must be specified for features and datums of size in the feature control frame. Not for single plane surfaces.

Rule 3 : All Geometric Tolerances Except Position-RFS understood w/o specification MMC specified where allowed by design for economy/producibility.

Tolerances of Orientation or Position or Datum References are understood to apply to the Pitch Diameter of a thread unless otherwise specified (e.g. Ø MAJOR or Ø MINOR)

Tolerances apply at 68°F (20°C) unless otherwise specified.

Datum features establishing a Datum Reference Frame without orientation tolerances are considered oriented to 0 at MMC for Virtual Conditions used in Gagemaking.

VIRTUAL CONDITION
EXTERNAL FEATURE:
MMC Size + Geometric Tolerance
INTERNAL FEATURE:
MMC Size - Geometric Tolerance

Counterbore and Spotface

Countersink

Depth/Deep

All Around

Square

Conical Taper

Arc Length

Origin Dimension

Datum Target

Slope

S Ø Spherical Dia

R Radius

(p) Conversion chart

FIGURE 16.31 Summary Fact Data Sheets—*Continued*

form, and orientation. Profile tolerances are specified as follows:

1. An appropriate view or section is drawn showing the desired basic profile.
2. Depending on design requirements, the tolerance may be divided bilaterally to both sides of the true profile or applied unilaterally to either side of the true profile. If an equal bilateral tolerance is intended, it is necessary to show only the feature control frame, with a leader directed to the surface. For a unilateral tolerance, phantom lines are drawn parallel to the true profile to indicate the line is extended to the feature control frame. If some segments of the profile are controlled by a profile tolerance and other segments by individually toleranced dimensions, the extent of the profile tolerance must be indicated.

16.7.1 Profile of a Line

A **profile of a line tolerance** specifies the limits of the boundaries of individual line elements of a surface [Fig. 16.31(g)]. The tolerance zone is two dimensional. BASIC dimensions define the true profile. The shape of the tolerance zone is two parallel boundaries offset above and below the true profile.

16.7.2 Profile of a Surface

A **profile of a surface tolerance** specifies the limits of all surface elements at the same time [Fig. 16.31(h)]. If the surface is made up of one or more basic curves, arcs, straight lines, or other shapes, all are described by BASIC dimensions. Some segments of a surface may be controlled by profile tolerancing and other segments by different tolerances. Reference letters serve to define the extent of a controlled segment, such as FROM A TO B. Points A and B are directed to the appropriate location on the surface. If the relationship of features is to be zero at MMC, specify by placing a 0 in the control frame or with a note, e.g., PERFECT ORIENTATION REQUIRED AT MMC. The orientation tolerance may then be equal to or less than the amount the feature deviates from MMC.

16.8 ORIENTATION TOLERANCES

Orientation tolerances cover parallelism, perpendicularity, and angularity. All require at least one datum specification. Some, such as perpendicularity, may involve an additional (secondary) datum. Orientation tolerances may employ element controls rather than surface requirements, in which case *each element of each radial element* is specified below the feature control frame.

Angularity, parallelism, perpendicularity, and in some instances profile are orientation tolerances applicable to related features. These tolerances control the orientation of features to one another. They are sometimes referred to as **attitude tolerances.** Relation to more than one datum feature should be considered if required to stabilize the tolerance zone in more than one direction. Note that angularity, perpendicularity, and parallelism, when applied to plane surfaces, control flatness if a flatness tolerance is not specified. Tolerance zones require an axis, or all elements of the surface, to fall within this zone.

16.8.1 Angularity

Angularity is the condition in which a surface or an axis is at a specific angle other than 90° from a datum plane or axis [Fig. 16.31(i)]. An **angularity tolerance** specifies one of the following:

- A tolerance zone defined by two parallel planes at the specified basic angle from a datum plane or axis within which the surface of the considered feature must lie
- A tolerance zone defined by two parallel planes at the specified basic angle from a datum plane or axis within which the axis the feature must lie

16.8.2 Perpendicularity

Perpendicularity is the condition in which a surface, center plane, or axis is at a right angle to a datum plane or axis [Fig. 16.31(j)]. A **perpendicularity tolerance** specifies one of the following:

- A tolerance zone defined by two parallel planes perpendicular to a datum plane or axis within which the surface or center plane of the considered feature must lie
- A tolerance zone defined by two parallel planes perpendicular to a datum axis within which the axis of the considered feature must lie
- A cylindrical tolerance zone perpendicular to a datum plane within which the axis of the considered feature must lie
- A tolerance zone defined by two parallel lines perpendicular to a datum plane or axis within which an element of the surface must lie

16.8.3 Parallelism

Parallelism is the condition in which a surface or axis is equidistant at all points from a datum plane or in which an axis is equidistant along its length from a datum axis [Fig. 16.31(k)]. A **parallelism tolerance** specifies one of the following:

- A tolerance zone defined by two planes or lines parallel to a datum plane or axis within which the line elements of the surface or axis of the feature must lie
- A cylindrical tolerance zone whose axis is parallel to a datum axis within which the axis of the feature must lie

16.9 RUNOUT TOLERANCES

A **runout tolerance** controls the functional relationship of one or more features of a part to a datum axis. The types of features controlled by runout tolerances include those surfaces constructed around a datum axis and those constructed at right angles to a datum axis.

Runout tolerances control the composite form, orientation, and position relative to a datum axis. Each feature must be within its runout tolerance when the part is rotated about the datum axis. The tolerance specified for a controlled surface is the total tolerance, or full indicator movement (FIM).

The two types of runout control are circular and total. The type specified depends on design requirements and manufacturing considerations. Circular runout is normally a less complex requirement than total runout.

16.9.1 Circular Runout

Circular runout is the condition of a circular element on the surface with respect to a fixed point during one complete revolution of the part about the datum axis [Fig. 16.31(l)]. Circular runout controls circular elements of a surface. The tolerance is applied independently at any circular cross section as the part is rotated 360°. If applied to surfaces constructed around a datum axis, circular runout can control the cumulative variations of circularity and coaxiality. If applied to surfaces at right angles to the datum axis, circular runout controls circular elements of a plane surface (*wobble*).

16.9.2 Total Runout

Total runout [Fig. 16.31(m)] is the condition of a surface with respect to a perfect counterpart of itself, perfectly oriented and positioned. The indicator is moved across the feature, relative to the desired geometry, as the part is rotated about the datum axis.

Total runout provides composite control of all surface elements. The tolerance is applied simultaneously to all circular and profile-measuring positions as the part is rotated 360°.

16.9.3 Position

Position is a total zone specification, such as a diameter or total width centered on the basic location of the axis, center plane, or center point of a feature, from the true position with respect to datum(s) [Fig. 16.31(n)].

Locating a hole with rectangular coordinates and plus–minus tolerances yields a square or rectangular zone. The worst-case location for the axis of the mating features is at the diagonal. Inscribing this square with a circle does not change the mating relationship, but it does yield a 58% greater area.

Another improvement in the positional tolerancing system is the change from a "chain" (feature-to-feature) basis to a "basic grid" system. Tolerance accumulations are therefore avoided (Fig. 16.32). The grid for a pattern of zones is perfect in all respects. The locations of each of these zones are in perfect relationship to each other. A grid is established by placing **BASIC dimensions** between the features. Figure

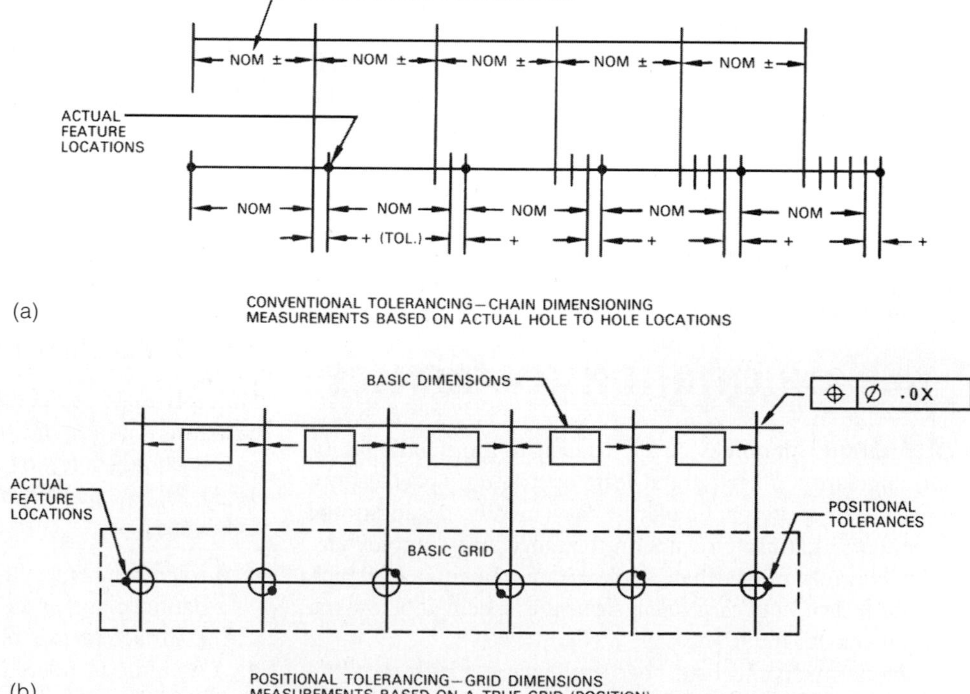

FIGURE 16.32
Conventional Chain Versus the Positional Grid System

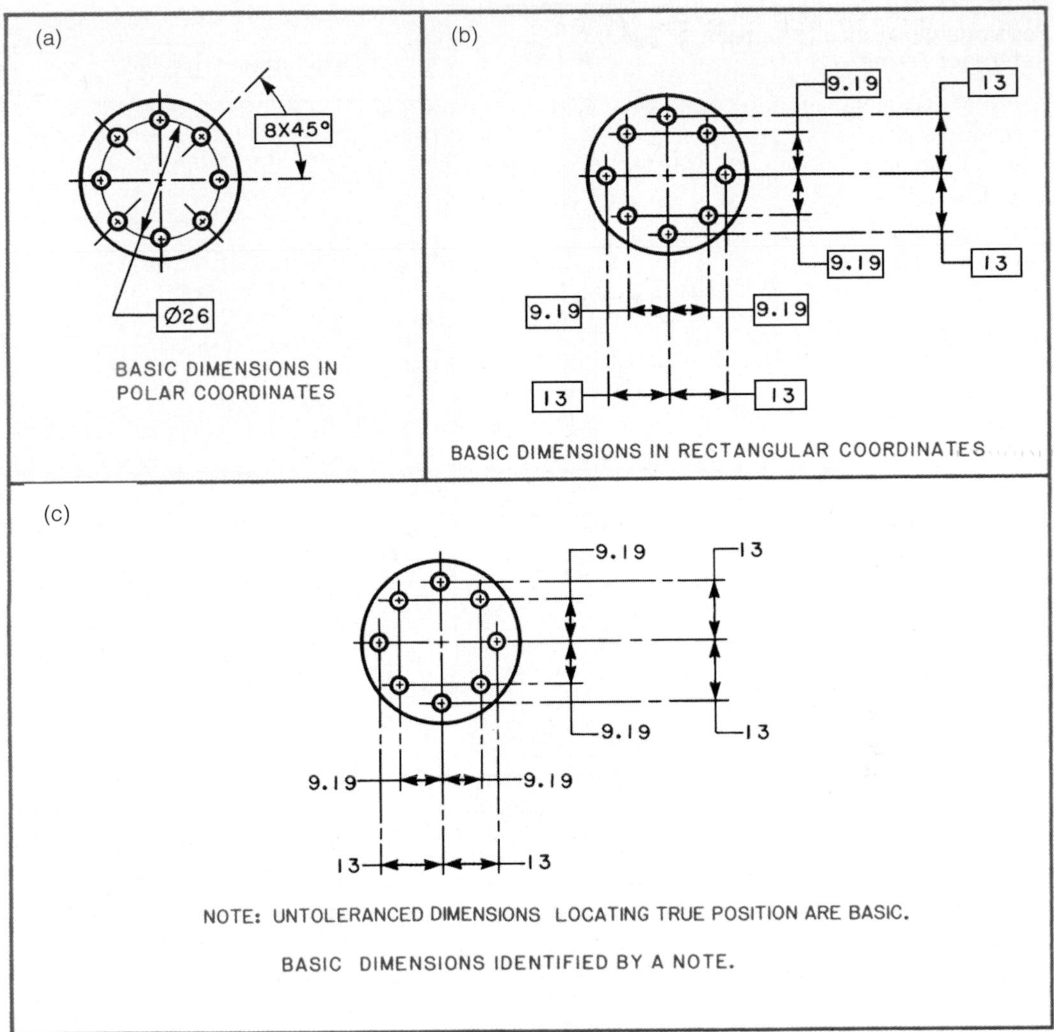

FIGURE 16.33 Identifying Basic Dimensions

16.33 shows examples of how to identify basic dimensions for patterns.

16.9.4 Positional Patterns

Figure 16.34 shows how **patterns** are located on parts. The preference is for composite positional tolerancing, as shown in the figure. The use of plus–minus dimensions to locate a pattern is *not* recommended.

16.10 LIMITS OF SIZE

The **limits of size** of a feature describe the extent within which variations of geometric form are allowed. Where only a size tolerance is specified, the limits of size of an individual feature describe the extent to which variations in its geometric form, as well as size, are allowed.

The **actual size** of an individual feature at any cross section must be within the specified tolerance of size. The form of an individual feature is controlled by its limits of size.

The surface or surfaces of a feature must not extend beyond a boundary of perfect form at MMC. This boundary is the true geometric form represented by the drawing. No variation in form is permitted if the feature is produced at its MMC limit of size. Where the actual size of a feature has departed from MMC toward LMC, a variation in form is allowed equal to the amount of such departure. There is no requirement for a boundary of perfect form at LMC. Thus, a feature produced at its LMC limit of size is permitted to vary from true form to the maximum variation allowed by the boundary of perfect form at MMC. The control of geometric form by limits of size does not apply to the following:

- Stock such as bars, sheets, tubing, structural shapes, and other items produced to established industry or government standards that prescribe limits for straightness, flatness, or other geometric characteristics
- Parts subject to free state variation in the unrestrained condition

FIGURE 16.34 Composite Positional Tolerance to Datum Reference Frame

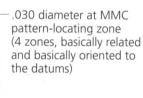

(a) Whole patterns

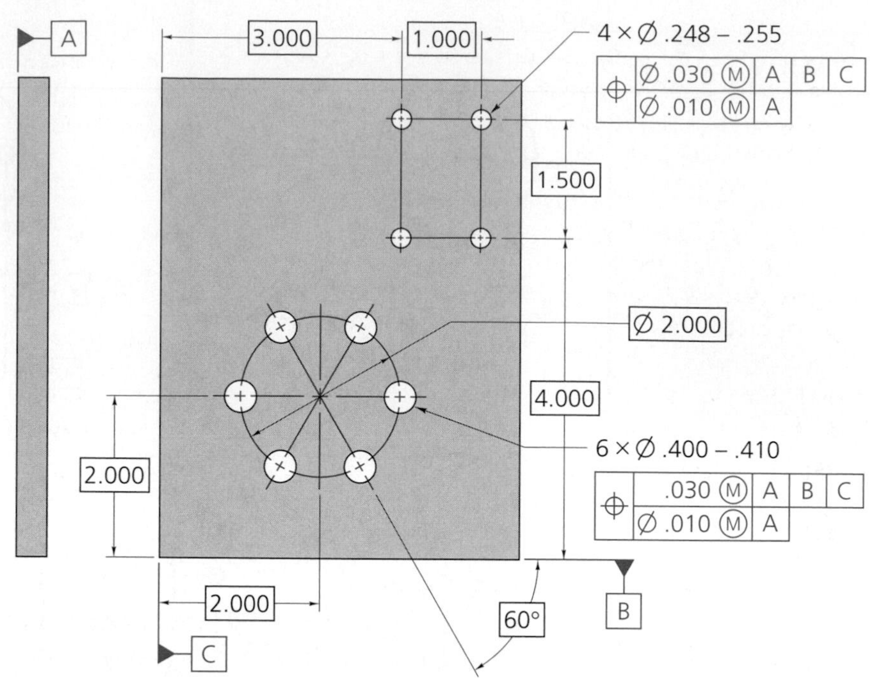

(b) Square patterns

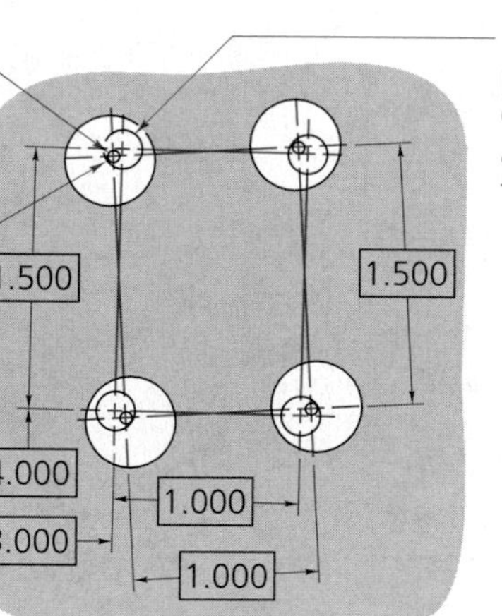

(c) Circular patterns

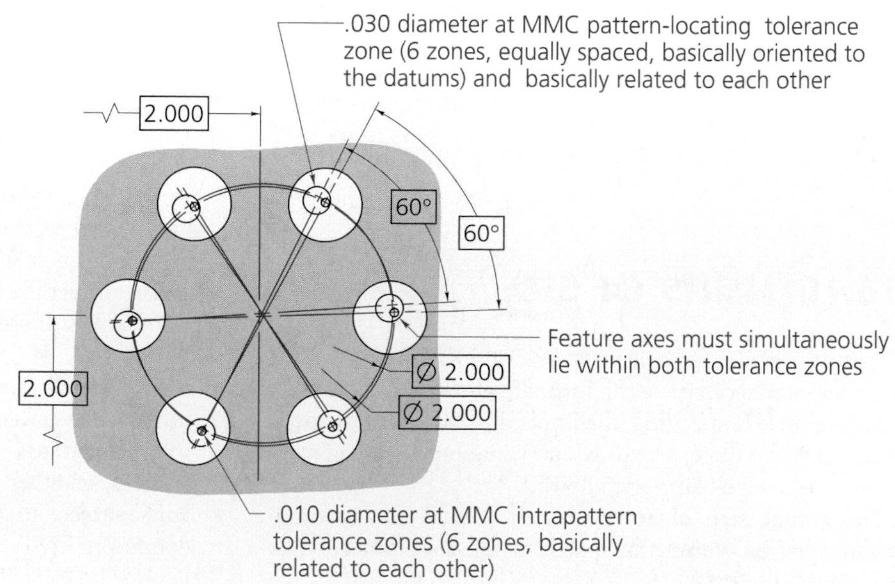

The limits of size do not control the orientation or location relationship among individual features. Features shown perpendicular, coaxial, or symmetrical to each other must be controlled for location or orientation. If it is necessary to establish a boundary of perfect form at MMC to control the relationship between features, use the following:

1. Specify a zero tolerance of orientation at MMC, including a datum reference (at MMC, if applicable), to control the angularity, perpendicularity, or parallelism of the feature.
2. Specify a zero positional tolerance at MMC, including a datum reference at MMC, to control coaxial or symmetrical features.
3. Indicate this control for the features involved with a note such as

   PERFECT ORIENTATION (or COAXIALITY or SYMMETRY) AT MMC REQUIRED FOR RELATED FEATURES.

4. Relate dimensions to a datum reference frame.

16.10.1 ISO Interpretation of Limits of Size

Where datums are specified in the ISO system, measurements are taken from the datums and made relative to them. Where datums are not specified, linear dimensions are intended to apply on a point-to-point basis or directly between the points indicated on the drawing. Unfortunately, caliper measurements float relative to one another and the exact shape is not known (Fig. 16.35). If the configuration is controlled, a form tolerance such as straightness or flatness is given.

Additionally, the direction of measurement can be a problem for a geometry that is not ideal. In Figure 16.36, the vertical measurements are not perpendicular to the horizontal ones. If the sides of a part are not parallel, finding the center plane to orient measurements is another problem.

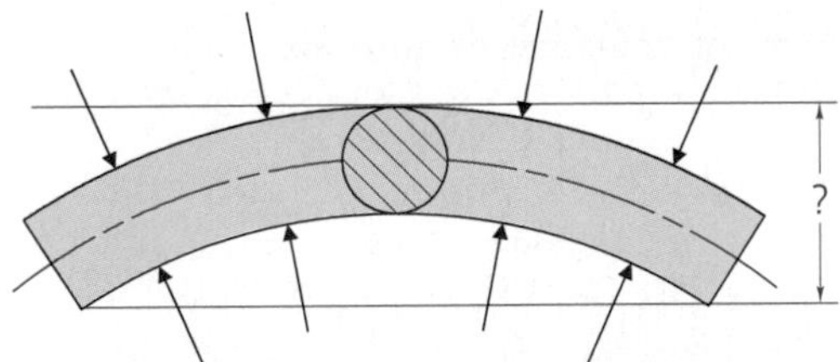

FIGURE 16.35 Caliper Measurements Do Not Measure Form. Illustration shows a cylindrical part.

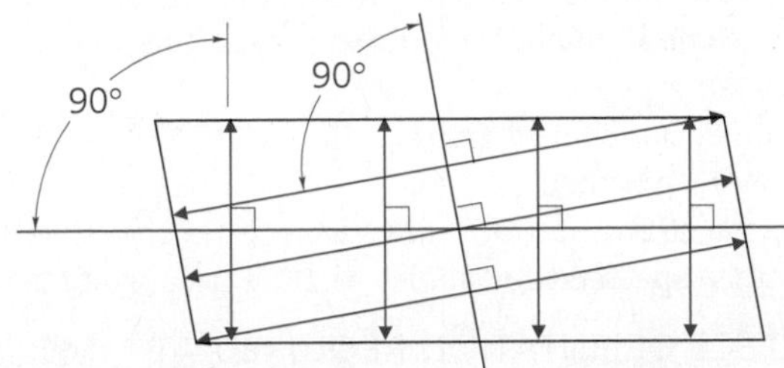

FIGURE 16.36 Measuring Orientation for Caliper Measurement. Illustration shows a rectangular part.

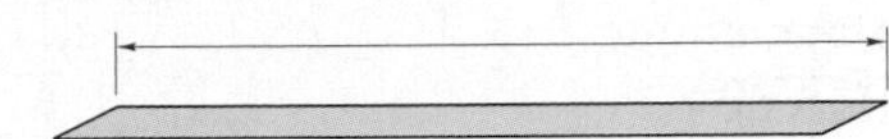

FIGURE 16.37 Measuring Thin Parts

For thin parts, the rule changes to taking measurements parallel to the base (Fig. 16.37). Furthermore, to make this system work, a rule of independence was devised:

> Every requirement on a drawing is intended to be applied independently, without reference to other dimensions, conditions, or characteristics, unless a particular relationship is specified.

This rule is voided, however, when "limits and fits" are specified, in which case the Taylor principle applies (the basis of ANSI). Rule 1 of the ANSI standard regarding limits of size follows:

> *Rule 1:* The surface(s) of a feature shall not extend beyond a boundary (envelope) of perfect form at MMC. This boundary is the true geometric form represented by the drawing. There is no requirement for a boundary of perfect form at LMC (Fig. 16.38).

Rule 1 does not apply to stock materials that use established industry or government standards; to parts specified in the "free state" (nonrigid); and to those specifically excluded, such as straightness of the axis or where the note **PERFECT FORM AT MMC NOT REQUIRED** is specified. Rule 1 does apply to individual features and, although they control the form of an individual feature of size, they do not control the orientation, location, or runout of features to each other. These relationships are defined by tolerances, notes, or other specifications called out directly on the drawing.

Advances in metrology—especially with computerized mathematical models and algorithms such as on coordinate measuring machines (CMMs)—lend themselves to the ANSI version of limits of size. A ring gage made to the MMC size of a shaft, and as long as the shaft, can verify a shaft for Rule 1 compliance. A micrometer or caliper can verify the LMC limit. A plug gage, made to the MMC size of a hole, and as long as the hole, can verify a hole for Rule 1 compliance. An inside micrometer or caliper is used to verify the LMC limit.

16.10.2 U.S. Interpretation of Limits of Size

In the United States, the **limits of size** of a feature describe the extent within which variations of geometric form, as well as size, are allowed. This control applies solely to individual features of size. **Feature of size** refers to one cylindrical or

FIGURE 16.38 Limits of Size Interpretation for Individual Features

(a)

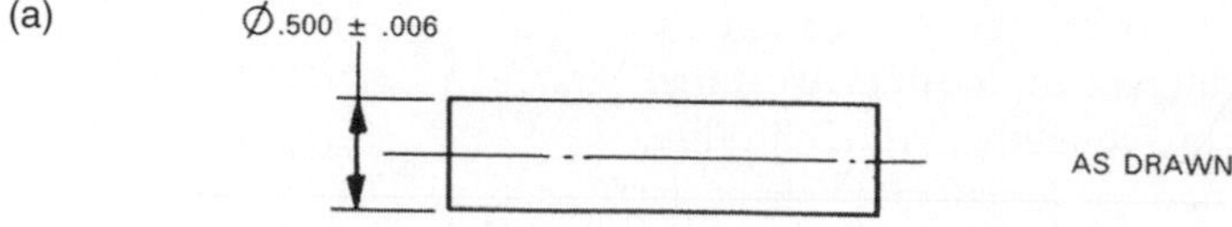

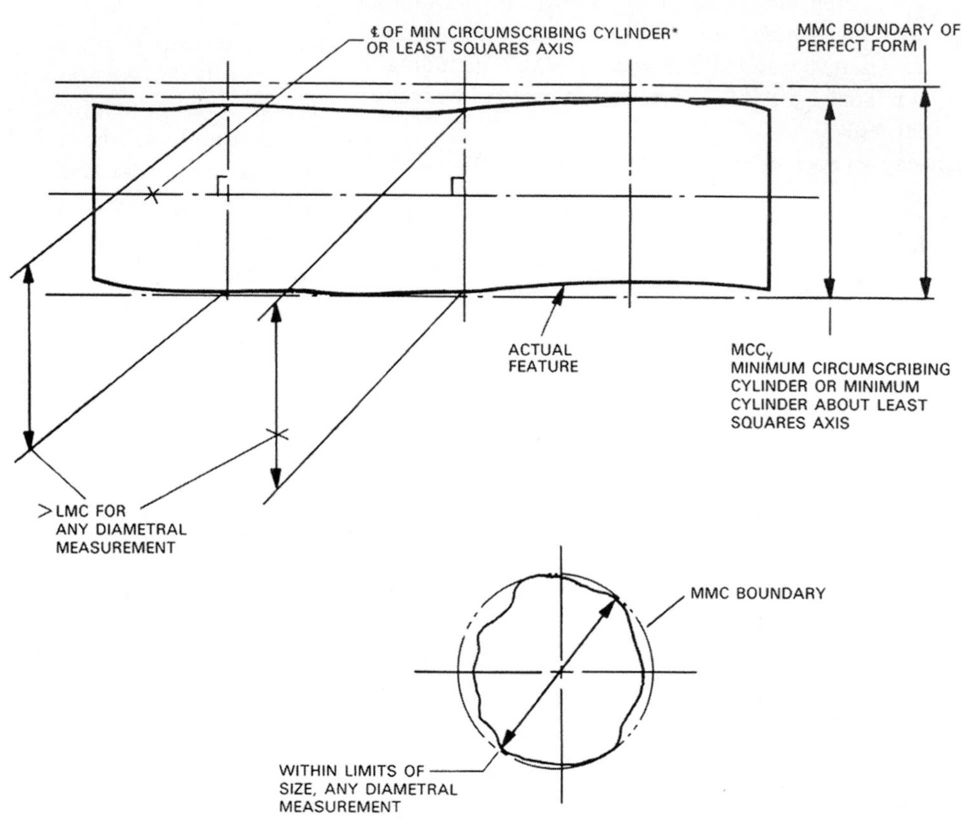

*Where a preference for a least squares or ℄ of envelope axis exists, it must be specified on the drawing.

spherical surface, or to a set of two plane parallel surfaces each of which is associated with a size dimension. Where only a **tolerance of size** is specified, the limits of size of an individual feature describe the extent to which variations in its geometric form, as well as size, are allowed (Fig. 16.39). **The actual size** of an individual feature at any cross section is within the specified tolerance of size.

16.11 GENERAL TOLERANCING RULES

Rules have been established to ensure uniform interpretation and to avoid costly errors and misunderstandings. Study the following six rules carefully.

- The system of indicating tolerances (whether size, location, or geometry) does not necessarily require any particular method of production or quality.
- Regardless of the number of places involved, all toleranced limits are considered to be absolute. Each limit is considered to be continued with trailing zeros. For example:

1.22 = 1.220 000 000 . . .
1.20 = 1.200 000 000 . . .

1.2 = 1.200 000 000 . . .
1.0 = 1.000 000 000 . . .

1.20 + .02 = 1.220 000 000 . . .
1.20 − .00 = 1.200 000 000 . . .

This rule applies to all limits (plus–minus or limit dimensioned), including those where title block tolerances are applied.

- All dimensions and tolerances are at 68°F (20°C) unless otherwise specified.
- Surfaces drawn at 90° are subject to the title block tolerance specified for angles or by a note, such as

PERFECT ORIENTATION REQUIRED AT MMC.

This rule also applies to features that have a common centerline or axis of revolution. Where function or inter-

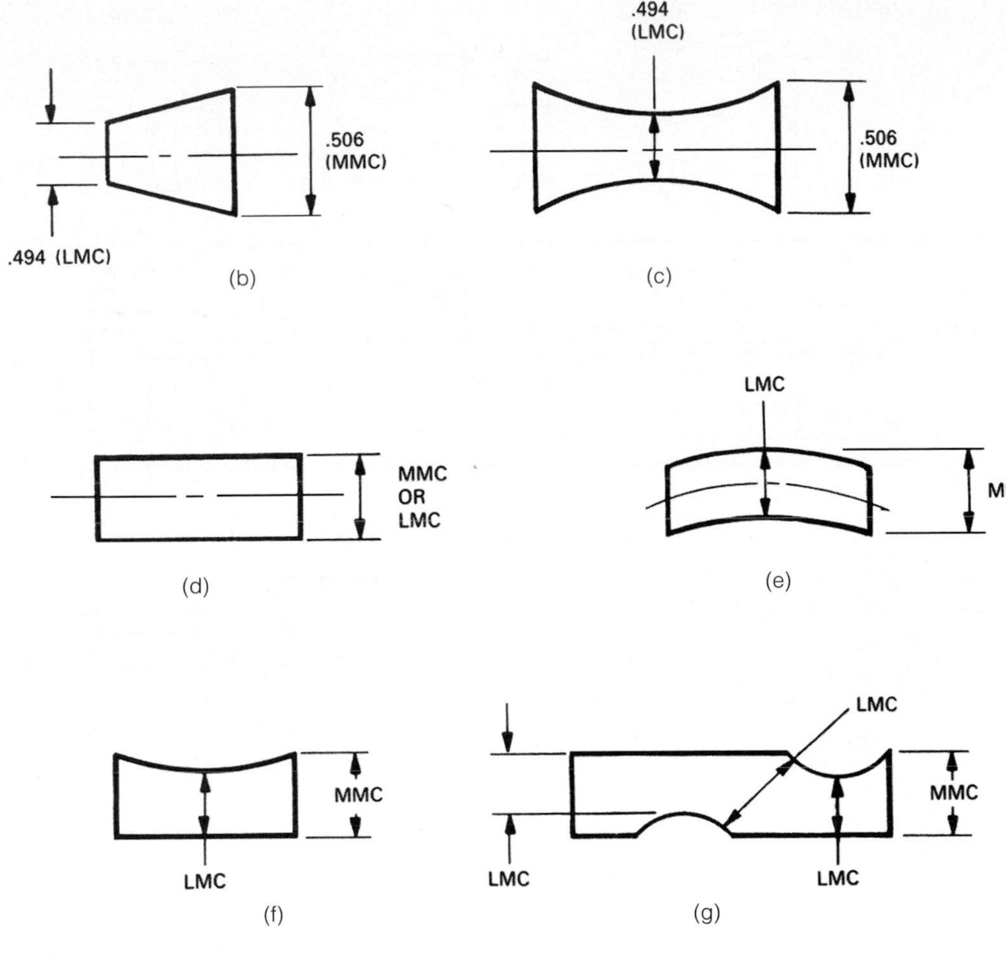

FIGURE 16.38 Limits of Size Interpretation for Individual Features—*Continued*

changeability is affected, the tolerances are to be specified.

- Theoretical constructions such as centerlines or planes, shown at right angles, and from which features such as holes or pins are dimensioned, are considered to be at 90° BASIC. Variations in the inspection setup are subtracted from the allowable tolerances during the verification process.
- The tolerance specified on the drawing is the total amount allowable, including manufacturing, inspection, and gaging variations. To ensure rapid part acceptance, manufacturing usually does not use more than 90° of the available tolerance.

16.11.1 General Rules of Geometric Tolerancing

Use the following rules to apply geometric tolerancing to a part.

- The surface(s) of a feature must not extend beyond a boundary (envelope) of perfect form at MMC. There is no requirement for a boundary of perfect form at LMC.
- Position tolerance requirements for modifiers are specified in the feature control frame. A modifier, M or L, is specified after the feature tolerance and after each datum for features and datums of size. No modifier is specified for a single-plane surface.

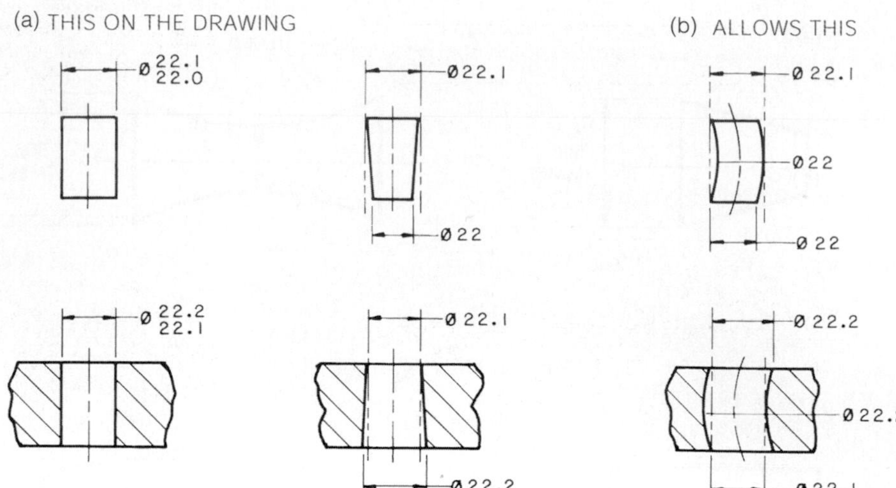

FIGURE 16.39 Tolerance Variations Allowed for Individual Features

- Requirements for modifiers of tolerances other than position are specified in the feature control frame. RFS applies, unless another modifier is specified, for all features and datums. The RFS modifier is not shown in the feature control frame. MMC is specified for features and datums of size where the design allows.

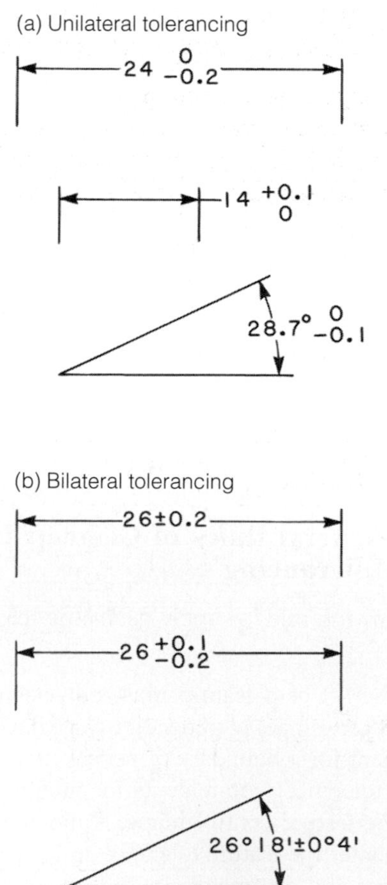

FIGURE 16.40 Plus-or-Minus Tolerancing on Dimensions

16.11.2 Setting Tolerances

The **nominal size** is often referred to as the **basic size** or **design size.** The nominal and the associated tolerances have the same number of decimal places, except in the metric system. The "plus" value is shown above the "minus" value. European drawings also use +, + and −, and − tolerances.

In **bilateral tolerancing** [Fig. 16.40(b)], the tolerance is applied in both directions from the nominal:

$.500 \pm .005$ or $1.200\begin{smallmatrix}+ .002\\ - .005\end{smallmatrix}$

In **unilateral tolerancing** [Fig. 16.40(a)], the tolerance is applied in one direction; the other value is zero:

$1.200\begin{smallmatrix}+ .002\\ - .000\end{smallmatrix}$ $1.200\begin{smallmatrix}+ .000\\ - .006\end{smallmatrix}$

16.11.3 Limit Dimensioning

In **limit dimensioning,** the maximum value is placed above the minimum value (Fig. 16.41). In note form, the larger value is placed to the right of the lesser value, separated by a dash. Both limits have the same number of decimal places:

$\begin{matrix}.750\\ .748\end{matrix}$ or .748 − .750

Even values are preferred. Although there is usually a trailing zero, the number of decimal places is minimized. Plus-or-minus and limit dimensions may appear on the same drawing. Generally, limit dimensions specify the size of features, and plus-or-minus dimensions specify the location of features. Plus-or-minus dimensions, in bilateral form, are preferred for numerical control production, where the mean is used.

16.11.4 Title Block Tolerances

Title block tolerances are used where there is a uniformity in tolerances (Fig. 16.42). In Figure 16.43, the nominal

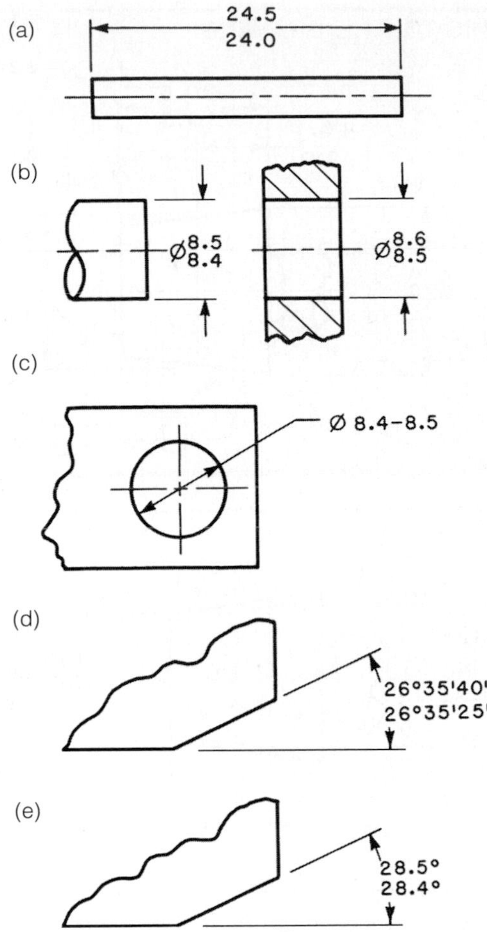

(a) 24.5 / 24.0

(b) Ø8.5 / 8.4   Ø8.6 / 8.5

(c) Ø 8.4–8.5

(d) 26°35'40" / 26°35'25"

(e) 28.5° / 28.4°

FIGURE 16.41 Limit Dimensioning on Drawings

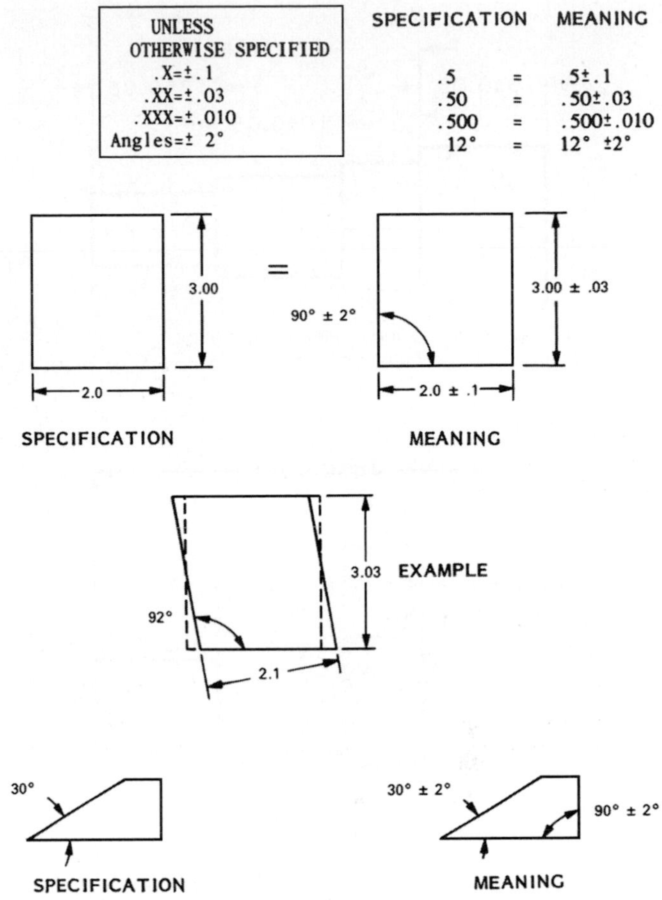

dimension is given alone on the face of the drawing and a bilateral tolerance is shown in the title block. If larger tolerances are allowed for a particular feature, they should be specified. In European title blocks, tolerances are based on feature size; in the United States they are based on the number of decimal places specified (Fig. 16.43).

UNLESS OTHERWISE SPECIFIED
.X=±.1
.XX=±.03
.XXX=±.010
Angles=± 2°

SPECIFICATION		MEANING
.5	=	.5±.1
.50	=	.50±.03
.500	=	.500±.010
12°	=	12° ±2°

SPECIFICATION: 3.00, 2.0 = MEANING: 3.00 ± .03, 90° ± 2°, 2.0 ± .1

EXAMPLE: 3.03, 92°, 2.1

SPECIFICATION: 30° — MEANING: 30° ± 2°, 90° ± 2°

FIGURE 16.43 Application of Title Block Tolerance

16.11.5 Tolerance Accumulation

Figure 16.44 compares the tolerance values from three methods of dimensioning.

Chain dimensioning The maximum variation between two features is equal to the tolerances on the intermediate

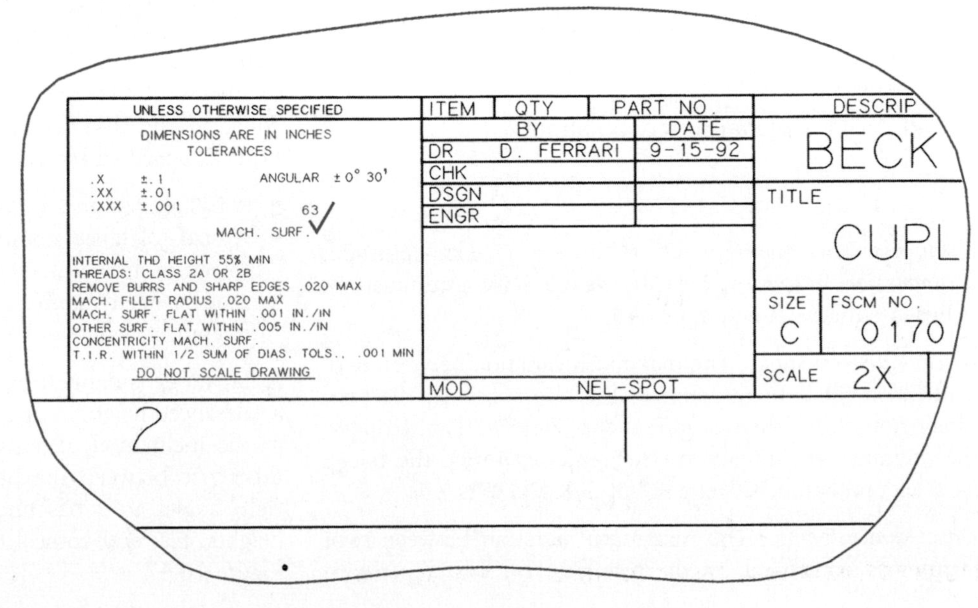

UNLESS OTHERWISE SPECIFIED
DIMENSIONS ARE IN INCHES
TOLERANCES
.X ±.1
.XX ±.01
.XXX ±.001
ANGULAR ±0° 30'
MACH. SURF. 63√
INTERNAL THD HEIGHT 55% MIN
THREADS: CLASS 2A OR 2B
REMOVE BURRS AND SHARP EDGES .020 MAX
MACH. FILLET RADIUS .020 MAX
MACH. SURF. FLAT WITHIN .001 IN./IN
OTHER SURF. FLAT WITHIN .005 IN./IN
CONCENTRICITY MACH. SURF.
T.I.R. WITHIN 1/2 SUM OF DIAS. TOLS., .001 MIN
DO NOT SCALE DRAWING

ITEM	QTY	PART NO.
	BY	DATE
DR	D. FERRARI	9-15-92
CHK		
DSGN		
ENGR		
MOD	NEL-SPOT	

DESCRIP
BECK
TITLE
CUPL
SIZE C
FSCM NO. 0170
SCALE 2X
2

FIGURE 16.42 Title Block Tolerances

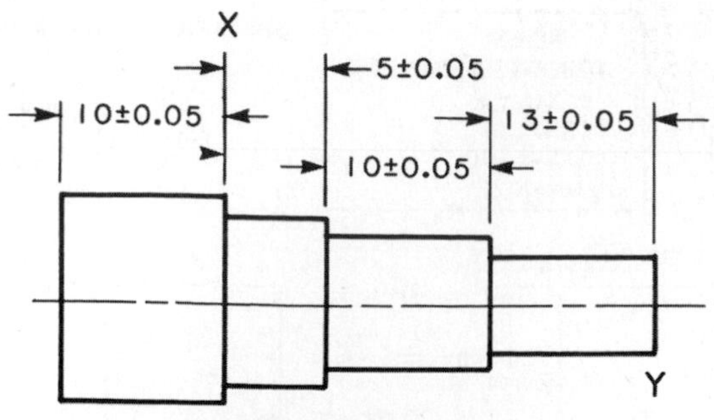

(a) Chain dimensioning—greatest tolerance accumulation between X and Y

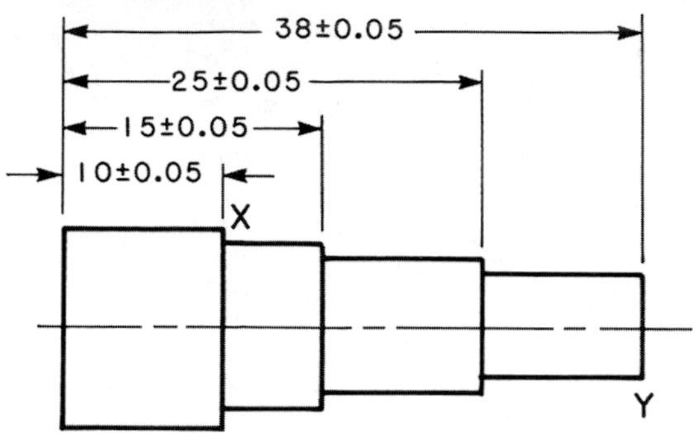

(b) Baseline dimensioning—less tolerance accumulation between X and Y

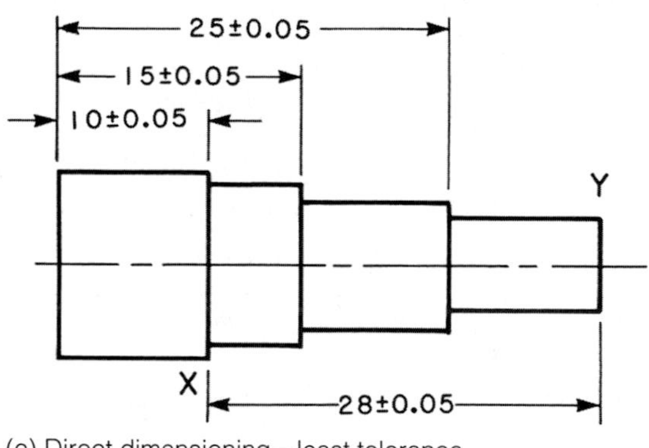

(c) Direct dimensioning—least tolerance between X and Y

FIGURE 16.44 **Tolerance Accumulations**

distances. This method results in the *greatest tolerance accumulation.* In Figure 16.44(a), the tolerance accumulation between surfaces **X** and **Y** is ±.15.

Baseline dimensioning The maximum variation between two features is equal to the sum of the tolerances on the two dimensions from their origin to the features. This reduces the tolerance accumulation. In Figure 16.44(b), the tolerance accumulation between surfaces **X** and **Y** is ±.1.

Direct dimensioning The maximum variation between two features is controlled by the tolerance on the dimension

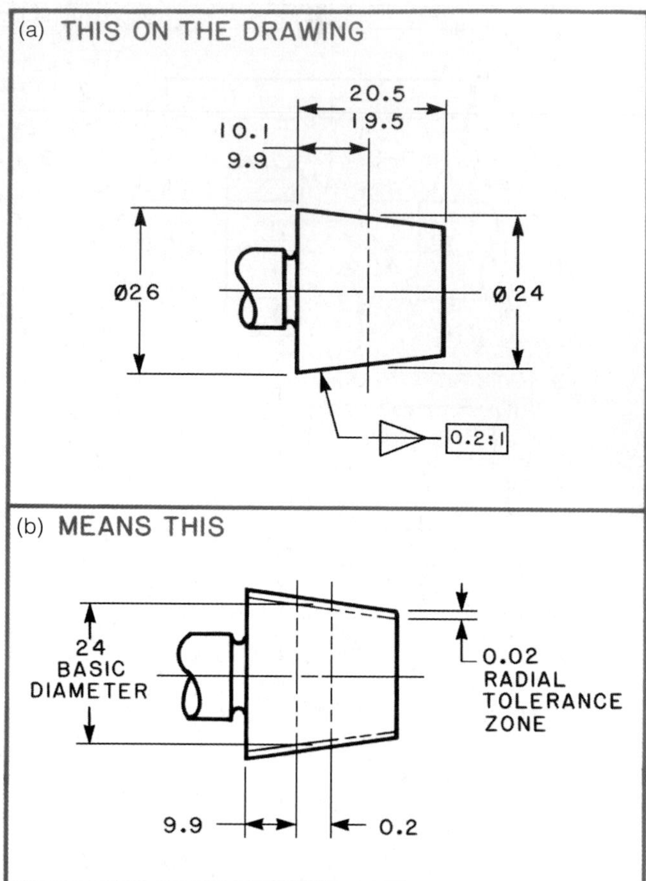

FIGURE 16.45 **Specifying a Basic Taper and a Basic Diameter**

between the features. This results in the *least tolerance.* In Figure 16.44(c), the tolerance between surfaces **X** and **Y** is ±.05.

16.11.6 Tolerances for Flat and Conical Tapers

Taper is defined as the ratio of the difference between the diameters of two sections, perpendicular to the axis of a cone, to the distance between these sections. A **conical taper** is specified by one of the following methods:

- A basic taper and a basic diameter (Fig. 16.45)
- A size tolerance combined with a profile of a surface tolerance applied to the taper
- A toleranced diameter at both ends, or a taper and a toleranced length

A **flat taper** is defined by specifying a toleranced slope and a toleranced height at one end (Fig. 16.46). **Slope** is defined as the inclination of a surface expressed as a ratio of the difference between the heights at each end, above and at right angles to a baseline, to the distance between those heights. Flat and conical tapers are toleranced as shown in Figure 16.47.

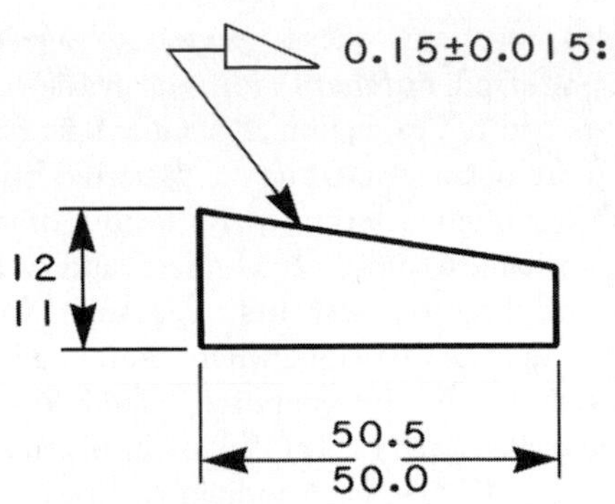

FIGURE 16.46 Slope Designation on a Drawing

16.11.7 Single Limits: Min and Max

The unspecified limit in minimum dimensions (the maximum limit) approaches infinity. Therefore overall lengths are not specified as minimum. The unspecified value in maximum dimensions (the minimum limit) approaches zero.

16.11.8 Reference Dimensions

Reference dimensions, as discussed in Chapter 15, are specified by enclosing the dimension in parentheses, e.g., **(.500)**. No tolerance is given. Reference dimensions are not intended to govern production or inspection; that is, they are informational, not controlling.

16.11.9 Functional Dimensions

Tolerances accumulate (Fig. 16.44). An example of how to control this situation is shown for a firing pin in Figure 16.48. The most important function of the firing pin is to project far enough to detonate the primer, but not far enough to pierce the primer. Also, the point must be fully below the bolt face, in the retracted position, to prevent premature detonation in the cartridge. This function is controlled by dimension **A**, a direct dimension from the point face to the interface with the bolt in the full forward position. Dimension **B** is established similarly. Dimensions that affect function should be dimensioned directly to avoid tolerance accumulation. Conversely, dimension C_1 was replaced by **(C)** during a producibility team review. This dimension must be long enough so that the hammer will drive the pin to its full forward position; but the length is not critical, since the pin has plenty of overtravel. Dimension **(C)**, for ease of manufacture, was taken to the end of the spherical surface that is contacted by the hammer. The tapered section doesn't have to be accurate, but it must be located. This is accomplished by dimension **D**.

16.11.10 Nonmandatory Dimensions

If practical, the finished part is defined without specifying the manufacturing method. For example, the diameter of a hole is given without indicating whether it should be drilled, reamed, punched, or made by any other operation. If manufacturing, processing, verification, or environmental

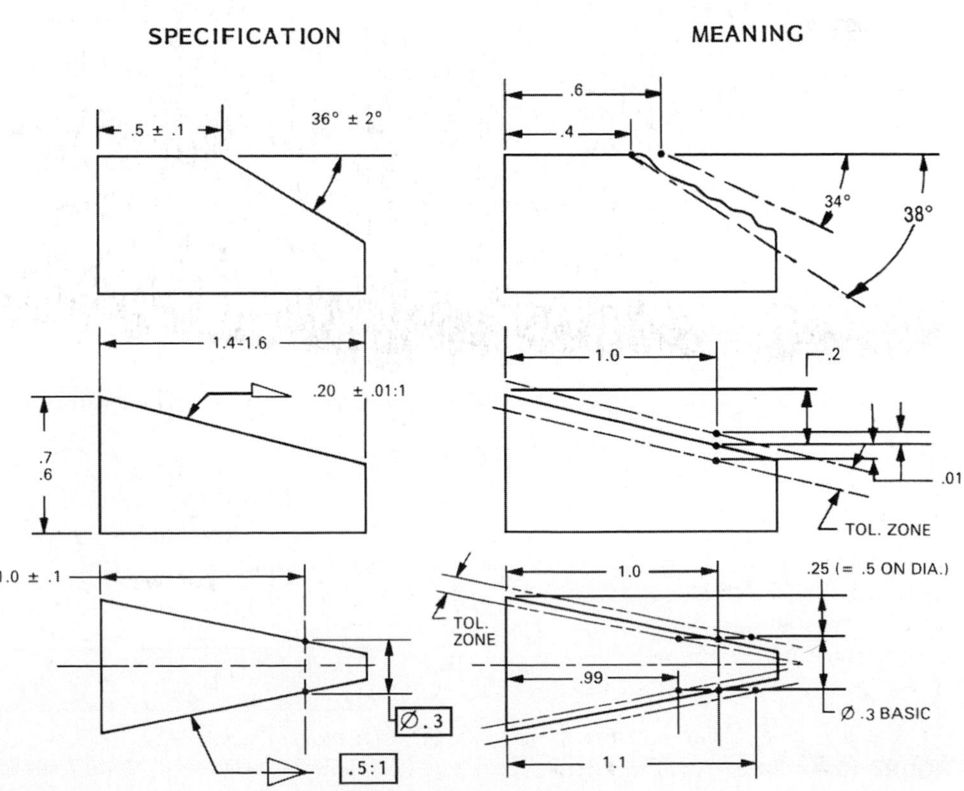

FIGURE 16.47 Flat and Conical Taper Tolerance Zones

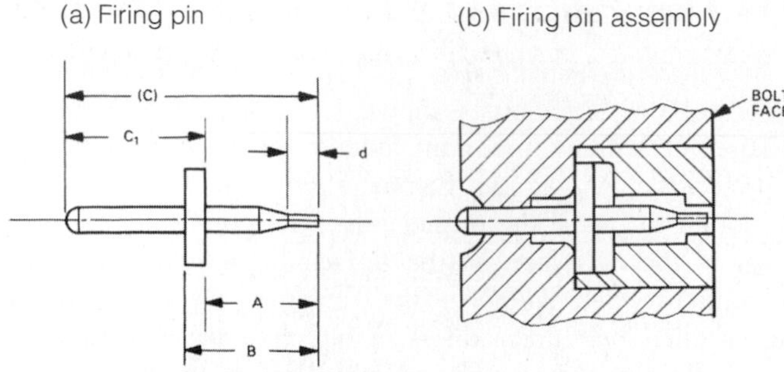

FIGURE 16.48 Functional Dimensioning: Firing Pin Assembly

information is essential to the definition, it is specified on the drawing. The affected dimensions are identified as NONMANDATORY (MFG DATA). This allows improved or superior methods to be used at the discretion of the manufacturing or quality-control departments.

16.11.11 Coordination, Interface Control, and Correlation Dimensions/Tolerances

On large projects or programs, dimensions and tolerances are agreed on by all parties. A coordination drawing has agreement on function, mating, shipping, equipment removal, etc. These dimensions are then "flagged" on the hardware drawings. This protects the design from inadvertent changes. Interface-control and correlation drawings are handled the same way. The only difference is that coordination drawings are prepared for the total system, whereas correlation and interface-control drawings are prepared for major subsystems. Dimensions on these drawings are flagged to be in compliance with the coordination drawings.

16.12 LIMITS AND FITS

Production and inspection benefit from standard limits. ANSI B4.2 and ISO 286 describe these systems. The ISO system has more than 500 possible tolerance zones for holes and shafts; ANSI has about 150. Many products can be standardized via the system of limits and fits: drills, reamers, clevis pins, bushings, keys, keyways, gages, and bolts. **Renard preferred numbers** are used in the metric system with limits and fits to maximize standardization. The tables presented are not restricted to the preferred numbers. Sizes in design are often determined by factors other than cost, such as mechanical and thermal stress, and weight.

There are three types of **fits**: **clearance**, where there is always clearance; **transition**, where there may be clearance or interference; and **interference**, where there is always interference (Fig. 16.49). The Taylor principle is applied to limits and fits; that is, each individual feature is in perfect form at MMC.

Limits and directly applied tolerance values are specified as follows:

Limit dimensioning The high limit (maximum value) is placed above the low limit (minimum value). When expressed in a single line, the low limit precedes the high limit and a dash separates the two values.

Plus-or-minus tolerancing The dimension is given first and is followed by a plus-or-minus expression of tolerance.

16.12.1 Single Limits

For **single limits**, MIN or MAX is placed after a dimension where other elements of the design definitely determine the other unspecified limit (depth of holes, length of threads, corner radii, chamfers, etc.). Single limits are used where the intent is clear and the unspecified limit can be zero or can approach infinity without interfering with the designed function of the part.

16.12.2 Tolerance Expression

The conventions regarding the number of decimal places carried are different for metric and inch drawings. For millimeter dimensions use the following rules.

For **unilateral tolerancing**, when either the plus or the minus value is nil, a single zero is shown without a plus or a minus sign:

Example:

$$32\,^{\;0}_{-.02} \quad \text{or} \quad 32\,^{+.02}_{\;0}$$

With **bilateral tolerancing**, both the plus and the minus

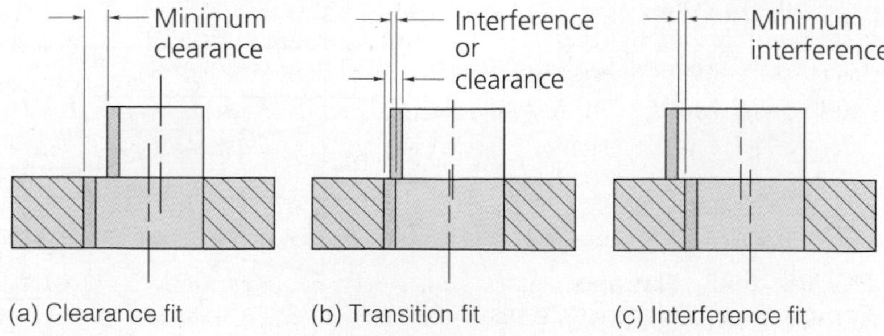

FIGURE 16.49 Basic Types of Fits

values have the same number of decimal places, using zeros where necessary:

Example:

$32 \begin{smallmatrix} +.25 \\ -.10 \end{smallmatrix}$ not $32 \begin{smallmatrix} +.25 \\ -.1 \end{smallmatrix}$

Where **limit dimensioning** is used and either the maximum or minimum value has digits following a decimal point, the other value has zeros:

Example:

$\begin{matrix} 25.45 \\ 25.00 \end{matrix}$ not $\begin{matrix} 25.45 \\ 25 \end{matrix}$

For **inch dimensions,** both limit dimensions, or the plus-or-minus tolerance and its dimension, are expressed with the same number of decimal places:

Examples:

.5 + .005 not .50 + .005

$\begin{matrix} +.005 \\ -.000 \end{matrix}$ not $\begin{matrix} +.005 \\ 0 \end{matrix}$

25.0 + .2 not 25 + .2

16.12.3 Preferred Metric Fits

For metric application of limits and fits, the tolerance may be indicated by a basic size and tolerance symbol. See ANSI B4.2 for complete information on this system. The preferred metric fits are defined as follows:

Loose Running (H11c11) Suitable for wide commercial tolerances or allowances on external members

Free running (H9/d9) Not suitable for use where accuracy is essential, but good for large temperature variations, high running speeds, or heavy journal pressures

Close running (H8/f7) Suitable for running on accurate machines and for accurate location at moderate speeds and journal pressures

Sliding fit (H7/g6) Not intended to run freely, but to move and turn freely and to locate accurately

Locational clearance (H7/h6) Provides snug fit for locating stationary parts, but can be freely assembled and disassembled

Locational transition (H7/k6) Suitable for accurate location; a compromise between clearance and interference

Locational transition (H7/n6) For more accurate location where greater interference is permissible

Locational interference (H7/p6) Suitable for parts requiring rigidity and alignment, with prime accuracy of location but without special bore pressure required

Medium drive (H7/s6) Suitable for ordinary steel parts or for shrink fits on light sections; tightest fit usable with cast iron

Force fit (H7/u6) Suitable for parts that may be highly stressed or for shrink fits where the heavy pressing forces required may be impractical

16.12.4 Preferred Inch Fits

There are three general groups of fits: running and sliding fits, locational fits, and force fits. **Running and sliding fits** provide similar running performance, with a suitable lubrication allowance, throughout the range of sizes. The first ten preferences for inch fits are as follows: RC 4, RC 7, RC 9, LC 2, LC 5, LT3, LT6, LN 2, FN2, and FN4. Running and sliding fits are defined as follows:

RC 1 Close sliding fits are intended for the accurate location of parts that must be assembled without perceptible play.

RC 2 Sliding fits are intended for accurate location, but with greater maximum clearance than class RC 1. Parts made to this fit move and turn easily, but are not intended to run freely; in the larger sizes, they may seize with small temperature changes.

RC 3 Precision running fits are about the closest fits that can be expected to run freely, and they are intended for precision work at slow speeds and light journal pressures, but are not suitable where appreciable temperature differences are likely to be encountered.

RC 4 Close running fits are intended chiefly for running fits on accurate machinery with moderate surface speeds and journal pressures, where accurate location and minimum play are desired.

RC 5 and RC 6 Medium running fits are intended for higher running speeds, or heavy journal pressures, or both.

RC 7 Free running fits are intended for use where accuracy is not essential, or where large temperature variations are likely to be encountered, or under both these conditions.

RC 8 and RC 9 Loose running fits are intended for use where wide commercial tolerances may be necessary, together with an allowance, on the external member.

16.12.5 Locational Fits

Locational fits are intended to determine only the location of the mating parts; they may provide rigid or accurate location, as with interference fits, or provide some freedom of location, as with clearance fits. They are divided into three groups: **clearance fits (LC), transition fits (LT),** and **interference fits (LN).**

LC Locational clearance fits are intended for parts that are usually stationary but that can be freely assembled or disassembled. They range from snug fits for parts requiring accuracy of location, through the medium-clearance fits for parts such as spigots, to the looser fastener fits where freedom of assembly is the prime consideration.

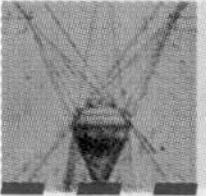

Applying Parametric Design . . .

TOLERANCING AND PARAMETRIC FEATURES

The manufacturing of parts and assemblies requires a degree of precision determined by **tolerances.** A typical parametric design system supports three types of tolerances:

- **Dimensional** tolerancing specifies allowable variation of size (see Fig. A)
- **Geometric** tolerancing controls form, profile, orientation, and runout
- **Surface finish** tolerancing controls the deviation of a part surface from its normal value

When you design a part, you specify dimensional tolerance—**allowable variations in size.** All dimensions are controlled by tolerances. The exception applies only to "**basic**" dimensions, which for the purpose of reference are considered to be exact (see Fig. B). The radius value in this example was changed from a "limits" format to "basic." You may also modify the upper or lower tolerance value (see Fig. C). **Dimensional tolerances** on a drawing can be expressed in two forms:

- As **general tolerances**—presented in a tolerance table. These apply to those dimensions that are displayed in nominal format, that is, without tolerances.
- As **individual tolerances**—specified for individual dimensions.

You can use general tolerances given as defaults in a table or set individual tolerances by modifying default values of selected dimensions. Default tolerance values are used at the moment you start to create a model (see Fig. D); therefore, default tolerances must be set prior to creating geometry. The system recognizes six decimal places for which you can specify the tolerance values. When you start to create a part (see Fig. E), the table at the bottom of the window will display the current defaults for tolerances (Fig. F). If you have not specified tolerances, the system defaults are assumed, and the

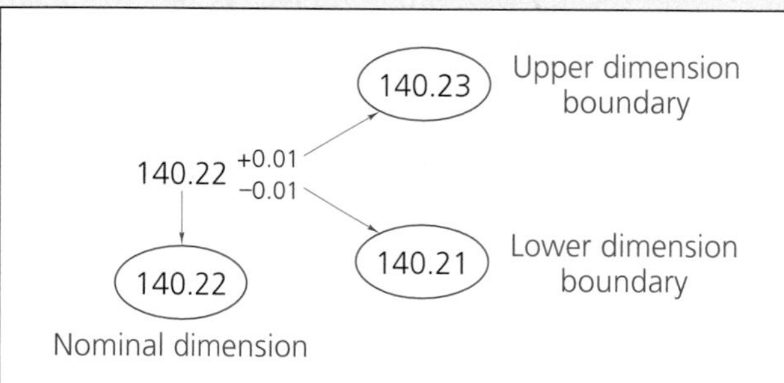

FIGURE A Dimensional Tolerance

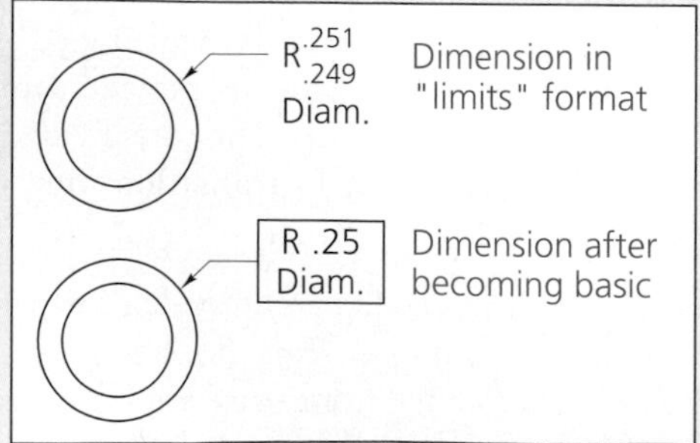

FIGURE B Limits Dimension and Basic Dimension

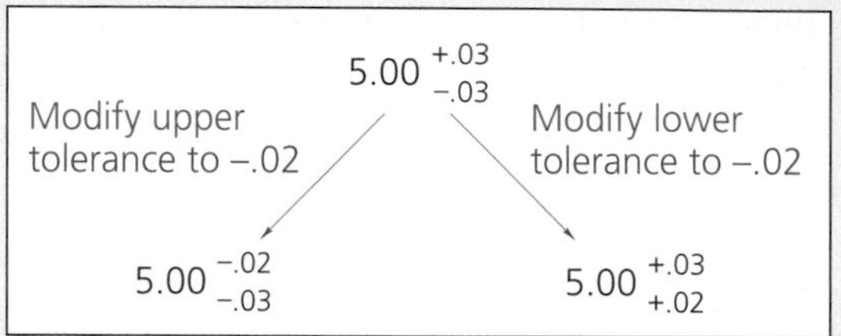

FIGURE C Modifying Upper and Lower Tolerance Values

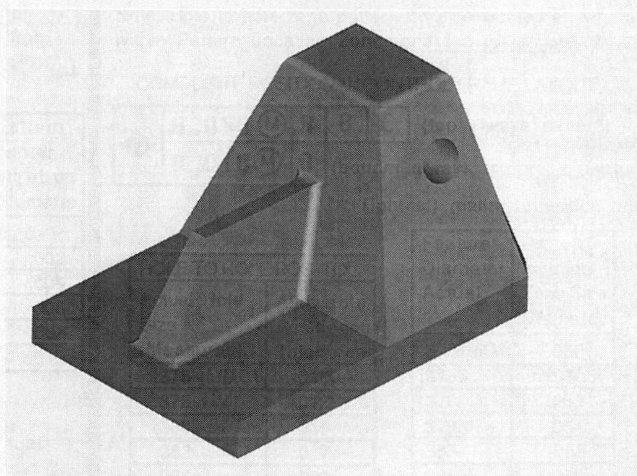

FIGURE D Shaded Model of Part

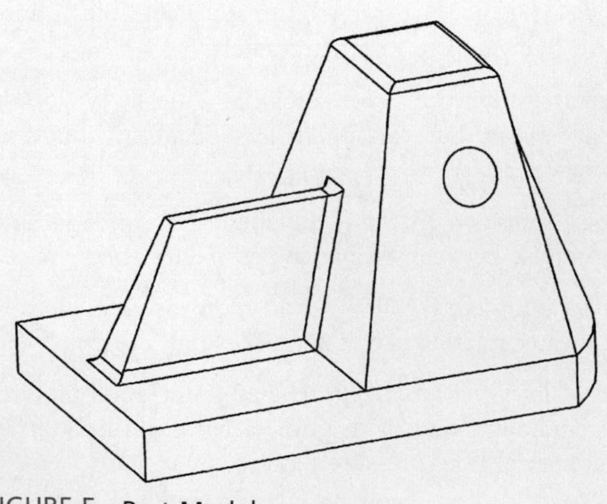

FIGURE E Part Model

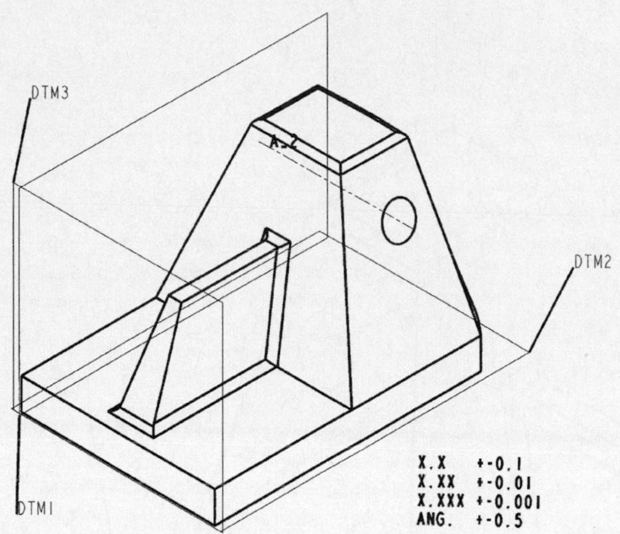

FIGURE F Part with Default Tolerances Displayed

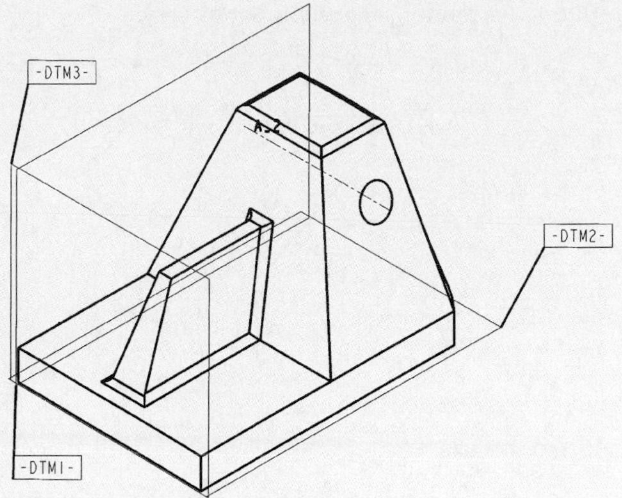

FIGURE G Tolerances Not Displayed; Datums Set as Basic

table will look as follows:

*X.X	±0.1
*X.XX	±0.01
*X.XXX	±0.001
*ANG.	±0.5

You have a choice of displaying or blanking tolerances. Even if tolerances are not displayed, the system still stores dimensions with their default tolerances. You can specify geometric tolerances, create "basic" dimensions, and set selected datums as reference datums for geometric tolerancing (Fig. G). Figure H provides an example of the part dimensions in the limits format, and Figure I shows the same dimensions as basic.

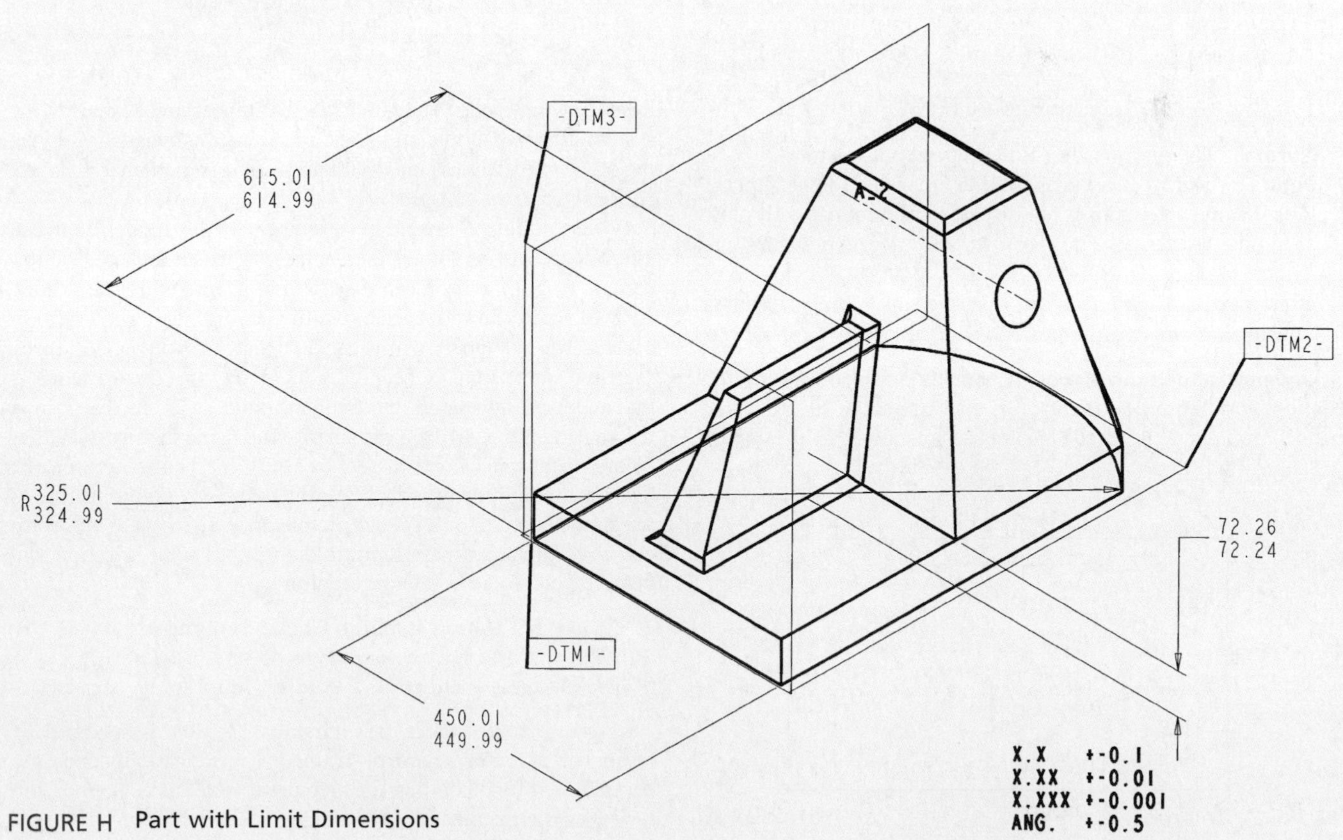

FIGURE H Part with Limit Dimensions

FIGURE I Part with Dimensions Set as Basic

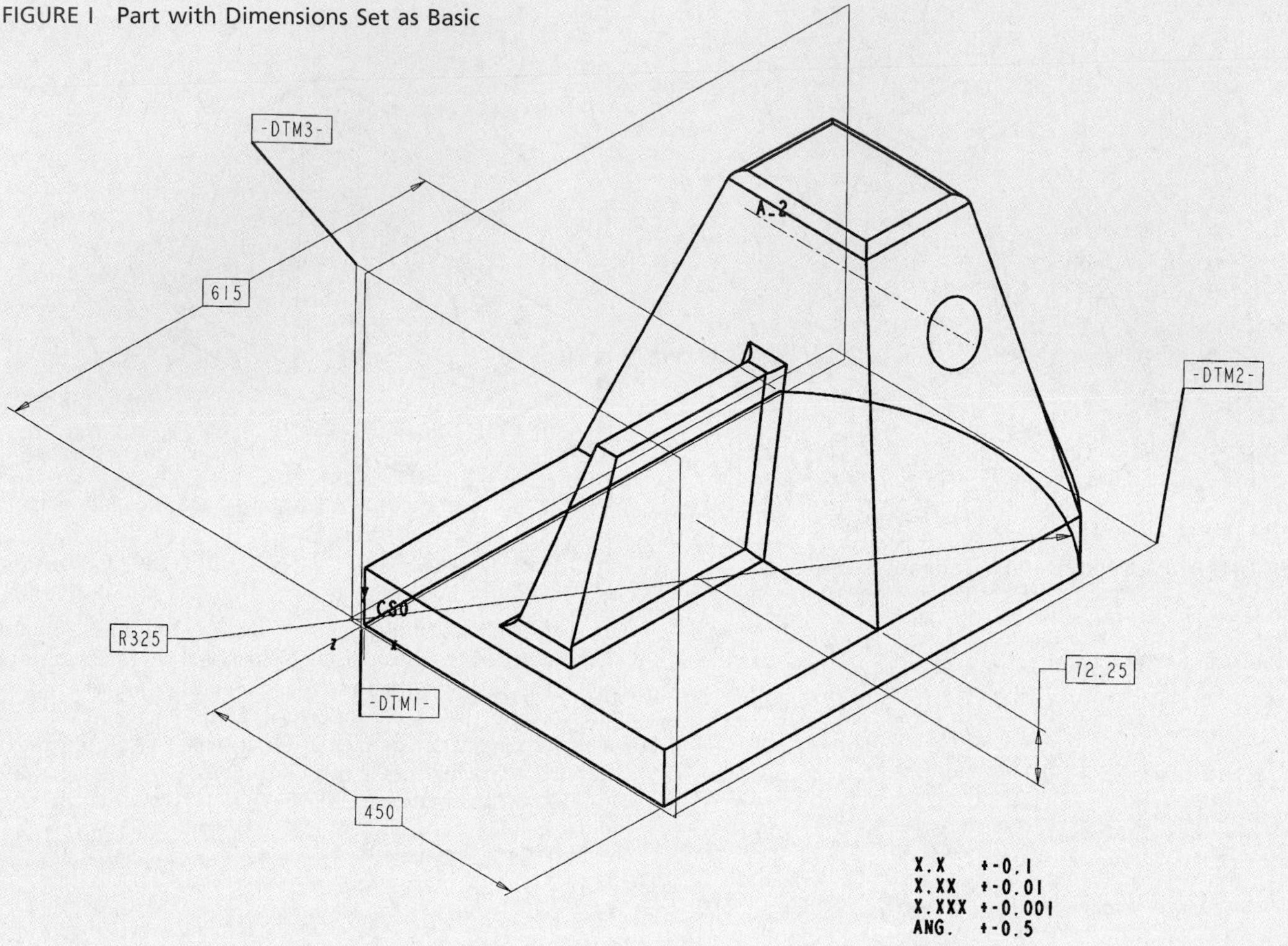

The available tolerance formats are (Fig. J):

- **Normal** Dimensions are displayed without tolerances.
- **Limits** Tolerances are displayed as upper and lower limits.
- **Plus–Minus** Tolerances are displayed as nominal with plus-or-minus tolerance. The positive and negative values are independent.
- **±Symmetric** Tolerances are displayed as nominal, with a single value for both the positive and the negative tolerances.

Geometric tolerances provide a method for controlling the location, form, profile, orientation, and runout of features (see Fig. K). You are able to add geometric tolerances to the model

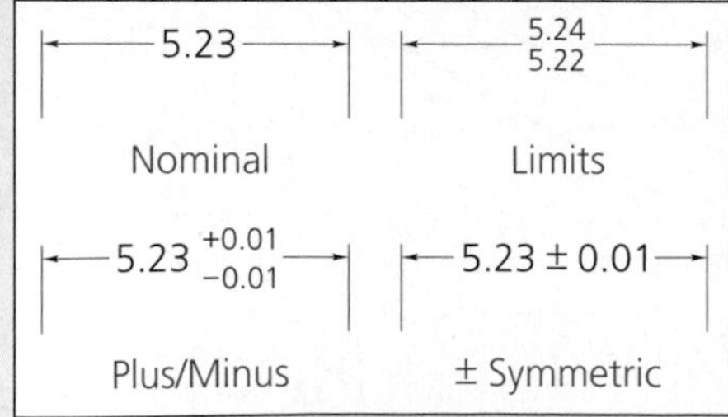

FIGURE J Tolerance Formats

from drawing mode. The geometric tolerances are treated by the system as annotations, and they are always associated with the model. *Unlike dimensional tolerances, geometric tolerances do not have any effect on part geometry.*

When adding a geometric tolerance to the model, you can attach it to existing dimensions, edges, or existing geometric tolerances (Fig. L), or you can display it as a note without a leader.

Before you can reference a datum (see Figs. D–L sequence) in a geometric tolerance, you must first indicate your attention by "**setting**" the datum. Once a datum is set, the datum name is prefixed and appended by hyphens, and it is enclosed in a rectangle (see Fig. G). You can change the name of a datum either before or after it has been "set" by using the **Name** item on the SET UP menu in Part mode. You can choose any datum feature as a reference datum for a geometric tolerance; the system will warn you if you pick an inappropriate datum, but your selection will be accepted. To set a reference datum:

1. Choose **Set Datum** from the GEOM TOL menu.
2. Select the datum plane or axis to be set.
3. The datum is enclosed in a feature control frame (Fig. M).

A geometric tolerance for individual features is specified by means of a **feature control frame** (a rectangle) divided into compartments containing the geometric tolerance symbol followed by the tolerance value (see Fig. M). Where applicable, the

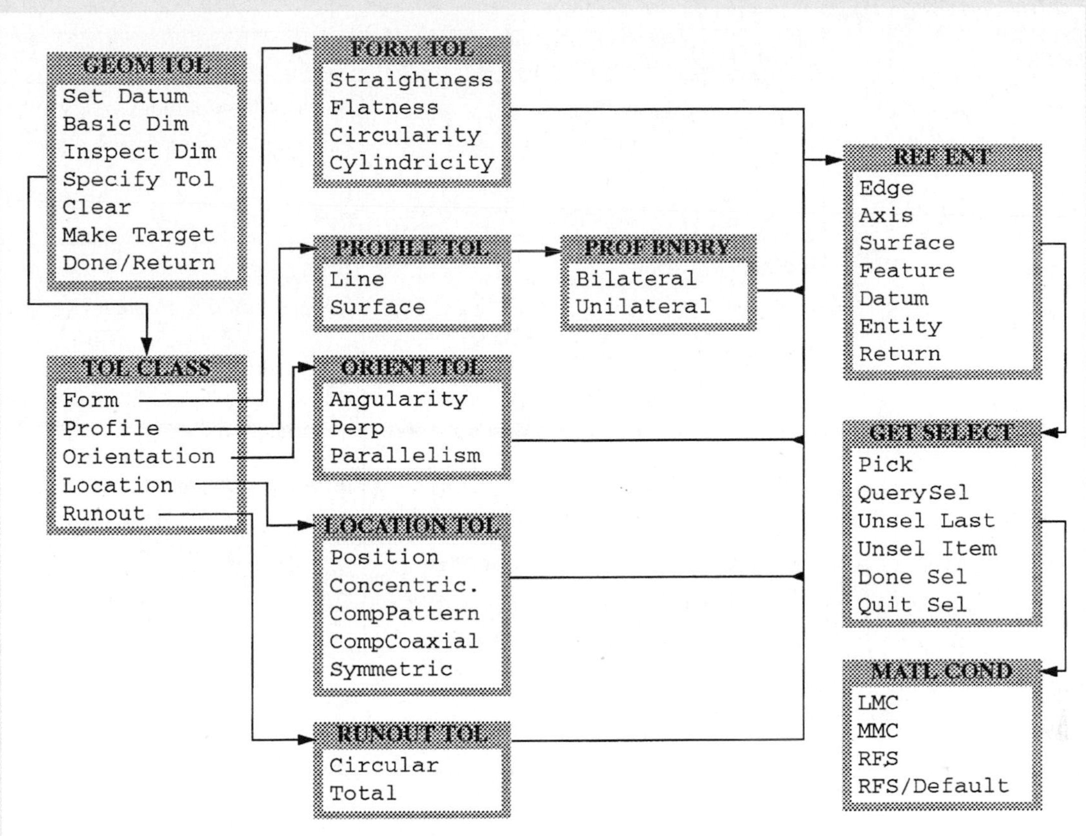

FIGURE K Geometric Tolerancing Menu

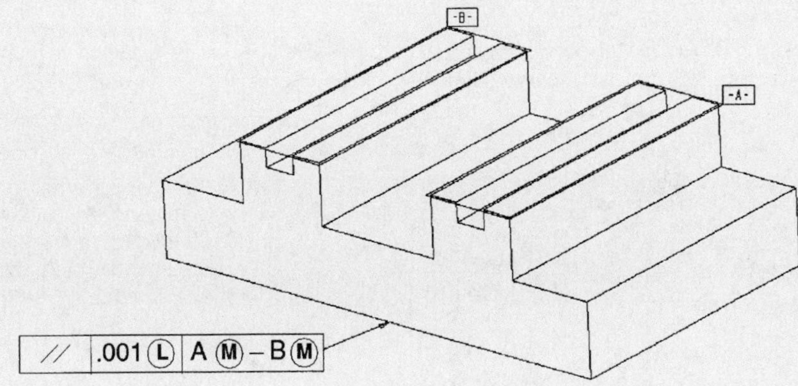

FIGURE L Displaying Geometric Tolerance with a Leader

tolerance is followed by a **material condition symbol.**

Where a geometric tolerance is related to a datum, the reference datum name is placed in a compartment following the tolerance value. Where applicable, the datum reference letter is followed by a material condition symbol.

For each class of tolerance, the types of tolerances available and the appropriate types of entities can be referenced (see Fig. N). The available material condition symbols are also shown in Figure N.

The system guides you in building a geometric tolerance by requesting each piece of information. You respond by making menu choices, entering a tolerance value, and selecting entities and datums (see Fig. O). As the tolerance is built, the choices are limited to those items that make sense in the context of the information you have already provided. For example, if the

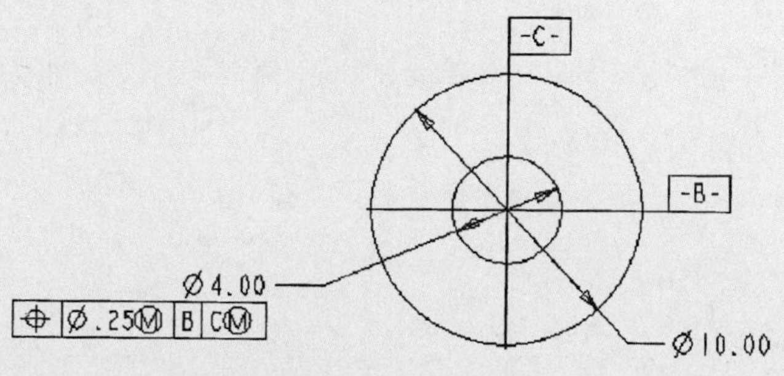

FIGURE M Feature Control Frame

FIGURE N Class, Type, Symbol, and Material Condition

Class	Type	Symbols	Entities
Form	Straightness	—	Surface of revolution, axis, straight edge
	Flatness	▱	Plane surface (not datum plane)
	Circularity	○	Cylinder, cone, sphere
	Cylindricity	⌭	Cylindrical surface
Profile	Line	⌒	Edge
	Surface	⌓	Surface (not datum plane)
Orientation	Angularity	∠	Plane, surface, axis
	Parallelism	//	Cylindrical surface, axis, planar surface
	Perpendicularity	⊥	Cylindrical surface, axis, planar surface
Runout	Circular	↗	Cone, cylinder, sphere, plane
	Total	⌰	Cone, cylinder, sphere, plane
Location	Position	⌖	Any
	Concentricity	◎	Axis, surface of revolution
	Symmetry	⌯	Any

LMC	Ⓛ	Least material condition
MMC	Ⓜ	Maximum material condition

geometric characteristic is one that does not require a datum reference, you will not be prompted for one. Other checks are made to help prevent mistakes in the selection of entities and datums.

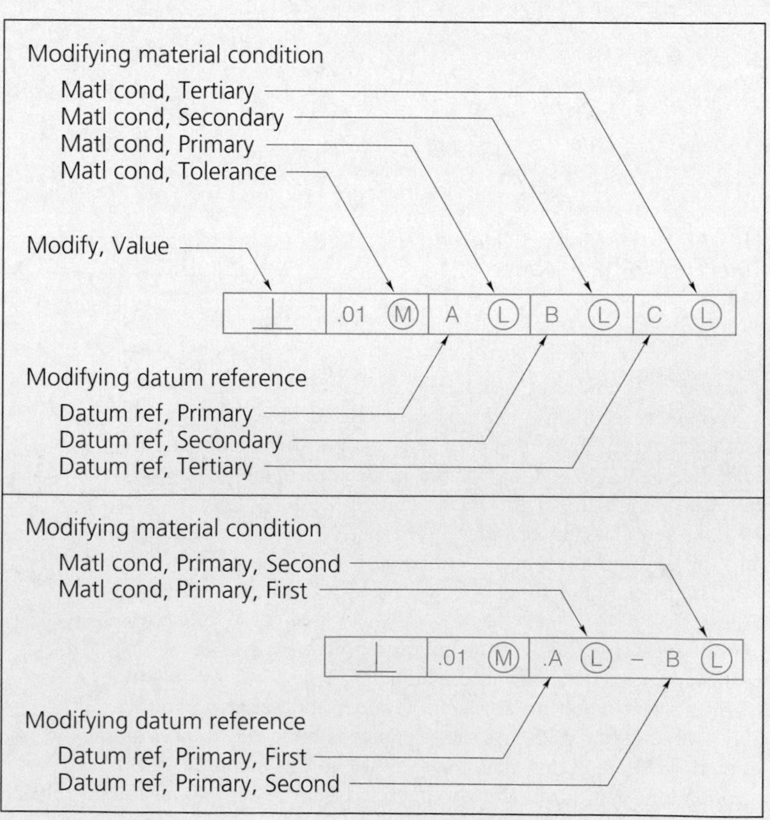

FIGURE O Building a Geometric Tolerance

LT Locational transition fits are a compromise between clearance and interference fits, for applications where accuracy of location is important but either a small amount of clearance or interference is permissible.

LN Locational interference fits are used where accuracy of location is of prime importance and for parts requiring rigidity and alignment with no special requirements for bore pressure. Such fits are not intended for parts designed to transmit frictional loads (these are covered by force fits).

16.12.6 Force or Shrink Fits

Force or **shrink fits** are a special type of interference fit, normally characterized by maintenance of constant bore pressures throughout the range of sizes. The interference varies almost directly with diameter, and the difference between its minimum and maximum values is small, to maintain the resulting pressures within reasonable limits.

FN 1 Light drive fits are those requiring light assembly pressures, and they produce more or less permanent assemblies. They are suitable for thin sections or long fits, or in cast-iron external members.

FN 2 Medium drive fits are suitable for ordinary steel parts or for shrink fits on light sections. They are the tightest fits that can be used with high-grade cast-iron external members.

FN 3 Heavy drive fits are suitable for heavier steel parts or for shrink fits in medium sections.

FN 4 and FN 5 Force fits are suitable for parts that can be highly stressed or for shrink fits where the heavy pressing forces required are impractical.

16.12.7 Preferred Tolerance Zones

A profile tolerance may be applied to an entire surface or to individual profiles taken at various cross sections through the part. **Preferred tolerance zones** are shown in Figure 16.50.

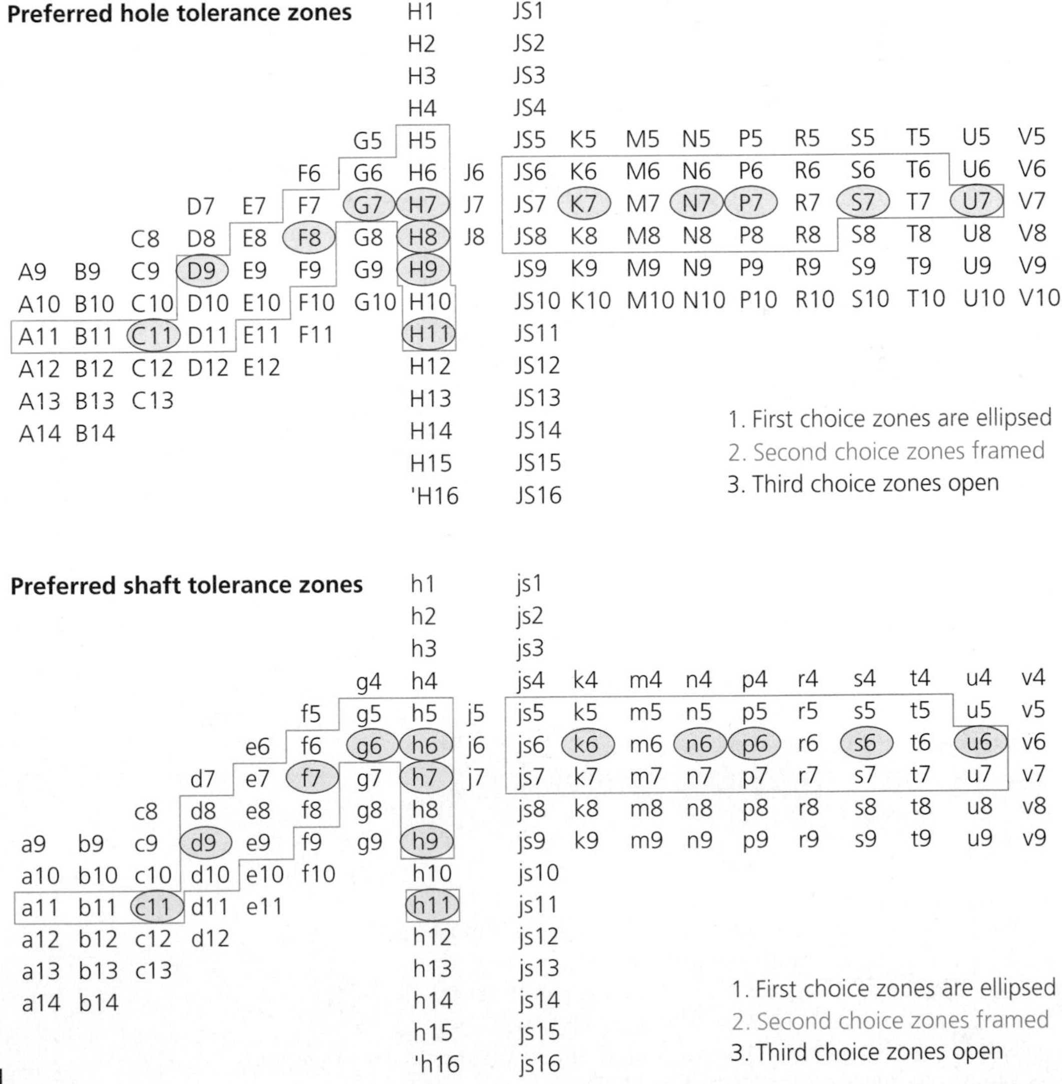

FIGURE 16.50 Preferred (Standardized) Tolerance Zones

A **positional tolerance** defines a zone within which the center, axis, or center plane of a feature of size is permitted to vary from true position. Basic dimensions establish the true position from specified datum features and between interrelated features. A positional tolerance is indicated by the position symbol, a tolerance, and appropriate datum references placed in a feature control frame.

16.12.8 Metric Preferred Sizes

Metric **preferred sizes** are based on the Renard series of preferred numbers. The first choice is rounded from the R10 series, where succeeding numbers each increase by 25%. The second choice is rounded from the R20 series, which has 12% increments. The rationale for first-choice sizes is the selection of every second number in the series, such as 1, 1.6, 2.5. This series is rounded from the R5 series of preferred numbers, in which the increments are 60%. Preferred sizes from 1 to 300 are given in metric (Table 16.2) and .01 to 20.00 in inches (Table 16.3). The **hole basis system** is the preferred system for selecting standard tools and gages.

16.12.9 Standardized Tolerances

Standardized **metric tolerances** are given in Table 16.4. International tolerance (IT) grade values are used. The basis for these is the tolerance unit *i*, which is defined as follows:

$$i = .45\sqrt[3]{D} + 0.001D$$

where D = the nominal dimension in millimeters.

Standardized **inch tolerances** are given in Table 16.5. The equivalents to IT values are based on the following formula (in inches):

$$i = .052\sqrt[3]{D} + .001D$$

where D = the nominal dimension in inches.

IT grades for manufacturing processes are shown in Figure 16.51. Production costs may be reduced by limiting dimensions or grades to those for which gaging equipment is available. This allows production personnel to apply "Go" (MMC) and "Not Go" (LMC) gages to the inspection of small parts.

16.13 CALCULATING LIMITS AND FITS

Metric tolerancing makes extensive use of limits and fits and symbology. In the United States, the symbology is supplemented by the limits, or the limits are specified and the symbology referenced on drawings, to prevent misinterpretation. Tables 16.6 and 16.7 are, respectively, metric and inch shaft position tables. These are used in conjunction with Tables 16.4 and 16.5 to calculate limits.

TABLE 16.2 Preferred Metric Basic Sizes (B.S.4318)

Choice			Choice			Choice		
1st	*2nd*	*3rd*	*1st*	*2nd*	*3rd*	*1st*	*2nd*	*3rd*
1					23			122
	1.1				24	125		
1.2			25					128
		1.3			26	130		
	1.4			28				132
		1.5	30				135	
1.6				32				138
		1.7			34	140		
	1.8		35					142
		1.9			36		145	
2				38				148
		2.1	40			150		
	2.2			42				152
		2.4			44		155	
2.5			45					158
		2.6			46	160		
	2.8			48				162
3			50				165	
		3.2		52				168
	3.5				54	170		
		3.8	55				175	
4					56			178
		4.2		58		180		
	4.5		60					182
		4.8		62			185	
5					64			188
		5.2	65			190		
	5.5				66			192
		5.8		68			195	
6			70					198
		6.2		72		200		
	6.5			74				205
		6.8	75				210	
	7				76			215
		7.5		78		220		
8			80					225
		8.5			82		230	
	9			85				235
		9.5			88	240		
10			90					245
	11				92		250	
12				95				255
		13			98	260		
	14		100					265
		15			102		270	
16				105				275
		17	110					285
	18				108		290	
		19			112			295
20				115		300		
		21			118			
	22		120					

TABLE 16.3 Preferred Basic Sizes in Inches

Decimal			**Fractional**					
0.010	2.00	8.50	$\frac{1}{64}$	0.015625	$2\frac{1}{4}$	2.2500	$9\frac{1}{2}$	9.5000
0.012	2.20	9.00	$\frac{1}{32}$	0.03125	$2\frac{1}{2}$	2.5000	10	10.0000
0.016	2.40	9.50	$\frac{1}{16}$	0.0625	$2\frac{3}{4}$	2.7500	$10\frac{1}{2}$	10.5000
0.020	2.60	10.00	$\frac{3}{32}$	0.09375	3	3.0000	11	11.0000
0.025	2.80	10.50	$\frac{1}{8}$	0.1250	$3\frac{1}{4}$	3.2500	$11\frac{1}{2}$	11.5000
0.032	3.00	11.00	$\frac{5}{32}$	0.15625	$3\frac{1}{2}$	3.5000	12	12.0000
0.040	3.20	11.50	$\frac{3}{16}$	0.1875	$3\frac{3}{4}$	3.7500	$12\frac{1}{2}$	12.5000
0.05	3.40	12.00	$\frac{1}{4}$	0.2500	4	4.0000	13	13.0000
0.06	3.60	12.50	$\frac{5}{16}$	0.3125	$4\frac{1}{4}$	4.2500	$13\frac{1}{2}$	13.5000
0.08	3.80	13.00	$\frac{3}{8}$	0.3750	$4\frac{1}{2}$	4.5000	14	14.0000
0.10	4.00	13.50	$\frac{7}{16}$	0.4375	$4\frac{3}{4}$	4.7500	$14\frac{1}{2}$	14.5000
0.12	4.20	14.00	$\frac{1}{2}$	0.5000	5	5.0000	15	15.0000
0.16	4.40	14.50	$\frac{9}{16}$	0.5625	$5\frac{1}{4}$	5.2500	$15\frac{1}{2}$	15.5000
0.20	4.60	15.00	$\frac{5}{8}$	0.6250	$5\frac{1}{2}$	5.5000	16	16.0000
0.24	4.80	15.50	$\frac{11}{16}$	0.6875	$5\frac{3}{4}$	5.7500	$16\frac{1}{2}$	16.5000
0.30	5.00	16.00	$\frac{3}{4}$	0.7500	6	6.0000	17	17.0000
0.40	5.20	16.50	$\frac{7}{8}$	0.8750	$6\frac{1}{2}$	6.5000	$17\frac{1}{2}$	17.5000
0.50	5.40	17.00	1	1.0000	7	7.0000	18	18.0000
0.60	5.60	17.50	$1\frac{1}{4}$	1.2500	$7\frac{1}{2}$	7.5000	$18\frac{1}{2}$	18.5000
0.80	5.80	18.00	$1\frac{1}{2}$	1.5000	8	8.0000	19	19.0000
1.00	6.00	18.50	$1\frac{3}{4}$	1.7500	$8\frac{1}{2}$	8.5000	$19\frac{1}{2}$	19.5000
1.20	6.50	19.00	2	2.000	9	9.0000	20	20.0000
1.40	7.00	19.50	—	—	—	—	—	—
1.60	7.50	20.00						
1.80	8.00	—						

All dimensions are given in inches.

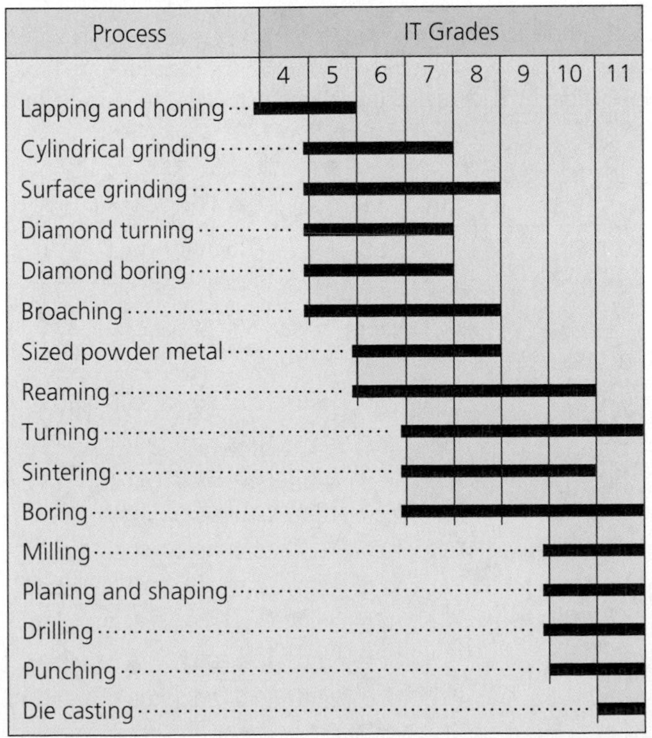

FIGURE 16.51 IT Grades for Manufacturing Processes

16.13.1 Calculating Metric Hole Limits

The hole basis system places the low limit of a hole at exactly the basic or design size. The high limit is calculated by adding to it the IT value (Table 16.4). For example:

$\varnothing$ 80 H7 = 80 + 0.03, − 0

(.03 is from Table 16.4.)

16.13.2 Calculating Inch Hole Limits

The low limit of the hole is at the basic or design size. The high limit is calculated by adding to it the IT value (Table 16.5). For example:

$\varnothing$ 3.1500 H7 = 3.1500 + 0.0012, − .0000

(.0012 is from Table 16.6.)

TABLE 16.4 Metric Table—Standard Tolerances

Nominal[1] Size		IT Tolerance Grade												IT = ISO Series of Tolerances					
Over (mm)	**Up to and includ-ing (mm)**	**IT01**	**IT0**	**IT1**	**IT2**	**IT3**	**IT4**	**IT5**	**IT6[3]**	**IT7**	**IT8**	**IT9**	**IT10**	**IT11**	**IT12**	**IT13**	**IT14[2]**	**IT15[2]**	**IT16[2]**
—	3	0·3	0·5	0·8	1·2	2	3	4	6	10	14	25	40	60	100	140	250	400	600
3	6	0·4	0·6	1	1·5	2·5	4	5	8	12	18	30	48	75	120	180	300	480	750
6	10	0·4	0·6	1	1·5	2·5	4	6	9	15	22	36	58	90	150	220	360	580	900
10	18	0·5	0·8	1·2	2	3	5	8	11	18	27	43	70	110	180	270	430	700	1100
18	30	0·6	1	1·5	2·5	4	6	9	13	21	33	52	84	130	210	330	520	840	1300
30	50	0·6	1	1·5	2·5	4	7	11	16	25	39	62	100	160	250	390	620	1000	1600
50	80	0·8	1·2	2	3	5	8	13	19	30	46	74	120	190	300	460	740	1200	1900
80	120	1	1·5	2·5	4	6	10	15	22	35	54	87	140	220	350	540	870	1400	2200
120	180	1·2	2	3·5	5	8	12	18	25	40	63	100	160	250	400	630	1000	1600	2500
180	250	2	3	4·5	7	10	14	20	29	46	72	115	185	290	460	720	1150	1850	2900
250	315	2·5	4	6	8	12	16	23	32	52	81	130	210	320	520	810	1300	2100	3200
315	400	3	5	7	9	13	18	25	36	57	89	140	230	360	570	890	1400	2300	3600
400	500	4	6	8	10	15	20	27	40	63	97	155	250	400	630	970	1550	2500	4000
500	630	—	—	—	—	—	—	—	44	70	110	175	280	440	700	1100	1750	2800	4400
630	800	—	—	—	—	—	—	—	50	80	125	200	320	500	800	1250	2000	3200	5000
800	1000	—	—	—	—	—	—	—	56	90	140	230	360	560	900	1400	2300	3600	5600
1000	1250	—	—	—	—	—	—	—	66	105	165	260	420	660	1050	1650	2600	4200	6600
1250	1600	—	—	—	—	—	—	—	78	125	195	310	500	780	1250	1950	3100	5000	7800
1600	2000	—	—	—	—	—	—	—	92	150	230	370	600	920	1500	2300	3700	6000	9200
2000	2500	—	—	—	—	—	—	—	110	175	280	440	700	1100	1750	2800	4400	7000	11000
2500	3150	—	—	—	—	—	—	—	135	210	330	540	860	1350	2100	3300	5400	8600	13500

Tolerance unit 0.001 mm
[1]Standard tolerance in microns (1μ = 0.001 mm)
[2]Not applicable to sizes below 1 mm
Not recommended for fits in sizes above 500 mm
ISO tolerance grade 6 in abbreviated form is IT6

16.13.3 Calculating Metric Shaft Limits

With a hole basis system, unless the shaft is at position *h* (see figure at the bottom right of Table 16.6), the value in Table 16.6 must be added algebraically to calculate the upper limit

TABLE 16.5 Inch Values—Standard Tolerances

IT Grade	01	0	1	2	3	4	5	6	7	8	9	10	11	12	13	14*	15*	16*
≤ 0.12	0.012	0.02	0.03	0.05	0.08	0.12	0.15	0.25	0.4	0.6	1.0	1.6	2.5	4.0	6.0	10.0	16.0	25.0
> 0.12 to 0.24	0.015	0.025	0.04	0.06	0.10	0.15	0.2	0.3	0.5	0.7	1.2	1.8	3.0	5.0	7.0	12.0	18.0	30.0
> 0.24 to 0.40	0.015	0.025	0.04	0.06	0.10	0.15	0.25	0.4	0.6	0.9	1.4	2.2	3.5	6.0	9.0	14.0	22.0	35.0
> 0.40 to 0.71	0.02	0.03	0.05	0.08	0.12	0.2	0.3	0.4	0.7	1.0	1.6	2.8	4.0	7.0	10.0	16.0	28.0	40.0
> 0.71 to 1.19	0.025	0.04	0.06	0.10	0.15	0.25	0.4	0.5	0.8	1.2	2.0	3.5	5.0	8.0	12.0	20.0	35.0	50.0
> 1.19 to 1.97	0.025	0.04	0.06	0.10	0.15	0.3	0.4	0.6	1.0	1.6	2.5	4.0	6.0	10.0	16.0	25.0	40.0	60.0
> 1.97 to 3.15	0.03	0.05	0.08	0.12	0.2	0.3	0.5	0.7	1.2	1.8	3.0	4.5	7.0	12.0	18.0	30.0	45.0	70.0
> 3.15 to 4.73	0.04	0.06	0.1	0.15	0.25	0.4	0.6	0.9	1.4	2.2	3.5	5.0	9.0	14.0	22.0	35.0	50.0	90.0
> 4.73 to 7.09	0.05	0.08	0.12	0.2	0.3	0.5	0.7	1.0	1.6	2.5	4.0	6.0	10.0	16.0	25.0	40.0	60.0	100.0
> 7.09 to 9.85	0.08	0.12	0.2	0.3	0.4	0.6	0.8	1.2	1.8	2.8	4.5	7.0	12.0	18.0	28.0	45.0	70.0	120.0
> 9.85 to 12.41	0.10	0.15	0.25	0.3	0.5	0.6	0.9	1.2	2.0	3.0	5.0	8.0	12.0	20.0	30.0	50.0	80.0	120.0
> 12.41 to 15.75	0.12	0.2	0.3	0.4	0.5	0.7	1.0	1.4	2.2	3.5	6.0	9.0	14.0	22.0	35.0	60.0	90.0	140.0
> 15.75 to 19.69	0.15	0.25	0.3	0.4	0.6	0.8	1.0	1.6	2.5	4.0	6.0	10.0	16.0	25.0	40.0	60.0	100.0	160.0

Table shows standard tolerances in 0.001 inches for diameter steps in inches.
*Up to .04 in., grades 14 to 16 are not provided.

TABLE 16.6 Metric Tolerance Zone Position—Standard Fits

METRIC-TOLERANCE ZONE POSITION TABLE-SHAFT UPPER LIMITS FROM ZERO LINE (BASIC SIZE) SEE GRAPHIC AT LOWER RIGHT.

Loose, free & close running, sliding, locational, drive, and force fits

Over-To	c11	d9	f7	g6	h6	k6	n6	p6	s6	u6
≤3	−60	−20	−6	−2	0	6	10	12	20	24
3 to 6	−70	−30	−10	−4	0	9	16	20	27	31
6 to 10	−80	−40	−13	−5	0	10	19	24	32	37
10 to 14	−95	−50	−16	−6	0	12	23	29	39	44
14 to 18	−95	−50	−16	−6	0	12	23	29	39	44
18 to 24	−110	−65	−20	−7	0	15	28	35	48	54
24 to 30	−110	−65	−20	−7	0	15	28	35	48	61
30 to 40	−120	−80	−25	−9	0	18	33	42	59	76
40 to 50	−130	−80	−25	−9	0	18	33	42	59	86
50 to 65	−140	−100	−30	−10	0	21	39	51	72	106
65 to 80	−150	−100	−30	−10	0	21	39	51	78	121
80 to 100	−170	−120	−36	−12	0	25	45	59	93	146
100 to 120	−180	−120	−36	−12	0	25	45	59	101	166
120 to 140	−200	−145	−43	−14	0	28	52	68	117	195
140 to 160	−210	−145	−43	−14	0	28	52	68	125	215
160 to 180	−230	−145	−43	−14	0	28	52	68	133	235
180 to 200	−240	−170	−50	−15	0	33	60	79	151	265
200 to 225	−260	−170	−50	−15	0	33	60	79	159	287
225 to 250	−280	−170	−50	−15	0	33	60	79	169	313
250 to 280	−300	−190	−56	−17	0	36	66	88	190	347

1. Basic hole system (unilateral hole basis) employed (table covers shafts).
2. Values are in thousandths of a millimeter (microns); sizes in mm.
3. Values represent the upper limit (relative to the zero line) of shafts.
4. The selected fits indicated are recommended in ANSI B4.1.
These are somewhat similar to those in (UK standard) BS 4500.
5. Add value from table algebraically to basic size for upper shaft limit.

Note:
- Uppercase letters represent holes/bores. (e.g., H7).
- Lowercase letters represent shafts (e.g., f6).
- The letter (location symbol) represents the position/distance to the "zero line"/Basic size.
- H and h are on the zero line.
- The number (quality no.) represents the tolerance grade. Higher nos. yield coarser fits.

* See tolerance grade (IT) table for limits not shown in these tables.
* Add IT to hole for max limit (Basic size is min hole)
* Subtract IT from shaft limit calc. from table for min.

METHODS OF INDICATING
1. Ø30 f7
2. Ø29.980 +.000, 2.021 (Ø30 f7)
3. Ø29.959–29.980 (Ø30 f7)

INDICATING FITS
1. Ø.30 H8/f7 (hole first)
2. Ø30 H8 (30.000−30.033)
f7 (29.959−29.980)

Clearance Fits		
FIT	HOLE	SHAFT
loose	H11	c11
free	H9	d9
close	H8	f7
sliding	H7	g6
locational	H7	h6

Transition Fits		
FIT	HOLE	SHAFT
locational	H7	k6
locational	H7	n6

Interference Fits		
FIT	HOLE	SHAFT
locational	H7	p6
med. drive	H7	s6
force	H7	u6

USING THE TABLE ABOVE
Ø30 f7 (Shaft)

zero line 30.00

Basic size "−20 (.02) from above" table to get upper limit

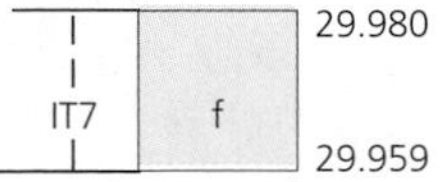

29.980
IT7 f
29.959

IT7 (other table) = .021

30.000 2 .020 5 29.980
29.980 2 .021 5 29.959

•BASIC size is min. hole size.
•Add IT(X) from table for max. hole. Upper limit from table

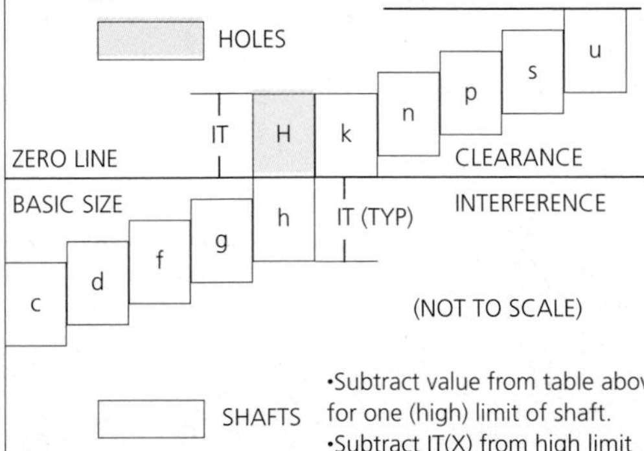

HOLES
u s p n k H IT
ZERO LINE
CLEARANCE
BASIC SIZE
h IT (TYP)
INTERFERENCE
g f d c
(NOT TO SCALE)

SHAFTS
•Subtract value from table above for one (high) limit of shaft.
•Subtract IT(X) from high limit of shaft for low limit.

POSITIONS OF TOLERANCE ZONES TO ZERO LINE.

of a shaft; subtracting the IT value (Table 16.4) from the upper limit yields the lower limit.

Example:

∅ 80 k6 = 80 + .021, + .002

or

80.002–80.021 (.021 – .019 = .002)

(.021 is from Table 16.6 and .019 from Table 16.4.)

TABLE 16.7 Inch Tolerance Zone Position—Standard Fits

INCH-TOLERANCE ZONE POSITION TABLE-SHAFT UPPER LIMITS FROM ZERO LINE (BASIC SIZE) SEE GRAPHIC ON METRIC TABLE PAGE.

RUNNING, SLIDING, CLEARANCE, TRANSITION, AND INTERFERENCE LOCATIONAL FITS

Over-To	c9&c10	d8	d9	e7&E8	e9	f6,f7	f8	g4,g5	g6	h5,6,7&9	s6	s7	k6	k7	n5	n6	n7	p6	r6	Sp-10	Sp-11	Sp-12
0-.12	−2.50	−1.0	−1.0	−.6	−.6	−.3	−.3	−.10	−.10	0	0.1	0.2	-	-	0.45	0.5	0.65	0.65	0.75	−4.0	−4.0	−5
.12-.24	−2.80	−1.2	−1.2	−.8	−.8	−.4	−.4	−.15	−.15	0	0.15	0.25	-	-	0.5	0.6	0.8	0.8	0.9	−4.5	−4.5	−6
.24-.40	−3.00	−1.6	−1.6	−1.0	−1.0	−.5	−.5	−.20	−.20	0	0.2	0.3	0.5	0.7	0.65	0.8	1	1	1.2	−5.0	−5.0	−7
.40-.71	−3.50	−2.0	−2.0	−1.2	−1.2	−.6	−.6	−.25	−.25	0	0.2	0.35	0.5	0.8	0.8	0.9	1.2	1.1	1.4	−6.0	−6.0	−8
.71-1.19	−4.50	−2.5	−2.5	−1.6	−1.6	−.8	−.8	−.30	−.30	0	0.25	0.4	0.6	0.9	1	1.1	1.4	1.3	1.7	−7.0	−7.0	−10
1.19-1.97	−5.00	−3.0	−3.0	−2.0	−2.0	−1.0	−1.0	−.40	−.40	0	0.3	0.5	0.7	1.1	1.1	1.3	1.7	1.6	2	−8.0	−8.0	−12
1.97-3.15	−6.00	−4.0	−4.0	−2.5	−2.5	−1.2	−1.2	−.40	−.40	0	0.3	0.6	0.8	1.3	1.3	1.5	2	2.1	2.3	−9.0	−10.0	−14
3.15-4.73	−7.00	−5.0	−5.0	−3.0	−3.0	−1.4	−1.4	−.50	−.50	0	0.4	0.7	1	1.5	1.6	1.9	2.4	2.5	2.9	−10.0	−11.0	−16
4.73-7.09	−8.00	−6.0	−6.0	−3.5	−3.5	−1.6	−1.6	−.60	−.60	0	0.5	0.8	1.1	1.7	1.9	2.2	2.8	2.8	3.5	−12.0	−12.0	−18
7.09-9.85	−10.00	−7.0	−7.0	−4.0	−4.0	−2.0	−2.0	−.60	−.60	0	0.6	0.9	1.4	2	2.2	2.6	3.2	3.2	4.2	−15.0	−16.0	−22
9.85-12.41	−12.00	−8.0	−7.0	−5.0	−4.5	−2.5	2.2	−.80	−.70	0	0.6	1	1.4	2.2	2.3	2.6	3.4	3.4	4.7	−18.0	−20.0	−28
12.41-15.75	−14.00	−10.0	−8.0	6	−5.0	−3.0	2.5	−1.00	−.70	0	0.7	1	1.6	2.4	2.6	3	3.8	3.9	5.9	−22.0	−22.0	−30

FORCE AND SHRINK FITS

Over-To	s6	t6	u6	x7	Sp-5
0-.12	0.85	-	0.95	1.3	0.5
.12-.24	1	-	1.2	1.7	0.6
.24-.40	1.4	-	1.6	2	0.75
0.4-.56	1.6	-	1.8	2.3	0.8
.56-.71	1.6	-	1.8	2.5	0.9
.71-.95	1.9	-	2.1	3	1.1
.95-1.19	1.9	2.1	2.3	3.3	1.2
1.19-1.58	2.4	2.6	3.1	4	1.3
1.58-1.97	2.4	2.8	3.4	5	1.4
1.97-2.56	2.7	3.2	4.2	6.2	1.8
2.56-3.15	2.9	3.7	4.7	7.2	1.9
3.15-3.94	3.7	4.4	5.9	8.4	2.4
3.94-4.73	3.9	4.9	6.9	9.4	2.6
4.73-5.52	4.5	6	8	11.6	2.9
5.52-6.30	5	6	8	13.6	3.2
6.30-7.09	5.5	7	9	13.6	3.5
7.09-7.88	6.2	8.2	10.2	15.8	3.8
7.88-8.86	6.2	8.2	11.2	17.8	4.3
8.86-9.85	7.2	9.2	13.2	17.8	4.3
9.85-11.03	7.2	10.2	13.2	20	4.9
11.03-12.41	8.2	10.2	15.2	22	4.9
12.41-13.98	9.4	11.4	17.4	24.2	5.5
13.98-15.75	9.4	13.4	19.4	27.2	6.1
$15.75-17.72	10.6	13.6	21.6	30.5	7
17.72-19.69	11.6	15.6	23.6	32.5	7

1. Basic hole system employed (table covers shafts).
2. Values are in thousandths of an inch.
3. Values represent the upper limit (relative to the zero line) of shafts.
4. Values indicated "Sp-X" are not used in the ISO (International ISO 286).
*5. Add value from table algebraically to basic size for upper shaft limit.

Running and Sliding Fits

FIT	HOLE	SHAFT
RC1	H5	g4
RC2	H6	g5
RC3	H7	f6
RC4	H8	f7
RC5	H8	e7
RC6	H9	e8
RC7	H9	d8
RC8	H10	c9
RC9	H11	Sp-10

Clearance Locational Fits

FIT	HOLE	SHAFT
LC1	H6	h5
LC2	H7	h6
LC3	H8	h7
LC4	H10	h9
LC5	H7	g6
LC6	H9	f8
LC7	H10	e9
LC8	H10	d9
LC9	H11	c10
LC10	H12	Sp11
LC11	H13	Sp12

Clearance Locational Fits

FIT	HOLE	SHAFT
LT1	H7	ls6
LT2	H8	ls7
LT3	H7	k6
LT4	H8	k7
LT5	H7	n6
LT6	H7	n7

Interference Locational Fits

FIT	HOLE	SHAFT
LN1	H6	n5
LN2	H7	p6
LN3	H7	r6

Force and Shrink Fits

FIT	HOLE	SHAFT
FN1	H6	Sp5
FN2	H7	s6
FN3	H7	t6
FN4	H7	u6
FN5	H8	x7

Note:
- Uppercase letters represent holes/bores (e.g., H7).
- Lowercase letters represent shafts (e.g., f6).
- The letter (location symbol) represents the position/distance to the "zero line"/Basic size.
- H and h are on the zero line.
- The number (quality no.) represents the tolerance grade. Higher nos. yield coarser fits.

* See tolerance grade (IT) table for limits not shown in these tables.
* Add IT(x) for hole limit (from 0). (Basic hole is min size.)
* Subtract IT from max shaft limit calculated from basic size and value in table for other limit.

METHODS OF INDICATING
1. Ø.30 f7
2. Ø.2995 +.000, −.0006 (Ø.30f7)
3. Ø2989–.2995 (Ø.30f7)

INDICATING FITS
1. Ø.30 H8/f7 (hole first)
2. Ø 30 H8 (.3000–.3009)
f7 (.2989–.2995)

IT Grade (7)
Location on zero line (H)
Ø30 H7
Basic Size (Ø30) Hole Designation

IT Grade (7)
Location to zero line (f)
Ø30 f7
Basic Size (Ø30) Shaft Designation

Example:

∅ 80 c11 = .80 − .150, − 340

or

79.660 − 79.850 (−.150 − .190) = −.340

(−.150 is from Table 16.6 and .190 from Table 16.4.)

16.13.4 Calculating Inch Shaft Limits

With a hole basis system, unless the shaft is at position *h* (see figure at the bottom right of Table 16.7), the value in Table 16.7 must be added algebraically to arrive at the upper limit of a shaft; subtracting the IT value (Table 16.6) from the upper limit yields the lower limit.

Example

∅ 3.15 k6 = 3.1500 − .0008, − .0015

or

3.1485–3.14992 (−.0008 − .0007 = − .0015)

(− .0008 is from Table 16.7 and .0007 from Table 16.6.)

Example

∅ 12.00 d9 = 12.00 − .007, − .012

or

11.988–11.993 (−.007 − .005 = − .012)

(.007 is from Table 16.7 and .005 from Table 16.6.)

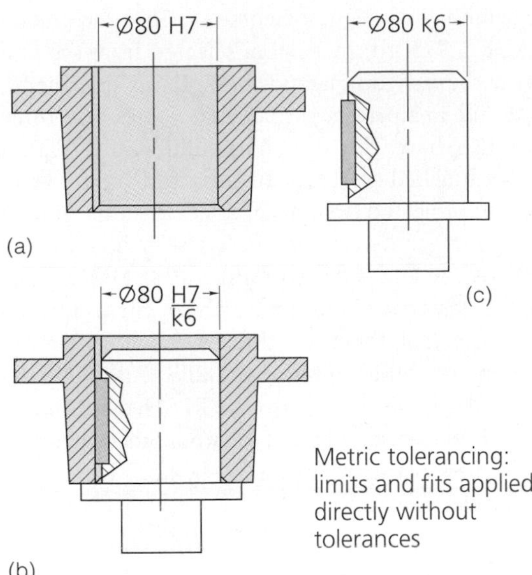

FIGURE 16.52 Metric Symbology for Limits and Fits

16.13.5 Calculating Fits

Once the limits are computed, the **fit calculation** is simple. A fit consists of two sets of limits and the maximum and minimum clearances. Except for interference, force, or shrink fits, the shaft is given a tolerance grade one number less than the hole. For the example in Figure 16.52 of ∅80 H7/k6 (LT3, clearance locational fit; see Table 16.6) the calculated limits are:

Hole	80.000–80.030
Shaft	80.002–80.021

Subtracting the largest (MMC) shaft from the smallest (MMC) hole, we get 80.000–80.012 = –.012 (minimum clearance or maximum interference). Subtracting the smallest (LMC) shaft from the largest (LMC) hole gives 80.030–80.002 = .028 (maximum clearance or minimum interference).

Tables for the most popular fits are in Appendix C.12.

16.14 CAD AND GDT

Many CAD systems provide an easy and quick way to create GDT symbols and feature control frames. Some systems, like the newest release of AutoCAD (R13), have features that allow you to create feature control frames, GDT symbols, and datum references automatically (Fig. 16.53) simply by choosing from a menu.

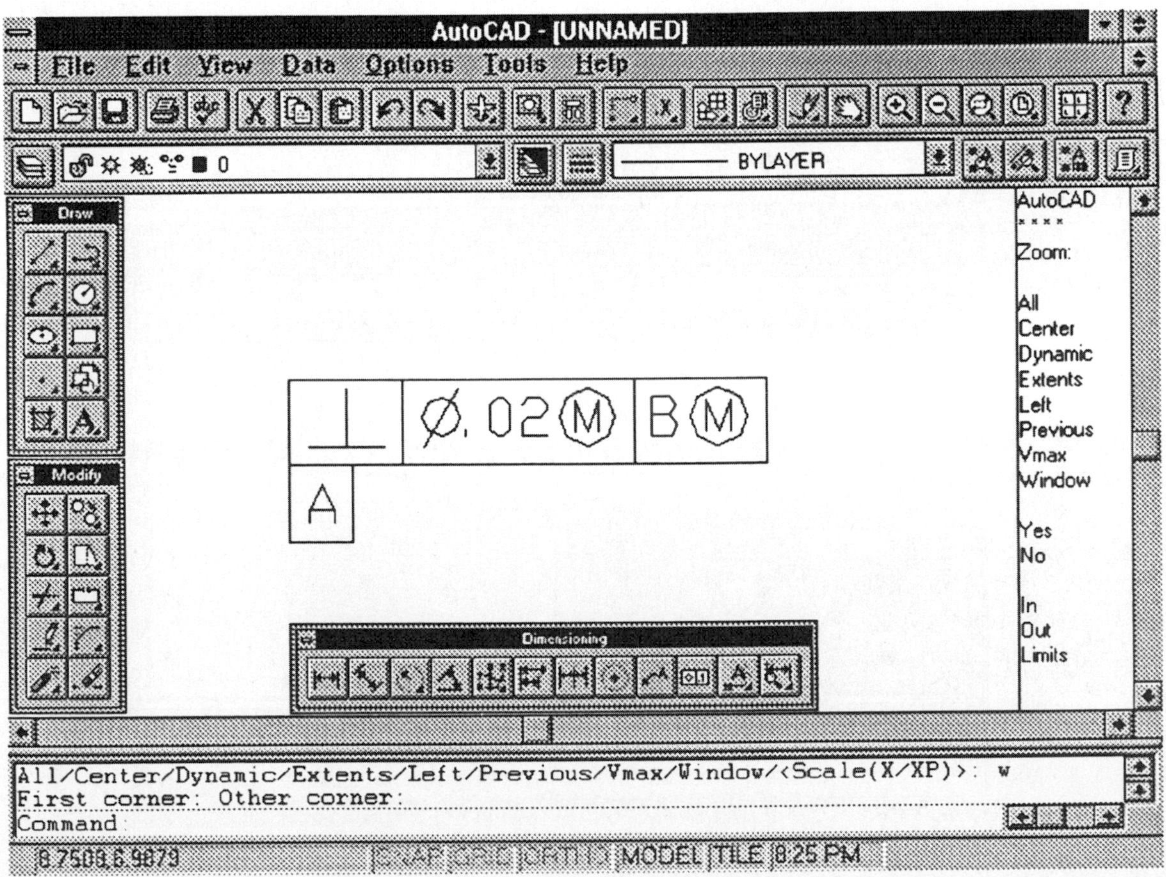

FIGURE 16.53 GDT Symbols Can Be Created Automatically in CAD Systems

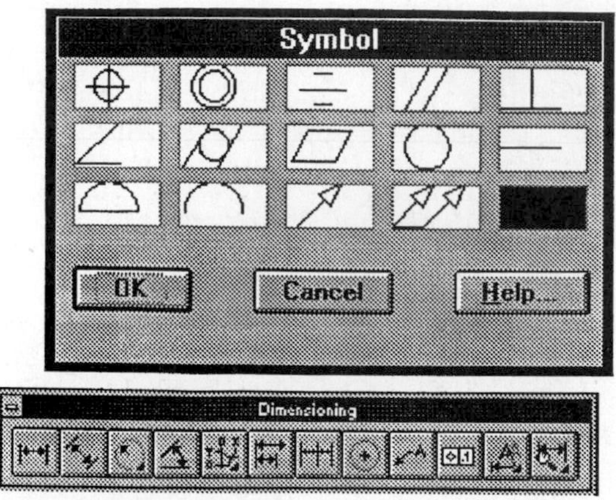

FIGURE 16.54 **Creating a Feature Control Frame—Step 1**

The first step in creating a feature control frame in R13 AutoCAD is to select the automatic-creation feature simply by picking the GDT tool from the dimensioning toolbar (third button from the right in Fig. 16.54). As shown in Figure 16.54, this first brings up a GDT Symbol menu. From that menu, simply select the symbol you wish to place in the feature control frame—position, concentricity, perpendicularity, flatness, straightness, etc. To create a datum only, you simply select the empty box (perpendicularity in our example).

After the symbol is chosen, a Geometric Tolerance menu appears (Fig. 16.55), with the symbol selected from the first menu filled in the appropriate position. From this menu, you can easily fill in up to two tolerance values and three datums. You also have the option of filling in a datum identifier to be attached to the feature control frame (**A** in this case) or a projected tolerance zone. In this simple example, only one geometric tolerance is selected—.02-in. diameter at MMC, which refers to Datum **A** at MMC.

To select the Material Condition, a third menu appears (Fig. 16.56). Note that there are three symbols to choose from on that menu: MMC, LMC, and RFS. Although the 1994 ANSI standards no longer use the RFS symbol, many people will be applying the older standards. Since RFS is implied in the new standard when no symbol is used, it makes no real difference to the part being manufactured if a RFS symbol appears in the specification. Implying RFS is the same as making an actual reference to RFS with the symbol. This is an extremely minor variation in the new standard, and the RFS symbol will, in all likelihood, continue to be used.

The final step involves inserting the feature control frames and datum identifiers that have been created automatically. Simply select the position required (Fig. 16.57), and the feature control frame is inserted in the drawing automatically.

You May Complete Exercises 13.1 Through 13.8 at This Time

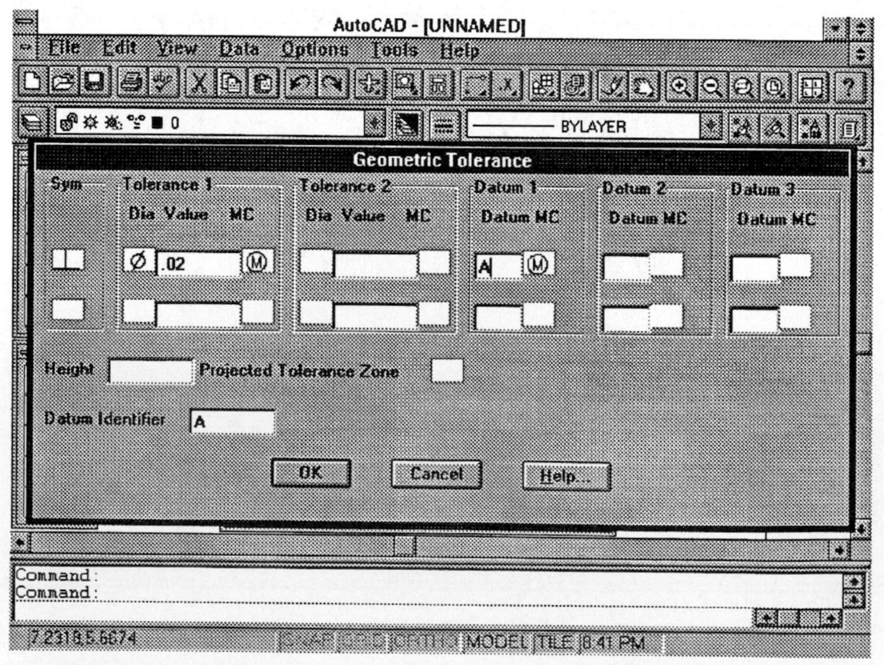

FIGURE 16.55 **Creating a Feature Control Frame—Step 2**

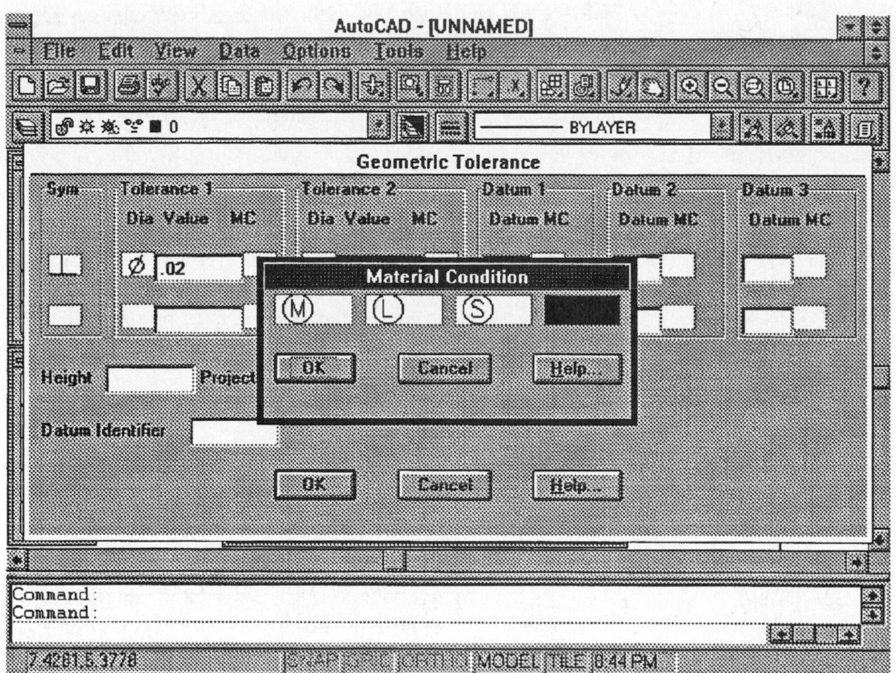

FIGURE 16.56 Creating a Feature Control Frame—Step 3

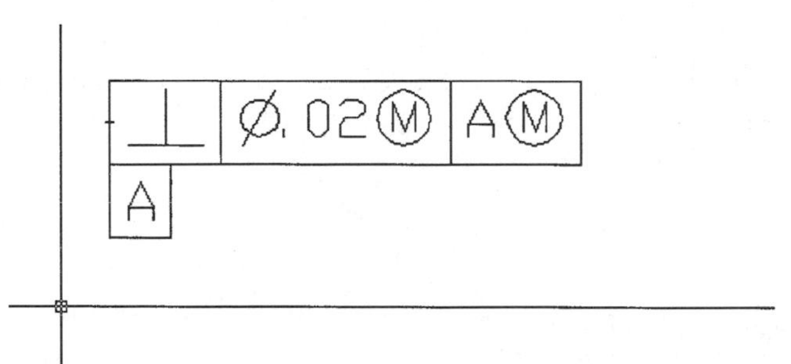

FIGURE 16.57 Creating a Feature Control Frame—Step 4

QUIZ

True or False

1. Bilateral tolerancing allows variation in both the positive and the negative directions.
2. In a feature control frame, a separator is not required between the geometric characteristic and the tolerance.
3. A tolerance of 1.2–1.4 allows a feature of 1.202 to be accepted.
4. A tertiary datum may be established by a single point of contact.
5. The four basic types of fit are clearance, interference, transition, and running.
6. The ANSI system of limits and fits has been standardized at about 500 fits.
7. Tolerances are understood to apply at 68°F unless otherwise specified.
8. A datum is identified, located, and established in a feature control frame.

Fill in the Blanks

9. A theoretically exact dimension is a ________ dimension.
10. A datum may be a ________, a ________, or a ________.
11. The abbreviations for the modifiers are ________, ________, and ________.
12. The surfaces of a feature must not extend beyond a ________ ________ ________ at MMC.
13. ________, ________, and ________ are the basic types of fits.
14. In ________ and ________ tolerancing, the________ is given first and is followed by a ________ and ________ expression of tolerance.
15. The classes of fits are arranged into three groups:________ and ________ fits, ________ fits, and ________ fits.
16. ________ means producing parts relative to standard measures and forms.

Answer the Following

17. What is the difference between circularity and cylindricity?
18. What is a tolerance zone?
19. What does the following statement mean? "Every manufactured part varies in size, but as long as it is understood and controlled, the part will function as designed."
20. Define the three datum planes, and describe how they are located.
21. How is perpendicularity defined?
22. What is title block tolerance, and how is it applied to part features?
23. Explain MMC of an internal feature.
24. Explain what RFS means.

EXERCISES

Exercises may be assigned as sketching, instrument or CAD projects. Transfer the given information to an "A"-size sheet of .25 in. grid paper. Exercises that are not assigned by the instructor can be sketched in the text to provide practice and to enhance understanding of the preceding instructional material. Complete all views by showing all hidden lines, centerlines, tolerances, datums, and dimensions.

Exercise 16.1 The surface between points D and E must lie between two profile boundaries .001 apart, perpendicular to plane A, equally disposed about the true profile, and positioned with respect to datum planes B and C. All dimensions given on the exercise sheet are basic.

Exercise 16.2 Specify different tolerances for each segment of the profile; between A and B use .005, between B and C use .004, and between C and D use .002. Complete the views and dimension the part.

Exercise 16.3 The two holes are to be parallel, with a maximum tolerance of .002. Complete the views and dimension the part.

Exercise 16.4 The large hole at MMC is to be perpendicular to datum plane A, with a maximum tolerance of .004. Complete the views and dimension the part.

EXERCISE 16.1

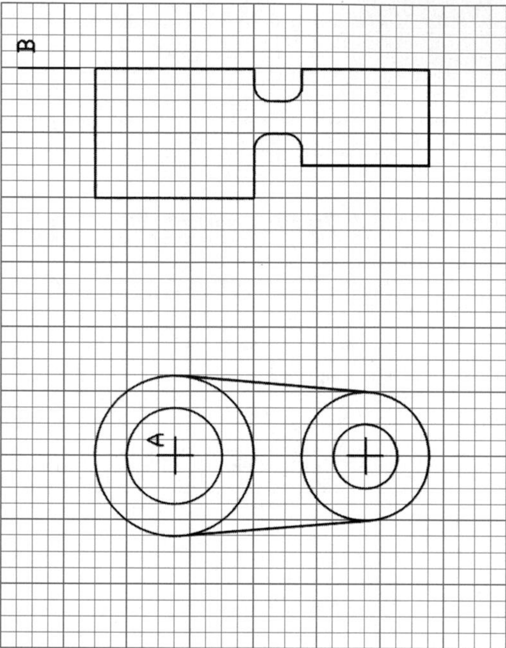

EXERCISE 16.3

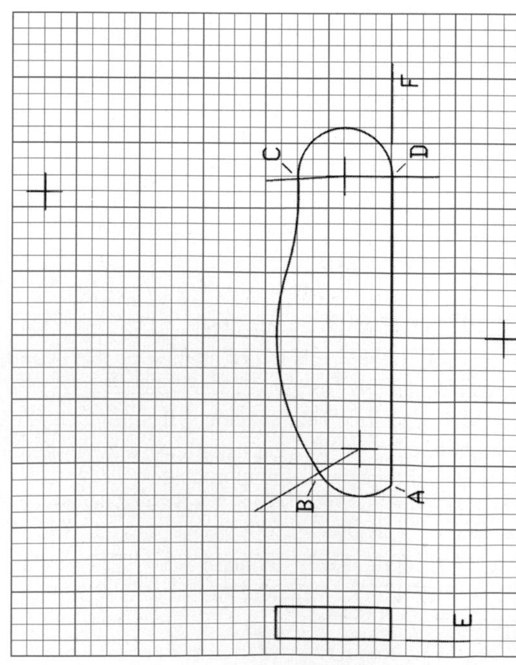

EXERCISE 16.2

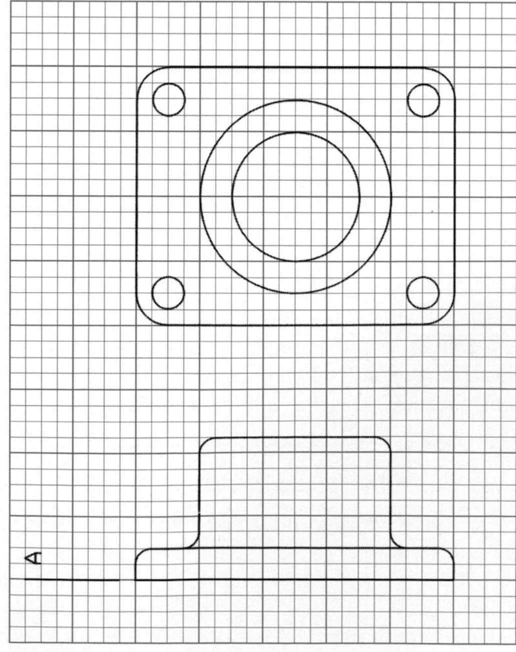

EXERCISE 16.4

Exercise 16.5 Use positional tolerancing for the part. The holes are to be at a depth of one-half of the part thickness. Show the bolt circle diameter as a reference dimension.

Exercise 16.6 Use positional tolerancing for the part. The large hole is to be toleranced at .016 at MMC from datums A, B, and C. The small holes are to be toleranced at .001 at MMC from the large hole. Dimensions for the hole pattern are basic.

Exercise 16.7 Dimension the part using composite positional tolerancing. All hole patterns are to be basic. The bolt circle hole pattern is 6 x 60° basic.

Exercise 16.8 Dimension the part with positional tolerancing. Use symbology to call out the counterbored holes. The counterbores are to have a .001-diameter tolerance zone at MMC in relation to datum B.

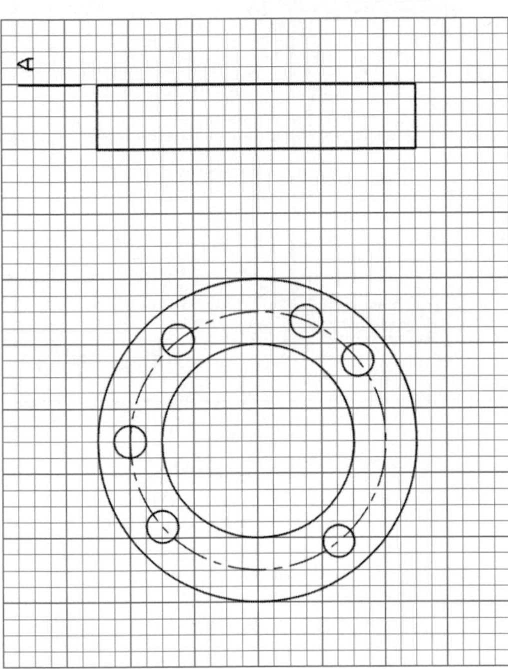

EXERCISE 16.5

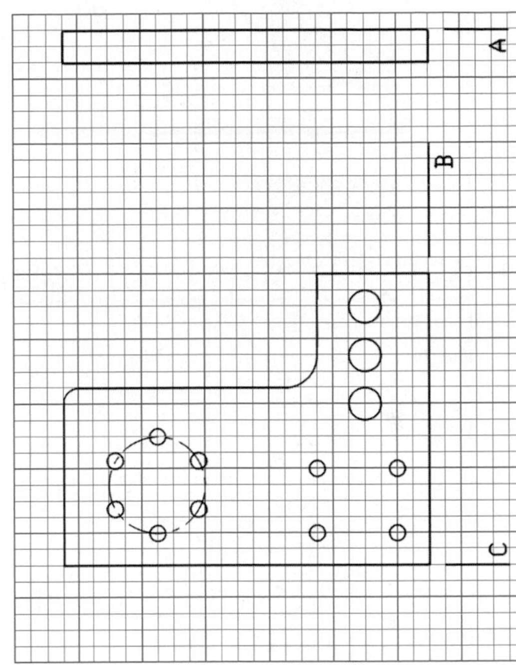

EXERCISE 16.7

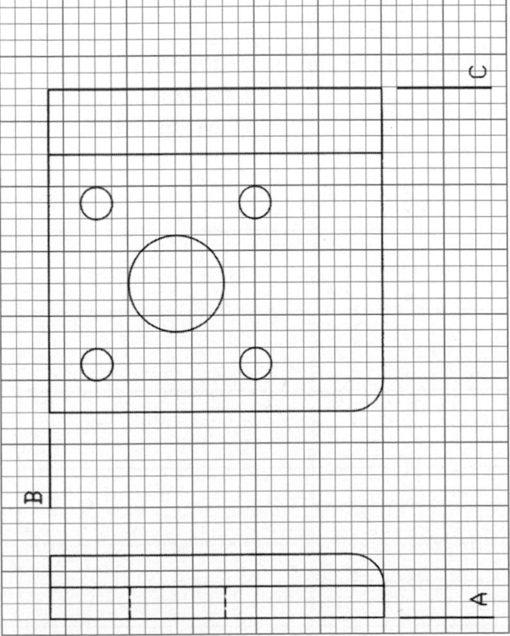

EXERCISE 16.6

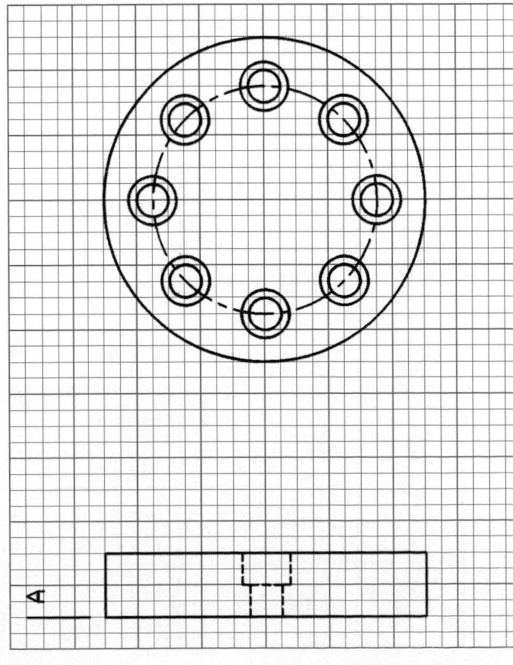

EXERCISE 16.8

PROBLEMS

The concepts and methods presented in the chapter should be applied for drawing projects throughout the text. The problems presented here are meant to introduce and familiarize you with simple geometric tolerancing situations. On problems that have no units, use either metric or decimal-inch scales and transfer directly from the text using 2× scale.

Problem 16.1 Complete the table for each of the four cases. Use Tables 16.1 through 16.7 to check the results.

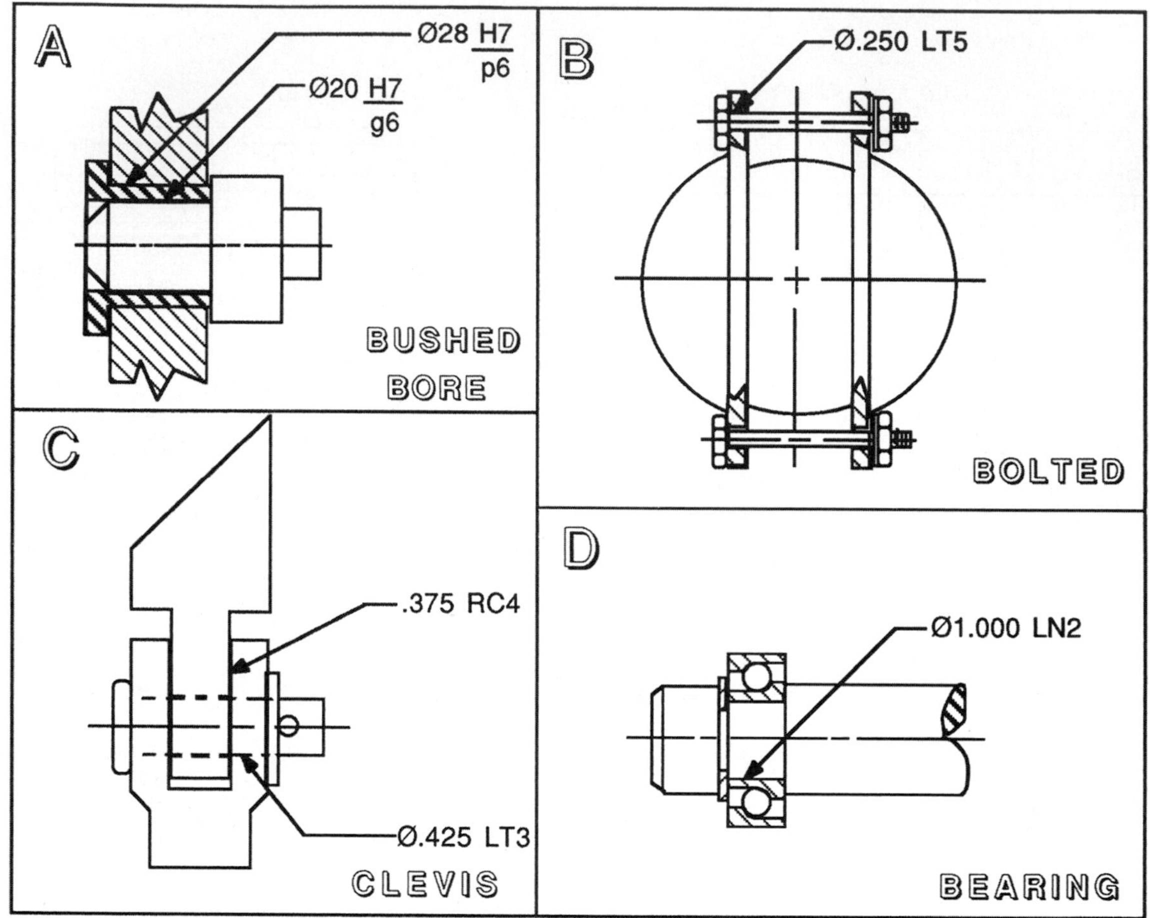

FIT IDENT	Ø or width mm or in.	FIT CALLOUT	FEATURE	SIZE LIMITS	CLEARANCE/ INTERFERENCE
A	Ø28 mm	H7/p6	MALE		
			FEMALE		
	Ø20 mm	H7/g6	MALE		
			FEMALE		
B	Ø.250 in.	LT5 (H7/n6)	MALE		
			FEMALE		
C	.375 in.	RC4 (H8/f7)	MALE		
			FEMALE		
	.425 in.	LT3 (H7/k6)	MALE		
			FEMALE		
D	1.00 in.	LN2 (H7/p6)	MALE		
			FEMALE		

PROBLEM 16.1

Problem 16.2 Follow the instructions at the bottom of the figure.

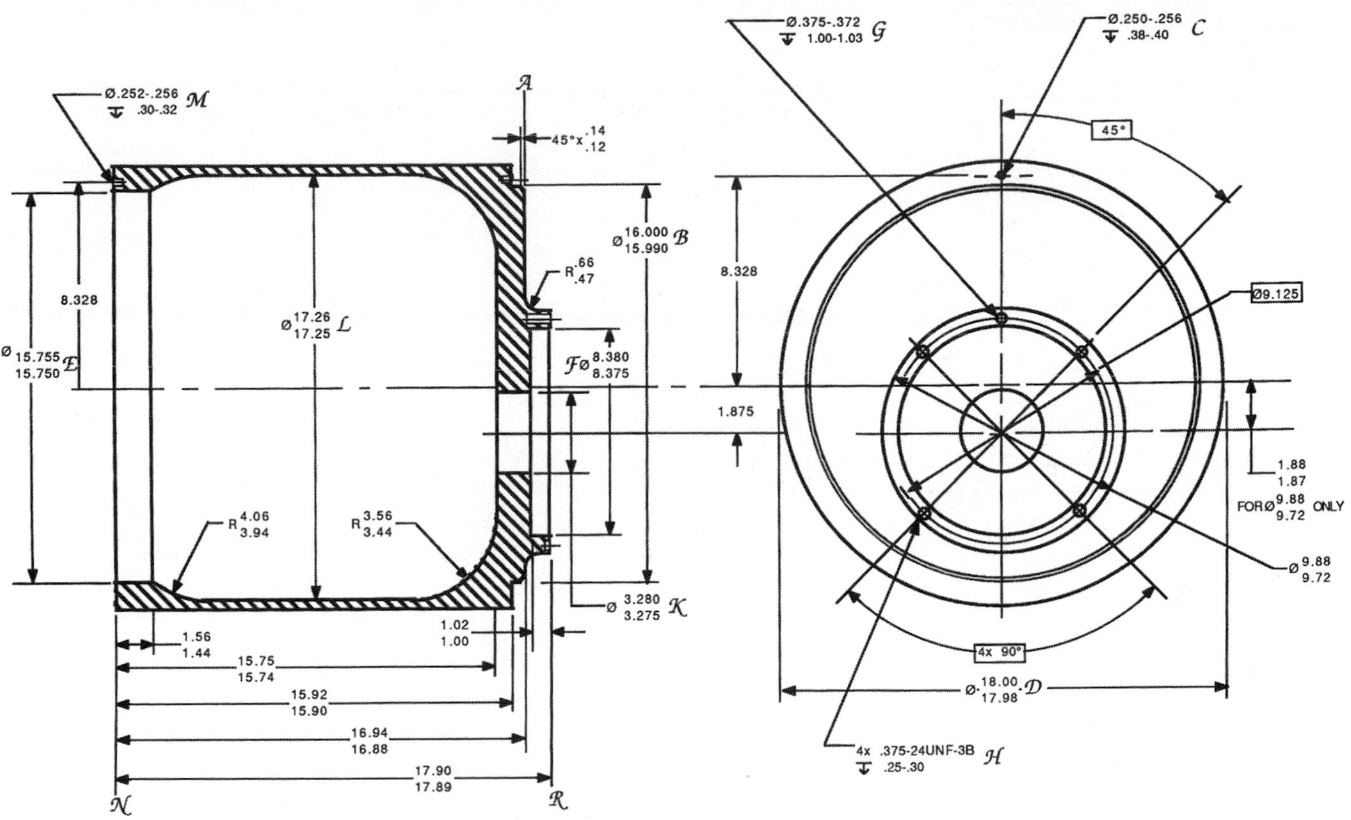

1. Establish a Datum Reference Frame using features *A, B and C.*
2. *A* is flat to .001. *B* is perpendicular to *A* within .010 at MMC. *C* is positioned within .005 at MMC to *A* and *B* at MMC.
3. Feature *D* has a positional tol. of .020 at MMC to *A* and *B* at MMC.
4. *E* has an .008 circ. runout to *A* and *B*
5. *F* is positioned within .004 at MMC to *R, B* at MMC and *C* at MMC.
6. *G* is positioned to .005 at MMC to *R, F* at MMC and *C* at MMC.
7. *H* has a composite positional tol. of .020 at MMC to *R, F* at MMC and *G* at MMC, and positioned to .006 at RFS to *R* the zone is projected .510.
8. *K* is positioned to .010 at *MMC* to *R* and *F* at MMC.
9. *L* has a Circ. Runout of .025 to *D*.
10. *M* is positioned to .008 at MMC to *N. E* at MMC and *C* at MMC.
11. *N* and *R* are parallel within .005 & .003 to *A* respectively.

PROBLEM 16.2

Problem 16.3 and Problem 16.4 Redraw each of the frames, and note the parts of each.

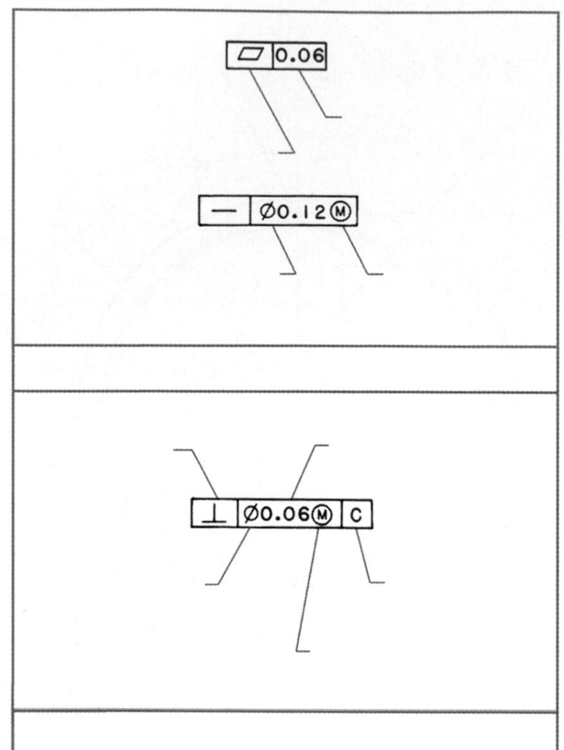

PROBLEM 16.3

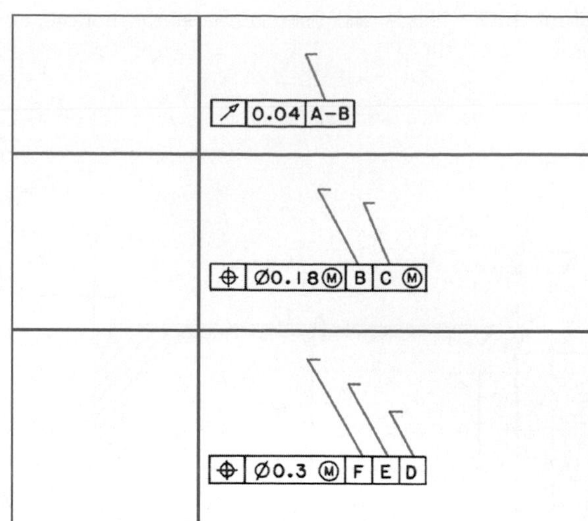

PROBLEM 16.4

Problem 16.5 The surfaces all around the part outline must lie between parallel boundaries .06 (1.5 mm) apart and perpendicular to datum A

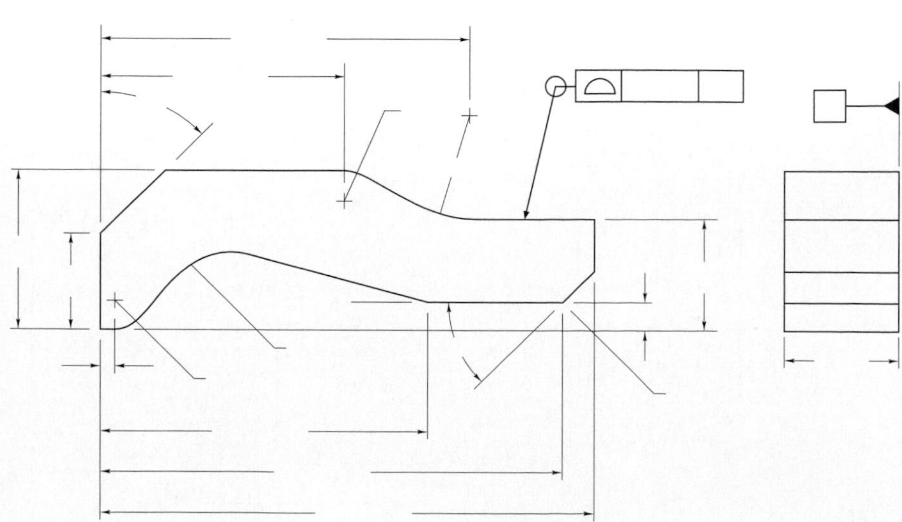

PROBLEM 16.5

Problem 16.6 Draw and dimension the part.

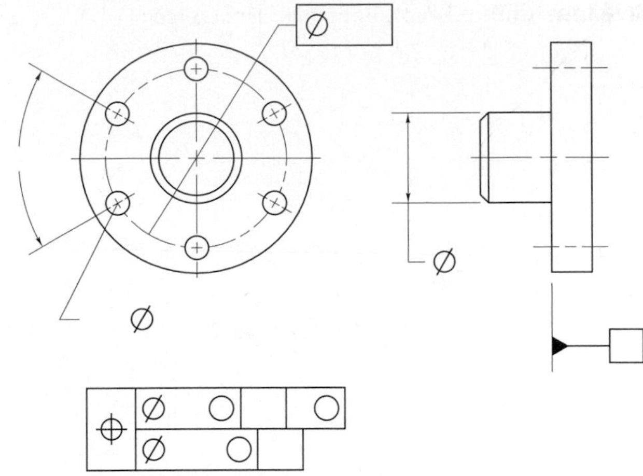

PROBLEM 16.6

Problem 16.7 Complete the part's dimensions and tolerancing.

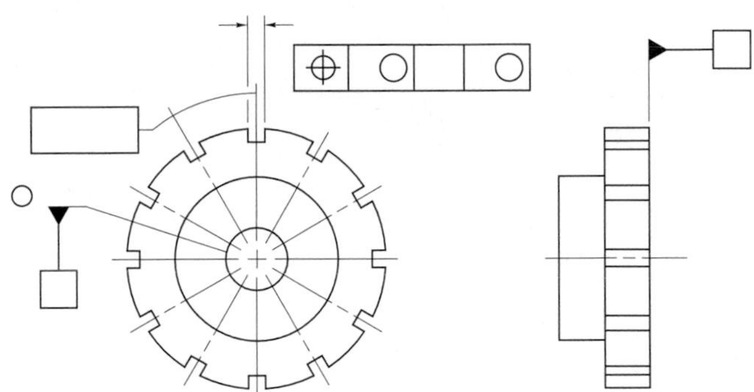

PROBLEM 16.7

Problem 16.8 Draw the part and complete the dimensioning.

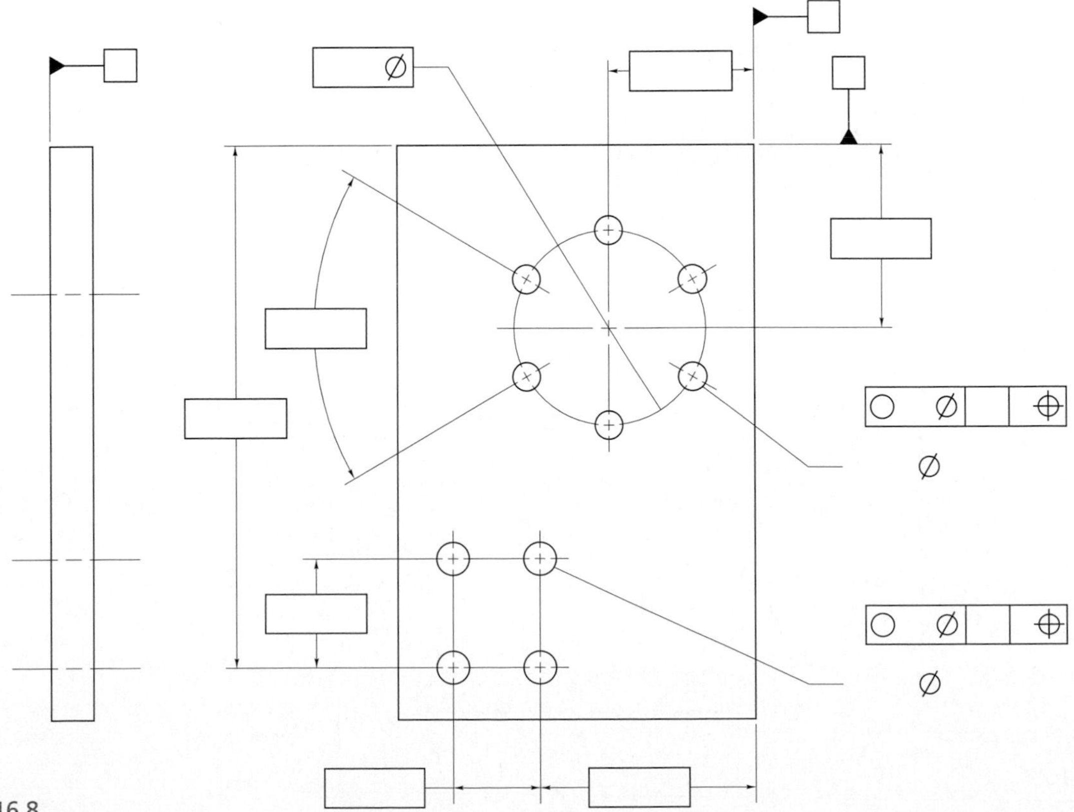

PROBLEM 16.8

Problem 16.9 Complete the part as required.

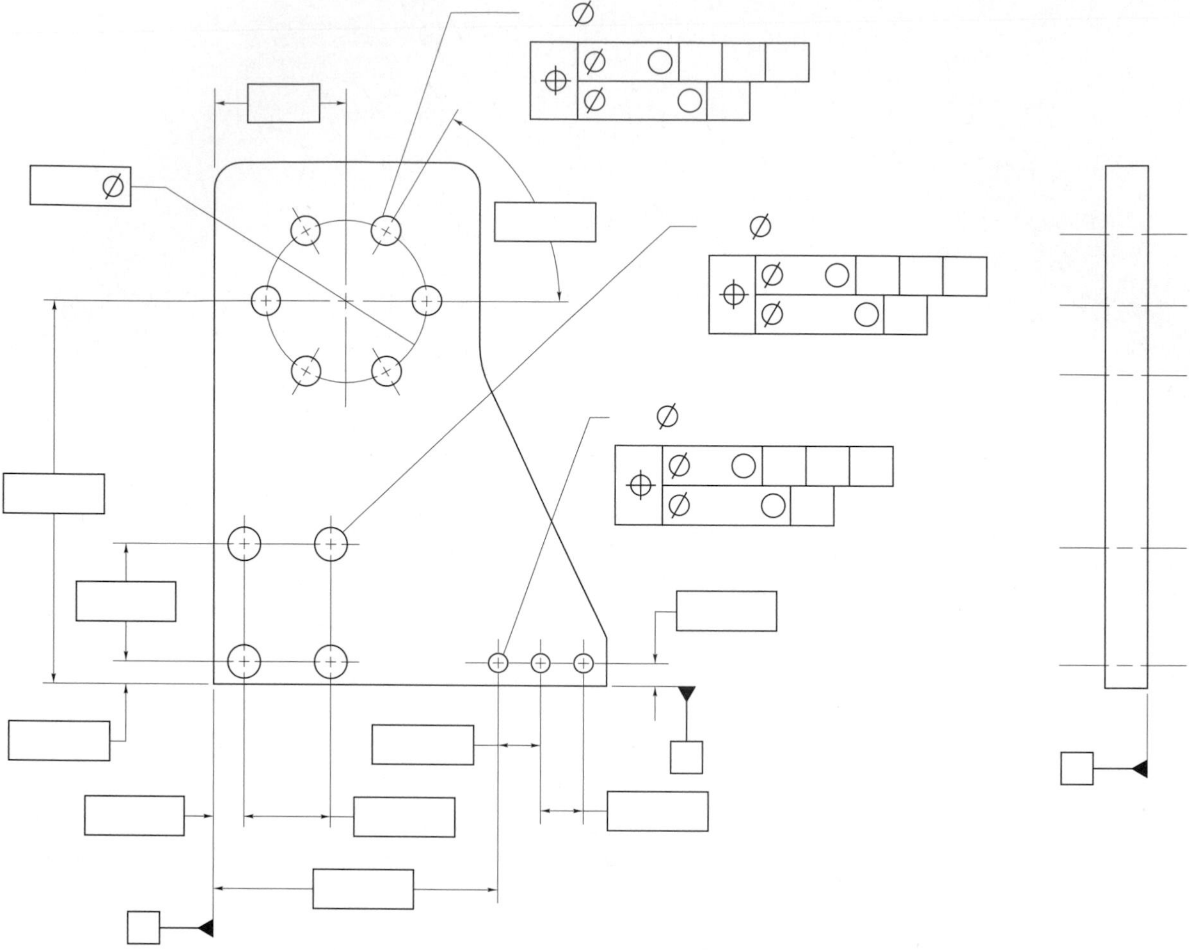

PROBLEM 16.9

Problem 16.10 Draw and dimension the part as required.

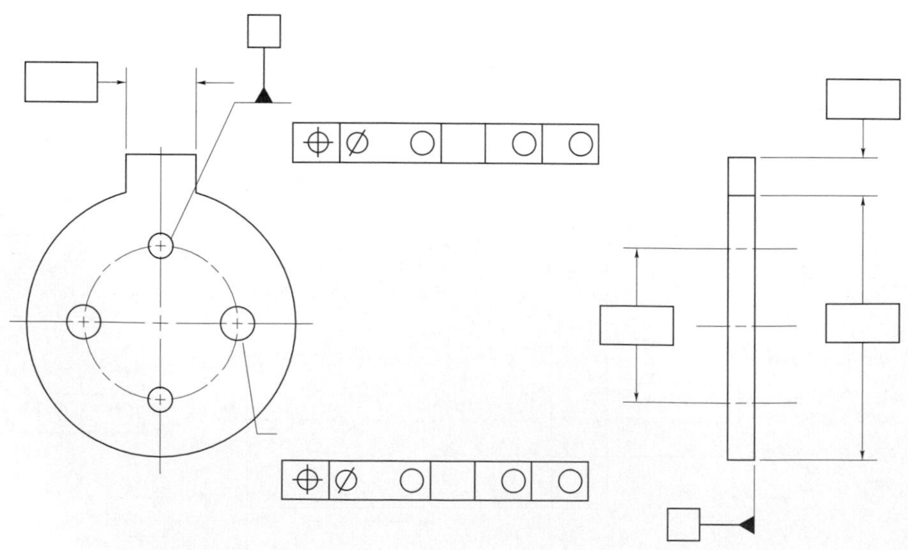

PROBLEM 16.10

Problem 16.11 Complete the portion of the part as shown.

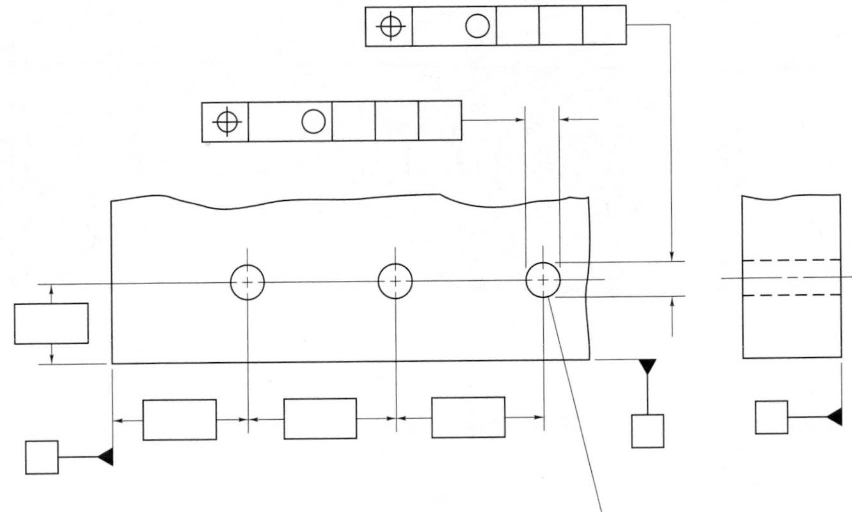

PROBLEM 16.11

Problem 16.12 Complete the project as required. Specify the different profile tolerances between the segments: .12 (3 mm) between A and B, .10 (2.5 mm) between B and C, and .05 (1.2 mm) between C and D.

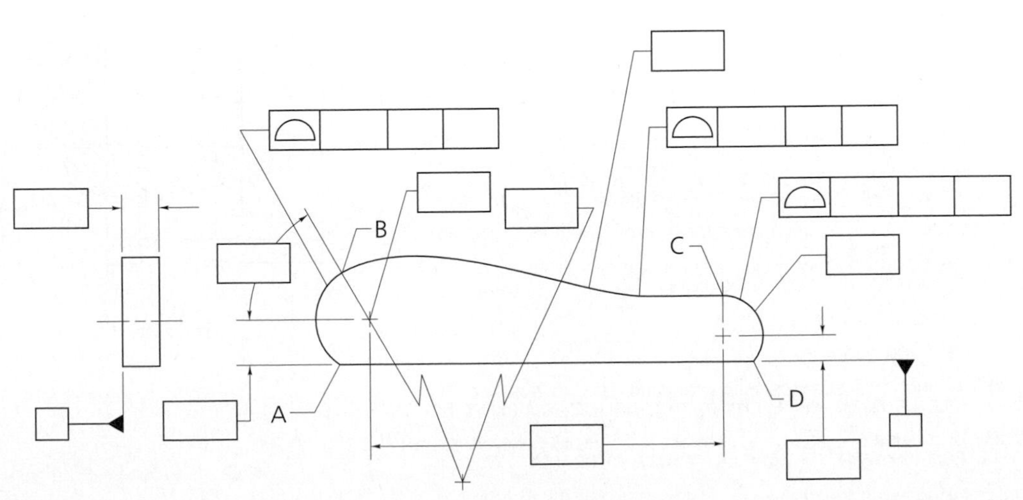

PROBLEM 16.12

Problem 16.13 Redraw or model the rotor, and show all dimensions. Use 1994 ANSI standards,

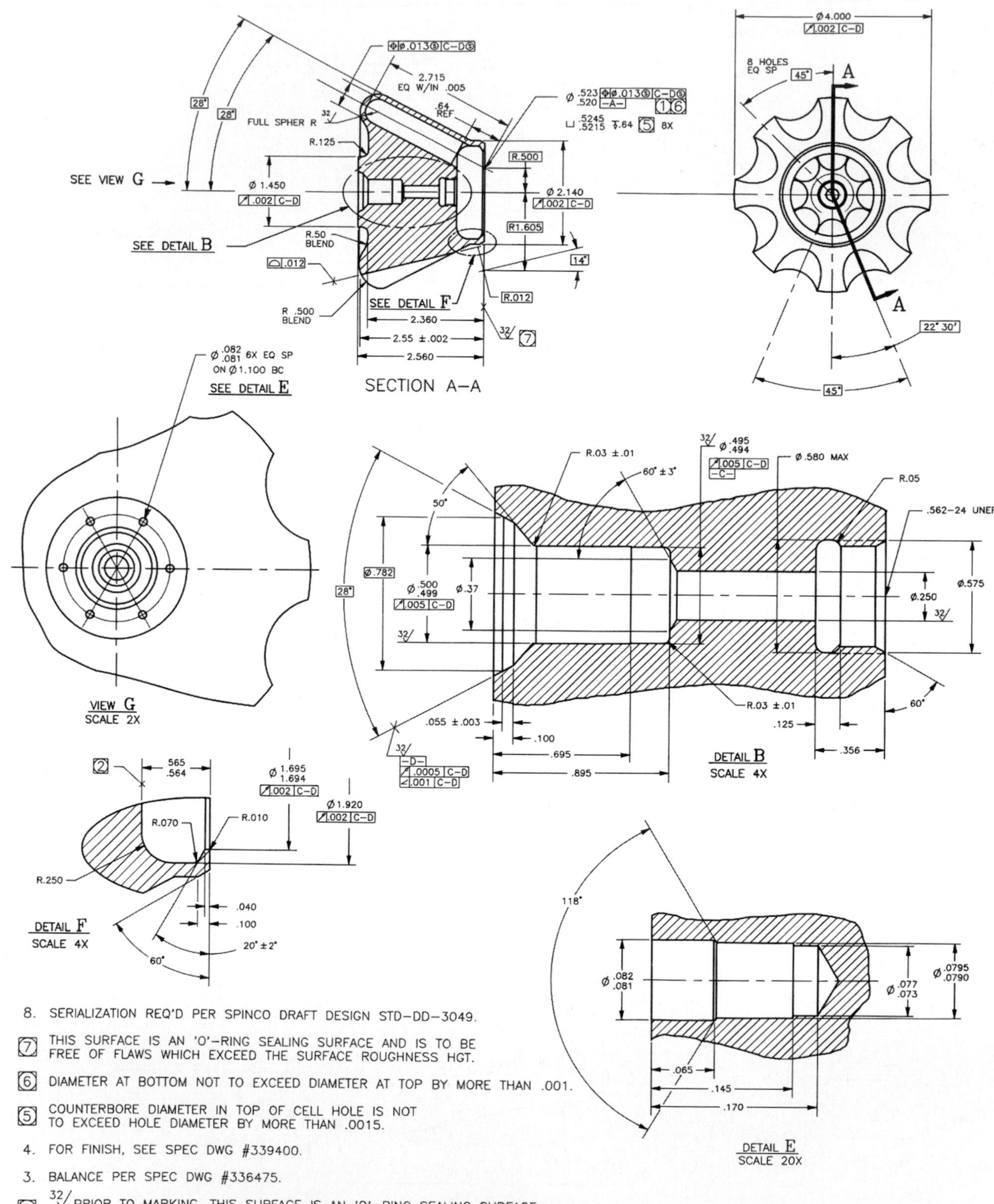

8. SERIALIZATION REQ'D PER SPINCO DRAFT DESIGN STD–DD–3049.

7 THIS SURFACE IS AN 'O'–RING SEALING SURFACE AND IS TO BE FREE OF FLAWS WHICH EXCEED THE SURFACE ROUGHNESS HGT.

6 DIAMETER AT BOTTOM NOT TO EXCEED DIAMETER AT TOP BY MORE THAN .001.

5 COUNTERBORE DIAMETER IN TOP OF CELL HOLE IS NOT TO EXCEED HOLE DIAMETER BY MORE THAN .0015.

4. FOR FINISH, SEE SPEC DWG #339400.

3. BALANCE PER SPEC DWG #336475.

2 32/√ PRIOR TO MARKING. THIS SURFACE IS AN 'O'–RING SEALING SURFACE AND IS TO BE FREE OF FLAWS WHICH EXCEED THE SURFACE ROUGHNESS HGT.

1 TRUE POSITION OF DIAMETER -A- TO BE WITHIN THE CONICAL ZONE AS SHOWN. THE MAX TRUE POSITION VARIATION BETWEEN CAVITIES TO BE .004.

NOTE: (UNLESS OTHERWISE SPECIFIED)

PROBLEM 16.13

MECHANICAL PARTS, PROCEDURES, AND LAYOUT

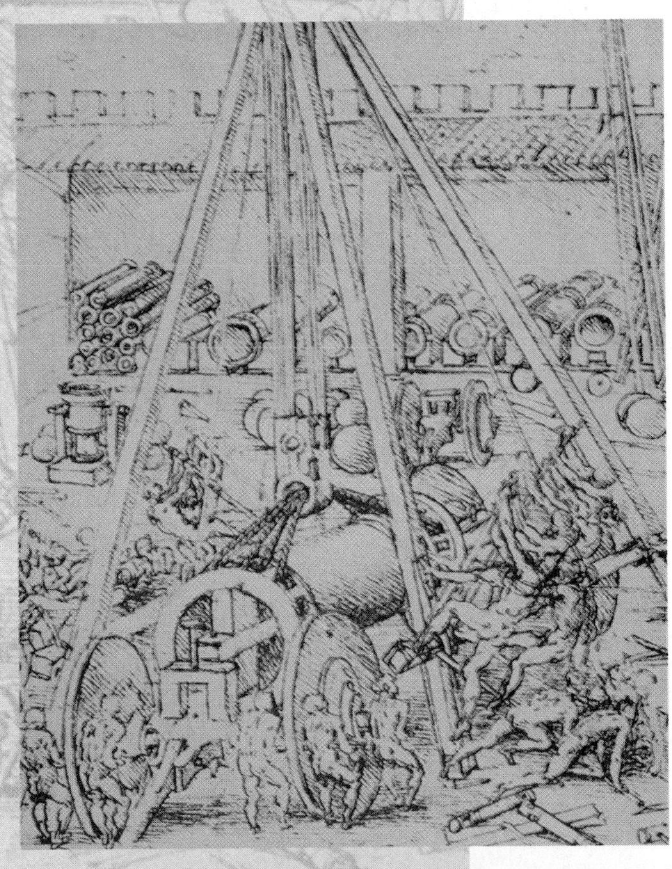

THREADS AND FASTENERS

Chapter 17

LEARNING OBJECTIVES

Upon completion of this chapter you will be able to:

1. Identify the variables, requirements, and considerations necessary for fastener selection.
2. Understand thread function while recognizing standard thread forms, series, terms, and parts.
3. Differentiate between and produce ANSI-standard detailed, schematic, and simplified screw thread representations.
4. Identify and compare Acme, buttress, metric, and pipe threads.
5. Understand bolt, nut, and screw representation.
6. Identify quick-release and semi-permanent pins.
7. Discuss key and keyseat variations and design considerations.
8. Understand the use of CAD libraries of fasteners and other standard mechanical parts to produce engineering drawings.

17.1 INTRODUCTION

Fasteners (Fig. 17.1) are used to join components in an assembly. They are interchangeable, readily available as standard parts, and manufactured to specific requirements to maintain a high degree of precision and quality. Most, but not all, fasteners have threads. There are more than a million types of fasteners. This chapter presents the common types of fasteners, covers thread specifications, and discusses nonthreaded types of fasteners.

17.1.1 Fastener Selection

There are many factors to consider when selecting the proper fastener. Design for manufacturability (DFM) concepts are considered at this stage, including:

- Use off-the-shelf, readily available standard fasteners.
- Use the minimum number of fasteners.
- Use fewer large fasteners rather than many small fasteners.
- Avoid separate washers.
- Design for automated assembly.
- Design for drop-in assembly.
- Eliminate separate fasteners by design (for example, snap fits).

The selection of the proper fastener for a project involves:

- Assembly requirements for assembly and disassembly during manufacturing, shipping, installation, service, and maintenance
- Conditions of operation: temperature, vibration, movement, corrosion, and impact
- Quantity of fasteners required to secure the parts adequately
- Variety of fasteners on the assembly
- Function of the fasteners in the assembly: location and fastening

FIGURE 17.1 Fasteners and Threads

17.2 SCREW THREADS

A **thread** is a helical or spiral groove formed on the outside (external) surface or inside (internal) surface of a cylinder. Screw threads support and transfer loads and transmit power. A variety of thread styles are found in the valve shown in Figure 17.2. Threads on round parts such as shafts and bolts are external threads [Fig. 17.3(a)]; threads on interior surfaces of a cylindrical hole are internal threads [Fig. 17.3(b)]. A die is used to cut external threads; a tap is used to cut internal threads.

In many cases, threads are modeled in a simplified form when designing on a CAD system. These threads, called cosmetic threads on some systems, will contain all the thread information on an imbedded thread file attached to the geometry (Fig. 17.4).

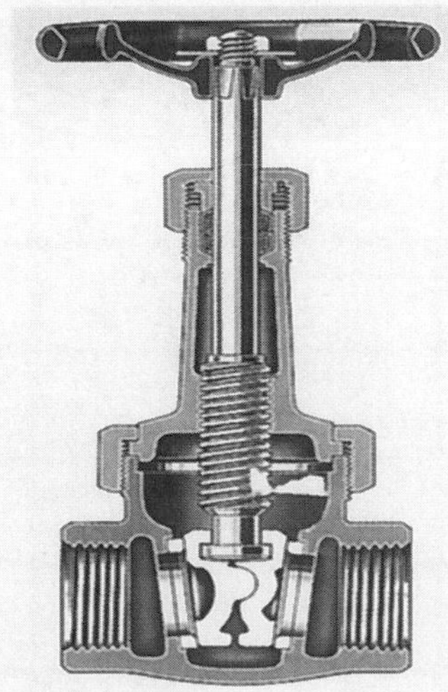

FIGURE 17.2 UNC, Acme, and NPT Threads Used in the Design of This Rising Stem Gate Valve

(a) External threads

(b) Internal threads

FIGURE 17.3 Threads

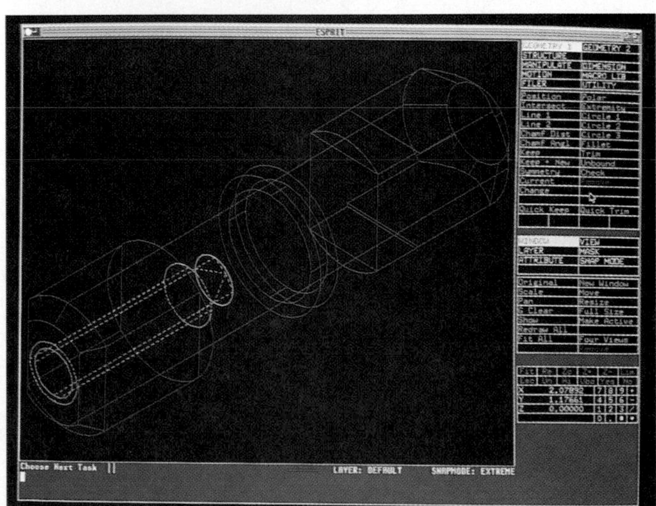

FIGURE 17.4 Threads Modeled on a Part via a 3D CAD System

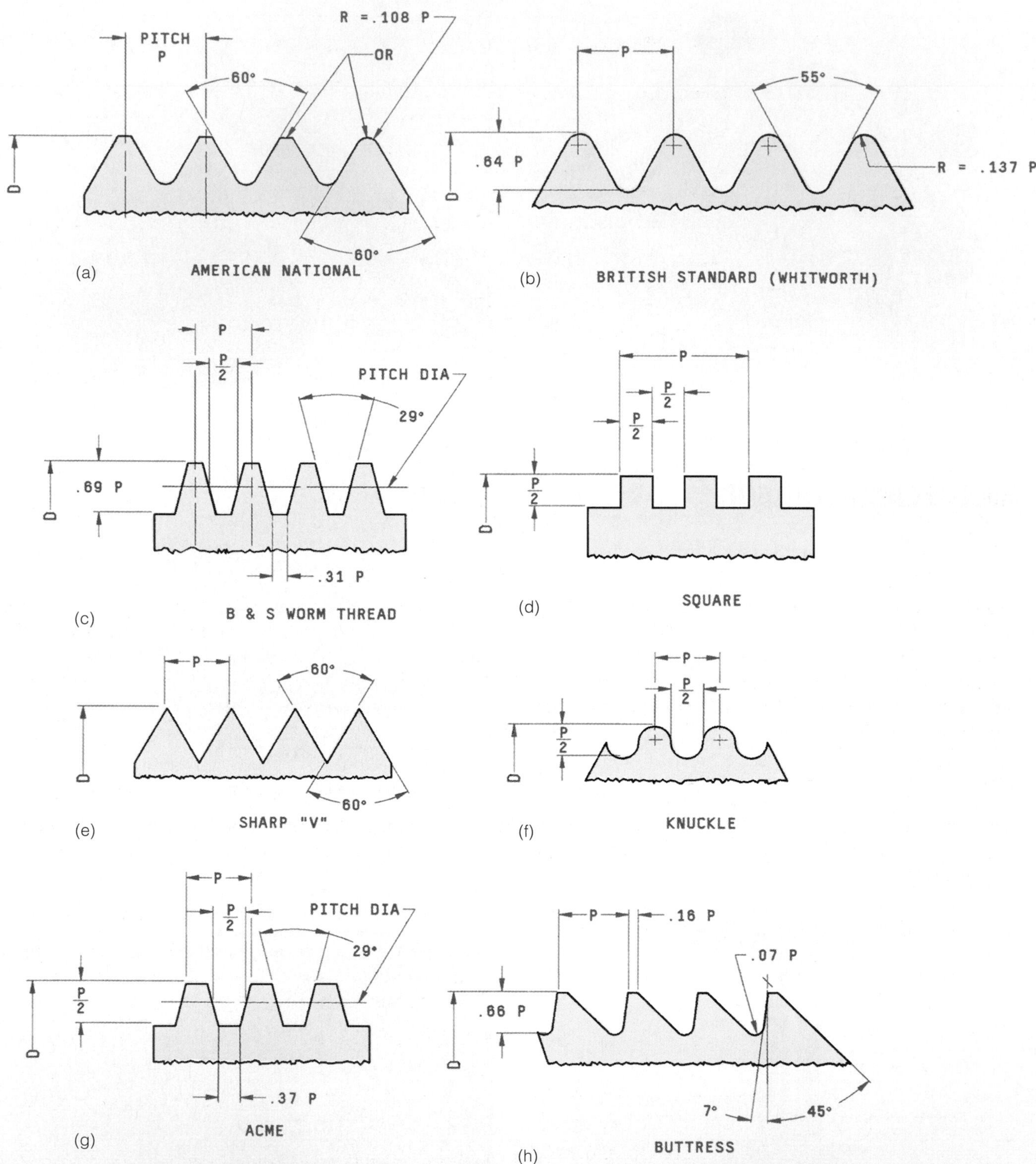

FIGURE 17.5 Standard Thread Forms

The different forms of threads are selected based on the requirements of the design. Eight standard styles are presented in Figure 17.5: (a) American National thread form, (b) the British Standard (Whitworth) thread form, (c) the worm thread form, (d) the square thread form, (e) the sharp V thread form, (f) the knuckle thread form, (g) the Acme thread form, and (h) the buttress thread form. The ISO metric thread form is shown in Figure 17.6, and the Unified National (UN) thread form is shown in Figure 17.7.

The Acme and square thread forms serve to transmit power. Acme threads (Fig. 17.2) function to move the valve stem up and down to open and close the valve. Worm

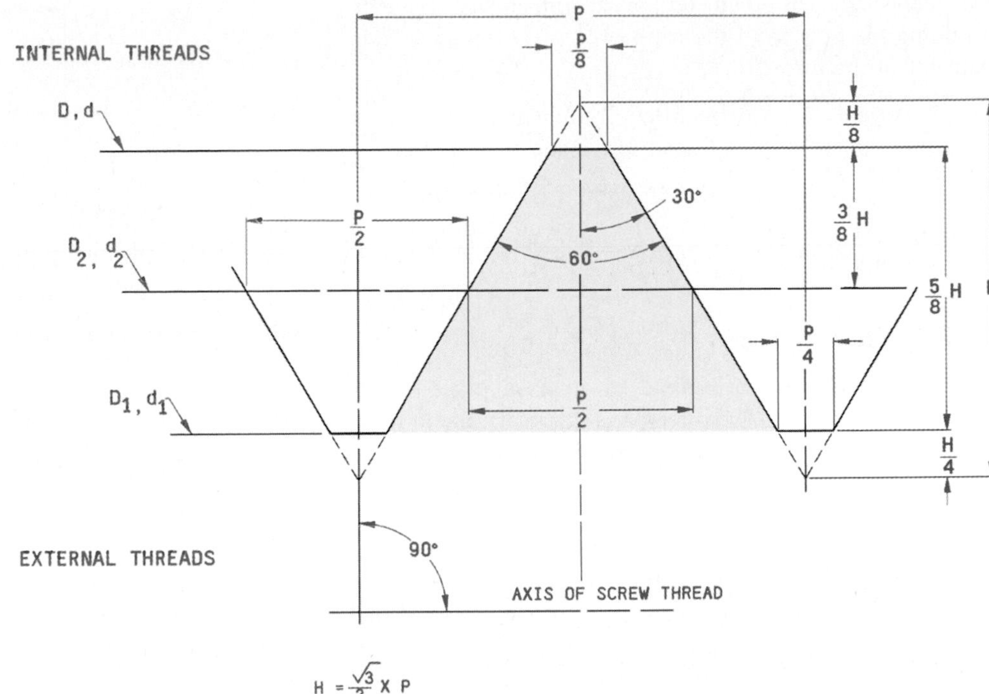

FIGURE 17.6 Basic M Thread Profile (ISO 68 Basic Profile)

threads are similar to Acme threads and also are used to transmit power.

The knuckle thread form is for sheet metal products such as the base of a light bulb, bottle and jar tops, and plastic bottles and caps. Buttress threads are found in high-stress designs and can transmit power along the axis in one direction.

ISO metric threads (Fig. 17.6) are the internationally recognized standard for thread forms. The ISO thread is very similar to the UN thread form except that its thread depth is not as great. The ISO thread has the same basic profile as the UN thread form.

The Unified National thread form (Fig. 17.7) is used in the United States and is practically identical to the obsolete American National thread form. In fact, threads manufactured to either form are functionally interchangeable. American National threads are designated as N, NC, NF, NEF, or NS. Unified National threads are designated similarly: UN, UNC, UNF, UNR, UNEF, UNS, or UNM.

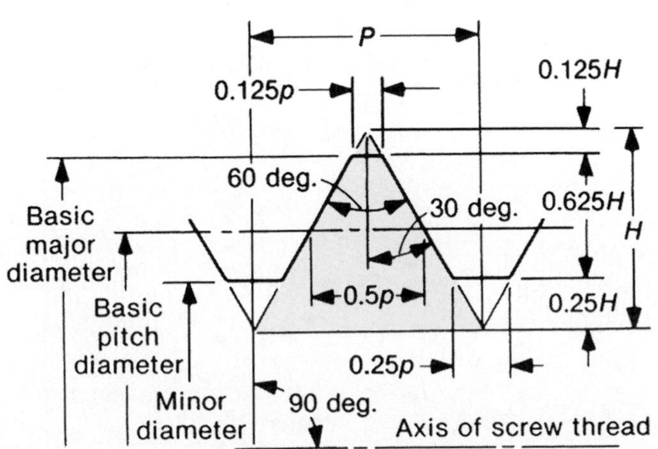

FIGURE 17.7 Basic Profile for UN and UNR Screw Threads

17.2.1 Thread Terms

The following terms are used throughout the chapter.

Class of thread An alphanumerical designation to indicate the standard grade of tolerance and allowance specified for a thread

Crest The top surface joining the two sides of the thread

Depth of thread engagement The radial distance, crest to crest, by which the thread forms overlap between two assembled mating threads

Major diameter The diameter of the major cylinder, that is, the distance across the crests of the thread

Minor diameter The diameter of the minor cylinder, that is, the root diameter of the thread

Nominal size The designation used for general identification of a thread, based on the major diameter

Pitch The axial distance from a point on one screw thread to the corresponding point on the next screw thread; equals the lead divided by the number of thread starts

Profile of thread The contour of a screw thread ridge and groove delineated by a cutting plane passing through the thread axis; also called *form of thread*

Root The bottom surface joining the two sides of the thread

Root diameter The diameter of an imaginary cylinder bounding the bottom of the roots of a screw thread (minor diameter of the thread)

Thread designations A capital letter abbreviation of names used to designate various thread forms and thread series

Thread series Groups of diameter/pitch combinations distinguished from each other by the number of threads per unit of measurement

17.2.2 Thread Parts

The configuration of the thread in an axial plane is the **thread form** (profile). The three parts that make the form of a thread are the crest, the root, and the flank (Fig. 17.7). The **crest** of a thread is at the top, the **root** is on the bottom, and the **flank** joins them. The **fundamental triangle** (shaded part of Fig. 17.7) is the triangle formed when the thread profile is extended to a sharp **V** at both the crest and the root. The height of the fundamental triangle (H) is the distance between the crest and the root diameters (for Unified threads, $H = 0.866025 \times$ thread pitch).

A thread having full form at both the crests and the roots is a complete or **full-form thread.** When either the crest or the root is not fully formed, it is an **incomplete thread.** Incomplete threads occur at the ends of externally threaded fasteners that are pointed (conical), at thread runouts where the threaded length blends into the unthreaded shank, and at the countersinks on the faces of nuts and tapped holes.

Thread pitch (P) is the distance, measured parallel to the thread axis, between corresponding points on adjacent threads. Unified screw threads are designated in **threads per inch,** which is the number of complete threads occurring in one inch of threaded length. Thread pitch is the reciprocal of threads per inch. The standard inch scale can be placed along the threads when a screw thread pitch gage is unavailable (Fig. 17.8). Counting the number of threads in one inch will give the threads-per-inch measurement.

The **pitch diameter** is the diameter of a theoretical cylinder that passes through the threads such that the widths

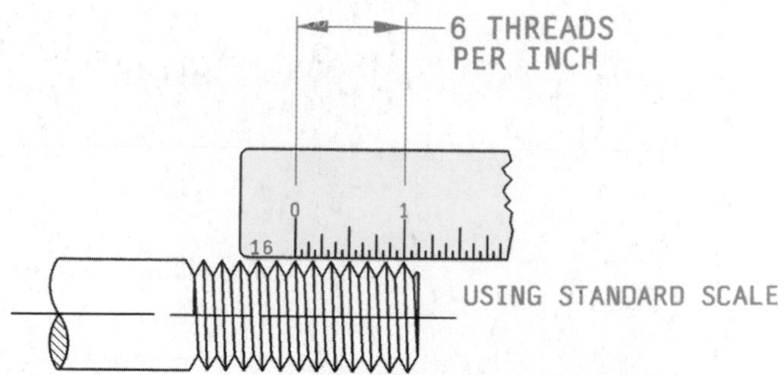

FIGURE 17.8 Using a Scale to Measure Threads per Inch

of the thread ridges and the thread widths would each equal one-half of the thread pitch (Fig. 17.9).

The combination of allowances and tolerances in mating threads, called the **fit,** is a measure of tightness or looseness between them. A **clearance fit** is one that always provides a free-running assembly. An **interference fit** is one that always results in a positive interference between the threads.

When assembling externally threaded fasteners into internally threaded nuts or tapped holes, the axial distance of contact of the fully formed threads is the **length of thread engagement** (Fig. 17.10). The distance these threads overlap in a radial direction is the **depth of thread engagement.**

17.2.3 Right-Hand and Left-Hand Threads

Unless otherwise specified, threads are right-hand. A left-hand thread turns counterclockwise to advance (Fig. 17.11). Figure 17.12 shows a turnbuckle that is designed with both right-hand and left-hand threads. When the buckle is turned in one direction, it will pull both rods together, thus tightening the connection.

17.2.4 Thread Lead

The **lead** of a thread is the axial distance it travels in one complete turn (the axial distance between two consecutive crests). Since the lead is the axial distance a crest will

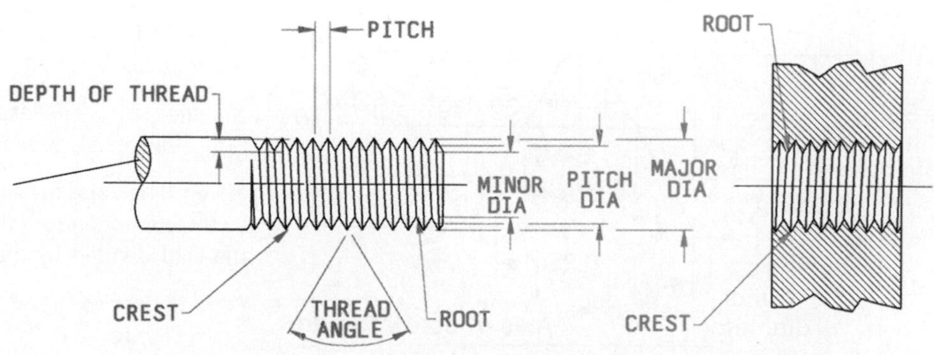

FIGURE 17.9 Unified National Thread Terminology

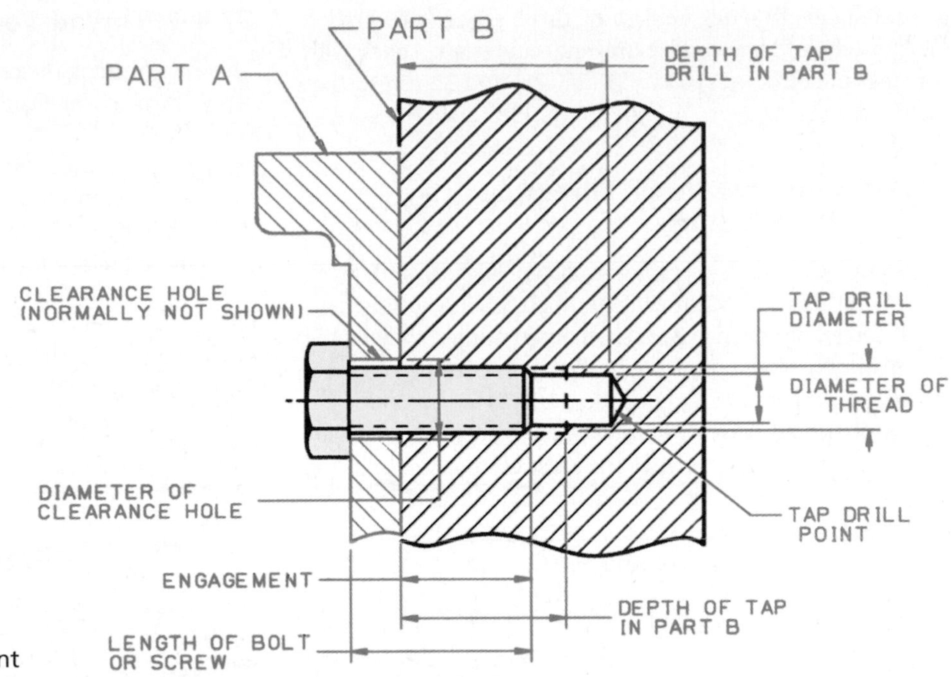

FIGURE 17.10 Thread Engagement

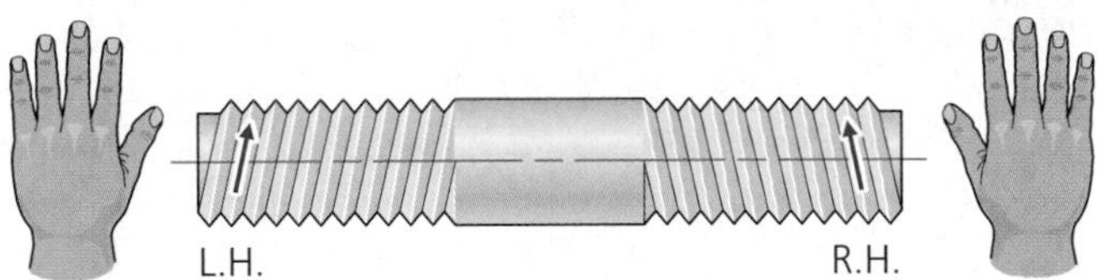

FIGURE 17.11 Right-Hand and Left-Hand Threads

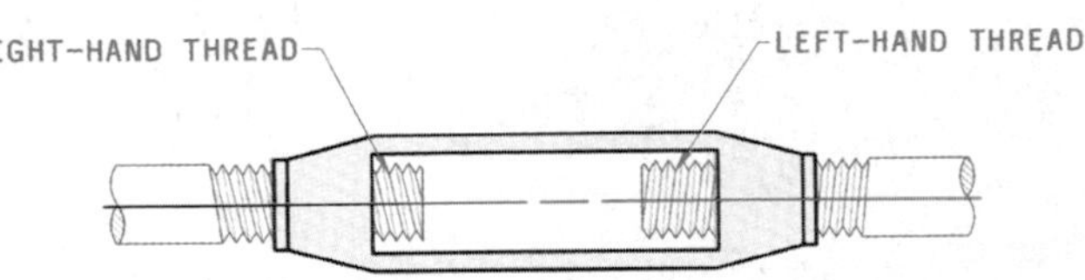

FIGURE 17.12 Turnbuckle

advance in one complete turn, **single threads** have a lead equal to the pitch, **double threads** have a lead equal to twice the pitch, and **triple threads** have a lead of thrice the pitch (Fig. 17.13).

17.3 UNIFIED NATIONAL THREAD SERIES

Thread series are groups of diameter–pitch combinations that differ by the number of threads per inch. For fasteners, the popular thread series are Unified coarse, fine, and 8-pitch. The two general series classifications are *standard* and *special*.

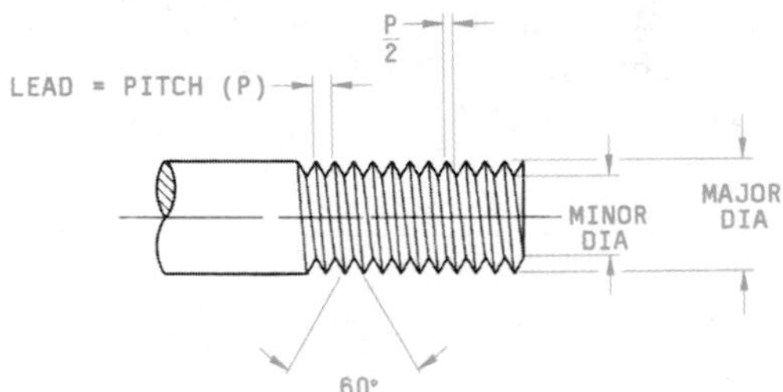

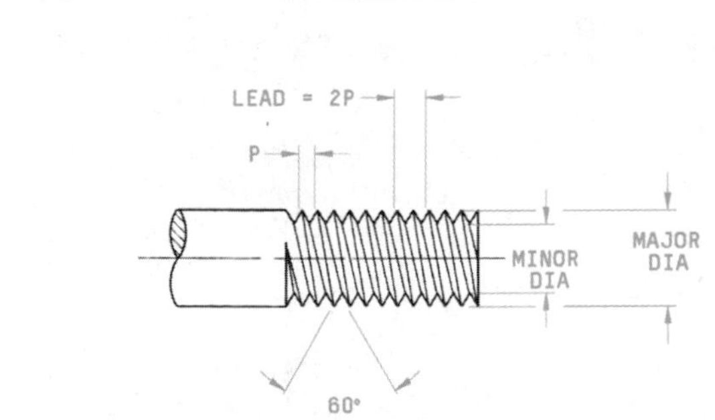

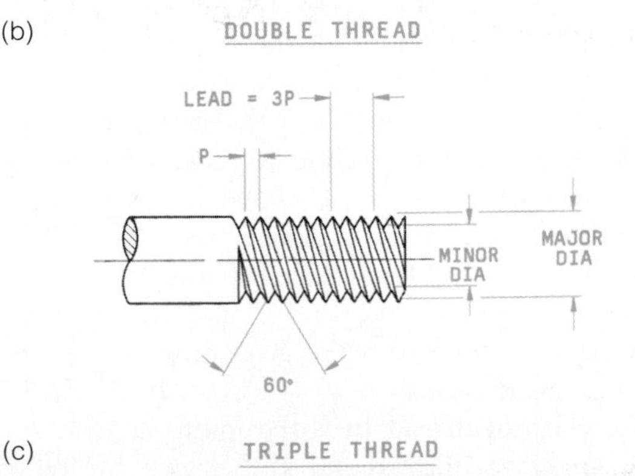

FIGURE 17.13 Single, Double and Triple Threads

The standard series consist of three series with graded pitches (coarse, fine, and extra-fine) and eight series with constant pitches (4, 6, 8, 12, 16, 20, 28, and 32 threads per inch).

17.3.1 Constant-Pitch Thread Series Applications

The various constant-pitch series (UN/UNR), with 4, 6, 8, 12, 16, 20, 28, and 32 threads per inch, offer a comprehensive range of diameter–pitch combinations where the threads in the coarse, fine, and extra-fine series do not meet the particular requirements of the design.

The **8-thread series** (8UN) is a uniform-pitch series for large diameters or is a compromise between coarse and fine thread series. Although originally intended for high-pressure-joint bolts and nuts, it is now widely used as a substitute for the coarse thread series for diameters larger than 1 inch.

The **12-thread series** (12UN) is a uniform-pitch series for large diameters requiring threads of medium-fine pitch. Although originally intended for boiler applications, it now serves as a continuation of the fine thread series for diameters larger than 12 inches.

The **16-thread series** (16UN) is a uniform-pitch series for large diameters requiring fine-pitch threads. It is suitable for adjusting collars and retaining nuts, and also serves as a continuation of the extra-fine thread series for diameters larger than $1\frac{11}{16}$ inch.

17.4 SCREW THREAD SELECTION

The first consideration in selecting a screw thread is the length of thread engagement required between threaded components (Fig. 17.10). For fastening applications, the lengths of engagement are derived from thread formulas based on the basic major diameter, the nominal size of the thread, and the material of the internal threaded part. The basic diameter of the thread is D. For steel screws, the length of engagement in mating materials should equal D for steel; 1.50 × D for cast iron, brass, bronze, or zinc; 2.00 × D for forged aluminum; 2.50 × D for cast aluminum and forged magnesium; and 3.00 × D for cast magnesium or plastic.

Thread form is the second consideration. Normally, the choice is limited to UNC, UNF, or SI metric for fasteners. Other thread forms, such as square, Acme, buttress, knuckle, and worm, are used for special applications.

Thread series is the third consideration. The Unified Screw Thread Standard Series gives preference to the coarse and fine thread series.

The **class of thread fit** is the fourth consideration. The class of threads determines the degree of looseness or tightness between mating threads.

17.4.1 Thread Form

There are dozens of screw thread forms. However, for inch series mechanical fasteners, only three have significance: UN, UNR, and UNJ. All are 60° symmetrical threads with essentially the same profile. The principal difference between them is the contour at the root of the external thread. For metric fasteners, SI metric threads are designated.

UNR applies only to external threads. The difference between UN and UNR threads, in addition to designation, is that a flat or optional rounded root contour is specified for UN threads, while only a rounded root contour is specified for UNR threads. The design of UNJ threads developed from a search for an optimum thread form. This thread has root radius limits of 0.150 to 0.180 × thread pitch.

17.5 STANDARD THREAD FITS

Thread fit is a measure of looseness or tightness between mating threads. **Classes of fit** are specific combinations of allowances and tolerances applied to external and internal threads.

Unified inch screw threads have three thread classes for external threads, 1A, 2A, and 3A, and three for internal threads, 1B, 2B, and 3B. All are clearance fits, which means they assemble without interference. *The higher the class number, the tighter the fit.* The designator "A" denotes an external thread; "B" denotes an internal thread. The mating of Class 1A and 1B threads provides the loosest fit; the mating of Class 3A with 3B the tightest.

Additionally, there is a Class 5 thread fit. This is an interference fit, which means that the external and internal threads are toleranced so that a positive interference occurs when they are assembled. Class 5 interference fits are standard only for coarse thread series in sizes 1 in. and smaller.

The requirements of screw-thread fits are determined by use and should be specified by indicating the proper classes for the components. For example, a Class 2A external thread should be used with a Class 2B internal thread. When choosing a class fit for threads, no tighter thread fit should be selected than the function of the parts requires.

Classes 1A and 1B are very loosely toleranced threads, with an allowance applied to the external thread. These classes are ideally suited when quick and easy assembly and disassembly are a prime design consideration. They are standard only for coarse and fine thread series in sizes $\frac{1}{4}$ in. and larger. They are rarely specified for mechanical fasteners.

Classes 2A and 2B are by far the most popular thread classes specified for inch series mechanical fasteners. Approximately 90% of all commercial and industrial fasteners produced in North America have this class of thread fit.

Classes 3A and 3B are suited to closely toleranced fasteners, such as socket cap screws, set screws, and other high-strength fasteners. Classes 3A and 3B have restrictive tolerances and no allowance.

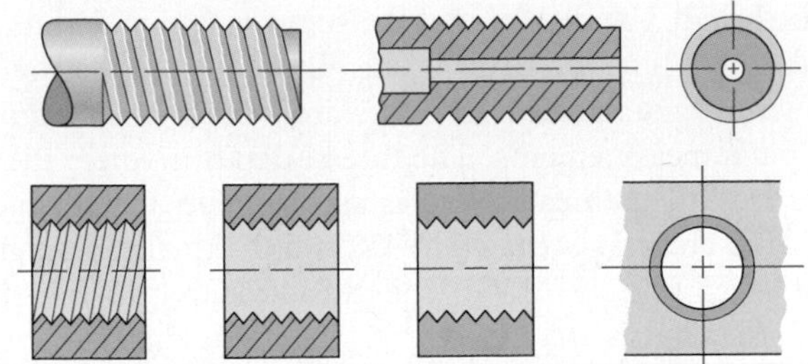

FIGURE 17.14 Detailed Thread Representation

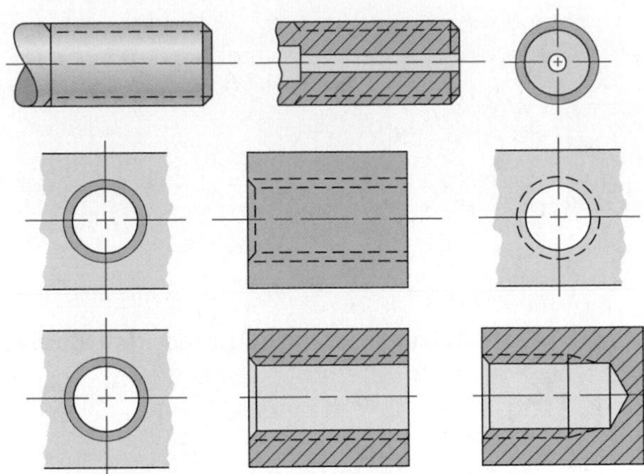

FIGURE 17.16 Simplified Thread Representation

17.6 THREAD REPRESENTATION

On working drawings, threads are seldom drawn as they would actually appear; instead, notes and specifications are given. The American National Standards Institute (ANSI) recognizes three conventions for representing screw threads on drawings: **detailed** (Fig. 17.14), **schematic** (Fig. 17.15), and **simplified** (Fig. 17.16) representations.

The detailed representation is an approximation of the actual appearance of screw threads. Minor modification includes showing the thread profile as a sharp V, where the actual thread has flat crest and root. Also, the normal helices are shown as straight lines connecting the thread, crest to crest and root to root. The detailed conventional representation is limited to cases in which the basic diameter is more than 1 in. and where detail or relation of component parts could be confused by less realistic thread representation. When internal holes are drawn by the detailed method, the lines representing the threads are sometimes omitted.

The **simplified method** showing internal threads and the simplified method to represent internal threads in a section are shown in Figure 17.17. Figure 17.18(b) shows how the simplified method represents external threads.

The **schematic method** is used only for external threads [Fig. 17.18(a)] or sectioned internal threads (Fig. 17.19), *not* for internal nonsectioned threads.

Figure 17.20 shows the **detailed method** of representing internal threads in a section. Notice that the detailed method can include or exclude the lines of the threads. External threads drawn with detailed representation are shown in Figure 17.18(c).

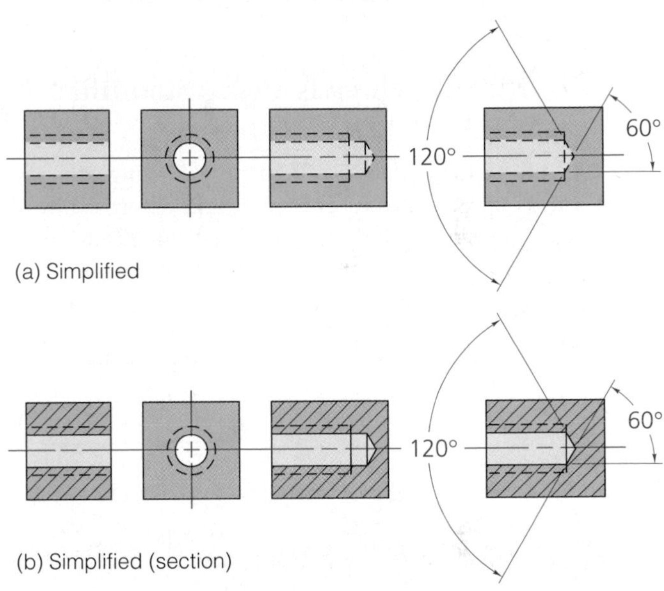

FIGURE 17.17 Internal Simplified Thread Representation

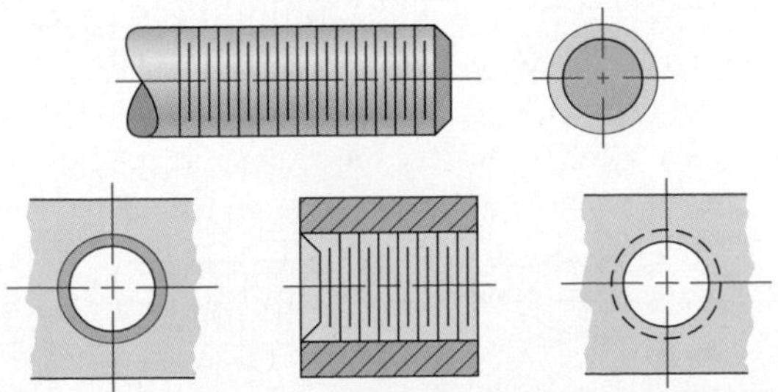

FIGURE 17.15 Schematic Thread Representation

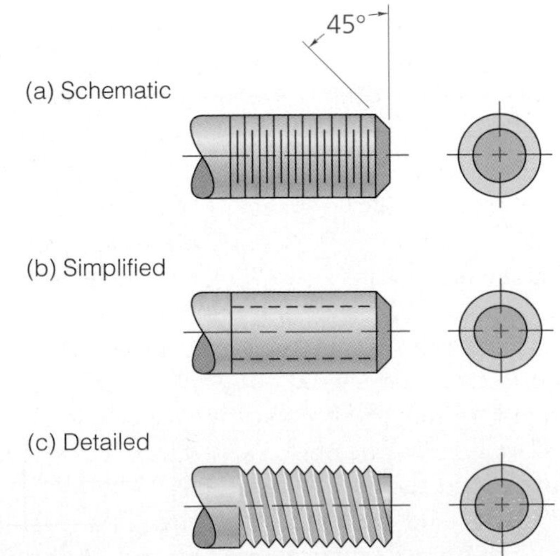

FIGURE 17.18 External Thread Representation

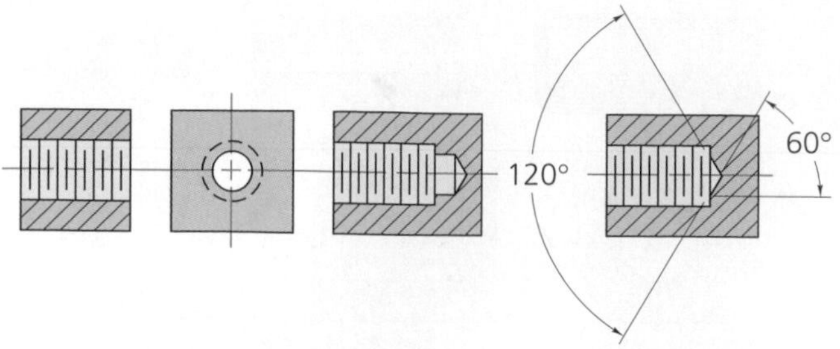

FIGURE 17.19 Internal Schematic Thread Representation

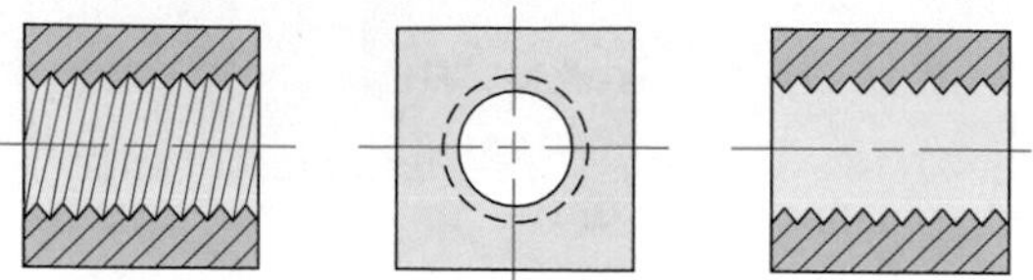

FIGURE 17.20 Internal Detailed Thread Representation

17.6.1 Drawing Threads Using Simplified Representation

The simplified method is executed by following the steps shown in Figure 17.21. Both internal and external threads are drawn by this method. Here, external threads are being constructed. The diameter of the screw is drawn and its end established [Fig. 17.21(a)]. The pitch (*P*) is measured as shown in Figure 17.21(b). Lines are drawn at 60° through the pitch measurements. The thread depth is where the 60° lines cross. The thread depth is used to draw the chamfered end. The chamfer is drawn at 45° and the threaded length is established [Fig. 17.21(c)]. The thread depth is used to draw the dashed lines that represent the minor diameter of the thread [Fig. 17.21(d)].

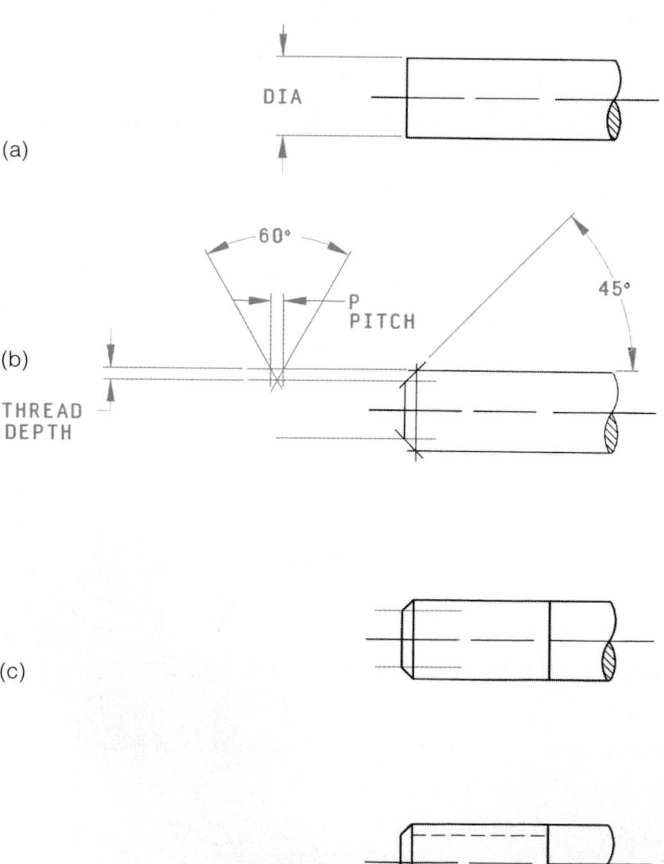

FIGURE 17.21 Drawing Threads Using Simplified Thread Representation

17.6.2 Drawing Threads Using Schematic Representation

Schematic representation is almost as effective as detailed representation and is much easier to draw. The alternating lines, symbolic of the thread roots and crests, are usually drawn perpendicular to the axis of the thread or sometimes slanted to the approximate angle of the thread helix. This construction should not be used for internal threads or sections of external threads.

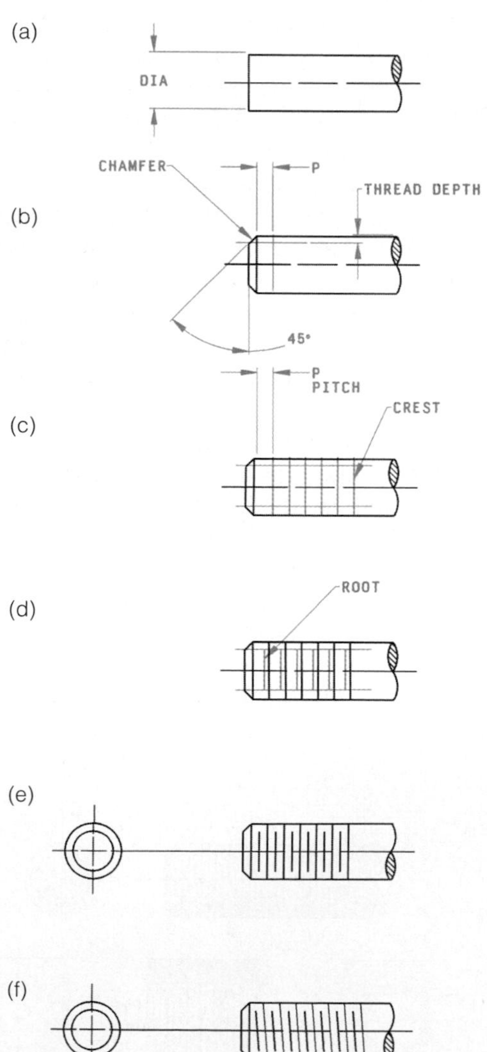

FIGURE 17.22 Drawing Threads Using Schematic Thread Representation

Drawing schematic threads is similar to the simplified method. The screw diameter and end are drawn first [Fig. 17.22(a)]. The chamfer is completed using 45° and the thread depth [Fig. 17.22(b)]. The pitch (*P*) is used to establish the spacing of the thread crests [Fig. 17.22(c)]. The root lines are drawn up to the thread depth [Fig. 17.22(d)]. The thread is completed by darkening in the lines [Fig. 17.22(e)]. This is called the **uniform-line method.** The slope-line representation is shown in [Fig. 17.22(f)]. The slope angle is equal to one-half the pitch. In actual industrial practice, drafters draw the screw diameter, construct a 45° chamfer, and use the chamfer depth to locate the thread root.

17.6.3 Drawing Threads Using Detailed Representation

The detailed thread representation is drawn only when a mechanical advantage must be calculated or analyzed graphically (or for illustrations). Figure 17.23 shows four steps in drawing threads with detailed representation. Step (a) is the same as for simplified and schematic thread representation. The diameter of the screw thread is layed out and one-half of the pitch is measured. Using the pitch (*P*), the top and the bottom lines of the shaft are divided along its length into the required number of threads. The sloped lines (crest lines) are drawn with an angle of one-half the pitch. The threads are drawn as sharp V's at 60°, as in Figure 17.23(b). The ends of the root lines will be established where the thread lines cross at the root. The root lines are drawn by connecting the roots [Fig. 17.23(c)]. Figure 17.23(d) shows the threads darkened.

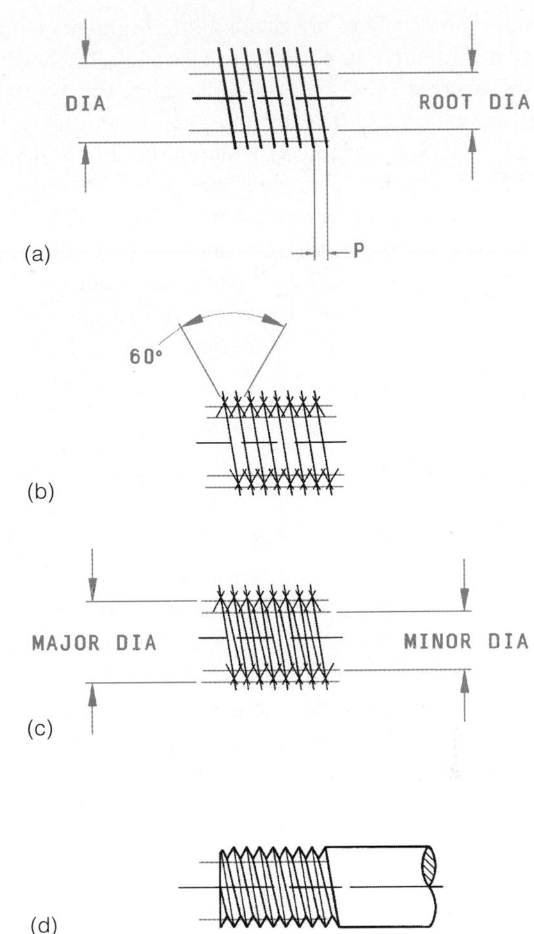

FIGURE 17.23 Drawing Threads Using Detailed Thread Representation

17.6.4 How to Draw Acme Threads

A step-by-step procedure for drawing Acme threads is given in Figure 17.24. The Acme thread has a depth equal to one-half its pitch. The drawing is begun by sketching the shaft diameter (major diameter), the minor diameter, and the pitch diameters with construction lines [Fig. 17.24(a)].

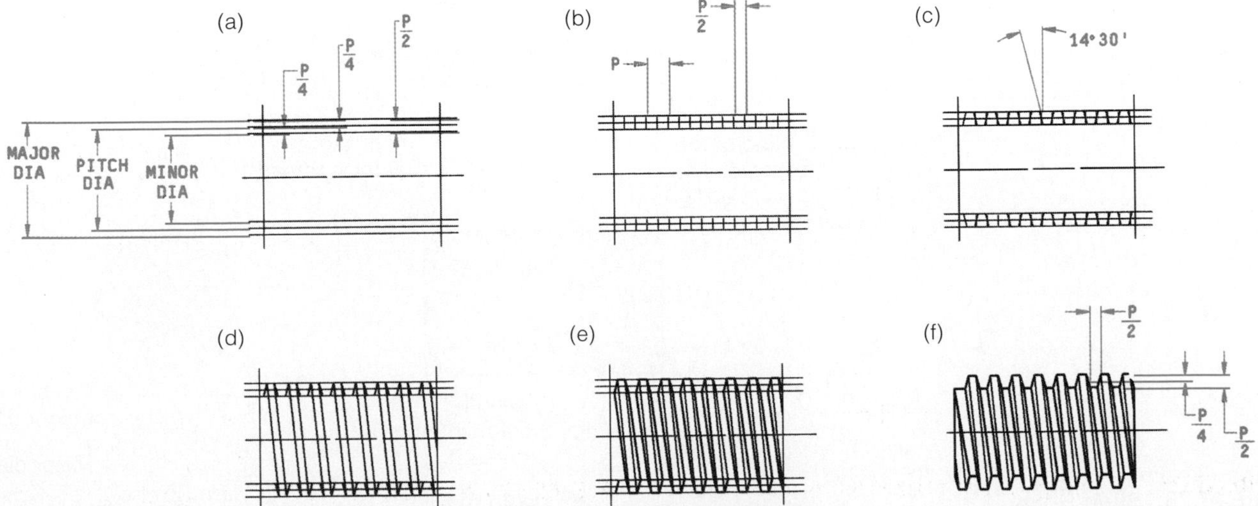

FIGURE 17.24 Drawing Acme Threads Using Detailed Thread Representation

The pitch diameter lines are divided into segments equaling one-half the pitch [Fig. 17.24(b)]. The angle of the thread profile is one-half of 29° ($14\frac{1}{2}$°). Usually, 15° is used to simplify the procedure. The 15° lines are drawn through the half-pitch distances established along the pitch diameter lines [Fig. 17.24(c)]. The angled lines will fall between the major diameter and the minor diameter [Fig. 17.24(d)]. The crests are completed and the root lines are then drawn [Fig. 17.24(e)]. The ends of the threads are completed, the construction lines are erased, and the drawing is darkened [Fig. 17.24(f)]. Detailed Acme threads are shown in Figure 17.25.

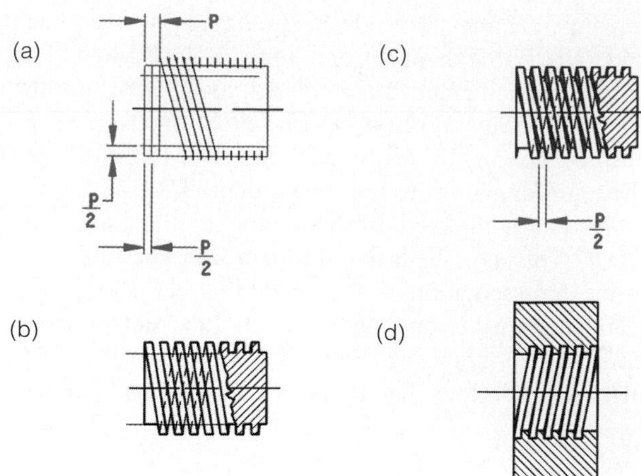

FIGURE 17.25 Detailed Acme Threads

17.6.5 Tap Drills

Threaded holes are first drilled and then tapped (Fig. 17.26). Because the tapping tool extends far enough into the hole to thread the required length of full threads, the tap drill must extend beyond the required thread depth. The major diameter represents the outside diameter of the thread, and the minor diameter represents the tap drill diameter.

Figure 17.27 shows how to represent tapped holes by the simplified method. The drilled hole is drawn accurately, with its diameter and depth as shown. The drill tip is 118°, but for simplicity it is drawn at 170° (30° from the horizontal). The tap drill is represented the same for holes. For drilled and tapped holes, the depth of the full thread is drawn accurately. The tap drill is drawn 3 × the pitch below the threaded portion. This distance includes a number of incomplete threads created by the chamfer end of the tapping tool. Although normally drawn at 3 × the pitch, this distance is actually determined by the drill size as to whether to use a bottoming tap or a plug tap. In some cases, the thread will

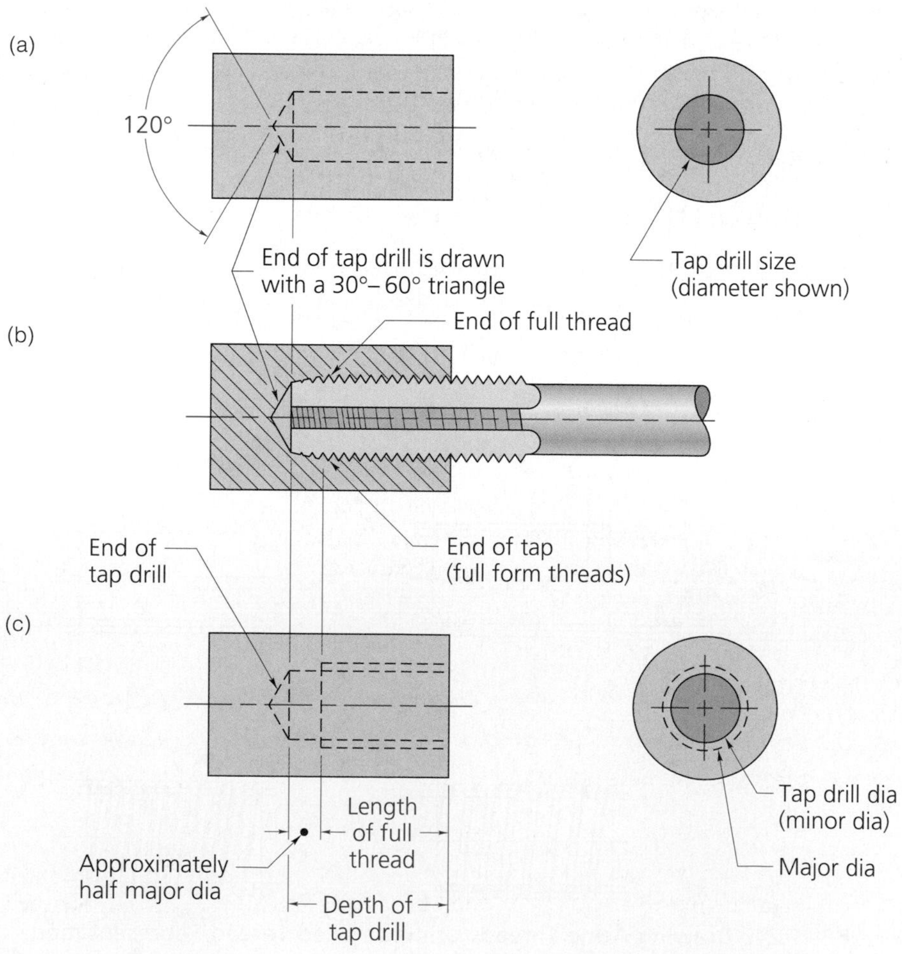

FIGURE 17.26 Blind Holes and Taps

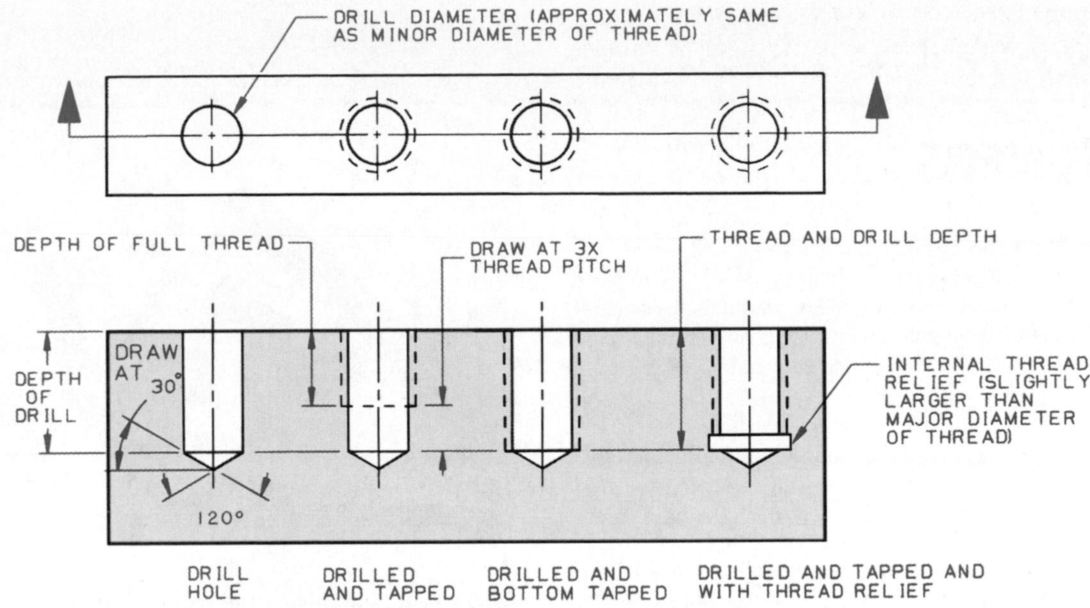

FIGURE 17.27 Drilling and Tapping Holes

extend to the bottom of the drilled hole, or a **thread relief** will be required.

An internal thread relief is slightly larger than the major diameter of the thread (Fig. 17.27). The circular views of the threaded holes show the tap drill as a solid line and the major thread (major diameter) as a dashed line.

17.7 DESIGNATING THREADS AND THREAD NOTES

The thread designation includes the nominal diameter, the number of threads per inch (or the pitch and lead), the letter symbol of the thread series, the number and letter of the thread class, and any qualifying information. The thread length, the hole size, and the chamfer or countersink may be included in the note or dimensioned on the drawing of the part.

The series symbols and the class numbers identify the controlling thread standard and define the details of thread design, dimensions, and tolerances not specifically covered on the drawing.

Series, Class, and Dimensional Letters in Thread Designations

A	external, American, aeronautical
B	internal
C	coupling, coarse, centralizing
EXT	external
EF	extra-fine
F	fine, fuel and oil
G	general purpose, gas, pitch allowance
H	house
I	intermediate
INT	internal
J	controlled radius root
L	lead, locknut
LE	length of engagement
LH	left-hand (absence of LH indicates RH, or right-hand)
M	metric, mechanical, microscope, miniature
MOD	modified
N	national
O	outlet, objective
P	pipe, pitch
R	railing, rounded root, American National Class 1 allowance
RH	right-hand
S	straight
SE	special engagement
SPL	special
T	taper
UN	unified

17.7.1 Thread Designation Examples

The designation and the pitch diameter limits are in note form and referenced to the drawing of the thread with a leader line. The following example illustrates the elements of a designation of the screw thread:

.250-20 UNC-2A

where

.250 = nominal diameter in decimal form
20 = number of threads per inch of pitch and lead

Focus On . . .

FASTENERS

How a product is fastened together is important to both the manufacturer and the customer or user of the product. We have all complained about the difficulty and cost to replace some minor component in an assembled product. Obviously, if rapid and easy disassembly were considered early in the design stage of the product, everyone would save time and money.

A fastener is any kind of device or method that is used to hold parts together. The permanent fastener choices are soldering, brazing, riveting, welding, and adhesives. Removable fasteners include nuts and bolts, screws, studs, pins, rings, and keys. Snap fits can also be designed into the part itself, eliminating the need for separate fasteners.

The choice of a suitable material for the fastener is also important. Because new materials, like carbon-fiber composites, are being employed, the choice of fastener material is becoming increasingly complex. Also, fasteners used on assemblies (for instance, aircraft and automobiles) must function in all weather conditions without deteriorating in a reasonable amount of time.

Various fasteners.

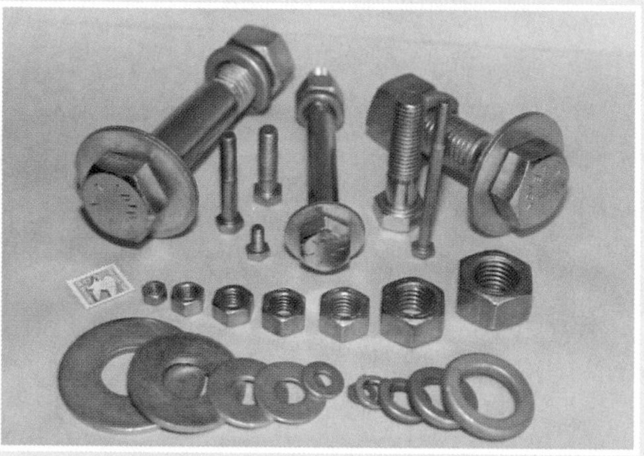

Industrial fasteners.

One of the most popular removable fasteners is the screw. Archimedes, the Greek mathematician, first used the idea in a screw conveyor to raise water. The threads on a screw provide a fast and easy method for fastening two parts together. However, screws are not the method of choice in automated assembly because of the complex motion required for insertion. Standards are being established to unify screw threads throughout the world. These standards would cut the costs of parts, reduce paperwork, simplify the inventory process, and improve quality control.

The selection of the proper fastening method and material is crucial for a product to be an economic success. The cost of the fastener itself is small compared to the costs associated with that fastener over the lifetime of the assembly. Every designer and drafter in industry knows how complicated the proper selection of a fastener can be, particularly when design for disassembly might be as important or more important than design for assembly.

UNC = thread form, series, and tolerance formulation symbol
2 = class number
A = internal or external symbol (A is external)

Thread sizes are shown as decimal callouts, except for fractional sizes. When specifying decimal sizes, a minimum of three or a maximum of four decimal places, omitting any zero in the fourth decimal place, should be shown as the nominal size:

1.000-8 UNC-2A

$1\frac{3}{4}$-8 UN-2A

Numbered sizes may also be shown; the decimal equivalent should be in parentheses:

No. 10(.190)-32 UNF-2A

Unless otherwise specified, threads are right-hand; a left-hand thread is designated LH:

$\frac{1}{4}$-20 UNC-3A-LH

17.8 ACME THREADS

There are four classes of general-purpose Acme threads and five classes of centralizing Acme threads. The general-purpose Acme threads have clearances on all diameters for free movement and may be used in assemblies where both internal and external members are supported to prevent movement.

There is only one class of stub Acme thread for general usage. It is the Class 2G (general-purpose) thread, which uses two threads with modified thread depths. Stub Acme threads are for power applications.

When designating Acme threads, the designation covers the nominal size, the number of threads per inch, the thread form symbol, and the thread class symbol:

1.750-4 ACME-2G

where

1.750 = nominal decimal size
4 = number of threads per inch
ACME = thread form and series symbol
2G = thread class symbol

17.9 BUTTRESS THREADS

Buttress threads are for high-stress applications where the stress is along its axis in only one direction. The buttress thread is designated either **butt** or **push-butt.** Since the design of most components having buttress threads is so special, no diameter–pitch series is recommended. The two classes of buttress threads are Class 2 (standard grade) and Class 3 (precision grade).

When only the "butt" designation is used, the thread is a "pull"-type buttress, with the clearance flank angle of 45° leading and the pressure flange angle of 7° following. In thread designations on drawings and in specifications, the designation should be shown as in the following example:

2.500-8 BUTT-2A-LH

where

2.500 = nominal size (basic major diameter in inches)
8 = threads per inch (TPI)
BUTT = buttress form of thread, pull-type
2 = class 2 (medium) thread
A = external thread
LH = left-hand

17.10 METRIC THREADS

A wide variety of threaded fasteners are manufactured with metric threads. This section contains general metric standards for a 60° symmetrical screw thread with a basic ISO 68 profile designated "M."

The simplified, schematic, and detailed methods of thread representation also apply to metric screw threads. The following additional definitions apply to metric threads: In ISO metric thread standards, **bolt thread (external thread)** describes all external threads. All symbols associated with external threads are designated with lowercase letters.

In ISO metric thread standards, **nut thread (internal thread)** describes all internal threads. All symbols associated with internal threads are designated with uppercase letters.

17.10.1 Metric Classes of Fit

There are two recognized classes of thread fit. One is for general-purpose applications and contains tolerance classes 6H/6g; the other is used where closer thread fits are required and contains tolerance classes 6H/4g to 6g.

The **tolerance grade** is indicated by a number. The system provides for a series of tolerance grades for each of the four screw thread parameters: minor diameter, internal thread (4, 5, 6, 7, 8); major diameter, external thread (4, 6, 8); pitch diameter, internal thread (4, 5, 6, 7, 8); and pitch diameter, external thread (3, 4, 5, 6, 7, 8, 9).

The **tolerance position,** the allowance, is indicated by a letter. A capital letter is for internal threads and a lowercase letter for external threads. The system provides a series of tolerance positions for internal and external threads:

Internal threads G, H
External threads g, h

The tolerance grade is given first, followed by the tolerance position—for example, 4g or 5H. To designate the tolerance class, the grade and position of the pitch diameter is shown first followed by the major diameter (external thread) or the minor diameter (internal thread)—for example, 4g6g for an external thread and 5H6H for an internal thread. If the two grades and positions are identical, it is not necessary to repeat the symbols. Thus, 4g alone stands for 4g4g, and 5H alone means 5H5H.

17.10.2 Designation of Metric Screw Threads

Metric screw threads are identified by the letter M for the thread form profile, followed by the nominal diameter size and the pitch, expressed in millimeters, separated by a × sign and followed by the tolerance class separated by a dash (-) from the pitch.

The simplified international practice for designating coarse-pitch M-profile metric screw threads is to leave off the pitch. Thus, an M14 × 2 thread is designated just M14. However, to prevent misunderstanding, it is mandatory to use the value for pitch in all designations shown on drawings.

The thread acceptability gaging system requirements of ANSI B1.3M may be added to the thread size designation. The numbers are shown in parentheses: (22), (21). The following is an example of a close-tolerance external thread designation:

M8 × 1.25-4g6g (22)

Here are two examples of internal thread designation:

M6 × 1-6H (21)

M6 × 1-5H6H (21)

Unless otherwise specified in the designation, the screw thread helix is right-hand. When a left-hand thread is specified, the tolerance class designation is followed by a dash and **LH**. The following is an example of a left-hand external thread with an **M** profile:

M6 × 1-4969-LH

where

- M = metric thread symbol, ISO 68 metric thread form
- 6 = nominal size in millimeters
- 1 = pitch in millimeters
- 4g6h = tolerance class
- 4g = major diameter tolerance symbol (4 = tolerance position; G = tolerance grade)
- 6g = pitch diameter tolerance symbol (6 = tolerance position; G = tolerance grade)
- LH = left-hand

A fit between *mating threads* is indicated by the internal thread tolerance class, followed by the external thread tolerance class, separated by a slash, for example:

M6 × 1-6H/6g

M6 × 1-6H/4g6g

17.11 DIMENSIONING THREADS

The thread length dimensioned on the drawing should be the gaging length, or the length of threads having full form. That is, the incomplete threads are outside or beyond the length specified.

Should there be reason to control or limit the number of incomplete threads on parts having a full-body diameter shank, the overall thread length, including the vanish (runout or incomplete) threads, are represented and dimensioned on the drawing, in addition to the full thread length (Fig. 17.28). All representation of fully formed threads should indicate the *thread runout* (incomplete threads), as shown in the figure. Overall thread length should be represented and dimensioned on the drawing, and should include the thread runout.

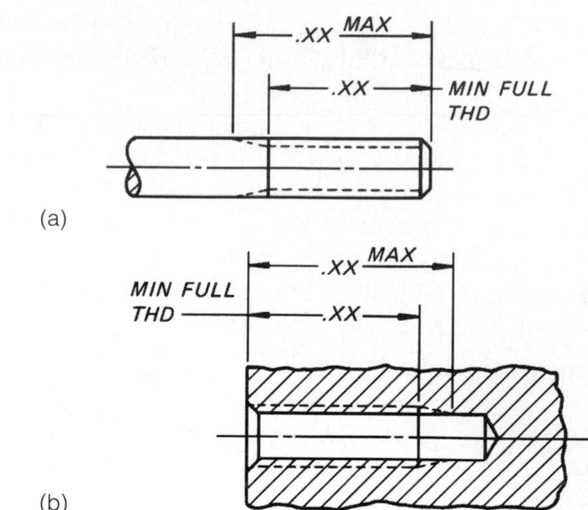

FIGURE 17.28 Dimensioning Thread Length

17.11.1 Thread Chamfers

If required, thread **chamfers**, or **countersinks**, should be specified on the drawing. It is preferable to specify the chamfer by length and diameter, to avoid confusion. Figure 17.29 shows three methods of dimensioning an external chamfer. The chamfer length should be 0.75 to 1.25 times the pitch, rounded off to a two- or three-place decimal.

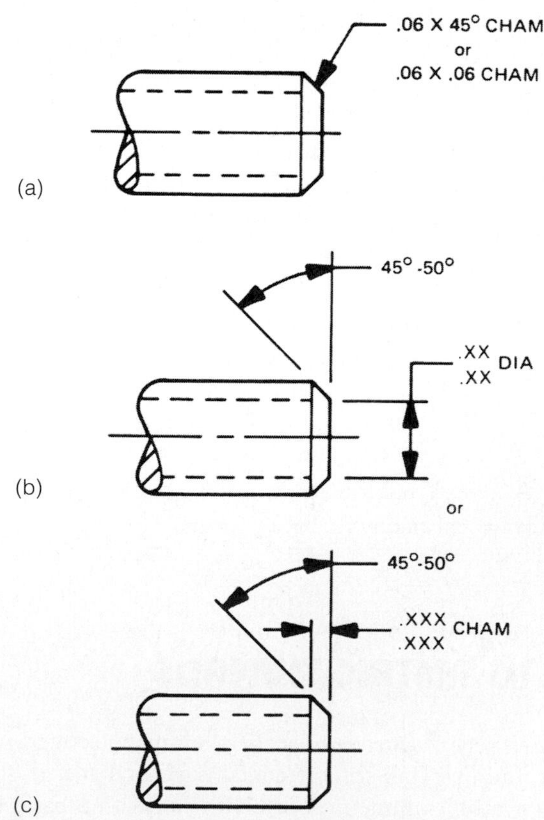

FIGURE 17.29 Dimensioning Chamfers at the End of External Threads

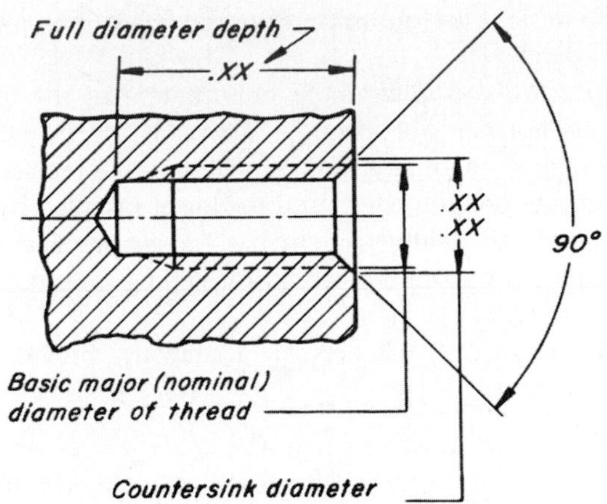

FIGURE 17.30 Dimensioning Countersink, Drill Depth, and Size on Internal Threaded Holes

When a callout cannot properly or clearly designate an internal threaded hole, the depth, size, and countersink (chamfer) are dimensioned (Fig. 17.30). If the chamfer and minor diameter are very close to being the same, the minor diameter of a thread may be eliminated to improve clarity. On end views of countersunk threaded holes where countersunk diameters and the major diameters of threads are close to being the same, the major diameter may be eliminated for clarity.

17.11.2 Threads on Drawings

Holes are located by their centers. Leaders have the arrowheads pointing toward the center in the circular views.

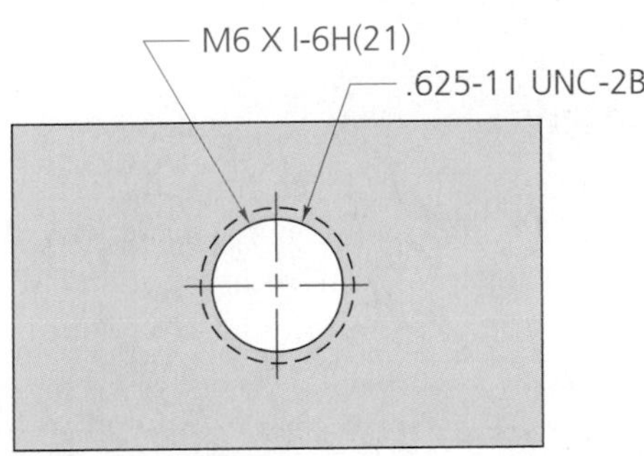

(a) With circular view

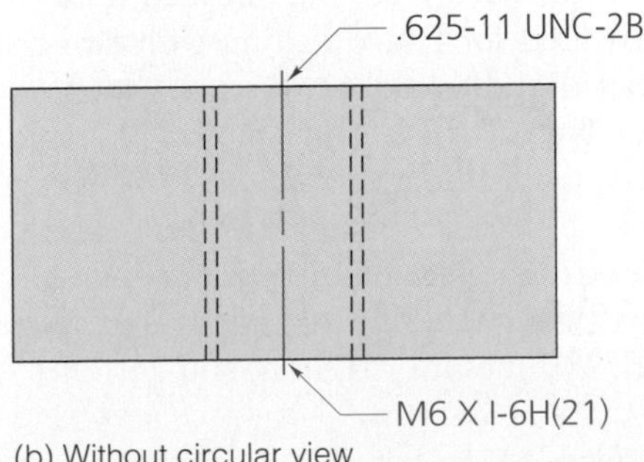

(b) Without circular view

FIGURE 17.31 Calling Out Threads on a Drawing

When the circular view is not available, the arrow of the leader line should touch the axial centerline of the hole. Figure 17.31 shows an example of UN thread callouts (they are not meant to be equivalents in the example).

The full depth of the drilled hole for **blind tapped holes** should be specified on the drawing (Figs.17.27 and 17.30). Blind holes do not go all the way through the part. If the wall at the drill point is the limiting consideration in addition to, or instead of, the full-diameter depth, the drill point depth or the *wall thickness* may be dimensioned or stated in a note. In some cases, the depth may be specified as a minimum full-diameter depth and the note DO NOT BREAK THRU should be added. Hole size limits should be shown on the drawing.

17.12 PIPE THREADS

The American National Standard taper pipe thread is tapered $\frac{1}{16}$ in. per inch ($\frac{3}{4}$ in. per ft) to ensure a tight joint at the fitting (Fig. 17.32). The crest of the thread is flattened, and the root is filled so that the depth of the thread is equal to 80% of the pitch. The number of threads per inch for a given nominal diameter can be found in Appendix C.1.

Pipe threads are designated in established trade sizes that signify a nominal diameter only. The designation of tapered threads includes the nominal size, the number of threads per inch, the thread form, and thread series symbols as shown in the following examples:

6-8 NPT		**.125-27 NPT**
	Explanation	
6 =	nominal pipe diameter in inches	= .125
8 =	number of threads per inch	= 27
N =	American Standard National thread	= N
P =	pipe	= P
T =	taper	= T

.750-14 NPSL	**12-8 NPTR**	
	Explanation	
.750 =	nominal pipe diameter in inches	= 12
14 =	number of threads per inch	= 8
N =	American National Standard thread	= N
P =	pipe	= P
S =	straight	
	taper	= T
L =	locknuts and locknut pipe threads	
	rail fittings	= R

17.12.1 Drawing Pipe Threads

Figure 17.33 shows a male (external) and female (internal) pipe thread drawn in simplified representation. The taper on a pipe thread is so slight that it does not show up on

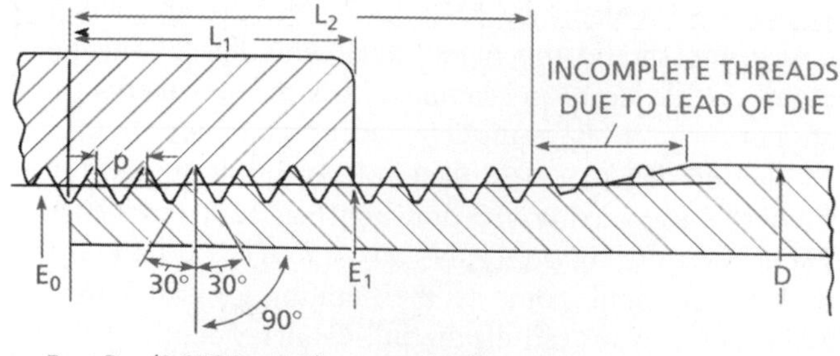

$E_0 = D - (0.050D + 1.1)p$ p = Pitch

$*E_1 = E_0 + 0.0625\ L_1$ Depth of thread = $0.80p$

$L_2 = (0.80D + 6.8)p$ Total Taper 3/4-inch per Foot

FIGURE 17.32 American National Pipe Thread (NPT)

Nominal Pipe Size	D	TPI	P	E0	E1	L1	L2
.750	.840	14	.071	.758	.778	.320	.533
3.000	3.500	8	.125	3.340	3.388	.766	1.200

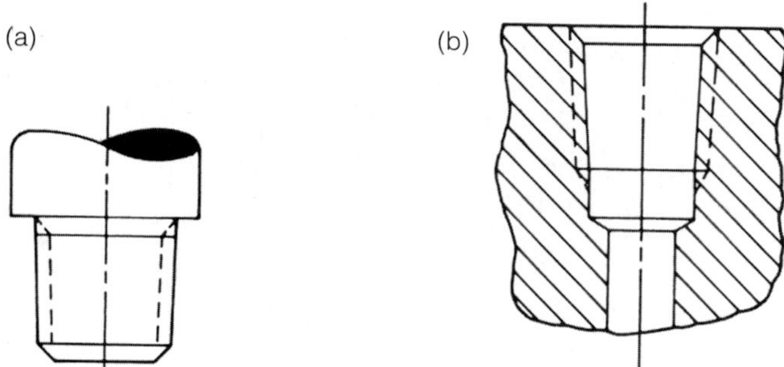

FIGURE 17.33 Internal and External Pipe Thread Representation

drawings unless it is exaggerated. It is drawn to 8 in. taper per inch. The ANSI recommendation for representing pipe threads is the same as for all other threads. The simplified form is the most common, the detailed form the least.

You May Complete Exercises 17.1 Through 17.4 at This Time

17.13 FASTENERS

Basic industrial **fasteners** (Fig. 17.34) include square and hex bolts, cap screws, carriage bolts, machine screws, plow bolts, lag screws, studs, nuts, and rivets. Other fasteners have also been standardized over the years as to type, style, usage, properties, dimensions, and tolerances.

Semipermanent assembly fasteners include bolts, screws, studs, nuts, washers, snap rings, nails, and pins. Rivets are considered **permanent fasteners**. Fastener selection is made by considering strength, appearance, durability, corrosion resistance, materials to be joined, total cost of assembly parts, and assembly and disassembly labor involved or machines and power tools required. Whenever possible, design for automated assembly with common standard parts.

The *installed cost* is far more important than the initial cost of the fastener. For example, a rivet is much cheaper than the high-strength bolt, nut, and washer that replaced it, but the greater holding power and the lower installed cost of the high-strength bolting system has for all practical purposes displaced riveting as standard fastening for structural joints.

When designating fasteners on a drawing, provide the following:

- Product name
- Nominal or actual size in fractions, decimal-equivalent, or metric units
- Thread specification, if appropriate
- Length in fractions, decimal-equivalent, or metric units
- Material and protective coating, if applicable
- Finish, where required

17.13.1 Representing Fasteners

In general, a template is employed for constructing standard fasteners. With a CAD system, a standard library of parts is normally available.

Figure 17.35 shows a sketch of two typical fasteners. The *head styles* shown are the **hex** and **socket** varieties. The *bearing surface* is that portion of the fastener that is in contact with the part being fastened (or a washer when one is used). The *point* is at the opposite end from the head and is normally chamfered. The *threaded* part of the *body* extends from the point toward the bearing surface. Some fasteners are completely threaded (the whole body) and some are partially threaded.

17.13.2 Studs

Studs are fasteners with no head but with threads at both ends of the shank. Studs come in *continuous threaded* types and *double-ended* varieties. In most applications, the stud is screwed into a workpiece on one end, and a nut is used on the other end (Fig. 17.36). In other applications, the stud has a nut on both ends and is used to secure two pieces. In Figure 17.37 the cover plate for the check valve has eight studs and sixteen nuts.

Continuous threaded studs are threaded from end to end and are often used for flange bolting with two nuts. Continuous threaded studs come in two types: Type 1, for general purpose, and Type 2, for pressure piping. If a stud is to be inserted into a tapped hole (Fig. 17.36), it is recommended that it be held in place by jamming it against the bottom of the hole. A Class 5 fit is recommended for such service. The thread engagement should be $1\frac{1}{4}$ times the diameter of the stud for steel, $1\frac{1}{2}$ times for cast iron, and $2\frac{1}{2}$ times for softer materials.

Double-ended studs come in four types: Type 1 is unfinished, Type 2 is finished and has an undersize body,

Description	Military Reference	Description	Military Reference	Description	Military Reference
—1— Pan head	MS 35204 thru MS 35219 and MS 35221 thru MS 35236	—12— Socket head cap screw	MS 35455 thru MS 35461	—23— Flat washer	MS 15795
80° to 82° —2— 82° Flat head	MS 35188 thru MS 35203 and MS 35237 thru MS 35251 and MS 35262	—13— Set screw	AN 565	—24— Lockwasher-spring	MS 35337 MS 35338 MS 35339 MS 35340
99° to 101° —3— 100° Flat head	AN 507	—14— Self-locking	Plastic pellet can be applied to all types of screws	—25— Lockwasher-ext. tooth	MS 35335
—4— Fillister head	MS 35361 and MS 35366	—15— Hex nut	MS 35649 MS 35650 MS 35690	—26— Lockwasher-int. tooth	MS 35333 MS 35334
—5— Drilled fillister head	MS 35263 thru MS 35278	—16— Self-locking nut (non-metallic collar)	Can be supplied with fibre or plastic collar. All sizes and material	—27— Lockwasher-csk. tooth	MS 35336 MS 35790
—6— Slotted hex head	Made to order in 1020 Bright. 1035 Heat Treat and Alloy Steel	—17— Self-locking nut (deflected beam)	Can be supplied in Steel, Brass, Stainless - all sizes	—28— Spring pin	MS 9047 MS 9048 MS 171401
—7— Tapping screw-Type 1	AN 504 AN 506	—18— Clinch nut	Supplied to order for special applications	—29— Grooved pin	MS 35671 thru MS 35679
—8— Tapping screw-Type 23	AN 504 AN 506	—19— Clinch nut	Supplied with fibre locking collar in various shank lengths	—30— Taper pin	AN 385
—9— Tapping screw-Type 25	AN 530 AN 531	—20— Self-locking nut	Made with Nylon pellets in standard and special sizes	—31— Weld stud	Supplied with welding nibs under and top of head
—10— Drive screw	AN 535	—21— Semi-tubular	MS 20450	—32— Weld nut (self locating)	Supplied with standard thread sizes
—11— Sems	Supplied with all types of heads, also with Internal and External Lockwashers	—22— Shoulder	Made to specifications in steel and brass	—33— Weld nut	Supplied with standard thread sizes

FIGURE 17.34 Industrial Fasteners

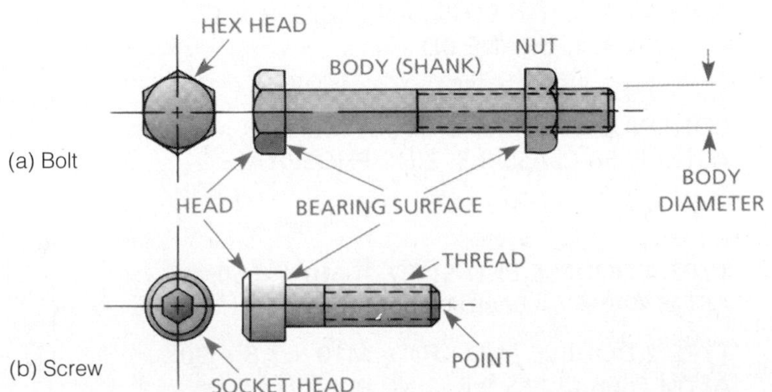

FIGURE 17.35 Bolt and Screw Terminology

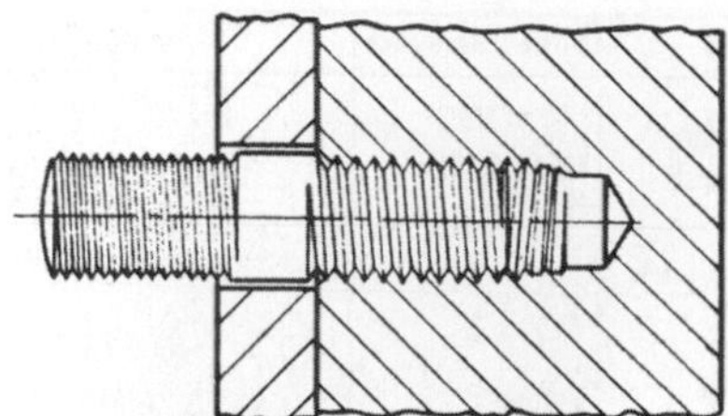

FIGURE 17.36 Threaded Stud in Blind Hole

FIGURE 17.37 Check Valve

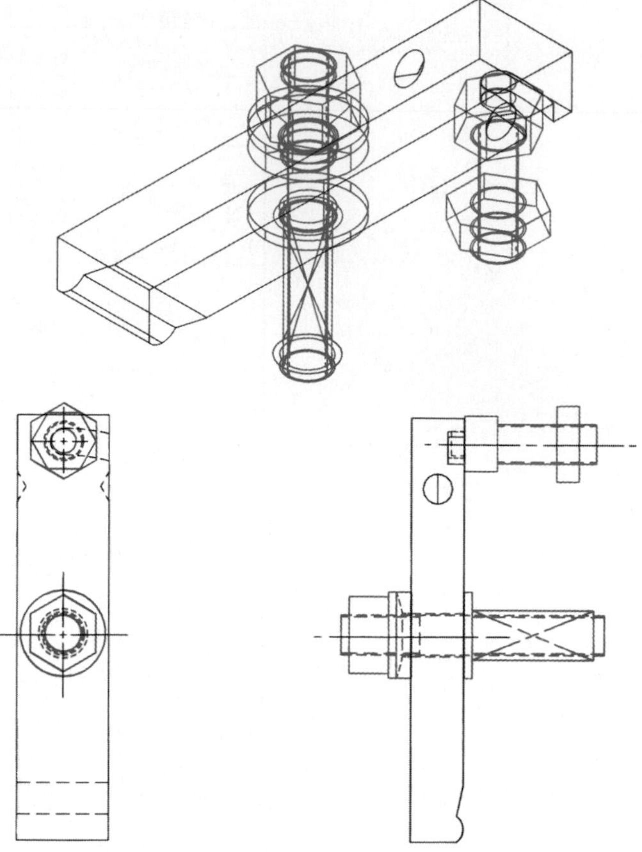

FIGURE 17.38 Swing Clamp for Tooling

Type 3 is full bodied and finished, and Type 4 is finished and is close-body, milled to specifications.

A typical stud application is shown in Figure 17.38 (a swivel-heel clamp assembly). Here, two studs are used in the design of this tooling component. Studs are designated on drawings as in the following examples.

For Type 1 continuous:

CONTINUOUS THREAD STUD, $\frac{1}{2}$-13 × 8,
ASTM A307, ZINC PLATED

For Type 2 continuous:

ANSI/ASME B16.5 STUD BOLT, .875-9 × 12,
ASTM A 354, GRADE BD

For metric continuous:

CONTINUOUS THREAD STUD, M24 × 3 × 200,
ASTM F568 CLASS 8.8, ZINC PHOSPHATE
AND OIL

For double-ended:

TYPE 4 DOUBLE END STUD $\frac{3}{4}$ - 10 × 8.50,
ASTM A499, CADMIUM PLATED

TYPE 2 DOUBLE END STUD, M10 × 1.5 × 90,
ASTM F568 CLASS 9.8, ZINC PLATED

17.13.3 Bolts

A **bolt** is a device with a head on one end of a shank and a thread on the other end. Designed for insertion through holes in assembly parts, it is mated with a tapped nut. The diameter of all bolts is measured as the outside (major) diameter of the thread; the length of a headed bolt is measured from under the head to the end of the bolt. The length of a bolt with a countersunk (flat) head is the overall length. The point (tip) of a bolt is always included in the measured length.

Figure 17.39 illustrates the common types of bolts available. **Hexagon bolts** (Fig. 17.40) can be used in a threaded hole or with a nut. A typical application of a hexagon bolt is shown in Figure 17.41. Hexagon bolts are available with either plain or slotted heads, and also come in metric sizes.

Square-head bolts (Fig. 17.42) and **round-head bolts** (Fig. 17.43) are usually made of low-carbon steel and are referred to as "black bolts." They are available in an unfinished style and with coarse threads. Square-head bolts are adequate for heavy machinery, conveyors, and fixtures. Round-head bolts have various-shaped necks under the head that are embedded in wood or metal and act as a locking device. **Countersunk bolts** are shown in Figure 17.44.

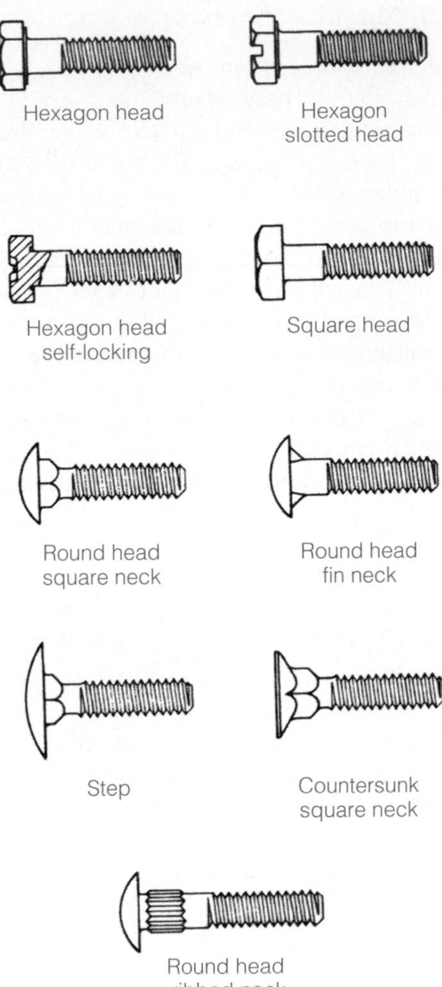

FIGURE 17.39 Bolt Head Types

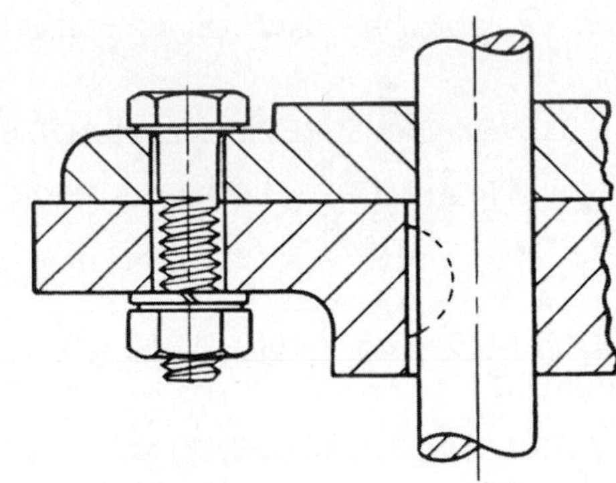

FIGURE 17.41 Hex Bolt Used on Assembly

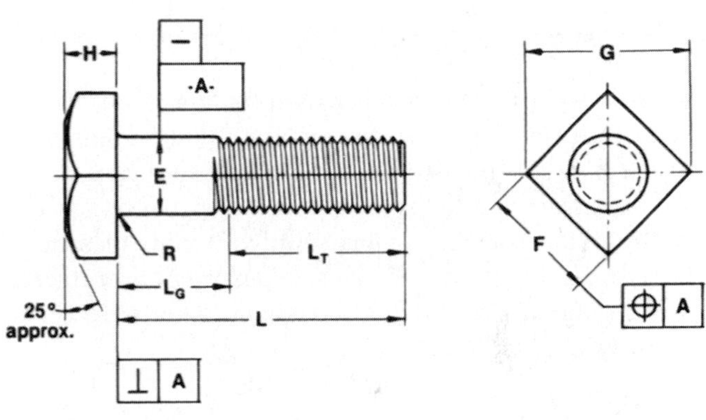

FIGURE 17.42 Square-Head Bolt

Nominal Size	E	F	G	LT	L
.875	.875	1.312	1.856	2.00	6.00 or less
1.500	1.50	2.250	3.182	3.25	6.00 or less

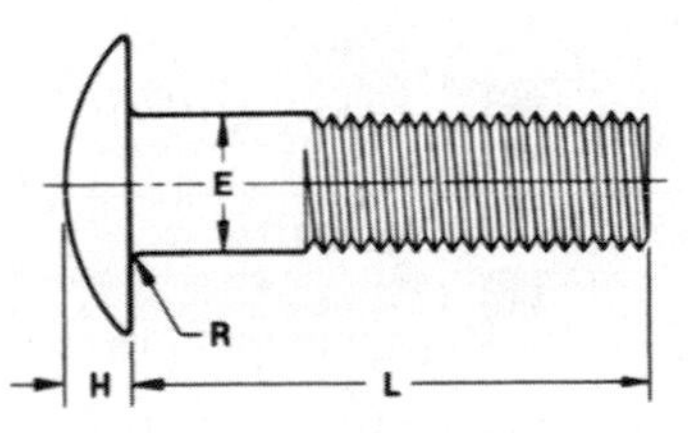

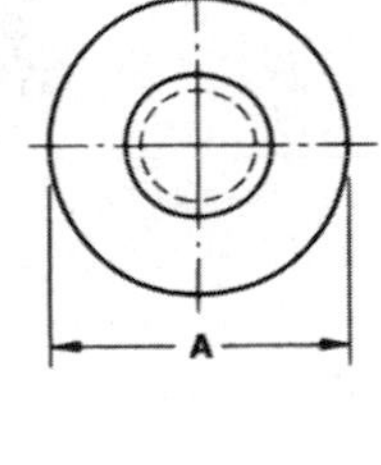

FIGURE 17.43 Round-Head Bolts

Nominal Size	A	E	H
.312	.719	.312	.176
.625	1.344	.625	.344

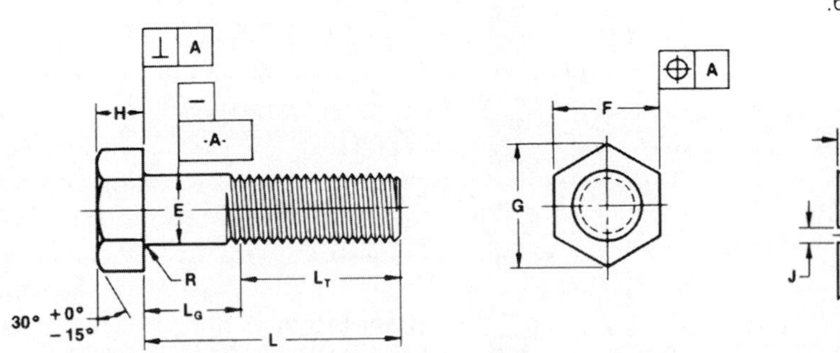

FIGURE 17.40 Hex Bolt

Nominal Size	E	F	G	LT	L
.627	.627	.938	1.08	1.50	6.00 or less
1.000	1.000	1.500	1.73	2.25	6.00 or less

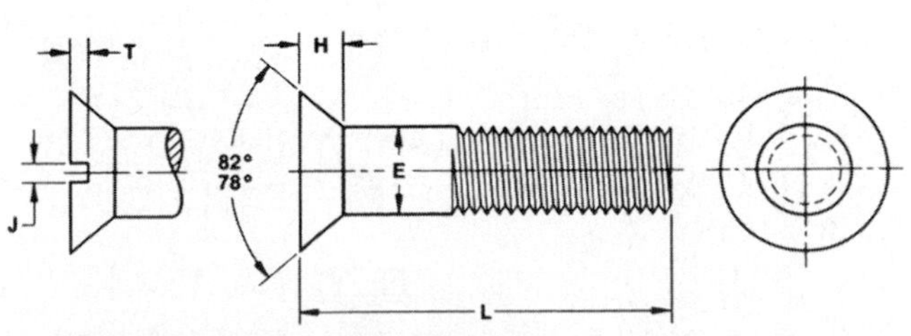

FIGURE 17.44 Countersunk Bolts

Nominal Size	Head Dia	E	H	J	T
.750	1.16	.750	.40	.14	.17
1.25	2.33	1.250	.67	.22	.29

Bolts are designated on drawings as in the following examples:

$\frac{1}{2}$-13 × 3$\frac{1}{2}$ HEX CAP SCREW, SAE GRADE 8 STEEL

.625-11 × 2 ROUND HEAD SQUARE NECK BOLT, STEEL

For metric:

HEX BOLT, M20 × 2.5 × 160, CLASS 4.6, ZINC PLATED

HEAVY HEX STRUCTURAL BOLT, M22 × 2.5 × 160, ASTM A325M

17.13.4 Screws

A **screw** is a threaded fastener used without a nut. Screws are inserted through a clearance hole and into an internally tapped hole in the mating part. The clearance hole is only slightly larger than the screw diameter; therefore, it is not shown on the assembly drawing. Only the body diameter of the screw is shown, as is the outside diameter of the threads. When sectioning assemblies, screws and other fasteners are not sectioned.

17.13.5 Machine Screws

Machine screws differ from cap screws mainly in the range of basic diameters, head shapes, and driver provisions. Machine screws are so named because they are machined completely from bar stock. They are usually restricted to light assemblies, such as instrument panel mountings, moldings, and clip fasteners. The size selection is determined by the tightness required of the parts to be fastened. Machine screws can be assembled into a nut or into a threaded hole in a functional part. Figure 17.45 shows various screw head shapes available as standard parts. Screw selection is made by considering design needs such as surface condition, appearance, size of hole, cover clearance, driving provisions, and expected environmental exposure.

Machine screws come in either fine or course thread and are normally confined to light assembly applications. Machine screw sizes are divided into two categories: fractional sizes and numbered sizes. Numbered sizes are confined to those below $\frac{1}{4}$ in. diameter. Fractional sizes range between $\frac{1}{4}$ and $\frac{3}{4}$ in. diameter. Number 0 has a diameter of .06 inches; .013 inches is added to each numbered size above number #0. Figure 17.46 shows a slotted flat-countersunk-head machine screw. Machine screws 2 in. and under in length come fully threaded. All lengths greater than 2 in. have a 1$\frac{3}{4}$ inch thread.

PAN Low large diameter with high outer edges for maximum driving power. With slotted or Phillips recess for machine screws. Available plain for driving screws.	FLAT UNDERCUT Standard 82° flat head with lower ⅓ of countersink removed for production of short screws. Permits flush assembles in thin stock.
TRUSS Similar to round head, except with shallower head. Has a larger diameter. Good for covering large diameter clearance holes in sheet metal. For machine screws and tapping screws.	100° FLAT, 100° Has larger head than 82° design. Use with thin metals, soft plastics, etc. Slotted or Phillips driving recess.
BINDER Undercut binds and eliminates fraying of wire in electrical work. For machine screws, slotted or Phillips driving recess.	FLAT TRIM Same as 82° flat head except depth of countersink has been reduced. Phillips driving recess only.
ROUND Used for general-purpose service. Used for bolts, machine screws, tapping screws and drive screws. With slotted or Phillips driving recess.	OVAL Like standard flat head. Has outer surface rounded for added attractiveness. Slotted, Phillips or clutch driving recess.
ROUND WASHER Has integral washer for bearing surface. Covers large bearing area than round or truss head. For tapping screw only; with slotted or Phillips driving recess.	OVAL UNDERCUT Similar to flat undercut. Has outer surface rounded for appearance. With slotted or Phillips driving recess.
FLAT FILLISTER Same as standard fillister but without oval top. Used in counter bored holes that require a flush screw. With slot only for machine screws.	OVAL TRIM Same as oval head except depth of countersink is less. Phillips driving recess only.
FILLISTER Smaller diameter than round head, higher, deeper slot. Used in counterbored holes. Slotted or Phillips driving recess. Machine screws and tapping screws.	ROUND COUNTERSUNK For bolts only. Similar to 82° flat head but with no driving recess.
HEXAGON Head with square , sharp corners, and ample bearing surface for wrench tightening. Used for machine screws and bolts.	SQUARE (SET-SCREW) Square, sharp corners can be tightened to higher torque with wrench than any other set-screw head.
HEXAGON WASHER Same as Hexagon except with added washer section at base to protect work surface against wrench disfigurement. For machine screws and tapping screws.	SQUARE (BOLT) Square, sharp corners, generous bearing surface for wrench tightening.
82° FLAT, 82° Use where flush surface is desired. Slotted, clutch, Phillips, or hexagon-socket driving recess.	SQUARE COUNTERSUNK For use on plow bolts, which are used on farm machinery and heavy construction equipment.

FIGURE 17.45 Machine Screw Head Styles

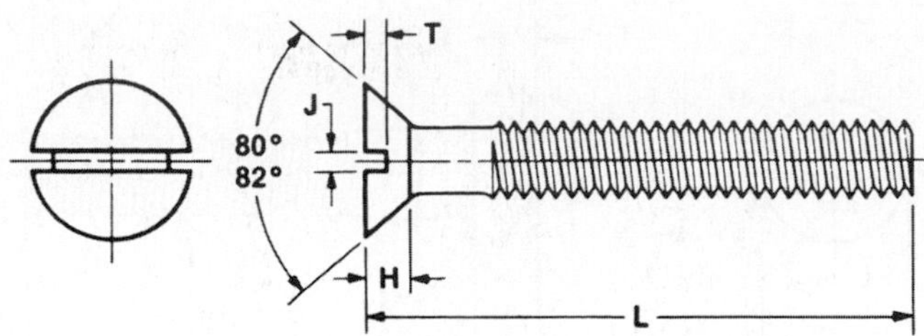

FIGURE 17.46 Slotted Flat-Countersunk-Head Machine Screw

Nominal Size	Head Dia	H	J	T
#5 (.125)	.25	.075	.04	.03
.500	.875	.223	.10	.10

Machine screws are called out in the same way as bolts, for example:

.25-20 x 1.5 SLOTTED PAN HEAD MACHINE SCREW, STEEL, ZINC PLATED

6-32 × 1.50 SLOTTED FLAT COUNTERSUNK HEAD MACHINE SCREW

For metric:

M8 × 1.25 × 30 SLOTTED PAN HEAD MACHINE SCREW, CLASS 4.8 STEEL, ZINC PLATED

M4 × 0.7 × 40 RECESSED PAN HEAD MACHINE SCREW, BRASS

17.13.6 Cap Screws

Cap screws are similar to machine screws except that there are fewer head styles available. Cap screws have their heads cold-formed from smaller-diameter stock. Cap screws are for applications that require closer tolerances and greater holding power per diameter. Figure 17.47 shows three examples of cap screws. Cap screws are finished and are more expensive than similar-size bolts and machines screws. Cap screws come in course, fine, and special threads. Cap screws 1 in. in diameter and under have a Class 3A thread; those greater than 1 in. in diameter have a Class 2A thread.

Cap screws are available in steel, brass, bronze, aluminum, and titanium. Steel hex-head cap screws (Fig. 17.48) are available in diameters from $\frac{1}{4}$ to 3 in. and have their

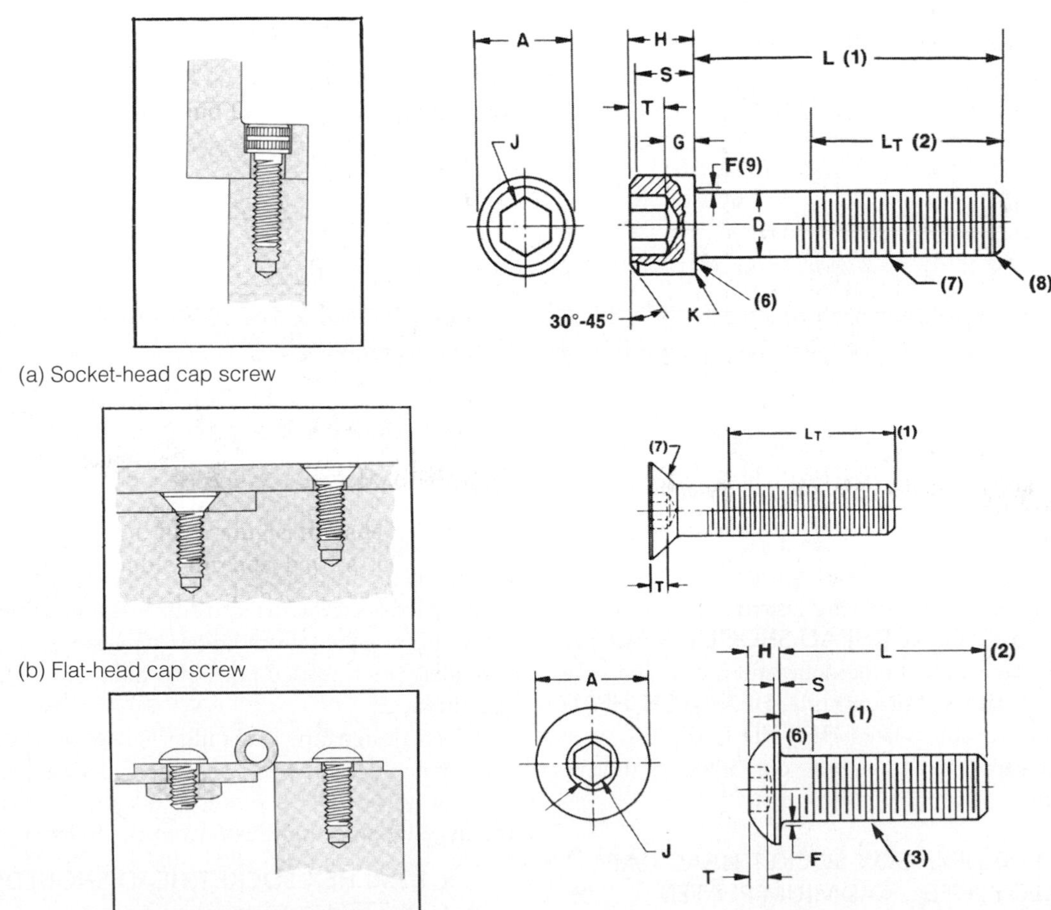

FIGURE 17.47 Cap Screw Applications

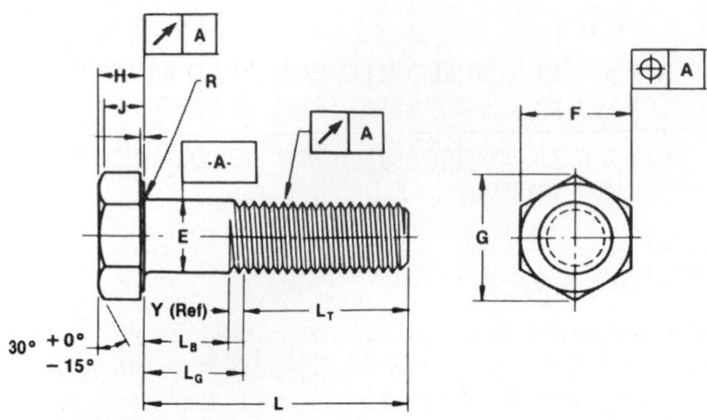

FIGURE 17.48 Hex Cap Screws

Size	E	F	G	H	J	LT	L
.500	.500	.750	.86	.32	.21	1.25	6.00 or less
.75	.750	1.125	1.29	.48	.32	1.75	6.00 or less

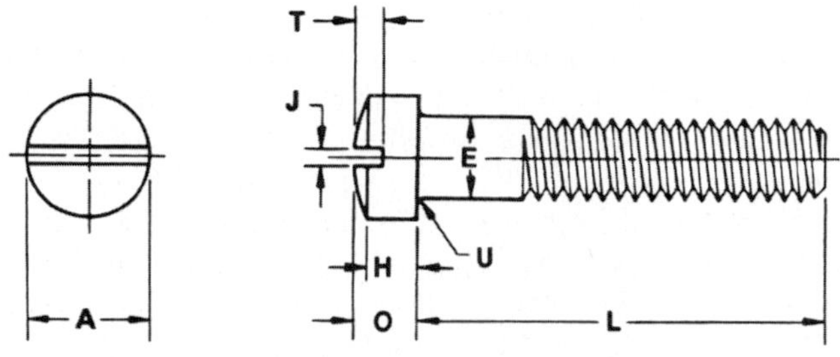

FIGURE 17.49 Slotted Round-Head Cap Screws

Nominal Size	A	E	H	J	T
.250	.437	.250	.19	.07	.11
.500	.812	.500	.35	.10	.21

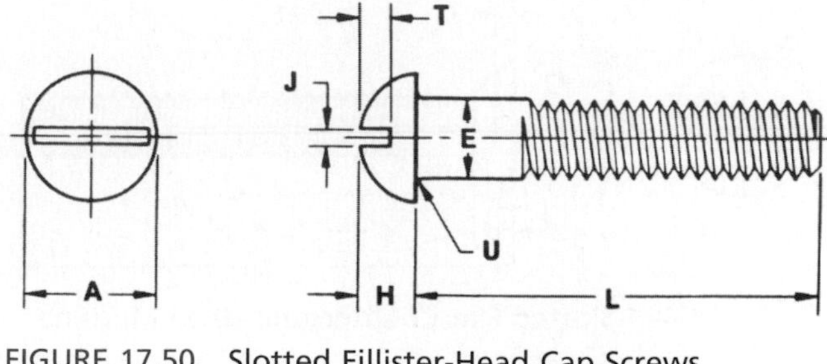

FIGURE 17.50 Slotted Fillister-Head Cap Screws

Nominal Size	A	E	H	J	O	T
.312	.437	.312	.20	.08	.25	.11
.562	.812	.562	.37	.11	.46	.21

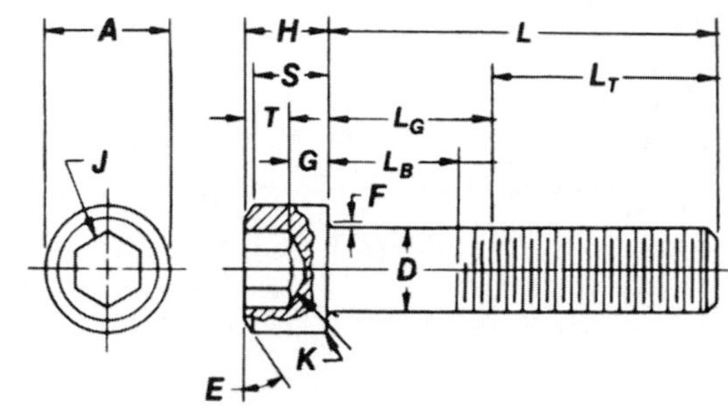

FIGURE 17.51 Socket-Head Cap Screws

Nominal Size	A	D	H	J	LT
.375	.56	.375	.372	.312	1.25
1.000	1.50	1.000	1.000	.750	2.50

strength indicated on their hex head by a geometric symbol. Slotted-head cap screws come in round (Fig. 17.49), fillister (Fig. 17.50), and flat heads.

Socket-head cap screws (Fig. 17.51) are used throughout industry for precision and high-strength fastening and where the head of the screw must be flush or below the part's surface. A clearance hole for the head is counterbored into the part (Fig. 17.47). Socket-head cap screws are also made with socket button heads and socket flat heads.

The metric format for designating fasteners can be abbreviated. For example, SOCKET HEAD SHOULDER SCREW becomes SHSS. American standard fasteners can also have abbreviated designations. For example, HEXAGON HEAD CAP SCREW can be abbreviated HEX HD CAP SCR.

When designating cap screws on your drawing, use the following format:

.138-32 × 1.00 HEXAGON SOCKET HEAD CAP SCREW, ALLOY STEEL, CADMIUM PLATED

$\frac{1}{4}$ - 28 × 1.75 HEXAGON SOCKET FLAT COUNTERSUNK HEAD CAP SCREW, ALLOY STEEL

For metric:

B18.3.1M-M6 × 1 × 20 HEXAGON SOCKET HEAD CAP SCREW

IFI-535 - 6 × 1 × 8 SOCKET COUNTERSUNK HEAD CAP SCREW, ZINC PLATED

Socket-head shoulder screws are used for location and fastening by combining the features of dowels and screws, and for applications requiring a pivot. This type of screw has an enlarged, toleranced, unthreaded portion of the screw body called a *shoulder* (Fig. 17.52). The length of a shoulder screw is measured from under its head to the end of its shoulder. The threaded portion is not included in the length specification.

When designating a shoulder screw on a drawing, give the nominal size or basic shoulder diameter in fractions or decimal equivalent, a shoulder length, the product name, the material, and the finish, as in the following examples:

$\frac{1}{4}$ × 1.250 HEX SOCKET HEAD SHOULDER SCREW, ALLOY STEEL

1.25 × 4.25 HEX SOCKET HEAD SHOULDER SCREW, ALLOY STEEL, PHOSPHATE COATED

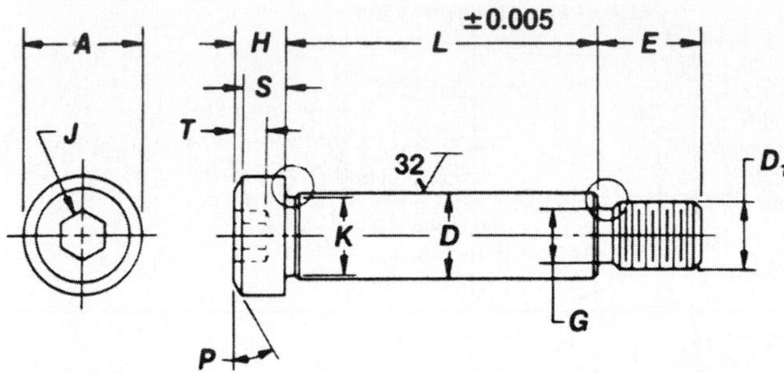

FIGURE 17.52 Hexagon Socket-Head Cap Shoulder Screw

Nominal Size	A	D	D1	E	G	H	J	K
.500	.75	.500	.375	.625	.30	.31	.25	.47
1.000	1.31	.998	.750	1.000	.63	.625	.50	.97

For metric:

B18.3.3M-8 × 25 SOCKET HEAD SHOULDER SCREW

B18.3.3M-10 × 50 SHSS, ZINC PLATED

17.13.7 Set Screws

There are three types of **set screws:** slotted, socket, and square head. In a set screw, there are three types of holding power: torsional (resistance to rotation), axial (resistance to lateral movement), and vibrational. Set screws serve in a variety of applications, such as securing components to shafts (Fig. 17.53).

Set screws are available in number sizes from 0 to 12 and in fractional sizes from $\frac{1}{4}$ to 2 in. Metric set screws come in nominal diameters of 1.6, 2, 2.5, 3, 4, 5, 6, 8, 10, 12, 16, 20, and 24 millimeters.

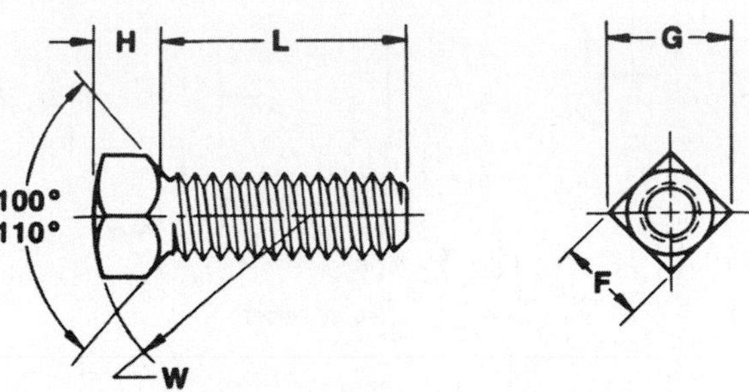

FIGURE 17.54 Square-Head Set Screws

Nominal Size	F	G	H	W
.250	.250	.35	.19	.62
.500	.500	.70	.38	1.25

The size of a set screw is an important factor in holding power. A rough rule of thumb is that the set screw diameter be 25% of the shaft diameter. When more than one set screw is used, the second should be placed near and in line with the first one. If the second set screw must be in the same location as the first, it should be staggered at an angle of 60°.

Square-head set screws protrude above the surface of the part (Fig. 17.54). Headless types disappear below the work surface when tightened. **Socket set screws** have spline or hex sockets (Fig. 17.55). Slotted set screws are tightened with screw drivers (Fig. 17.56). Figure 17.56 also shows examples of six standard point forms available for both socket and slotted set screws. The *cone point* is used where two parts must be joined in a permanent position relative to each other. The *cup point* is for applications that require rapid assembly. The *oval point* serves in applications similar to the cup point. The *flat point* is valued where fine adjustments are needed. Since the half-dog and full-dog points penetrate a mating hole drilled in the shaft, they have the greatest holding power.

A set screw is designated on a drawing by giving the nominal size, threads per inch, length, product name, point style, material, and protective coating (if needed), as in the

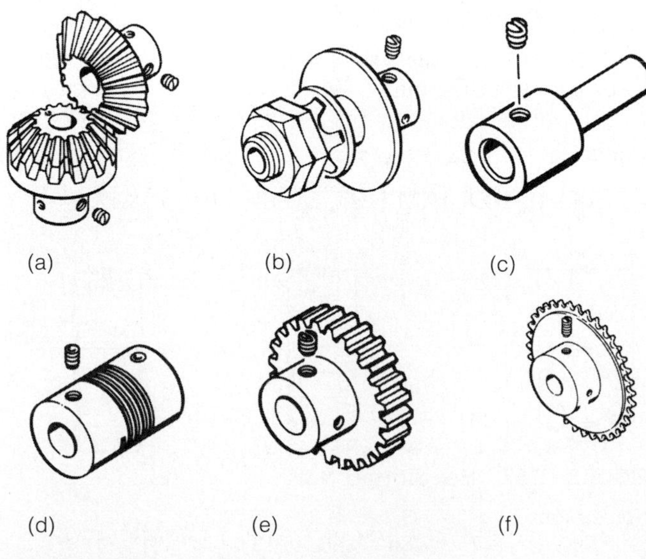

FIGURE 17.53 Set Screws in Use

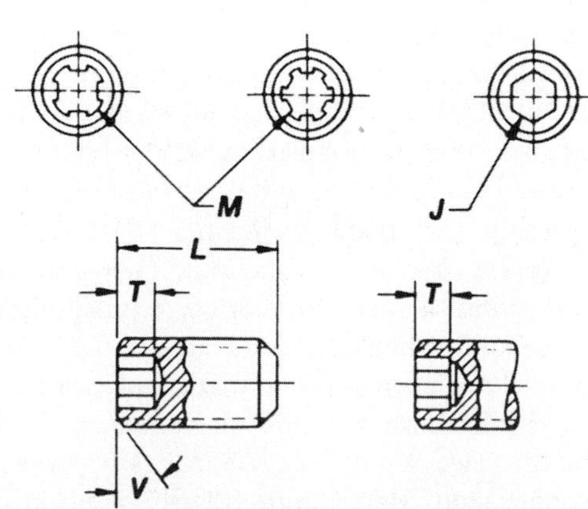

FIGURE 17.55 Socket-Head Set Screws

Nominal Size	J	M	T
.250	.125	.14	.13
.375	.188	.21	.18

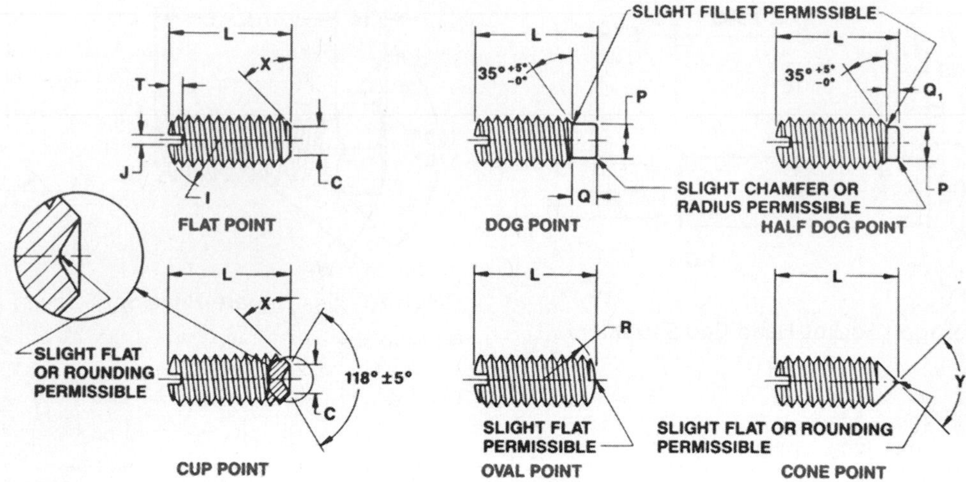

FIGURE 17.56 Slotted Headless Set Screws

Nominal Size	J	P	Q	Q1	T
.250	.04	.15	.13	.06	.06
.375	.06	.25	.19	.09	.09

following examples:

$\frac{1}{4}$-20 × .375 HEXAGON SOCKET SET SCREW, CUP POINT, ALLOY STEEL

.250-20 × 50 SLOTTED HEADLESS SET SCREW, HALF DOG POINT, STEEL

For metric:

B18.3 6M-10 × 1.5 CUP POINT SOCKET SET SCREW, ZINC PLATED

17.14 NUTS

Many types of nuts are available to satisfy specific design and functional requirements. Lock nuts, swivel nuts, hex nuts,flange nuts, coupling nuts, square nuts, slotted nuts, and jam nuts are just a few of the types used in industry. Most nuts are either hex-head or square-head varieties. Nuts are identified by the size of bolt they fit, not by their outside dimensions.

Flange nuts incorporate a washer into the nut that increases the bearing area of the nut. **Hexagon nuts** are available as unfinished, plain, slotted, regular, heavy, and jam types. Semifinished hex nuts are available in plain, slotted, jam, thick plain, thick slotted, and castle varieties. Semifinished nuts have one side machined on the bearing side of the nut. Heavy nuts are .125 inches wider across the flats on the hexagon. **Slotted nuts** (Fig. 17.57) have slots for use with cotter pins, which prevent the nut from coming off or untightening. Regular hex nuts (Fig. 17.58) are thinner than their size designations. A $\frac{1}{2}$ in. regular hex nut is actually $\frac{7}{16}$ in. thick, and a $\frac{1}{2}$ in. heavy hex nut is $\frac{31}{64}$ in. thick. Metric nuts are also thinner than their designated size. An M6 × 1 metric hex nut, Style 2, is 5.70 mm thick. There are two types of metric nuts, Style 1 and Style 2.

The nominal size, threads per inch, product name, material, and protective finish are given to designate a hex nut on a drawing, as in the following examples:

$\frac{1}{2}$ - 13 HEX NUT, STEEL, ZINC PLATED

750-20 HEX NUT, SAE J995 GRADE 5, CORROSION RESISTANT STEEL

For metric:

HEX NUT, STYLE 2, M20 × 2.5, ASTM A563, CLASS 9, ZINC PLATED

HEAVY HEX NUT, M30 × 3.5, ASTM A563M, CLASS 105, HOT DIP GALVANIZED

Jam nuts are thin hex nuts and are used where height is restricted, or as a means of locking the working nut, if assembled as in Figure 17.59.

Jam nuts are designated in the same way as hex nuts, for example:

.500-16 HEX JAM NUT, STEEL, ZINC PLATED

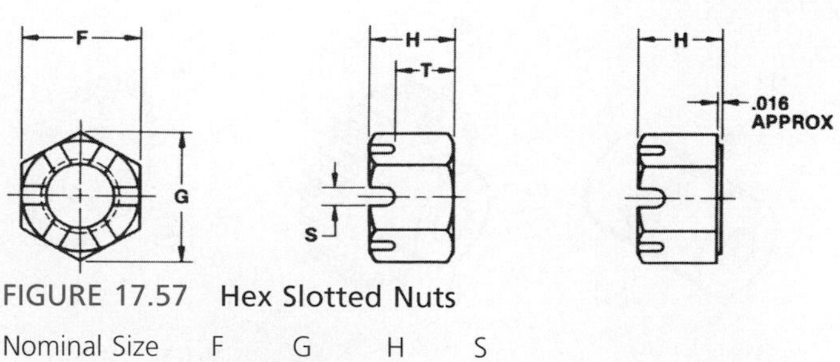

FIGURE 17.57 Hex Slotted Nuts

Nominal Size	F	G	H	S
.500	.75	.86	.56	.18
1.000	1.50	1.72	1.018	.30

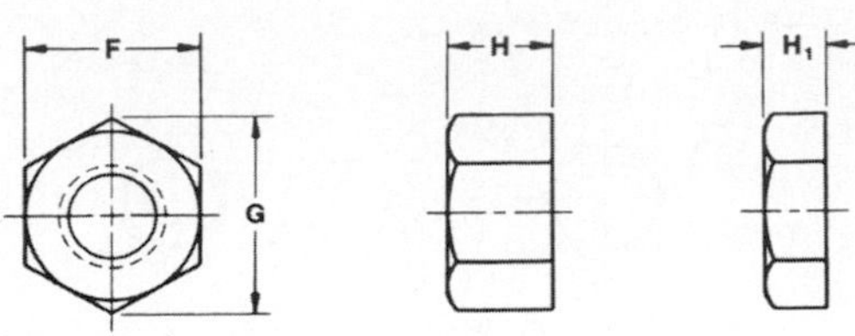

FIGURE 17.58 Hex Flat and Jam Nuts

Nominal Size	F	G	H	H1
.500	.75	.86	.43	.31
.750	1.12	1.29	.66	.44

For metric:

HEX JAM NUT, M10 × 1.5, ASTM A563M CLASS 04 ZINC PLATED

Square nuts, because they must be installed with an open-ended wrench and not a socket wrench, are less common. Square nuts are designated on drawings in the same way as hex nuts, for instance:

1.000-8 SQUARE NUT, STEEL

17.15 STANDARD BOLT, NUT, AND SCREW REPRESENTATION

Bolts, screws, and nuts should be drawn with the aid of a template. When a template is not available, use the fastener's dimensions for drawing the part. A simplified method is also acceptable (Fig. 17.60). These dimensions are acceptable when constructing bolts and screws. The most important dimensions on fasteners are their diameter and length, which must be constructed accurately because they affect clearances.

Figure 17.60 shows some approximate dimensions that can be used to draw fasteners. Although they do not correspond exactly to the fastener's actual dimensions, it is standard practice to simplify the constructions. In this figure, *the basic sizes of each part of a fastener are given relative to the diameter dimension*. Each dimension is a fraction of the diameter. Chamfered endpoints are normally drawn at 45°. When rendering the end view of a slotted fastener, the slots are drawn at 45°, not at 90° or 180°. The head of hex-head bolts and nuts is drawn so that three surfaces are visible from an elevation view. The depth of the hex on a hex socket-head cap screw is not drawn. Figure 17.61 shows three steps in the drawing of a hex-head bolt and nut. Figure 17.62 shows the dimensions for drawing a square-head bolt.

17.16 WASHERS

Washers are used in conjunction with threaded fasteners. The three basic types of washers are *plain, spring lock,* and *tooth lock*. Plain washers spread the bearing area of the fastener head or nut and are normally used with soft metals. Spring washers maintain tension on the nut or bolt head, and tooth-lock washers have teeth that dig into the fastener and the part to prevent the fastener from loosening. **Plain washers** are flat and ring shaped (Fig. 17.63).

Washers are designated on drawings by providing the product name and type, size (ID), material, and finish, as in the following:

TYPE A PLAIN WASHER, $1\frac{1}{2}$ STEEL, CADMIUM PLATED

TYPE B PLAIN WASHER, NO. 12, STEEL

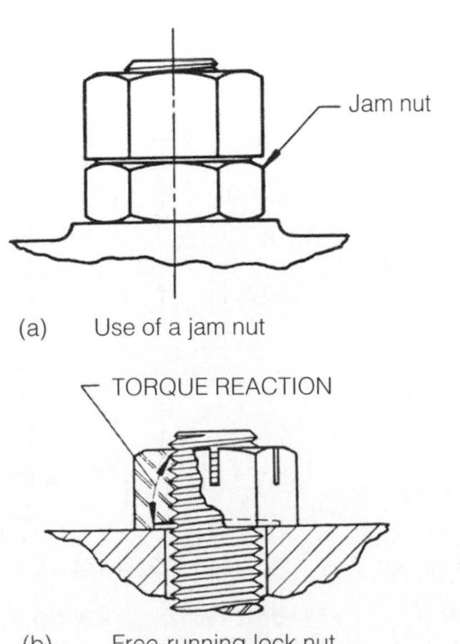

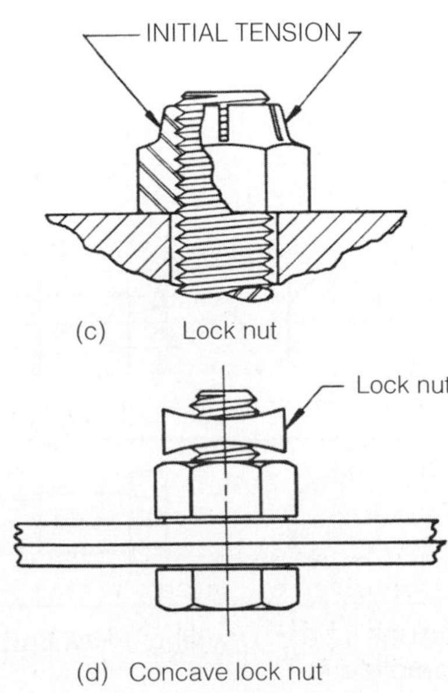

FIGURE 17.59 Lock and Jam Nut Applications

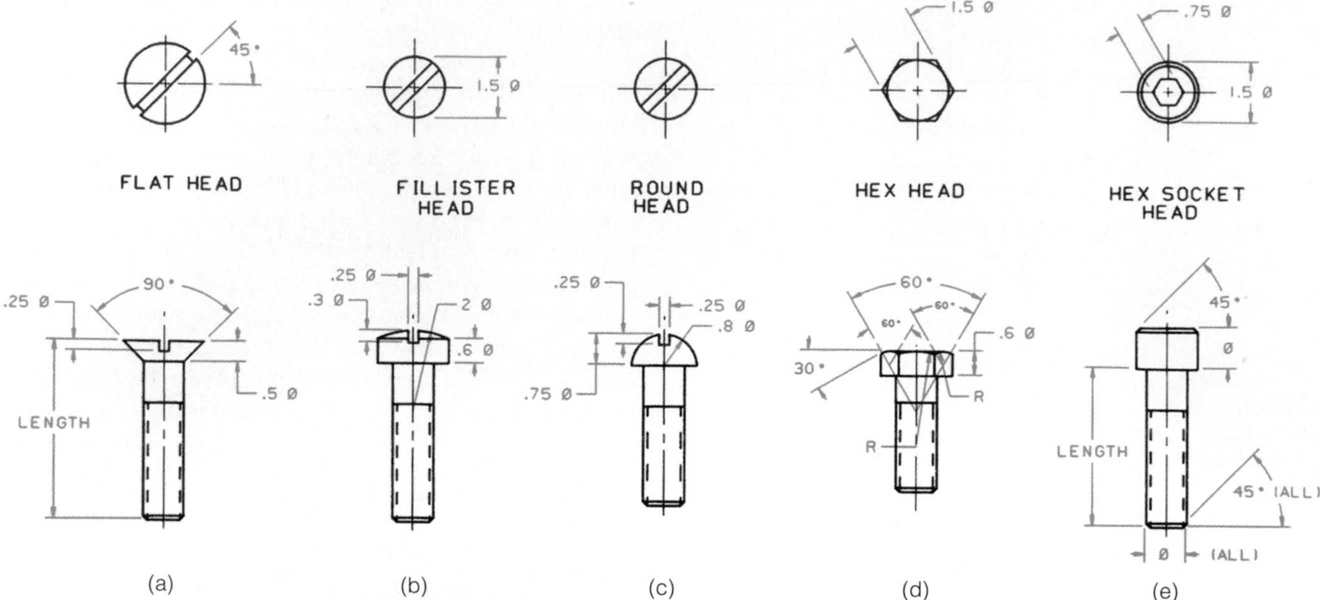

FIGURE 17.60 Approximate Sizes for Drawing Screws

For metric:

PLAIN WASHER, 6MM, NARROW, SOFT, STEEL, ZINC PLATED

Spring-lock washers are split on one side and are helical in shape. They have the dual function of acting as a spring take-up, to compensate for developed looseness and a loss of tension between component parts of an assembly, and as a hardened thrust bearing, to aid in assembly and disassembly of bolted fastenings. Lock washer (Fig. 17.64) sizes are selected by the nominal bolt or screw sizes. Figure 17.65 shows two common types of **tooth-lock washers:** Type A and Type B. Both are internal–external types.

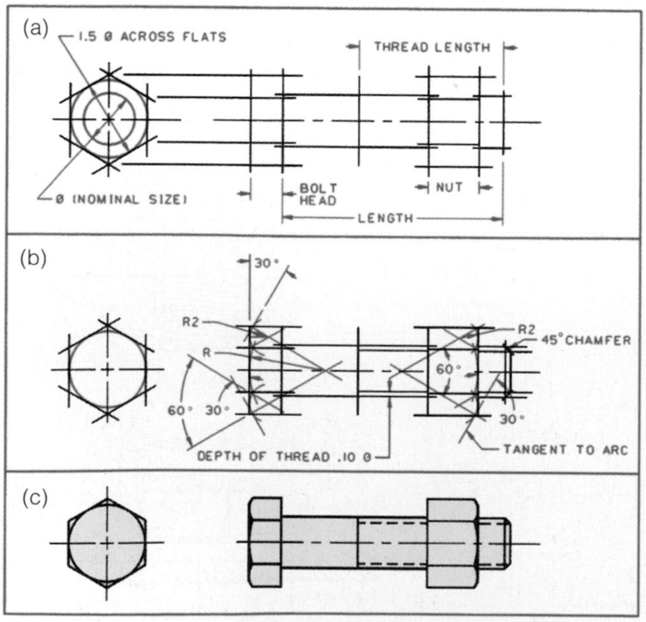

FIGURE 17.61 Drawing a Hex Bolt and Nut Without a Template

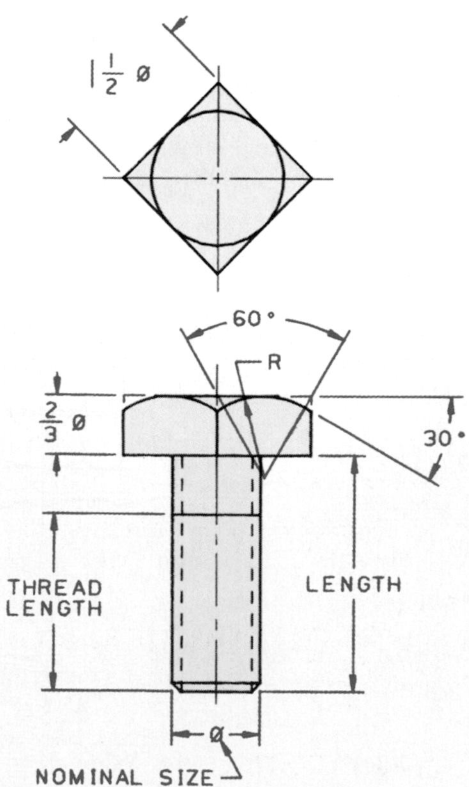

FIGURE 17.62 Drawing a Square-Head Bolt Without a Template

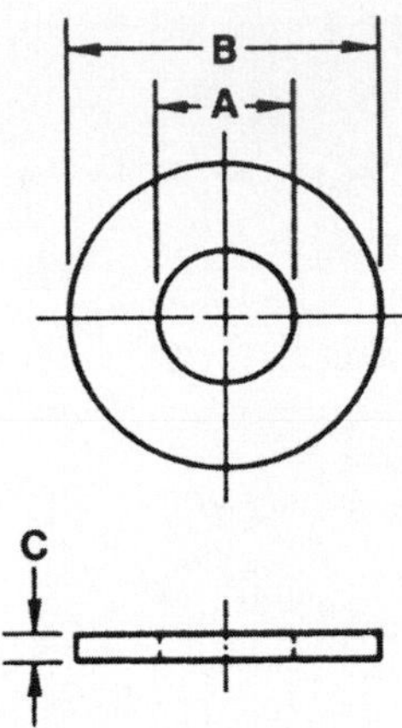

FIGURE 17.63 Plain Washers

Nominal Size	A	B	C
.500	.531	1.06	.09
1.000	1.062	2.50	.16

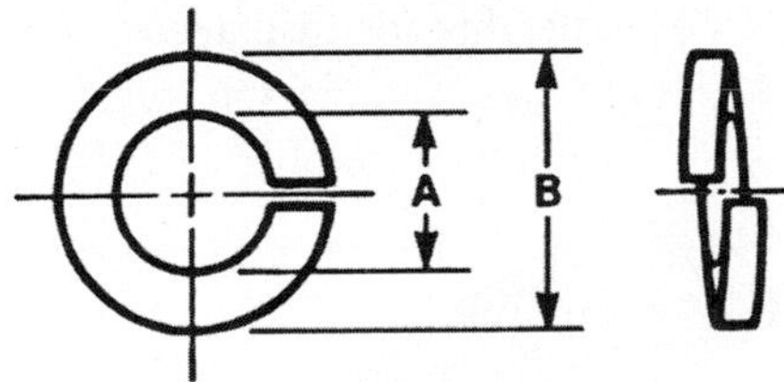

FIGURE 17.64 Spring-Lock Washers

Nominal Size	A	B	Width
.500	.518	.87	.125
.625	.65	1.07	.156

Designate lock washers on drawings as in the following examples:

HELICAL SPRING LOCK WASHER, .125 REGULAR, CORROSION RESISTANT STEEL, CADMIUM PLATED

HELICAL SPRING LOCK WASHER, $\frac{3}{8}$ EXTRA DUTY, STEEL, PHOSPHATE COATED

INTERNAL-EXTERNAL TOOTH LOCK WASHER, NO. 10 (.760 O.D.), TYPE A, STEEL, CADMIUM PLATED

EXTERNAL TOOTH LOCK WASHER, .625, TYPE B, STEEL, PHOSPHATE COATED

For metric:

4MM INTERNAL TOOTH, TYPE A

You May Complete Exercises 17.5 Through 17.8 at This Time

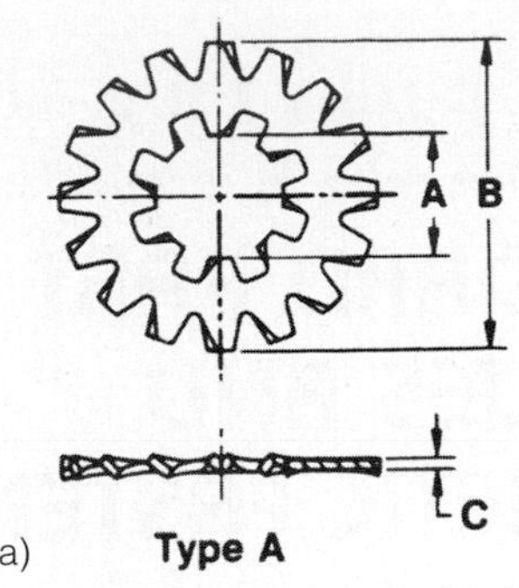

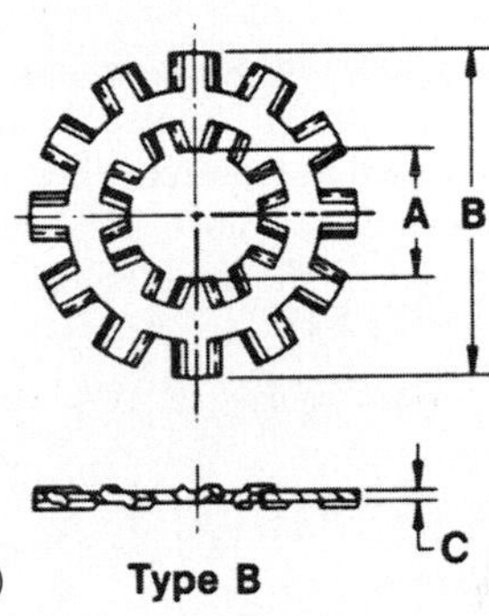

FIGURE 17.65 Tooth-Lock Washers

Nominal Size	A	B	C
#10 (.190)	.20	.76	.04
.500	.53	1.41	.06

17.17 MACHINE PINS

Standard machine pins are used throughout industry wherever there is a need for the assembly and alignment of mating parts, and for attaching gears, cams, collars, pulleys, sprockets, and other mechanical parts to shafts. Three types of pins are shown securing a gear to a shaft in Figure 17.66: (a) a straight pin, (b) a taper pin, and (c) a spring pin. Most of the pin types have metric-sized standard equivalents.

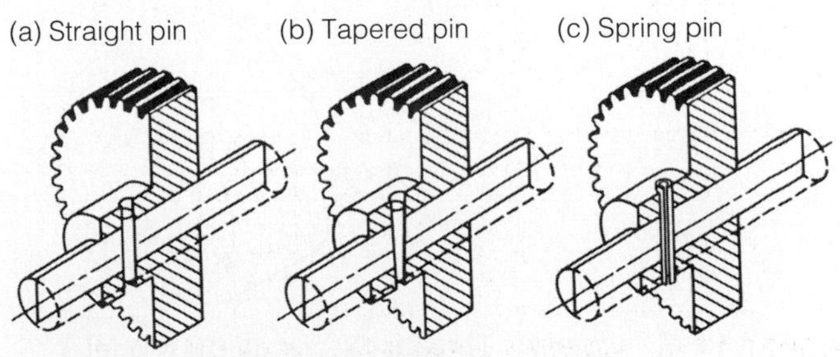

FIGURE 17.66 Pinning Applications

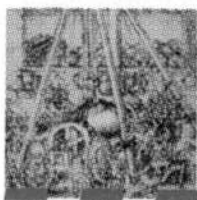

Applying Parametric Design . . .

STANDARD PART FAMILIES AND COSMETIC FASTENER THREADS

In parametric design, **threads** are a cosmetic feature representing the diameter of a thread and having the capability of imbedding information into the feature (see Fig. A). It is displayed in a unique color (magenta), and can be displayed, blanked, or suppressed as required when plotting. Threads are created with the default tolerance setting of limits. The socket-head cap shoulder screw shown in Figure A has a threaded end

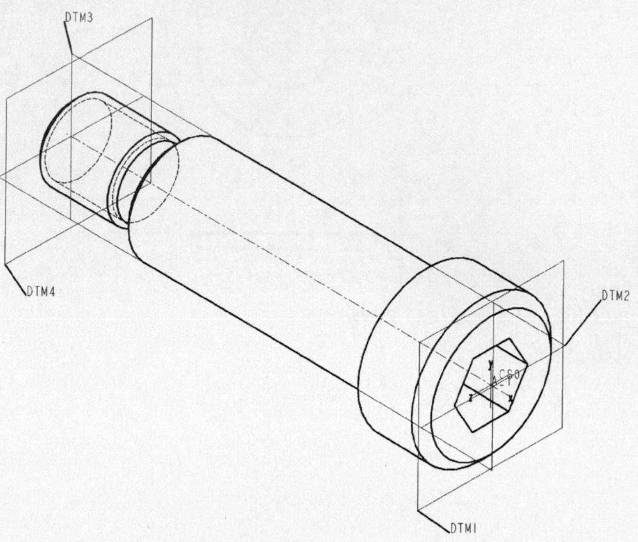

FIGURE C Datum, Planes, Datum Axes, Coordinate System, and Cosmetic Threads Displayed

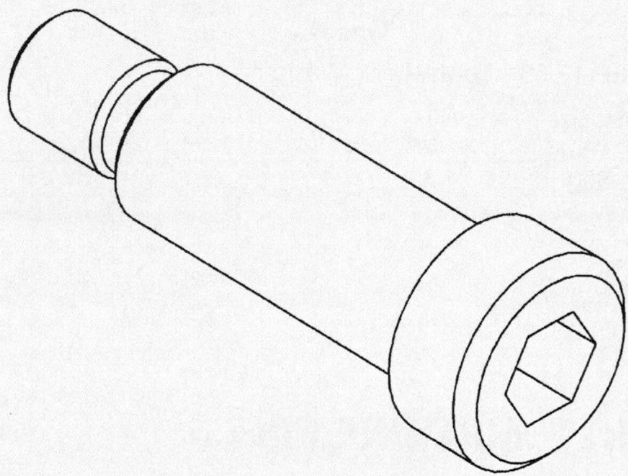

FIGURE A Socket-Head Cap Shoulder Screw

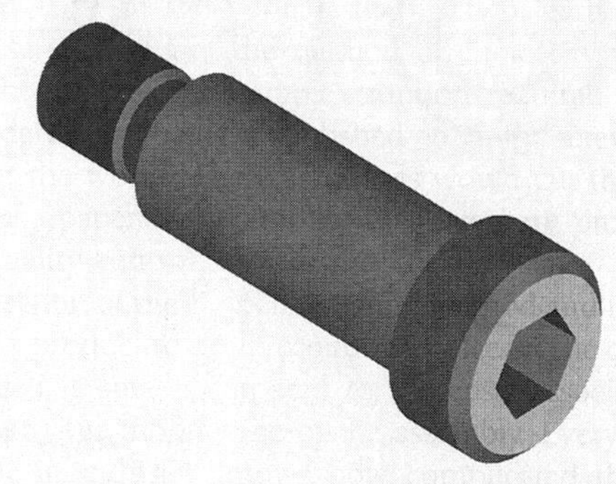

FIGURE D Shaded Image of Shoulder Screw

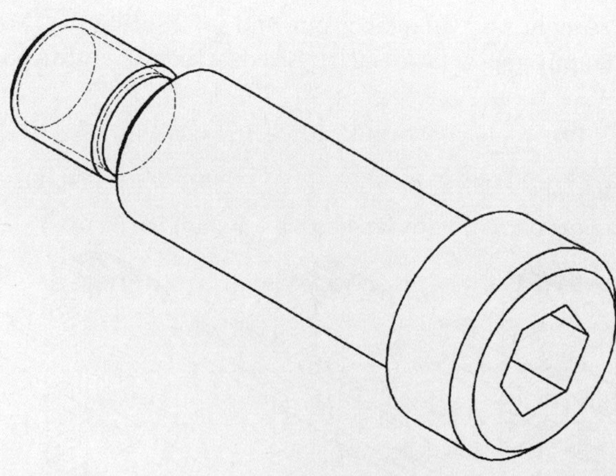

FIGURE B Cosmetic Threads Displayed on Model

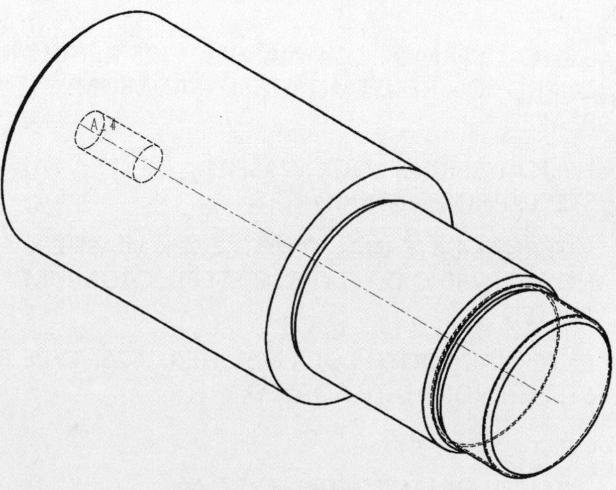

FIGURE E Shaft with External and Internal Cosmetic Threads

in Figure B. The cosmetic threads are displayed with dashed lines representing the threads' external thread root diameter. In Figure C, the datum planes, datum lines, coordinate system, and cosmetic threads are displayed (the hidden lines are now shown). A shaded image of the screw (Fig. D) completes the sequence.

Cosmetic threads can be external or internal, blind or through. In the shaft example, one end has external blind threads and the opposite end has internal blind threads (Fig. E). The shaft was modeled by creating a revolved protrusion (Fig. F). The geometry of the revolved feature is shown in section and pictorially (Fig. G). After the protrusion (base feature) was created, the hole, chamfers, and slot (relief) were modeled.

The cosmetic threads for the external shaft end (Figs. H and I) and the internal hole threads (Fig. J) were added last. They are created by specifying the minor or major diameter (for external and internal threads, respectively), starting plane (here a datum plane was used—DTM4), and thread length or ending edge. A half-section-removed view shows the blind hole and the cosmetic threads. Note that the cosmetic feature is not cut (Fig. K).

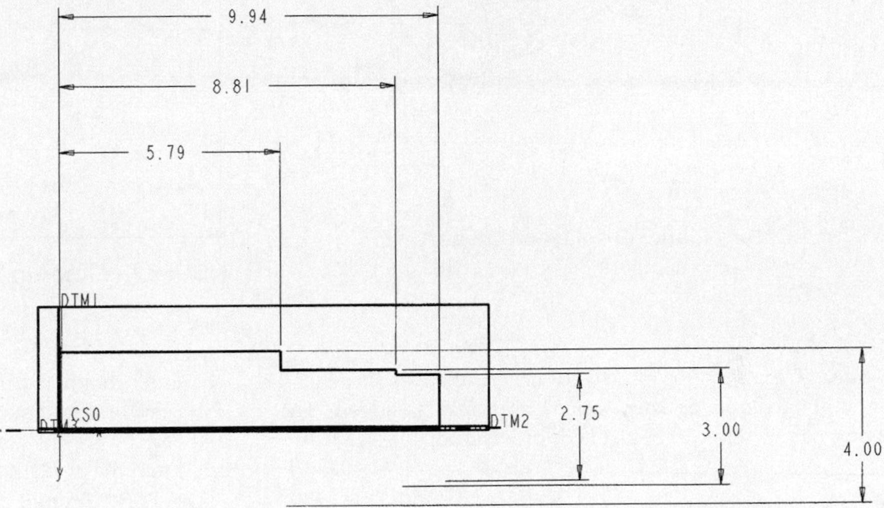

FIGURE F Sketch for Revolved Protrusion

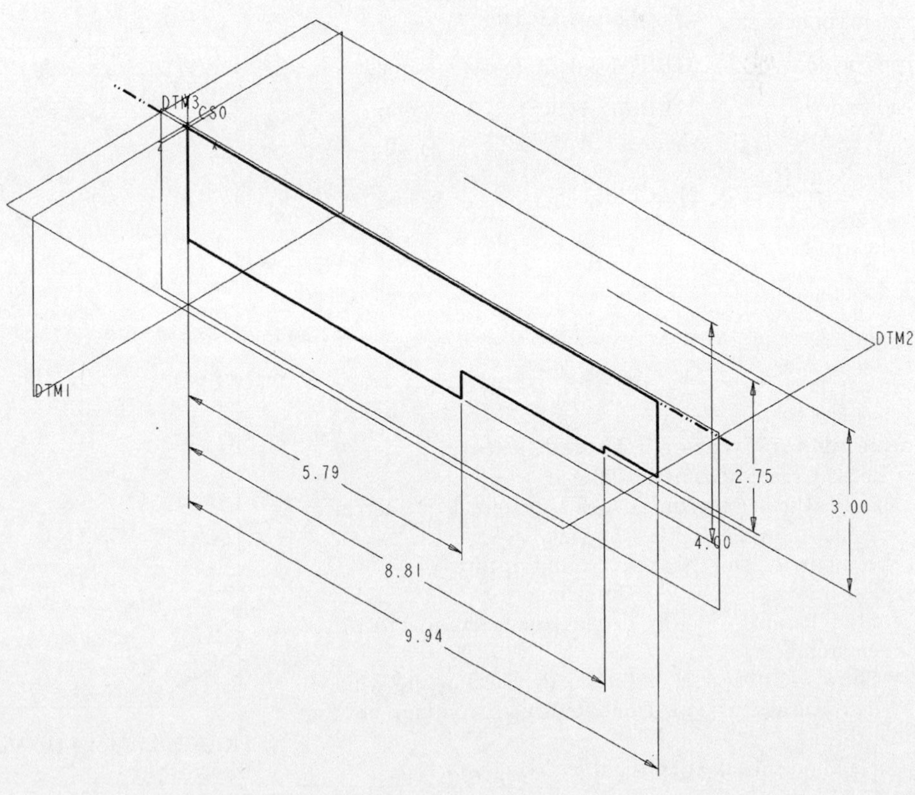

FIGURE G Pictorial View of Sketch

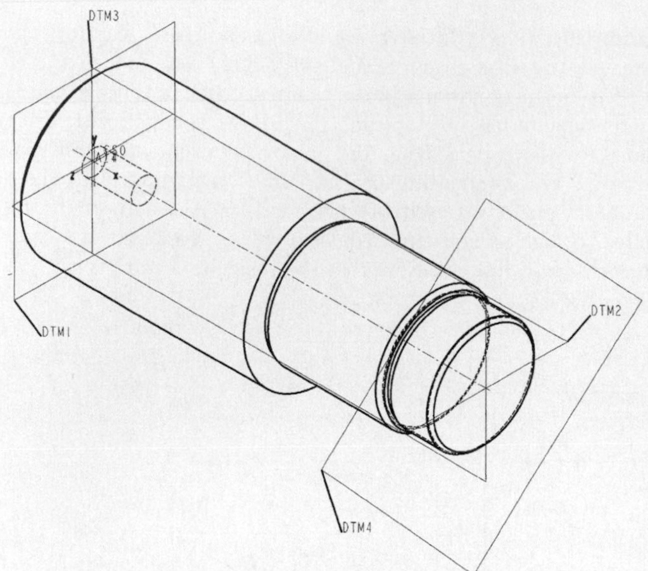

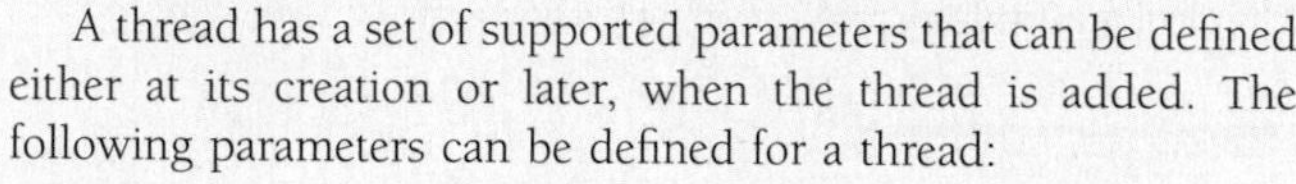

FIGURE H Datum Planes Displayed on Shaft

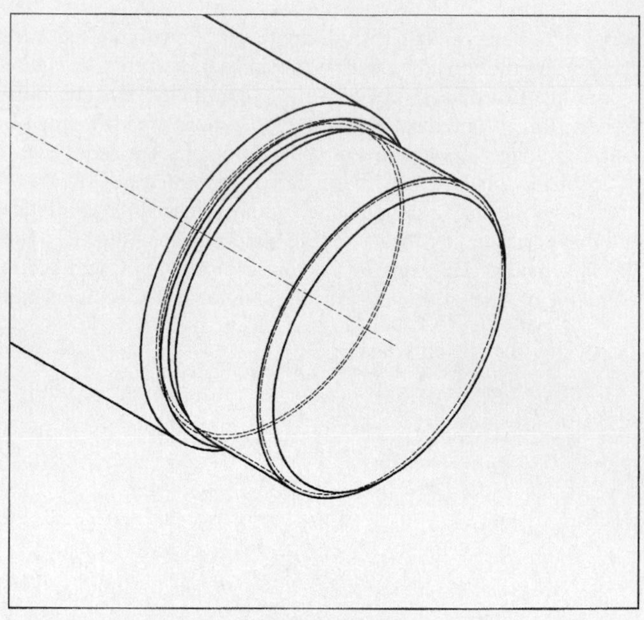

FIGURE I Close-Up View of External Threads

A thread has a set of supported parameters that can be defined either at its creation or later, when the thread is added. The following parameters can be defined for a thread:

Parameter Description	Parameter Name	Parameter Value
Thread major diameter	MAJOR_DIAMETER	Number
Threads per inch (pitch)	THREADS_PER_INCH	Number
Thread form	THREAD_FORM	String
Thread class	CLASS	Number
Thread placement (A—external, B—internal)	PLACEMENT	Character
Thread is metric	METRIC	TRUE/FALSE

Commands for Creating a Thread Feature

1. Choose **Create, Cosmetic, Thread.**
2. Specify whether the thread will be external or internal by selecting from the THREADS menu.
3. Specify the type of the thread: **blind** or **thru.**
4. Select from the FEAT PARAM menu:
   - **Mod Params** Modify thread parameters in Pro/TABLE environment.
   - **Show** Display a set of thread parameters in Info Window.
5. When finished, choose **Done/Return** to continue creating the thread.
6. For a blind thread, enter the thread length.
7. Enter the thread major/minor diameter.
8. Select a thread surface.
9. Select a thread starting plane.
10. From the MODIF PREV menu, select one of the options:
    - **Prev Prompt** Reselect references for the previous prompt. When finished, choose **Done.**
    - **Done** Accept previous specifications and conclude thread creation.

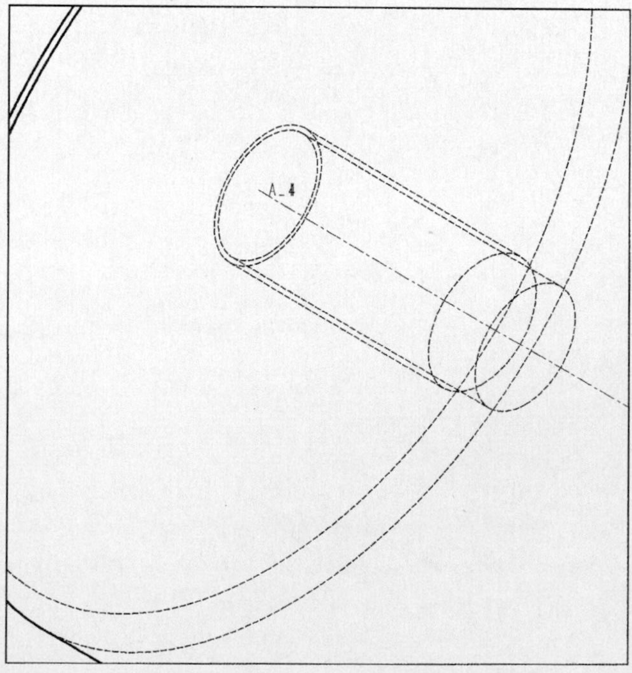

FIGURE J Close-Up View of Internal Threads and Blind Hole

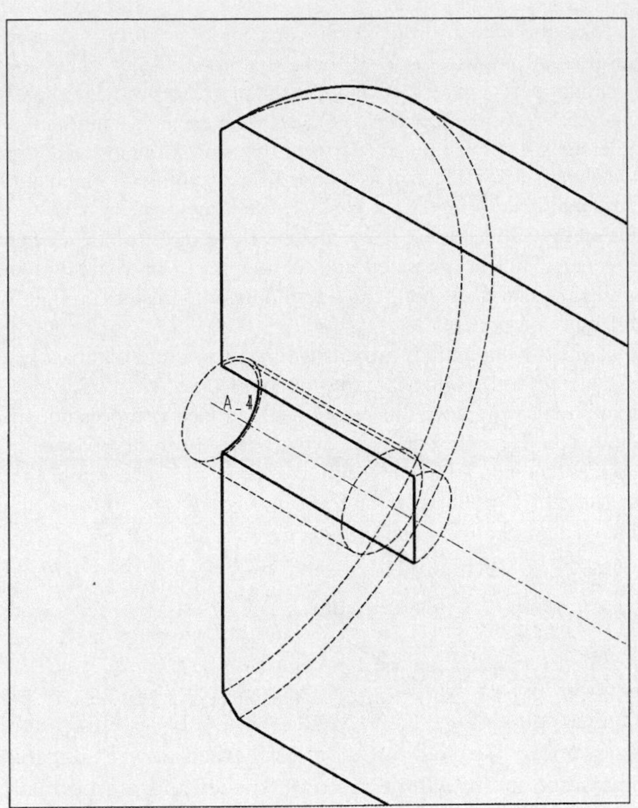

FIGURE K Cutaway of Blind Hole and Cosmetic Threads

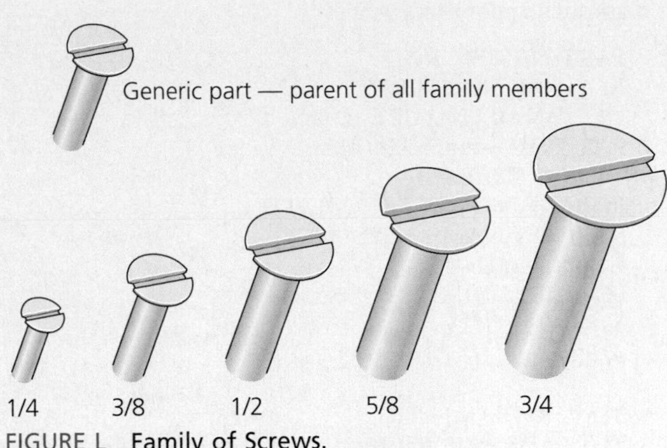

FIGURE L Family of Screws.

Thread parameters can be manipulated as are other user-defined parameters: They can be added, modified, deleted, or displayed via options in the MODEL PARAMS menu. The following information was extracted with the **Info** command:

Part---Feature---Info---Feature Info--- (select the external thread)

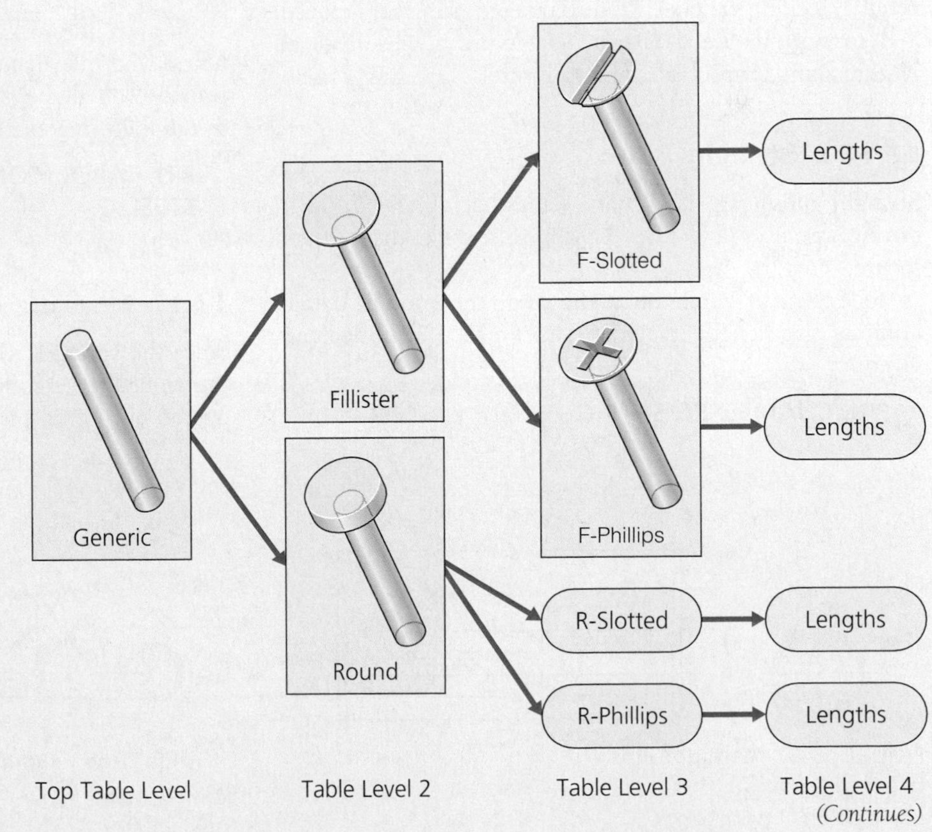

FIGURE M Generic Screw and Family Tree

(Continues)

Information appears in a window:

PART NAME = ROD
FEATURE NUMBER 13
INTERNAL FEATURE ID 246
PARENTS = 9(#5) 224(#12)
TYPE = THREAD
FORM = 360 DEG. REVOLVED
SECTION NAME = S2D0003
OPEN SECTION
FEATURES DIMENSIONS:
d28(d11) = 1.25
d29(d12) = .63 Dia.

MAJOR_DIAMETER	.625
THREADS_PER_INCH	11
FORM	UNC
CLASS	2A

Like the standardized parts you purchase from a catalog, **families of parts** (also called "table-driven parts") are collections of similar parts that are available in different sizes or have slightly different detailing features. For example, screws come in all different sizes, but they all perform the same function and look somewhat alike. Thus, it is convenient to think of them as a family of parts (Fig. L). Likewise, we can create a family of assemblies and features. These all have the same attributes, where a "generic" object is created and all members of the family look somewhat like the generic but are of different sizes or use slightly different components.

Table-driven families provide a very simple and compact way of creating and storing large numbers of objects. In additional, family tables promote the use of standardized components and allow you to represent your actual part inventory. Moreover, families facilitate interchangeability of parts and subassemblies in an assembly; instances from the same family are automatically interchangeable with each other (Fig. M).

Eight common types of pins are found in industry and are recognized as American National standards:

- Straight
- Tapered
- Spring
- Grooved
- Dowel
- Cotter
- Clevis
- Push–pull

Pins can be either quick-release or semipermanent. Quick-release pins include the cotter, clevis, push–pull, and positive locking varieties. Dowel, tapered, straight, grooved, and spring pins are semipermanent types because they all require some form of pressure to insert.

17.17.1 Straight Pins

Straight pins (Fig. 17.67) are somewhat difficult to align during assembly and must be a precise fit to make them secure.

To designate a pin on a drawing, the product name, nominal size, length, material, and finish (if required) are given:

PIN, CHAMFERED STRAIGHT, $\frac{5}{16}$ × 2, STEEL

17.17.2 Tapered Pins

Tapered pins (Fig. 17.68) add to ease of assembly and disassembly. They fall out more easily than dowels. Tapered pins come in sizes from $\frac{1}{16}$ to $1\frac{1}{2}$ inches and are normally steel. Tapered pins are called out by a number, from 0 (small diameter) to 14 (large diameter), and by their length requirement. The large end of a tapered pin is constant for a particular-size pin, but the small end changes according to the length. Tapered pins have a taper of $\frac{1}{4}$ in. per foot.

Step drilling or tapered reaming is required for tapered holes. The information contained Figure 17.69 should be provided on all taper details. Tapered pins are designated as in the following example:

PIN, TAPER (COMMERCIAL CLASS) NO. 2 × $1\frac{1}{4}$, STEEL

17.17.3 Spring Pins

Since the spring force retains the pin in the hole, a **spring pin** (rolled pin) reduces the possibility of falling out during operation. The hole for a spring pin is drilled slightly smaller

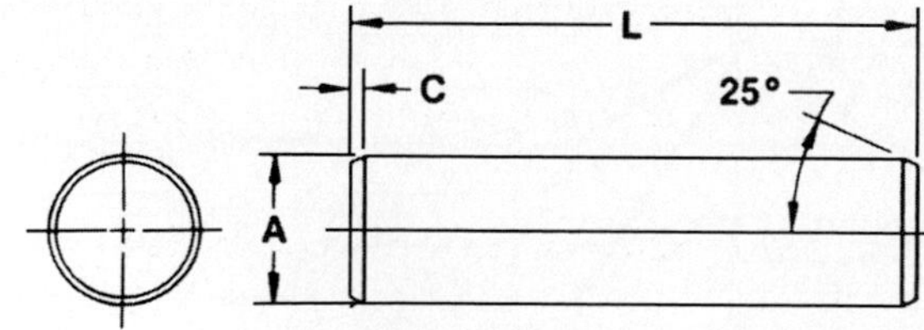

FIGURE 17.67 Straight Pins

Nominal Size	A	C
.250	.2500	.025
.375	.3750	.040

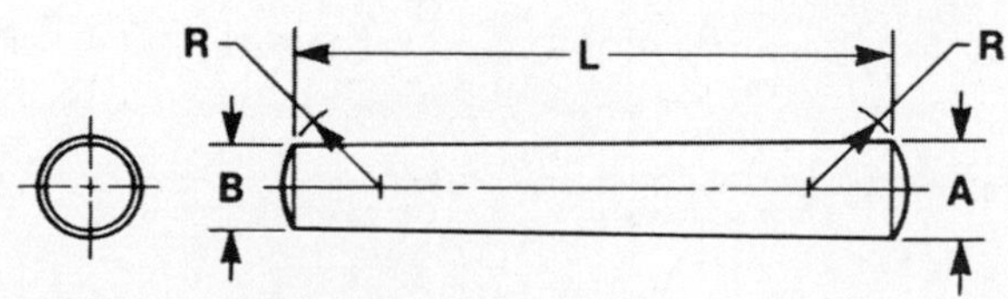

FIGURE 17.68 Tapered Pins

Nominal Size	A	R
#4 (.2500)	.2500	.26
#8 (.4920)	.4920	.50

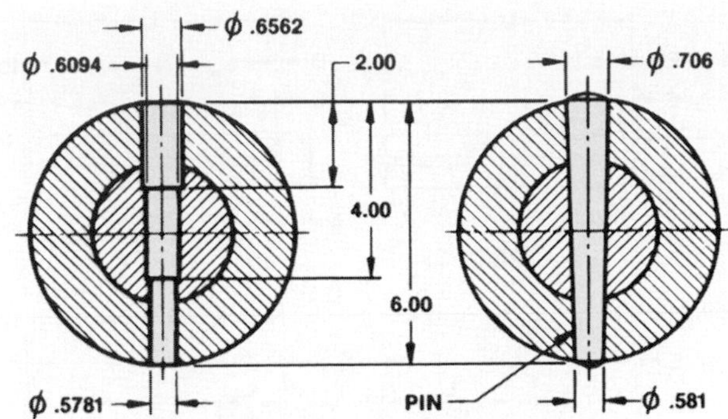

FIGURE 17.69 Dimensioning Tapered Pins

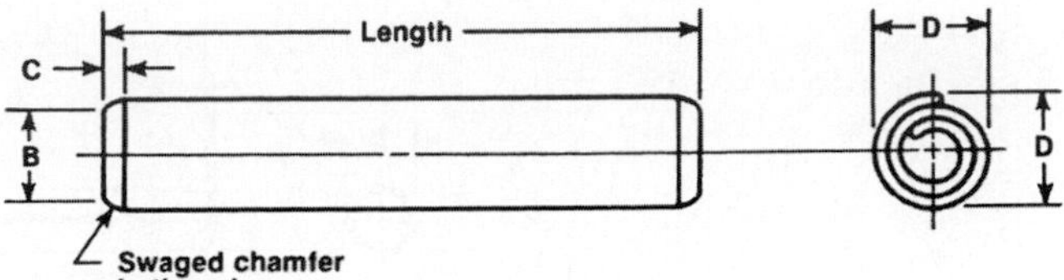

FIGURE 17.71 Metric Coiled Spring Pins

Nominal Size	B	C	D
10	9.75	2.5	10.80
20	19.6	4.5	21.10

than the pin. Spring pins are reusable and can be removed repeatedly without distortion or without losing their locking efficiency

Spring pins come in two basic styles. One type has a slot throughout its length (Fig. 17.70), and the other is shaped in the form of a coil (Fig. 17.71). Spring pins are designated on drawings as in the following examples:

PIN, COILED SPRING, $\frac{1}{2} \times 2\frac{1}{4}$, STANDARD DUTY, STEEL, ZINC PLATED

PIN, SLOTTED SPRING, .250 × .75, AISI 420 CORROSION RESISTANT STEEL

For metric:

PIN, COILED SPRING, 10 × 40, HEAVY DUTY, STAINLESS STEEL, PHOSPHATE COATED

PIN, SLOTTED SPRING, 20 × 60, STANDARD DUTY, CHROME-NICKEL AUSTENITIC STAINLESS STEEL, CADMIUM PLATED

17.17.4 Grooved Pins

Grooved pins (Fig. 17.72) are tapered or straight, with longitudinal grooves pressed into the body The pin will deform when pressed into the part. Because they hold securely even after repeated removal and reassembly, grooved pins are employed in situations where repeated disassembly is required. Grooved pins are designated as in the following example:

PIN, TYPE B GROOVED, $\frac{5}{16}$ × 2, CORROSION RESISTANT STEEL

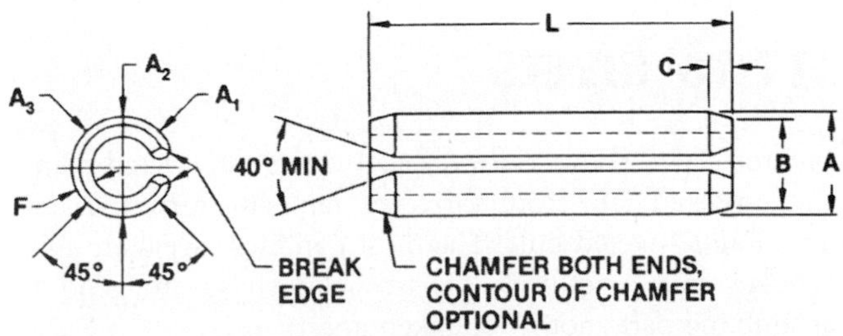

FIGURE 17.70 Slotted Spring Pins

Nominal Size	A	B	C
.375	.39	.36	.09
.500	.521	.48	.11

17.17.5 Dowel Pins

Dowel pins (Fig. 17.73) are heat-treated, precision-ground pins. Dowels align mating parts precisely or retain parts in a fixed position; they are not used as fasteners. Since the dowels are press-fit, holes for dowels are reamed and not drilled. The dowel is slightly larger than the hole and the dowel pin is forced ("press-fit") into the hole to ensure accurate alignment between mating parts. Dowels provide alignment and the screws serve to fasten. A general rule is to use dowels that are close to the same diameter as the screws. The dowel length should be $1\frac{1}{2}$ to 2 times its diameter in each plate or part to be doweled. Dowel pins are designated as in the following examples:

PIN, HARDENED GROUND PRODUCTION DOWEL, .500 × 1.75, STEEL, PHOSPHATE COATED

PIN, UNHARDENED GROUND DOWEL, $\frac{3}{4} \times 1\frac{1}{2}$ STEEL

For metric:

PIN DOWEL, 16 × 70, STAINLESS STEEL

17.17.6 Clevis Pins and Cotter Pins

Clevis pins (Fig. 17.74) are used with cotter pins to retain parts on a shaft or to lock a nut and bolt. **Cotter pins** (Fig. 17.75) are used with clevis pins to retain parts on a shaft or to lock a slotted nut and bolt. Cotter pins are good where quick-and-easy assembly and disassembly are required. Clevis pins and cotter pins are designated as in the following examples:

PIN, CLEVIS, .438 × 1.19, STEEL, CADMIUM PLATED

PIN, CLEVIS, $\frac{1}{4}$ × 0.77, STEEL

PIN, COTTER, $\frac{1}{8} \times 1\frac{1}{2}$, EXTENDED PRONG TYPE, STEEL, ZINC PLATED

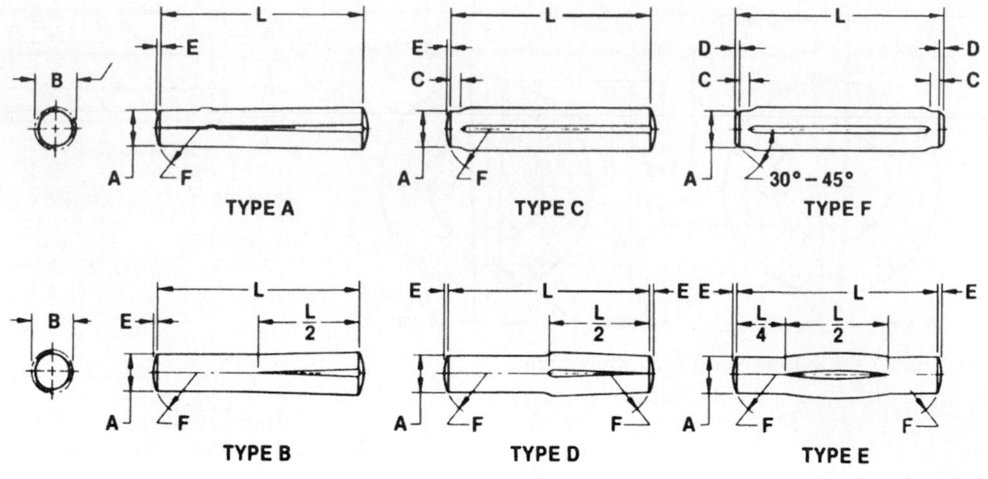

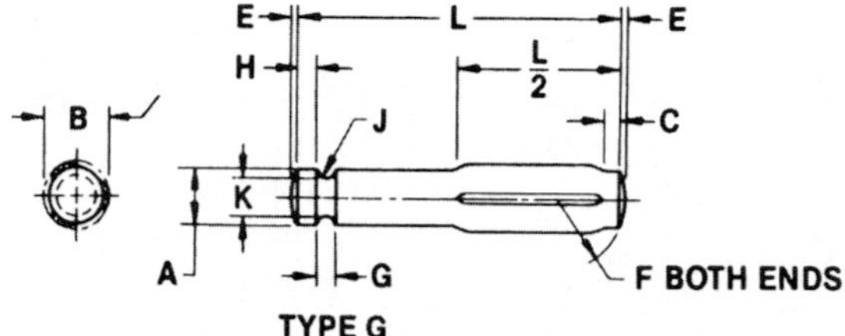

FIGURE 17.72 Grooved Pins

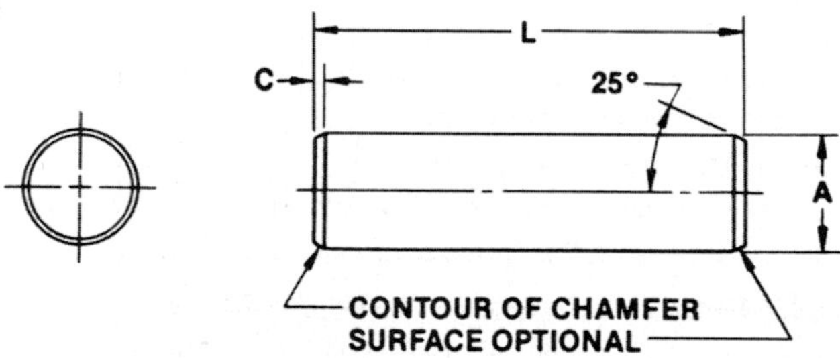

FIGURE 17.73 Dowel Pins

Nominal Size	A	C
.375	.371	.04
.500	.496	.04

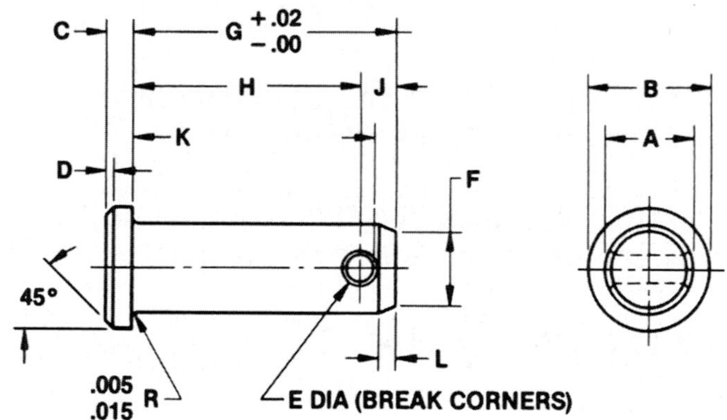

FIGURE 17.74 Clevis Pins

Nominal Size	A	B	C	D	F	G	H	J	L	Pin Size
.375	.37	.51	.13	.03	.33	1.06	.95	.12	.07	.093
.500	.49	.63	.16	.04	.44	1.36	1.22	.15	.08	1.250

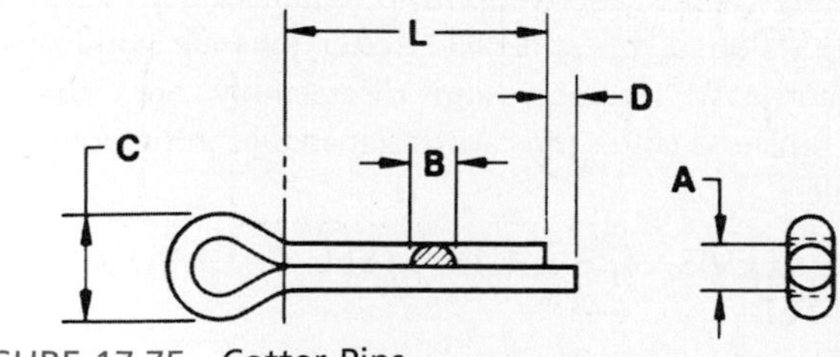

FIGURE 17.75 Cotter Pins

Nominal Size	A	B	C	D
.135	.12	.12	.25	.06
.188	.17	.17	.38	.09

17.18 RIVETS

Figure 17.76 shows four typical types of riveted joints: single-riveted lap, double-riveted lap, single-riveted butt, and double-riveted butt. The most common rivets are solid, tubular, split, and blind rivets. Solid rivets are good for assembling parts not to be taken apart.

Solid rivets are shown on drawings as in Figure 17.77. If plans, elevations, or sections show the conventional signs for the head of the shop rivets or field rivets, the corresponding lengthwise view of the rivet fastenings is normally omitted.

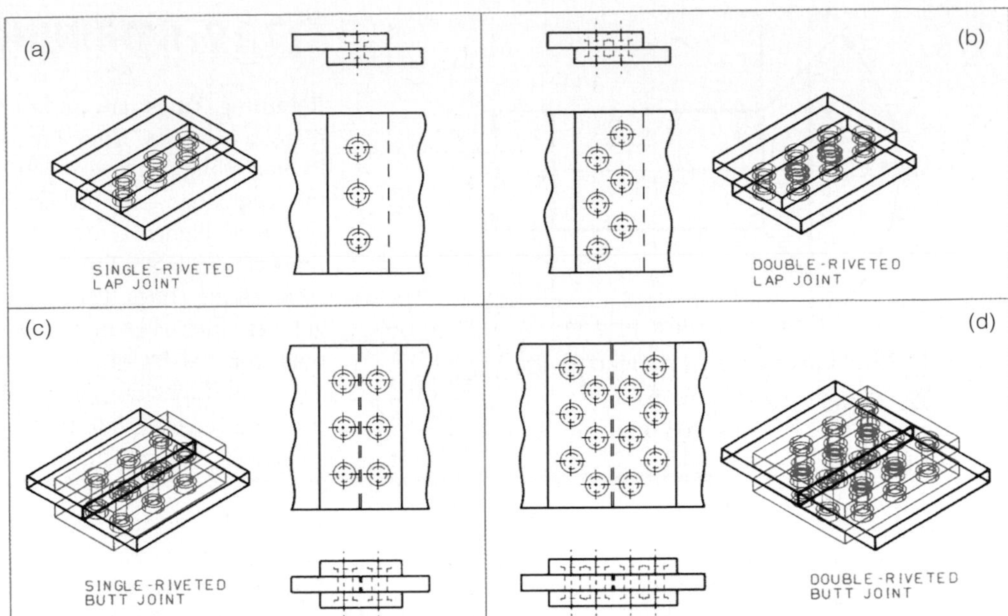

FIGURE 17.76
Riveted Joints

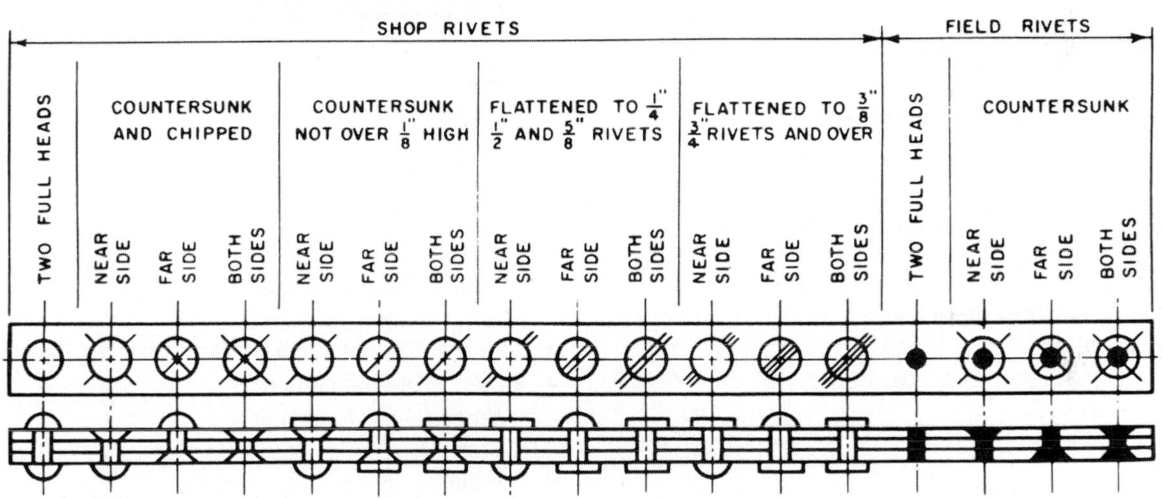

FIGURE 17.77 Drawing Conventions for Solid Rivets

Rivets are available in a variety of endpoints. The choice of head and endpoint is determined by the application. The hole size and type will be determined by the rivet choice. Figures 17.78 through 17.81 show four standard types of rivets.

Designate rivets on drawings as in the following examples:

.146 × .500 SEMI-TUBULAR, OVAL HEAD, STEEL, CADMIUM PLATED

$\frac{1}{4}$ × $1\frac{1}{4}$ FLAT HEAD SMALL SOLID RIVET, STEEL, ZINC PLATED

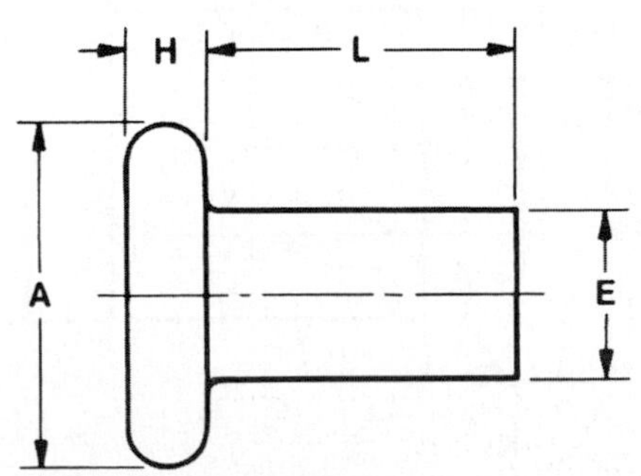

FIGURE 17.78 Flat-Head Rivets

Nominal Size	A	E	H
.125	.125	.25	.04
.250	.250	.50	.09

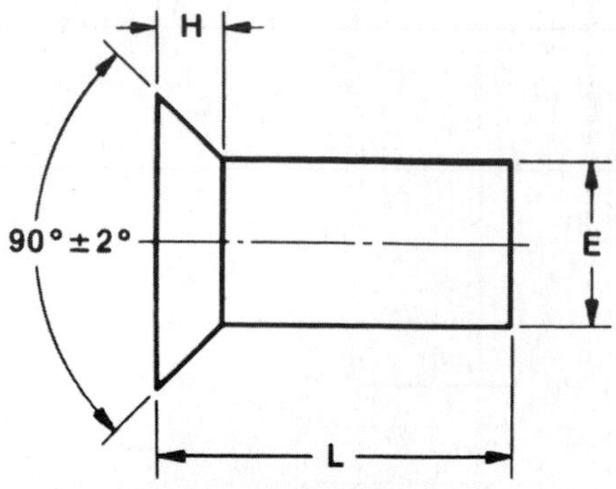

FIGURE 17.79 Flat-Countersunk-Head Rivets

Nominal Size	Head Dia.	E	H
.156	.29	.15	.06
.312	.58	.31	.13

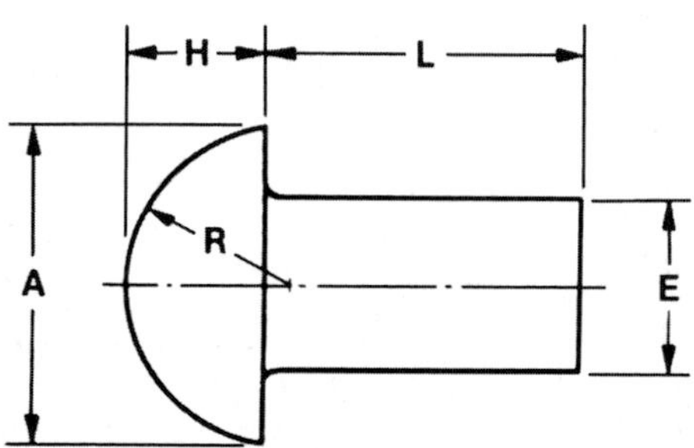

FIGURE 17.80 Button-Head Rivets

Nominal Size	A	E	H	R
.094	.18	.094	.07	.08
.281	.51	.281		

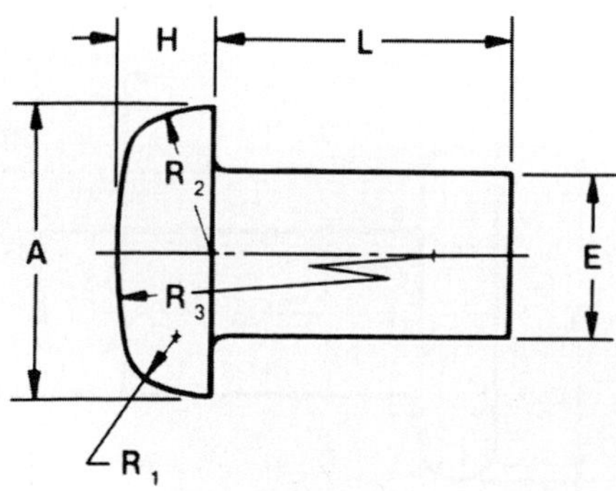

FIGURE 17.81 Pan-Head Rivets

Nominal Size	A	E	H	R1	R2	R3
.188	.33	.187	.11	.05	.15	.64
.312	.55	.312	.18	.09	.26	1.07

17.19 RETAINING RINGS

Retaining rings are semipermanent fasteners found on many assemblies. They are used as shoulders that can be located along a shaft (or pin) or in a recessed hole to keep the components of an assembly properly positioned, as shown in Figure 17.82. Many different styles of retaining rings are available (Fig. 17.83).

Retaining rings can easily be installed in machined grooves, internally in housings or externally on shafts or pins. Some styles of retaining rings require no grooves but have a self-locking spring-type action. The two types of retaining rings are internal and external.

Radially assembled rings are designed to be snapped directly onto a shaft. Axially assembled rings require special tools to expand the ring (for external rings) or to contract the ring (for internal rings) to slide over a shaft (external) or slip into a grooved housing (internal) while installing.

17.20 COLLARS

A **collar** (Fig. 17.84) is a ring installed over a shaft and positioned adjacent to a machine element such as a pulley, a gear, or a sprocket. A collar is held in position in most cases by a set screw. The advantage of a collar is that axial location can be established virtually anywhere along the shaft to allow adjustment of the position at the time of assembly.

Typical Collar Applications

- Spacer on a machine shaft
- Thrust collar on pillow block
- Hub or plate on a sprocket
- Adjustment for torsion spring
- Clutch part
- Locating a gear or cam on a shaft.

17.21 KEYS AND KEYSEATS

A key is a machine component used to assemble a shaft and the hub of a power-transmitting element (gear, sprocket, pulley) to transmit torque. Keys are removable to facilitate assembly and disassembly of the shaft and components. A key is installed in an axial groove machined into the shaft, called a **keyseat** (Fig. 17.85). A similar groove in the hub of the power-transmitting element is usually called a keyway but is more properly called a keyseat.

Square keys (the width and the height are equal) are preferred on shaft sizes up to 6.50 inches in diameter. Square keys (Fig. 17.86) are sunk halfway into the shaft and extend halfway into the hub of the assembly. Above 6.50 inches in diameter, rectangular keys are recommended. The **rectangular key** (flat key) is recommended for larger shafts

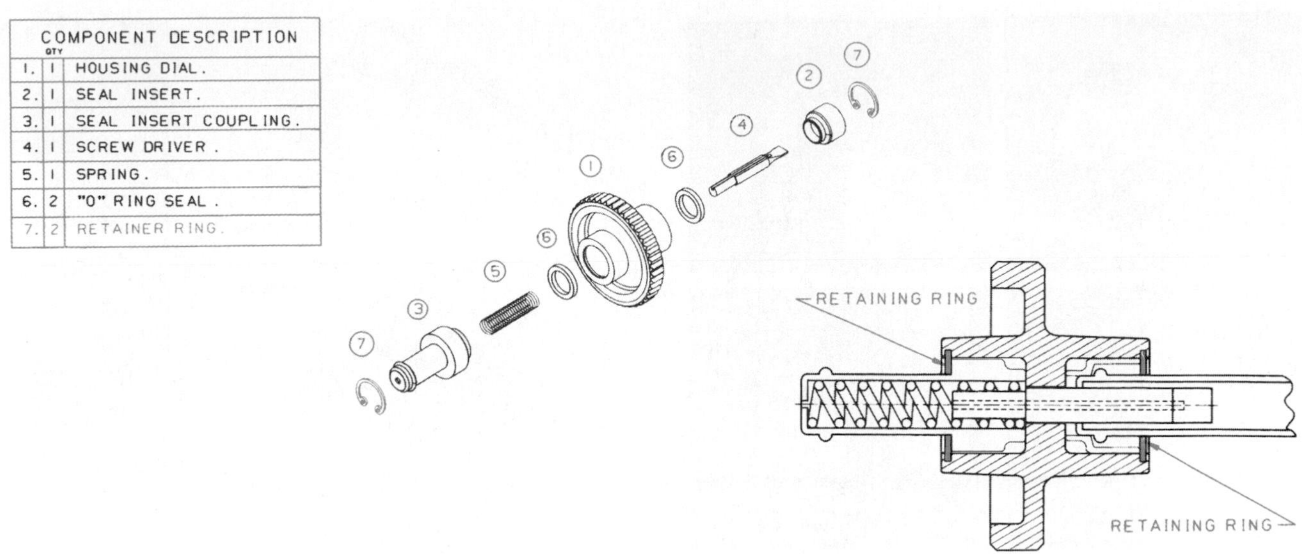

	QTY	COMPONENT DESCRIPTION
1.	1	HOUSING DIAL.
2.	1	SEAL INSERT.
3.	1	SEAL INSERT COUPLING.
4.	1	SCREW DRIVER.
5.	1	SPRING.
6.	2	"O" RING SEAL.
7.	2	RETAINER RING.

FIGURE 17.82 Internal Retaining Rings Used on an Assembly

and is used for smaller shafts where the shorter height is acceptable for the design requirements.

The **taper key** (Fig. 17.86) permits the key to be inserted from the end of the shaft after the hub is in position. If the opposite end of the key is not accessible to be driven out, the gib-head key provides the means for extracting the key

Type	Style	Number	Use	Size Range (in.)	Size Range (mm)
INTERNAL	BASIC	N5000	For housings and bores	250—10.0 in	6.4—254.0 mm
INTERNAL	BOWED	N5001	For housings and bores	.250–1.750 in.	6.4–44.4 mm.
INTERNAL	BEVELED	N5002	For housings and bores	1.0—10.0 in	25.4—254.0 mm
INTERNAL	CIRCULAR	5005	For housings and bores	.312—2.0 in	•
INTERNAL	INVERTED	5008	For housings and bores	.750—4.0 in.	19.0—101.6 mm
EXTERNAL	BASIC	5100	For shafts and pins	.125—10.0 in.	3.2—254.0 mm.
EXTERNAL	BOWED	5101	For shafts and pins	.188–1.750 in.	4.8–44.4 mm.
EXTERNAL	BEVELED	5102	For shafts and pins	1.0—10.0 in	25.4—254.0 mm.
EXTERNAL	CRESCENT®	5103	For shafts and pins	.125—2.0 in.	3.2—50.8 mm.
EXTERNAL	CIRCULAR	5105	For shafts and pins	094—1.0 in.	•
EXTERNAL	INTERLOCKING	5107	For shafts and pins	.469—3.375 in.	11.9—85.7 mm.
EXTERNAL	INVERTED	5108	For shafts and pins	.500—4.0 in.	12.7—101.6 mm.
EXTERNAL	REINFORCED	5115	For shafts and pins	094—1.0 in.	•
EXTERNAL	BOWED E-RING	5131	For shafts and pins	110—1.375 in.	2.8—34.9 mm.
EXTERNAL	E-RING	5133	For shafts and pins	040—1.375 in.	1.0—34.9 mm.
EXTERNAL	PRONG-LOCK®	5139	For shafts and pins	.092—.438 in.	•
EXTERNAL	REINFORCED E-RING	5144	For shafts and pins	.094—.562 in.	2.4—14.3 mm.
EXTERNAL	HEAVY-DUTY	5160	For shafts and pins	.394—2.0 in.	10.0—50.8 mm.
EXTERNAL	TRIANGULAR NUT	5300	For threaded parts	6-32 and 8-32, 10-24 and 10-32, 1/4-20 and 1/4-28	
EXTERNAL	KLIPRING	5304 T-5304	For shafts and pins	.156–1.000 in.	4.0–25.4 mm.
EXTERNAL	TRIANGULAR	5305	For shafts and pins	.062—.438 in.	•
EXTERNAL	GRIPRING®	5555	For shafts and pins	.079—.750 in.	2.0—19.0 mm.
EXTERNAL	HIGH-STRENGTH	5560	For shafts and pins	.101—.328 in.	•
EXTERNAL	PERMANENT SHOULDER	5590	For shafts and pins	.250–.750	6.4–19.0 mm.

FIGURE 17.83 Retaining Ring Styles

FIGURE 17.84 Coupling Applications

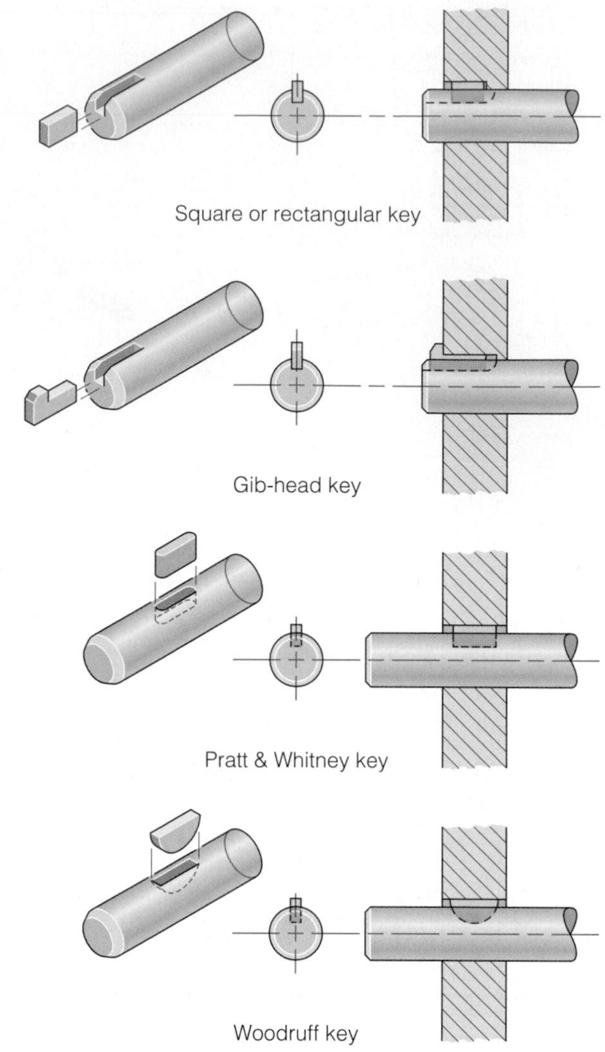

FIGURE 17.85 Types of Keys

On both the plain-taper and the gib-head key, the taper is 8 in. per foot. The cross-sectional dimensions of the key, *W* and *H,* are the same as for parallel keys, with the height *H* measured at the position specified in Figure 17.86.

17.21.1 Key Size Versus Shaft Diameter

For a stepped shaft (one that has multiple diameters), the size of a key is determined by the diameter of the shaft at the

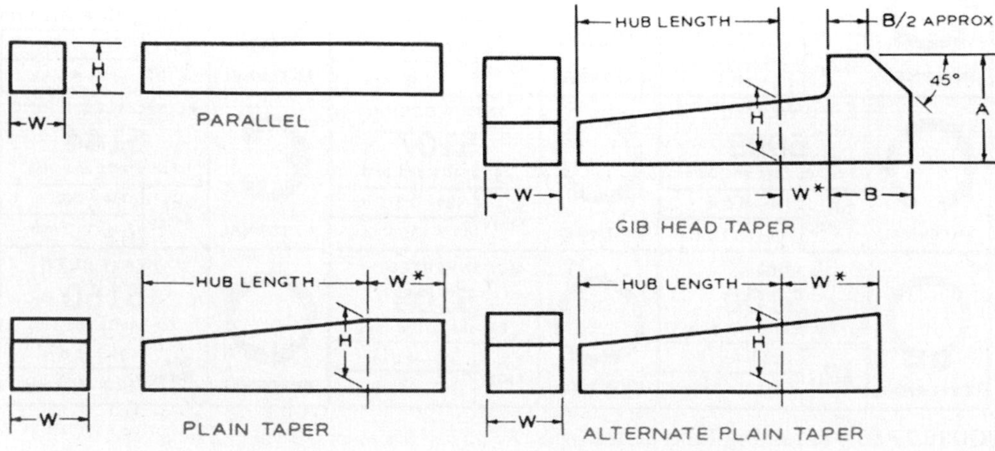

FIGURE 17.86 Keys

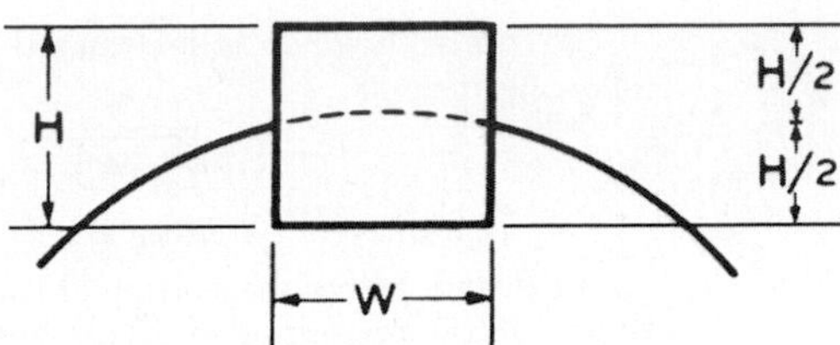

FIGURE 17.87 Key Sizes for Square Keys

Nominal Shaft Dia.	H	W
.875.1.25	.25	.25
1.750.2.25	.50	.50

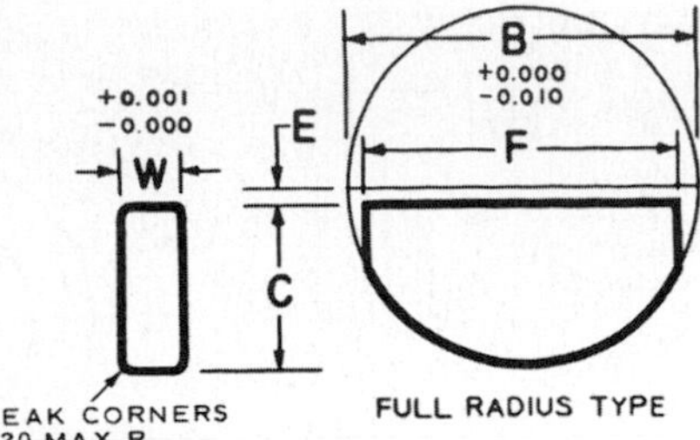

FIGURE 17.89 Woodruff Keys

Key #	W × B	C	D	E	F
817.1	.250 × 2.125	.40	.39	21/32	1.38
1217.1	.375 × 2.125	.40	.29	21/32	1.38

point of location of the key, regardless of the number of different diameters on the shaft. Sizes and dimensions for keys are found in tables in the *Machinery's Handbook* and in ANSI B17.1. Figure 17.87 shows the preferred dimensions for parallel keys as a function of the shaft diameter. The width is normally one-fourth of the diameter of the shaft.

17.21.2 Woodruff Keys

Woodruff keys, which are almost in the shape of a half circle, are used where relatively light loads are transmitted. One advantage of Woodruff keys is that they cannot change their axial location on a shaft, because they are retained in a pocket. Woodruff keys can be either the full-radius type (Figs. 17.88 and 17.89) or the flat-bottom type.

17.21.3 Design of Keys and Keyseats

The key and keyseat are designed after the shaft diameter is determined. Then, with the shaft diameter as a guide, the size of the key is selected from ANSI B17.1 or ANSI B17.2. The only remaining variables are the length of the key and its material. One of these can be specified, and the requirements for the other can then be computed. Typically, the length of a key is specified to be the hub length of the element in which it is installed, to provide for good alignment and stable operation. Figure 17.90 shows keyseat dimensions for Woodruff keys. Keys are designed to fail *before* the shaft or hub fails, to lower the cost for replacement.

For rectangular and square keys, keyseats in the shaft and the hub are designed so that exactly one-half of the height of the key is in the shaft keyseat and the other half is in the hub keyseat. Figure 17.91 shows the resulting geometry. The distance Y is the radial distance from the theoretical top of the shaft, before the keyseat is machined, to the top edge of the finished keyseat, to produce a keyseat depth of exactly $H/2$. To assist in machining and inspecting the shaft or the hub, the dimensions S and T can be computed and shown on the part drawings. The equations are given in Figure 17.91. Tabulated values of Y, S, and T (Fig. 17.92) are available in the standard and in the *Machinery's Handbook.* Standard key sizes are also listed in Appendix C.9.

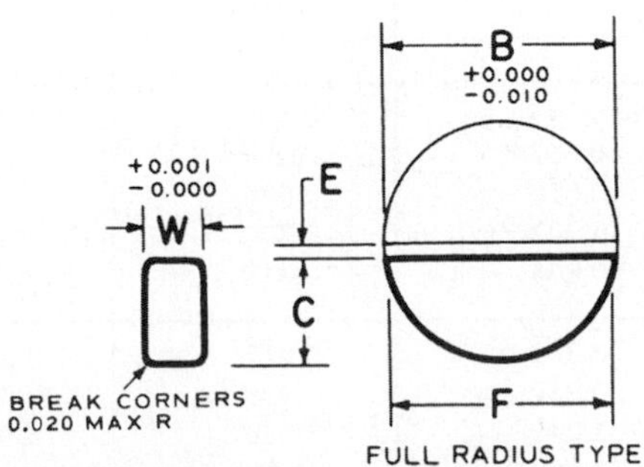

FIGURE 17.88 Full-Radius Woodruff Keys

Key #	W × B	C	D	E	F
403	.125 × .375	.17	.17	1/64	.37
806	.250 × .7501	.31	.30	1/16	.74

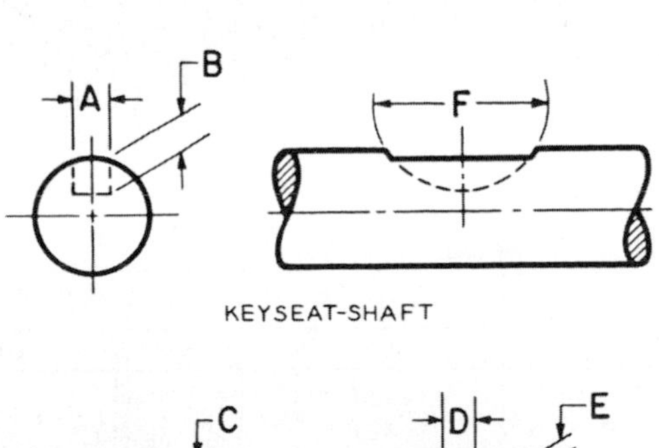

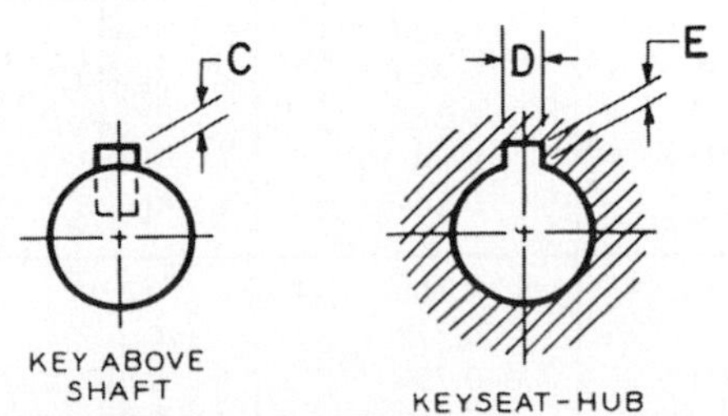

FIGURE 17.90 Keyseat Dimensions

Key #	Nominal Size	A	B	C	D	E	F
403	.125 × .375	.12	.10	.06	.12	.06	.375
806	.250 × .750	.24	.18	.12	.25	.13	.750

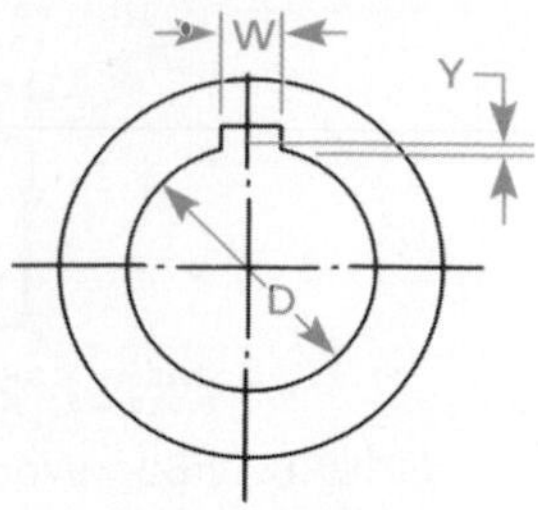

The chordal height Y is determined from the following formula:

$$Y = \frac{D - \sqrt{D^2 - W^2}}{2}$$

The distance from the bottom of the shaft keyseat to the opposite side of the shaft is specified by dimension S. The following formula may be used for calculating this dimension:

$$S = D - Y - \frac{H}{2} = \frac{D - H + \sqrt{D^2 - W^2}}{2}$$

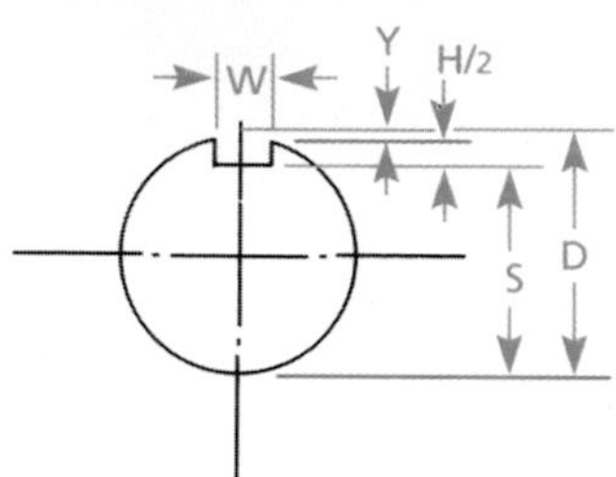

The distance from the bottom of the hub keyseat to the opposite side of the hub bore is specified by dimension T. For taper keyseats, T is measured at the deeper end. The following formula may be used for calculating this dimension:

$$T = D - Y + \frac{H}{2} + C = \frac{D + H + \sqrt{D^2 - W^2}}{2} + C$$

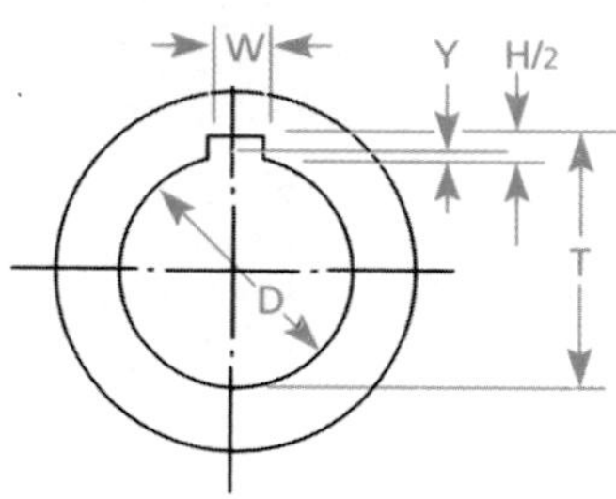

Symbols
- C = Allowance
  - + 0.005 inch clearance for parallel keys
  - – 0.020 inch interference for taper keys
- D = Nominal shaft or bore diameter, inches
- H = Nominal key height, inches
- W = Nominal key width, inches
- Y = Chordal height, inches

FIGURE 17.91 Calculating Keyseats

NOMINAL SHAFT DIAMETER	PARALLEL AND TAPER		PARALLEL		TAPER	
	SQUARE	RECTANGULAR	SQUARE	RECTANGULAR	SQUARE	RECTANGULAR
	S	*S*	*T*	*T*	*T*	*T*
1/2	0.430	0.445	0.560	0.544	0.535	0.519
9/16	0.493	0.509	0.623	0.607	0.598	0.582
5/8	0.517	0.548	0.709	0.678	0.684	0.653
11/16	0.581	0.612	0.773	0.742	0.748	0.717
3/4	0.644	0.676	0.837	0.806	0.812	0.781
13/16	0.708	0.739	0.900	0.869	0.875	0.844
7/8	0.771	0.802	0.964	0.932	0.939	0.907
15/16	0.796	0.827	1.051	1.019	1.026	0.994
1	0.859	0.890	1.114	1.083	1.089	1.058
1-1/16	0.923	0.954	1.178	1.146	1.153	1.121

FIGURE 17.92 Shaft Diameter and Keyseat Dimensions

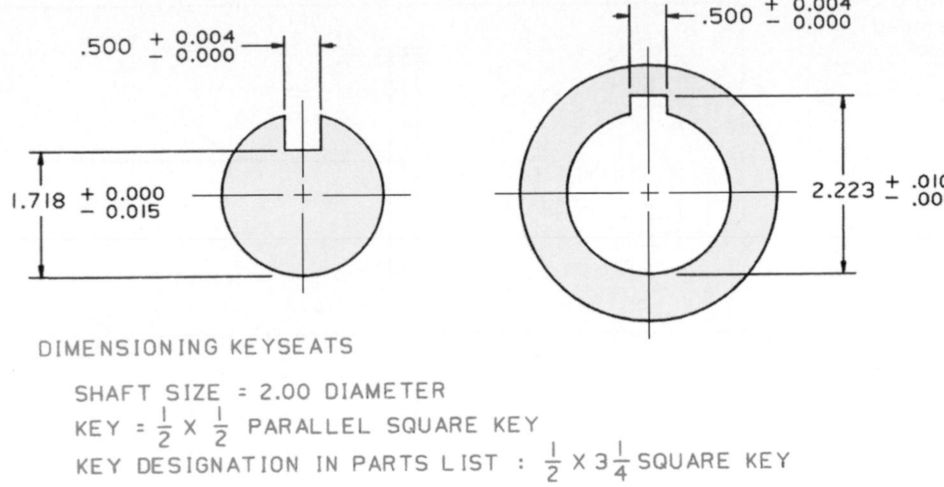

FIGURE 17.93 Dimensioning Keyseats

17.21.4 Dimensioning Keyseats

Keyseats (Fig. 17.93) are dimensioned by giving the width, depth, location, and, if required, length. For shafts, the width of the keyseat, the distance from the bottom of the shaft to the bottom of the keyseat, and the length are given. For the hub, the width of the keyseat and the distance from the bottom of the shaft hole to the top of the keyseat are given.

When designating keys on drawings, the key number or size, length, and product name are given, as in the following:

$\frac{1}{2}$ × 3 SQUARE KEY

NO. 403 WOODRUFF KEY

$\frac{1}{4}$ × $1\frac{1}{2}$ SQUARE GIB HEAD KEY

$1\frac{1}{4}$ × 4 SQUARE PLAIN TAPER KEY

NO. 8 PRATT & WHITNEY KEY

$\frac{1}{8}$ × $\frac{3}{32}$ × $\frac{3}{4}$ RECTANGULAR KEY

You May Complete Exercises 17.9 Through 17.12 at This Time

17.22 USING A CAD SYSTEM TO DRAW THREADS

Drawing threads with a 2D CAD system is similar to the processes already described for detailed and Acme threads (see Sections 17.6.3 and 17.6.4). However, the thread profile of only one thread is constructed; the other threads are constructed simply through CAD commands such as **COPY** and **ARRAY**. Figures 17.94 and 17.95 show projects that were completed on a CAD system. AutoCAD was used to create the threads in Figure 17.94. The **ARRAY** command created the additional threads.

```
Command: ARRAY
Select Objects: W (D1 and D2 are used to window the entities)
Rectangular or polar array (R/P): R
Number of rows (---) <1>: Return/Enter
Number of columns (:::) <1>:7
Unit cell or distance between rows (---): Return/Enter
Distance between columns (:::): .125
```

The socket-head cap screw in Figure 17.95 was drawn with Computervision's Personal Designer software. The command that generated the threads is different (**MOVE COPY**), but the results are the same for both examples.

With a CAD system, a standard library of parts is normally available for rapid and accurate insertion of standard fasteners as a 3D model or a 2D part (Fig. 17.96). Many standard parts are now available with 2D and 3D parts libraries for CAD systems. A library of standard parts eliminates the need to redraw each part. The part can be recalled and inserted as required anywhere on the design, in as many places as required. Library parts are a CAD system's version of a manual drafter's template.

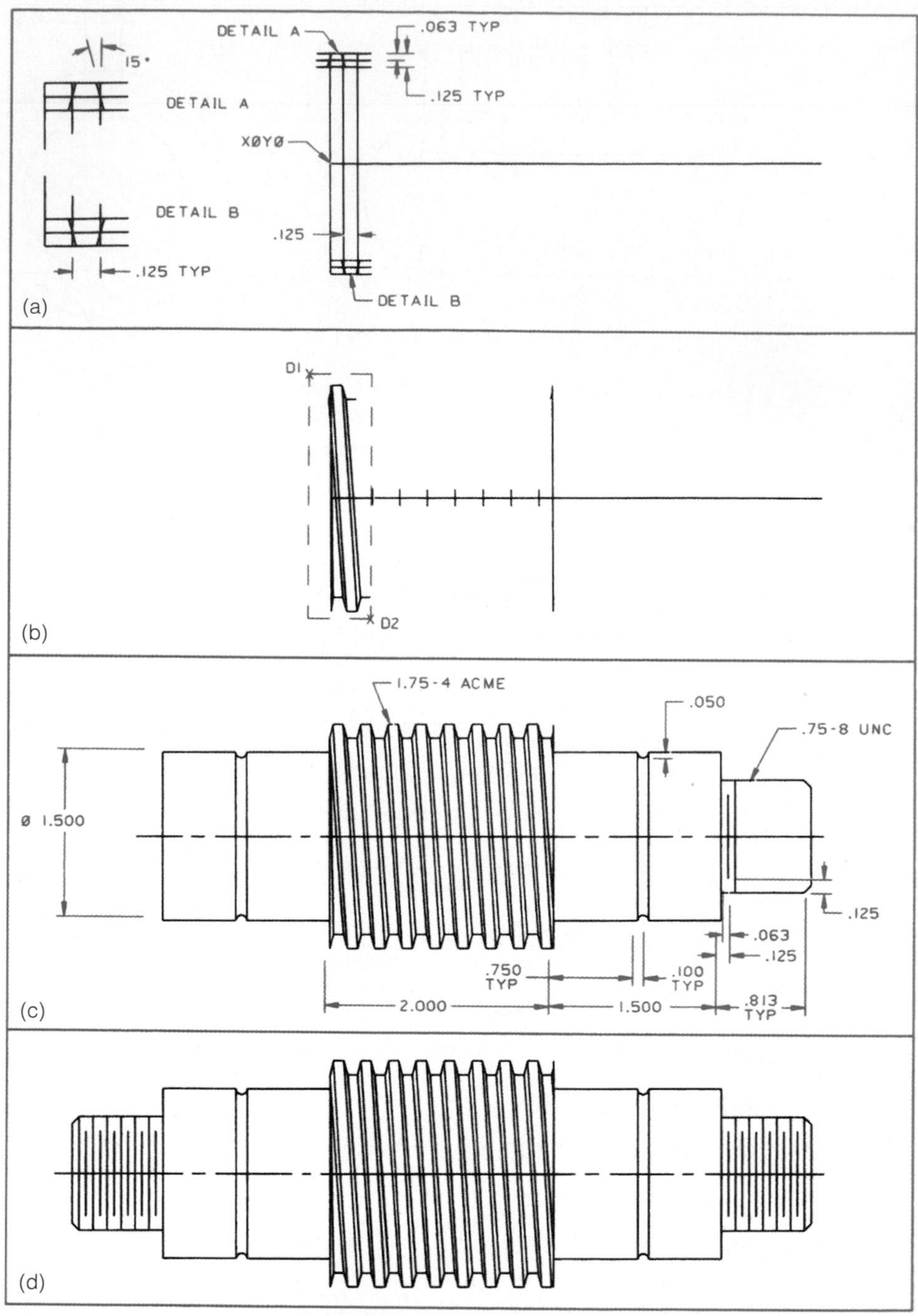

FIGURE 17.94 Using a CAD System to Draw Detailed Acme Threads

The fasteners shown in Figures 17.97 and 17.98 are additional examples of fasteners created on CAD systems. Both the model of the fastener and its orthographic projection are available to the designer.

The bolt shown in Figure 17.99 was created on Pro/ENGINEER's parametric design modeling system and has threads modeled on the bolt. In most cases, cosmetic or simplified threads are used for 3D models. The threads on this fastener were cut on the bolt shank. This method requires a huge amount of processing power and a very large file size. The shaded-image-plot file for this illustration took 24 Mbytes, and the part file took over 3 Mbytes! The access, process, regeneration, and repaint time (let alone the storage space on disk) make this type of modeling unrealistic for most situations, for example, a simple assembly with six pieces and twenty-four bolts.

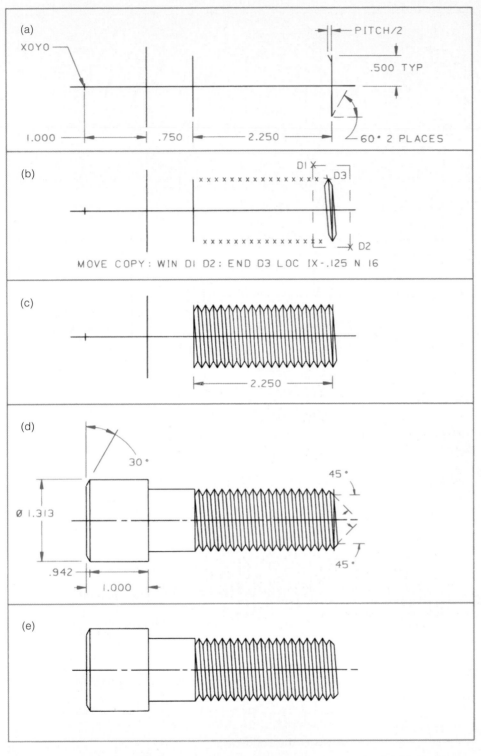

FIGURE 17.95 Using a CAD System to Draw Detailed Threads

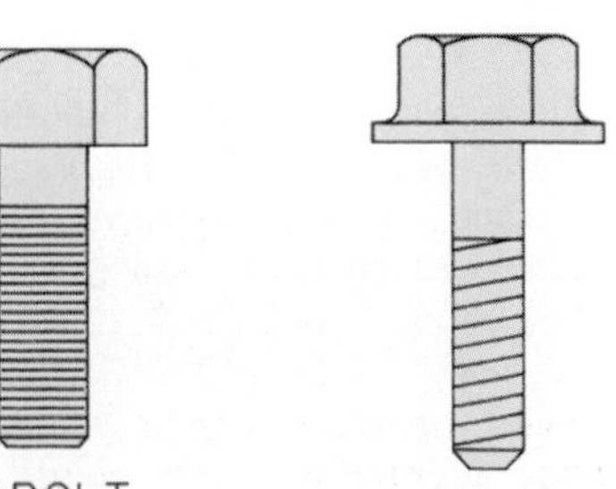

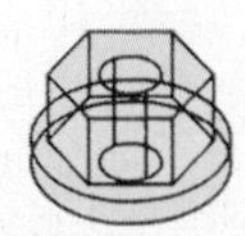

FIGURE 17.96 2D and 3D CAD Library Parts

This chapter has presented only a few of the millions of standard fasteners available on the market. Understanding the basic sizes, threads (where appropriate), and design uses of the fasteners is more important than knowing every style. When designing, remember to consult a variety of trade magazines, part catalogs, and design manuals before creating any new nonstandard fastener for your design project.

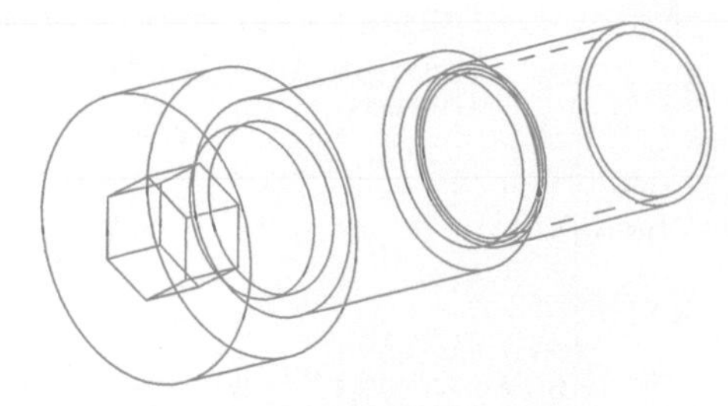

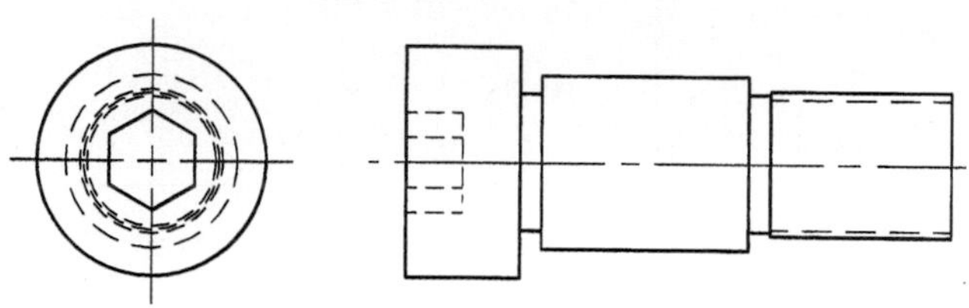

FIGURE 17.97 A Fastener Design That Was Created on a CAD System

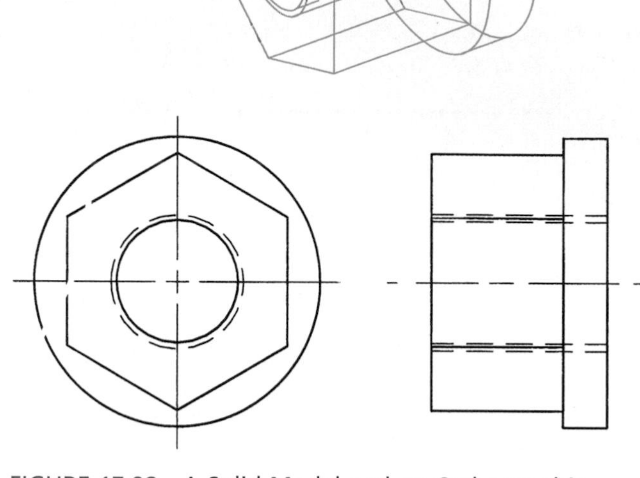

FIGURE 17.98 A Solid Model and an Orthographic Projection of a Fastener

FIGURE 17.99 Parametric Model of a Bolt with Modeled Threads

QUIZ

True or False

1. M5 × 1.50-6g is a designation for an American National thread.
2. UNC means United National thread form.
3. The B symbol for threads indicates that the thread is external.
4. Dowel pins are used to align and locate parts.
5. Studs are fasteners that secure two left-handed parts together.
6. Carriage bolts have a square body under the head.
7. The 13 in ".500-13 UNC-2B" means the number of threads per foot.
8. Tapered pins are tapered $\frac{1}{8}$ in. per foot.

Fill in the Blanks

9. ________, ________, and ________ are types of keys.
10. ________, ________, and ________ are primarily for power transmission.
11. ________ pins are used to retain parts such as slotted nuts and ________ pins.
12. ________ threads are used in place of the old ________ threads.
13. ________ ________ rings are installed on ________ machined grooves in housings.
14. A ________ key is shaped similar to a half circle.
15. Basic industrial fasteners include ________ and ________ bolts, ________, carriage bolts, studs, ________, and ________.
16. ________ are fasteners with no head but with threads at both ends of the shank.

Answer the Following

17. Describe how an axially assembled external retaining ring might be used in a design.
18. What is a set screw? Describe some of its possible design functions.
19. Name and describe three types of locating pins.
20. What are the meanings of UN, UNF, and UNC?
21. What is the difference between Class 1, 2, and 5 threads?
22. List four considerations in the selection of a fastener.
23. Describe two types of studs.
24. What is the difference between a right-hand and a left-hand thread?

EXERCISES

Exercises may be assigned as sketching or instrument projects. Transfer the given information to an "A"-size sheet of .25 in. grid paper. Complete all views, and solve for proper visibility, including centerlines, object lines, and hidden lines. Exercises that are not assigned by the instructor can be sketched in the text to provide practice and to enhance understanding of the preceding instructional material. Dimensions for fasteners used in exercises can be located in figures throughout the chapter and in Appendix C.

After Reading the Chapter Through Section 17.12.1, You May Complete the Following Four Exercises

Exercise 17.1 Complete the three parts using the appropriate threads. Use detailed thread representation.

Exercise 17.2 Draw the detailed representation of the Acme threads.

Exercise 17.3(A) Calculate the normal engagement, effective thread, and pipe end. Draw the flange and pipe as shown. The NPT pipe thread has a taper of $\frac{3}{4}$ in. per foot. The pipe has a 3 in. nominal size.

Exercise 17.3(B) Complete the pipe plug and flange. The plug has a standard NPT $\frac{3}{4}$ in. nominal pipe thread with a taper of $\frac{3}{4}$ in. per foot. Calculate and draw the effective thread, normal thread engagement, and length. Use simplified thread representation. Complete the end views showing only details that are visible and the threads.

Exercise 17.4 Draw the threaded shaft as shown. Include all chamfers, reliefs, and threads. Use schematic thread representation.

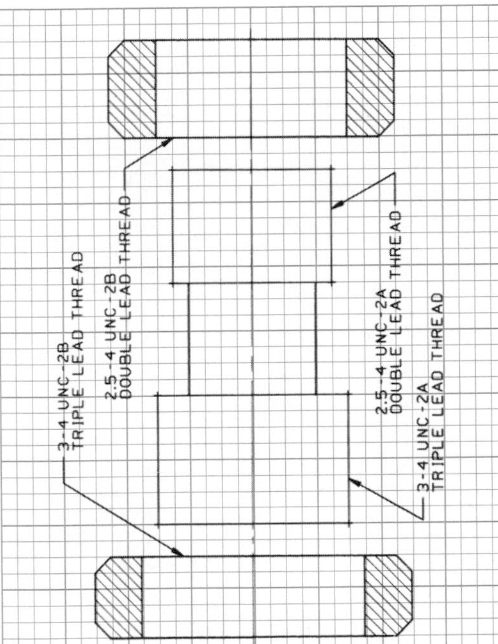

EXERCISE 17.1

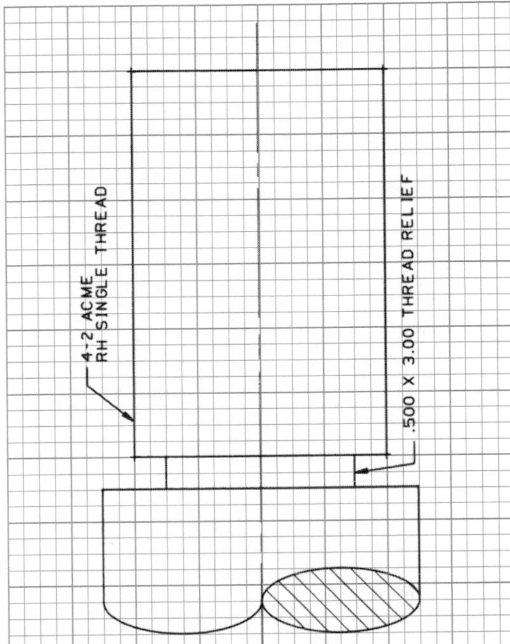

EXERCISE 17.2

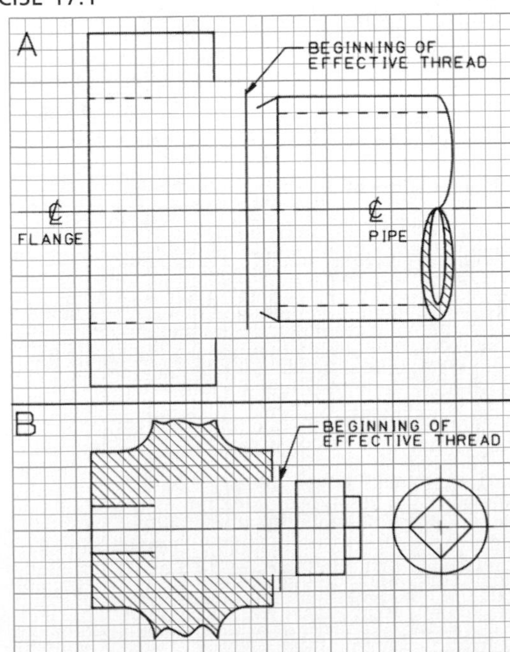

EXERCISE 17.3

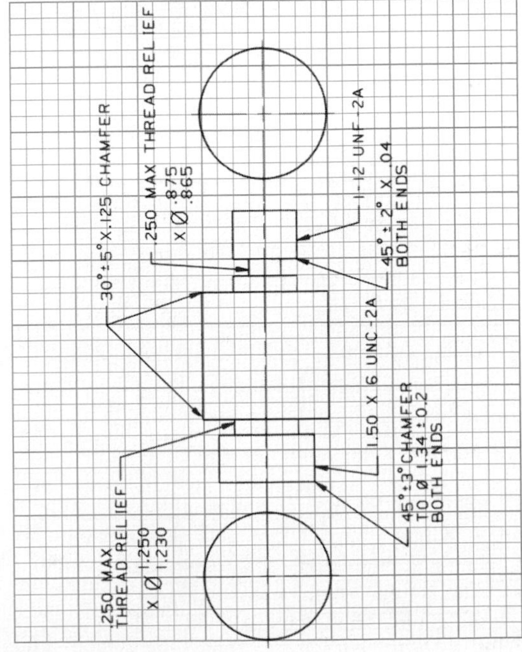

EXERCISE 17.4

After Reading the Chapter Through Section 17.16, You May Complete Exercises 17.5 Through 17.8

Exercise 17.5(A) Using detailed representation, draw a 1.50-6 UNC-2A × 4 square-head bolt. Draw only the axial (side) view in the given space.

Exercise 17.5(B) Draw a detailed representation of the 1-8 UNC-2A × 3 hex socket-head cap screw. Show the side and end views in the given space, and label the drawing correctly.

Exercise 17.6(A) Fasten the rest block to the plate with four $\frac{3}{8}$ in. diameter hex socket-head cap screws (S) and two $\frac{3}{8}$ in. diameter steel dowel pins (D). Calculate the screw and dowel lengths. The plate will have threaded through-holes. The rest block will have clearance through-holes for the screws to pass through. Calculate the screw's length of engagement, and counterbore the block so that the screw's head will be flush with the top surface. Calculate the counterbore diameter and depth. The dowel will be press-fit (interference-fit) into the block and the plate. Calculate the ream hole diameter for the dowels.

Exercise 17.6(B) Dimension the hole pattern for the screws and the dowels. Call out the proper clearance hole size for the drilled clearance holes, the screws, and the reamed holes for the dowels.

Exercise 17.7 Draw the moving shaft pivot as shown. Use two hex socket-head shoulder screws. Show the screws in both views. The screws have different diameters and lengths.

Exercise 17.8 Read Section 17.13.7 on set screws, and complete the exercise as described. Determine the proper diameter and length of the set screws as per shaft diameter. There are two hex socket set screws required for each shaft. They are installed at 90° to one another. Use a cup point for the small set screws and a dog point for the two larger set screws.

A

TOP OF BOLT HEAD

B

TOP OF SCREW HEAD

EXERCISE 17.5

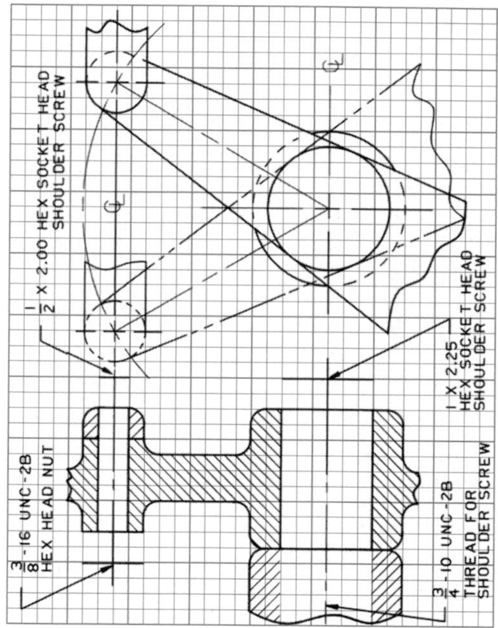

EXERCISE 17.7

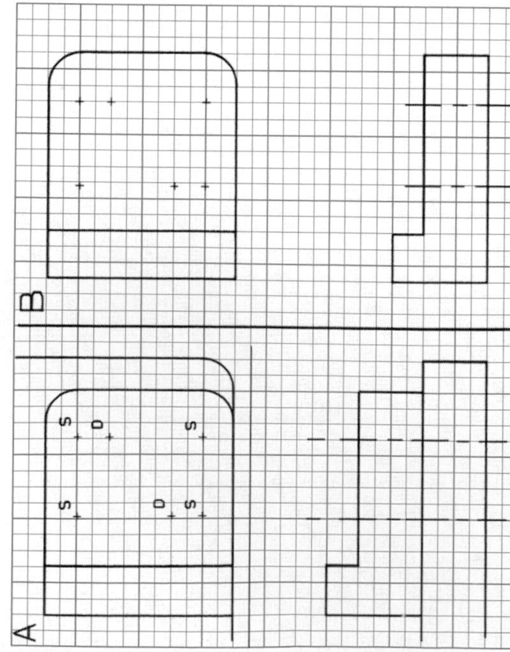

EXERCISE 17.6

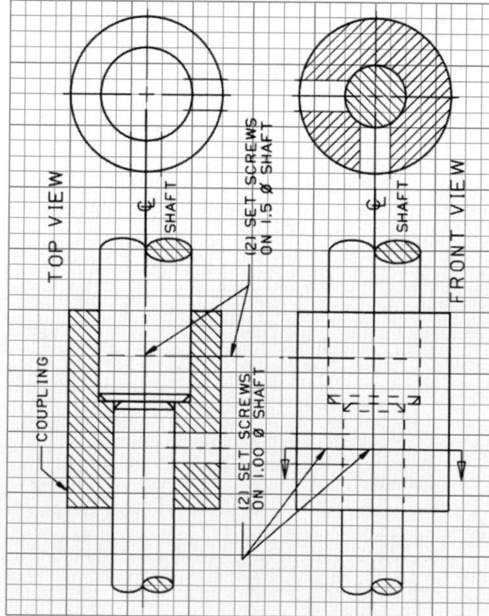

EXERCISE 17.8

After Reading the Chapter Through Section 17.21.4, You May Complete the Following Exercises

Exercise 17.9(A) Attach the collar to the shaft using one of the two following types of spring pins:

Pin, Coiled Spring, 10 × 100, Metric, Steel
Pin, Slotted Spring, .500 × 4.00, ANSI 302

Exercise 17.9(B) Attach the collar to the shaft with a tapered pin. Call out the hole size and dimensions for tapered holes, and use the following pin: Pin, Tapered, No. 8 × 2.50, Steel.

Exercise 17.10 Fasten the hitch at C with a .500 in. clevis pin. Use two .500 in. plain washers above and below the hitch and plate. Show a .175 in. diameter cotter pin to secure the clevis pin. Fasten the plates at B with three .625 in. diameter hex bolts. Use lock washers on both sides and hex flat nuts on the bottom. Show fasteners in both views. You will need to determine the length of the bolts and the clevis pin based on the fastening requirements. Call out the clevis pin, cotter pin, washers, nuts, and bolts on a separate parts list, and attach it to the drawing.

Exercise 17.11(A) Calculate the size and length of a Woodruff key or a square key (ask your instructor). Draw the key in the view provided. The shaft has a 2.00 in. diameter.

Exercise 17.11(B) Secure the shaft to the sprocket using a tapered gib key or a tapered key. Determine the size and length of a key for the 1.50 in. diameter shaft.

Exercise 17.12(A) Draw and dimension the shaft and a basic 5100 external retaining ring. See Appendix C.6 or manufacturing catalogs for the ring dimensions.

Exercise 17.12(B) Repeat Exercise 17.12(A), except use an N5000 basic 3 in. internal retaining ring for the housing. Draw and dimension completely.

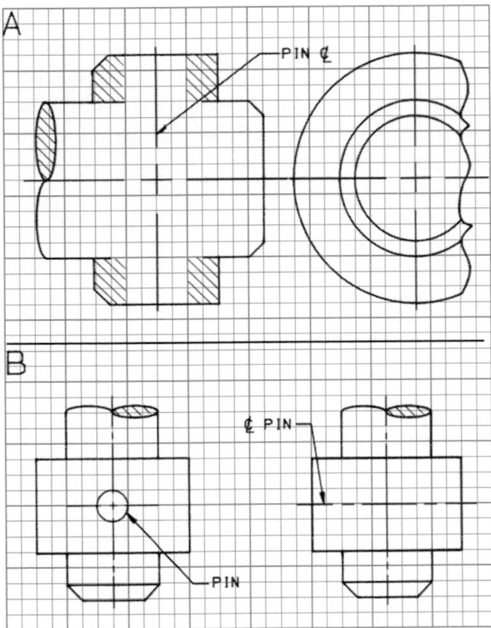

EXERCISE 17.9

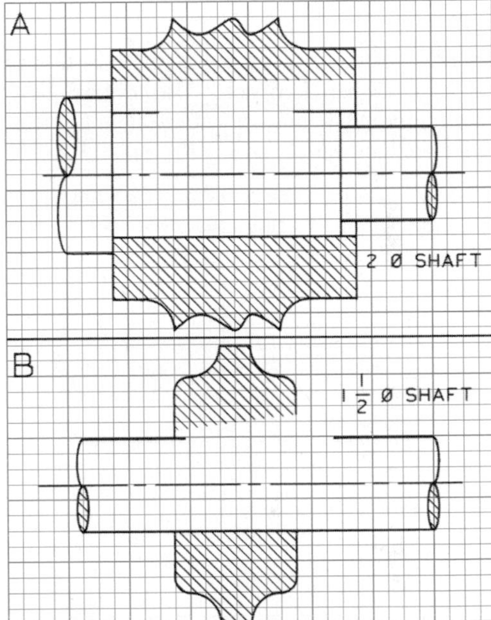

EXERCISE 17.11

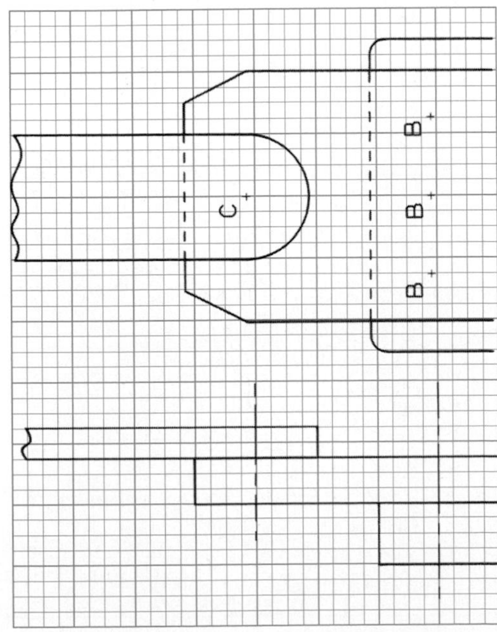

EXERCISE 17.10

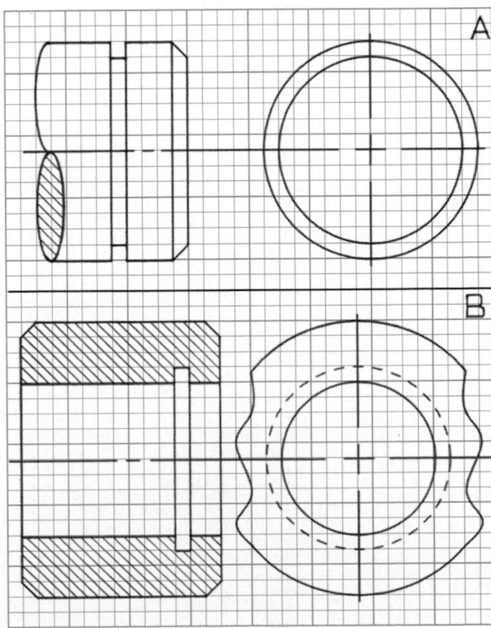

EXERCISE 17.12

PROBLEMS

Problem 17.1 Draw a 1.00 in. pitch thread (2× size) of the following thread types: Acme, square, and UNC.

Problem 17.2 Draw 3–2 Acme thread with a length of 5.00 in. using detailed thread representation.

Problem 17.3 Draw a 1.25 × 4.50 hex socket-head shoulder screw full size. Show the length view and the end view of the head. Use schematic method to display the threads.

Problem 17.4 Fasten a 1.25 in. plate to an aluminum casting (3.00 in. thick) using a .500-13 UNC socket-head cap screw. Calculate and show the screw in two views. Dimension and call out the tap drill, clearance hole, and tap size.

Problem 17.5 Connect a 1.50 in. and a 1.375 in. plate with a 1.00 in. socket-head shoulder screw and appropriate nut. Show in views, and call out all hole sizes.

Problem 17.6 Bolt together two 1.50 in. thick steel plates with two 1.25-12 UNF hex-head bolts. Use lock washers on both ends and the appropriate nut. Show in section. Construct a small parts list for the hardware.

Problem 17.7 Fasten a 4.0 × 4.0 × 4.0 × 2.00 in. thick steel angle plate to a steel part using four .375-16 UNC socket-head caps screws and two .375 in. diameter dowels. Design the bolt pattern, and calculate all fastener sizes. Dimension and call out all fasteners. Counterbore the plate so that the screw heads will be below the surface.

Problem 17.8 Draw a 50 mm diameter shaft and a 74 mm wide collar (O.D. 100 mm/I.D. 51 mm). Fasten the collar to the shaft with appropriately sized socket set screws with a dog point. Show in two views.

Problem 17.9 Draw a 2.50 in. diameter shaft and a 4.00 in. wide (O.D. 5.00 in./I.D. 2.51 in.). Connect the two parts with a square key 2.00 in. long. Calculate the key size, and show in two views. Dimension the views as required.

Problem 17.10 Repeat Problem 17.9, but use a Woodruff key and keyseat. Dimension the views as required.

Problem 17.11 Connect two sheets of .125 in. thick aluminum with a .125 in. diameter button-head rivet. Show in two views at 2× size.

Problem 17.12 Using a butt joint, connect two .500 in. thick sheets of steel (6.00 in. wide) with twelve 1.125 in. diameter rivets. Use double rivets on each side of the joint. Show in two views, and dimension completely.

SPRINGS

Chapter 18

LEARNING OBJECTIVES

Upon completion of this chapter you will be able to:

1. Understand the purposes and uses of springs in mechanical assemblies.
2. Identify the various types of springs used in mechanical assemblies.
3. Differentiate between left-hand and right-hand springs.
4. Produce drawings of basic spring types.
5. Select the proper spring type and design requirements for a given engineering application.

18.1 INTRODUCTION

A **mechanical spring** is an elastic body whose mechanical function is to store energy when deflected by a force and to return the equivalent amount of energy on being released. In machines, mechanical springs exert a particular force, provide a means of flexibility, or store or absorb energy. Springs come in a variety of styles and sizes as off-the-shelf standard parts (Fig. 18.1), and can be designed for specific engineering applications in an infinite number of nonstandard configurations. In general, springs are classified as wire springs, flat springs, or specialty springs. Helical springs (Fig. 18.2) are similar to threads in that they are spiral shaped and made from round or square wire. They are designed to resist tensile, compressive, or torsional loads.

You can probably think of a number of engineering applications where springs are important mechanical components—the suspension system of an automobile, for example. Constant-force springs are found in many door openers. Springs are used in valves to position various components or to return components to a particular location after the force has been removed. Automation assemblies employ springs to absorb and store energy. Of course, most mechanical methods of keeping time have some kind of spring assembly. Fixturing in manufacturing and machining applications depends heavily on springs to absorb and release energy.

Most springs are represented by their centerline and the phantom lines defining their outside diameter when drawn in 2D, and as circles connected by crossing lines (from end to end) when represented in 3D (see "Focus On . . ." and "Applying Parametric Design" boxes). Seldom are springs drawn or modeled pictorially (coils drawn or modeled). However, at the end of the chapter, a step-by-step procedure for drawing spring coils is provided. Some CAD systems have macros programmed to generate 3D solid or surface models of springs automatically. This capability is seldom exercised unless the spring is nonstandard and must be represented accurately in order to be manufactured correctly.

FIGURE 18.1 Industrial Springs

A number of requirements are applicable to all spring drawings, including material specifications and inspection notes. Since most springs are standard configurations and sizes, specifications and notes are more important than the drawing itself. Material specifications are designated in a general note on the drawing.

Springs are produced according to specific standards and specifications. ANSI recognizes six types of springs:

- **Compression**—helical, cylindrical, volute, coned disk (Belleville)
- **Extension**—helical
- **Garter**—helical
- **Torsion**—helical, torsion bar, spiral
- **Flat**—cantilever
- **Constant-force**—flat

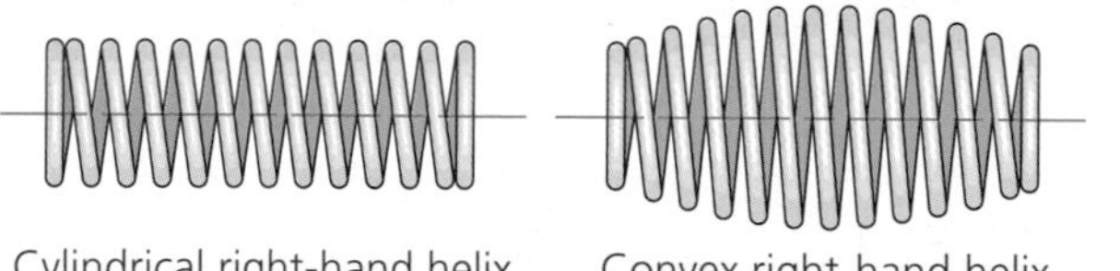

Cylindrical right-hand helix Convex right-hand helix

Cylindrical with coned end left-hand helix

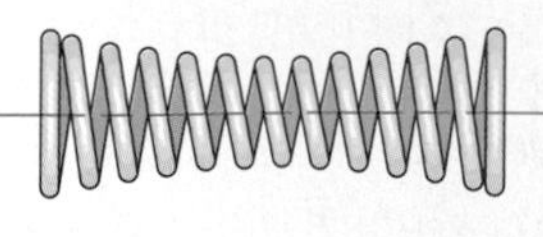

Concave right-hand helix

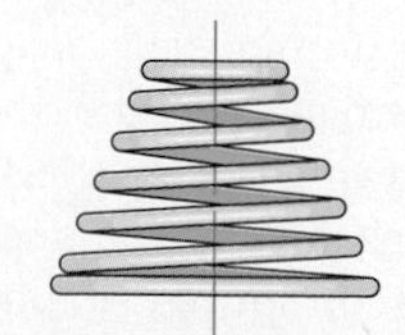

Conical right-hand helix

FIGURE 18.2 Helical Compression Spring Forms

18.1.1 Spring Terms

The following terms are used throughout this chapter and on drawings of mechanical springs.

Coils, active The number of coils used in computing the total deflection of a spring; those coils that are free to deflect under load

Deflection, total The movement of a spring from its free position to maximum operating position; in a compression spring, the deflection from the free length to the solid (compressed) length

Force The force exerted on a spring to reproduce or modify motion, or to maintain a force system in equilibrium

Helix The spiral form (open or closed) of compression, extension, and torsion springs

Length, free The overall length of a spring in the unloaded position

Length, solid The overall length of a compression spring when all coils are fully compressed

Load The force applied to a spring that causes deflection

Pitch The distance from center to center of the wire in adjacent active coils (recommended practice is to specify number of active coils rather than pitch)

Set The permanent distortion of the spring when stressed beyond its elastic limits

Total number of coils The number of active coils n plus the coils forming the ends

18.2 RIGHT-HAND AND LEFT-HAND SPRINGS

If dictated by design requirements, the direction of helix is specified as LEFT-HAND (LH) or RIGHT-HAND (RH). Otherwise, the direction of helix is specified as OPTIONAL. Usually, the direction is not important, except when a plug is screwed into the end or when one spring fits inside another. In the latter case, one spring is designated left-hand and the other spring right-hand. Figure 18.3 shows how the coils look for right-hand and left-hand springs: When you look at the back of your hands, the spring will be coiling either to the left or to the right.

Focus On . . .

SPRING DESIGNS DRAWN FROM TOOLING LIBRARIES

Springs are found on a wide variety of designs throughout industry. Many standard off-the-shelf mechanical fasteners use springs. The choice of spring depends on the function of the spring. The size and force requirements are determined by the required application. Here, we see compression springs in the stainless spring plunger and the spring hook clamp. Both of these mechanical components are taken from Carr Lane's tooling library, which contains more than 6,000 3D modeled parts. The library is available for industry and schools and comes in a wide variety of CAD/CAM formats and for most CAD systems.

The spring plunger employs a spring to keep a required force on the nosepiece of the unit. The drawing of the plunger shows the nose in the extended and the retracted (compressed) positions. This mechanical device can quickly locate a part being positioned on a jig or fixture, or lift the part after it is machined. The spring must be strong enough to overcome the weight of the part in this latter application.

The hook clamp uses a spring to keep pressure on the body and arm of the clamp. This design is extremely compact and well suited for tight spaces and where high clamping forces are required.

In the 2D views of the plunger device, the spring is represented pictorially. The 3D wireframe model of the plunger and the clamp use a simplified version of representation—showing the spring's end circles (diameters) connected by a crossing pair of lines. Seldom are springs modeled with 3D surface modeling or created as solid models.

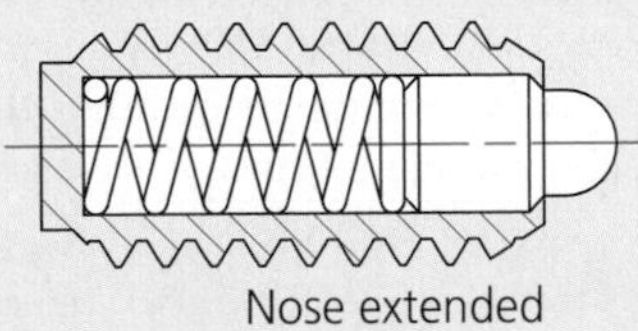

Nose extended

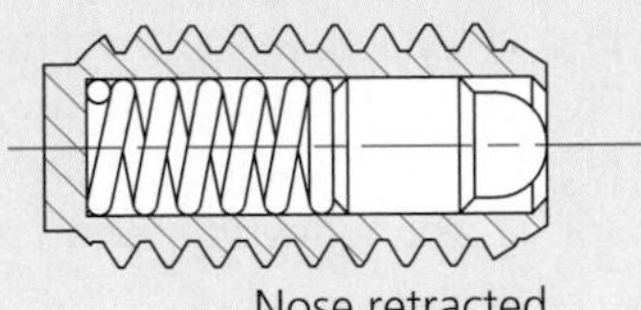

Nose retracted

Stainless short spring plunger.

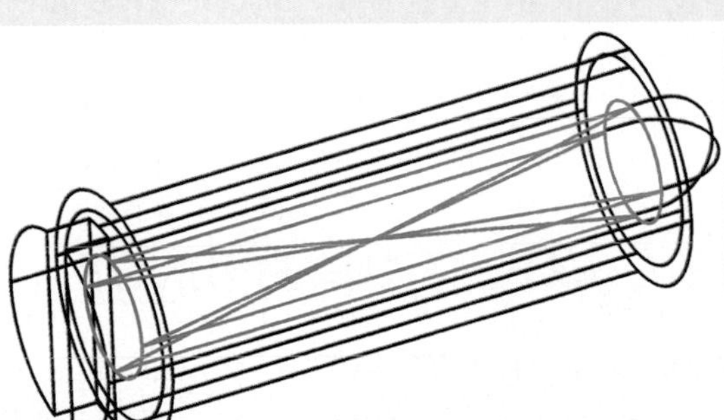

Wireframe model of spring plunger.

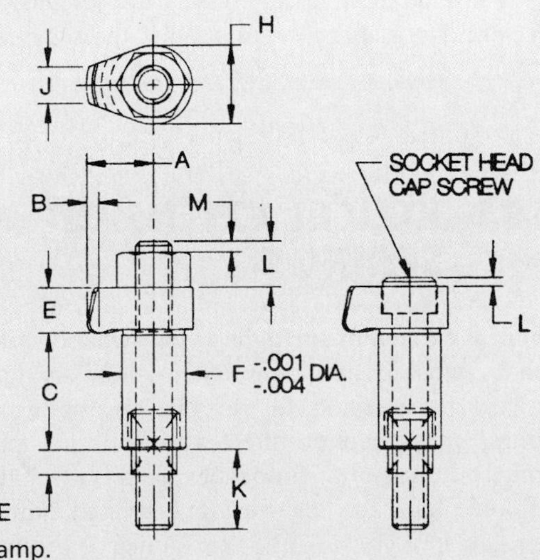

Hook clamp.

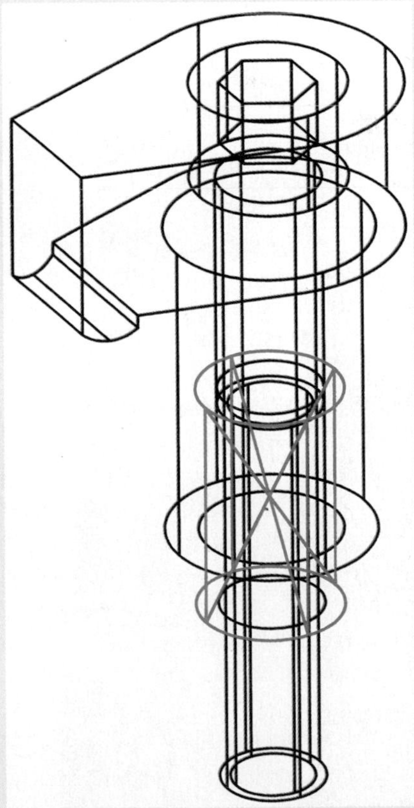

Wireframe model of hook clamp.

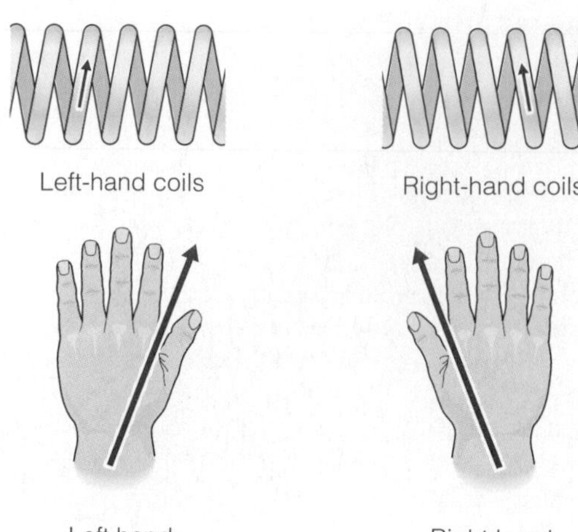

FIGURE 18.3 Left-Hand and Right-Hand Springs

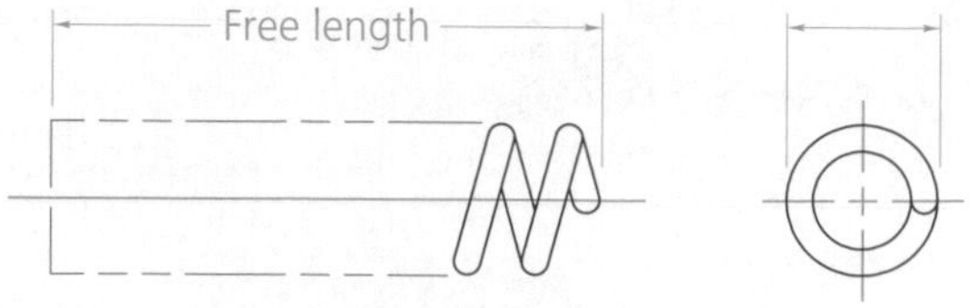

18.3 COMPRESSION SPRINGS

A **compression spring** is an open-coil helical spring that resists a compressive force applied along the axis. Compression springs are coiled as a constant-diameter cylinder. Figure 18.4 shows an industrial application of a compression spring. Here, a large safety valve at a power plant has a compression spring incorporated into its design. Other common forms of compression springs, such as conical, tapered, concave, convex, and various combinations of these, are utilized as required by the application. While square, rectangular, or special-section wire may have to be

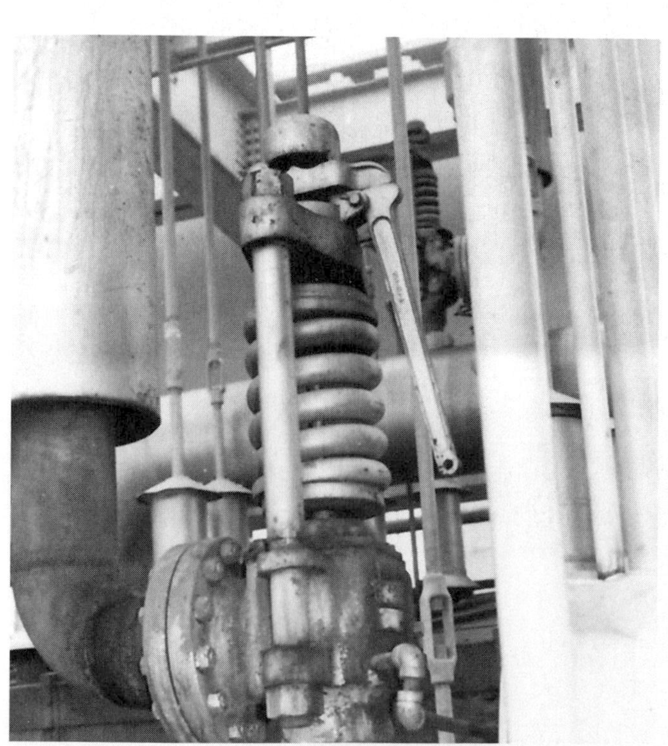

FIGURE 18.4 Compression Spring on a Safety Valve

Free length

Spring Data

Material specification . . . .
Wire diameter. . . . .
Direction of helix. . . . .
Total coils . . . .

FIGURE 18.5 Drawing Requirements for Helical Compression Springs

specified, round wire is predominant in compression springs. Figure 18.5 shows the recommended way to specify compression springs.

There are four basic types of compression spring ends, as shown in Figure 18.6. The particular type of ends specified affect the pitch, solid height, number of active and total coils, free length, and seating characteristics of the spring. The type of ends is specified on the drawing and dimensioned as required. Depending on the application of the compression spring, the following requirements are specified:

TO WORK OVER ____ MAX. DIAMETER ROD
TO WORK IN ____ MIN. DIAMETER BORE
ID (with tolerance) ________________
OD (with tolerance) ________________

18.4 EXTENSION SPRINGS

Extension springs (Fig. 18.7) absorb and store energy by resisting a pulling force. Various types of ends attach the extension spring to the source of the force. Most extension springs are wound with an initial tension, which holds the coils tightly together. The load necessary to overcome the internal force and just start coil separation is the same as the initial tension.

18.5 HELICAL EXTENSION SPRINGS

A **helical extension spring** is a close-wound spring, with or without initial tension, or an open-wound spring that resists an axial force trying to elongate the spring. Extension springs are formed or fitted with ends for attaching the spring to an assembly. Guidelines for specifying dimensional and force data on engineering drawings showing helical extension springs (Fig. 18.8) are similar to those established for helical compression springs. Usually, all coils in an

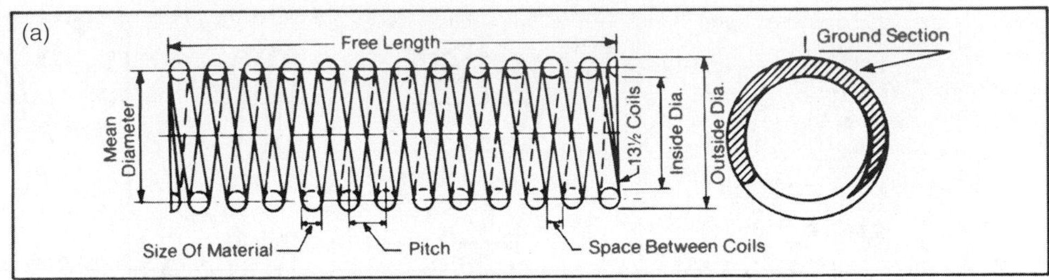

Type of End Finishes

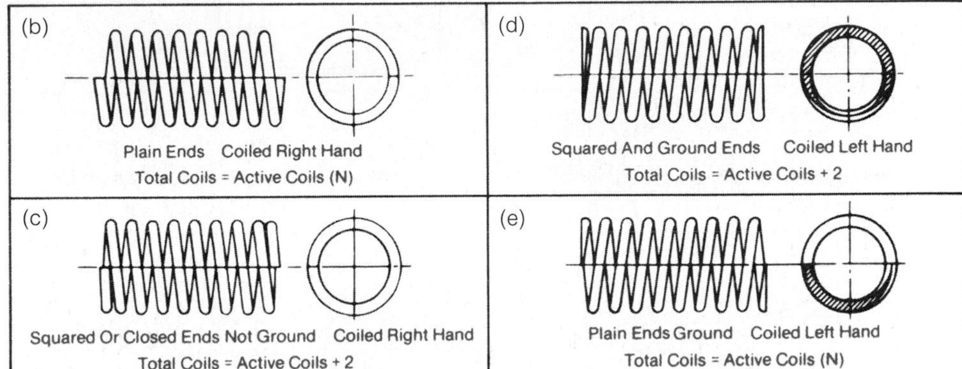

FIGURE 18.6 End Finishes for Compression Springs

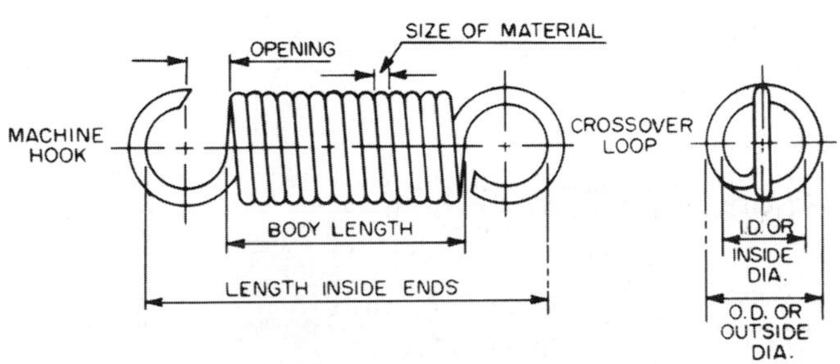

FIGURE 18.7 Extension Springs

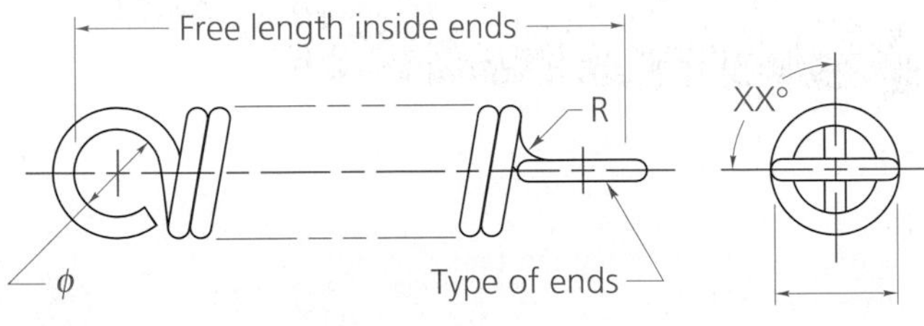

Spring Data

Material specification . . . .
Wire diameter. . . . .
Direction of helix. . . . .
Total coils . . . .
Extended length without permanent set . . . .
Relative position of ends . . . .
Initial tension . . . .
Force at operating length of ______

FIGURE 18.8 Drawing Requirements for Helical Extension Springs

extension spring are active. Exceptions are those with plug ends and those with end coils coned over swivel hooks. The total number of coils required is specified.

18.6 GARTER EXTENSION SPRINGS

A **garter spring** (Fig. 18.9) is a long, close-coiled extension spring with its ends joined to form a ring. Garter springs are used in mechanical seals on shafting, to hold round segments together, as a belt, and as a holding device. The diameter over which the spring is to function is specified.

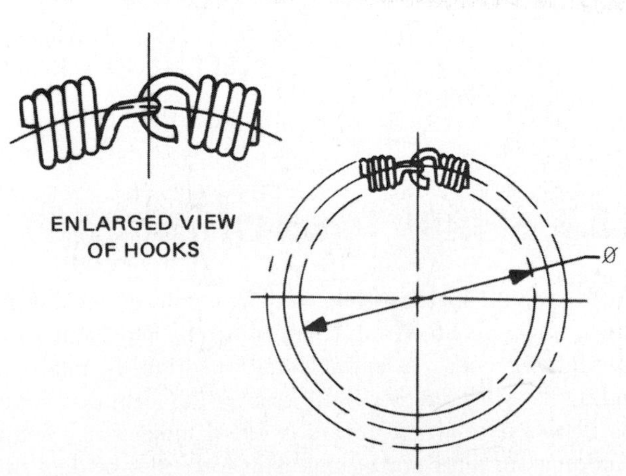

FIGURE 18.9 Drawing Requirements for Garter Springs

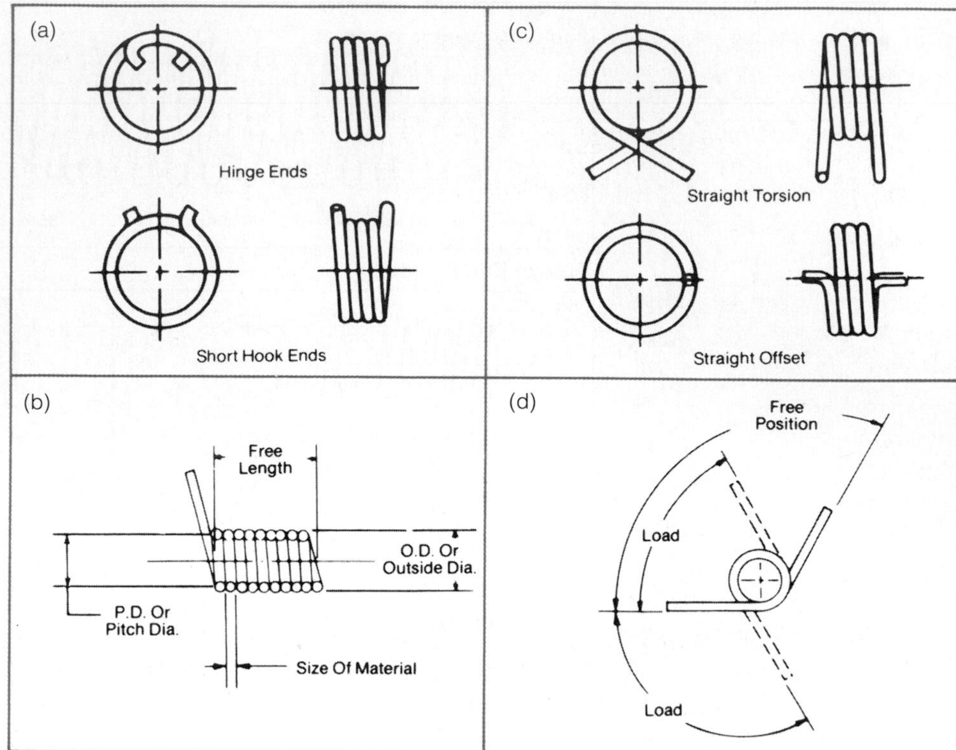

FIGURE 18.10 Drawing Requirements for Helical Torsion Springs

For example, a shaft diameter may be given, although other than an actual shaft may be involved.

18.7 HELICAL TORSION SPRINGS

Helical torsion springs (Fig. 18.10) are springs that resist a force or exert a turning force in a plane at right angles to the axis of the coil. The wire itself is subjected to bending stresses rather than torsional stresses. Usually, all coils in a torsion spring are active. The total number of coils required and the length in the free position are specified. The helix of a torsion spring is important. Either LEFT-HAND or RIGHT-HAND is specified.

18.8 SPIRAL TORSION SPRINGS

Spiral torsion springs (Fig. 18.11), made of rectangular section material, are wound flat, with an increasing space between the coils. A spiral torsion spring is made by winding flat spring material on itself in the form of a spiral. It is designed to wind up and exert a force in a rotating direction around the spring axis. This force may be delivered as torque, or it may be converted into a push or pull force.

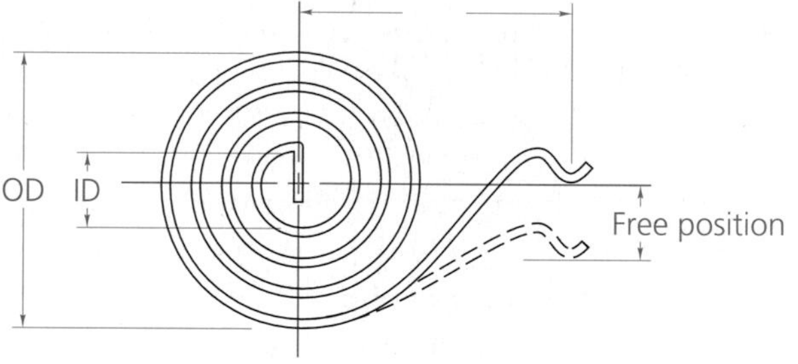

Spring Data

Material specification . . . .
Material size . . . .
Outside diameter. . . . .
Inside diameter . . . .
Developed length of material . . . .
Active length of material. . . . .
Number of coils in free position. . . . .
Torque at final position . . . .
Maximum deflection beyond final position without set . . . .
Type of ends . . . .

FIGURE 18.11 Drawing Requirements for Spiral Torsion Springs

18.9 SPRING WASHERS

Because of trends toward miniaturization and greater compactness of design, **spring washers** are widely employed in industrial designs. They have space and weight advantages

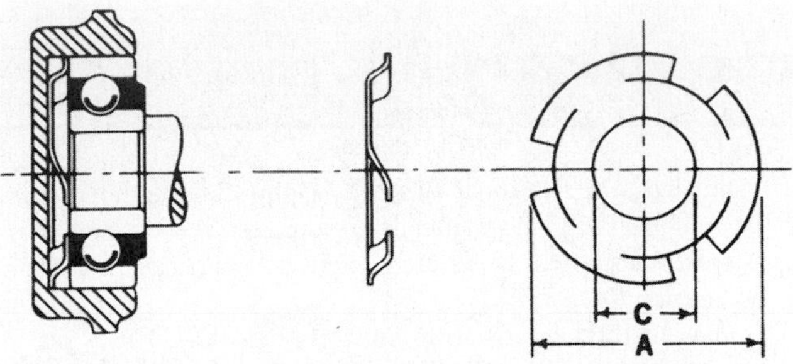

FIGURE 18.12 Finger Spring Washer Installed in a Bearing Housing

over conventional wire springs and are often more economical. Their applications include keeping fasteners secure, distributing loads, absorbing vibrations, compensating for temperature changes, eliminating side and end play, and controlling end pressure. Figure 18.12 shows a finger spring washer used for preloading ball bearings.

A **coned disk (Belleville) spring** (Fig. 18.13) is a spring washer in the form of the frustum of a cone. It has constant material thickness and functions as a compression spring.

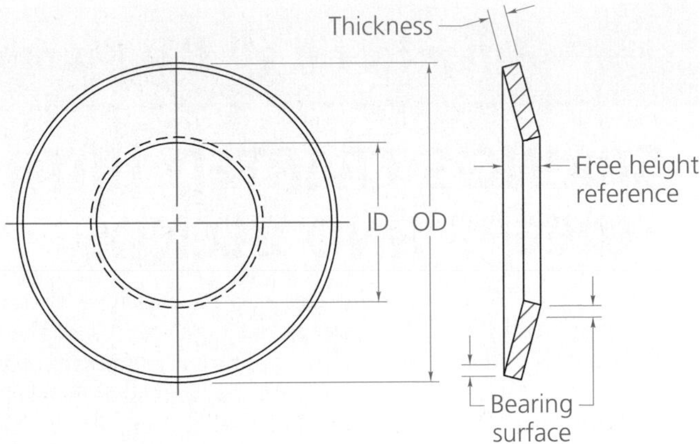

Spring Data

Material specification . . . .
Thickness of material. . . . .
Free height . . . .
Force at compressed height of ______
(Special data) . . . .

FIGURE 18.13 Drawing Requirements for Coned Disk (Belleville) Springs

18.10 FLAT SPRINGS

The term **flat springs** covers a wide range of springs or stampings fabricated from flat strip material, which, when deflected by an external load, releases stored energy. Only a small portion of a complex-shaped stamping may actually be functioning as a spring. Leaf springs on the rear of cars and vans are examples of flat springs.

Flat springs include all springs made of flat strip or bar stock that deflects as a cantilever or as a simple beam. Figure 18.14 is an example of a detail drawing of a flat spring. A pictorial view shows the part in its finished state and gives the bending angle in degrees. The dimensioned view is of the flat (developed) part.

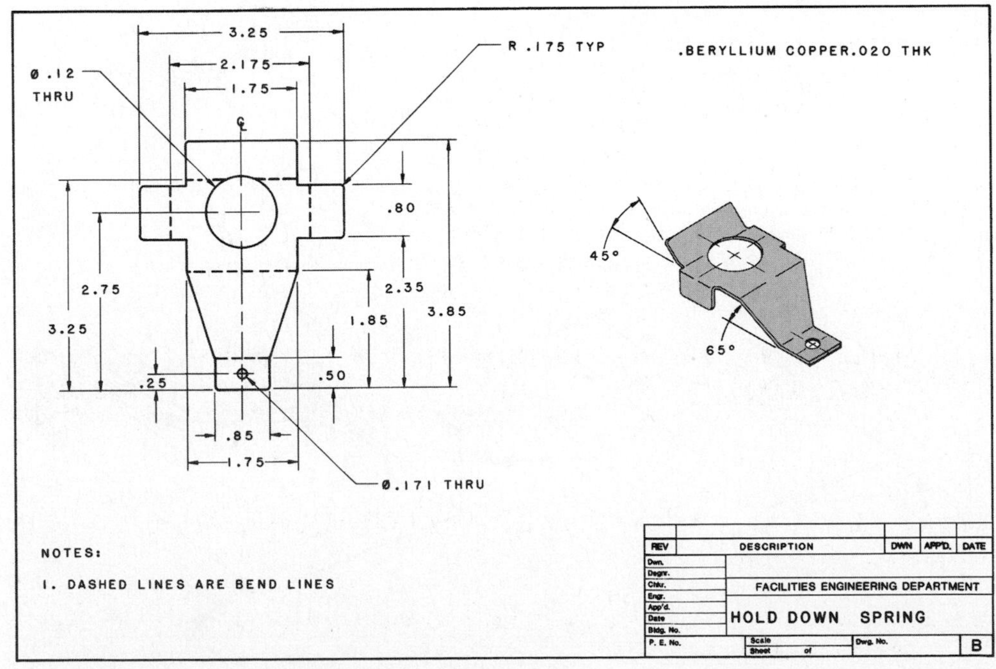

FIGURE 18.14 Hold-Down Spring

Applying Parametric Design . . .

SPRINGS CREATED WITH SWEEPS AND BLENDS

Springs and other helical features can be created with the sweep or blend commands. **Sweeps** (see Fig. A) are established along a three-dimensional path by creating a three-dimensional (3D) spline for the sweep trajectory. You can modify the Z coordinates of spline points (all other sketcher entities must lie on a 2D sketching plane) in order to establish points in space. In all other respects, 3D sweeps are created in the same way as are 2D sweeps. Sweeps are created by sketching a trajectory and then sketching a section to follow along it (Fig. B).

To Create a 3D Spline:

1. Create a 2D spline and dimension it to a coordinate system.
2. Modify the X, Y, and Z coordinates for one or more spline points. You can modify the spline coordinates manually or by using a spline definition file.

A **rotational blend** (Fig. C) is created by rotating sections about the Y axis. Angular dimensions are entered to control section orientation, and sections can be dimensioned from their Sketcher coordinate system to control radial placement.

If you define a rotational blend as being closed, the first section will be used automatically as the last section and a closed solid feature will be created; there is no need to sketch the last section.

Another method for creating springs (Figs. D–G) uses an advanced curve command called a **helical sweep.** A helical sweep is created by sweeping a section along a trajectory that lies in the *surface of revolution:* The trajectory is defined by both the profile of the surface of revolution and the distance between coils.

Helical Sweep

1. **Part---part name: spring---Feature---Create---Datum---Plane---Default---Create---Datum---Coord System---Default---Done**
2. **Create---Protrusion---Advanced---Done---Helical Sweep---Done---Constant---Thru Axis---Right Handed---Done---Plane** (pick DTM3) **---Okay---Top** (pick DTM2) --- (sketch a line as shown in Fig. D) **---Alignment** (align the end of the line to DTM2) **---Regenerate---Dimension** (add dimensions as shown) **---Regenerate---Axis** (add an axis line along DTM3) **---Sketch---Line---Centerline---Vertical---Alignment** (align the axis line to DTM3) **---Regenerate---Done**

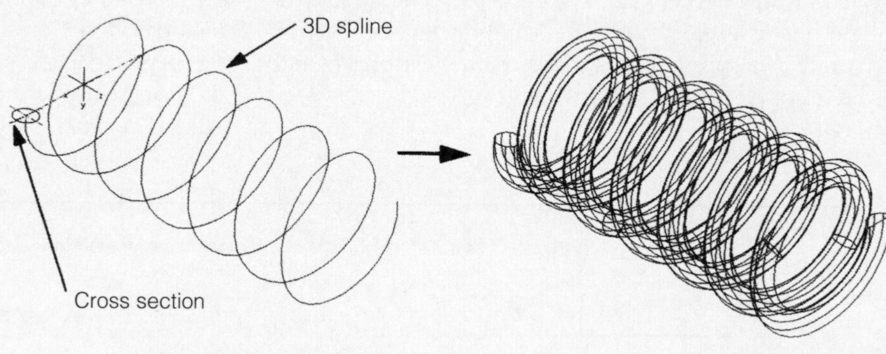

FIGURE A A Spring Created from a 3D Spline

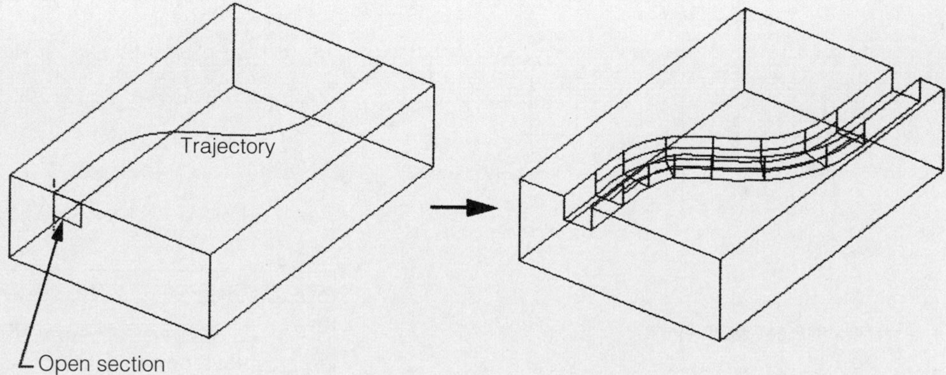

FIGURE B A Swept Cut

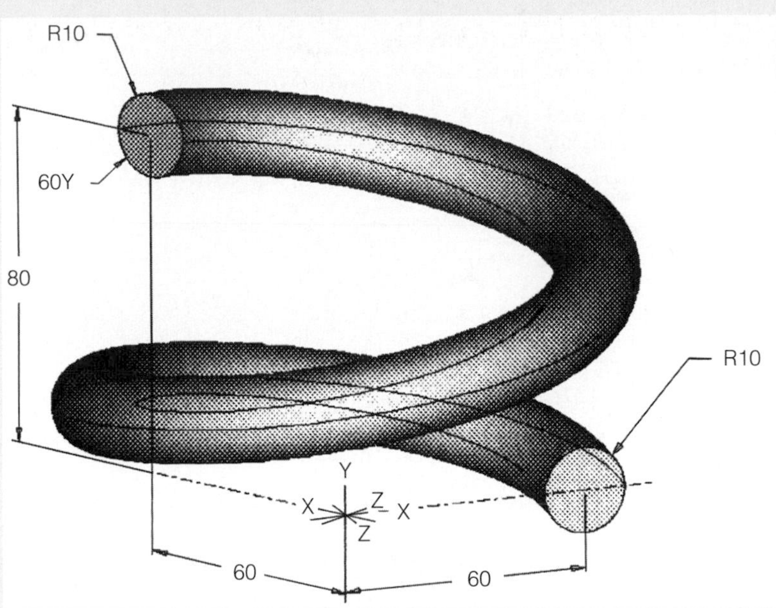

FIGURE C A Sketched Rotational Blend with the First and Last Sections Displayed

3. Enter Pitch Value [40] --- (Now sketch the cross section, here a ∅15 circle) ---**Sketch---Circle---Ctr/Point--- Dimension** (add diameter dimension) ---**Modify** (make dimension 15) ---**Alignment** (align center of circle) --- **Regenerate---Done**
4. [Spring is done (see Fig. E). Add the cut line as shown. This will create a ground end] **Create---Cut---Extrude---Solid ---Done---Both side---Thru All---Done---Plane** (pick DTM3) ---**Okay---Bottom** (pick DTM3) --- **Sketch---Line ---Horizontal---Alignment** (align the line to DTM1) --- **Dimension** (dimension the line as in Fig. F) ---**Regenerate ---Modify** (modify dimensions to 200 and 240 as shown) ---**Done---Okay** (see Figs. G–J)

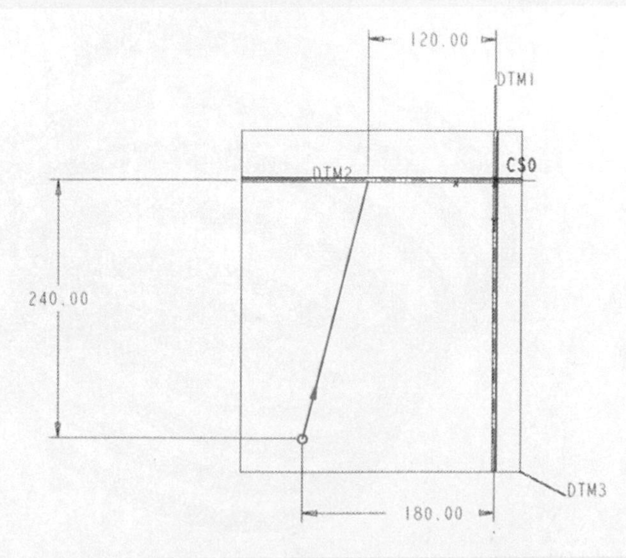

FIGURE D Sketch of Spring Trajectory

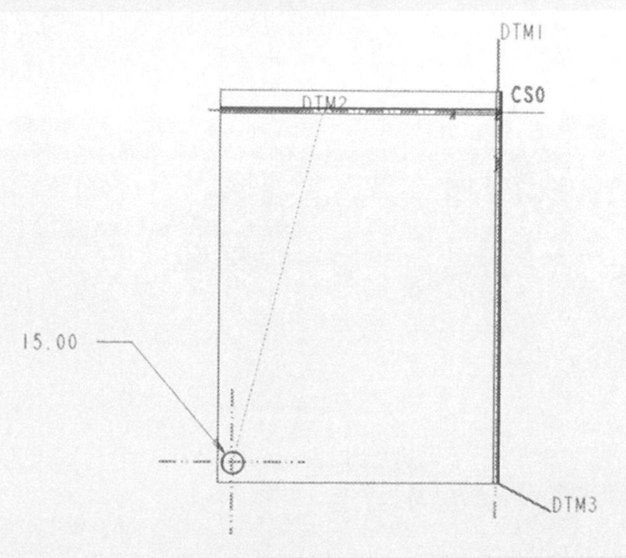

FIGURE E Section of Spring Geometry

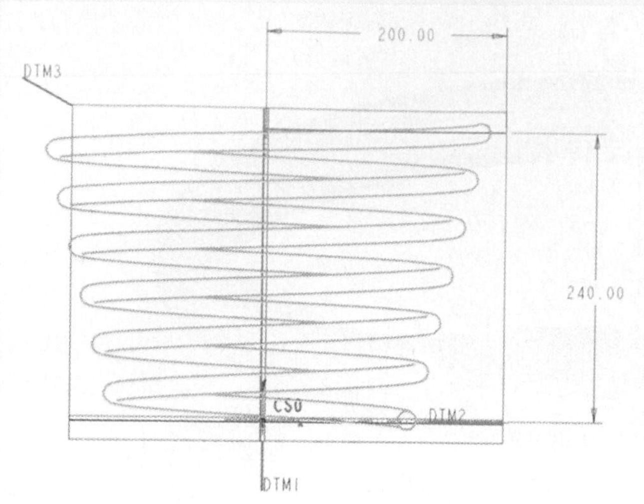

FIGURE F Adding a Cut to Create Ground End

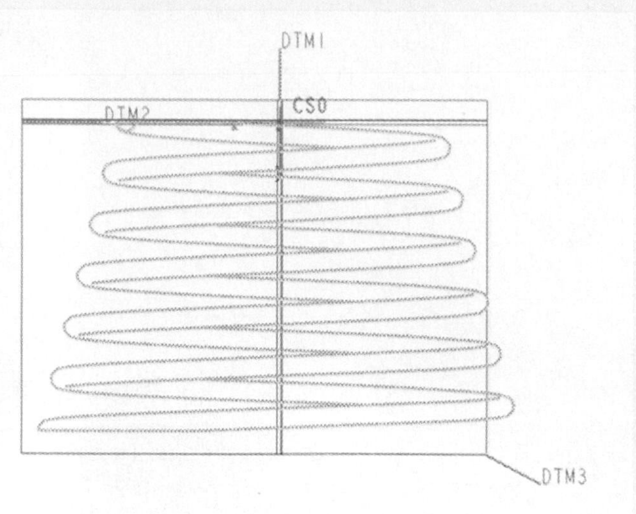

FIGURE G Completed Spring

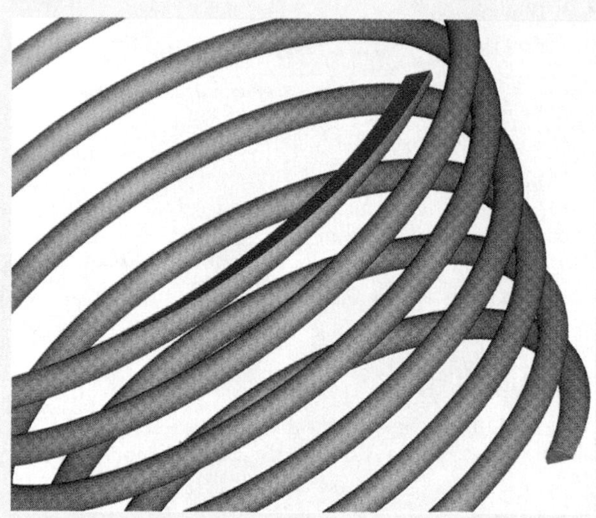
FIGURE H Close-Up of Ground Edge

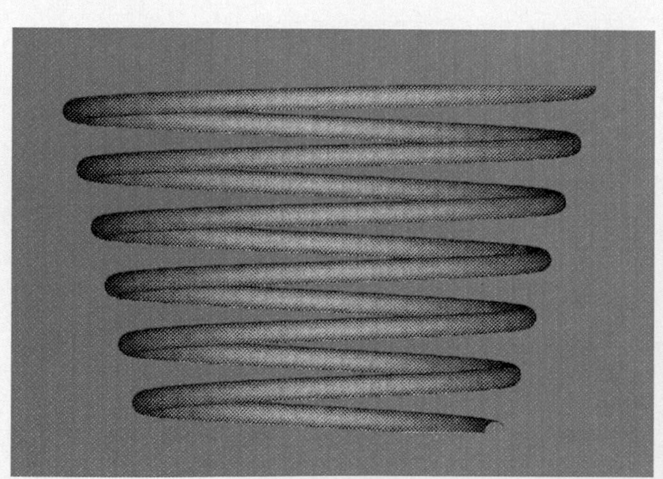
FIGURE I Shaded Image of Spring

FIGURE J Shaded Image Showing Ground End

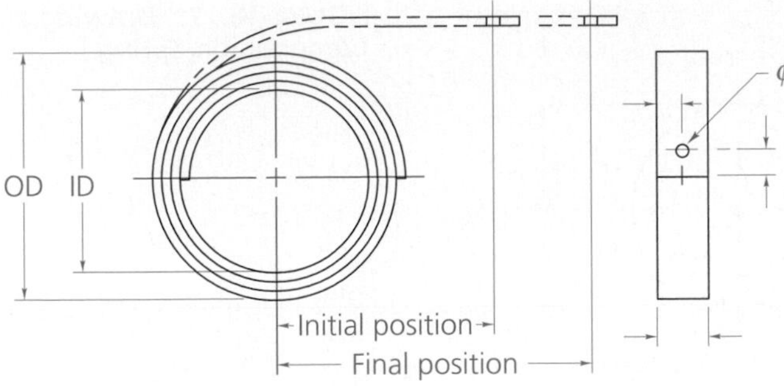

Spring Data

Material specification . . . .
Material size . . . .
Active length. . . . .
Number of coils. . . . .
Force. . . . .
Fits over. . . . .

FIGURE 18.15 Drawing Requirements for Constant-Force Springs

NOTES:
1. ASSOCIATED SPRING
PART NO. T054-180-421-R

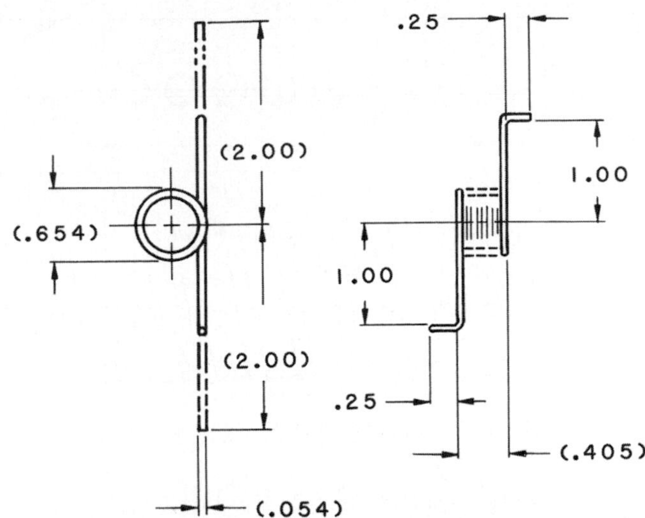

FIGURE 18.16 Torsion Spring Detail

18.11 CONSTANT-FORCE SPRINGS

A **constant-force spring** (Fig. 18.15) is a strip of flat spring material that has been wound to a given curvature so that, in its relaxed condition, it is in the form of a tightly wound coil or spiral. A constant force is obtained when the outer end of the spring is extended tangent to the coiled body of the spring. A constant torque is obtained when the outer end of the spring is attached to another spool and wound in either the reverse or the same direction as originally wound. Because the material for this type of spring is thin and the number of coils would be difficult to show in actual form, it is acceptable to exaggerate the thickness of the material and to show only enough coils to depict a coiled constant-force spring.

18.12 DRAWING SPRINGS

Springs are drawn using simplified methods, except when the spring must be pictorially correct for dimensioning. Even when these situations occur, it is normal practice to show only a limited number of coils and to use the simplified method for the remaining coils. The simplified method of representing springs employs phantom lines to establish the spring's outside diameter, and a centerline to locate its axis. Figure 18.16 shows an industrial detail of a torsion spring. The ends are drawn true, and the coils are shown with phantom lines. In Figure 18.17, six active coils were required, along with plain open ends.

To Draw the Coils of a Compression Spring:

1. Lay out the free length (overall length), the coil centerline, and the outside diameter of the spring. These dimensions are blocked in with construction lines. The *mean diameter* is drawn as shown in the side view (end view) of the spring. The mean diameter equals the outside diameter of the coil minus the wire diameter.

   One coil diameter (wire diameter) is drawn in the side view (Fig. 18.17). The inside diameter and the outside diameter of the coil are drawn in the side view (end view).

   The front view of the spring is divided into even spaces based on the total number of coils. Each of the coil cross-section diameters is drawn lightly along the top and bottom of the coil length, at the appropriate divisions.
2. Lightly draw the coil winding (left- or right-hand) as shown. The appropriate end style is then constructed. (The plain open end is used in this example.)
3. Darken the coil, using appropriate line weights, and dimension accordingly. (Dimensions are not shown in this example; refer to previous examples throughout the chapter.)

Drawing an *extension spring* is similar to constructing a compression spring except that the coils are solid in the relaxed (unloaded) position; in other words, the coils touch.

To draw a Full-Loop-over-Center Extension Spring (Fig. 18.18):

1. Draw centerlines and the outside and inside diameters. Then draw the end loops (they will be the same as the end view) at the required length, and complete the construction.

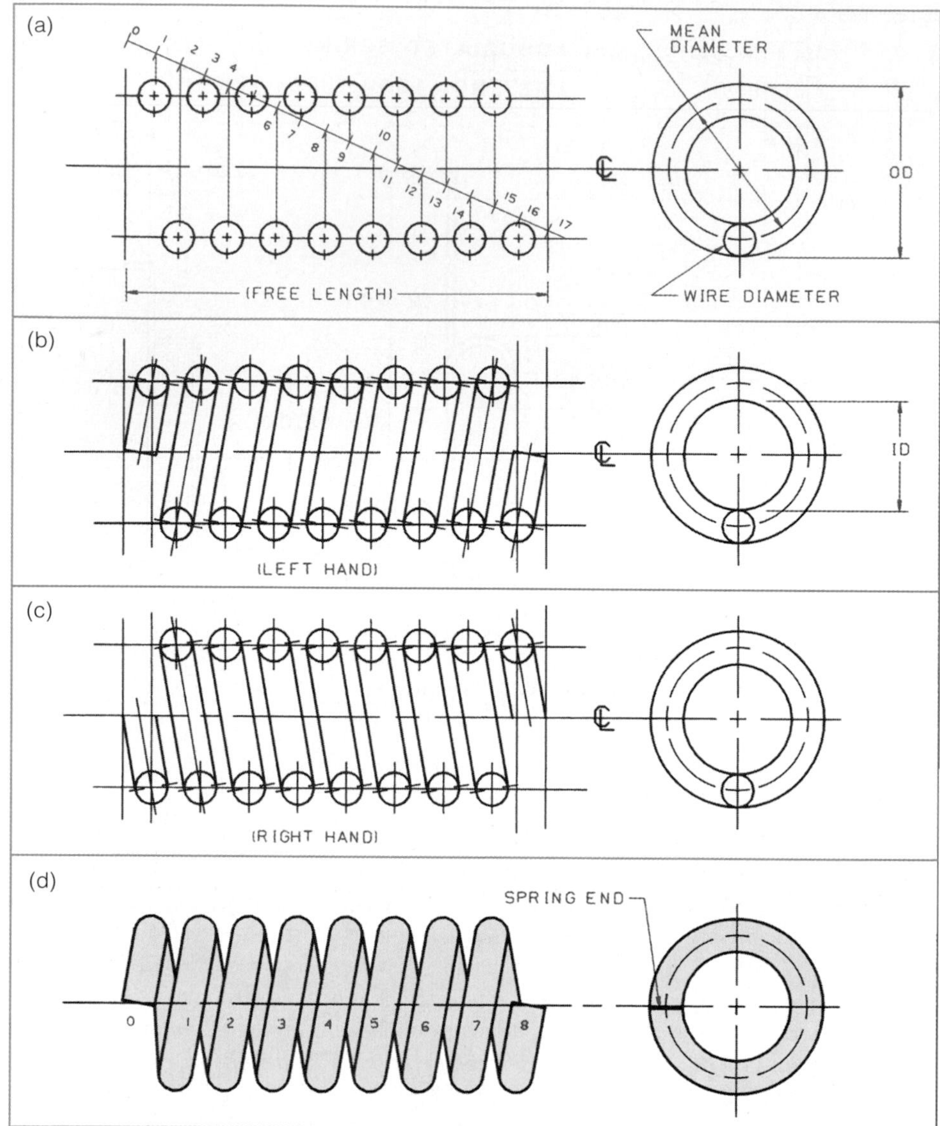

FIGURE 18.17 Drawing a Compression Spring

2. Using a circle template and the appropriate diameter (wire size), draw the wire diameters on the top and the bottom.
3. Extend a construction line from the end of the edge of the wire diameter on the lower left to the edge of the upper left diameter. Draw lines parallel to the first construction line along the total length of the spring coils.
4. Draw circles that represent the wire diameters along the upper portion of the coil length, as shown. Then adjust the spring end as shown. The spring ends are established by a 30° construction line extended from the coil end diameter.
5. Complete the coil and end visibility carefully. Use appropriate line weights to darken and complete the drawing. Add dimensions as required to manufacture the spring.

QUIZ

True or False

1. Spring washers should not be used in applications where weight and space are the prime considerations.
2. The solid length of a spring is its overall length in the unloaded position.
3. Usually, all coils in a torsion spring are active.
4. A Belleville spring is a coned disk spring.
5. *Set* is the permanent distortion of the spring when stressed beyond its elastic limits.
6. A garter spring may not be used to hold round segments together.
7. There is really only one basic type of compression spring end.
8. The force that is applied to a spring that causes deflection is known as load.

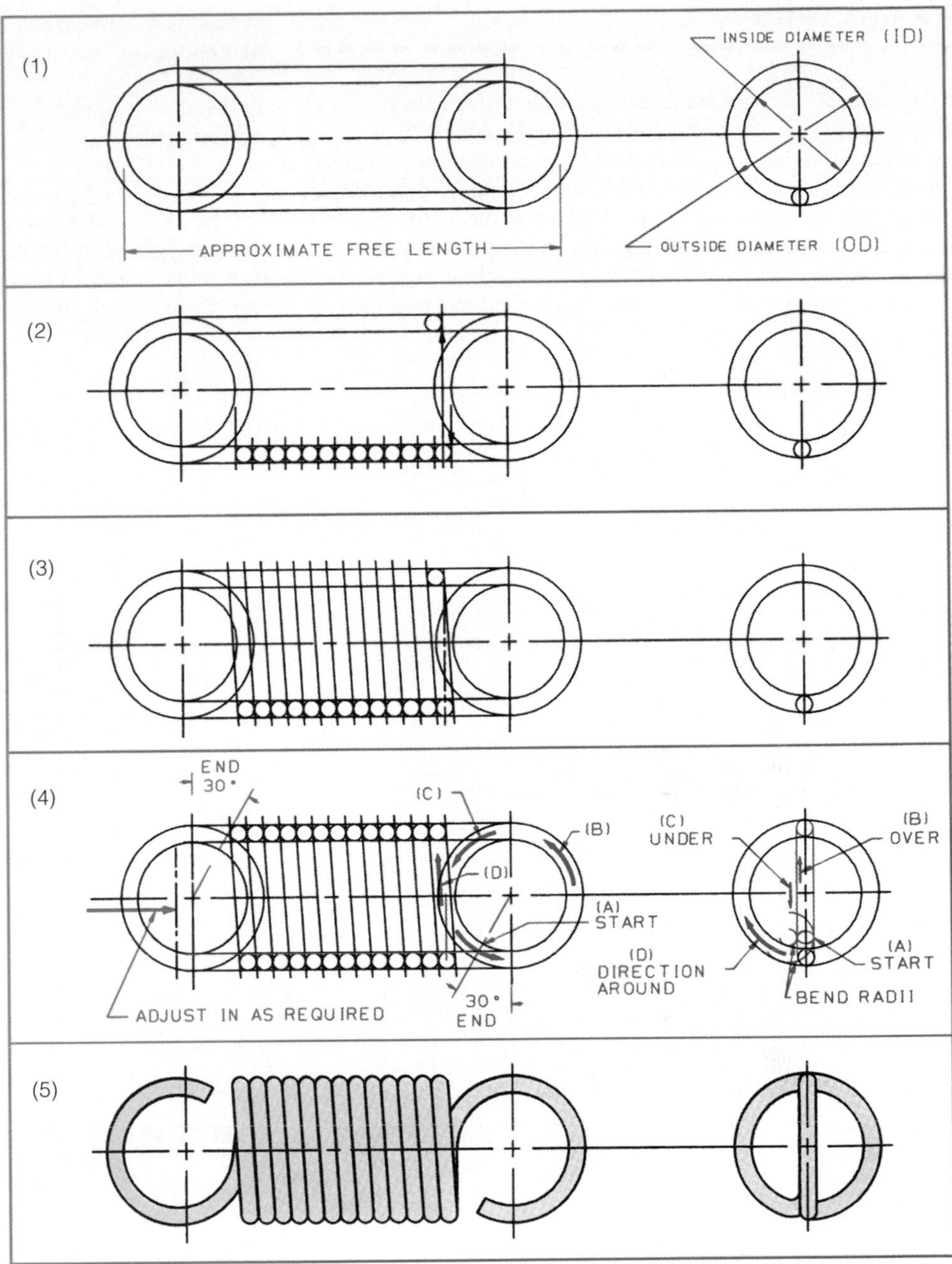

FIGURE 18.18 Drawing an Extension Spring

Fill in the Blanks

9. __________, __________, and __________ are three types of end configurations used on extension springs.
10. A __________ is a spring washer in the form of the frustum of a cone.
11. A __________ is the spiral form of compression, extension, and torsion springs.
12. A __________ is an open-coil helical spring that resists a compressive force along the axis.
13. The __________ is the movement of a spring from its free position to maximum operating position.
14. __________ absorb and store energy by resisting a pulling force.
15. A __________ spring is made by winding flat spring material on itself in the form of a spiral.
16. A __________ spring is a strip of flat spring material that has been wound to a given curvature so it is in the form of a tightly wound coil.

Answer the Following

17. What is the difference between the free length and the solid length of a spring?
18. What is the difference between the terms *active number of coils* and *total number of coils?*
19. Describe the difference between a left-hand spring and a right-hand spring.
20. What is a compression spring?
21. Describe how *pitch* is defined for springs.
22. What is the difference between a helical extension spring and a garter extension spring?
23. Describe the basic function of an extension spring.
24. What is a spring washer?

EXERCISES

Exercises may be assigned as sketching or instrument projects. Transfer the given information to an "A"-size sheet of .25 in. grid paper. Complete all views, and solve for proper visibility, including centerlines, object lines, and hidden lines. Exercises that are not assigned by the instructor can be sketched in the text to provide practice and to enhance understanding of the preceding instructional material. Dimensions for fasteners used in these exercises can be located in figures throughout the chapter and in Appendix C.

Exercise 18.1 Using detailed representation, draw the compression spring as shown. List all pertinent specifications on the drawing. The spring is steel, has a wire diameter of .250 in., is left-hand wound, with square ends, and has eight active coils and ten total coils.

Exercise 18.2 Draw all coils for the compression spring. The spring is right-hand wound, has a wire diameter of .187 in., with plain ends, and has a total of eighteen active coils (also eighteen total coils). List all controlling specifications.

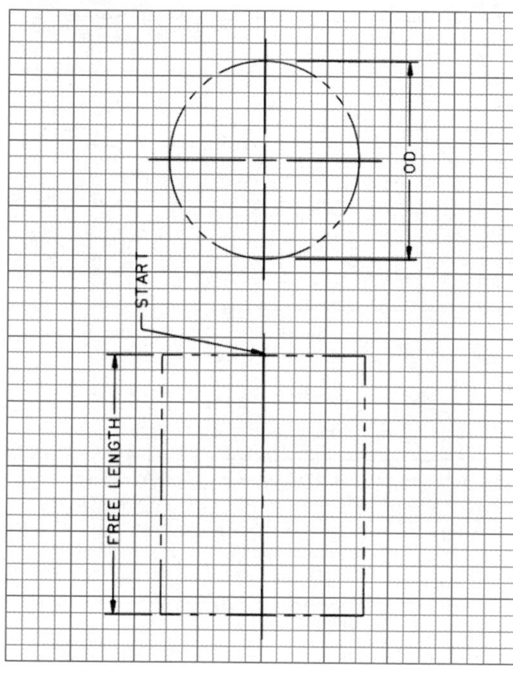

EXERCISE 18.1

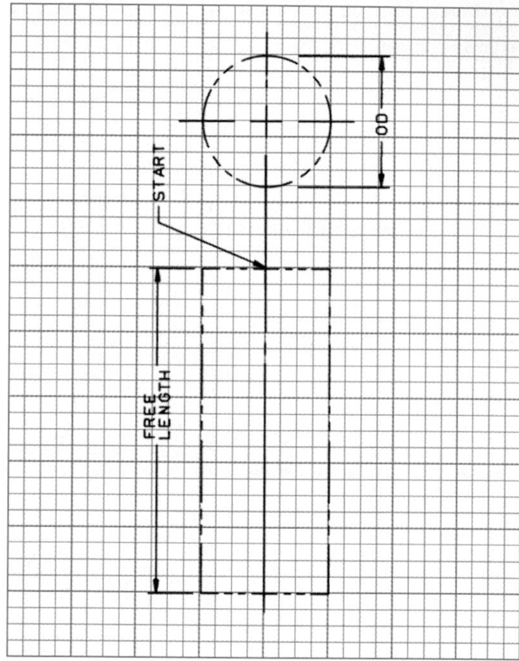

EXERCISE 18.2

Exercise 18.3 Complete the helical extension spring. The spring is to be right-hand wound, has a .250 in. wire diameter, and comes with round ends, as shown. Draw all coils. List all specifications.

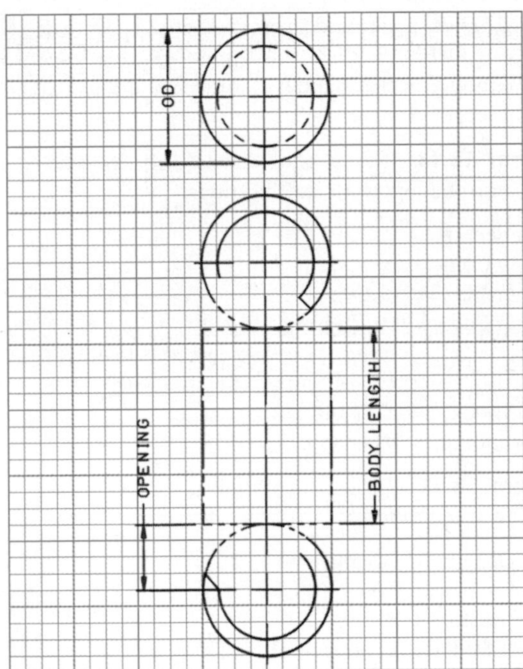

EXERCISE 18.3

Exercise 18.4 Complete the helical torsion spring using a wire diameter of .200 in. and seventeen coils. The spring is left-hand wound. Draw all coils. List all specifications.

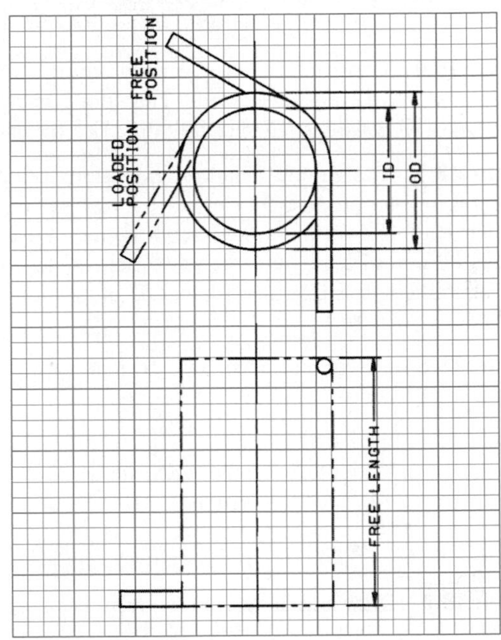

EXERCISE 18.4

PROBLEMS

Problem 18.1 Draw a detailed representation of a compression spring. List all specifications on the drawing. The spring is steel, has a wire diameter of .200 in., is right-hand wound, with square ends, and has ten active coils and twelve total coils. Use the same OD.

Problem 18.2 Draw a compression spring showing five coils at each end and the remainder with phantom lines. The spring is left-hand wound, has a wire diameter of .125 in., comes with plain ends, and has a total of twenty active coils (also twenty total coils). List all controlling specifications. Use the same OD.

Problem 18.3 Draw a helical extension spring. The spring is to be left-hand wound, has a .200 in. wire diameter, and comes with round ends. Draw all coils, list the specifications, and use the same OD.

Problem 18.4 Construct a helical torsion spring with a wire diameter of .187 in. and fifteen coils. The spring is right-hand wound. Draw all coils. List all specifications. Use the same OD.

Problem 18.5 Design and detail an extension spring with a full loop over center on the right end and a long hook over center on the left end. The spring is right-hand wound and has a free length of 180 mm with a 6 mm wire size. There are fourteen total coils. The coil length is 80 mm with an OD of 50 mm. Show all dimensions.

Problem 18.6 Design and detail an extension spring with the following specifications:

Approximate free length = 1700 mm
Winding = left-hand (spiral)
Wire size = 5 mm
OD = 50 mm
Ends = full loop over center for both

Problem 18.7 Draw and dimension a compression spring with plain closed ends and a wire diameter of 10 mm. The spring will be left-hand wound, with an OD of 48 mm. The free length is 160 mm. Calculate the solid length. There are ten total coils (eight are active).

Problem 18.8 Design and detail a compression spring with the following specifications:

Free length = 4.00 in.
Coils = 6 total; 3 active
Wire size = .50 in.
Ends = closed ground
OD = 3.75 in.
Winding = left-hand
Solid length = (calculate)

Problem 18.9 Design and detail a compression spring with the following specifications:

Free length = 190 mm
Coils = 18 total; 12 active
Wire size = 6 mm
Ends = plain open
OD = 60 mm
Winding = right-hand
Solid length = (calculate)

Problem 18.10 Design and detail a compression spring with the following specifications:

Free length = 5.00 in.
Coils = 7 total; 5 active
Wire size = .375 in.
Ends = ground open
OD = 3.00 in.
Winding = left-hand
Solid length = (calculate)

Problem 18.11 Design and detail (draw 2× size) a torsion spring with the following specifications:

Free length = .875 in.
Coils = 5
Wire size = .125 in.
Ends = straight and turned to follow radial lines to center of spring and to extend .375 in. from OD of spring
OD = 1.375 in.
Winding = left-hand

Problem 18.12 Design and detail a torsion spring with the following specifications:

Free length = 50 mm
Coils = 10
Wire size = 6 mm
Ends = as assigned by instructor
OD = 70 mm
Winding = right-hand

GEARS, SHAFTS, AND BEARINGS

Chapter 19

LEARNING OBJECTIVES

Upon completion of this chapter you will be able to:

1. Recognize mechanical devices that are designed to transmit motion from one machine element to another.
2. Analyze gear blank stock material, types of hubs, and methods of attaching gears to shafts.
3. Define the various gear categories and basic specifications for manufacture and inspection.
4. Explain common gear terms and symbols.
5. Demonstrate an understanding of gear, shaft, and bearing drawing practices.
6. Communicate gear, shaft, and bearing data by means of ANSI-standard dimensioning and notation.
7. Describe the types and purposes of bearings and their respective housings and mountings.
8. Explore the use of CAD in gear design.

19.1 INTRODUCTION

This chapter covers mechanical devices designed to transmit motion from one machine element to another. Most gears (Fig. 19.1) are mounted on shafts, which, in turn, are secured by **bearings** installed in a variety of housings. **Gears** are designed to transfer rotary motion from one **shaft** to another. The speed of the motion is increased or decreased by changing the size of the *drive gear* and the *driven gear*.

The selection of gear types is based on the relative position of the shafts. The shafts will be either intersecting, nonintersecting, or parallel. Shafts can be positioned perpendicular, parallel, or at any given angle to each other, depending on the design application. Figure 19.2 shows two spur gears mounted on parallel shafts. Shaft A holds the drive gear; shaft B holds the driven gear. Spur gears are commonly used to transfer motion from one parallel shaft to another. In this example, the drive gear is smaller than the driven gear; therefore, the driven gear will take longer to complete one revolution and its speed will be less than that of the drive gear.

Some gears are designed to change rotary motion into reciprocating (linear—back-and-forth) motion. These machine elements are called **pinions** and **gear racks.** Another method of transmitting rotary motion into reciprocating (linear—up-and-down) motion utilizes a cam-and-follower assembly. This method is discussed in Chapter 20.

Whether the transfer of motion is rotary-to-rotary or rotary-to-linear, the rotary element must be mounted on some kind of a shaft and that shaft must rotate freely. Therefore, shafts ride on bearings [Fig. 19.3(a)]. The gear itself may have an integral keyseat to provide a positive connection to the shaft [Fig. 19.3(b)].

FIGURE 19.1 Gears

19.2 GEARS

This chapter introduces the most common types of gears, shows how they are represented on drawings, and presents methods for calling out their specifications. **Gear specifications** are the most important information that is supplied to the gear manufacturer. Gears come in many styles, including spur gears, pinions, ring gears, worm gears, bevel gears, miter gears, hypoid bevel gears, and racks, among others. Gears are made of metals and nonmetals. Spur gears are the most common type manufactured.

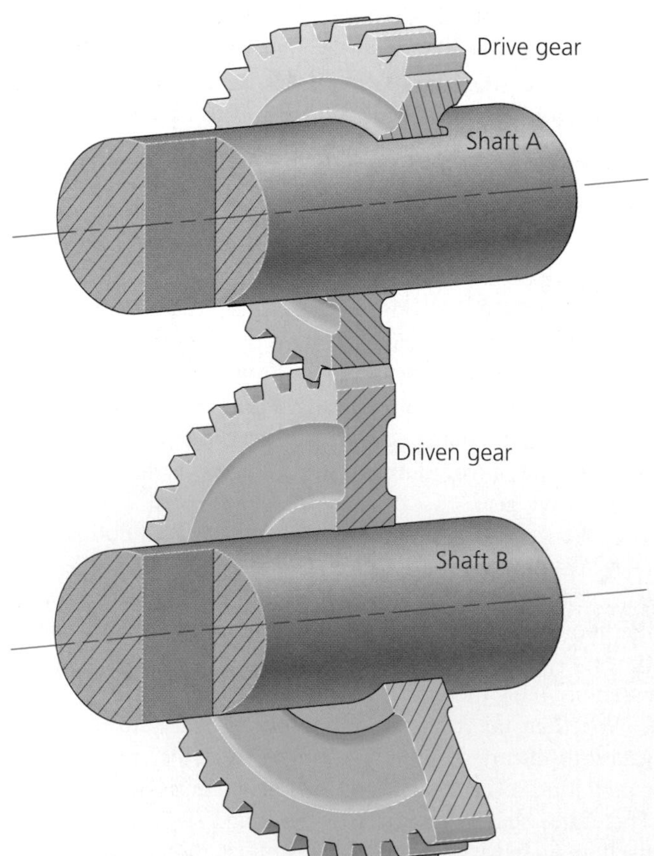

FIGURE 19.2 Gears and Shafts

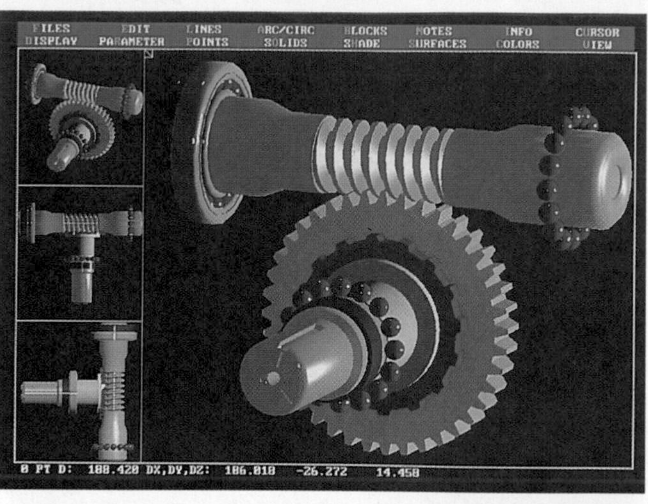

(a) Gears, shafts, and bearings

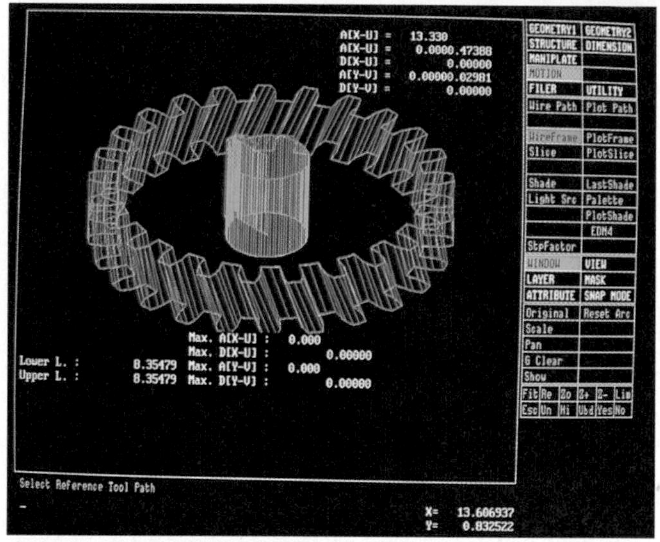

(b) Gear

FIGURE 19.3 Gear Design Using CAD

19.2.1 Gear Teeth

Gear teeth are projections designed to fit into the tooth spaces of mating gears and to contact mating teeth along a common line known as the **pressure line**, also called the **line of action** (Fig. 19.4). The most common form for the tooth flank is involute. The pressure line determines the particular involute shape. The American National Standards Institute (ANSI) has standardized two pressure angles: $14\frac{1}{2}°$ (now rarely used) and 20° (Fig. 19.5).

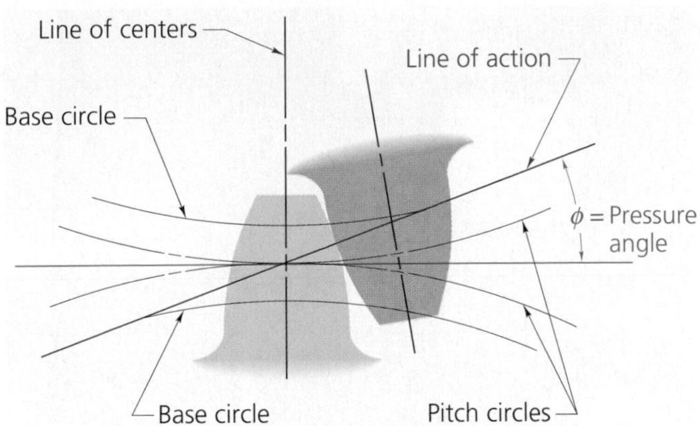

FIGURE 19.4 Pressure Angle and Line of Action

19.2.2 Gears, Splines and Serrations, and Racks

The following terms and descriptions define the general gear categories covered in the chapter.

Spur gears Gears connecting parallel shafts and having straight teeth elements (parallel to the axis of the shafts). The smaller gear of a pair of gears is called a **pinion.**

Helical gears Gears connecting shafts with projected non-intersecting centerlines. Helical gear teeth elements are spiral, or helical, in shape.

Bevel and miter gears Gears that are conical in form and that operate on shafts having projected intersecting centerlines. When the gears are different sizes, they are called bevel gears. Bevel gears of the same size (one-to-one ratio) and with shafts intersecting at right angles are called miter gears.

Internal gears Gears connecting parallel shafts, with teeth elements that are either straight or helical and with a pitch circle that is tangent internally to the mating spur or spiral gear.

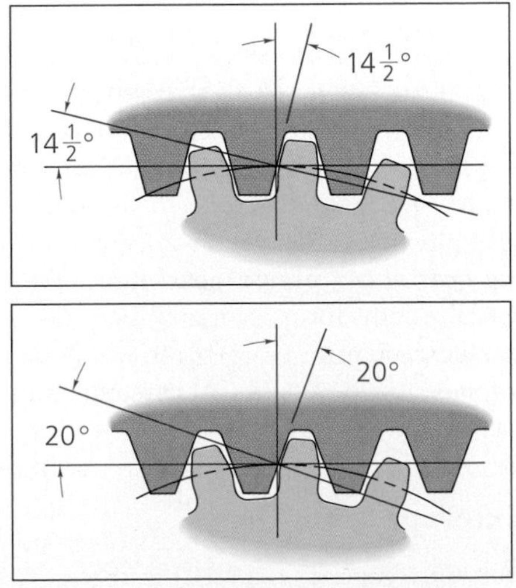

FIGURE 19.5 $14\frac{1}{2}°$ and 20° Pressure Angles

Worm gears Gears connecting nonparallel, nonintersecting shafts. They have teeth elements that are helical. Worm gearing generally is composed of a worm (screw) and a worm wheel (gear), in matched sets.

Rack gear A rack can be considered a gear of infinitely long pitch radius. The pitch line of a rack is a straight line; the pitch is described as linear pitch. A rack gear is a flat spur gear.

Splines and serrations Splines and serrations are multiple keys used to prevent relative rotation between two members, in the general form of internal and external gear teeth. Splines act primarily to transmit torque.

19.2.3 Gear Blanks

The **gear blank** is the stock material from which the gear is cut. The blank must have sufficient rigidity to prevent distortion during tooth cutting. The type of *hub* (split, solid, or hubless) and the type of gear (spoked, flanged, or flat) must also be determined. Hub variations are shown in Figure 19.6. Still another factor to consider in selecting the gear blank is the method of attaching the gear to its shaft. Here are some of the more common methods employed.

Key Permits easy assembly and disassembly. The design must ensure that the key is captive when the assembly is complete.

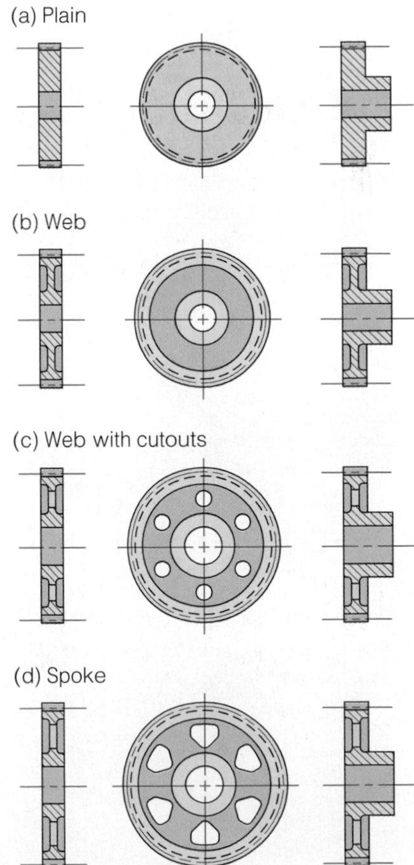

FIGURE 19.6 Hub Options

Pin Requires drilling at assembly. This tends to weaken small shafts and does not permit replacement of gear or shaft. This method provides a positive engagement between gear and shaft.

Set screw Permits easy assembly and disassembly. This method should always use two set screws at 45°–90° to each other. Set screws at a 60° angle are the strongest. The design of the shaft should provide flats on the shaft as a bearing surface for the set screw. Some method of retaining the set screw must be provided. This method is inappropriate when large torque loads are transmitted.

Adhesive bond Requires considerable care at assembly to ensure a good bond. Adhesive has temperature and torque limitations. Disassembly is very difficult without destroying parts of the assembly. The adhesive chosen must be compatible with gear and shaft materials.

Mechanical stake This method has moderate torque-transmitting capacity and may not permit replacement of gear or shaft.

Clamp Can only be used with split hub gears, is bulky in size, and has only moderate torque capacity. This method allows for easy assembly and disassembly.

Press This method is unacceptable when the shaft cannot be isolated from the bearings, as in a motor. Disassembly is difficult. Materials must not expand or contract and cause a loose fit at temperature extremes.

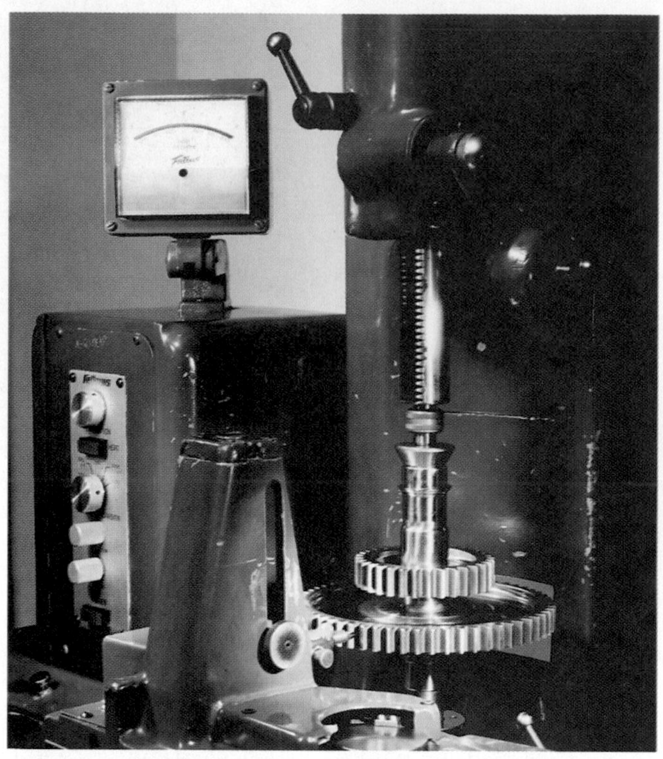

FIGURE 19.8 Machining Gear Teeth

19.3 SPUR GEARS

Two friction wheels with surfaces in contact are shown in Figure 19.7. If one of the wheels is turned—and no slippage occurs—the other one will turn. To prevent slipping, gear teeth may be added to both wheels, with corresponding recesses in each wheel. In Figure 19.8 the spaces are being cut on a spur gear by a machine tool. **Spur gears** are mounted on parallel axes and are manufactured in both internal and external versions. Terms are given in Figure 19.9 for gears with the involute form of gear teeth. A gear and pinion are shown in this figure. A **pinion** is the smaller of two gears in a mating set. The **pitch circles** in Figure 19.9(a) are tangent and might be thought of as representing the friction wheels. The pitch circles on spur gears are tangent circles.

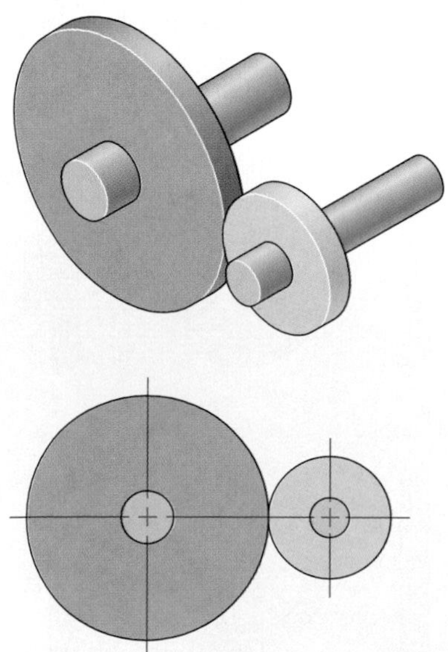

FIGURE 19.7 Friction Wheels

19.3.1 Internal Spur Gear (Ring Gear)

An **internal gear** has greater tooth strength for a given tooth size. Internal spur gears permit a closer *center distance* that may enable a more compact design and allow input (drive) and output (driven) shafts to rotate in the same direction. Figure 19.10 illustrates the center-to-center distance between a **ring gear** and a **pinion gear.** Ring gears can have spur or helical tooth forms. Figure 19.11(a) shows an internal spur gear; Figure 19.11(b) shows a pinion. This matching set was designed on a CAD system and physically modeled via stereolithography.

19.3.2 External Spur Gear

The **external spur gear** (Fig. 19.12) is the most common and best-known type of gear. It transmits motion between

FIGURE 19.9 Gear Teeth

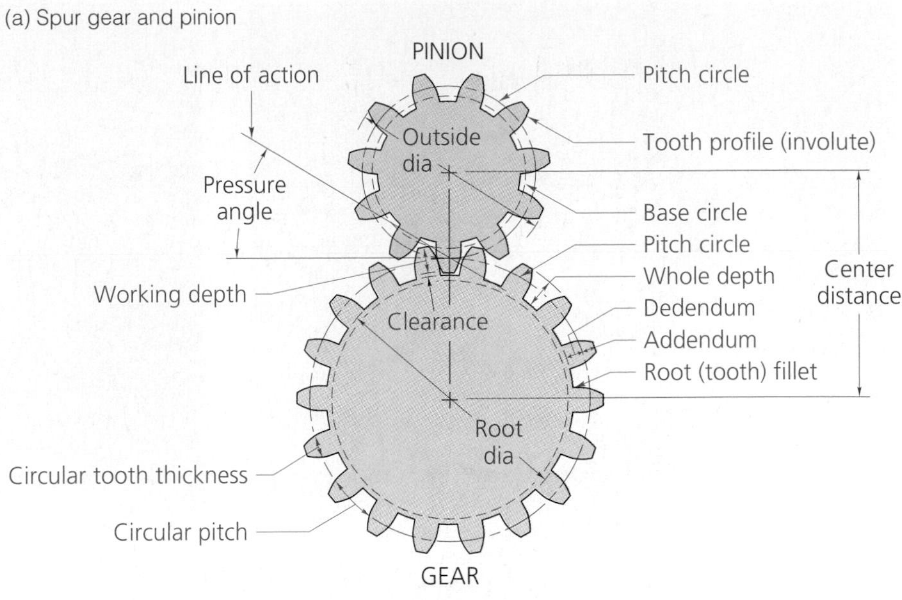

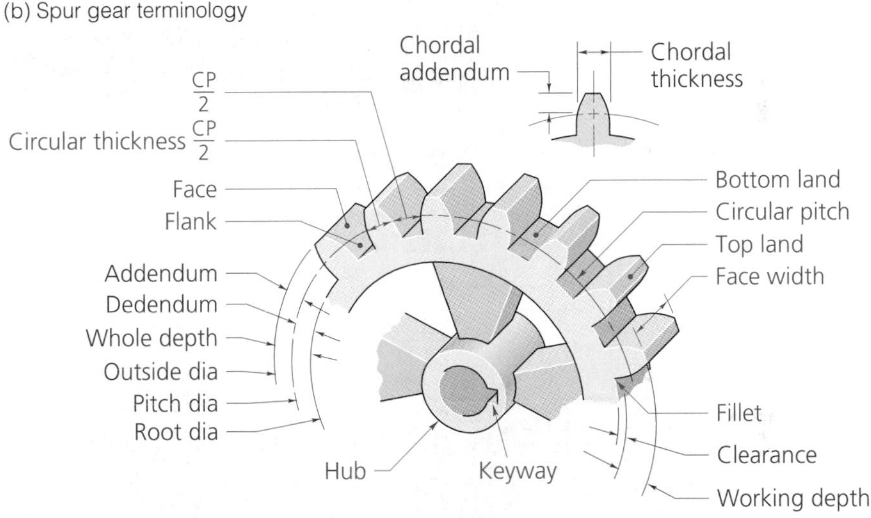

parallel shafts that rotate in opposite directions. Spur gears generate radial bearing loads. Because of their availability and ease of manufacture, they should be given first consideration as the choice of gear type.

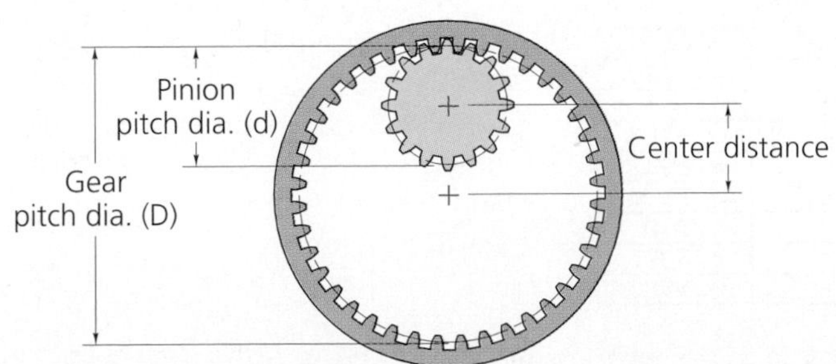

FIGURE 19.10 Ring Gear and Pinion

19.3.3 Spur Gear Specifications

The basic specifications for both manufacturing and inspection for a spur gear are as follows.

- Pressure angle
- Tooth form
- AGMA quality number
- Diametral pitch
- Tooth thickness, circular
- Measuring-wire size
- Total composite error
- Testing pressure
- Outside diameter
- Number of pinion teeth
- Material
- Number of gear teeth
- Face width
- Pitch diameter
- Measurement over wires
- Gear testing radius
- Surface finish

To provide these required data, the application requirements must be known. This information should include speed, ratio, power, accuracy, life, temperature, and application.

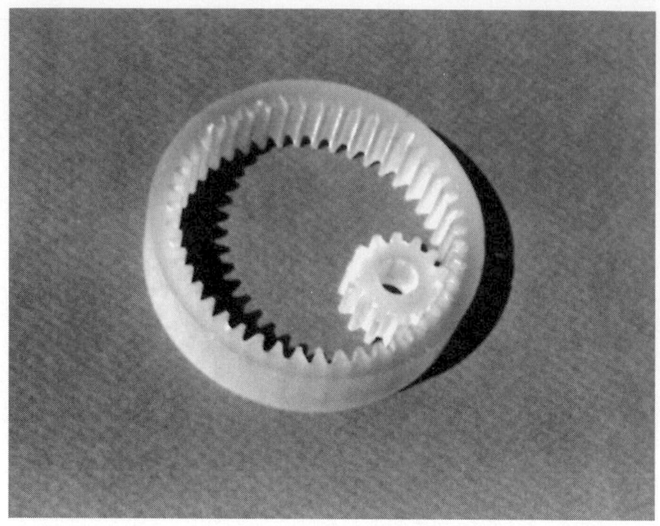

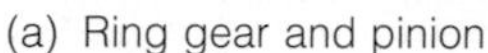

(a) Ring gear and pinion

(b) Pinion

FIGURE 19.11 Gears Modeled using Stereolithography

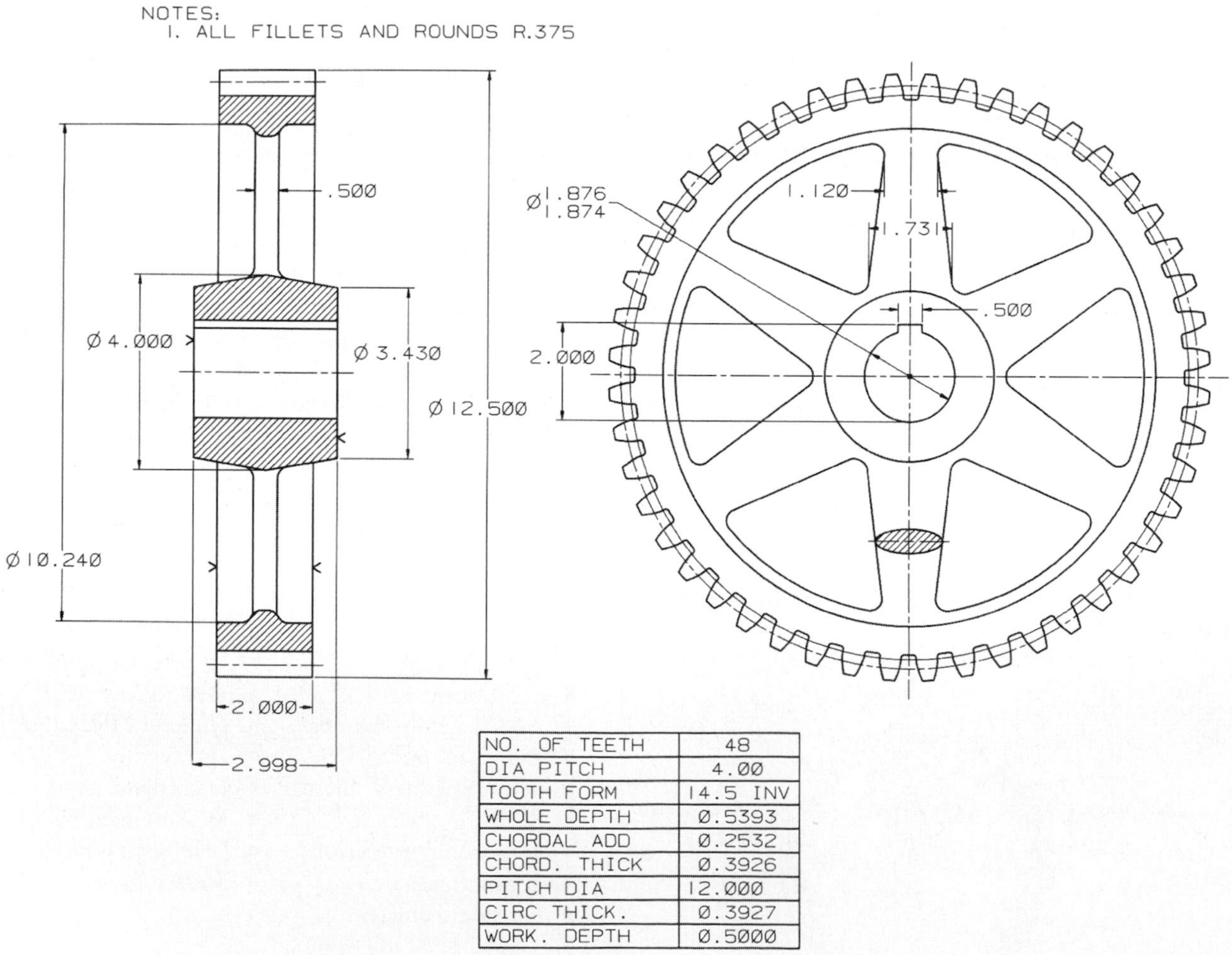

NOTES:
1. ALL FILLETS AND ROUNDS R.375

NO. OF TEETH	48
DIA PITCH	4.00
TOOTH FORM	14.5 INV
WHOLE DEPTH	0.5393
CHORDAL ADD	0.2532
CHORD. THICK	0.3926
PITCH DIA	12.000
CIRC THICK.	0.3927
WORK. DEPTH	0.5000

FIGURE 19.12 Detail Drawing of a Spur Gear

19.3.4 Spur Gear Terms and Symbols

Many terms will be understood by an examination of Figure 19.9. The addendum is the height of the tooth, from the pitch circle to the outside circle. The **base circle** is used to generate the involute curve. The **line of action** is the line along which the contact between the teeth takes place. Symbols used for gears include the following:

a = addendum	b = dedendum
c = clearance	D = pitch diameter
OD = outside diameter	N = number of teeth
P = diametral pitch	p = circular pitch

The following terms are used throughout the chapter to describe spur and helical gears.

Addendum The height that a tooth projects beyond the pitch circle or pitch line.

Base diameter The diameter of the base cylinder from which the involute portion of a tooth profile is generated.

Backlash The amount by which the width of a tooth space exceeds the thickness of the engaging tooth on the pitch circles.

Center distance The distance between the parallel axis of spur gears and parallel helical gears, or the crossed axes of crossed helical gears.

Circular pitch The distance along the pitch circle or pitch line between corresponding profiles of adjacent teeth.

Dedendum The depth of a tooth space below the pitch line; normally greater than the addendum of the mating gear, to provide clearance.

Diametral pitch The ratio of the number of teeth to the pitch diameter, in inches.

Face width The length of the teeth in an axial plane.

Hub diameter The outside diameter of a gear, sprocket, or coupling hub.

Hub projection The distance the hub extends beyond the gear face.

Involute teeth The teeth of spur gears, helical gears, and worms where the active portion of the profile in the transverse plane is the involute of a circle.

Lead The axial advance of a helix for one complete turn, as in the threads of cylindrical worms and the teeth of helical gears.

Normal diametral pitch The value of the diametral pitch as calculated in the normal plane of a helical gear or worm.

Normal plane The plane normal to the tooth surface at a pitch point and perpendicular to the pitch plane.

Outside diameter The diameter of the addendum (outside) circle of a gear.

Pinion A machine part with gear teeth. When two gears run together, the one with the smaller number of teeth is called the pinion.

Pitch circle The circle derived from a number of teeth and a specified diametral or circular pitch; the circle on which spacing or tooth profiles is established and from which the tooth proportions are constructed.

Pitch diameter The diameter of the pitch circle. In parallel shaft gears, the pitch diameters can be determined directly from the center distance and the number of teeth.

Pressure angle The angle between a tooth profile and a radial line at its pitch point. In involute teeth, pressure angle is often described as the angle between the line of action and the line tangent to the pitch circle.

Root diameter The diameter at the base of the tooth space.

Transverse diametral The ratio of the number of teeth to the pitch diameter, in inches, for a helical gear.

Whole depth The total depth of a tooth space, equal to addendum plus dedendum, which is equal to working depth plus variance.

Working depth The depth of engagement of two gears.

19.3.5 Diametral Pitch System

All stock gears are made in accordance with the diametral pitch system. The **diametral pitch** of a gear is the number of gear teeth for each inch of pitch diameter. Therefore, the diametral pitch specifies the size of the gear tooth; a smaller diametral pitch indicates a larger tooth. An eight-pitch gear has eight teeth for each inch of pitch diameter (for a 6-in. pitch diameter, $6 \times 8 = 48$ teeth). The **circular pitch** is the distance from a point on one tooth to the corresponding point on the next tooth, measured along the pitch circle.

Gear teeth can be manufactured in a wide variety of shapes and profiles. The **involute profile** is the most common system for gearing today, and most standard spur and helical gears are of involute form. An **involute** is a curve that is traced by a point on a taut cord unwinding from a circle, called a **base circle.** The involute is a form of spiral, the curvature of which becomes straighter as it is drawn from a base circle. Eventually, if drawn far enough, it would become a straight line.

Focus On . . .

ELEVATORS

If asked, the average person would tell you that an elevator is a mechanical device for moving people or objects to a higher or lower level. They might also tell you that it is a rectangular car that moves up and down on guides in a shaft, has doors that open onto each floor, has a mechanism of some sort, has controls, and uses safety devices. Virtually no one would think to tell you that the elevator is the world's most used and safest method of transportation. Many would consider automobiles, planes, and trains before the elevator. Most would not even consider the elevator at all.

The total number of passengers riding in elevators in any two-week period is more than the world's population. Records show that there are fewer than 1000 accidents per year that involve elevators. However, if you have ever been stranded in an elevator during a malfunction, you know that the elevator is the kind of important technology no one notices until it malfunctions.

Elevators are based on the principle of the counterweight: The weight of one object balances the weight of another object.

In the early nineteenth century, the English were the first to hook up a steam engine to a pulley, but it was not until 1853 that Elisha Graves Otis really improved the safety of the elevator. He displayed his spring safety elevator at the World's Fair in New York City at the Crystal Palace. He invented a governor that allowed the cable holding the car to be cut without moving the car. Everyone was amazed and wanted to know how he stopped the elevator from plunging to the ground.

In 1857, Otis installed the first commercial passenger elevator in a department store. This elevator took fifteen minutes to arrive at the top of a skyscraper (back then that was fast!). The elevator was one of the key factors in the development of our cities. Otis, because of his patents on the steam elevator, created the Otis Elevator Company—a familiar name because their products are very visible in our modern tall buildings.

Today, the manufacturing, installation, and use of elevators are regulated by the national code of the American Society of Mechanical Engineers, the American Institute of Architects, and the National Institute of Standards and Technology. One wonders if Otis could have imagined the impact his invention would have on us when he first exhibited it at the 1853 World's Fair. It's one of those inventions you don't notice until you have to climb stairs to the twenty-fifth story of your office building. Then you know how important Otis is to your life.

An early steam elevator.

A modern elevator.

19.3.6 Pressure Angle

Pressure angle (PA) (Fig. 19.5) is defined as the angle formed between the normal to the tooth profile at the pitch circle and the tangent to the pitch circle at that point.

Standard gears are manufactured in both $14\frac{1}{2}°$ and 20° PA involute full-depth system gears. Although a 20° PA has a higher load-carrying capacity, $14\frac{1}{2}°$ PA gears are still in existence. The spur gear detail shown in Figure 19.12 has a pressure angle of $14\frac{1}{2}°$, a pitch diameter of 12.00 in., and a diametral pitch of 4; therefore, the gear has $12 \times 4 = 48$ teeth. *For gears to mesh, they must have the same diametral pitch.*

19.3.7 Spur Gear Formulas

Table 19.1 shows a complete set of spur gear formulas for full-depth involute teeth.

Tooth Proportions for Standard 20° Fine-Pitch System

N = number of teeth
P = diametral pitch = N/D
a = addendum = $1.000/P$
b = dedendum = $1.200/P + 0.002$
c = clearance = $0.200/P + 0.002$
h_k = working depth of tooth = $2.000/P$
h_l = total depth of tooth = $2.200/P + 0.002$
D = pitch diameter = N/P
OD = D_O (or D_o) = outside diameter = $D + 2/P$

Tooth Proportions for Standard $14\frac{1}{2}$° Full-Depth Involute System

N = number of teeth
P = diametral pitch = N/D
a = addendum = $1/P$
b = dedendum = $1.157/P$
c = clearance = $0.157/P$
h_k = working depth = $2/P$
h_l = total depth = $2.157/P$
D = pitch diameter = N/P
OD = outside diameter = $D + 2/P$

TABLE 19.1 Spur Gear Teeth Formulas (20° Pressure Angle) for Full-Depth Involute Teeth

To Obtain:	Having:	Formula
Diametral pitch (P)	Circular pitch (p)	$P = \frac{3.1416}{p}$
	Number of teeth (N) and pitch diameter (D)	$P = \frac{N}{D}$
	Number of teeth (N) and outside diameter (D_o)	$P = \frac{N+2}{D_o}$
Circular pitch (p)	Diametral pitch (P)	$p = \frac{3.1416}{P}$
Pitch diameter (D)	Number of teeth (N) and diametral pitch (P)	$D = \frac{N}{P}$
	Outside diameter (D_o) and Diametral pitch (P)	$D = D_o - \frac{2}{P}$
Base diameter (D_b)	Pitch diameter (D) and pressure angle (ø)	$D_b = D \cos ø$
Number of teeth (N)	Diametral pitch (P) and pitch diameter (D)	$N = P \times D$
Tooth thickness (t) @ pitch diameter (D)	Diametral pitch (P)	$t = \frac{1.5708}{P}$
Addendum (a)	Diametral pitch (P)	$a = \frac{1}{P}$
Outside diameter (D_o)	Pitch diameter (D) and addendum (a)	$D_o = D + 2a$
Whole depth (h_t) (20P and finer)	Diametral Pitch (P)	$h_t = \frac{2.2}{P} + .002$
Whole depth (h_t) (coarser than 20P)	Diametral pitch (P)	$h_t = \frac{2.157}{P}$
Working depth (h_k)	Addendum (a)	$h_k = 2a$
Clearance (c)	Whole depth (h_t) and addendum (a)	$c = h_t - 2a$
Dedendum (b)	Whole depth (h_t) and addendum (a)	$b = h_t - a$
Contact ratio (M_c)	Outside radii,* base radii,* center distance (C), and pressure angle (ø)	$M_c = \frac{\sqrt{R_o^2 - R_b^2} + \sqrt{r_D^2 - r_b^2} - C \sin ø}{P_c \cos ø}$
Root diameter (D_r)	Pitch diameter (P) and dedendum (b)	$D_r = D - 2b$
Center distance (C)	Pitch diameter (D)	$C = \frac{D_1 + D_2}{2}$
	Number of teeth (N) and pitch (P)	$C = \frac{N_1 + N_2}{2P}$

*R_o = outside radius, gear; r_o = outside radius, pinion; R_b = base circle radius, gear; r_b = base circle radius, pinion.

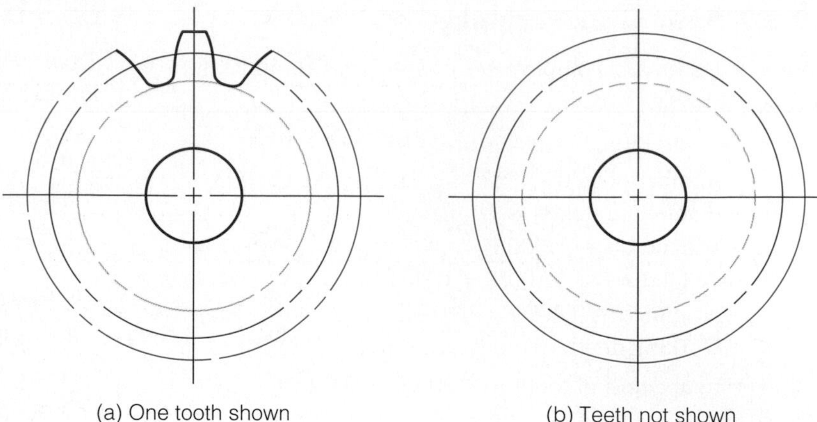

FIGURE 19.13 Representing Gear Teeth (a) One tooth shown (b) Teeth not shown

19.3.8 Spur and Helical Gear Teeth Representation

Views of external spur and helical gears are drawn as shown in Figure 19.13. Gear tooth outlines can normally be omitted from the drawing. Outlines are shown where needed for orientation with other features of the gear or where details, such as tip chamfers or reliefs, require dimensioning. Where required, one tooth may be shown [Fig. 19.13(a)]. Notice that all the teeth are shown in Figure 19.12. This is because a CAD system was used to draw the gear detail. The designer constructed only one tooth and then rotated and copied (**ARRAY** on AutoCAD) the tooth the required number of times (48 in the example). When gears are drawn manually, a template is almost always used to construct the gear teeth.

19.3.9 Gear Tooth Thickness

Circular or arc **tooth thickness** is the preferred specification; chordal tooth thickness may be used. Tooth thickness is normally specified at the referenced pitch circle. Figure 19.14 shows gear teeth terminology in detail. If measurements such as with pins or balls (Fig. 19.14) are specified in addition to the actual tooth thickness, these measurements must be labeled "reference," or labeled as in Figure 19.15, where the dimension is given **OVER PIN**. The diameter of pins or balls (Fig. 19.15) must be expressed beyond four decimal places as appropriate. The diameter of pins or balls is basic.

Tooth thickness must be designated "actual" or "functional." Functional tooth thickness is a specification at the referenced pitch circle for definitive backlash control. It may be used in place of, or in addition to, actual tooth thickness. However, if the actual tooth thickness is critical, it should be specified in addition to the functional tooth thickness. Table 19.2 shows standard tooth dimensions for spur gears.

19.3.10 Backlash on Spur Gears

Backlash is the motion of a meshed gear when its mate is held fixed. An increase or decrease in center distance will cause an increase or decrease in backlash. Stock spur gears are cut to operate at **standard center distances** (Figs. 19.9 and 19.10). The standard center distance is defined as follows:

$$\text{Standard center distance} = \frac{\text{pinion pitch diameter} + \text{gear pitch diameter}}{2}$$

19.4 HELICAL GEARS

The information already given for spur gears is also applicable to helical gears, with the addition of helix angle and lead. **Helix angle** is the angle between any helix and an

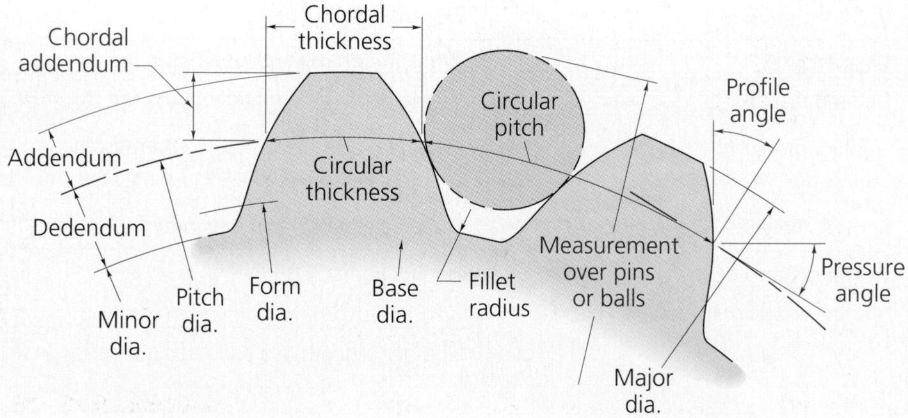

FIGURE 19.14 Spur Gear Teeth Terminology

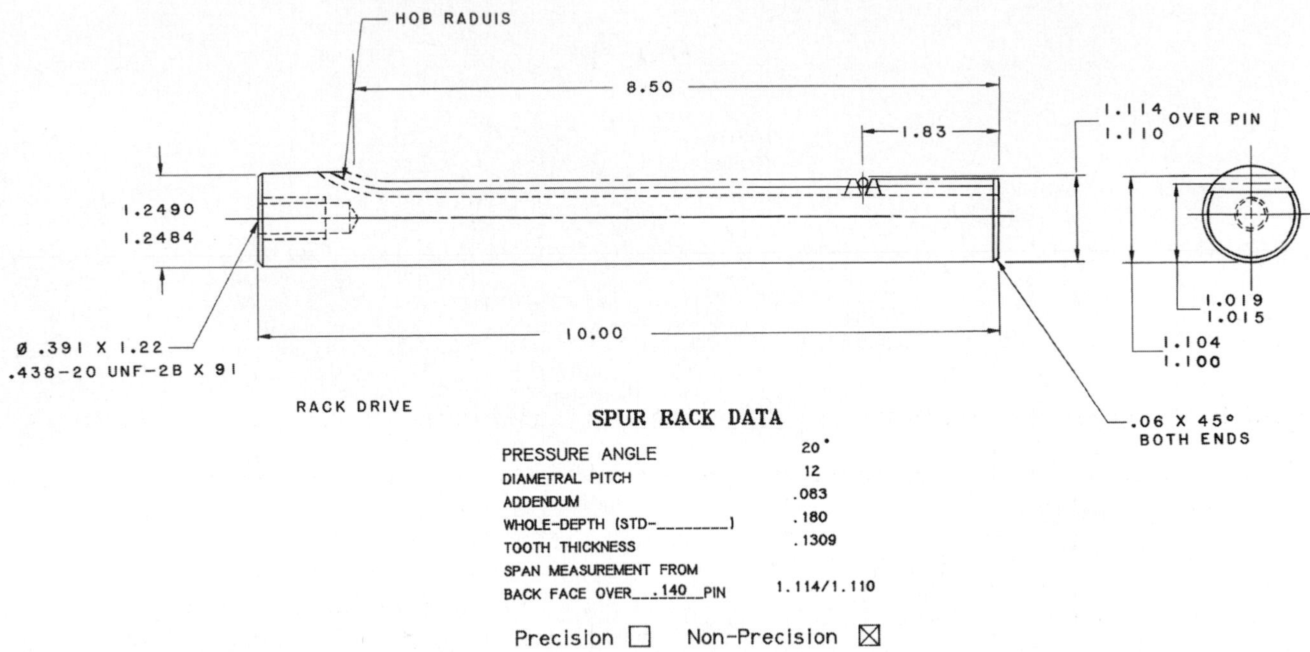

FIGURE 19.15 Spur Rack Detail

element of its cylinder; in **helical gears** (Fig. 19.16) it is at the pitch diameter, unless otherwise specified. **Lead** for helical gears is the axial advance of a helix for one complete turn, for instance, as in the threads of cylindrical worms and the teeth of helical gears. Figure 19.17 presents helical gear terminology.

Many standard helical gears are cut to the diametral pitch system. This results in a normal pitch that is smaller than the diametral pitch. **Normal diametral pitch** is the diametral pitch calculated in the normal plane.

Helical gears of the same hand operate at right angles. Helical gears of opposite hands run on parallel shafts.

The helical tooth form is involute in the plane of rotation and can be developed in a manner similar to that for the spur gear. However, unlike the spur gear, which may be viewed as two-dimensional, the helical gear must be viewed as three-dimensional to show changes in axial features. Formulas for helical gears are provided in Table 19.3.

TABLE 19.2 Spur Gear Tooth Dimensions

Diametral Pitch	Circular Pitch (inches)	Thickness of Tooth on Pitch Line (inches)	Depth to Be Cut in Gear (inches) (Hobbed Gears)	Addendum (inches)
3	1.0472	.5236	.7190	.3333
4	.7854	.3927	.5393	.2500
5	.6283	.3142	.4314	.2000
6	.5236	.2618	.3565	.1667
8	.3927	.1963	.2696	.1250
10	.3142	.1571	.2157	.1000
12	.2618	.1309	.1798	.0833
16	.1963	.0982	.1348	.0625
20	.1517	.0785	.1120	.0500
24	.1309	.0654	.0937	.0417
32	.0982	.0491	.0708	.0312
48	.0654	.0327	.0478	.0208
64	.0491	.0245	.0364	.0156

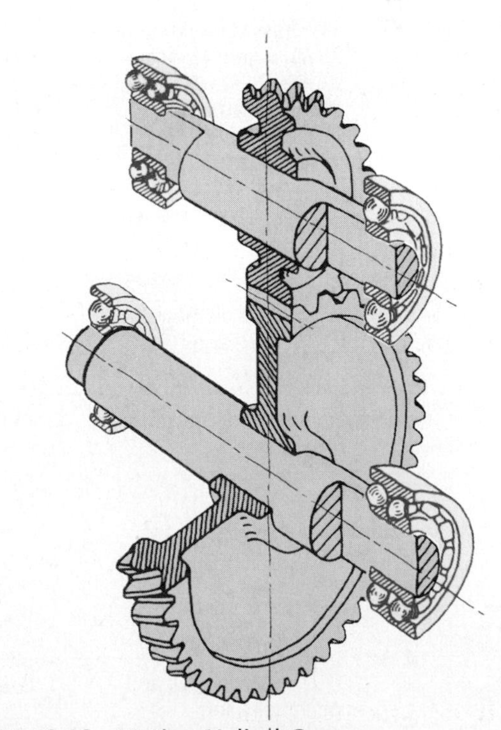

FIGURE 19.16 Mating Helical Gears

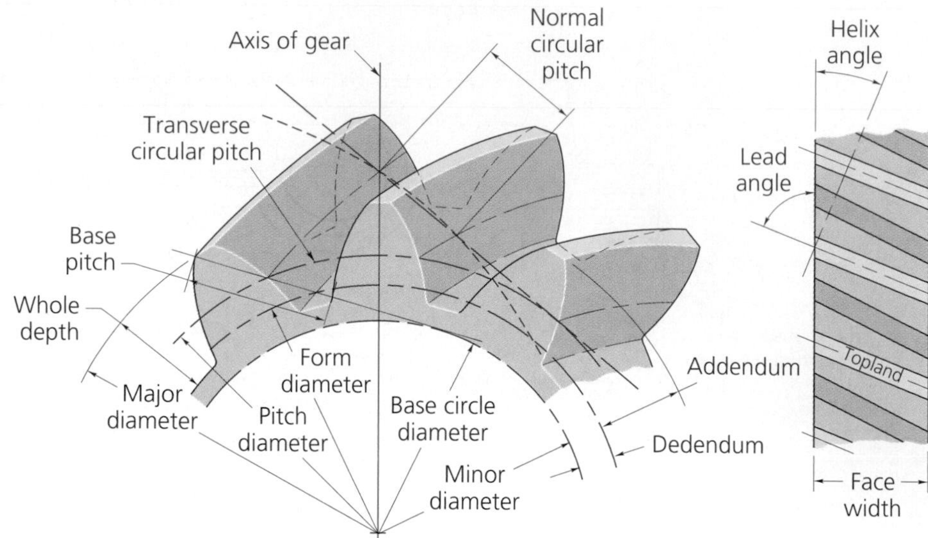

FIGURE 19.17 Helical Gear Teeth Terminology

19.5 RACKS AND PINIONS

A **rack** may be considered a gear of infinitely long pitch radius. The pitch line of a rack is a straight line; the pitch is described as the **linear pitch.** Racks can have spur or helical teeth. Figure 19.18 shows a standard rack detail. Racks are designed to mate with a **pinion** (gear) and are used to convert rotary motion into linear motion or the reverse.

TABLE 19.3 Helical Gear Teeth Formulas

To Obtain:	Having:	Formula
Transverse diametral pitch (P)	Number of teeth (N) and pitch diameter (D)	$P = \frac{N}{D}$
	Normal diametral pitch (P_N) and helix angle (ψ)	$P = P_N \cos \psi$
Pitch diameter (D)	Number of teeth (N) and transverse diametral pitch (P)	$D = \frac{N}{P}$
Normal diametral pitch (P_N)	Transverse diametral pitch (P) and helix angle (ψ)	$P_N = \frac{P}{\cos \psi}$
Normal circular tooth thickness (τ)	Normal diametral pitch (P_N)	$\tau = \frac{1.5708}{P_N}$
Transverse circular pitch (p_t)	Diametral pitch (P) (transverse)	$p_t = \frac{\pi}{P}$
Normal circular pitch (p_n)	Transverse circular pitch (p_t) and pitch helix angle (ψ)	$p_n = p_t \cos \psi$
Lead (L)	Pitch diameter (D) and pitch helix angle (ψ)	$L = \frac{\pi D}{\tan \psi}$

19.6 SPLINES

Splines are multiple keys, in the general form of internal and external gear teeth, used to prevent relative rotation between two members. Splines act primarily to transmit torque and are usually integral with shafts that include other features, as in Figure 19.19, where the end of the shaft is a spline and the center is a worm screw. Splines (Fig. 19.20) normally have three applications:

- For coupling shafts when heavy torques are transmitted without slippage
- For attaching parts that require removal for indexing or for change of angular position
- For transmitting power to permanently fixed gears, pulleys, or other rotating devices

Involute splines (Fig. 19.20) are similar in form to external or internal involute gears. The general graphic format for depicting spline teeth is the same as for spur gears. Standard involute splines are manufactured with 30°, $37\frac{1}{2}$°, and 45° pressure angles.

19.7 GEAR DRAWING PRACTICES

An axial view and a plane of rotation view are generally sufficient to illustrate a gear. Additional views may be used to show construction and special features or relations. The axial view is usually made in section, on a plane parallel to the axis (Fig. 19.12). A helical gear or a gear, pinion, or worm integral with a shaft is shown in full view, on a plane parallel to the axis (Fig. 19.19). The pitch diameter is shown by conventional centerlines and the root diameter by hidden

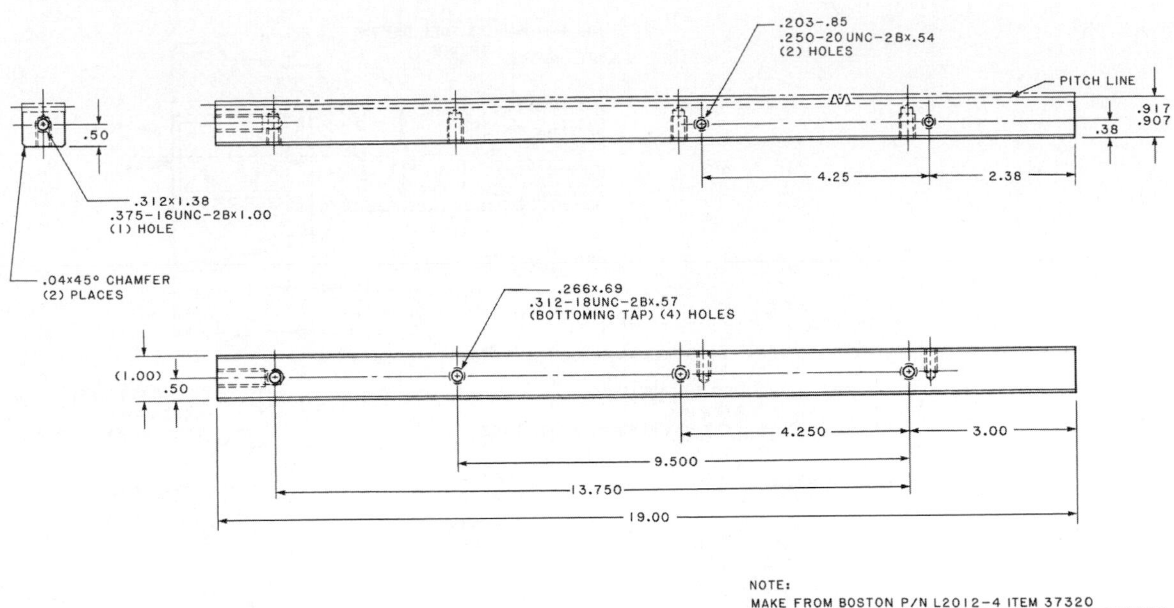

FIGURE 19.18 Rack Detail

lines. In an axial section view, visible lines represent the outside and root diameters, and centerlines show the pitch diameter.

In views representing planes of rotation, the outside and root diameters are shown by phantom lines and, when several teeth are shown, the pitch diameter is shown by a centerline [Fig. 19.13(a)]. *When no teeth are shown,* the outside diameter is represented by a visible object line and the root diameter by a hidden line [Fig. 19.13(b)]. The pitch diameter is still represented by a centerline. Figure 19.21 is an actual industry detail drawing of a gear.

In most cases, it is not necessary to draw all gear teeth when detailing gears. When it is necessary to illustrate a relation to some other feature, such as a keyseat or a bolt hole, or to show dimensions across pins, one or more teeth may be shown. An enlarged view or section can show special

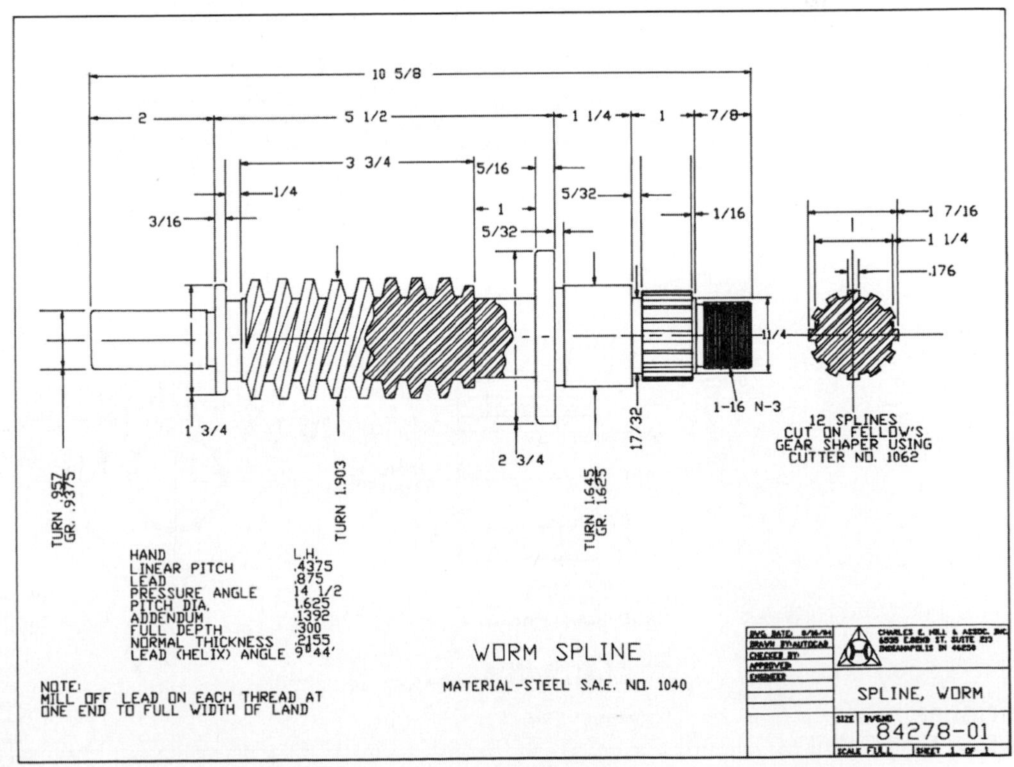

FIGURE 19.19 Worm Spline

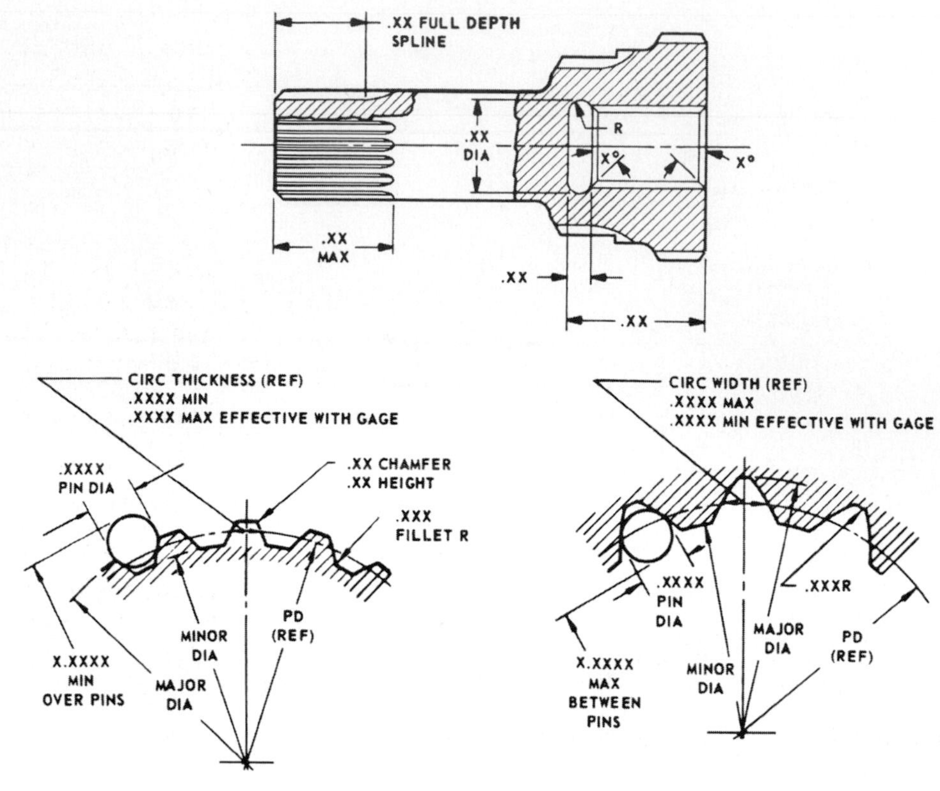

INVOLUTE SPLINE DATA – EXTERNAL	
NUMBER OF TEETH	XX
DIAMETRAL PITCH	XX/XX
PRESSURE ANGLE	XX°
PITCH DIA (REF)	X.XXXX
MAJOR DIA	X.XXXX – X.XXXX
MINOR DIA	X.XXXX – X.XXXX
TRUE INVOLUTE FORM DIA	X.XXXX
*MAX LEAD ERROR	.XXXX

INVOLUTE SPLINE DATA – INTERNAL	
NUMBER OF TEETH	XX
DIAMETRAL PITCH	XX/XX
PRESSURE ANGLE	XX°
PITCH DIA (REF)	X.XXXX
MAJOR DIA	X.XXXX – X.XXXX
MINOR DIA	X.XXXX – X.XXXX
TRUE INVOLUTE FORM DIA	X.XXXX
*MAX LEAD ERROR	.XXXX

FIGURE 19.20 Spline Dimensioning

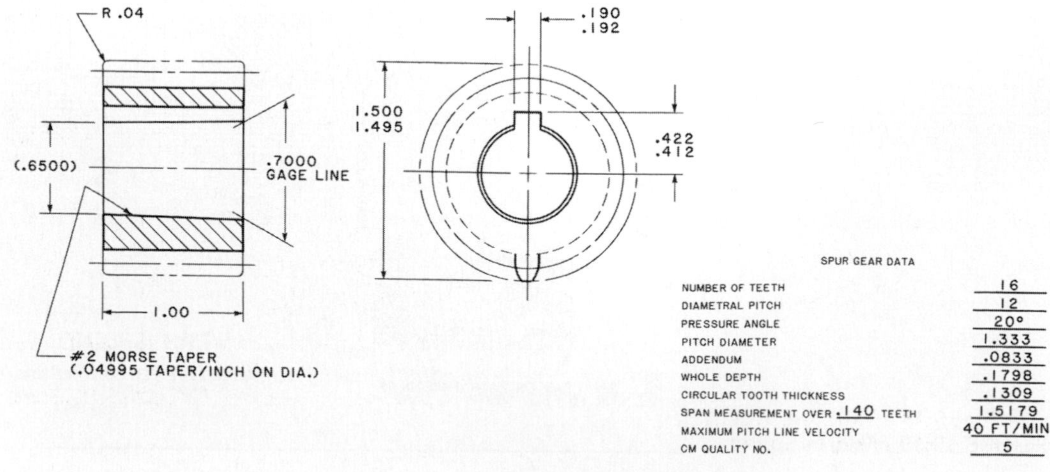

SPUR GEAR DATA	
NUMBER OF TEETH	16
DIAMETRAL PITCH	12
PRESSURE ANGLE	20°
PITCH DIAMETER	1.333
ADDENDUM	.0833
WHOLE DEPTH	.1798
CIRCULAR TOOTH THICKNESS	.1309
SPAN MEASUREMENT OVER .140 TEETH	1.5179
MAXIMUM PITCH LINE VELOCITY	40 FT/MIN
CM QUALITY NO.	5

FIGURE 19.21 Spur Gear Detail

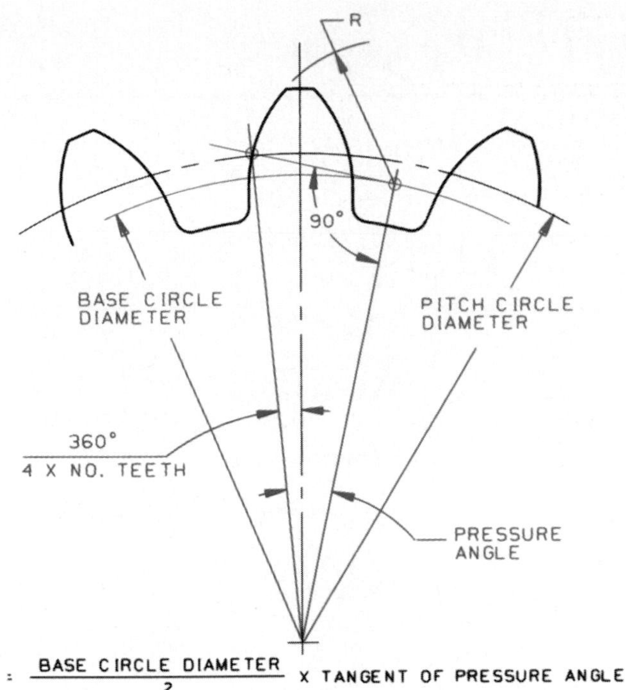

FIGURE 19.22 Drawing an Approximate Involute for Construction of Gear Teeth

features of gear teeth or a gear profile. Gear teeth may be drawn by the approximate method shown in Figures 19.22 and 19.23. The relative size of gear teeth in terms of diametral pitch is illustrated full size in Figure 19.24.

19.7.1 Dimensioning and Notes

Gear data must be grouped as shown in Figures 19.12 and 19.15. The location of the gear data on the drawing is arbitrary. However, if more than one gear is depicted on a drawing, the groups of gear data must be clearly referenced to the appropriate gear.

The major diameter may be specified as the outside diameter; the minor diameter may be specified as the root diameter. This is for external gears only. On internal gears, the major diameter may be specified as the root diameter and the minor diameter as the inside diameter.

Illustrations show only those dimensions that control the gear teeth and their relation to the specified mounting. All other dimensions and specifications must conform to recommended drafting practice (ANSI). For the rack in Figure 19.25, dimensional values are indicated by X's that show the number of decimal places recommended in each instance.

A completely defined rack or gear contains two sets of dimensions: those of the gear blank and those of the gear teeth. This information is shown as a composite on one set of views. Information required for the production of a gear blank is shown on the face of the gear drawing, integral with the graphic depiction. Information required for the production of the gear teeth is shown on the same drawing in a data block. Local and general notes are added as required. Angular dimensions are expressed in degrees and decimal portions thereof (where desired, the angle may be given in degrees, minutes, and seconds). Figure 19.26 shows a matching set of spur gears, along with all dimensions required for manufacture.

19.8 BEVEL GEARS

Portions of two cones in frictional contact (Fig. 19.27) might be used to transmit motion from one shaft to another. However, to prevent slipping, teeth may be used. The cones then become **bevel gears** (Fig. 19.28). Two bevel gears of the same size, with shafts at right angles, are called **miter gears** (Fig. 19.29). Bevel gears are the most common way to transmit motion between shafts with intersecting axes. The addendum and dedendum are measured the same as for a spur gear, and measurements are taken on a cone called the **back cone.** The diametral pitch, circular pitch, etc. are the same as for a spur gear.

The shafts for bevel gears may make any angle, called the

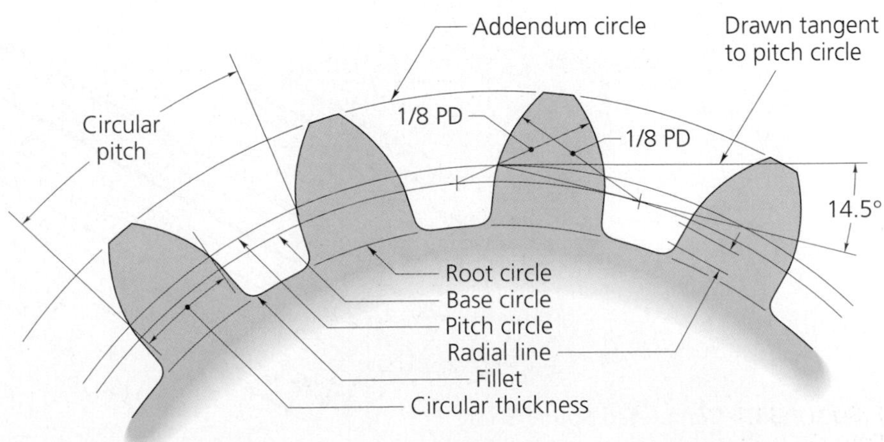

FIGURE 19.23 Simplified Gear Tooth Construction

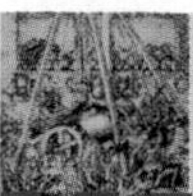

Applying Parametric Design . . .

SPLINE GEAR TEETH AND PATTERNING

Patterns are multiple features created from a single feature (see Fig. A). After it is created, a pattern behaves as if it was a single feature. When you create a pattern, you create instances (copies) of the selected feature.

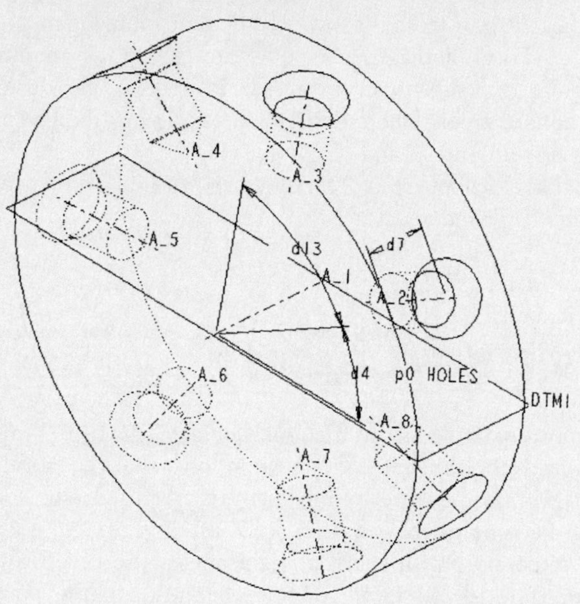

FIGURE A A Rotational Pattern of Radially Placed Holes

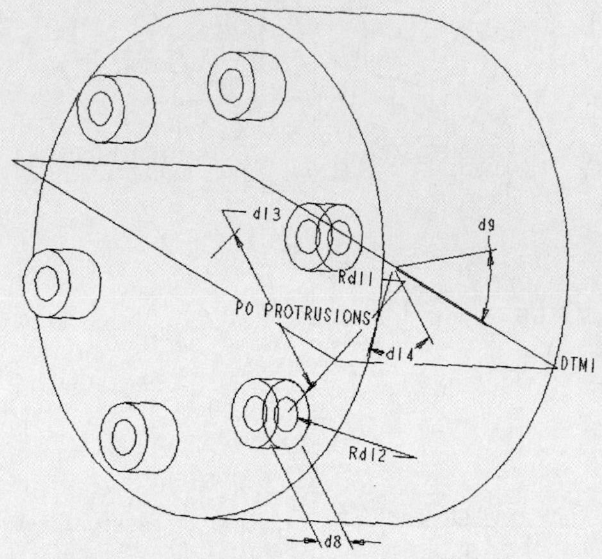

FIGURE B A Rotational Pattern of Sketched Features

Patterns have many uses. Creating a pattern is a quick way to reproduce a feature (Fig. B). Manipulating a pattern may be more advantageous than operating individual features. In fact, you can easily suppress a pattern (temporarily remove it from the screen) or add it to a layer.

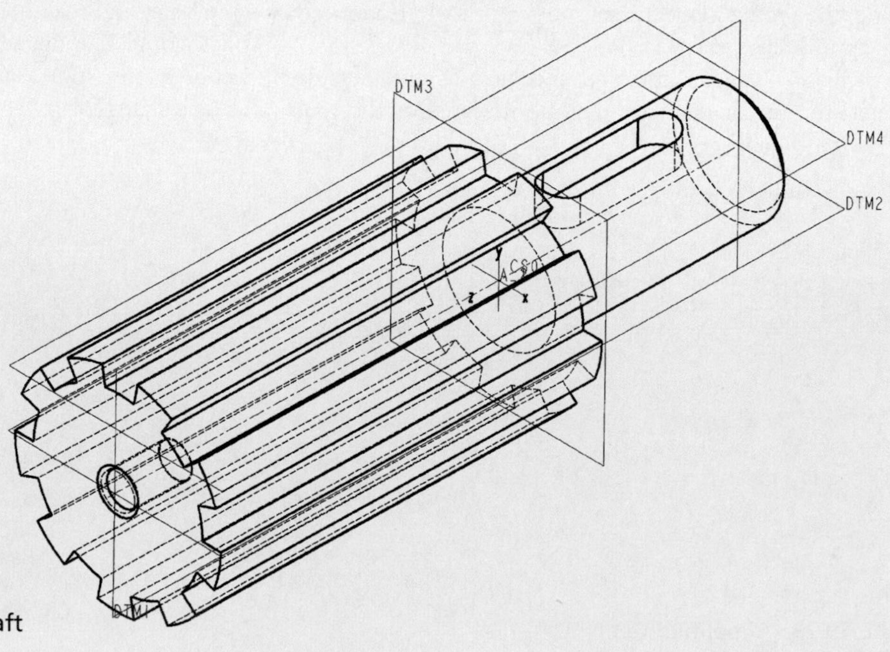

FIGURE C Completed Spline Shaft

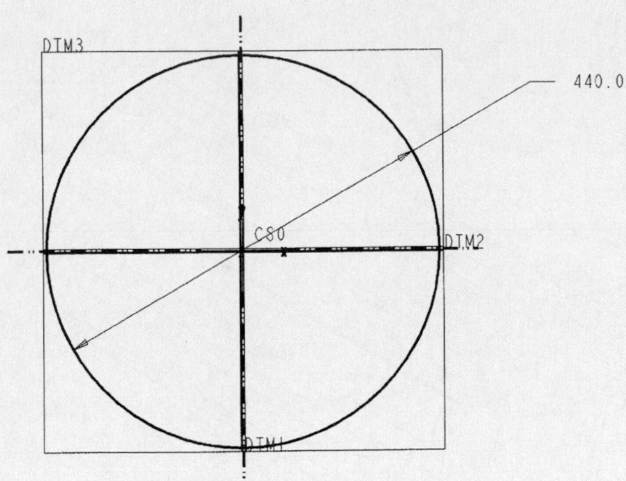

FIGURE D Sketched Circle OD

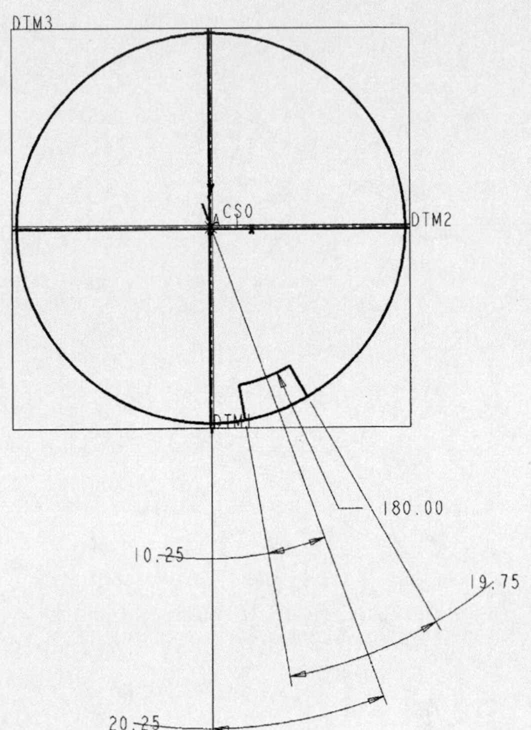

FIGURE E Sketched Spline Tooth

Modifying patterns is more efficient than modifying individual features. In a pattern, when you change dimensions of the original feature, the whole pattern will be updated automatically. Because a pattern is controlled parametrically, it can be modified by changing pattern parameters, such as the number of instances, spacing between instances, and the original feature dimensions.

The following features can be patterned:

Slots	Cuts	Protrusions
Holes	Shafts	Necks
Flanges	Ribs	Cosmetics
Ears	Local pushes	Datum planes
Thin features	Surface features	Datum point arrays
Gear teeth	Spline teeth	Features copied by translation

To create a gear spline on a parametric design system involves a simple set of commands. The following figure sequence and description presents the creation of a spline and shaft (see Figure C):

1. Sketch the circle representing the OD of the spline using the system's default datum planes (see Fig. D). The depth of the spline surface is given after the circle is dimensioned and regenerated.
2. Sketch the dimensions for one spline tooth. Make the tooth at an angle to one of the datum planes—here DTM1 (see Figs. E and F). This will allow you to use the angle dimension when

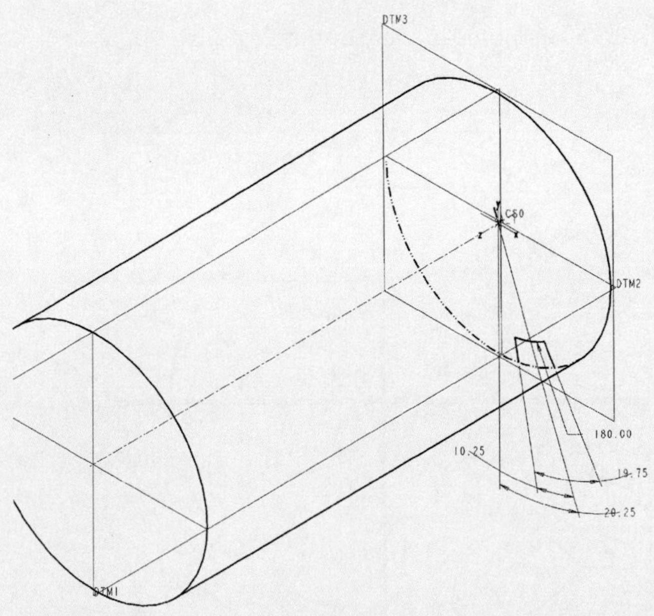

FIGURE F Dimensioned Sketch of the Spline Tooth

(Continues)

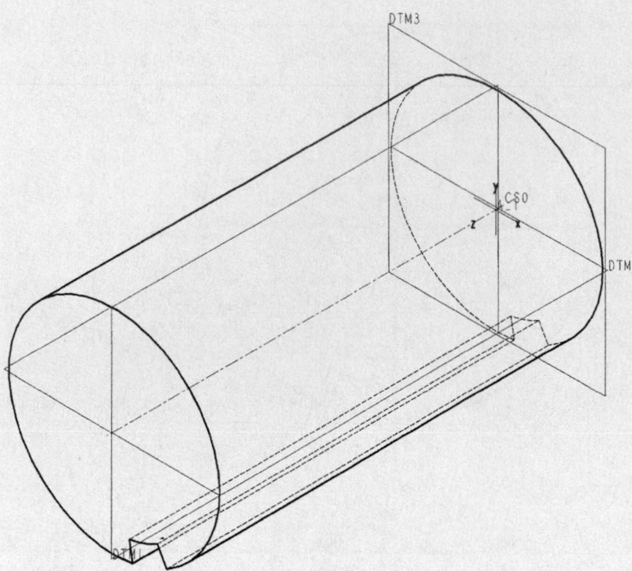

FIGURE G Spline Cut Created Through the Shaft

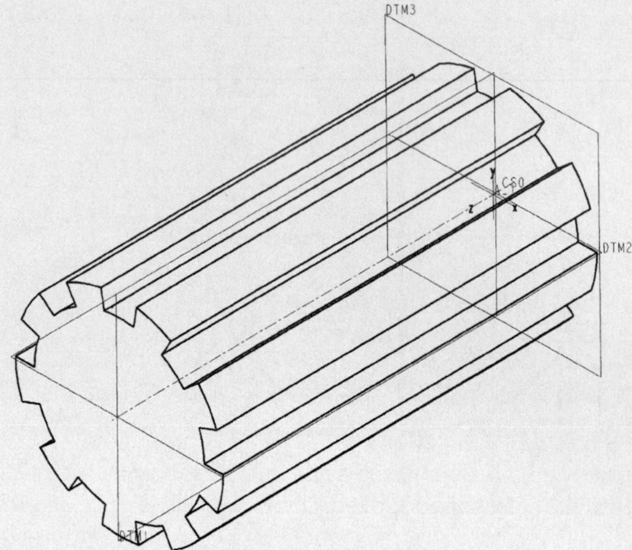

FIGURE J Spline Shaft

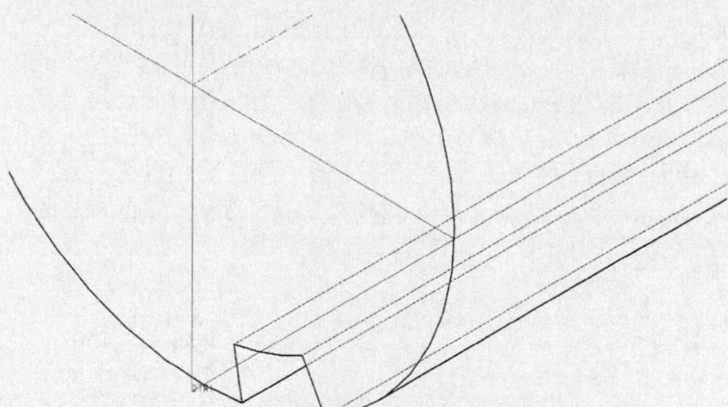

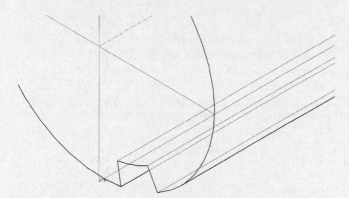

FIGURE H Close-Up View of Cut Feature

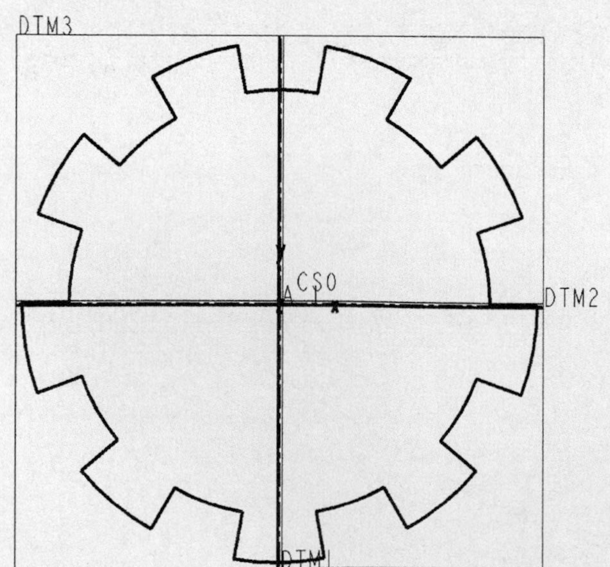

FIGURE I Patterned Spline

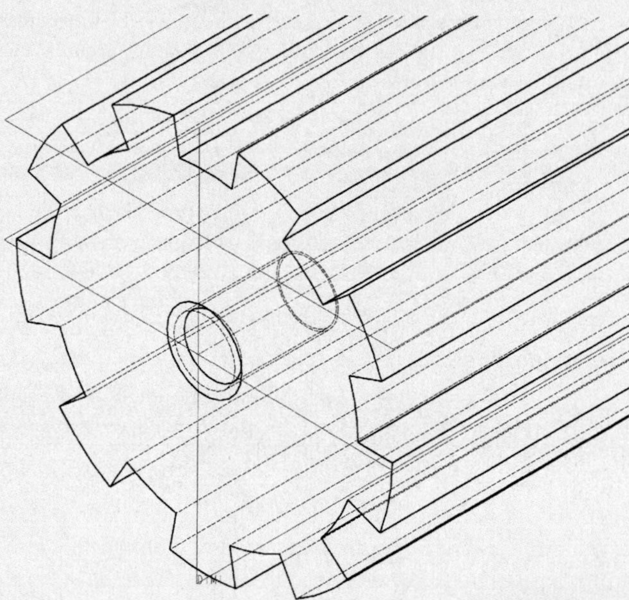

FIGURE K Countersunk Hole and Cosmetic Threads

patterning the feature. The depth of the spline tooth is given after its shape is sketched, aligned, regenerated, and dimensioned (see Figs. G and H).

3. Create the pattern by selecting the feature to be patterned, providing the angle for the radial displacement, and the number of instances (see Figs. I and J).
4. Model the shaft, keyseat, and countersunk hole last (see Figure C).
5. Add cosmetic threads to complete the part (see Fig. K).

20° P.A.	$14\frac{1}{2}$° P.A.
64 D.P.	
48 D.P.	48 D.P.
32 D.P.	32 D.P.
24 D.P.	24 D.P.
20 D.P.	20 D.P.
16 D.P.	16 D.P.
12 D.P.	12 D.P.
10 D.P.	10 D.P.
8 D.P.	8 D.P.
6 D.P.	6 D.P.
5 D.P.	5 D.P.
4 D.P.	4 D.P.
	3 D.P.

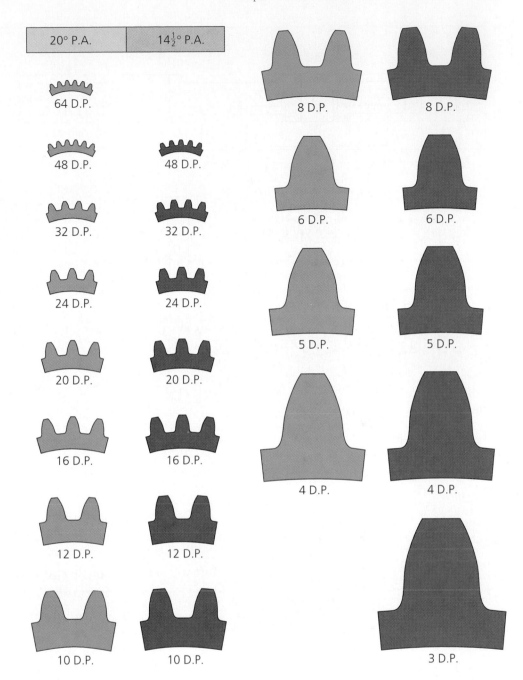

FIGURE 19.24 Spur Gear Teeth Outlines (shown full size)

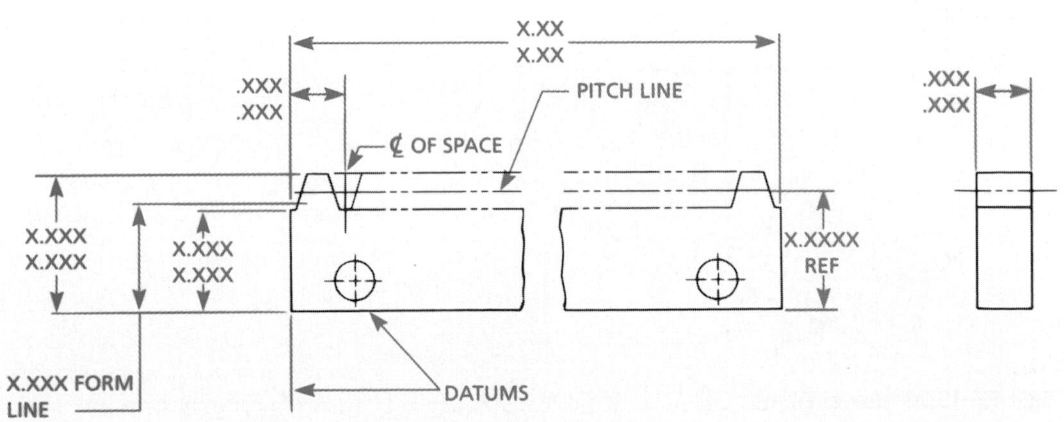

FIGURE 19.25 Rack Dimensioning

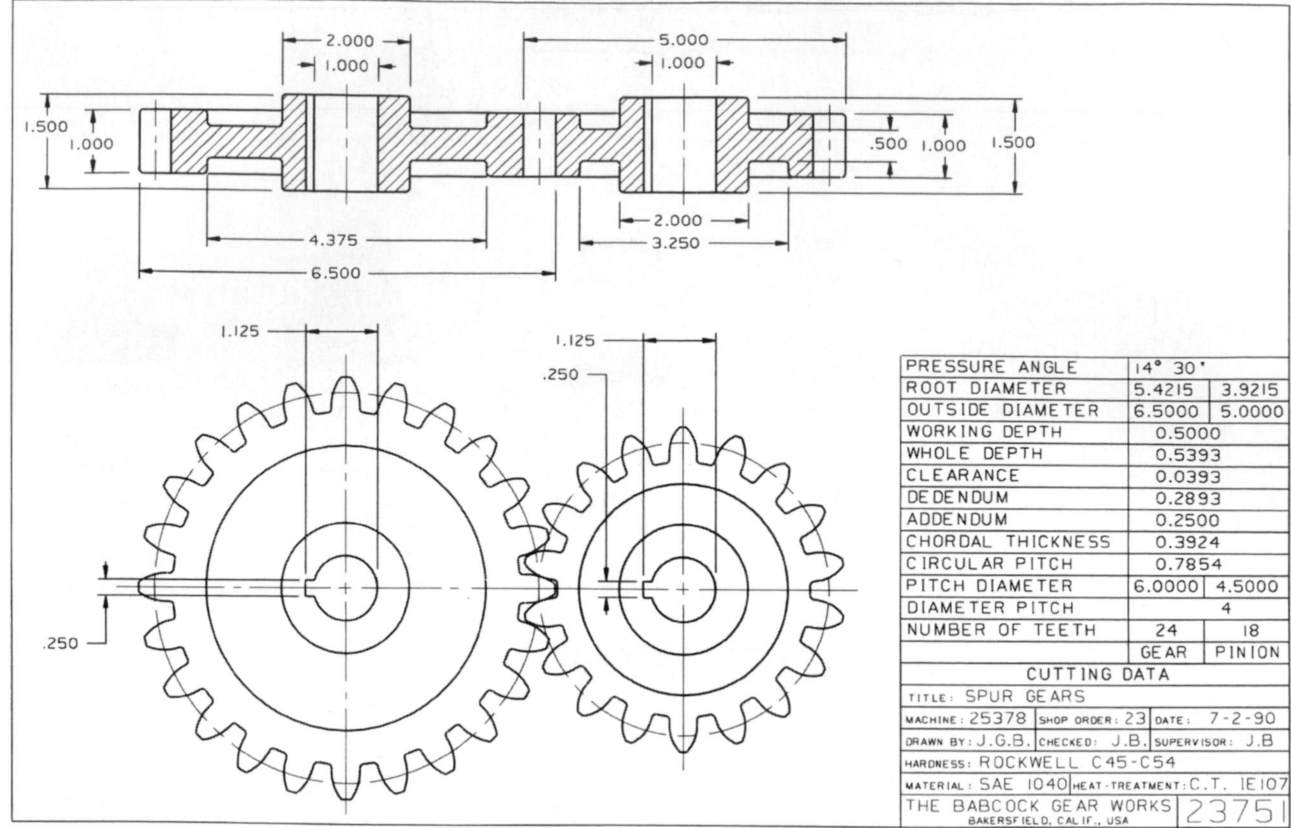

2.000
1.000
5.000
1.000
1.500
1.000
.500 1.000 1.500
2.000
3.250
4.375
6.500
1.125
1.125
.250
.250
PRESSURE ANGLE 14° 30'
ROOT DIAMETER 5.4215 3.9215
OUTSIDE DIAMETER 6.5000 5.0000
WORKING DEPTH 0.5000
WHOLE DEPTH 0.5393
CLEARANCE 0.0393
DEDENDUM 0.2893
ADDENDUM 0.2500
CHORDAL THICKNESS 0.3924
CIRCULAR PITCH 0.7854
PITCH DIAMETER 6.0000 4.5000
DIAMETER PITCH 4
NUMBER OF TEETH 24 18
GEAR PINION
CUTTING DATA
TITLE: SPUR GEARS
MACHINE: 25378 SHOP ORDER: 23 DATE: 7-2-90
DRAWN BY: J.G.B. CHECKED: J.B. SUPERVISOR: J.B
HARDNESS: ROCKWELL C45-C54
MATERIAL: SAE 1040 HEAT-TREATMENT: C.T. IE107
THE BABCOCK GEAR WORKS 23751
BAKERSFIELD, CALIF., USA

FIGURE 19.26 Detail of Mating Spur Gears

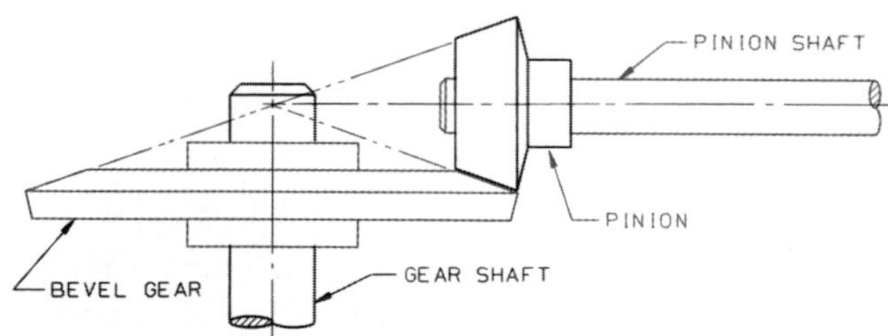

FIGURE 19.27 Bevel Gear Cones

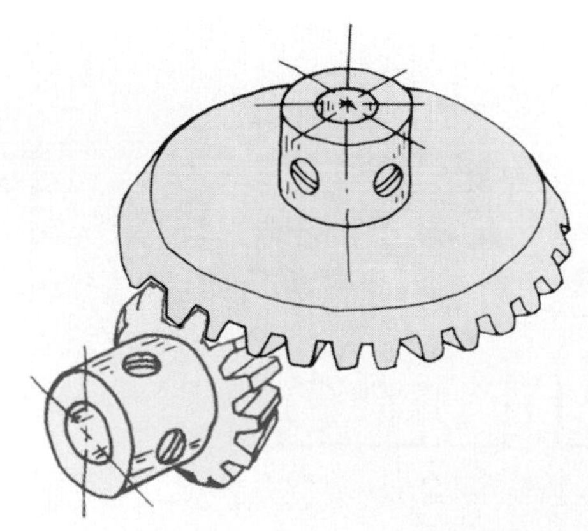

FIGURE 19.28 Bevel Gears

shaft angle, with each other. The terms used for bevel gears are given in Figure 19.29.

19.8.1 Bevel Gear Terminology and Formulas

Bevel gears (Fig. 19.30) are frequently matched in sets or pairs during sequence of the manufacturing process. They are maintained as a matched set in assembly. Formulas for straight bevel gears are given in Table 19.4. Since bevel gears differ from spur gears, the gear tooth nomenclature that follows is presented to familiarize you with general terms used on the bevel gear drawings.

Addendum The distance from the pitch cone to the top of the tooth, as measured at the large end of the tooth.

Axial plane A plane that contains the gear axis.

Back angle distance The perpendicular distance from the intersection of the gear axis with the locating surface at the back of a bevel gear to the back cone element.

Circular thickness The length of arc between the two sides of a gear tooth on the pitch circle.

Face angle distance The perpendicular distance from the intersection of the gear axis with the locating surface at the back of a bevel gear to the face cone element.

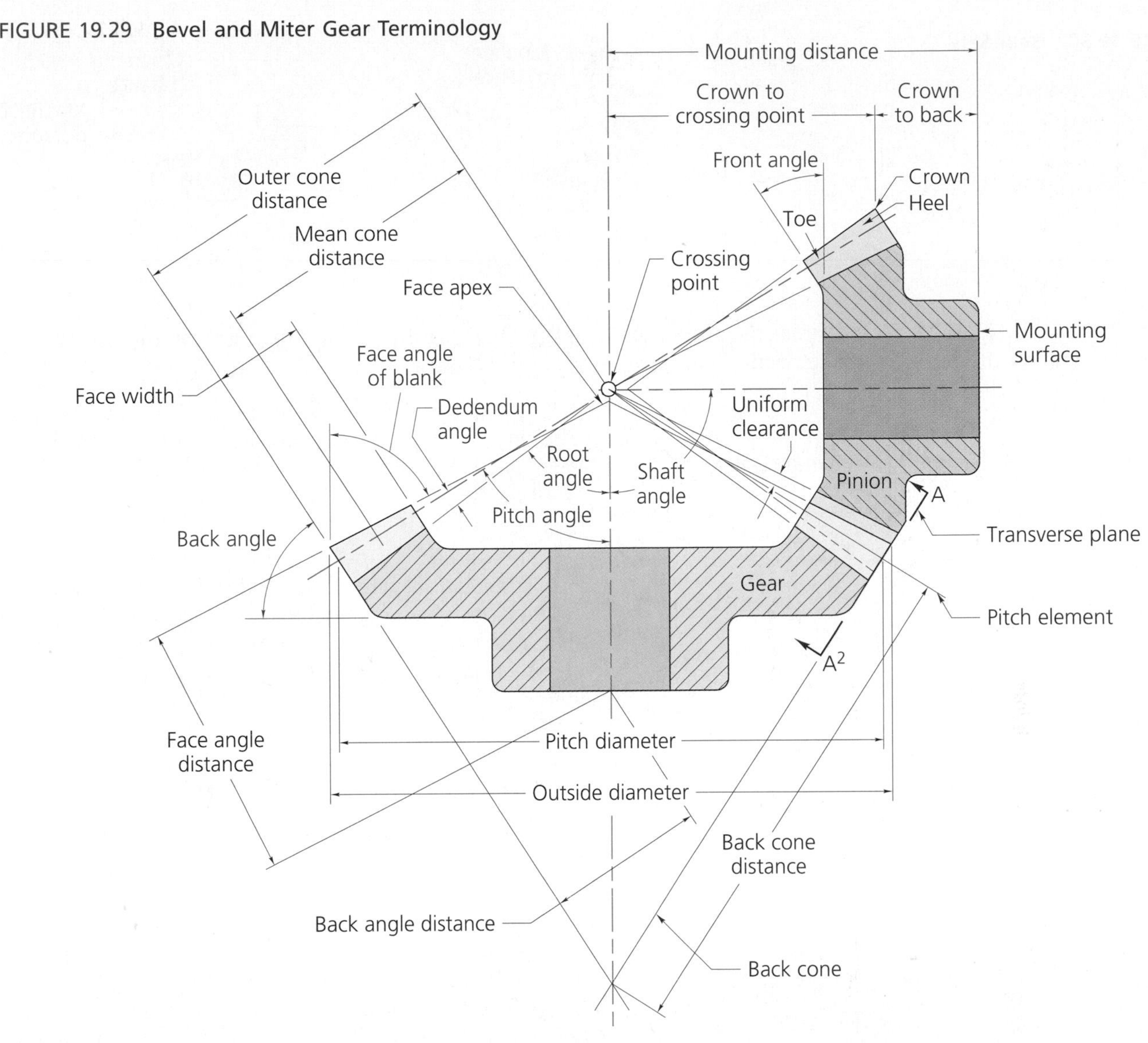

FIGURE 19.29 **Bevel and Miter Gear Terminology**

TABLE 19.4 **Straight-Tooth Miter and Bevel Gear Formulas**

To Obtain:	**Having:**	**Formula**	
		Pinion	***Gear***
Pitch diameter (*D, d*)	Number of teeth (*N*) and diametral pitch (*P*)	$d = \frac{N}{P}$	$D = \frac{N}{P}$
Whole depth (h_r)	Diametral pitch (*P*)	$h_T = \frac{2.188}{P} = .002$	$h_T = \frac{2.188}{P} = .002$
Addendum (*a*)	Diametral pitch (*P*)	$a = \frac{1}{P}$	$a = \frac{1}{P}$
Dedendum (*b*)	Whole depth (h_T) and addendum (*a*)	$b = h_T - a$	$b = h_T - a$
Clearance (*c*)	Whole depth (h_T) and addendum (*a*)	$c = h_T - 2a$	$c = h_T - 2a$
Circular tooth thickness (τ)	Diametral pitch (*P*)	$\tau = \frac{1.5708}{P}$	$\tau = \frac{1.5708}{P}$
Pitch angle (L_P, L_G)	Number of teeth in pinion (N_P) and gear (N_G)	$L_P = tan^{-1}\left(\frac{N_P}{N_G}\right)$	$L_G = 90 - L_P$
Outside diameter (D_O, d_O)	Pinion and gear pitch diameter ($D_p + D_G$), addendum (*a*), and pitch angle ($L_P + L_G$)	$d_O = D_P + 2a(\cos L_P)$	$D_o = D_G + 2a(\cos L_G)$

FIGURE 19.30 Gear Sets

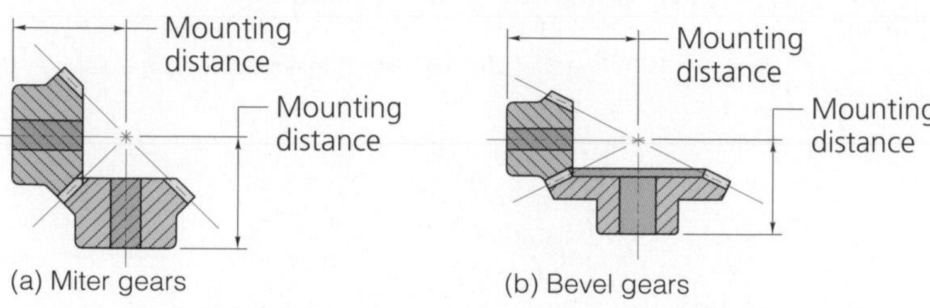

Mounting distance (MD) The distance from the end of the hub of one gear to the centerline of its mating gear (Fig. 19.30).

Pitch plane A plane tangent to the gear pitch surface. For bevel gears, the pitch plane is tangent to the pitch cone.

Pressure angle The angle at the pitch point between a line normal to the tooth profile and the pitch plane.

Spiral angle The angle between the tooth trace and an element of the pitch cone.

Tooth form The shape of the tooth profile. Since bevel gears are manufactured with a variety of tooth forms, it is essential to specify the desired form on the gear drawing.

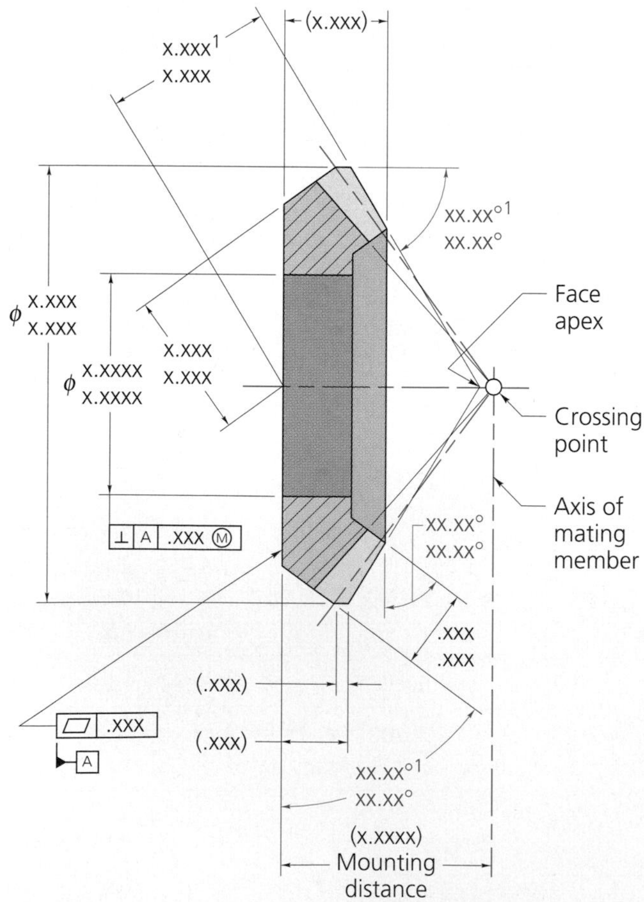

FIGURE 19.31 Dimensions Required for Spiral Bevel Gears

19.8.2 Drawing and Dimensioning Bevel Gears

A bevel gear drawing consists of a side view or axial section illustrating the general configuration and tabulated gear tooth data. Generally, only one view is needed. A front view is added where necessary to show the relationship of the gear teeth to other features.

The spiral bevel gear illustration in Figure 19.31 shows only those dimensions that control the gear teeth and their relation to the mounting surfaces. Dimensional values are indicated by X's, to show the number of decimal places recommended in each instance.

19.9 WORMS AND WORM GEARS

Worm gears (Fig. 19.32) transmit motion from one shaft to another at a high speed. **Worm gears** (wheel) and **worm screws** are designed to transmit motion between nonintersecting, perpendicular shafts. A worm is, in effect, a screw. When a worm wheel (similar to a spur gear) has teeth shaped to fit the threads on the worm, the worm will turn the wheel. The worm may have single, double, or multiple threads. A large speed ratio is possible with this type of

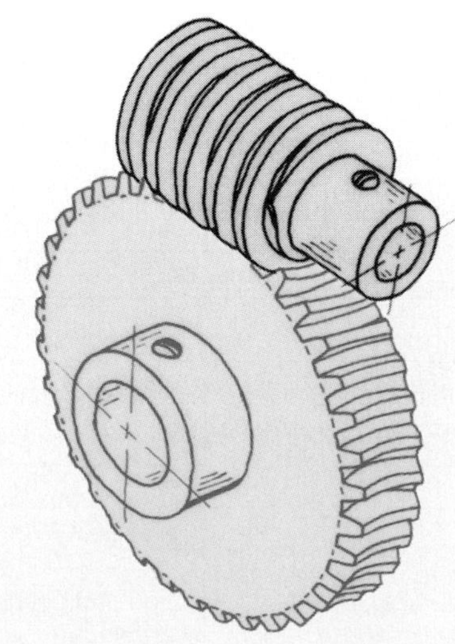

FIGURE 19.32 Worm and Worm Gear

gearing; however, a worm drive only works as a reducer. When the worm gear drives the worm screw (speed increases), the drive locks up.

Specifications and dimensions required for a worm gear set are provided in Figure 19.33. A detail of a worm wheel and a worm gear are shown in Figure 19.34. Sometimes a worm gear is combined with a pinion.

Standard stock worms and worm gears transmit motion and/or power between nonintersecting shafts at right angles (90°). Worm gear drives are considered the smoothest and quietest form of gearing. In most cases, a worm and a worm wheel are detailed on separate sheets. Worm and worm gear formulas are provided in Table 19.5.

19.10 CAD AND GEARS

CAD systems can be used to design and detail gears. Since the system can rotate and copy graphics (even in 3D), only one tooth is drawn and then time-saving commands are used. Figure 19.34 was drawn on a CAD system. The designer in Figure 19.35 is working at his terminal creating a 3D surface model of a spur gear tooth.

If a CAD system had not been involved, only one tooth would have been drawn for each gear. For AutoCAD the **ARRAY** command with the `Polar` option is used to rotate and copy the gear teeth:

```
Command: ARRAY Select Objects: Window the tooth that was drawn.
Rectangular or Polar Array (R/P): P
Center point of array: Pick the center of the gear.
Number of items: 32
Angle to fill (+=CCW, -=CW) <360>: <Return> to choose 360° default.
Rotate objects as they are copied? <y>: <Return> for default.
```

You May Complete Exercises 19.1 Through 19.4 at This Time

TABLE 19.5 Worm and Worm Gear Formulas

To Obtain:	Having:	Formula
Circular pitch (p)	Diametral pitch (P)	$P = \frac{3.1416}{P}$
Diametral pitch (P)	Circular pitch (p)	$P = \frac{3.1416}{P}$
Lead (of worm) (l)	Number of threads in worm and circular pitch (p)	$L = p \times$ (No. threads)
Addendum (a)	Diametral pitch (P)	$a = \frac{1}{P}$
Pitch diameter of Worm (D_W)	Outside diameter (dO) and addendum (a)	$D_W = d_O - 2a$
Pitch diameter of worm gear (D_G)	Circular pitch (p) and number of teeth (N)	$D_G = \frac{N_p}{3.1416}$
Center distance between worm and worm gear (CD)	Pitch diameter of worm (DW) and of worm gear (DG)	$CD = \frac{P_W + D_G}{2}$
Whole depth of teeth (hT)	Circular pitch (p)	$h_T = .6866p$
	Diametral pitch (P)	$h_T = \frac{2.157}{P}$
Bottom diameter of worm (dr)	Whole depth (hT) and outside diameter (dO)	$d_r = d_O - 2h_T$
Throat diameter of worm gear (DT)	Pitch diameter of worm gear (D_G) and addendum (a)	$D_T = D_G + 2a$
Lead angle of worm	Pitch diameter of worm (D_W) and the lead (L)	$Angle = tan^{-1}\left(\frac{L}{3.1416\ D_W}\right)$
Ratio	No. of teeth on gear (NG) and number of threads on worm	$Ratio = \frac{N_G}{No.\ threads}$

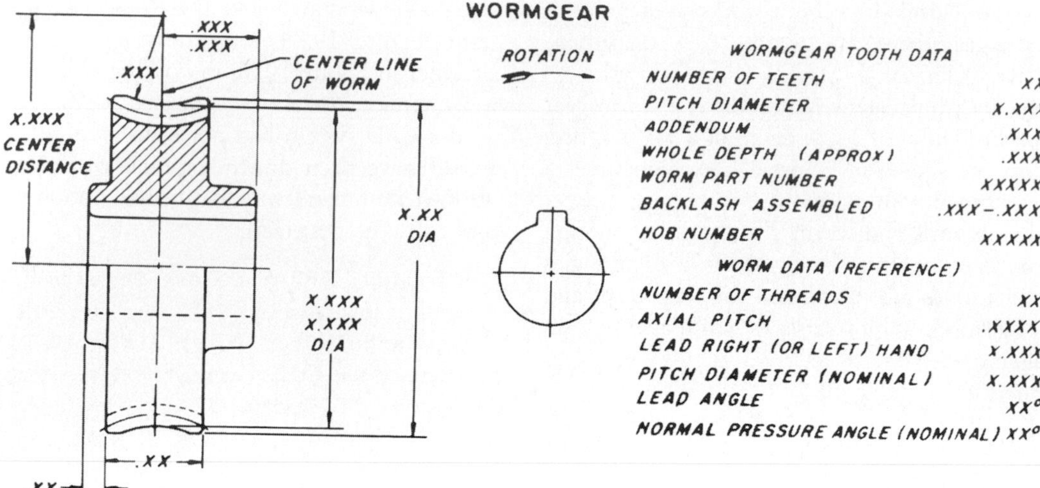

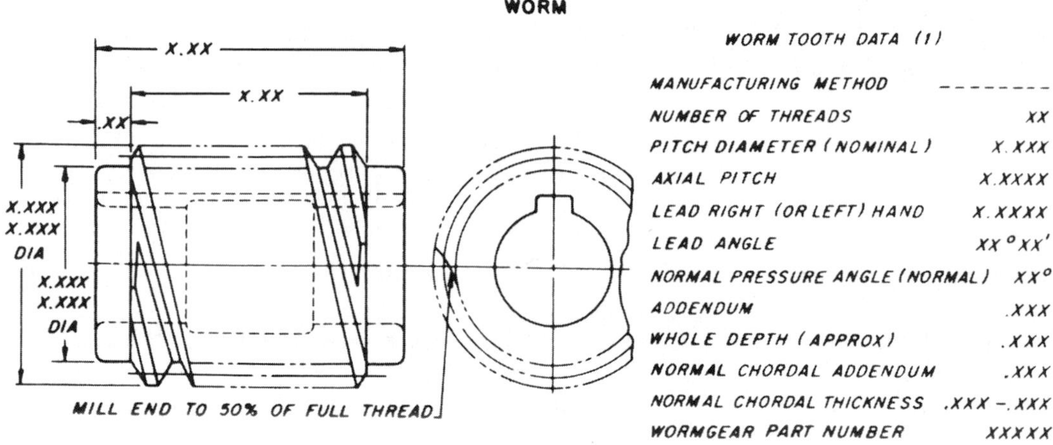

FIGURE 19.33 Dimensions Required for Worms and Worm Gears

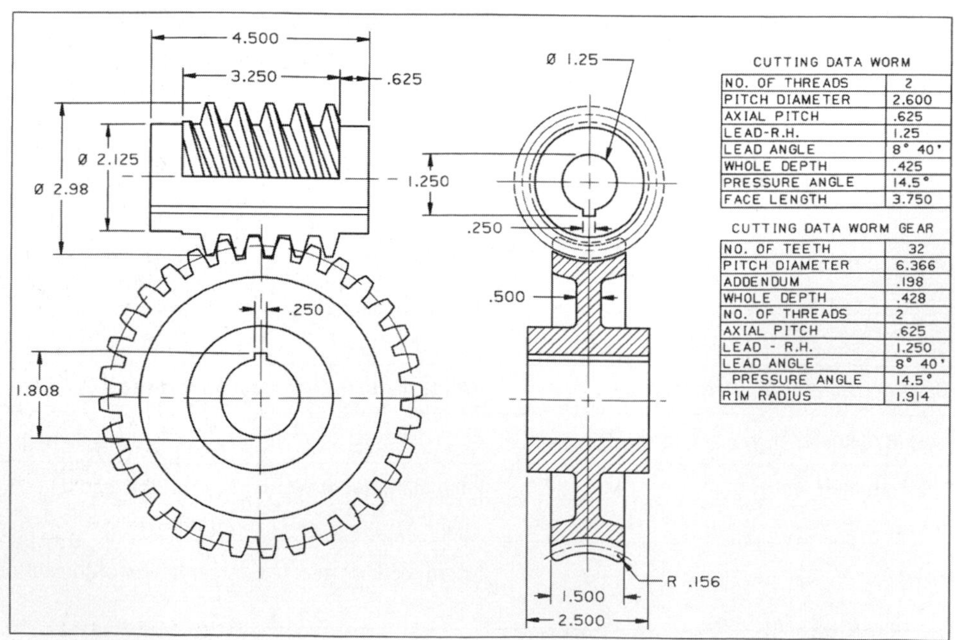

CUTTING DATA WORM

NO. OF THREADS	2
PITCH DIAMETER	2.600
AXIAL PITCH	.625
LEAD-R.H.	1.25
LEAD ANGLE	8° 40'
WHOLE DEPTH	.425
PRESSURE ANGLE	14.5°
FACE LENGTH	3.750

CUTTING DATA WORM GEAR

NO. OF TEETH	32
PITCH DIAMETER	6.366
ADDENDUM	.198
WHOLE DEPTH	.428
NO. OF THREADS	2
AXIAL PITCH	.625
LEAD - R.H.	1.250
LEAD ANGLE	8° 40'
PRESSURE ANGLE	14.5°
RIM RADIUS	1.914

FIGURE 19.34 Worm and Worm Gear Detail

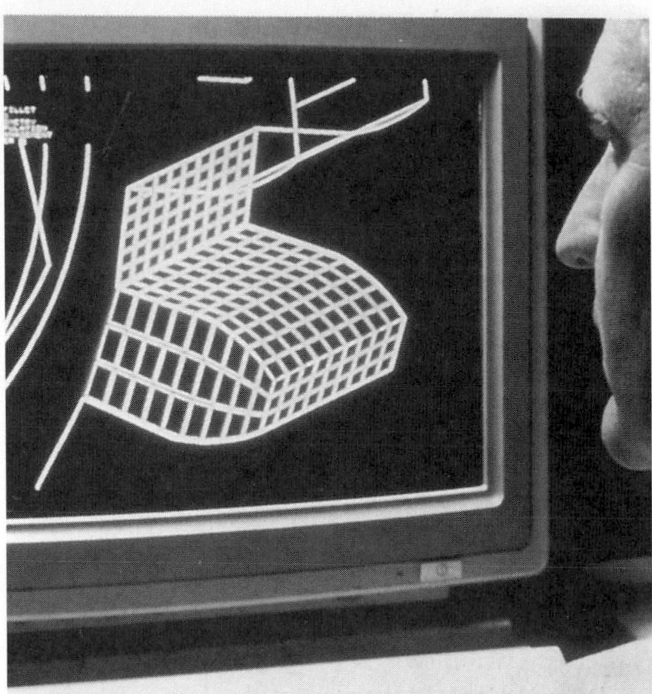

FIGURE 19.35 Spur Gear Teeth Design using CAD

19.11 SHAFTS

Shafts are rotating machine elements that are subjected to torsional stress (twisting) during operation. Shafts rotate freely when held by bearings at each end (Fig. 19.36). The shaft in Figure 19.37 is secured in a housing with a bearing.

Gears and cams are normally mounted on a shaft. The shaft is rotated by a drive mechanism, such as an electric motor. Gears are secured to the shaft by a collar set screw, keys, a dowel pin, a taper pin, threaded bearings, housing caps, or a bolted bearing flange.

Most shafts transmit power and must be sufficiently strong and rigid to avoid interfering with bearing and gear operation. Figure 19.16 shows a gearing assembly in which a helical gear on one shaft is being used to turn a mating helical gear on a parallel shaft. The shafts are held in place by bearings at both ends. Each shaft has a single-row ball bearing at one end and a double-row ball bearing at the other end. Double-row ball bearings carry a greater load than single-row ball bearings. The two gears are of different sizes; therefore, they provide reduced or increased shaft speed, depending on which shaft is the drive shaft and which the driven shaft.

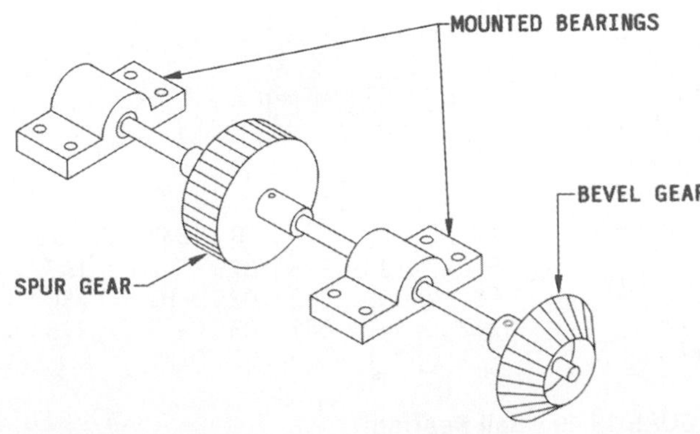

FIGURE 19.36 Shaft, Bearings, and Gears

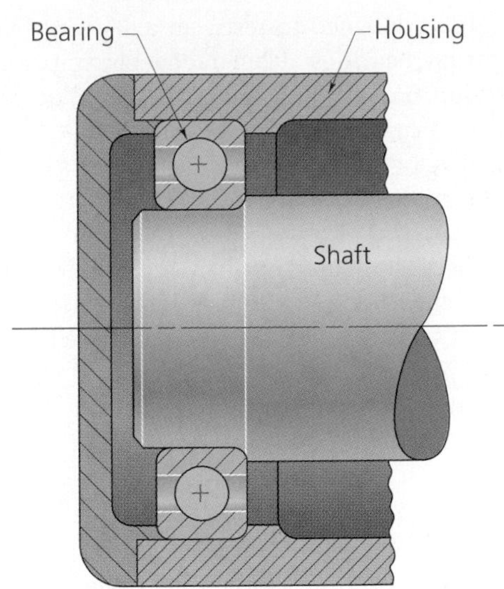

FIGURE 19.37 Bearing, Shaft, and Housing

19.12 BEARINGS

Bearings (Fig. 19.38) are designed to take radial loads, axial loads, or a combination of the two. Bearings designed to resist a load perpendicular to the axis of the shaft are **radial**

FIGURE 19.38 Bearings and Housings

bearings. Those designed to resist an axial load (along the axis) are **thrust bearings**. Plain radial bearings are sometimes called **journal bearings** (bushing type). The portion of a shaft that is in contact with the bearing is called a **journal**. Figure 19.39 shows the difference between axial (thrust) load and radial load. Bearings are manufactured from a variety of metals and plastics.

Bearing selection is based on shaft size, application, speed of rotation, required design life, load requirements, physical geometry, cost, and mounting requirements. When specifying bearings, you must consider the method of retaining the bearings, lubrication requirements, and sealing of the housing and the bearing. Shaft tolerance and diameter, shaft shoulder diameter, and the housing's internal bore and tolerance are also important. Many types of bearings are on the market, and they can be divided into two categories: **plain bearings** and **rolling contact bearings.**

19.12.1 Plain Bearings

When two mechanical members rest on one another and move in relation to one another, they create a *bearing surface.* In general, bearings are separate mechanical devices that reduce friction between moving parts. The two basic types of **plain bearings** are those in which the parts in contact slide and those in which the members revolve. Since the surfaces of each part or member make contact, bearings that do not incorporate some form of roller or ball are plain surface bearings.

Bearings that provide sliding contact between mating surfaces fall into three general classes: **radial bearings,** which support rotating shafts or journals; **thrust bearings** which support axial loads on rotating members; and **guide (slipper) bearings,** which guide moving parts along a straight line.

Radial sliding bearings, more commonly called **sleeve bearings,** may be of several types, the most common being the plain full journal bearing, which has 360° contact with its mating journal, and the partial journal bearing, which has less than 180° contact. Plain bearings look like bushings and, in many cases, what is referred to as a bushing is actually a plain bearing. Since the bearings in Figure 19.39 (drawn sectioned) do not have balls or rollers, they would be considered plain bearings. Plain bearings are manufactured both with and without flanges.

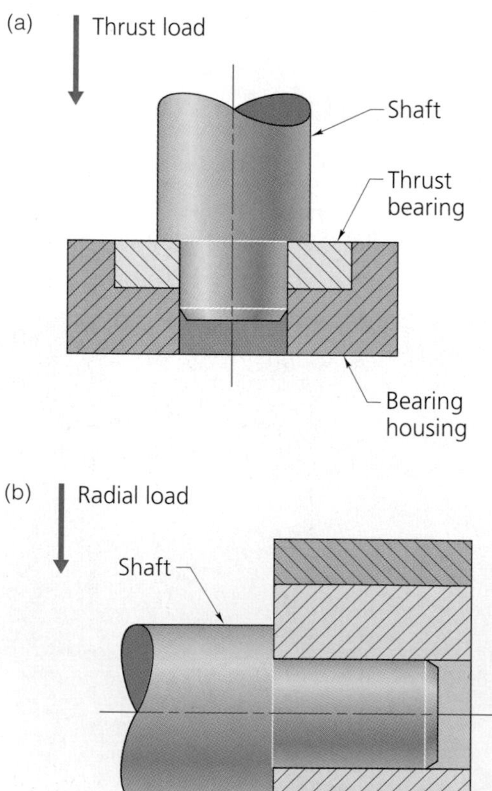

FIGURE 19.39 **Bearing Loading**

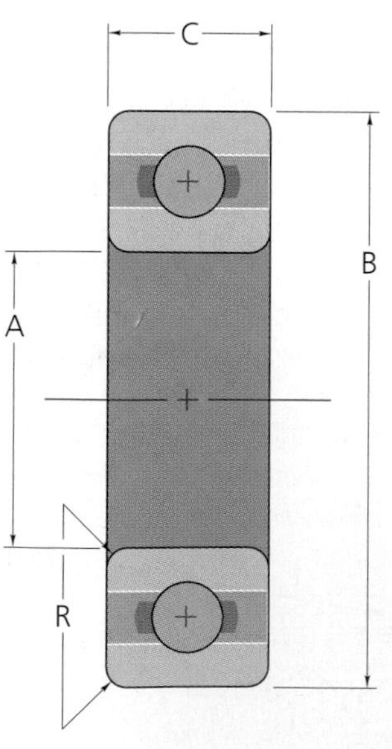

Dimensions	A	B	C	R	Balls	Ball dia.
	.500	1.125	.375	.025	7	.187
	1.000	2.000	.562	.035	10	.250
	1.312	2.562	.687	.035	9	.375

FIGURE 19.40 **Ball Bearing**

FIGURE 19.41 Roller Bearings

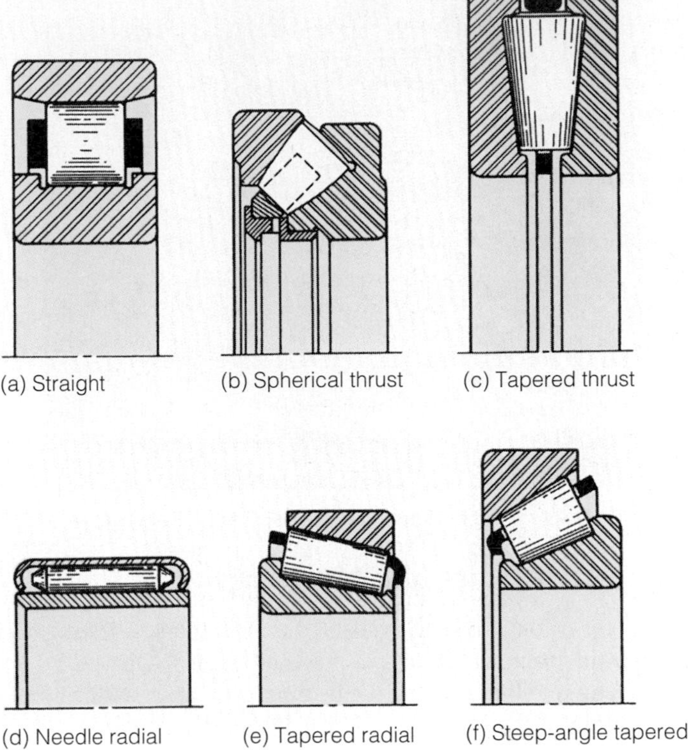

19.12.2 Rolling-Contact Bearings

Rolling-contact bearings substitute a rolling element, a ball (Fig. 19.40), or a roller for a hydrodynamic or hydrostatic fluid film to carry an impressed load without wear and with reduced friction. Because of their greatly reduced starting friction compared to the conventional journal bearing, they have acquired the common designation of *antifriction bearings*. The balls of a rolling ball bearing can be any size from 0.05 to 320 mm and can be manufactured from a wide variety of metals and plastics.

The most common antifriction bearing application is the deep-groove **ball bearing** (Fig. 19.40) with a ribbon-type separator in which sealed-grease lubrication helps to support a shaft with radial and thrust loads in rotating equipment. The two basic types of rolling bearings are those that use a **ball** as the rolling element and those that use a **roller.** Rollers may be either cylindrical, tapered, spherical, or needle shaped (Fig. 19.41). The internal construction of a typical tapered roller bearing is illustrated in Figure 19.42.

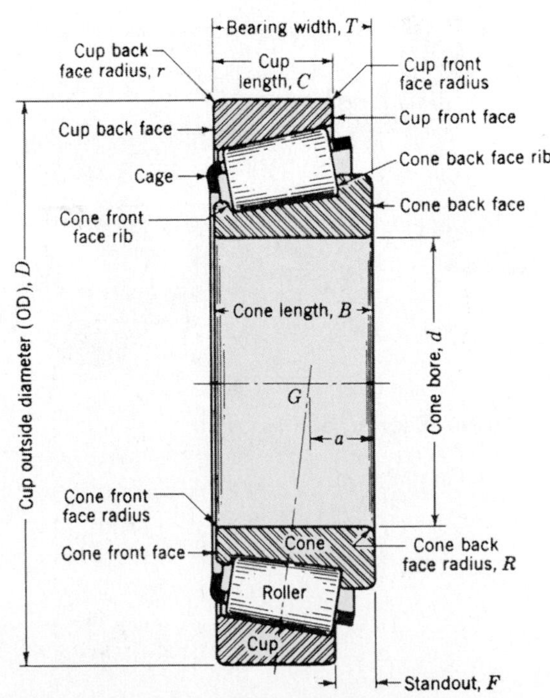

FIGURE 19.42 Tapered Roller Bearing

19.12.3 Thrust Bearings

Thrust bearings, as the name implies, either absorb axial shaft loads or position vertical shafts. Thrust bearings are designed to take thrust loads either alone or, in some cases, in combination with radial loads. Thrust bearings (Fig. 19.43) have been manufactured in sizes up to 8 m in diameter.

FIGURE 19.43 Large-Diameter Thrust Roller Bearing

19.12.4 Housings and Mountings

A number of methods are available to ensure that a bearing remains in place within a housing (Fig. 19.44). One common technique for retaining the bearing is to press or shrink the bearing in the housing with a light interference fit.

In applications where lubricants or process fluids are utilized in operation, provision must be made to prevent leakage. This is accomplished with a seal. All seals perform two functions: preventing the escape of fluid, and preventing the introduction of foreign matter.

You May Complete Exercise 19.5 at This Time

FIGURE 19.44 Bearing and Housing

QUIZ

True or False

1. The shaft relationship for mating spur gears is for them always to be perpendicular to one another.
2. A journal is that portion of a bearing that touches the balls or rollers.
3. The center distance for an internal spur gear (ring spur gear) and a pinion is closer than for external gears.
4. All needle bearings provide sealed housings.
5. Gear teeth are seldom drawn on the gear detail unless the gear is a special order.
6. Some thrust bearings can carry a radial load.
7. A pressure angle of 20° has a higher load-carrying capacity than one of $14\frac{1}{2}°$.
8. Thrust bearings are limited to smaller sizes (.5 in. to 6.00 in. diameter) and are found on high-speed machinery.

Fill in the Blanks

9. __________ bearings are the most common type of bearing found in industry.
10. A __________ is a straight machine element that has teeth cut into its surface that engage with a __________ gear to produce linear movement.
11. __________ gears connect parallel shafts, __________ gears connect shafts whose axes intersect, and __________ gears connect shafts whose axes are not parallel and do not intersect.
12. __________ are used to support and align.
13. A __________ gear is the same as a spur gear, but is usually smaller and has less __________ .
14. A __________ is designed to transmit power and is under __________ stress.
15. __________ are used to secure bearings.

Answer the Following

16. Describe the difference between a thrust bearing and a radial bearing.
17. What information is needed on a bevel gear drawing in addition to the graphical representation?
18. How are gears attached to shafts?
19. Why do plain bearings require special lubrication?
20. What are the three classes of bearings that provide sliding contact?
21. How do worm screws and worm gears work, and what type of motion is transmitted during operation?
22. What are the types of roller bearings?
23. Describe four common gear types.

EXERCISES

Exercises may be assigned as sketching, instrument, or CAD projects. Transfer the given information to an "A"-size sheet of .25 in. grid paper. Complete all views, and solve for proper visibility, including centerlines, object lines, and hidden lines. Exercises that are not assigned by the instructor can be sketched in the text to provide practice and to enhance understanding of the preceding material.

After Reading the Chapter Through Section 19.14.1 You May Complete the Following Four Exercises

Exercise 19.1 Draw a standard spur gear. Show three teeth. The cast-iron spur gear has a pressure angle of 20°, 48 teeth, 6.000 pitch diameter, 1.00 bore diameter, 2.00 hub diameter (1.00 hub projection), 8 diametral pitch, with a gear face width of 1.50 and a total width of 2.50. Design the gear to have a standard keyseat per the shaft diameter (see Chapter 17). The gear hub is to have a set screw at 90° to the keyseat. Determine the set screw size based on the shaft diameter (see Chapter 18).

Exercise 19.2 Draw the spur gear and rack. Show three teeth on the rack and the gear. Design the gear's keyseat and set screw per Exercise 19.1. The steel rack has the following specifications: 20° pressure angle, 5 diametral pitch, 1.500 overall thickness, 1.300 pitch line to back, 2.500 face width. The steel gear has the following specifications: 20° pressure angle, 5 diametral pitch, 1.125 shaft bore diameter, 20 teeth, .750 hub projection, 2.500 face width, 3.25 total width, and a 3.00 hub diameter.

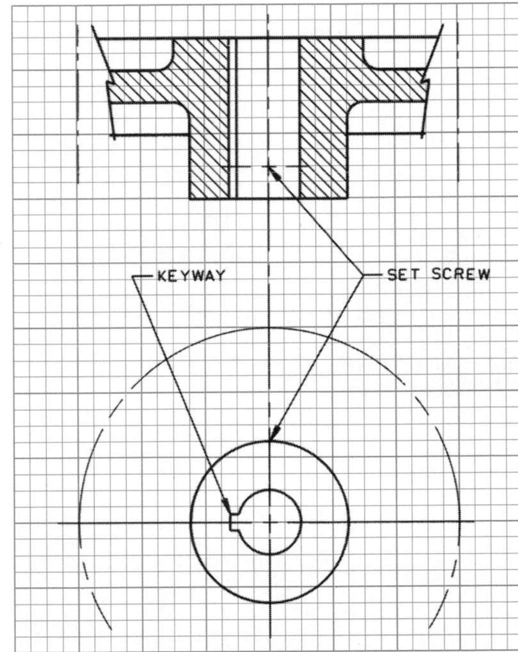

EXERCISE 19.1

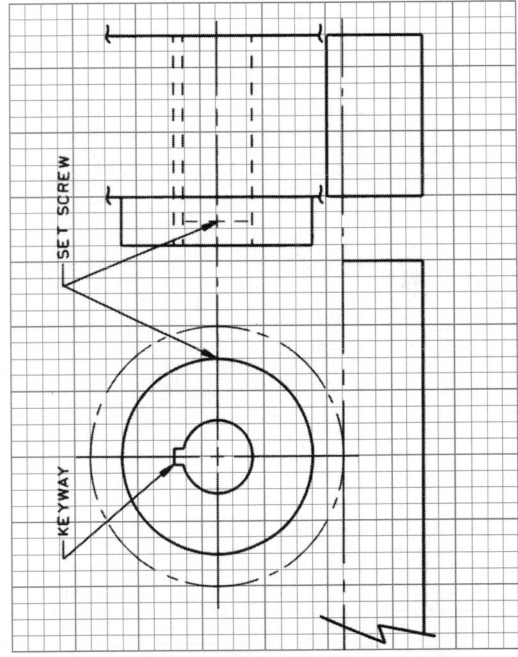

EXERCISE 19.2

Exercise 19.3 Design and draw bevel gears with the following specifications:

Gear A		Gear B
6	Diametral pitch	6
18	Teeth	36
2:1	Ratio	2:1
1.06	Face width	1.25
3.500	Mounting distance	4.750
2.25	Gear width	2.75
2.50	Hub diameter	3.25
6.00	Pitch diameter	3.00
1.125	Hub bore diameter	1.125
Calculate	Keyseat	Calculate
Calculate	Set screw	Calculate

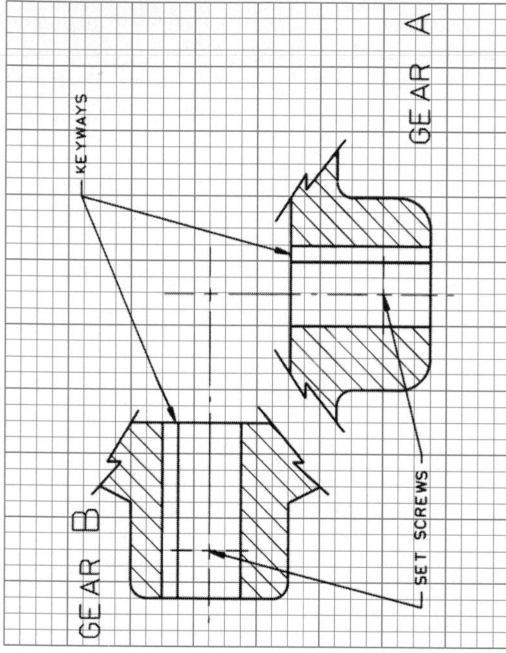

EXERCISE 19.3

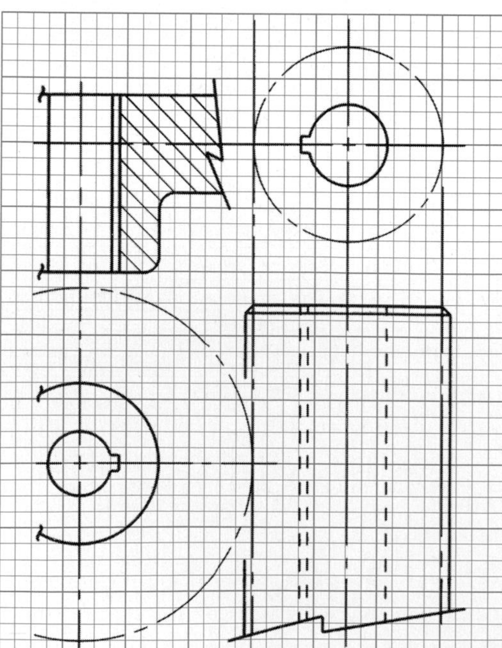
EXERCISE 19.4

Exercise 19.4 Design and draw the worm and the worm gear as in Figure 19.34. The worm (screw) is to have a $14\frac{1}{2}°$ pressure angle, 4 diametral pitch, 3.500 face width, .7854 lead, 4.76° lead angle, 1.250 bore shaft diameter, 3.000 pitch diameter. Design the keyseat per the shaft size. The worm gear is to have a $14\frac{1}{2}°$ pressure angle, 4 diametral pitch, 20 teeth, 5.000 pitch diameter, 1.00 diameter bore for a shaft, 2.50 hub diameter, 1.250 hub projection, and a face width of 1.500. Design an appropriate-size keyseat for the shaft

After Reading the Chapter Through Section 19.12.4 You May Complete the Following Exercise

Exercise 19.5 Using the bearing dimensions from Figure 19.40, design and draw a bearing housing to retain the bearings and support the stepped shaft.

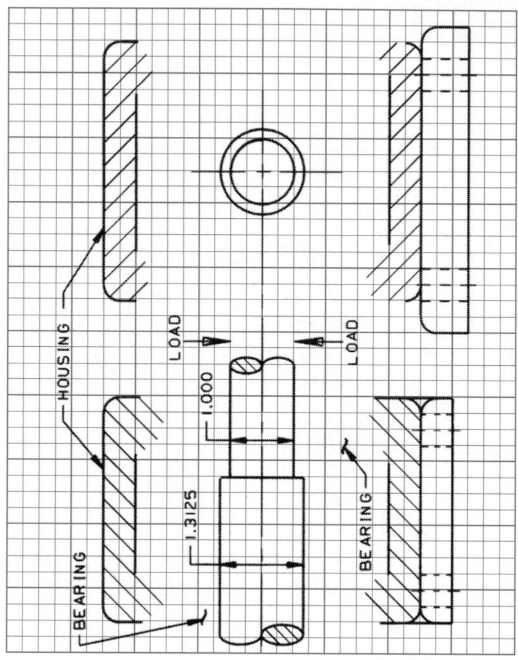

EXERCISE 19.5

PROBLEMS

For gear problems completed manually, show only one tooth. For projects drawn on a CAD system, show all teeth.

Problem 19.1 Redraw the spur gear detail in Figure 19.12.

Problem 19.2 Draw the spur rack detail shown in Figure 19.15.

Problem 19.3 Detail the rack shown in Figure 19.18.

Problem 19.4 Draw the worm spline detail provided in Figure 19.19.

Problem 19.5 Detail each of the spur gears in Figure 19.26.

Problem 19.6 Redraw the worm and worm gear shown in Figure 19.34. Split the two into separate details and also draw an assembly. Use Figure 19.33 as a guide for dimensioning.

Problem 19.7 Design a spur gear rack and mating gear with the following specifications. Compute the required specifications for the rack and gear. Show all information data blocks on the drawing. Draw an assembly of the gear and rack using appropriate ANSI dimensioning.

1. **Gear**—6 in. pitch diameter

   20° pressure angle (20° involute teeth)
   2.00 in. face width
   Keyseat in hub
   1.25 diameter shaft
   Spoked gear blank

2. **Rack**—will move laterally 5 in.

Problem 19.8 Using the same format as in Problem 19.7, complete a spur gear and rack assembly with 20° involute teeth, gear face width of .75 in., solid gear blank, shaft diameter of 2.00 in., 7 in. pitch diameter for the gear, 56 teeth, and diametral pitch of 8. The rack will move 8 in. laterally.

Problem 19.9 Design spur gears with the following specifications:

Gear A—Spur Gear
- 44 teeth
- 20° full-depth involute teeth
- Diametral pitch of 12
- Spoke gear blank
- 1.00 face width
- Keyseat in hub
- 2.00 diameter shaft

Gear B—Spur Gear
- 18 teeth
- 20° full-depth involute teeth
- Diametral pitch of 8
- Webbed hub with lightning holes
- .750 face width
- Keyseat in hub
- 1.00 diameter of shaft

Gear C—Internal Ring Gear
- 32 teeth
- $14\frac{1}{2}$° teeth
- 32 diametral pitch
- 2.00 pitch diameter
- 2.75 OD
- 1.96 ID
- .315 face width

Problem 19.10 Design bevel gears with the following specifications. Show all dimensions. Design the appropriate keyseat for each gear.

	Gear A	*Gear B*	*Gear C*	*Gear D*
Teeth	20	45	19	20
Pitch diameter	2.000	7.500	4.000	50 mm
Diametral pitch	10	6	4	1
Face	.570	1.070	1.400	18 mm
Bore	.750	1.125	1.125	30 mm
Hub diameter	1.750	3.250	3.250	40 mm
Hub projection	1.000	1.250	1.875	24 mm
Hub width	1.500	2.125	3.500	30 mm

Problem 19.11 Design mating miter gears with the following specifications. Show all dimensions. Design the appropriate keyseat for each gear.

	Set A	*Set B*	*Set C*
Teeth	36	32	30
Pitch diameter	1.500	2.000	2.500
Diametral pitch	24	19	12
Face	.220	.400	.540
Bore	.3125	.500	.625
Hub diameter	.6875	1.250	1.625
Hub projection	.3125	.375	.843
Hub width	.609	.875	.484
Mounting distance	1.188	1.562	2.312

Problem 19.12 Design and detail a worm gear set with the following specifications: *worm*—1.250 pitch diameter, diametral pitch of 10, $14\frac{1}{2}$° pressure angle; *worm gear*—40 teeth, .750 face width.

Problem 19.13 Design and detail a worm gear set with the following specifications: *worm*—1.000 pitch diameter, diametral pitch of 12, $14\frac{1}{2}$° thread; *worm gear*—30 teeth, .625 face width, .750 bore, 2.50 pitch diameter.

Problem 19.14 Design and detail a helical gear with the following specifications: normal diametral pitch = 12, 20° pressure angle, 48 teeth, face width = 1.75, helix angle = 45°.

Problem 19.15 Design and lay out a shaft-and-bearing assembly capable of supporting any of the gear sets described in Problems 19.7, 19.8, 19.11, or 19.12. Use standard mounted bearings or design a housing for the bearings.

CAMS

Chapter 20

LEARNING OBJECTIVES

Upon completion of this chapter you will be able to:

1. Recognize cam types and motions.
2. Demonstrate an understanding of cam drawing practices.
3. Communicate cam data by means of ANSI-standard dimensioning and notation.
4. Demonstrate familiarity with cam follower functions and terminology.
5. Identify cam motions, and describe them through displacement diagrams.
6. Explore the use of CAD in cam design.

20.1 INTRODUCTION

Cams (Fig. 20.1) are machine elements designed to transmit or change motion by direct rolling or sliding contact with another part, called a **follower.** Cams can translate rotary motion into rotary or linear motion, and linear motion into rotary or linear motion. Cams are either radial or cylindrical. **Radial cams** move followers perpendicular to the cam shaft; **cylindrical cams** move followers parallel to the shaft.

Most cams are designed to transform rotary motion into **reciprocating** motion. An example is the automobile engine cam shaft [Fig. 20.2(a)], which is called a *lobe cam* and which can be seen in the close-up in Figure 20.2(b). The cam raises and lowers the valve lifters of the motor. The movement of the cam imparts motion to the follower. Cams are designed to accomplish a wide variety of motion changes and are manufactured in an almost unlimited number of configurations (Fig. 20.3). A detail of a cam is provided in Figure 20.4.

For most cams, the follower moves perpendicular to the axis about which the cam is rotating. This type of cam has a **translating follower**, which might be a roller, though it is

FIGURE 20.1 Computer-Aided Cam Design

(a) Automobile engine crank shaft

(b) Lobe cam on an engine crank shaft

FIGURE 20.2 Crank Shaft

normally a **flat plate cam.** A cam that moves the follower axially, or parallel to the axis of the cam, is called a **cylindrical cam** or **drum cam.** Follower systems of a cam mechanism usually consist of one or more rods, gears, levers, springs, and/or other mechanical devices.

Some cams perform other types of work, such as clamping. Figure 20.5 shows a standard cam-clamp assembly that can be ordered off the shelf from a tooling fixture company (Carr Lane) in this instance. The cam design on the end of the clamp allows the machinist to secure and release quickly and easily a workpiece requiring machining.

Cams are sometimes mounted on shafts with keys (Fig. 20.6). In some cases, the drive mechanism employs a gear.

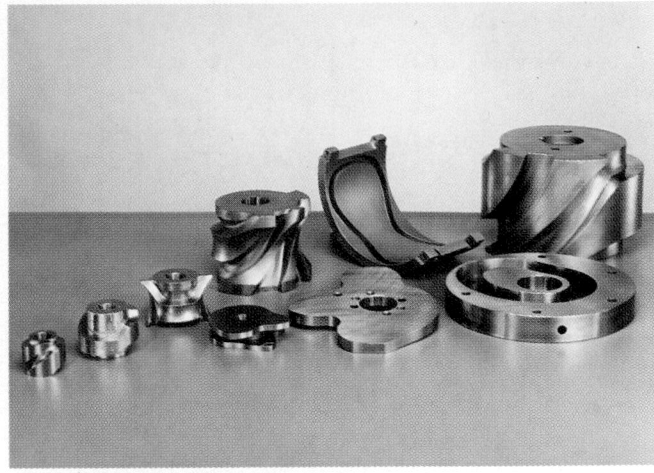

FIGURE 20.3 Cam Styles

20.1.1 Cam Terminology

The following terms are used when describing cams (Fig. 20.7).

Base circle A circle drawn with the center line of the shaft as its center and a radius equal to the distance to the center of the follower wheel when it is in its lowest position.

Cam profile The cam surface edge on which the follower moves.

Displacement diagram A curve that illustrates the movement of a cam. The diagram is drawn by laying out a stretch-out line equal to the circumference of the working circle. The line is divided into even units, based on angular divisions on the cam, and then plotted as a series of points corresponding to the cam's outline.

Dwell When a cam's follower rests or stops movement. A dwell is designed into the cam profile by allowing the cam outline to be a constant distance from its center for a period of time.

Follower A machine element that moves with reciprocating motion by following the cam as it rotates. Followers usually move up and down, although followers on drum cams move back and forth.

Harmonic motion A type of motion that produces a smooth start and stop with nonuniform speed.

Height The total vertical rise of the follower during operation of the cam. Its value is established by subtracting the base circle from the working circle.

Pitch curve (pitch line) A curve generated by the motion of the follower about the cam. The distance between the shaft center and each position of the follower's center generates the pitch curve as it moves about the cam profile.

Reciprocating motion Linear movement of the follower, either back and forth or up and down, that is caused by the rotary movement of the shaft-and-cam assembly. A follower can also oscillate in rotation.

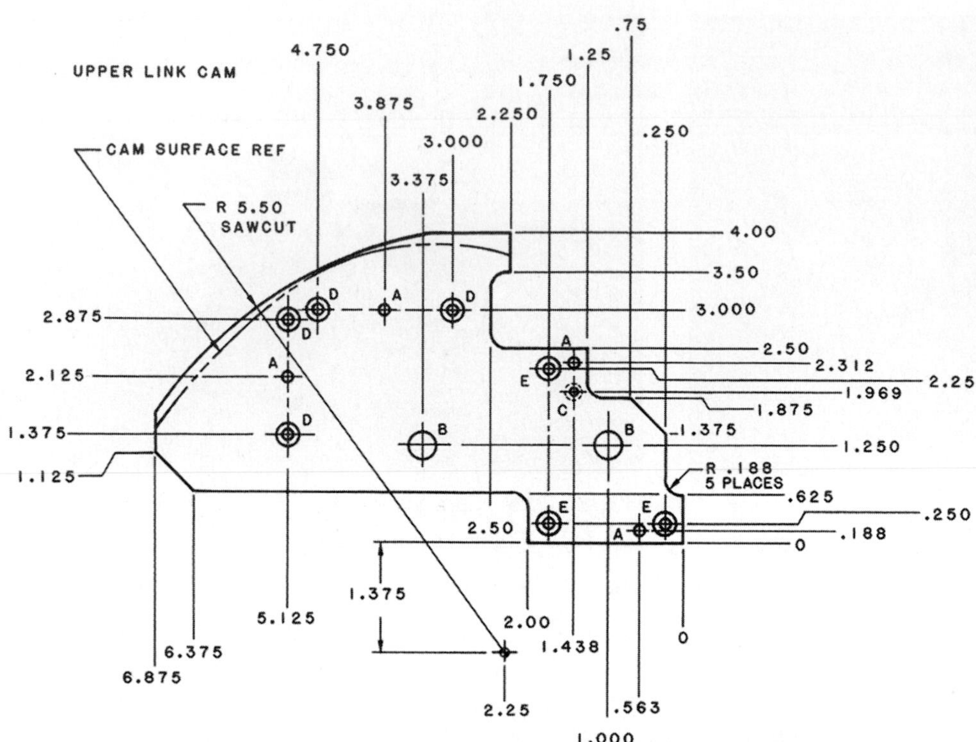

.25 ALY ALUM ANODIZE BLACK

HOLE	DESCRIPTION	QTY
A	Ø .125 THRU	4
B	Ø .375 THRU	2
C	8-32 UNC-2B	1
D	Ø .149 Ø .266 CBORE X .138 DP	4
E	Ø .171 Ø .313 CBORE X .164 DP	3

FIGURE 20.4 Cam Detail

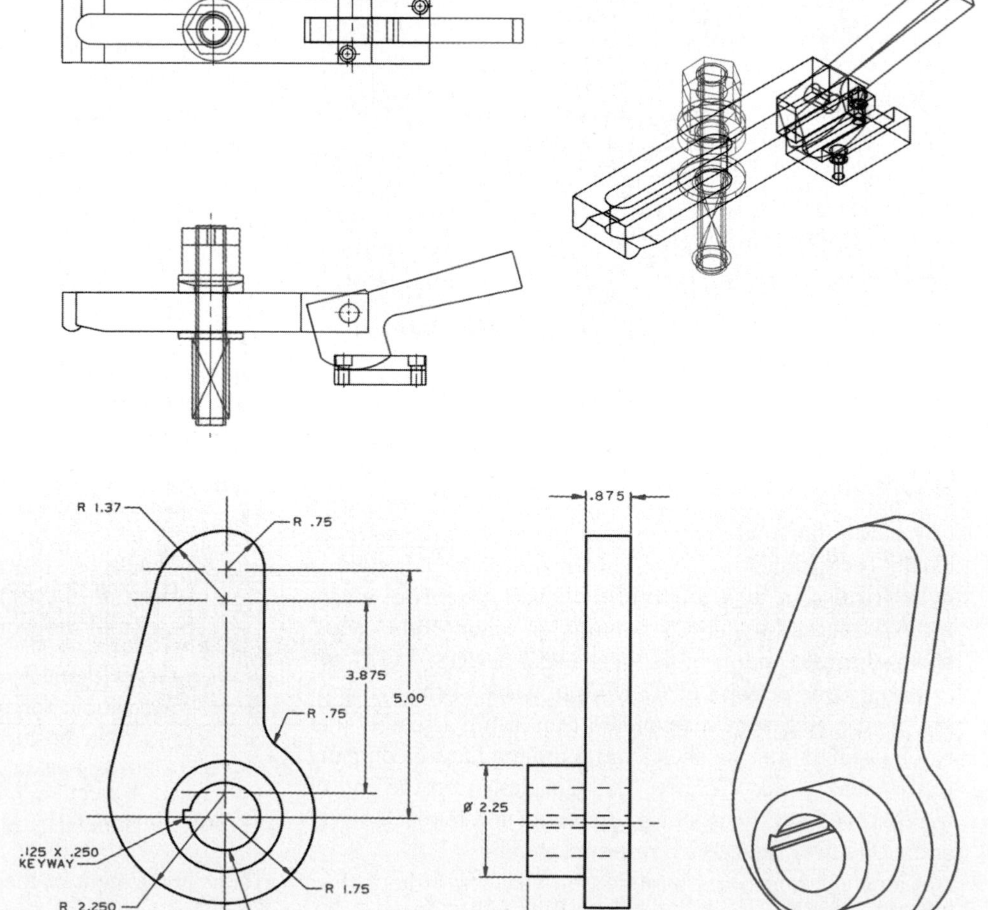

FIGURE 20.5 Carr Lane Cam-Clamp Assembly

FIGURE 20.6 Cam

FIGURE 20.7 Cam Terminology

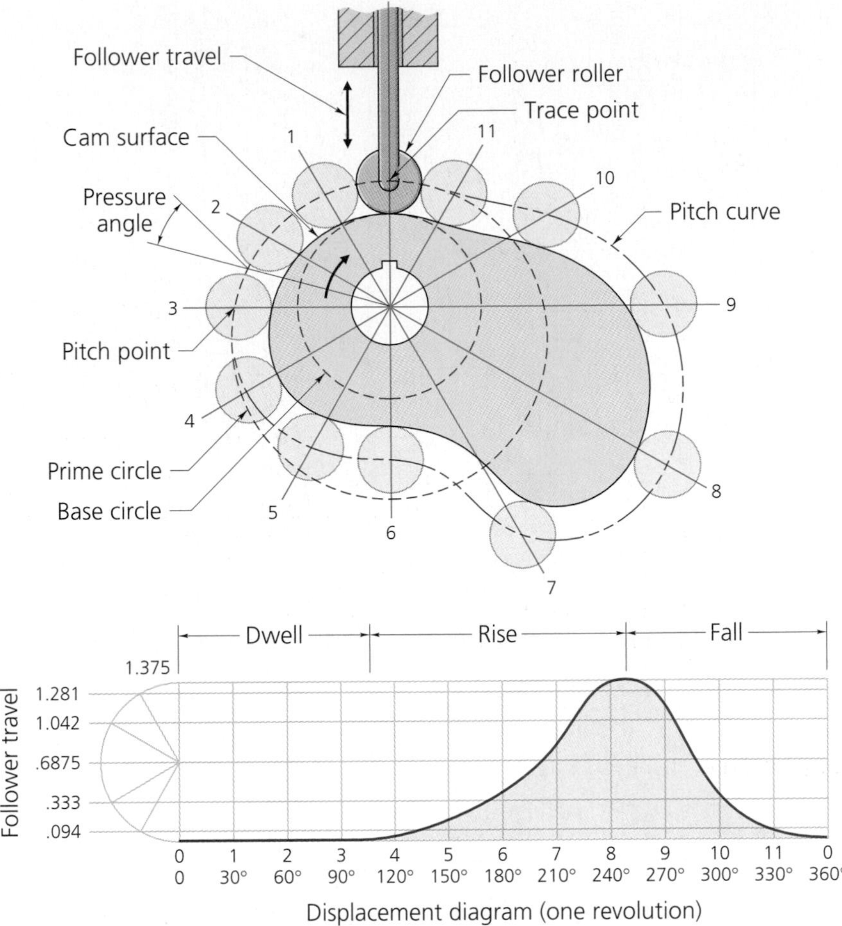

Rise and fall Movement of the cam through one cycle.

Roller A cylindrical element mounted at the end of a follower to follow the cam outline.

Time interval The time needed to move the follower from its lowest to its highest position.

Transition point The position where the acceleration changes from plus to minus and the follower reverses directions.

Uniform acceleration Change in speed that is constant throughout the cam movement.

Uniform velocity The constant speed at which a cam follower might rise and fall.

Working circle A circle with the center of the shaft as its center and a radius equal to the distance to the center of the follower wheel when it is in its highest position. The working circle is not normally shown on the cam drawing. The distance between the base circle and the working circle is equal to the follower displacement (rise, or height).

20.1.2 Classes of Cams

Cams can usually be divided into two classes: **uniform motion cams** and **accelerated motion cams.** The uniform motion cam moves the follower at the same speed from the beginning to the end of the stroke. Because the movement is started and stopped abruptly, a shock can occur. If the movement is rapid, there is a significant shock at the beginning and at the end of the stroke. Therefore, in high-speed machinery, cams must be designed so that sudden shocks are avoided throughout the motion of the follower. The various cam motions can be described in diagrams (Fig. 20.8):

Uniform motion Equal distances are traveled in equal intervals of time [Fig. 20.8(a)].

Uniform motion modified A radius is introduced at the beginning and the end to smooth the starting and stopping [Fig. 20.8(b)].

Parabolic motion (a) The displacement curve is created through parabolic construction [Fig. 20.8(c)]. (b) The displacement curve is constructed using the uniformly accelerated and retarded method, in which the ratio of increase and decrease is 1:3:5:5:3:1 [Fig. 20.8(d)].

Harmonic motion The distances moved vertically are obtained by projecting from the equally divided semicircle; **gravity motion** is the motion of a falling body [Fig. 20.8(e)].

Cycloidal motion The displacement curve is generated from a cycloid that is the locus of a point on a circle rolling on a straight line [Figure 20.8(f)].

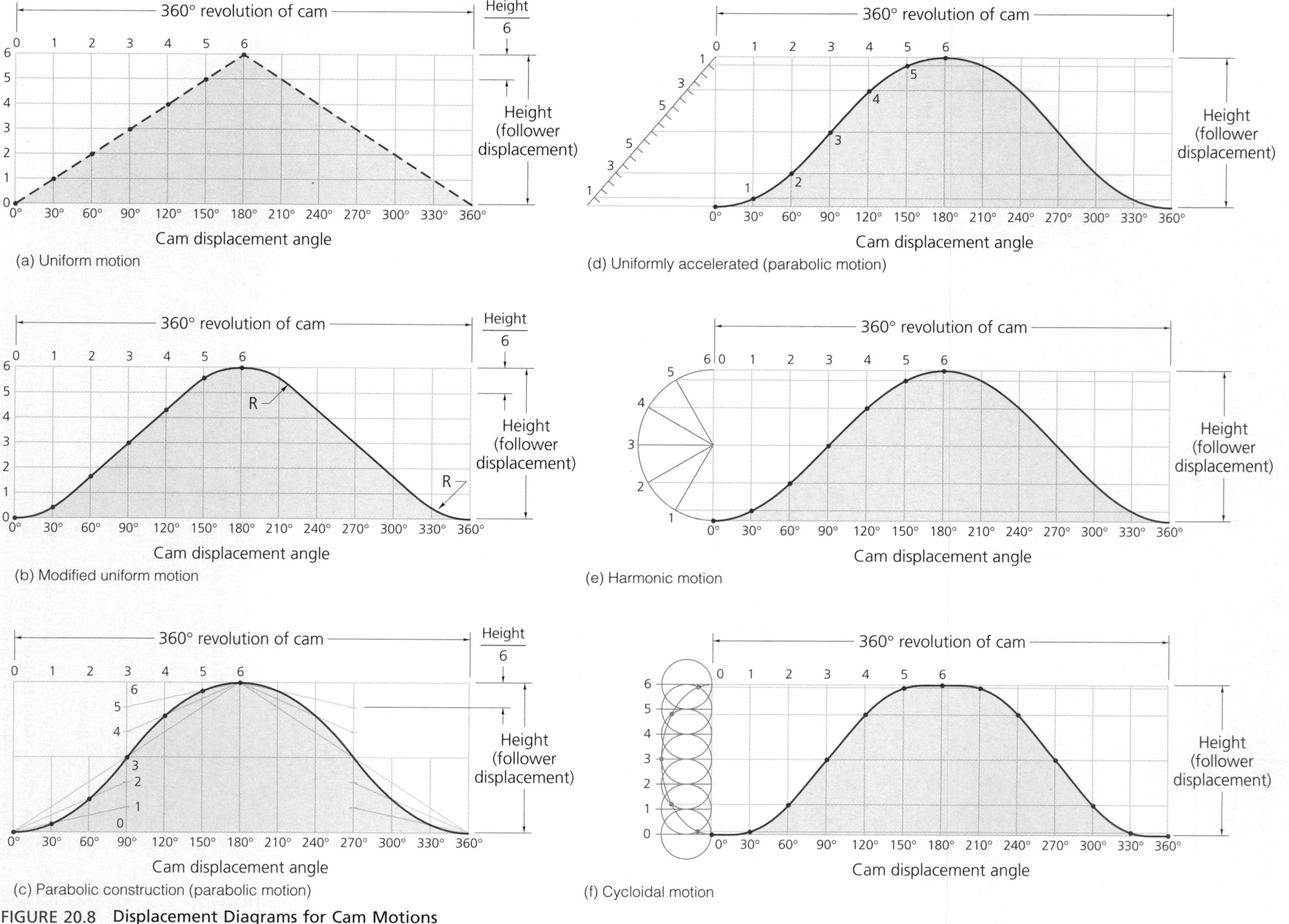

FIGURE 20.8 **Displacement Diagrams for Cam Motions**

Focus On . . .

ENGINE CAMSHAFTS

In its most basic form, a camshaft would be a simple shaft with an eccentric lobe or cam on it. One cylinder of an engine would use two such simple camshafts: one for the inlet valve, the other for the exhaust valve. However, multiple-cylinder engines usually have as many cams as there are valves to be operated. For a multi-valve engine, all the cams are placed at intervals on one shaft (the camshaft). On most engines, the camshaft is directly above the crankshaft or is located to one side and is placed in the crankcase. In this type of design, the camshaft is driven directly from the crankshaft by gears or by a silent chain.

Porsche Indy car racing engine in Porsche chassis.

Although the cams appear simple in shape, cam designs are actually worked out in painstaking mathematical detail and then verified by experimentation in the laboratory. If the shape of the cam is altered by wear, then the efficiency of the engine drops dramatically. The desired smooth running of the engine is also quickly destroyed.

There is a lot more to cam design than simply opening and closing a valve. The cam is designed to lift the valve at precisely the correct position of the piston movement and keep it open long enough to obtain the most efficient filling and emptying of the cylinder. For a passenger car, the cams open the valves smoothly and gently to make for quiet operation of the engine, and the design is usually a compromise between efficiency and quiet operation. For a race car engine, however, noise is acceptable, so cams are designed for the highest possible efficiency, deliberately aiming to open the valve faster, wider, and longer and to close it more quickly. Of course, race car engines are noisy, idle roughly, and wear more quickly. A camshaft designed for a race car engine would be totally unacceptable for a family sedan. Many sports cars on the market today offer a compromise between efficiency and operating parameters.

The design of the cams on camshafts is vitally important to the basic operation of the engine and also affects how the customer perceives the smooth operation of the car.

A displacement diagram of a cam might utilize many types of motions to accomplish specific design tasks. Figure 20.9 shows a displacement diagram that has three dwells and three types of motion: modified, parabolic, and harmonic. *Modified motion* is simply a straight line that has radii introduced at each end. *Harmonic motion* is plotted by drawing a half circle and dividing it evenly, with each division corresponding to a division on the diagram (horizontally). The points are projected from the half circle to the vertical lines and connected with a smooth curve (using an irregular curve). *Parabolic motion* is plotted by proportionally dividing the vertical distance of the rise or fall using a ratio of 1:3:5:5:3:1 and projecting the points to the vertical lines, as shown.

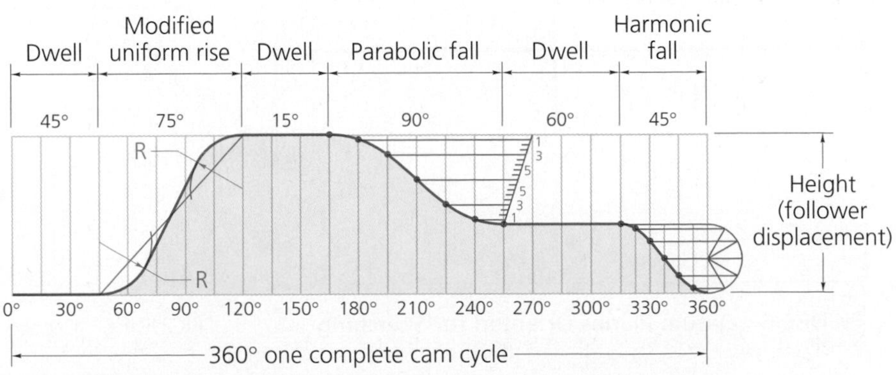

FIGURE 20.9 Cam Displacement Diagram Showing a Variety of Motions and Dwells

Applying Parametric Design . . .

SPLINE CAMS

Cams in parametric design are created by sketching a **spline** (similar to an irregular curve) feature through a series of specific points and then giving the depth of the protrusion-cam thickness. To create a spline:

- Choose **Spline** from the GEOMETRY menu.
- The SPLINE MODE menu appears with the following commands:

  Sketch Points Create a spline by picking screen points for the spline to pass through.

  Select Points Create a spline by selecting existing sketcher points. Once the point has been selected, there is no further link between the point and the spline.

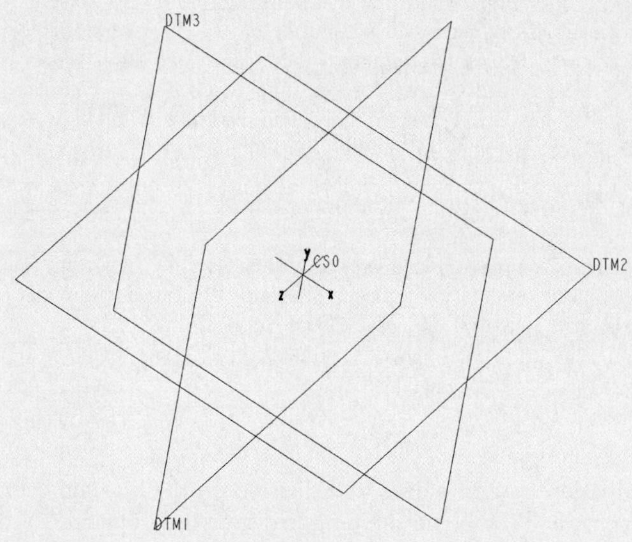

FIGURE A Default Datums

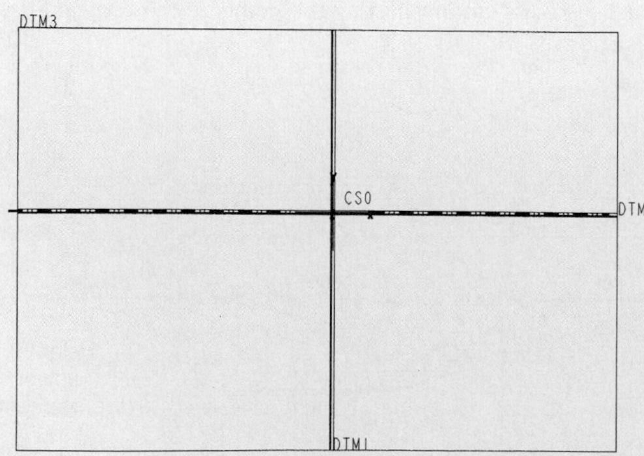

FIGURE B Datum Planes Oriented for Sketching

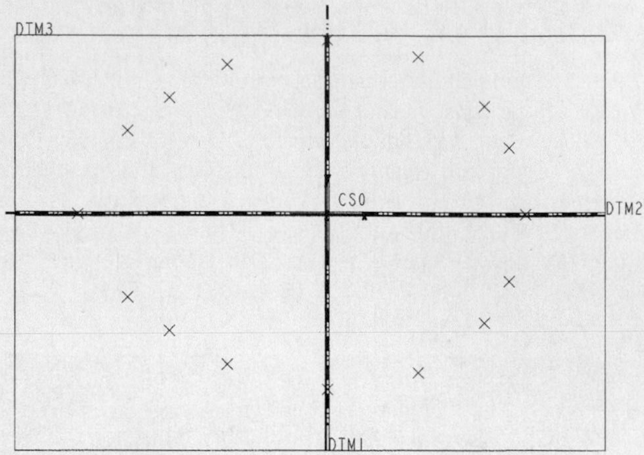

FIGURE C Sketching Points

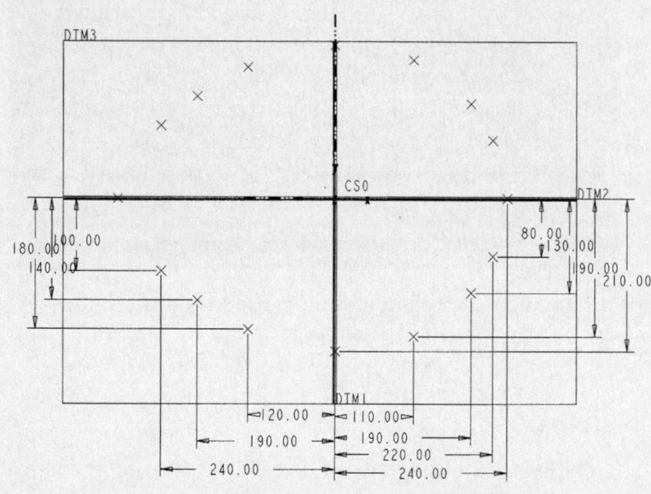

FIGURE D Dimensioning and Modifying Points

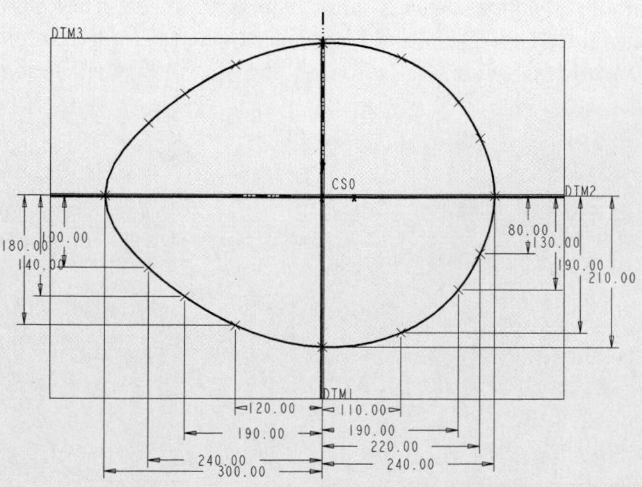

FIGURE E Create Spline Through Selected Points

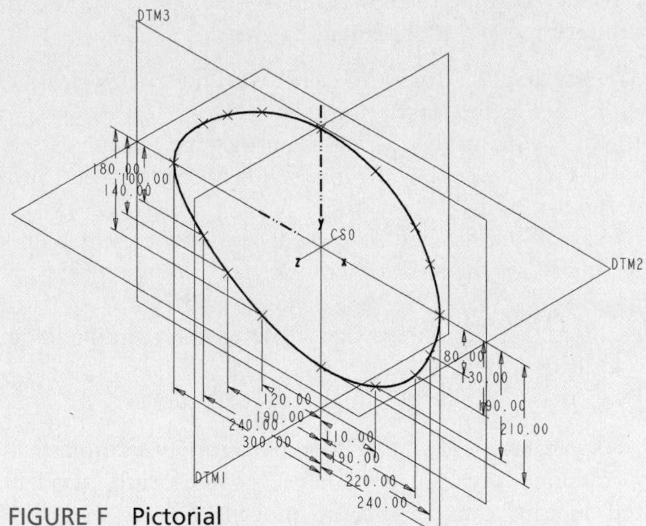

FIGURE F Pictorial Orientation of Spline and Dimensions

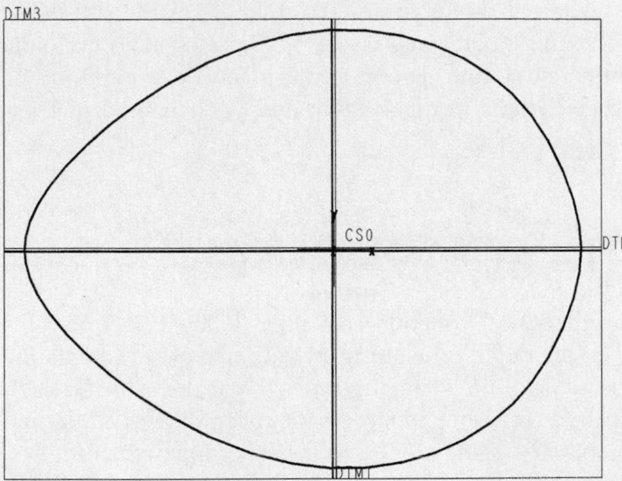

FIGURE G Completed Spline Feature

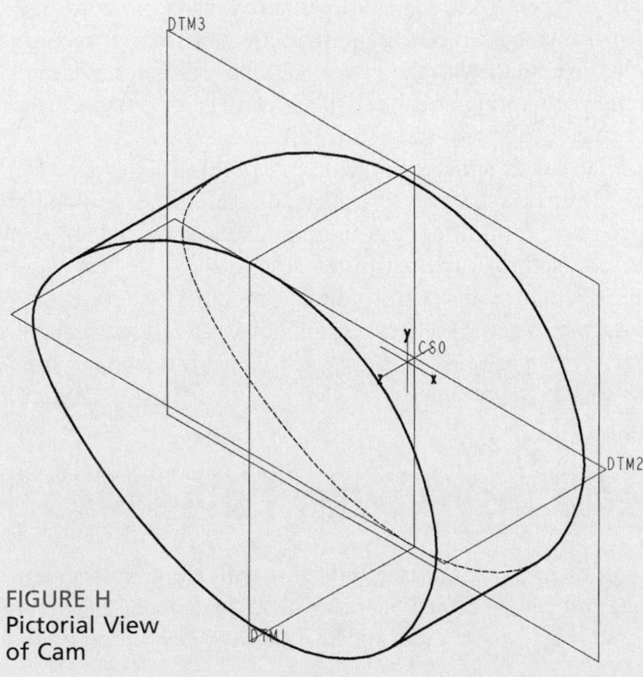

FIGURE H Pictorial View of Cam

The cam in the example shown here was created through the following commands.

1. Define a set of default planes (Fig. A).
2. Orient datum planes for sketching (Fig. B).
3. Sketch points approximately (Fig. C).
4. Dimension points and modify them to required coordinates (Fig. D).
5. Create a spline via **Select Points** (Fig. E).
6. Use point locations for dimensioning the spline (Fig. F).
7. Regenerate the part and add depth (Fig. G).
8. Orient the view to see depth (Fig. H).
9. Add the hole, and then cut the keyseat (Fig. I).
10. Display the part in a pictorial orientation (Fig. J).

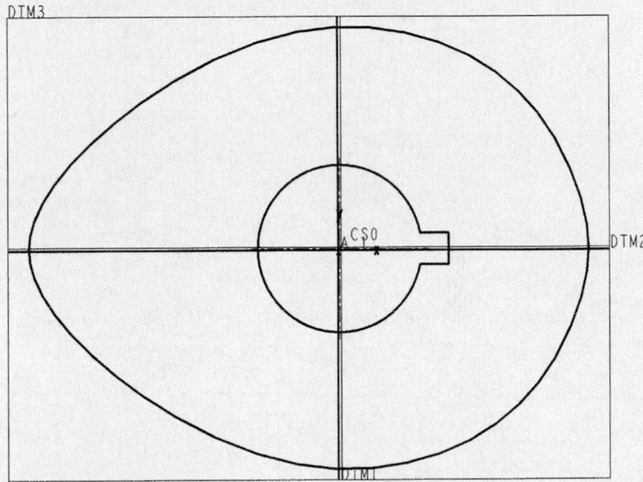

FIGURE I Hole Added to Cam Center and Keyseat Cut Through the Part

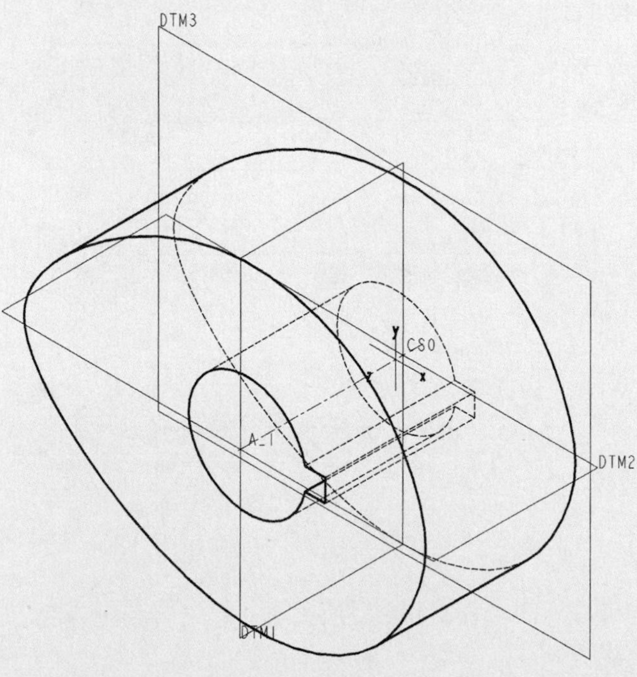

FIGURE J Pictorial View of Cam

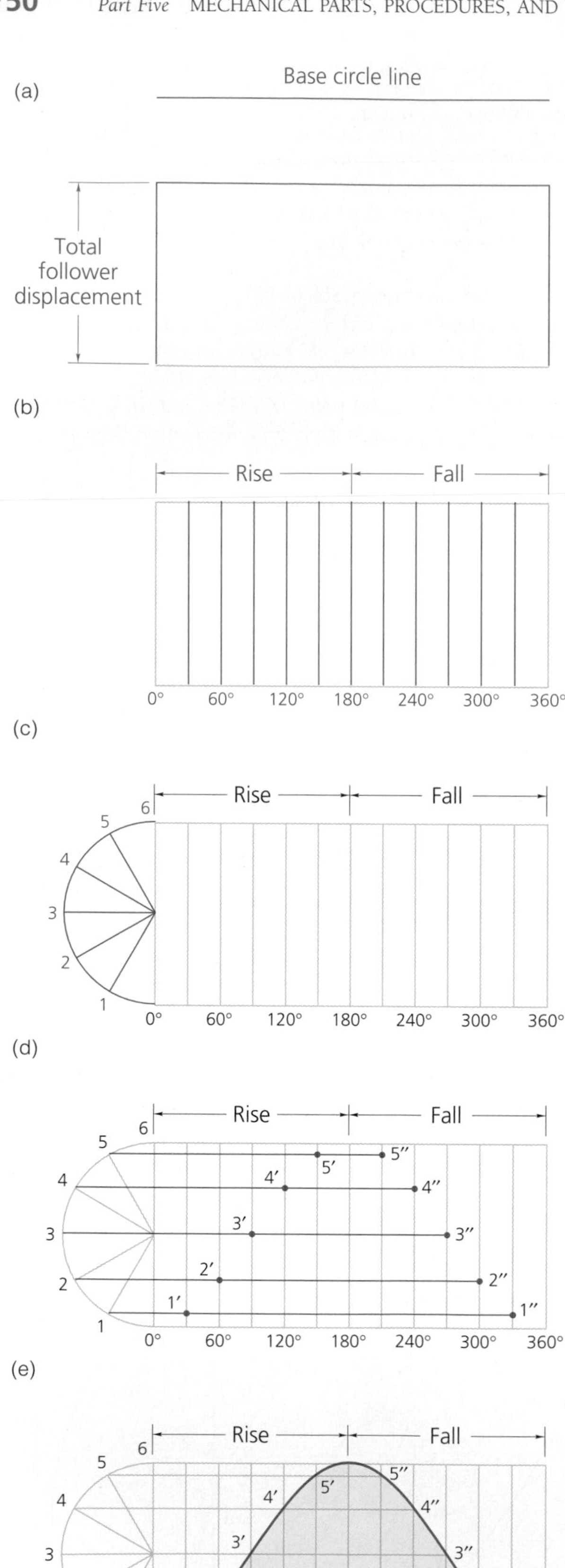

FIGURE 20.10 Constructing Displacement Diagrams

Figure 20.10 presents the step-by-step construction of a harmonic motion displacement diagram:

(a) First draw the base circle line, with the circle's circumference as the length of the layout line.
(b) The height of the displacement diagram represents the distance covered by the total follower displacement, also known as the *follower travel*.
(c) Lay off the rise and the run on the the base circle line and locate the angles there.
(d) Draw the half circle, and divide it as shown.
(e) Project points on the half circle to the corresponding "degrees" lines.
(f) Connect the points with an irregular curve.

Some cams are designed to employ **gravity motion**, that is, uniformly accelerated motion. The **uniformly accelerated motion cam** is appriate in cam designs requiring moderate speeds. However, if sudden changes in acceleration occur at the beginning, the middle, or the end of the stroke, this type of cam is not the best design. A **cycloidal motion curve cam**, since it results in low noise, produces no abrupt changes in acceleration and is often used in high-speed machinery.

20.2 CAM FOLLOWERS

The three most common cam roller followers (Fig. 20.11) are (a) the **radial translating** style, (b) the **offset translating** style, and (c) the **swinging** style. When the cam rotates, it imparts a translating motion to the roller followers in (a) and (b) and a swinging motion to the roller follower in (c).

Figure 20.12(a) shows a **closed-track single roller** cam. In (b), the roller is forced to move in a **closed-track double roller.** Open-track cams are usually smaller than closed-track cams, but, in general, springs are necessary to keep the roller in contact with the cam at all times. Closed-track cams require no spring and have the advantage of positive drive throughout the rise-and-return cycle.

Flat-faced, spherical-faced, and **pointed** followers (Fig. 20.13) are good styles for when the cam is not moving at high speeds and when heat buildup and wear of the follower are not factors in the machine's design.

As a cam moves with a rotating motion, its curved-edge surface moves the reciprocating follower as in Figure 20.14, where five positions of the roller follower are shown, from the lowest to the highest.

20.3 DISPLACEMENT DIAGRAMS

The design of a cam usually begins with the **displacement diagram.** A simplified displacement diagram is shown in Figure 20.15. One cycle means one 360° revolution of the

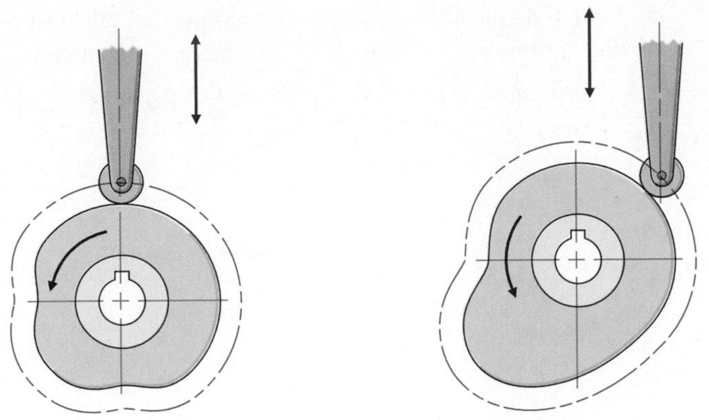

(a) Radial translating

(b) Offset translating

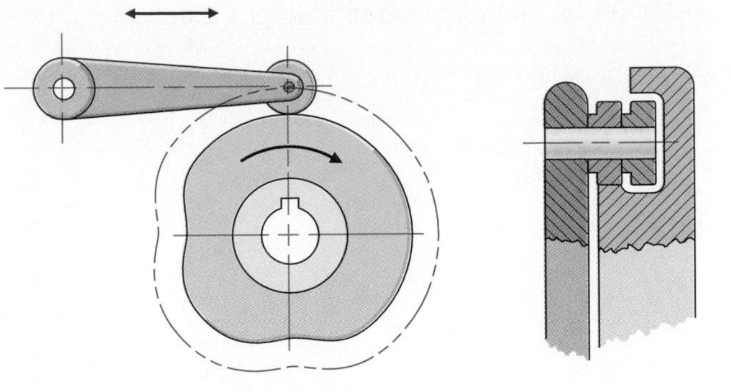

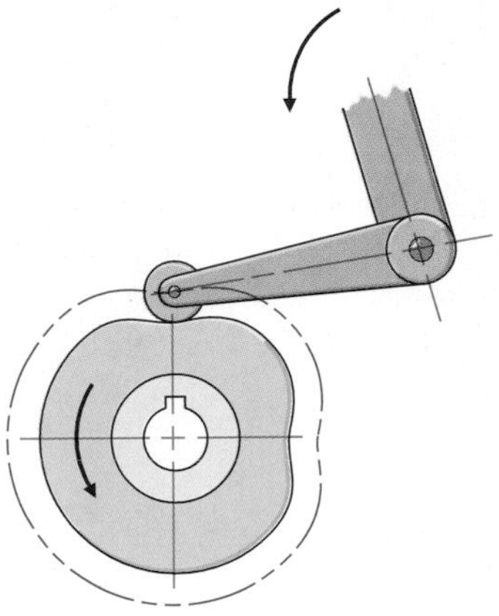

(c) Swinging

FIGURE 20.11 **Roller Follower Styles**

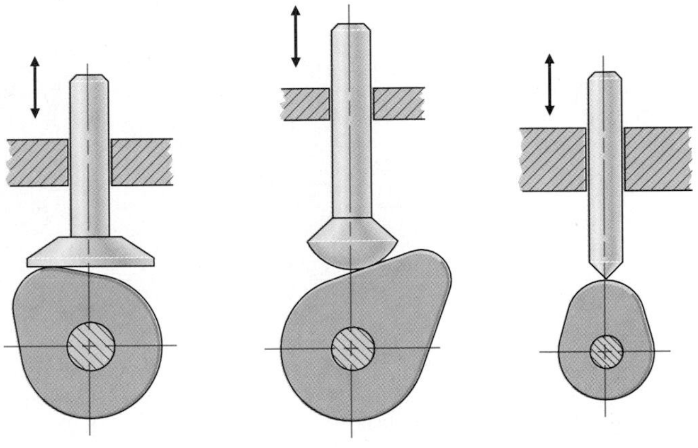

(a) With one follower

(b) With two followers

FIGURE 20.12 **Closed-Track Followers**

(a) Flat-Faced

(b) Spherical-Faced

(c) Pointed

FIGURE 20.13 **Nonrolling Cam Followers**

cam. The horizontal distances A, B, C, and D are expressed in either units of time (seconds), radians, or degrees. The vertical distance (height) represents the maximum "rise" (stroke) of the follower.

The time-displacement diagram for a cam with a radial translating roller follower is shown in Figure 20.16(a). This diagram is read from left to right, as follows: For 100° of cam shaft rotation, the follower rises (AB), dwells in its upper position for 20° (BC), returns over 180° (CD), and finally dwells in its lowest position for 60° (DE).

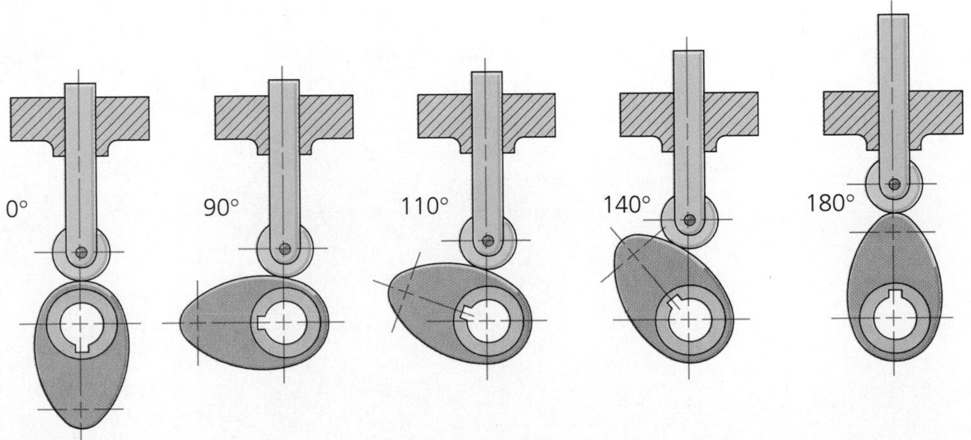

FIGURE 20.14 **Five Positions of a Lobe Cam and Roller Follower**

FIGURE 20.15 Simplified Displacement Diagram

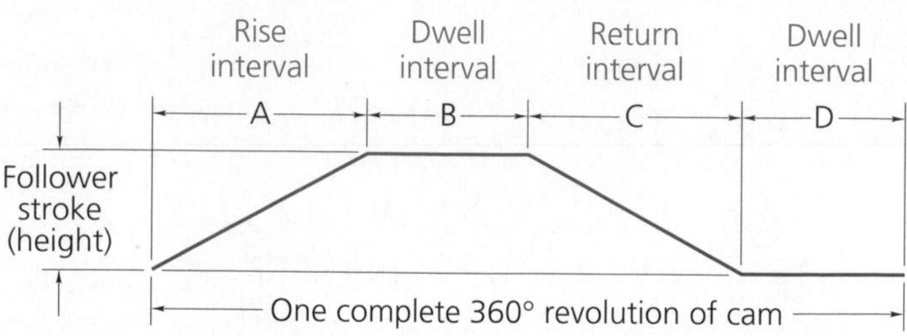

FIGURE 20.16 (a) Displacement Diagram and (b) Cam Layout

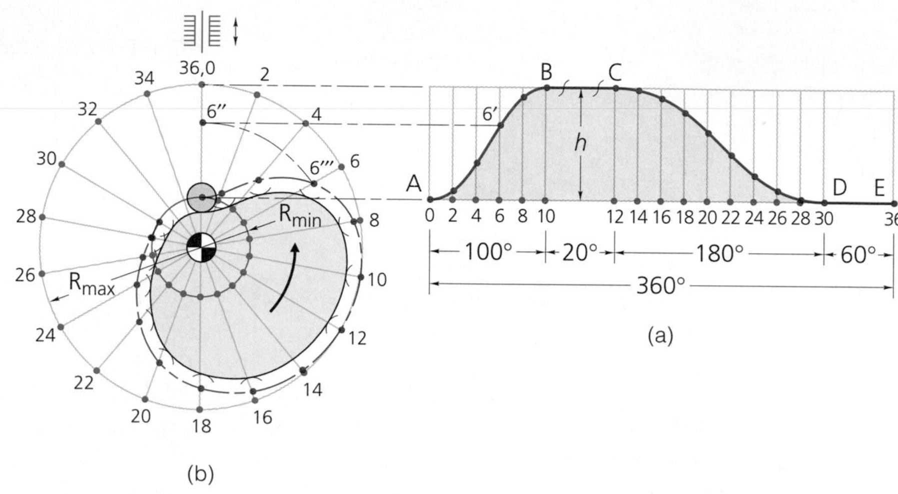

20.4 DRAWING CAMS

When drawing the cam and follower, instead of revolving the cam, it is assumed that the follower rotates around the fixed cam. This requires the drawing of many follower positions, but because this is accomplished more or less diagrammatically, it is relatively simple.

When a roller, rather than a point, is used as the follower, the cam outline will be smaller. The **pitch curve** (pitch line) becomes the line of centers of the roller (Fig. 20.17). With the radius of the roller and the centers on the pitch line, a number of arcs are drawn to which a tangent working curve

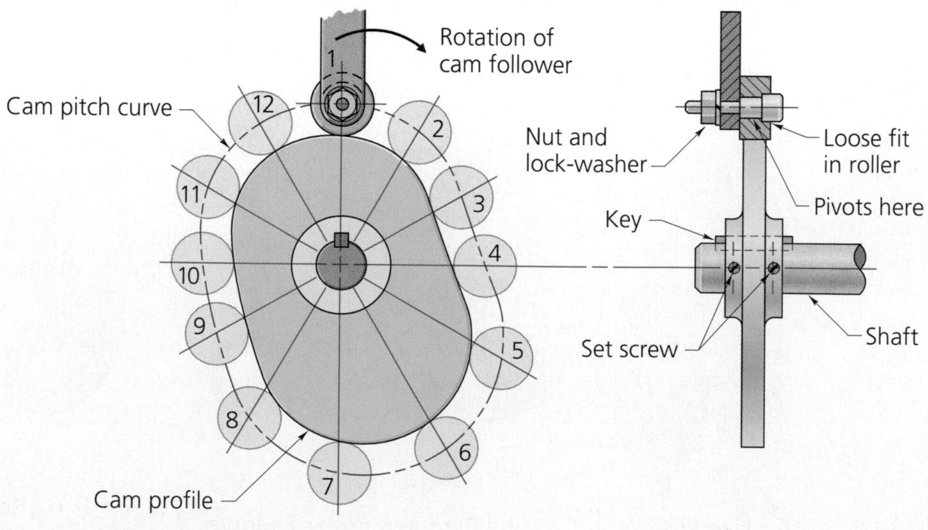

FIGURE 20.17 Cam-and-Roller-Follower Assembly

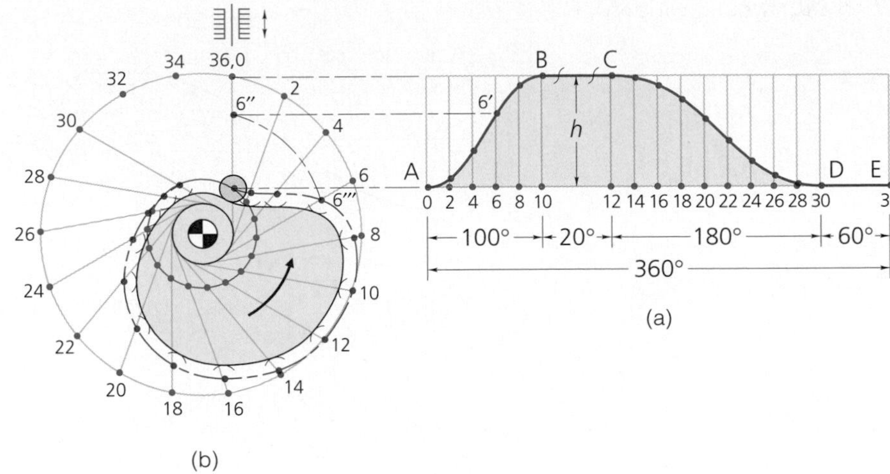

FIGURE 20.18 Cam with Offset Translating Roller Follower

can be drawn to give the cam outline. You can also transfer the distances with a compass or dividers. The **cam pitch curve** is the actual profile or working surface when a flat, pointed, or spherical follower is involved. To obtain the profile or working surface for a cam with a roller follower, a series of circles is drawn, with centers on the pitch curve and radii equal to the radius of the roller. The inner envelope drawn tangent to these arcs is the cam working surface or profile.

As part of the inversion process, the direction of rotation is important. To preserve the correct sequence of events, the artificial rotation of the follower must be the reverse of the cam's prescribed rotation. Thus, in Figure 20.17, the cam rotation is counterclockwise, whereas the artificial rotation of the follower is clockwise.

Figure 20.16 shows the cam construction layout with the cam pitch curve as a centerline. To locate a point on this curve, a point on the displacement curve, such as 6′ at the 60° position, is projected horizontally to point 6″ on the 0° position of the cam construction diagram. Using the center of cam rotation, an arc is struck from point 6″ to intercept the 60°-position radial line. This gives point 6″ on the cam pitch curve. The smaller circle in the cam construction layout has a radius R_{min} equal to the smallest distance from the center of cam rotation to the pitch curve. The larger circle has a radius R_{max} equal to the largest distance to the pitch curve. The difference in radii of these two circles is equal to the maximum rise (height) of the follower.

Figure 20.18 shows the construction of a cam with an offset translating roller follower. The time-displacement diagram, the cam layout, and an offset follower are also shown. The follower's angular position lines are not drawn radially from the cam shaft center in the construction of this type of cam. Instead, they are tangent to a circle having a radius equal to the amount of offset of the centerline of the cam follower from the center of the cam shaft.

Figure 20.19 shows a timing cam and displacement diagram used in a paper copier. This cam was designed and modeled on a CAD system. After the points were established on the cam layout, a **SPLINE** command was used to draw a smooth curve through the points. This eliminates the need for an irregular curve.

20.4.1 Dimensioning Cams

Standard ANSI dimensioning practices are employed to dimension all cams (Fig. 20.20). When a displacement diagram is not provided, the detail must show all radii for the cam profile outline. In this detail, the cam's shaft hole must be perpendicular to surface A within .002 in. The cam is held in place on the shaft with a keyseat and set screw. The eight 1.00 in. diameter holes reduce the total mass weight of the cam. In Figure 20.21, a cylindrical drum or cam is detailed and a displacement diagram provided. This is a typical industrial cam detail drawn on a CAD system.

You May Complete Exercises 20.1 Through 20.3 at This Time

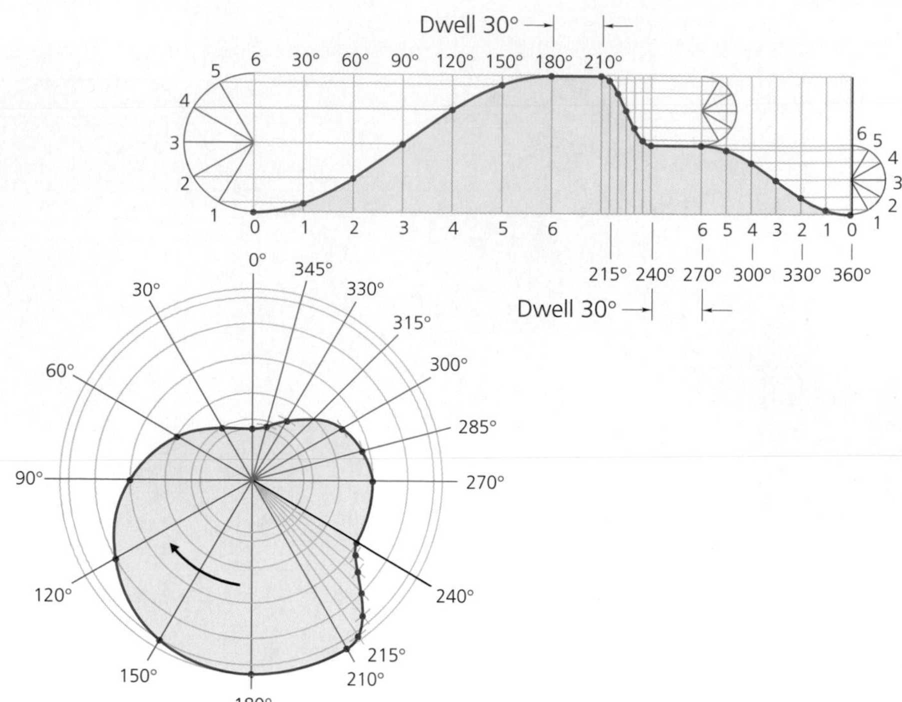

FIGURE 20.19 Construction of a Cam Using a Displacement Diagram

FIGURE 20.20 Cam Detail

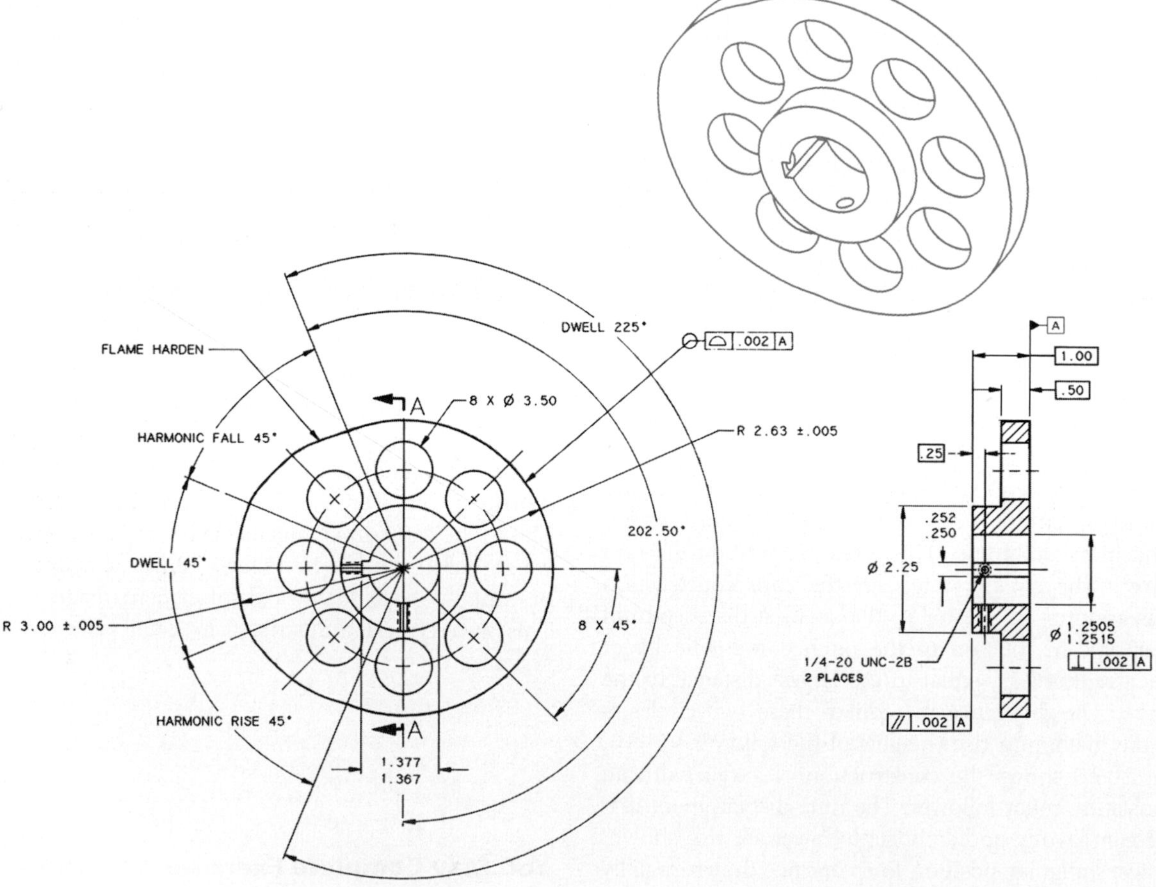

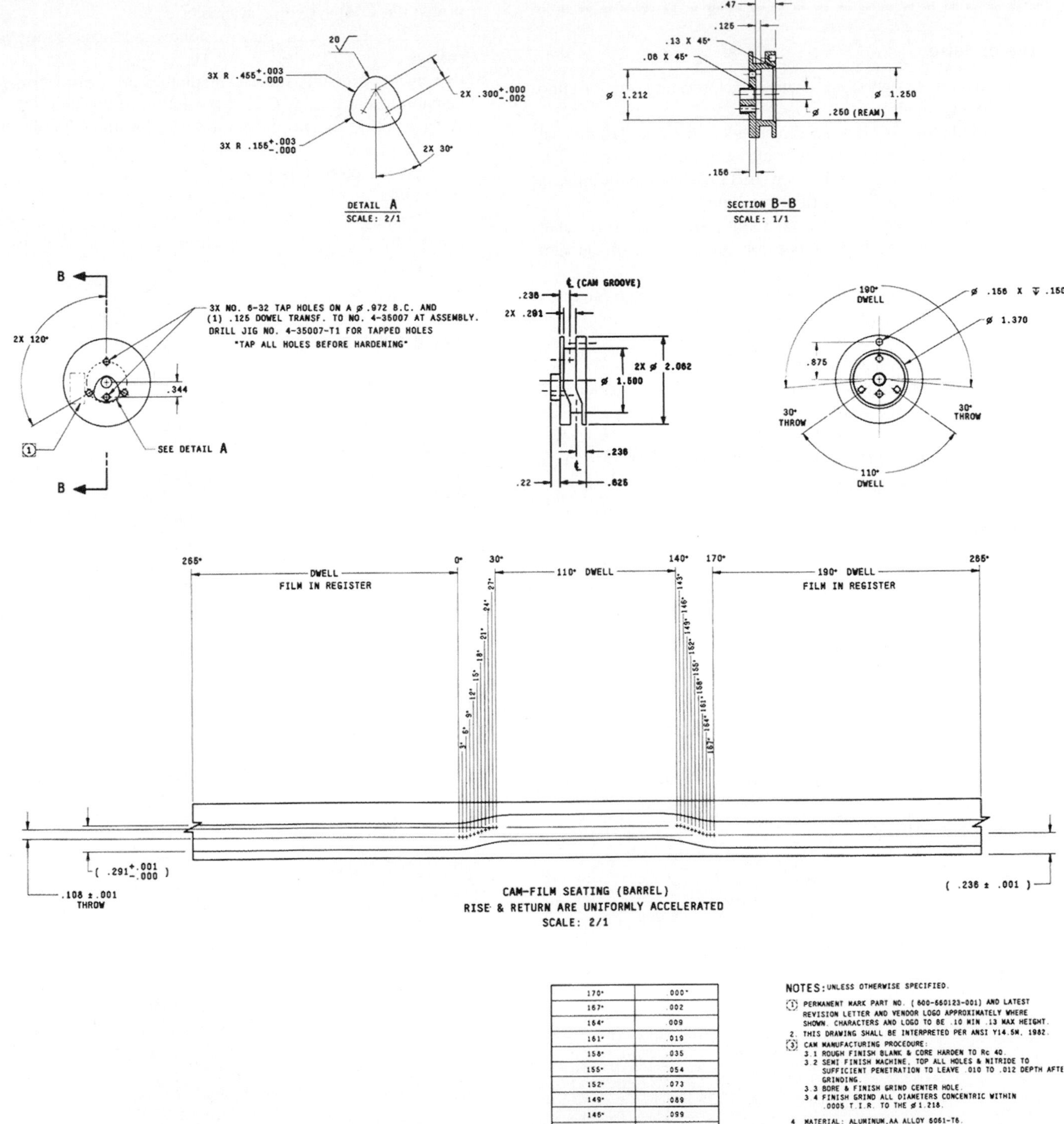

DEGREES	TOTAL RISE FROM DWELL
170°	.000"
167°	.002
164°	.009
161°	.019
158°	.035
155°	.054
152°	.073
149°	.089
146°	.099
143°	.106
140°	.108
30°	.108
27°	.106
24°	.099
21°	.089
18°	.073
15°	.054
12°	.035
9°	.019
6°	.009
3°	.002
0°	0"
DEVELOPMENT SEATING (BARREL CAM)	

NOTES: UNLESS OTHERWISE SPECIFIED.

1. PERMANENT MARK PART NO. (600-660123-001) AND LATEST REVISION LETTER AND VENDOR LOGO APPROXIMATELY WHERE SHOWN. CHARACTERS AND LOGO TO BE .10 MIN .13 MAX HEIGHT.
2. THIS DRAWING SHALL BE INTERPRETED PER ANSI Y14.5M, 1982.
3. CAM MANUFACTURING PROCEDURE:
   3.1 ROUGH FINISH BLANK & CORE HARDEN TO Rc 40.
   3.2 SEMI FINISH MACHINE, TOP ALL HOLES & NITRIDE TO SUFFICIENT PENETRATION TO LEAVE .010 TO .012 DEPTH AFTE GRINDING.
   3.3 BORE & FINISH GRIND CENTER HOLE.
   3.4 FINISH GRIND ALL DIAMETERS CONCENTRIC WITHIN .0005 T.I.R. TO THE ø 1.218.
4. MATERIAL: ALUMINUM, AA ALLOY 6061-T6.

FIGURE 20.21 Detail of a Cylindrical Cam

QUIZ

True or False

1. Cams are designed to change reciprocating motion into revolving motion.
2. A rolling follower is a machine element used on designs that operate at a high speed. It is also employed where there is considerable wear, and when friction (heat) buildup is a factor in the operation of the machine.
3. The working circle of a cam is the distance from the shaft centerline to the highest position on the edge of the cam profile.
4. Cylindrical cams transmit motion perpendicular to the cam's shaft.
5. Drum cams serve to move the follower axially.
6. The time interval is the time needed to move the follower through its motion from its highest to its lowest position and back again to the starting position at the top.
7. There are three classes of cams.
8. In uniform motion the displacement curve is created through parabolic construction.

Fill in the Blanks

9. An __________ __________ is not in line with the cam centerline.
10. Harmonic motion of a cam is __________, but the __________ is not __________.
11. The __________ command can be used to draw the cam profile if a CAD system is available.
12. __________ __________ follower designs require no springs.
13. One cycle of a cam's movement plotted on a displacement diagram means a __________ revolution of the cam.
14. When a roller, instead of a point, is used as the follower, the __________ __________ becomes __________.
15. __________ motion is plotted by drawing a __________ circle and __________ it evenly.
16. __________ are normally mounted on __________ and secured with __________. The drive mechanism may be a __________.

Answer the Following

17. Name four types of cam motion, and give a short description of each.
18. What are displacement diagrams? Why are they used in cam design?
19. Name and describe the classes of cams.
20. What is a cam's dwell?
21. What are the three most common types of followers?
22. When are flat-faced followers not used?
23. What is the difference between open-track and closed-track follower systems? Which requires the use of a spring?
24. Describe the difference between the cam profile and the base circle.

EXERCISES

Exercises may be assigned as sketching, instrument, or CAD projects. Transfer the given information to an "A"-size sheet of .25 in. grid paper. Complete all views, and solve for proper visibility, including centerlines, object lines, and hidden lines. Exercises that are not assigned by the instructor can be sketched in the text to provide practice and to enhance understanding of the preceding material.

After Reading the Chapter Through Section 20. 4.1 You May Complete the Following Exercises

Exercise 20.1 Draw the displacement diagram using the given cam motions, dimensions, and displacement. The cam is symmetrical about its vertical centerline. Use the diagram for both halves to construct the cam in Exercise 20.2.

Exercise 20.2 Using the displacement diagram from Exercise 20.1, lay out the cam and follower as shown. Calculate the proper keyseat and set screw for the shaft. The set screw is to be at 90° to the keyseat.

Exercise 20.3 Lay out the offset cam with the following specifications:

0°–90° modified uniform motion rise, total 1.50 displacement
90°–120° dwell
120°–180° parabolic motion fall, 100
180°–300° harmonic motion rise, .50
300°–330° dwell
330°–360° harmonic fall, 1.00

Construct a displacement diagram on a separate sheet to establish the cam's outline. Show the follower at 30° intervals. Design a proper-size keyseat, and secure the cam to a shaft with two set screws at 90° to the keyseat.

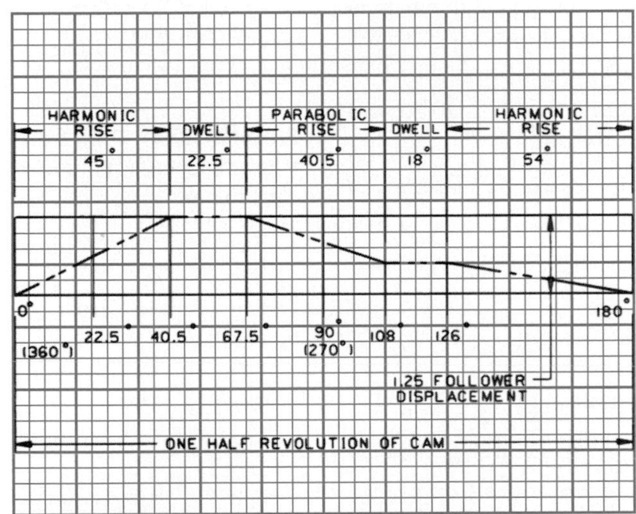

EXERCISE 20.1

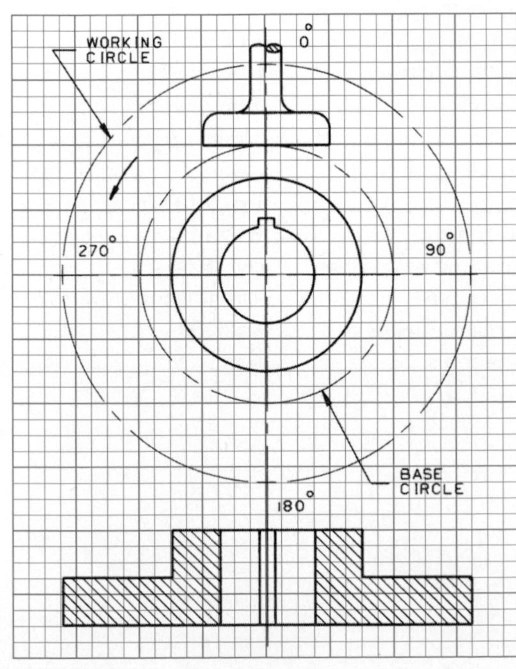

EXERCISE 20.2

EXERCISE 20.3

PROBLEMS

Problem 20.1 Redraw the upper link cam shown in Figure 20.5.

Problem 20.2 On a CAD system, model the cam in Figure 20.7 in 3D. Dimension completely using geometric tolerancing.

Problem 20.3 Design a cam based on the displacement diagram shown in Figure 20.10(f). The cam will have a shaft diameter of 1.50 and an appropriately sized keyseat. The cam will be .75 thick and have a 1.50 thick shaft hub with a 3.00 diameter. Design the shaft hub to have two appropriately sized set screws to secure the cam to the shaft. The cam will employ a radial translating roller follower. The roller is 1.25 in diameter. Show the roller in twelve positions using phantom lines. The height of the displacement diagram (the rise of the follower) is 4.00. The working circle is 10.00 diameter, and the base circle is 6.00. Dimension the cam completely using two views. If you're working with a 3D CAD system, model the part and display it as a rotated (pictorial, isometric) view. For modifying the uniform rise use a radius value of one-third the rise. The harmonic fall will be 1.625, and the parabolic fall will be 2.375.

Problem 20.4 Redraw the cam shown in Figure 20.20, and construct a displacement diagram for the cam.

Problem 20.5 Redraw the cylindrical cam detail shown in Figure 20.21.

Problem 20.6 Draw a displacement diagram and construct a cam with the following specifications:

Rise	20°, harmonic motion, 50 mm
Dwell	30°
Rise	60°, harmonic motion, 24 mm
Dwell	30°
Fall	60°, modified uniform motion, 40 mm
Dwell	15°
Fall	45°, harmonic motion, to starting level

Height	100 mm
Working circle	280 mm
Base circle	100 mm
Cam rotation direction	Clockwise
Shaft diameter	40 mm
Shaft hub diameter	78 mm
Shaft hub thickness	60 mm
Keyseat and set screws	Per shaft size
Follower type	Pointed
Cam plate thickness	30 mm
Cam cutouts	Six at 24 mm diameter

Problem 20.7 Draw a displacement diagram and cam with the following specifications (for metric cam use SI dimensions in parentheses):

Rise	90°, harmonic motion, 1.50 (38)
Dwell	15°
Rise	60°, uniform acceleration, 1.50 (38)

Height	4.00 (100)
Working circle	12.50 (318)
Base circle	4.50 (114)
Cam rotation direction	Counterclockwise
Shaft diameter	1.75 (45)
Shaft hub diameter	2.75 (70)
Shaft hub thickness	2.50 (64)
Keyseat and set screws	Per shaft size
Follower type	Flat face
Cam plate thickness	1.00 (25)
Cam cutouts	Six holes at .75 (20) diameter

Problem 20.8 Draw a displacement diagram and cam with the following specifications (for metric cam use SI dimensions in parentheses):

Rise	45°, modified uniform motion, 2.00 (50)
Dwell	45°
Fall	45°, harmonic motion, .75 (19)
Dwell	45°
Fall	45°, modified uniform motion, 1.00 (25)
Dwell	15°
Rise	°60, harmonic motion, 1.50 (38)
Dwell	15°
Fall	45°, parabolic motion, to starting level

Height	2.00 (50)
Working circle	7.50 (187)
Base circle	3.50 (89)
Cam rotation direction	Clockwise
Shaft diameter	1.00 (25)
Shaft hub diameter	1.875 (48)
Shaft hub thickness	1.75 (45)
Keyseat and set screws	Per shaft size
Follower type	Radial translating roller
Cam plate thickness	.75 (18)
Cam cutouts	None

Problem 20.9 Draw a displacement diagram and cam with the following specifications:

Fall	75°, modified uniform motion, 90 mm
Dwell	30°
Rise	45°, harmonic motion, 60 mm
Dwell	15°
Fall	60°, uniformly accelerated motion, 50 mm

Height	310 mm
Working circle	270 mm
Base circle	100 mm
Cam rotation direction	Clockwise
Shaft diameter	50 mm
Shaft hub diameter	70 mm
Shaft hub thickness	60 mm
Keyseat and set screws	Per shaft size
Follower type	Offset translating roller; offset 50 mm to the right side of cam center
Cam plate thickness	30 mm
Cam cutouts	Four holes at 20 mm diameter

Problem 20.10 Draw a displacement diagram and cam with the following specifications:

Rise	45°, harmonic motion, 4.00 (100)
Dwell	30°
Fall	60°, gravity motion, 3.50 (90)
Dwell	15°

Height	4.00 (100)
Working circle	14.00 (355)
Base circle	6.00 (127)
Cam rotation direction	Clockwise
Shaft diameter	2.00 (50)
Shaft hub diameter	4.00 (100)
Shaft hub thickness	3.00 (76)
Keyseat and set screws	Per shaft size
Follower type	Swinging roller follower
Cam plate thickness	2.00 (50)
Cam cutouts	Six at .50–1.00 (12–24) diameter

Problem 20.11 Draw a cyindrical cam with a 15 mm diameter roller moving counterclockwise 80 mm with a constant velocity through 180° revolution of the cylinder. The remaining 180° will be harominic motion. The cam axis is horizontal with 110 mm diameter cylinder with a length of 200 mm and on a 30 mm shaft diameter. Key the cam to the shaft.

FLUID POWER

Chapter 21

LEARNING OBJECTIVES

Upon completion of this chapter you will be able to:

1. Describe the differences between pneumatic and hydraulic fluid power applications and systems.
2. Understand Pascal's Law and its significance to fluid power systems.
3. Know how basic pneumatic and hydraulic circuits operate and how they are represented with ANSI and ISO symbols.
4. List the most important functions and characteristics of hydraulic and pneumatic fluids.
5. Understand the basic operation and function of hydraulic and pneumatic components.
6. Understand and construct simple graphical diagrams describing fluid power circuits.

21.1 INTRODUCTION

Fluid power systems use pressurized fluids such as air, water, and hydraulic fluid (oil) to control, transmit, or generate power. You are already familiar with many fluid power systems: power steering and power braking systems in automobiles, control systems and landing gears in airplanes, control systems in heavy machinery (forklifts, paving machines, earth movers, etc.), pneumatic tools, fuel pumps and carburation in automobiles, control of spacecraft, automation equipment such as robots and automated part loaders, hydroelectric power generation systems, and heating, ventilation, and air conditioning (HVAC) systems. Just about everywhere you look today you will find applications involving fluid power systems.

The fluid in a fluid power system can be either a liquid or a gas. **Pneumatic systems** use air because it is convenient, inexpensive, and ventable to the atmosphere. Air, however, is compressible, making pneumatic systems less stiff than hydraulic systems. This compressibility becomes a problem where precise motion and, therefore, rigidity is needed. Water was first employed in hydraulic systems because it is so abundant. But it rusts steel and iron components, is not a good lubricant, and freezes easily, so most modern **hydraulic systems** use hydraulic oils or synthetic oils.

Fluid power systems helped to produce useful work long before the Industrial Revolution. Early transportation systems relied on flowing water and capturing the power of the wind with sails. Water mills used flowing water to power water wheels that were connected to belts and pulleys for grinding grains. Before electricity, pressurized water and air mains in London and Paris powered the Industrial Revolution. In the twentieth century, hydraulic systems were developed to control ship and aircraft systems. An understanding of the principles of lift, drag, and viscosity played a key role in the development of the modern airplane. Modern CNC lathes, turning centers, and injection molding machines are all based on hydraulic systems. Theme park rides and fighter aircraft simulators make extensive use of fluid

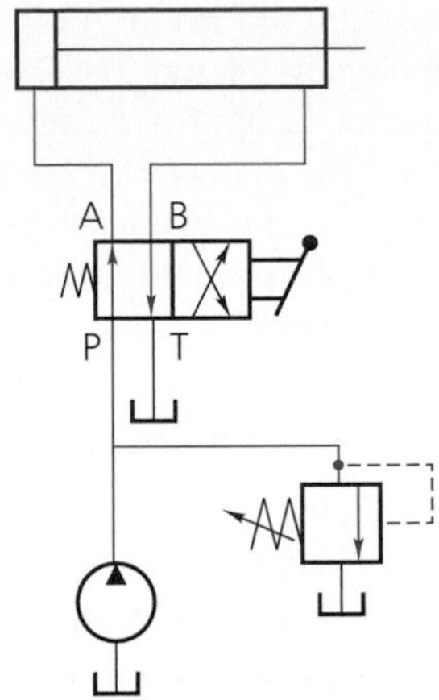

FIGURE 21.1 Double-Acting Cylinder with a Four-Way, Two-Position, Lever-Operated, Spring-Returned Directional Control Valve

power systems. Although few people realize the importance of fluid power applications in modern life, about 90% of North American industries use fluid power in some way.

Several organizations produce standards that affect the fluid power industry in the United States: the National Fluid Power Association (NFPA), the Society of Automotive Engineers (SAE), the American Society for Testing and Materials (ASTM), and the American Petroleum Institute (API). The American National Standards Institute (ANSI) resolves any differences among the standards. Committee B93 is the ANSI group that governs fluid power standards. Internationally accepted standards are the responsibility of the International Organization for Standardization (ISO).

There are three types of symbols for describing fluid power systems: pictorial, cutaway, and graphic. **Pictorial** symbols are like pictorial drawings in that they show the physical appearance of the components. Although pictorial drawings can illustrate the physical layout of components well, they are difficult to standardize. **Cutaway** drawings are virtually impossible to standardize, are difficult to draw, and do not show how particular components function. They are useful in showing the fluid path in the system and the internal construction of the components. **Graphic** symbols (Fig. 21.1) show the function of each component and the operation of the circuit. Graphic symbols have been standardized by ANSI and ISO and are commonly employed to describe pneumatic and hydraulic systems. Therefore, this chapter concentrates on how **graphic symbols** describe various fluid power circuits.

21.2 UNITS AND TERMS

Pressure in a typical fluid power circuit develops when force is applied to a confined fluid and there is resistance to fluid flow. French scientist Blaise Pascal (1623–1662) showed that the pressure exerted on a confined liquid at rest is transmitted equally in all directions and acts perpendicular to the surfaces of the container. This is known as **Pascal's law**. As shown in Figure 21.2, a force of 1 lb applied to an area of 1 in.^{2} results in a pressure of 1 psi (pound per square inch). According to Pascal's law, a pressure of 1 psi is transmitted equally in all directions in the confined fluid.

Pressure can be defined mathematically by the following formula:

$$\text{Pressure} = \frac{\text{force}}{\text{area}}$$

$$P = \frac{F}{A}$$

where force (F) is in units of pounds of force or newtons [a newton is approximately one-fourth of a pound (force)], area (A) is in square inches (in.^{2}) or square meters (m^2), and pressure (P) is in pounds per square inch (psi) or newtons per square meter (N/m^2) (1 N/m^2 = 1 pascal, or 1 Pa). Newtons, pascals, and meters are, of course, SI units.

Appropriate Conversions

1 lb (force) = 4.448N
1 m = 39.37 in.
1 m^2 = 1550 in.^{2}
1 psi = 6895 N/m^2, or 6895 Pa

Though Pascal's law states that pressure is transmitted equally in all directions, it says nothing about the shape or size of the vessel containing the fluid. In fact, the shape and size of the container are of no consequence; the vessel can be any size or shape, even a whole series of connected vessels. Therefore, a pipeline containing a pressurized fluid can transmit force much like an aluminum or steel rod. This is why hydraulic systems are found in situations where a high amount of force or torque must be transmitted or used, such as in forklifts or earth-moving equipment.

However, pressurized fluid systems are not perfect. Hydraulic systems commonly leak because of defects in seals. Any high-pressure system is inherently dangerous. Most hydraulic fluids are flammable, although some are not quite

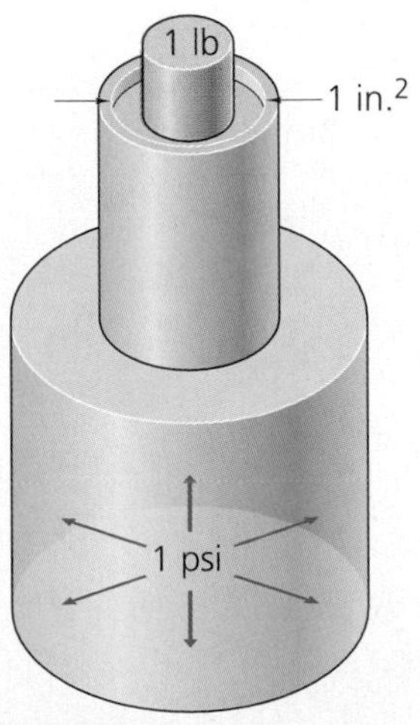

FIGURE 21.2 Pascal's Law

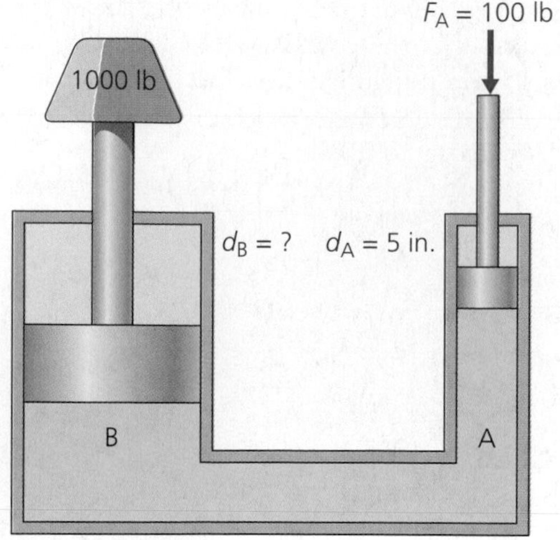

FIGURE 21.3 Mechanical Advantage (Multiplication of Force)

as flammable as fluids commonly used in hydraulic systems. Components in high-force and high-torque situations do wear, especially if the fluid is not kept free of particulates and filtered properly.

Perhaps the most interesting application of the principles of hydraulics lies in multiplying force. Simply stated, multiplication of force occurs when you use a small force to lift or move a larger force. You have seen this in hydraulic lifts in automotive applications. Since pressure is transmitted equally throughout the system and since $P = F/A$, doubling the size of the area (A) will double the force that can be applied; if the area is tripled, the force is tripled. We simply need to connect two vessels with different areas. This multiplication of force is known as **mechanical advantage.** In Figure 21.3, 100 lb is lifting 1000 lb, so the mechanical advantage (multiplication of force) is 10. Given that the area of a circle is (π × diameter^2)/4 and that $P = F/A$, the pressure in the example system is approximately 5 psi, and d_B is approximately 16 in. [The diameter is not 10 times the other diameter because area is (π × diameter^2)/4.]

The last concepts to be covered in this section are those of work and power. **Work** is defined mathematically as follows:

$$W = F \times d$$

where work (W) has units ft·lb or N·m. Recall that 1 N·m = 1 joule (J). Force (F) is in pounds of force or newtons, and d is the distance traveled, in feet or meters. Since the work we put into a system must equal the work taken out of the system, the distance traveled by the larger piston must be smaller than the distance traveled by the smaller cylinder in the hydraulic lift in Figure 21.3. If the smaller cylinder travels 5 in., the larger cylinder travels only 0.5 in. (Simply divide the distance the smaller cylinder travels by the mechanical advantage of the system.)

Power (P) is the rate at which work is done, that is, work per unit time:

$$P = W/t$$

Power has units of ft·lb/sec or N·m/sec or J/sec. 1 J/sec = 1 watt; 1 horsepower (hp) = 550 ft·lb/sec.

Input power in a hydraulic fluid power system is the power transmitted to the hydraulic pump from the prime mover, which is either an internal combustion engine or an electric motor. That is, the prime mover provides the rotational input power to the hydraulic pump, which converts the rotational energy into kinetic energy (flow) and pressure energy (resistance). (These values will be considered later when Bernoulli's equation is described.)

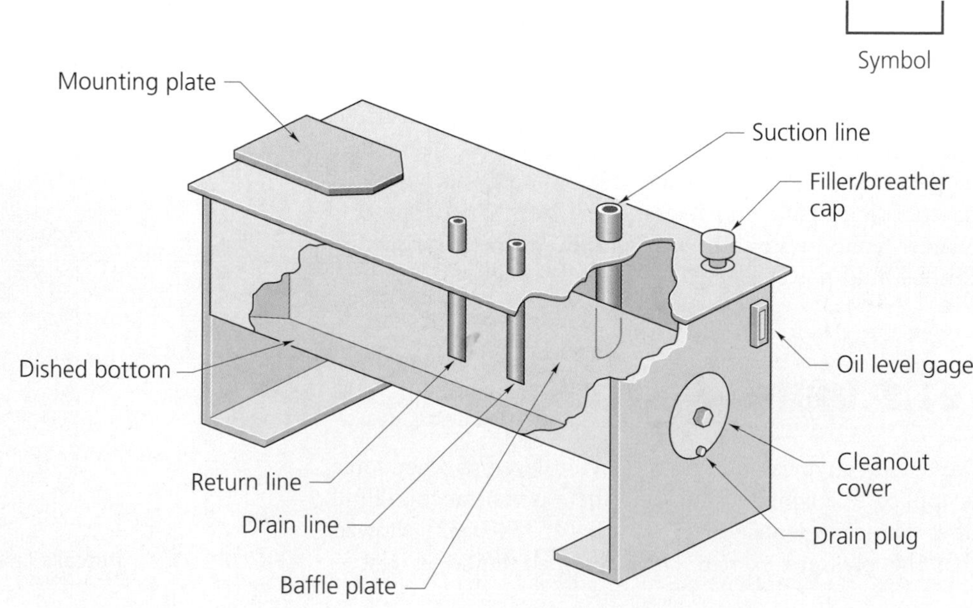

FIGURE 21.4 Reservoir to Hold and Cool Hydraulic Fluid

21.3 FLUID POWER SYSTEMS

Fluid power systems are designed to do useful work, sometimes applying thousands of pounds of force. For example, construction equipment such as excavators, graders, scrapers, and loaders all have fluid-power-based systems that apply large amounts of force. Hydraulic systems operate at pressures exceeding 1000 psi, whereas typical pneumatic systems operate at around 100 psi. Regardless of the complexity of the fluid power and control system, all pneumatic or hydraulic circuits build on the same basic components.

21.3.1 Basic Components

Basic Hydraulic Circuit Components

- A *reservoir (tank)*, to hold and cool the hydraulic fluid (Fig. 21.4)
- A *pump*, to move the fluid through the circuit (Fig. 21.5)
- A *power source (prime mover)*, such as an electric motor or an internal combustion engine, to drive the pump
- *Piping*, through which the fluid is moved from one location to another
- *Valves*, to control the direction, pressure, and flow rate of the fluid (Fig. 21.6)
- An *actuator*, to convert the fluid's motion into some sort of useful work (Fig. 21.7) (e.g., turning a motor or extending a hydraulic cylinder)

Basic Pneumatic Circuit Components

- A *tank*, to hold a supply of compressed air
- A *compressor*, to compress air
- A *power source*, such as an electric motor or other device, to power the compressor
- *Piping or tubing*, through which the pressurized air is moved around the circuit

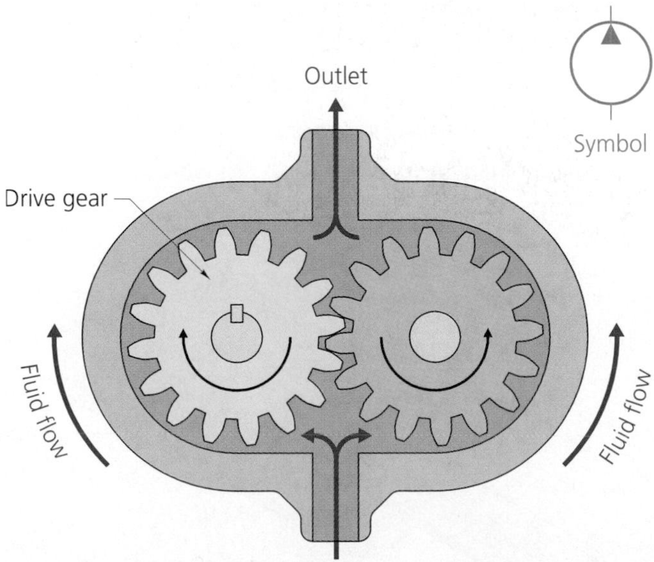

FIGURE 21.5 External Gear Pump, the Most Common Type of Gear Pump

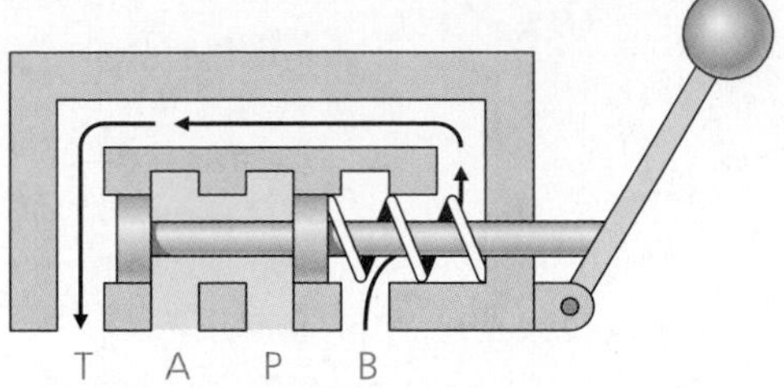

(a) Valve unactuated

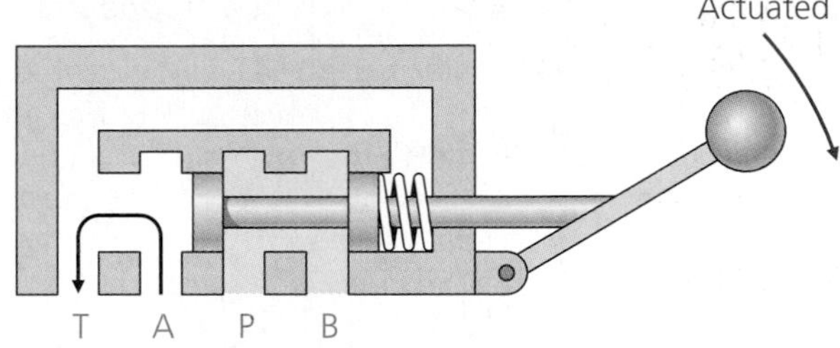

(b) Valve actuated

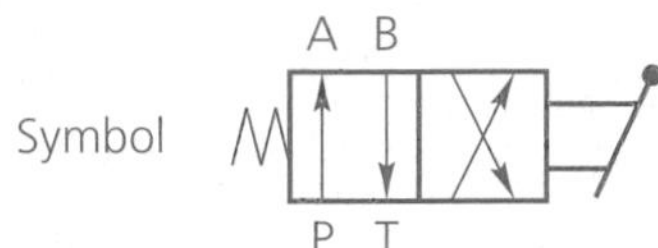

FIGURE 21.6 Cutaway of a Four-Way, Two-Position Directional Control Valve Showing Flow Through the Valve in Each Spool Position

- *Valves*, to control the direction, pressure, and flow rate of the air (Figs. 21.8 and 21.9)
- *Actuators*, to convert the motion of the air into some sort of useful work (e.g., turning a motor or extending a pneumatic cylinder) (Fig. 21.10)

The basic components of a pneumatic or hydraulic system can be assembled to apply either rotary motion (via a motor) or linear motion (via a cylinder) to the workpiece. Control of the fluid power valves can range from simple manual methods to complex microprocessor feedback control systems. In the hydraulic braking system for your car, you apply the brakes manually at the appropriate time. Whether or not the system is power-assisted, you choose the braking time. However, on new antilock braking systems (ABS brakes), a microprocessor program determines the optimum way to apply the brakes so that they do not "lock up" while the car is coming to a stop.

21.3.2 Fluid Power Symbols

Conveying the information about the design of a fluid power system through an engineering drawing is a matter of using the appropriate symbol for each fluid power component and line. ANSI and ISO have established standard fluid power symbols for the basic fluid power components. Figure 21.11 shows the standard ANSI symbols.

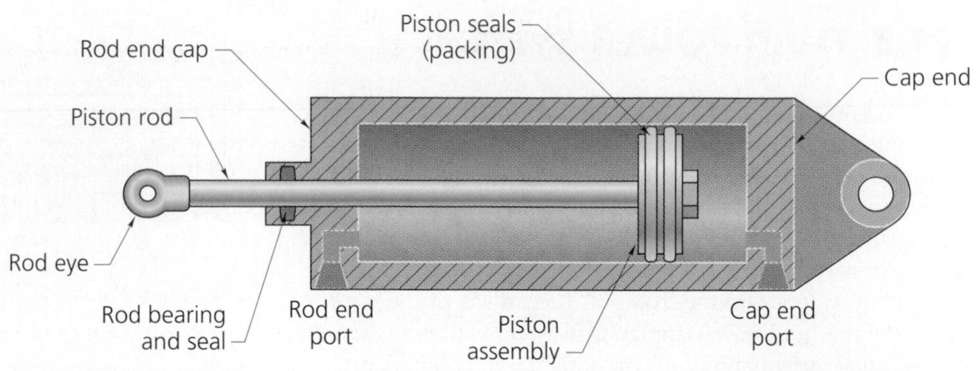

FIGURE 21.7 Cross Section of a Typical Double-Acting Cylinder

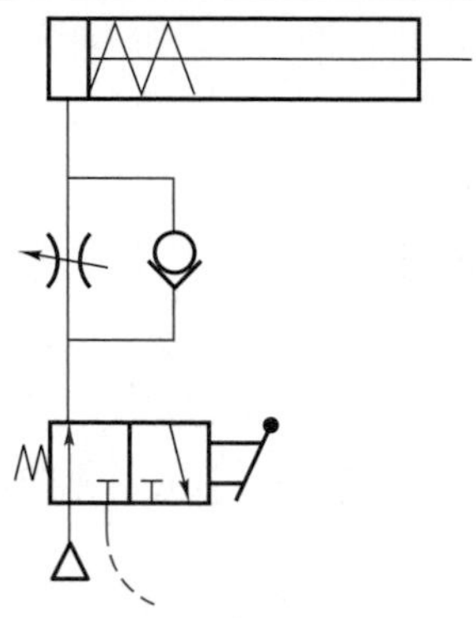

FIGURE 21.8 A Flow Control Valve Can Control the Retraction Speed of a Single-Acting Cylinder

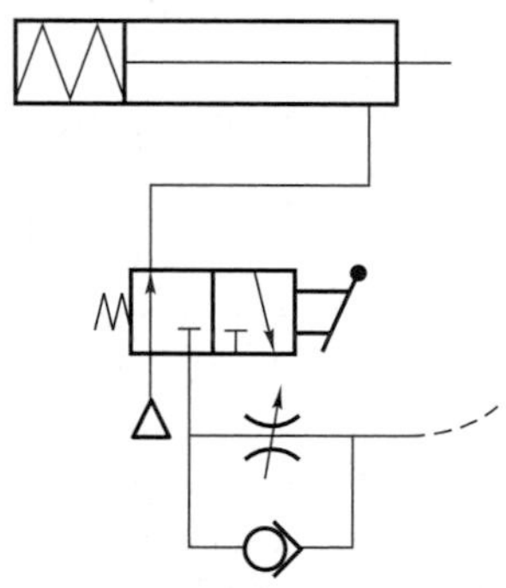

FIGURE 21.9 A Flow Control Valve Can Control the Extension Speed of a Single-Acting Cylinder

Notice that there are symbols for the listed basic components: motors and cylinders, pumps, valves, reservoirs, and instrumentation. Valves can be activated in several ways: springs, solenoids, levers, push buttons, pedal, ball, cam, etc. A solenoid is a way to activate a valve that is electrical and not mechanical in nature. For example, depending on the exact design of the valve, a solenoid uses an electrical signal to move the spool in the valve to change the direction of flow in the valve. Since a solenoid is electrically operated, solenoid actuation is employed extensively in computer- or microprocessor-controlled fluid power circuits.

Figure 21.12 is a drawing of a basic pneumatic fluid power circuit that controls a spring-return air cylinder. Though at first glance the circuit might seem complicated, there are only four parts to the diagram:

1. **FROM AIR SUPPLY** means that this circuit is hooked to a large air compressor and tank that can supply an unlimited amount of flow to the circuit.
2. The **FILTER, REGULATOR AND LUBRICATOR (FRL) UNIT** filters and regulates the air in the circuit to a certain pressure value. A lubricant is added to the air to lubricate the metal components. A safety relief valve is in the unit in case the regulator fails to keep the air pressure to a safe value.

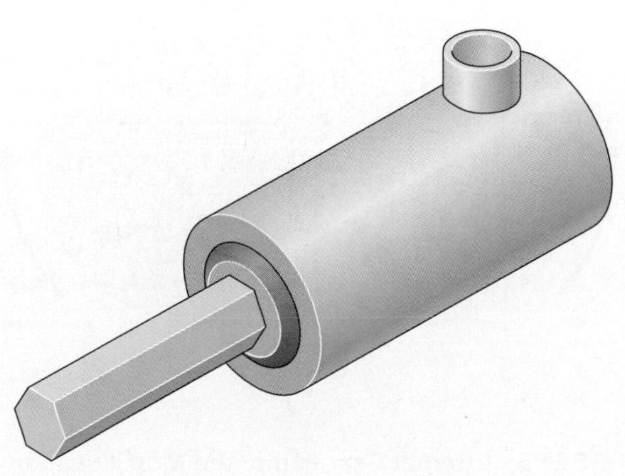

FIGURE 21.10 Single-Acting, Nonrotating Cylinder with a Hexagonal Shaft, Common in Pneumatic Applications

Motors	
	Motor— Fixed displacement
	Motor— Reversible
M	Motor— Electric
	Cylinder

Pumps	
	Compressor
	Pump— Single fixed displacement

Valves	
	Control valve
	Check valve
	Variable control valve
	Valve— Single flow, normally open
	Valve— Single flow, normally closed
	Safety relief valve
	Two-way three-port valve
Position 1 Position 2	Four-way two-position valve
Position 1 Position 2 (Closed) Position 3	Four-way three-position valve

Miscellaneous Symbols	
	Accumulator— Gas charged
	Accumulator— Spring loaded
	Pressure gauge
	Temperature gauge
	Flow meter
	Filter
	Filter with fluid trap
	Reservoir

Methods of Activation	
	Spring
	Solenoid
	Solenoid— Spring centered
	Lever
	Push button
	Pedal
	Ball or cam
	Pilot— Hydraulic
	Pilot— Pneumatic

FIGURE 21.11 Basic Fluid Power Symbols (ANSI)

Focus On . . .

PIPING SYSTEMS

As far back as 400 B.C. people built pipe systems to transfer products in bulk form. The Chinese were probably the first. They used hollow bamboo to carry water and smaller-diameter bamboo wrapped with waxed cloth to move marsh gas to various locations. Later, the Romans and Arab conquerors piped water through aqueducts of hollow stone. In approximately 600 A.D., the Japanese fashioned clay pipes by hand. Commercial production of pipe began about 200 years ago in Europe. These cast-iron pipes were used for sewage, water, and gas.

In 1859 the first successful oil well was drilled in Pennsylvania. An effective method to transfer the crude oil to refineries was soon required. Because of their low cost, pipelines were the method of choice. Of course, railroads opposed this method and even refused to let pipelines cross under their tracks. Regardless, the use of pipelines proliferated after that time.

Stone aqueducts.

Improvements in metallurgy, construction, and equipment steadily reduced the cost of pipelines until the 1970s. Then, higher labor and material costs caused the prices to increase. Government regulations and the effort to protect the environment added to the total price.

Since the first pipelines were produced in the mid-1800s, several improvements to the systems have been made. One such improvement was lap-welded wrought-iron pipe with threaded ends. Other improvements were made in the metallurgy of the pipe material. In the 1940s the maximum strength was 42,000 psi. Today the maximum strength is 70,000 psi, an increase that required about a 67% increase in the strength of the material.

Bamboo pipes.

Because of better equipment and materials, the total length possible for a pipeline increased. The 800-mile-long Trans-Alaska pipeline constructed in the 1970s illustrates the sophisticated technology available for modern pipelines. Because of the very low arctic temperatures, the oil is heated to lower its viscosity and increase its ability to flow. The pipeline is encased in heavy insulation to prevent heat loss as the oil travels through the pipeline.

By the 1980s most countries had some pipeline system that carried refined products to their major cities. The United States was the first country to use "batching" of several products into one pipeline. This permits products to be conveyed together without any separation.

New technology continues to improve the pipelines that crisscross the United States and other parts of the world. Need seems to dictate how quickly advances are made to existing systems. Today, the need to protect the environment has become very important to us. This will certainly play a key role in planning future pipelines.

3. A **SOLENOID** (electrically operated) **TWO POSITION THREE PORT TWO-WAY VALVE** controls the direction of air flow to the pneumatic cylinder. Pressurized air will extend the cylinder.
4. A **SPRING RETURN AIR CYLINDER** is the actuator in the circuit. The pressurized air in the system acts to extend the air cylinder. The air cylinder applies linear motion to accomplish some function, such as moving parts from one position to another. A spring functions to return the air cylinder.

If you wanted to apply a simple rotary motion with the same circuit, you would merely replace the linear pneumatic cylinder with an air motor. There are three common types of air motors: vane, axial piston, and rotary piston. Vane air motors are typically in pneumatic circuits. Of course, start-

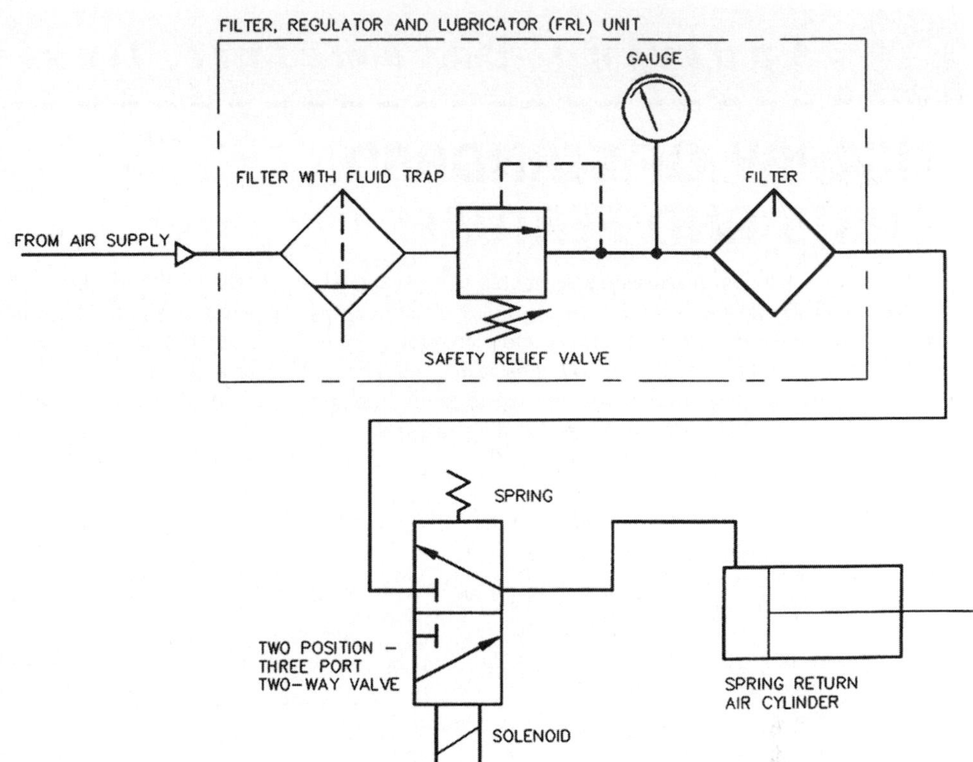

FIGURE 21.12 Pneumatic Fluid Power Circuit That Controls a Spring-Return Air Cylinder

ing torque and stall torque are the most common design considerations when selecting air motors. Complex fluid power systems are actually just basic systems linked together to accomplish some predefined function.

21.4 FLUID POWER COMPONENTS

Several basic components are common to many fluid power systems. The design of each such device is different if the device is an air (pneumatic) device or a hydraulic device, but the primary function is unchanged regardless of the fluid involved. Remember that the fluid may be a gas or a liquid. Liquid systems are more rigid than gas systems because liquids are more difficult to compress. Because most pneumatic systems are "spongy" due to the compressibility of air, pneumatic systems are not used when a large amount of force must be applied or where precise control of position is involved.

21.4.1 Fluids and Fluid Properties

There are many different fluids employed in hydraulic systems. Originally, all fluid power systems used water. Obviously, water was far from ideal, because it rusted steel components, froze in cold weather, provided no lubrication, and was difficult to seal due to its low viscosity. Despite these shortcomings, London and Paris in the nineteenth century had pressurized water lines to provide power. Water was the most abundant and inexpensive fluid available for those systems. In fact, as late as 1975 London still had 600 systems that used water to transmit power. However, the advantages of petroleum-based fluids (developed in the late nineteenth century) were so clear that the fluid power industry switched to them for most applications. Typical industrial hydraulic systems today operate at 1000 to 5000 psi or more.

The advantages of petroleum-based hydraulic fluids include good lubrication, good heat transfer, resistance to corrosion and to erosion of hydraulic system components, viscosity that allows easy seals, good electrical insulation, high incompressibility, and low specific gravity. Unfortunately, all petroleum-based fluids are flammable to some extent. However, some fire-resistant fluids are available today.

Viscosity is a fluid's resistance to flow. It is the ability of the fluid to resist internal shear at a particular temperature. Dynamic or absolute viscosity is measured in $\text{lb}\cdot\text{sec/ft}^2$ or slug/ft·sec. The SI units are $\text{N}\cdot\text{sec/m}^2$ or Pa·sec. Figure 21.13 describes internal shear resistance by showing the fluid velocity profile between stationary and moving plates. As a fluid moves, it develops a shear stress that depends on the viscosity of the fluid. Shear stress (τ) is the force required to slide one unit-area layer of a fluid over another. As a force

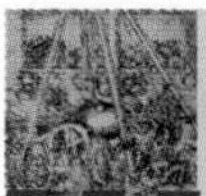

Applying Parametric Design . . .

LIBRARY OF STANDARD PARTS AND FEATURES

A variety of **parts** and **features** are accessible in a **3D library**. Pro/ENGINEER has available die, mold, tooling, casting, piping, HVAC, and a variety of electrical and electronic components. These parts and accompanying features are already modeled parametrically and can be inserted instantly into any design as a component of an assembly or diagram.

The bulkhead run tee shown in Figure A is an example of a pipe fitting and fluid power fitting that can be called up for use in your design. The part is available in a variety of standard sizes and styles.

The **pipe fitting library** also has a selection of standard features, such as the port shown in Figure B, which is a

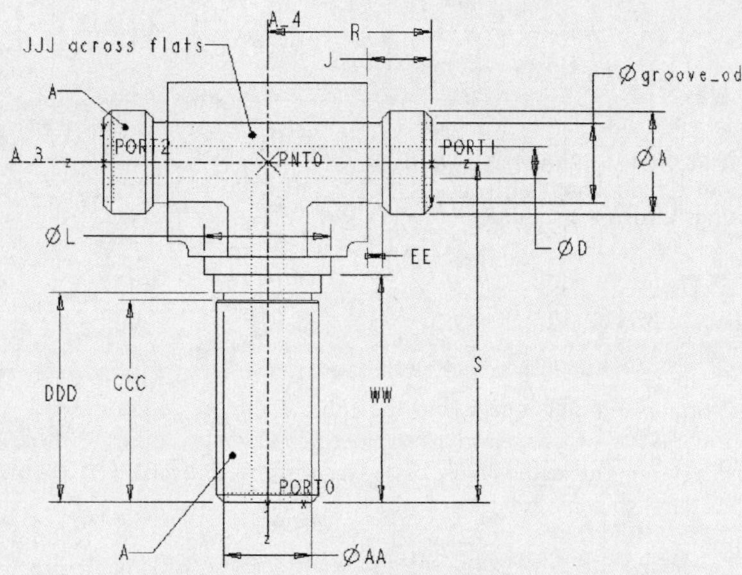

FIGURE A Bulkhead Run Tee from a Library of Piping Parts

Name	Nom Tube OD	Thread Size Face
JTBB01	0.25000	9/16 - 18
JTBB02	0.37500	11/16 - 16
JTBB03	0.50000	13/16 - 16
JTBB04	0.62500	1 - 14
JTBB05	0.75000	1-3/16 - 12
JTBB06	1.00000	1-7/16 - 12
JTBB07	1.25000	1-11/16 - 12
JTBB08	1.50000	2 - 12

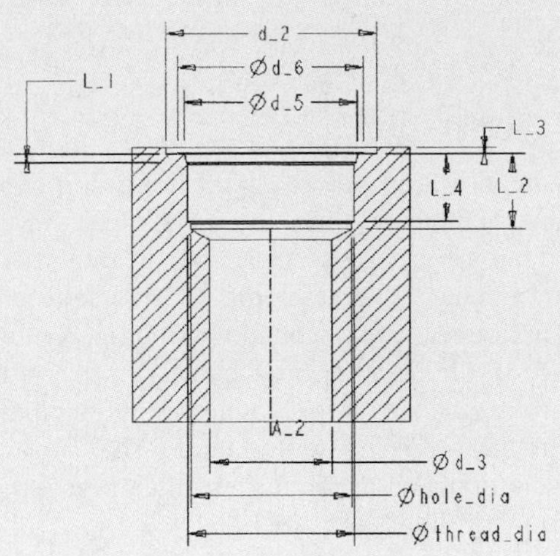

FIGURE B Port Feature from a Library of Features for Piping

Name	Tube OD	Thread Size
PORT01	4.0000	M8 x 1
PORT02	5.0000	M10 x 1
PORT03	6.0000	M12 x 1.5
PORT04	8.0000	M14 x 1.5
PORT05	10.0000	M16 x 1.5
PORT06	12.0000	M18 x 1.5
PORT07	16.0000	M22 x 1.5
PORT08	20.0000	M27 x 2
PORT10	22.0000	M30 x 2
PORT01	25.0000	M33 x 2
PORT11	30.0000	M42 x 2
PORT12	38.0000	M48 x 2
PORT13	50.0000	M60 x 2

standard port for **fluid power**. The library of features eliminates the need to create each hole and thread requirement individually. Ports are just one of the many features that come with the library.

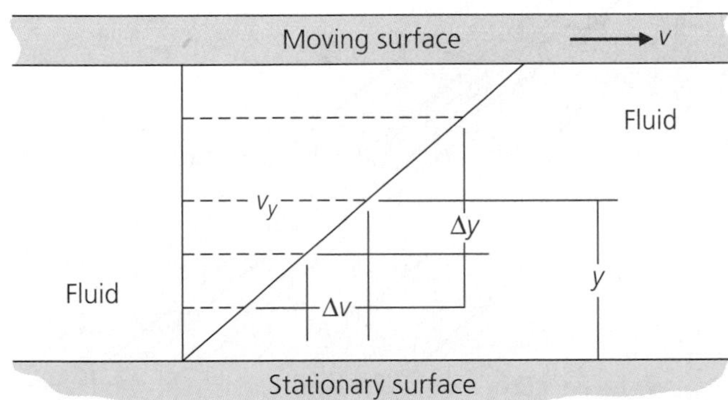

FIGURE 21.13 Fluid Velocity Profile Between Stationary and Moving Plates

divided by an area, shear stress has units of N/m^2 or psi. In many fluids, such as water, oil, hydraulic fluid, and alcohol, the magnitude of the shear stress developed is proportional to the change in velocity between different positions in the fluid. Mathematically, this is:

$$\tau = \mu(\Delta v/\Delta y)$$

Dynamic, or **absolute**, **viscosity** is the proportionality constant μ. **Kinematic viscosity** is the dynamic viscosity divided by the density of the fluid. Both properties must be measured at the same temperature. The units for kinematic viscosity are ft^2/sec or m^2/sec. Another, older common unit for kinematic viscosity is Saybolt seconds universal (SSU or, sometimes, SUS). When measured in the Saybolt Viscometer (ASTM D 88), the viscosity values are often expressed in SSU or SUS. Although ASTM has rescinded this standard, the SSU or SUS continues to be used today.

The study of how a substance deforms and flows is called **rheology**. A **newtonian fluid** is a fluid that exhibits the flow behavior described earlier, where the shear stress in the fluid is proportional to the velocity gradient in the fluid. Fluids that do not behave like this are termed **nonnewtonian fluids**. For example, Bingham or plug-flow fluids develop a significant amount of shear stress before flow begins. Catsup is an excellent example of this type of fluid.

The viscosity of a fluid changes with temperature. Engine oil is an excellent example of a fluid that exhibits day-to-day or season-to-season viscosity changes with temperature. The viscosity index (VI) is a measure of how the viscosity changes with temperature. A fluid with a high viscosity index has a small change in viscosity with temperature. The viscosity index is a dimensionless number that indicates the relative viscosity of a fluid between two limits. The original zero rating was based on oil from fields along the Gulf of Mexico, and the rating of 100 was based on oils form Pennsylvania that changed very little with temperature. Because of the nature of this rating, there are fluids with a viscosity index higher than 100 and lower than zero. Figure 21.14 shows the ASTM standard viscosity temperature charts for various fluids.

Ideally, you select a hydraulic fluid that would keep operating at its optimum viscosity regardless of the operating conditions. If the viscosity of an oil is too low, leakage is a prime concern. If the viscosity is too high, the system may overheat because of excessive friction, actuators may be sluggish, and the pumps will not operate efficiently or effectively.

21.4.2 Reservoirs

A **reservoir** in a fluid power circuit holds and supplies an appropriate volume of fluid for the circuit. An *air tank,* manufactured to exact specifications, is the reservoir for pneumatic circuits. The reservoir for hydraulic circuits is more complicated. It may contain a strainer, a filter, an oil level gage, an air breather, and baffles. As hydraulic fluid moves through the circuit, friction losses in the pipes, valves, and joints heat the hydraulic fluid. The *baffles* in the reservoir are designed to remove as much heat as necessary from the circuit fluid.

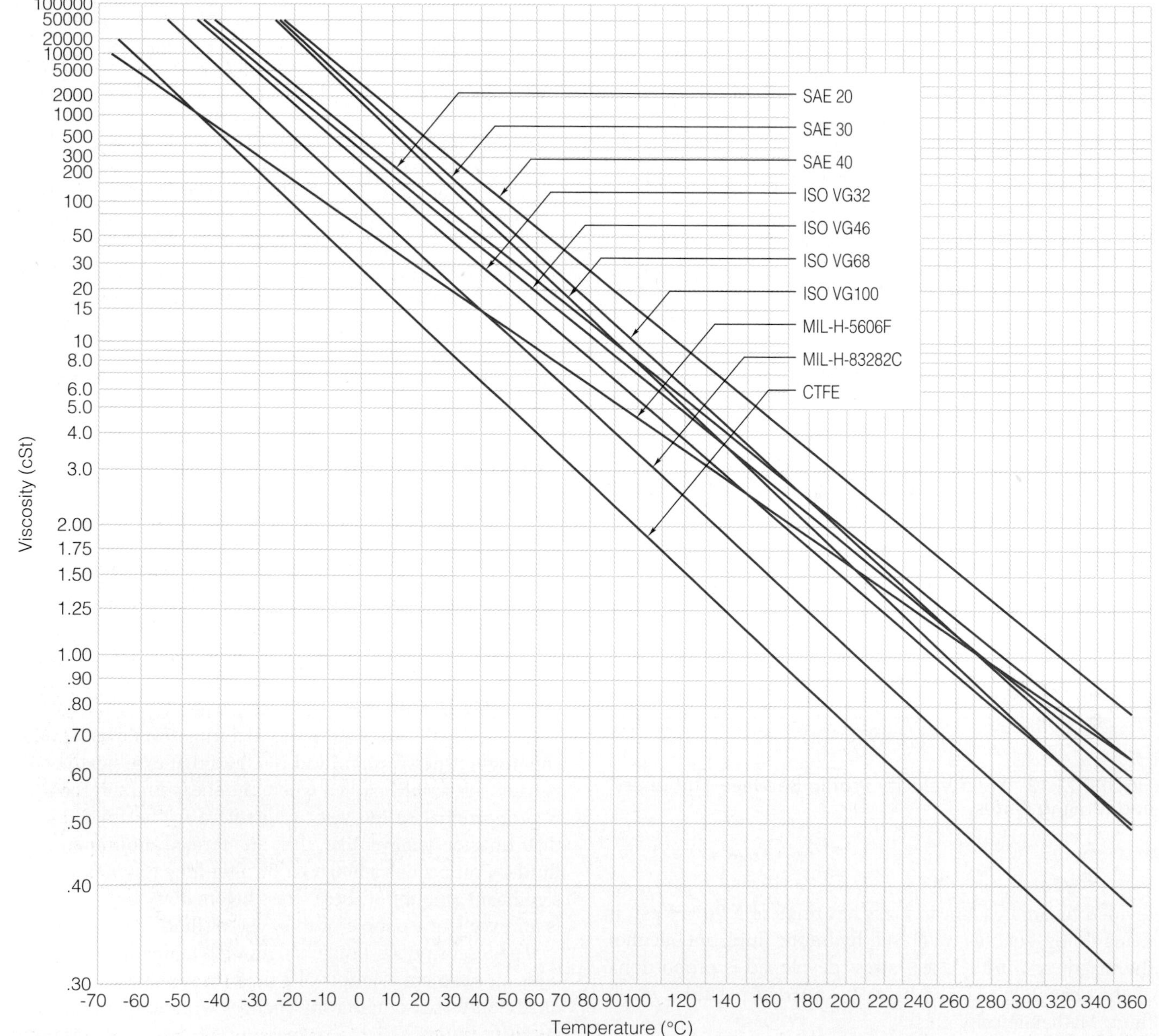

FIGURE 21.14 ASTM Standard Viscosity Temperature Charts for Liquid Petroleum Products

21.4.3 Pumps

Pumps in fluid power circuits convert mechanical energy into fluid power energy. Pumps are powered by prime movers, such as electrical motors, and convert that energy into fluid moving throughout the circuit. A **positive-displacement pump** delivers a fixed quantity of fluid with each revolution of the pump. The family tree of positive-displacement pumps is shown in Figure 21.15. The internal configuration of a pump determines the amount of fluid that is moved in one revolution of the pump. If you cannot change the internal configuration of the pump, then it is a **fixed-displacement** pump. If you can change the internal configuration of the pump, it is a **variable-displacement** pump. Most industrial hydraulic power systems use positive-displacement pumps to pump the fluid in the system. A nonpositive-displacement pump, or a **kinetic pump,** adds energy to the fluid by accelerating it through a rotating impeller. Such pumps are designed for low-pressure, high-volume applications that move fluids from one location to another. The pump in a dishwasher is an example.

A positive-displacement pump produces a pulsating flow, whereas a kinetic pump produces a continuous flow. Positive-displacement pumps are not affected by variations in system pressure. Types of positive-displacement pumps are *gear* (Fig. 21.16), *vane, screw, cam or lobe, piston, plunger,* and *diaphragm.* Types of kinetic pumps are *radial flow (centrifugal), axial flow (propeller),* and *mixed flow.*

Positive-displacement pumps contain a pumping chamber that increases then decreases in volume. Fluid enters the chamber as the chamber increases in volume and is pushed out of the chamber as the chamber decreases in volume. Internal leakage in the pump is called **slippage**.

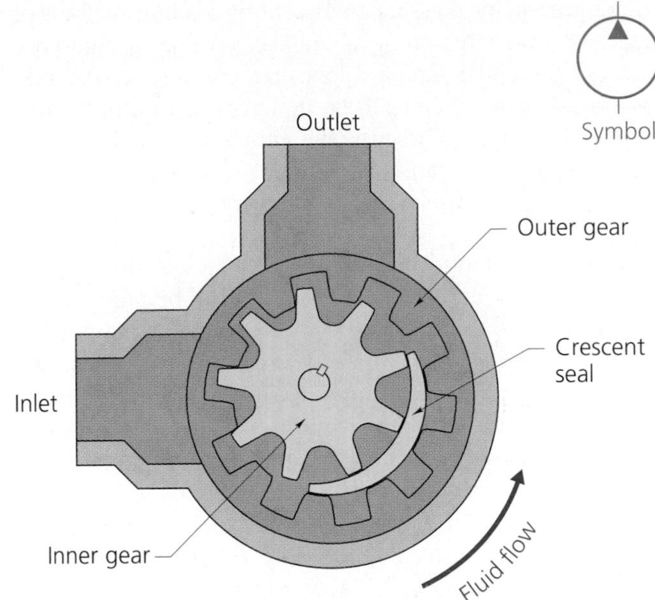

FIGURE 21.16 Crescent Pump, a Type of Internal Gear Pump

Perhaps the simplest of all positive-displacement pumps is the basic sliding-vane pump (Fig. 21.17). Each pair of vanes forms a pumping chamber that varies in volume as the pump rotates. The chamber enlarges from the eccentricity of the cam ring and the rotor. The partial vacuum that is created pushes the fluid into the chamber. As the pump rotates, the volume of the chamber is reduced and the fluid is pushed out of the pump. Fluid leakage around the vanes

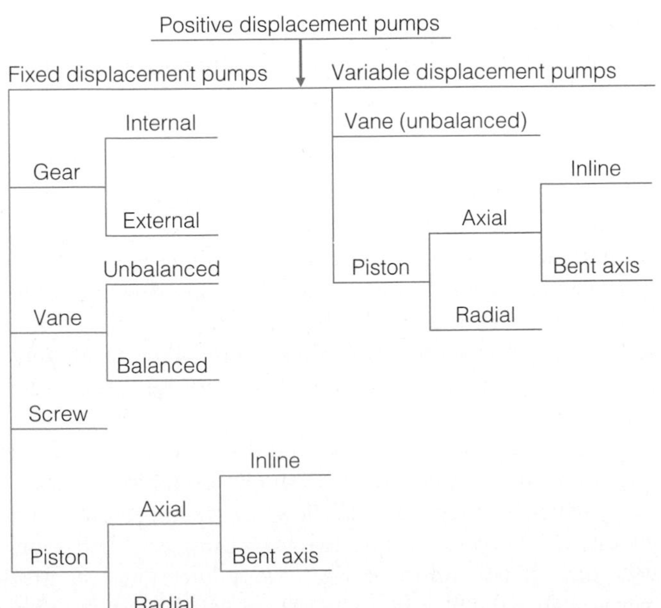

FIGURE 21.15 Family Tree of Positive-Displacement Pumps

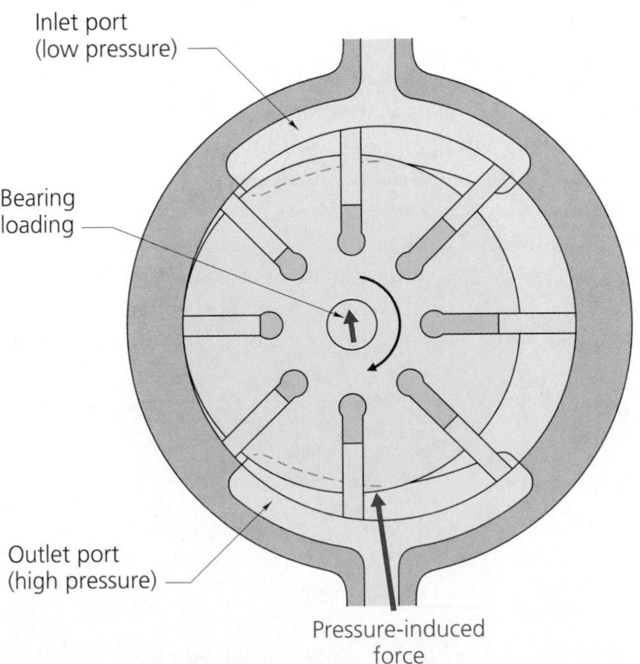

FIGURE 21.17 Force Imbalance in an Unbalanced-Vane Pump Causes High Bearing Loads

is minimized by pressure or by spring-loading of the side plates. Because this pump is unbalanced due to high pressure on the outlet side and low pressure on the inlet side, bearing wear is inherent to its design. The bearing wear is tolerated, however, because the pump is simple, easy to produce, and inexpensive. It can also be changed into a variable-displacement pump by changing the position of the cam ring.

Many factors must be considered when selecting a pump for a particular application: type of fluid to be pumped, the volume of fluid to be pumped, the total energy that must be delivered to the system by the pump, the power source for the pump (electric, steam turbine, diesel, etc.), configuration limitations (size), cost of the pump (installation and operation), and type of connections at the inlet and outlet.

Performance is often the most important consideration in pump selection. The operating pressure, the operating efficiency, and the delivered flow rate (often in gallons per minute) all are important. Other significant factors include physical size, mounting configuration and requirements, noise levels, and environmental effects. Unfortunately, no pump performance specifications exist that cover the entire fluid power industry.

Air compressors provide the energy to pneumatic circuits. They compress air (or another gas) from atmospheric pressure to a higher pressure for the fluid power circuit by reducing the volume of the gas. Air compressors usually are positive-displacement machines. They may be **reciprocating piston, rotary screw**, or **rotary vane** types. As air compresses, heat is generated. Portable and small industrial compressors are air cooled, but large industrial compressors must be water cooled. A single-piston air compressor can provide about 150 psi of pressure. Large, multistage compressors can provide 5000 psi.

21.4.4 Valves

Valves are important components in fluid power circuits because they control pressure, flow rate, and direction of fluid flow in circuits. Some flow control valve symbols are shown in Figure 21.18. **Flow control valves** control the volume flow rate of fluid through the circuit. The speed of hydraulic or pneumatic cylinders and motors is determined by their own displacement and the amount of fluid available: The slower the volume flow rate of fluid, the slower the volume displacement fills and the slower the motor turns or the cylinder extends or retracts.

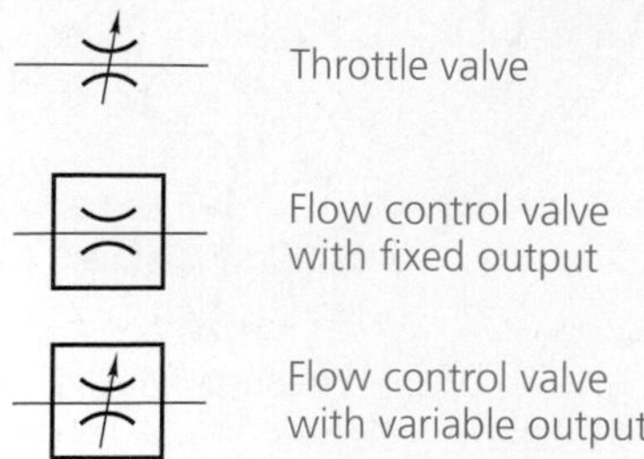

FIGURE 21.18 Flow Control Valve Symbols

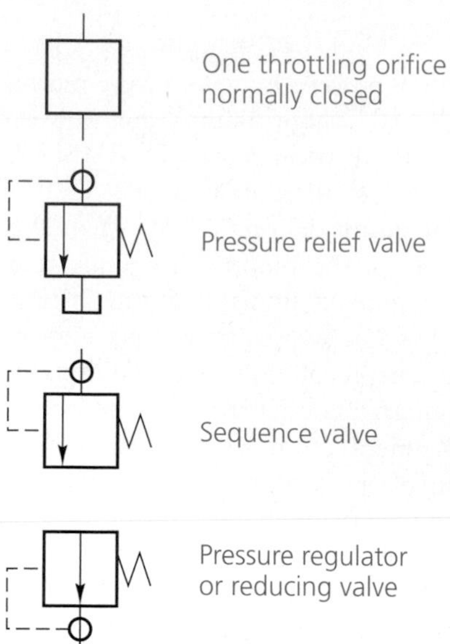

FIGURE 21.19 Pressure Control Valve Symbols

Pressure control valves (Fig. 21.19) control the pressure for some purpose in fluid power circuits. The most common type of pressure control valve is the **pressure relief valve**. Pressure relief valves are found in most fluid power circuits because they provide overload (overpressure) protection for the circuit. Since both hydraulic and pneumatic components are designed to operate under specific pressures, overloading the circuit with too much pressure is extremely dangerous. Safety pressure relief valves divert the flow back to the reservoir at a set pressure and, thus, prevent overpressure from developing within the circuit. Pressure relief valves may also vent the excess pressure and fluid into the atmosphere or another, external container.

Pressure regulating or pressure-reducing valves maintain specific (reduced) pressures at different locations in a circuit. You have probably seen or worked with air pressure regulating valves on small air compressors. Hydraulic pressure reducing valves maintain reduced pressures at different locations in the circuit.

Sequence valves are designed for machines that must act in proper sequence. Sequence valves operate when pressure has reached a certain level. Although they act much like a relief valve, a sequence valve diverts fluid flow to another part of the system to do useful work and not just back to the reservoir.

Directional control valves control the direction of fluid flow in a fluid power circuit. A simple example is a *check valve,* which ensures that fluid flows in one direction in the circuit. Other types include two-way, three-way, and four-way directional control valves. Most directional control valves change the path of the fluid by moving a sliding spool inside the valve. The spool is often actuated manually, but circuits that are controlled by computers use an electric

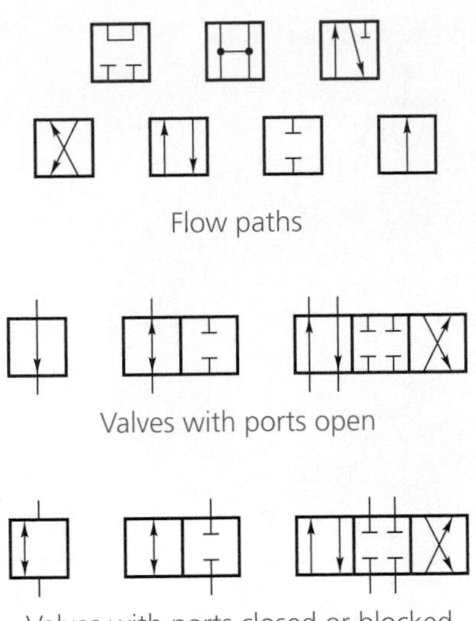

FIGURE 21.20 Valve Flow Paths and Ports Open and Closed

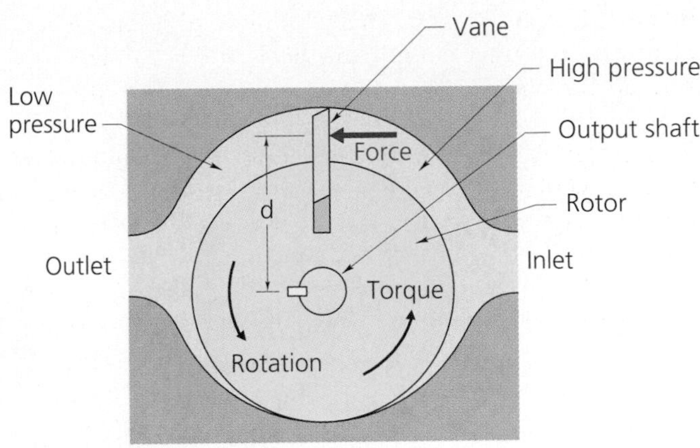

(a) Torque in an unbalanced vane motor

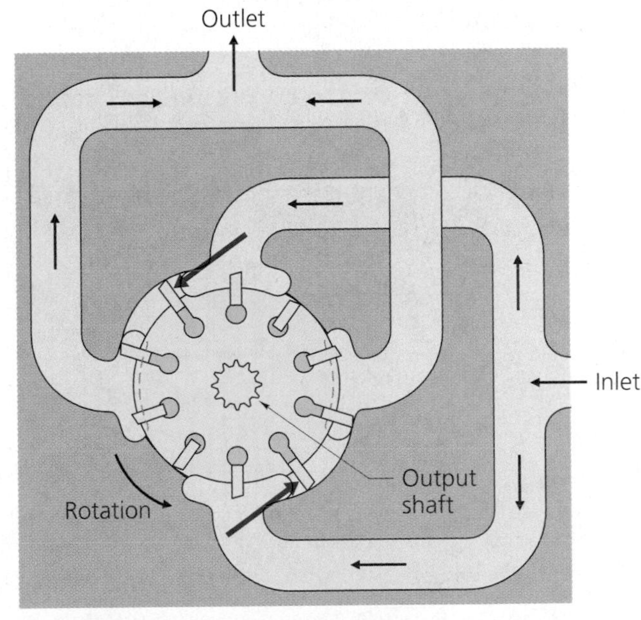

(b) Torque produced on both sides of a balanced vane motor

FIGURE 21.21 Torque Development in an Unbalanced- and a Balanced-Vane Motor

solenoid (coil) to move the spool. There are many styles of each directional control valve because of the many ways to actuate them and because of the many possible internal configurations of the spool inside the valve itself.

Several of the internal configurations (flow paths) of directional spool valves are shown in Figure 21.20. The top section, labled "Flow paths," shows that the fluid may take several paths through the circuit. The fluid flows differently throughout the circuit depending on whether the port is open or closed (blocked). Whatever configuration is required for your circuit, a directional control valve for it is available as a standard item from fluid power suppliers.

A two-way valve may be used to operate a pneumatic cylinder because air can be vented to the atmosphere. In other words, air can extend or retract the cylinder, but the exhaust gas can be vented to the air from the other side of the cylinder. However, to control a hydraulic cylinder you must use a four-way valve because a return path for the hydraulic fluid is needed for when the extended cylinder retracts. Hydraulic fluid must have a return path and cannot be vented to the environment. There are also different neutral positions for the valve (Fig. 21.20). Sometimes a cylinder will be locked in place in neutral. Other designs will call for a hydraulic motor to continue operating in neutral.

21.4.5 Actuators

An **actuator** in a fluid power system is a device that converts the fluid power energy to mechanical energy for doing useful work. *Linear actuators* are called pneumatic or hydraulic cylinders or rams. *Rotary actuators* are called pneumatic or hydraulic motors. Thus, the motion produced in fluid power systems is either linear or rotary.

A hydraulic motor is much like an electric motor except that the motion of the fluid causes the shaft to rotate. Cylinders extend and retract to perform one cycle of linear motion. Both cylinders and motors are types of *actuators*. There are several different types of rotary actuators (motors). Hydraulic pumps can usually serve as hydraulic motors with little or no modification. The function of a motor is opposite to that of a pump. Types of motors include vane motors (Fig. 21.21), gear motors (Fig. 21.22), and piston motors. Mathematically, torque = force × distance. Usual units for torque are lb·ft or in·lb. SI units are N·m.

The simplest type of cylinder is the single-acting cylinder (Fig. 21.23). A piston inside the housing (the barrel) is attached to a rod that extends outside the cylinder housing. Fluid force is applied on only one side of the piston. The cylinder retracts by gravity or by some external force only. A double-acting differential cylinder is shown in Figure 21.24. Fluid may flow on either side of the piston. Because of the

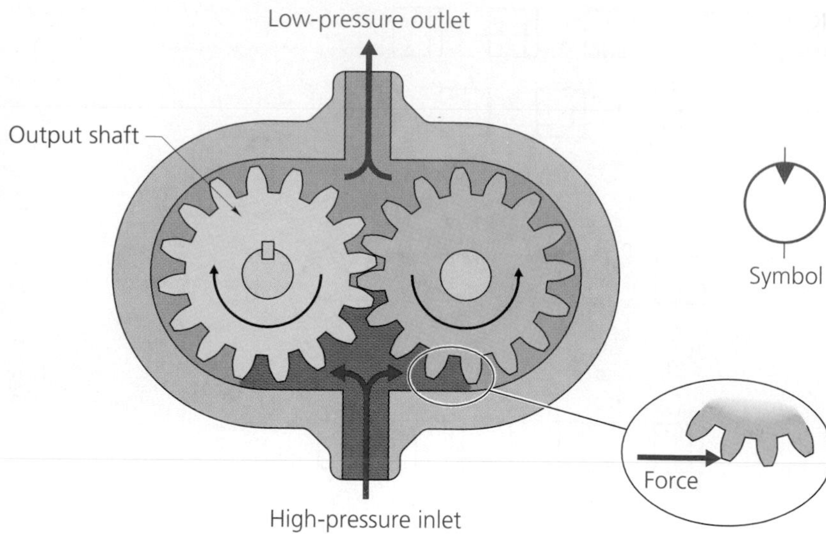

FIGURE 21.22 Torque Development in a Gear Motor

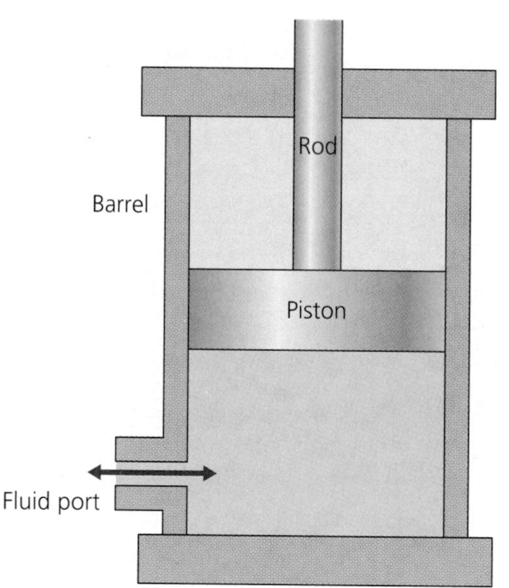

FIGURE 21.23 Single-Acting Linear Actuator

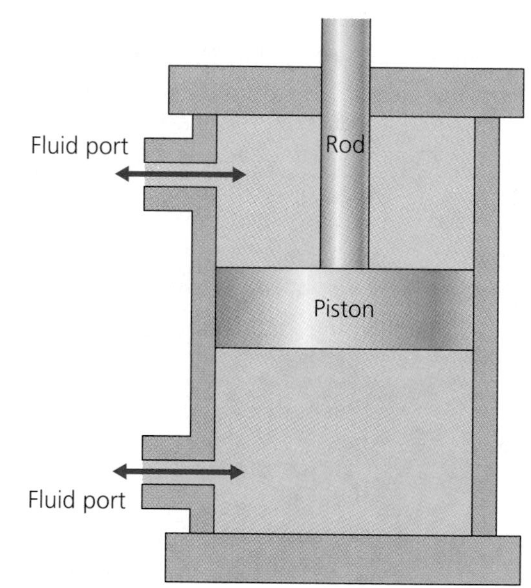

FIGURE 21.24 Double-Acting Differential Linear Actuator

volume taken up by the rod, the rod's extend and retract speeds will not be the same. The extend and retract forces will also be different, for the same reason. Double-acting nondifferential cylinders with rods on both sides of the piston that extend and retract at the same rate also exist.

21.5 FLUID POWER DIAGRAMS

The four types of fluid power circuit diagrams are pictorial, cutaway, graphical, and combination. Pictorial and cutaway diagrams, like other pictorial diagrams in engineering graphics, are visualization aids. **Fluid power pictorials** show the actual layout of the pipe, and the symbols on those drawings are outline symbols that show the actual shape of the components. **Cutaway drawings** show the internal features and are commonly used for understanding circuit operation and for construction. Pictorial and cutaway diagrams contain symbols that are not really standardized, and so they are not covered here.

Graphical diagrams employ standard symbols to represent components; the piping is represented by single lines. A diagram showing the operation of a simple reciprocating circuit is given in Figure 21.25. A diagram showing the operation of a pneumatic powered door opener is presented in Figure 21.26.

Interpreting a fluid power diagram is a simple matter of

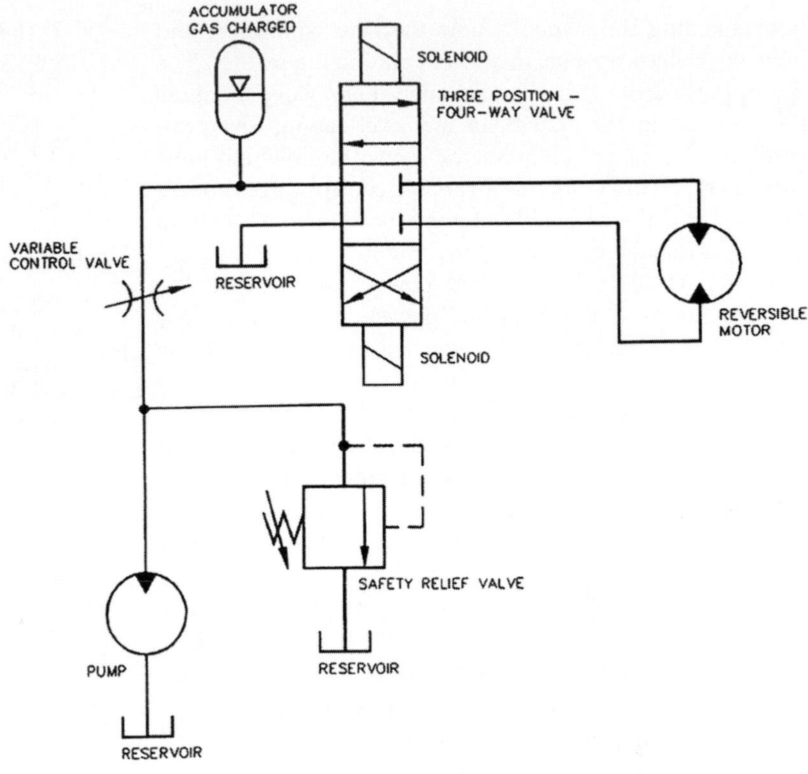

FIGURE 21.25 Simple Reciprocating Hydraulic Circuit

FIGURE 21.26 Circuit for Pneumatic Powered Door Opener

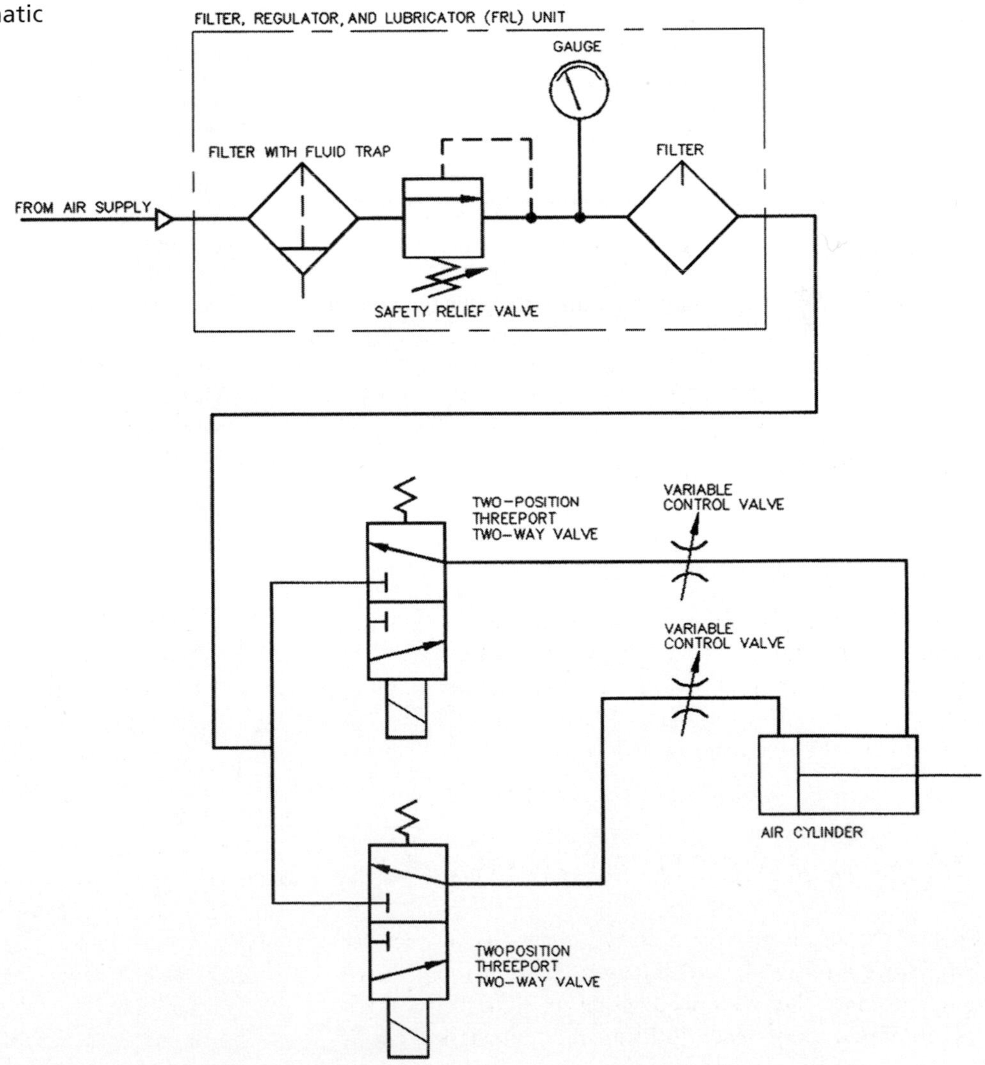

understanding the symbols, how they are connected, and how the valves operate in the circuit. In Figure 21.25, a pump powers the circuit and a safety relief valve monitors the pressure in the system for any overloading (overpressure). A gas-charged accumulator keeps the flow and pressure in the system constant. A variable control valve controls the speed of the reversible motor. The directional control valve controls the direction of the motor.

Figure 21.26's graphical fluid power diagram describes the operation of a pneumatic powered automatic door opener. A pneumatic cylinder attached to a bracket on the door actually opens and closes the door. Air is supplied from a large compressor and tank that is capable of providing all the needed volume flow rate of fluid. A filter, regulator, and lubricator (FRL) unit regulates the air pressure to an appropriate value (around 100 psi). The air is also filtered and lubricated. A safety relief valve prevents overpressure. Two solenoid-operated two-position three-port two-way valves extend and retract the cylinder (open and close the door). Two variable flow control valves control the speed at which the door opens and closes. Notice that the extend and retract steps are activated independently. A quadriplegic often has trouble going through an open door in the measured amount of time if the circuit is merely timed. Here, there is a way to actuate independently the open-and-close mechanism; that is, the door opens on command and closes only after a different control command.

QUIZ

True or False

1. Pneumatic systems are more rigid than hydraulic fluid power systems.
2. Safety relief valves are not really necessary components of fluid power circuits.
3. There is no difference between work and power in fluid power systems.
4. A linear actuator (cylinder) always extends and retracts at the same speed.
5. Mechanical advantage means that you can lift a small force with a large input force in a hydraulic system.
6. The only purpose of a hydraulic fluid is to transmit a force in a fluid power system.
7. A graphical diagram of a fluid power circuit shows the internal construction of each component.
8. All fluid power circuits should contain a safety relief valve.

Fill in the Blanks

9. The rate at which work is done in a fluid power system is called __________.
10. In the SI system, a newton per square meter (N/m^2) is called a __________.
11. The __________ __________ is a measure of how much the viscosity of a fluid changes with temperature.
12. The two type types of viscosity values are __________ and __________.
13. A __________ holds and cools the hydraulic fluid in a fluid power system.
14. The rate at which a pneumatic or hydraulic cylinder extends or retracts can be controlled with a __________ valve.
15. __________ __________ valves control the flow path in fluid power circuits.
16. __________, __________, __________, and __________ are types of positive-displacement hydraulic pumps.

Answer the Following

17. What are the basic differences between a pneumatic and a hydraulic fluid power circuit?
18. Describe two modern applications of fluid power circuits that have an impact on your life.
19. Name and describe the major components of a basic hydraulic fluid power system.
20. Other than holding fluid, what are the basic functions of a hydraulic reservoir?
21. Describe the concept of mechanical advantage as it relates to fluid power systems.
22. What is viscosity? Why is the concept so important to fluid power applications?
23. Describe the operation of a basic fluid power pump.
24. Describe the difference between a hydraulic or pneumatic motor and a hydraulic or pneumatic pump.

EXERCISES

Exercises may be assigned as sketching, instrument, or CAD projects. Transfer the given information to an "A"-size sheet of .25 in. grid paper. Complete all views, and solve for proper visibility, including centerlines, object lines, and hidden lines. Exercises that are not assigned by the instructor can be sketched in the text to provide practice and to enhance understanding of the preceding material.

Exercise 21.1 Draw a graphical diagram of a pneumatic circuit that extends and retracts a single-acting pneumatic cylinder. The circuit contains the following components:

Air supply
FRL unit
Air cylinder
Safety relief valve
Solenoid-operated two-position two-way valve
Check valve

Exercise 21.2 Draw a graphical diagram of a hydraulic circuit that extends and retracts a double-acting hydraulic cylinder. The circuit contains the following components:

Reservoir
Pump
Accumulator
Safety relief valve
Three-position four-way valve
Double-acting hydraulic cylinder
Check valve

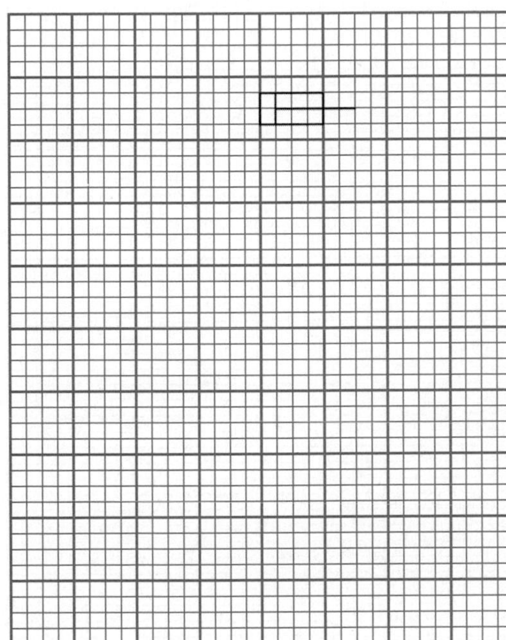

EXERCISE 21.1

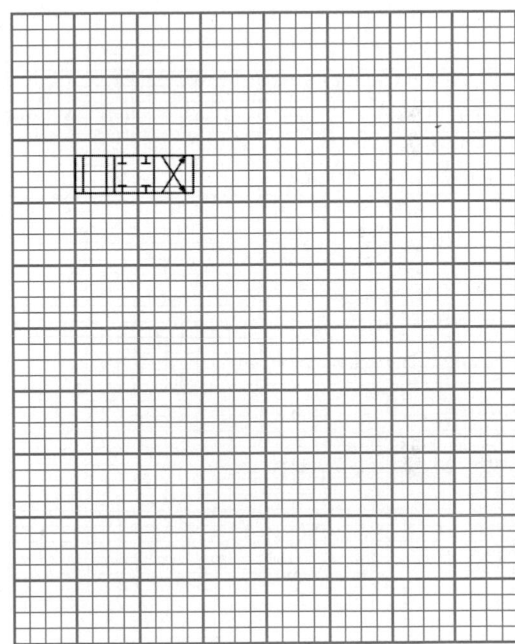

EXERCISE 21.2

Exercise 21.3 Draw a graphical diagram of a hydraulic circuit that runs a hydraulic motor in both directions. The circuit contains the following components:

Reservoir
Pump
Accumulator
Safety relief valve
Three-position four-way valve
Flow control valve
Hydraulic motor
Check valve

Exercise 21.4 Draw a graphical diagram of a pneumatic circuit that runs a pneumatic motor in both directions. The circuit contains the following components:

Air supply
Air tank
FRL unit
Safety relief valve
Four-way valve
Pneumatic motor
Check valve
Flow control valve

Exercise 21.5 Calculate the approximate force a pneumatic cylinder can apply if it has a diameter of 2 in. and is connected to shop air of 100 psi.

Exercise 21.6 Calculate the approximate force a hydraulic cylinder can apply if it has a diameter of 2 in. and is connected to a 2500 psi circuit.

Exercise 21.7 Calculate the mechanical advantage required to lift a 1000 lb object with a 10 lb force. Design one possible hydraulic lift that would produce such a mechanical advantage.

Exercise 21.8 Calculate the approximate force in newtons that is required to lift 1000N if the mechanical advantage of the system is 5. Design one possible hydraulic lift that would produce such a mechanical advantage. Use SI units.

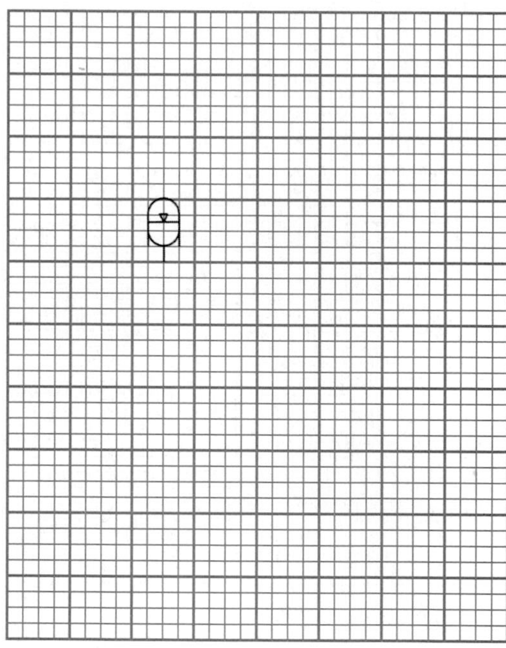

EXERCISE 21.3

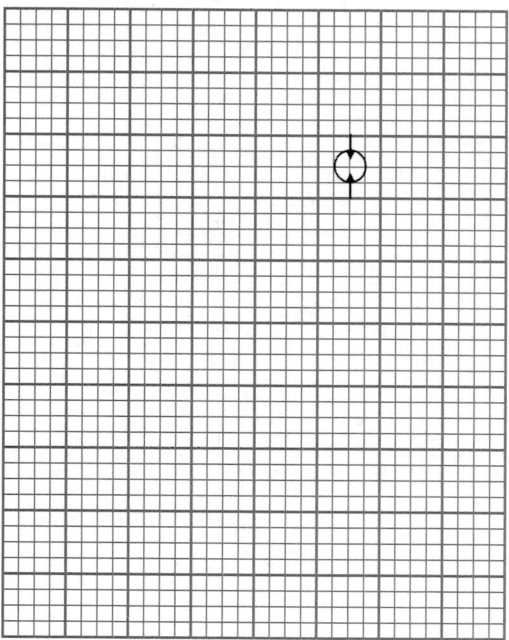

EXERCISE 21.4

PROBLEMS

Problems may be assigned as sketching, instrument, or CAD projects.

Problem 21.1 Redesign the pneumatic circuit in Figure 21.26 so that it runs two pneumatic motors simultaneously. Add the appropriate valves to make the circuit run efficiently.

Problem 21.2 Redesign the hydraulic circuit in Figure 21.25 so that it controls two double-acting hydraulic cylinders simultaneously. Add the appropriate valves to make the circuit run efficiently.

Problem 21.3 Design a hydraulic lift that will lift up to a 3500 lb vehicle with a mechanical advantage of at least 10. Make realistic assumptions concerning the areas in which the cylinders must be located to complete the operation safely.

Problem 21.4 Design a hydraulic circuit that runs three different hydraulic cylinders and one hydraulic motor. Each actuator must be able to run independently and must be controlled by electrically driven solenoid valves. Choose the appropriate port positions from Figure 21.20 to ensure that the cylinders remain extended and locked. The motor must also remain locked in position when its valve is not activated.

WELDING DRAWINGS

Chapter 22

LEARNING OBJECTIVES

Upon completion of this chapter you will be able to:

1. Understand welding methods and processes.
2. Determine the weldability of a material.
3. Identify various types of welds, symbols, and joint preparations.
4. Produce complete welding symbols.
5. Recognize supplementary welding symbols.
6. Apply and position appropriate weld type, size, length, and location for complete welding symbols.

22.1 INTRODUCTION

Knowledge of welding processes (Fig. 22.1) is essential for engineers because it is one of the basic manufacturing processes in industry. As an engineer, you will need to know how to communicate to the welder the type, dimensions, and position of the weld to be used. It is important to keep welds simple and to eliminate possible misunderstandings on engineering communications. Intricate welds take time and are expensive; moreover, time is often lost when interpreting the complex symbols. Through education and experience, you will learn the welding theory necessary for determining adequate weld sizes, placement, and welding procedures.

Welds are used to fasten an assembly together permanently. The parts to be fastened can be of the same type of metal or of dissimilar metals. Welding is for assemblies (Fig. 22.2) that require no disassembly for service or maintenance and where only one or a small number of assemblies is required. Because the heat that accompanies the welding process will distort the workpiece, any machining needed on a welded assembly is completed *after* the welding.

22.2 WELDING METHODS

Welding is the procedure by which two pieces of metal are fused together along a line or a surface between them or at a certain point. Welding can be classified by process or by source of energy. With **nonpressure welding** (fusion and brazing), no mechanical pressure is applied. The pieces of metal are welded at the point of contact by heat, which is created by an electric arc or a gas flame. **Pressure welding**, or **resistance welding**, forms a joint by passing an electrical current through the area of the joint as mechanical pressure is applied. Welding may also be classified by the source of energy for developing the temperatures required to produce the molten pool (chemical, electrical, mechanical, etc.). It is

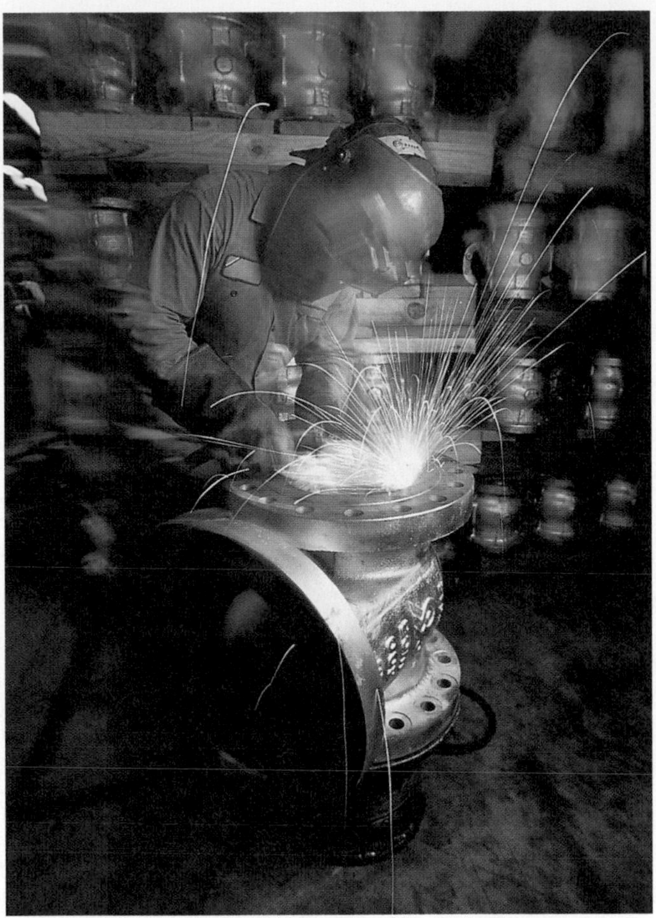

FIGURE 22.1 Welding

usually convenient, however, to classify welds into three separate categories: resistance welding, gas welding, and arc welding.

Resistance welding involves applying heat and pressure at the same time, usually by a machine. Two or more parts can be welded by passing an electric current through the work as pressure is applied. Electronic beam, laser, and ultrasonic methods are also used. The main types of resistance welds are spot, seam, projection, flash, and upset.

In **fusion welding**, also known as **gas** or **oxyfuel welding**, heat is created by the combustion of a gas and air or pure oxygen. In oxyacetylene welding, a flame is produced by the combustion of oxygen and acetylene gases. Today, this type of welding is less common (except when flame cutting). Besides guiding the torch, the welder may also introduce the filler rod as the welding material (Fig. 22.1).

22.2.1 Arc Welding

The most common method of welding is **arc welding,** which includes submerged arc welding, shielded arc welding, gas-metal arc welding, and gas-tungsten arc welding.

In **submerged arc welding,** coalescence is produced by the heating from an electric arc generated between the electrode and the workpiece. The workpiece is shielded by a blanket of granular, fusible material called **flux.** The flux protects the weld pool (floats on it). Leftover flux creates slag, which must be removed at the end of the process. The filler material is obtained from a supplementary welding rod or from the electrode itself. In this process, loose flux (also called *melt* or *welding composition*) is placed over the joint to be welded. After the arc is established, the flux melts to form a shield that coats the molten metal (Fig. 22.3). A bare wire electrode is used in this process instead of a coated electrode, and the flux is supplied separately.

In **shielded arc welding,** the electric arc is produced by passing a current from a coated metal electrode to the material to be welded. A gap exists between the electrode and the workpiece. Fusion takes place during the intermingling of the molten metals. Figure 22.4 illustrates manual shielded arc welding. Notice how slag is formed on top of the base metal or on top of the solidified weld metal. Slag must be removed *after* the welding. Figure 22.3, by way of contrast, shows how the electrode in submerged arc welding extends into the work itself and how the base materials are fused together in molten weld metal. The flux may have

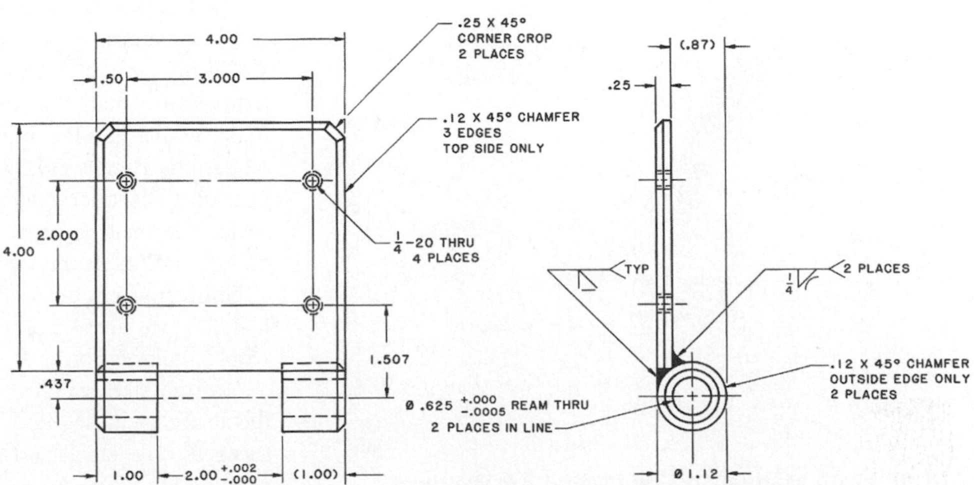

FIGURE 22.2 Weldment Detail

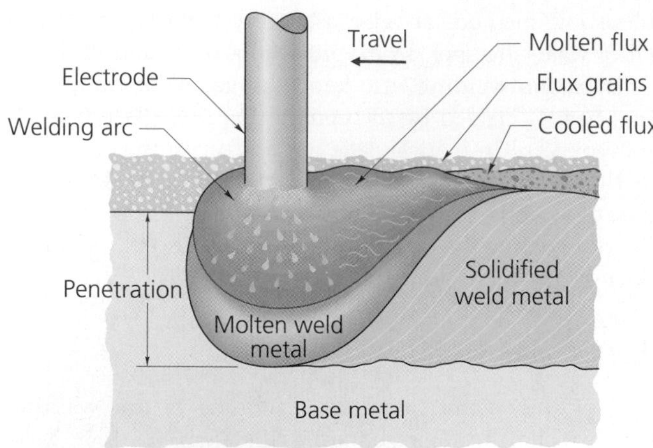

FIGURE 22.3 Submerged Arc Welding

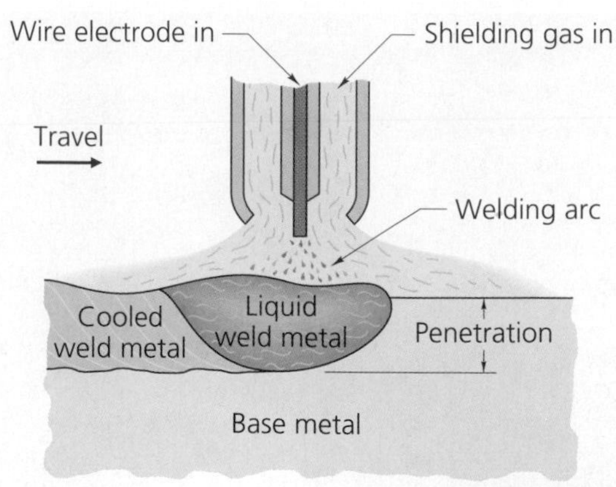

FIGURE 22.5 Gas-Metal Arc Welding

some additives that become part of the weld. The penetration is much deeper than in shielded arc welding.

Shielded arc welding is usually done manually by a trained welder. It is found quite often in structural systems (see Fig. 22.10) because it is easy to use in the field. It is also good for **tack welding** (holding parts in position prior to final welding).

In **gas-metal arc welding (GMAW),** heat is created electrically, as in the process just described, but the shielding is accomplished by a blanket of gas (Fig. 22.5). The term **MIG** is normally used when referring to this process, not GMAW. Pressure may or may not be involved, but welding is generally pressureless. The electrode is the filler metal and becomes an integral part of the weld. The filler metal may also be added to the welding zone *prior* to welding, in which case inert gases are fed into the welding area to form a blanket. This welding procedure is for magnesium, aluminum, and carbon steel.

Gas-tungsten arc welding (GTAW) is different from GMAW because the electrode is tungsten. The term **TIG** is commonly used when referring to this process, not GTAW. The electrode transmits electric current but is not a filler metal. The TIG process produces root beads of high quality and is seldom used for the entire weld unless there are special circumstances. TIG is typically for aluminum, stainless steel, and exotic materials.

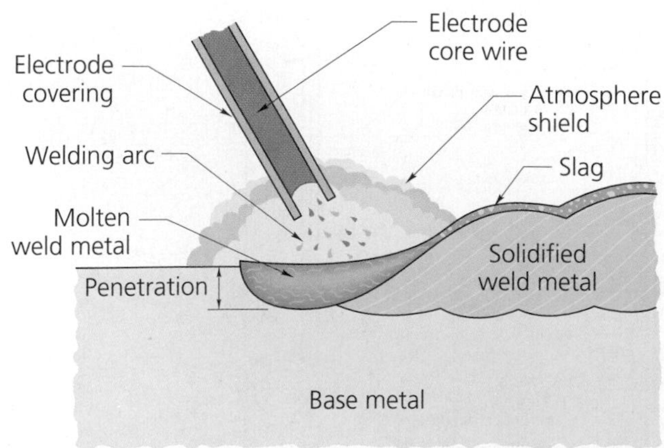

FIGURE 22.4 Manual Shielded Metal Arc Welding

22.3 WELDING MATERIALS

Weldability is the capacity of a metal to be welded in relation to its suitability to the design and service requirements. Metals that become fused during the welding process undergo changes similar to those that occur during manufacture. Chemical, thermal, physical, and metallurgical changes make it essential for the engineer to understand the nature of the materials to be fused. The metallurgy of welds is as complex as the metallurgy of the material. The weldability of different materials varies greatly, and so does the process by which the weld is completed. When welding cast iron to steel, for instance, cast-iron rods are the welding material and the steel must be preheated before an adequate weld can be made. When welding steel castings, there is no easy rule for the process because the carbon content can vary greatly between types of steel. Steel welding rods usually produce an adequate weld.

Brass is ordinarily brazed instead of welded because of the high temperature produced by the welding process and the low melting point of brass. **Brazing** is the process of soldering with a nonferrous alloy that melts at a lower temperature than that of the metals being joined. Copper must serve as a filler, and care must be taken not to produce oxidation when welding materials containing copper. The heat and the filler material create a metallurgical bond in which the melting point is above 840°F but still below the melting points of the materials being joined.

Soldering employs an alloy of tin and lead to join two metallic surfaces. Soldering requires nonferrous metals whose melting points are below 427°C (800°F).

Carbon steel welding is usually completed via shielded metal arc welding. Rod iron has characteristics similar to those of mild steel, and a similar process is involved in its welding.

Focus On . . .

USING THE LASER TO WELD

One of the most important and most widely used applications of the laser is in fiber-optic communication systems. Laser-based communication systems are prevalent in the United States and Japan and are rapidly spreading throughout Europe. Laser beams that are transmitted by glass fibers carry thousands of times more information than copper cables. Even though lasers are a relatively new technology (1960), they have become one of our most useful tools.

Laser applications in industry, ranging from manufacturing to the space program, have become quite popular. Laser-based tools serve for heat treating, cutting, drilling, and welding. Even though laser cutting and drilling are used, laser welding is by far the most common process.

There are two different laser welding processes. One is conduction, which occurs at the surface of the material; the other is deep penetration, in which heat is moved below the surface of the material. The conduction process is for joining thin sheets. The deep-penetration process creates a more efficient weld, with high tensile strength and hardness. Laser welding has achieved great success in shipbuilding, pipeline fabrication for the arctic, nickel steels, and low-alloy steels. The National Aeronautics and Space Agency developed a way to weld aluminum effectively with a laser. Aluminum is difficult to weld because it has a low melting temperature. Because of the developed process, aluminum vessels can now contain a high-pressure gas. Other precision aluminum pieces can be fabricated by the same process.

In laser welding, the welding rod is eliminated. The welding is accomplished without the excess heat that distorts and even destroys some materials in conventional welding. Even two dissimilar materials can be joined with laser welding. As larger and more powerful lasers are built, laser welding applications will grow in size and in number. Welding with lasers has made fabrications possible today that were impossible only forty years ago.

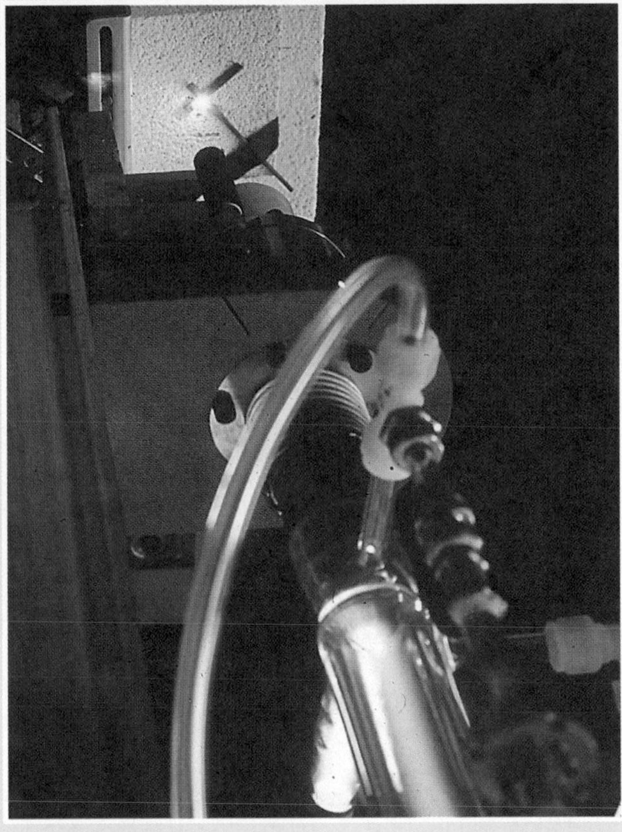

Laser welding.

Arc welding using robots.

For aluminum and aluminum alloys, most of the commercial welding and brazing processes can be used, though the most common are GTAW and GMAW. Various problems are encountered when employing the acetylene process to weld aluminum because of an oxide film that prevents metal flow at welding temperatures. Aluminum is characterized by its low melting point and high thermal conductivity.

22.4 TYPES OF WELDS

As an engineer, you will be concerned with specifying symbols for the various welds and joint preparations. Weld symbols and types of welds are classified by process. Resistance weld symbols are grouped under flash or upset,

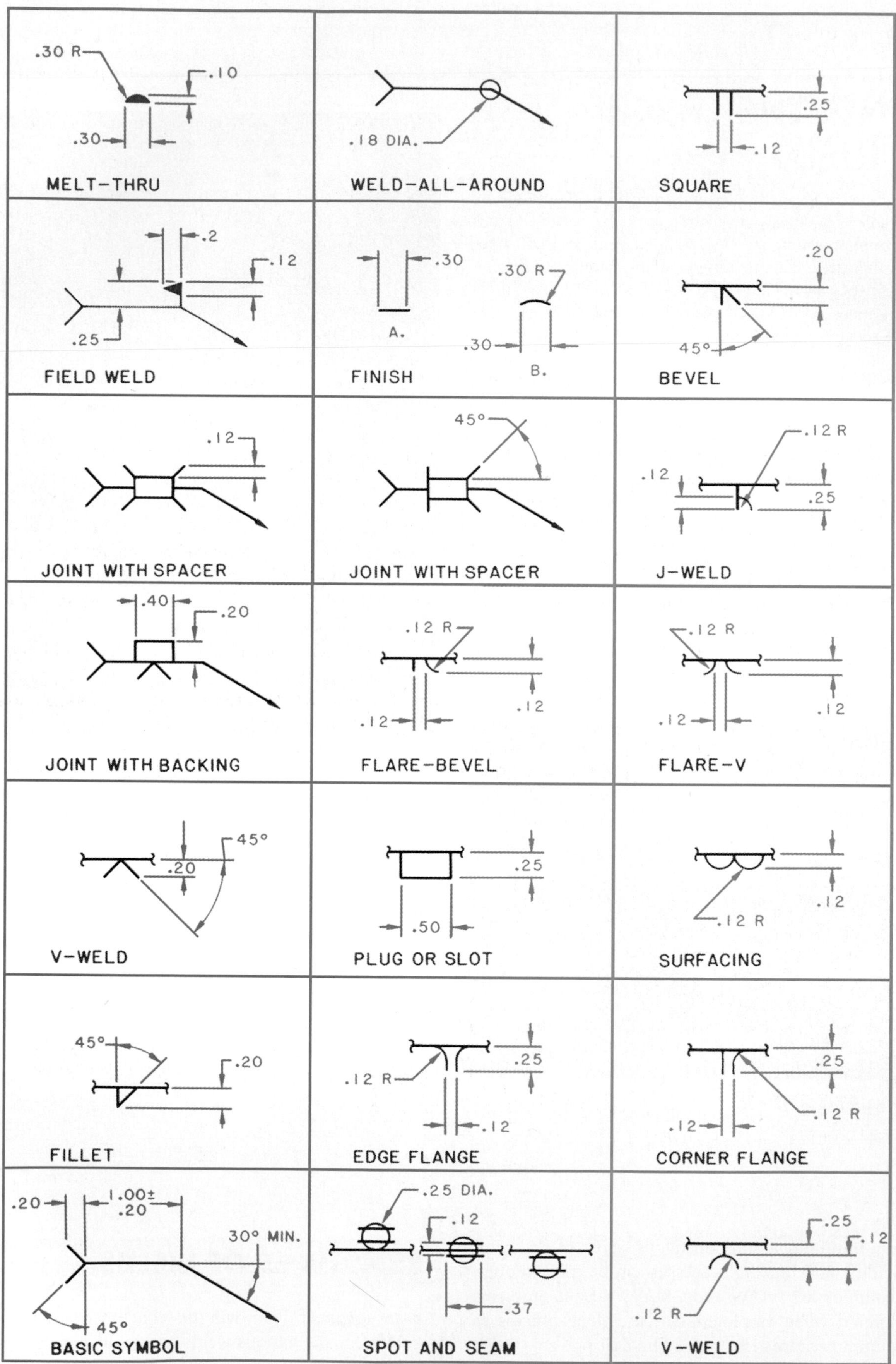

FIGURE 22.6 Weld Symbols

projection, seam, and spot, with supplementary descriptions such as contour weld and field weld.

Arc and gas weld symbols are divided into groove types (bevel, square, J, U, V), bead, fillet, plug, and slot welds. For bead and fillet welds, no special preparations are necessary for the metal. The essential difference between the various groove weld types is the edge preparation of the material to be welded—that is, whether it is to remain square, is to be beveled, or is to be machined into a V, U, or J shape. Although these welds can be combined, an effort should be made to keep welding symbols for similar joints both the same and simple.

22.4.1 Welding Symbols

Welding symbols communicate to the fabricator the weld type, size, and location. All welds can be identified by their profile or cross-sectional view. The welding drawing shows the parts or units that are to be made by welding (Fig. 22.2). Symbols define and locate the specific welds to be used. Each joint in the welding process must be fully described. The weld symbol (Fig. 22.6) denotes the desired type of weld: fillet, square, bevel, J, U, V, flare V, back, weld, arc seam, spot, plug, or slot. The complete welding symbol takes into account all welding information that might be needed: weld type, size, length, location, and place of construction (field or shop). Figure 22.7 shows the standard welding symbol and the location of its elements. This type of symbol, with the exception of the field weld flag, which is used by only a few companies, is standard throughout industry. The components of the complete welding symbol and their location are provided in this figure.

Welding symbols are composed of three basic parts:

- An **arrow** that points to the joint
- A **reference line** upon which all the dimensions and other data are placed
- The **weld symbol**, which indicates the type of weld required

The assembled welding symbol consists of the following eight elements or whatever number of these elements is necessary (Fig. 22.7):

Reference line
Arrow
Basic weld symbols
Dimensions and other data
Supplementary symbols
Finish symbols
Tail
Specifications, process, or other reference

Figure 22.8 shows five different joints that may be encountered in the construction of welded assemblies. Figure 22.9 offers a sample of various welds as applied to the particular joint. Besides the welding symbol, a cross-sectional view of the weld is drawn with the weld itself filled in. This provides a graphical description of the weld along with the symbolic description found in the welding symbol. The complete welding symbol is the most important information given to the welder. In many applications, the graphic representation of the weld is not shown on the drawing—only the symbol (see, for example, Fig. 22.13).

Usually the same welding process is referenced through-

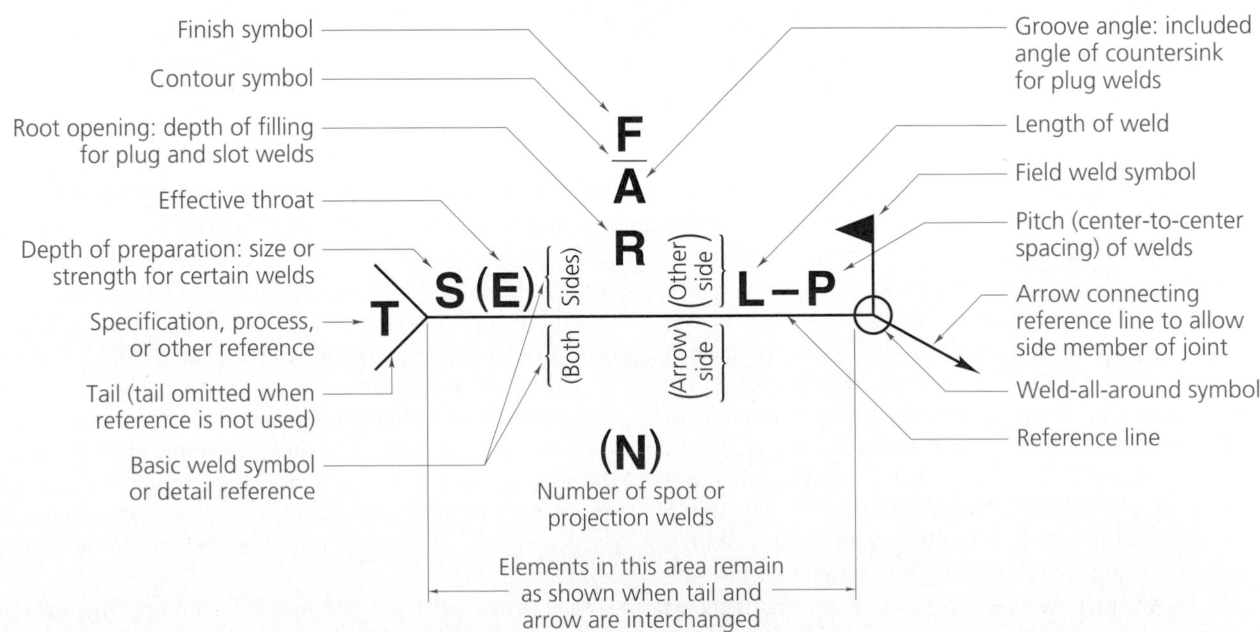

FIGURE 22.7 Standard Location of Elements of a Welding Symbol

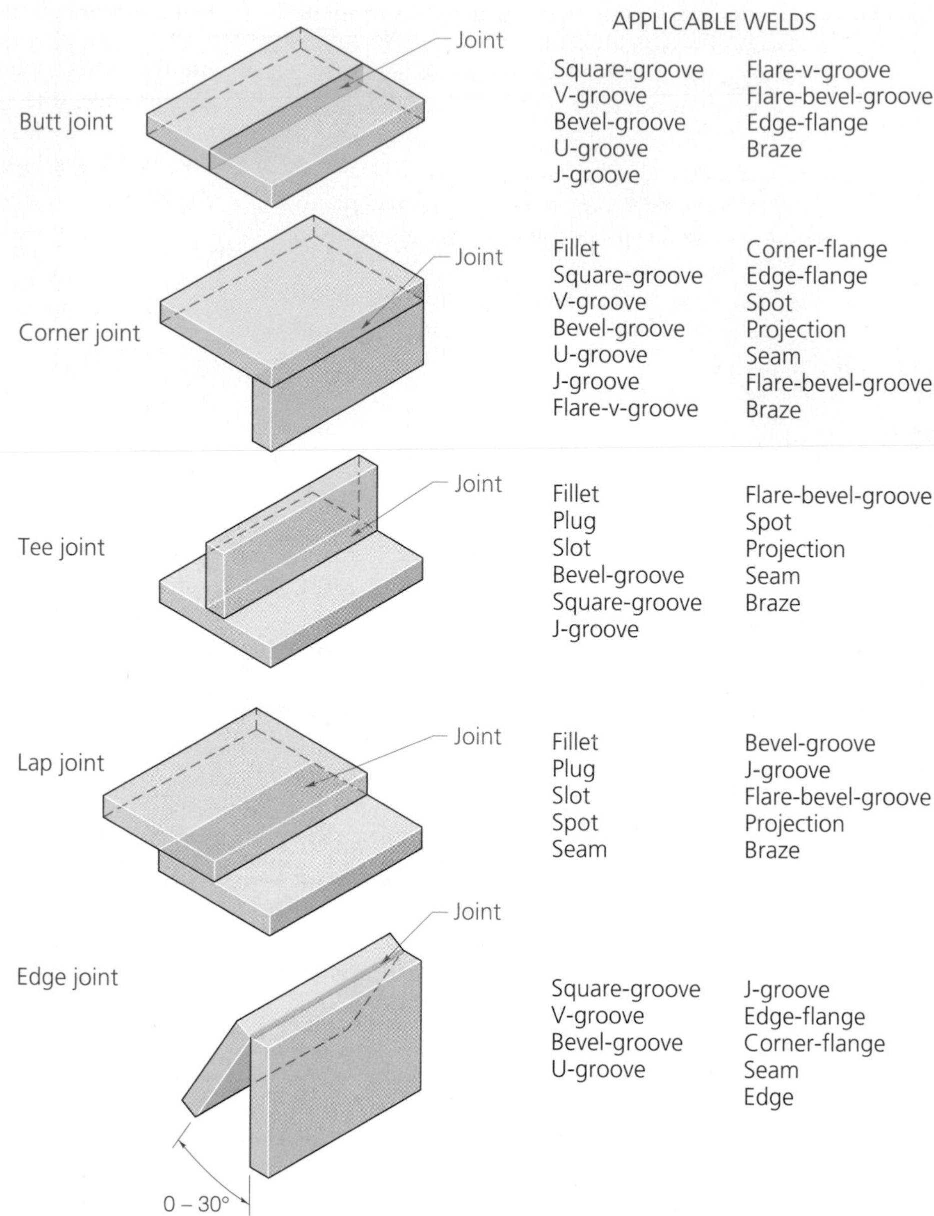

FIGURE 22.8 Basic Types of Joints

out a drawing, as in Figure 22.10. If this is not the case—for instance, when the drawing contains submerged arc welding by machine and by manual welding—each process must be noted on the symbol when pointing to the joint to be completed. The particular welding process should be placed at the tail of the welding symbol. The tail is omitted when references are not needed to supplement the symbol.

Engineers usually employ templates (or a library of standard parts on a computer) for drawing welding symbols. But you should not become dependent on templates, because drawings require various sizes of symbols, depending on whether or not it will be reduced onto microfilm. With a CAD system, welding symbols can be programmed into the menu for instant selection and placement by digitizing or explicit coordinates. Symbols are created as blocks, subfigures, or subparts and saved in a library. Inserting the symbol can then be done quickly and accurately.

The welding symbol should be of a size adequate to be readily visible to the fabricator. At the junction of the arrow and the reference line within the welding symbol a flag or a solid field weld designation may be placed. Work that is to be performed on the job site, rather than shop fabricated, will have a **field weld designation.** The edge preparation for such welds is completed at the fabricating plant (seldom at the job site itself), so shop drawings contain all the edge preparation designations. Only field drawings contain field weld symbols. For more information, see ANSI standard Y32.3.

The arrow in a welding symbol connects the reference line to the joint (Fig. 22.11). The side that the arrow is on is

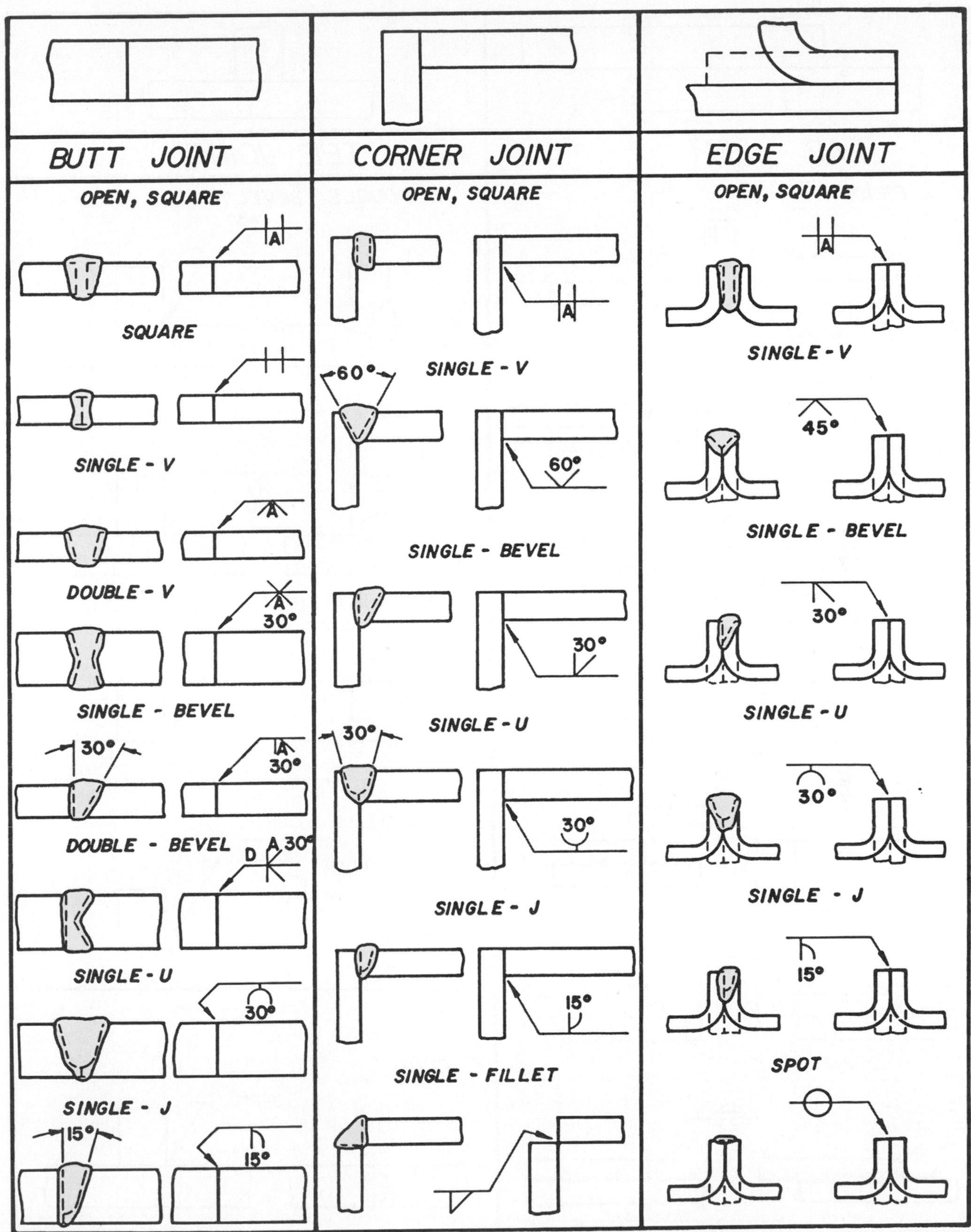

FIGURE 22.9 Joints and Appropriate Welds—*Continues*

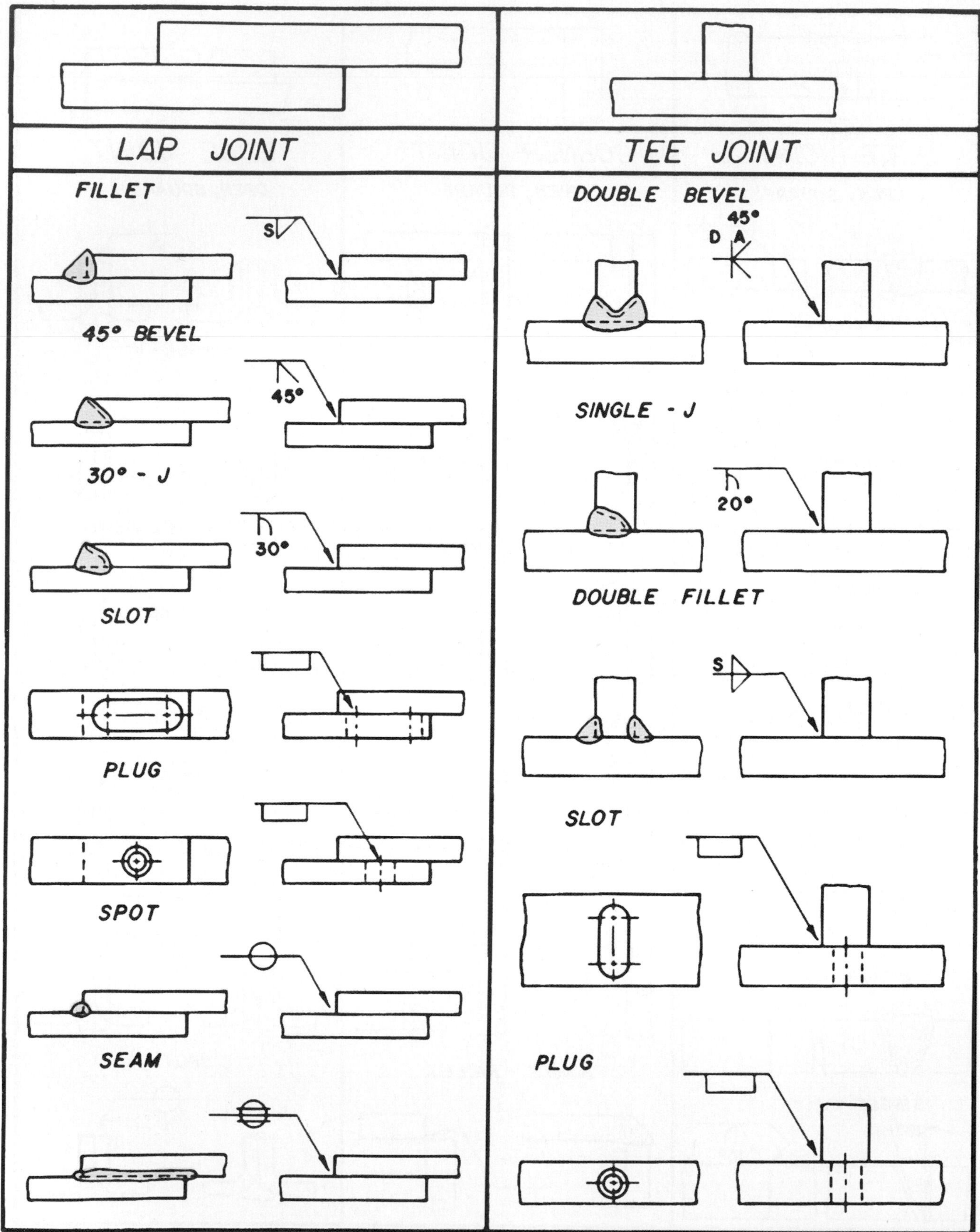

FIGURE 22.9 Joints and Appropriate Welds—*Continued*

DET.#	DESCRIPTION	QUAN
1	54 X 7.7, 2'-11" LG.	1
2	54 X 7.7, 13-1/4" LG.	2
3	54 X 7.7, 6-13/16" LG.	1
4	54 X 7.7, 8-3/4" LG.	1
	1/2" X 2-9/16", C.S. PLATE, 4" LG.	3
	8-P PART 298 FOR 3" PIPE	2

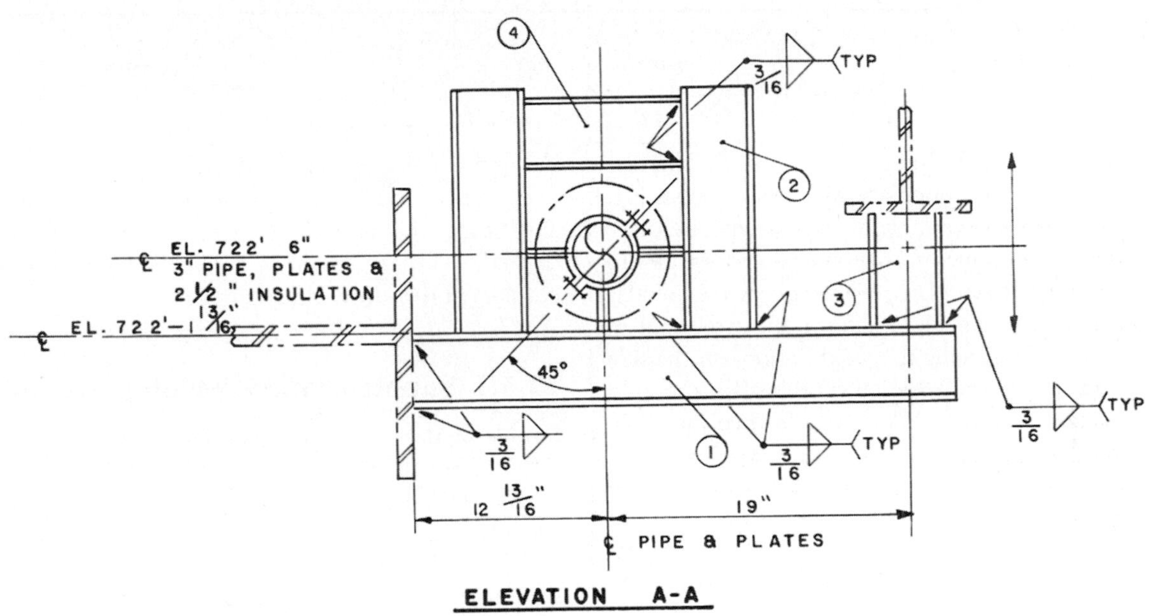

FIGURE 22.10 Welded Pipe Support Using Structural Steel

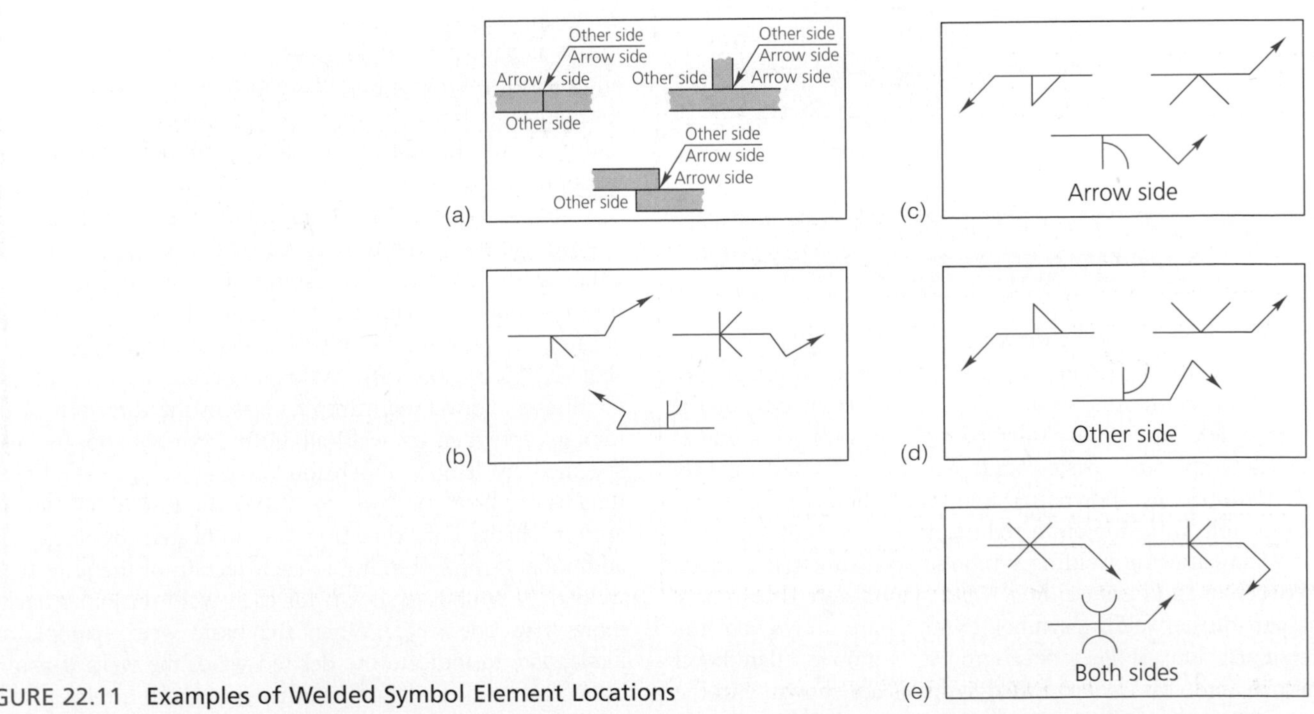

FIGURE 22.11 Examples of Welded Symbol Element Locations

FIGURE 22.12
Supplementary Symbols

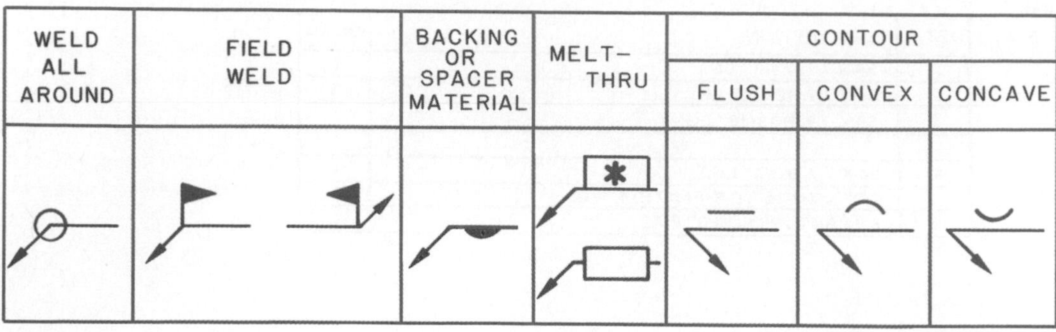

called the **arrow side** of the joint [Fig. 22.11(a)]. The side opposite the arrow is the **opposite side** [other side, Fig. 22.11(d)] of the joint, except for plug, slot, seam, and other projection welds, where the arrow connects the symbol to the surface to be acted on. The arrow side of the joint is always considered the near side. Welds on the arrow side of the joint are shown by placing the weld symbol on the side nearest to the reader. To show welds on both sides, the weld symbol is placed on both sides of the reference line [Fig. 22.11(e)].

In many situations one welding symbol is shown on the drawing and a note is included that specifies the type of weld to be used on the entire drawing—such as ALL WELDS TO BE 4 IN. UNLESS OTHERWISE NOTED. On welds that are to be on all sides of a particular joint, the **weld-all-around symbol** is placed at the junction of the arrow line and the reference line, which may also contain a field weld symbol at the same joint (Fig. 22.12). When welds are to be finished or contoured, this requirement must be shown on the symbol (Fig. 22.12). It is also possible to combine different weld symbols in one welding symbol. Remember, the weld symbol is always placed according to the side of the joint on which the weld is to be made.

22.5 WELDING SYMBOL SPECIFICATIONS

Weld symbols are to be drawn as in Figure 22.6. The sizes shown in that figure are a guide for symbol construction, with their minimum values given. The actual size of the weld symbol and the welding symbol will vary according to the drawing size. Basic weld symbols on drawings are proportioned as shown in Figure 22.6 and are of a size compatible with microfilm reduction requirements.

When drawing welding symbols, no distinction is made between arc and gas welding. Weld symbols are shown only as part of the welding symbol. Symbols are drawn "on" the reference line. Fillet, bevel-groove, J-groove, flare-bevel groove, and corner-flange weld symbols are shown with the *perpendicular leg always to the left.* Symbols are drawn a uniform size throughout the drawing. If the arrow is directed to the outer surface of one of the members of the joint (plug, slot, seam, and projection welds) at the centerline of the desired weld, the member to which the arrow points is considered the arrow-side member.

22.5.1 Supplementary Welding Symbols

Supplementary welding symbols, shown in Figure 22.12, are used as applicable to define specific welding requirements. The *weld-all-around* symbol indicates welds that extend completely around a joint (Figs. 22.13 and 22.14). Welds completely around a joint in which the metal intersections at the points of welding are in more than one plane are also indicated by the weld-all-around symbol. The **melt-thru** symbol (Fig. 22.15) is used only where 100% joint or member penetration plus reinforcement is required in welds made from one side only. Reinforcement (melt-thru) height may be shown on the welding symbol [Fig. 22.15(a)]. Melt-thru that is to be made flush by mechanical means is shown by adding both the flush contour symbol and the finish symbol [Fig. 22.15(b)]. Melt-thru that is to be mechanically finished to a convex contour is shown by adding both the convex contour symbol and the finish symbol.

Contour symbols serve, as applicable, to indicate the appropriate weld contour desired (flat, convex, or concave), either with mechanical finishing (in conjunction with a finish symbol) or without. Finishing of welds, other than cleaning, is indicated by suitable contour and finish symbols [Fig. 22.15(b) and (c)]. Welds indicated by symbols are continuous between abrupt changes in the direction of the joint except when the weld-all-around symbol appears, or as specified by length dimension on the welding symbol or dimension lines on the view. Welds extending beyond abrupt changes in direction are indicated by means of additional arrows pointing to each section of the joint to be welded. A symbol is shown for each weld on joints having more than one weld. When the basic weld symbols are inadequate to indicate the desired weld, the weld is shown by a cross section, detail, or other data, with a reference on the welding symbol.

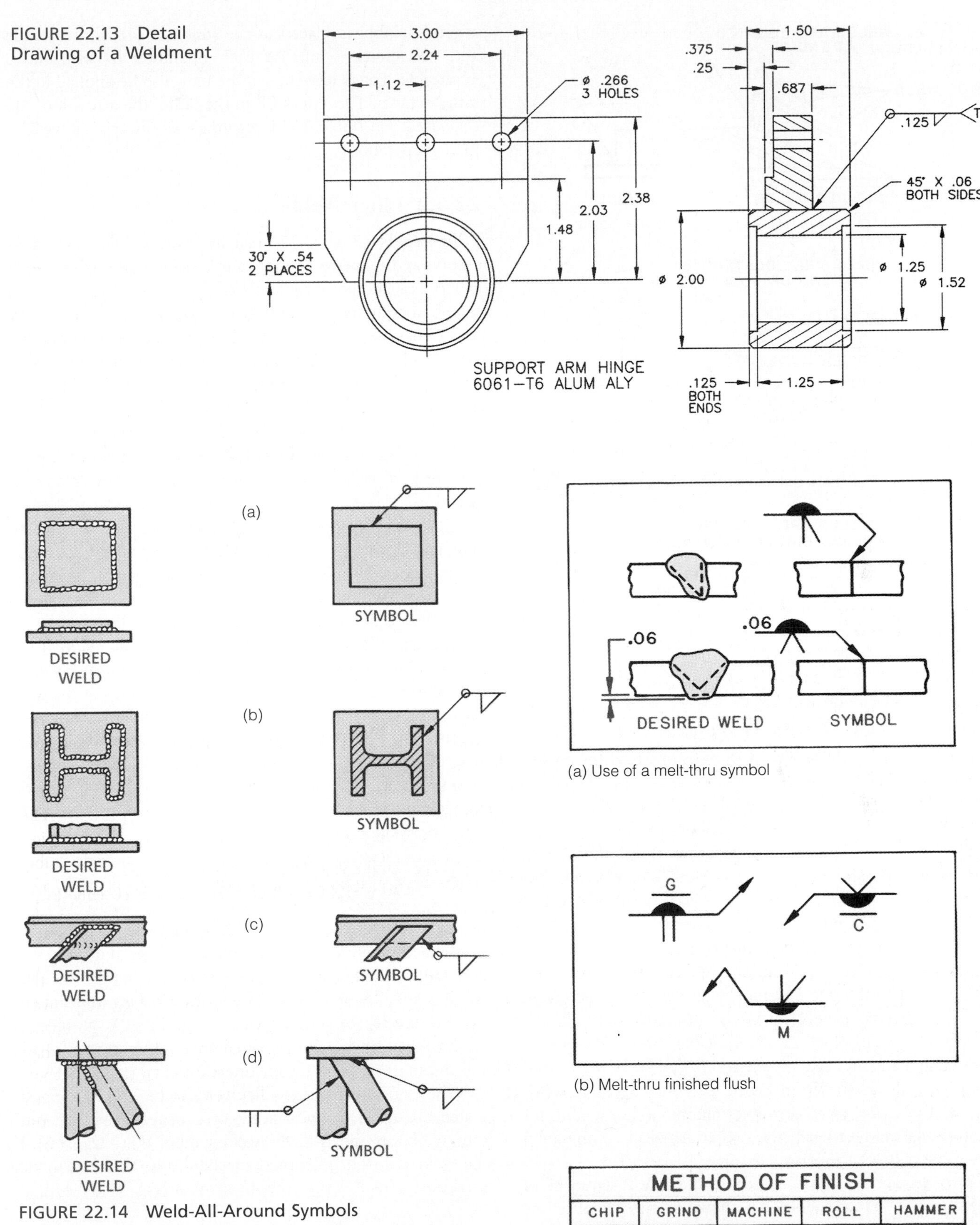

FIGURE 22.13 Detail Drawing of a Weldment

FIGURE 22.14 Weld-All-Around Symbols

(a) Use of a melt-thru symbol

(b) Melt-thru finished flush

METHOD OF FINISH				
CHIP	GRIND	MACHINE	ROLL	HAMMER
C	G	M	R	H

(c) Weld finish symbols

FIGURE 22.15 Melt-Thru and Finish Symbols

The **pitch** (center-to-center spacing) of intermittent welds is shown to the right of the length dimension and separated from it by a hyphen [Fig. 22.16(a)]. The pitch indicates the distance between centers of the welds on one

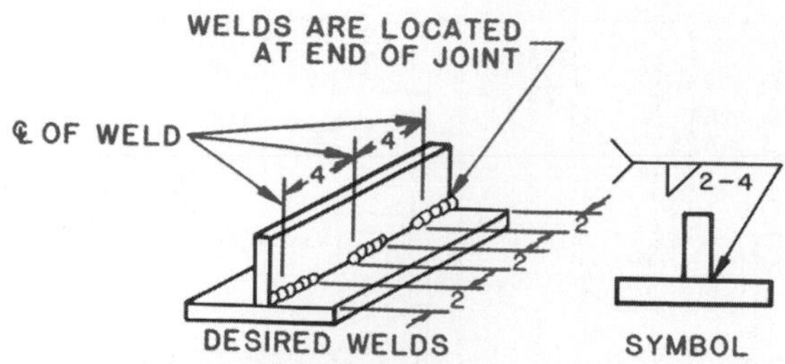

(a) Length and pitch of increments of intermittent welding

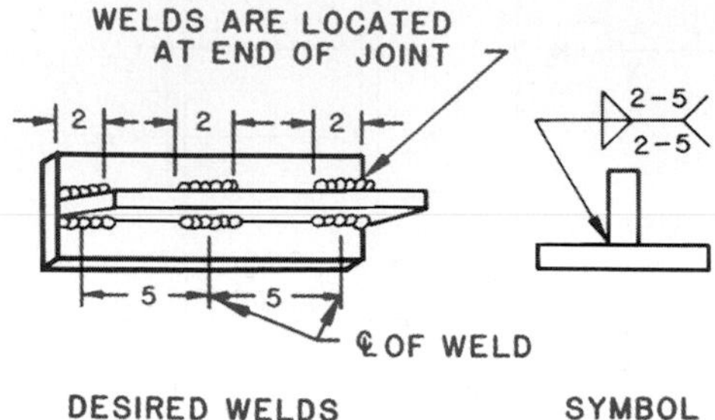

(b) Length and pitch of increments of chain intermittent welding

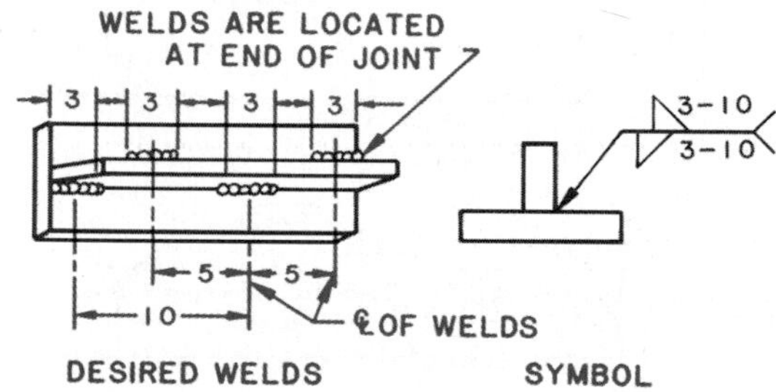

(c) Length and pitch of increments of staggered intermittent welding

FIGURE 22.16 Application of Dimensions to Intermittent Fillet Welding Symbols

side of the joint. Chain and staggered intermittent weld dimensions are shown on both sides of the reference line [Fig. 22.16(b) and (c)]. When intermittent welding is called out by itself, the symbol indicates that welds are located at the ends of the joint. When intermittent welding is called out between continuous welding, the symbol indicates that spaces equal to the pitch minus the length of one increment are left between the end of the continuous weld and the intermittent weld [Fig. 22.16(c)]. Unless otherwise specified, staggered intermittent welds on both sides are spaced symmetrically, as shown in Figure 22.16(c). Separate welding symbols are given for intermittent welding and for continuous welding when the two are used in combination along one side of the joint.

Two or more reference lines can indicate a sequence of operations. The first operation is shown on the reference line nearest the arrow. Subsequent operations are shown sequentially on other reference lines. Additional reference lines can show data supplementary to welding symbol information included on the reference line nearest the arrow. Test information may be shown on a second or third reference line away from the arrow. When required, the weld-all-around symbol is placed at the junction of the arrow line and the reference line for each operation to which it is applicable. The field weld symbol may also be applied in the same manner. The letters **CP** in the tail of the arrow indicate a *complete penetration* weld, regardless of the type of weld or joint preparation.

22.5.2 Fillet Welds

Fillet welds (Fig. 22.17) usually have a triangular cross section and join two or more surfaces at right angles—such as lap, tee, and corner joints (see Fig. 22.9). They are often found in combination with groove welds for corner joints. The dimensions of fillet welds are placed on the welding symbol. The weld size goes to the left of the fillet weld symbol; the length of the weld is placed to the right of the basic weld symbol when required.

Weld size is determined by the thicker of the two parts to be joined. Rule-of-thumb weld size is the thickness of the thinner part, unless the larger size is required by calculated stress.

Fillet welds are also good in larger holes and slots where plug and slot welds are inappropriate. Generally, fillet welds are not finished unless a specific finishing process is specified on the symbol. The two basic types of fillet welds are those with *equal legs* and those with *unequal legs.*

The size of fillet welds is shown on the same side of the reference line as the weld symbol and to the left of the weld symbol (Fig. 22.17). When welds on both sides of the joint have the same dimensions, both are dimensioned (Fig. 22.18). The size of a weld with unequal legs is shown in parentheses to the left of the weld symbol. Weld orientation is not indicated by the symbol and is shown graphically on the drawing when required (Fig. 22.18). Fillet weld size can also be specified in a general note such as:

NOTE: UNLESS OTHERWISE SPECIFIED
ALL FILLET WELDS SHALL BE 20 MM SIZE

Specified lengths of fillet welding may be indicated by symbols in conjunction with dimension lines [Fig. 22.19(a) and (b)]. When necessary for clarity, the length of fillet welding may be graphically shown by *hatching* and dimensioned directly on the drawing (Fig. 22.20). No length dimension need be shown when the weld extends for the full distance between abrupt direction changes.

When a design requires fillet welds to be welded approximately flat-faced, convex-faced, or concave-faced, the contour symbol is added to the weld symbol [Fig. 22.21(a)]. If the weld is to be contoured mechanically, the weld finish symbol is added to the contour symbol [Fig. 22.21(b)].

22.5.3 Plug and Slot Welds

The rectangular basic weld symbol (Fig. 22.22) designates **plug welds** and **slot welds.** All the rules for drawing symbols and their locations apply to these types of weld as well. Plug and slot welds are often found in butt joints and

FIGURE 22.17 Application of Fillet Welding Symbols

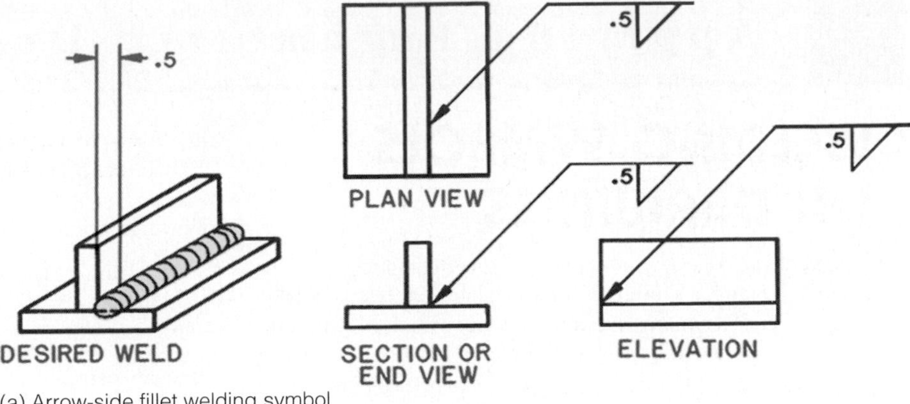

(a) Arrow-side fillet welding symbol

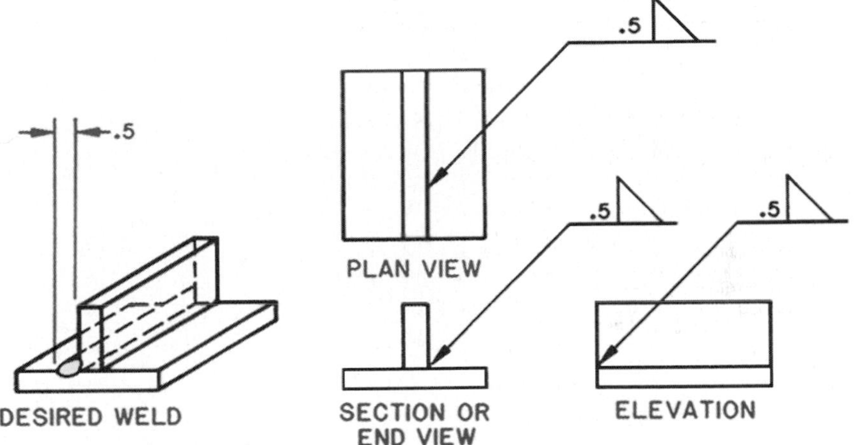

(b) Other-side fillet welding symbol

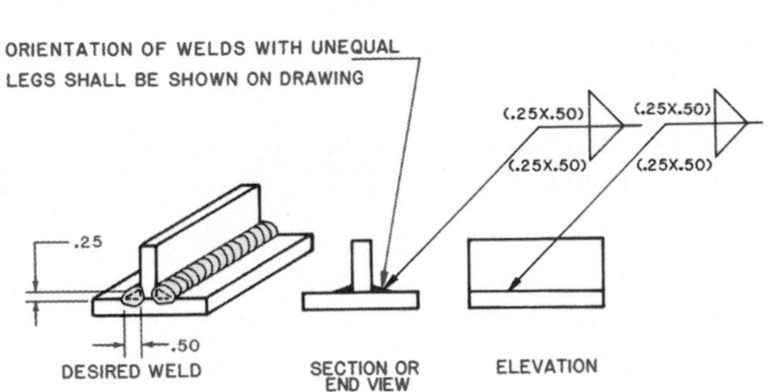

(a) Both-sides fillet welding symbol for one joint

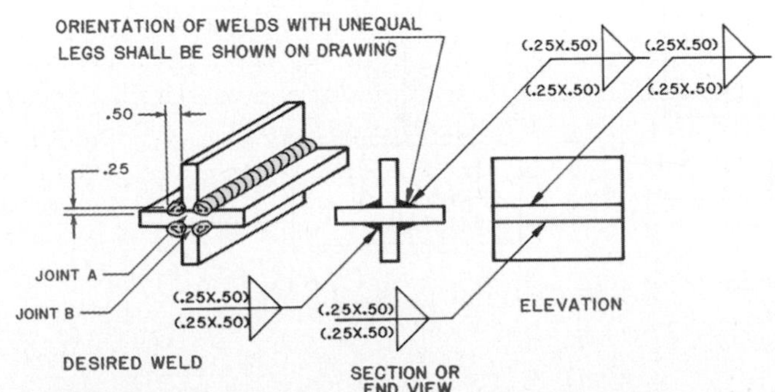

(b) Both-sides fillet welding symbol for two joints

FIGURE 22.18 Fillet Welding Symbol Application

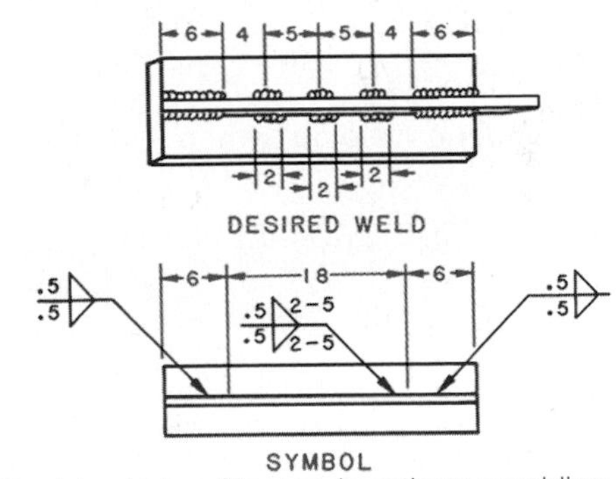

(a) Combined intermittent and continuous welding

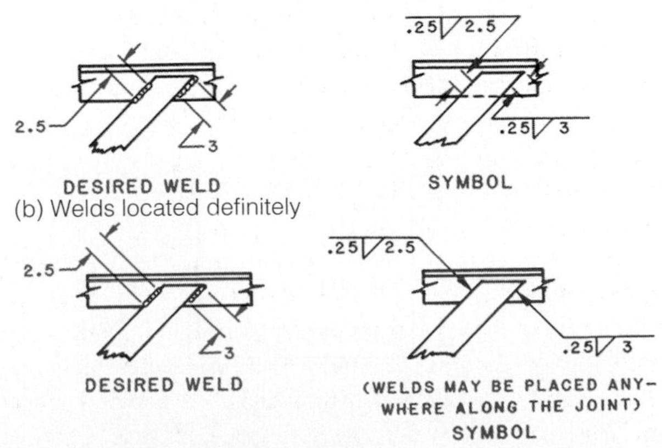

(b) Welds located definitely

(c) Welds located approximately

FIGURE 22.19 Location and Extent of Fillet Welds

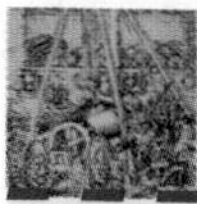

Applying Parametric Design . . .

WELDING SYMBOLS ON DRAWINGS

A **symbol** is a collection of drafting geometry and text (see Fig. A). In a drawing, a symbol becomes a single entity or instance. You can add as many instances of a symbol as you like. Symbols, stored in a specified directory, create a standard symbol library specific to a discipline, project, orientation, or company.

Pro/ENGINEER supports two kinds of symbols:

- **Simple symbol** Creates symbol instances identical to the symbol.
- **Generic symbol** Creates a variety of instances using entities included in the generic definition. Geometry and notes in a generic can be arranged in a tree definition structure (Fig. B); therefore, when creating an instance, you can specify groups to be included in a particular instance.

The symbol functionality is accessed through **Create** from the DETAIL menu and through **Symbol** from the DETAIL ITEM menu. This brings up the SYMBOL TYPE menu, with the following options:

- **Definition** Define/redefine a symbol.
- **Instance** Create an instance.

The general procedure for defining symbols includes the following steps:

1. Specify the name of the symbol.
2. Specify geometry to be included in the symbol.
3. For generic symbols, create a tree definition structure (Fig. C).
4. Define symbol attributes.
5. Specify the attachment point for the origin orientation leader.
6. If variable text is present, enter the default text.
7. Store the symbol to disk.

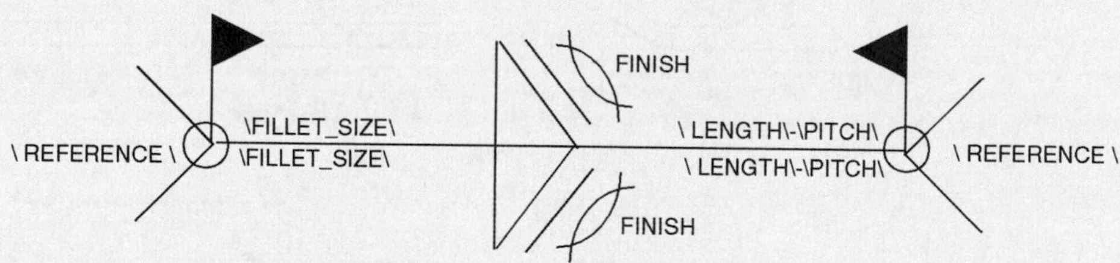

FIGURE A Generic Welding Symbol (Fillet Welding Symbol Shown)

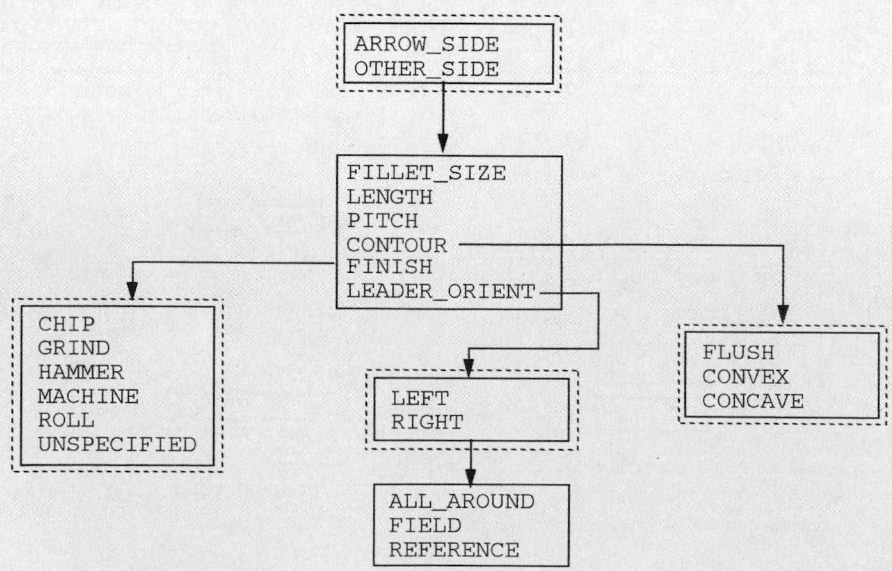

FIGURE C Symbol Definition Structure

FIGURE B Symbol Tree

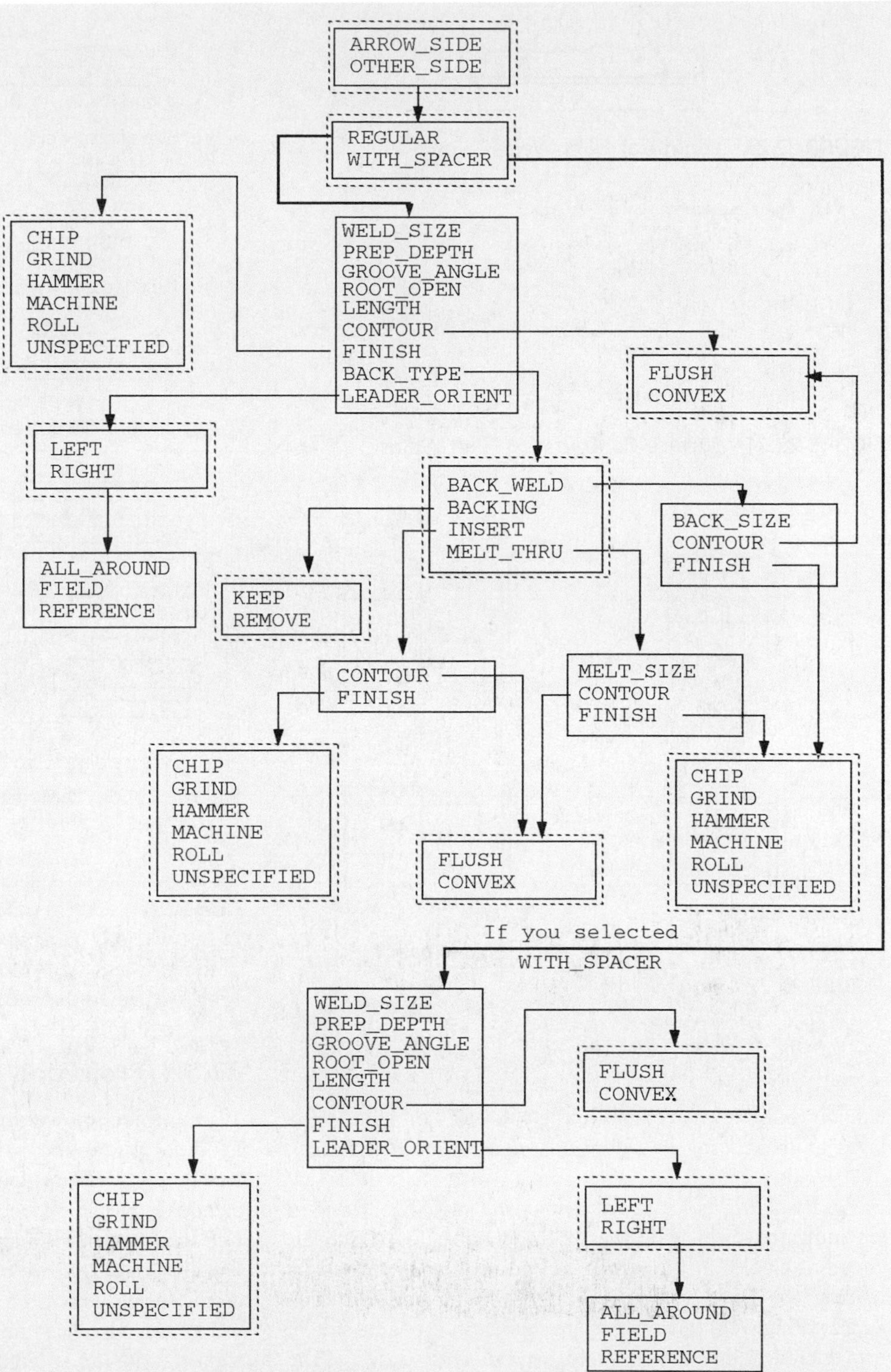

The **Generic Welding Symbol** command creates a welding symbol with welds on both sides or on either side of a reference line. The command provides forty-eight different welding symbols (excluding the choice of independent weld characteristics or variable leader orientation). Here are a few notes (see Fig. A):

1. When creating combined groove welds, the root opening of the weld must be specified only on one of the welding symbols.
2. When you create chained intermittent fillet welds, LENGTH and PITCH values for the arrow side and for the other side must be identical.
3. When you select FINISH, you must also consider CONTOUR.
4. ALL_AROUND should not be selected if LENGTH and PITCH are selected.
5. Arrow-side and other-side significance for text entry is indicated by the following suffixes:

   _AS for arrow side
   _OS for other side

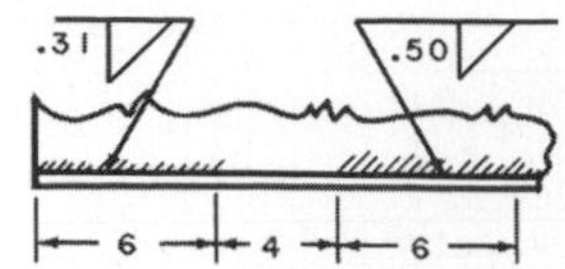

FIGURE 22.20 Length of Fillet Welds

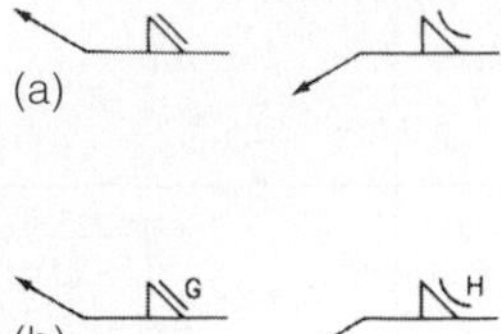

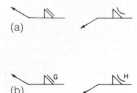

FIGURE 22.21 Surface Contours for Fillet Welds

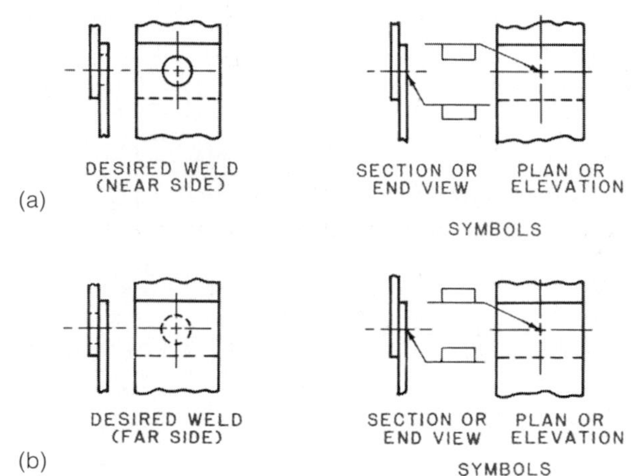

FIGURE 22.22 Plug Welds

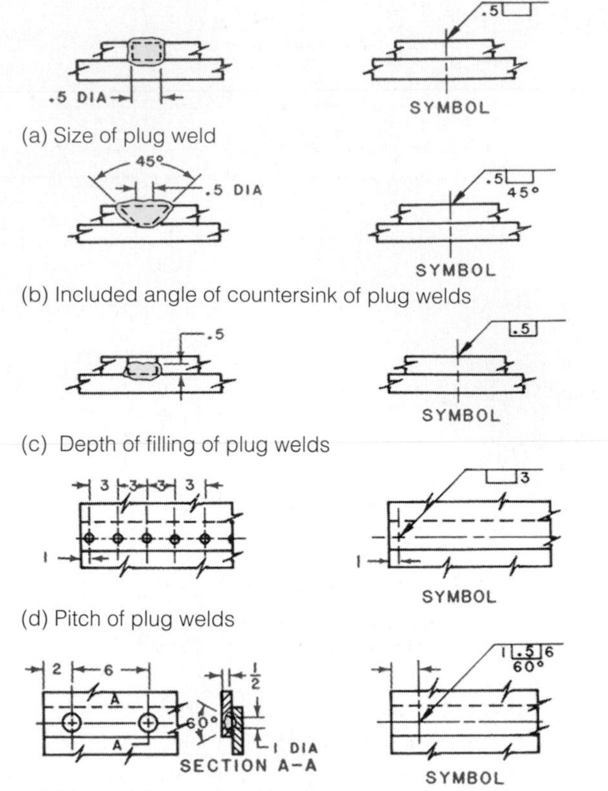

(a) Size of plug weld

(b) Included angle of countersink of plug welds

(c) Depth of filling of plug welds

(d) Pitch of plug welds

(e) Plug welding symbol showing use of combined dimensions

FIGURE 22.23 Dimensions on Plug Welding Symbols

lap joints for reinforcement. When the slot or hole is too large to make plug or slot welds effective or economical, fillet welds are used.

Plug welding holes in the arrow-side member of a joint are indicated by placing the weld symbol below the reference line. Holes in the other-side member are indicated by placing the weld symbol above the reference line (Fig. 22.22). Plug weld dimensions are shown on the same side of the reference line as the weld symbol (Fig. 22.23). The diameter of the base of the hole is shown to the left of the weld symbol. The hole is cylindrical, unless the included angle of countersink (taper) is shown above (other-side) or below (arrow-side) the weld symbol [Fig. 22.23(b)]. Plug welds completely fill the holes, unless depth of filling is shown inside the weld symbol [Fig. 22.23(c)]. The pitch of plug welds is shown to the right of the weld symbol [Fig. 22.23(d)].

Length, width, spacing, included angle of countersink (taper), orientation, and location of slot welds cannot be shown on the welding symbol. This information is given on the drawing, with a detail referenced on the welding symbol (Fig. 22.24). Unless otherwise indicated, the depth of filling of slot welds is understood to be complete. When the depth of filling is less than smooth or complete, the depth of filling is shown inside the weld symbol [Fig. 22.24(b)].

22.5.4 Projection Welds

When **projection welding** is required, the spot weld symbol is used, with the projection welding process reference in the tail of the welding symbol (Fig. 22.25). The spot weld symbol is placed above and below (never on) the reference line to indicate in which member the *embossment* is placed. Dimensions are shown on the same side of the reference line as the weld symbol, or on either side when the symbol is astride the reference line and has no arrow-side or other-side significance. The strength of spot welds is designated as the minimum shear strength per spot and, unless controlled by the applicable process, specification is shown to the left of the weld symbol (Fig. 22.26).

The pitch of spot and projection welds is shown to the right of the weld symbol [Fig. 22.26(b)]. When spot welding extends less than the distance between abrupt changes in direction or less than the full length of the joint, the extent is dimensioned on the drawing. When a definite number of spot welds is desired in a joint, the number is shown in parentheses either above or below the weld symbol [Fig. 22.26(c)].

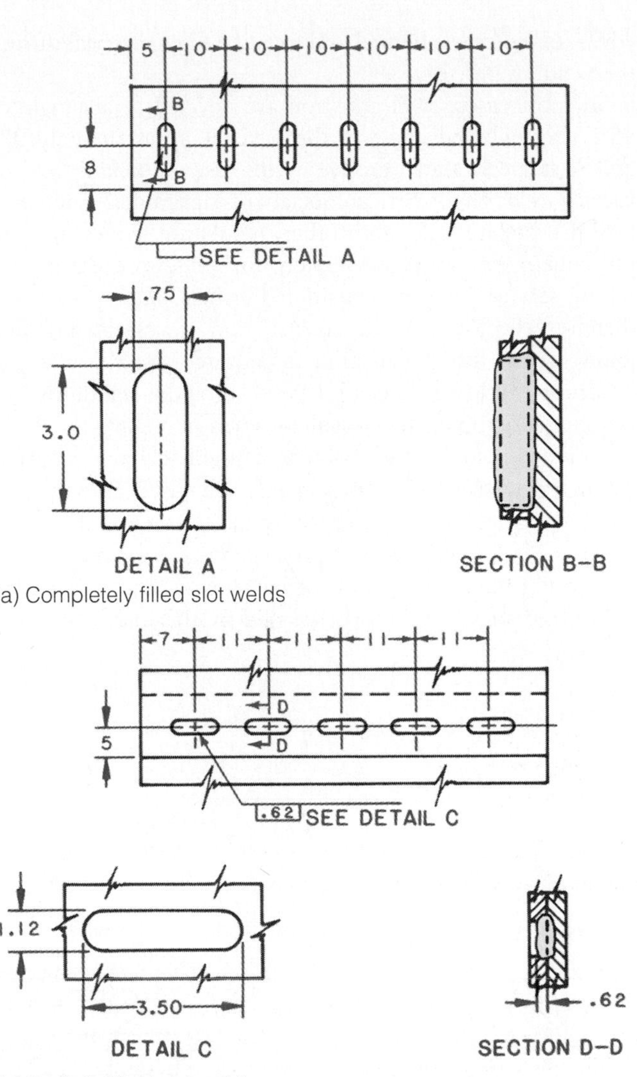

(a) Completely filled slot welds

(b) Partially filled slot welds

FIGURE 22.24 Dimensions on Slot Welding Symbols

22.5.5 Seam Welds

One symbol designates all **seam welds,** regardless of the welding process. The process reference is shown in the tail of the welding symbol. The weld symbol may or may not have location significance, depending on the welding process. Dimensions are given on the same side of the reference line as the weld symbol, or on either side when the symbol is astride the reference line and has no arrow-side or other-side significance (Fig. 22.27).

Seam welds are dimensioned by either size or shear strength. Weld size is designated as the width of the weld. Shear strength is designated in pounds per linear inch minimum, and is shown to the left of the weld symbol [Fig. 22.27(b)]. The length of a seam weld that extends less than the full length of the joint or less than the distance between abrupt changes in direction is either shown to the right of the weld symbol or dimensioned on the drawing [Fig. 22.27(c)]. The flush contour symbol can indicate flushness

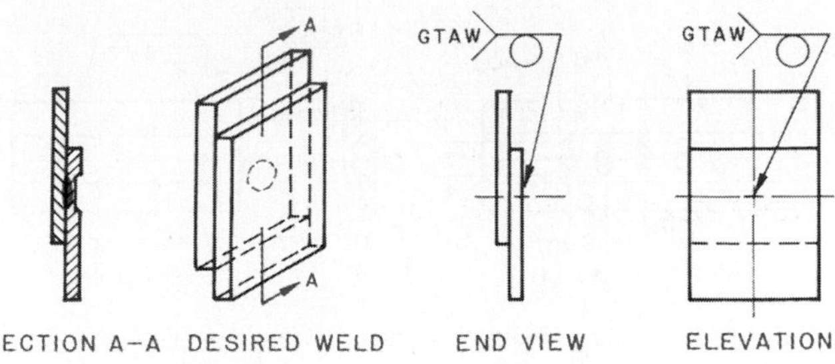

(a) Arrow-side spot weld symbol (gas tungsten-arc spot)

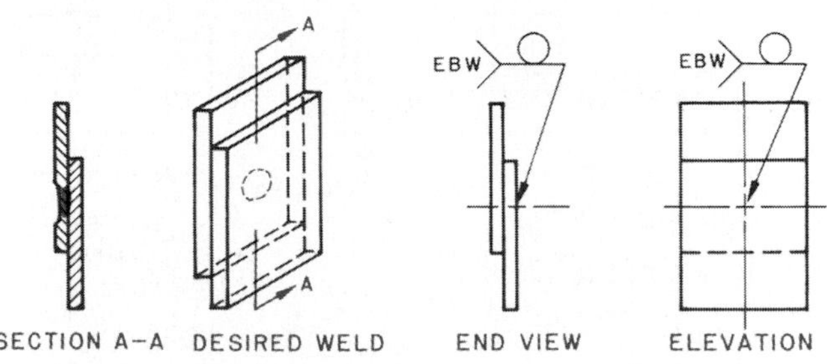

(b) Other-side spot weld symbol (electron beam spot)

FIGURE 22.25 Spot Welding Symbol Applications

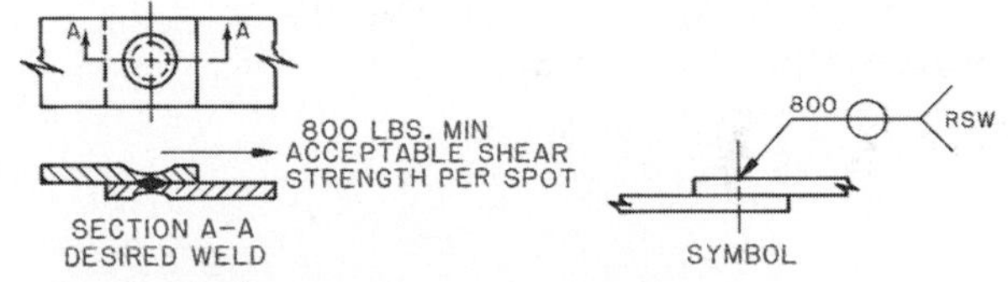

(a) Shear strength of spot welds (resistance spot)

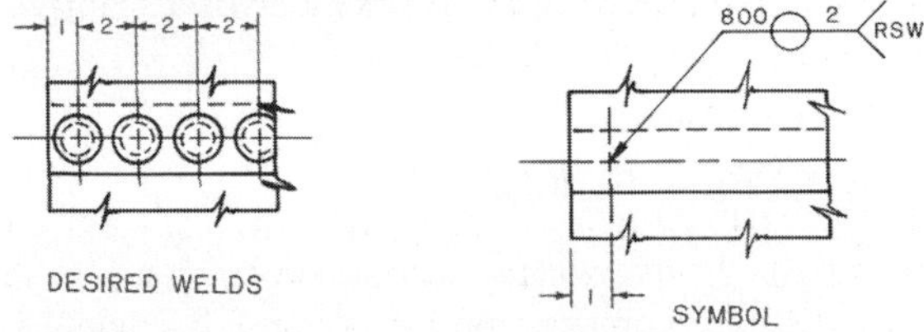

(b) Pitch of spot welds (resistance spot)

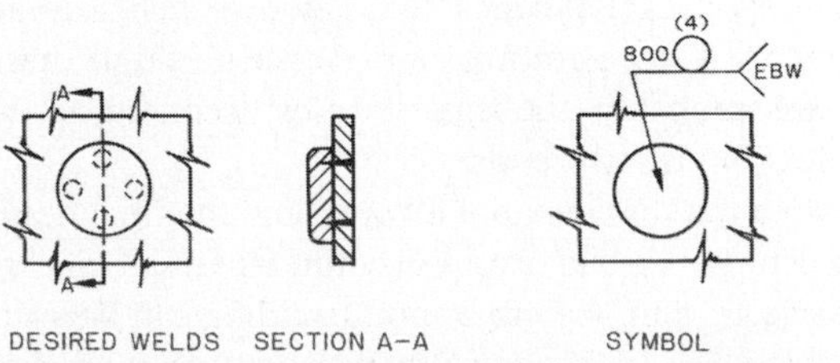

(c) Specified number of spot welds located at random (electron beam spot)

FIGURE 22.26 Application of Dimensions to Spot Welding Symbols

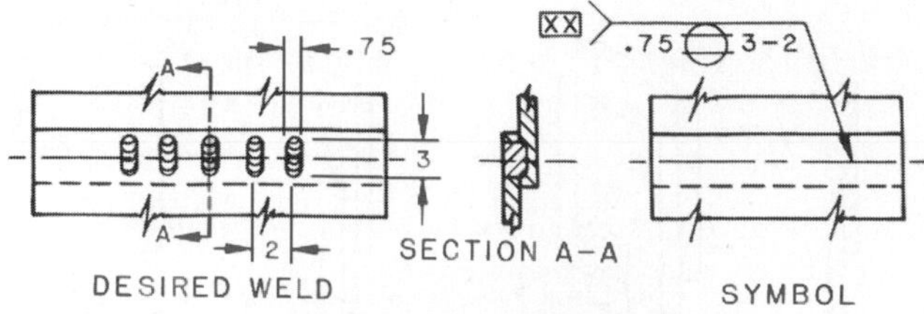

(a) Length and pitch of seam welds

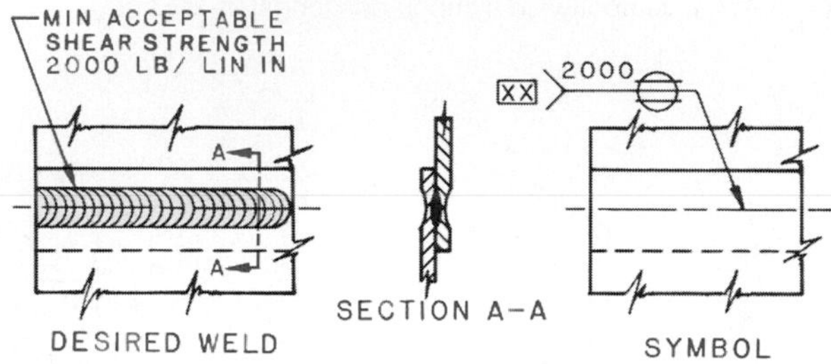

(b) Strength of seam welds

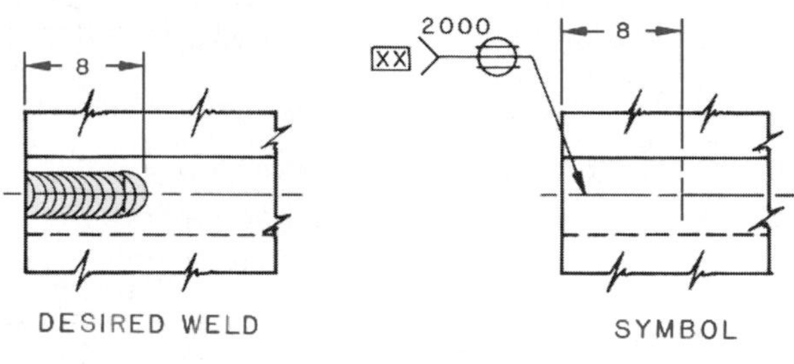

(c) Extent of seam welds

FIGURE 22.27 Application of Dimensions to Seam Welding Symbols

of the exposed surface of either member of a seam-welded joint.

22.5.6 Groove Welds

The five basic **groove welds** are beveled, square, J, U, and V. However, various combinations are also used: single V, single bevel, single J, single U, double V, double bevel, double J, and double U. The edges in a groove weld are usually prepared by a flame cutting torch. Whether single or double, these are probably the easiest, most economical welded joints for joining two ends.

When a joint is prepared for welding, the thickness of the material must be taken into account. In small thicknesses, such as $\frac{1}{16}$ to $\frac{1}{8}$ in. (1.5 to 3 mm), welding can be successful when the edges are square. When the edges are thicker than this, bevels must be made to ensure full penetration and create an adequate joint; otherwise, the flame will not be hot enough to produce adequate fusion. A general rule to follow when material is thicker than $\frac{1}{8}$ in. (3 mm) is to prepare the edges for a groove channel and to add a filler material during the welding process.

In most cases, steel and iron are beveled at an angle of 45°. The included angle of the bevel is approximately 90° and V-shaped. Many groove welds use a *backing bar* or *backing weld.* The American Society of Mechanical Engineers (ASME) boiler code and other regulating codes require full-penetration welds, especially for pressure vessels and piping services that are considered critical. *Backup rings* are therefore employed in the construction of vessels and pipe joints where full penetration is required. ASME and the American Welding Society (AWS) provide standards for welding and should be consulted when necessary.

Complete (full) penetration is defined to have occurred when the weld and the base metal are fused through the entire depth of the joint. This way may or may not require backing bars or bead welds. Partial-penetration groove welds are appropriate when full penetration is not necessary because of stress levels to be carried by the joint. The only

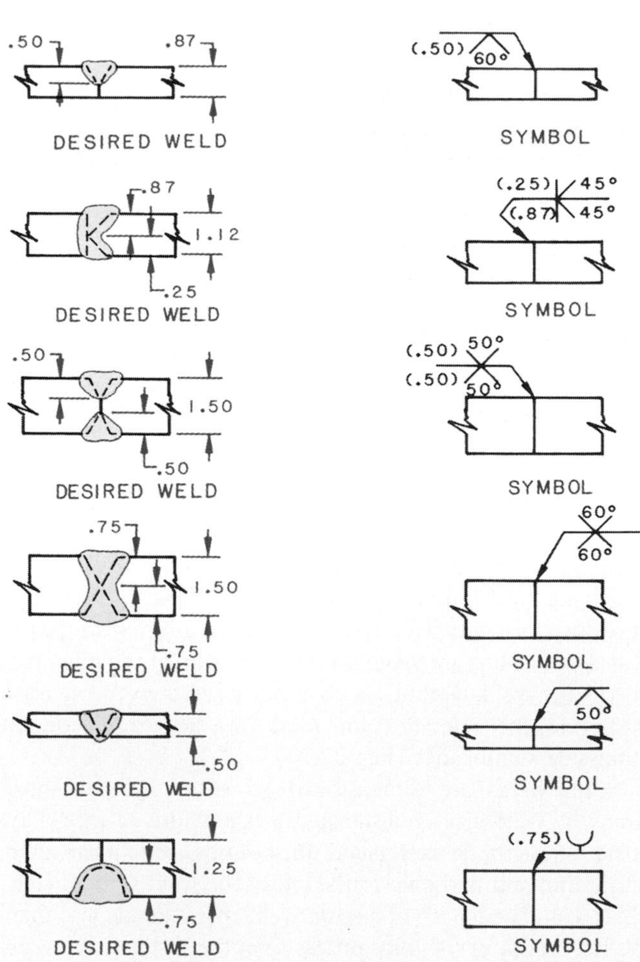

FIGURE 22.28 Designation of Size of Groove Welds with No Specified Root Penetration

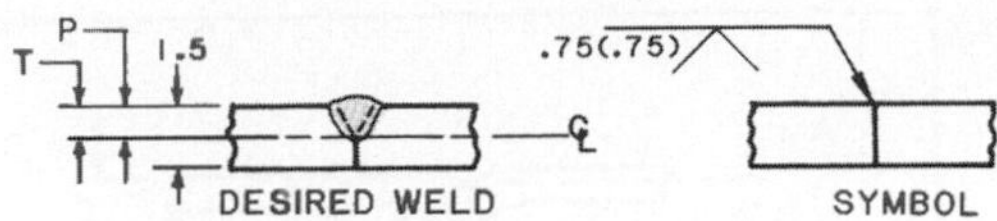

(a) Depth of preparation equal to effective throat

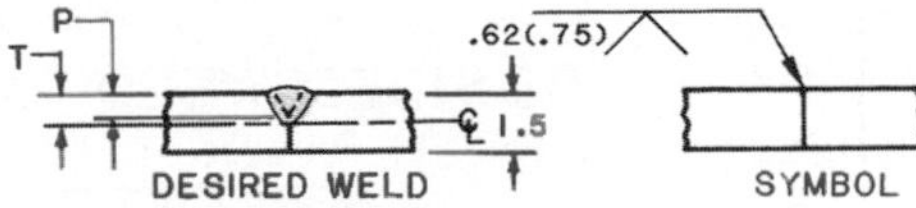

(b) Depth of preparation less than effective throat

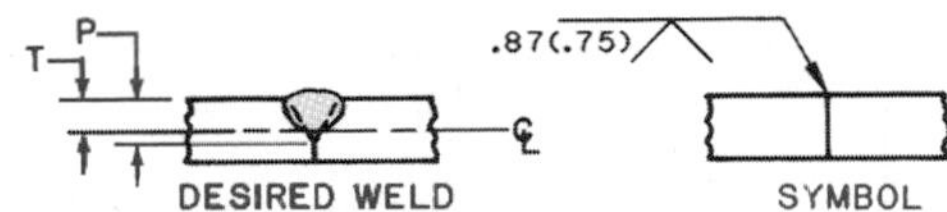

(c) Depth of preparation more than effective throat

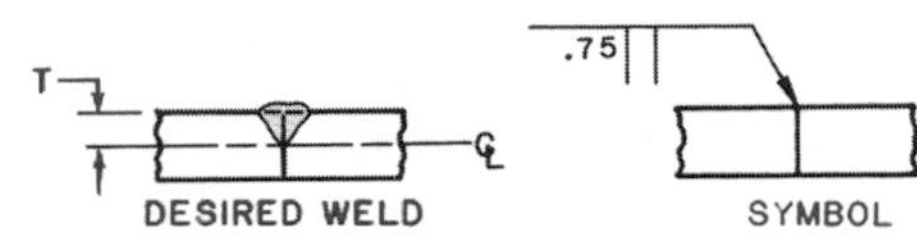

(d) No preparation

FIGURE 22.29 Depth of Groove Weld Preparation

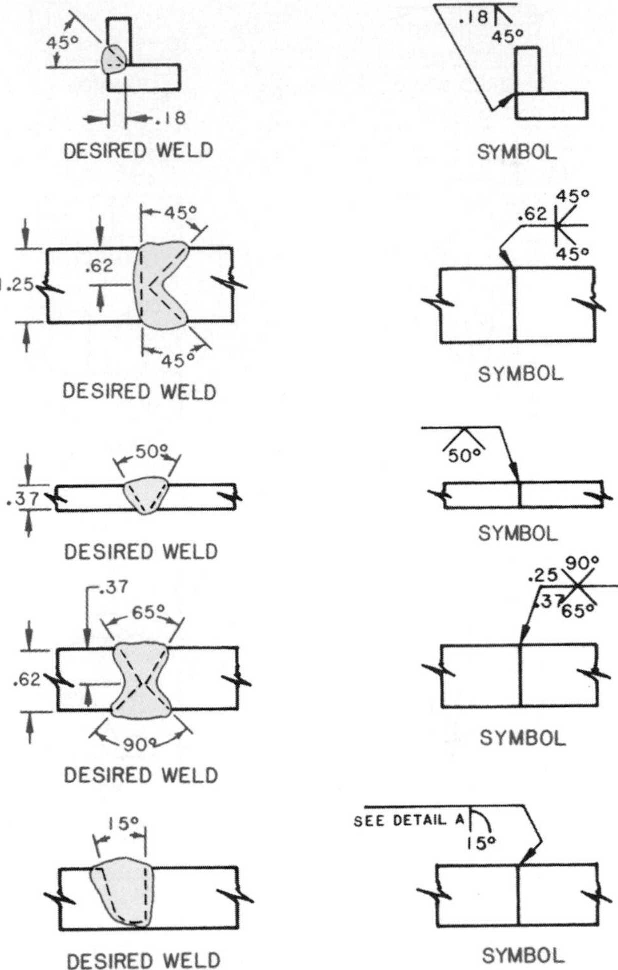

FIGURE 22.30 Groove Angle of Groove Welds

difference between the two penetrations is in the depth of the end preparation or edge preparation: Partial penetration does not cover the full thickness of the two materials to be joined. Root spacing will minimize lack-of-penetration notches caused by insufficient spacing or tight butting of joints. Root spacing is just one of the considerations that determine the quality of the joint. Alignment is also important, although slight imperfections are tolerable.

An engineer might be called on to detail different cross-sectional views of the joint geometry, including backing, space, or extension bars, and to show whether the weld is a full or partial penetration and its various angles and dimensions. **Joint geometry** is the basic cross-sectional shape of the joint prior to welding.

Dimensions of all types of groove welds (Fig. 22.28) are shown on the same side of the reference line as the weld symbol. If double-groove welds have the same dimensions, both are dimensioned. The depth of groove preparation and the effective throat of a groove weld are shown to the left of the weld symbol, with the effective throat in parentheses. The *effective throat* is the perpendicular depth of the groove cut. The total effective throat never exceeds the thickness of the thinner member of a joint. The effective throat is shown only for square groove welds in Figure 22.29, where P is the preparation thickness and T is the effective throat depth.

When no depth of groove preparation or effective throat is shown on the welding symbol for single-groove or symmetrical double-groove welds, complete penetration is required (Fig. 22.28). Unless specified in a general note, the groove angle or groove welds are shown *outside* the weld symbol (Fig. 22.30). And unless specified in a general note, the root opening of groove welds is shown *inside* the weld symbol (Fig. 22.31). Groove radii of U-groove and J-groove welds is specified in a general note, or by a detail view on the drawing, referenced on the welding symbol. The depth of preparation for flare-groove welds is considered as extending only to the tangent points (Figs. 22.32 and 22.33). Groove welds with contour requirements are indicated in the same manner as that prescribed for fillet welds.

The flush and convex supplementary weld symbols are also applied to groove welds—for instance, when the outer contour of the weld must be altered by grinding or machining.

You May Complete Exercises 22.1 Through 22.4 at This Time

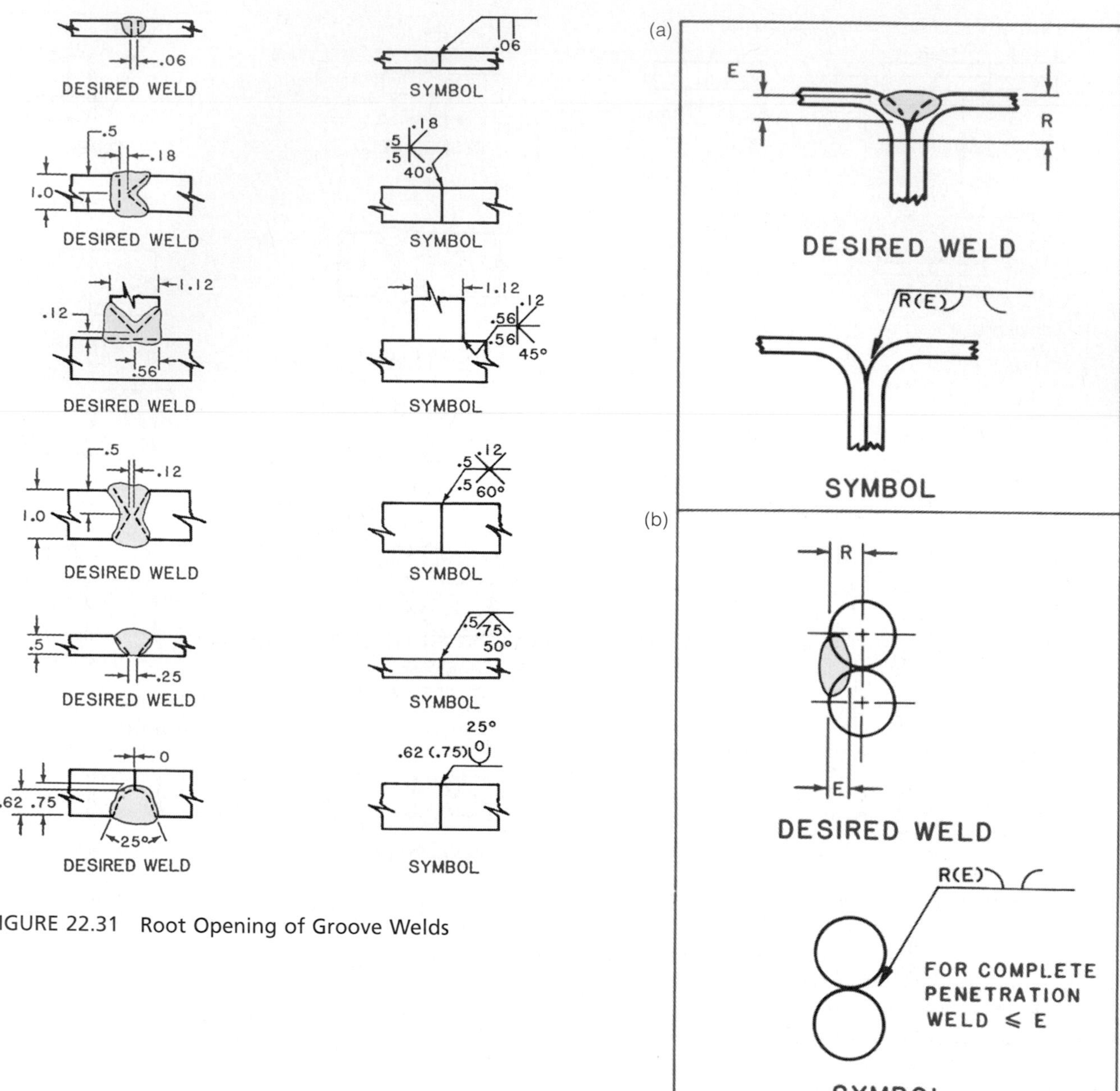

FIGURE 22.31 Root Opening of Groove Welds

FIGURE 22.32 Bead Welds

22.5.7 Back or Backing Welds

The **back** or **backing welds** of single-groove welds are shown by placing a back or backing weld symbol on the side of the reference line opposite the groove weld symbol (Fig. 22.34). The welding symbol does not indicate the welding sequence (groove weld made before or after backing weld) or backing weld passes (single or multiple). The height of the weld bead is shown to the left of the backing weld symbol, when required. No other backing weld dimensions are shown on the welding symbol. Other dimensions may be shown pictorially on a drawing detail.

Back or backing welds that are to be welded flush without recourse to any method of finishing are shown by adding the flush contour symbol to the back or backing weld symbol. Those to be made flush by mechanical means are shown by adding the flush contour symbol and the finish symbol. A joint with spacer is indicated with the groove weld symbol modified to show a rectangle within it, with the rectangle including a notation as shown in Figure 22.35.

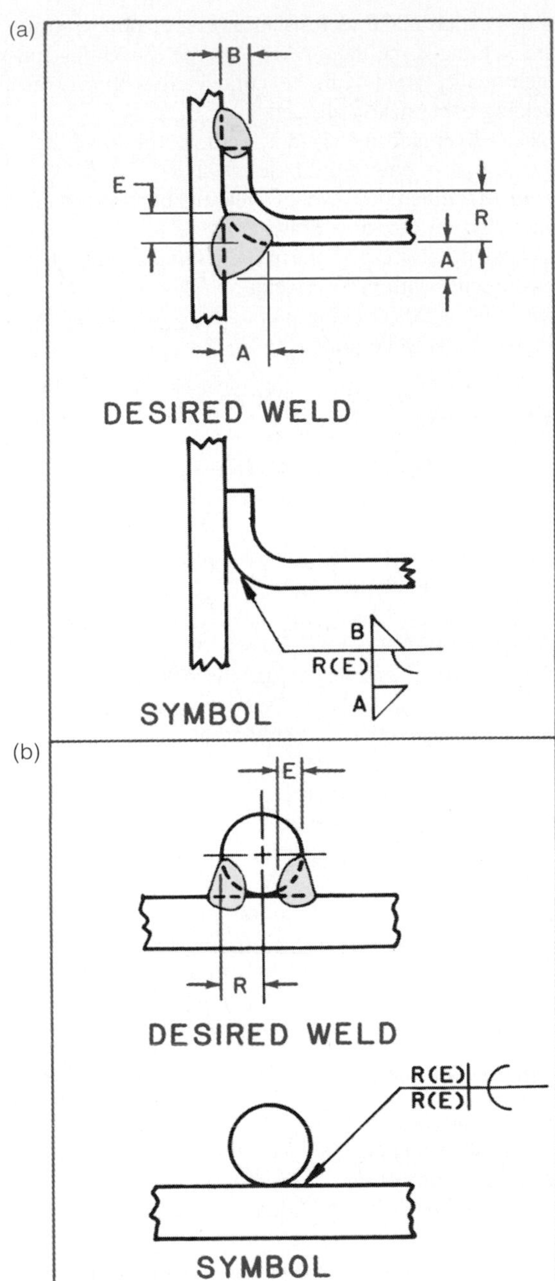

FIGURE 22.33 Bead Welds and Symbols

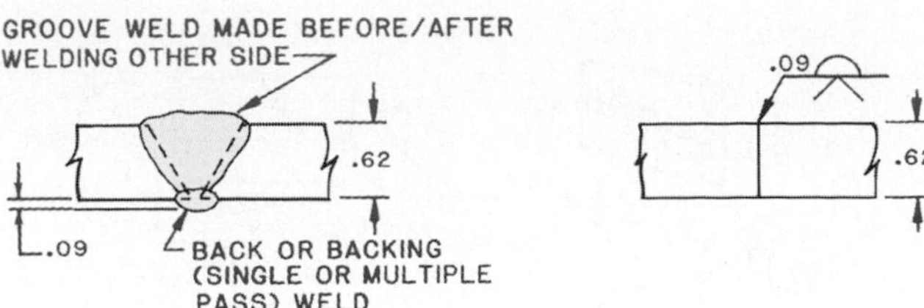

(a) DESIRED WELD SYMBOL

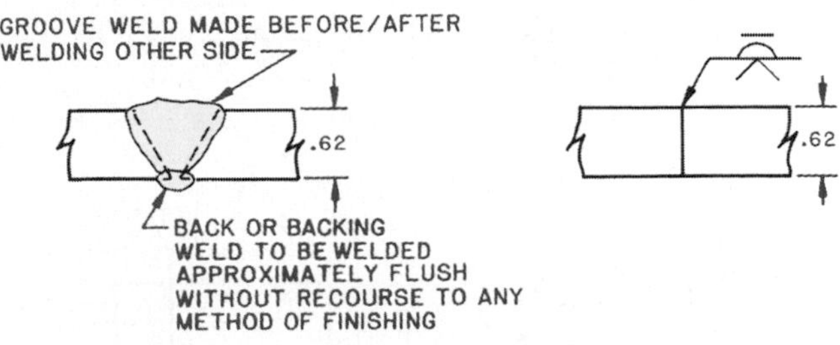

(b) DESIRED WELD SYMBOL

FIGURE 22.34 Bead Weld Symbols Used to Indicate Bead-Type Back and Backing Weld

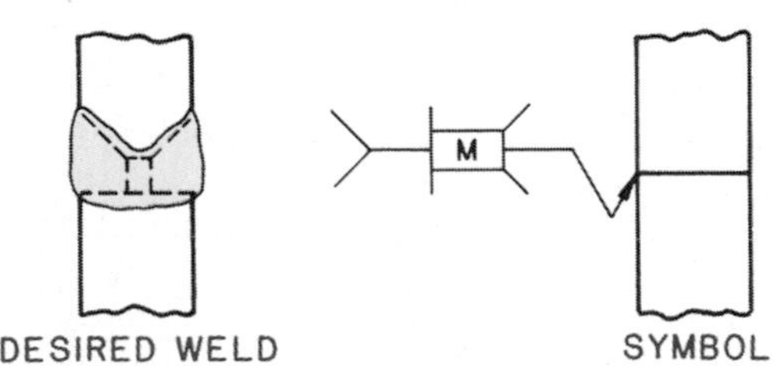

(a) Spacer in double-bevel-groove joint

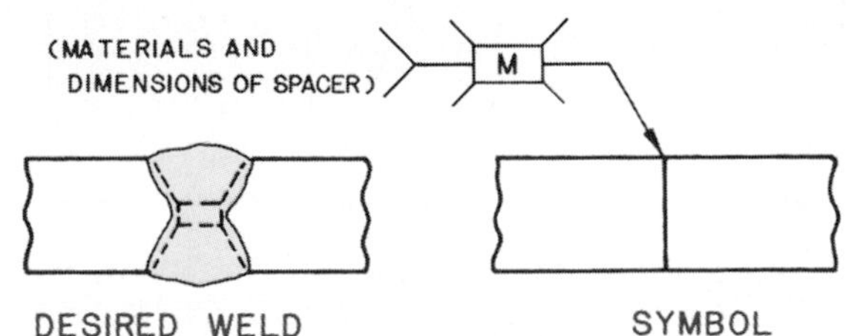

(b) Spacer in double-v-groove joint

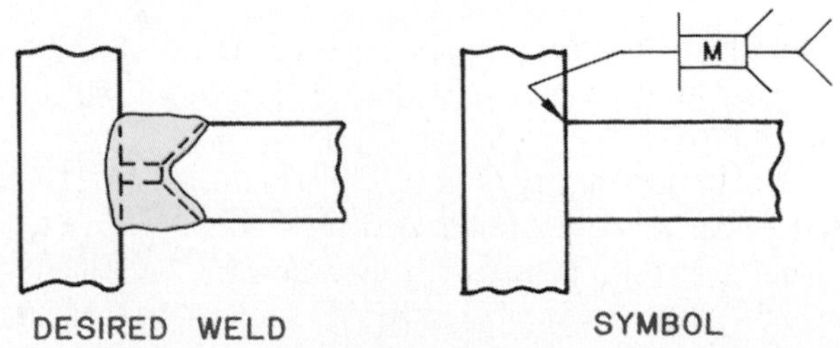

(c) Spacer in double-bevel-groove joint

FIGURE 22.35 Spacers for Welds

22.5.8 Surfacing Welds

Basically, **surface welds** function to reclaim worn part surfaces or to add alloying elements to the base metal for added protection. Often, "surfaced" parts outlast plain parts. The surfacing weld symbol does not indicate the welding of a joint; therefore it does not have arrow-side or other-side significance. The symbol is placed below the reference line, and the arrow points clearly to the surface on which the weld is to be deposited.

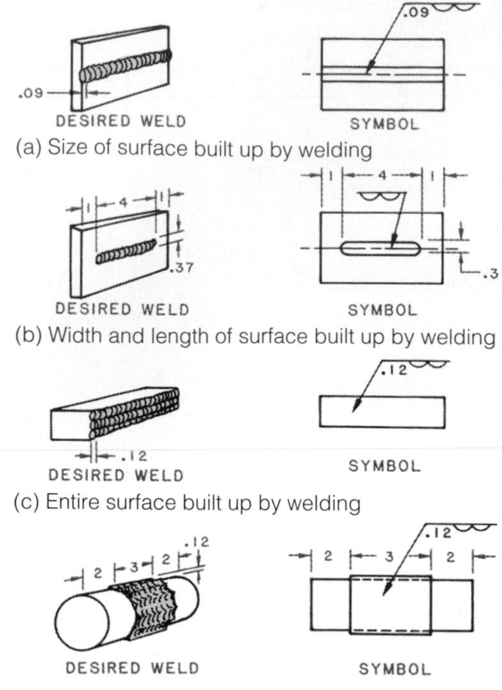

FIGURE 22.36 Dual Bead Weld Symbol to Indicate Surfaces Built Up by Welding

The minimum thickness of the weld buildup is the only dimension shown on the welding symbol and is placed to its left. When no specific thickness of weld is required, no size dimension is given. When only a portion of the area of a plane or curved surface is to be built up by welding, the extent, location, and orientation of the area to be built up are dimensioned on the drawing (Fig. 22.36).

You May Complete Exercises 22.5 Through 22.8 at This Time

QUIZ

True or False

1. Welding knowledge is important for engineers to understand because they will be called on to draw and design mechanical parts that may need to be fastened permanently.
2. Welds are classified as resistance, gas, or nonpressure.
3. Arc welding is the most common type of welding today.
4. High-quality welds can be completed with gas-metal arc welding using nearly all metals.
5. When dissimilar metals are welded, the weld deposit is always that of one of the base metals.
6. Normally, different types of welding processes can be encountered on the same drawing.
7. Lack of penetration is the most common type of problem encountered with groove welds.
8. With fillet welds, weld size is determined by the thinner of the two parts to be joined.

Fill in the Blanks

9. Dimensions for all types of groove welds are shown on ________ ________ of the reference line as the weld symbol.
10. The assembled welding symbol consists of the following eight parts: a reference line, ________, ________, ________, ________, ________, ________, and specifications.
11. The five basic groove welds are beveled, ________, ________, ________, and ________.
12. Deeper weld penetration results from ________ arc welding.
13. The main difference between V, bevel, U, and J welds is in the ________ of the parts to be joined.
14. The size of the fillet weld is shown to the ________ of the ________ symbol.
15. Plug and slot welds are found primarily in ________ joints.
16. The tail of the weld symbol should be omitted when ________ or ________ are not used.

Answer the Following

17. Describe slot and plug welds and their differences.
18. Explain the difference between shielded arc and unshielded arc welding processes.
19. What is the name for the granulated welding cover used in submerged arc welding?
20. What factors can affect the weldability of metals?
21. Which process is most commonly used to weld dissimilar materials?
22. Why is it important to bevel plates before groove welding?
23. Name the elements of a complete weld symbol.
24. What is meant by *arrow side* and *opposite side*? For what is the tail of the symbol used on the drawing?

EXERCISES

Exercises may be assigned as sketching, instrument, or CAD projects. Transfer the given information to an "A"-size sheet of .25 in. grid paper. Complete all views, and solve for proper visibility, including centerlines, object lines, and hidden lines. Exercises that are not assigned by the instructor can be sketched in the text to provide practice and to enhance understanding of the preceding instructional material.

After Reading the Chapter Through Section 22.5.6 You May Complete the Following Four Exercises

Exercise 22.1 Draw the requested welding symbol, far side only. Complete the symbol, including the arrowhead.

Exercise 22.2 Draw the requested weld and its associated symbol, for each joint.

Exercise 22.3 Complete the welding symbol and draw the weld on the given views. The shaft weld requires a surface weld.

Exercise 22.4 Use .25 in. or 6 mm fillet welds and appropriate groove welds to construct the all-welded assembly. Show the welds and the welding symbols.

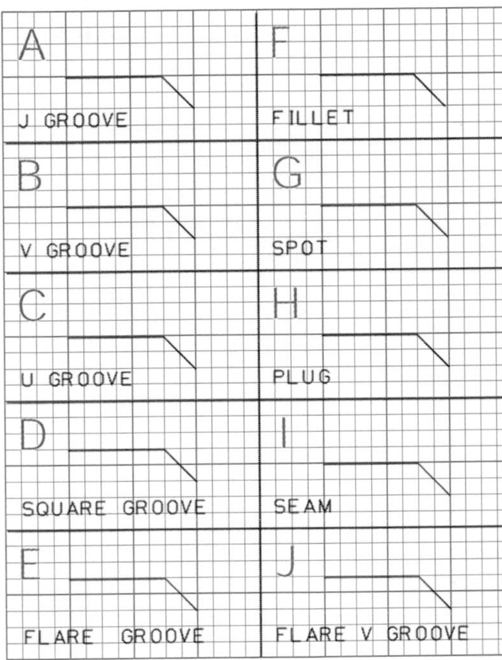

EXERCISE 22.1

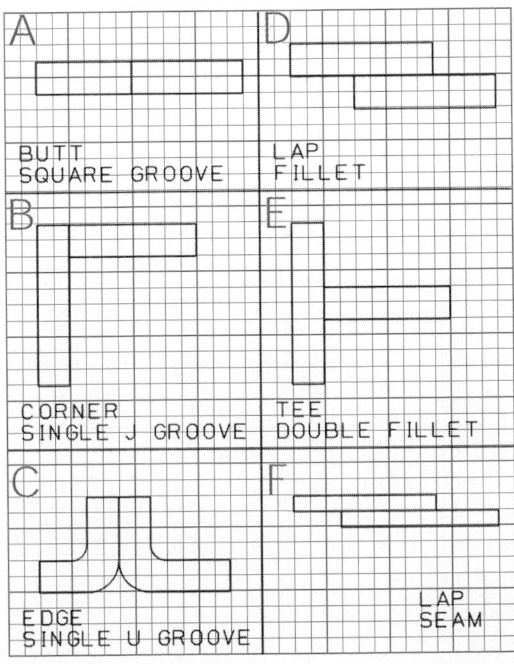

EXERCISE 22.2

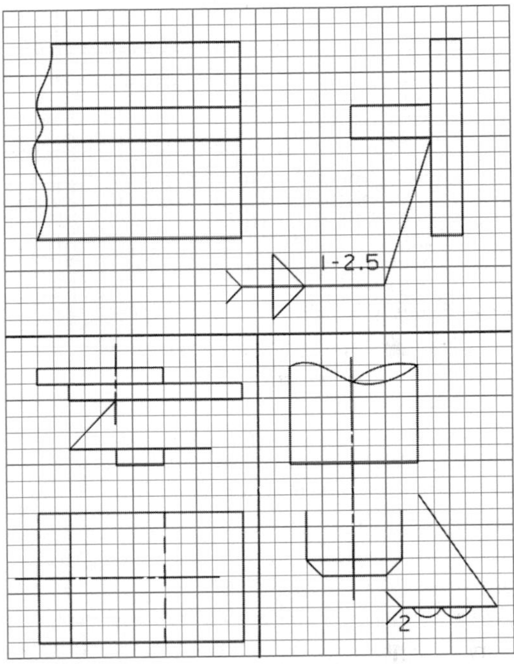

EXERCISE 22.3

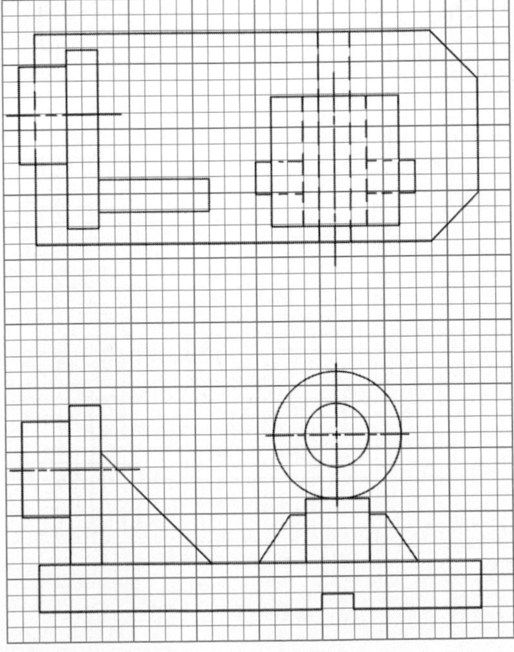

EXERCISE 22.4

After Reading the Chapter Through Section 22.5.8 You May Complete the Following Exercises

Exercise 22.5 Using .25 in. or 6 mm fillet welds, show all symbols and welds for the part.

Exercise 22.6 Show appropriate welds and welding symbols for the all-welded assembly.

Exercise 22.7 Draw the welds and welding symbols for the all-welded assembly.

Exercise 22.8 Using spot welding for the angle and plate weldment, show the appropriate weld and welding symbol to attach the pieces with welds placed at 1 in. (25 mm) increments. For the two plates, use plug welds. Draw the welds and the welding symbols.

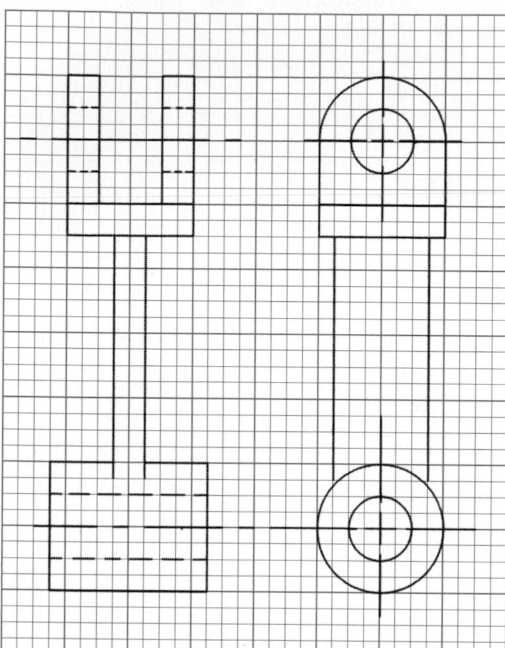

EXERCISE 22.5

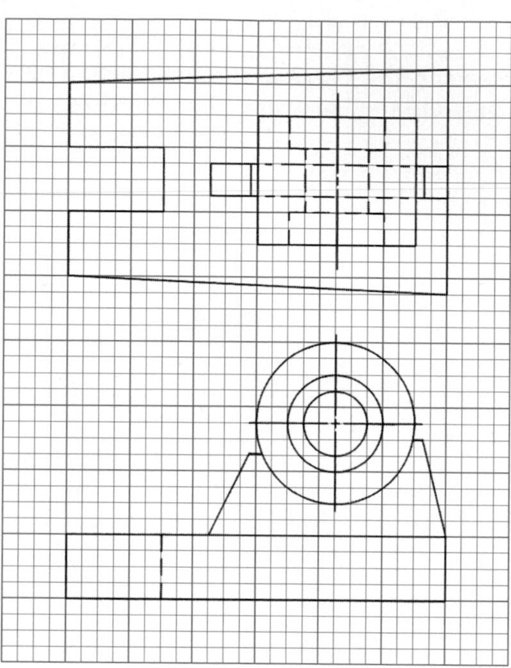

EXERCISE 22.7

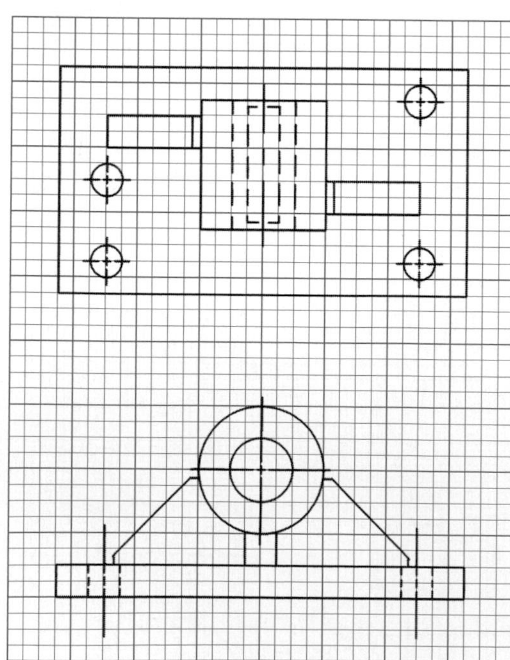

EXERCISE 22.6

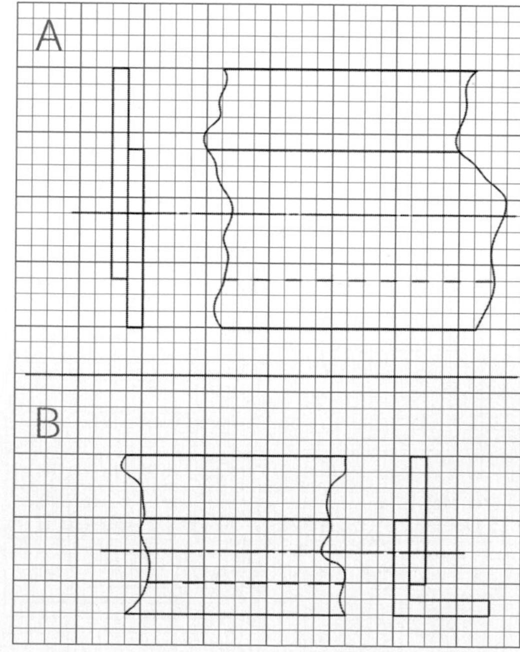

EXERCISE 22.8

PROBLEMS

Problems 22.1 through 22.8 Draw each of the given mechanical parts, dimension completely, and show all welds and welding symbols. Use the most recent ANSI dimensioning standards. Prepare a material or parts list for each project. Balloon and call out each separate weldment piece.

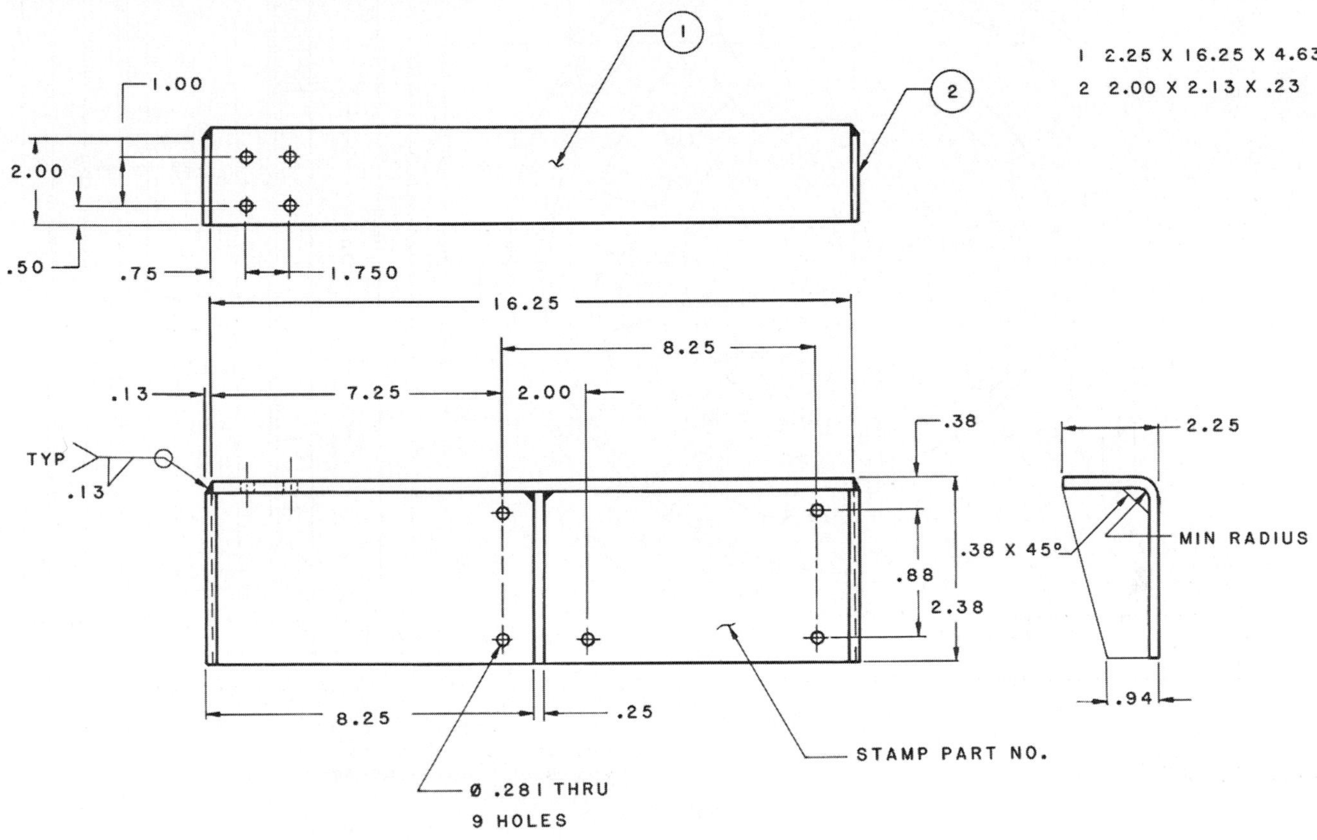

PROBLEM 22.1 Sensor Bracket

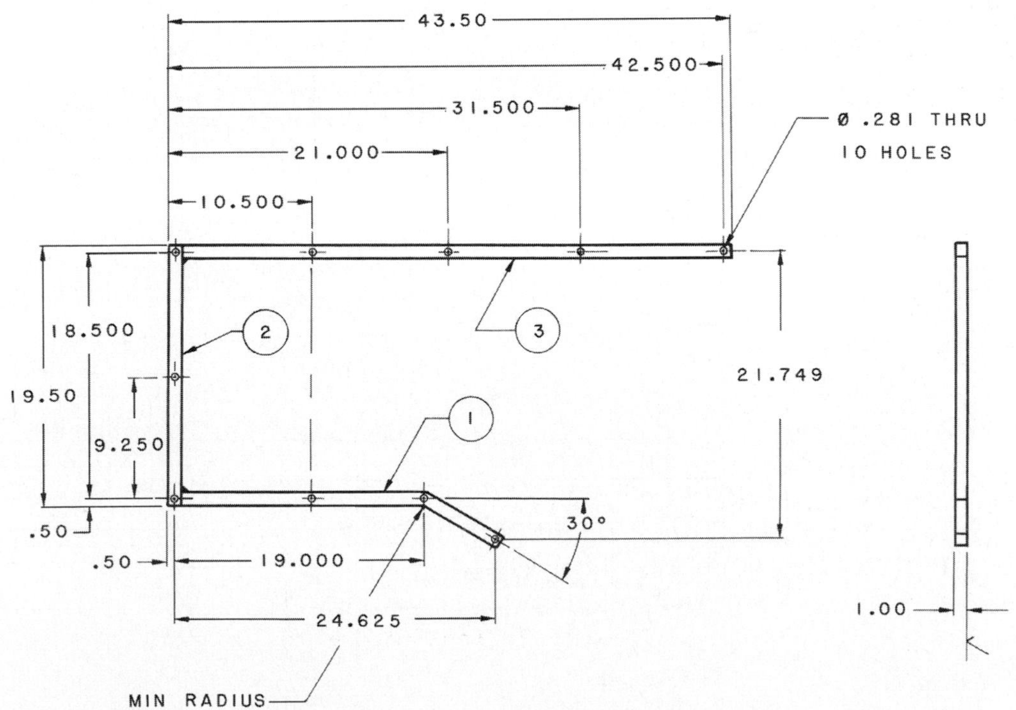

PROBLEM 22.2 Form Dam

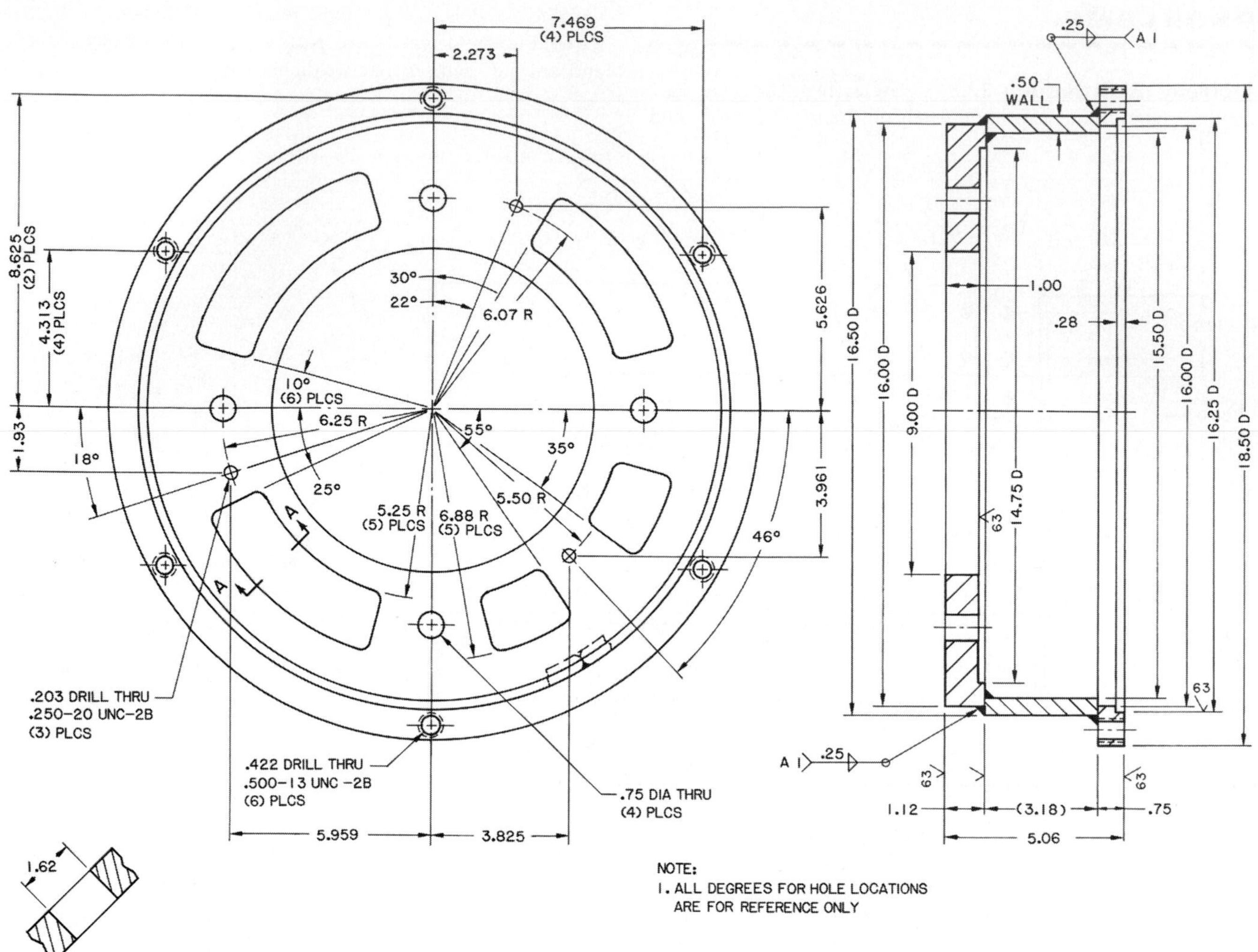

PROBLEM 22.3 Housing

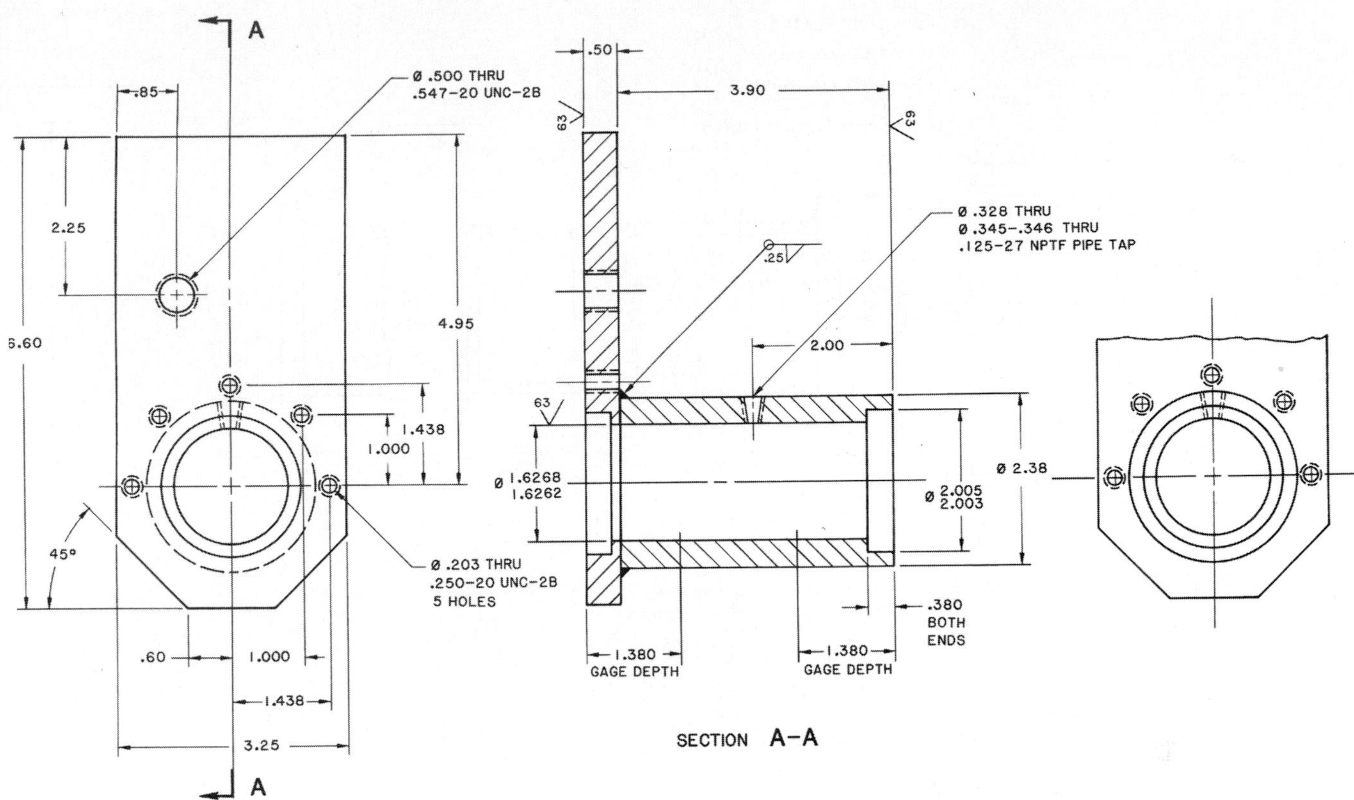

PROBLEM 22.4 Weldment Detail

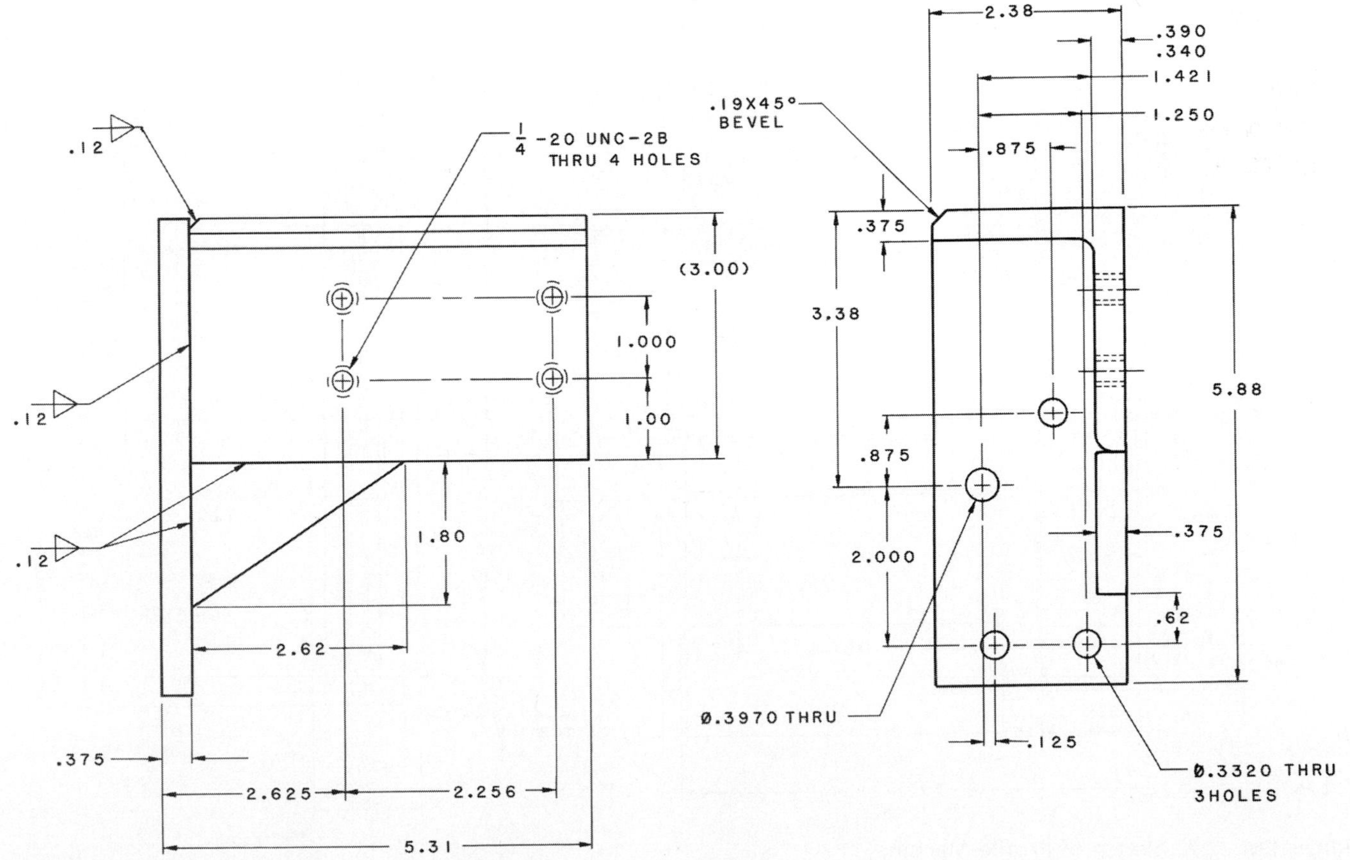

.12
$\frac{1}{4}$ -20 UNC-2B
THRU 4 HOLES
(3.00)
1.000
1.00
.12
.12
1.80
2.62
.375
2.625
2.256
5.31
2.38
.390
.340
1.421
1.250
.19X45°
BEVEL
.875
.375
3.38
5.88
.875
2.000
.375
.62
Ø.3970 THRU
.125
Ø.3320 THRU
3HOLES

PROBLEM 22.5 Weldment

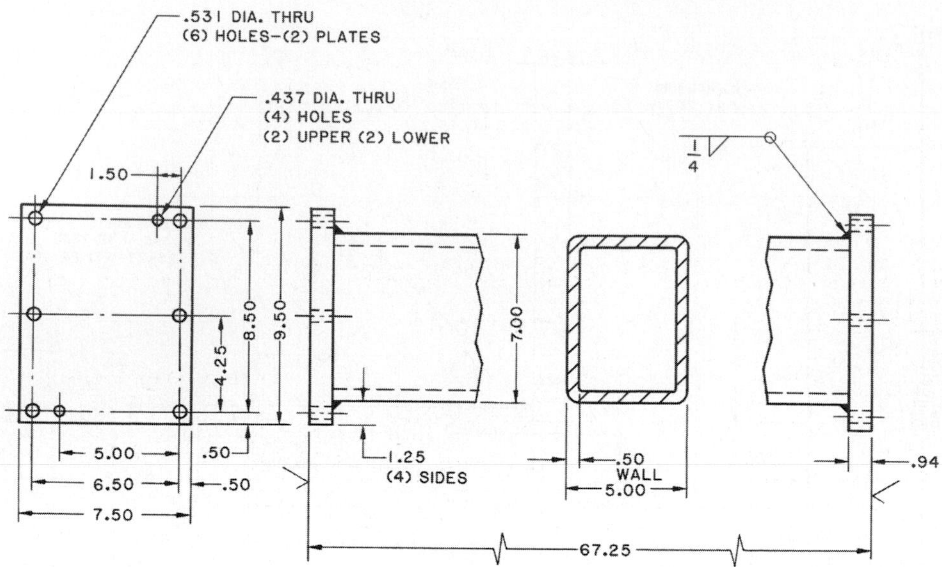

PROBLEM 22.6 Column Weldment

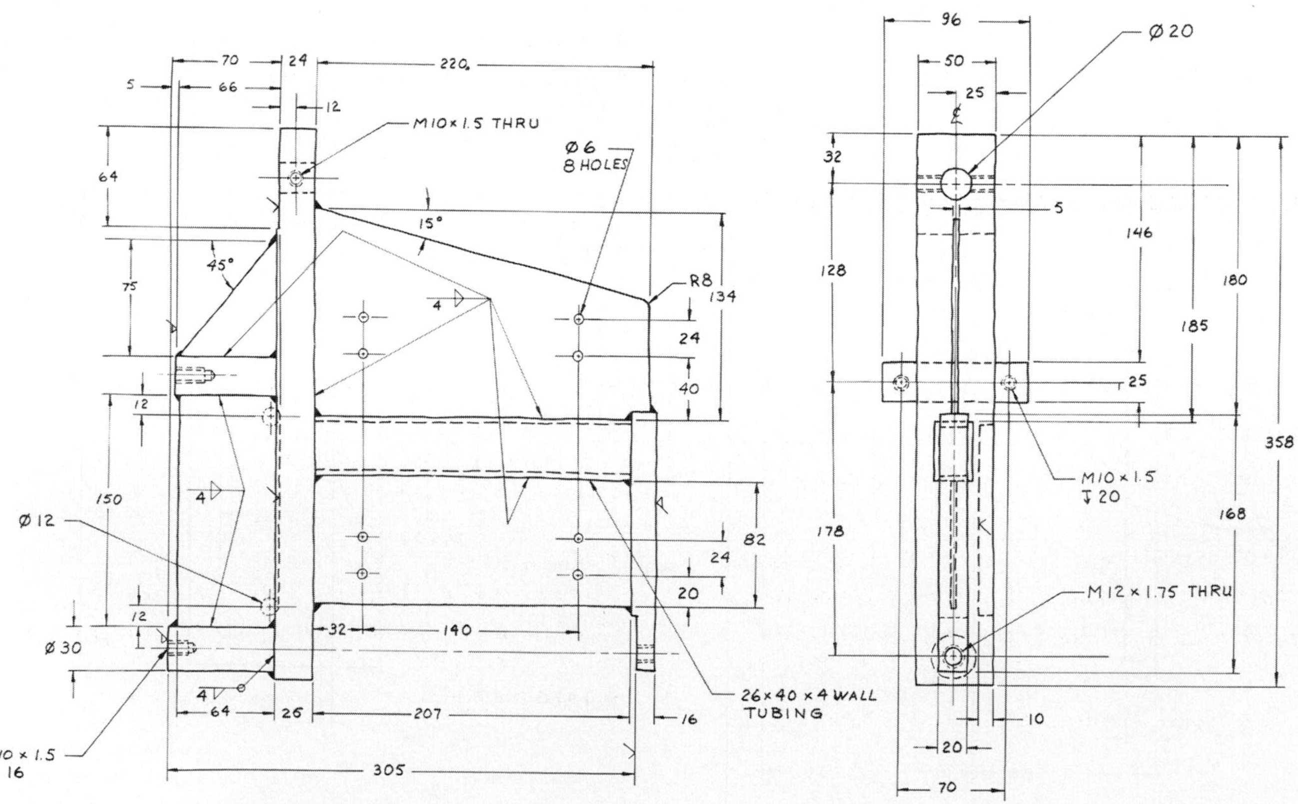

PROBLEM 22.7 Sketch of Profile Machine

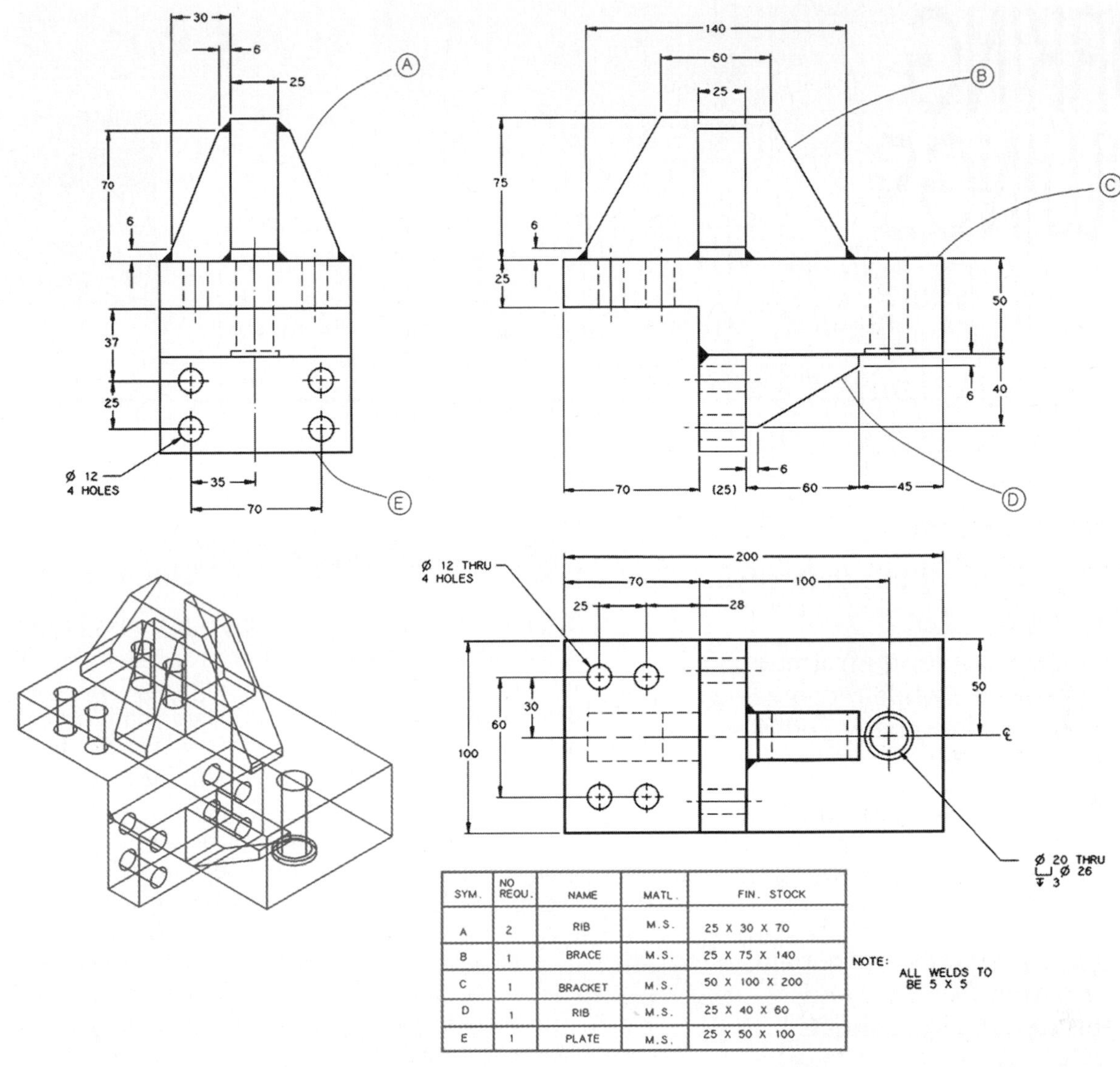

SYM.	NO REQU.	NAME	MATL.	FIN. STOCK
A	2	RIB	M.S.	25 X 30 X 70
B	1	BRACE	M.S.	25 X 75 X 140
C	1	BRACKET	M.S.	50 X 100 X 200
D	1	RIB	M.S.	25 X 40 X 60
E	1	PLATE	M.S.	25 X 50 X 100

PROBLEM 22.8 3D CAD Model and Weldment Detail

Problem 22.9 Draw the five major joints and a cross-sectional view of two different welds applied to each.

Problem 22.10 Sketch five basic joints.

Problem 22.11 Sketch three basic welds.

Problem 22.12 Draw a cross section of a fillet weld, and call out its basic parts.

Problem 22.13 Draw the basic arc and gas weld symbols.

Problem 22.14 Draw the basic resistance weld symbols.

Problem 22.15 Create the following symbols:

a. $\frac{1}{4}$ in. (6 mm) continuous fillet weld on arrow side

b. $\frac{3}{8}$ in. (9 mm) intermittent fillet weld on other side

Each weld is 3 in. (75 mm) long, spaced on 5 in. (15 mm) centers.

Problem 22.16 Create an appropriate symbol for a butt joint:

a. Single V-groove weld
b. 3 in. (9 mm) weld on opposite side
c. 60° groove weld on both sides
d. $\frac{1}{2}$ in. (12 mm) weld on arrow side
e. Workpieces to be placed $\frac{1}{8}$ in. (3 mm) apart
f. Grind welds flush with plate surface

Problem 22.17 Using Figure 22.2, redraw the part and dimension completely.

Problem 22.18 Using Figure 22.13, redraw the part.

WORKING DRAWINGS

Chapter 23

LEARNING OBJECTIVES

Upon completion of this chapter you will be able to:

1. Convey engineering information for production while recognizing basic types of assembly and drawing categories.
2. Understand, read, and produce assembly and detail drawings with appropriate view selection and dimensions.
3. Compile parts lists and supply information for notes and preprinted drawing sheets.
4. Identify and apply simplification and checking procedures.
5. Understand drawing reproduction and storage methods.
6. Use CAD to generate jig, fixture, die, and tooling designs.

23.1 INTRODUCTION

The primary purpose of a drawing is to convey engineering requirements to produce a finished product or part. **Working drawings** include **assembly drawings** and associated **detail drawings** of a project. Parts are drawn manually or modeled on a CAD system. The valve part and valve assembly in Figure 23.1(a) have been modeled via a solid modeling CAD/CAM program. Once the geometry is created, the solid modeler can explode the housing into its component parts, rotate the model to different viewing angles, create cross sections, and check for interferences [Fig. 23.1(b)]. Wireframe geometry is created automatically from the solid model. Exploded views and assemblies can be used for 2D drafting or design format [Fig. 23.1(c)]. Parametric modeling also allows for the automatic generation of part families [Fig. 23.1(d)]. Product drafting and detailing documentation is produced from common design geometry [Fig. 23.1(e)]. A finite-element model is generated from solid geometry and analyzed against design parameters [Fig. 23.1(f)]. Color schemes depict the results for a particular engineering analysis [Fig. 23.1(g)]. During the first stages of manufacturing, NC capability allows generation of NC data directly from the solid model [Fig. 23.1(h)]. Manufacturing engineers and part programmers can preview cutter paths before machining a part to obtain optimum cutter path design [Fig. 23.1(i)].

Drawings are required for all almost all product design, production requirements, and manufacturing specifications. Each of the parts in Figure 23.2 required working drawings—detail drawings for each separate piece and an assembly drawing. A set of drawings for a system, a tool, or a product contains sufficient engineering information so that the following functions may be performed:

- Ordering material
- Planning manufacturing operations, tooling, and manufacturing facilities
- Processing material

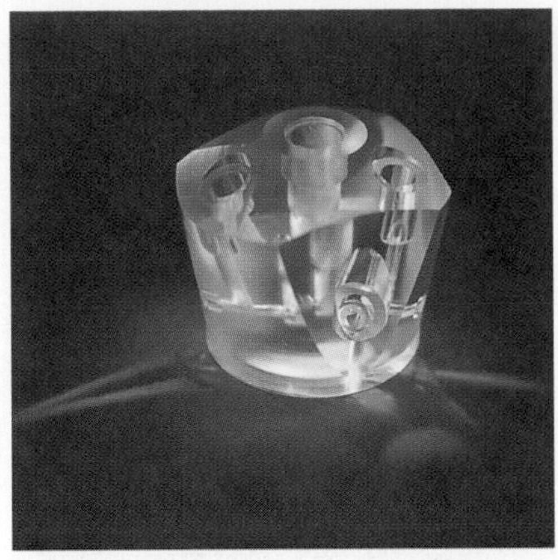

(a) Solid model of a valve housing

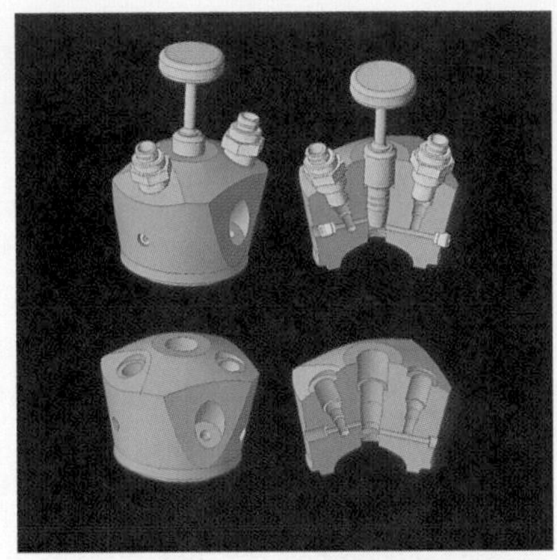

(b) Component parts

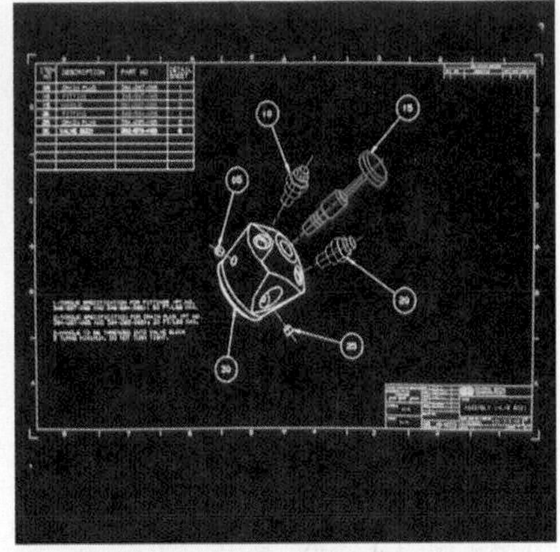

(c) Exploded valve housing

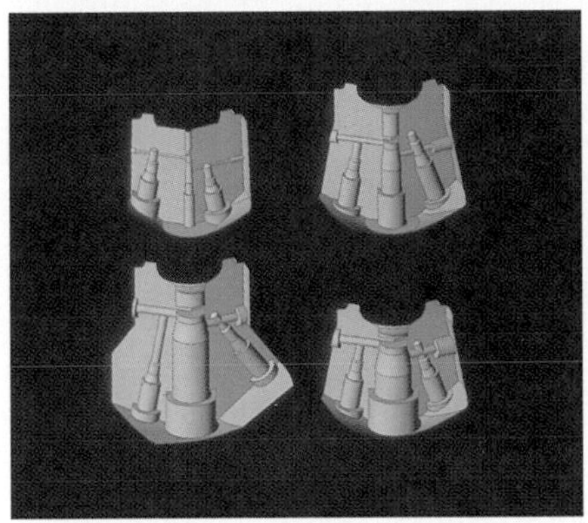

(d) Parametric modeling

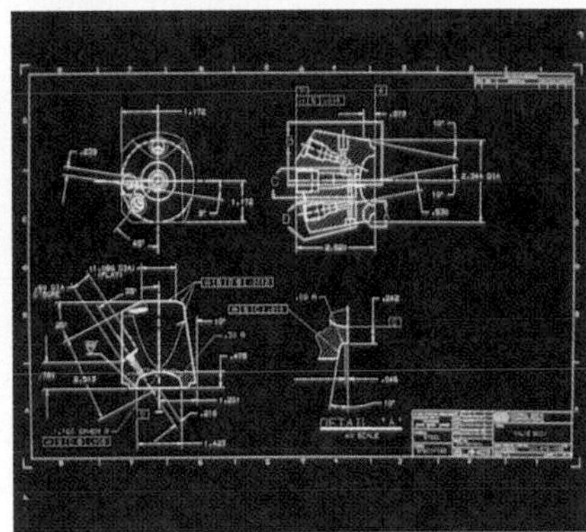

(e) Product documentation

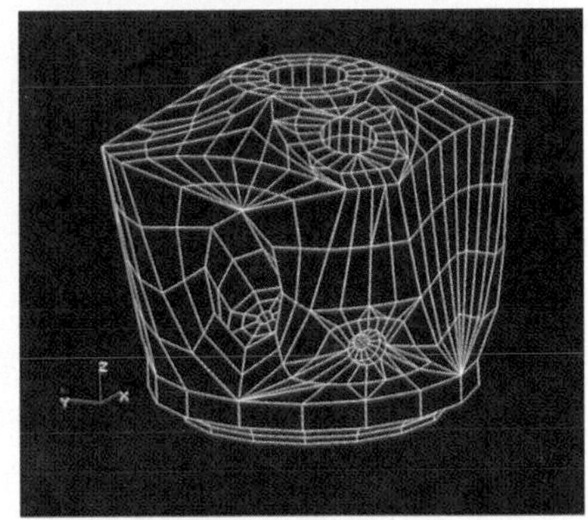

(f) Finite-element model

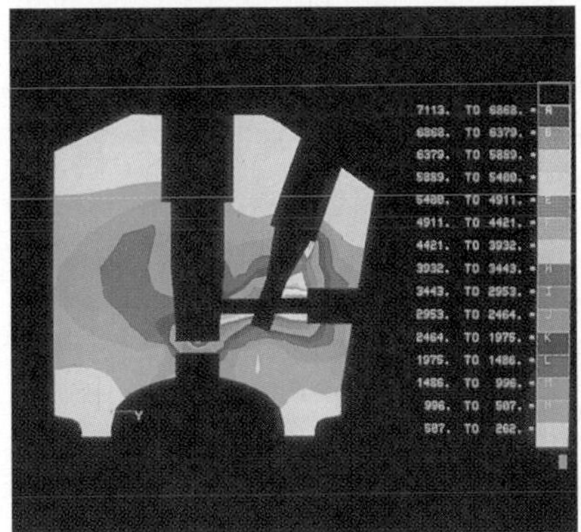

(g) Color schemes for analysis

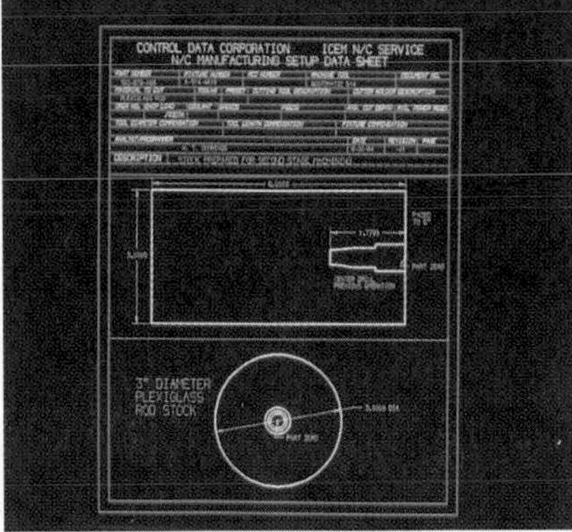

(h) NC generation

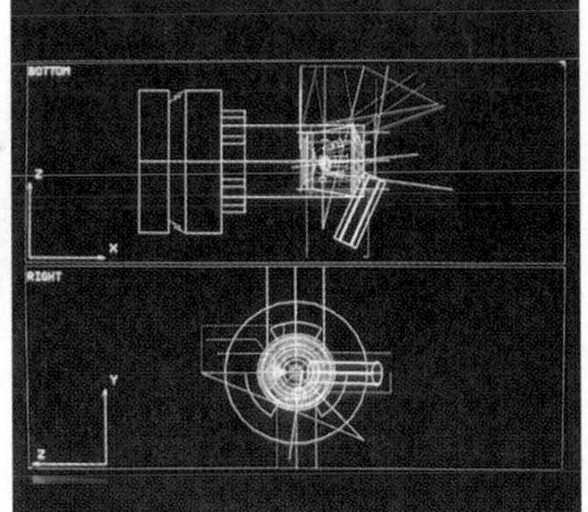

(i) Cutter paths before machining the part to obtain optimum cutter path design

FIGURE 23.1 Using CAD/CAM to Document and Manufacture a Part

- Inspection and control of product quality and reliability
- Assembly
- Testing and modeling
- Packaging, boxing, and shipping
- Determining cost
- Cataloging
- Installation and service
- Conducting final acceptance test
- Making alterations
- Recording for duplication, repair, or replacement

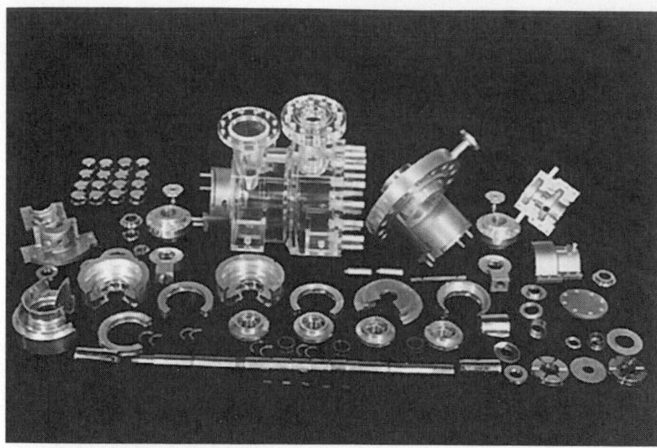

FIGURE 23.2 Disassembled Boiler Feed Pump

23.2 ASSEMBLY DESIGN CONSIDERATIONS

The way the product will be assembled must be considered early in the design phase. Perhaps as much as 80% of the cost to produce a part is set during the design phase. This is one of the many reasons why the design of the product and the design of the manufacturing process must occur simultaneously. **Design for manufacturability (DFM)** and **simultaneous** or **concurrent engineering (CE)** are keys to successful designs. The optimal method of assembly can be chosen early in the design process if the product and the production-assembly process are designed at the same time.

There are five basic types of assembly:

Manual assembly Performed manually, with the assistance of hand tools only.

Semiautomatic assembly A combination of manual and automated processes. The operator loads the product manually, the machine then performs one or more assembly operations, and the operator then unloads the product.

Adaptive assembly Programming the system to adapt itself automatically to certain variations based on sensors.

Automatic assembly All operations are performed automatically without human intervention or decisions; places constraints on the design for the assembly of the product as well as the orientation, presentation, and gripping of the parts.

Flexible assembly Uses flexible manufacturing equipment that builds families of related products or subassemblies on the same setup or with quick, automated setup changes built into the process.

23.3 CATEGORIES OF DRAWINGS

Engineering drawings can be classified into three broad categories:

- Layout and design study drawings
- Engineering and production detail drawings
- Assembly drawings

23.3.1 Layout and Design Study Drawings

Layout and design drawings depict proportions, dimensions, materials, and the relationship of parts in new or modified designs. Usually, they precede production drawings, are drawn to scale, and are useful in preparing and checking part drawings and assemblies.

Layout drawings, often effective in establishing patent claims, are completed by engineers and designers in conjunction with production personnel. When practical, layouts should be prepared in a form suitable for use in manufacturing, especially in situations where prototype or developmental models are required (Fig. 23.3).

23.3.2 Engineering and Production Detail Drawings

Detail drawings provide a complete engineering definition of the finished system, assembly, or part (Fig. 23.4). This includes design data references, laboratory instructions, and engineering specifications. These drawings are prepared for the shop floor and are used in the production of the desired product.

Individual parts of an assembly are machined separately during the manufacturing stage of the project. Parts are also called **workpieces**. A typical workpiece is detailed so the fixture designer can produce tools for holding and locating it during the machining operations.

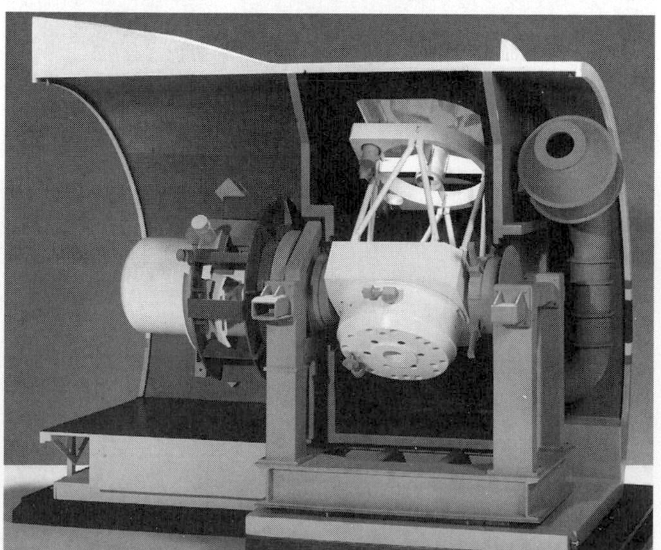

FIGURE 23.3 Model of an Infrared Telescope

Engineering production drawings are not created to accommodate a particular method of manufacture. They are meant to be used without additional explanation. If manufacturing or processing instructions are provided, this information is for reference only, unless such data is vital to the end definition and engineering control of the product.

23.3.3 Assembly Drawings

An **assembly drawing** defines the complete end-item requirements, and establishes item identification for the assembled configuration of two or more pieces, parts, subordinate assemblies, or any combination that are joined together to form an assembly (Fig. 23.5). Assembly drawings always include a **parts list** or a **bill of materials.** The sleeve valve in Figure 23.6 required an assembly drawing to show the proper relationship of the parts. During the design phase, a design layout was employed to establish and control the relationship between parts with regard to tolerancing and fits.

23.4 ASSEMBLY DRAWINGS AND THE DESIGN PROCESS

In most cases, the assembly is conceived as a whole (layout assembly) and broken into individual pieces (detail drawings) for manufacture and later assembly. This is called the **top-down** approach to design.

Assemblies are seldom designed from the bottom up, unless the individual parts are standard items that are to be assembled into a unit. **Bottom-up design** means that each component of a unit is designed separately and then put together in an assembly.

The sleeve valve in Figure 23.6 comes in four pieces. The design is *limited to the minimum number of parts*. Each piece fits inside the other. Since each piece was toleranced in relationship to the housing, the product was *designed as a unit*. The housing and end cap hold the other parts together. The bolts and nuts needed for assembly are not shown in the figure.

After the design and layout of a project are complete, a detail drafter pulls separate parts from the assembly and draws them on individual sheets. This process is called **detailing**. Details include appropriate views and dimensions.

Standard items that can be purchased off the shelf are shown on the assembly drawing and listed in the parts list. They do not require a separate detail, unless they are modified in some way. Standard parts include bolts, screws, nuts, retaining rings, dowels, pins, springs, gears, bearings, clamps, and purchased subassemblies.

As a product is designed and detailed, the manufacturing department begins to determine the tooling requirements. **Tool designers** create appropriate fixtures to hold the individual parts during manufacture. Machining involves the use of fixtures to locate, hold, and position the part for accurate, economical, and efficient production. Jigs and fixtures are also assemblies and are designed, laid out, and detailed in a manner similar to product assemblies.

23.4.1 Assembly Drawing Types

An **assembly drawing** may contain the detailed design requirements for one or more parts required in the assembly. It is prepared for each group of items that are to be joined together to form an assembly and reflects one of the following:

- A logical level in the assembly or disassembly sequence
- A functional unit
- A stocked, standard, off-the-shelf purchased item

The assembly may be shown on the same drawing sheet on which the details appear or on a separate sheet. If the assembly is on a separate sheet, this will be sheet number 1, and the details will be shown on sheet number 2, etc. All sheets bear the same drawing number.

An assembly drawing may define either a **separable** or an **inseparable** assembly. **Welded assemblies** are inseparable assemblies. Figure 23.7 is an example of a welded assembly. The parts list is a **material stock list** and simply gives the stock steel sizes of each piece. On most weldments, the assembly is considered a detail of a part and each piece is dimensioned on the drawing. The detail of the weldment in Figure 23.8 is such a case. Here, even though the weldment is three separate pieces of aluminum joined together by welding, it is not considered an assembly. The drawing is simply a detail of the weldment. Each piece is not separately called out, ballooned, or listed in a material stock list. Instead, it is dimensioned on the sheet. (See Chapter 22 for more information concerning weldments and welded assemblies.)

23.4.2 Mechanical Assemblies and Drawing Requirements

A mechanical assembly may have parts made from sand, permanent mold, or die castings (Fig. 23.9); rolled, extruded, or pressed-shape forgings; plates; bars; sheet metal; or a combination of any two or more of these. These parts may be assembled into a complete unit by welding, brazing, soldering, riveting, bolting, or other fastening methods. After assembly, additional work, such as a machining, may be necessary to complete the item.

The function of an assembly drawing is to provide a complete specification for joining together, in proper relationship, two or more detail parts or subassemblies to form an assembly. This type of drawing usually includes a graphic layout of component parts, necessary notes, and, if a separate list or bill of material is not involved, a tabulated list of parts. It should show the spatial relation of each part or

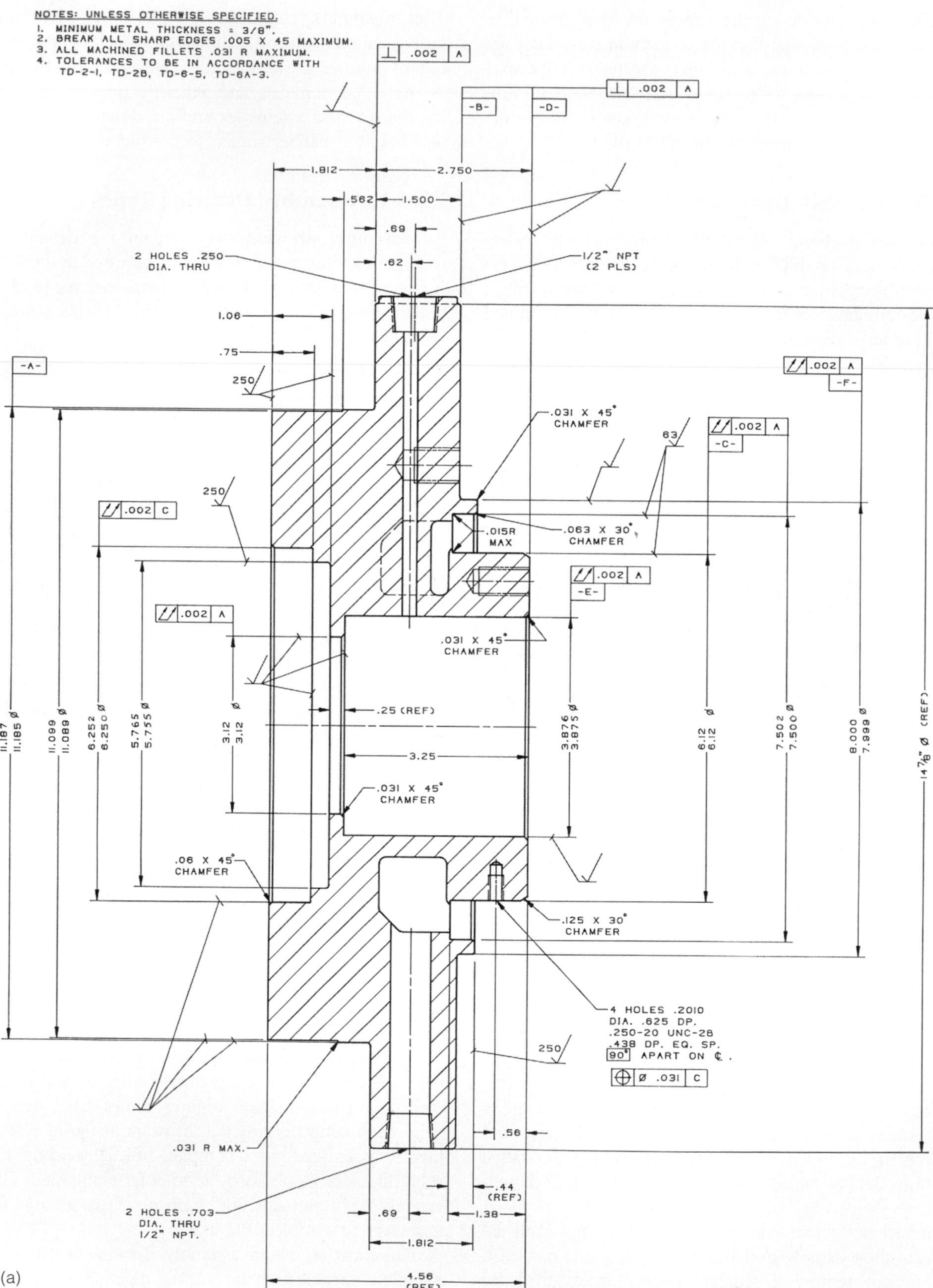

(a)

FIGURE 23.4 Cover Detail

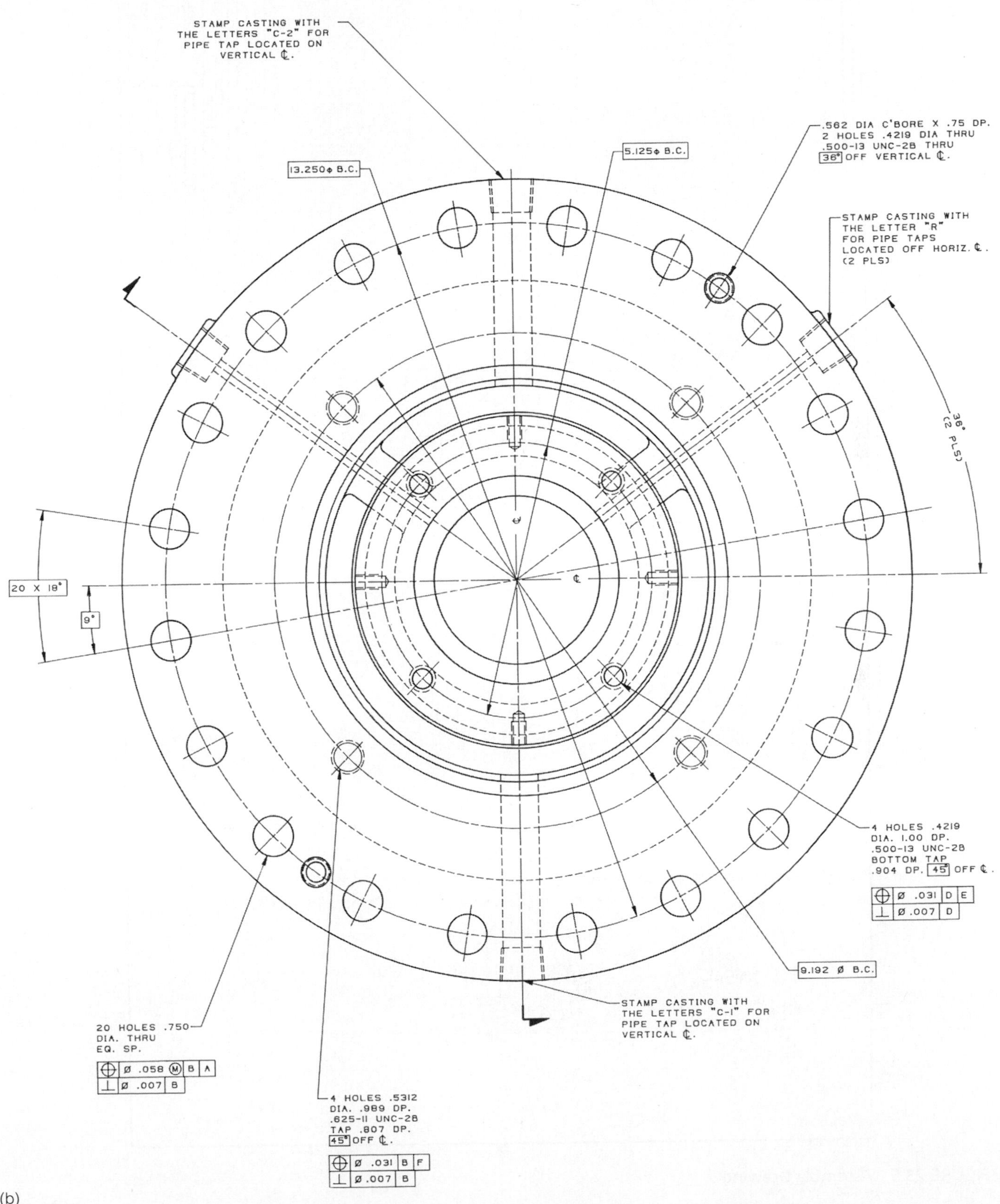
STAMP CASTING WITH THE LETTERS "C-2" FOR PIPE TAP LOCATED ON VERTICAL ℄.
.562 DIA C'BORE X .75 DP. 2 HOLES .4219 DIA THRU .500-13 UNC-2B THRU 36° OFF VERTICAL ℄.
5.125⌀ B.C.
13.250⌀ B.C.
STAMP CASTING WITH THE LETTER "R" FOR PIPE TAPS LOCATED OFF HORIZ. ℄. (2 PLS)
36° (2 PLS)
20 X 18°
9°
℄
4 HOLES .4219 DIA. 1.00 DP. .500-13 UNC-2B BOTTOM TAP .904 DP. 45° OFF ℄.
⌖ Ø .031 D E
⊥ Ø .007 D
9.192 Ø B.C.
STAMP CASTING WITH THE LETTERS "C-1" FOR PIPE TAP LOCATED ON VERTICAL ℄.
20 HOLES .750 DIA. THRU EQ. SP.
⌖ Ø .058 Ⓜ B A
⊥ Ø .007 B
4 HOLES .5312 DIA. .989 DP. .625-11 UNC-2B TAP .807 DP. 45° OFF ℄.
⌖ Ø .031 B F
⊥ Ø .007 B

(b)

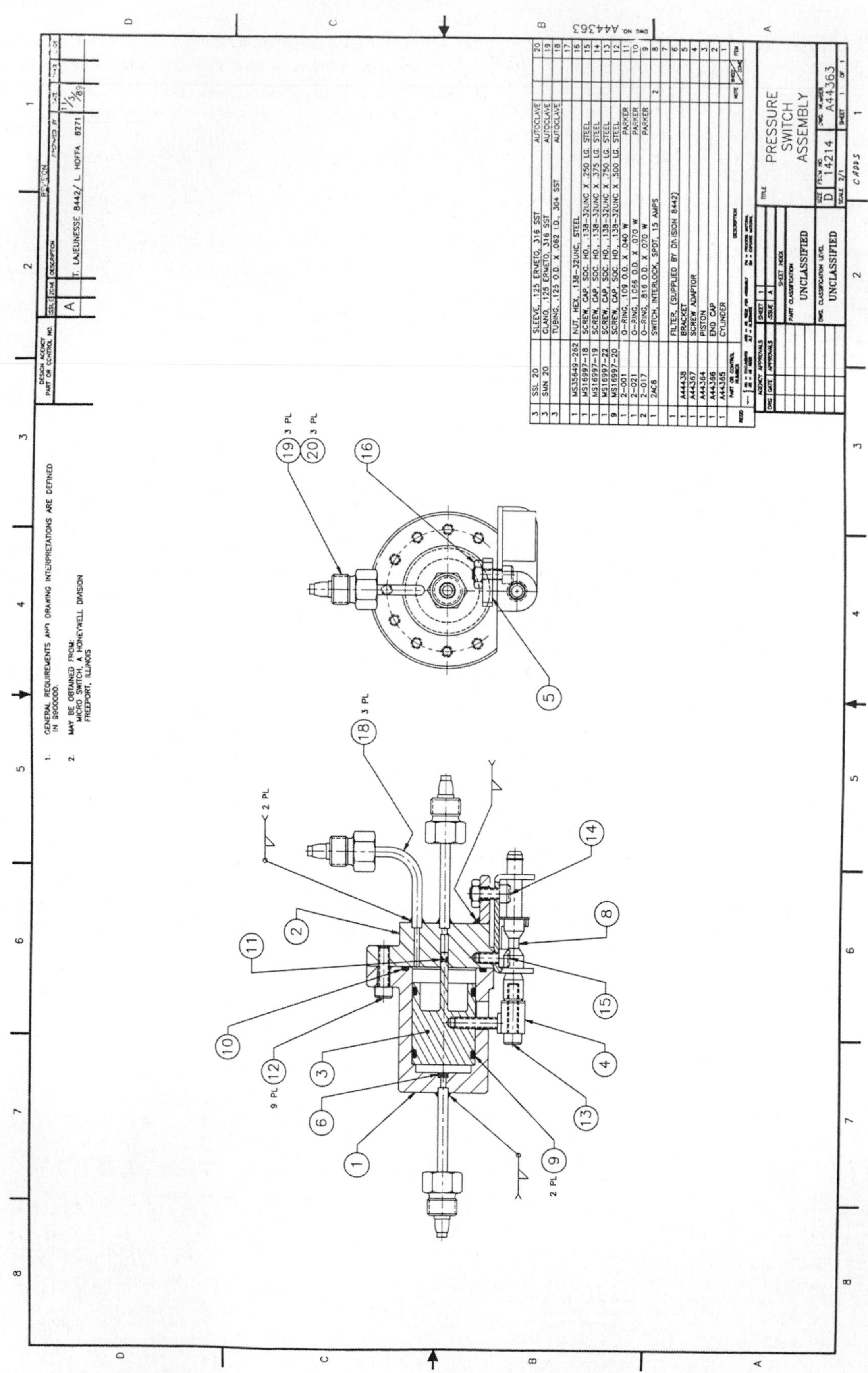

FIGURE 23.5 Assembly Drawing

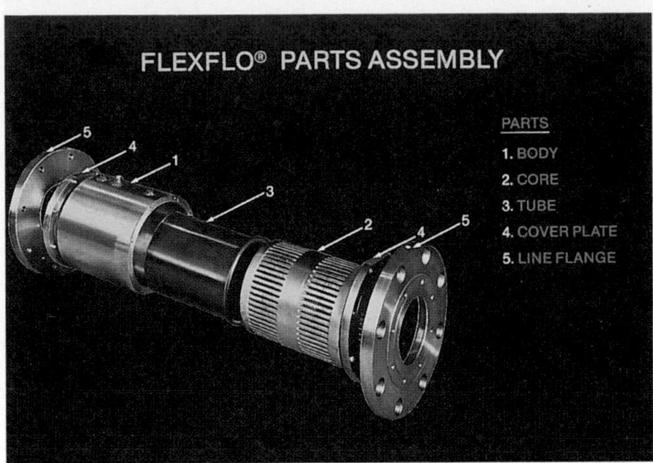

FIGURE 23.6 Disassembled Grove Flexflo Flexible Rubber Sleeve Valve

subassembly, the method of fastening, and the type of fasteners.

When necessary, the assembly drawing indicates subsequent operations to form the completed item. For example, heat treatment, machining dimensions, and finishes are specified here. If a mechanical assembly is made entirely from cut shapes with sufficient information for cutting each piece, the information to fasten them together and finish them might be given on a single drawing.

23.4.3 Detail Drawings

Detail drawings are fully dimensioned, accurately laid-out engineering drawings of individual parts (Fig. 23.10). All information needed to manufacture and produce the part is included. Adequate view description, correct dimensioning and tolerancing, accurate notes, and material designation are shown on the detail drawing. Components may appear on the assembly drawings or on separate details, or be established by written description.

23.4.4 Assembly Drawing Considerations

Assembly drawings for production parts may also be created from the detail drawings *after they have been approved by the checker*. This procedure gives a final check of the detail drawings for space clearances, limits, and satisfactory function in assembly.

Assembly drawings for jigs and fixtures are produced from the designer's sketches that are accurate layout drawings. The final assembly is broken into individual components that are detailed separately. The checker checks the assembly and the details in the final stage.

Product design, production volume, and facilities are the determining factors influencing the need for an assembly drawing. The quality of the finished product depends on the effective attachment methods, regardless of the quality of the individual parts.

Welded, soldered, or brazed parts that have characteristics requiring the parts to have a particular relation to one another and parts that are permanently assembled are shown in their assembled positions. Necessary dimensions and specifications are included for size control and other conditions. Parts that are pressed and line-reamed in place, parts that are secured together with pins, bushings, and similar assemblies, and parts that are machined after assembly require an assembly to show these operations and specifications for assembly control. Parts for which a surface finish must be applied after assembly may require an assembly drawing to ensure proper overall finish. The cam boxes in Figure 23.11 are examples of assembled devices.

The subassembly in Figure 23.12(a) shows the relationship and orientation of the components of a complicated mechanical assembly. This example illustrates the use of CAD in the design of a typical mechanical assembly. Assemblies, components, drawings, and animated working models of the project are generated by the engineer and designer directly on the system before any drawings are created. A solid model of a component in the assembly is shown in Figure 23.12(b). A model, the wireframe assembly, and a multiview drawing of the component document the part [Fig. 23.12(c)]. A solid model of the mechanical assembly animates the working conditions of the assembly [Fig. 23.12(d)].

23.4.5 View Selection and Dimensions on Assembly Drawings

Usually, views are chosen to depict the assembly in its natural position in space, to define clearly how the parts fit together, and to describe the functional relationship of the parts. The minimum number of views needed to define the assembly should be given. Often, only one view is required.

Dimensions on assembly drawings are confined to setup dimensions, dimensions needed for assembly, dimensions required for machining after assembly, and clearance dimensions. Overall dimensions (height, width, and depth) may be included on the assembly for packaging assistance. When necessary, open and closed positions of movable parts on the assembly are given.

23.4.6 Hidden Lines, Crosshatching, and Phantom Lines on Assembly Drawings

Hidden lines should not be shown on assembly drawings, especially if they would confuse the reader. Instead, section views can show the relationship of internal parts (see later Figs. 23.30 and 23.31). Conventional section lining may be used. Material symbols are optional on assembly drawing sections. The section lines are drawn at angles to the object outlines and should be at a different angle for each adjacent part.

If there is some doubt, the note **FRONT**, to indicate the forward operating position, should be added to the detail

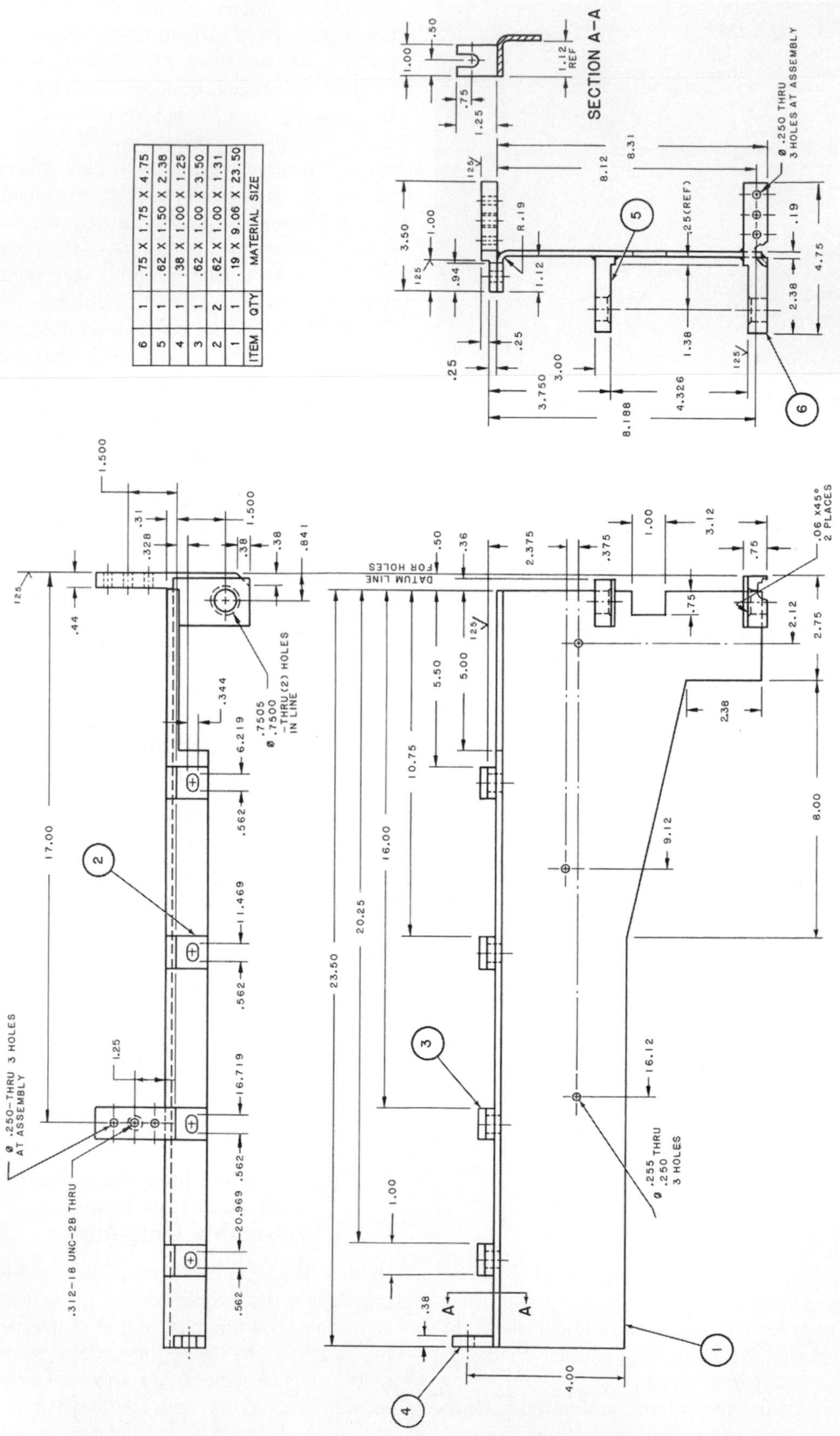

ITEM	QTY	MATERIAL SIZE
6	1	.75 X 1.75 X 4.75
5	1	.62 X 1.50 X 2.38
4	1	.38 X 1.00 X 1.25
3	1	.62 X 1.00 X 3.50
2	2	.62 X 1.00 X 1.31
1	1	.19 X 9.06 X 23.50

FIGURE 23.7 Welded Assembly

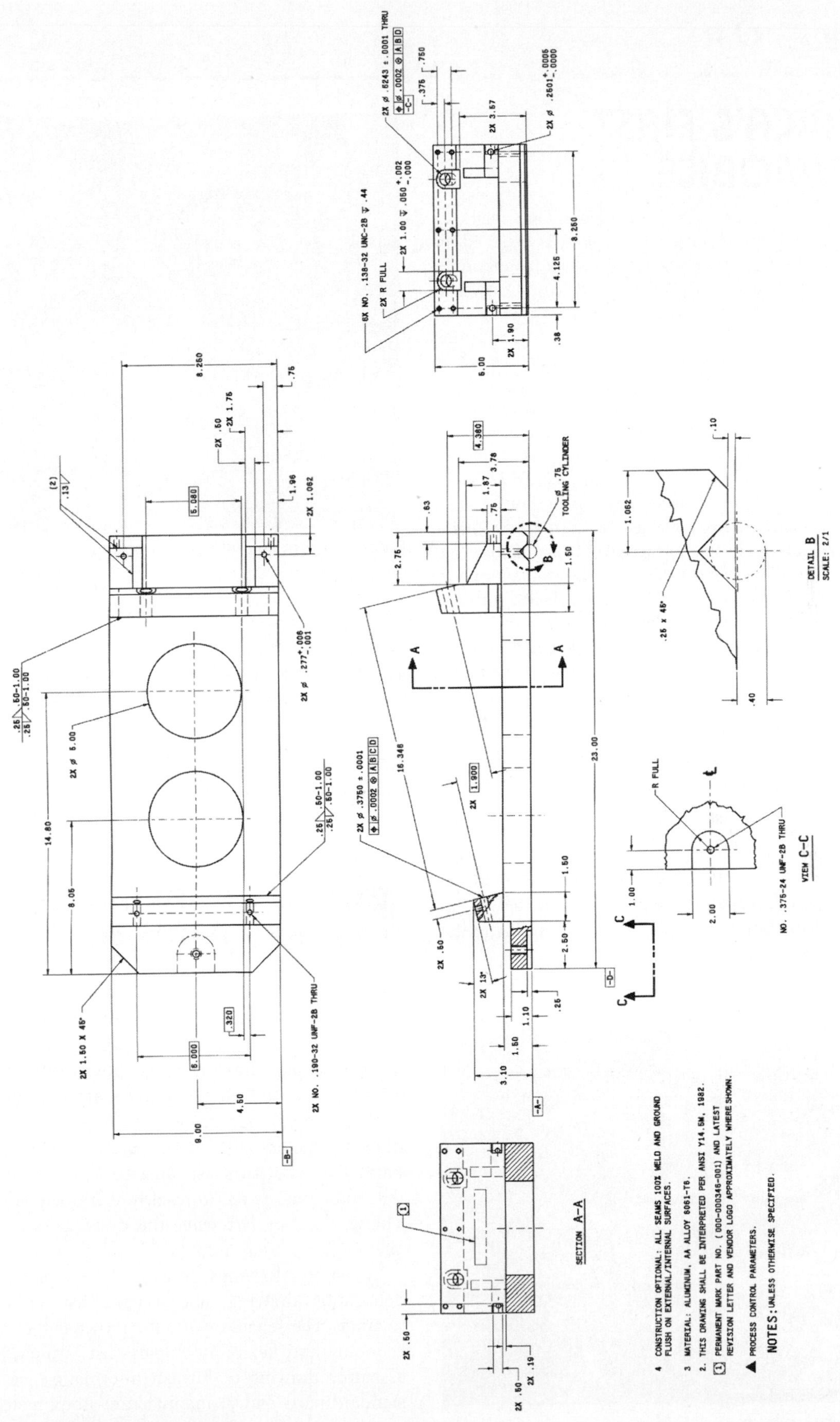

FIGURE 23.8 Welded Assembly Detail

Focus On . . .

AMERICA'S FIRST AUTOMOBILE

Who produced America's first automobile? One might be tempted to name Henry Ford, or maybe even Thomas Edison because of his electric car. However, the first car manufactured in the United States was the creation of Charles Duryea in Springfield, Massachusetts, in 1895.

Duryea was born on a farm in 1861 at a time when people relied on mechanical devices to accomplish their farm work. At seventeen, he began to cultivate his mechanical aptitude by assembling discarded farm parts into bicycles. Later on, he sold bicycles built from parts manufactured to his specifications.

He first saw a gasoline engine while he was displaying bicycles at the Ohio State Fair. The engine was much larger than could possibly be used in an automobile, but he knew that smaller engines were possible. He also knew that a German, Karl Benz, had recently patented the first automobile. He decided to build and patent the first American automobile.

After many years of thinking about his horseless carriage, Duryea and his brother finally built their first car in 1892. It had a gasoline-powered internal combustion engine with an electric ignition. The engine was attached to a converted horse buggy.

In 1893, the Duryeas produced a prototype called the *buggaut* and established themselves as the makers of the first successful American automobile. By 1895, they offered an improved 700-pound version for $2000.

Modern internal combustion engine.

Charles Duryea continued work on his dream machine and obtained nineteen patents, one of which was the first automobile patent issued to an American manufacturer. In 1896, the Duryea Motor Wagon Company produced thirteen cars of the same design. They were the first manufacturers to produce many copies of a single design. The car won several races against domestic and foreign automobiles.

drawing of a part to indicate the position of the part in the assembly. It is also acceptable to show a part before an assembly process operation with phantom lines and after the operation with object lines.

FIGURE 23.9 Die Cast Parts

23.5 ASSEMBLY DRAWINGS AND PARTS LISTS

An **assembly** is a combination of two or more parts joined together in one working unit. A **subassembly** is an assembly of parts that aid in producing a larger assembly. The purpose of an assembly drawing is to show the spatial relation of each part to the others and to identify all parts in the assembly by a number for each unique part. Assembly drawings include a list of all parts of the assembly, called a **parts list**. The parts list must be keyed to the drawing so that individual parts are clearly identified on the assembly. This is done by *ballooning* the drawing (see Fig. 23.5 and later Figs. 23.30 and 23.31).

Assembly drawings consist of two parts: an assembly delineation drawing, and a parts list, either integral or separate. The separate parts list provides the greatest overall economy and flexibility. A parts list is included with each assembly drawing to furnish information needed to order standard parts and to manufacture stock materials for non-standard parts.

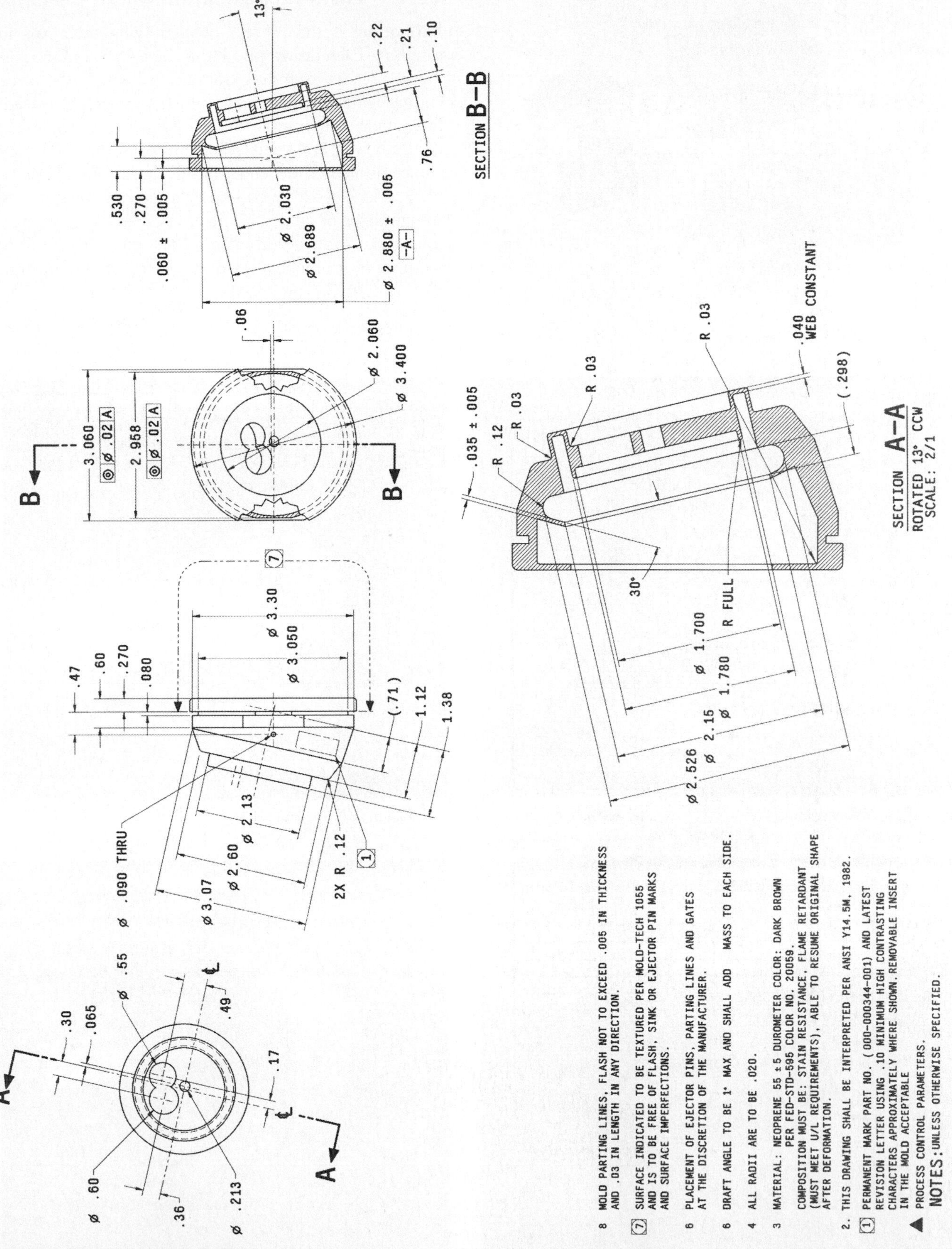

SECTION B-B
SECTION A-A
ROTATED 13° CCW
SCALE: 2/1
Ø .090 THRU
2X R .12
.040 WEB CONSTANT
R FULL
30°
13°
-A-
Ø 2.880 ± .005
.060 ± .005
.035 ± .005
8 MOLD PARTING LINES, FLASH NOT TO EXCEED .005 IN THICKNESS AND .03 IN LENGTH IN ANY DIRECTION.
7 SURFACE INDICATED TO BE TEXTURED PER MOLD-TECH 1055 AND IS TO BE FREE OF FLASH, SINK OR EJECTOR PIN MARKS AND SURFACE IMPERFECTIONS.
6 PLACEMENT OF EJECTOR PINS, PARTING LINES AND GATES AT THE DISCRETION OF THE MANUFACTURER.
5 DRAFT ANGLE TO BE 1° MAX AND SHALL ADD MASS TO EACH SIDE.
4 ALL RADII ARE TO BE .020.
3 MATERIAL: NEOPRENE 55 ±5 DUROMETER COLOR: DARK BROWN PER FED-STD-595 COLOR NO. 20059.
COMPOSITION MUST BE: STAIN RESISTANCE, FLAME RETARDANT (MUST MEET U/L REQUIREMENTS), ABLE TO RESUME ORIGINAL SHAPE AFTER DEFORMATION.
2. THIS DRAWING SHALL BE INTERPRETED PER ANSI Y14.5M, 1982.
1 PERMANENT MARK PART NO. (000-000344-001) AND LATEST REVISION LETTER USING .10 MINIMUM HIGH CONTRASTING CHARACTERS APPROXIMATELY WHERE SHOWN. REMOVABLE INSERT IN THE MOLD ACCEPTABLE
PROCESS CONTROL PARAMETERS.
NOTES: UNLESS OTHERWISE SPECIFIED.

FIGURE 23.10 Acoustic Microphone Cup

FIGURE 23.11 Cam Boxes

23.5.1 Parts Identification on an Assembly

Ballooning is the process of identifying each part in the assembly. Each drawn part has a circle with a number inside it and a leader extending from the balloon to the piece and ending with an arrowhead. Balloons either are placed in a line along the middle of the drawing (horizontally or vertically) or are scattered throughout the drawing. The choice of method depends on the complexity of the assembly. Leader lines from balloons should not cross and can be straight lines or curved. Balloon circles are drawn anywhere from .5 to .75 inches in diameter (12 mm to 20 mm) with a template on manually drawn assemblies or with a command such as **CIRCLE** on a CAD system.

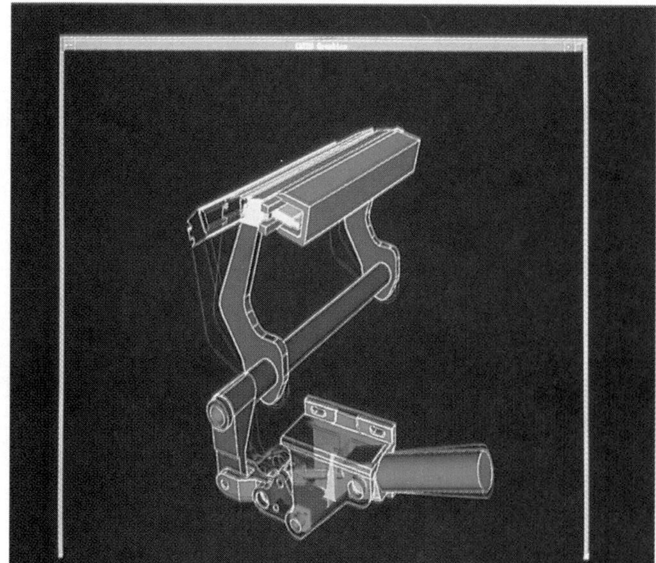

(a) Mechanical assembly

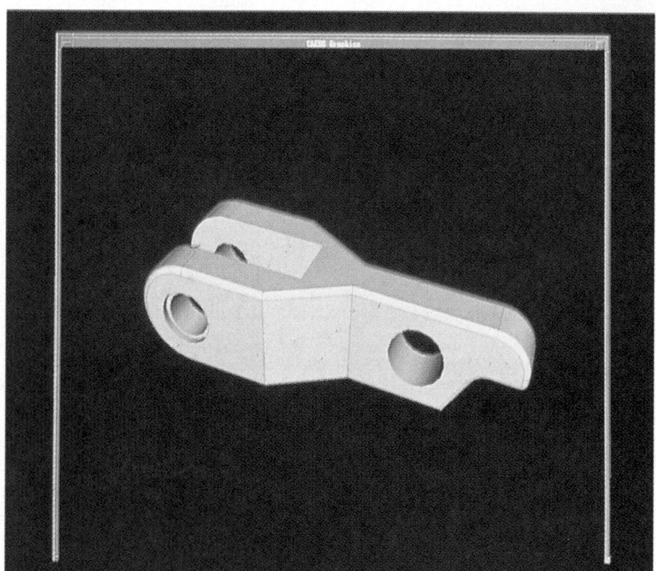

(b) Solid model of component

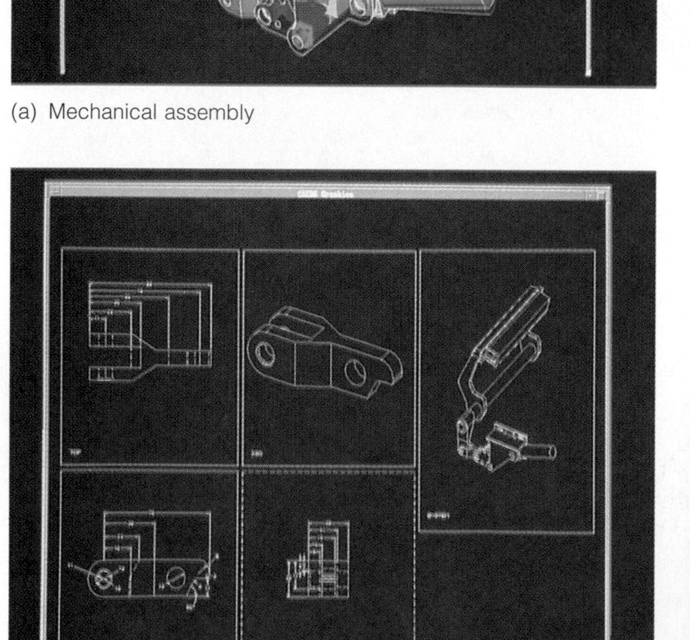

(d) Assembly animation

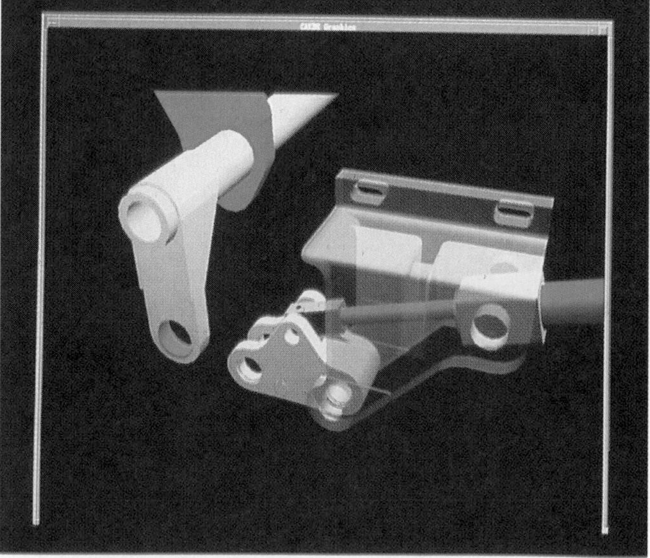

(c) Component documentation

FIGURE 23.12 CAD and Design

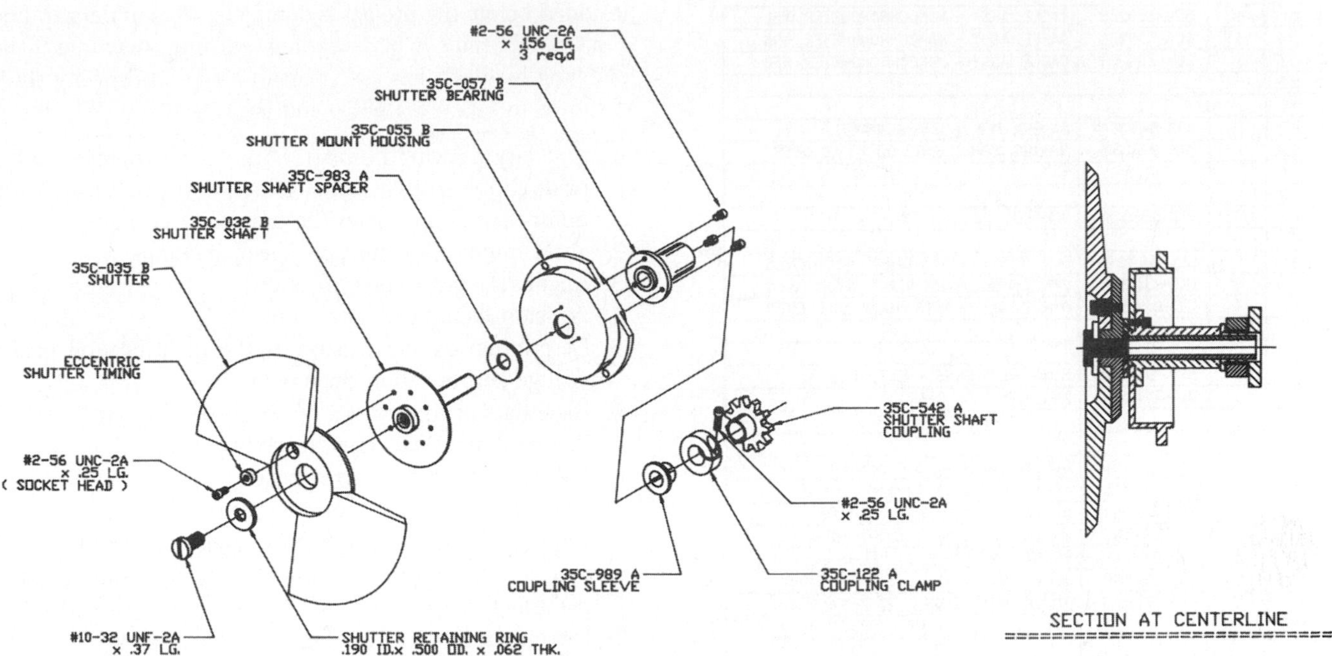

FIGURE 23.13 UltraCam Shutter Assembly

Many CAD systems allow you to enter a command that will insert a balloon with the appropriate text within the circle. The **BALLOON** command is picked, the text is entered via keyboard, the part edge is selected, and the balloon is positioned on the drawing. The system draws the balloon, the leader, the arrowhead, and the text. Some systems have automatic sequence number capability.

In some cases, the parts of an assembly are called out on the drawing without the aid of numbered balloons. In Figure 23.13, the shutter assembly has been displayed pictorially. Each of the parts is described in notes that have leaders pointing to the part.

23.5.2 Parts Lists

The assembly drawing must have a complete **parts list**. Each parts list includes individual part numbers, the name and a description of each part, and the material and quantity of all items required for one complete assembly (Fig. 23.14).

On tool and die drawings, the parts list is sometimes called a **stock list**. Here, material allowance is added for purchase information. Die drawings also have a stock list on the assembly drawing sheet.

The assembly parts list is placed above the title block when on the same sheet as the drawing. The part numbers are arranged to read upward so that new parts can be added if needed. The precise method of listing parts varies among companies. The parts or stock list sometimes uses the vertical line divisions of the revision record (block at top right of the drawing form). Spacing of horizontal divisions is uniform in both revision blocks and the parts list.

Parts List Heading Arrangement When an integral parts list is included on a drawing sheet, the heading **PARTS LIST** is placed on the bottom of the list and the part numbers read upward. Figure 23.15 is an example of a company title block with a parts list. The quantity, item number (balloon number), part number, and description are shown here.

When the parts list is separate from the part drawing, the heading **PARTS LIST** is at the top and the list is constructed from the top down. The following describes the four basic columns on a parts list (Fig. 23.16):

QUANTITY REQUIRED The number entered in this column denotes the quantity, volume, length, or other unit of measure required to complete one of the items to which the column applies. When this number applies to something other than quantity, the unit of measure is entered in this column or in an optional unit of measure column.

FSCM The Federal Supply Code for Manufacturer's number assigned to the originating design activity whose part or identifying number appears in column 3 is shown in this column. Many company title blocks exclude this entry.

PART OR IDENTIFYING NUMBER The identifying number for each item on the parts list is shown in this column.

NOMENCLATURE OR DESCRIPTION The assigned noun or name of the item whose identifying number is in the part number column appears in this column.

ITEM	QTY	PART NO.	DESCRIPTION
55	1	664-359239	CABLE, ASSY - MONOCHRONOMETER, YEL
54	1	664-359238	CABLE, ASSY - MONOCHRONOMETER, GRN
53	1	664-359237	CABLE, ASSY - MONOCHRONOMETER, RED
52			
51			
50	1	693-349584	BOARD, P.W. - U.V. SCANNER
49	1	301-961283	SPRING, CPRSN-.063 OD X 1 LG CRES
48			
47			
46	12	165-359506	WASHER, FLT .127 TFL-
45			
44	1	125-362041	PIN, DOWEL -.1553 DIA X .450L CRES
43	4	125-811591	PIN, DOWEL -.1251 DIA X .375L CRES
42	4	125-824305	PIN, DOWEL -.0626 DIA X .312L CRES
41			
40			
39	3	130-961281	RING, RETAINING - EXT, .073 ID
38	2	105-828447	NUT, HEX 2-56 S-BK
37			
36			
35	6	101-827620	SCREW, CAP 4-40 X 1" S-HXSO
34	2	101-961013	SCREW, CAP 2-56 X 1-3/8 S-HXSO
33	2	101-803947	SCREW, CAP 2-56 X .875 S-HXSO
32	1	101-961282	SCREW, CAP 2-56 X .750 S-HXSO
31	2	101-961201	SCREW, MACH 2-56 X 1" FL-S-SL
30	2	101-828409	SCREW, MACH 2-56 X .375 P-S-BK-SL
29	3	101-828408	SCREW, MACH 2-56 X .25 P-S-BK-SL
28			
27			
26	2	201-361974	GEAR, (MODIFIED) 42 TEETH
25	1	201-359899	GEAR, (MODIFIED) 84 TEETH
24	3	201-349033	GEAR, (MODIFIED) 132 TEETH
23			
22			
21	1	150-359263	BUSHING, MIRROR HOUSING
20	6	145-863274	BEARING
19			
18			
17	1	201-356344	RACK, GEAR U.V. MODIFICATION
16	1	520-348987	GRATING
15	1	333-349032	PLATFORM, GRATING
14	1	223-356345	SHAFT, CROSSOVER U.V. MODIFICATION
13	4	223-349019	SHAFT, GEAR
12			
11	1	548-361969	ASSY. FILTER
10			
9	1	499-348983	SPUD
8	1	105-348982	NUT, RETAINER
7	1	178-348984	EXTENSION TUBE #1, U.V. SCANNER
6	1	178-349027	EXTENSION TUBE #2, U.V. SCANNER
5	1	178-347010	EXTENSION TUBE #3, U.V. SCANNER
4	1	299-348981	HOUSING, MIRROR
3			
2	1	299-349023	DIRECTION CHAMBER U.V. LIGHT (LEFT)
1	1	299-348989	DIRECTION CHAMBER U.V. LIGHT (RIGHT)

E SIZE 223-356367 DWG. NO.

	BY	DATE	
DR	D.M.DUARTE	1/18/90	BECKMAN
CHK			TITLE MONOCHRONOMETER ASSEMBLY
DSGN			
ENGR			E SIZE · CODE IDENT NO. 07978 · DWG NO. 223-356367
MOD	LIO-A		SCALE 1/2 · 1ST USE 355899 · SHEET 1 OF 1

FIGURE 23.14 Monochrometer Assembly Parts List

23.5.3 Drawing Sheets

Drafting sheets are polyester film, vellum, bond, or other type of paper preprinted with the border, title block (Fig. 23.17), and revision block. You must know what each aspect of the drawing sheet means, and what information needs to be added before the project is complete. This understanding is also important when reading existing drawings. The following list describes each part of a typical drawing sheet as shown in Figure 23.18(a) and (b):

1. Ancillary drawing number. Permits the engineer to file print copies so that, when folded correctly, all drawing numbers will appear in the upper left corner.
2. Sheet number for multiple sheet drawings
3. Ancillary revision identification
4. Revision identification symbol
5. Description of the revision or the identification of the change authorization document
6. Issue date of the revised drawing
7. Required approval signature for revisions
8. Microfilm alignment arrowheads
9. DSJ—distribution key or code, if used
10. Company name and address. Must agree with FSCM number for companies with multidivisions and departments.
11. Drawing title
12. Assigned drawing number
13. Weight record. Should indicate whether it is actual, estimated, or calculated, when required, and if it is gross (before machining) or net (after machining).
14. FSCM number, if required for identification of the company or design activity whose drawing number is used
15. Predominant scale of the drawing
16. Drawing size letter designation
17. Signature of the drafter and the date the drawing was started
18. Signature of the responsible person who checked the drawing and the date of signing
19. Signature of the responsible engineer, to signify approval of the design by engineering, and the date of signing
20. Signature of the responsible issuing person and the initial date of issue
21. Notes
22. Approval by an activity other than those described above
23. The appropriate surface texture designation that applies
24. The general tolerances that apply to the overall document
25. The appropriate material specification, which should include type, grade, class, or other classifications as applicable
26. Zones: letters vertically (bottom up, starting with A) and numbers horizontally (right to left, starting with 1)

23.6 NOTES

Notes on drawings (Fig. 23.19) supply information that cannot be presented in any other descriptive way. A standard method of applying, placing, and revising notes on engineer-

FIGURE 23.15 Parts List

-001	ITEM NO.	VERSATEC PART NO.	DESCRIPTION
2	13	140-862005-606	STUD,SELF-CLINCH-FH, NO. 10-32 X.750 LG
2	12	140-862005-206	STUD,SELF-CLINCH-FH, NO.4-40 X .750
4	11	104-044042-014	FASTENER,SELF-CLINCHING, NO. 10-32
26	10	140-862005-404	STUD SELF-CLINCH-FH, NO.8-32 X .500
22	9	104-044042-002	FASTENER,SELF-CLINCHING, NO. 8-32
4	8	106-044316-006	WASHER EXTERNAL TOOTH, NO. 6
8	7	102-044729-003	LOCKNUT, HEX, NO. 2-56
2	6	140-017322-011	FASTENER,SELF-CLINCHING SS NO. 4-40
8	5	102-044629-001	NUT, SADDLE
7	4	104-045364-001	NUT, HEX JAM, NO. 1/4-20
6	3	104-044356-003	INSERT,THREADED STAINLESS STEEL,NO. 8-32 X.248 LG
3	2	140-021009-001	NUT-HEX, NO. 8 LIGHT
1	1	000-012345-051	COVER,CONTROL,FREQUENCY PANEL (13)
QUANTITY PER VERSION			PARTS LIST

PROPRIETARY
The contents of this document are PROPRIETARY TO VERSATEC INC. and are not to be disclosed to others or used for purposes other than intended without the written approval of Versatec

MATERIAL:
SEE ABOVE P/L
DATA BASE B.O.M
AVAILABLE.

UNLESS OTHERWISE SPECIFIED
DIMENSIONS ARE IN INCHES. ALL PARTS TO BE DEBURRED AND EDGES BROKEN .010 MAXIMUM

TOL.	1PLC.	2PLC.	3PLC.	ANG.
±	.1	.03	.010	1°--

THIRD ANGLE PROJECTION

FINISH: (7)

SIGNATURE	DATE
DRN. VALENZUELA	9-10-90
CHK.	- -
APPV.	- -
APPV.	- -
APPV.	- -

DO NOT SCALE DRAWING

VERSATEC
A XEROX COMPANY
SANTA CLARA
CALIFORNIA 95051

TITLE:
COVER,CONTROL,
FREQUENCY PANEL

SIZE	CODE IDENT.	DRAWING NO.	REV.
E	50804	000-012345	17

SCALE: 1/2 , AS NOTED SHEET 1 OF 1

2 1 A

ing drawings is used, to maintain company-wide uniformity. Although there are standard formats, placements, and sequences for notes on the drawing, each company will have its own **company standards**.

General notes (Fig. 23.19) are those that apply to the total drawing and, if placed on the drawing at each point of application, would be repetitive and time consuming to apply. **Local notes** are those that apply to a specific portion, surface, or dimension on a drawing. The following rules can serve as a guide when putting notes on a drawing.

Use Notes To:

- Clarify features that can be defined more accurately through words than by graphical delineation and dimensions

QTY REQD	FSCM	PART OR IDENTIFYING NO.	NOMENCLATURE OR DESCRIPTION
PARTS LIST			

(a) Columnar arrangement for integral parts list

PARTS LIST			
QTY REQD	FSCM	PART OR IDENTIFYING NO.	NOMENCLATURE OR DESCRIPTION

(b) Columnar arrangement for separate parts list

FIGURE 23.16 Parts List Arrangement

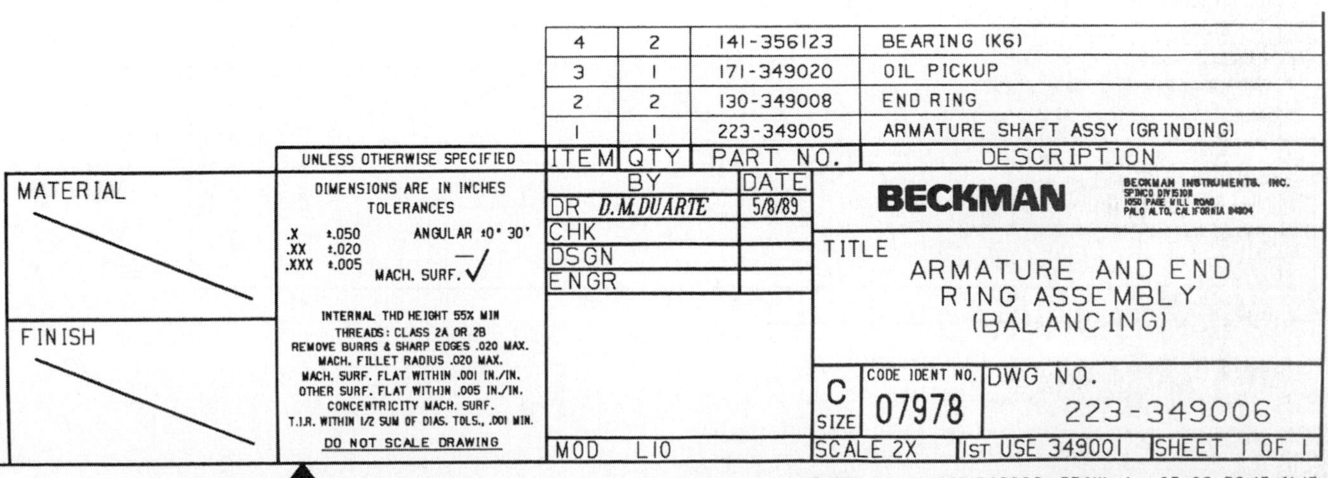

ITEM	QTY	PART NO.	DESCRIPTION
4	2	141-356123	BEARING (K6)
3	1	171-349020	OIL PICKUP
2	2	130-349008	END RING
1	1	223-349005	ARMATURE SHAFT ASSY (GRINDING)

MATERIAL

FINISH

UNLESS OTHERWISE SPECIFIED
DIMENSIONS ARE IN INCHES
TOLERANCES
.X ±.050 ANGULAR ±0° 30'
.XX ±.020
.XXX ±.005
MACH. SURF. √
INTERNAL THD HEIGHT 55% MIN
THREADS: CLASS 2A OR 2B
REMOVE BURRS & SHARP EDGES .020 MAX.
MACH. FILLET RADIUS .020 MAX.
MACH. SURF. FLAT WITHIN .001 IN./IN.
OTHER SURF. FLAT WITHIN .005 IN./IN.
CONCENTRICITY MACH. SURF.
T.I.R. WITHIN 1/2 SUM OF DIAS. TOLS., .001 MIN.
DO NOT SCALE DRAWING

	BY	DATE
DR	D.M.DUARTE	5/8/89
CHK		
DSGN		
ENGR		

MOD L10

BECKMAN
BECKMAN INSTRUMENTS, INC.
SPINCO DIVISION
1050 PAGE MILL ROAD
PALO ALTO, CALIFORNIA 94304

TITLE
ARMATURE AND END
RING ASSEMBLY
(BALANCING)

C SIZE | CODE IDENT NO. 07978 | DWG NO. 223-349006

SCALE 2X | 1ST USE 349001 | SHEET 1 OF 1

PART: 04.ME.2235.349006 DRAW: A 05-08-89 15:41:13

FIGURE 23.17 Armature and End Ring Assembly Title Block and Parts List

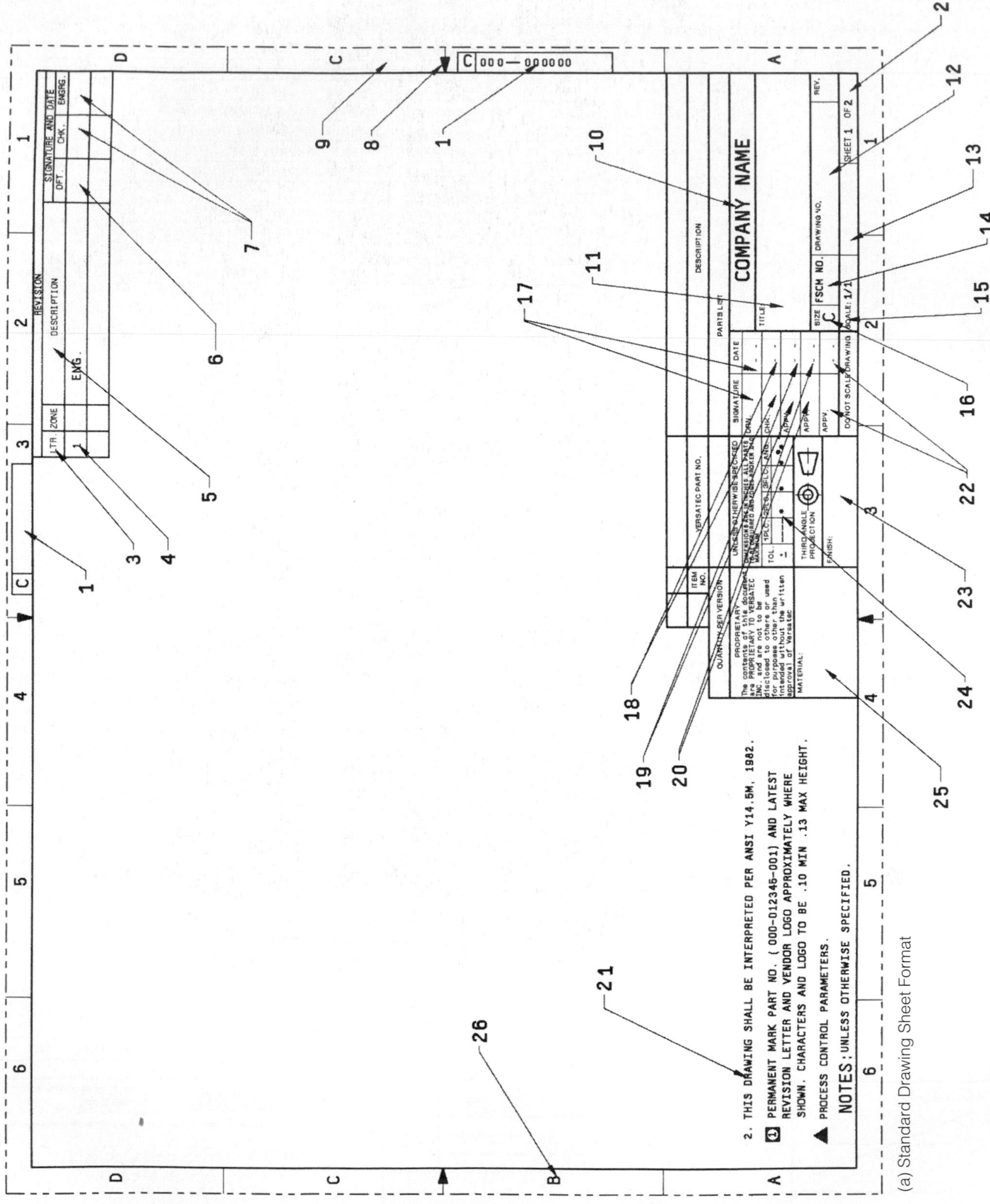

(a) Standard Drawing Sheet Format

FIGURE 23.18 Standard Drawing Sheet Format

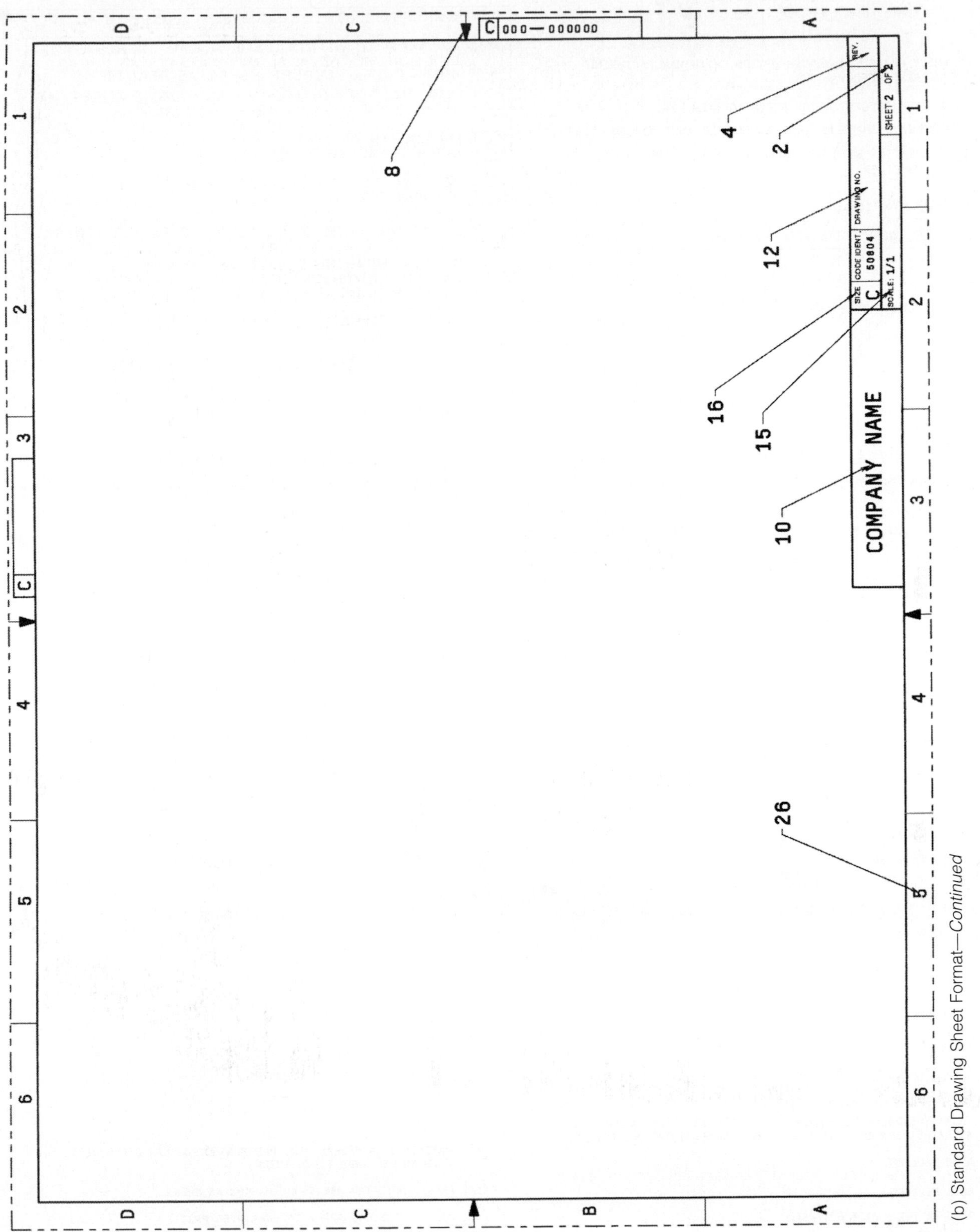

(b) Standard Drawing Sheet Format—*Continued*

FIGURE 23.18 Standard Drawing Sheet Format—*Continued*

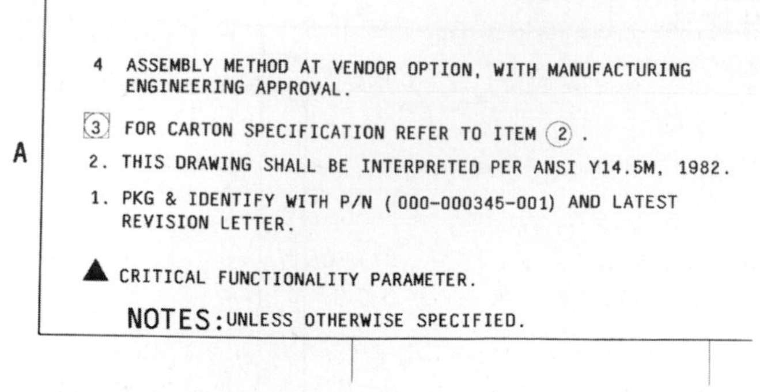

4 ASSEMBLY METHOD AT VENDOR OPTION, WITH MANUFACTURING ENGINEERING APPROVAL.
3 FOR CARTON SPECIFICATION REFER TO ITEM 2 .
A
2. THIS DRAWING SHALL BE INTERPRETED PER ANSI Y14.5M, 1982.
1. PKG & IDENTIFY WITH P/N (000-000345-001) AND LATEST REVISION LETTER.
▲ CRITICAL FUNCTIONALITY PARAMETER.
NOTES: UNLESS OTHERWISE SPECIFIED.

FIGURE 23.19 General Notes

NOTES: (UNLESS OTHERWISE SPECIFIED)

1 BALANCE TO WITHIN 3 MILLIGRAM-INCHES BY DRILLING BETWEEN ALUMINUM BARS AS SHOWN (BOTH ENDS). DEBURR HOLES AS REQUIRED.

2 .020 DIA (REF) IN ITEMS 1 AND .040 DIA (REF) IN ITEM (3) TO BE ASSEMBLED ALIGNED.

3 MAX DEPTH OF MATERIAL REMOVED FOR BALANCING TO BE .035.

4 BEARING PRESS FORCE TO BE BETWEEN 100 AND 300 LBS.

5 LETTERING SIDE OF BEARING TO FACE OUTWARD.

6 OPTION: BEARING 356122 (K5) MAY BE USED ON TOP AND/OR OPTIONAL BEARING 356124 (K1419) MAY BE USED ON BOTTOM AS REQUIRED

FIGURE 23.21 Notes Listed from the Top Down

- Give instructions for applying special treatments
- Give instructions for utilization of specific processes
- Describe instructions to supplement standard symbols
- Provide additional information to the drawing document or for its use
- Add clarifying notes so the part can be made correctly the first time

Notes Should Be:

- Clear and concise
- In the present tense
- Positioned parallel to the bottom edge of the drawing
- Carefully composed to relay one message; capable of one interpretation
- Preprinted on appliqués or, if the drawings are computerized, entered in a standard library for repeated use

Notes Should Not:

- Be underlined on the drawing
- Contain abbreviations other than the most commonly understood shop trade terms
- Duplicate information on an associated parts list or shop practices reference document
- Contain dimensions that are already documented elsewhere on the drawing
- Describe complex processes (which should instead be documented either in a specification or a process document)
- Reference information that is given elsewhere in the product documentation

23.6.1 General Notes

General notes on drawing sizes "B" through "F" are placed in the upper or lower left-hand corner of the sheet. Some companies construct their note sequence from the bottom up, as in Figure 23.20; others list theirs from the top down (Fig. 23.21). Notes at the top of a sheet are numbered from the top down; those at the bottom of a sheet are numbered from the bottom up. The width of the general note column should not exceed 6 to 8 in. (150 to 200 mm).

When the drawing is completed on a CAD system, it is possible to reuse notes that are common to a number of situations and designs. Such notes are saved as a **text file** and inserted as blocks on the drawing. Because text files can be edited, variations and changes can be incorporated before they are inserted into a drawing.

7 PAINT YELLOWISH GREY (CODE BAP) AND REIDENTIFY PAINTED PART AS BAP-012345-001, PER PAINT SPECIFICATION DWG 000-014123.
6 NOTE DELETED.
5 NOTE DELETED.
4 BEND RELIEF Ø .125 OPTIONAL.
3 ALL BEND RADII ARE TO BE MINIMUM.
2. THIS DRAWING SHALL BE INTERPRETED PER ANSI Y14.5M, 1982.
A
1 PERMANENTLY MARK PART NO. (000-012345-001) AND LATEST REVISION LETTER AND VENDOR LOGO APPROXIMATELY WHERE SHOWN. CHARACTERS AND LOGO TO BE .10 MIN .13 MAX HEIGHT.
▲ PROCESS CONTROL PARAMETERS.
NOTES: UNLESS OTHERWISE SPECIFIED.

13 MATERIAL: GALVANEAL ZINC PRE-PLATED, CARBON STEEL,AISI COLD ROLLED 14GA (.075 THICK).
12 AREAS INDICATED ARE TO BE MASKED AS SHOWN.
11 HOLE DIMENSIONS APPLY TO UNPAINTED PART.
10 FEATURE TO BE FREE OF PAINT.
9 FEATURE TO BE SINGLE PUNCHED SUCH THAT FEATURE SIZE SURFACE IS FREE OF BURRS/PROTRUSIONS GREATER THAN .002.
8 PAINT SPECIFICATION TEXTURE APPLIES TO THESE SURFACES ONLY.

8 7 6 5

FIGURE 23.20 Notes Listed from the Bottom Up

23.6.2 Local Notes

Local notes on the drawing must be placed outside the outline of the part and close to the item that is being referenced.

Fabrication operations such as BEND, DRILL, TAP, PUNCH, and BORE are *not* shown on the drawing. This permits manufacturing to determine the type of operation required to produce the part within the required tolerances. Features such as SPOTFACE, COUNTERBORE, COUNTERSINK, UNDERCUT, and THREAD may be given in notes.

23.7 REVISION OF ENGINEERING DRAWINGS

The **revision block** (Fig. 23.22), located in the upper right-hand corner of the drawing, is for recording changes to the drawing. Because revisions initiate a substantial number of change documents in all functions of a business, the need for accuracy and completeness in the revision process should not be underestimated.

23.7.1 Revision Terminology

The following terms describe the process of revising drawings and are found in revision blocks on drawings.

Added A new feature or view introduced to the document

2 | 1

REVISION					
LTR.	ZONE	DESCRIPTION	SIGNATURE AND DATE		
			DFT.	CHK.	ENGRG.
1		ENGRG.	VICTOR.V 2/22/89		
2	E5	ADDED ITEM 5 THRU 7 AND HOLES MFG.	VICTOR.V 3/07/89		
3	B2	ADDED HOLE CHART & PAGE 2 INPUT MFG.	VICTOR.V 3/12/89		
4	C7	REVISED SHT 1 & 2 PER ENG. CHANGES	VICTOR.V 3/26/89		
5	D3	ADDED BOTTOM VIEW & DETAIL F REV TOP VIEW LOCATION AND ADDED V15 THRU V22 ON HOLE CHART	VICTOR.V 4/03/89		
6	A5	REVISED LOCATION U1 ON CHART AND SHT 2 REV RADII WAS:.313 IS: .375	VICTOR.V 4/07/89		
7	F4	ADDED N5, N6, R2, R3, Y3 AND Y4	VICTOR.V 9/18/89		
8	C2	INCORP PROTO CHANGES PILOT RELEASE	VICTOR.V 9/18/89		
9	D6	REVISED PER ACO NO. 147	VICTOR.V 11/01/89		
10	E5	REVISED DIMENSIONS WAS: 3.50 & 8.25 IS: 4.00 & 6.00	VICTOR.V 11/16/89		
11	G8	ADDED ITEMS 2 & 3	VICTOR.V 12/06/89		
12	H3	REVISED ITEM 4 & 5 PER DETAILED PART	VICTOR.V 1/26/90		
13	F7	REVISED QTY OF ITEMS 7 & 9	VICTOR.V 3/08/90		
14	A6	ADDED SECTION A-A AND DETAIL B	VICTOR.V 6/01/90		
15	C5	REVISED NOTES 4, 7 AND 9	VICTOR.V 6/25/90		
16	E6	DELETED NOTES 5 AND 6	VICTOR.V 8/06/90		
17	G4	REVISED PER ACO NO. 353	VICTOR.V 9/10/90		

H

G

FIGURE 23.22 Revision Block

Approval An endorsement attesting to a revision made on a drawing or a parts list

Change A specific alteration made as part of a revision on a drawing. A revision may include one or more changes.

Deleted A feature or view removed from the document

Obsolete (inactive, canceled) A condition in which the drawing has been discontinued by the design activity. The word *inactive* or *canceled* may be used.

Redrawn A new original drawing with the same drawing number that has been substituted for a previous drawing

Revision (revised) One or more changes to a drawing, made after distribution or release, according to an established revision procedure

Revision designation Alphabetic, numeric, or alphanumeric characters that identify a revision

23.7.2 Revising Drawings

Revisions are made by erasure, crossing out, addition, redrawing, or, for the case of CAD-generated drawings, editing. When picking the method to be used to revise a drawing, first consider achieving and maintaining the best possible quality, legibility, and reproducibility by the most economical means. Unless otherwise specified, use the most recently approved graphics symbols, designations and letter symbols, abbreviations, and drawing practices. The exception is the use of geometric and position tolerance symbols that may be different from the latest issue of ANSI Y14.5. If the latest symbol is desirable, an explanatory note should be provided on the drawing. Superseded symbology on the drawing should remain unchanged, provided the interpretation is clear.

23.7.3 Incorporating Changes

Dimensional changes entered on a drawing are made to the same scale as the portion of the drawing undergoing revision. If the drawing is not to scale, and the pictorial portion of the drawing is made to proportion, all dimensional changes are made to the proportions of the delineation affected.

When information is added to a drawing, the additions must match the lettering style and line weight of the existing drawing as closely as possible.

23.7.4 Simplifying the Design Process and Saving Time

Saving time on a project may mean bringing it to market ahead of the competition. Overdrawn and detailed designs add time and cost to a project. The following list can help you check for simplicity:

1. Use text description wherever possible to eliminate drawing completely.

2. Use text description wherever practical to eliminate projected views.
3. Eliminate views where the shape can be given by description, e.g., HEX, SQ, DIA.
4. Show partial views of symmetrical objects.
5. Avoid elaborate, pictorial or repetitive detail.
6. When necessary to detail threads, do not show them over the full length of the stud, bolt, or tapped hole.
7. Eliminate detail of nuts, bolt heads, and other standard hardware. Show outlines when it is necessary to show position.
8. Reduce detail of parts on assembly drawings. Simply show the part position.
9. Avoid unnecessary hidden lines that add no clarification.
10. Use sectioning only when it is necessary for the clarity of the drawing.
11. Simplify graphics for holes and tapped holes by use of symbols.
12. Omit views with no dimensional or written instruction.
13. Within limits, a small drawing is usually easier and quicker to make than a large one.
14. When two parts are only slightly different, complete graphical representation of both parts is not required. The note SAME AS EXCEPT _______ or OTHERWISE SAME AS _______ may be given.
15. Drawings made to modify stock or commercial parts should be as plain as possible. Avoid detail.
16. Use standard abbreviations wherever possible.
17. When necessary, enlarge small details on larger parts for clarity.
18. Draw small parts large enough to avoid crowding so that they may be easily read, but not unnecessarily large so as to waste space on the drawing.
19. Do not duplicate dimensions.
20. Substitute recognized standard symbols, to simplify greatly the drawing of common objects.
21. Eliminate repetitive data by use of general notes.
22. When drafting, do as much free-hand drawing as the work permits, in preference to using instruments.
23. Where practical, use geometric symbols instead of notes.
24. Where acceptable, give rectangular coordinate or tabular dimensioning instead of dimension lines.

23.8 A CHECKLIST FOR ENGINEERS AND DESIGNERS

A drawing should be checked after it has been completed. Compare it against the following.

Readability

1. Is the drawing easy to read?
2. Are the part outlines distinct from dimension lines?
3. Is the lettering neat and clear?
4. Is all of the information on the drawing?
5. Will the drawing make a good print?
6. Have all the rules of standard drafting practice been followed?
7. Is the nomenclature correct? Will everyone understand it the same way?
8. Is the drawing title truly descriptive?

Completeness

9. Are all necessary views given?
10. Are some views unnecessary?

Notes

11. Are the general notes properly located?
12. Are any exceptions to the general notes clearly pointed out?
13. Are any notes crowded or hard to find?
14. Could any of the notes be misunderstood?
15. If a specially purchased item is required, is procurement information given?
16. If special procedures are required in making or assembling, have they been noted on the drawing?

Parts List

17. Does the parts list agree with the drawing?
18. Have overall dimensions been given?
19. Are standard parts specified correctly?

Dimensioning

20. Are out-of-scale dimensions (if any) clearly marked?
21. Is it necessary to leave a dimension out of scale?
22. Are all dimensions given?
23. Are there any duplicate dimensions?
24. Are dimensions kept well away from the outline of the part?
25. Is the scale designated?

Tolerances

26. Have all tolerances given been carefully considered?
27. Are all tolerances to the maximum possible?
28. Are any tolerances too large? too small?
29. Has the drawing been checked for possible tolerance stackups?

Finishes

30. Are all machine finishes given, and do they conform to applicable specifications?
31. Are all paint and plating finishes specified?

Processes

32. Is heat treatment needed?
33. Have standard manufacturing processes been followed?
34. Can the part be produced simply and economically?

Materials and Parts

35. Are standard or purchased parts used to the maximum extent?
36. Are all special or reworked parts noted?

Assembly
37. Are there no mechanical interferences?
38. Will parts assemble without difficulty?
39. Does the work agree with associated mechanisms?
40. Are all parts properly numbered or designated?

Cost
41. Could the function have been accomplished at less expense with the same results?
42. Could the design have contained fewer parts?
43. Have you given thought as to how this would be built?

Reliability
44. Have you checked the design for possible failure?
45. Have you considered safety factors?

23.9 REPRODUCTION AND STORAGE OF DRAWINGS

The last step in the design-detailing process is outputting the drawings of the project. Reproduction of manual or CAD drawings involves a process called *whiteprinting*. Before a CAD drawing can be printed, it must be plotted on one of many types of plotters available.

23.9.1 Whiteprinting

Whiteprinters (Fig. 23.23) make copies of drawings. The whiteprinter is still referred to as a "blueprint machine" by many people. As an engineer you can expect to run prints of drawing projects.

Regardless of the type of "paper," the whiteprinter makes a "positive" image of the drawing on whiteprint paper. The process depends on the transmission of light through the drawing paper and onto the developing surface. The lines, lettering, or other graphics block the light in order for a positive image to be developed on the print. Because they must block light, the lines must be high quality, crisp, and dark. Use H or HB grade lead, and press sufficiently hard to create a dark, crisp drawing. CAD-plotted drawings employ black ink, so the drawing's lines and lettering block light well.

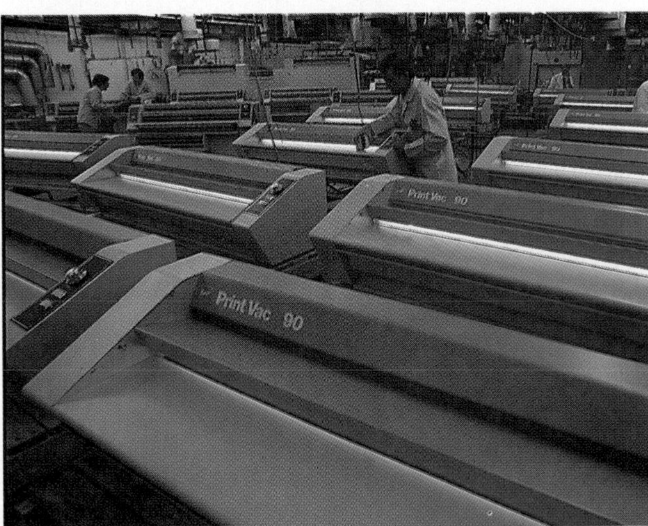

FIGURE 23.23 Blueprint Duplicating Machines

23.9.2 Plotting

Output devices include printers, plotters, and photocopy equipment. The **plotter** allows you to produce drawings on paper, vellum, or drafting film in a multitude of colors. Some plotters are limited by the size of the plotting surface. Others can plot drawings of any length, although they are limited to standard paper widths. Pen plotters use ballpoint pens, felt-tip pens, or liquid-ink pens. When plotting a drawing, you have many options for scaling the drawing, rotating it, selecting colors, and selecting different line widths.

After the drawing is plotted on vellum or polyester film, a whiteprinter can make copies. Multiple copies can be made on the plotter, but plotting is slow and tedious. Elesctrostatic plotters are much faster than pen plotters and can plot a drawing without the mess of wet-ink technical pens. Figure 23.24 shows COM units, one of the latest innovations in plotting technology. A laser plotter is faster than an electrostatic plotter, and is as accurate as a pen plotter.

A CAD plotter can output as many high-quality originals as required. However, having more than one original could cause considerable document control problems! The "old" original should be removed from circulation or destroyed.

FIGURE 23.24 COM Units

Applying Parametric Design . . .

ASSEMBLIES, EXPLODED ASSEMBLY MODELS, AND REPORTS (BOM)

The **Assembly mode** allows you to place together component parts and subassemblies to form assemblies (Fig. A). These assemblies can then be modified, documented (Fig. B), analyzed, or reoriented. **Assembly mode** is used for the following functions:

- Placing components into assemblies
- Exploding views of assemblies
- Part modification, including feature construction
- Analysis

With Pro/ENGINEER You Can:

- Assemble Place together component parts and subassemblies to form assemblies
- Delete or replace Remove or replace assembly components
- Modify assembly placement offsets, create and modify assembly datum planes, coordinate systems and cross sections
- Modify parts directly in assembly mode
- Get assembly engineering information, perform viewing and layer operations, create reference dimensions, and work with interfaces

With Pro/ASSEMBLY You Can:

- Create new parts in assembly mode
- Create sheet metal parts in assembly mode
- Mirror parts in assembly mode (create a new part)
- Replace components automatically by creating interchangeability groups.
- Create assembly features, existing only in assembly mode and intersecting several components
- Create families of assemblies, using the family table
- Simply the assembly representation
- **Move** and **Multiply** commands for assembly components
- Use Pro/PROGRAM to create design programs that allow user entries to program prompts to alter the design model

Creating an assembly is accomplished by adding components (parts) to a base component (parent part) using a variety of constraints. A **placement constraint** specifies the relative position of a pair of surfaces on two components. The **mate, align, insert,** and **orient** commands and their variations can accomplish this task.

General Principles for Constraint Placement

- The two surfaces must be of the same type (for example, plane–plane, revolved–revolved). The term "revolved surface" means a surface created by revolving a section or by extruding an arc or a circle. Only the following surfaces are allowed: plane, cylinder, core, torus, sphere.
- If you put a placement constraint on a datum plane, you should specify which side of it you are going to use, yellow or red.
- When using **Mate Offset** or **Align Offset** and entering a value, you will be given the offset direction. If you need an offset in the opposite direction, make the offset value negative.
- When a surface on one window is selected, another window may become hidden. For a description of how to bring the hidden window to the front, see the appropriate manual for the hardware used.
- Add constraints one at a time. For example, it is not possible to align two different holes in one part with two different holes in another part via a single align command; two different align constraints must be defined.

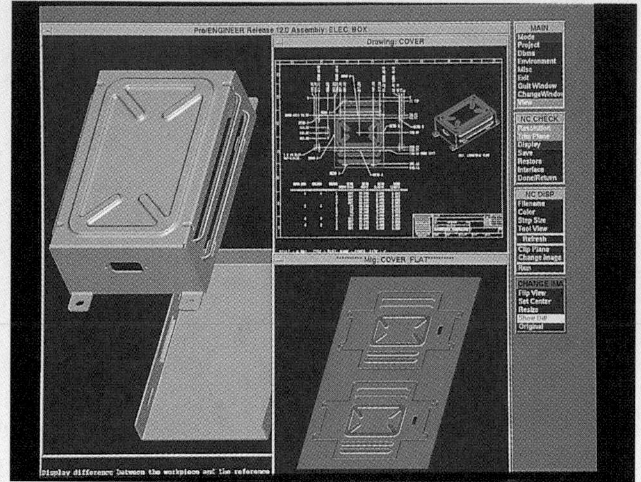

FIGURE A Electronic Product Assembly, Including Printed Circuit Board and Package

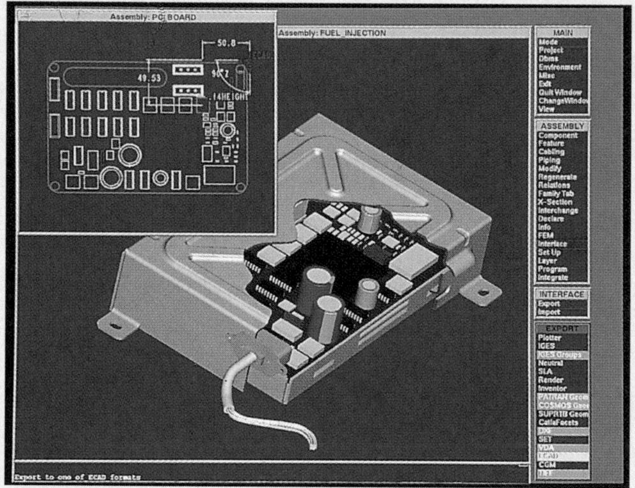

FIGURE B Assembly Package and Documentation

- Placement constraints are used in combinations in order to specify completely placement and orientation. For example, one pair of surfaces may be constrained to mate, another pair to insert, and a third pair to orient.

Mate (Fig. C) makes two surfaces touch one another: coincident and facing each other. When using datums, this means that two yellow sides, or two red sides, will face each other. **Mate Offset** (Fig. D) makes two planar surfaces parallel and facing each other. The offset value determines the distance between the two surfaces.

The **Align** command (Fig. E) makes two planes coplanar: coincident and facing in the same direction; or aligns revolved surfaces or axes to be coaxial. You can also align two datum points, vertices, or curve ends; selections on both parts must be of the same type (that is, if a datum point is selected on one part, only a datum point on another part can be selected). The **Align Offset** command (Fig. F) aligns two planar surfaces at an offset: parallel and facing in the same direction.

The **Insert** command inserts a "male" revolved surface into a "female" revolved surface, aligning axes.

The **Orient** command (Fig. G) orients two planar surfaces to be parallel and facing in the same direction; offset is not specified.

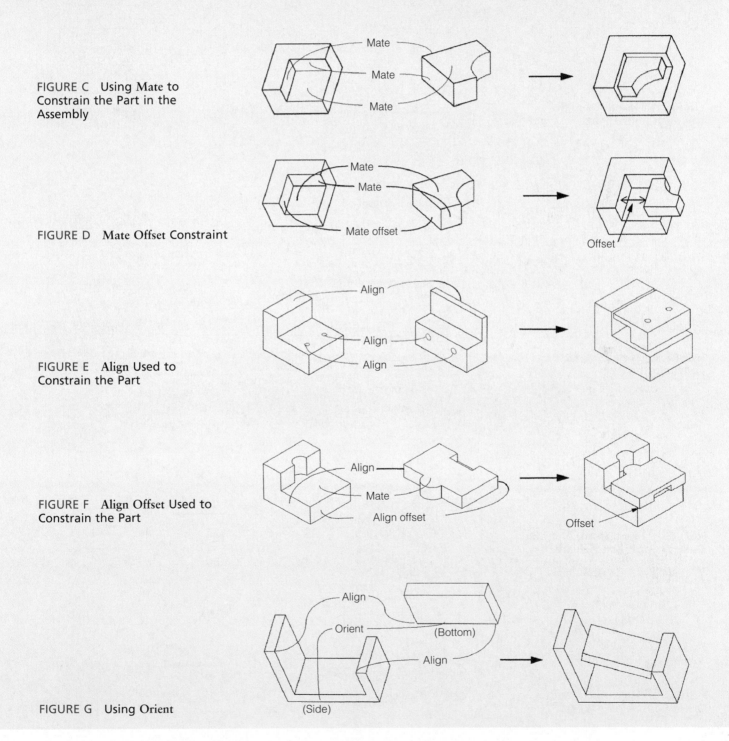

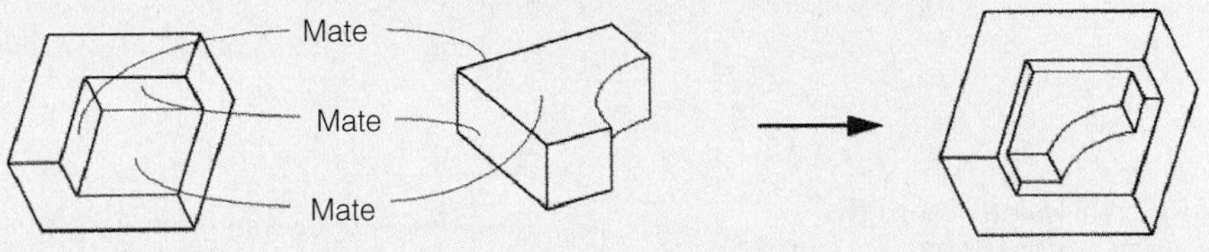

FIGURE C Using **Mate** to Constrain the Part in the Assembly

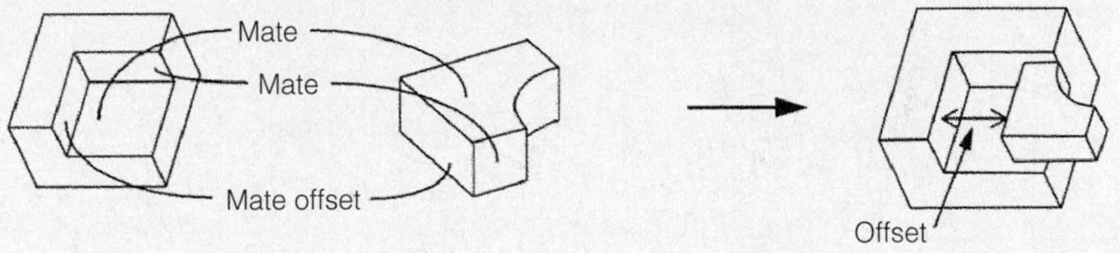

FIGURE D **Mate Offset** Constraint

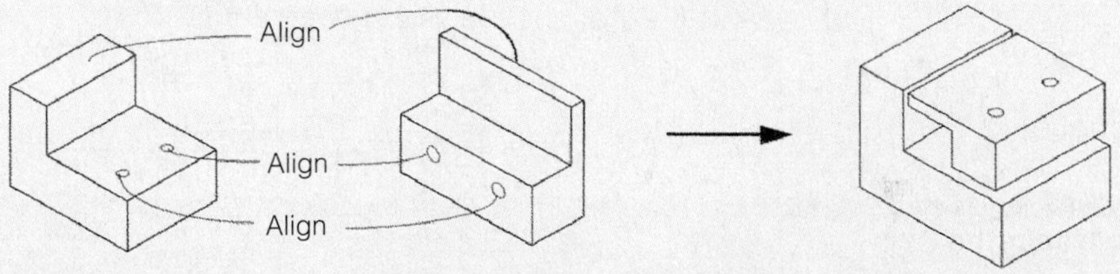

FIGURE E **Align** Used to Constrain the Part

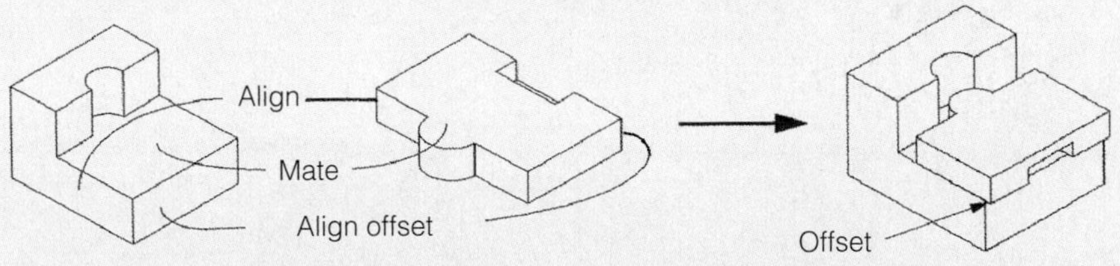

FIGURE F **Align Offset** Used to Constrain the Part

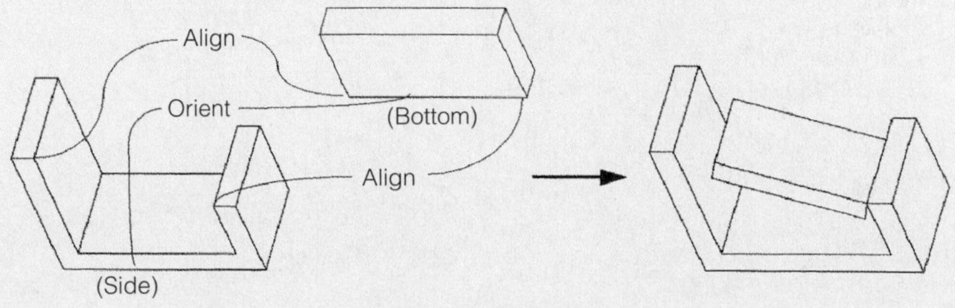

FIGURE G Using **Orient**

The **Coord Sys** command (Fig. H) places a component into the assembly by aligning its coordinate system with a coordinate system in the assembly (both assembly or part coordinate systems can be used). Both coordinate systems must exist before starting the assembly process. Coordinate systems can be picked or selected by name from namelist menus. The components will be assembled by aligning X, Y, and Z axes of the selected coordinate system.

The **Tangent, Pnt On Surf,** and **Edge On Surf** commands control the contact of two surfaces at their tangency, at a point, or at an edge (Fig. I). An example of use of these placement commands is the contact surface or point between a cam and its actuator.

In most cases, a combination of constraints will be required. **Mate, mate,** and **insert** constrain the two parts shown in Figure J. **Mate, insert,** and **orient** are also a possibility, depending on the parts (Fig. K).

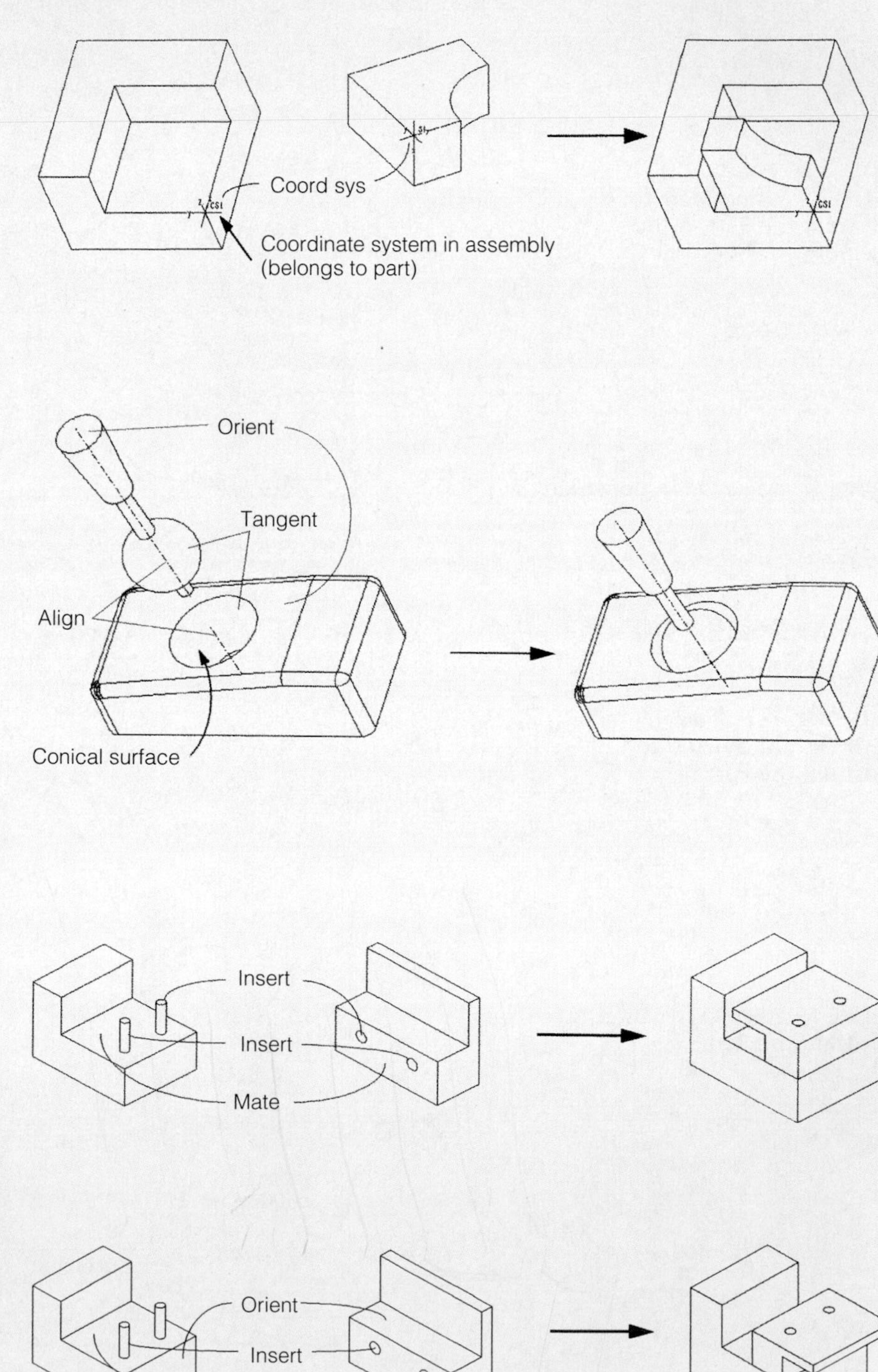

FIGURE H Using Coord Sys to Constrain the Part

FIGURE I Using Tangent to Constrain the Part

FIGURE J Insert, Insert, and Mate Used to Constrain the Part

FIGURE K Mate, Insert, and Orient Constraining a Part

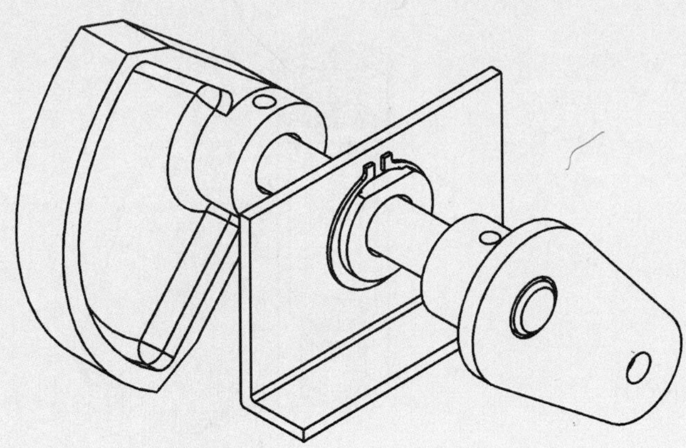

FIGURE L Assembly

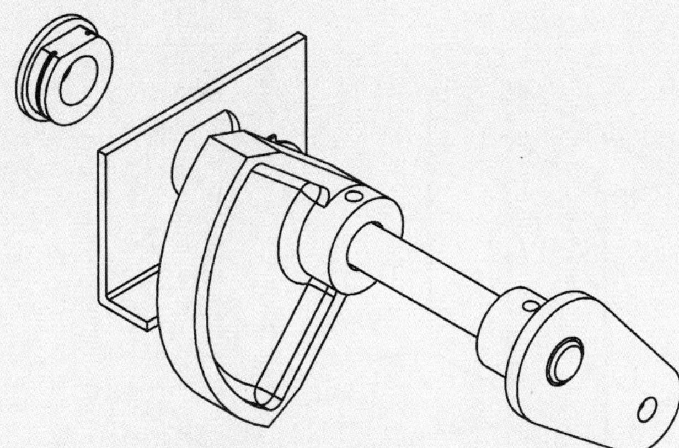

FIGURE M Exploded Assembly

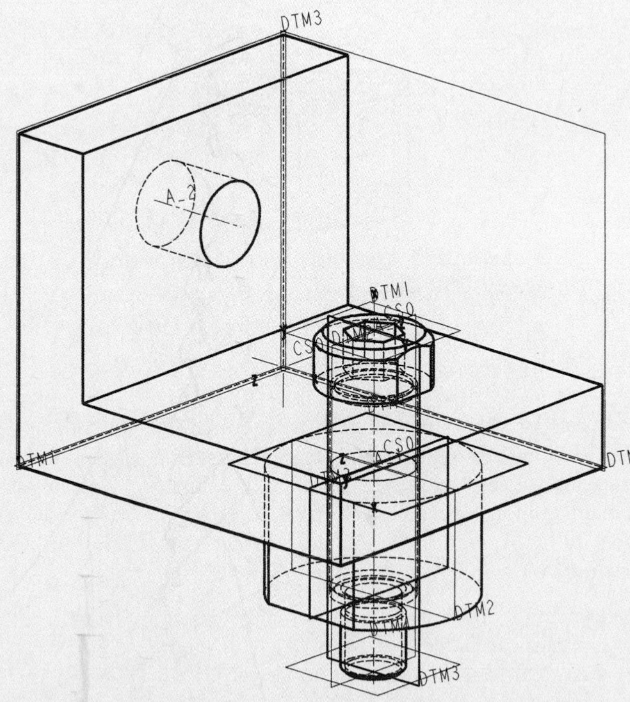

FIGURE N Angle, Socket-Head Shoulder Screw, and Sleeve Assembly

Assemblies (Fig. L) can also be displayed exploded (Fig. M). The explode distance can be modified to any value.

The angle, screw, and sleeve assembly shown in Figure N is an example of the type of capabilities available. The angle part is the base part (Fig. O). The screw is constrained via **insert** and **mate** (Fig. P), and the sleeve is constrained by **mate**, **insert**, and **orient** (Fig. Q). The completed assembly (Fig. R) can be modified by redefining the constraints. An exploded cosmetic view of the assembly can be displayed with the reference planes, coordinate system, and hidden lines (Fig. S) or without them (Fig. T). The last stage of the project involves putting the assembly in the draw mode and displaying the appropriate views (Fig. U).

After the assembly is complete, an assembly drawing is created. With Pro/REPORT you can then generate a bill of

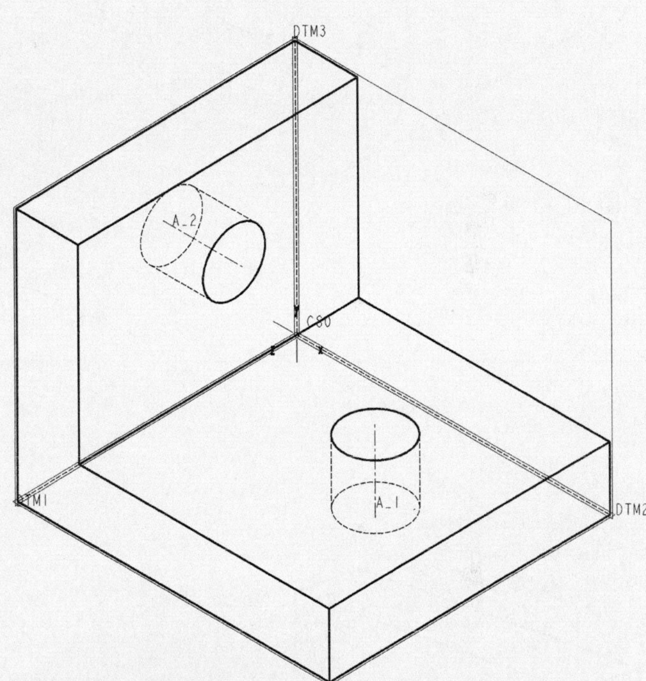

FIGURE O Angle Part

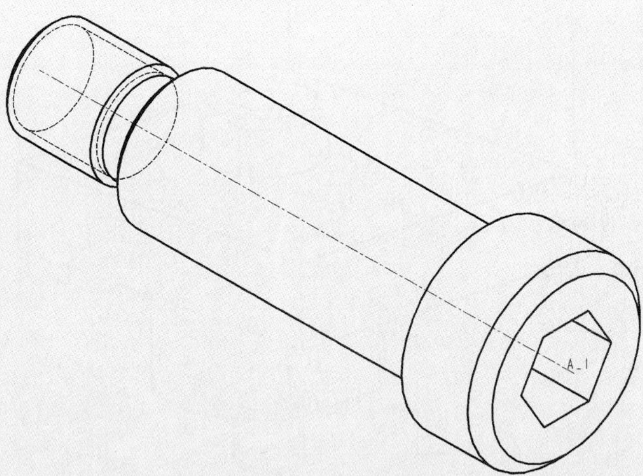

FIGURE P Socket-Head Shoulder Screw

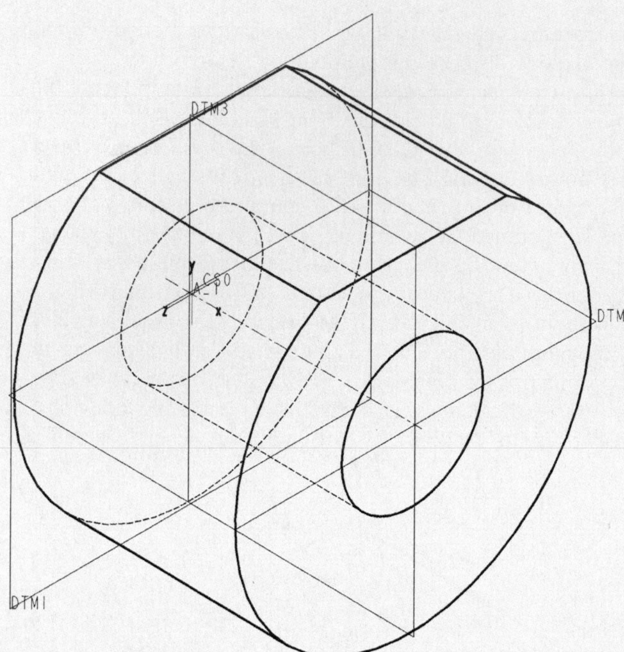

FIGURE Q Sleeve

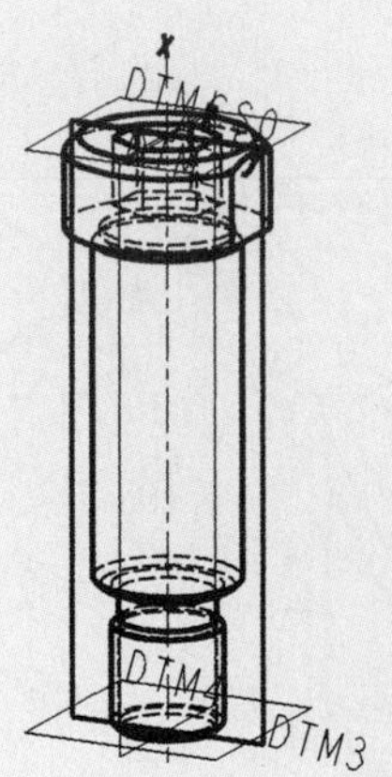

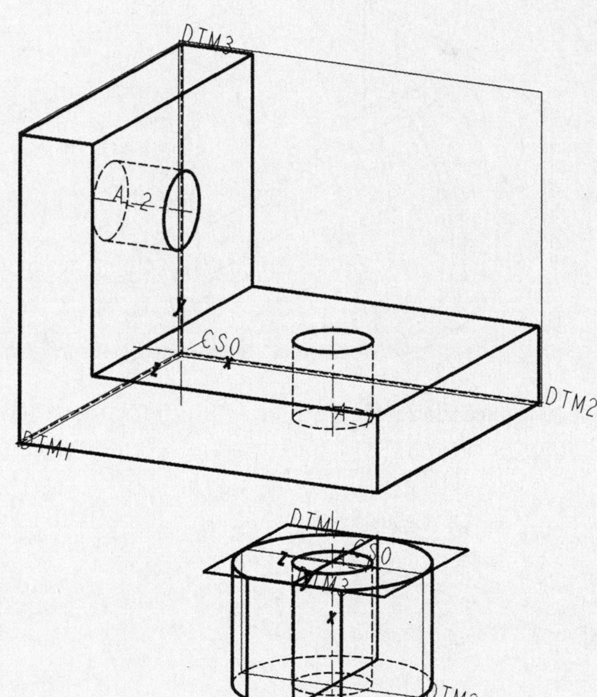

FIGURE S Exploded Assembly with Datums and Coordinate System Displayed

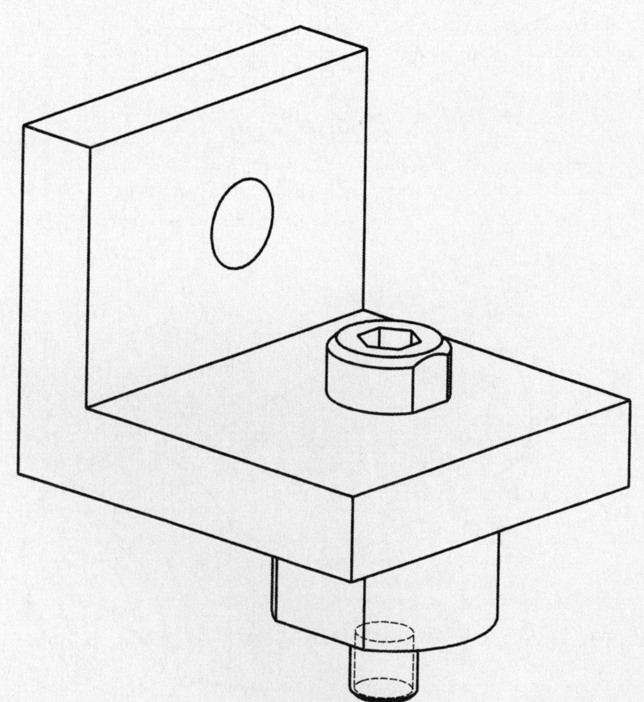

FIGURE R Constrained Parts

materials or other tabular data as required for the project. **Pro/REPORT** introduces a formatting environment where text, graphics, tables, and data may be combined to create a dynamic report. Specific tools enable you to generate customized **bills of materials** (BOMs), family tables, and other associative reports, including the following.

- Dynamic, customized reports with drawing views and graphics can be created (Fig. V).
- User-defined or predefined model data can be listed on reports, drawing tables, or layout tables. This reported data can be sorted by any individual requested data type display.

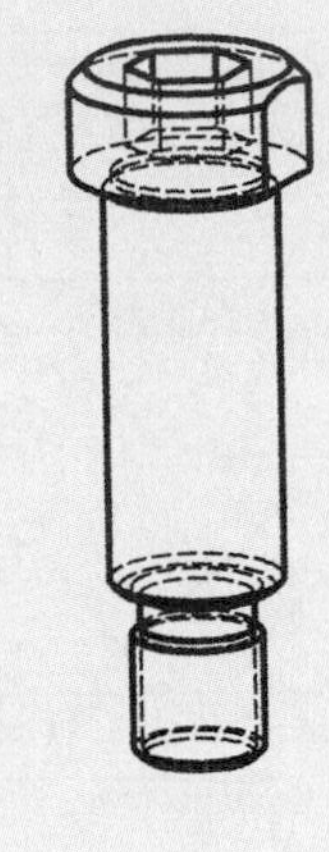

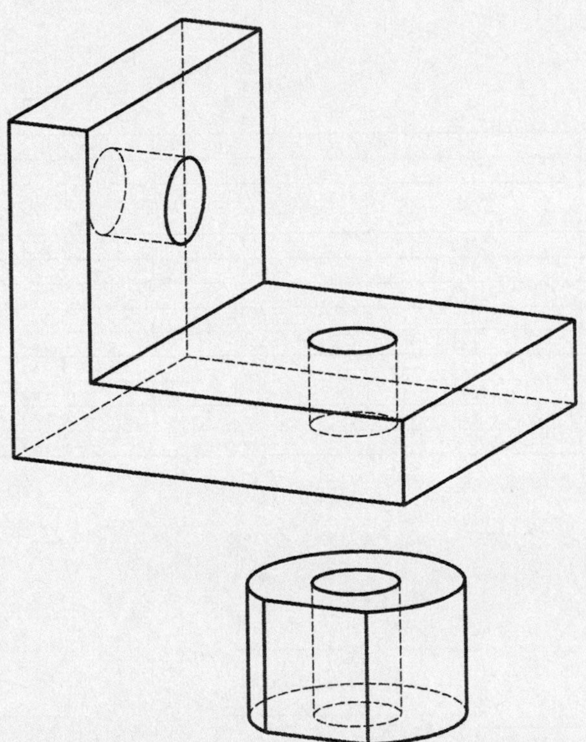

FIGURE T Exploded Assembly with Hidden Lines Only

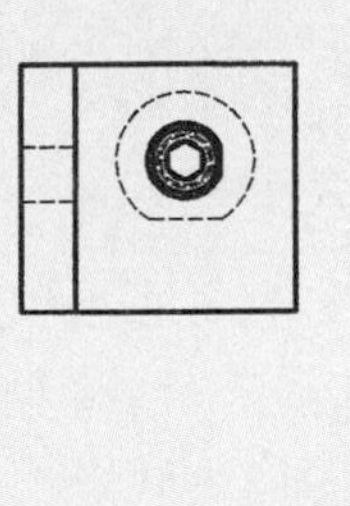

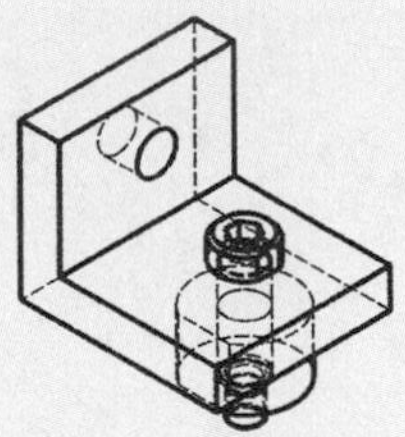

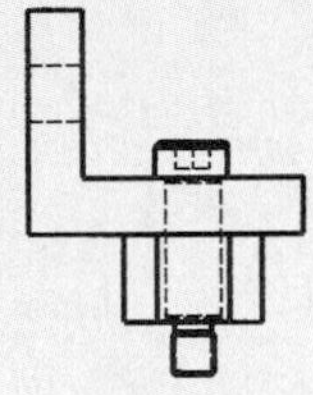

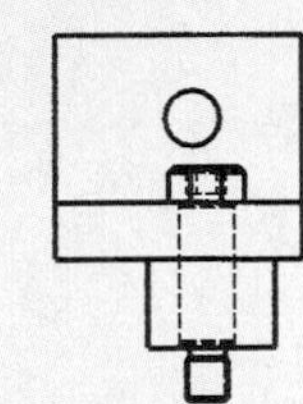

FIGURE U Assembly in Drawing Format

- Duplicate occurrences of model data can be listed individually or as a group in a report, drawing table, or layout table.
- Assembly component balloons can be linked directly to a customized **BOM** (Fig. W) and updated automatically when assembly modifications are made.

In **Report Mode,** data can be displayed in a tabular form on reports just as it is in drawing tables. The data reported on the tables is taken directly from a selected model and updates automatically when the model is modified or changed. A common example of a report is a bill of materials report or a generic part table (Fig. X).

- Regions in drawing tables, report tables, and layout tables can be defined to expand and shrink automatically with the available model information that has been requested to display.
- Filters can be added to eliminate specific types of data from displaying in reports, drawing tables, or layout tables.
- Recursive or top-level assembly data can be searched for display.

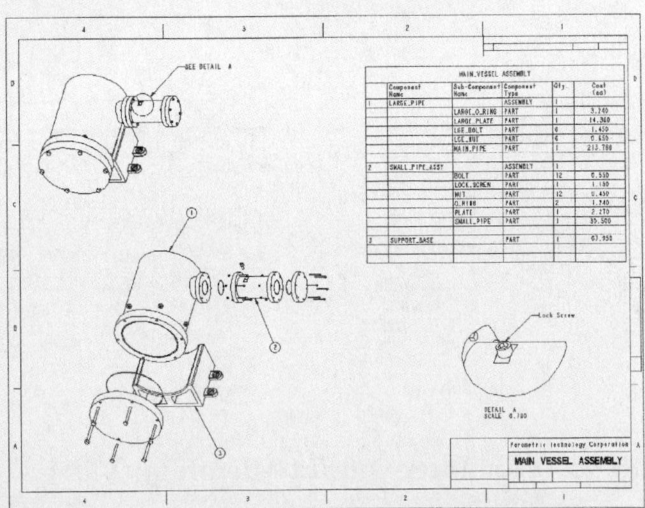

MAIN_VESSEL ASSEMBLY

	Component Name	Sub-Component Name	Component Type	Qty.	Cost (ea)
1	LARGE_PIPE		ASSEMBLY	1	
		LARGE_O_RING	PART	1	3.240
		LARGE_PLATE	PART	1	14.300
		LGE_BOLT	PART	6	1.450
		LGE_NUT	PART	6	0.650
		MAIN_PIPE	PART	1	213.700
2	SMALL_PIPE_ASSY		ASSEMBLY	1	
		BOLT	PART	12	0.550
		LOCK_SCREW	PART	1	1.150
		NUT	PART	12	0.450
		O_RING	PART	2	1.740
		PLATE	PART	1	2.270
		SMALL_PIPE	PART	1	30.500
3	SUPPORT_BASE		PART	1	63.950

FIGURE V Assembly, Exploded Assembly, and Bill of Materials

(Continued)

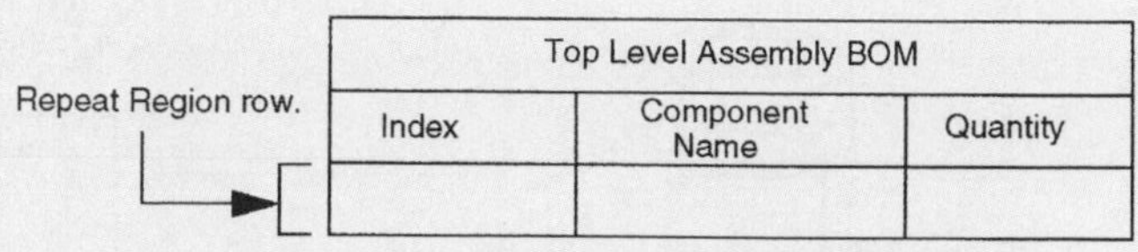

Top Level Assembly BOM		
Index	Component Name	Quantity

Report table BEFORE update for model data.

Top Level Assembly BOM		
Index	Component Name	Quantity
1	LARGE_PIPE	1
2	SMALL_PIPE_ASSY	1

Expanded Repeat Region.

Report table AFTER model added.

FIGURE W Creating a Bill of Material

GENERIC PART NAME: *PINA*				
	MODEL PARAMETERS			
INSTANCE NAME	*a*	*head_dia*	*NOM_SIZE*	*prong*
PINA01	0.032	0.060	.0312	0.010
PINA02	0.048	0.090	.0468	0.020
PINA03	0.060	0.120	.0625	0.030
PINA04	0.076	0.160	.0781	0.040
PINA05	0.090	0.190	.0937	0.040
PINA06	0.104	0.220	.1093	0.050
PINA07	0.120	0.250	.125	0.060
PINA08	0.134	0.280	.1406	0.060
PINA09	0.150	0.310	.1562	0.070

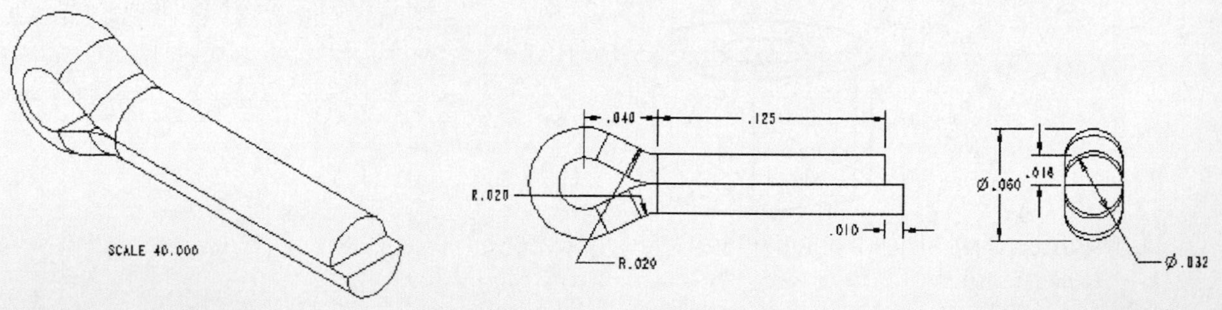

FIGURE X Drawing Table

23.9.3 Computer-Output Microfilm (COM) Units

Computer-output microfilm (**COM**) units provide fast and accurate plotting of drawings. The microfilm is usually mounted on an aperture card. The CAD-generated database is transferred from the system to a graphics controller (Fig. 23.26), and the laser film plotter creates the aperture card directly from a variety of data formats (Fig. 23.25). The microfilm can be enlarged.

FIGURE 23.25 Aperture Card Laser Plotter

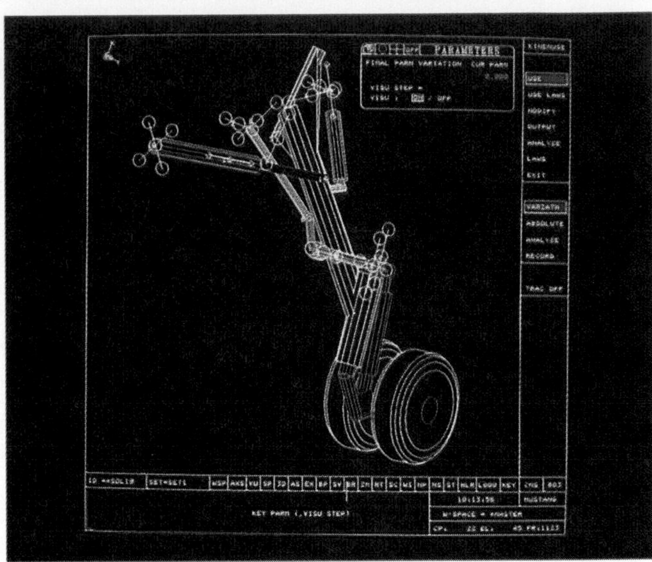

FIGURE 23.27 CAD Assembly

23.10 PREPARING ASSEMBLIES AND DETAILS WITH A CAD SYSTEM

A 3D CAD system makes it easier to check the spatial relationship between parts in an assembly, and the parameters in the model may be varied to produce different-size components (Fig. 23.27). The assembly can be rotated to view it from any angle to examine it for interferences (Fig. 23.28). With a 2D system, as with manual drafting, complex projections are required to achieve the same results. Since the 3D system can view a part from any angle, isometric and perspective views can be created with little extra effort.

Exploded views of the assembly are easy to create from a 3D assembly model (Fig. 23.29). In Figure 23.30 the assembly was modeled on a CAD system and plotted on an electrostatic plotter. The assembly was displayed pictorially, which enhances the assembly because each part is realistically depicted in its assembled position. Since the pictorial illustration clearly displays the parts of the assembly and each part is ballooned appropriately, separate views were not required. A separate section (**VIEW A–A**) is provided in Figure 23.30.

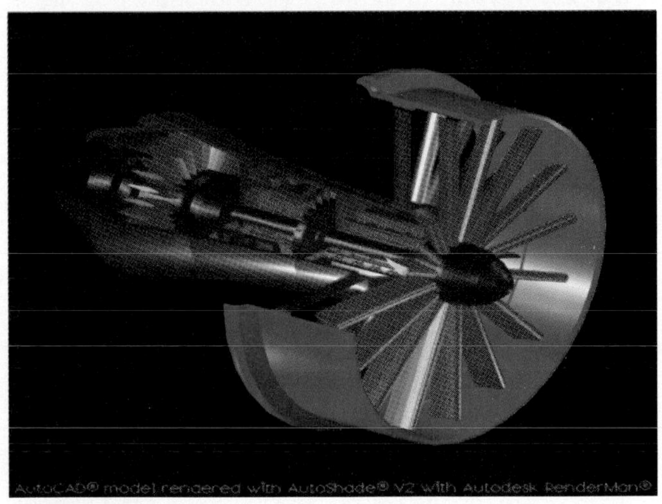

FIGURE 23.28 Turbine Assembly

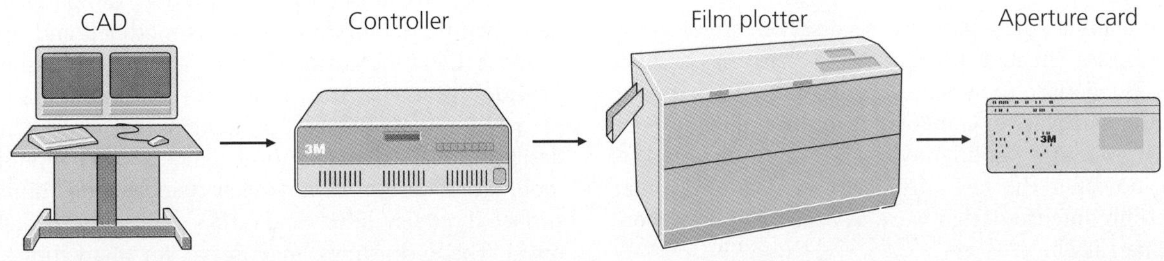

FIGURE 23.26 Aperture Card Output

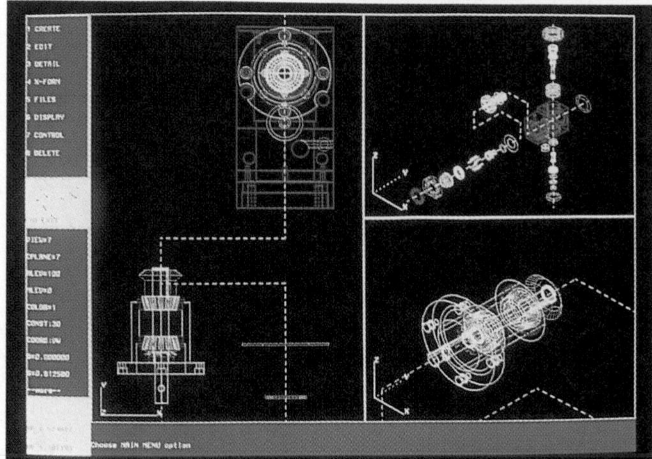

FIGURE 23.29 Exploded Mechanical Assembly

The assembly in Figure 23.31 was also created with a CAD system. Here, the traditional method of providing appropriate views of the assembly and ballooning is illustrated. The notes are in the lower left corner, the parts list is above the title block, and the revision information is at the upper right of the page.

Since a CAD system was involved, the title block, parts list format, revision block, and note format were all added to the drawing as subparts or drawings, or what some systems call **blocks** (AutoCAD). Because these company (and ANSI) standard formats are used on every drawing for this company, they are predefined formats that are retrieved and placed on any detail or assembly without reconstructing them each time a project is completed. Predefined formats are also accompanied by standard sheet sizes.

With a CAD system, hidden lines can be removed automatically from the assembly. For solid modeling systems, the combined parts can be displayed with proper visibility, as shown in Figure 23.32. Figure 23.33 shows a jig box that was designed on a 3D CAD system. The hidden line removal command (**HIDE**) was used to show visibility on this assembly model.

After the model of the assembly is completed, a designer separates the parts and files them individually. Each part may now be recalled and detailed. The model can serve to generate any views required by the engineer to detail the part properly.

23.10.1 Jigs, Fixtures, Dies, and Tooling

In order to manufacture a part, it is necessary to establish the tools. Tools are created to produce a part or product efficiently. Previously, tools were created after the part was engineered and designed. **Concurrent tooling development** involves considering tooling requirements as the part is designed, not after the fact. Jigs, fixtures, dies, and other tooling require intense design work as much as, if not more than, the part itself.

Changes in production methods, the development of new manufacturing products, and, in particular, the perfecting of economical production methods involve many design problems with tooling, dies, jigs, and fixtures. Making drawings requires special experience, and is done either by a company division maintained for that purpose or by independent tool specialists.

In general, a **tool** is a piece of equipment that helps create a finished part. It may be anything that must be designed and/or made in order to manufacture the part. The following is a list of tools found in industry.

Molds Used to form a variety of parts for consumer, industrial, and medical applications (Fig. 23.34)

Dies Used to forge, cast, extrude, and stamp materials in various physical states (solid through fluid)

Tooling The individual component of a mold or a die; might include a cavity, nest, core, punch, bushing, slide, or sleeve

Fixtures Used to hold and locate parts of assemblies during machining or other manufacturing operations (Fig. 23.35). The accuracy of the product being produced determines the precision with which the fixture is designed. Figure 23.36 shows a fixture for holding a part while machining.

To design and manufacture a finished part efficiently, product design engineers work with tool and fixture designers as well as manufacturing engineers. CAD systems promote this interaction by providing a common source of information for the product design and the associated tool/fixture design, manufacture, and production. When designing a tool or fixture, the 3D model of the part to be produced is retrieved to determine how the tool or fixture should be built to produce the finished product. The tool or fixture is then designed directly on the system (Fig. 23.35).

Since duplicating the design for CAM-related purposes is eliminated, time is saved. This also helps eliminate errors caused by misinterpreting design information. A CAD system handles large amounts of information that the engineer or designer needs to determine complex relationships between the tool/fixture and the part. The visual representation of the tool/fixture on the display, as it relates to the part, provides an important link between engineering and manufacturing. This eliminates the tedious work of interpreting the detailed part drawing and then manually calculating individual fits and tolerances of the tool or fixture required to produce the finished part. If product design changes are necessary, the tool/fixture design is modified and updated.

Once the tool/fixture is designed, a detail drawing to provide a geometric description of each part of the fixture is prepared. Detail drawings, an integral part of all steps in the design-through-manufacturing process, can represent the tool/fixture design in any view and include dimensions, surfaces, hidden lines, and other appearance control features. These drawings may serve for marketing, design,

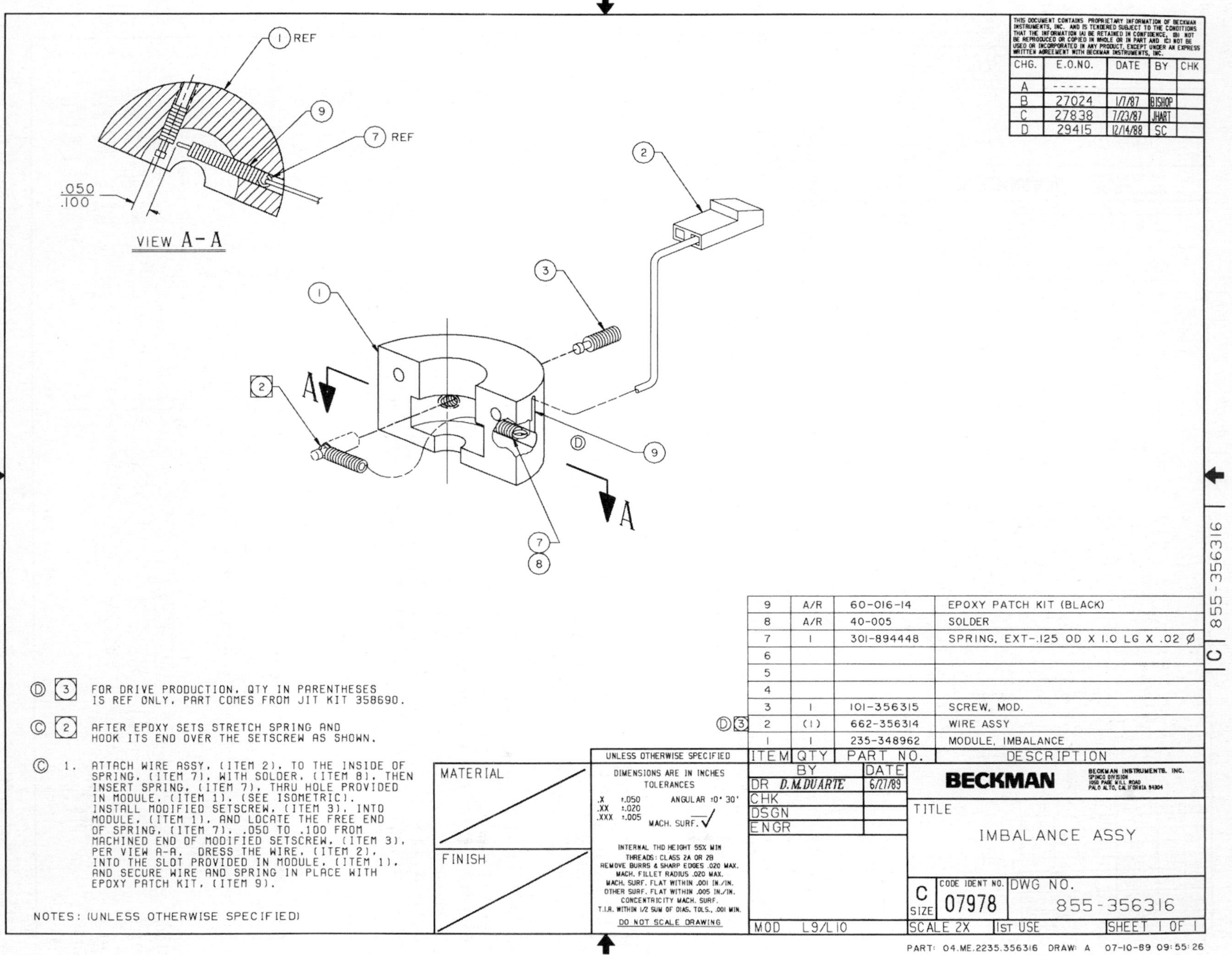

FIGURE 23.30 Imbalance Assembly

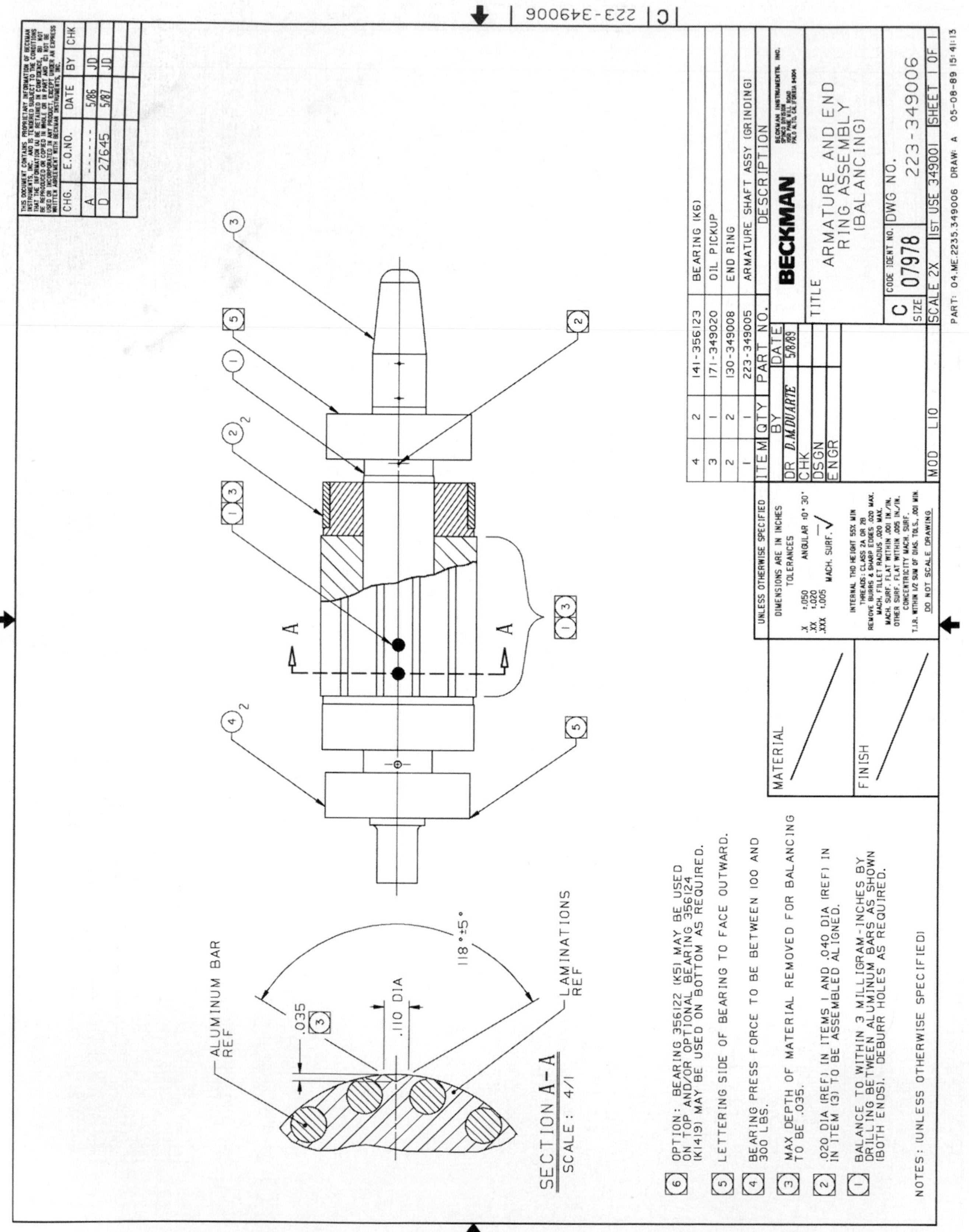

FIGURE 23.31 Armature Assembly

FIGURE 23.32 Solid Model Assembly

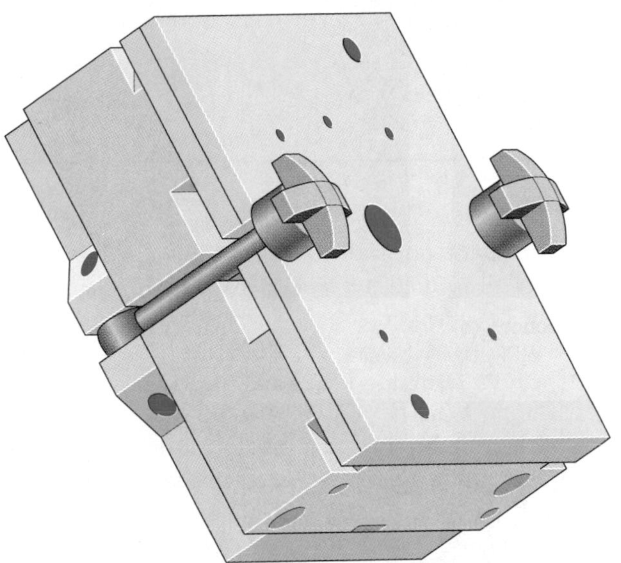

FIGURE 23.33 Jig Box Assembly with Hidden Lines Removed

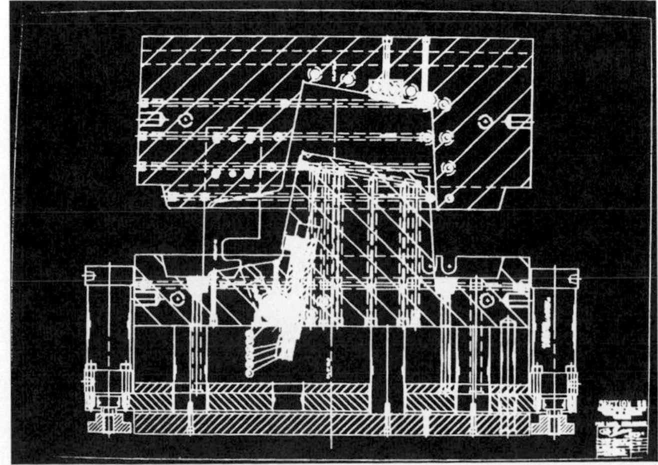

FIGURE 23.34 Mold Design Using a CAD System

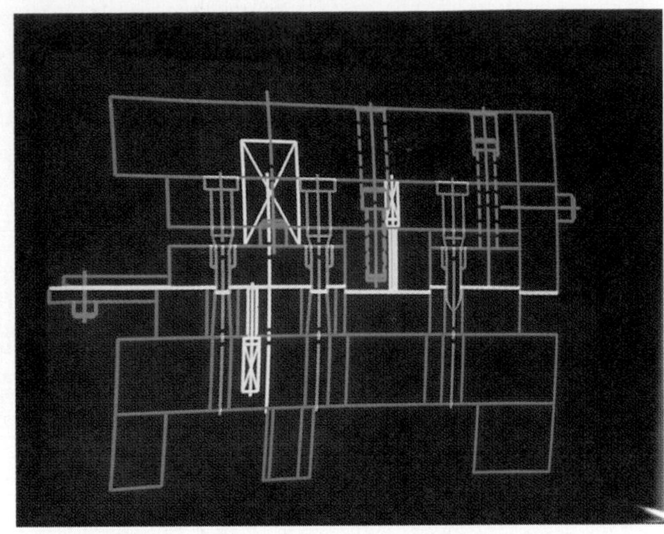

FIGURE 23.35 Tooling Fixture Designed on a CAD System

review, and manufacturing approval, or as input to the documentation, purchasing, and production departments.

To list the parts and materials needed to produce a tool/fixture designed on the system, CAD systems can automatically output a bill of materials for the planning and purchasing departments.

23.10.2 Visual Simulation to Verify Tool and Fixture Design

To provide clearances between the tool/fixture and the part, the designer can check and verify the minimum clearance needed by enlarging the view on the graphics display with the **ZOOM** and **MEASURE** commands. This ensures optimum use of materials. Color can help discriminate components for ease of viewing and highlighting.

To evaluate a tool design, a CNC programmer generates a toolpath (cutter path) and visually simulates the movement of a cutting tool around a part. The simulated cutter moves on the display screen to verify the result of the toolpath definition. The toolpath is plotted on a drawing along with the part and the fixture. This reduces costs for test machining, machine setup, and prototype creation by eliminating reruns. Process planners can then use this information to create process instructions and plans for the same part (Fig. 23.36).

23.10.3 Tool Design Using Standard Library Parts and CAD

Fixture design is an important application for computer-aided design. Tool designers can often benefit more than anyone from CAD/CAM. Since part size and shape are key factors in deciding how to locate and clamp, one obvious advantage of a CAD system for tool design is that workpiece geometry is already stored on the system. The ability to use

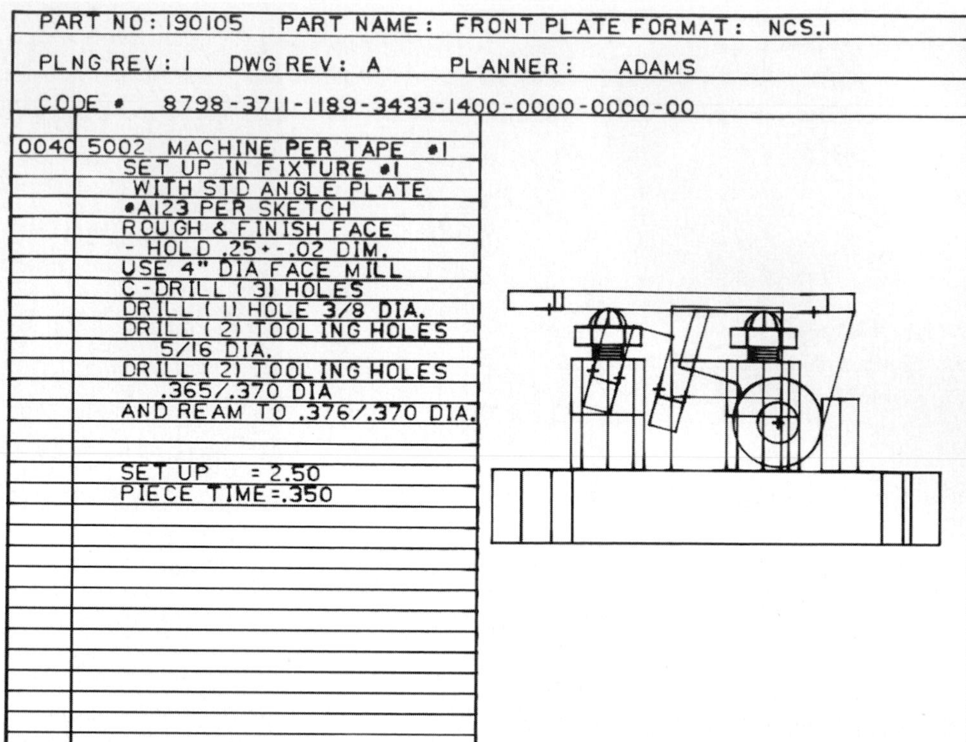

PART NO: 190105 PART NAME: FRONT PLATE FORMAT: NCS.1
PLNG REV: 1 DWG REV: A PLANNER: ADAMS
CODE • 8798-3711-1189-3433-1400-0000-0000-00
0040 5002 MACHINE PER TAPE •1
SET UP IN FIXTURE •1
WITH STD ANGLE PLATE
•A123 PER SKETCH
ROUGH & FINISH FACE
- HOLD .25+-.02 DIM.
USE 4" DIA FACE MILL
C-DRILL (3) HOLES
DRILL (1) HOLE 3/8 DIA.
DRILL (2) TOOLING HOLES
5/16 DIA.
DRILL (2) TOOLING HOLES
.365/.370 DIA
AND REAM TO .376/.370 DIA.
SET UP = 2.50
PIECE TIME=.350

FIGURE 23.36 Planning Machine Operations on a CAD System

and reuse a **standard library** of tooling components, made up of standard components plus in-company standards, is important to fixture layout and design.

Figure 23.37 demonstrates the steps taken to design a fixture out of standard components from a tooling library of parts. In the following example, CARR LANE components are used. The CARR LANE library of parts has more than 5000 standard items available in 2D and 3D versions.

CARR LANE provides schools with the library of parts free of charge. CARR LANE supports micro-based CAD systems, including AutoCAD, CADKEY, VersaCad, and Personal Designer, as well as workstation systems such as ComputerVision and Anvil. The following describes a set of steps in the design of a fixture from standard components already modeled on the CAD system and saved as a parts library.

1. Workpiece Geometry [Fig. 23.37(a)] Part geometry, before and after machining, is the key to deciding how to hold a part. Our sample part will be pocket milled, then drilled. When parts are designed on a CAD system and represented graphically, there is an extra advantage. After retrieving the workpiece, drawing layers containing unneeded dimensions and notes are turned off. Parts are normally shown in phantom lines and/or different colors. Parts are not a component of the fixture itself. Before proceeding further, tool sizes and cutting forces must be considered.

2. Fixture Base [Fig. 23.37(b)] Our example involves a standard, off-the-shelf *mill fixture base*. Whether you use a premachined base or make your own tooling plate, it must be big enough to hold the workpiece and any clamps you may need. Usually, you should allow some gap under the part for supports. The base must be thick enough to resist distortion from clamping forces and vibration from cutting forces. Standard cast angles, cubes, and other sections are also available off-the-shelf, and easily can be modified for fixtures. For cylindrical parts, the "fixture base" may be a set of blank chuck jaws, custom-shaped to fit the part.

3. Supports [Fig. 23.37(c)] For proper part location, designers commonly pick multiple fixed support points and occasionally some adjustable supports. In this example, three *rest buttons*, all underneath the workpiece, are the fixed supports. Geometric tolerancing considerations may dictate where the rest buttons are placed. Although you would usually place the supports by eye, you could also rely on your CAD system's center-of-mass function for heavy or complicated parts to distribute weight evenly. If the parts are thin and require additional backup against machining forces, you could add adjustable supports (hydraulically operated if you want the greatest accuracy).

4. Locators [Fig. 23.37(d)] Next, we locate our part laterally. In the example, we bring in three *round pins*, tangent to the part's side reference surfaces, to orient it correctly. We choose locators strong enough to resist anticipated lateral cutting forces. Three *spring stop buttons* hold the workpiece firmly against the round pins while we clamp.

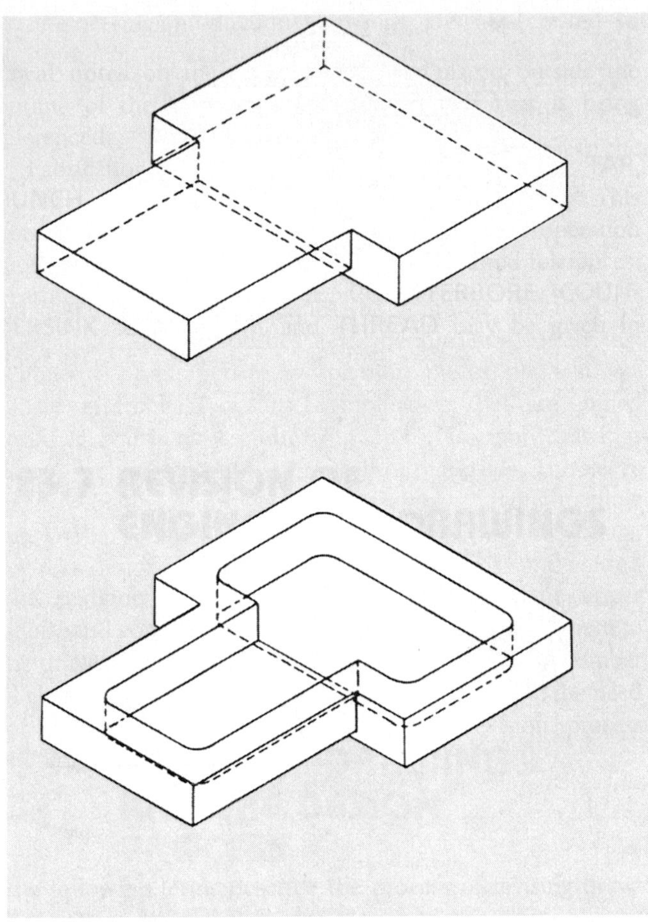

(a) Workpiece geometry

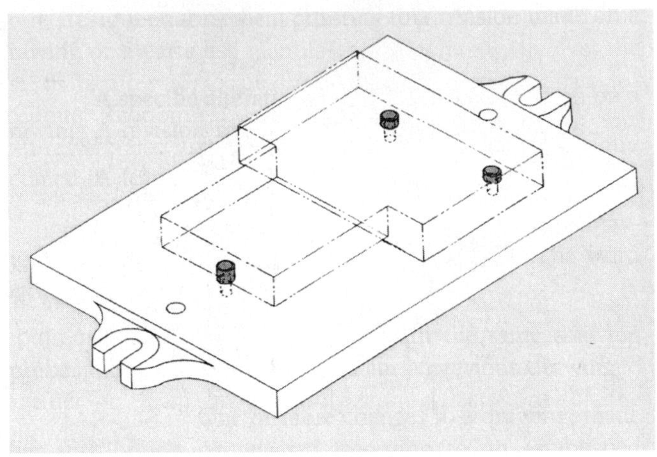

(c) Supports

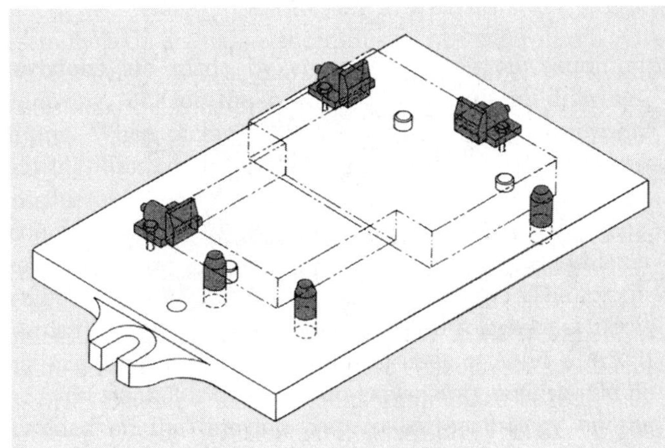

(d) Locators

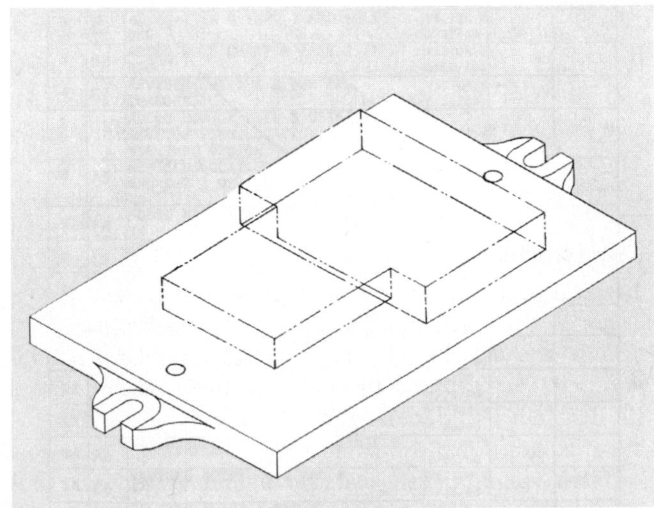

(b) Fixture base

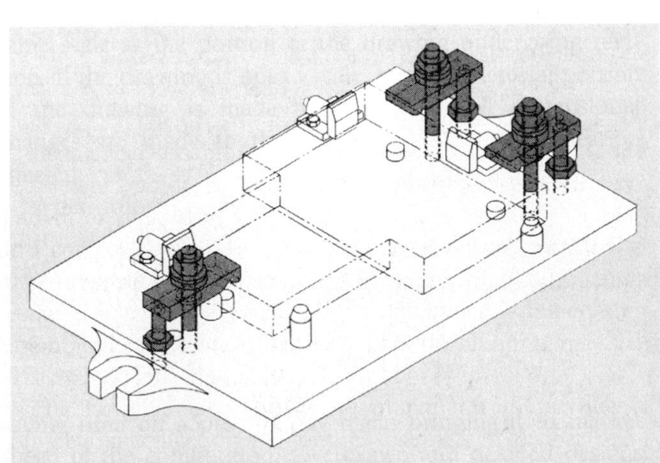

(e) Clamps

FIGURE 23.37 Tool Design Process Using a CAD System and a Component Library of Parts

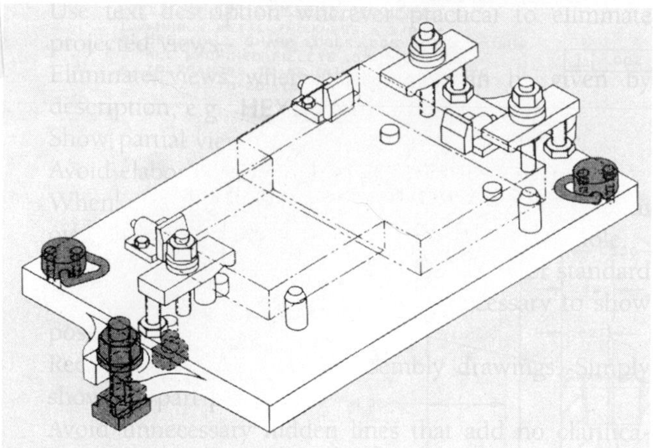

(f) Fixture accessories

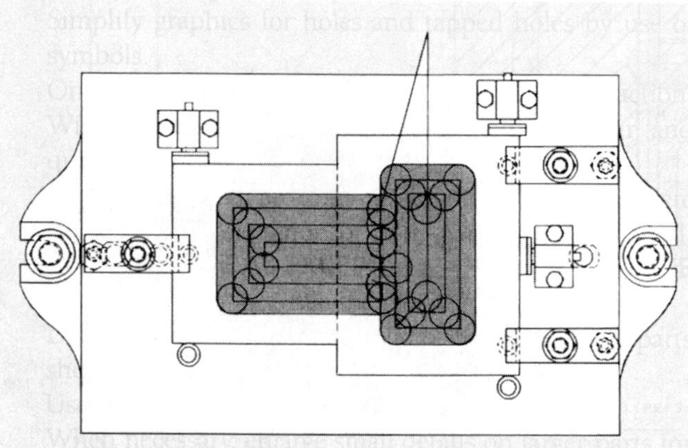

(g) Checking tool clearance

FIGURE 23.37 Tool Design Process Using a CAD System and a Component Library of Parts—*Continued*

ITEM	QTY.	PART NO.	DESCRIPTION
1	2	CL-4-FN	FLANGE NUT
2	2	CL-5/8-11X2.50	STUD
3	2	CL-10-TN	T-NUT
4	4	48223	SOCKET HEAD CAP SCREW
5	2	CL-20-HR	HOIST RING
6	6	53896	HEX HEAD CAP SCREW
7	3	CL-20C-SSB	SPRING STOP BUTTON
8	2	CL-6-RB	REST BUTTON
9	3	CL-12-SHA-1	CLAMP STRAP ASSEMBLY
10	2	CL-687-SLFK	FIXTURE KEY
11	3	CL-5-RP	ROUND PINS
12	1	CL-7-RB	REST BUTTON
13	1	CL-4-MFB	MILL FIXTURE BASE

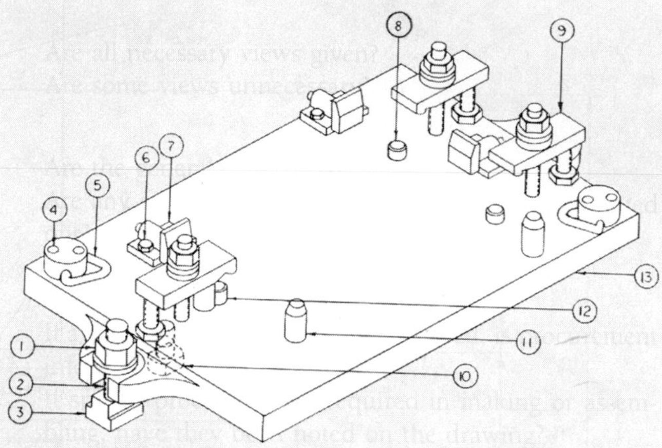

(h) Assembly drawing and parts list

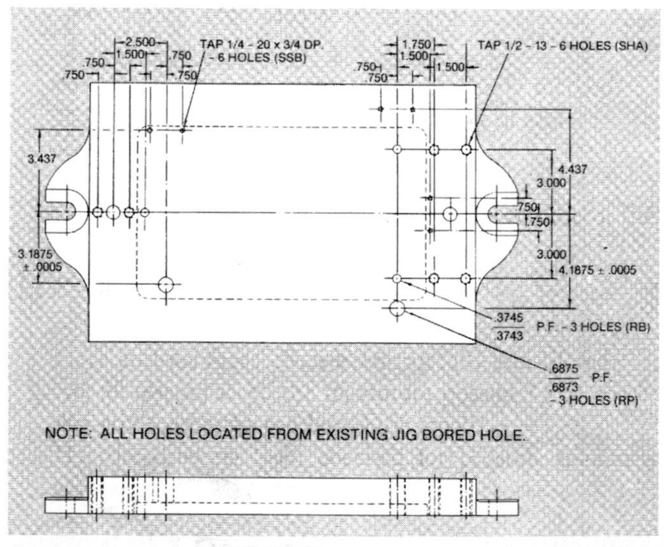

(i) Base detail drawing

5. Clamps [Fig. 23.37(e)] Cutter forces are considered when choosing the type, size, and number of clamps. In this example, we use three simple *clamp strap assemblies,* placed directly above the supports to avoid part distortion. We keep our clamps clear of the areas to be machined. If the entire top surface were to be milled, we could use *edge clamps* to keep the top totally clear.

6. Fixture Accessories [Fig. 23.37(f)] Fixture accessories are the final components we select. We choose two *hoist rings* to help lift our fixture into place. Two *sure-lock fixture keys* locate the fixture base accurately on the machine table. Two *T-nuts*, studs, and *flange nuts* fasten the base to the machine.

7. Checking Tool Clearance [Fig. 23.37(g)] After tentatively placing all fixture components, you can check tool clearance. Using the CNC graphics capabilities of your CAD/CAM system, you can determine tool paths, then, ultimately, generate CNC programs. This machining verification step ensures that the part is entirely machined and that tools do not interfere with the fixture.

8. Assembly Drawing and Parts List [Fig. 23.37(h)] The first step in documenting the fixture design is an assembly drawing. Assembly drawings are produced easily by turning off the drawing layer containing the workpiece. You can then use your system's capabilities to add item callouts and create a bill of material.

9. Base Detail Drawing [Fig. 23.37(i)] A detail drawing of the fixture base is also easy to produce by turning off the drawing layers containing other components. Here, two views, top and front, were selected to add machining dimensions. As a final step, we could generate a CNC program to machine the base.

You May Complete Exercises 23.1 Through 23.4 at This Time

QUIZ

True or False

1. The revision block is one of the most important things you should look at when reading an existing drawing for the first time.
2. Dimensions are given on all assemblies to locate and define the parts geometry.
3. Sections are used on assemblies to provide a convenient way of displaying clearly the unit's geometry.
4. A parts list and a bill of materials are two distinct and different aspects of an assembly drawing.
5. Since they will normally differ for each project, general notes are seldom standardized.
6. Hidden lines are shown whenever possible on the assembly drawing to clarify each part's geometry.
7. A parts list that is on the assembly drawing is listed from the top down and is placed below the revision block.
8. Ballooning is the process of calling out each part of an assembly by providing a circle attached to a leader that points to the piece on the drawing.

Fill in the Blanks

9. __________ provides prints of a drawing that have white lines with a blue background.
10. __________ are used to hold and locate a part during machining operations.
11. Layout drawings help to establish and depict __________, __________, and the relationship of __________.
12. __________ is the process of taking individual pieces of an assembly and redrawing them with sufficient views and __________.
13. Working drawings serve to order __________, plan operations, determine __________, and assemble the unit.
14. Welded assemblies are considered __________ assemblies.
15. Assemblies are fastened by one or more of the processes including __________, __________, __________, __________, and __________.
16. __________ on assemblies are provided for setup, assembly, and clearance.

Answer the Following

17. What are jigs, fixtures, and dies?
18. Why are notes required for most drawings? What is the difference between local and general notes?
19. What is the function of the assembly drawing?
20. Explain the difference between the concept of bottom-up design versus the top-down design approach.
21. Describe a parts list and each of its major headings.
22. How are views selected for an assembly drawing?
23. Explain the difference between a separable and an inseparable assembly.
24. Name three ways that you could simplify a drawing.

EXERCISES

Exercises may be assigned as sketching, instrument, or CAD projects. Transfer the given information to an "A"-size sheet of .25 in. grid paper. Exercises that are not assigned by the instructor can be sketched in the text to provide practice and to enhance understanding of the preceding instructional material. Draw the drawing format, title block, and other standard information for the exercise. If using AutoCAD or another system that provides standard formats, use them instead of the one provided here or in the worksheets.

After Reading the Chapter Through Section 23.11.1, You May Complete the Following Exercises

Exercise 23.1 Do a complete parts list for Problem 23.27 or Problem 23.22.

Exercise 23.2 Do a complete parts list for Problem 23.28 or Problem 23.23.

Exercise 23.3 Do a complete parts list for Problem 23.29 or Problem 23.24.

Exercise 23.4 Do a complete parts list for Problem 23.30 or Problem 23.25.

ITEM	QTY	PART NO.	DESCRIPTION

EXERCISE 23.1

ITEM	QTY	PART NO.	DESCRIPTION

EXERCISE 23.2

ITEM	QTY	PART NO.	DESCRIPTION

EXERCISE 23.3

ITEM	QTY	PART NO.	DESCRIPTION

EXERCISE 23.4

PROBLEMS

Jig and Fixture Assembly Design Projects

Design a jig and fixture to hold the following parts while machining. Do a layout of the fixture, a finalized assembly, a parts list, and details of each nonstandard item in the assembly. Show the workpiece part in phantom lines, or plot in a second color. Use Chapters 17, Threads and Fasteners, Chapter 18, Springs, and Appendix C (and CARR LANE parts if available) for standard parts.

Figure 23.38 shows an example of a student-designed fixture. The journal bearing housing provided in Problem 23.7 was used as the part to be machined. A wireframe model was completed first [Fig. 23.38(a)]. A surface model of the part was completed next [Fig. 23.38(b)]. Figure 23.38(c) shows a dimensioned detail of the journal bearing housing. An assembly was designed from standard CARR LANE parts [Fig. 23.38(d)], and an assembled detail was completed along with a parts list, as shown in Figure 23.38(e).

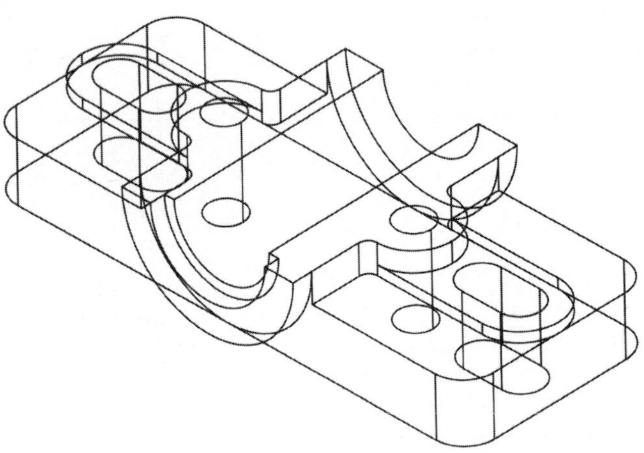

(a) Wireframe model of the journal bearing housing shown in Problem 23.7

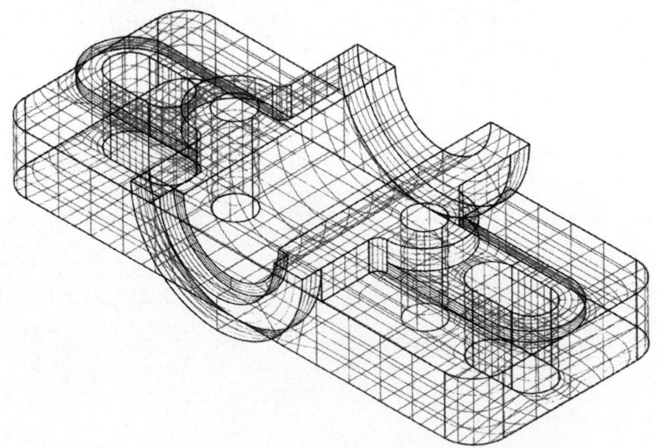

(b) Surface model of the journal bearing housing

FIGURE 23.38 Journal Bearing Fixture

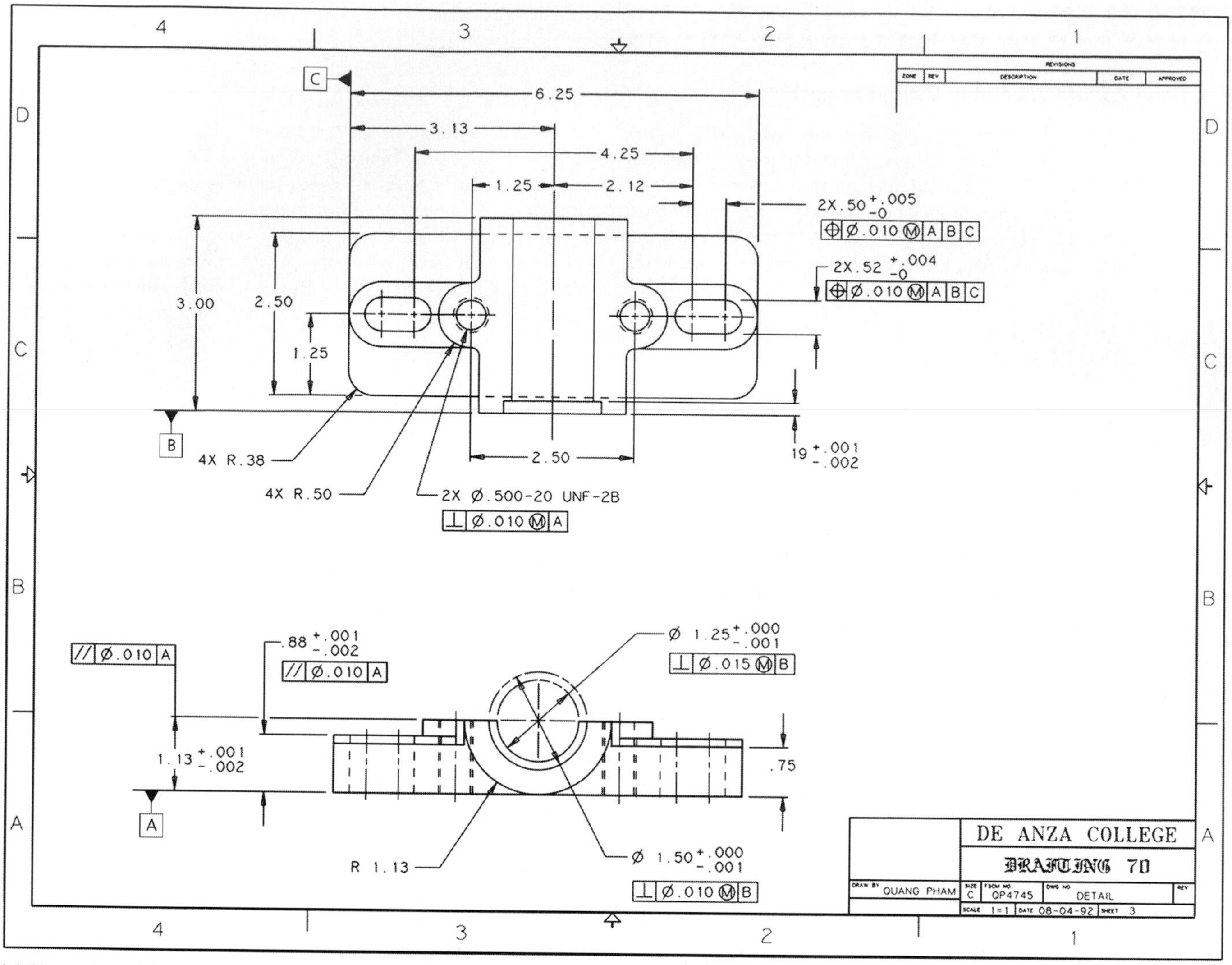

6.25
3.13
4.25
1.25
2.12
2X .50 +.005 −0
⊕ Ø.010 Ⓜ A B C
2X .52 +.004 −0
⊕ Ø.010 Ⓜ A B C
3.00
2.50
1.25
19 +.001 −.002
B
4X R.38
4X R.50
2.50
2X Ø.500-20 UNF-2B
⊥ Ø.010 Ⓜ A
// Ø.010 A
.88 +.001 −.002
// Ø.010 A
Ø 1.25 +.000 −.001
⊥ Ø.015 Ⓜ B
1.13 +.001 −.002
A
.75
R 1.13
Ø 1.50 +.000 −.001
⊥ Ø.010 Ⓜ B

DE ANZA COLLEGE
DRAFTING 70
DRAWN BY QUANG PHAM
SIZE C FSCM NO OP4745 DWG NO DETAIL
SCALE 1=1 DATE 08-04-92 SHEET 3

(c) Dimensioned detail of the journal bearing housing

FIGURE 23.38 Journal Bearing Fixture—*Continued*

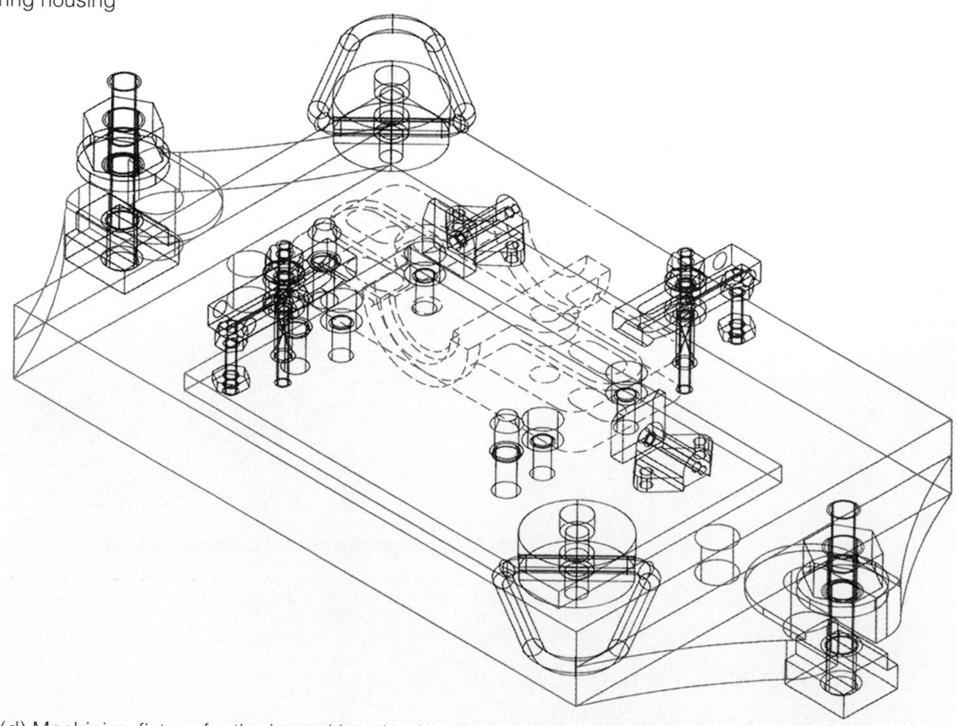

(d) Machining fixture for the journal bearing housing

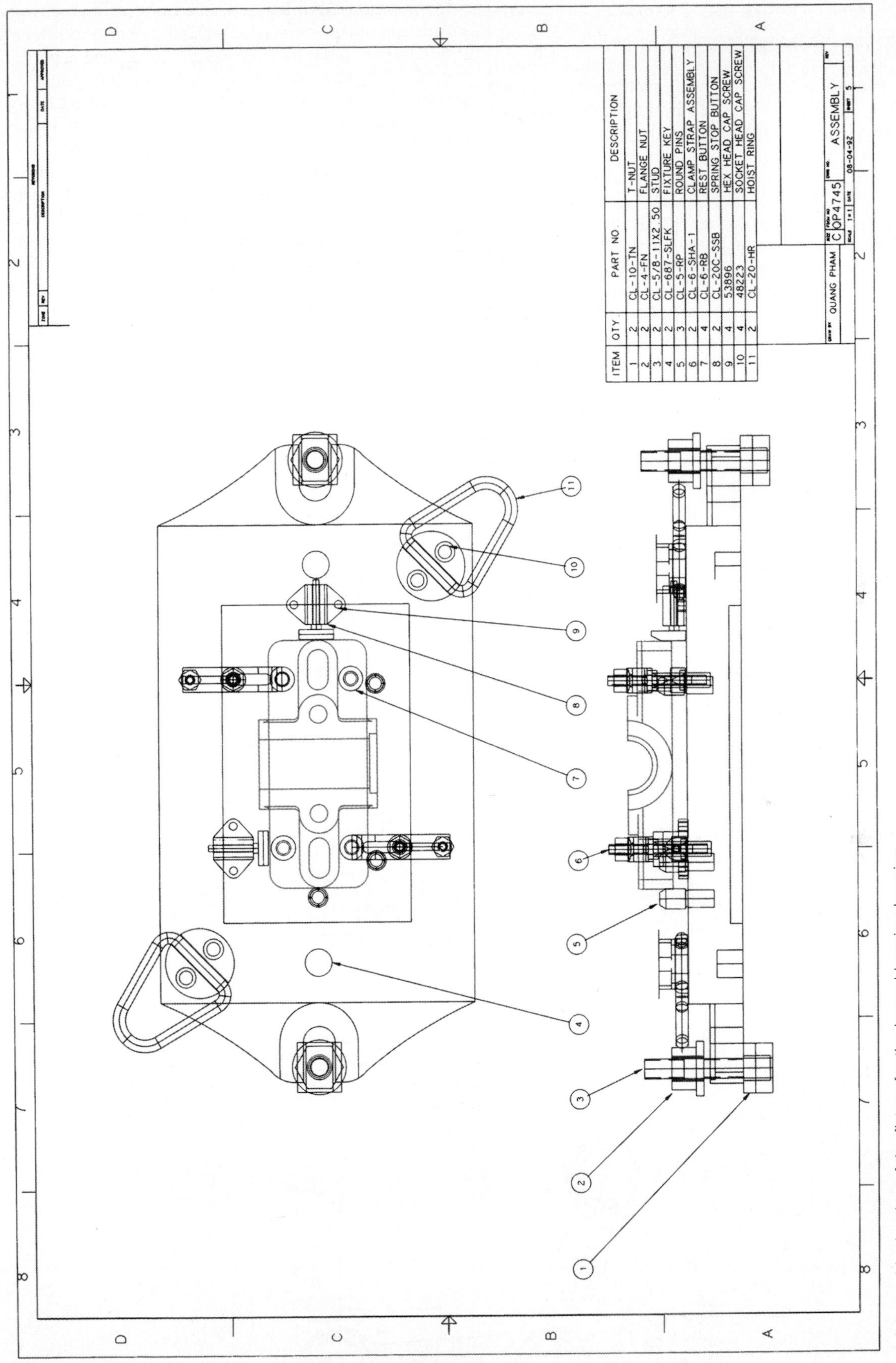

(e) Assembly drawing of the fixture for the journal bearing housing

FIGURE 23.38 Journal Bearing Fixture—*Continued*

Detail Drawings

For detail drawings, use appropriate ANSI standards for dimensioning and tolerancing for all problems. Complete a rough sketch of the part before drawing it with instruments or a CAD system. Choose an appropriate-size drawing sheet for each project. If a 3D system is available, model the part first and then generate a dimensioned detail.

For all drawings, use ANSI or ISO standard sheet sizes, parts list format, revision block, and title blocks, as shown in this chapter. The dimensions given for individual parts are in most cases for construction of the part's geometry only. With the exception of a few of the projects shown in the chapter body, the problems shown here are by no means meant to represent the correct way of dimensioning the part. The given dimensions will enable you to draw the part. *It will be your responsibility to select the proper views and place the dimensions, notes, and other information on the drawing.* Show all finish marks and use symbology wherever possible.

All pictorial drawings are to be converted to multiview details with appropriate view selection and proper dimensioning methods. In most cases, the drawings presented here as projects can be drawn full scale. If a project prohibits full-scale rendering, a reduced scale can be used. All projects done on a CAD system are to be modeled/drawn full scale and then plotted according to your instructor and the limitations of your plotter.

Decimal-inch projects and metric drawings are provided. You may convert any of the projects to the other measurement system. In many cases, you will find that converting the dimensions will give odd and inappropriate sizes. You may redesign any of the parts using even and logical sizes for that measurement system. For example, though 1.00 in. converts to 25.4 mm, it is acceptable to change the metric dimension to 25 mm or 24 mm. The same is true for standard parts such as screws, nuts, washers, and other off-the-shelf items; look up the closest standard size before ordering the item (placing on the parts list).

Problem 23.1 Draw and detail the adjustable guide.

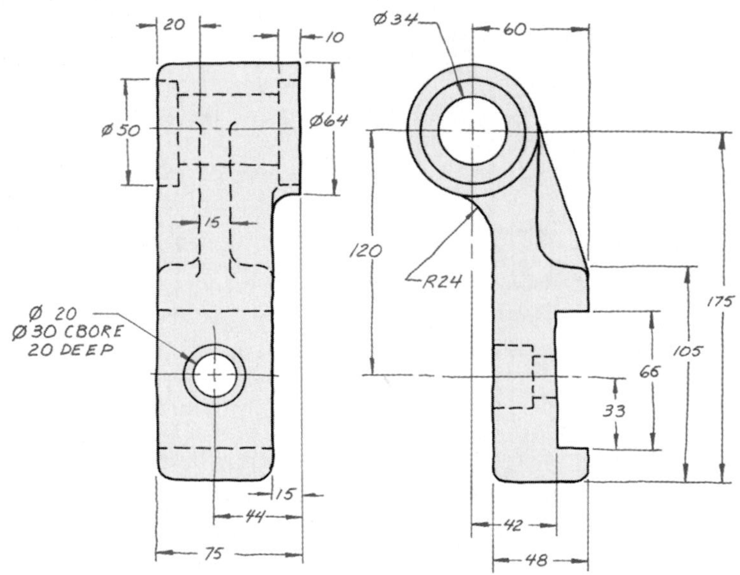

Problem 23.2 Do a detail drawing of the crank arm.

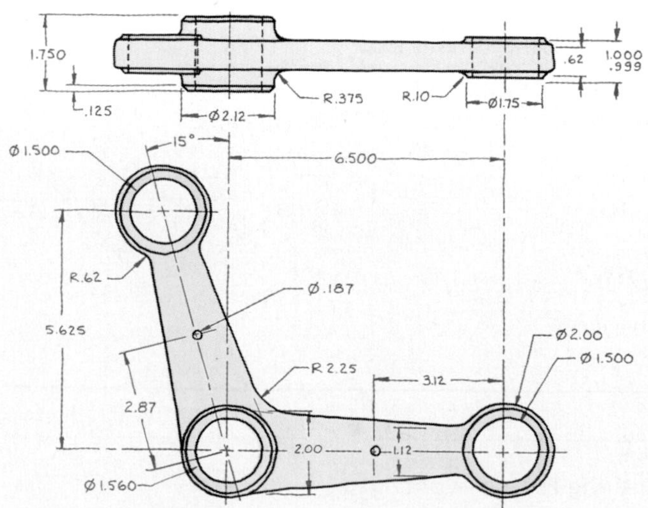

Problem 23.3 Draw and detail the shifter fork.

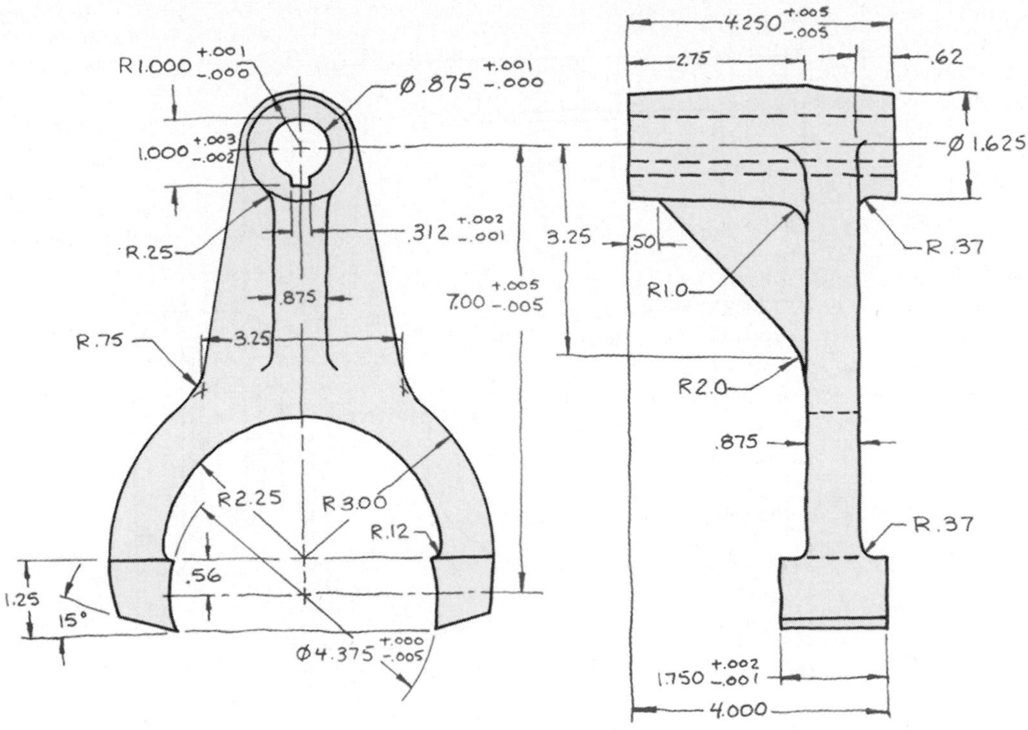

Problem 23.4 Draw and detail the flywheel.

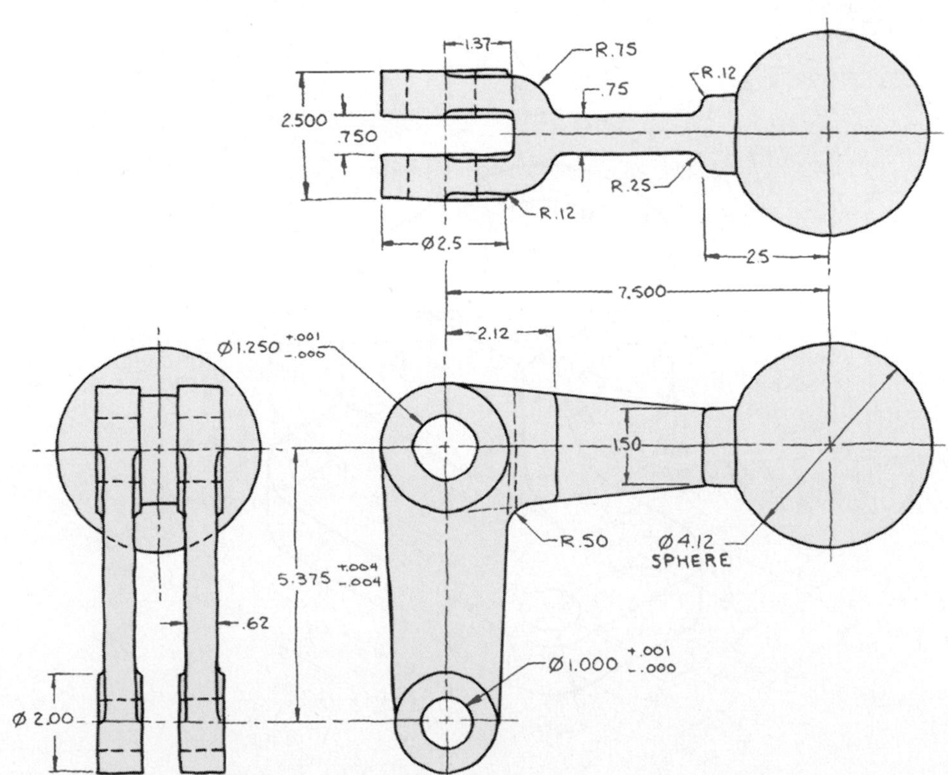

Problem 23.5 Do a detail drawing of the bearing adjustment.

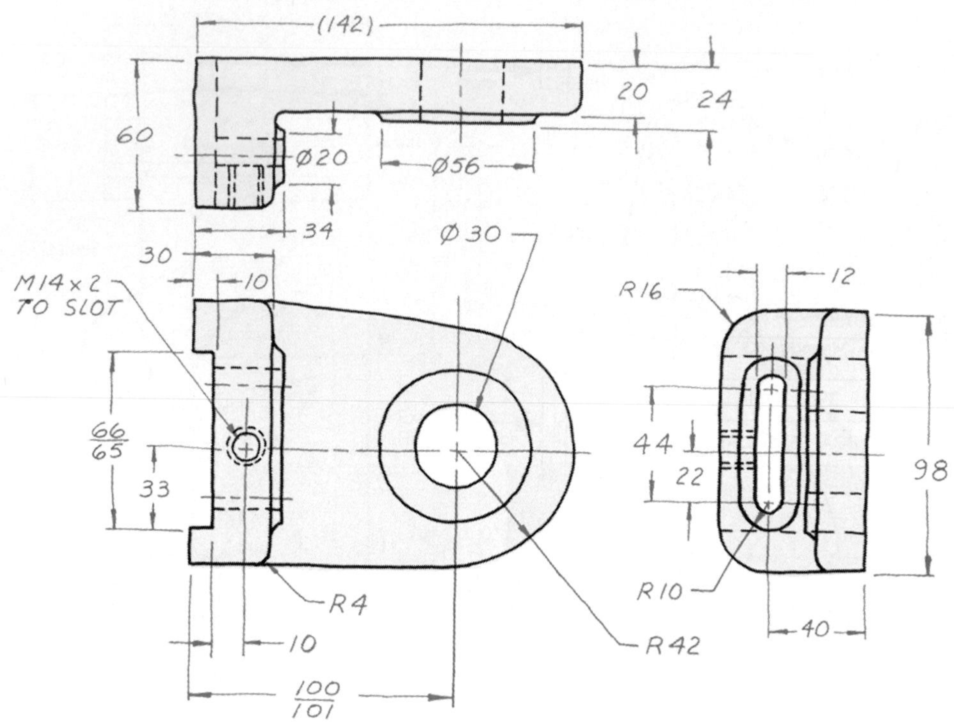

Problem 23.6 Draw and detail the guide bracket.

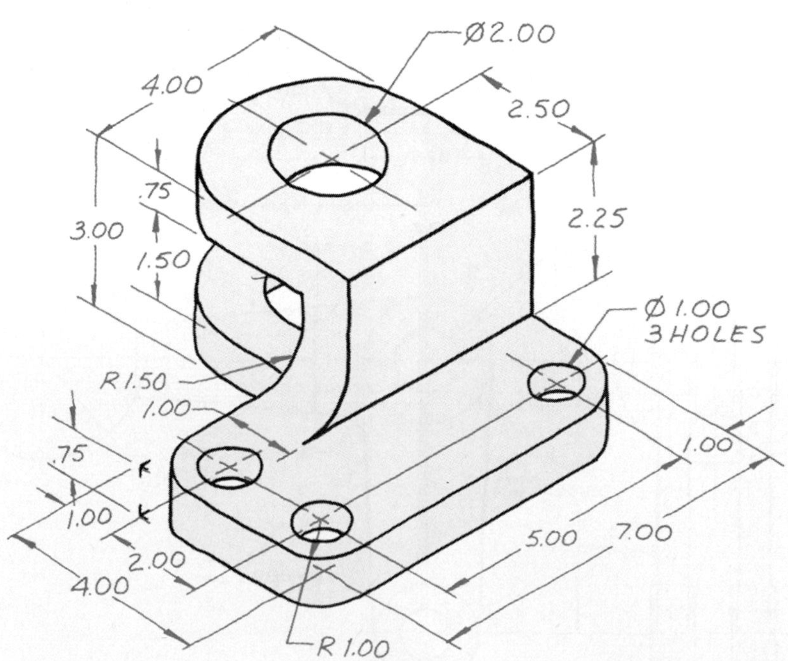

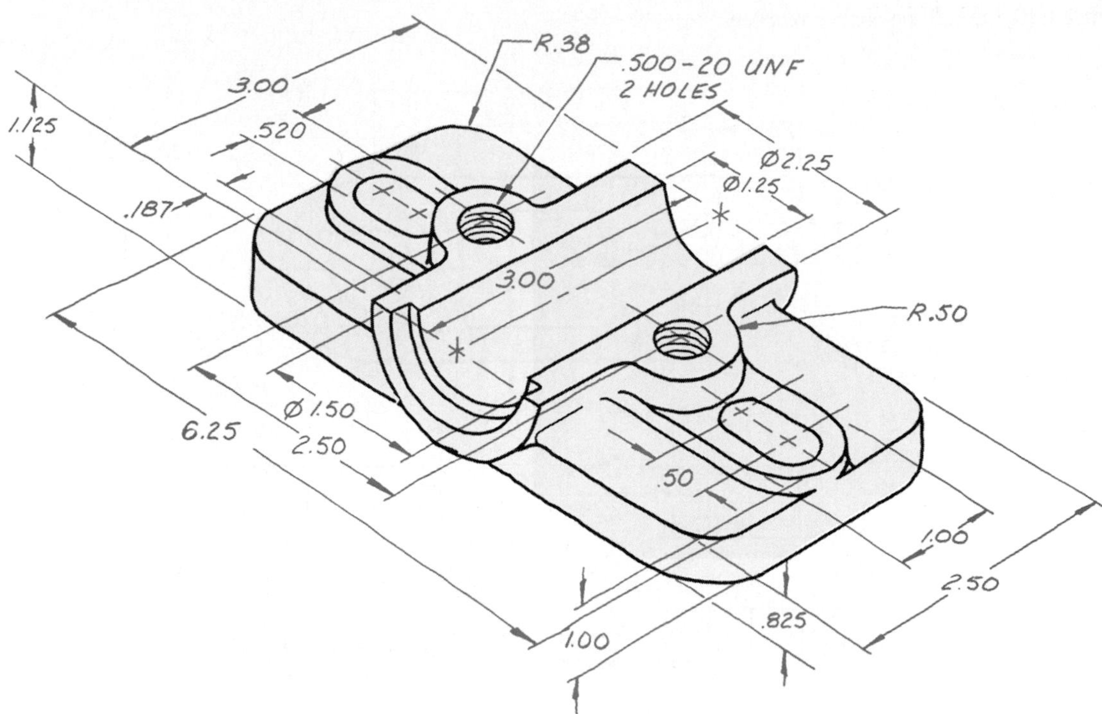

Problem 23.7 Detail the journal bearing housing.

Problem 23.8 Draw and detail the offset bracket.

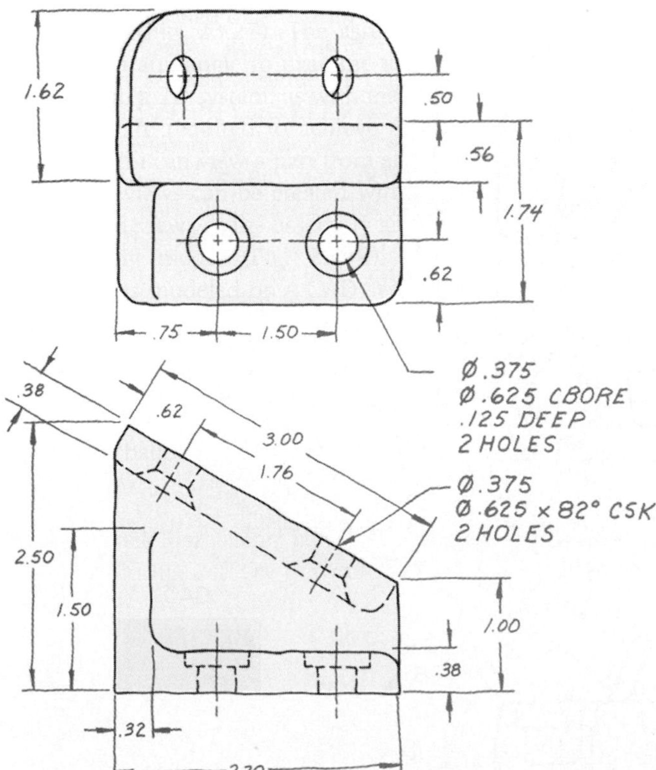

Problem 23.9 Complete a detail of the thrust bearing cap.

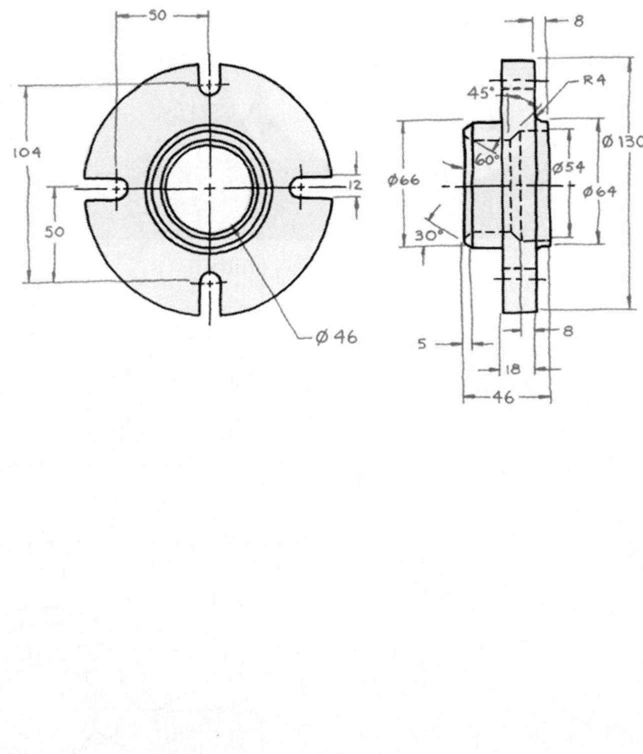

Problem 23.10 Detail the anchor bracket.

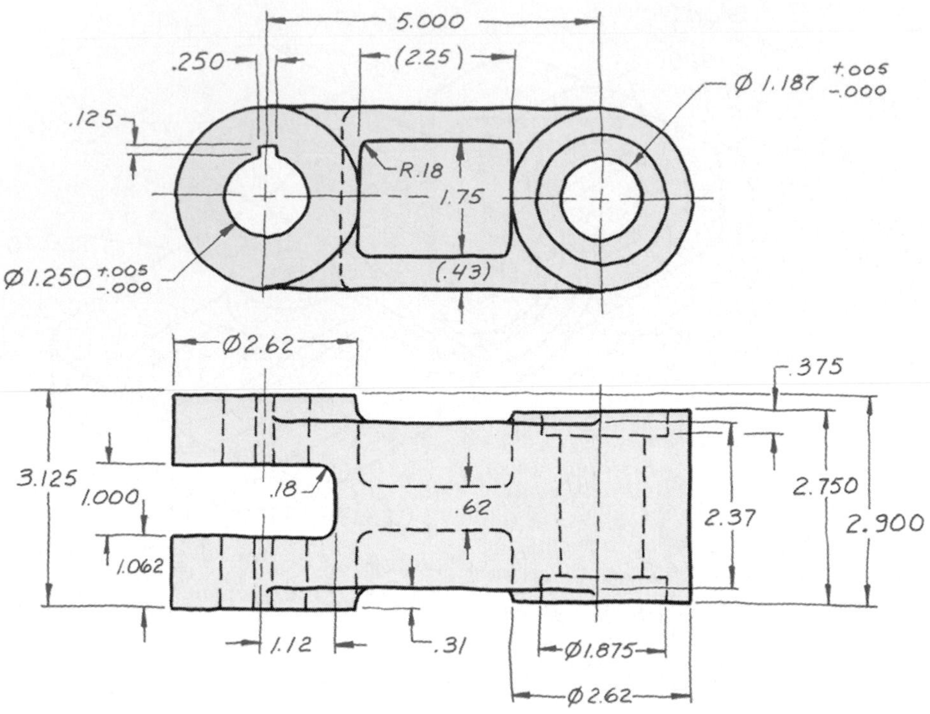

Problem 23.11 Draw and detail the bracket.

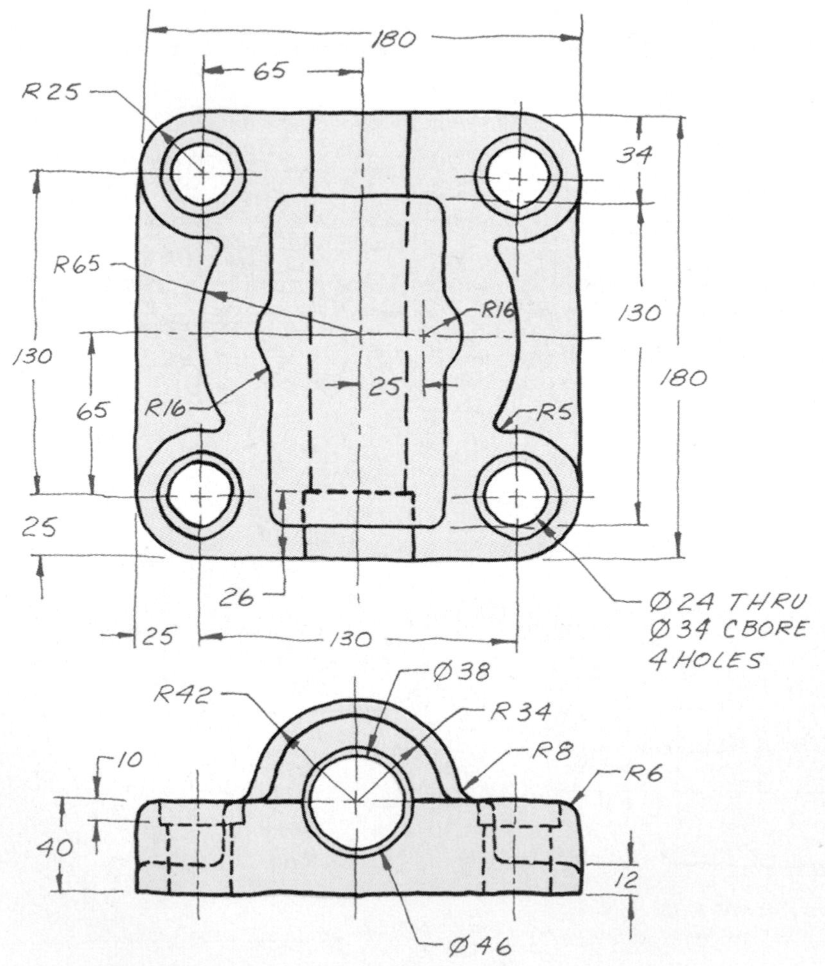

Problem 23.12 Draw and detail the part.

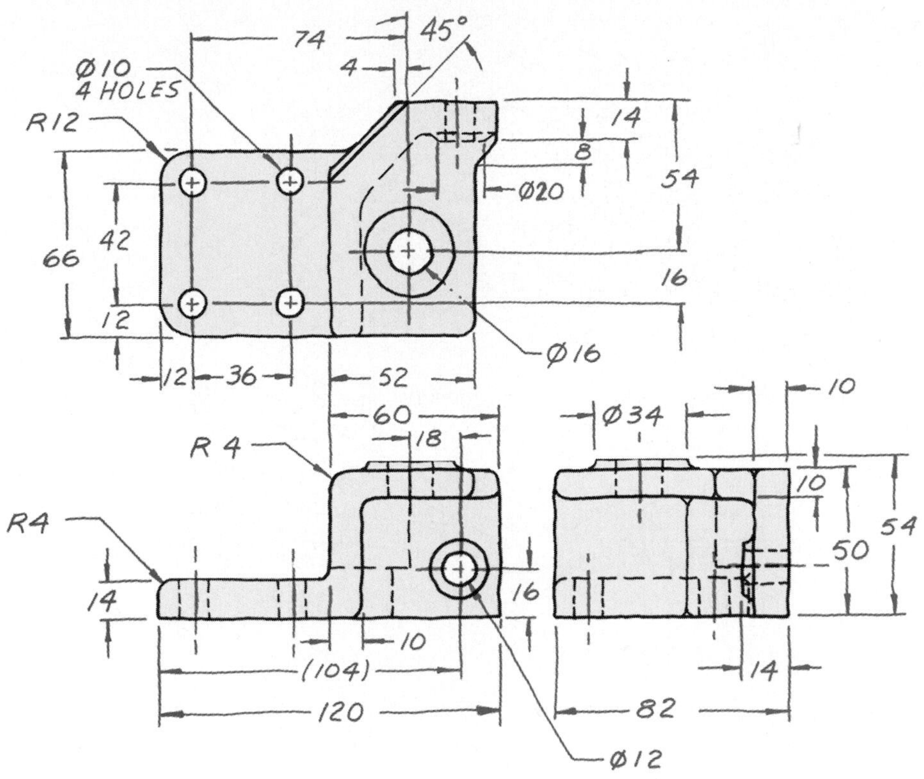

Problem 23.13 Draw and detail the master connecting rod.

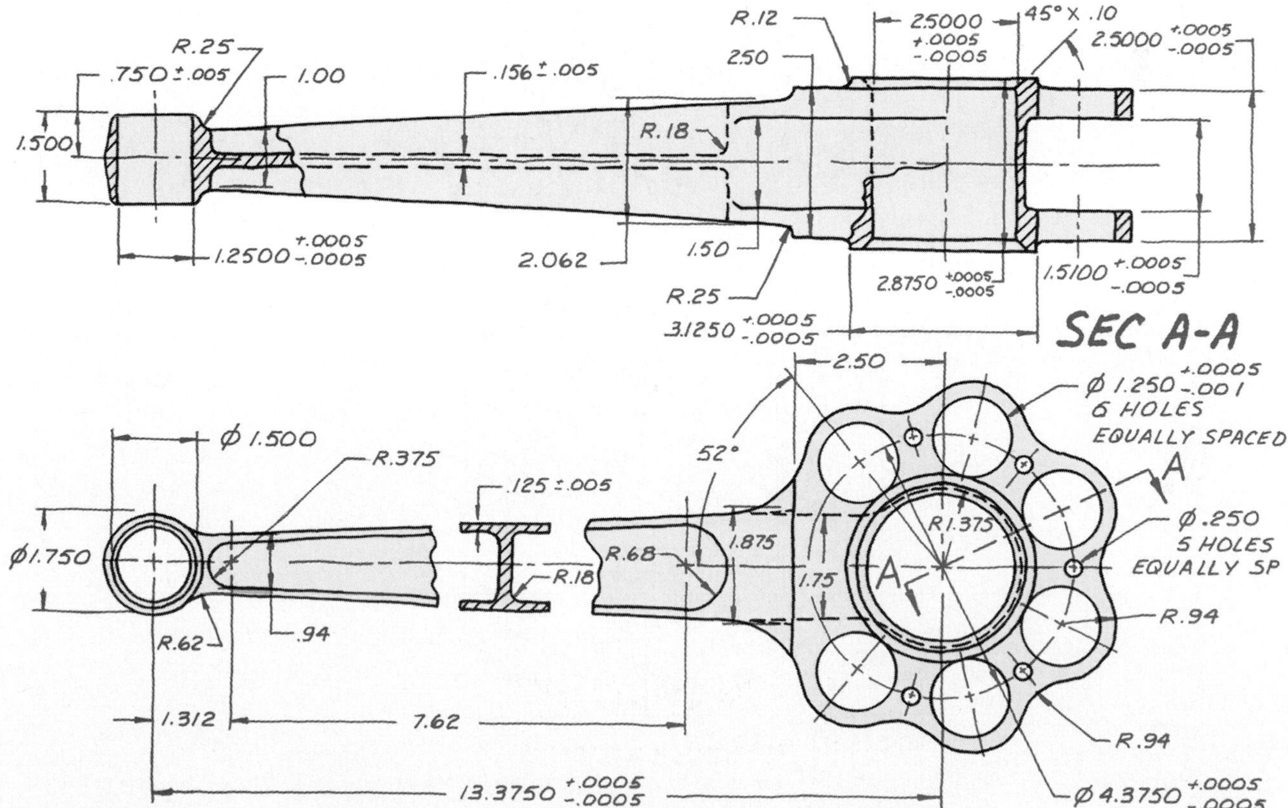

Problem 23.14 Draw and detail the CARR LANE mill base.

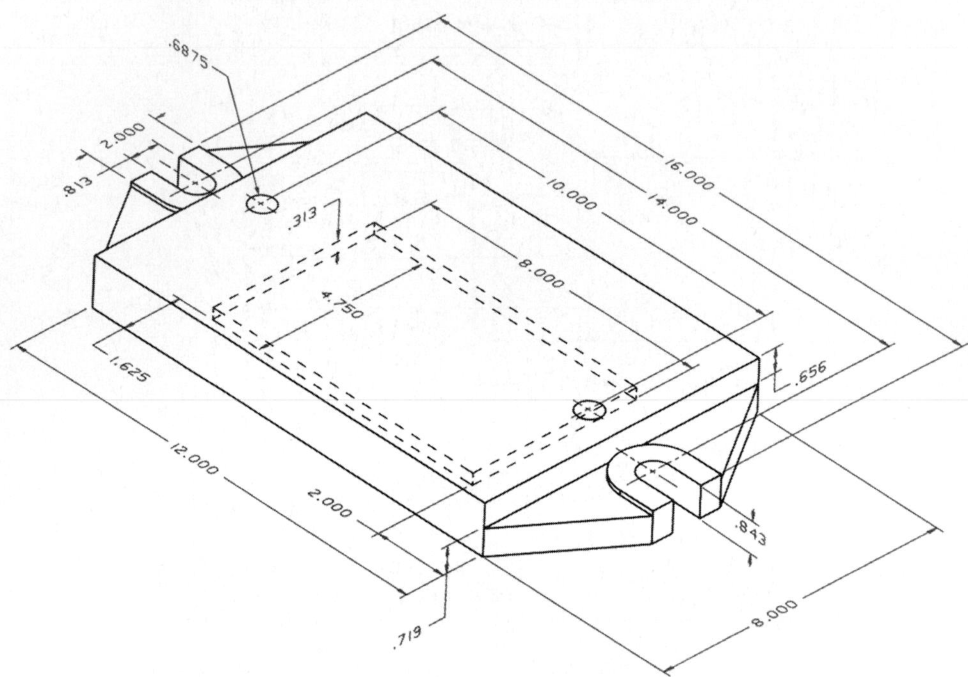

Problem 23.15 Draw and detail the CARR LANE cylinder mount.

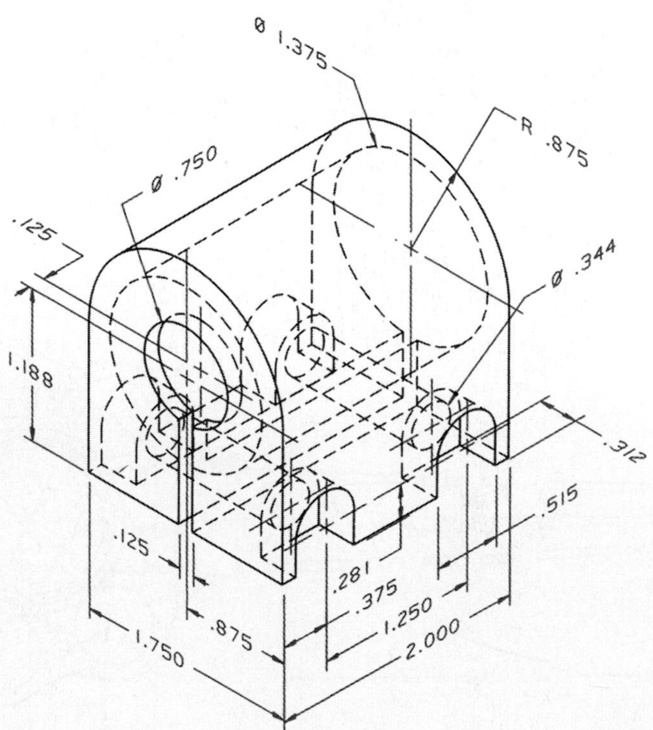

Problem 23.16 Draw and detail the casting.

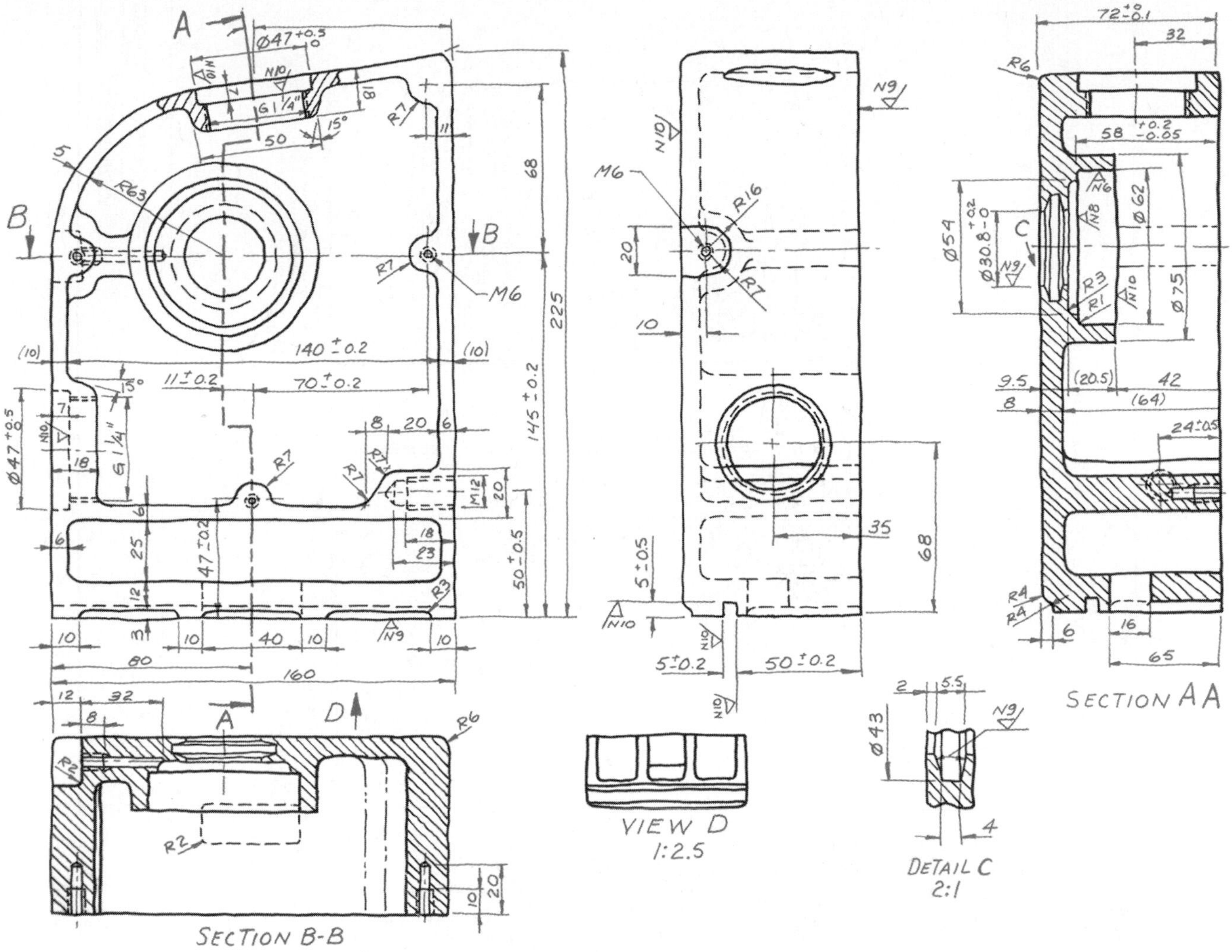

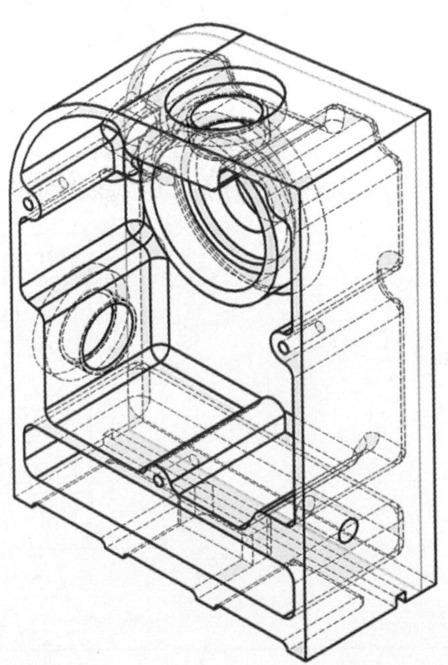

Problem 23.17 Redraw the chassis.

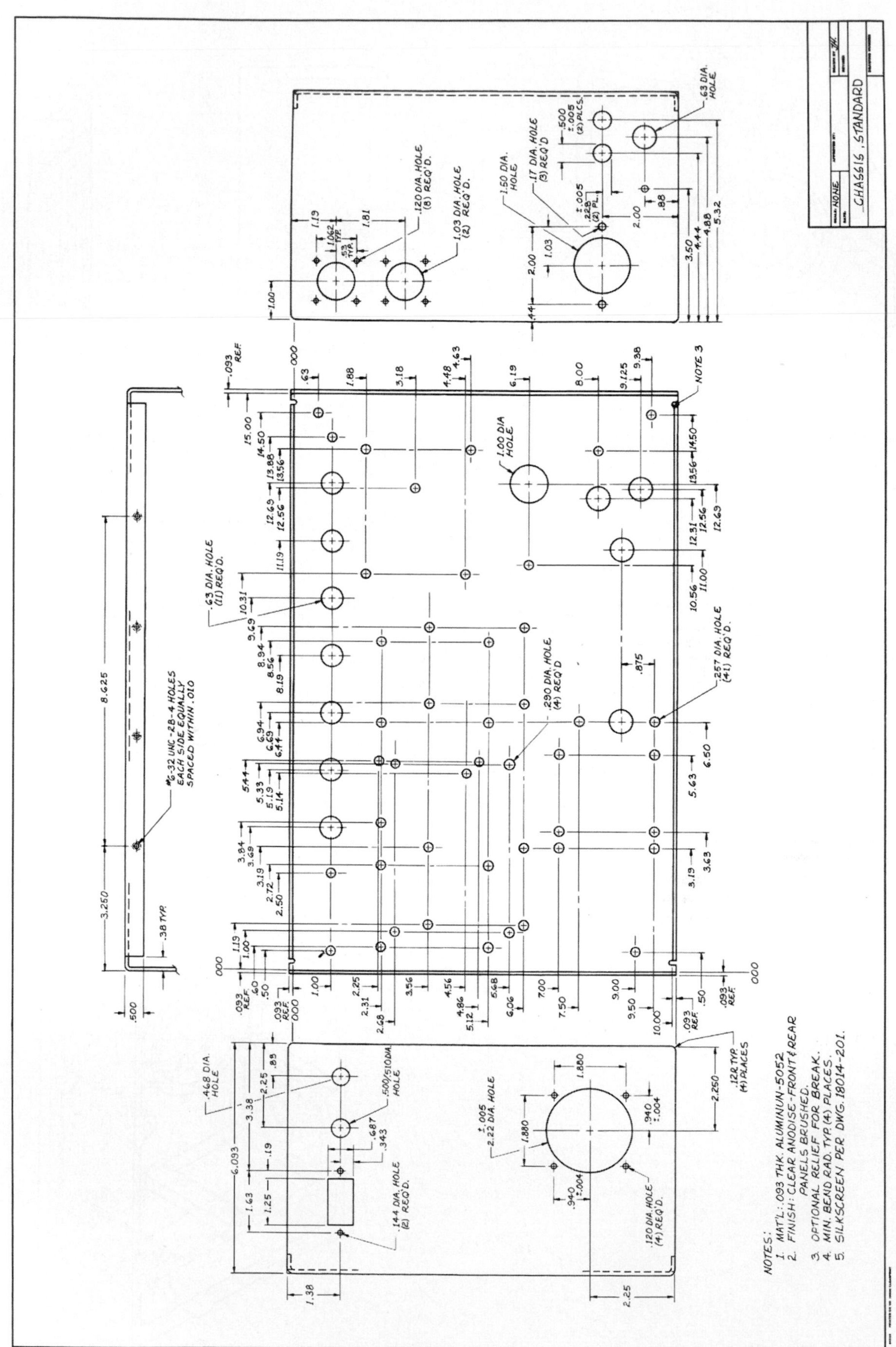

Problem 23.18(A) and (B) Draw and detail the cleaning kit package, and dimension completely. Make a full-size model of the box out of cardboard.

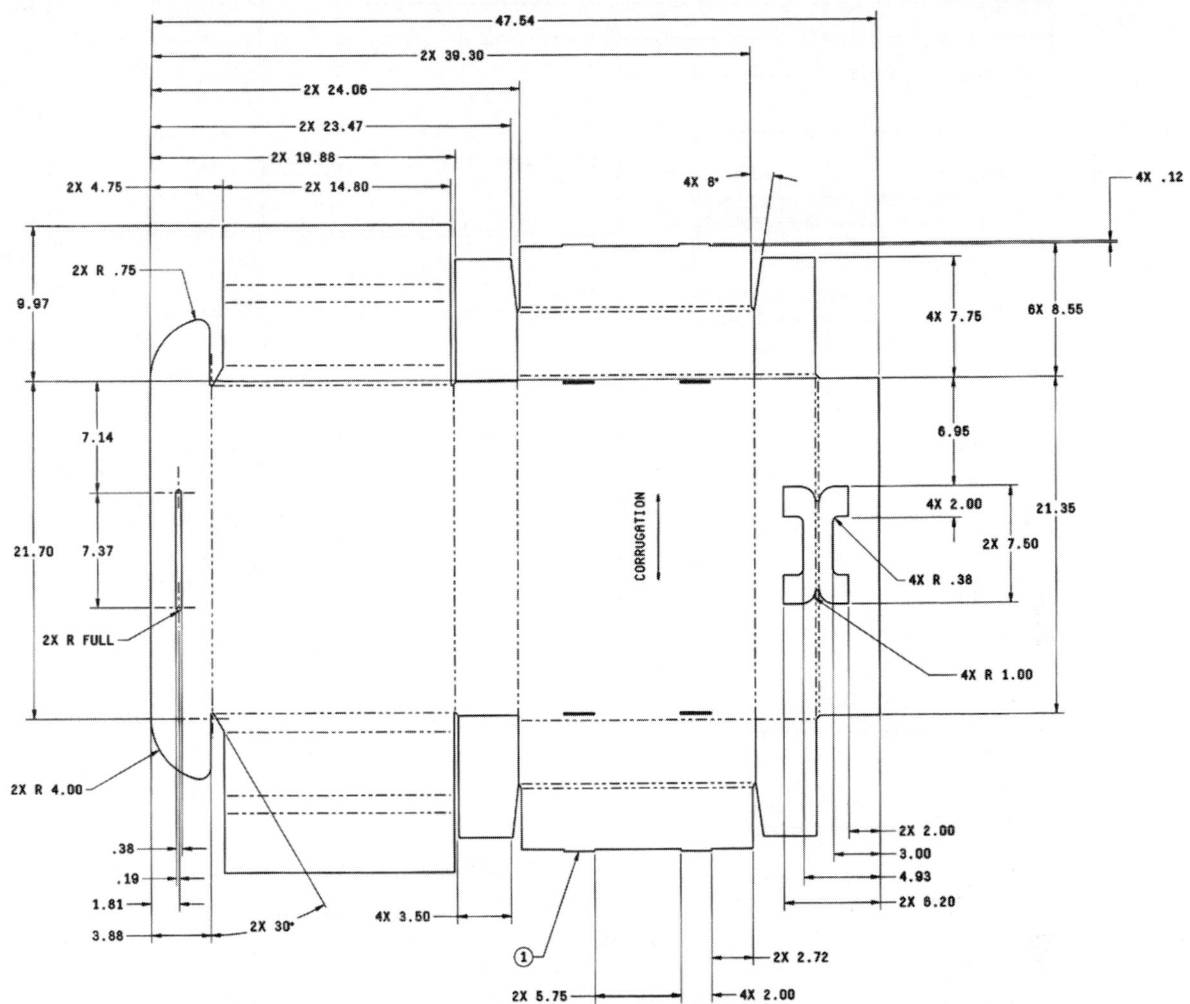

4 ASSEMBLY METHOD AT VENDOR OPTION, WITH MANUFACTURING ENGINEERING APPROVAL.

3 BOX MATERIAL: 200 B FLUTE NO. 3 WHITE

2. THIS DRAWING SHALL BE INTERPRETED PER ANSI Y14.5M, 1982.

1. PKG & IDENTIFY WITH P/N (000-000345-001) AND LATEST REVISION LETTER.

▲ CRITICAL FUNCTIONALITY PARAMETER.

NOTES: UNLESS OTHERWISE SPECIFIED.

BOX, CLEANING KIT

PROBLEM 23.18(A)

PROBLEM 23.18(B)

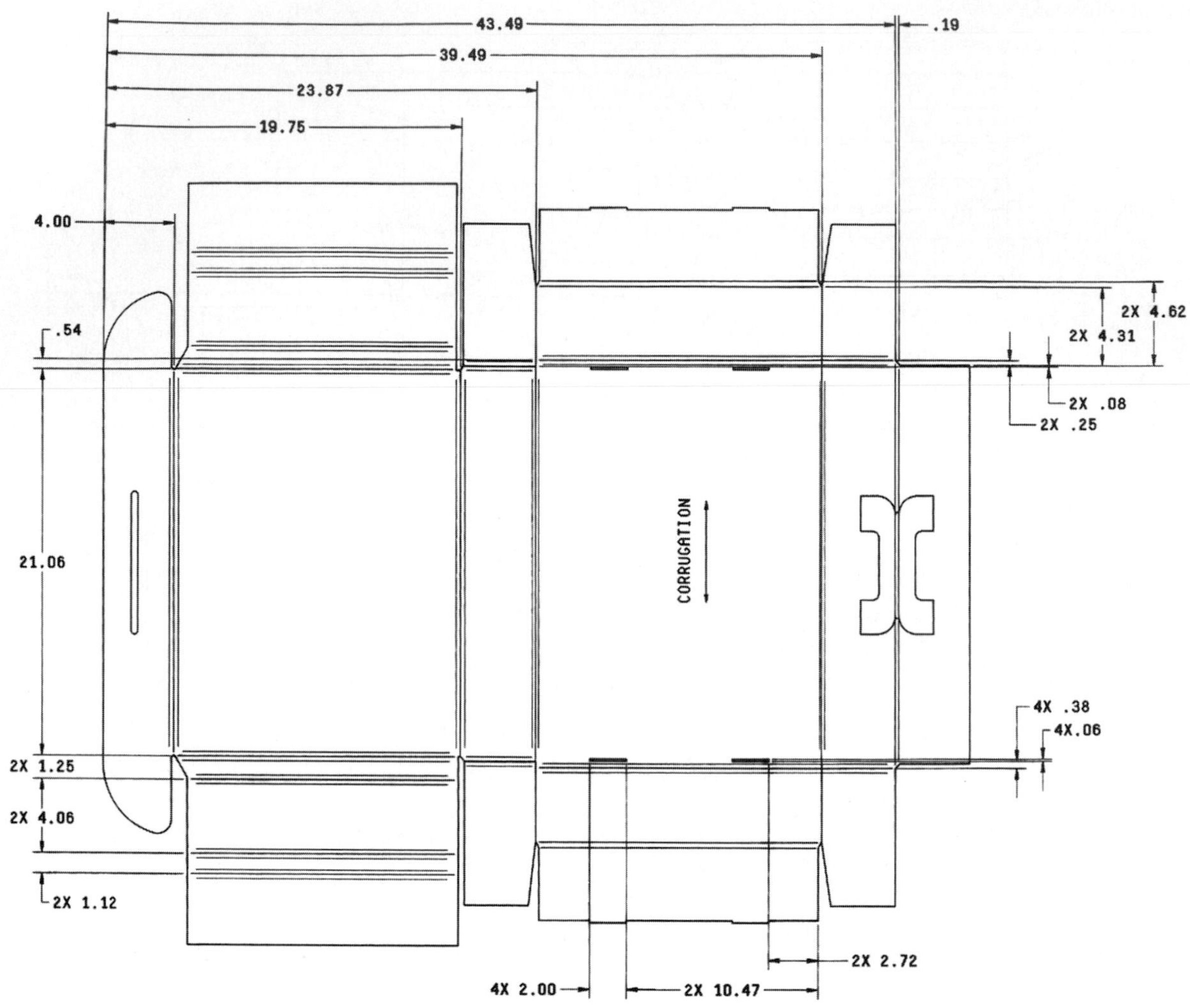

Assembly Drawing Projects

For assembly projects, prepare a layout assembly of the parts by blocking them in for each view required. Be sure to provide sufficient space on the sheet for the assembly and the parts list. The parts list can be generated on a word processor or a CAD system and printed on a separate sheet.

Problem 23.19(A) and (B) Do an assembly (A) and details (B) for the hydraulic valve assembly.

NO.	PART NAME	REQD	MATL
8	BALL BEARING Ø 3/16	I	STEEL
7	BALL CHECK VALVE SPRING	I	SPG STL
6	PLUNGER SPRING	I	SPG STL
5	RETAINER RING	I	SPG
4	BALL RETAINER	I	STL
3	PUSH ROD SEAT	I	STL
2	PLUNGER	I	STL
I	LIFTER BODY	I	STL

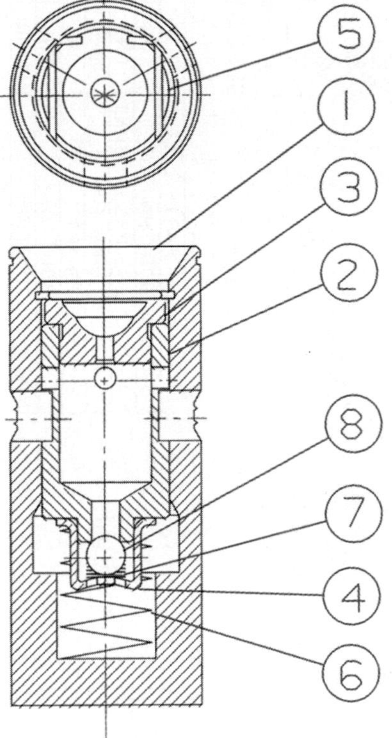

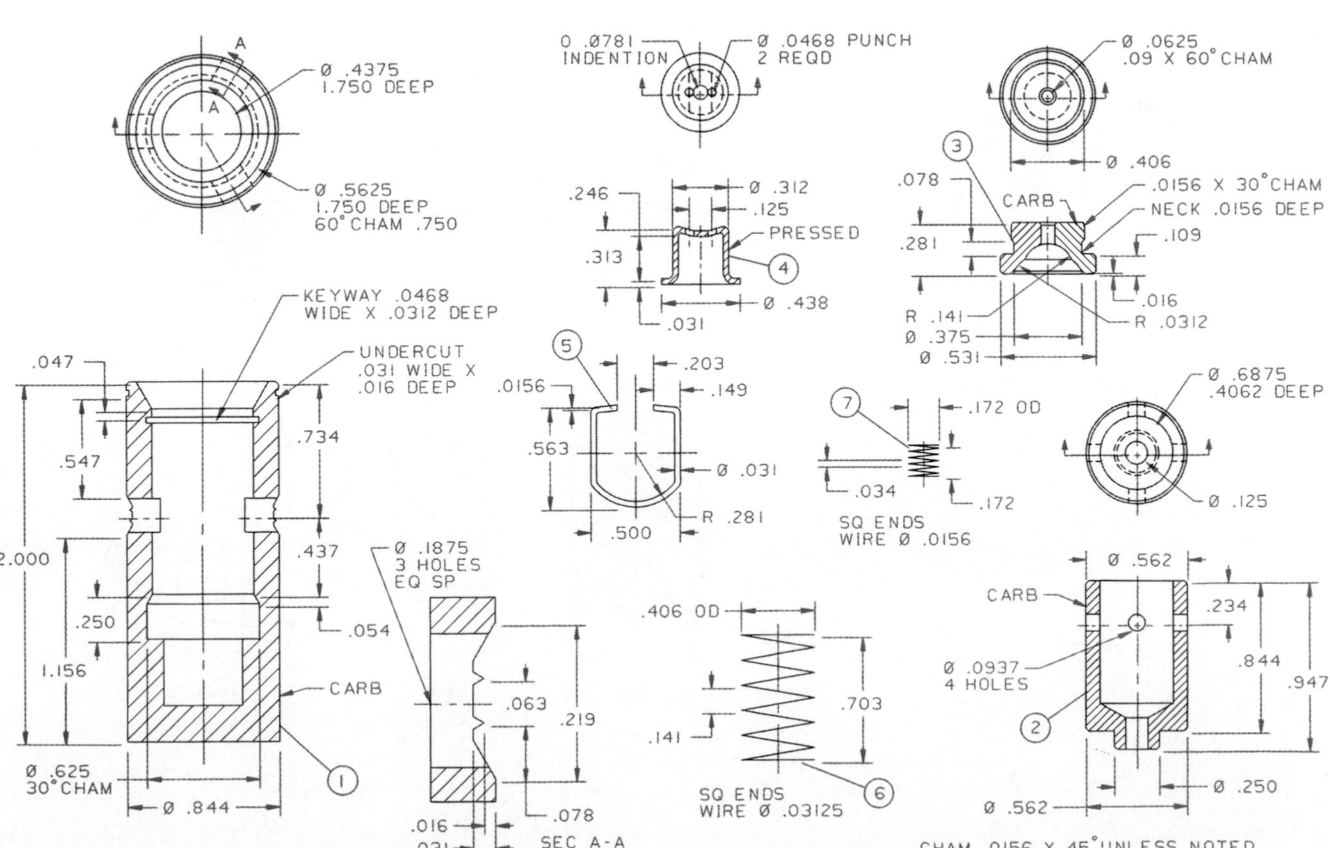

Problem 23.20 Do an assembly and details of the bike chain puller assembly.

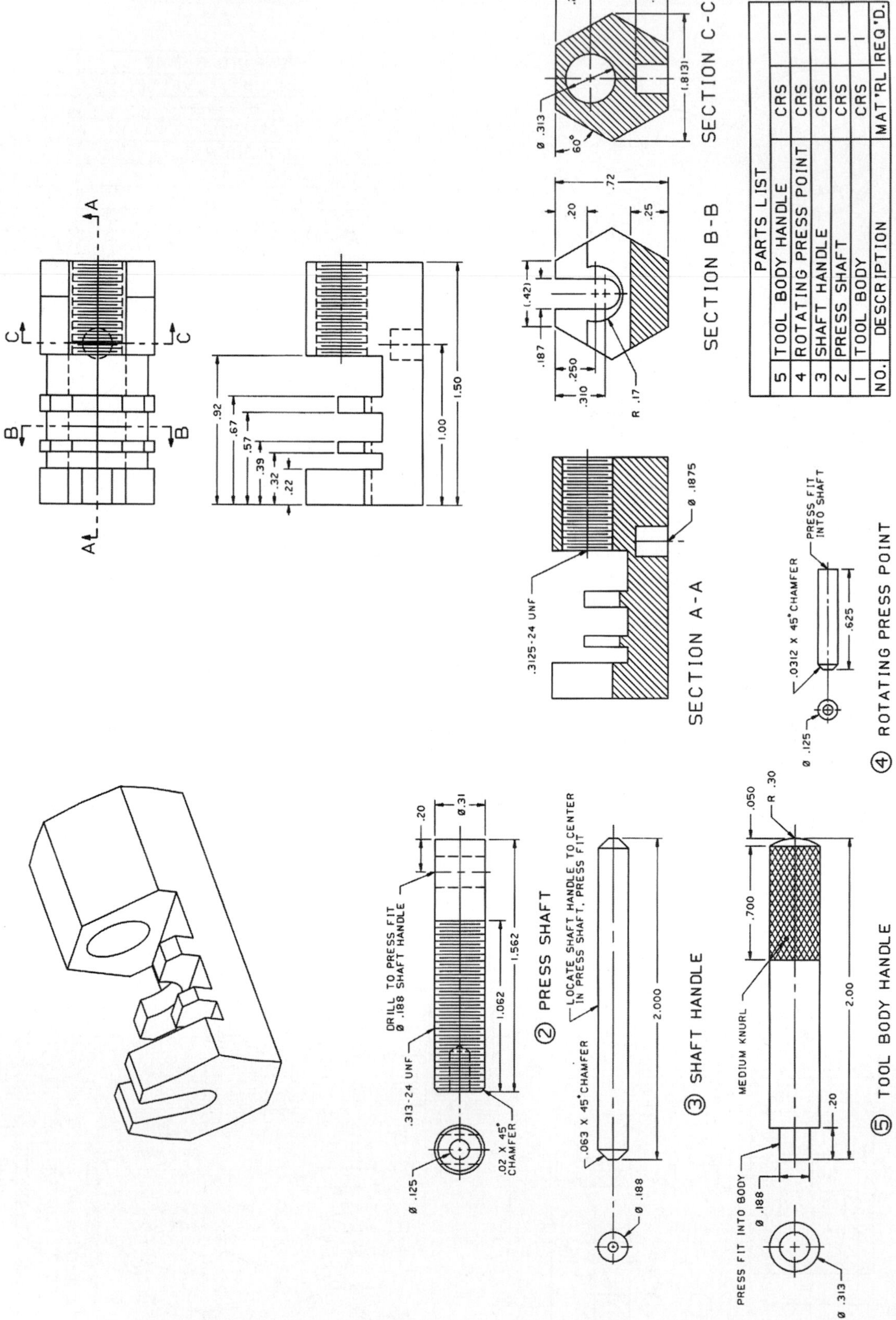

PARTS LIST			
5	TOOL BODY HANDLE	CRS	1
4	ROTATING PRESS POINT	CRS	1
3	SHAFT HANDLE	CRS	1
2	PRESS SHAFT	CRS	1
1	TOOL BODY	CRS	1
NO.	DESCRIPTION	MAT'RL	REQ'D.

Problem 23.21(A) and (B) Draw and detail the assembly and details for the coupling.

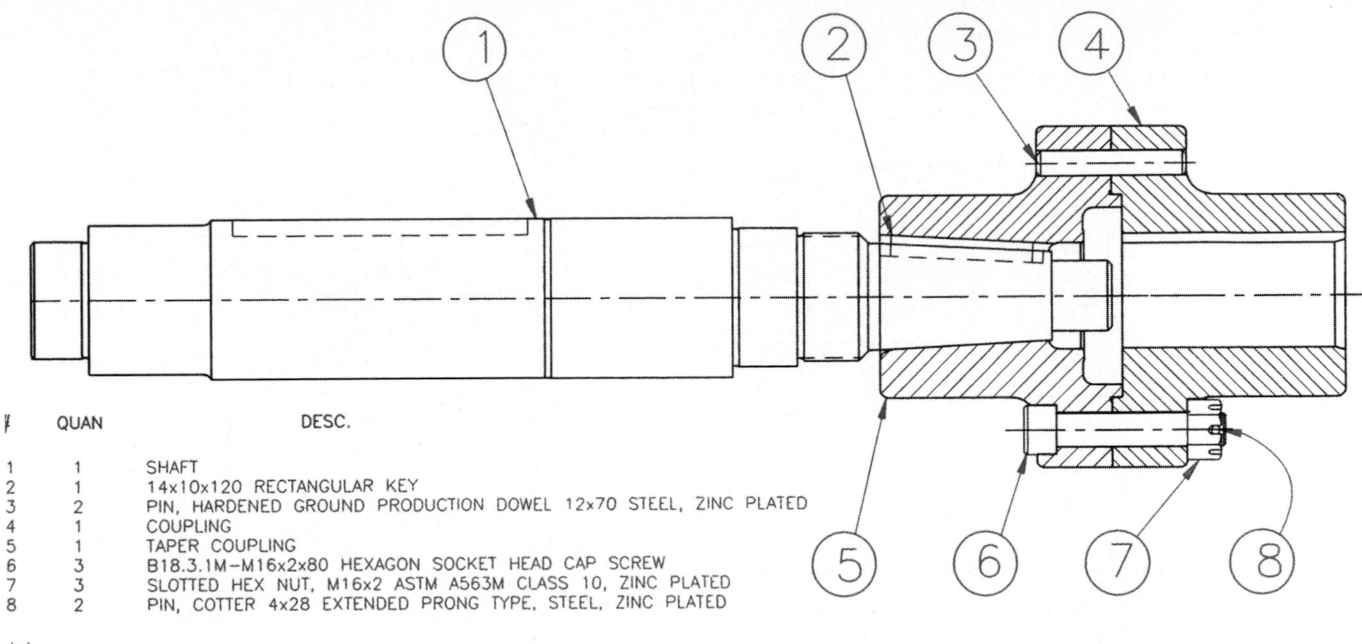

#	QUAN	DESC.
1	1	SHAFT
2	1	14x10x120 RECTANGULAR KEY
3	2	PIN, HARDENED GROUND PRODUCTION DOWEL 12x70 STEEL, ZINC PLATED
4	1	COUPLING
5	1	TAPER COUPLING
6	3	B18.3.1M–M16x2x80 HEXAGON SOCKET HEAD CAP SCREW
7	3	SLOTTED HEX NUT, M16x2 ASTM A563M CLASS 10, ZINC PLATED
8	2	PIN, COTTER 4x28 EXTENDED PRONG TYPE, STEEL, ZINC PLATED

(a)

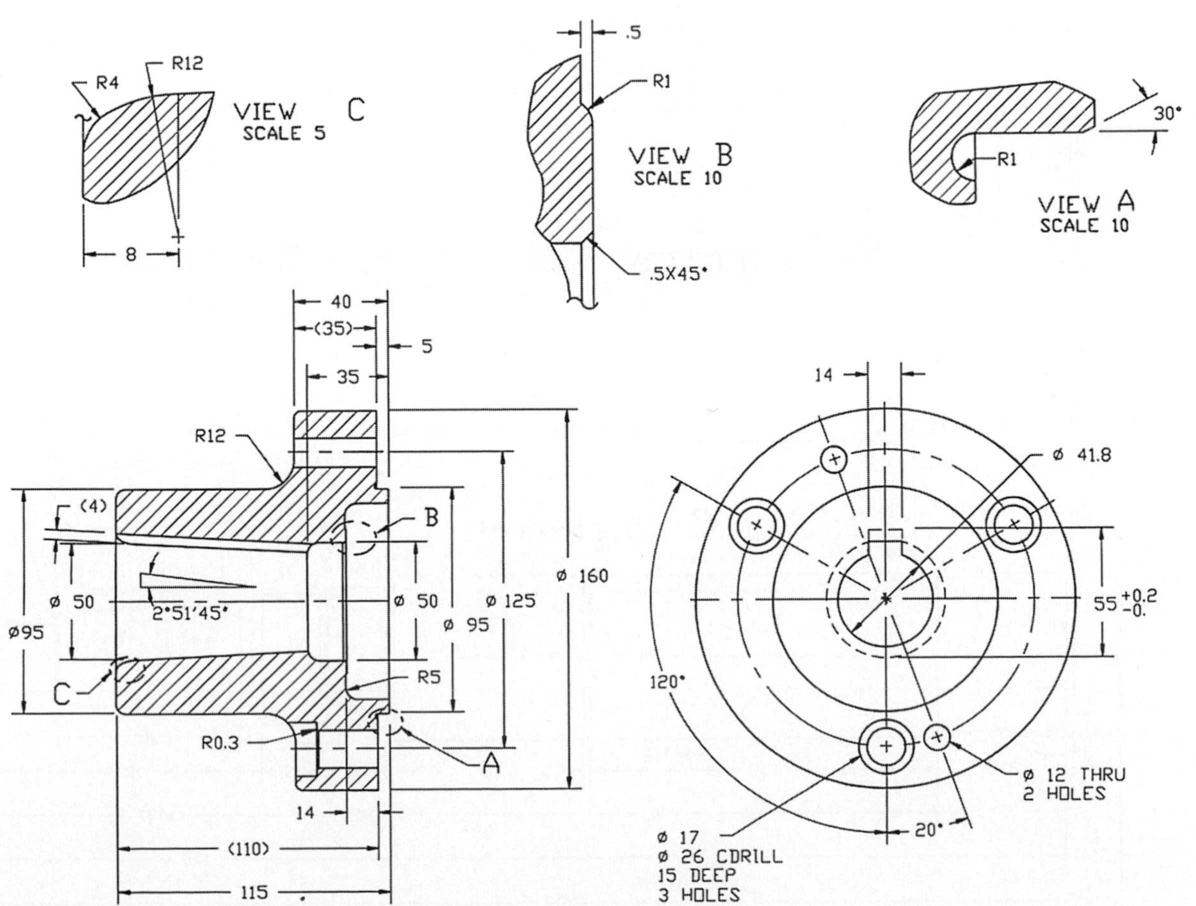

(b)

Problem 23.21(C) and (D) Draw and detail the assembly and details for the coupling.

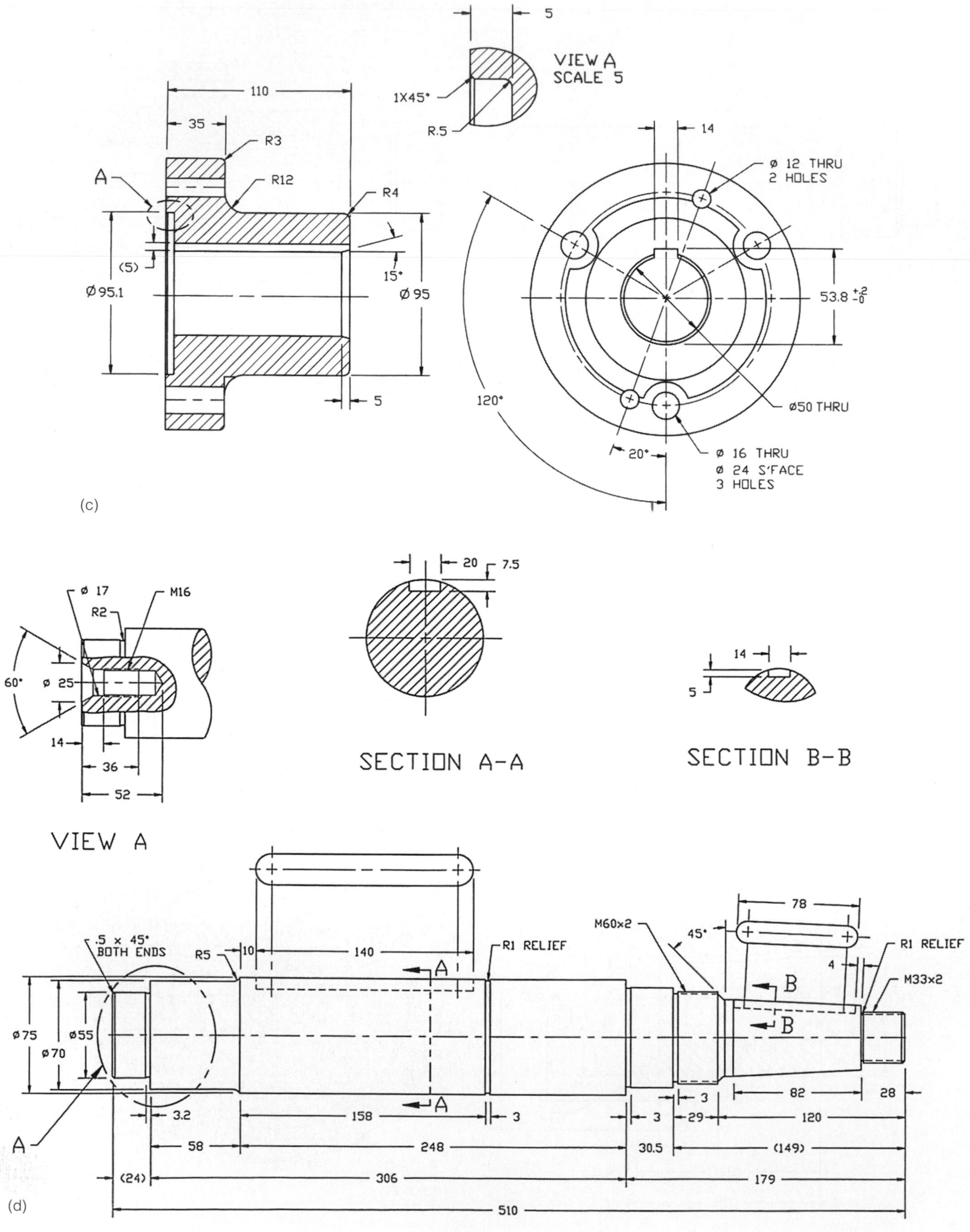

(c)

(d)

Problem 23.22(A) Through (I) Draw and detail the die set. Do a complete assembly and set of details.

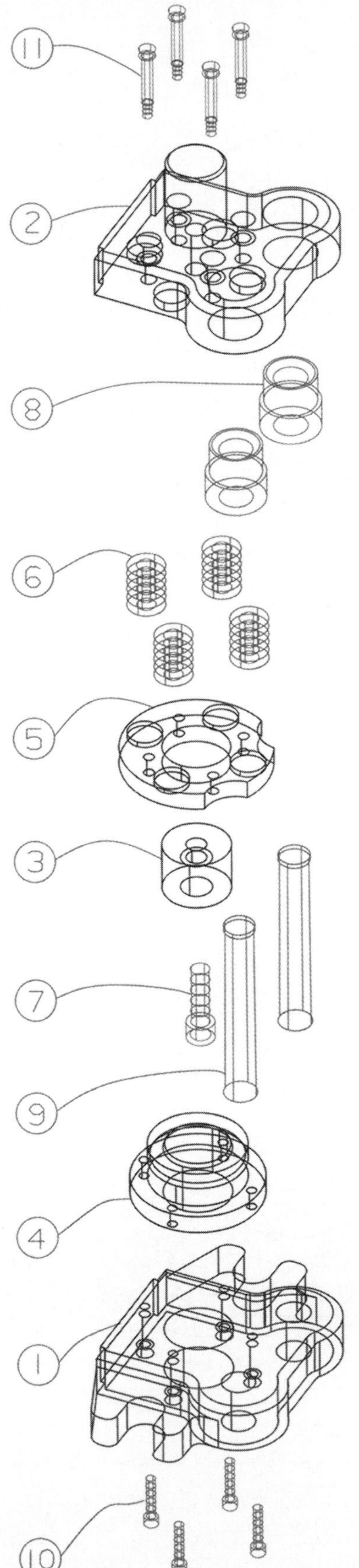

(a)

ITEM	QTY	PART NO.	DESCRIPTION
1	1		DIE BASE, CAST STEEL
2	1		UPPER DIESHOE, CAST STEEL
3	1		DIE PUNCH, STEEL
4	1		WASHER DIE, STEEL
5	1		DIE PLATE, STEEL
6	2	9-1606-21	SPRING, DANLY MEDIUM-HIGH PRESSURE, STEEL RETANGULAR WIRE, HOLE Ø 1.00, ROD Ø .500, 1.50 FREE LENGTH (REF .980 OD .150 ID)
7	1		SCREW, SOCKET HEAD CAP .500-20 X 2.00
8	2	6-07-61	BUSHING, DANLY PRECISION PRESS FIT SHORT SHOULDER, STEEL, .875 ID, 1.375 OD, 1 9/16 SHOULDER ID, LENGTH 1.75, 13/16 LONG SHOULDER
9	2	5-0720-1	GUIDE POST, DANLY MICROME PRECISION STEEL, Ø .875 X 5.00
10	4		SCREW, SOCKET HEAD CAP SHOULDER Ø .3125 X 1.50
11	1		SCREW, SOCKET HEAD CAP Ø .250-20 X 1.25

SH | REV. | DWG. NO.

DRAWN 8-2-91 | ISSUED 8-15-91 | SIZE A | FSCM NO. | SCALE 1:1 | DIE SET | REV. | JAIME GUERRERO

(b)

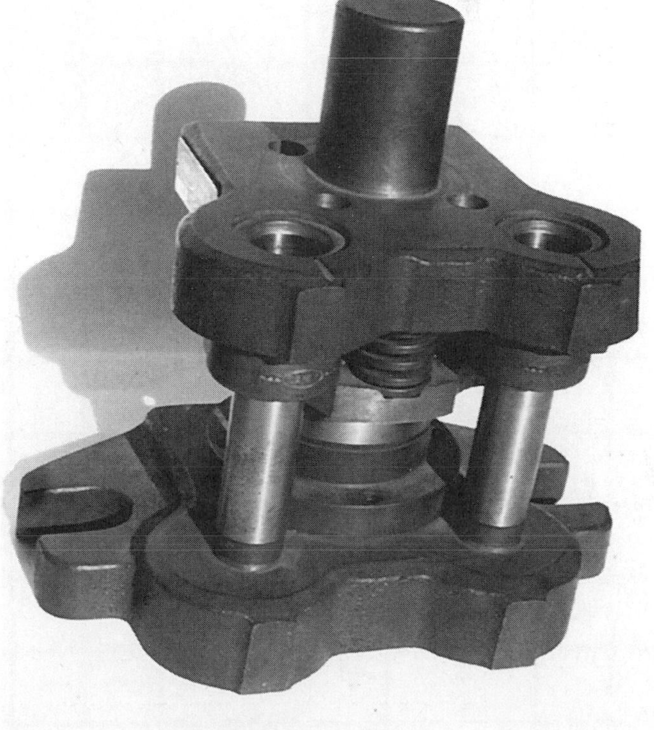

(c)

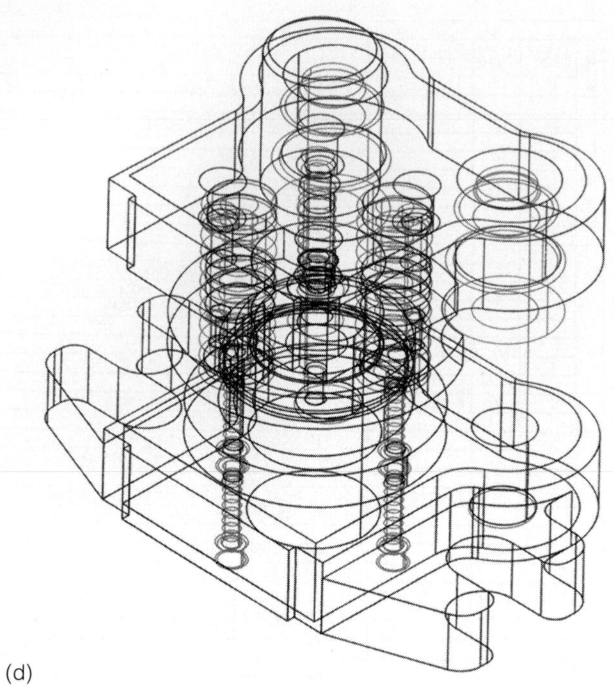

(d)

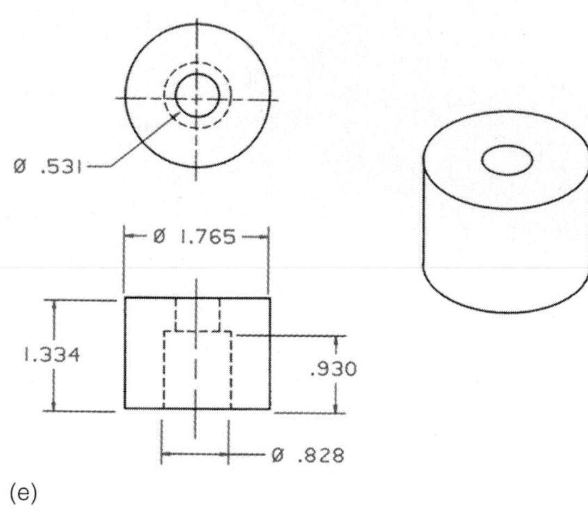
Ø .531
Ø 1.765
1.334
.930
Ø .828

(e)

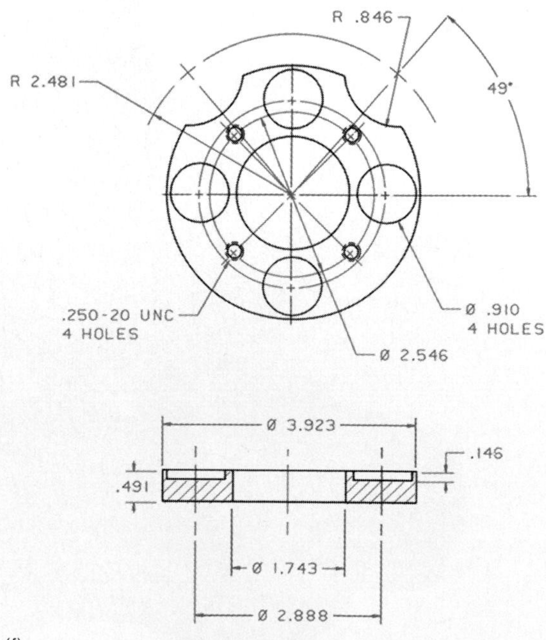
R .846
R 2.481
49°
.250-20 UNC
4 HOLES
Ø .910
4 HOLES
Ø 2.546
Ø 3.923
.146
.491
Ø 1.743
Ø 2.888

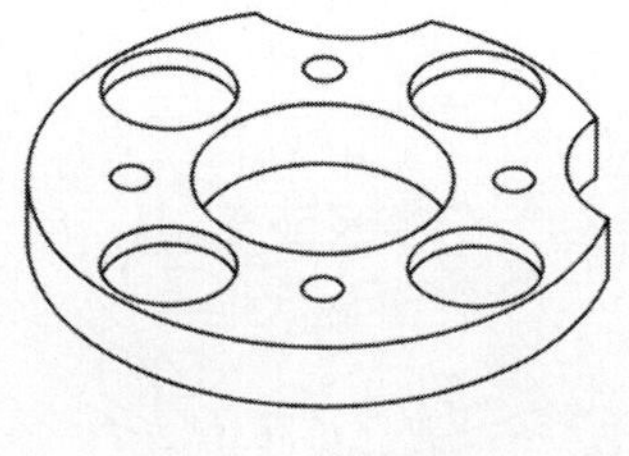

(f)

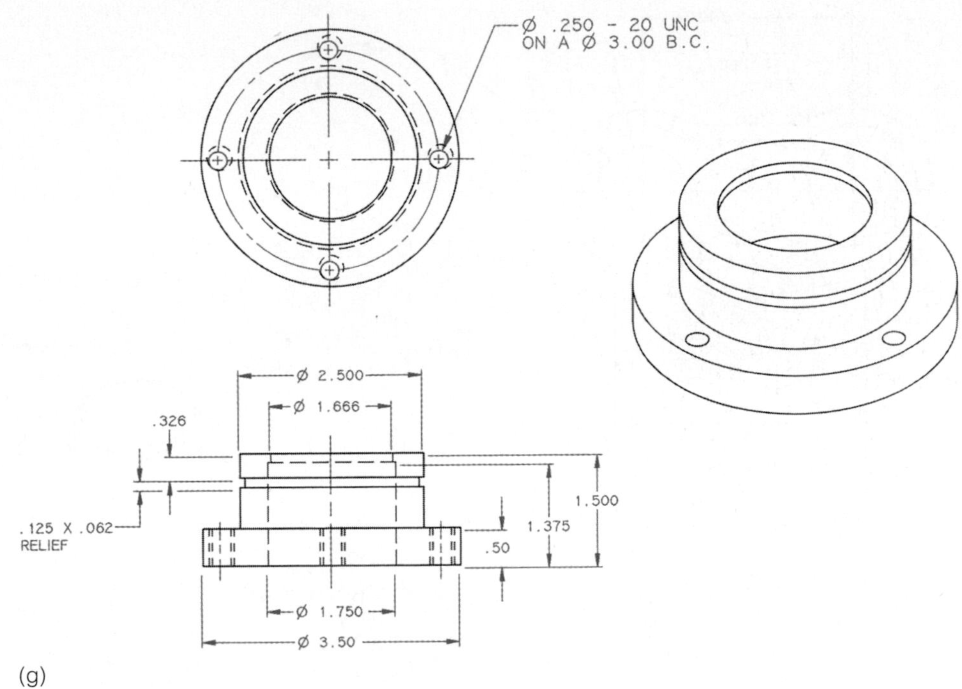

Ø .250 - 20 UNC
ON A Ø 3.00 B.C.
Ø 2.500
Ø 1.666
.326
.125 X .062
RELIEF
1.500
1.375
.50
Ø 1.750
Ø 3.50

(g)

Ø .3106 +.001 -.000
Ø .453 CBORE
.328 DEEP
4 HOLES
FROM FAR SIDE
Ø .875 +.000 -.001
3.250
R .250
R 1.000
R 1.250
.250
1.000
R .250
R .375
.750
1.875
3.875
R .250
1.000
21°
.125
.250
R .375
Ø 3.000
3.125
Ø 1.750
R .125
3.625
4.125
6.375
8.00
.125
1.250
.875

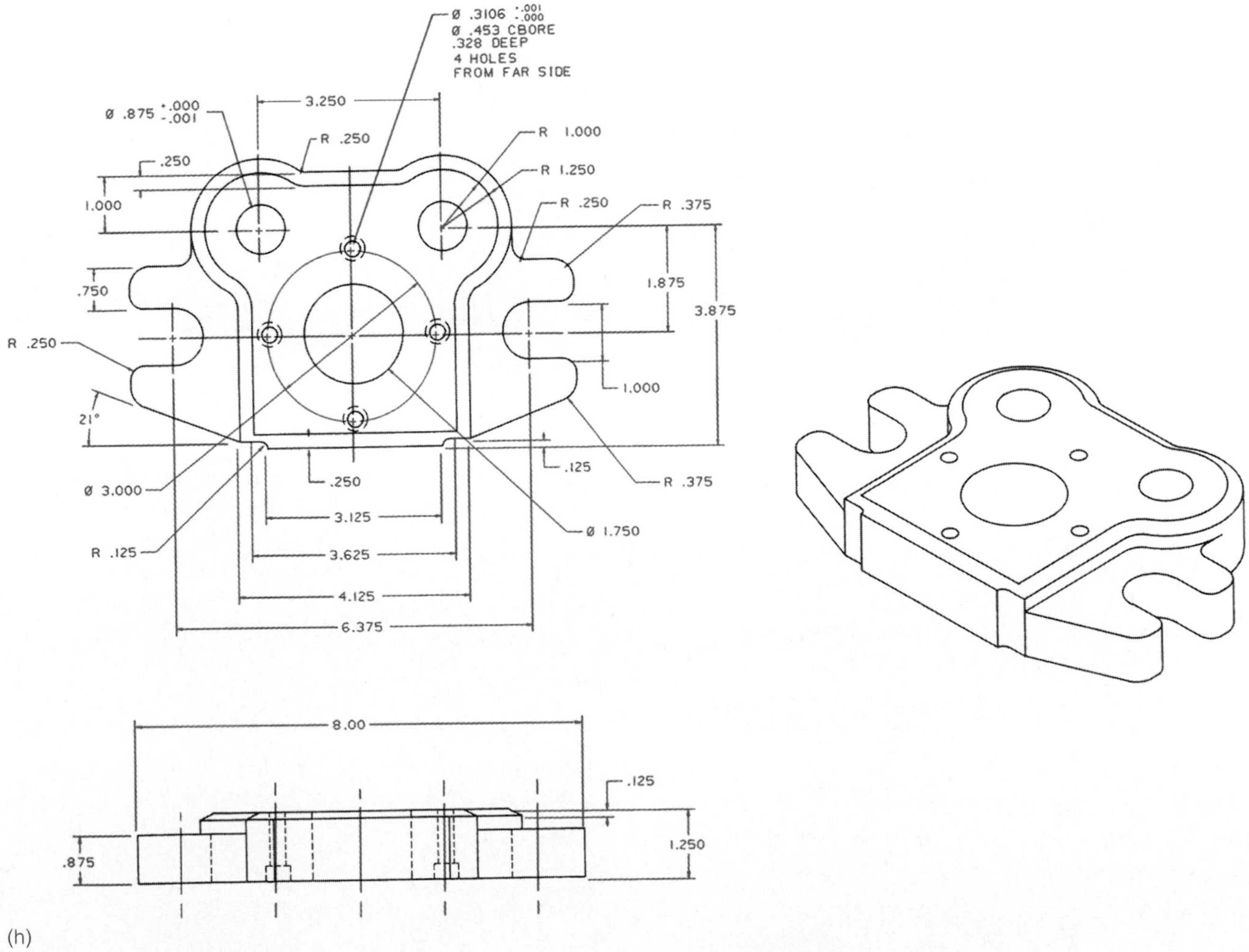

(h)

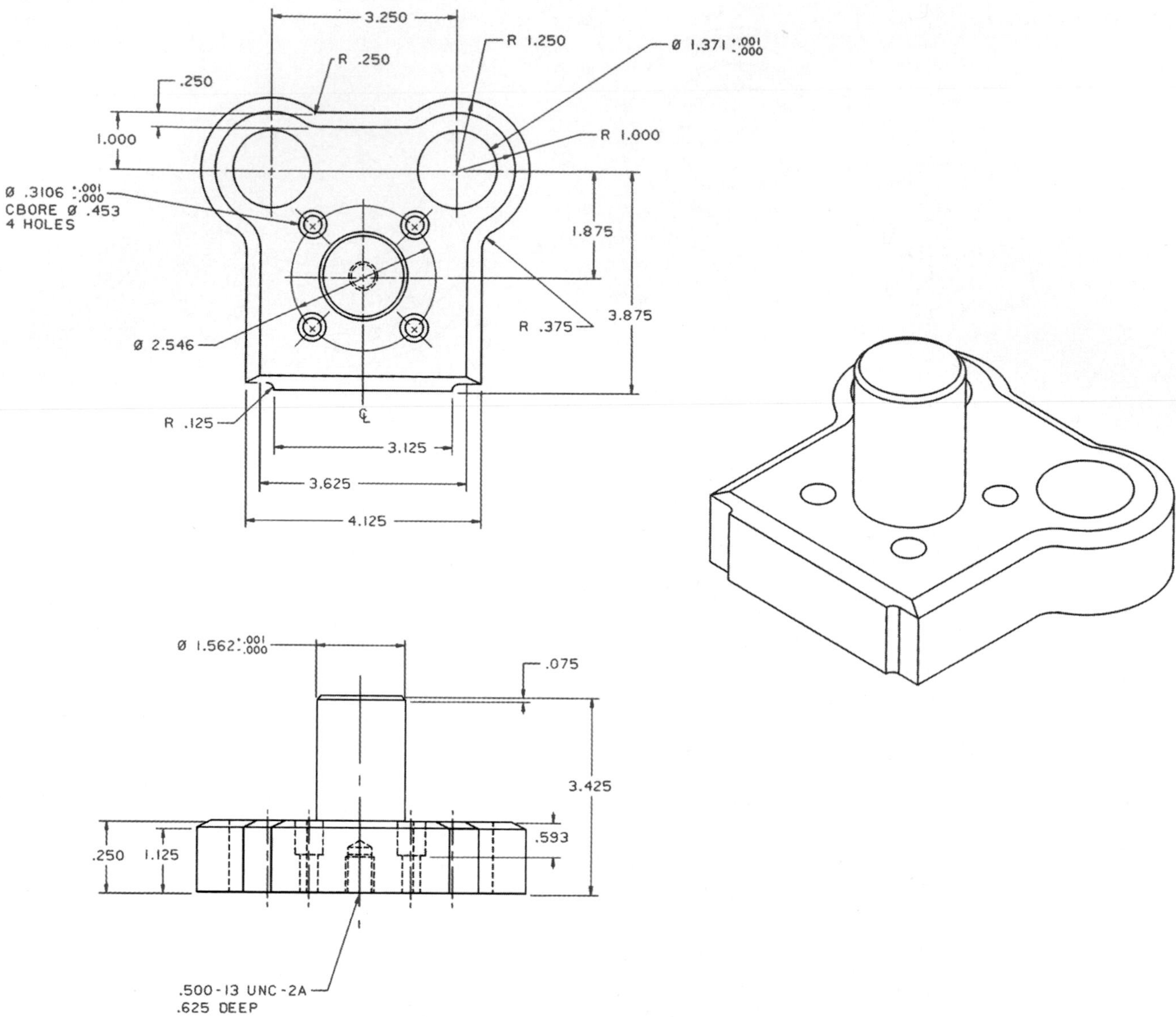

3.250
R 1.250
Ø 1.371 +.001 -.000
R .250
.250
1.000
R 1.000
Ø .3106 +.001 -.000
CBORE Ø .453
4 HOLES
1.875
3.875
R .375
Ø 2.546
R .125
3.125
3.625
4.125
Ø 1.562 +.001 -.000
.075
3.425
.593
.250
1.125
.500-13 UNC-2A
.625 DEEP

(i)

Problem 23.23(A) Through (H) Draw and detail the jig and fixture assembly.

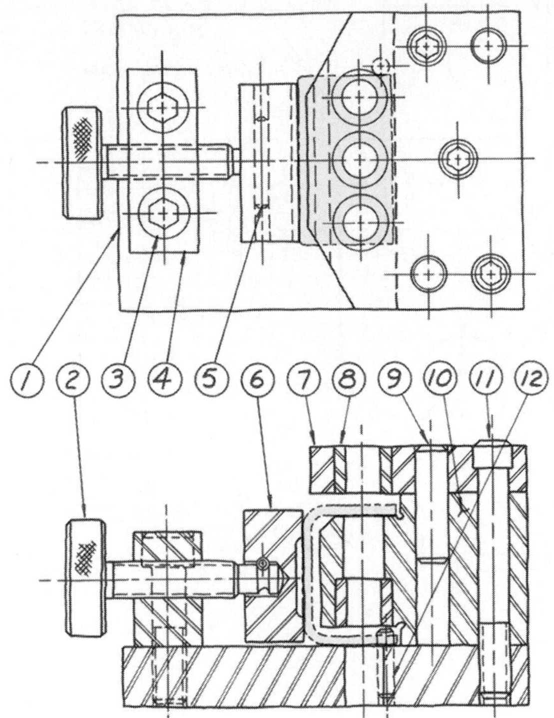

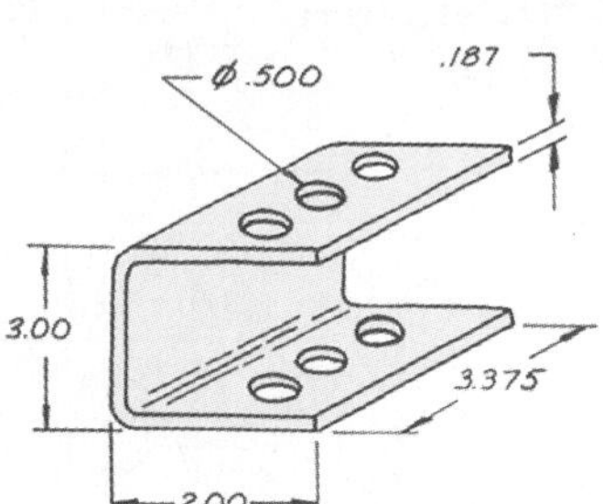

(a)

ITEM	QTY	PART NO.	DESCRIPTION
1	1		BASE PLATE, 1.375 X 6.50 X 9.00, STEEL
2	1		SCREW, KNURLED HEAD, STEEL
3	2		SCREW, HEX SOC HD CAP, .750-10 X 3.00
4	1		CLAMP BLOCK, 1.50 X 2.50 X 4.00, STEEL
5	1		PIN, MACHINE DOWEL, Ø .250 X 2.00
6	1		CLAMP, 1.375 X 3.00 X 3.50, STEEL
7	1		BUSHING PLATE, 1.00 X 4.75 X 6.50, STEEL
8	6		BUSHING, TYPE P HEADLESS PRESS FIT MODIFIED ID = .500, 1.25 OD X 1.00 LG
9	2		PIN, MACHINE DOWEL, Ø .750 X 2.50
10	1		LOCATOR BLOCK, 3.25 X 4.50 X 6.50
11	3		SCREW, HEX SOC HD CAP, .625-11 X 5.00
12	1		PIN, MACHINE DOWEL, Ø .375 X 1.50

DRAWN 3-4-91	SIZE A	FSCM NO.	PLATE JIG, DRILL	REV.
ISSUED 7-30-91	SCALE 1:1			

(b)

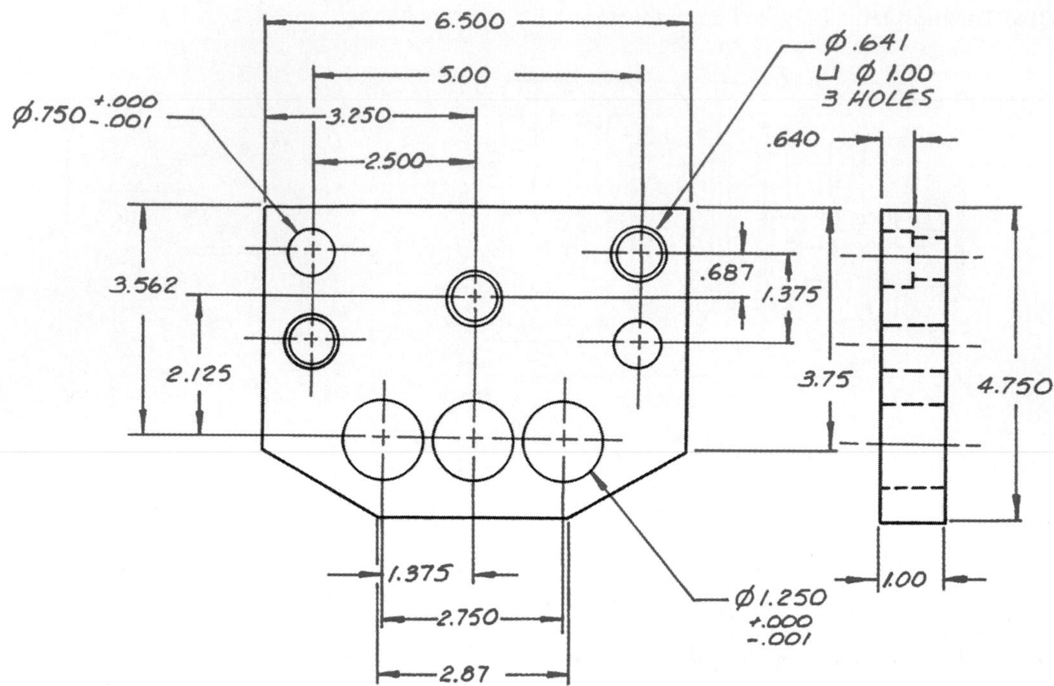
6.500
5.00
3.250
2.500
Ø.750 +.000 -.001
Ø.641
⊔ Ø 1.00
3 HOLES
.640
3.562
2.125
.687
1.375
3.75
4.750
1.375
2.750
2.87
Ø 1.250 +.000 -.001
1.00

(c)

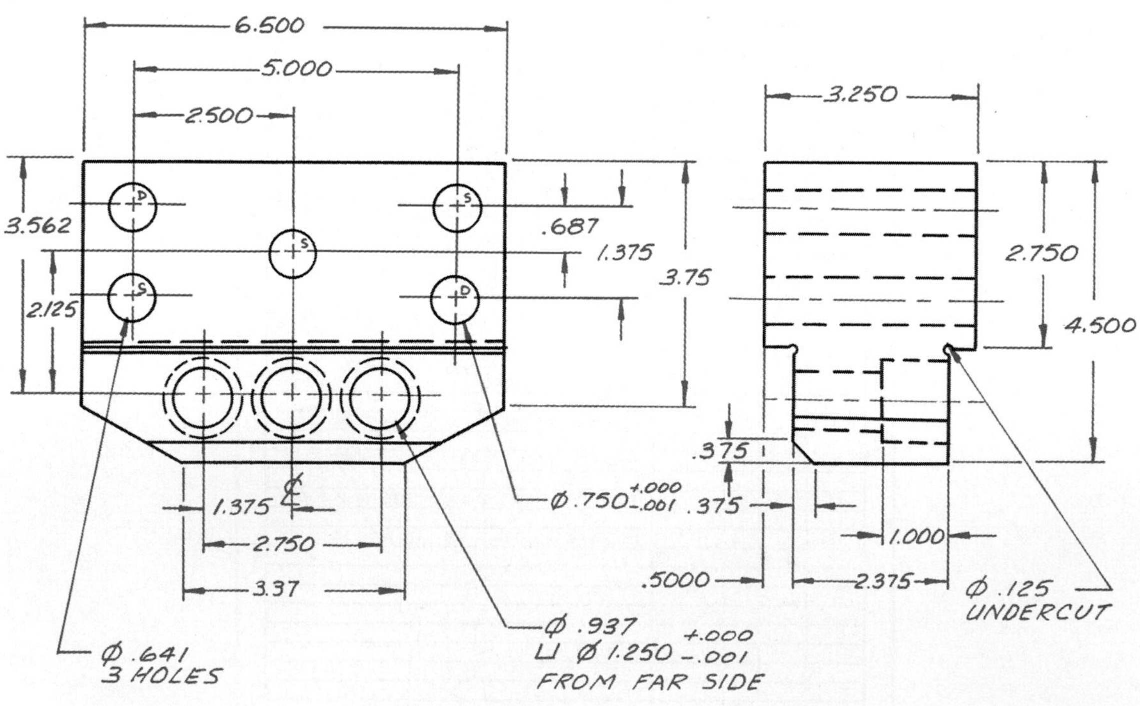
6.500
5.000
2.500
3.562
2.125
.687
1.375
3.75
3.250
2.750
4.500
.375
1.375
2.750
3.37
Ø.750 +.000 -.001
.375
1.000
.5000
2.375
Ø .125
UNDERCUT
Ø .641
3 HOLES
Ø .937
⊔ Ø 1.250 +.000 -.001
FROM FAR SIDE

(d)

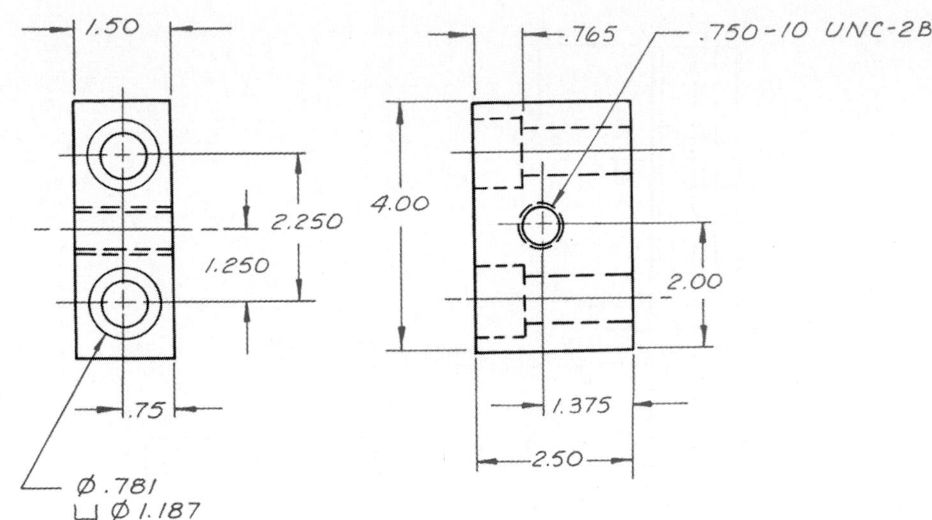
1.50
.765
.750-10 UNC-2B
2.250
4.00
1.250
2.00
.75
1.375
2.50
Ø.781
⌴ Ø1.187

(e)

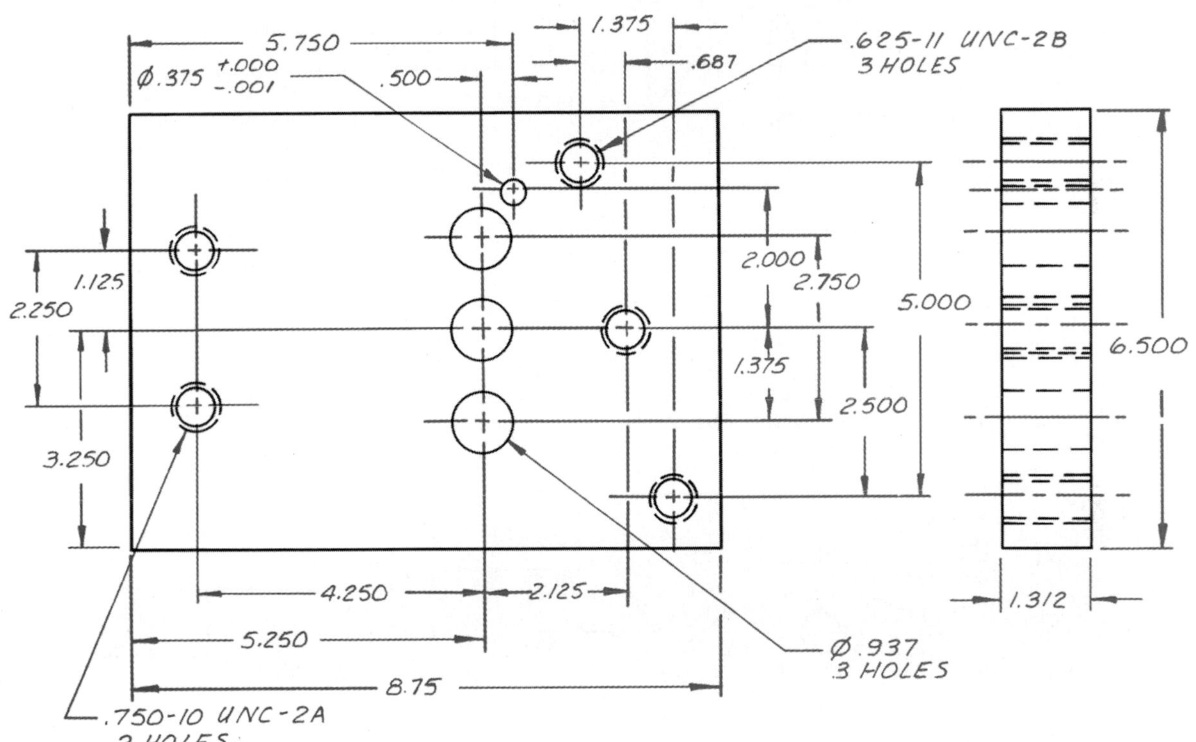
5.750
1.375
.625-11 UNC-2B
3 HOLES
Ø.375 +.000 -.001
.500
.687
2.000
2.750
1.125
2.250
5.000
6.500
1.375
2.500
3.250
4.250
2.125
1.312
5.250
Ø.937
3 HOLES
8.75
.750-10 UNC-2A
2 HOLES

(f)

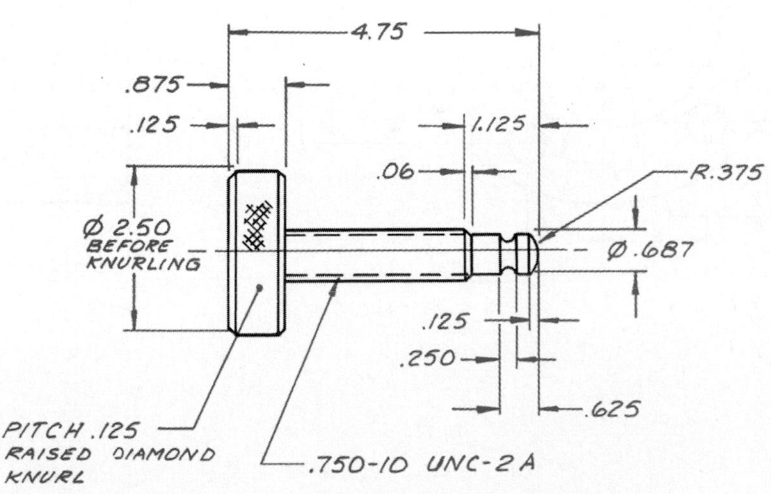
4.75
.875
.125
1.125
.06
R.375
Ø2.50
BEFORE
KNURLING
Ø.687
.125
.250
.625
PITCH .125
RAISED DIAMOND
KNURL
.750-10 UNC-2A

(g)

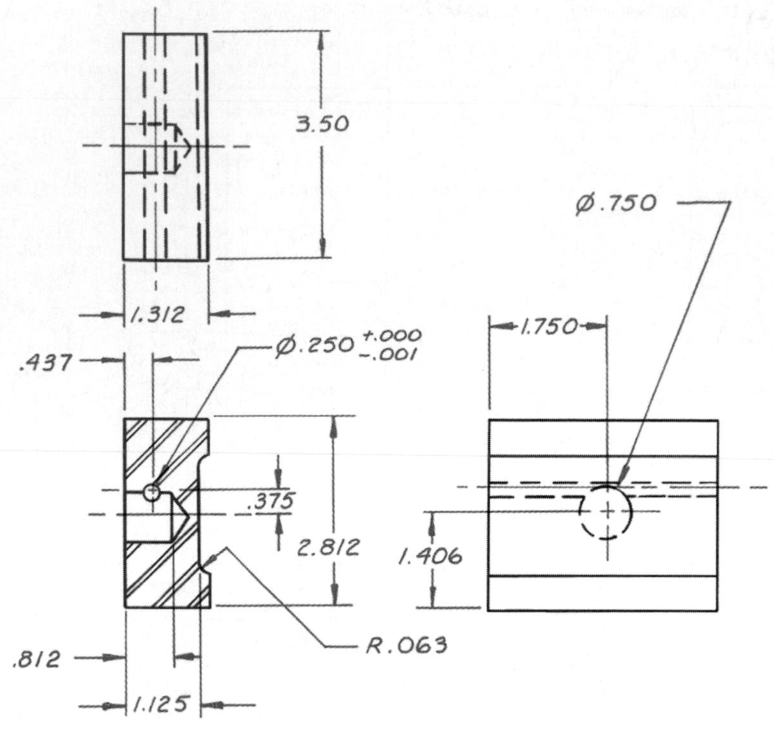

(h)

Problem 23.24 Design a fixture to hold the ring while machining the center hole and the six small holes.

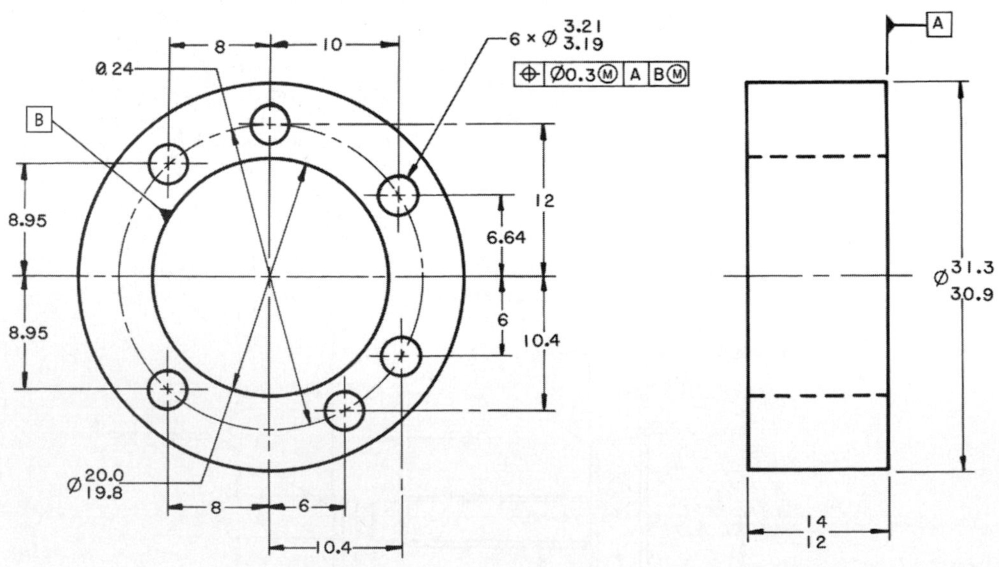

Jig and Fixture Assembly Design Projects

Problem 23.25 Design a fixture to hold the plate while machining the 6 mm and 20 mm holes.

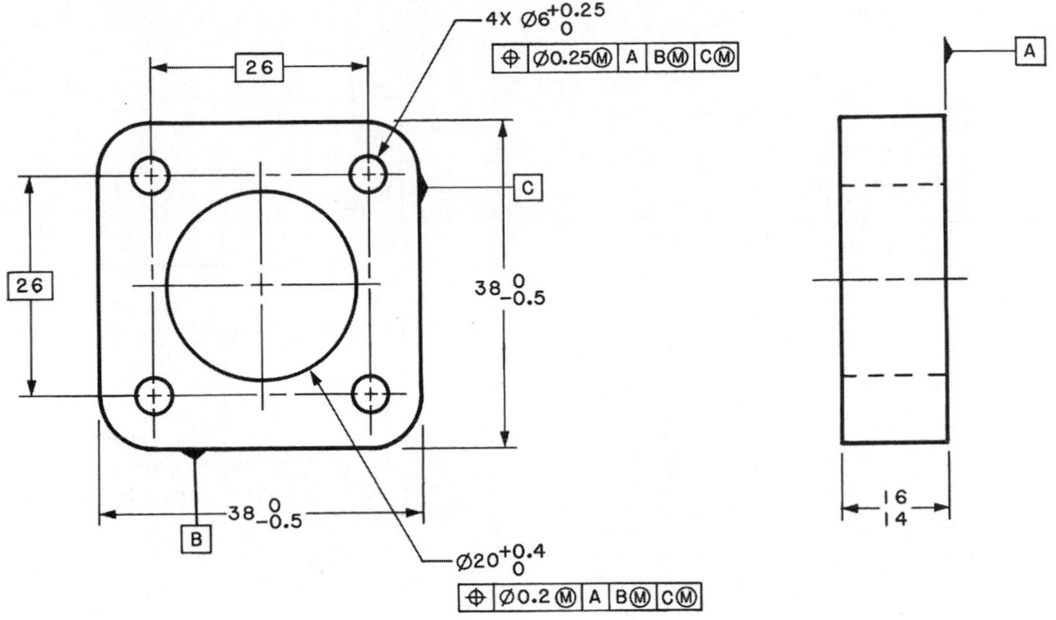

Problem 23.26 Design a jig and fixture to hold the adjustable guide shown in Problem 23.1 while machining the slot.

Problem 23.27 Design and detail a jig and fixture to hold the crank arm shown in Problem 23.2. The three holes are to be created during this machining operation.

Problem 23.28 Design a fixture to hold the shifter fork shown shown in Problem 23.3 while machining the bottom of the part.

Problem 23.29 Design a fixture to hold the flywheel while machining the clevis ends, not the holes, using the part in Problem 23.4.

Problems from Figures in the Chapter

Problem 23.30 Redraw the welded assembly shown in Figure 23.7.

Problem 23.31 Draw and dimension the weldment in Figure 23.8.

Problem 23.32 Redraw the acoustic cup in Figure 23.10.

Problem 23.33 Model the SmartLevel rail [Fig. 23.39(a)], the wood insert [Fig. 23.39(c)], and the end cap [Fig. 23.39(d)]. Put all parts into an assembly, balloon, and complete a parts list.

Problem 23.34 Draw and detail the housing module shown in Figure 23.39(i) and (j).

Problem 23.35 Draw and detail the front panel shown in Figure 23.39(k).

Problem 23.36 Model and detail the keytop in Figure 23.39(l).

Additional Problems

Problem 23.37 Draw and detail the assembly.

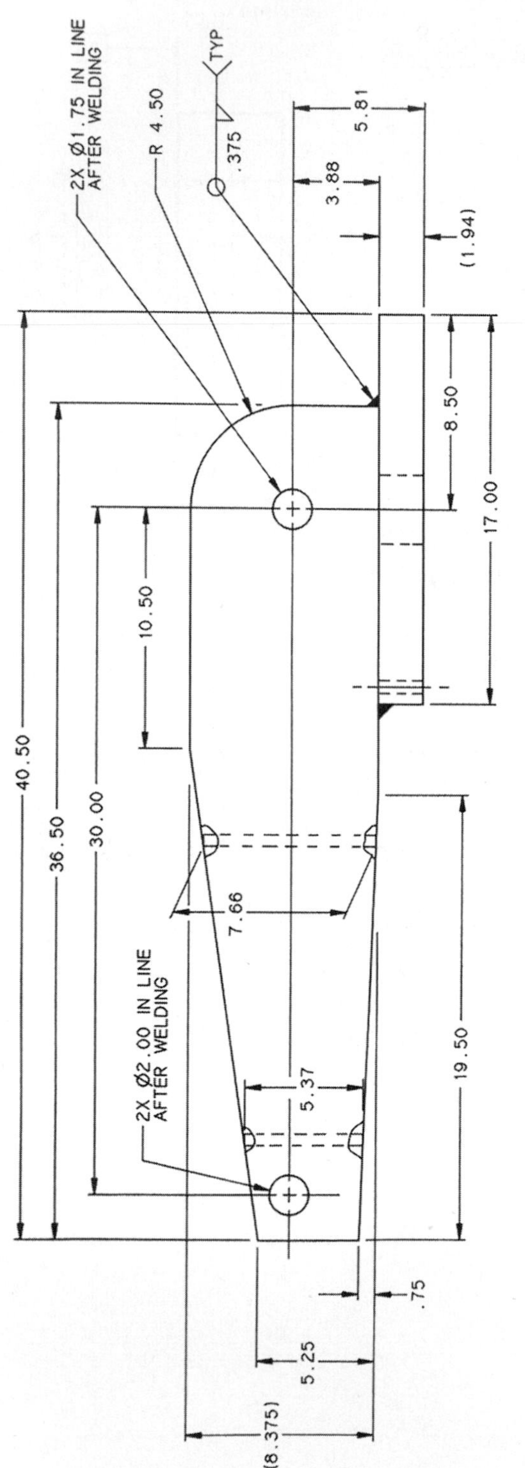

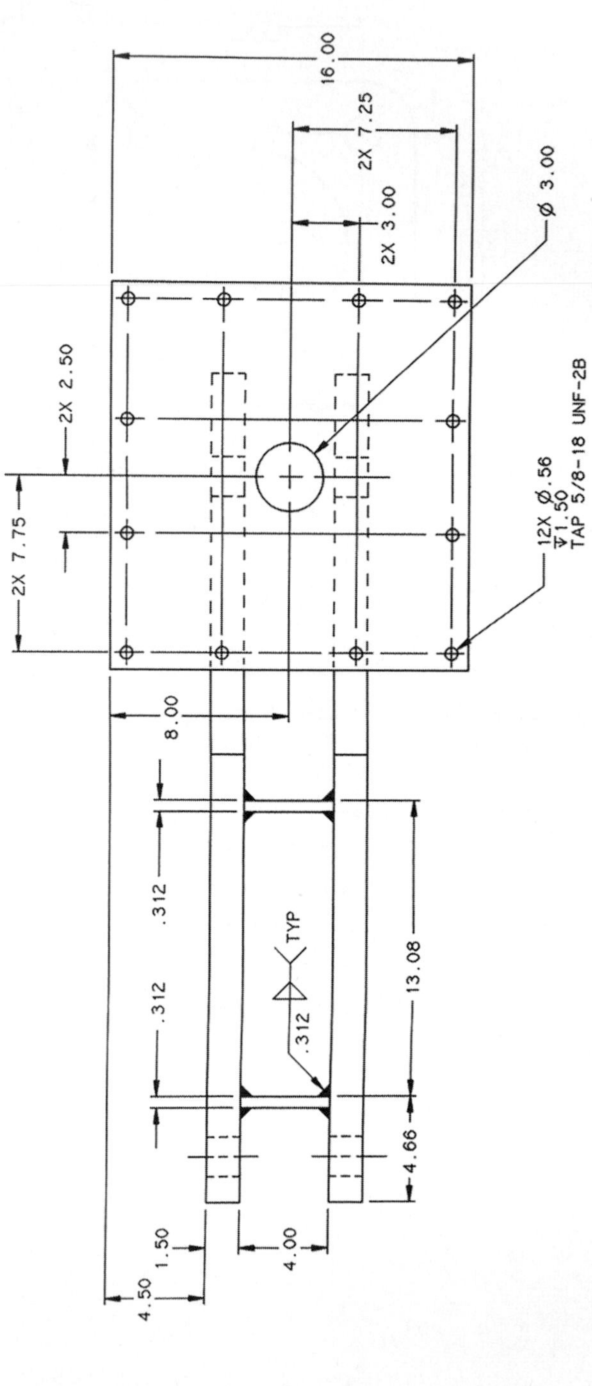

Problem 23.38 Draw and detail the assembly.

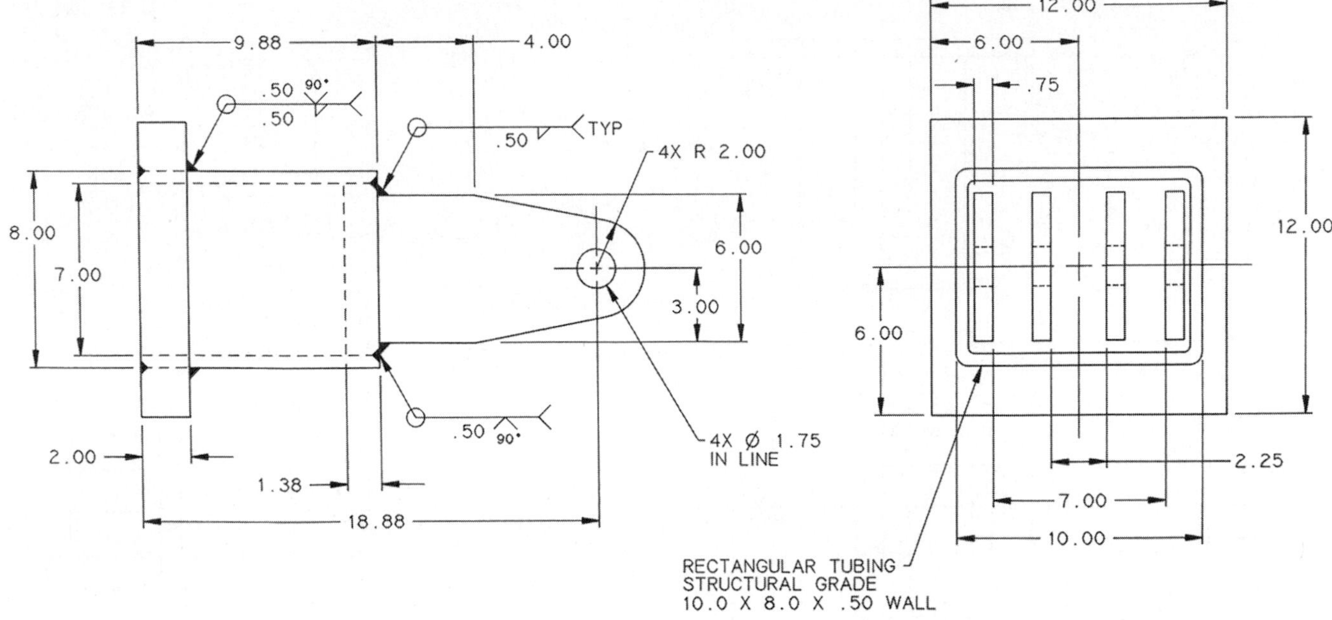

Problem 23.39 Draw and detail the assembly.

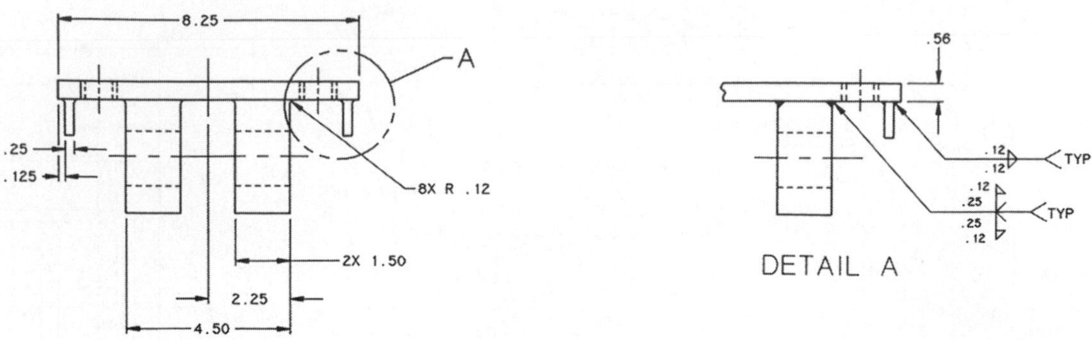

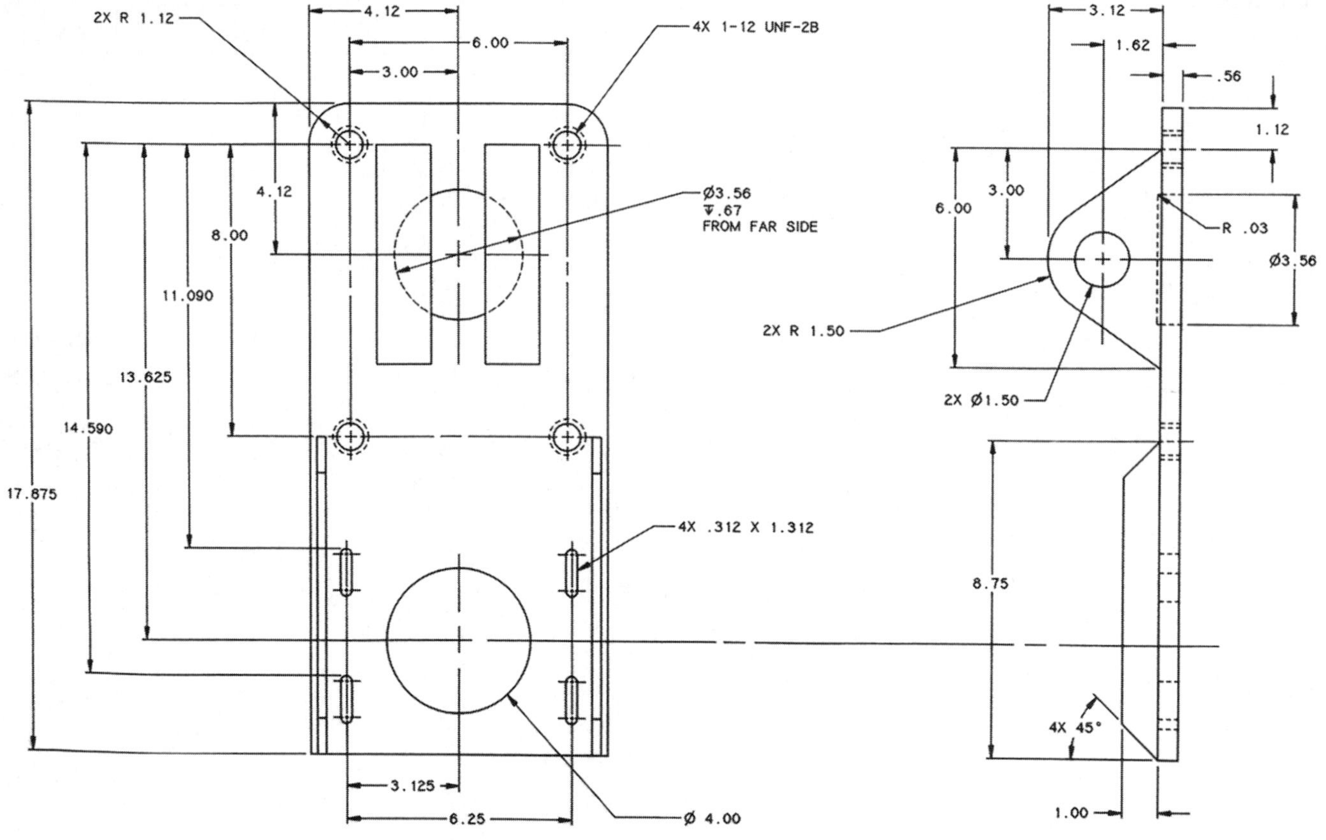

ENGINEERING GRAPHICAL ANALYSIS

Part Six

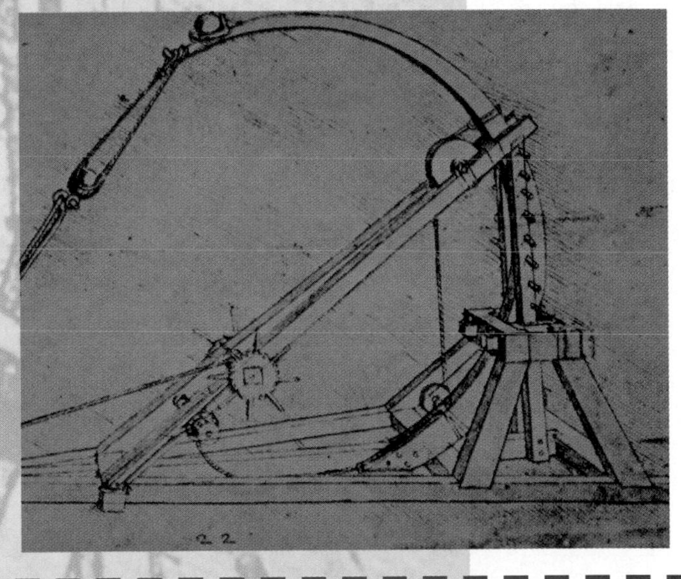

POINTS AND LINES

Chapter 24

LEARNING OBJECTIVES

Upon completion of this chapter you will be able to:

1. Apply descriptive geometry solutions to three-dimensional problems involving points and lines.
2. Recognize the importance of notational elements in descriptive geometry.
3. Define and differentiate between principal lines and line types.
4. Understand spatial description and coordinate dimensions.
5. Apply the concepts of parallelism and perpendicularity.
6. Recognize the significance of 2D and 3D CAD integration into geometric problem-solving.

24.1 INTRODUCTION

Descriptive geometry (Fig. 24.1) is the use of orthographic projection to solve three-dimensional problems on a two-dimensional surface. This chapter is the first chapter in the descriptive geometry sequence presented in this text. The core of most courses in descriptive geometry is formed from the topics covered in Chapter 25, Planes, Chapter 26, Revolutions, Chapter 27, Intersections, Chapter 28, Developments, and Chapter 29, Vector Analysis.

Practical industrial applications for descriptive geometry techniques include sheet metal layout, piping clearances, intersections of heating and air conditioning ducting, transition pieces for farm product systems, range-of-movement studies in mechanical design, structural steel design and analysis, topographical and civil engineering projects, and a variety of mechanical engineering problems. Descriptive geometry is not only a means to communicate a particular aspect of a technical problem, it is the actual solution in graphical form. The descriptive geometry worksheet or drawing is the equivalent of the final numerical answer derived via a mathematical method.

Linework, lettering, and drawing standards are no less important here than in other forms of drafting. Lettering and notation are the primary means of communication on drawings. No matter how accurate and precise the drawing, if it is poorly lettered and inadequately labeled, it cannot communicate a solution or present ideas properly. Therefore, concise, well-formed lettering, properly positioned notes, and sufficient labeling are essential to the solution of a descriptive geometry worksheet or drawing.

Figure 24.2 is a typical descriptive geometry drawing using the special language and notation that has been developed for this subject. It is essential that the format, symbols, and notation become part of your technical vocabulary. As you progress through the chapter, frequent referrals to this figure will reinforce this new language.

Figure 24.3 presents a line and symbol key that defines the type and thickness of the lines and symbols appropriate

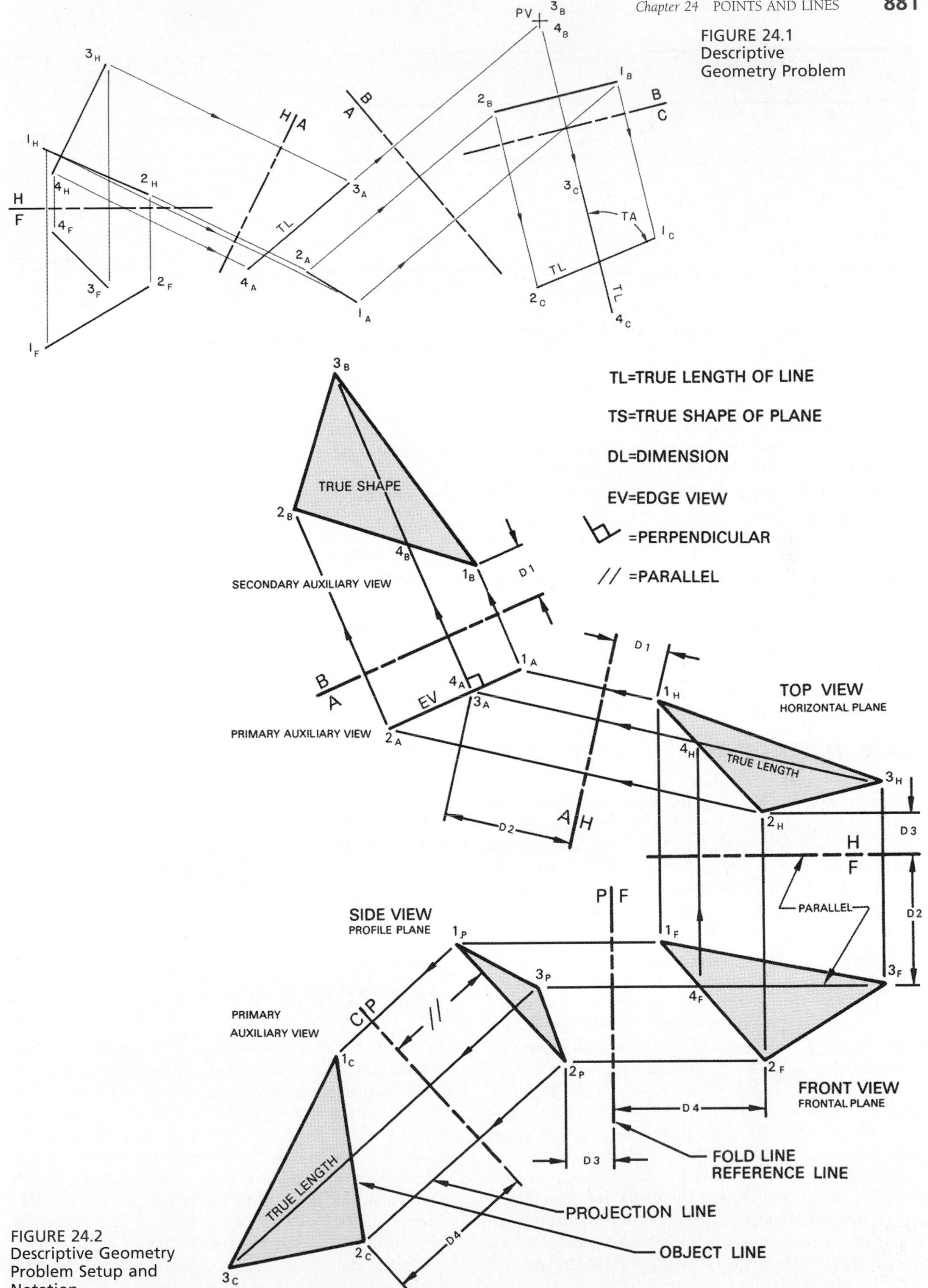

FIGURE 24.1
Descriptive
Geometry Problem

FIGURE 24.2
Descriptive Geometry
Problem Setup and
Notation

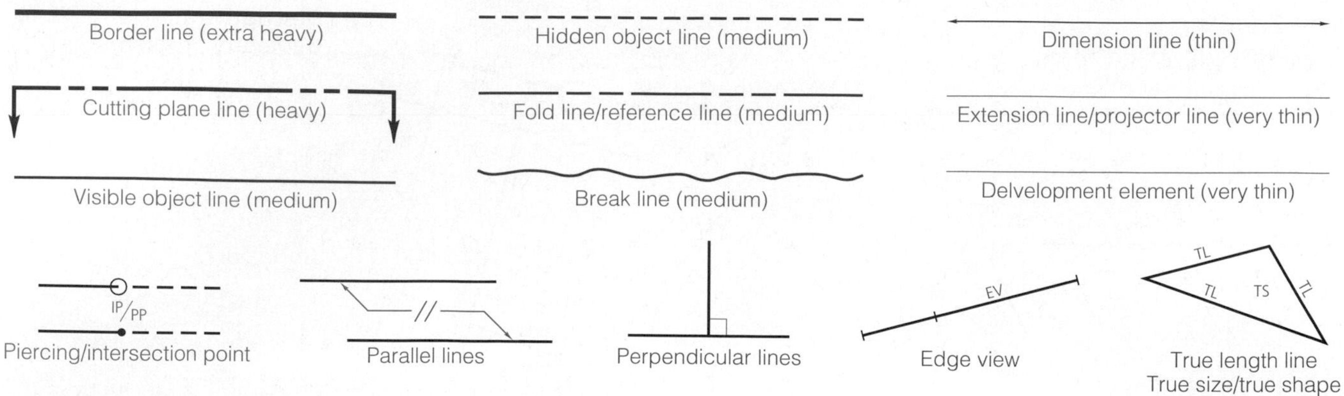

FIGURE 24.3 **Descriptive Geometry Line and Symbol Key**

to descriptive geometry. Many of the line weights and line types are similar to those found in mechanical/engineering drafting. Two unique lines are also shown—the fold line and the development element. As discussed in Chapters 10 and 12, the fold line serves to divide each view and to establish a reference from which to take dimensions when projecting from view to view.

The development element is employed extensively when developing curved surfaces and for triangulation of surfaces; it is explained in Chapter 28. Both development lines and fold lines are needed in the solution of a variety of descriptive geometry problems.

24.2 NOTATION

The nearby notation key gives the abbreviations and notational elements used throughout descriptive geometry problems. **EV** is the **edge view** of a plane. **IP** refers to the **intersection** of a line and a surface, whereas **PP** is the **piercing point** of a line (that is, part of a plane) and another surface; theoretically, **IP** and **PP** are the same. **PV** is the **point view** of a line. **True shape** and **true size** mean the same thing and are abbreviated as **TS. TL** is the true length of a line. **D** denotes a dimension.

H, F, and **P** identify the three primary views in orthographic projection: **horizontal** (top), **frontal** (front), and **profile** (side). "**A**" will always be the first auxiliary view on a problem, followed by "**B**", "**C**", "**D**", etc.

Whole numbers **1, 2, 3, 4,** etc., establish points in space. They can be individual points, or they can be combined to determine the extent of lines, planes, or solids. In a few cases, capital letters establish points, for clarity.

Subscripts establish the view in which a point is located, such as 2_H, which means point 2 in the H (horizontal) view. **Superscripts** are found when an aspect of a point appears in more than one place in a view, for instance, when a line of a prism is called $3\text{-}3^1$, or when for clarity, the piercing point of a line is noted as an aspect of the original point, e.g., 2^1.

After reading the text and completing a few of the problems, these notations will become second nature and enable you to label, notate, and communicate via descriptive geometry and its specialized language.

Notation Key

EV = edge view
IP = intersection point
PP = piercing point
PV = point view
TL = true length
TS = true shape
TS = true size
D = dimension
H = horizontal view
F = frontal view
P = profile view
A, B = auxiliary views

1, 2, 3, 4, 5, 6, etc. = points
H, F, P, A, B, C, etc. = view identifications
2_F, 3_P, 4_A, etc. = view subscript
2^1, 3^2, 4^2, etc. = superscript
2R, 3R, 4R, etc. = revolved points

24.3 POINTS

Geometric shapes must be reduced to **points** and their connectors, which are lines. In descriptive geometry, points are the most important geometric element and the primary building block for any graphical projection of a form. All projections of lines, planes, or solids can be physically located and manipulated by identifying a series of points that represent the object or part. Understanding this will help you to design both on the board and with a CAD system. Establishing endpoints in space is one of the primary means of constructing geometry on a CAD system.

A point can be located in space and illustrated by establishing it in two or more adjacent views. Two points

Focus On . . .

MINING APPLICATIONS OF DESCRIPTIVE GEOMETRY

A geologist or geological engineer borrows concepts and procedures from descriptive geometry to solve various types of mining and geology problems. The Earth's surface is covered with a thin layer of soil and vegetation. Beneath this layer lies a series of stratified layers (*strata*) of sedimentary rock. These layers were formed mechanically (sandstone, limestone), chemically (salt, gypsum), or organically (coal) from sediment. The process of *sedimentation* includes the transportation and the formation/solidification (cementing, bonding) of the sediments into solid layers, also called *beds,* of rocks.

Sedimentary rock was formed in the Earth's oceans, and subsequent upheavals and disturbances have faulted, sheared, folded, tilted, fractured, and distorted the original plane tabular formations. Therefore most strata are inclined and cover only limited areas. The upper and lower surfaces of these strata are assumed to be more or less parallel, with a uniform thickness, within limits.

Layered rock formations/beds/strata/*veins* may contain valuable minerals, especially at the intersection of two strata. Such a vein can have any type of configuration. Other strata—for instance, coal beds—are normally bounded by parallel surfaces and will at times intersect the surface of the Earth along outcroppings. This type of stratum is also referred to as a *vein.* The line along which a vein or stratum intersects the surface is called an *outcrop* line. Identification and location of outcrops plays an important part in the finding and mining of valuable ore deposits.

Contour maps describe and establish the limits of a particular deposit of rock. The strike, dip/slope, and thickness of a stratum of rock describe its physical orientation. Since a stratum is a sheetlike mass of sedimentary rock that lies between two stratum of different compositions, its *strike* can be determined by measuring the bearing of a level line on either of its bounding surfaces (upper bedding plane/headwall, lower bedding plane/footwall). The surface of a bedding plane can be located by three or more points. Points on the upper or lower plane surfaces are found by drilling boreholes. The slope of a deposit/stratum is established by finding the angle, referred to as the *dip,* of a plane and includes the general direction of its tilt. Therefore, the dip of a vein/stratum includes its slope angle and dip direction of tilt. The strike and dip are measured as compass directions deviating from a north/south line toward the east or the west. The strike is always given from the north or the south, depending on its orientation to the strike and the low side of the plane.

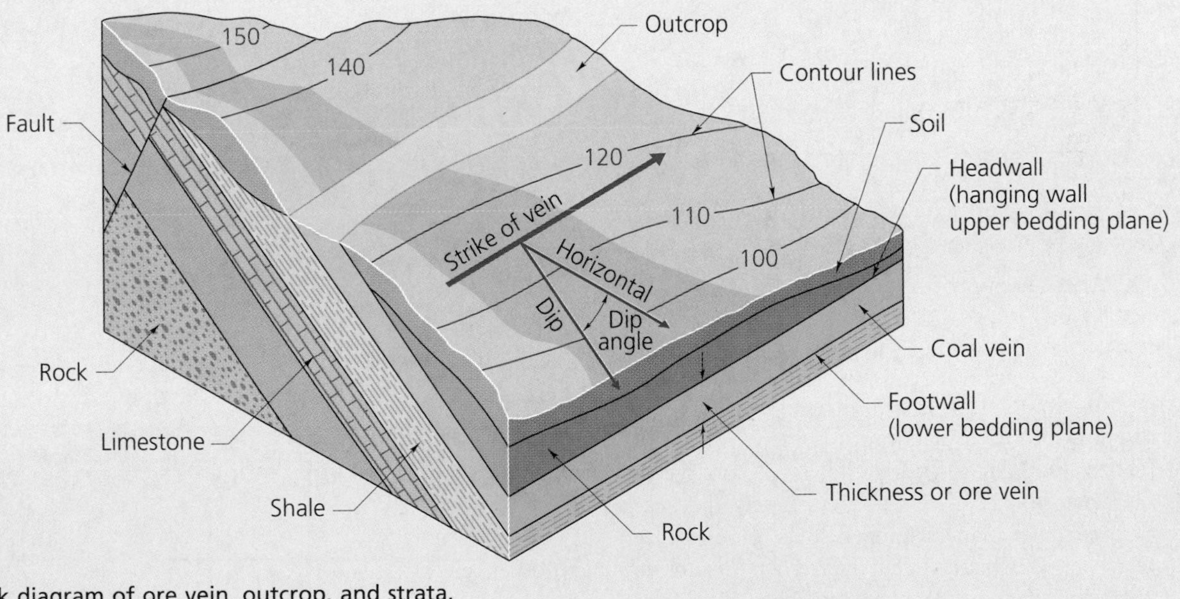

Block diagram of ore vein, outcrop, and strata.

that are connected are called a **line.** Points can also served to describe a plane or a solid, or can be located in space by themselves, though they have no real physical dimension. All of descriptive geometry is based on the orthographic projection of points in space.

24.3.1 Views of Points

Since a **point** is a location in space and not a dimensional form, it must be located by measurements taken from an established reference line, such as that in the glass box

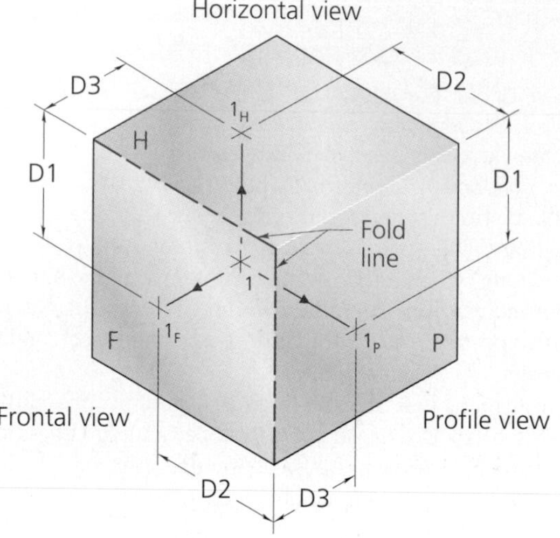

(a) Isometric pictorial

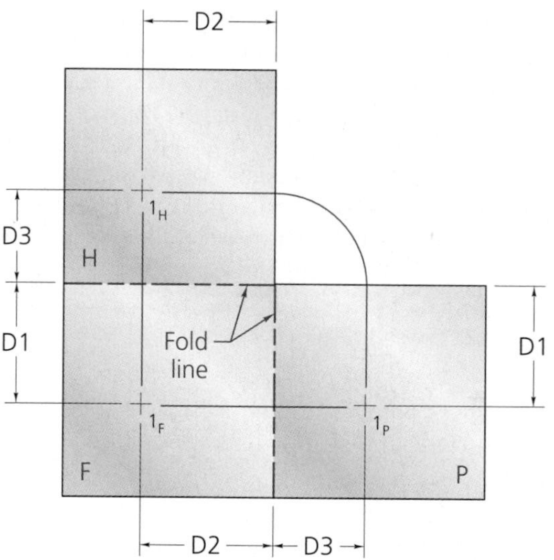

(b) Orthographic projection

FIGURE 24.4 Three Views of a Point in Space

method of orthographic projection illustrated in Figure 24.4. This figure represents the projection of point 1 in the three principal planes: frontal (1_F), horizontal (1_H), and profile (1_P). In the glass box method, it is assumed that each mutually perpendicular plane is hinged so as to be revolved into the plane of the paper. *The intersection line of two successive (perpendicular) image planes is called a fold line/reference line.* All measurements are taken from fold lines to locate a point (line, plane, or solid) in space. A fold line/reference line can be visualized as the edge view of a reference plane.

A point can be located through verbal description by giving dimensions from fold/reference lines. In Figure 24.4, point 1 is below the horizontal plane (D1), to the left of the profile plane (D2), and behind the frontal plane (D3). D1 establishes the elevation (height) of the point in the front and side views, D2 the right–left location (width) in the front and top views, and D3 the distance behind the frontal plane (depth) in the top and side views.

24.3.2 Primary Auxiliary Views of a Point

Auxiliary views taken from one of the three principal views are **primary auxiliary views.** A primary auxiliary view of a point will be perpendicular to one of the principal planes and inclined to the other two. Another name for this type of view is **first auxiliary view,** being the first view off of a principal plane. Figure 24.5 shows a primary auxiliary view taken from each of the three principal planes. Primary auxiliary view A is taken perpendicular to the horizontal plane, primary auxiliary view B is drawn perpendicular to the frontal plane, and primary auxiliary view C is perpendicular to the profile plane.

24.3.3 Secondary Auxiliary Views of a Point

Auxiliary views projected from a primary auxiliary view are called **secondary auxiliary views.** Secondary auxiliary views are drawn perpendicular to one primary auxiliary view and so will be oblique projections, since they will be inclined to all three principal views. All views projected from a secondary auxiliary view are called *successive auxiliary views,* as are all subsequent views. In most cases, solutions to descriptive geometry problems require only secondary auxiliary projections. Figure 24.6 shows point 1 in the H and F views. View C is a primary auxiliary view, as is view A. View B is a secondary auxiliary view, since it was projected from auxiliary view A.

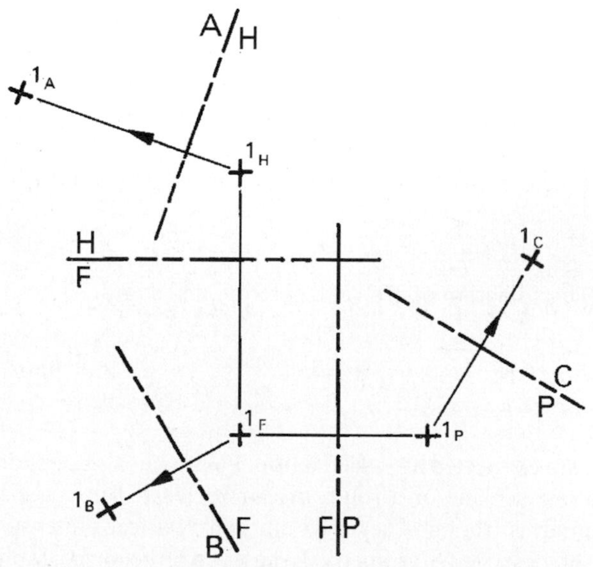

FIGURE 24.5 Views of Points in Space

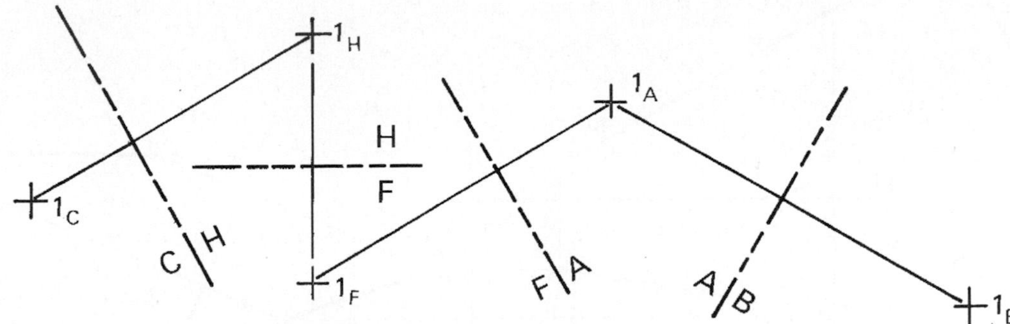

FIGURE 24.6
Auxiliary Views of Points

24.4 LINES

Lines can be thought of as a series of points in space, having magnitude (length) but not width. A line is assumed to have a thickness so as to be drawable. Though a line may be located by establishing its endpoints and may be of a definite specified length, all lines can be extended in order to solve a problem. Therefore, a purely theoretical definition of a line could be as follows: *Lines are straight elements that have no width but are infinite in length (magnitude); they can be located by two points that are not at the same location.* When two lines lie in the same plane, they will either be parallel or intersect.

Throughout the text, numbers have been used to designate the endpoints of a line. The view of a line and its locating points are labeled with a subscript corresponding to the plane of projection, as in Figure 24.7, where the endpoints of line 1-2 are notated 1_H and 2_H in the horizontal view, 1_F and 2_F in the frontal view, and 1_P and 2_P in the profile view. For many figures in the chapter, subscripts are eliminated if the view is obvious, or only one point per view may be labeled.

24.4.1 Multiview Projection of a Line

Lines are classified according to their orientation to the three principal planes of projection or how they appear in a projection plane. They can also be described by their relationship to other lines in the same view. As with points, lines are located from fold lines/reference lines.

In Figure 24.7, line 1-2 is projected onto each principal projection plane and located by dimensions taken from fold lines. The end points of line 1-2 are located from two fold lines in each view, using dimensions or projection lines that originate in a previous (adjacent) view. Dimensions D1 and D2 establish the elevation of the endpoints in the profile and frontal views, since these points are horizontally in line in these two views. D3 and D4 locate the endpoints in relation to the F/P fold line (to the left of the profile plane), in both the frontal and horizontal views, since these points are aligned vertically. D5 and D6 locate each endpoint in relation to the H/F and the F/P fold lines, since these dimensions are the distance behind the frontal plane and will show in both the horizontal and profile views.

24.4.2 Auxiliary Views of Lines

Lines can be projected onto an infinite number of successive projection planes. As with points, the first auxiliary view from one of three principal planes is called a primary

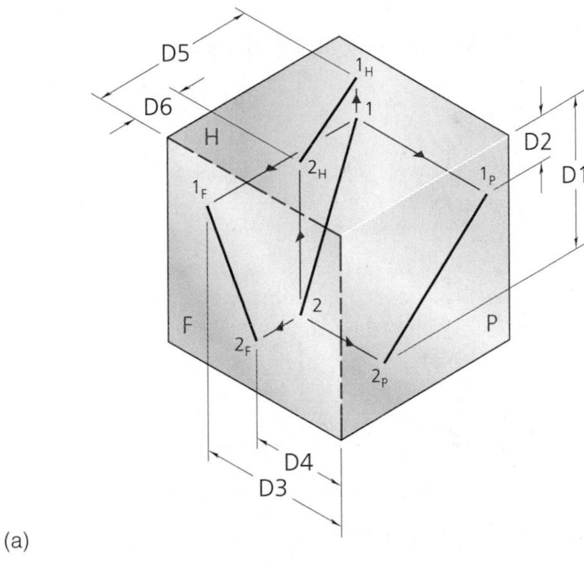

(a)

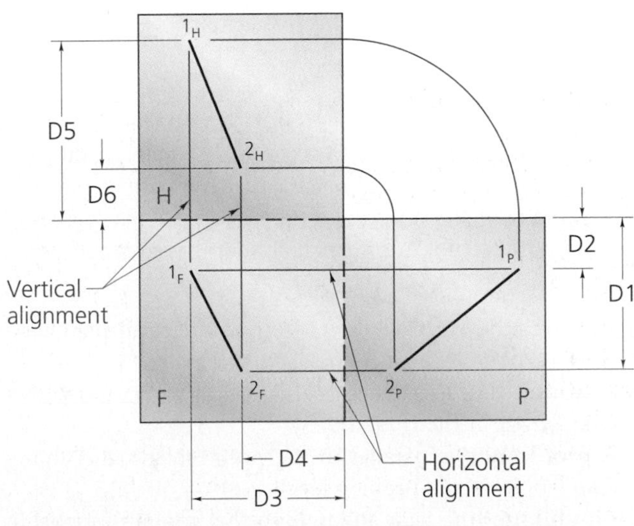

(b)

FIGURE 24.7 Three Views of a Line in Space

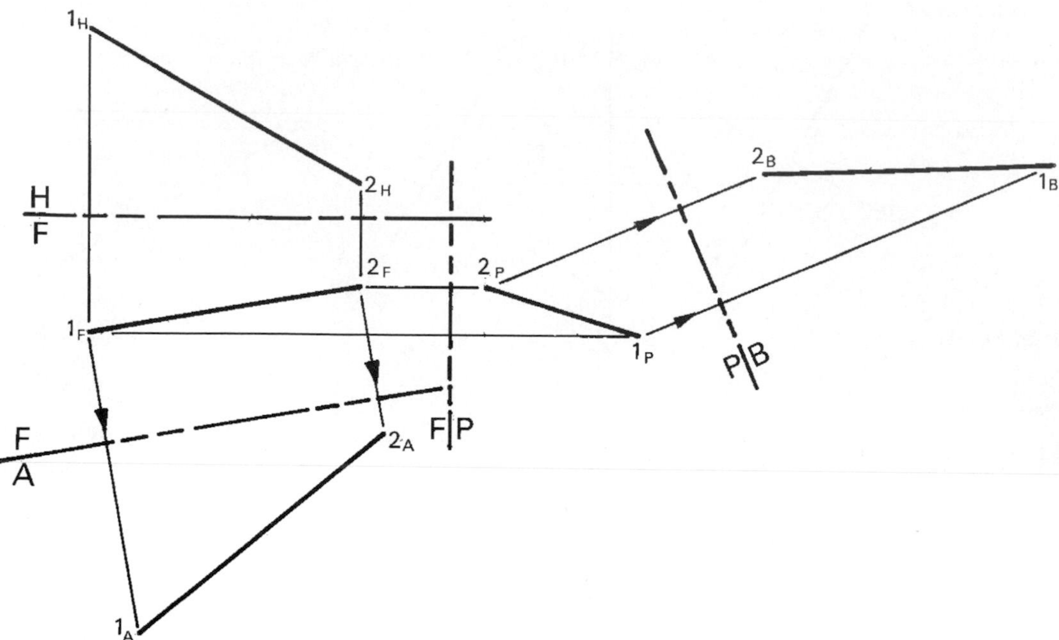

FIGURE 24.8 Auxiliary Views of a Line

auxiliary view. Any auxiliary view projected from a primary auxiliary is a secondary auxiliary view, and all auxiliary views projected from these are called successive auxiliary views. A line will appear as a point, as true length, or as foreshortened in orthographic projections. In Figure 24.8, line 1-2 is shown in the frontal, horizontal, and profile views. Primary auxiliary view A is projected perpendicular to the frontal view (and is inclined to the other two principal planes). Primary auxiliary view B is perpendicular to the profile view (and inclined to the other two principal views). The line of sight for an auxiliary view is determined by the requirements of the problem. In this example, the line of sight for view A is perpendicular to line 1-2 in the frontal view. View B is a random projection. An infinite number of auxiliary projections can be taken from any view.

24.4.3 Principal Lines

A line that is parallel to a principal plane is called a **principal line**, and is *true length* in the principal plane to which it is parallel. Since there are three principal planes of projection, there are three principal lines: horizontal, frontal, and profile (Fig. 24.9):

- A **horizontal line** is parallel to the horizontal plane and shows true length in the horizontal view.
- A **frontal line** is parallel to the frontal plane and shows true length in the frontal view.
- A **profile line** is parallel to the profile plane and shows true length in the profile view.
- An **oblique line** is at an angle to the frontal, horizontal, and profile planes and therefore does not show true length in any of these projections.

24.4.4 Line Types and Descriptions

The following terms describe lines.

Vertical line Any line that is perpendicular to the horizontal plane and that appears true length in the frontal and profile views (consequently such lines will be both frontal and profile principal lines). Vertical lines appear as a point (point view) in the horizontal view and show true length in all elevation views.

Level line Any line that is parallel to the horizontal plane. Level lines are horizontal lines.

Inclined line Any line that is parallel to the frontal or profile plane (and therefore a profile or frontal principal line) and at an angle to the horizontal plane. An inclined line is always at an angle to the horizontal.

Oblique line Any line that is inclined to all three principal planes and therefore not true length in a principal view (Fig. 24.9).

Foreshortened line Any line that is shorter than true length in a specific view.

Point view When a view is projected perpendicular to a true-length line, that line appears as a point view; the endpoints are therefore coincident. A point view is a view of a line in which the line of sight is parallel to the line.

True length A view in which a line can be measured true distance between its endpoints shows the line as true length. A line appears true length in any view where it is parallel to the plane of projection.

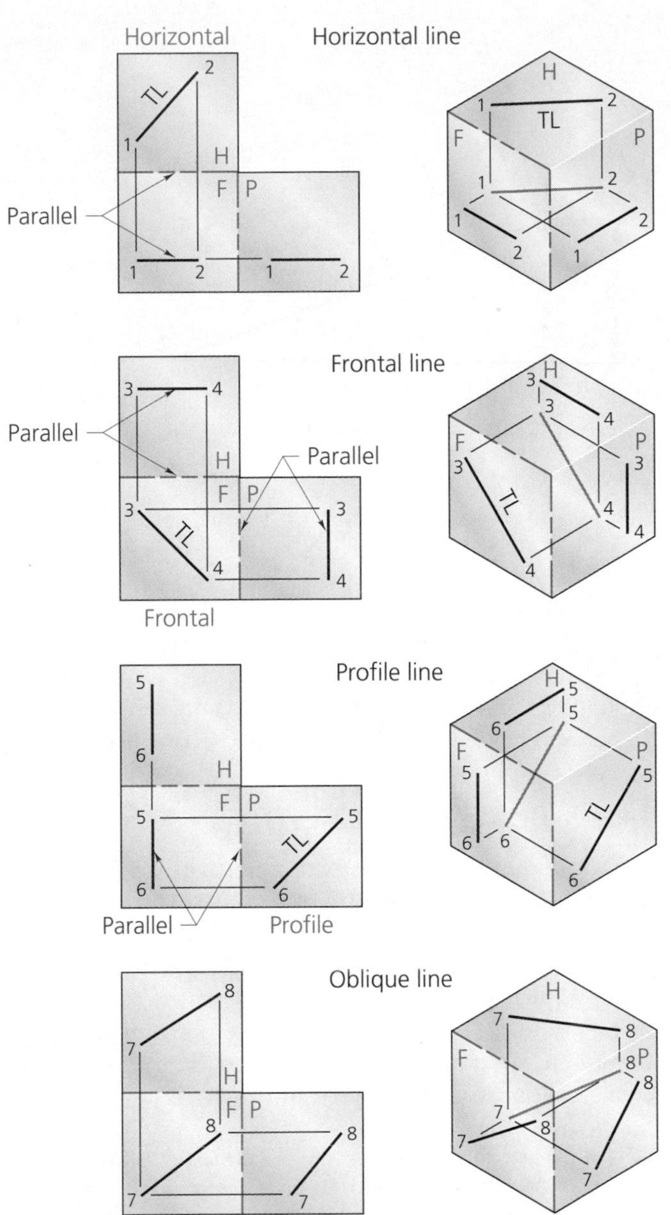

FIGURE 24.9 Types of Lines

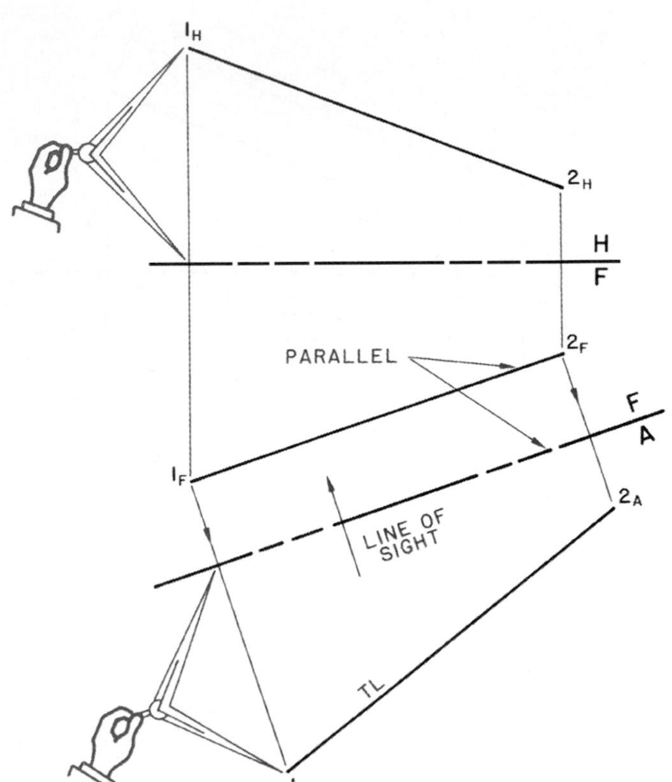

FIGURE 24.10 Oblique Line Shown in Horizontal, Frontal, and Auxiliary Views. Note that auxiliary view A shows the lines and a true-length projection.

24.4.5 True Length of a Line

A **true-length** view of an oblique line can be projected from any existing view by establishing a line of sight perpendicular to a view of the line and drawing a fold line parallel to the line (perpendicular to the line of sight). Note that fold lines are always drawn perpendicular to the line of sight. The following steps describe the procedure for drawing a true-length projection of an oblique line from the frontal view (Fig. 24.10):

1. Establish a line of sight perpendicular to oblique line 1-2 in the frontal view.
2. Draw fold line F/A perpendicular to the line of sight and parallel to oblique line 1-2.
3. Extend projection lines from points 1 and 2 perpendicular to the fold line (parallel to the line of sight). The distance from line 1_F-2_F is random.
4. Transfer the endpoints of the line from the horizontal view to locate points 1_A and 2_A along the projection lines in auxiliary view A. Connect points 1_A and 2_A. This is the true length of projection of line 1-2.

24.4.6 True-Length Diagrams

An alternative to the auxiliary view method of solving for the true length of a line is the **true-length diagram.** This method is employed extensively when developing complicated shapes such as transition pieces and other developments where there may be a large number of elements in one view that are oblique and not parallel to one another. In this type of situation it would be impossible to project auxiliary views of every line. A true-length diagram can establish the true-length measurement of an oblique line from any two adjacent (successive) views of that line, thereby eliminating the necessity of projecting an auxiliary view.

In Figure 24.11(a), oblique line 1-2 is shown in the frontal and horizontal views. Instead of projecting an auxiliary view to establish its true length, a true-length diagram [Fig. 24.11(b)] has been used. To construct the diagram, draw two construction lines at 90° to the side of the given views. Transfer the vertical dimension D1 from the frontal view to the vertical leg of the construction line, to locate point 2. Dimension D2 can then be transferred from the horizontal view to the horizontal construction line to locate

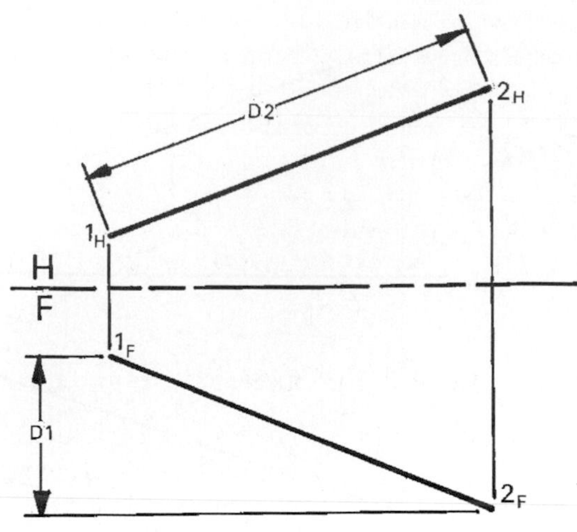

(a) H and F views of a line

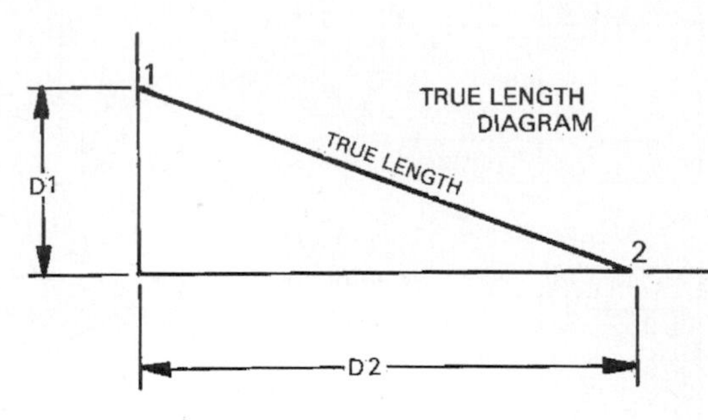

(b) True-length diagram

FIGURE 24.11 Constructing a True-Length Diagram

point 1. This newly formed right triangle has a hypotenuse equal to the true length of line 1-2, and can be measured from the drawing. The true length can also be calculated algebraically from the Pythagorean theorem, $C = \sqrt{A^2 + B^2}$. C is the hypotenuse (true length of line 1-2), A is the altitude/height (D1), and B is the base (D2):

$$\text{Hypotenuse} = \sqrt{(D1)^2 + (D2)^2}$$

For oblique lines the following formula applies:

$$TL = \sqrt{(D1)^2 + (D2)^2 + (D3)^2}$$

24.4.7 Point View of a Line

A line will project as a point view when the line of sight is parallel to a true-length view of the line. In other words, the **point view** is projected on a projection plane that is perpendicular to the true-length line. Finding the true length and the point view of a line is required for many situations involving the application of descriptive geometry to engineering problems. The first requirement for a point view is that the line be projected as true length. This procedure has been discussed previously.

The point view of an oblique line can be drawn only after the line is projected as true length in an auxiliary view. In Figure 24.12, line 1-2 is projected as true length in auxiliary view A. To establish the point view, a secondary auxiliary view (B) is projected perpendicular to the true-length line. The following steps describe this process.

1. Project a true-length view of line 1-2.
2. Establish a line of sight parallel to the true-length line 1-2.
3. Draw the fold line (A/B) perpendicular to the line of sight. Notice that the fold line is perpendicular to the true-length line.
4. Transfer dimension D3 from the horizontal view to locate both points along the projection line in auxiliary view B.

24.4.8 Bearing of a Line

The angle that a line makes with a north–south line in the horizontal view is the **bearing** of that line. The bearing can be measured only in the horizontal view and is always measured from the north or the south. Since the bearing of a line is the angle the line makes with the north–south meridian, it can be measured from the north or the south toward the east or the west. *The bearing is the map direction of a line, and is measured in degrees, with a protractor or compass,*

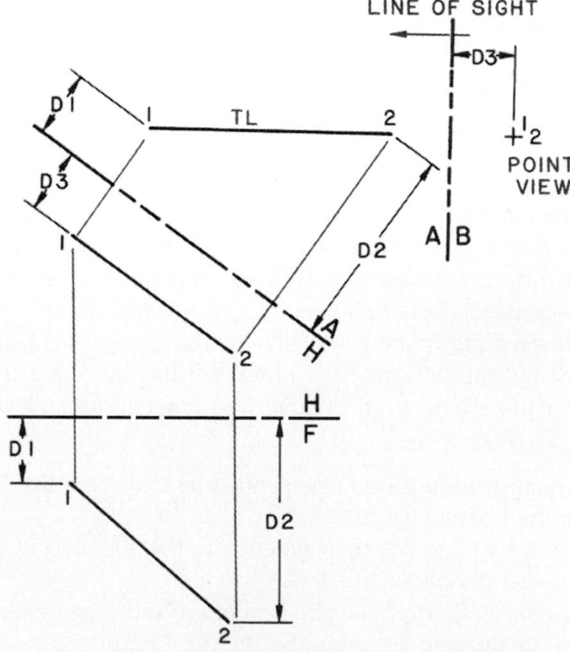

FIGURE 24.12 True Length and Point View of a Line

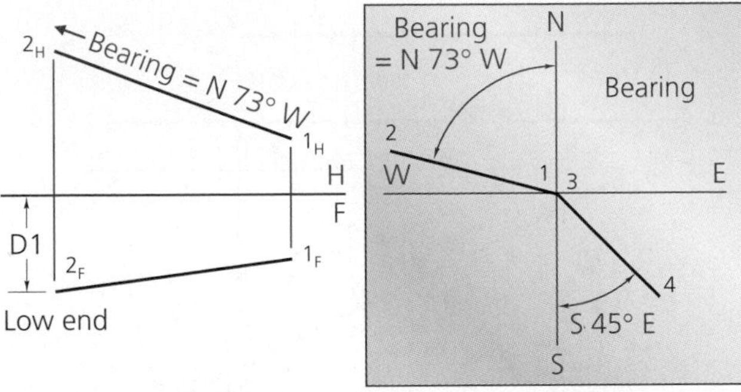

FIGURE 24.13 Bearing of a Line

from the north or the south. The bearing indicates the quadrant in which the line lies.

Normally, the originating point is the lowest numerical value. For example, line 1-2 starts at point 1. The low end is the lowest point on a line as seen in a frontal or elevation view. In some cases, the bearing is measured from the high end of the line toward the low end, as is done, for instance, for a sloping cross-country pipeline.

In Figure 24.13, line 1-2 has a bearing of north 73° west (N 73° W), measured from the north 73° toward the west. The bearing is measured from the north toward the west, from point 1 toward point 2. Figure 24.13 also shows the horizontal view of line 1-2, located in relation to the compass meridian. Line 1-2 lies in the second quadrant. Therefore, it is measured from the north toward the west. Remember, the bearing is always measured in the top (horizontal) view.

The bearing of line 3-4 is south 45° east (S 45° E), which means that line 3-4 forms a 45° angle with the north–south meridian and is measured from the south toward the east. The low end is always determined in the frontal view, where the elevation of the line is shown. Line 3-4 is located in relation to the meridian and lies in the fourth quadrant, since it is measured from the south toward the east.

In Figure 24.14, the bearing of the pipeline, line 3-4, is S 45° E. This means that line 3_H-4_H forms a 45° angle with the north–south meridian and is measured from the south toward the east. Here the concept of *low end* has been applied. The low end is always determined in the frontal view, where the elevation of the line is shown.

The bearing of a line is used in engineering work to locate lines by compass directions. The bearing of a road, for instance, would be measured on a map, normally from the north. Note that the concept of low end is useless in surveying, since the elevation may not be known or needed in regard to the bearing.

24.4.9 Azimuth of a Line

The **azimuth** bearing of a line is the angle the line makes with the north–south meridian, and is always measured from the north in a clockwise direction. In Figure 24.15, line 4-5 has an azimuth reading of 135° and line 7-8 has an azimuth of 288°. Note that the azimuth is always measured from the north and that the directions of the compass are not required. Both the azimuth bearing and the compass bearing are used in engineering and mapping work. The bearing for line 7-8 is N 72° W, and for line 4-5 is S 45° E. *Measurements of azimuth or bearing are always taken in the horizontal view, since a compass direction will show only in the plan view and north can be determined only by looking down on a map,* as in Figure 24.16(a).

In Figure 24.16, line 5-6 has a bearing of N 38° W and a corresponding azimuth of 322°. Normally a line's bearing is not affected by its elevation view (usually the front view), though for some applications, such as the slope of a tunnel or angle of slope for a pipeline, the low point determines the direction of bearing. In this figure the bearing of line 5-6 could be given as either N 38° W or S 38° E, but since the low end, or down side, of the line is at point 6, the bearing was given from the north toward the west. This method of determining the bearing direction is not accepted in all engineering fields but is employed for portions of this text.

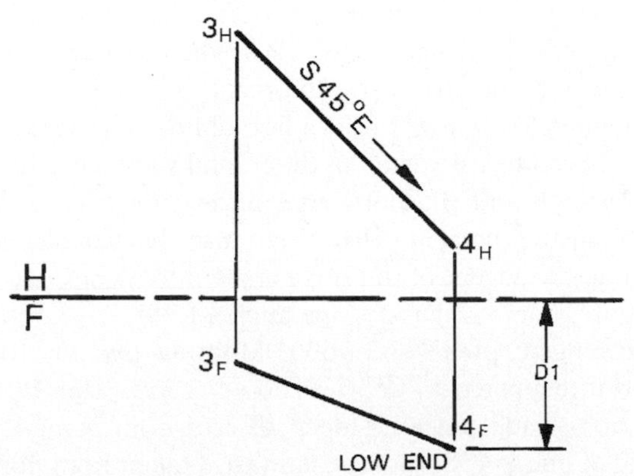

FIGURE 24.14 Bearing and Low End of a Line

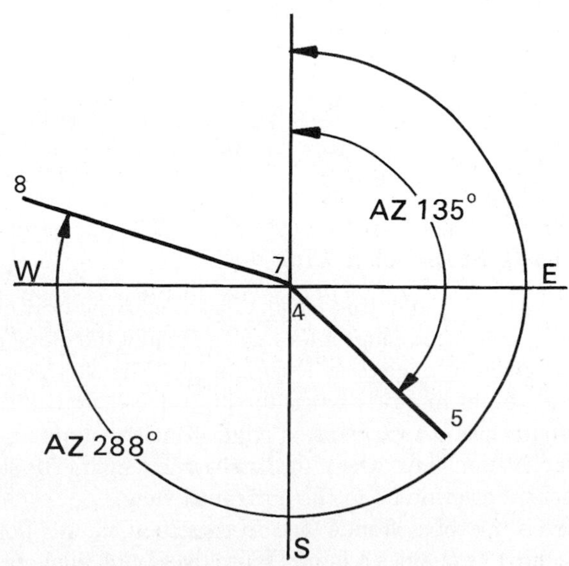

FIGURE 24.15 Azimuth Readings

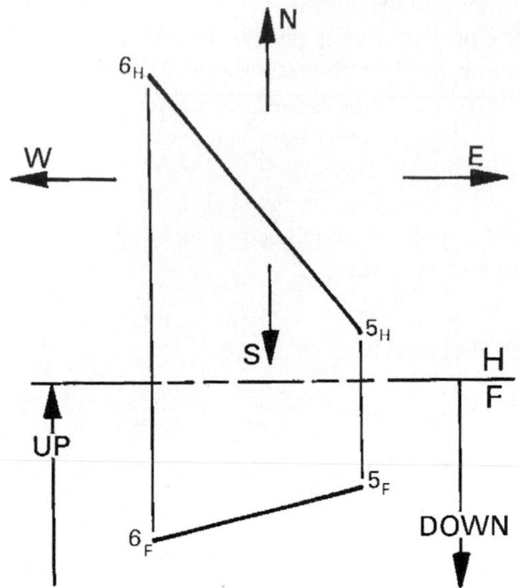

(a) Bearing N 38° W

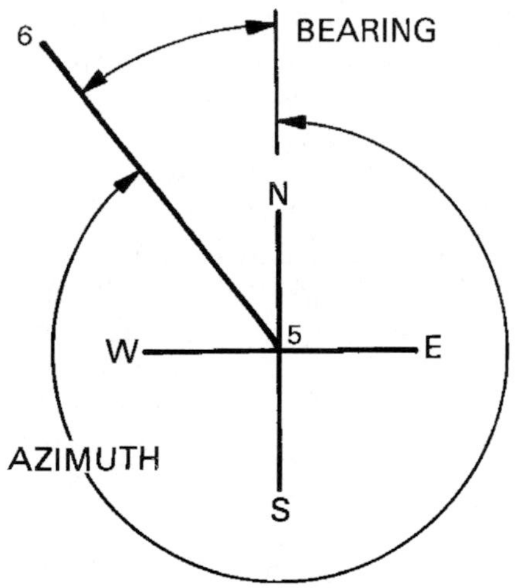

(b) Azimuth 322°

FIGURE 24.16 Bearing and Azimuth

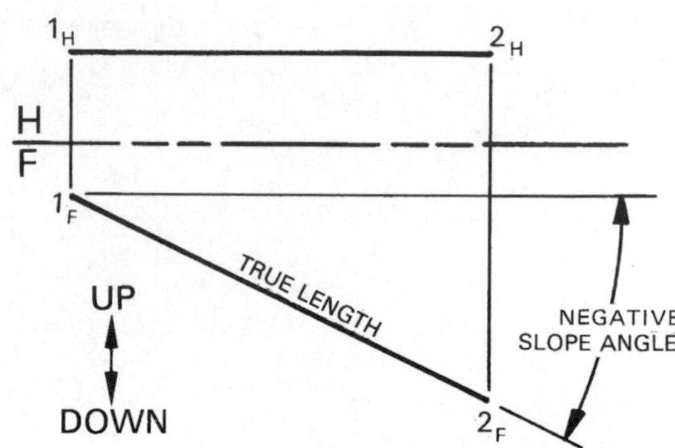

FIGURE 24.17 Slope of a Frontal Line

Note that the first point listed for a line could be assumed to be the starting point for the direction of the line instead of using the low-side method.

24.4.10 Slope of a Line

The angle that a line (true length) makes with the horizontal plane is called the **slope** of a line. Normally the slope of a line is given in degrees as a slope angle. The slope can be measured only in a view where the line is true length and the horizontal plane appears as an edge. Thus the slope is seen in an elevation view, where the line is true length. The slope cannot be determined in the horizontal view.

The slope of a frontal line is measured in the frontal (elevation) view, since it is parallel to the frontal plane in the horizontal view and therefore shows as true length in the frontal view. In Figure 24.17, line 1-2 is a frontal line (true length in the frontal view). The slope angle is the angle formed by true-length line 1_F-2_F and the H/F fold line. Since point 1_F is above point 2_F, the line slopes down; in other words, it has a negative slope (−26°). By the low-end method, the bearing of line 1-2 is due east. The bearing would also be due east if the first-numerical-value procedure was followed, since the line slants down from point 1_F to point 2_F. Notice that the slope would be positive if the line originated at point 2_F and consequently sloped upward.

The slope of a profile line is measured in the profile view. A horizontal line is not a slope, since it is a level line and is parallel to the horizontal plane. To establish the slope of an oblique line, a primary auxiliary view must be projected from the horizontal view, parallel to the oblique line.

In Figure 24.18, line 1-2 is oblique. To measure its slope, auxiliary view A is projected parallel to line 1_H-2_H. Draw fold line H/A parallel to line 1_H-2_H. Line 1_A-2_A appears true length in auxiliary view A, and the slope angle (−16°) is measured between the line and fold line H/A. Line 1-2 has a negative slope, since it slants from point 1 downward toward point 2.

24.4.11 Grade of a Line

Another way of stating a line's slope is to give the grade of the line. The **grade,** or **percent grade,** of a line is the ratio of its rise (vertical height) to its run (horizontal distance). The percent grade is calculated in a view where the line appears as true length and the horizontal plane is an edge.

In Figure 24.19, line 1-2 is a frontal line. The slope angle and grade can be calculated in the frontal view, since the line is true length and the horizontal plane shows as an edge. Note that the percent grade can also be calculated by changing the tangent of the slope angle into a percentage. In this figure, line 1-2 has a slope angle of 44°.

The tangent of 44° is .9656. Multiply this by 100 to convert it to a percent: .9656 × 100 = 96.56%. Line 1-2 has a +96.56% grade, since it slopes upward from point 1. The bearing of line 1-2 would be due west if taken from point 1.

When calculating the percent grade as the ratio of rise to

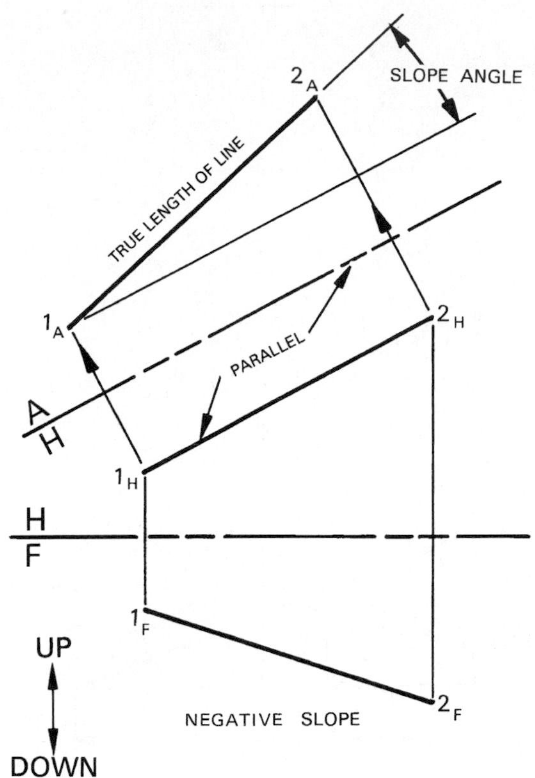

FIGURE 24.18 Slope of an Oblique Line

run, always use 100 units for the run and measure the rise with the same type of units, for this will yield the percent grade directly. In Figure 24.20, line 1-2 is oblique. Auxiliary view A is projected parallel to line 1_H-2_H (1). Line 1_A-2_A is true length and the grade can be calculated in this view. In Figure 24.20(b), line 1-2 has been drawn so as to illustrate this procedure better. Note that a true-length diagram could have been used. One hundred units are set off along the run and the rise has been measured at 40 units (the type of units is irrelevant). So percent grade = 40/100 × 100 = 40%. The grade of line 1-2 is –40%, since it slopes downward from point 1. The tangent of the slope angle is equal to the percent grade divided by 100: –40%/100 = –.4. Converting a tangent value of –.40 to an angle gives a slope angle of –21°48′.

24.4.12 Slope Designations

The slope of a line can be noted in a variety of ways. The slope ratio (vertical rise over horizontal run) can be expressed as percent grade, as a fraction, as a decimal, or as a slope angle. Each engineering field has developed a specific procedure and name to designate the slope of a line as it pertains to a given aspect of the field's work. In structural engineering the angle of slope is called the *slope* or *bevel* of a structural member (beam, truss element) and is designated by a slope triangle, as shown in Figure 24.21(a). The longest leg of the slope triangle is always 12 units and the shorter one is measured in the same units and designated as in Figure 24.21. For architectural projects the slope is designated as the ratio of rise to span (run), as in Figure 24.22, where the roof pitch = rise/span (10/12 = 5/6, 5/10 = 1/2).

24.4.13 To Draw a Line Given the True Length, Bearing, and Slope (Grade)

A line can be located in space if its length, bearing, and slope (or grade) are known. The bearing of a line will fix the line's position in the horizontal view that can be drawn without regard to its true length. Since the slope and the grade of a line show in a view where the line is true length and the horizontal plane appears as an edge, a primary auxiliary view projected from the horizontal view will fix the line in space. This auxiliary view must be projected parallel to the

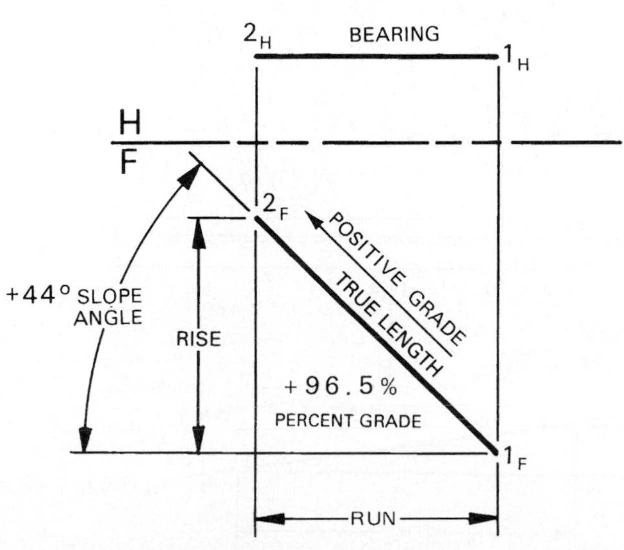

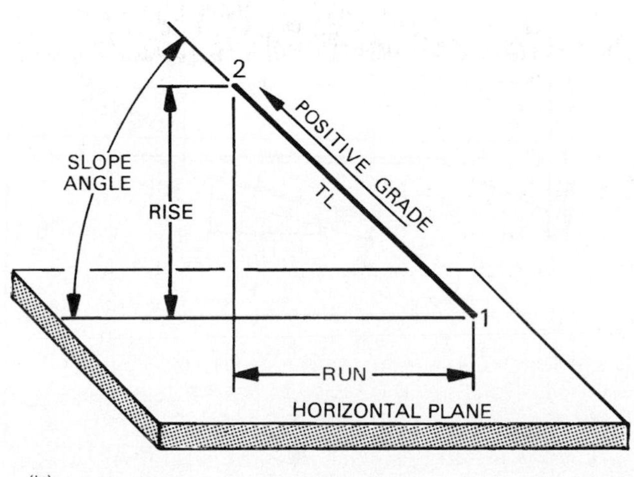

FIGURE 24.19 Grade of a Line

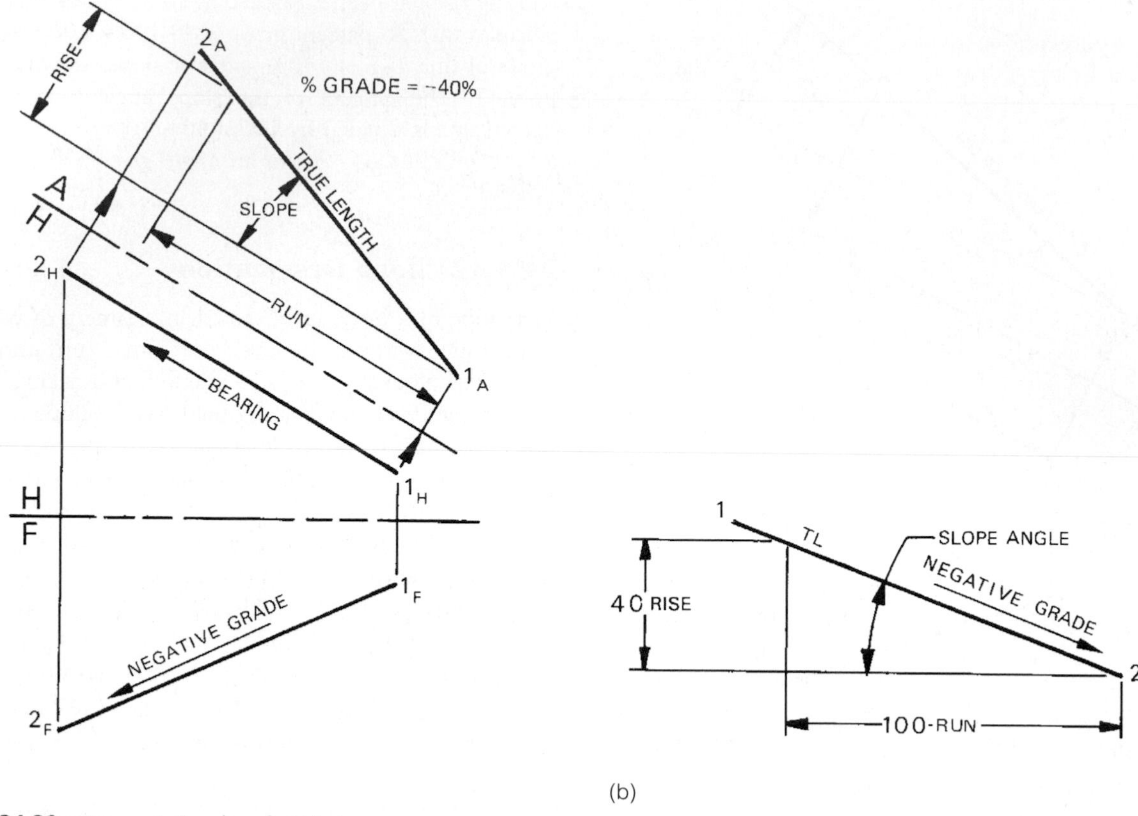

FIGURE 24.20 Percent Grade of a Line

line that is established in the horizontal view by its bearing only. In the auxiliary view, the slope or grade of the line can be used to draw the line an indefinite length and the true length can then be established by measurement along the slope line. With both ends of the line fixed it can be projected back to the horizontal and frontal views.

The following steps describe the construction of line 1-2 in Figure 24.23. Line 1-2 is 500 ft long, has a bearing of N

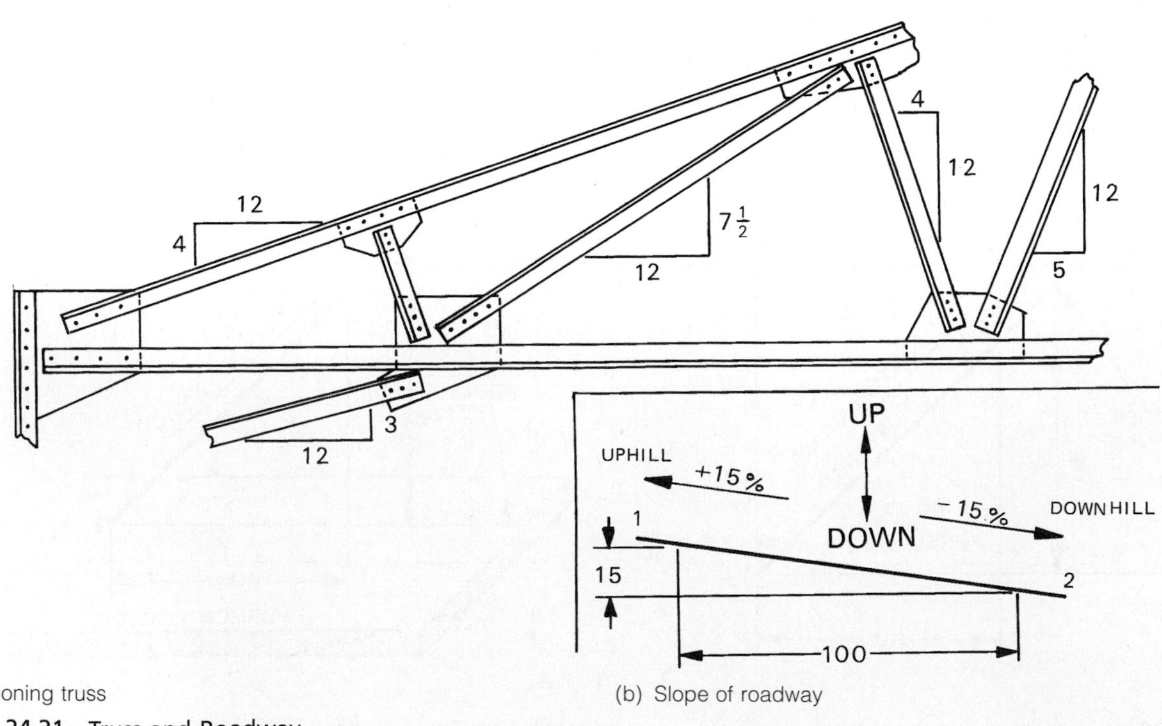

(a) Sectioning truss (b) Slope of roadway

FIGURE 24.21 Truss and Roadway

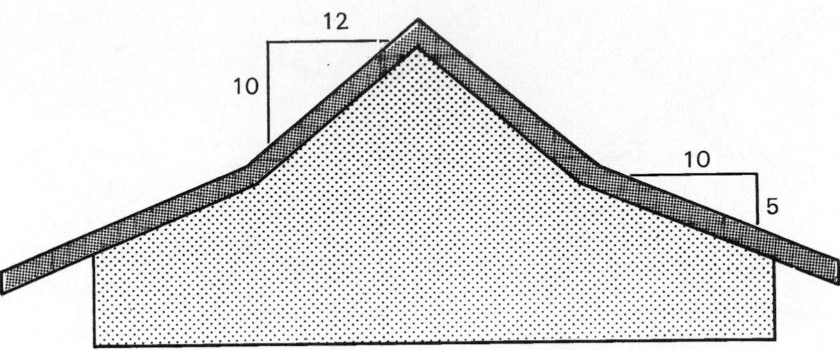

FIGURE 24.22 Pitch of Roof

70° W, and an upward grade of +25% from point 1 to point 2. Notice that the bearing in this problem is not oriented toward the low end of the line.

1. Establish and label point 1 in the frontal and horizontal views (1). From point 1, draw a line having a bearing of N 70° W (in horizontal view). Draw this line a convenient length.
2. Draw A/H parallel to the bearing line and project point 1 in auxiliary view A (2). Draw a construction line from point 1_A parallel to H/A and lay off 100 units for the run and 25 units for the rise, as shown.The rise is perpendicular to the run and extends toward the H/A fold line, since the line has a positive grade. Draw the line from point 1_A an indefinite length and touching the 25-unit rise. This fixes the grade and slope angle of the line.
3. Measure off 500 ft along the line from point 1_A and label the other endpoint 2_A (3). Locate point 2_H in the horizontal view by projection.
4. Locate point 2_F in the frontal view by projection and by transferring dimension D2 from auxiliary view A (4). Connect the two points to complete the frontal view.

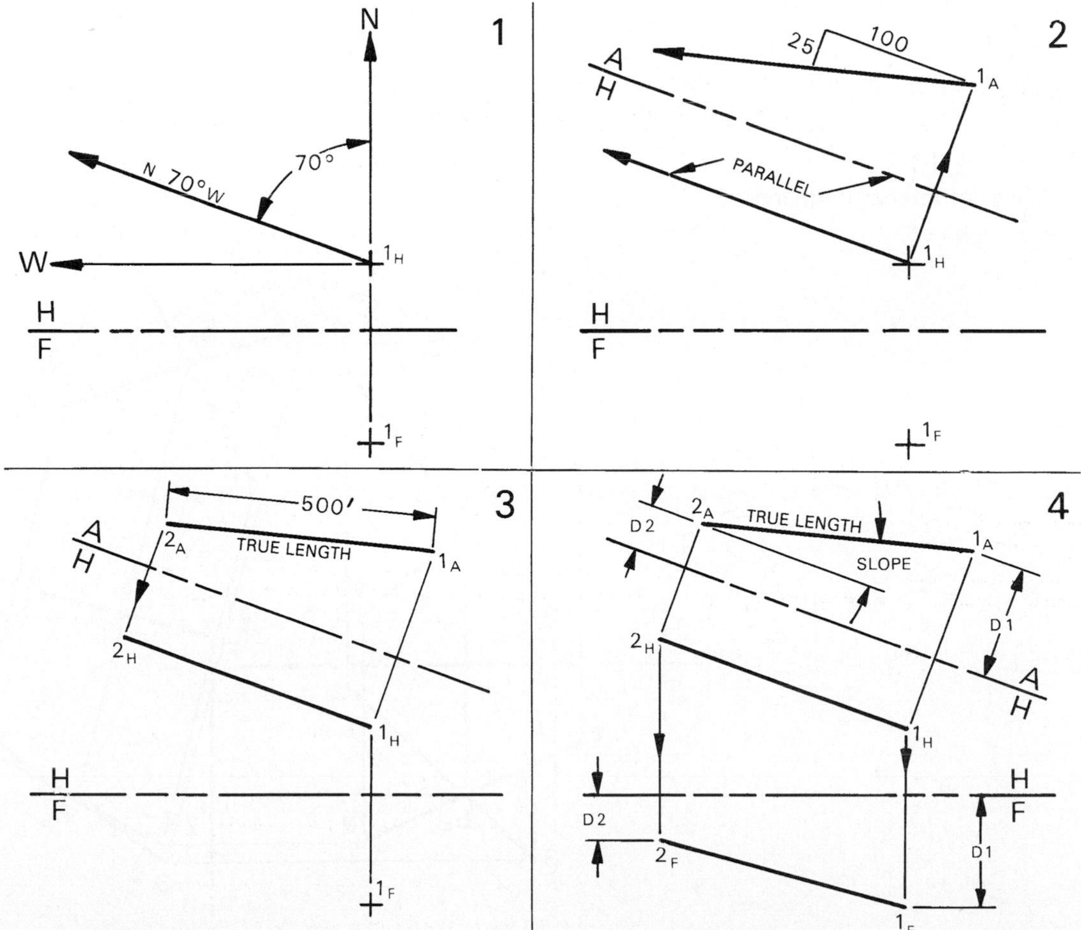

FIGURE 24.23 Locating a Line Given the Bearing, Slope (Grade), and True Length

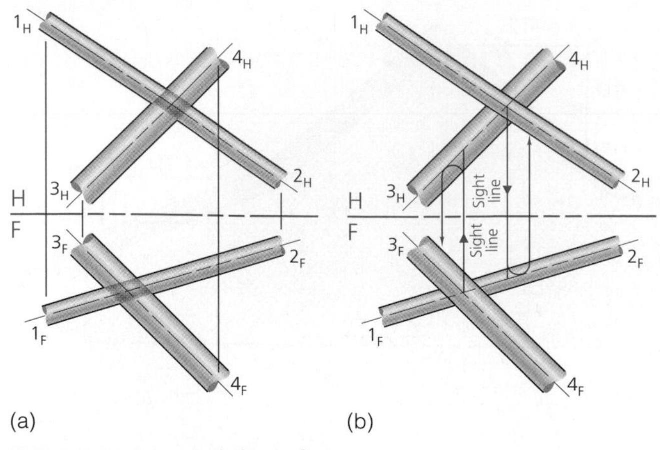

FIGURE 24.24 Visibility of Lines

24.4.14 Visibility of Lines

When two lines cross in space, they may intersect or one may be visible and the other hidden at the crossing point. A *visibility check* determines the proper relationship of the lines. Note that the visibility of two lines can change in every view; first one line may be visible, then in the next view the other line, or the same line may be visible in adjacent views. For example, when two pipes or structural members cross in a construction project, one will be above or in front of the other. This relationship of construction elements is one of the applications of descriptive geometry in industry.

In Figure 24.24(a), lines 1-2 and 3-4 cross. It must be determined which line lies in front of the other in the frontal view and which line is on top in the horizontal view. A visibility check must be made. The following steps describe this process.

1. Where line 1_H-2_H crosses line 3_H-4_H in the horizontal view, extend a sight line perpendicular to H/F until it meets one of the lines in the frontal view [Fig. 24.24(b)]. Here, line 1_F-2_F is the first line to be encountered; therefore, line 1_H-2_H is the visible line in the horizontal view.
2. Extend a sight line from the crossing point of line 1_F-2_F and 3_F-4_F in the frontal view until it meets the first line in its path in the horizontal view. Since line 3_H-4_H is encountered first, it will be the visible line in the frontal view.
3. Complete the visibility of lines by showing the proper solid (visible) and dashed (hidden) lines in both views. (The visible line has been shaded for clarity, though this is not standard practice.) Note that line 1-2 is visible in the horizontal view (is above line 3-4), and line 3-4 is visible in the frontal view (is in front of line 1-2).

24.4.15 Intersecting Lines

Intersecting lines must have a common point, one where the two lines meet and therefore "intersect." Parallel lines and skew lines do not intersect. Perpendicular lines can be intersecting or nonintersecting.

The two lines in Figure 24.25 are intersecting lines since they have a common point, point 5, which remains the same

FIGURE 24.25 Views of Intersecting Lines

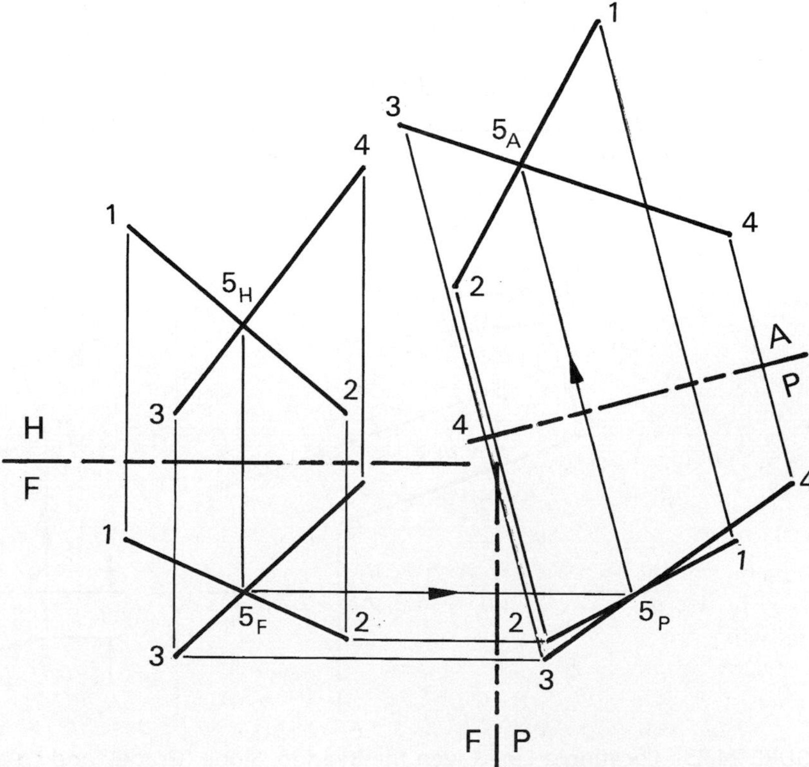

in all projections. In this example, three principal views and one auxiliary view are shown for lines 1-2 and 3-4. Notice that the intersecting (common) point is aligned vertically between the horizontal and frontal views and that all projection lines between the views are parallel. If the apparent common point projected between two lines is not parallel to the other projection lines (and therefore to the line of sight), the two lines do not intersect.

For all auxiliary projections of intersecting lines, the common point must be projected parallel to the other projection lines and perpendicular to the fold line.

Intersecting lines have a common point that will project parallel to the line of sight for each adjacent view. The projection/extension line of a common point will be perpendicular to the fold line between the views. In the case of **nonintersecting lines**, the crossing point of two lines is different in each adjacent view.

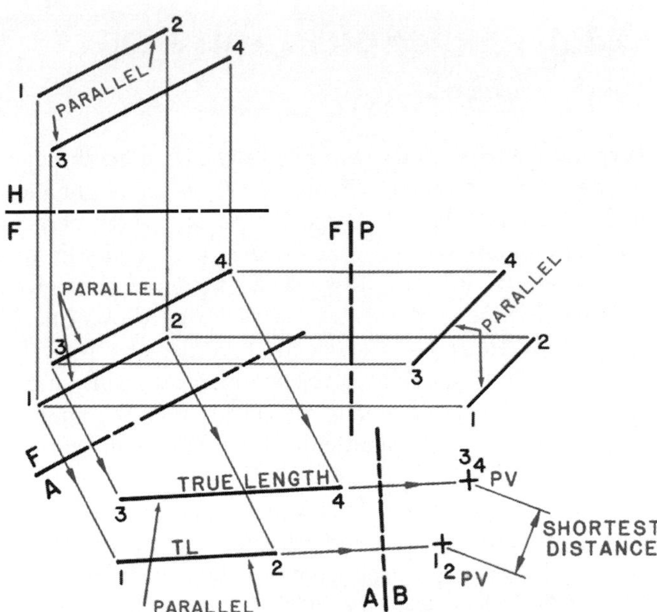

FIGURE 24.26 Solving for the Shortest Distance Between Two Lines

24.5 PARALLELISM OF LINES

Two lines in space will be intersecting, skew, parallel, or perpendicular. Parallel lines project parallel in all views (Fig. 24.26). Note that in each view, lines 1-2 and 3-4 are parallel. **Parallel lines** may also appear as points (in the same view) or their projections may coincide.

Two oblique lines that project parallel or coincide in all views will always be parallel. Two lines that are parallel or perpendicular to a principal plane and appear parallel to each other may not be parallel lines, and a third view will be needed to establish their relationship.

The true distance between two parallel lines is shown in a view where the lines appear as points. In Figure 24.26, oblique lines 1-2 and 3-4 are parallel. Auxiliary view A is projected parallel to both oblique lines from the frontal view (fold line F/A is drawn parallel to 1-2 and 3-4). View A shows both lines as true length. *Note that parallel lines show true length in the same view.* Auxiliary view B is then projected perpendicular to the true-length lines (fold line A/B is drawn perpendicular to true-length lines 1-2 and 3-4). In auxiliary view B, both lines appear as point views; therefore, true distance (shortest distance) between the lines can be measured here.

24.5.1 Construction of a Line Parallel to a Given Line

A commonly required construction in descriptive geometry is drawing a line parallel to a given line and through an established point. Since parallel lines are parallel in all views it is simply necessary to draw a line through a point parallel to another line. Normally only two views are required for oblique lines. When the given line is parallel to the horizontal or profile plane it is necessary to draw three views of the lines.

In Figure 24.27(a), line 1-2 and point 3 are given. A line is to be drawn parallel to line 1-2, with its midpoint at point 3. Since line 1-2 is oblique, only two views are necessary. The new line is drawn through point 3 and parallel to line 1-2 in both views [Fig. 24.27(b)]. A specific length was not required, only that the new line be parallel and have point 3 at its midpoint. The endpoints of the new line must be aligned so that the line is of equal length in both views.

You May Complete Exercises 24.1 Through 24.4 at This Time

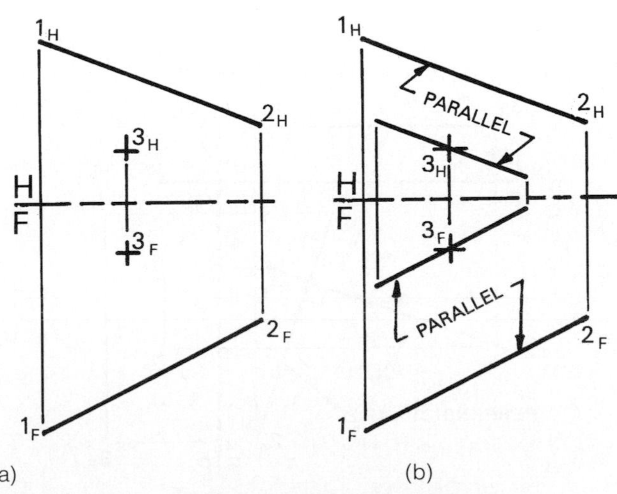

FIGURE 24.27 Line Parallel to a Given Line

24.6 PERPENDICULARITY OF LINES

Perpendicularity, along with parallelism, is used throughout descriptive geometry to solve a wide range of graphical problems. Lines that are perpendicular will show perpendicularity in any view in which one or both of the lines is true length. Because two lines may be oblique in their given views, it is necessary to project a view that shows one or both of the lines as true length in order to check for perpendicularity. If two lines appear to be perpendicular in a given view and neither one is true length, then the lines are not perpendicular. **Perpendicular lines** can be either intersecting or nonintersecting lines.

Frontal perpendicular lines appear parallel in the horizontal and profile views and perpendicular in the frontal view. Both lines show true length in the frontal view (Fig. 24.28). In a view where one line is a point view and the other line is true length, the lines are perpendicular.

24.6.1 Intersecting Perpendicular Lines

Intersecting lines have a common point that lies on a single projection line, parallel to all other projection lines between adjacent views. Perpendicular lines make right angles with one another and appear perpendicular in a view where one or both of the lines is true length. Thus, two lines that intersect at a common point and form 90° with each other where one or both lines appears as true length are intersecting perpendicular lines.

When two intersecting lines are oblique in the frontal and horizontal views, project a view where one or both of the lines is true length to check for perpendicularity. Lines 1-2 and 3-4 in Figure 24.29 are intersecting lines, since they have a common point that is aligned in adjacent views. In this example, fold line H/A is drawn parallel to oblique line 1-2 (auxiliary view A is parallel to line 1-2). Both lines are then projected into auxiliary view A. Line 1-2 is true length and forms a 90° angle with (is perpendicular to) line 3-4. Lines 1-2 and 3-4 are perpendicular. Point 5 is the point shared by both lines.

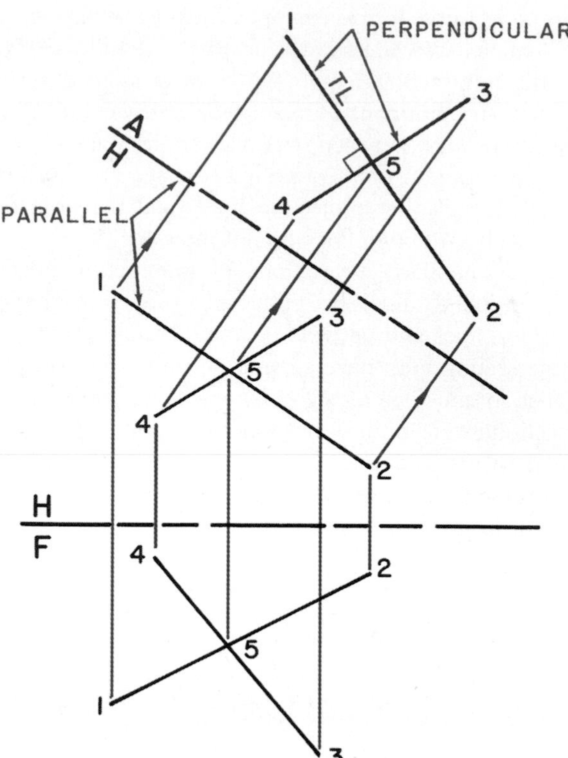

FIGURE 24.29 Intersecting Perpendicular Lines

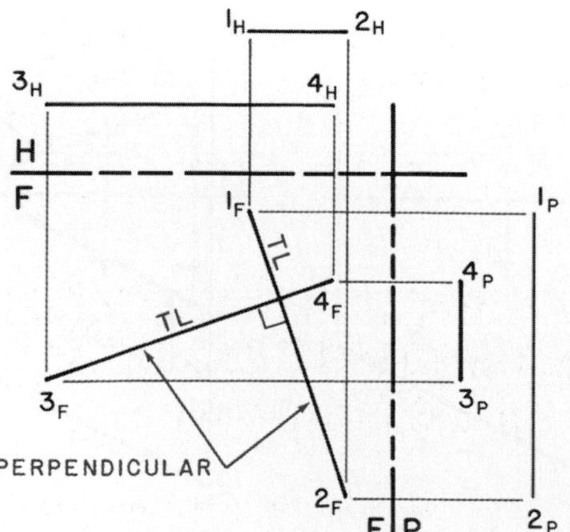

FIGURE 24.28 Nonintersecting Perpendicular Lines

24.6.2 Nonintersecting Perpendicular Lines

Two **nonintersecting lines** are perpendicular lines if they form right angles in a view where one or both are shown true length. For oblique lines, project an auxiliary view where at least one of the lines is true length and measure the angle between the lines in that new view.

In Figure 24.30 the principal views of the two lines establish that they are nonparallel, nonintersecting, and oblique. Auxiliary view A is projected parallel to line 3-4 by drawing fold line F/A parallel to line 3_F-4_F. Projection lines are then drawn perpendicular to the fold lines from all points in the frontal view. Measurements to locate each point are transferred from the horizontal view to establish the points along the projection lines in auxiliary view A. Line 3_A-4_A is true length and line 1_A-2_A is oblique. The lines are perpendicular, since they are at right angles in auxiliary view A.

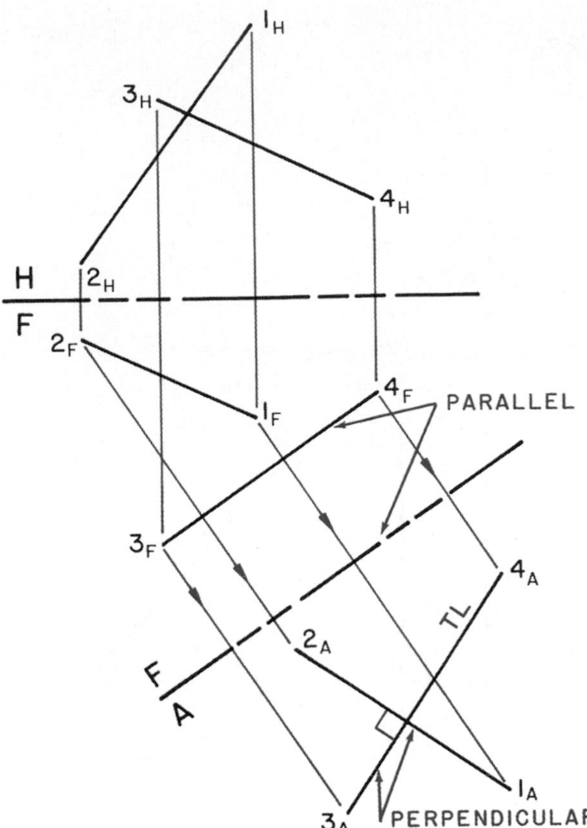

FIGURE 24.30 Perpendicular Lines in Space

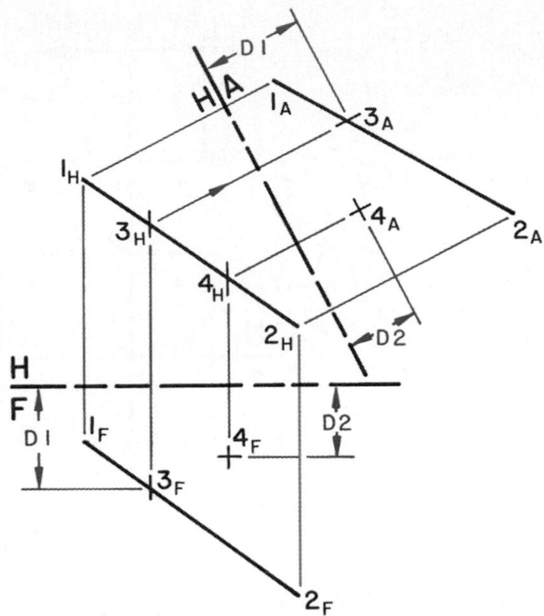

FIGURE 24.31 Points On and Off a Line

24.7 POINTS ON LINES

Successive views (principal or auxiliary) of a point on a line may be projected to all adjacent views by extending a projection line from the point perpendicular to the fold line until it crosses the line in the next view. In Figure 24.31, points 3 and 4 *appear* to be on line 1-2 in the horizontal view, but their frontal and auxiliary views show that only point 3 is on the line, whereas point 4 lies directly above the line, as shown in the horizontal view. If a point is centered on a line, then it must be centered on the line (true length or oblique) in all views.

24.7.1 Point on a Line by Spatial Description

The location of a point on a line can be determined by spatial description and one coordinate dimension. Points can be located by describing their relationship to another point (Fig. 24.32). The frontal view locates a point above or below and to the right or left of a given point. The horizontal view locates a point to the front or back and to the right or left of a given point, and the profile view locates a given point above or below and to the front or back of a given point. Notice that each view has one location direction in common with an adjacent view: in the frontal and horizontal views, the left/right distance; in the frontal and profile views, the above/below distance; and in the horizontal and profile views, the front/back distance.

In Figure 24.32, point 3 is on line 1-2. To locate the point, we need to know only one coordinate distance and its spatial description. Point 3 can be said to lie on line 1-2 at distance D1 behind point 1. This would fix the point in all views by measurement or projection. Another way of describing the location of point 3 would be to say that point 3 is on line 1-2, distance D2 below point 1; or point 3 is on line 1-2, distance D3 to the right of point 1. Of course, point 3 could also be located in respect to point 2. The distance dimension would be given in specific units of measurement.

If point 3 were to lie midpoint on line 1-2, then it would only be necessary to state that fact, since a point on the midpoint of a line is at its midpoint in every view. The above description allows for the spatial description of a point as referenced from an existing point. The new point need not lie on the line to use this method. Also note that a point on a line can simply be projected from view to view, since the point will remain on the line (Fig. 24.33). A point on a line divides the line in the same proportions in every view.

24.8 SHORTEST CONNECTOR BETWEEN TWO LINES (LINE METHOD)

The shortest connector between two skew lines is required in a variety of industrial situations. In Figure 24.34, finding the distance between the chutes is a typical engineering

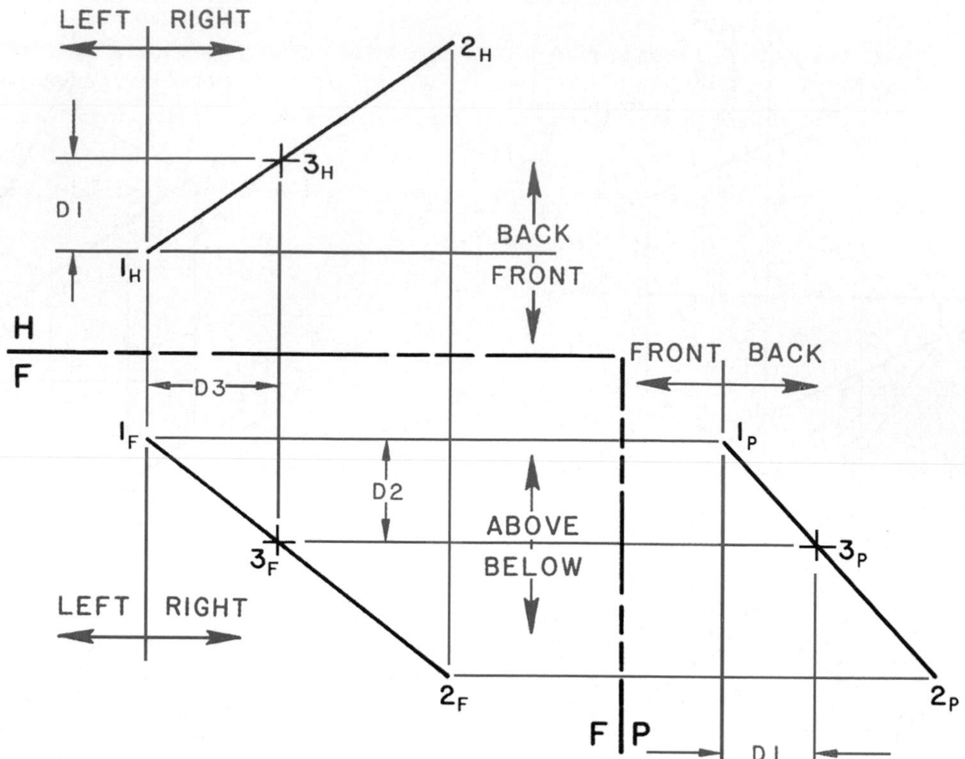

FIGURE 24.32 Points on Lines by Spatial Description

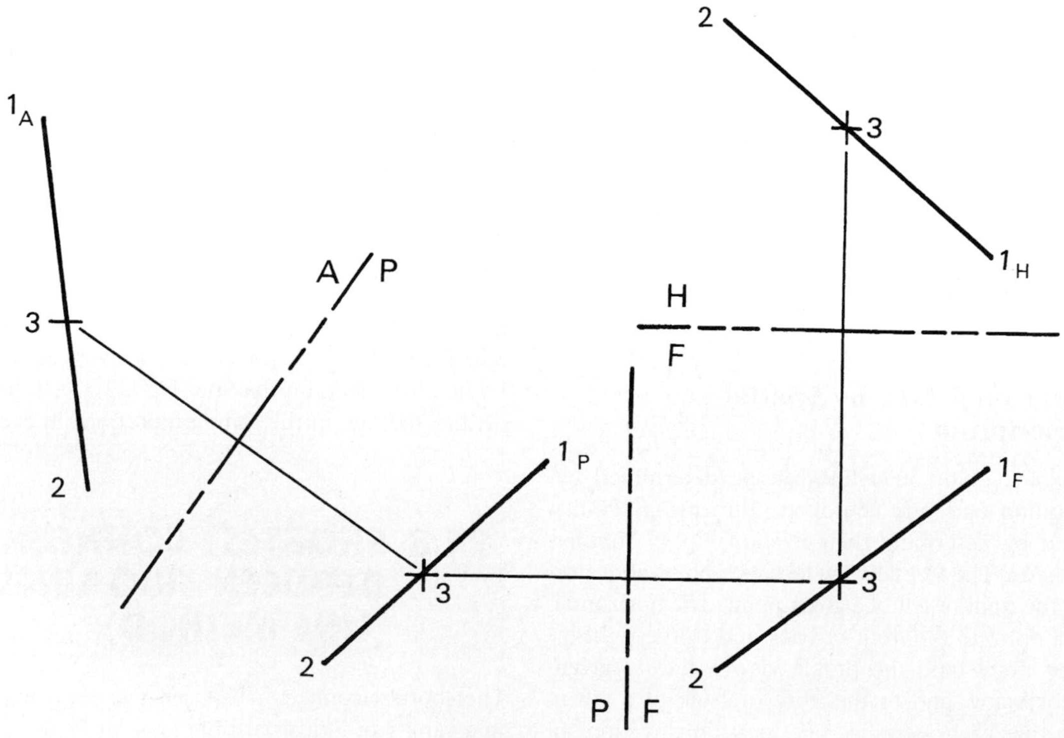

FIGURE 24.33 Locating a Point on a Line

FIGURE 24.34 Industrial Application of Descriptive Geometry

problem. The procedure for finding the shortest distance between a point and line (Section 24.8.1) or between two lines (Section 24.8.2) could have been used to design these elements.

24.8.1 Shortest Distance Between a Point and a Line

A perpendicular line between a given point and line is the shortest connection (distance). The shortest distance between a point and a line is measured along a perpendicular connector in a view where the line appears as a point view.

In Figure 24.35, oblique line 1-2 and point 3 are given. The shortest connector between the line and the point is required. This connector must be shown in all views. The following steps describe the procedure for finding the shortest distance between a point and a line.

1. Draw auxiliary view A parallel to oblique line 1-2. Start by drawing fold line F/A parallel to the line.
2. Project line 1-2 and point 3 into auxiliary view A. Line 1-2 shows true length.
3. Draw a perpendicular connector between point 3 and true-length line 1-2, and label this new point 4. Project auxiliary view B parallel to line 3-4 (and perpendicular to true-length line 1-2). Notice that fold line A/B is parallel to line 3-4 and perpendicular to line 1-2.

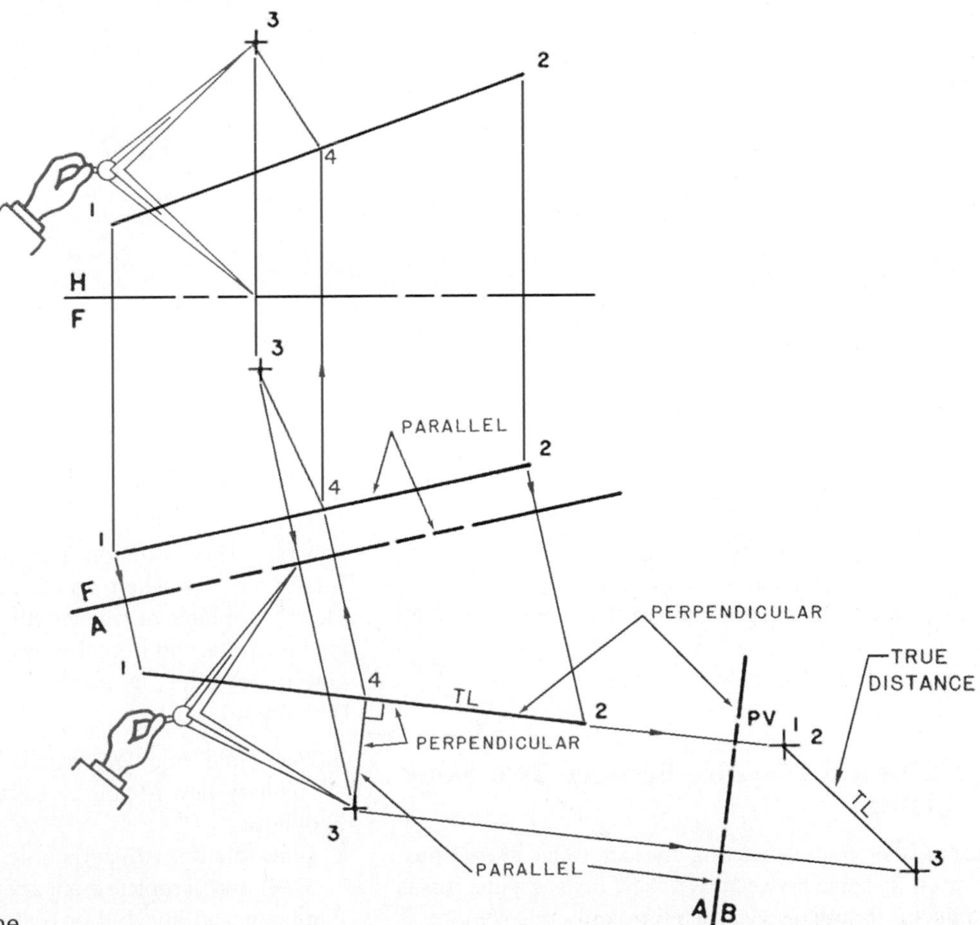

FIGURE 24.35 Shortest Connector (True Distance) Between a Point and a Line

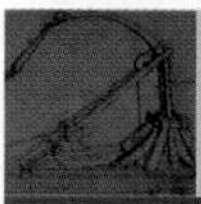

Applying Parametric Design . . .

DATUM AXES

Datum axes can serve as references for feature creation. They are particularly useful for making a datum plane, for placing an item's concentricity, and for creating radial patterns. Axes can be used to measure from, to place coordinate systems, and to place specific features such as a coaxial hole. The angle between features and an axis, the distance between an axis and a feature, and so on can be established with the **Info** command. Axes (appearing as centerlines) are created automatically for (Fig. A):

Revolved features All features whose geometry is revolved, such as revolved base features, holes, shafts, and revolved slots, cut, and protrusions.

Extruded circles An axis will be created for each extruded circle in any extruded feature.

Extruded arcs An axis can be created automatically for extruded arcs only when you set the configuration options.

How to Create a Datum Axis

1. Choose **Datum** from the FEATURES menu and the **Axis** from the DATUM menu.
2. Select **Single** or a pattern option **Dim Pattern** or **Ref Pattern.** Choose **Done.**
3. Choose the desired constraint option from the DATUM AXIS menu:
   - **Thru Edge** Create a datum axis through a straight edge. Select the edge.

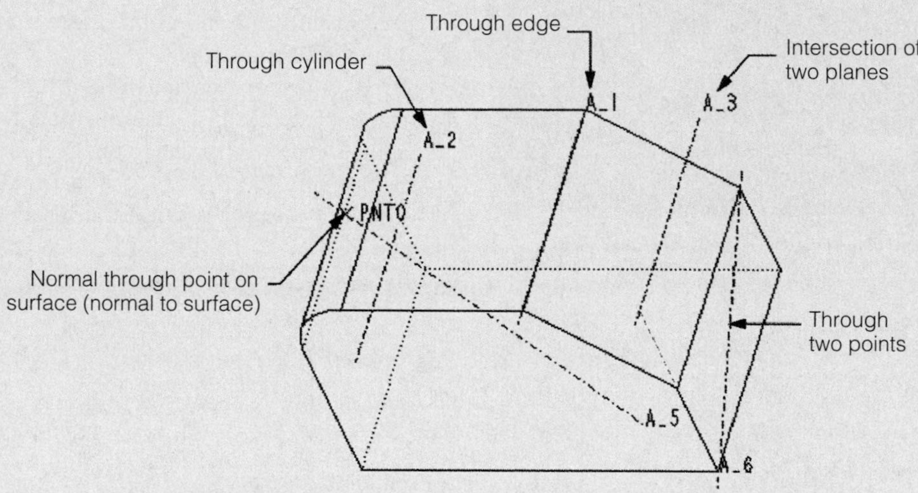

FIGURE A Datum Axis Options

4. Auxiliary view B shows line 1-2 as a point view and line 3-4 (the shortest connector) as true length. The true distance between the point and the line can be measured here.
5. Project line 3-4 back into each view.

24.8.2 Shortest Distance Between Two Skew Lines

Two nonparallel, nonintersecting lines are called **skew lines.** The shortest distance between two skew lines is a line that is perpendicular to both lines. Therefore, only one solution is possible. This common perpendicular is shown as true length in a view where one line appears as a point view and the other oblique or true length. Given lines 1-2 and 3-4 in the horizontal and frontal views, the following steps describe how to solve for the shortest distance between skew lines (Fig. 24.36).

1. Draw fold line F/A parallel to line 3-4, and project auxiliary view A. Line 3-4 is true length and line 1_A-2_A is oblique.
2. Draw fold line A/B perpendicular (90°) to true-length line 3_A-4_A and complete auxiliary view B. Line 3-4 projects as a point and line 1-2 as oblique.

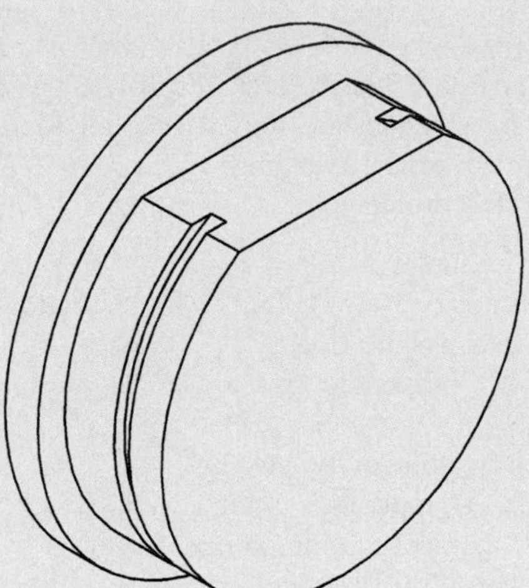

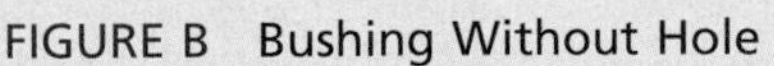

FIGURE B Bushing Without Hole

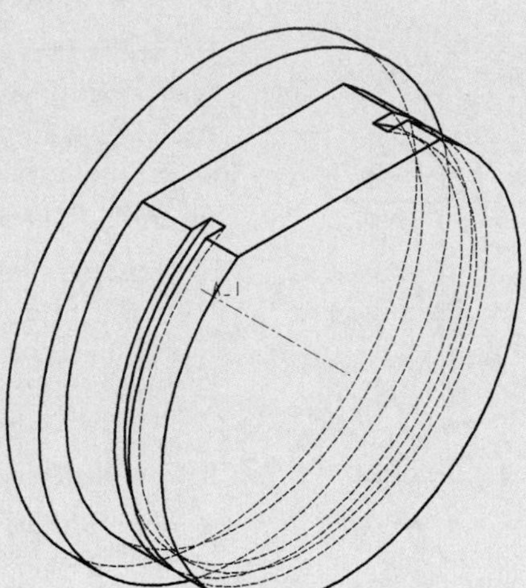

FIGURE C Axis Placed Through cylindrical Feature of Bushing

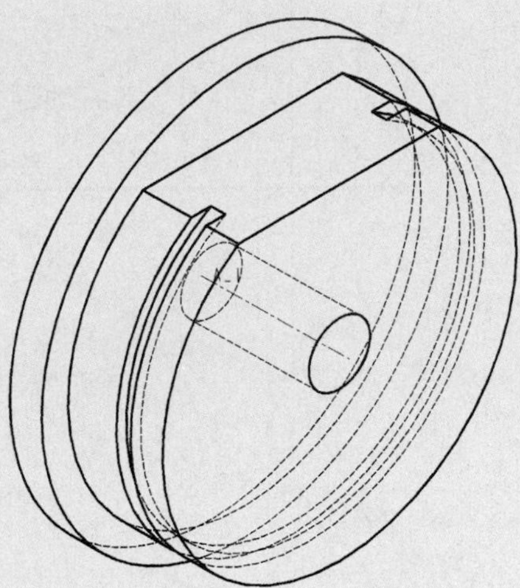

FIGURE D Hole Created Coaxial

- **Norm Pln** Create an axis that is normal to surface, with linear dimensions locating it on that surface.
- **Pnt Norm Pln** Create an axis through a datum point and normal to a specified plane.
- **Thru Cyl** Create an axis through the "imaginary" axis of any surface of revolution (where an axis does not already exist). Select a cylindrical surface or a revolved surface. Note that some features that only appear to be cylindrical, such as a remove surface round, cannot be selected (Fig. A).
- **Two Planes** Create a datum axis at the intersection of two planes (datum planes or surfaces). Select two planes; they cannot be parallel, but they don't have to be shown to intersect on the screen.
- **Two Pnt/Vtx** Create an axis between two datum points or edge vertices. Select datum points or edge vertices.
- **Pnt on Surf** Create an axis through any datum point located on a surface; the point does not need to have been created via **On Surface.** The axis will be normal to the surface at that point.
- **Tan Curve** Create an axis that is tangent to a curve or an edge at its endpoint. Select the curve/edge to be tangent to, then select an endpoint of the curve/edge.

4. Pick the necessary references for the selected option.

A hole can be placed at a required location with the coaxial option (Fig. B). The hole on the bushing was created by the following commands.

1. Create—-Datum—-Axis—-Single—-Thru Cylinder—- (pick the bushing cylinder's curved surface) (Fig. C)
2. Create—-Hole—-Linear—-Single—-Coaxial—-Thru All—-Straight—-One Side—-Thru All—-(give diameter size)—-(select the axis)—-(select the placement plane–front surface of the bushing) (Fig. D)

3. Draw a line from point view 3_B-4_B perpendicular to line 1_B-2_B. Point 5_B is on line 1_B-2_B. This is the shortest distance between the two skew lines. Notice that this shortest-distance line is perpendicular to both skew lines. The distance between PV 3-4 and point 5 is the true distance between line 1-2 and line 3-4.

In Figure 24.37, the shortest distance between the two lines is required. View A establishes the true length of line 1-2, and view B shows its point view. The shortest connector between lines 1-2 and 3-4 is established in view B as shown. Since it is the shortest connector, it is true length. Connector 5-6 is fixed in view A by projection. Point 5 is on line 3-4, and line 5-6 is drawn parallel to fold line B/A. The horizontal and frontal views of line 5-6 are completed by projection.

24.9 ANGULARITY

The angle between two lines is required in a variety of industrial problems, including the angle formed by two structural elements on a power transmission tower and between two pipes in a piping system.

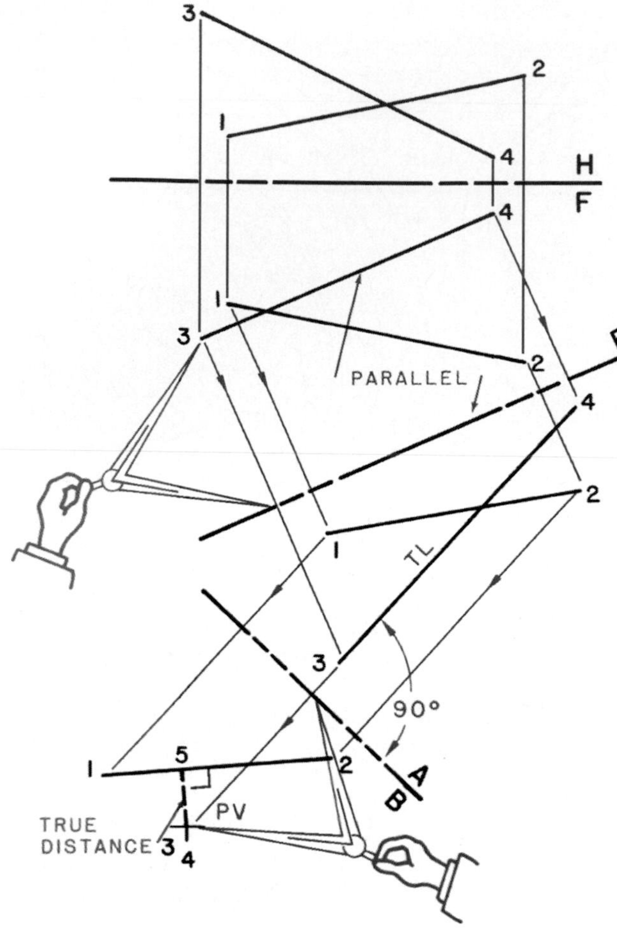

FIGURE 24.36 **Shortest Connector Between Two Lines**

24.9.1 Angle Between Two Skew Lines

The angle formed by two skew lines is measured in a view where both lines appear true length. In Figure 24.38, skew lines 1-2 and 3-4 are given in the frontal and horizontal views; the angle formed by the two lines is required. The following steps solve the problem.

1. Draw fold line F/A parallel to line 3_F-4_F.
2. Project primary auxiliary view A. Line 1_A-2_A is oblique and line 3_A-4_A shows as true length.
3. Draw fold line A/B perpendicular to true-length line 3_A-4_A.
4. Complete secondary auxiliary view B. Line 1_B-2_B is oblique and line 3_B-4_B appears as a point view.
5. Draw fold line B/C parallel to oblique line 1_B-2_B.
6. Project auxiliary view C. Since auxiliary view C is projected parallel to oblique line 1_B-2_B, line 1_C-2_C shows as true length in auxiliary view C. Lines 1-2 and 3-4 both show as true-length lines in this view.

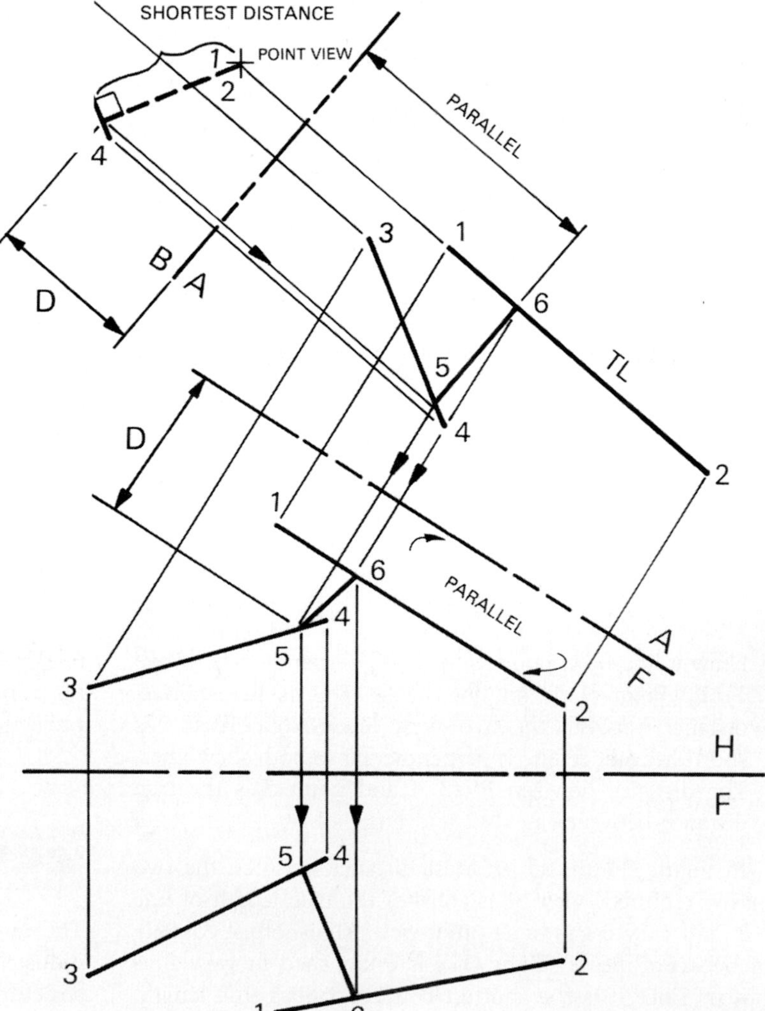

FIGURE 24.37 **Shortest Distance Between Two Lines**

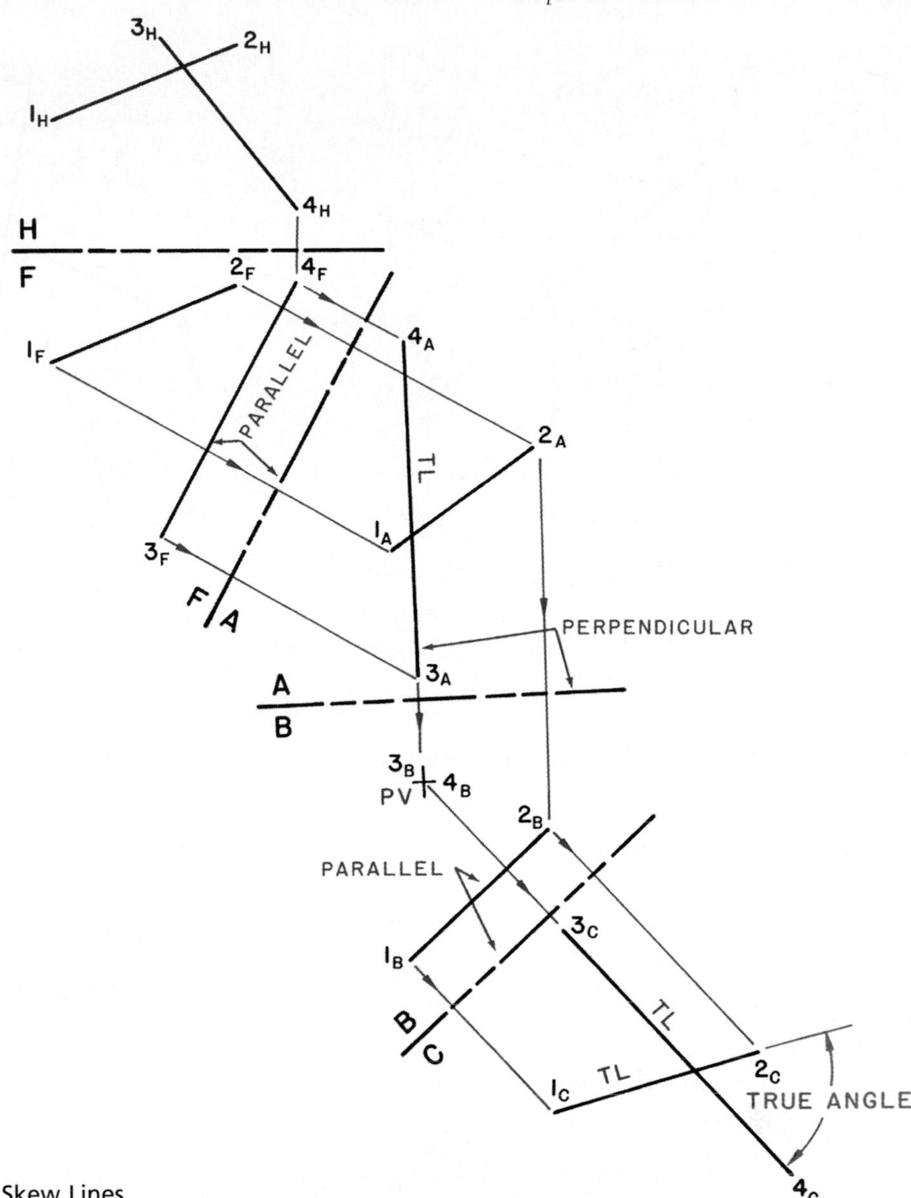

FIGURE 24.38 Angle Between Two Skew Lines

7. The true angle (acute) formed by the two lines can be measured in auxiliary view C, since both lines show true length.

24.9.2 Angle Between Two Intersecting Lines

Since two intersecting lines form a plane, the true angle between the lines is seen in a view where the plane appears true shape. In Figure 24.39, lines 5-6 and 7-8 are intersecting lines; the true angle between them is required.

1. Assuming that lines 5-6 and 7-8 are a plane, draw frontal line 8_H-10_H parallel to H/F, and project to the frontal view, where it appears true length.
2. Draw F/A perpendicular to true-length line 8_F-10_F, and project auxiliary view A. Line 8_A-10_A appears as a point view; therefore "plane" 5_A-6_A-7_A-8_A shows as an edge.
3. Draw A/B parallel to the edge view of "plane" 5_A-6_A-7_A-8_A, and project auxiliary view B. Intersecting lines 5_B-6_B and 7_B-8_B are both true length and thus determine the true size of plane 5_B-6_B-7_B-8_B.
4. The true angle formed by lines 5_B-6_B and 7_B-8_B can be measured in this view. Notice that the acute angle is measured.

24.9.3 Angle Between a Line and a Principal Plane

The true angle between a line and a principal plane shows in a view where the line is true length and the principal plane appears as an edge. It follows that principal lines form a true angle with the edge view of the adjacent principal plane. The angle formed by a horizontal line and the H/F fold line is the true angle between the line and the frontal plane. The angle formed by a frontal line and the H/F fold line is the true angle between the line and the horizontal plane, and the angle it makes with F/P is the true angle between it and the profile plane. The angle formed by a profile line and the F/P

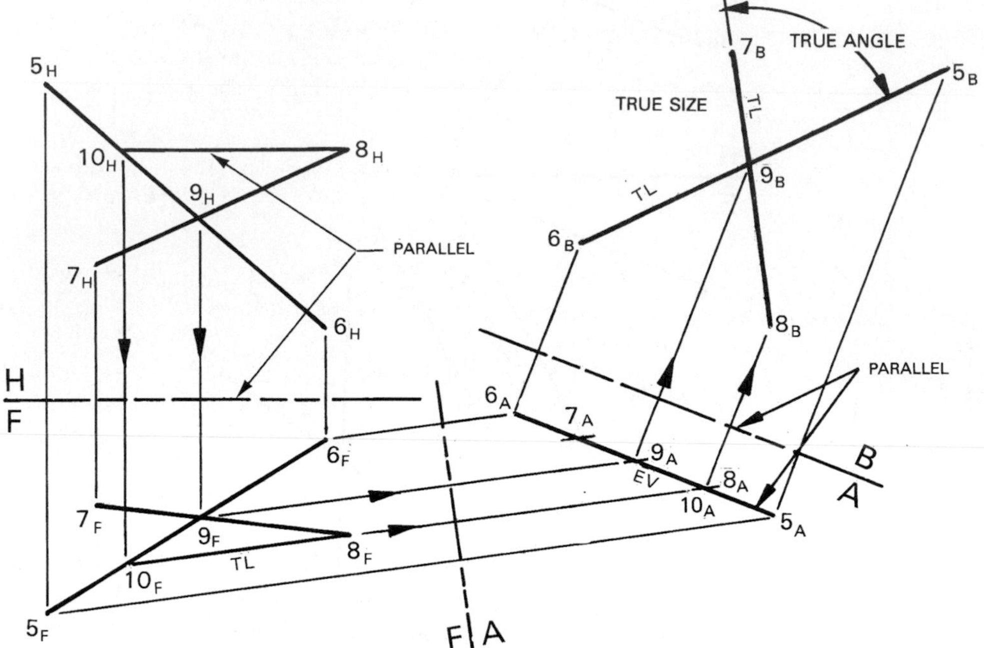

FIGURE 24.39 Angle Between Two Intersecting Lines

fold line is the angle that the line makes with the frontal plane.

When a given line is oblique, it is necessary to project a primary auxiliary view where the line is true length and the principal plane shows as an edge. In Figure 24.40(a), oblique line 5-6 is given and the angle between it and the horizontal plane is required. Primary auxiliary A is projected parallel to line 5_H-6_H. Draw H/A parallel to line 5_H-6_H, and complete auxiliary A. In this new view, line 5_A-6_A appears true length and the horizontal plane shows as an edge. The true angle between line 5_A-6_A and fold line H/A is the true angle between the line and the horizontal plane.

The true angle formed by oblique line 1-2 and the frontal plane in Figure 24.40(b) can be measured in a primary auxiliary view that shows the line as true length and the frontal plane as an edge. In this example F/A is drawn parallel to line 1_F-2_F. Auxiliary view A shows line 1_A-2_A as true length and the frontal plane as an edge. Therefore the true angle between them is measured between line 1_A-2_A and the F/A fold line.

In Figure 24.40(c), line 7-8 is oblique and the angle it makes with the profile plane is required. Auxiliary view A is projected parallel to line 7_P-8_P. The true angle can be measured in this view, since line 7_A-8_A is true length and the profile plane appears as an edge.

You May Complete Exercises 24.5 through 24.7 at This Time

24.10 DESCRIPTIVE GEOMETRY USING CAD

Traditionally, engineers and designers have conceptualized a design in three dimensions and then presented the concept by constructing 2D views on paper. With the manual method for projection and solving problems with descriptive geometry, you must rely on the accuracy of your linework and projection proficiency instead of the quality of the 3D model database. Designing with a 3D CAD system is a much more realistic way to produce the model of a part. The 3D model is the starting point for engineering analysis, design, and manufacturing. Via computer commands, you mold or model the part. The part exists in 3D space and is defined mathematically within the computer by 3D coordinates.

Even though 2D systems are limited when compared to 3D systems, the use of 2D CAD in descriptive geometry and in projects requiring orthographic projection is still advantageous. Verifying (listing), measuring, and calculating are very accurate with a CAD system, whereas the manual methods of scaling and calculating are prone to errors and inaccuracies.

Model geometry is constructed in a 3D coordinate system. Therefore, all spatial relationships of the design can be determined accurately from the model itself, not a 2D representation of the part. The location and the true length of each element, the size and area of each face plane, and the intersections of surfaces or shapes can be determined directly from the model database; descriptive geometry and

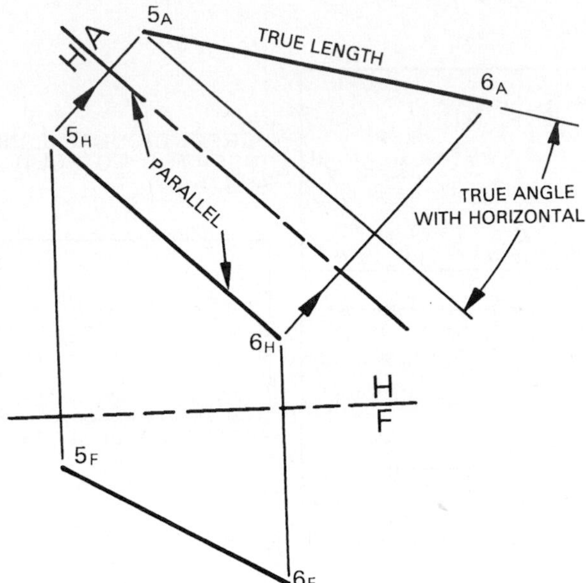

(a) The angle a line makes with the horizontal plane

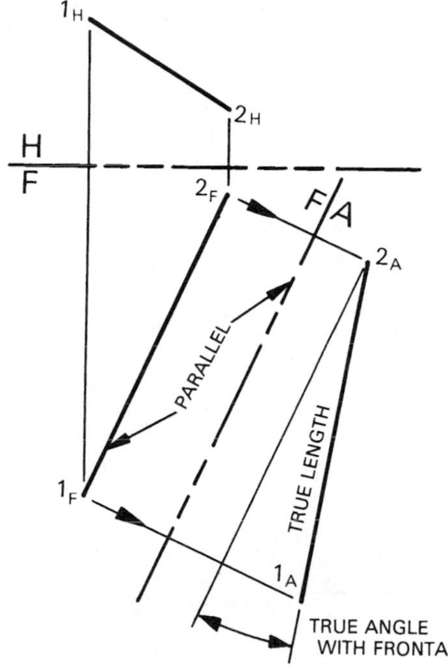

(b) The angle a line makes with the frontal plane

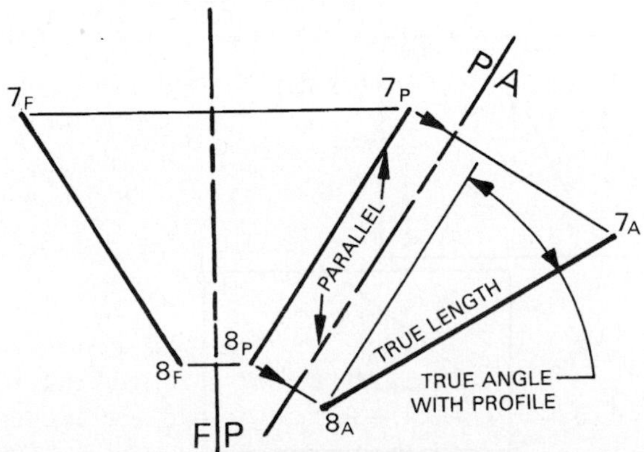

(c) The angle a line makes with the profile plane

FIGURE 24.40 Angle Between Lines and Principal Planes

orthographic projection have limited use. Views of the part are generated automatically from the model by the system. Sections can also be constructed automatically by the system and analysis can be performed on the computer part.

24.10.1 Descriptive Geometry Versus 2D and 3D CAD Capabilities

Depending on the type of modeling available, the use of orthographic projection and descriptive geometry may be similar, lessened, or possibly eliminated. Based on the type of computer model that was built, both 2D and 3D systems allow automatic extraction of a certain amount of information. A 2D system will extract accurate measurements for each view of the part. Therefore, measurements, like the length of a line, can be easily verified. The area of a surface can be calculated automatically. The distance between two points or a point and a line can be extracted. Parallelism, the angle between two lines, and perpendicularity can be determined. All of these measurements are possible as long as the elements being measured lie in the plane of the 2D coordinate system used by the system.

A 3D system can also perform any of these 2D measurements. However, the 3D system offers many more capabilities. A 3D system can calculate volume. It can measure the distance between two points, lines, or planes regardless of their placement in space, and can perform a variety of tasks beyond the capabilities of a 2D system.

24.10.2 Traditional Descriptive Geometry Problems and CAD

Traditional descriptive geometry problems involve the relationship of points, lines, and planes, solving for intersections, and laying out developments (intersections and developments using CAD will be discussed in Chapters 27 and 28). Since a 3D system builds a model in 3D space, many of the traditional descriptive geometry techniques can be replaced. The true length of a line, the distance between a point and a line, the shortest distance between two lines, and problems in parallelism, perpendicularity, and revolution can be extracted automatically. The true angle between lines and the dihedral angle between planes are determined by the system. Revolution of lines, planes, or solids is completed in 3D space instead of simulated on paper.

The true length of a line is one of the most common requirements to the solution of a multitude of descriptive geometry problems. For a solution, a minimum of a three-view drawing with an auxiliary projection is required. The true length of an oblique line is solved for in Figure 24.41. The auxiliary true-length projection is simply folded from a view of the line. In the CAD-generated solution, the true length is established by verifying the entity. Verifying (**LIST** command on AutoCAD) an entity is a process in which you request the data establishing the entities, type, layer, color, position in space, and size. In Figure 24.41 the line is oblique in the given frontal view. The line is folded about

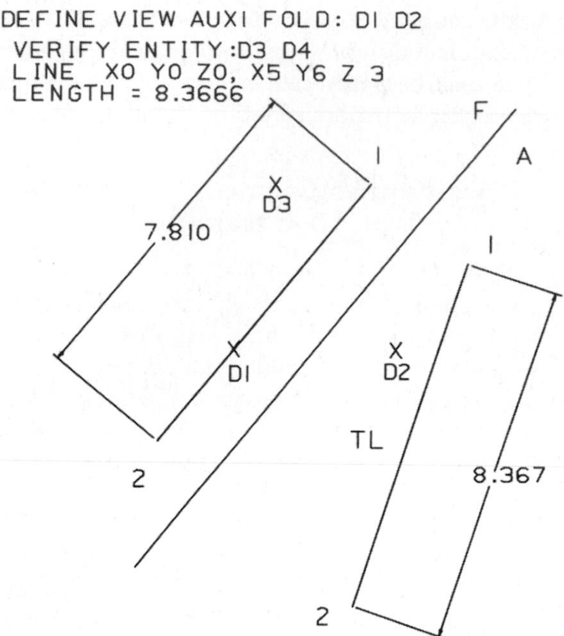

FIGURE 24.41 Solving for the True Length of an Oblique Line Using CAD

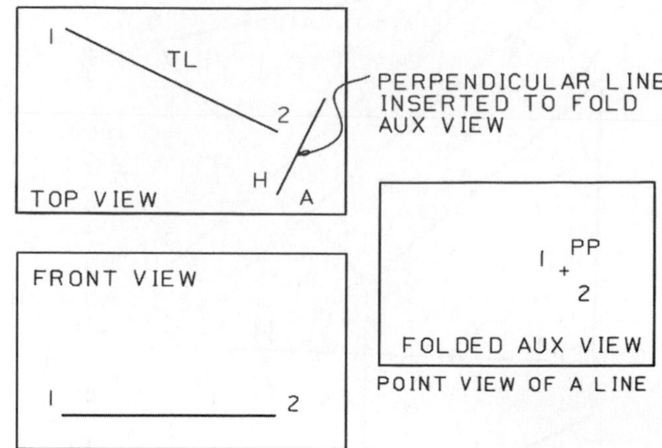

FIGURE 24.42 Point View Using CAD

F/A. The verification establishes the length as 8.3666 in. Measurements were placed on the frontal view and auxiliary view A, as shown. Notice that the frontal view shows the line's length to be 7.810. This is the oblique view of the line; therefore it shows as foreshortened. The dimension in view A establishes the true-length measurement as 8.367 (rounded). Originally, the line was input using coordinates, and the system responds to the verifying command with the precise location of the endpoints of the line and its length. The auxiliary projection showing the line as true length was not necessary to extract the line's length and location.

With AutoCAD, verification of an entity is accomplished with the **LIST** command. **LIST** provides the X, Y, and Z locations of the endpoints of the line, the length of the line, the angle the line makes with the X-Y plane, and the layer, as shown here:

```
Command: LIST
Select objects: pick line <enter>
LINE Layer: xxxx
     Space: Model space or Paper space
     Handle= xxxx
From point, X= xxxx   Y= xxxx   Z= xxxx
Length= xxxx
Angle in XY Plane= xxxx
Delta X= xxxx
Delta Y= xxxx
Delta Z= xxxx
```

Typically, the next step after the projection of the true length of a line is to solve for the point view. A second auxiliary projection is necessary for lines that are oblique in the given view. In Figure 24.42, the CAD solution required inputting of the coordinates of the line and folding each successive view from the model view that was first created.

To establish the relationship of lines in space, a minimum of two views is necessary in traditional descriptive geometry, and often three projections will be required. The CAD solution requires inputting of the line's coordinates and picking the **MEASURE ANGLE** command. In Figure 24.43, the front and top views are included, but only one view was really necessary. The **MEASURE ANGLE** (Personal designer) command extracted the obtuse and acute angles between the lines and the relationship of the lines in space.

Lines in space can have any of three spatial relationships: intersecting, parallel, or skew. When two lines appear parallel in a view, a second or third view is necessary to prove

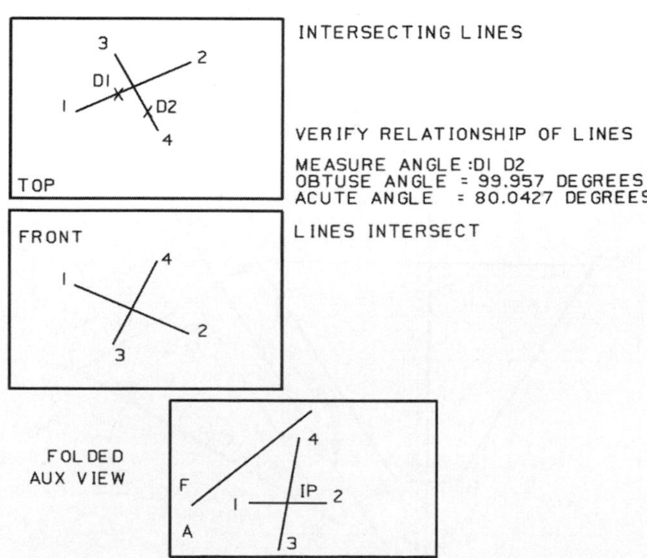

FIGURE 24.43 Angle of Two Lines in Space Using the MEASURE Command

PARALLELISM CHECK
ANGLE BETWEEN LINES
SHORTEST DISTANCE

5 7 DI D2 6 8

MEASURE DISTANCE :DI D2
LINES SKEW
OBTUSE ANGLE = 107.65°
ACUTE ANGLE = 72.34°
MINIMUM DISTANCE = 1.5

FIGURE 24.44 **Parallelism, Angle, and Shortest Distance Solutions Using CAD**

parallelism. In Figure 24.44, the profile view would normally be needed when using descriptive geometry. The CAD solution requires inputting of the lines using coordinates and selecting the **MEASURE DISTANCE** command. Besides extracting the relationship of the lines (skew), the system provided the angle between the lines and the minimum distance. AutoCAD has a similar command called **DISTANCE**, which asks you to pick the endpoints of the entities you wish to measure. The distance, the angle in the X-Y plane, and the angle from the X-Y plane are then provided, as shown here:

```
Command: DISTANCE
'dist from point: use OSNAP and pick position on object
Second point: use OSNAP and pick second position on object
Distance= xxxx
Angle in XY Plane= xxxx
Angle from XY Plane= xxxx
Delta X= xxxx
Delta Y= xxxx
Delta Z= xxxx
```

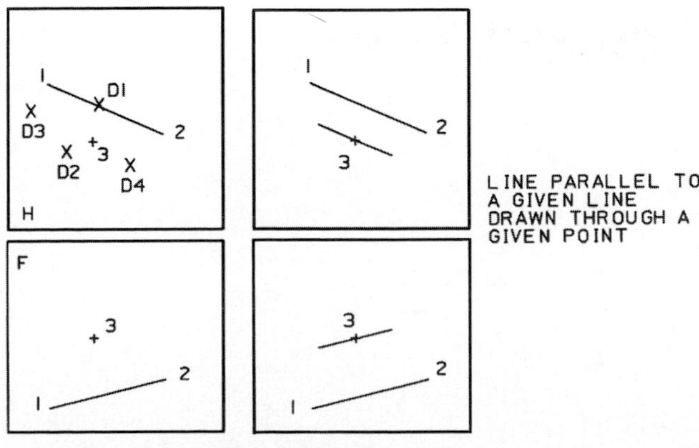

FIGURE 24.45 **Inserting a Line Parallel to Another Line and Through a Given Point Using CAD**

To draw a line parallel to a given line and through a point (Fig. 24.45) is a fairly simple, but typical, problem in descriptive geometry. The CAD-generated solution requires inputting of the X, Y, Z locations of the given line and point, as shown in Figure 24.45 (left). An **OFFSET** command, or a **DRAW LINE PARALLEL** command as shown, is input. The given line is selected (D1), then the side of the line where the parallel line is to be drawn is established (D2). Last, the endpoints of the new line (D3 and D4) are picked [Fig. 24.45 (right)]. The line will show in all views since this was drawn on a 3D system.

The AutoCAD **OFFSET** command could also accomplish the same thing if the required line were exactly the same length as the original line:

```
Command: OFFSET
Offset distance or Through <Through>: give distance
Select object to offset: pick line
Side to offset? pick offset side
```

In Figure 24.46 only one view of the lines in space is provided. Since the **MEASURE** command establishes that they are at 90°, they are perpendicular lines. Therefore, the lines are nonintersecting (skew).

The procedure for constructing a line perpendicular to a given line and through an established point is provided in Figure 24.47. A third projection, in which one of the lines is true length, is normally necessary. The CAD-generated solution was established by giving the coordinates of the given line and then the **DRAW LINE PERPENDICULAR** command (Personal Designer CAD system). This is also called the shortest distance between a line and a point and is a common problem in descriptive geometry. The manual solution normally requires two auxiliary projections. The CAD solution simply requires the insertion of a perpendicular line between the point and the given line. The **DRAW LINE PERPENDICULAR** command meant selecting the original line (D1), the given point (D2), and the given line again with the **ON** option (mask) (D3). The system constructed the line from the point to the line (on the line). The views for this solution show the lines as skew. Since a 3D CAD system was involved, it was unnecessary to draw the lines in a view in which they show perpendicular. The

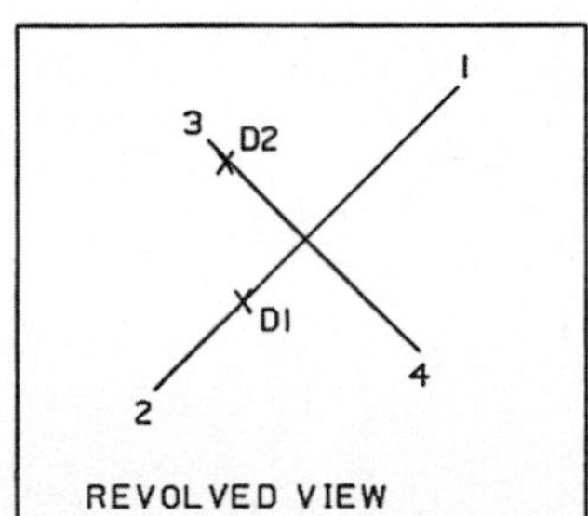

FIGURE 24.46 **Perpendicularity Check Using the MEASURE Command**

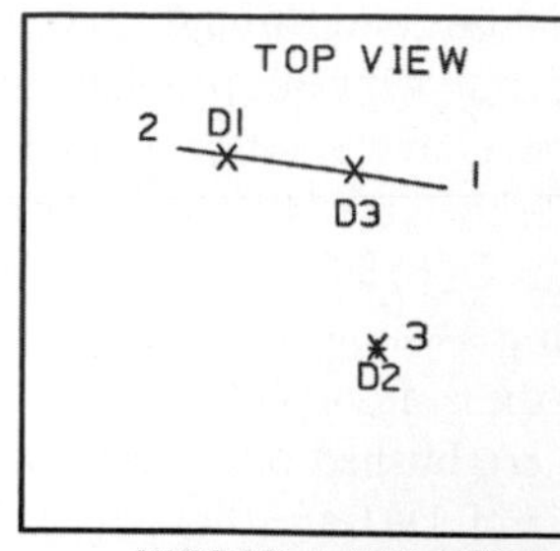

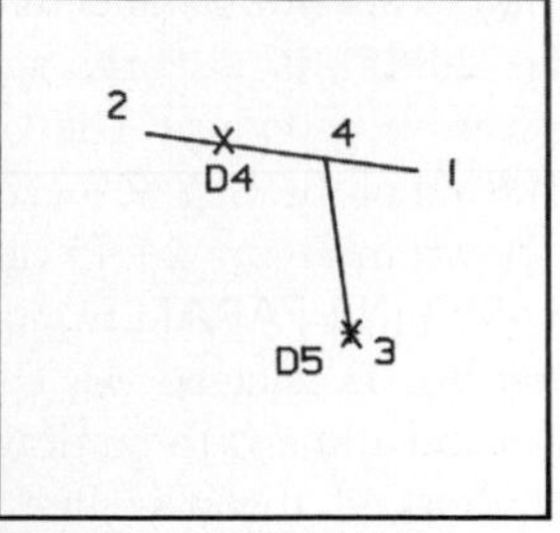

INSERT LINE PERPENDICULAR: DI D2 ON D3
MEASURE DISTANCE :D4 D5

NORMAL DISTANCE 1.75

1. SHORTEST DISTANCE BETWEEN A LINE AND A POINT
2. LINE DRAWN PERPENDICULAR TO A LINE AND THROUGH A GIVEN POINT
3. LINE 3-4 IS THE SHORTEST (PERPENDICULAR) CONNECTOR

FIGURE 24.47 Inserting a Line Perpendicular to Another Line and Through a Given Point Using CAD

MEASURE DISTANCE, VERIFY, or LIST command then provides the length of the shortest connector, which is the normal distance.

The preceding discussion of CAD-generated solutions to descriptive geometry problems is not meant to show all the possible descriptive geometry problems encountered in engineering and design.

QUIZ

True or False

1. Perpendicular lines show in any view in which one or both of the lines is true length.
2. Parallelism of two lines can always be established with only two views.
3. The bearing of a line is measured from the north toward the east or the west.
4. Revolutions will in many cases eliminate the need for an auxiliary view.
5. Parallel planes can be determined in a view in which both planes project as edges.
6. The shortest distance between two parallel lines can be measured in a view in which the lines appear as point views.
7. Oblique lines are never true length in a principal view.
8. The cutting plane method for finding the intersection of a line and a plane requires only two views.

Fill in the Blanks

9. Two oblique lines that appear ________ in two or more views will always be ________.
10. The angle between two intersecting lines can be measured in any view in which the ________ both appear________ ________.
11. Two lines on the same plane must be either ________ or ________.
12. To establish the angle between a line and a plane, the plane must appear as an ________ ________ and the line ________ ________.
13. To establish the point of intersection between a line and a plane, project a view in which the plane is shown as an ________ ________.
14. A point view of a line can be projected in a view in which the ________ ________ is parallel to a true-length view of the ________.
15. Frontal lines and frontal planes are ________ to or lie in the frontal ________ ________.
16. The path of a point as it is revolved about an ________ ________ will scribe a ________ arc.

Answer the Following

17. How many views are necessary to fix the position of a point or a line in space?
18. Define a vertical line. In what views will it appear vertical?
19. If a line is vertical in the profile plane, what type of line is it in the top and front views?
20. What is the bearing and the slope of a line?
21. How can you obtain a true length of an oblique line?
22. How can you tell if two lines are perpendicular?
23. Explain how to check for perpendicularity of two lines.
24. What is a point view of a line?

EXERCISES

Exercises may be assigned as sketching, instrument, or CAD projects. Transfer the given information to an "A"-size sheet of .25 in. grid paper. Complete all views, and solve for proper visibility, including centerlines, object lines, and hidden lines. Exercises that are not assigned by the instructor can be sketched in the text to provide practice and to enhance understanding of the preceding instructional material.

After Reading the Chapter Through Section 24.5.1 You May Complete Exercises 21.1 Through 21.4

Exercise 24.1(A) Locate the three points in all views.

Exercise 24.1(B) Locate the following three points in the given views. Point 1 is seven units below point 2. Point 2 is two units behind point 1. Point 3 is three units to the left of point 2. Point 1 is given in the horizontal view, point 2 is given in the frontal view, and point 3 is given in the profile view.

Exercise 24.1(C) Locate points 1 and 2 in all four views. Point 1 is given. Point 2 is .25 in. (6 mm) in front of, .75 in. (20 mm) to the right of, and 1.25 in. (32 mm) below point 1.

Exercise 24.1(D) Locate the following points: Point 1 is four units behind the frontal plane, nine units to the left of the profile plane, and twelve units below the horizontal plane. Point 2 is three units behind the frontal plane, seven units below the horizontal plane, and seven units to the right of point 1. What is the distance between the two points in the front view?

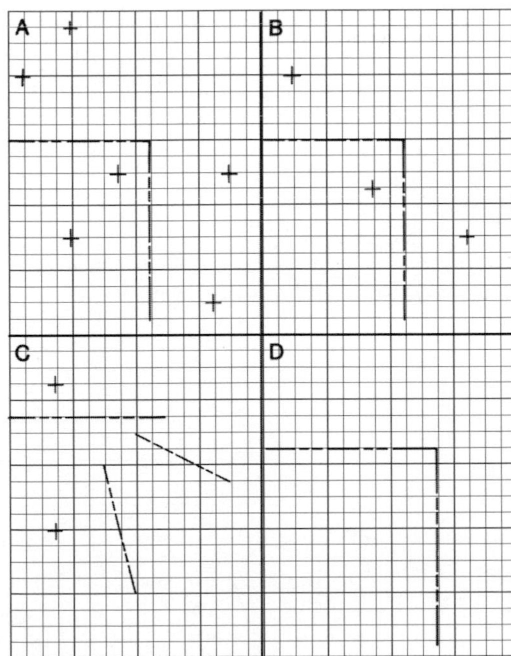

EXERCISE 24.1

Exercise 24.2(A) Complete the three views of the profile line.

Exercise 24.2(B) Complete the three views of the profile lines.

Exercise 24.2(C) Locate the given line in the required auxiliary views.

Exercise 24.3(A) and (B) Complete the three views of the given lines. Label lines where they appear as principal lines, and note if a line is oblique, inclined, true length, or parallel with a projection plane. Show all possible solutions.

Exercise 24.3(C) Solve for the true length of the line and the point view. Note the bearing of the line. Point 1 is above point 2. What are the bearing, azimuth, slope, and grade of the line?

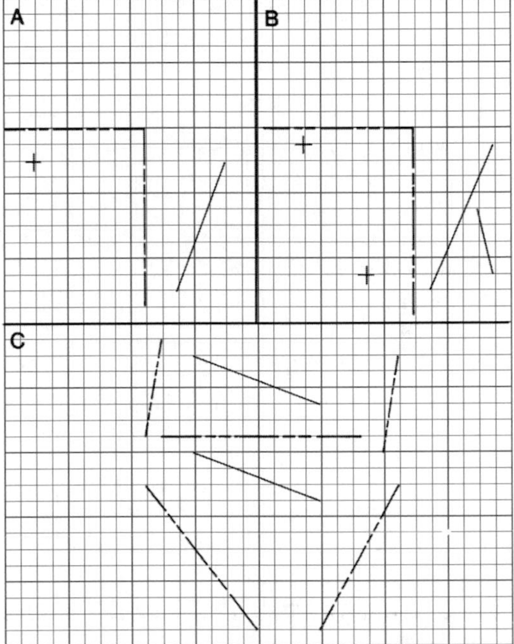

EXERCISE 24.2

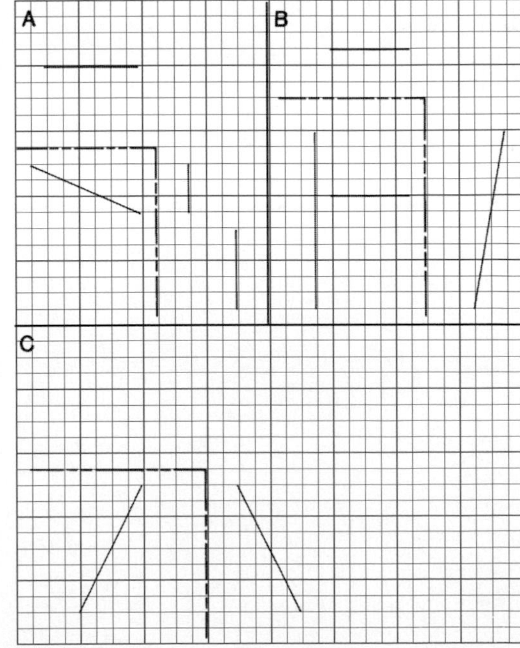

EXERCISE 24.3

Exercise 24.4(A) and (B) Complete the views of the pipes, and solve for visibility. Shade the pipe that is visible in each view.

Exercise 24.4(C) Complete the three views of the parallel lines.

Exercise 24.4(D) Complete the views of the lines. Are they parallel?

After Reading the Chapter Through Section 24.9.3 You May Complete the Following Exercises

Exercise 24.5(A) Complete the views of the two lines. Line 3-4 shows as a point view in the horizontal view. Are they perpendicular? Note all true-length lines.

Exercise 24.5(B) Project the three views of the two intersecting perpendicular lines.

Exercise 24.5(C) Construct a line through the point, perpendicular to and on the given line.

Exercise 24.5(D) Draw a line through the point and perpendicular to the line in the horizontal view.

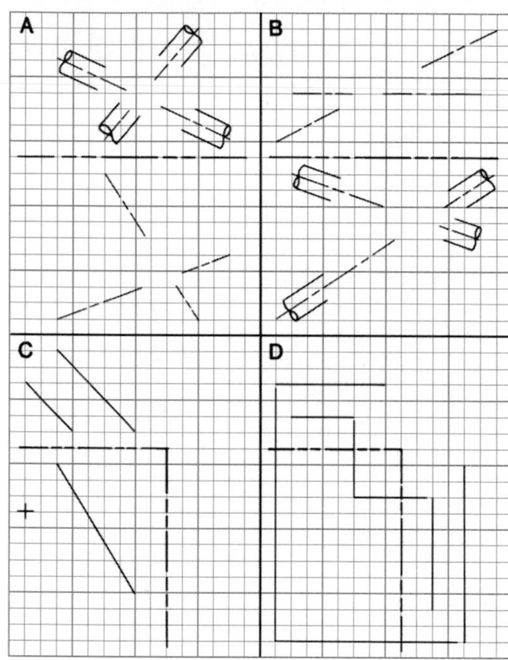

EXERCISE 24.4

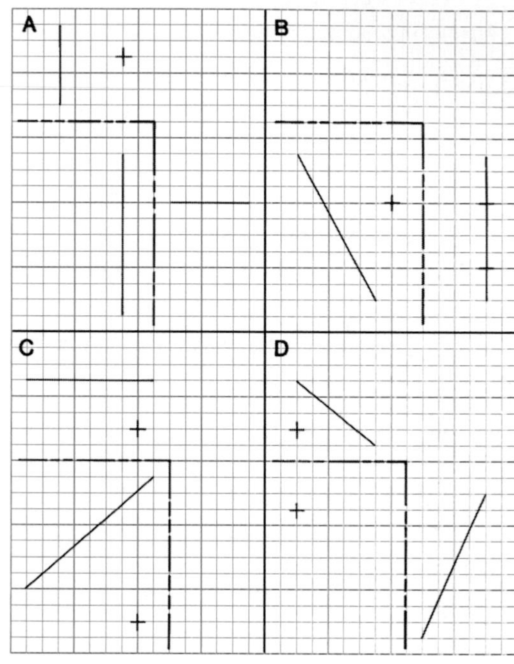

EXERCISE 24.5

Exercise 24.6(A) Draw the given line in each view, and locate the points on the line in each projection.

Exercise 24.6(B) Locate point 3, which is three units to the right of point 1 and lies on the line. Point 4 is eight units below point 1 and on line 1-2. Point 1 is above point 2.

Exercise 24.6(C) Solve for the true-length distance between the line and the point. Show the connector and the point in each view.

Exercise 24.6(D) Find the shortest (perpendicular) distance between the two lines. Project the line back into all views.

Exercise 24.7 Solve for the angle between the two lines. Show the shortest connector between the lines, and show it in all views.

EXERCISE 24.6

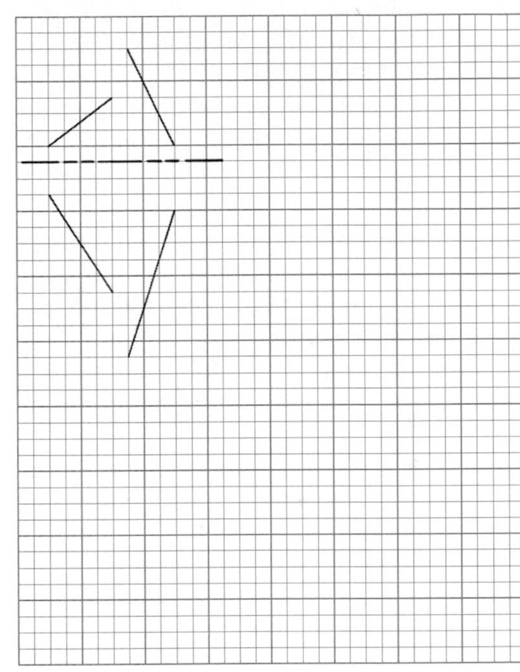

EXERCISE 24.7

PROBLEMS

Problems may be assigned as sketching, instrument, or CAD projects. For Problem 24.1, transfer the given problem to a separate "A"-size sheet. Complete all views, and solve for proper visibility, including centerlines, object lines, and hidden lines. Use dividers to transfer the positions of the points and lines. Note that a $\frac{1.5}{1}$ scale is suggested, but a $\frac{2}{1}$ scale could also be used. Two problems can be put on each sheet. Make a rough trial sketch of the problem and the solution before finalizing its position on drafting paper. This will avoid placement of the problem without enough work space to complete the project.

Problem 24.1(A) Project the profile view of point 1. Locate a point 2 that is .75 in. (1.9 cm) in front of, .50 in. (1.27 cm) to the right of, and 1 in. (2.54 cm) below point 1. Show point 2 in all views.

Problem 24.1(B) Project three views of the line 1-2. Point 2 is .75 in. (1.9 cm) in front of, 1 in. (2.54 cm) to the right of, and 1.25 in. (3.17 cm) below point 1. If there is a true-length projection of line 1-2, label it TL.

Problem 24.1(C) Complete the three views of line 2-3, and project an auxiliary view showing the line as true length. Take the auxiliary projection from the frontal view.

Problem 24.1(D) Complete the profile view of line 5-6. Solve for the true length of the line in two separate auxiliary projections and label as TL.

Problem 24.1(E) Solve for the correct visibility of the pipes. Note that the fold line is not shown.

Problem 24.1(F) Project the missing view of the two horizontal lines. Are they parallel? Label any true-length projections.

Problem 24.1(G) Construct line 1-2 perpendicular to line 3-4. Point 2 will lie on line 3-4. Project the profile view.

Problem 24.1(H) Construct line 3-4 perpendicular to line 1-2. Point 4 will be at the midpoint of line 1-2.

Problem 24.1(I) Project the shortest connector, line 3-4, between the two skewed lines. Point 4 is to be on line 7-8. Show line 3-4 in the horizontal and frontal views.

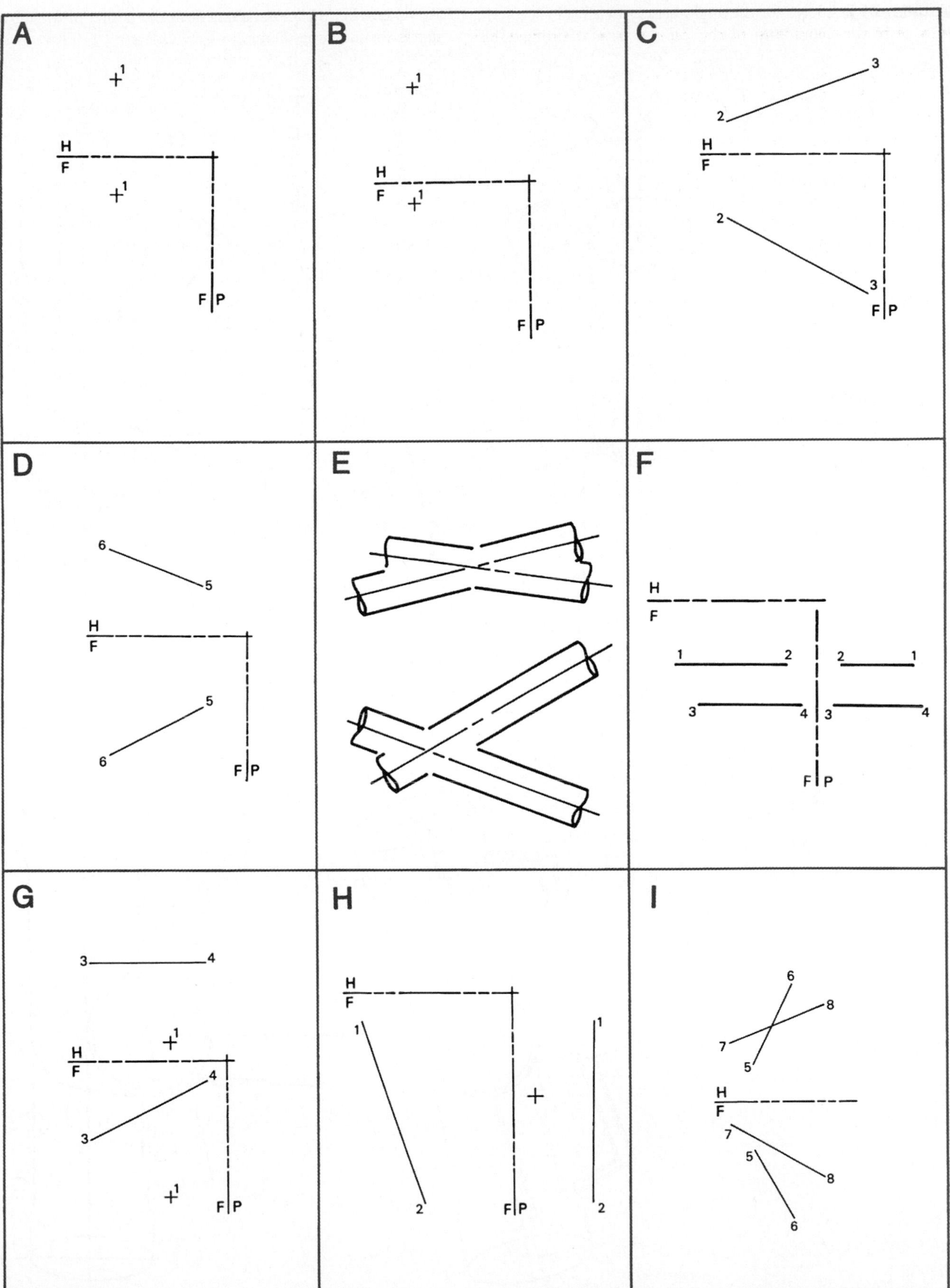
A
1
H
F
1
F P
B
1
H
F
1
F P
C
3
2
H
F
2
3
F P
D
6
5
H
F
5
6
F P
E
F
H
F
1
2
2
1
3
4
3
4
F P
G
3
4
1
H
F
4
3
1
F P
H
H
F
1
1
2
F P
2
I
6
8
7
5
H
F
7
5
8
6

PROBLEM 24.1

Problem 24.2 Solve for the angle between each of the pipes. Draw only the centerlines of the pipe structural fitting. This assembly was a structural element in the design of the moveable stands for the Super Dome in New Orleans.

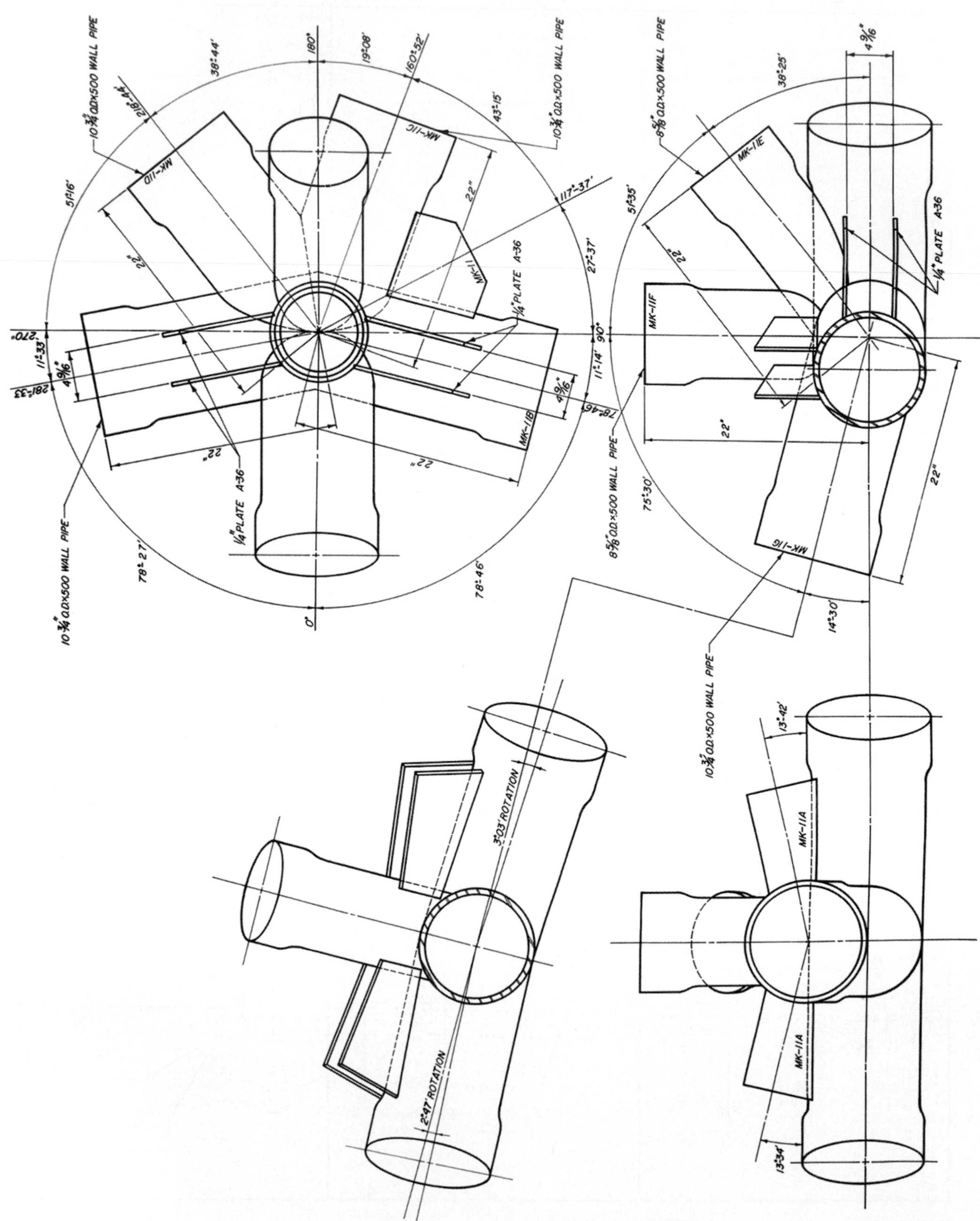

PROBLEM 24.2

Problem 24.3 Draw the part and solve for the angle between each bend.

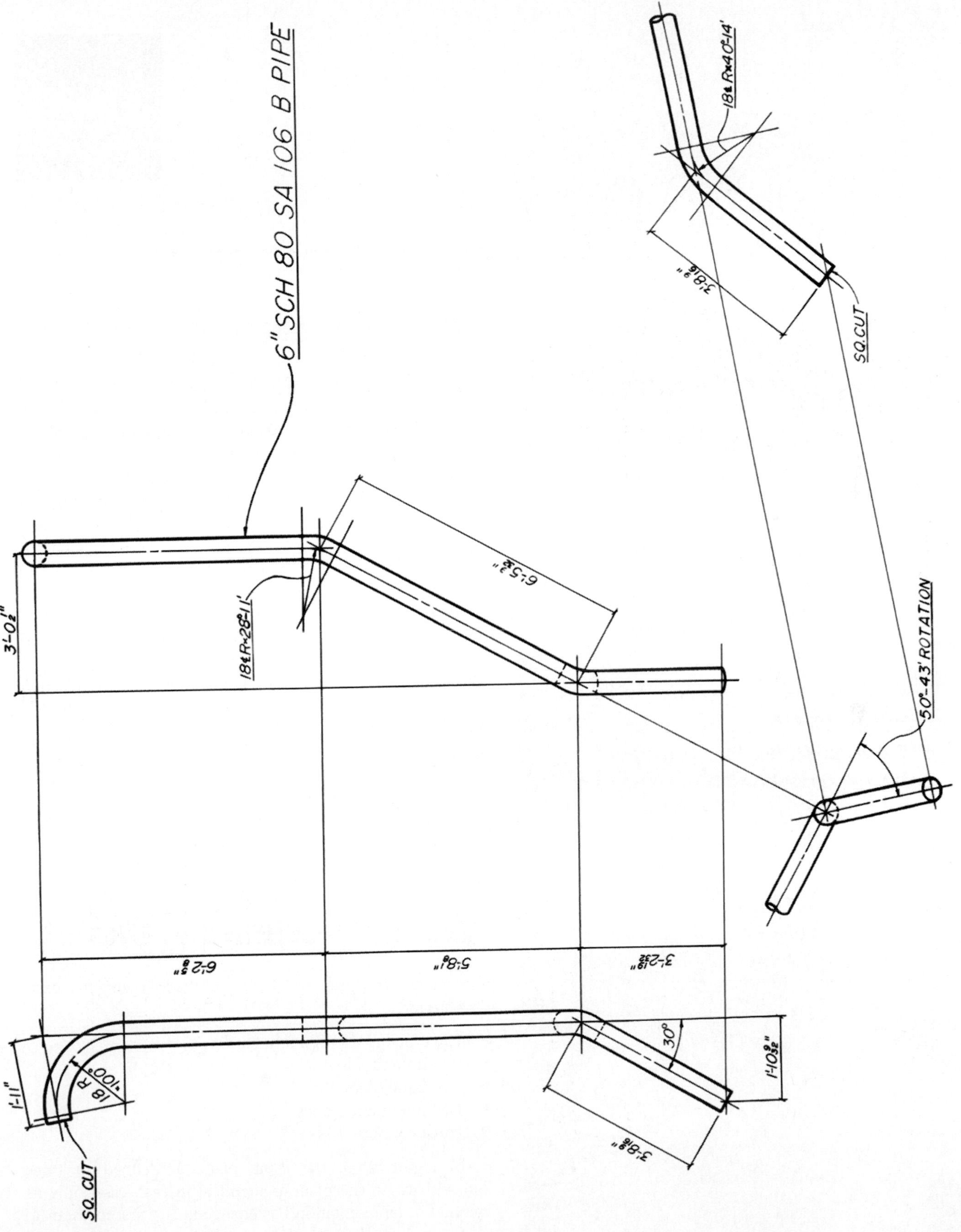

PROBLEM 24.3

PLANES

Chapter 25

LEARNING OBJECTIVES

Upon completion of this chapter you will be able to:

1. Determine the intersection of a line and a plane.
2. Solve for the angle between two intersecting planes.
3. Find the edge view and true shape of a plane in space.
4. Construct parallel and perpendicular planes.
5. Establish the strike, slope, and dip of a plane.
6. Determine the shortest distance between a point and plane and between a line and a plane.

25.1 INTRODUCTION

A **plane** can be defined as a flat surface that is neither curved nor warped. If any two points on it were connected to form a line, that line would be wholly in the surface of the plane. In general, a plane will be considered a constrained, limited, defined shape. Though a plane may be limited, its borders can be extended indefinitely to solve for specific information concerning a problem. The video device design concept shown in Figure 25.1 is an example of a product incorporating planar surfaces in most of its design. Planes are primary construction entities on a CAD system.

Planes also serve in the construction of parts when modeling in 3D. The part shown in Figure 25.2 is composed of a number of planar shapes and other geometric forms. The part was modeled using datum planes as construction features. The ability to incorporate datum planes directly into a design enables the engineer to model the part with greater flexibility and to establish the design intent by controlling relationships between features. The datum planes can also help to assemble a component part in a subassembly or assembly by controlling the placement and constraints of the part and the base part.

25.2 REPRESENTING PLANES

A plane can be represented by any of the following five basic conditions:

- Three points not in a straight line
- A point and a line
- Two parallel lines
- Two intersecting lines
- Three connected lines

In Figure 25.3, the same plane is defined in three different ways. The plane is identical in each case; only its method of representation has changed. The first method (a) is three individual unconnected points. In the second method (b), two of the points are connected; therefore, the plane is defined by a point and a line. In method (c), the same three points are connected to form plane 1-2-3. The three points could also be three random points on the plane, identifying not shape but only position in space. All three examples locate the endpoints of the same plane and define its surface when connected.

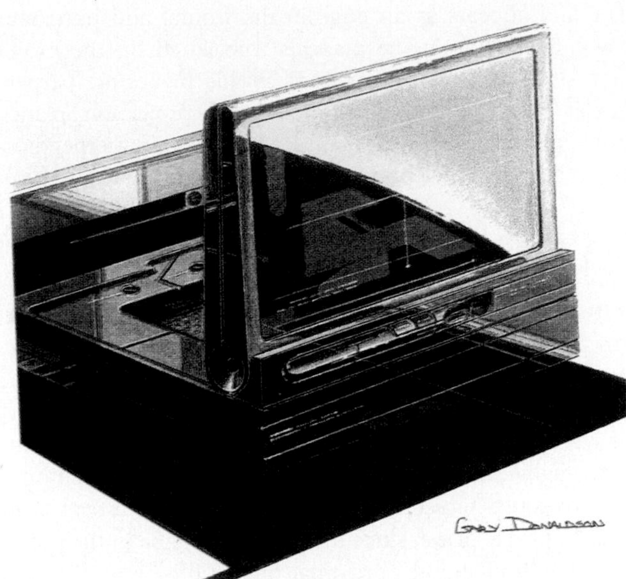

FIGURE 25.1 Video Product Development Using Plane Shapes

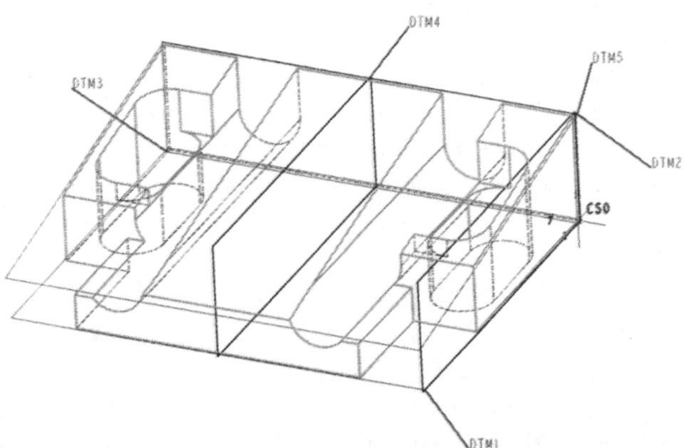

FIGURE 25.2 Parametric Model Designed with Datum Planes as Primary Features

25.2.1 Principal Planes

When a plane is parallel to a principal projection plane, it is called a **principal plane**. A principal plane can be a horizontal plane, a frontal plane, or a profile plane, depending on its relationship to a principal projection plane (Fig. 25.4). Because all lines in a horizontal, frontal, or profile plane are true-length lines, principal planes are composed of principal lines.

Remember, principal projection planes are imaginary sides of the unfolded glass box used to expedite the orthographic projection of an object (point, line, plane, solid). On the other hand, principal planes are limited definite forms that happen to lie parallel to one principal projection plane. To determine if a plane is a principal plane, you must have at least two views, unless the given view shows the plane as parallel to a principal projection plane. In either case, two views are required to fix the position of any plane in space.

A **horizontal plane** [Fig. 25.4(a)] is parallel to the horizontal projection plane. It is true size (true shape) in the horizontal view, since all of its lines are principal lines and, therefore, true length. The frontal and profile views of a horizontal plane always show the plane as an edge view (EV). A horizontal plane is a level plane and shows as an edge in all elevation projections. Horizontal planes are perpendicular to the frontal and profile projection planes. The profile and frontal planes have been unfolded from the horizontal plane in order to show parallelism.

A **frontal plane** [Fig. 25.4(b)] lies parallel to the frontal projection plane, where it shows as true size. In the horizontal and profile views, the plane appears as an edge view. All

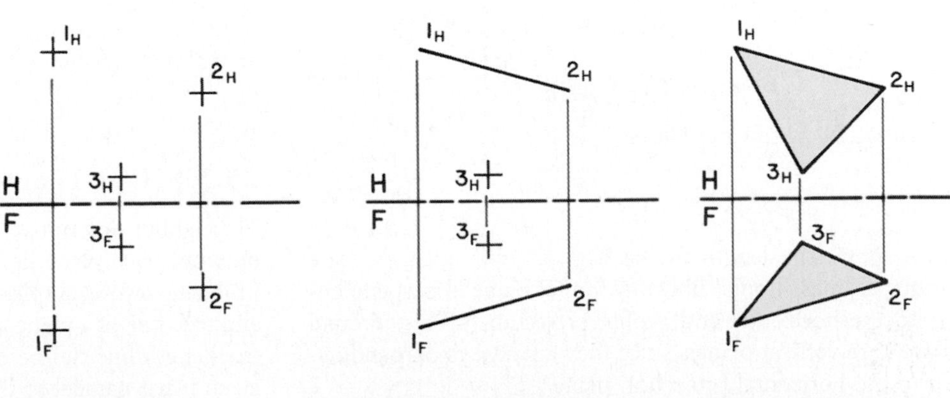

FIGURE 25.3 Representation of a Plane

(a) Three points (b) A line and a point (c) Three lines

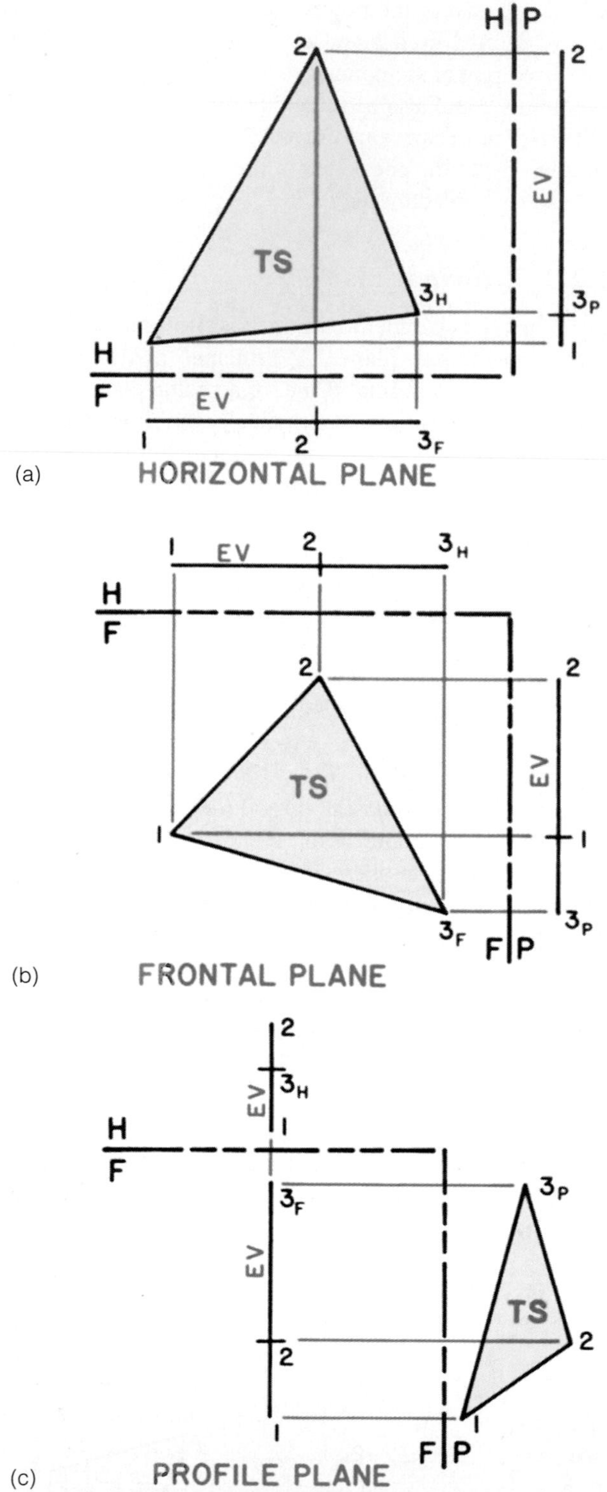

FIGURE 25.4 Principal Planes

lines show true length in the frontal view, since they are principal lines (frontal lines). A frontal plane is perpendicular to the horizontal and profile projection planes. Frontal planes are vertical planes, since they are always perpendicular to the horizontal projection plane.

A **profile plane** [Fig. 25.4(c)] is true size in the profile view and appears as an edge in the frontal and horizontal views. Every line in the plane is true length in the profile view, since they are profile lines. Profile planes are perpendicular to the frontal and horizontal projection planes. Profile planes are vertical planes, since they are perpendicular to the horizontal projection plane.

25.2.2 Vertical Planes

Vertical planes are perpendicular to the horizontal projection plane. The horizontal view of all vertical planes shows the plane as an edge. There are three basic positions for a vertical plane, as shown in Figure 25.5. In Figure 25.5(a), the vertical plane appears as an edge in the frontal and horizontal views. Plane 1-2-3 is perpendicular to the frontal and horizontal projection planes. This type of vertical plane is also a profile plane, since it shows true shape in the profile view. The frontal and horizontal projections show the edge view of the plane parallel to the profile projection plane.

In Figure 25.5(b), plane 1-2-3 is not parallel to a principal projection plane. Therefore it does not show as true shape in any of the three principal views. The horizontal view of the plane establishes it as a vertical plane, since it appears as an edge. The frontal and profile projections are foreshortened.

The third example of a vertical plane [Fig. 25.5(c)] is a frontal plane, since it is true shape in the frontal view. The horizontal and profile views show the plane as an edge and parallel to their adjacent projection planes.

25.2.3 Oblique and Inclined Planes

The classification of planes is determined by their relationship to the three principal projection planes: frontal, horizontal, and profile. Principal planes (normal planes) appear as true shape in one of the three principal projections and as edges in the other two. An **oblique plane** (Fig. 25.6) is inclined to all three principal projection planes, which results in foreshortening (distortion) of each view. *Oblique planes* [Fig. 25.7(a)] *do not appear true size in any of the three principal views.*

Inclined planes do not appear true shape in any of the three principal views either, but they do show as edges in the frontal or the profile view [Fig. 25.7(b) and (c)]. The angle an inclined plane makes in elevation can be measured in one of these views.

25.2.4 True-Length Lines on Planes

Throughout descriptive geometry, a *true-length line* that lies on an oblique plane needs to be found to solve a particular problem. Two examples of this situation are the edge view and true size of a plane and the angle between two planes. A true-length line can be established by drawing a line on the given plane parallel to the fold line. The adjacent projection shows the line as true length and on the given plane. In

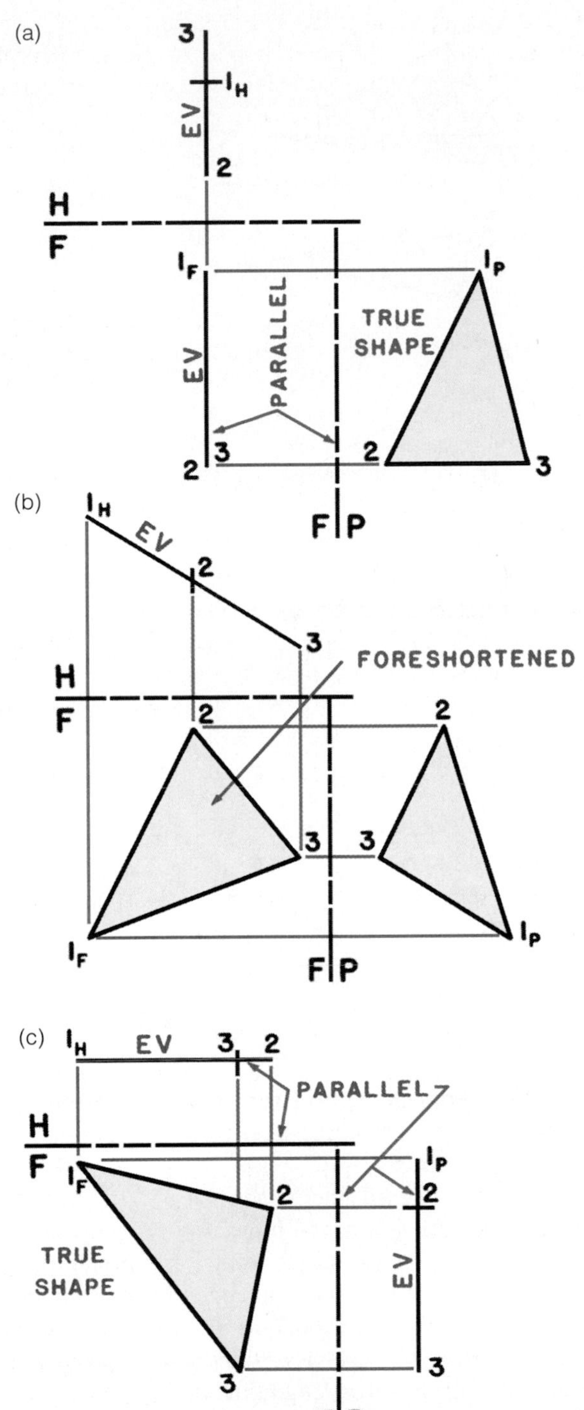

FIGURE 25.5 **Vertical Planes**

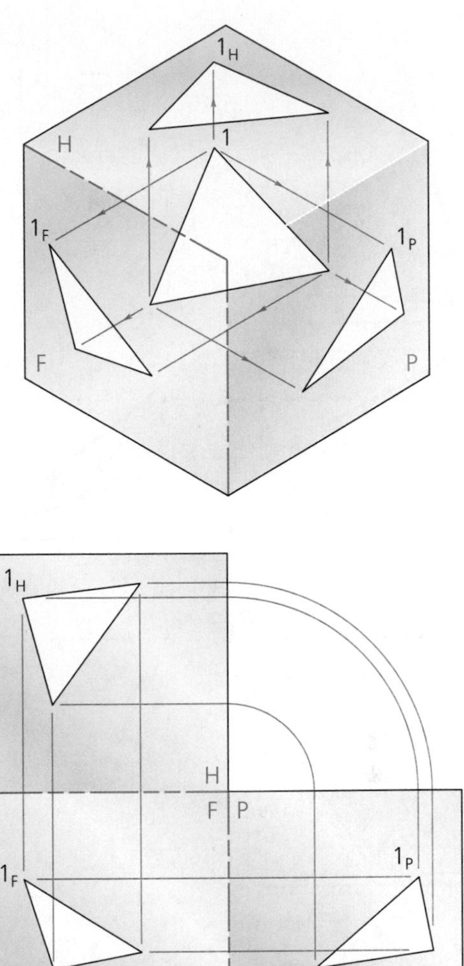

FIGURE 25.6 **Three Views of a Plane in Space**

Figure 25.8, lines have been located in each example so that they are parallel to the fold line in one view and project true length in the adjacent view.

Because the Figure 25.8 examples are oblique planes in the three principal projection planes—frontal, horizontal, and profile—these newly introduced lines must be principal lines. The true length of a line can be found in any view by using its adjacent projection to construct the line parallel to the fold line. When these views are not principal views, the lines will not be principal lines. The only requirement to finding a true-length line on a plane is that the line be drawn parallel to the projection plane in one view and, therefore, that it project true length in the adjacent view.

In Figure 25.8(a), line 3-4 is drawn on the given oblique plane and parallel to H/F. The frontal projection of the line is on the plane and true length (a frontal line). In example (b), line 3-4 is drawn parallel to H/F and on the given plane. The horizontal view shows the line as a horizontal line (true length) and on the plane. In example (c), line 2_F-4_F is drawn on plane 1-2-3 and parallel to F/P. Line 2-4 appears true length in the profile view; it is a profile line.

25.2.5 Edge View of a Plane

The **edge view** of a plane is seen in a view in which the line of sight is parallel to the plane, that is, when it is parallel to a true-length line that lies on the plane. Since a projection plane is always perpendicular to the line of sight, it follows that a view drawn perpendicular to a given plane shows the plane as an edge. This can be seen in a vertical plane, which

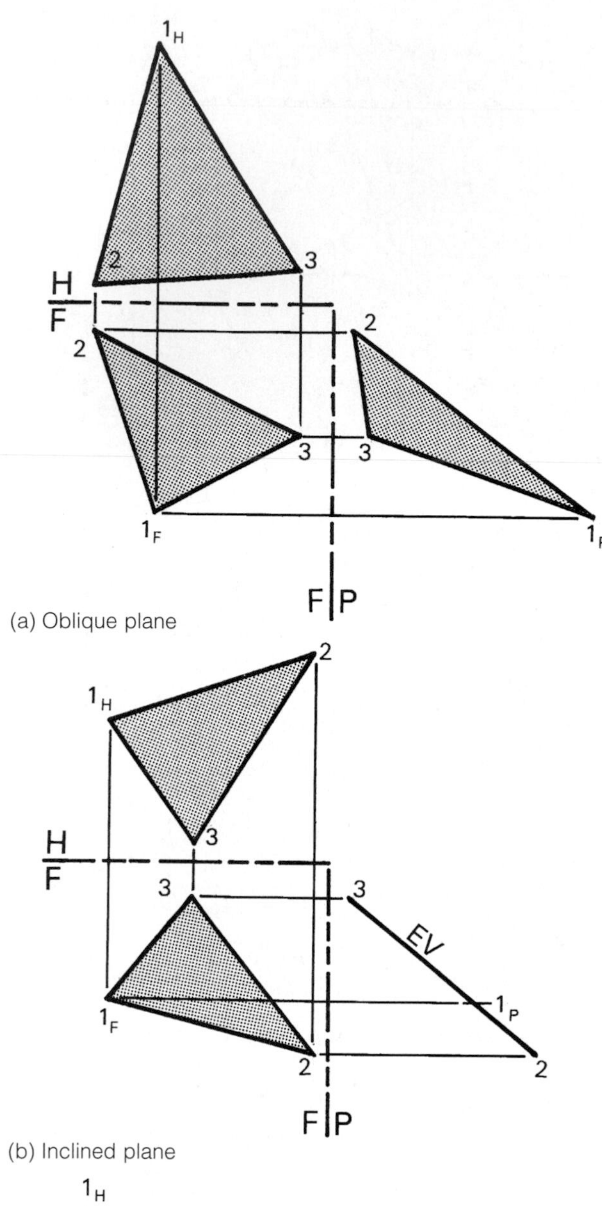

(a) Oblique plane

(b) Inclined plane

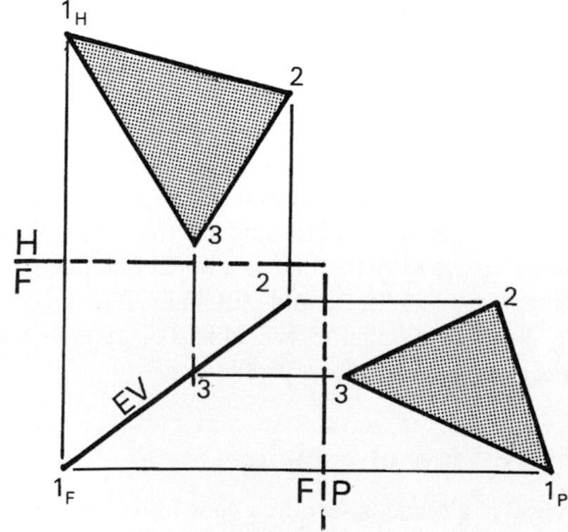

(c) Inclined plane

FIGURE 25.7 Planes in Space

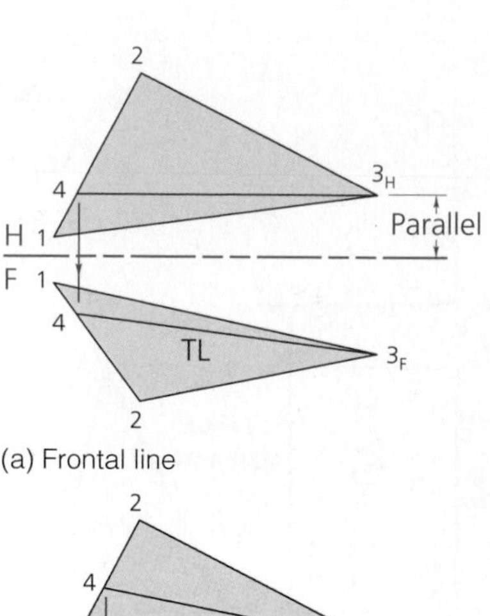

(a) Frontal line

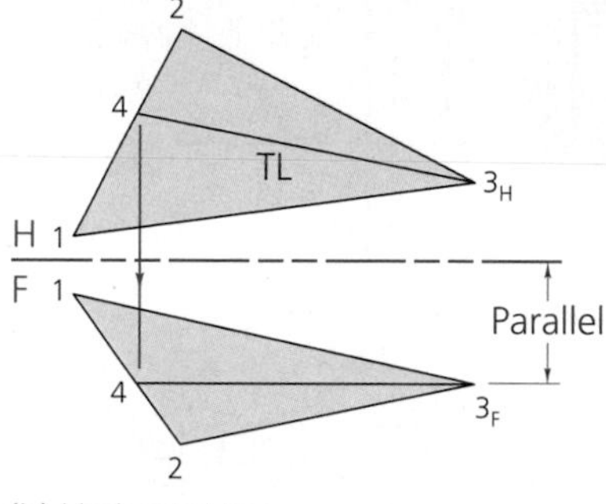

(b) Horizontal line

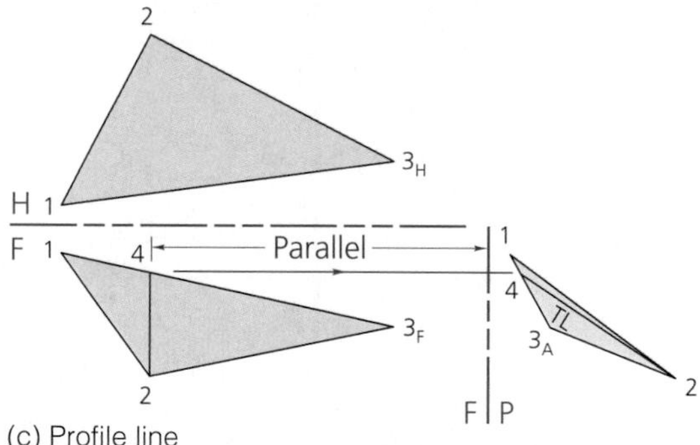

(c) Profile line

FIGURE 25.8 Principal Lines (True Length) on Planes

appears as an edge in the horizontal view, since it is perpendicular to the horizontal projection plane. A horizontal plane is perpendicular to the frontal and profile projection planes and thus appears as an edge in these two views.

When the given plane is oblique, an auxiliary projection is needed to show the edge view. To establish a line of sight parallel to the plane, a true-length line that lies on the plane needs to be drawn. An auxiliary view in which the line appears as a point view shows the plane as an edge. In Figure 25.9, plane 1-2-3 is given and an edge view is required. The following steps were used in the solution.

1. Draw line 1_H-4_H on plane 1-2-3 in the frontal view, parallel to H/F, and complete the horizontal view by projection. Line 1_F-4_F is true length.
2. Project auxiliary view A perpendicular to plane 1-2-3 (perpendicular to line 3-4). The line of sight for this projection is parallel to the plane and parallel to true-length line 1-4.
3. Draw F/A perpendicular to 1-4 and complete auxiliary

Focus On . . .

DESCRIPTIVE GEOMETRY IN GEOLOGY

The *strike*, *dip*, and *thickness* of an ore view is determined by drilling four *bore holes*. These holes establish three points on the upper surface (*upper bedding/headwall*) of the stratum and one on the lower surface (*lower bedding plane/footwall*). The upper and lower surfaces of the *stratum* are assumed to be parallel, within limits. The drill positions are located on the plan/contour map as shown. Note that point 1 is at the surface, so it is on the *outcrop line*. The strike, dip, and thickness of the plane require a frontal view showing plane 1-2-3 (as an edge view) and point 4, using the elevations of the four points to set up the view.

The *strike* of a plane is a bearing measurement of a horizontal (level) line on the plane. The *dip* of a plane is a geologist's term for its slope. The dip is measured as an angle the plane stratum makes in elevation. The *dip direction* (slope direction) is determined by drawing a line perpendicular to the strike line and toward the low end of the plane stratum. The general compass direction of this line is the dip direction, SE in the figure.

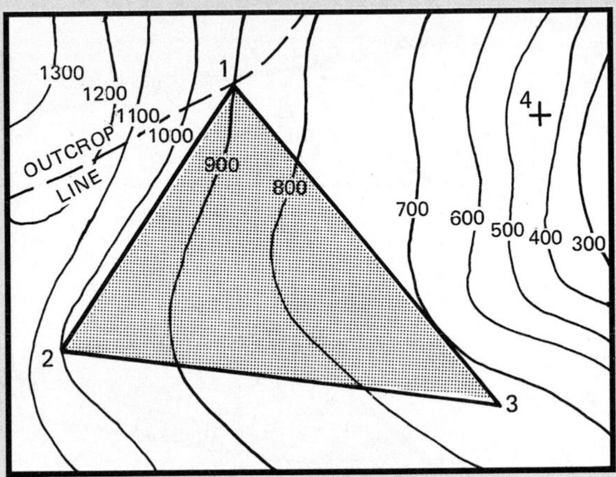

Contour map and bore holes.

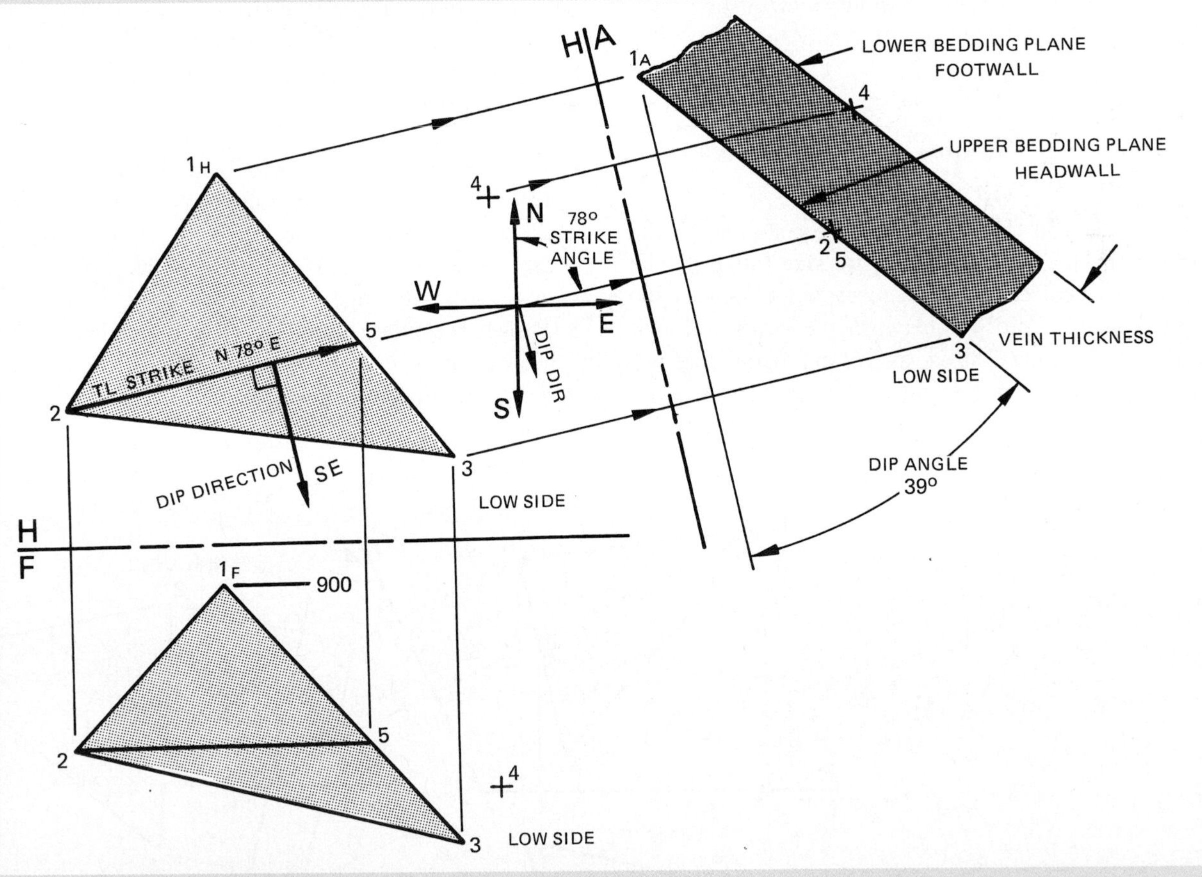

Strike, dip, and thickness of one vein.

FIGURE 25.9 Edge View

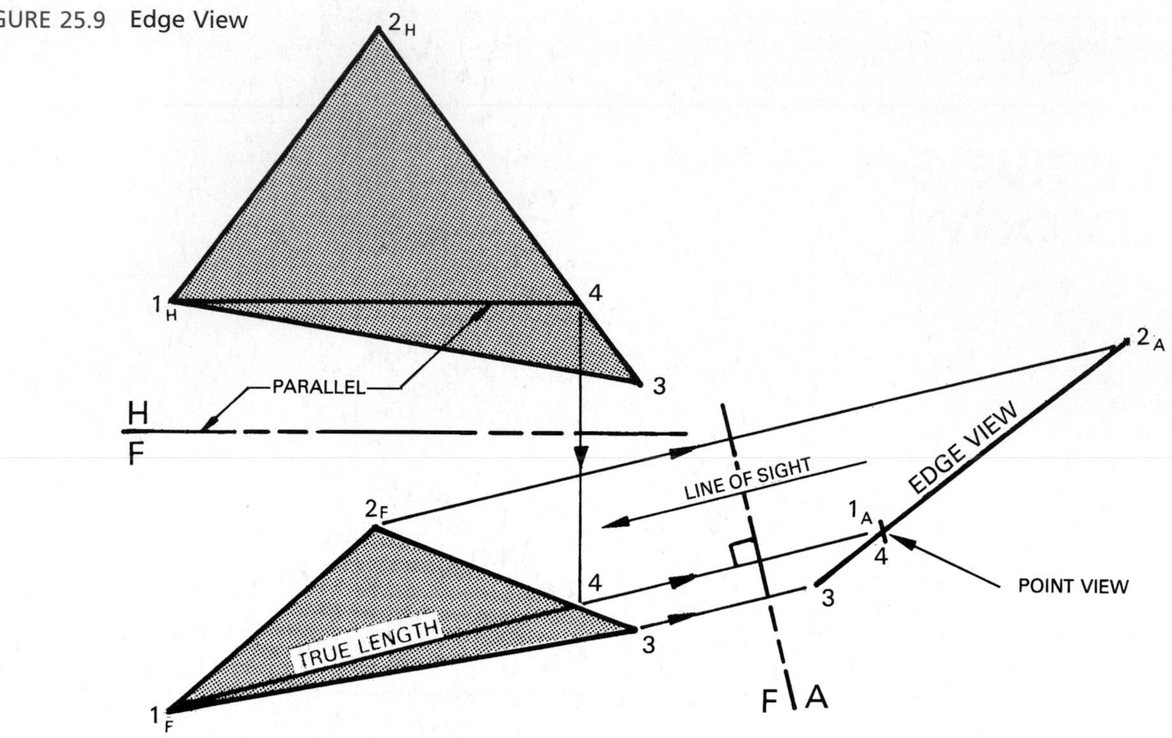

view A by projection. Because auxiliary view A shows line 1-4 as a point view, plane 1-2-3 appears as an edge view.

25.2.6 True Size (Shape) of an Oblique Plane

When the *line of sight* (Fig. 25.10) is perpendicular to the edge view of a plane, it projects as **true size (shape)**. The true-size view is projected parallel to the edge view of the plane. Therefore, the fold line between the views is drawn parallel to the edge view. Because an oblique plane does not appear true size in any of the principal projection planes, a primary auxiliary view and a secondary auxiliary view are needed to solve for the true shape of an oblique plane.

In Figure 25.11, oblique plane 1-2-3 is given and its true shape is required. The following steps were used to solve the problem.

1. Draw horizontal line 3-4 parallel to H/F and project as true length in the horizontal view.
2. Draw A perpendicular to line 3_A-4_A and complete auxiliary view B. Line 3_A-4_A is a point view and plane 1_A-2_A-3_A is an edge.
3. Project secondary auxiliary view B parallel to the edge view of plane 1-2-3. Draw A/B parallel to the edge view.
4. Complete auxiliary view B. Plane 1-2-3 projects true size (shape).

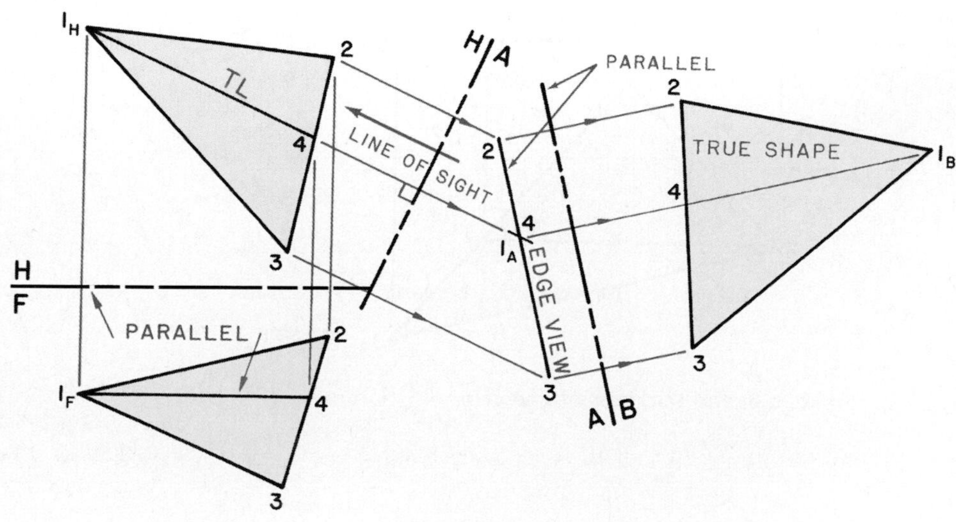

FIGURE 25.10 Edge View and True Size of an Oblique Plane

FIGURE 25.11 True-Shape View of an Oblique Plane

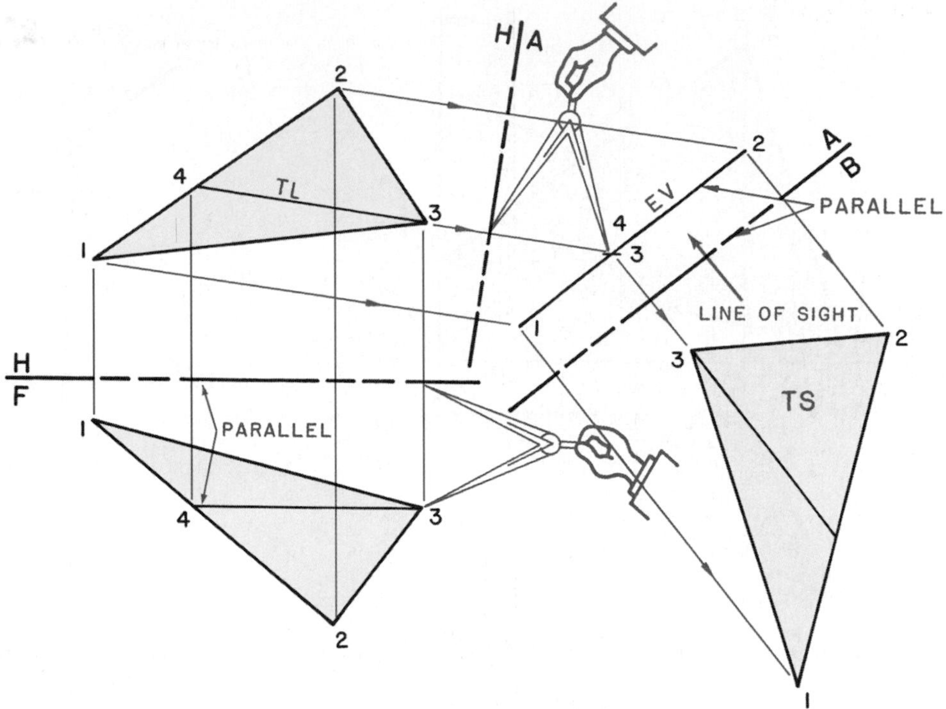

You May Complete Exercises 25.1 Through 25.4 at This Time

25.3 STRIKE AND SLOPE OF A PLANE

The most common applications of the strike and the slope (dip) of a plane are in mining and geology. The **strike** of a plane is the *bearing of a horizontal line that lies in the plane.* The strike is normally measured from the north as an acute angle. The strike line is a level line (horizontal line) and is therefore not slanted toward one of its endpoints. The strike is measured from a north–south meridian toward the east or the west. Any true-length line in the horizontal view can be used to measure the strike of the plane.

The angle that an edge view of a plane makes with the horizontal plane is the **slope** of the plane. The **slope angle** can be measured only in an elevation view where the plane is an edge and the horizontal projection plane is an edge. The slope cannot be seen in a primary auxiliary taken from the frontal or the profile view. The slope must be established in the frontal view or in a primary auxiliary view taken from the horizontal view (an elevation view). Both the plane and the horizontal projection plane must appear as edges in the same view in order to see the slope angle of the plane. In mining and geology the slope of a plane is referred to as the **dip**.

25.3.1 Strike of a Plane

In Figure 25.12(a), plane 1-2-3 is given and its strike is required. Line 1-2 is a horizontal line, being parallel to H/F in the frontal view and true length in the horizontal view. Note that line 1_F-2_F is "level" and therefore does not slope in the elevation view. The strike of the plane is equal to the bearing of horizontal line 1_H-2_H. The angle that line 1_H-2_H makes with the north–south meridian is measured as an acute angle from north [Fig. 25.12(b)]. Line 1_H-2_H makes a 54° angle with the north–south reference and bears toward the west. The bearing of line 1_H-2_H is north 54° west, N 54° W. An azimuth reading can also be used, N 306°.

In Figure 25.13, plane 1-2-3 is oblique. In order to solve for the strike of the plane, a horizontal line must be constructed. Line 2-4 is drawn parallel to H/F. The horizontal projection of line 2_H-4_H shows the line as true length. The strike of plane 1-2-3 is measured from north as an acute angle. The strike equals the bearing of true-length line 2_H-4_H. The bearing of horizontal line 2_H-4_H is north 70° east; therefore the strike of plane 1-2-3 is written N 70° E (AZ 70°).

5.3.2 Slope of a Plane

The slope (dip) of a plane includes the slope angle (dip angle) and the general direction that the plane tips toward its downward end (low end). The direction of slope is established by drawing a line perpendicular to the strike line and toward the low end ¥of the plane. The direction of the slope (dip) is read as the bearing of the line that is at a right angle to the strike line, given only as compass directions, not as degrees. There-

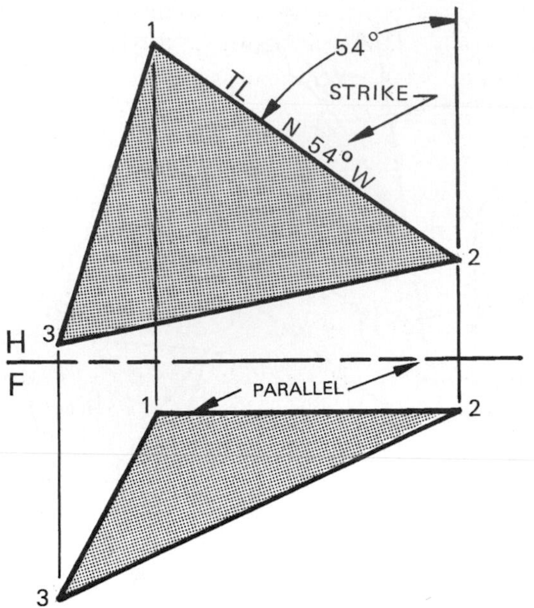

(a) Oblique plane

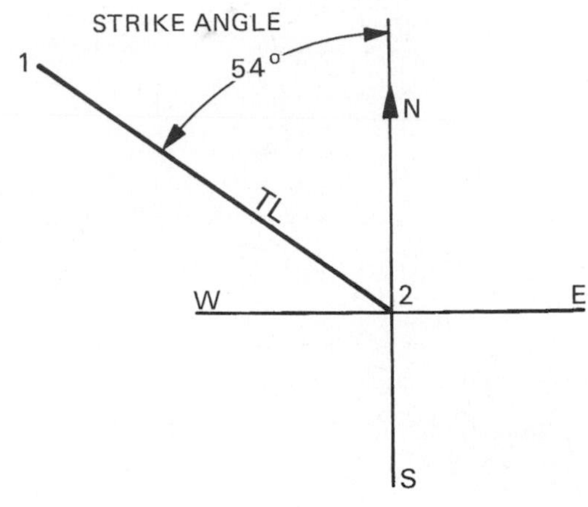

(b) Strike line

FIGURE 25.12 Strike of a Plane

fore the direction of slope is identified by NE, NW, SE, or SW or by the four cardinal directions: N, S, E, or W.

When giving the slope (dip) of a plane, the slope angle is stated first and the direction of slope (dip) second. For example: In 45° NW, 45° is the slope/dip angle and NW is the direction of slope/dip. This means we have a plane that slopes 45° toward the northwest.

In Figure 25.14, oblique plane 1-2-3 is given and the slope (dip) is required.

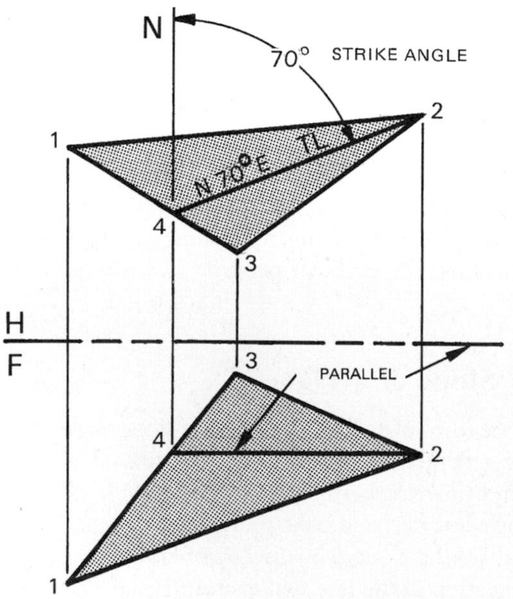

FIGURE 25.13 Strike of an Oblique Plane

1. A view in which the plane and the horizontal view are edges is needed. Draw horizontal line 3_F-4_F parallel to H/F in the frontal view and true length in the horizontal view by projection. Note the low end of the plane, and measure the bearing as an acute angle from the north. The bearing is N 81° W [Fig. 25.14(a)].
2. Draw H/A perpendicular to line 3_H-4_H and project auxiliary view A. Line 3_A-4_A is a point view and plane 1_A-2_A-3_A appears as an edge view. Measure the angle the edge view of plane 1_A-2_A-3_A makes with the edge view of the horizontal projection plane. The slope angle measures 33° [Fig. 25.14(b)].
3. In the horizontal view, draw a line perpendicular to the strike line toward the downward side of the plane, the *low end* (toward point 2). The direction of slope is the direction this line deviates from the north–south meridian. The direction of slope is NE in the example, since it falls in the first quadrant and points in a northeasterly direction. The slope (dip) of plane 1-2-3 is 33° NE.

25.4 SHORTEST DISTANCE BETWEEN A POINT AND A PLANE

The **shortest distance** between a point and a plane is a perpendicular line drawn between the point and the plane. In a view in which the plane is an edge, the shortest distance is measured as the perpendicular distance between the point and the plane. The following steps were used to solve the problem in Figure 25.15.

1. Draw horizontal line 3_F-5_F parallel to H/F, and project as true length in the horizontal view.
2. Drawn H/A perpendicular to horizontal line 3-5. In auxiliary view A, plane 1-2-3 appears as an edge. Draw

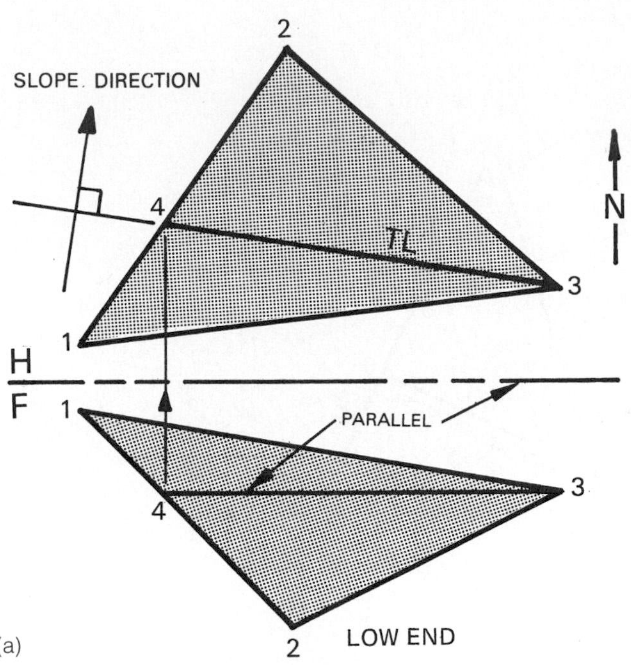

(a)

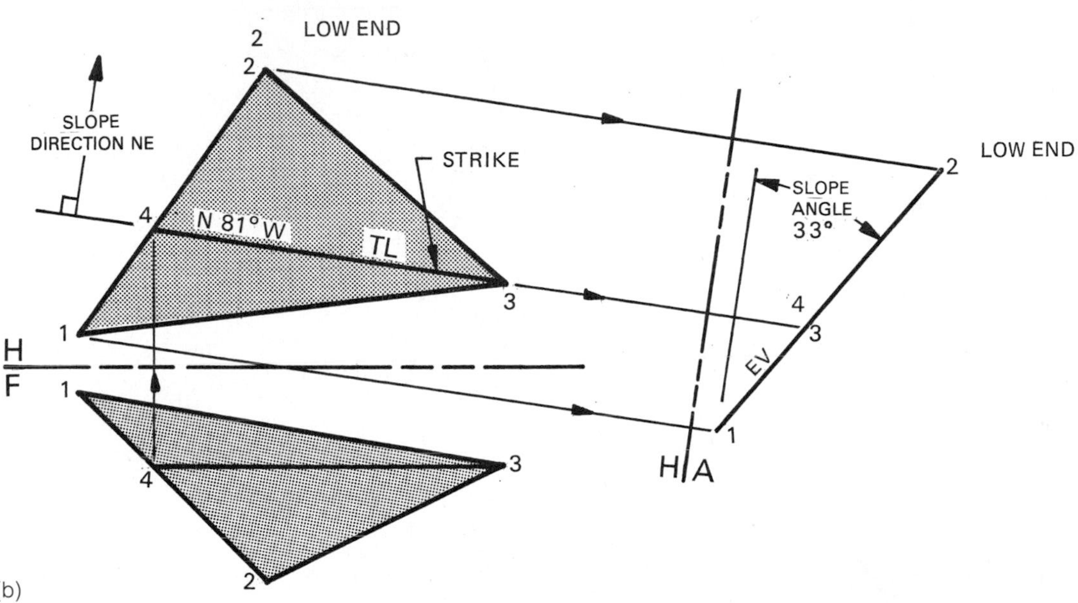

(b)

FIGURE 25.14 Strike, Dip, Slope Angle, and Dip Direction

a line from point 4 perpendicular to the edge view of the plane. Point 6 lies on the plane (at the point where the line pierces the plane). Line 4_A-6_A is the shortest distance between the point and the plane.

3. Line 4_A-6_A is true length in auxiliary view A; therefore, it projects to the horizontal view parallel to H/A. Point 6 is fixed by projection from auxiliary view A. Locate point 6 by transferring from auxiliary view A along its projection line in the frontal view.
4. Project auxiliary view B to establish the true shape of the plane and the true position of the line on the plane.

A line drawn from a point to a plane is its **shortest connector** if drawn perpendicular to an edge view of the plane. In Figure 25.16 the shortest distance was determined via the same general steps as described for Figure 25.15: After establishing

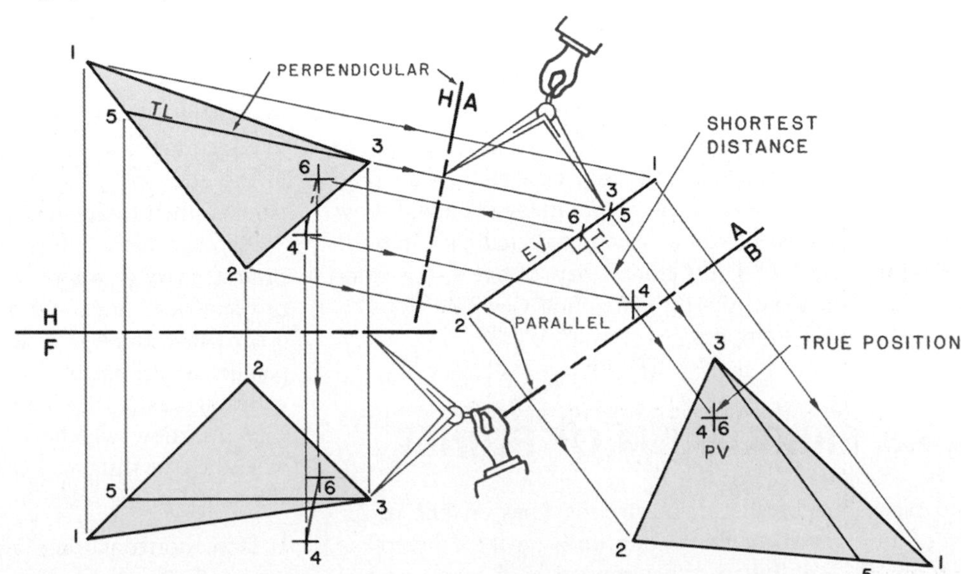

FIGURE 25.15 Shortest Connector (Shortest Distance) Between a Point and a Plane

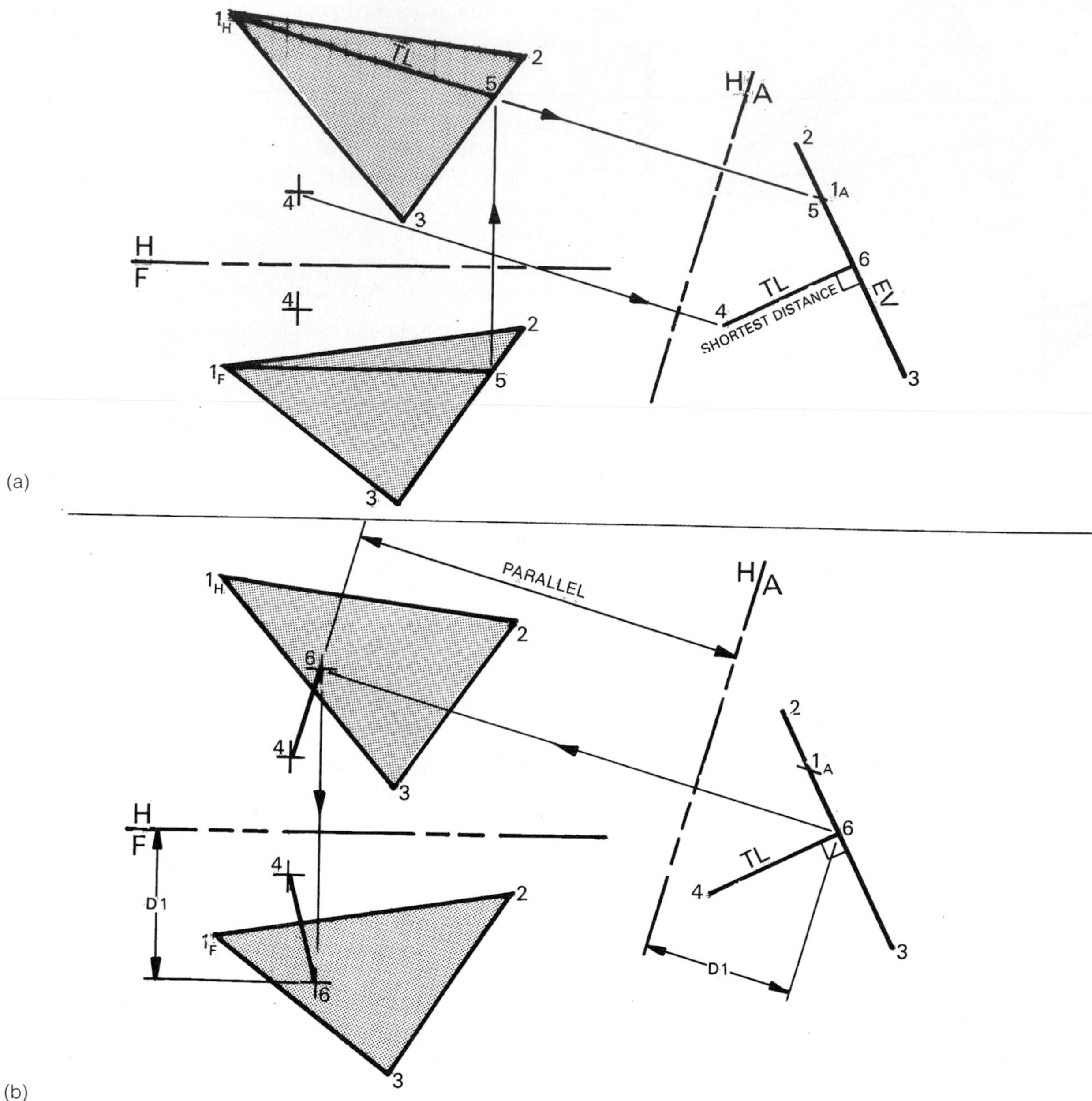

FIGURE 25.16 Shortest Connector

the distance in view A, draw the shortest connector (line 4-6) from point 4 perpendicular to the edge view of the plane [Fig. 25.16(a)]. Since line 4-6 is true length in view A it will show as parallel to the H/A fold line when projected back into the H view [Fig. 25.16(b)]. The frontal view of line 4-6 is completed by projection from the horizontal view and transferring distance D1 from view A.

25.5 PARALLELISM OF PLANES

Two planes are parallel if intersecting lines on one of the planes are parallel to intersecting lines on the other plane (Fig. 25.17). **Parallelism** is determined by drawing a set of intersecting lines parallel to any two of the intersecting lines in the other plane. If the two sets of intersecting lines are parallel, then the planes are parallel.

Another method of establishing parallelism of planes is to project an edge view of one of the planes. If one plane projects as an edge and as parallel to the edge view of the other plane, the true distance between the planes as well as parallelism are established.

In Figure 25.18, planes 1-2-3 and 4-5-6 are given. We want to know whether the planes are parallel and, if so, what the true distance between them is. The following steps were used in the solution.

1. Draw horizontal line 5_H-7_H on plane 4_H-5_H-6_H, parallel to H/F. It will project as true length in the frontal view.

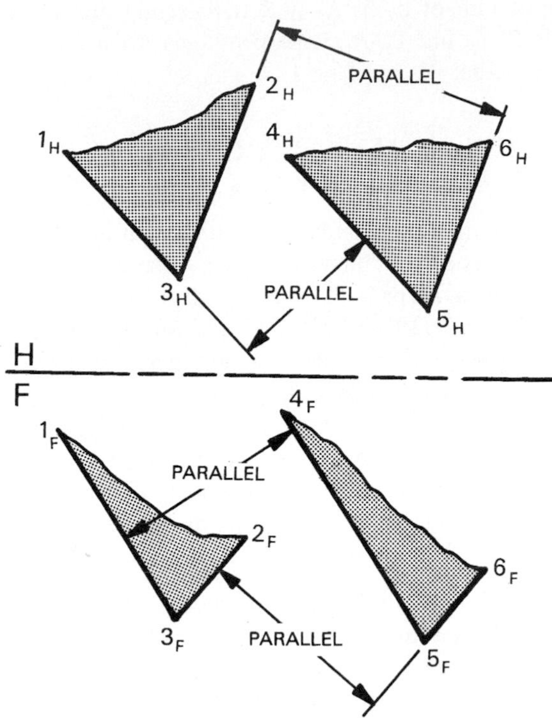

FIGURE 25.17 Parallelism of Planes

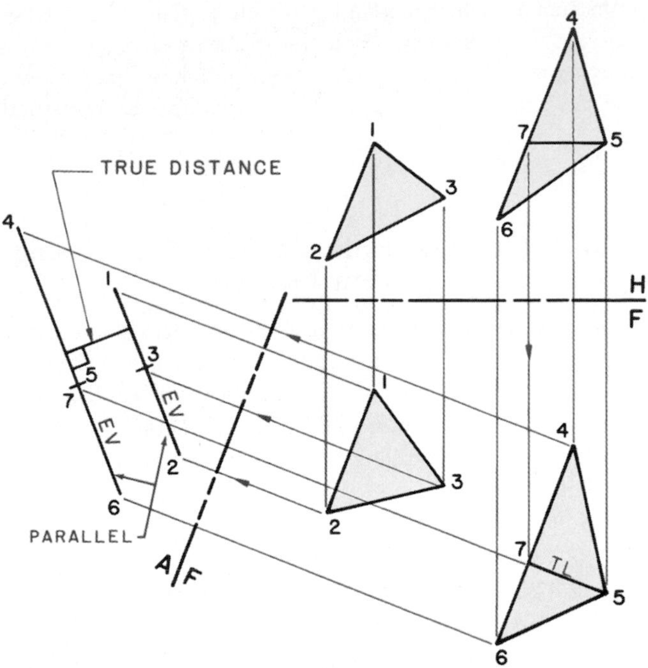

FIGURE 25.18 Shortest Connector (True Distance) Between Two Parallel Planes

2. Project auxiliary view A perpendicular to line 5-7 by drawing F/A perpendicular to it.
3. In auxiliary view A, both planes show as edges and also parallel to one another. The true distance between the planes is measured as the perpendicular distance between the two planes.

25.6 PERPENDICULARITY

A line is **perpendicular** to a plane if it is perpendicular to two intersecting lines that lie on the plane. If a line is perpendicular to a plane, it is perpendicular to all lines that fall on the plane and intersect the line (Fig. 25.19). To

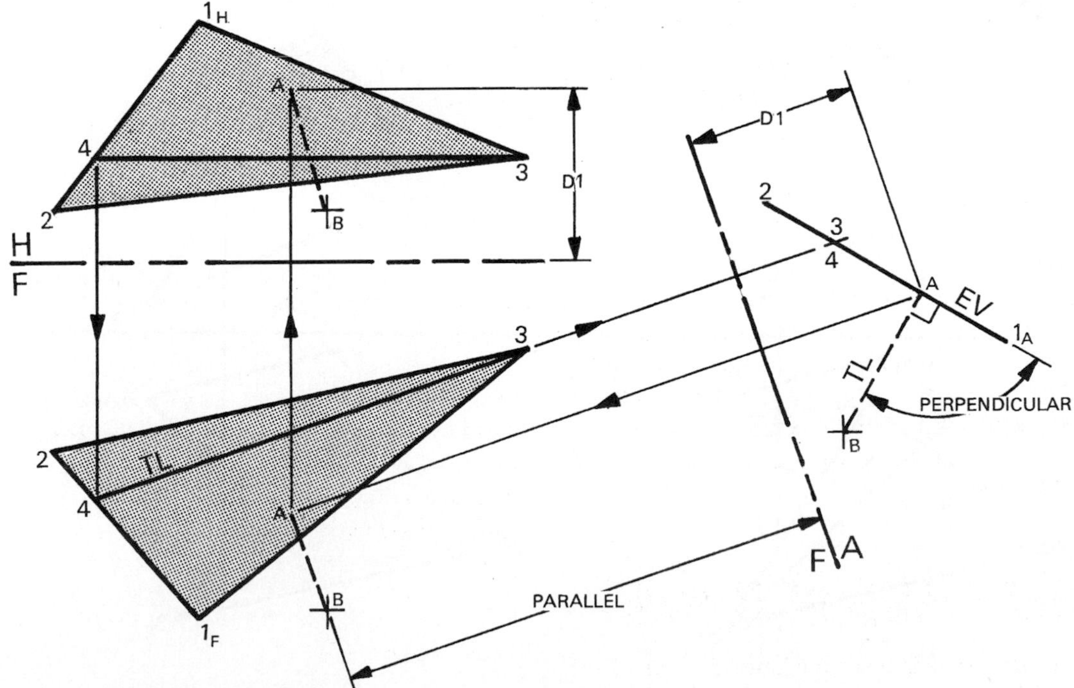

FIGURE 25.19 Line Through a Given Point Perpendicular to a Plane

construct a line perpendicular to a given plane, a true-length line must be established on the plane. A line can then be drawn perpendicular to the true-length line. Each view of the perpendicular line can be drawn via the same method.

25.6.1 Line Perpendicular to a Plane Using the Edge View Method

In a view where a plane appears as an edge, a line can be drawn through a given point and perpendicular to the plane. The point at which the line touches the plane is the piercing (intersection) point of the line and the plane. This perpendicular line is a true-length line in this view and projects parallel to the fold line in the previous adjacent view. The length of the perpendicular line is the shortest distance between the point and the plane. In Figure 25.19, plane 1-2-3 and point B are given. A perpendicular line from the point to the plane is required.

1. Draw frontal line 3-4 in both views. Project auxiliary view A perpendicular to line 3_H-4_H in order to show plane 1-2-3 as an edge. Complete auxiliary view A.
2. Draw a line from point B_A perpendicular to plane 1_A-2_A-3_A. Line B_A-A_A is the shortest perpendicular distance from the point to the plane. Line B_A-A_A pierces plane 1_A-2_A-3_A at point A_A.
3. Project line B-A back to all previous views. Line B_F-A_F is parallel to F/A and perpendicular to true-length line 3_H-4_H. Point A_F is fixed by projection from auxiliary view A. Locate the horizontal view of line B_F-A_F is by the projection of point A_F and transferring dimension D1. Note that line B_H-A_H is perpendicular to any true-length line 1 that lies in plane 1_H-2_H-3_H.

25.6.2 Plane Through a Given Line Perpendicular to a Plane

A line drawn perpendicular to a true-length line that lies in a given plane, and intersecting an existing external line, forms a plane perpendicular to the given plane.

In Figure 25.20, plane 1-2-3 and line 4-5 are given. A plane passing through the line and perpendicular to the plane is required. The simplest way to construct a plane is by drawing two intersecting lines. Also, in order for a plane to be perpendicular to another plane it must contain a line that is perpendicular to the given plane. Since line 4-5 is given, a line intersecting it must be drawn perpendicular to a true-length line that lies in the given plane.

1. Establish a true-length line in plane 1-2-3 in each view. Draw frontal line 3_H-6_H parallel to H/F, and project it to the frontal view, where it is true length. Draw horizontal line 1_F-7_F parallel to H/F and project it to the horizontal view, where it is true length [Fig. 25.20(a)].
2. In both views, from any point on line 4-5 draw an intersecting line perpendicular to the true-length lines in plane 1-2-3. From point 5_F, draw a line of a convenient length and perpendicular to the frontal line that lies in plane 1_F-2_F-3_F. In the horizontal view, draw a line from point 5_H perpendicular to the horizontal line that lies in plane 1_H-2_H-3_H. Locate endpoint 8 anywhere along this line, and align in both views [Fig. 25.20(b)].

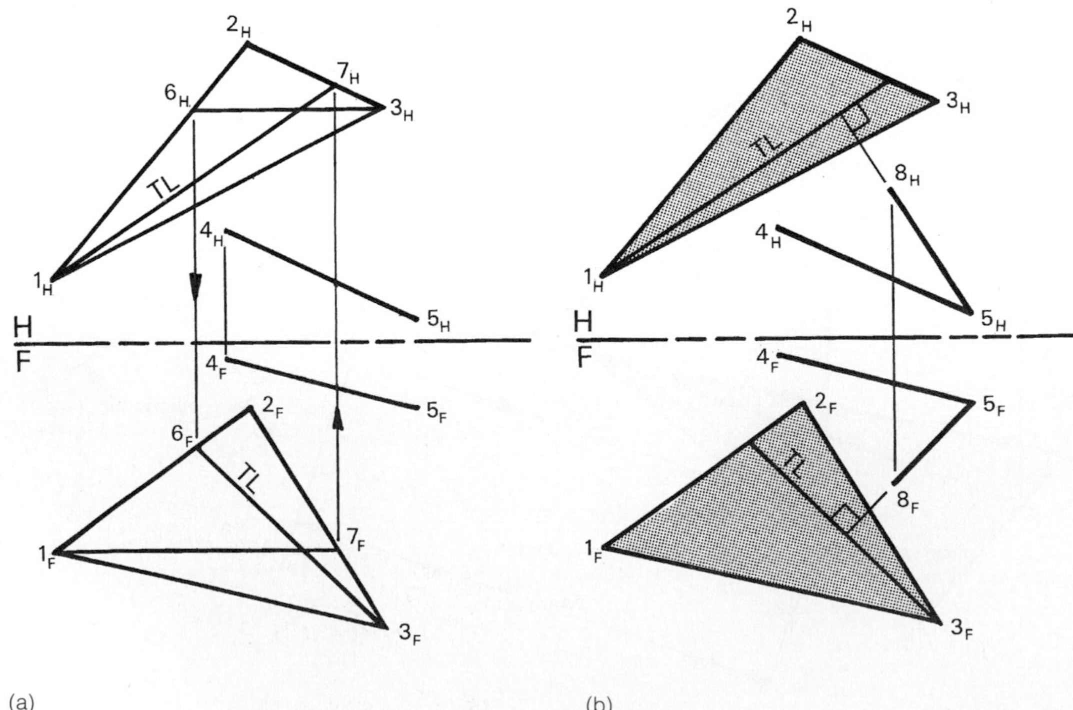

FIGURE 25.20 Plane Through a Given Line Perpendicular to a Plane

Applying Parametric Design . . .

DATUM PLANES

Datum planes can create a reference on a part where one does not already exist. For example, you can sketch or place features on a datum plane when there is no appropriate planar surface; you can also dimension to a datum plane as if it were an edge. When you are constructing an assembly, you can use datums with assembly commands.

Datum planes function as references, as sketching planes, and as parent features for a variety of nonsketched part features.

In most part designs the first feature created will be three default datums (Fig. A). The base features are created from the existing datums. In Figure B the cylindrical features are on DTM2, with DTM3 passing through the axes of both cylinders. Other features are then constructed (Fig. C). DTM4 is introduced parallel to DTM2 to create the arm feature (Fig. D). The shaded illustration in Figure E shows the completed part. DTM2 served as the sketching plane to create the base features.

A nondefault datum is created by specifying **constraints** that locate it with respect to existing geometry. For example, a datum plane might be made to pass tangent to a cylinder axis and parallel to a planar surface (Fig. F). Chosen constraints must locate the datum plane relative to the model without ambiguity. Other examples of constraining datums include: through an axis and normal to a selected surface (Fig. G), through an axis and at an angle to a surface (Fig. H), and through two edges (Fig. I).

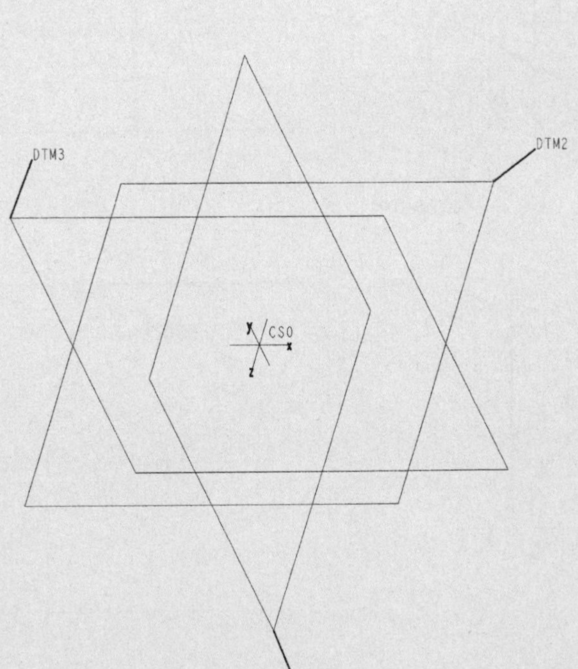

FIGURE A Default Datums

FIGURE B Base Features and Default Datum Planes

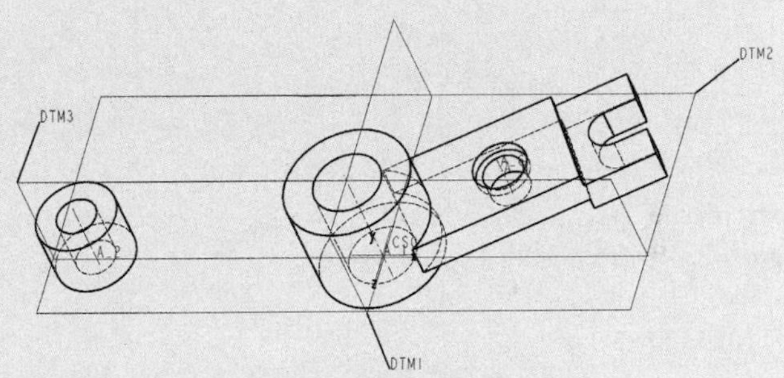

FIGURE C Features and Datum Planes

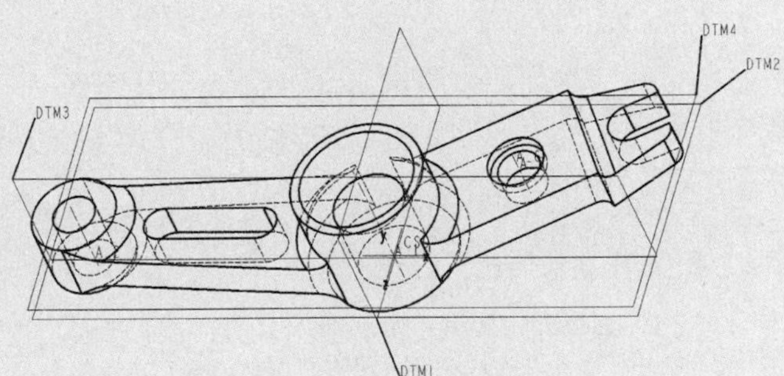

FIGURE D DTM4 Created Parallel to DTM2

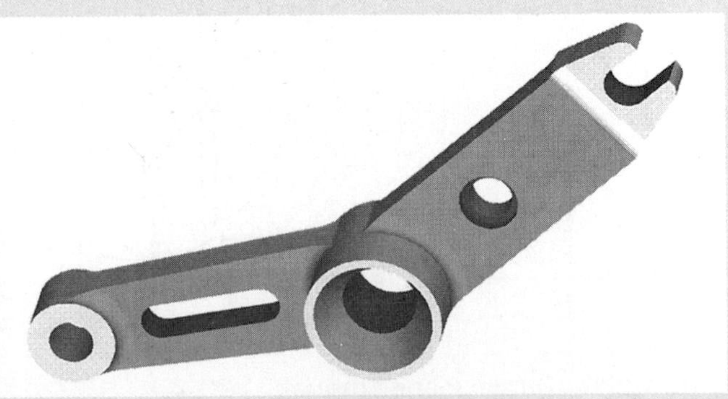

FIGURE E Shaded Image of Part

The following datum constraints can only be used alone, since each locates the datum plane completely:

- **Through/Plane** Creates a datum plane coincident with a planar surface
- **Offset/Plane** Creates a datum plane that is parallel to a plane and offset from the plane by a specified distance (Fig. J).
- **Offset/Coord Sys** Creates a datum plane that is normal to one of the coordinate system axes and offset from the origin of the coordinate system. When you select this option, you are prompted to select which axis the plane will be normal to, then to enter the offset along this axis.
- **BlendSection** Creates a datum plane through the section that was used to make a feature. If multiple sections exist,

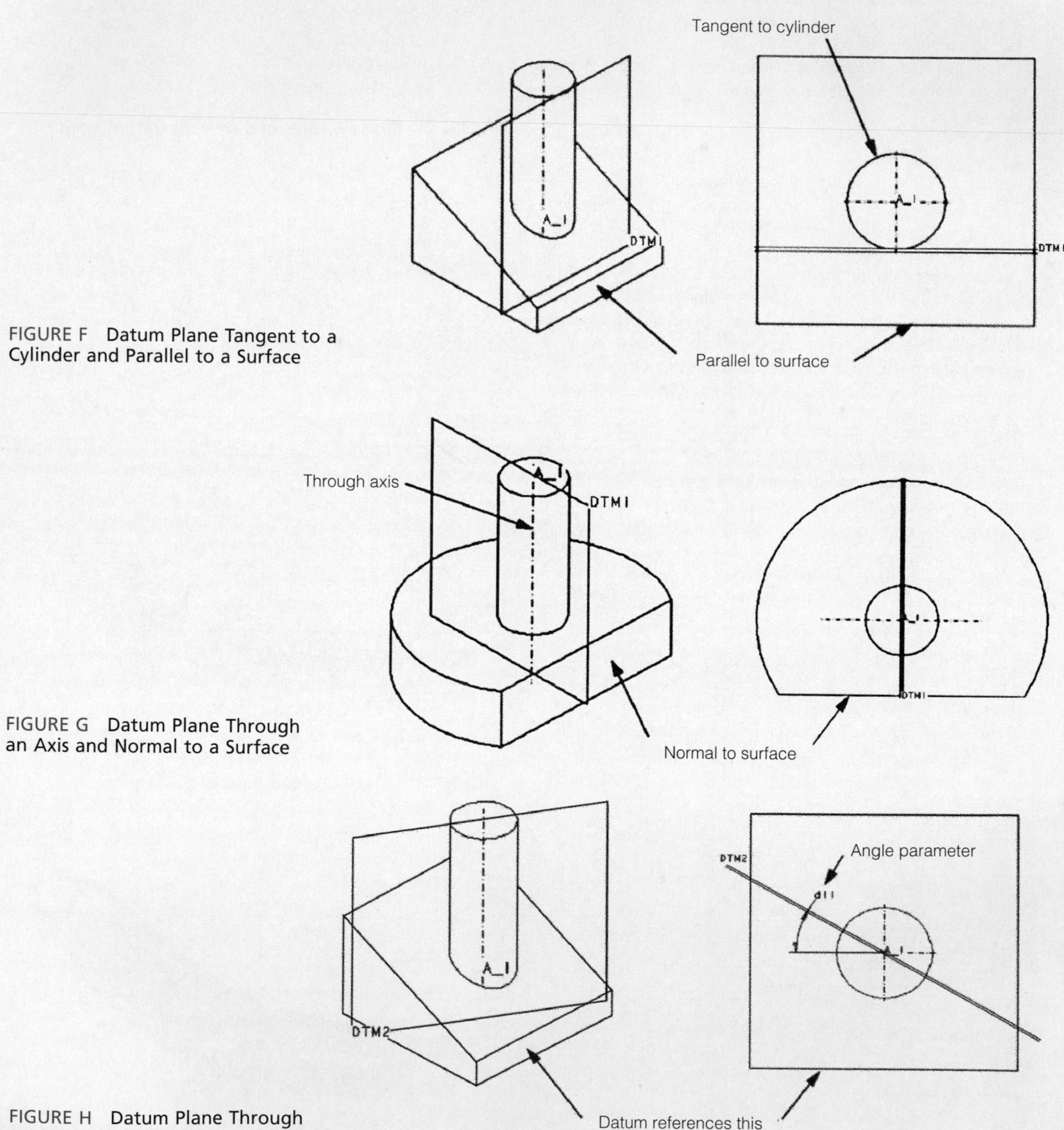

FIGURE F Datum Plane Tangent to a Cylinder and Parallel to a Surface

FIGURE G Datum Plane Through an Axis and Normal to a Surface

FIGURE H Datum Plane Through an Axis and at an Angle to a Surface

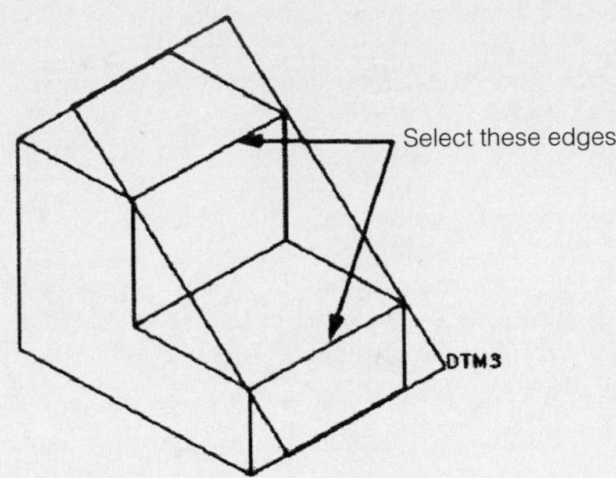

FIGURE I Datum Plane Through Two Edges

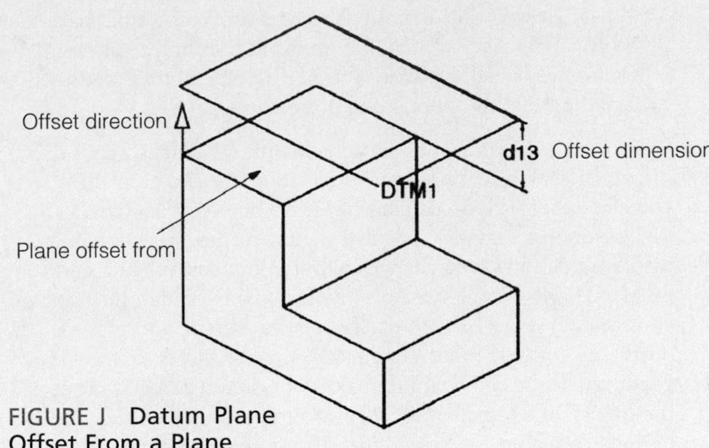

FIGURE J Datum Plane Offset From a Plane

as for a blend, you will be prompted for the section number.

How to Create a Datum Plane

1. Choose **Datum** from the FEAT CLASS menu (or **Make Datum** from the SETUP PLANE menu), and then choose **Plane** from the DATUM menu.
2. Specify a size for the datum, and select **Single** or a pattern option **Dim Pattern** or **Ref Pattern,** then **Choose Done.**
3. Choose the desired constraint option from the DATUM PLANE menu. All appropriate geometry options in the lower section of the menu will be selected automatically. If you want to limit the items to select, click on those highlighted menu options to unhighlight them.
4. Pick the necessary references.

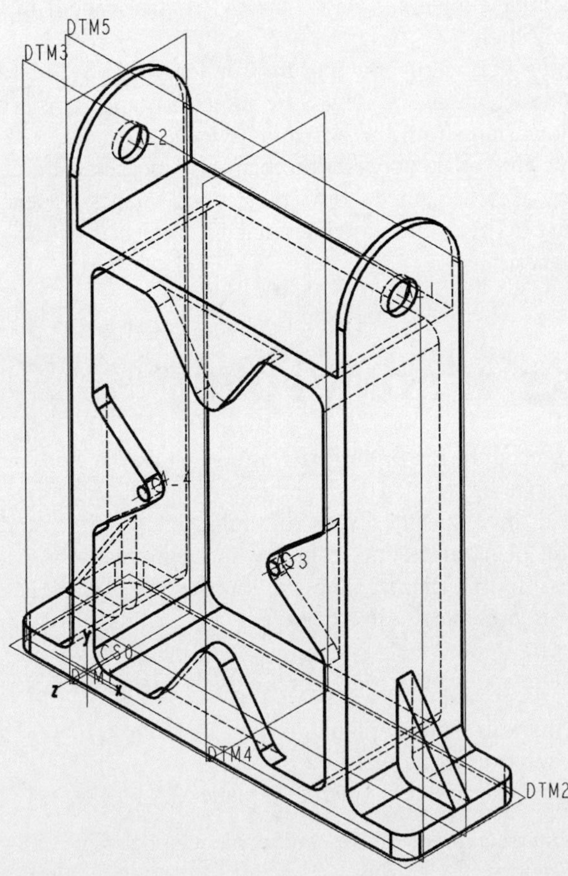

FIGURE K Casting

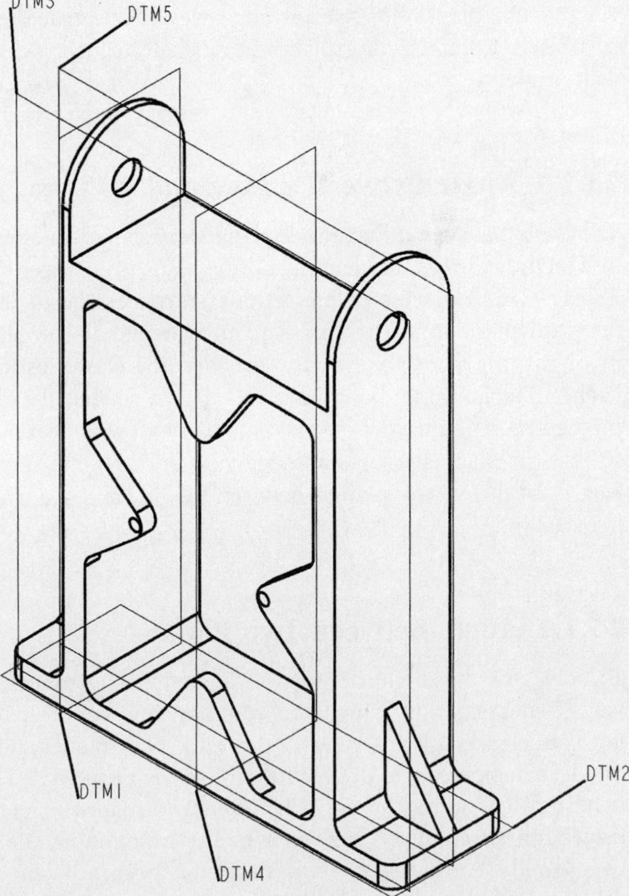

FIGURE L Casting and Datum Planes

5. Repeat steps 3 and 4 until the necessary constraints have been established. When the maximum number of constraints has been specified, Pro/ENGINEER notifies you by dimming out all options but **Done** and **Quit.**

Although datum planes are actually infinite planes, they are displayed scaled to the model size. To select a datum plane, you can either pick on its name or select one of its boundaries. The casting in Figure K has five datum planes. The size of a displayed datum plane changes with the dimensions of a part. DTM1–DTM5 are all sized per the features by which they are constrained (Fig. L). All datum planes except those made on-the-fly (within other commands) can be sized to specific geometry. These allow you to make your datum plane as big as the model, or as small as an edge or surface on the model. The options available for sizing the datum plane outline are as follows.

- **Default** Sizes the datum plane to the model (part or assembly)
- **Fit Part** (available in Assembly only) Sizes the datum plane to the selected part
- **Fit Feature** Sizes the datum plane to a part or assembly feature
- **Fit Surface** Sizes the datum plane to any surface
- **Fit Edge** Sizes the datum plane to fit an edge
- **Fit Axis** Sizes the datum plane to fit an axis
- **Fit Radius** Sizes the datum plane to fit a specified radius, centering itself within the constraints of the model

25.7 ANGULARITY

The angle between lines, between a line and a plane, or between two planes is a common industrial problem. The angle between two planes can be found in a projection in which both planes are seen as edge views. The true angle between two intersecting planes is normally called a **dihedral angle**.

25.7.1 Angle Between a Line and a Plane

The angle between a line and a plane is measured in a view in which the line is true length and the plane is an edge (Fig. 25.21). Three successive projections are necessary to produce this situation. The first step in solving this problem involves projecting a view in which the line shows as true length. The second auxiliary view is drawn so that the line projects as a point view. The last auxiliary view is projected so that the plane shows as an edge view and the line is true length. In this view the angle between the line and the plane is measured.

25.7.2 Angle Between Two Planes

To solve for the angle between two intersecting planes, a view is necessary in which the common line (intersecting line) appears as a point view. In this view both planes show as edges and the angle between them can be measured. The first step in finding the angle between two planes involves projecting an auxiliary view in which the common line is true length. An auxiliary view projected perpendicular to this true-length intersection line shows the common line as a point and both planes as edges. The true angle between the planes is measured in this secondary auxiliary view.

In Figure 25.22 two oblique planes with a common line are given. The dihedral angle formed by these two intersecting planes is required. The following steps were used to solve the problem.

1. Draw H/A parallel to line 1-2, which is the common (intersection) line of the two oblique planes.
2. Complete auxiliary view. Line 1-2 is true length in this projection.
3. Draw A/B perpendicular to true-length line 1-2, and complete auxiliary view B by projection and transferring dimensions from the horizontal view.
4. The true angle between the planes is measured in auxiliary view B, since both intersecting planes appear as edges. This is the dihedral angle (TA) formed by the two planes.

25.8 PIERCING POINTS

The procedure for finding the intersection of a line and a plane can be applied to intersections in all categories. If divided into specific types of intersections—line and a sphere, plane and cone, cylinder and pyramid—the list is endless. In this chapter, only the intersection of a line and a plane is presented. All other types are covered in Chapter 26.

A line and a plane have three possible relationships:

- A line can lie on a plane.
- A line can be parallel to a plane.
- A line can intersect (pierce) a plane

The intersection of a line and a plane forms the basis of intersections of all forms, since most objects are composed of lines and planes. Both the line and the plane can be extended to solve for theoretical intersections—those that lie

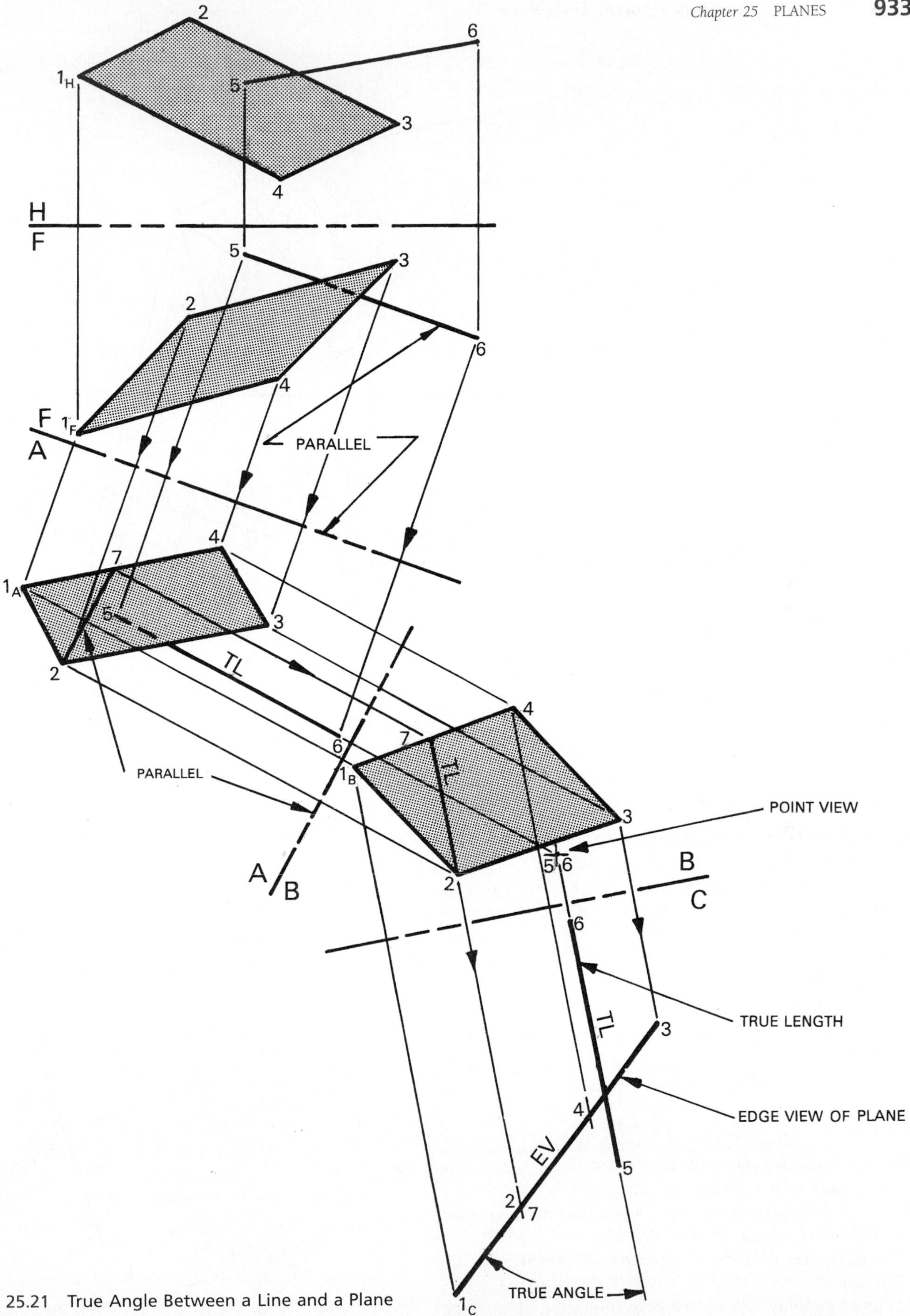

FIGURE 25.21 True Angle Between a Line and a Plane

outside the given bounded plane or beyond the given length of the line.

The point at which a line intersects (pierces) a plane is its **piercing point**. This piercing point can be obtained by the edge view (auxiliary view) method or the cutting plane method.

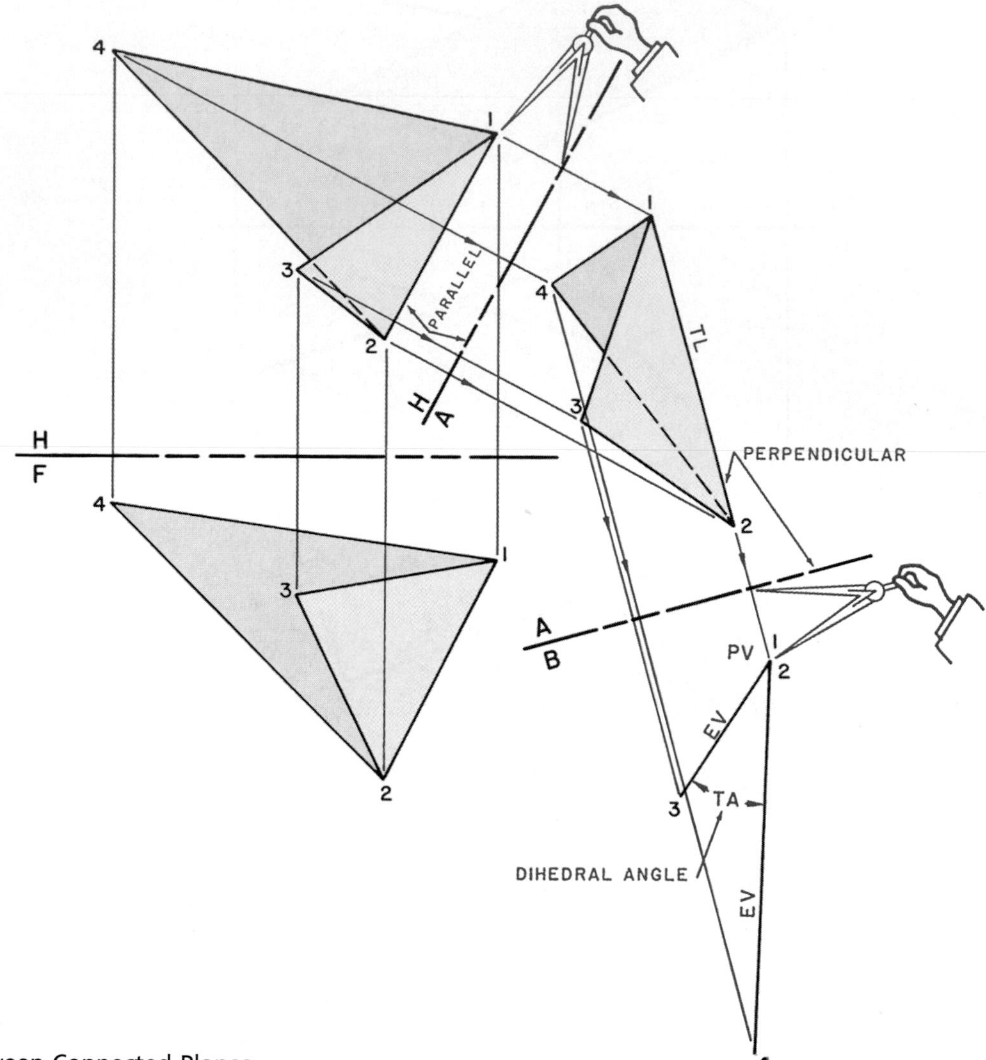

FIGURE 25.22 True Angle Between Connected Planes

25.8.1 Edge View Method

In Figure 25.23, plane 1-2-3 and line 4-5 are given. Their piercing point and proper visibility are required. The following steps were used to solve the problem by the edge view method.

1. Draw H/A perpendicular to horizontal line 1_H-2_H and project auxiliary view A. Plane 1-2-3 appears as an edge view and line 4-5 as oblique.
2. The piercing point (point 6) is where the line crosses the edge line of the plane.
3. Project point 6 to the horizontal and frontal views as shown.
4. Proper visibility is determined by inspection of auxiliary view A for the horizontal view and by the visibility test for the frontal view.

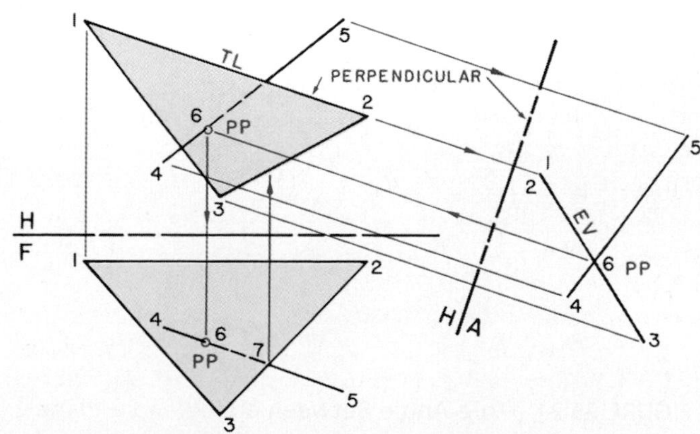

FIGURE 25.23 Piercing Point (Point of Intersection) of a Line and a Plane

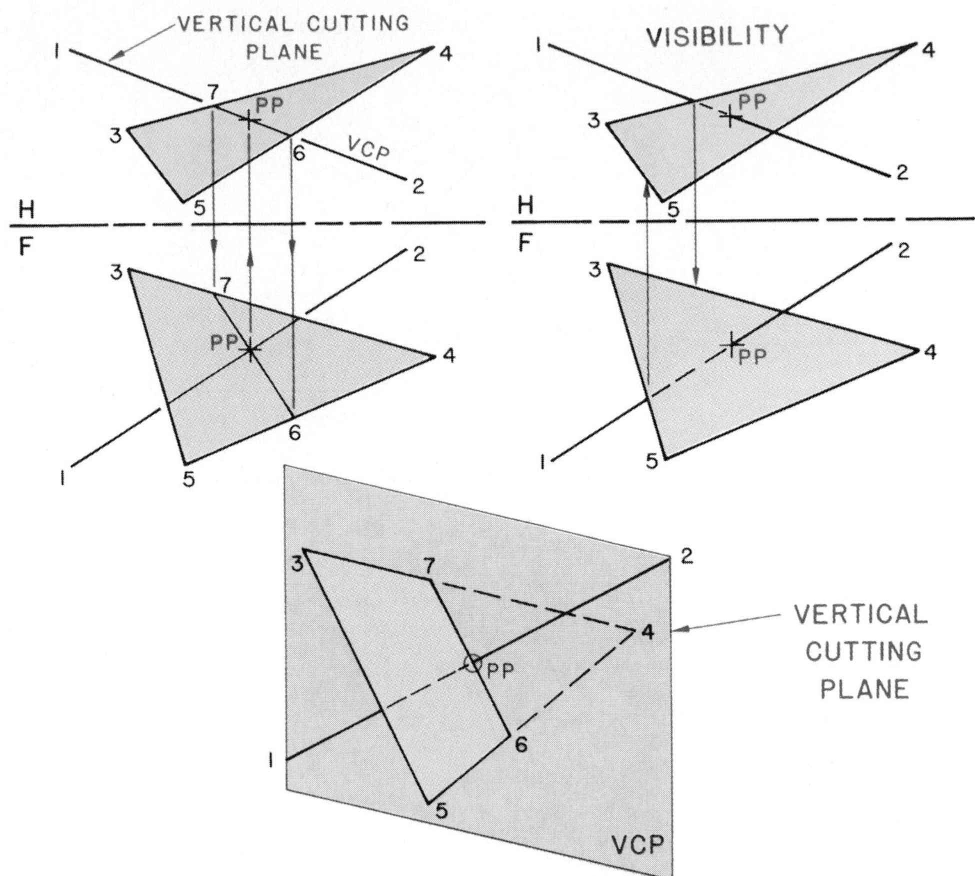

FIGURE 25.24 Intersection of a Line and a Plane Using the Cutting Plane Method

25.8.2 Cutting Plane Method

If two planes intersect, their line of intersection contains all lines that lie on one plane and pierce the other. The cutting plane method involves forming a new plane that contains the given line. A cutting plane is used that shows as an edge view in one of the principal projection planes.

In Figure 25.24, a **vertical cutting plane** (VCP) was formed by passing a plane through line 1-2. Line 1-2 represents the edge view of the VCP. Where this VCP "cuts" plane 3-4-5, it forms a line of intersection, line 6-7, common to both planes. This line of intersection is projected to the adjacent view, where it lies on both planes. The line of intersection between the two planes must either be parallel or intersect the given line. If the line of intersection intersects the given line in the adjacent projection, then it will establish the piercing point of the line and the plane, PP.

With a vertical cutting plane, the piercing point is established by projecting the line of intersection from the horizontal view. Points 6 and 7 are projected to the frontal view, where they form line 6_F-7_F. Line 6-7 crosses line 1-2 at PP. The horizontal view of PP can be located by projection. Visibility is determined through the visibility test, since inspection of an edge view is not possible.

If the line of intersection does not cross the given line, the line and plane do not intersect, in which case the given line is parallel to the given plane and lies in front of or behind and above or below the plane.

Figure 25.24 also provides a pictorial view of this problem. The vertical cutting plane contains line 1-2. The VCP cuts plane 3-4-5 along a line of intersection, line 6-7. Line 6-7 lies on both planes; that is, it is a common line. Where line 6-7 crosses line 1-2 they will intersect at PP, which is the piercing point of line 1-2 and plane 4-5-6.

You May Complete Exercises 25.5 Through 25.8 at This Time

25.9 DESCRIPTIVE GEOMETRY USING CAD

The piercing point problem shown in Figure 25.25 was completed on a CAD system. The cutting plane method was used to solve for the piercing point. This example was modeled in 3D, but the piercing point was established with 2D drafting techniques.

The true shape of a plane is another required solution in descriptive geometry. Figure 25.26 shows a plane as an edge in one view. An auxiliary view was folded from the given

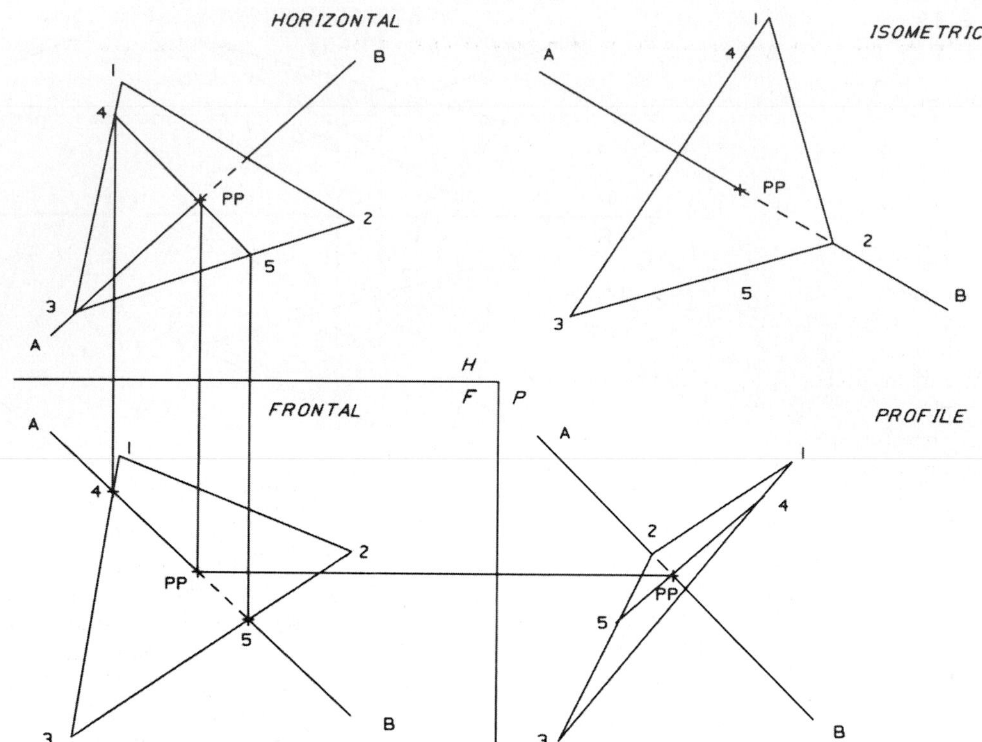

FIGURE 25.25 Using CAD to Solve for the Intersection of a Line and Plane. Note that the problem shows three views and an isometric projection.

view. The surface area of the plane could also have been established with an **AREA** command if this information was required. AutoCAD's **AREA** command is used to find the area of an entity (circle, ellipse) or an enclosed polyline.

```
Command: AREA
<First point>/Object/Add/Subtract: O
Select objects: pick object
Area= xxxx
Circumference= xxxx
Command: AREA
<First point>/Object/Add/Subtract: pick
points defining a boundary
Area= xxxx
Circumference= xxxx
```

The angle between two planes (Fig. 25.27) is called the dihedral angle. The CAD solution requires the projection of the common line (1-2) as true length (TL) and then as a point view (PV). These views are generated automatically on a CAD system with the **FOLD VIEW** or a similar command, depending on your system.

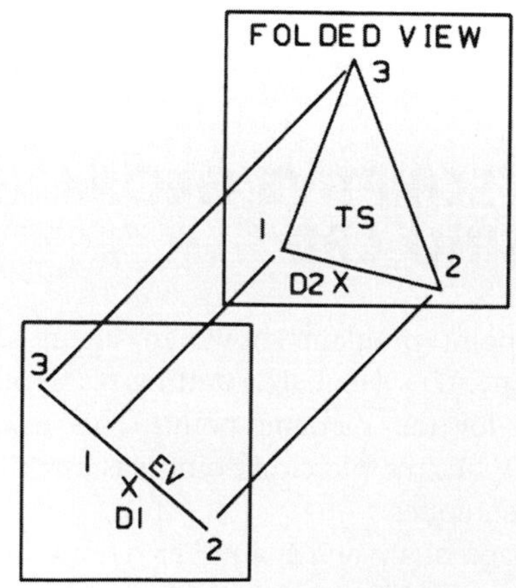

FIGURE 25.26 True Shape of a Plane Using CAD

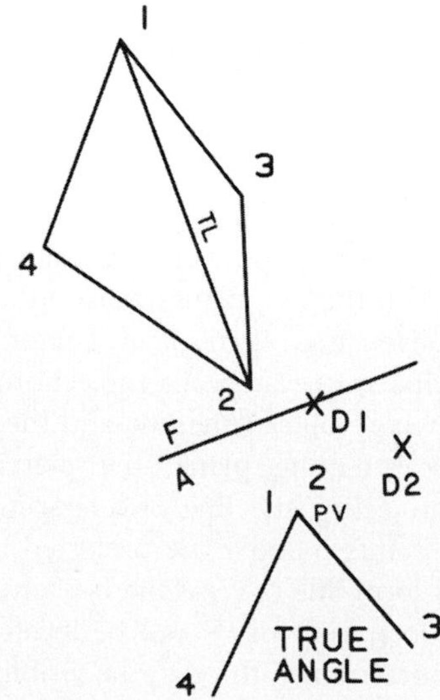

FIGURE 25.27 Angle Between Two Planes Using CAD

QUIZ

True or False

1. The slope angle and the dip are the same thing.
2. If one line in a plane is perpendicular to a true-length line that lies in another plane, then the planes form a dihedral angle.
3. The shortest distance between two parallel planes can be measured in a view in which both planes show as true shape.
4. The strike of a plane is the bearing of a horizontal line that lies in the plane.
5. Parallel planes can be determined in a view in which both planes project as edges.
6. The slope angle can be measured only in an elevation view where the plane is an edge and the frontal projection plane is an edge.
7. The shortest distance between a point and a plane is a perpendicular line drawn between the point and the plane.
8. The cutting plane method for solving for the intersection of a line and a plane requires only two views.

Fill in the Blanks

9. The strike, dip, and ________ of an ________ ________ are used by geologists.
10. The ________ ________ method requires only two views to solve for the intersection of a ________ and a ________ .
11. ________ of planes will show in the view in which both planes are edges.
12. To establish the angle between a line and a plane, the plane must appear as an ________ and the line ________ .
13. To establish the point of intersection between a line and a plane, project a view where the ________ is shown as an ________ .
14. The ________ ________ is the position where a line intersects a ________ .
15. Frontal lines and frontal planes are ________ to or lie in the frontal ________ ________ .
16. A ________ ________ is the angle formed by two ________ that are not parallel.

Answer the Following

17. What is the shortest connector between a line and a plane? How do you solve for this distance?
18. Describe the use of dip and dip direction in mining.
19. How can you construct a line perpendicular to a plane using two adjacent views?
20. What is the dihedral angle of two planes?
21. How do you solve for the edge view of a plane?
22. Explain how to solve for the piercing point of a line and a plane.
23. Describe two ways to use a CAD system to solve a traditional descriptive geometry problem involving planes.
24. What are the three possible relationships of a line and a plane?

EXERCISES

Exercises may be assigned as sketching, instrument, or CAD projects. Transfer the given information to an "A"-size sheet of .25 in. grid paper. Complete all views, and solve for proper visibility, including centerlines, object lines, and hidden lines. Exercises that are not assigned by the instructor can be sketched in the text to provide practice and to enhance understanding of the preceding instructional material.

After Reading the Chapter Through Section 25.2.6 You May Complete Exercises 25.1 through 25.4

Exercise 25.1(A) through (D) Complete the views of the planes. Where necessary, connect the points in each problem to form planes.

Exercise 25.2(A) through (D) Complete the views of the *principal* planes. Label for TS, TL, PV, EV, and principal plane.

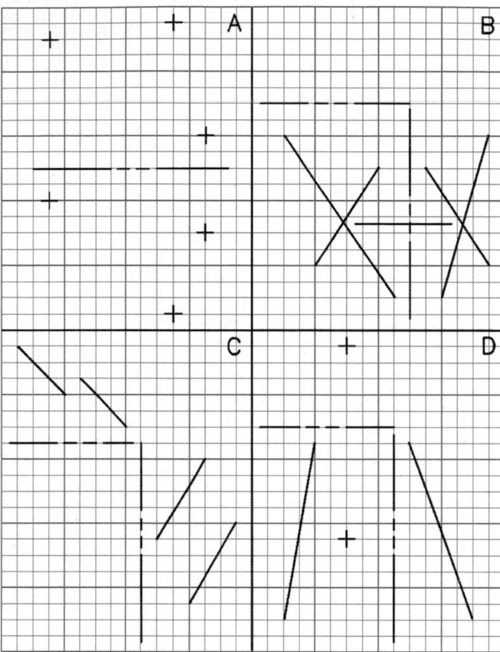

EXERCISE 25.1

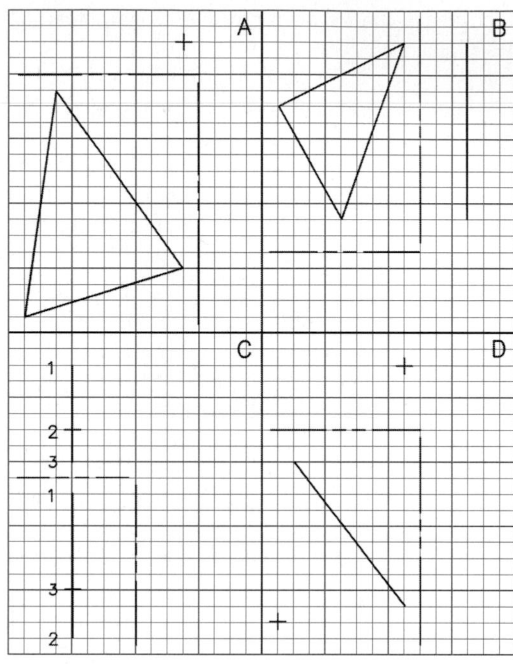

EXERCISE 25.2

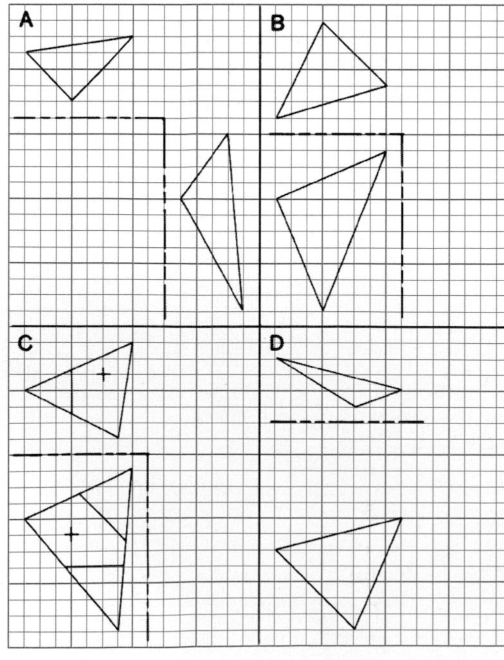

EXERCISE 25.3

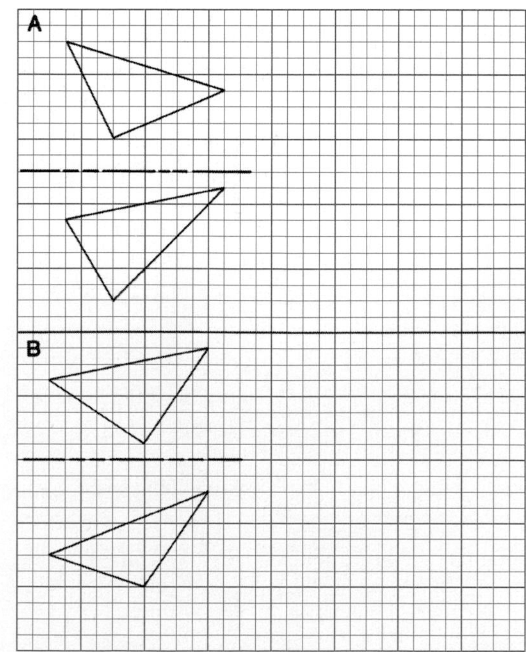

EXERCISE 25.4

Exercise 25.3(A) Project the front view of the plane. Draw three evenly spaced *frontal* lines on the plane, and show in all views.

Exercise 25.3(B) Establish a profile, horizontal, and frontal line on the plane, and show in all views.

Exercise 25.3(C) Show the points and the lines on the plane, and project into all views.

Exercise 25.3(D) Solve for the edge view of the plane.

Exercise 25.4(A) Solve for the largest circle within the plane. Establish an edge view from the horizontal view. Show the circle in all views.

Exercise 25.4(B) Project an edge view and a true-shape view of the plane. Project the edge view from the frontal view.

After Reading the Chapter Through Section 25.8.2 You May Complete the Following Exercises

Exercise 25.5(A) and (B) Determine the strike, slope, dip, and direction of slope of each plane.

Exercise 25.5(C) Solve for the slope, dip, strike, and true shape of the plane.

Exercise 25.6(A) Determine the shortest distance between the point and the plane. Show the connecting line in all views. What is the bearing of the line? (North is always at the top of the drawing.)

Exercise 25.6(B) Construct a plane parallel to the given plane and through the point.

Exercise 25.6(C) and (D) Project and measure the true angle between the two connected planes.

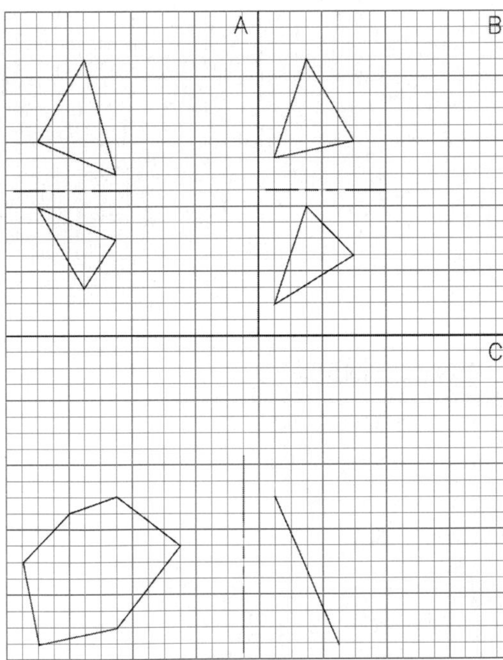

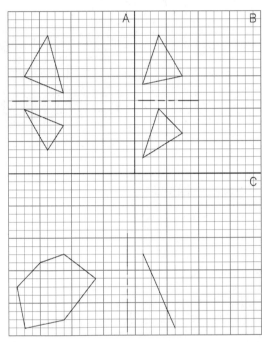

EXERCISE 25.5

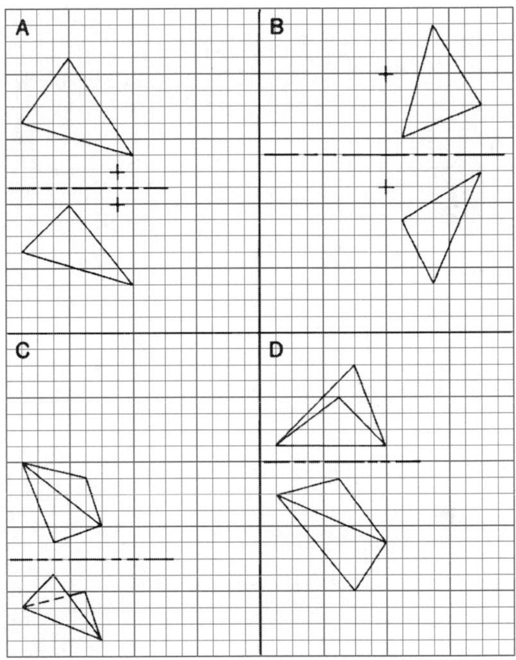

EXERCISE 25.6

Exercise 25.7(A) and (C) Using the edge view method, determine the piercing point, and show in all views, along with the proper visibility.

Exercise 25.7(B) Using the cutting plane method, solve for the piercing point of the line and the plane. Complete all views, and show the proper visibility.

Exercise 25.8 What is the relationship between the plane and the line? Solve for the shortest distance, shortest connector, angle between, piercing point, strike, dip, slope angle, and any other pertinent information as required.

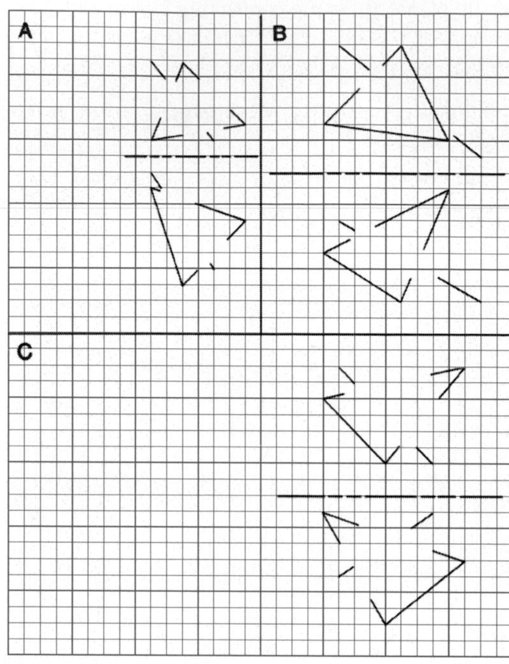

EXERCISE 25.7

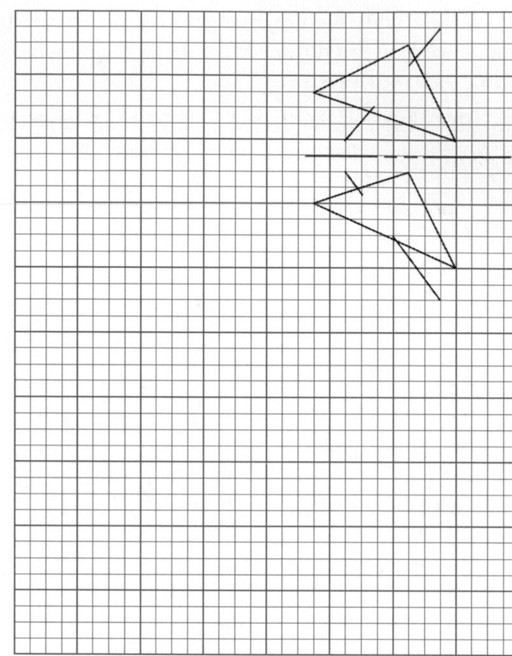

EXERCISE 25.8

PROBLEMS

Problems may be assigned as sketching, instrument, or CAD projects. Transfer the given problem to a separate "A"- or "B"-size sheet. Complete all views, and solve for proper visibility, including centerlines, object lines, and hidden lines. Use dividers to transfer the positions of the points and lines. A 1.5/1 scale is suggested, but a 2/1 scale could also be used. Make a rough trial sketch of the problem and the solution before finalizing its position on paper. This will avoid placement of the problem without enough work space to complete the project.

Problem 25.1 Establish the lines on the planes in all views. Complete the four views of the plane and the lines.

Problem 25.2 Establish the three views of the plane. Line 4-5 is on the plane.

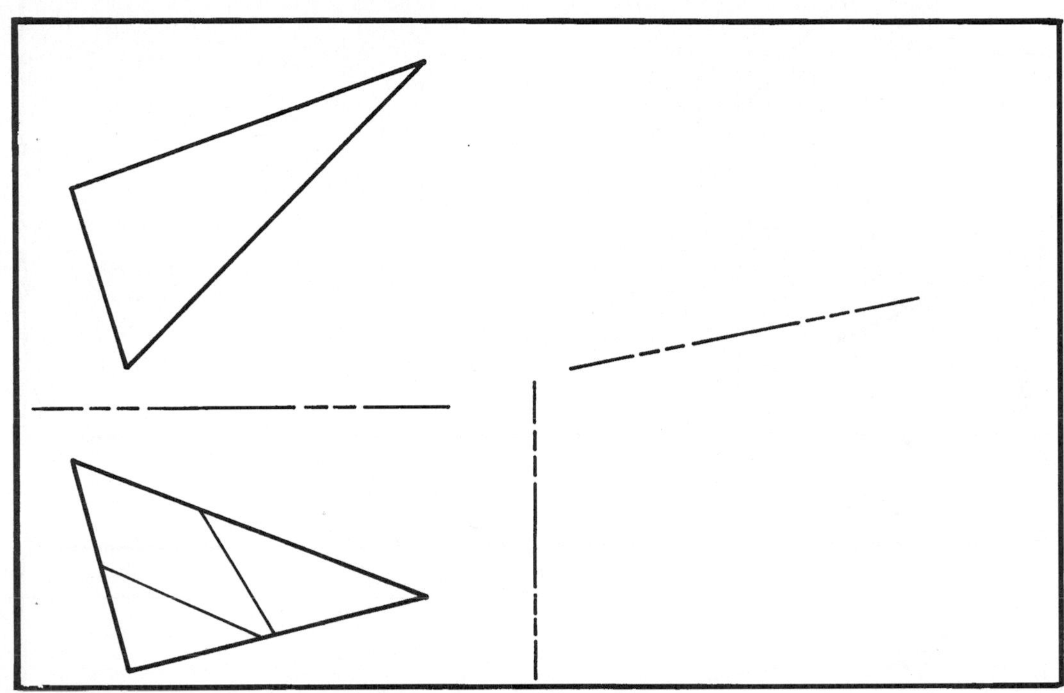

PROBLEM 25.1

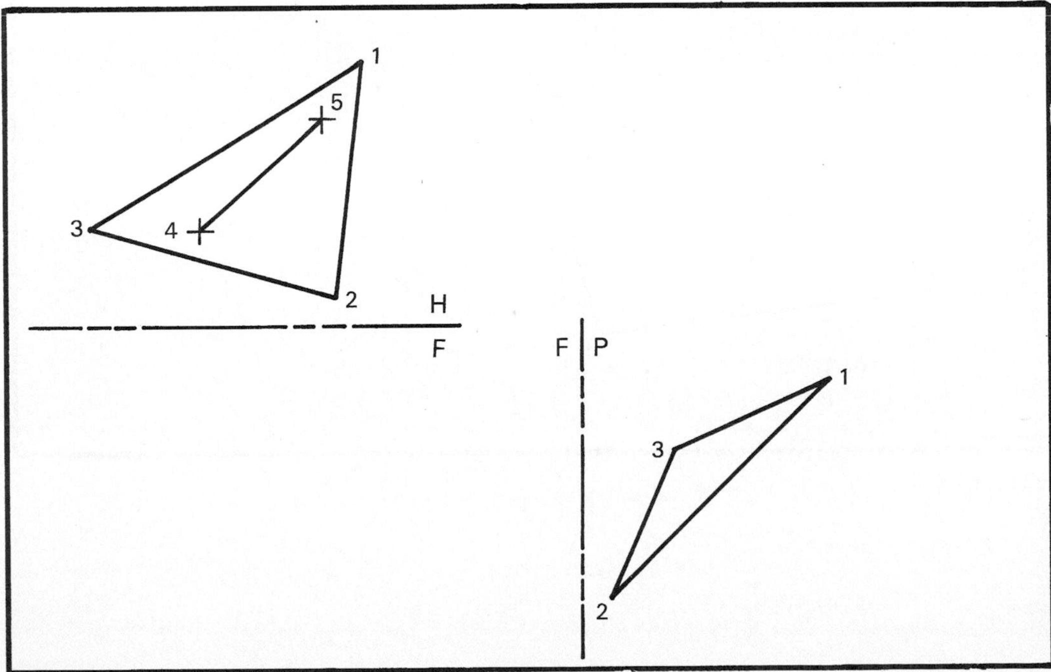

PROBLEM 25.2

Problem 25.3 Solve for the edge view, true shape, strike, slope angle, dip, and area of the plane.

Problem 25.4 Solve for the shortest distance between the point and the plane. Show the shortest connector in all views.

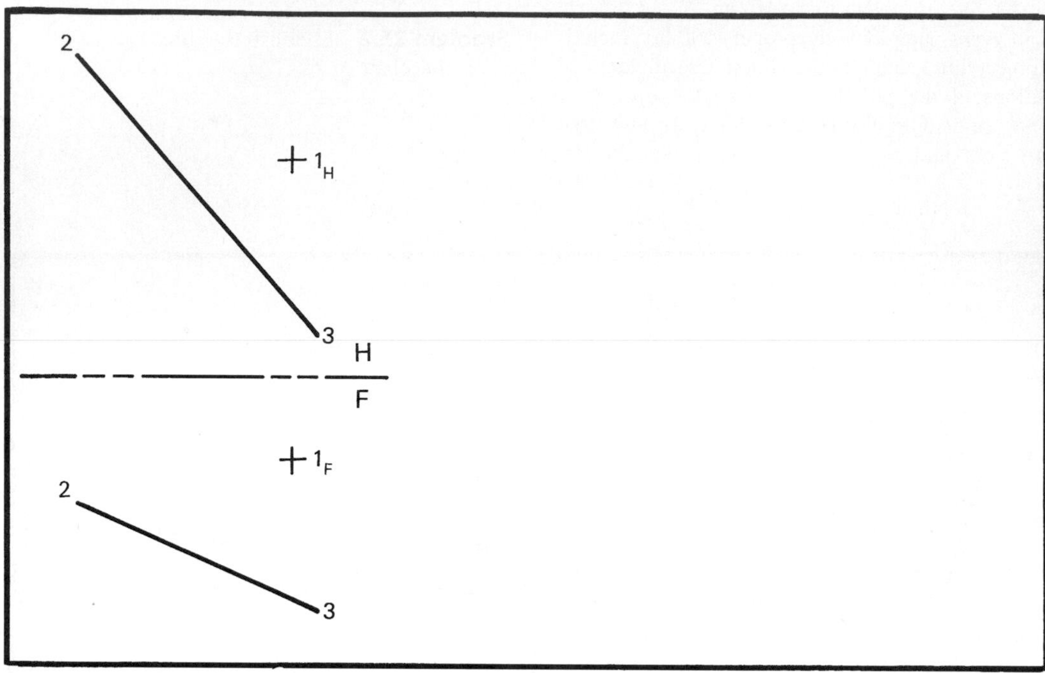

PROBLEM 25.3

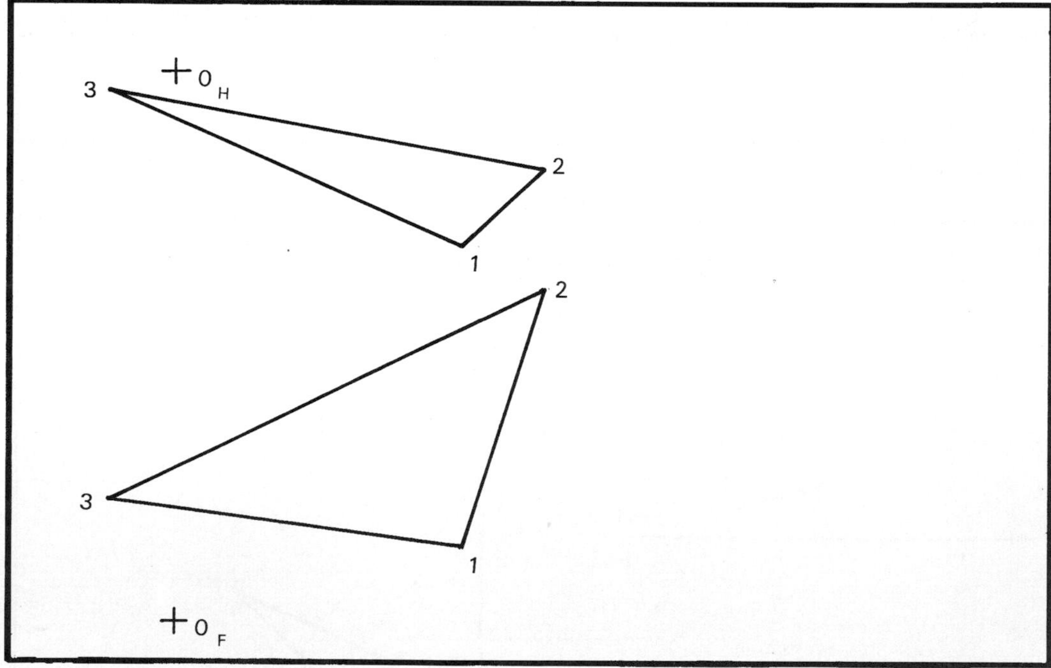

PROBLEM 25.4

Problem 25.5 What is the angle formed by the plane and each of the three principal views?

Problem 25.6 What is the dihedral angle between plane A and plane B?

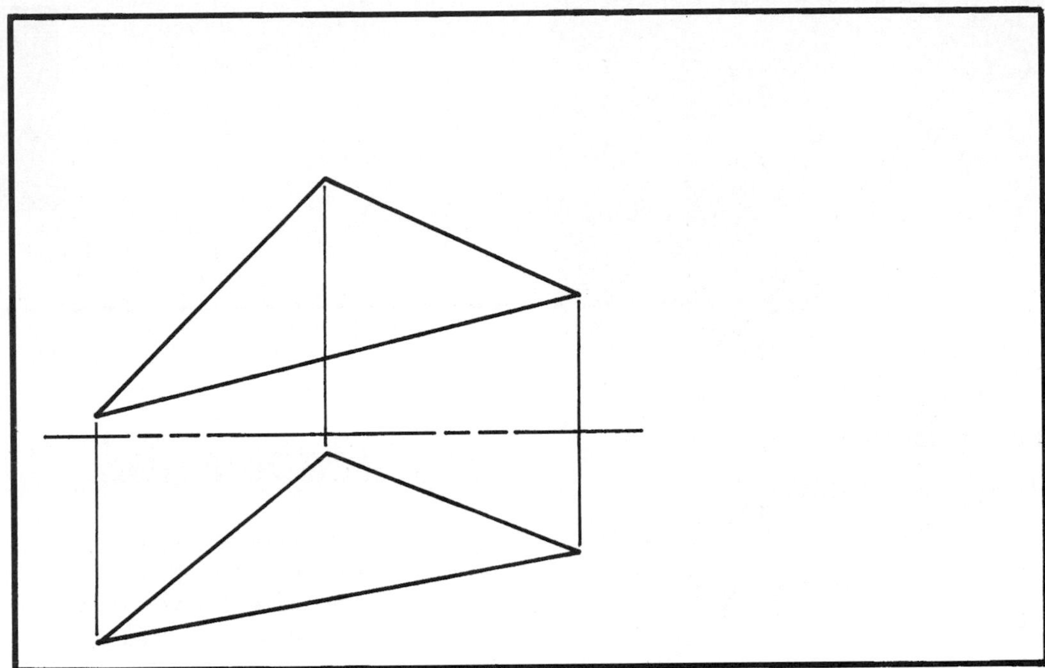

PROBLEM 25.5

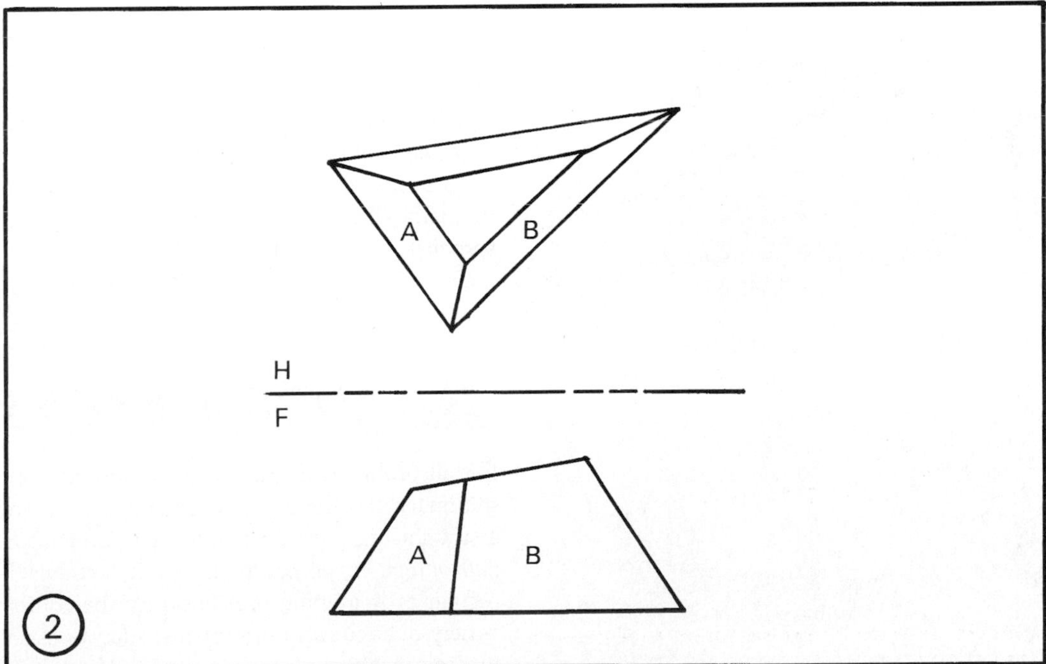

PROBLEM 25.6

REVOLUTIONS

Chapter 26

LEARNING OBJECTIVES

Upon completion of this chapter you will be able to:

1. Rotate a point or a line about a given axis line.
2. Revolve a line through a specific angular displacement.
3. Solve for the slope angle of a line using revolution.
4. Construct a line with a specific slope, bearing, and length.
5. Solve for the cone locus of a line.
6. Use double-revolution to find the true shape of a plane.
7. Measure the true angle between two planes using revolution.
8. Use CAD commands to rotate part features.

26.1 INTRODUCTION

Orthographic projection and descriptive geometry are normally associated with the projection of an object or a form onto a projection plane. The view of each projection plane assumes that the object is stationary and that the vantage point for each view differs. **Revolution/rotation** requires the object to be revolved or rotated and the observers to remain stationary. This procedure takes fewer views to accomplish a specific task, though it may clutter or crowd the given views.

Industrial applications of revolution are shown in Figure 26.1. In each application a rigid chain is employed to move, revolve, or lift. The chain in Figure 26.1(a) can extend and remain unsupported. The rigid chain in Figure 26.1(b) is mounted on top of forks on a lift truck, allowing the chain to slide the load on and off the forks. The chain revolves about an axis and the related mechanical part or material is moved. In many designs the chain retracts by revolving about a sprocket [Fig. 26.1(c) and (d)].

26.2 REVOLUTION OF A POINT

For all problems involving revolution, the observer remains stationary and the object (point) is rotated (revolved) about a straight-line axis. Each revolved point moves in a *circular path of rotation,* perpendicular to the *axis line.* Revolution and regular orthographic projection can be combined to solve a variety of engineering problems, such as clearances between moving machine parts (Fig. 26.1). The following principles apply to the revolution of a point. Since all objects, lines, and planes are composed of points, these principles form the theoretical foundation for *all* revolution problems.

- The **axis of revolution** (rotation) is always a straight line and must be established before a point can be revolved. The axis is a point view in which the path of rotation

(a) Rigid chain used to move material

(b) Rigid chain mounted on a lift truck

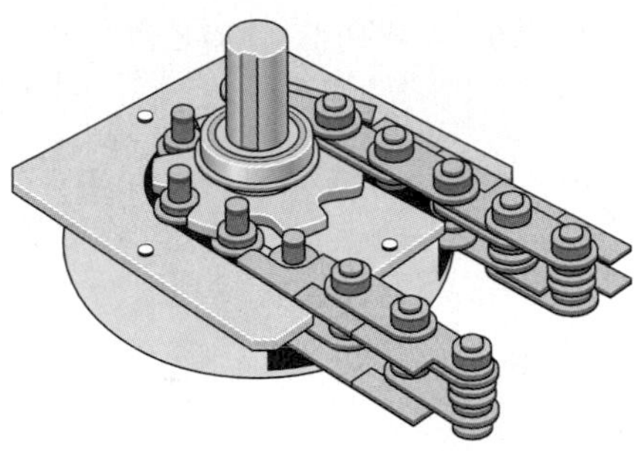

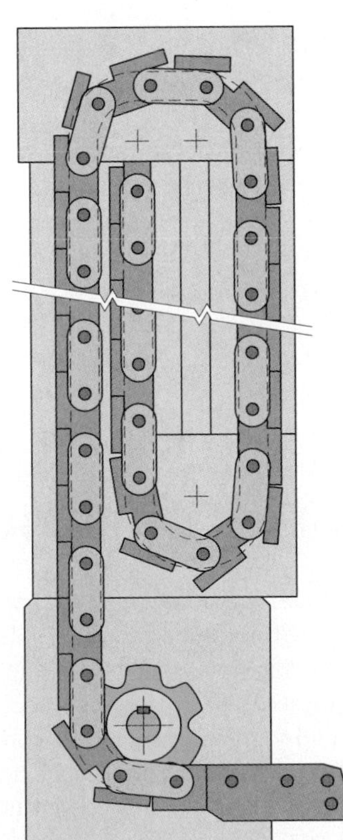

(c) Magazine illustrating the double recoil feature. The chain revolves 90° about the sprocket.

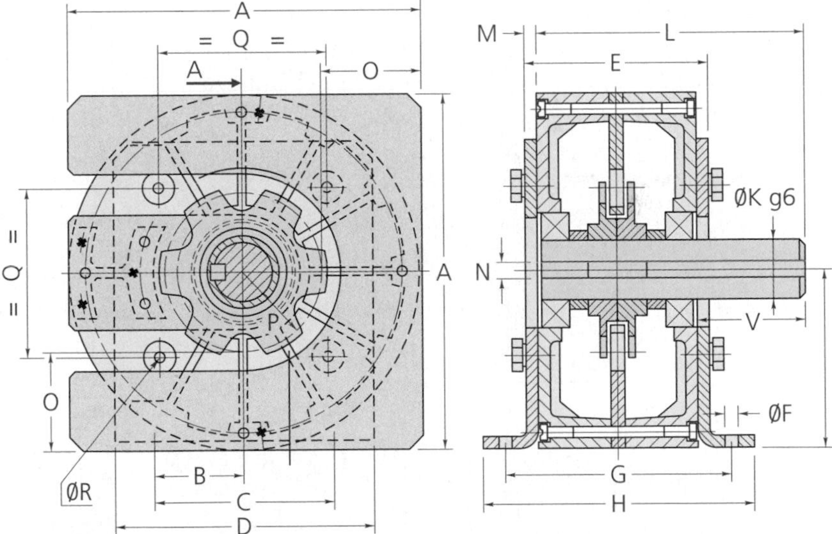

(d) 180° drive housing

FIGURE 26.1 Chains and Revolving Parts

is a circle, and it appears true length where the path of rotation is an edge.

- The revolution of a point is always perpendicular to the axis and moves in a circular path around the point view of the axis line. This circular path forms a plane perpendicular to the axis, which appears as a circle (or portion of a circle) when the axis is a point view.
- The **path of rotation** is formed by the revolving point and a line connected from it to the axis. This line is the radius of the circle (or arc) formed by revolution. When

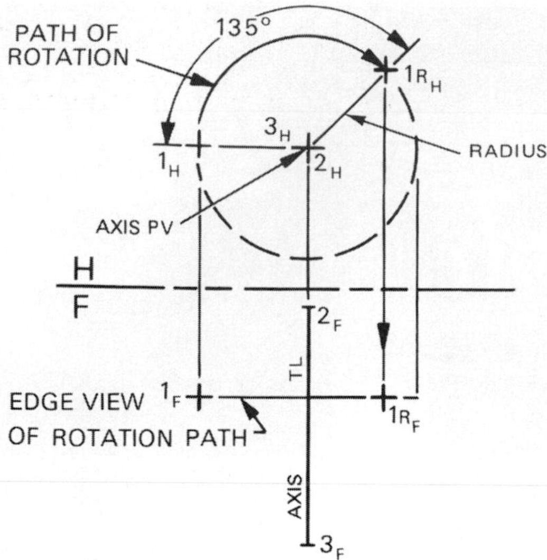

FIGURE 26.2 Rotation of a Point

the axis shows as true length, the path of rotation appears as an edge with a length equal to the diameter of the circle.

In Figure 26.2, point 1 is revolved around vertical axis line 2_H-3_H. Axis 2-3 is true length in the frontal view and is a point in the horizontal view. Point 1_H is revolved clockwise 135° to position $1R_H$. The path of rotation is an edge view in the frontal view, in which the axis is true length, and is a circular path in the horizontal view. The point in Figure 26.3 is rotated about a horizontal axis and moves clockwise 21° downward. The circle path shows as a circle in the frontal view and as an edge in the horizontal view.

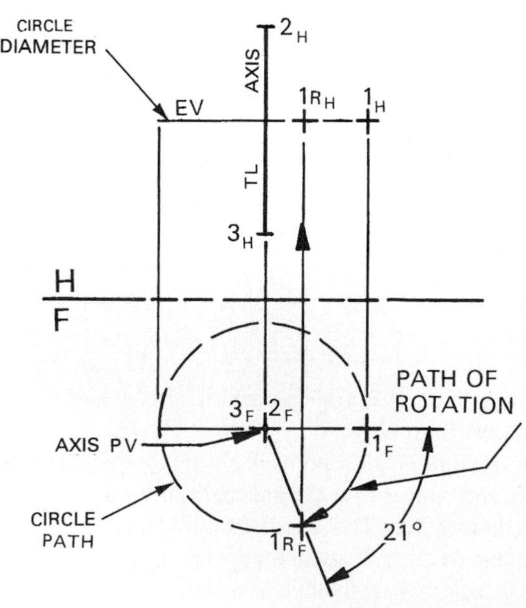

FIGURE 26.3 Rotation of a Point About a Horizontal Axis

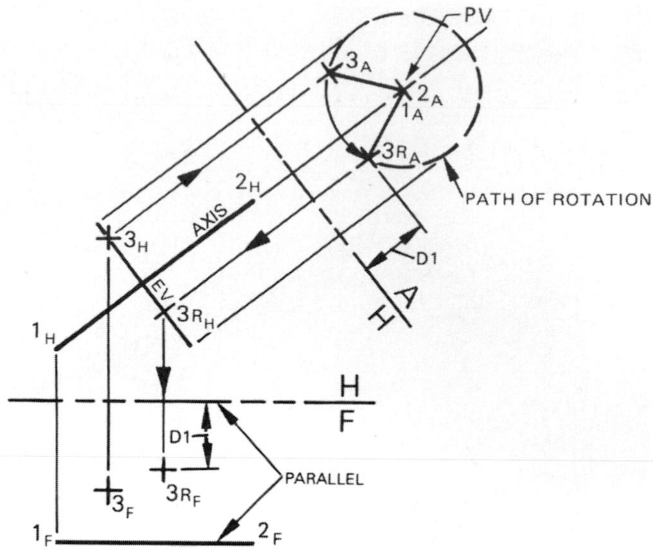

FIGURE 26.4 Rotation of a Point About a Given Line

26.2.1 Revolution of a Point About an Axis

When a point is revolved about an axis that does not appear as a point in the frontal or horizontal view, an auxiliary projection is required in which the axis appears as a point. In Figure 26.4, point 3 is to be revolved about line 1-2, which does not project as a point in the frontal or horizontal views. Therefore, the path of rotation would appear as an ellipse in the frontal projection (not shown). To revolve point 3 about horizontal line 1-2, an auxiliary view is projected perpendicular to the true length of axis 1_H-2_H. Fold line H/A is drawn perpendicular to line 1_H-2_H, and axis 1_A-2_A shows as a point view in this primary auxiliary view. Point 3_A is revolved to position $3R_A$ in this view. The path of rotation generated by moving the point creates a circular plane in this view. Point $3R_A$ is located in the horizontal plane by simple projection, since it falls on the edge view of the path of rotation. The frontal position of point 3R is located by transferring D1 from auxiliary view A to the frontal view along its projected line.

26.3 REVOLUTION OF A LINE

A line can be revolved in the same manner as a point. The axis must be established before a line can be revolved. The axis can be through either the endpoint of the line, a point on the line, or a point off the line. In the first case, the line revolves about a single endpoint and generates a cone. In the second case, both ends revolve and change position. Each endpoint remains in the same plane created by its path of rotation.

One of the most common uses of revolution is to find the true length of an oblique line without the need for an auxiliary view. Since revolution changes the position of a line

Focus On . . .

THE GYROCOMPASS

Have you ever heard the phrase "Let George do it"? If you have, you may have wondered who George is. That bit of advice, from World War II, encourages someone to avoid a burdensome or demanding task. George is the name given the aircraft automatic pilot device that removes some of the burden from the pilot and keeps the airplane on course.

Automatic navigation was unheard of until recently. For those who once sailed the seas by stars and by plotting complex navigational charts, it must have appeared magical indeed. The magic is performed by gyroscopes.

Though gyroscopes have been around a long time (since the early 1800s), they weren't put to use until the 1900s. At that time, Elmer Sperry was convinced they had great commercial possibilities. Sperry developed the gyrocompass from the elementary gyroscope. The invention filled an immediate Navy need for a compass that would be unaffected by steel ships.

By World War II, 200 of the merchant fleets in the world were guided by the Sperry gyrocompass. Other devices that relied on the gyroscope were developed, but the most important application was "George," the turn indicator and automatic pilot.

The autopilot relieves the human pilot from the physical effort of flying the plane. Today, autopilots are found in almost every size of aircraft. Electronic navigation and control are used extensively on all modern aircraft. Modern commercial airplanes give George much of the duties involved in navigation and control. Tell George where you want to go, and he can navigate the plane so it stays on course.

After you have studied descriptive geometry, you will probably be able to appreciate the relationship between points, lines, and planes in 3D. You may also be able to appreciate navigation at sea during eras before the gyrocompass. Electronic navigation and control play a large part in piloting a modern aircraft. Most pilots will be happy to tell you that life is a lot nicer now that George is around.

A gyrocompass.

but not its length, it is possible to revolve an oblique line so that it is parallel to the adjacent projection plane. The line will then project as true length in the adjacent view. The axis can be located through an endpoint or on the line and revolved in either given view. The axis line is a point view in one view and is assumed true length in the other, though it need not have a specific length.

Figure 26.5 compares the auxiliary view method with the revolution method. The auxiliary view method [Fig. 26.5(a)] requires the projection of a new view. In Figure 26.5(b), point 2_H is revolved about a vertical axis line passed through point 1_H until it is parallel to H/F in position $2R_H$. Point 2 is located in the frontal view by projection, since it falls on the edge view of the path of rotation. A construction line (which is really a portion of the edge view of the path rotation) is drawn parallel to H/F until it intersects the projection line and locates $2R_F$. The revolution of point 2 changes its position in the horizontal and frontal views. The revolved point does not alter its elevation, since it must remain in a plane perpendicular to the true-length axis of revolution. Line 1_F-$2R_F$ is true length.

In Figure 26.6 two revolved positions for line 1-2 are shown. Both solve for the true length of the line in the horizontal view. Choice of rotation directions is determined by the angular displacement required for the project and the space available on the paper.

26.3.1 Revolution of an Oblique Line

When a line is revolved about another line, it generates a cylinder if the lines are parallel, a circle if they are perpendicular, a cone if they intersect, or a hyperboloid of revolution if they are oblique. In Figure 26.7, oblique line 1-2 is revolved clockwise 110° about vertical line 3-4. Line 3_H-4_H is a point view in the horizontal view and true length in the frontal view. Line 1_H-2_H is revolved about the point view of axis line 3_H-4_H in the horizontal view by rotating both endpoints 110°. Because the whole line is revolved, it does not change its oblique shape in the horizontal view; only its position ($1R_H$-$2R_H$) is altered. The frontal projection of the revolved line is located by moving points 1_F and 2_F perpendicular to the true-length axis 3_F-4_F. Each point intersects the projection line drawn from its related revolved point in the horizontal view.

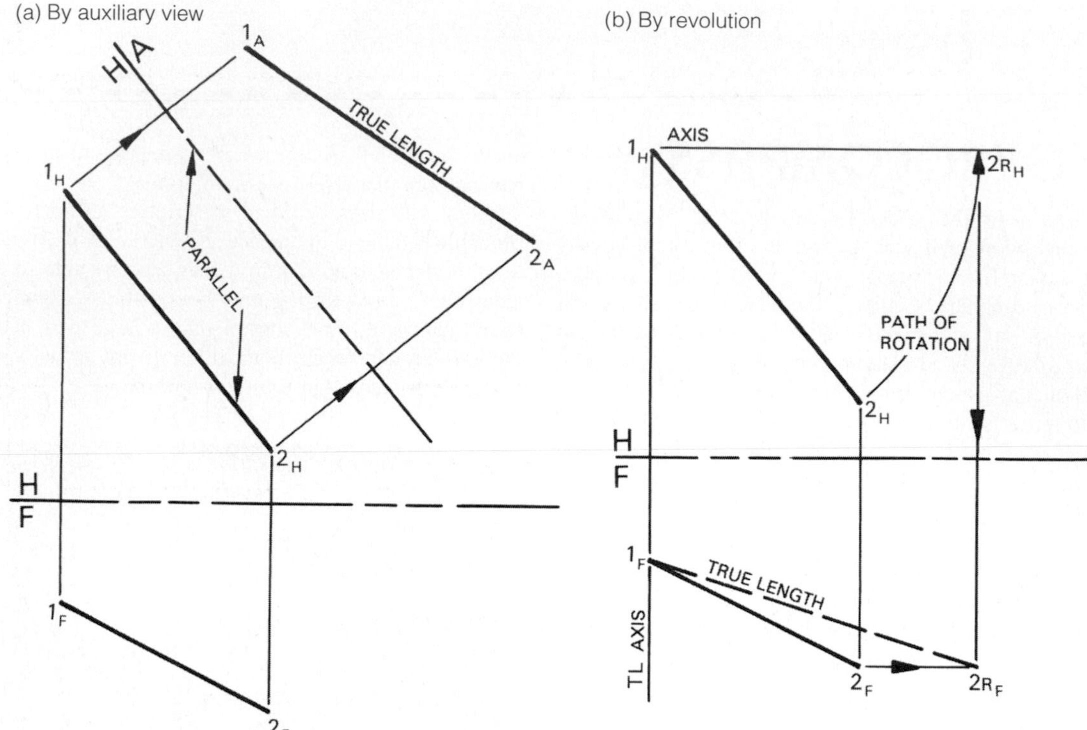

FIGURE 26.5 True Length of a Line

26.3.2 True Length and True Angle a Line Makes with a Principal Plane by Revolution

The true length of a line can be found by revolution using any two adjacent views of the line. In Figures 26.8 and 26.9, the true length of the lines have been established by revolution. The angle that the line makes with a principal view is measured as the angle between the true-length solution and the adjacent fold line. In Figure 26.8, the angle line 1-2 makes with the horizontal view is shown; in Figure 26.9, the angle line 1-2 makes with the frontal view is determined.

Note that a line can be revolved in any view to solve for the true length in the adjacent projection plane. The axis of revolution can pass through any point on the line, though

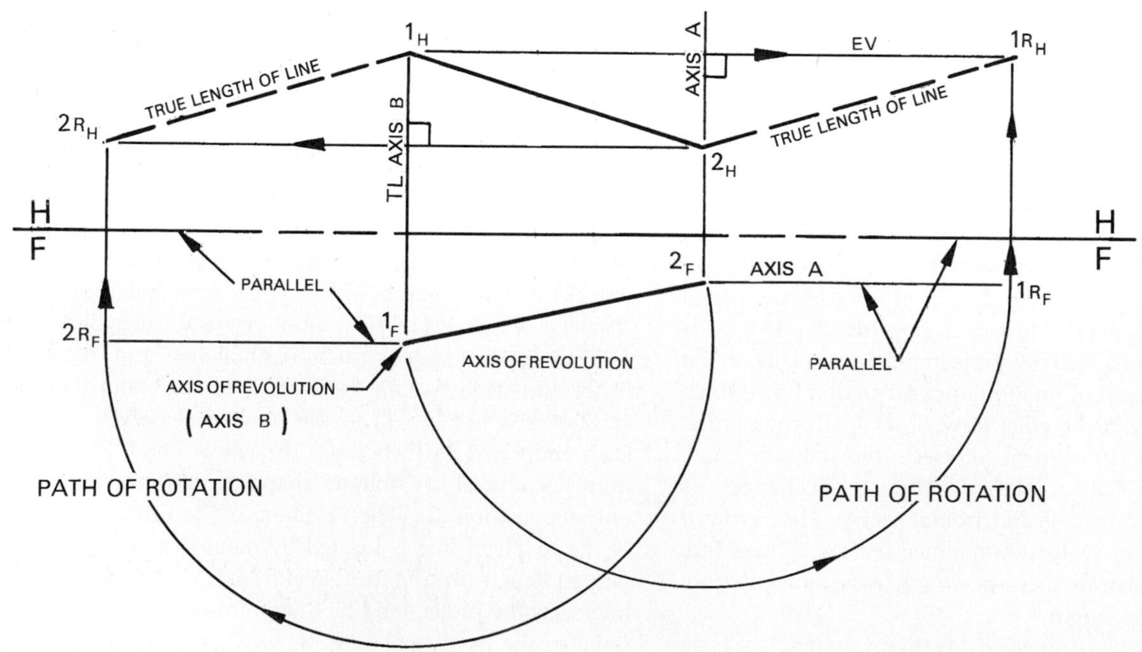

FIGURE 26.6 True Length by Revolution

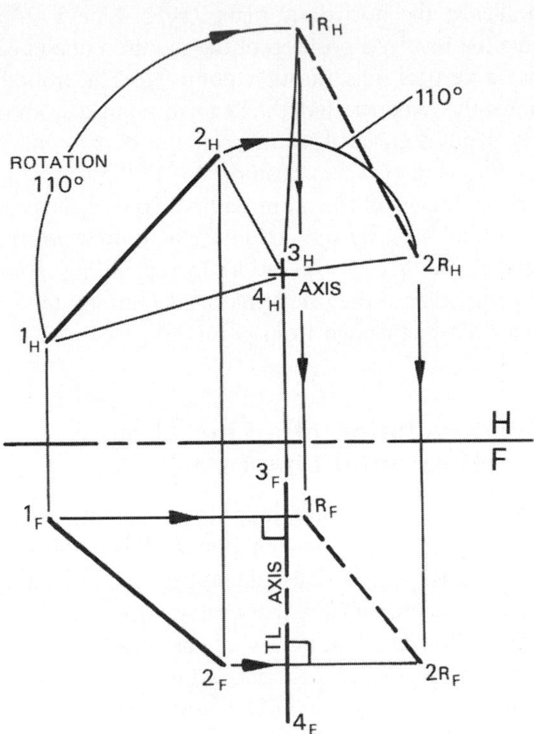

FIGURE 26.7 Revolution of a Line About a Vertical Axis

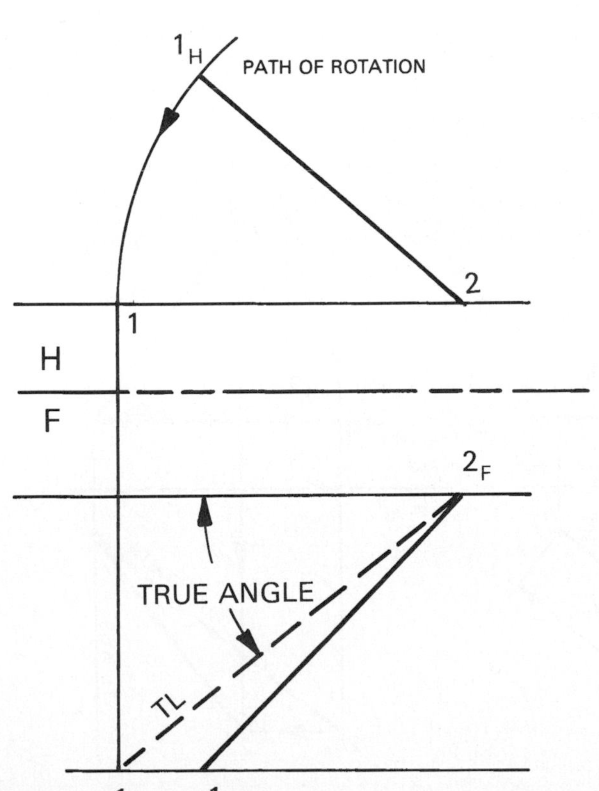

FIGURE 26.8 True Angle Between a Line and the Horizontal Plane

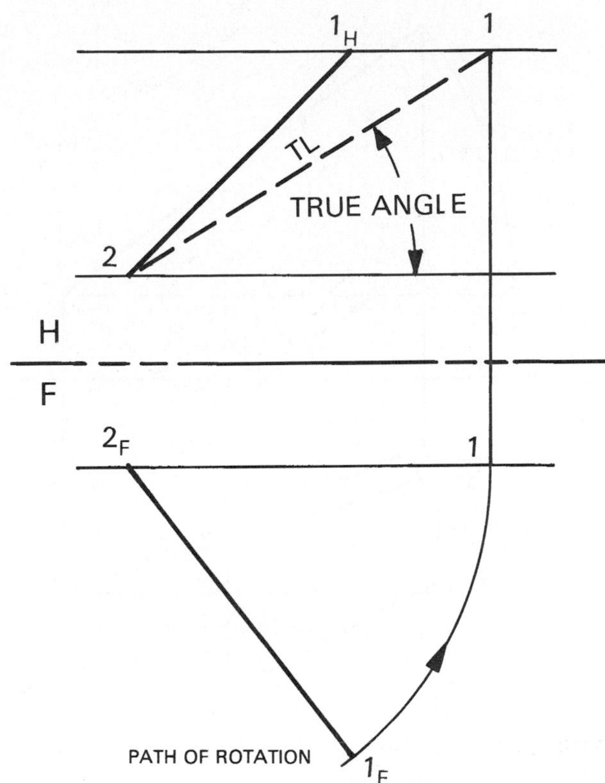

FIGURE 26.9 True Angle Between a Line and the Frontal Plane

the endpoints are the most convenient since only one end will need to be revolved.

26.3.3 Slope of a Line by Revolution

The **slope** of a line can be measured in an elevation view in which the line appears true length and the horizontal plane shows as an edge. To measure the slope of a line that is not a frontal or profile principal line, an auxiliary view projected parallel to the line in the horizontal view is needed. The true length of the line must show in an elevation view. In Figure 26.10, the slope of line 1-2 is found by revolving the line about a vertical axis that passes through point 2_H. Point 1_H is revolved about the point view of the axis at 2_H to position $1R_H$. Because line $1R_H$-2_H is parallel to H/F, its frontal projection shows as a true-length line (frontal line). The slope angle is measured between true-length line $1R_F$-2_F and a *level line* (or the edge view of the horizontal plane as represented by fold line H/F).

26.3.4 Slope, Bearing, and True length of a Line by Revolution

Revolution can serve to locate a line in space given its **bearing**, **slope**, and **length**. Only two views are necessary

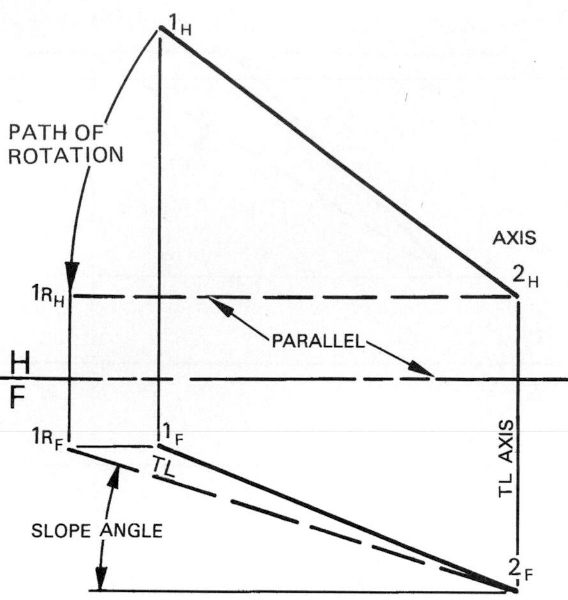

FIGURE 26.10 Slope Angle by Revolution

when revolution is used. In Figure 26.11, the bearing is given as N 37° W, with a 39° slope from point 1 toward point 2, and a true length of 200 ft. The following steps were used to solve the problem.

1. Locate point 1 in the frontal and horizontal views. From point 1_H, draw a line of indefinite length with a bearing of N 37° W (1).
2. From point 1_F, draw line 1_F-2_F at 39° downward toward point 2_F, using 200 ft as the true length. Line 1_H-$2R_H$ is parallel in the horizontal plane (H/F). Line 1-2R represents the revolved position of the required line (1-2) (2).
3. Pass a vertical axis through point 1_H. The frontal view shows the axis true length. Revolve point $2R_H$ about the axis at point 1_H until it intersects the bearing line. Point $2R_H$ is thus revolved to position 2_H, and line 1_H-2_H is the horizontal view of the required line. Point 2_F is located in the frontal view by projection; 2_F is located on the edge view of the path of rotation by extending point $2R_F$ perpendicular to the true-length axis until it intersects the projection line drawn from point 2_H.

26.3.5 Revolution of a Line About a Horizontal Line (Axis)

The axis of revolution must appear as a point view before rotating a given point, line, or object. When the axis is a horizontal line, which does not appear as a point in the frontal view, a primary auxiliary view is projected perpendicular to the true-length view of the axis to establish its point view. In Figure 26.12, oblique line 3-4 is rotated 180° counterclockwise (toward point 1 when viewed from point 2) about horizontal line 1-2.

1. Draw H/A perpendicular to the true-length view of line 1_H-2_H
2. Project auxiliary view A. Axis line 1_A-2_A appears as a point, D1.
3. Revolve point 3_A 180° counterclockwise to position $3R_A$, and point 4_A 180° counterclockwise to position $4R_A$.
4. Draw projection lines from points $3R_A$ and $4R_A$ perpen-

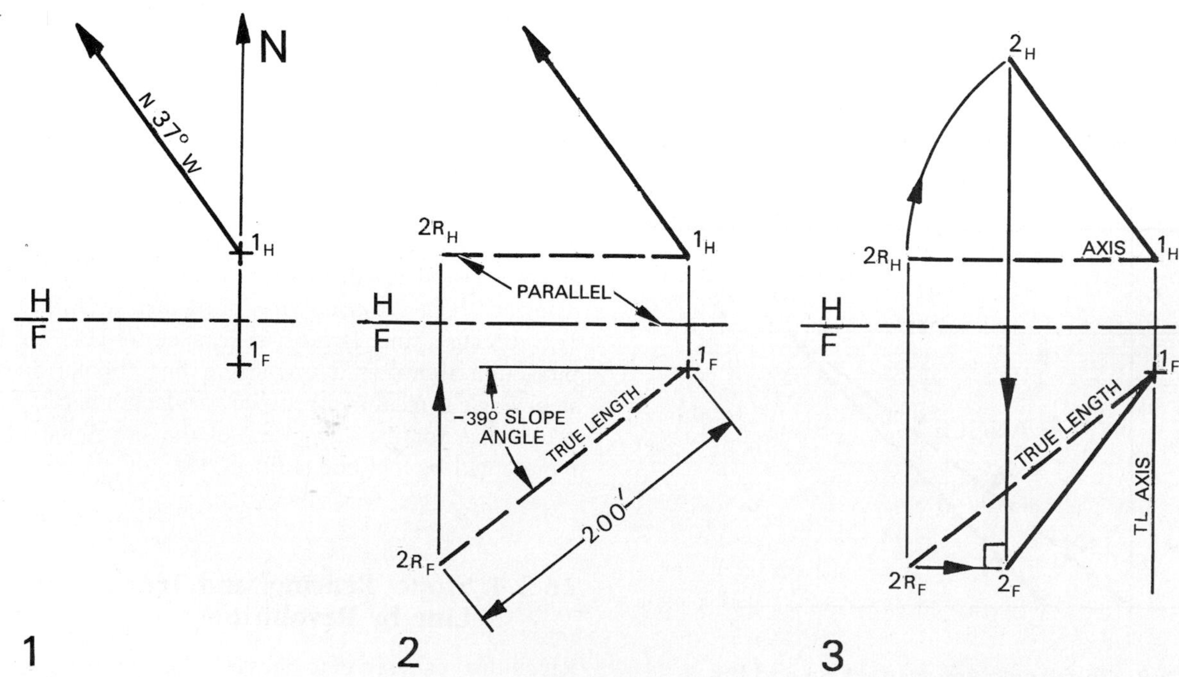

FIGURE 26.11 Construction of a Line by Revolution Given Its Bearing, Slope, and True Length

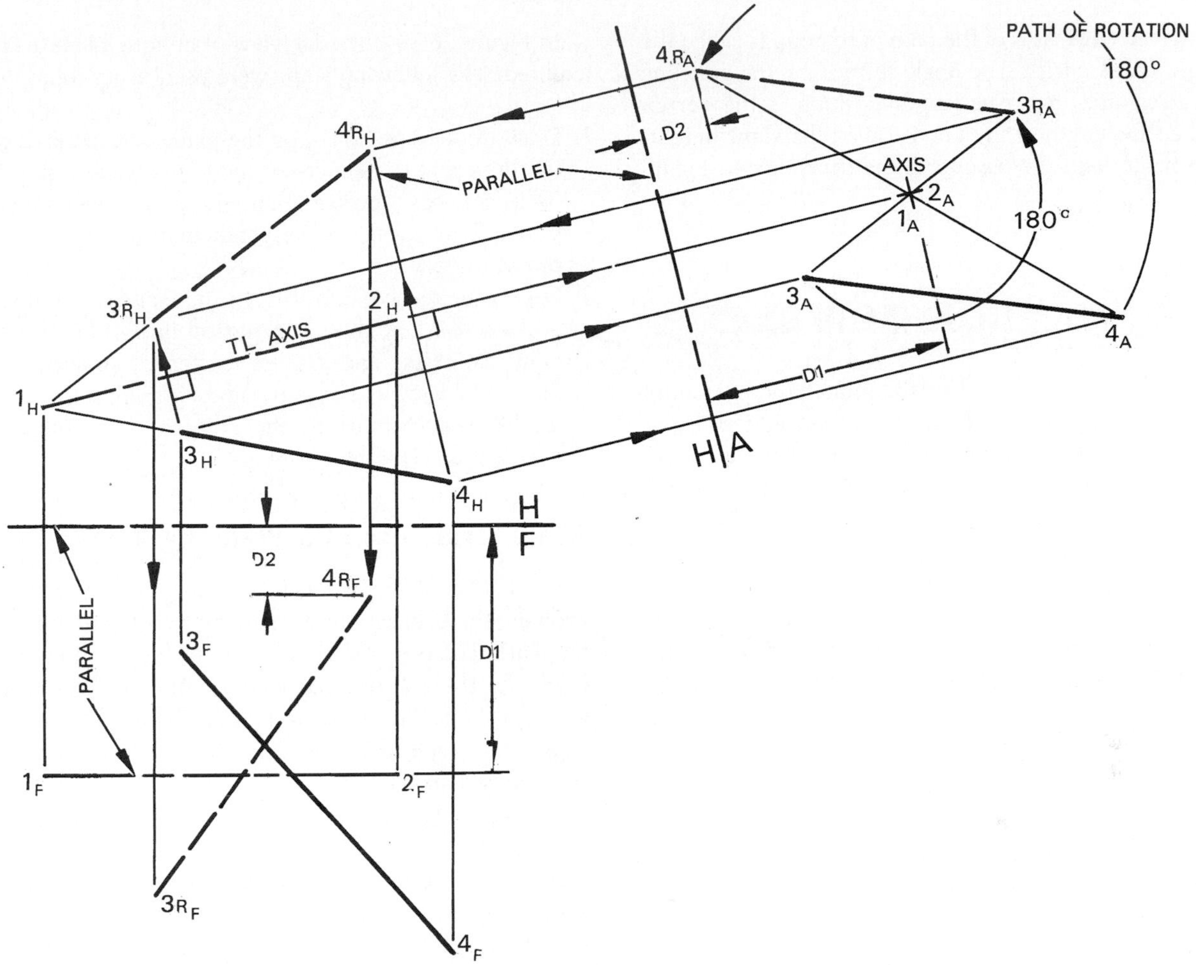

FIGURE 26.12 **Revolution of a Line About a Horizontal Axis**

dicular to H/A. Project points 3_H and 4_H perpendicular to the true-length axis to locate the revolved position of line $3R_H$-$4R_H$. Points $3R_H$ and $4R_H$ are on the edge view of their corresponding paths of rotation.

5. The frontal view of revolved line $3R_F$-$4R_F$ is established by projection and transferring distances from the auxiliary view (D2).

26.3.6 Cone Locus of a Line

The **locus** of a point or line is the set of all possible points (positions) formed by the movement of the point or line as determined by specified conditions. A *circle* results if a point is revolved to all possible positions around a given line axis. If the axis is a point, the movement of the point generates a *sphere*. When a line is revolved into all possible locations about a parallel axis line, the movement produces a *cylinder*, since all lines on the surface are the same distance from the center axis line. When an oblique line is revolved about an axis line that is not parallel to or intersecting the given line, a **hyperboloid of revolution** is formed.

The most commonly used locus of a line is generated by revolving the line about an axis that passes through (intersects) an endpoint of the given line; this is called a **cone locus** of a line (Fig. 26.13). The cone represents all possible positions that the line could be in, given a specified angle and a true-length element. The **true angle** that the line

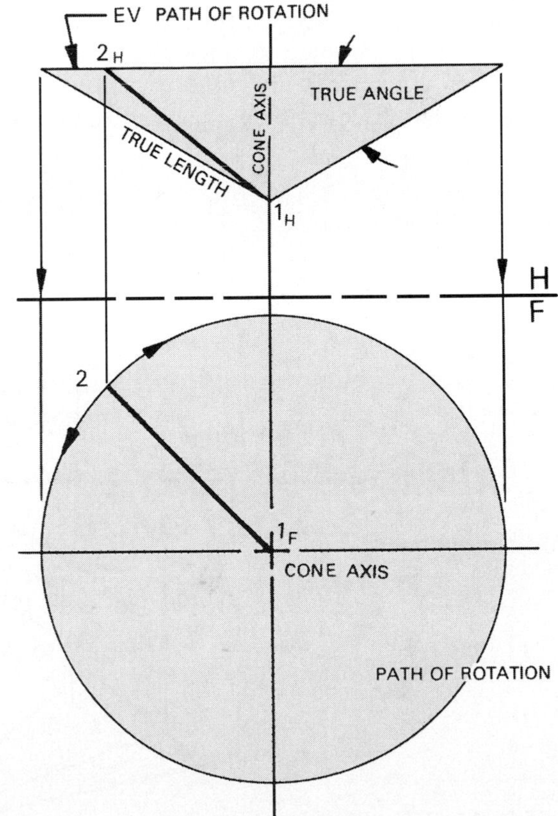

FIGURE 26.13 **Cone Locus of a Line**

makes with the edge view of the path of rotation is called the **base angle** (*slope angle*). The angle formed by the axis line and the given line in a true-length position is the **vertex angle.** The true length of the line is called the **slant height.** The slant height and the base form the true angle in Figure 26.13.

26.4 REVOLUTION OF PLANES

The revolution of planes involves the same basic procedure as for revolution of points and lines. Revolution is an excellent method for solving graphical problems in fewer views by eliminating time-consuming auxiliary projections. A variety of industrial applications involving revolving parts on machinery and aircraft or for showing clearance between moving parts and mechanisms must be solved by graphical revolution.

Revolution of any object (point, line, plane, solid) requires each individual point making up the form to be revolved about an established axis line. Each point of a given form is revolved through the same number of specified degrees, in the same direction.

26.4.1 Edge View of a Plane Using Revolution

The edge view of a plane is found in a view in which a line in the plane appears as a point. Normally an auxiliary projection is needed to solve for the edge view of a plane. Revolution can also establish an edge view. By revolving a plane until it is perpendicular to a principal projection plane, its adjacent view will show the plane as an edge.

In Figure 26.14, the edge view of oblique plane 1-2-3 is required. The following steps were used in its solution.

1. Draw frontal line 3_H-4_H on the plane and parallel to H/F (a). Project as true length in the frontal view. Using point 3_F as an axis, revolve plane 1_F-2_F-3_F clockwise until frontal line 3_F-$4R_F$ is perpendicular to the horizontal projection plane.
2. Project the revolved position of the plane to the horizontal view (b). Line 3-4R is a vertical line and appears as a point. Point $1R_H$ and $2R_H$ are located by projection from the frontal view and by moving each point perpendicular to the axis (parallel to the adjacent fold line). Plane $1R_H$-$2R_H$-3_H is an edge view.

26.4.2 True Size of a Plane by Revolution

The true size/shape of a plane can be determined by revolving the plane about a true-length axis line that lies on the plane. The plane is revolved about the axis in a view in which the plane appears as an edge and the axis line is a point view. The edge view of the plane is revolved until it is parallel to an adjacent projection plane. The revolved plane will then be parallel to the fold line and perpendicular to the line of sight for its adjacent projection.

Given two principal views of an oblique plane, the first step is to project the plane as an edge view. This can be done by establishing a principal (true-length) line that lies on the plane in either view and projecting an auxiliary view perpendicular to it. The plane appears as an edge in this primary auxiliary view. The second step is to revolve the edge view of the plane about the point view of the axis line (principal line) that lies on the plane, until the plane is parallel to the adjacent fold line. The revolved position of

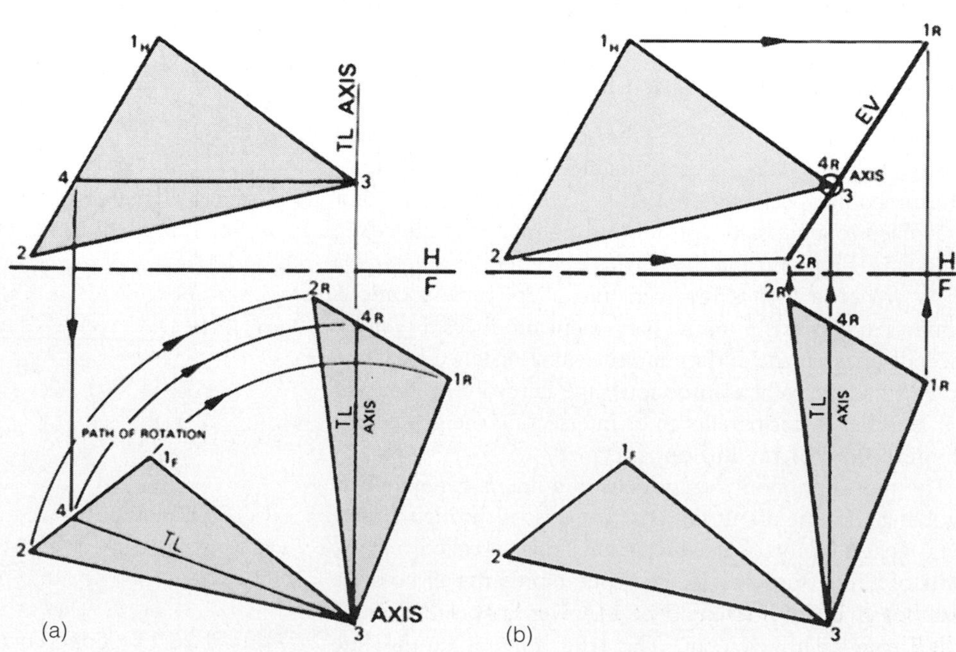

FIGURE 26.14 Edge View by Revolution

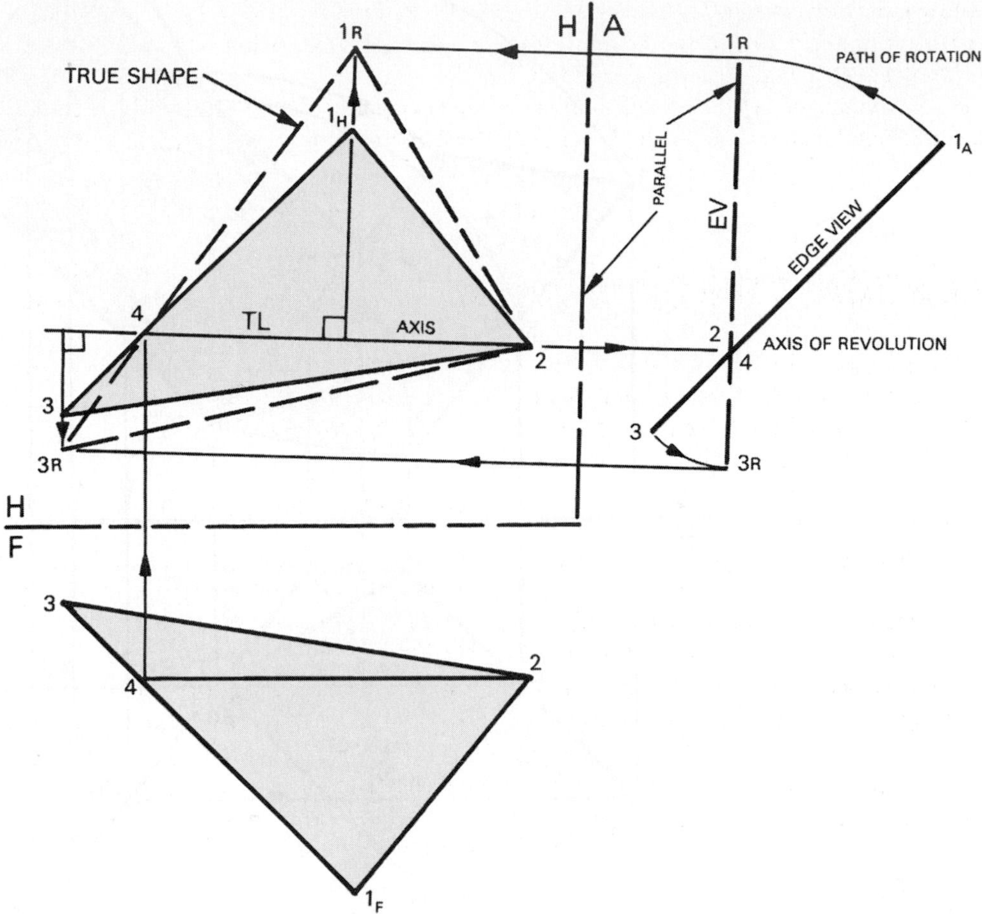

FIGURE 26.15 Edge View and True Shape by Revolution

the plane is then projected back to the previous view, in which it is true size in its revolved location.

In Figure 26.15, the frontal and horizontal projections of oblique plane 1-2-3 are given. The true shape is required. The following steps were used in the solution.

1. Draw horizontal line 2_F-4_F parallel to H/F and true length in the horizontal view.
2. Draw fold line H/A perpendicular to horizontal line 2_H-4_H, and complete auxiliary view A. Plane 1_A-2_A-3_A is an edge view in auxiliary view A.
3. Using the point view of horizontal line 2_A-4_A as the axis of revolution, rotate the plane until it is parallel to H/A. Point 1_A revolves to position $1R_A$ and point 3_A revolves to position $3R_A$. Both points move counterclockwise through the same angular displacement.
4. Project the revolved position of plane $1R_A$-2_A-$3R_A$ back to the horizontal view. Locate point $1R_H$ and $3R_H$ by moving points O_H and 3_H perpendicular to the true-length axis line 2_H-4_H, until they intersect projection lines extended from the revolved points in auxiliary view A.
5. Connect points $1R_H$, $3R_H$, and 2_H, thereby forming the true shape of the plane.

You May Complete Exercises 26.1 and 26.2 at This Time

26.4.4 Double Revolution of a Plane

The edge view and the true shape of an oblique plane can be solved for in the two given views by **double revolution.** An auxiliary projection is unnecessary with this method. However, double revolution can cause confusion and clutter the drawing if the plane is revolved so as to overlap the existing views. This confusion can be eliminated by revolving the plane away from the given projections.

The first step is to establish a true-length line on the plane (Fig. 26.16). Second, the plane is revolved until the true-length line is perpendicular to the fold line and projected to the adjacent view in which it appears as an edge. Third, the edge view is revolved until parallel to the fold line and then projected to the adjacent view in which it shows true size/shape.

26.4.5 Revolution of a Plane About a Given Line

A plane is revolved about a given external line in a view in which the line appears as a point. The true length of the line must be found before the point view can be established. The point view of the line is projected in a view taken perpendicular to the true-length line. In Figure 26.17, line 1-2 and

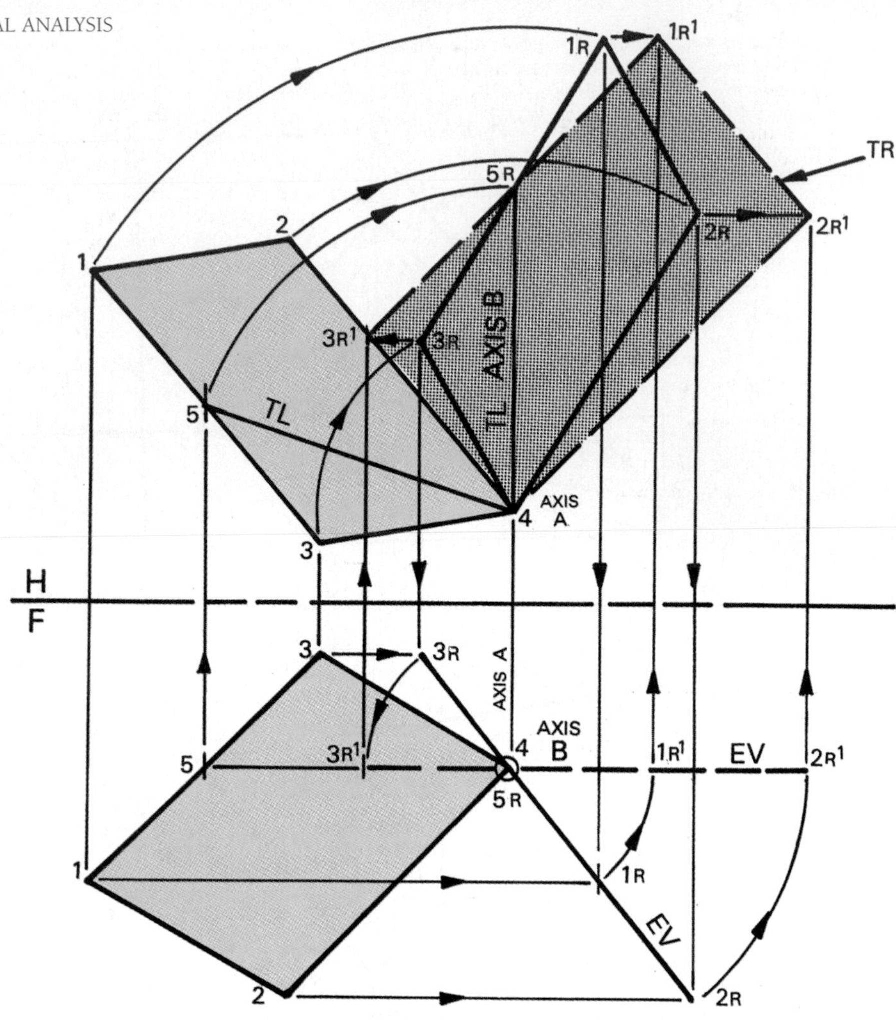

FIGURE 26.16 True Shape by Double Revolution

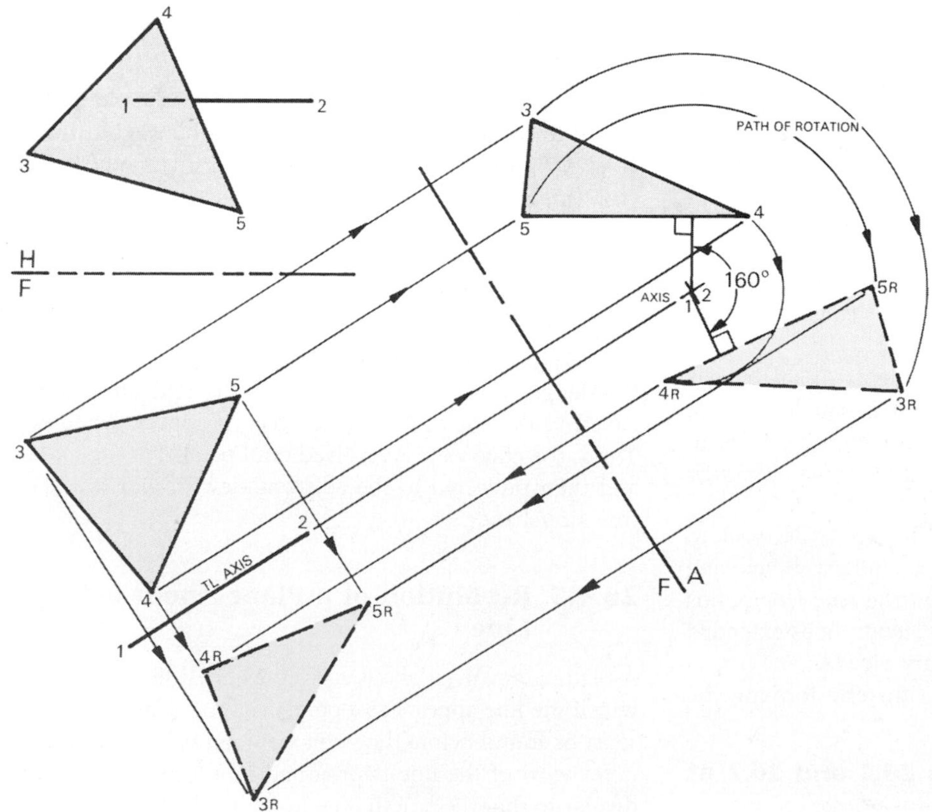

FIGURE 26.17 Revolution of a Plane About a Given Axis

plane 3-4-5 are given. The plane is to be revolved 160° clockwise about the line. Because line 1-2 is a frontal line, it appears true length in the frontal view. Plane 3-4-5 is oblique. The following steps were used to solve the problem.

1. Draw fold line F/A perpendicular to frontal line 1_F-2_F. The line of sight for auxiliary view A is parallel to frontal line 1_F-2_F.
2. Project auxiliary view A. Line 1_A-2_A is a point view. Plane 3_A-4_A-5_A appears oblique.
3. Using line 1_A-2_A as the axis of revolution, revolve every point in the plane clockwise 160°. Since all points of the plane are external to the axis line, they move through the same angular displacement. Plane $3R_A$-$4R_A$-$5R_A$ is the revolved position of the given plane.
4. The revolved position of the plane is projected back to the frontal view, where each of its points moves perpendicular to the axis line 1_F-2_F, parallel to F/A. Plane $3R_F$-$4R_F$-$5R_F$ is the frontal position of the revolved plane. The horizontal position of the plane is not shown.

26.4.6 Angle Between Two Planes by Revolution

Revolution can help find the **dihedral angle** between two planes. A cutting plane is passed perpendicular to the intersection (common) line between the two planes in a view in which the line appears true length. The plane formed by the cutting plane as it cuts the two intersecting planes is revolved until parallel to the adjacent fold line. This new plane is projected back to the previous view, where it appears true size. The true angle can be measured in this view as the angle formed by the cutting plane intersecting the given planes.

In Figure 26.18, two intersecting planes are given and their dihedral angle is required.

1. Draw F/A parallel to intersection line 2_F-3_F and project auxiliary view A. Intersection line 2_A-3_A is true length in auxiliary view A. Both planes are oblique.
2. Pass a cutting plane perpendicular to true-length inter-

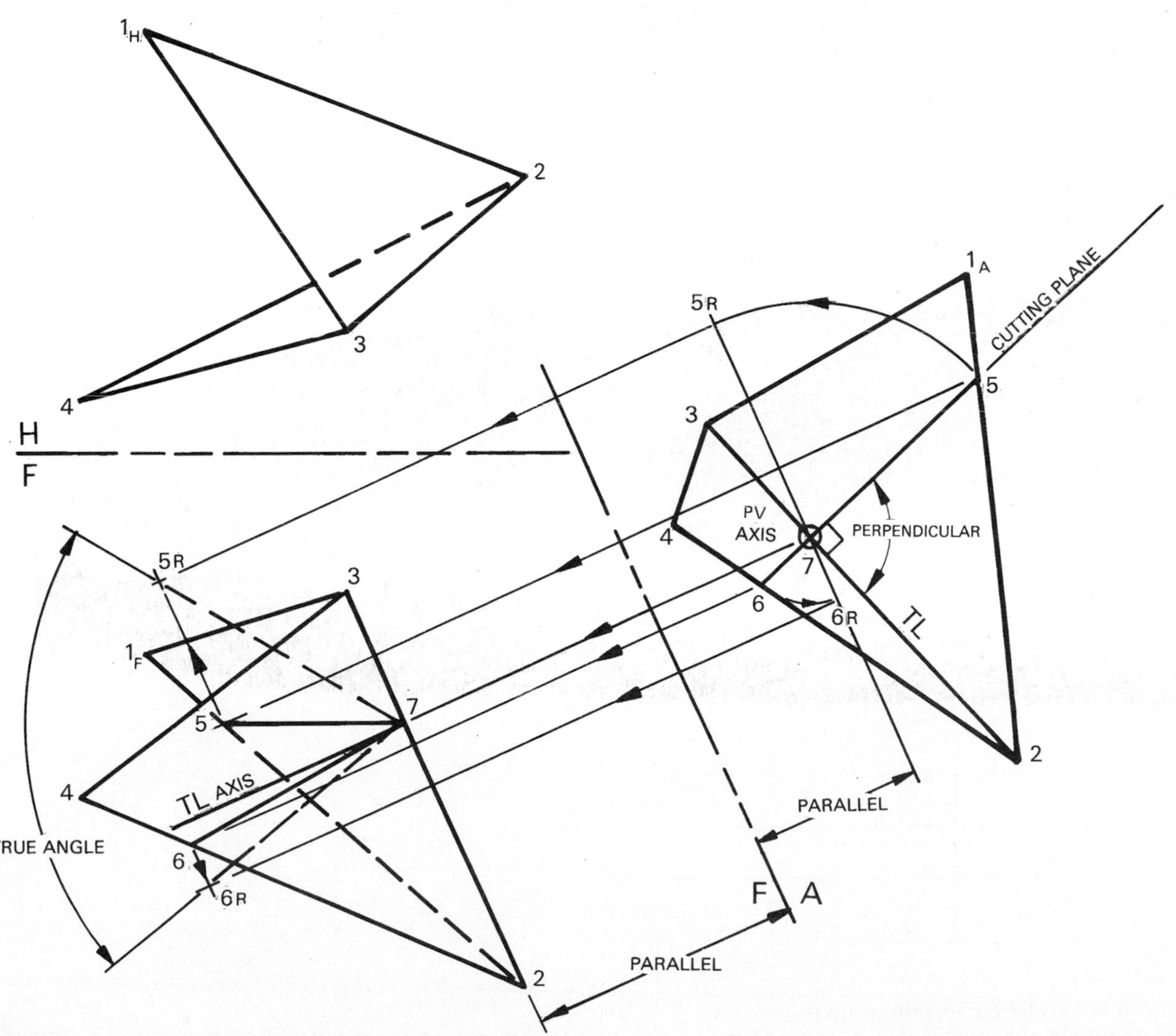

FIGURE 26.18 Dihedral Angle by Revolution

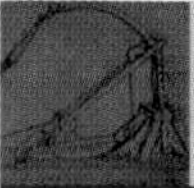

Applying Parametric Design . . .

REVOLVING FEATURES AND PARTS

The pivot pin part shown in Figure A as a shaded image is an example of a part created entirely by revolving one section about a centerline. The **revolve** option creates a feature by revolving the sketched section around a centerline from the sketching plane into the part (Fig. B). The pin was created from one **revolved protrusion.** The holes were added last (Fig. C).

When sketching a feature to be revolved, the first centerline sketched is the **axis of revolution.** The section must lie completely on one side of this centerline and must be closed (Fig. D).

A revolved feature can be created either entirely on one side of the sketching plane or symmetrically on both sides of the sketching plane. The **One Side** and **Both Sides** options are available for any but the first feature. If you choose **Both Sides,** the feature will be revolved symmetrically in each direction for one-half of the angle specified in the OPTIONS menu or for the variable angle of revolution that you enter when prompted.

After choosing **Revolve,** the OPTIONS menu appears. This menu allows you to specify the feature's angle of revolution and whether that angle is to be measured entirely on one side of the sketching plane or symmetrically on both sides of the sketching plane. You can choose the **Variable** option for a user-defined angle of revolution, or you can choose from one of four preset angles: **90, 180, 270,** and **360.** If you choose **Variable,** the angle may be specified and modified after the section is created. This angle must be greater than 0° and less than 360°. The angle will be controlled by a dimension that will appear when modifying the part and in drawings. A corresponding dimension will not appear if a preset angle is chosen. The base feature of the pin was created with a 360°-revolved section (Fig. E). Note that the pin could have been created first without the chamfers and the neck cuts. This is the preferred design sequence, since the chamfers and the necks will then become children of the pin rather than be part of the base

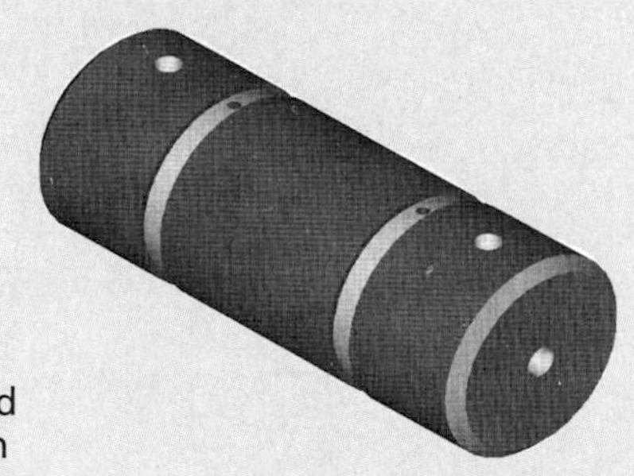

FIGURE A Shaded Image of Pivot Pin

FIGURE B Sketched Section, Dimensions, and Datum Planes

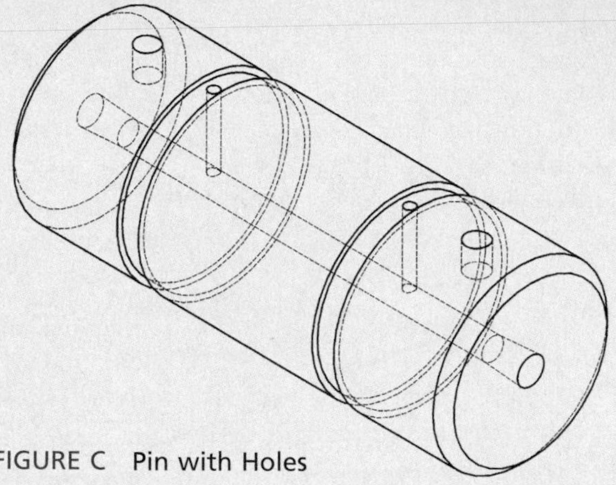

FIGURE C Pin with Holes

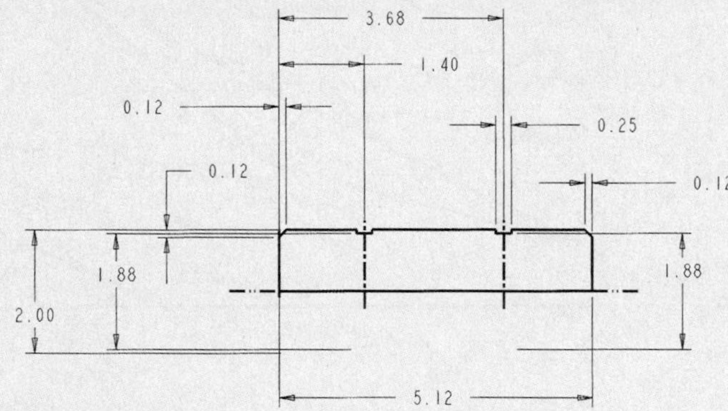

FIGURE D Sketched Section Showing Centerline

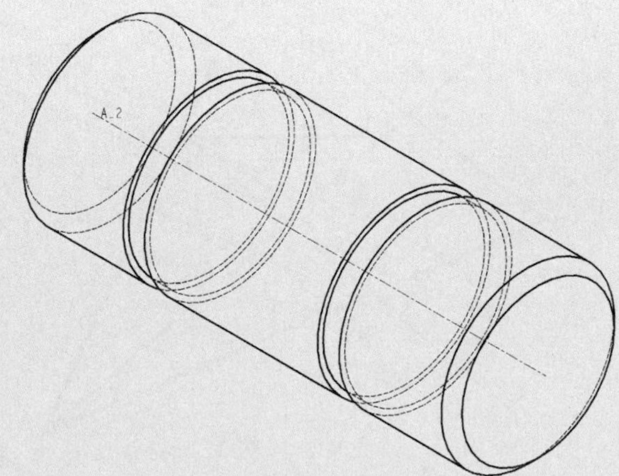

FIGURE E Completed Revolved Base Feature

feature. The pin's holes and cosmetic threads were added using the datum planes (Fig. F) as parent features (Fig. G).

To rotate an existing **component** of an **assembly,** simply select the coordinate system to serve as a reference, pick one or more components, and give the rotation angle. The valve assembly in Figures H, I, J, and K has an arm, a shaft, and a disk that can be rotated during operation. The following sequence of commands was used to rotate them.

Assembly—-(the valve is open at this position)—-**Modify**—-Modify
Assembly—-**Move**—-(select coordinate system)—-(select CSO)—-(select components to move)—-(pick the arm, shaft, and disk plate)—-**Rotate**—-**X Axis**—-(input the angle about the X direction)—-(the valve is now closed)

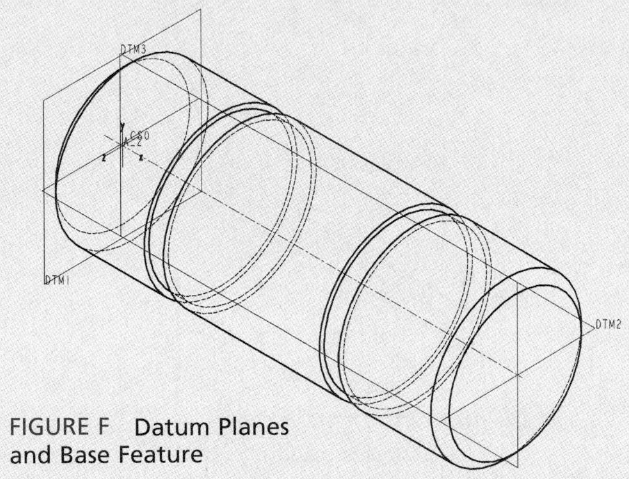

FIGURE F Datum Planes and Base Feature

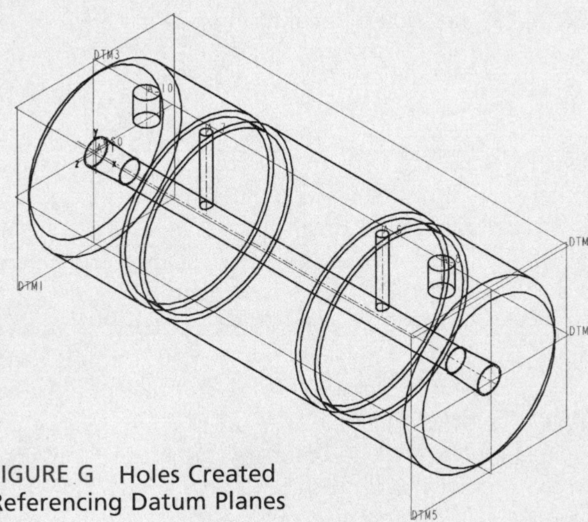

FIGURE G Holes Created Referencing Datum Planes

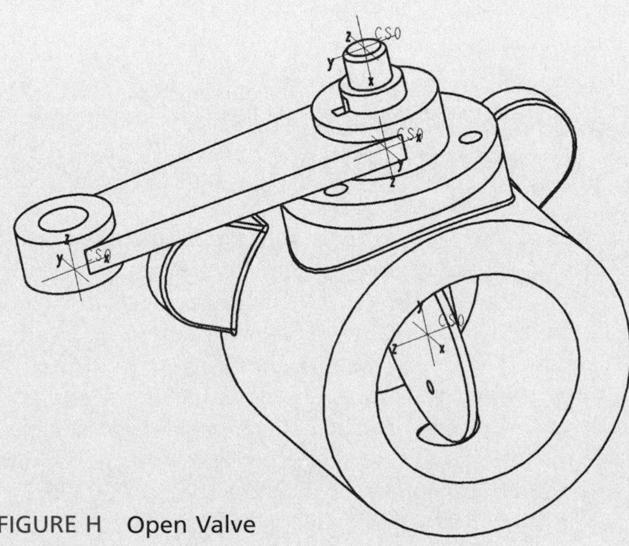

FIGURE H Open Valve

FIGURE I Shaded Open Valve

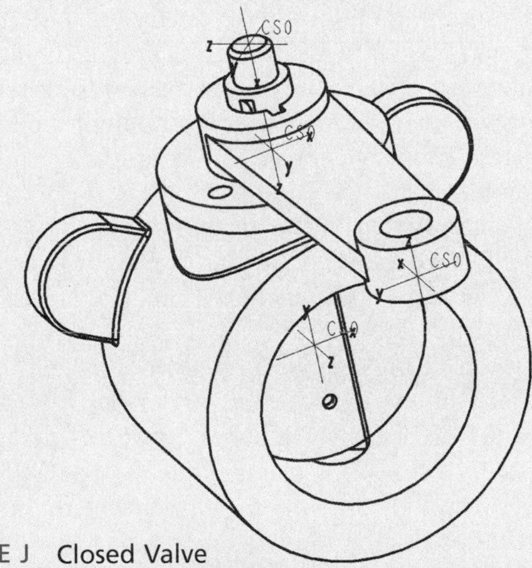

FIGURE J Closed Valve

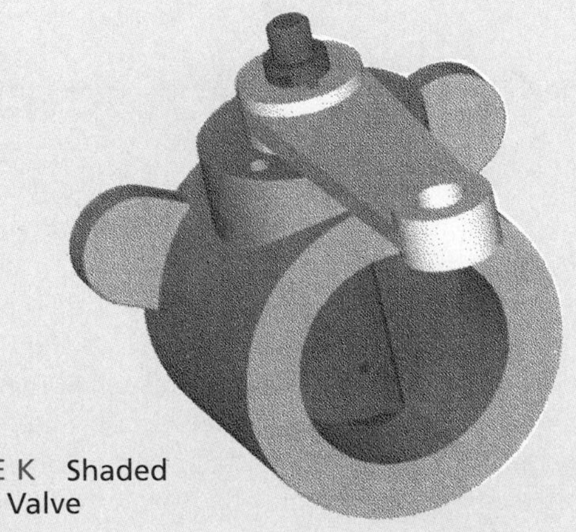

FIGURE K Shaded Closed Valve

section line 2_A-3_A. Establish the cutting plane anywhere along the true-length intersection line. For greater accuracy, locate the cutting plane where the given planes are shown clearly, preferably through a wide portion of each plane. This is the edge view of the cutting plane.

3. Where the cutting plane intersects (cuts) the two given planes, label these points 5_A, 6_A, and 7_A. The cutting plane is now defined by plane 5_A-7_A-6_A.
4. Revolve the new plane formed by the cutting plane and the given intersecting planes about one of its points until parallel to the fold line. Then revolve plane 5_A-7_A-6_A about point 7_A until parallel to F/A, $5R_A$-7_A-$6R_A$. Point 7_A is the point view of the axis line.
5. Draw the axis line true length and perpendicular to line 2_F-3_F and F/A in the frontal view. Points 5_F and 6_F move perpendicular to the axis line (parallel to F/A) to position $5R_F$ and $6R_F$, respectively. Cutting plane $5R_F$-7_F-$6R_F$ is true size in this view.
6. The dihedral angle $5R_F$-7_F-$6R_F$ is measured as shown.

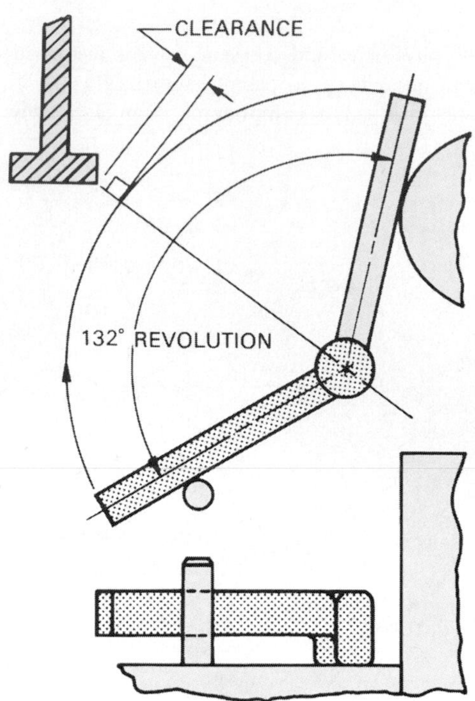

FIGURE 26.19 Restricted Revolution and Clearance

26.5 RESTRICTED REVOLUTION AND CLEARANCE

When a machine part or any type of mechanical device must be free to rotate about an axis through a circle or circular arc, revolution is used to find the extent of the piece's movement. The circular arc created by the extreme point of the revolving part determines its **clearance** with surrounding surfaces. The circular plane created by the rotating part scribes an arc, which equals the extreme line of intersection. If the part is to move through its prescribed angular displacement, all surrounding surfaces must lie outside the circular plane scribed by the outer edge of the part.

The lever in Figure 26.19 can move in a circular arc of 132° before it hits an obstruction. Its forward position is fixed by a dowel pin. The clearance between the moving lever and the steel beam is measured as the perpendicular distance between the beam and the circular line of intersection, along a line passing through the axis.

26.6 REVOLUTION OF A SOLID

A designer may find it necessary to revolve an object or a solid about a given axis line. Most often, the object will be revolved to a new position where some operation can be performed on it or with it. Usually, the revolved position shows the object in a normal (true-shape) or edge view perspective. A more complicated situation is when the given object is oblique and its rotated position is also oblique.

In Figure 26.20, a rectangular prism is revolved 90° about a given external axis. Note that the revolution of a given object requires that each point on the form revolve through the same angle. In the example, all points in the horizontal view revolve clockwise through 90°, since axis A is given as external to the prism. In the view in which the axis is a point, the prism retains the exact shape it had before it was revolved; only its position has changed.

The revolved frontal view is located by drawing projection lines from each point on the rotated prism in the horizontal view. Every point of the given projection in the frontal view moves perpendicular to the axis line (parallel to fold line H/F), until intersecting the projection lines extended from the revolved prism in the horizontal view. The frontal position of the revolved prism changes shape as well as position.

26.7 CAD-GENERATED REVOLUTIONS

Two-dimensional CAD systems will require the same techniques as described for the manual construction of revolutions. The solid model of the planetary gear system in Figure 26.21 can be dynamically revolved on the screen via revolve commands. This capability allows the design to be displayed in all its revolved positions and tested without a physical model of the prototype. Three-dimensional CAD systems enable the designer to revolve the part into any position by executing the appropriate command. The part in Figure 26.22 is shown in six separate revolved positions. This

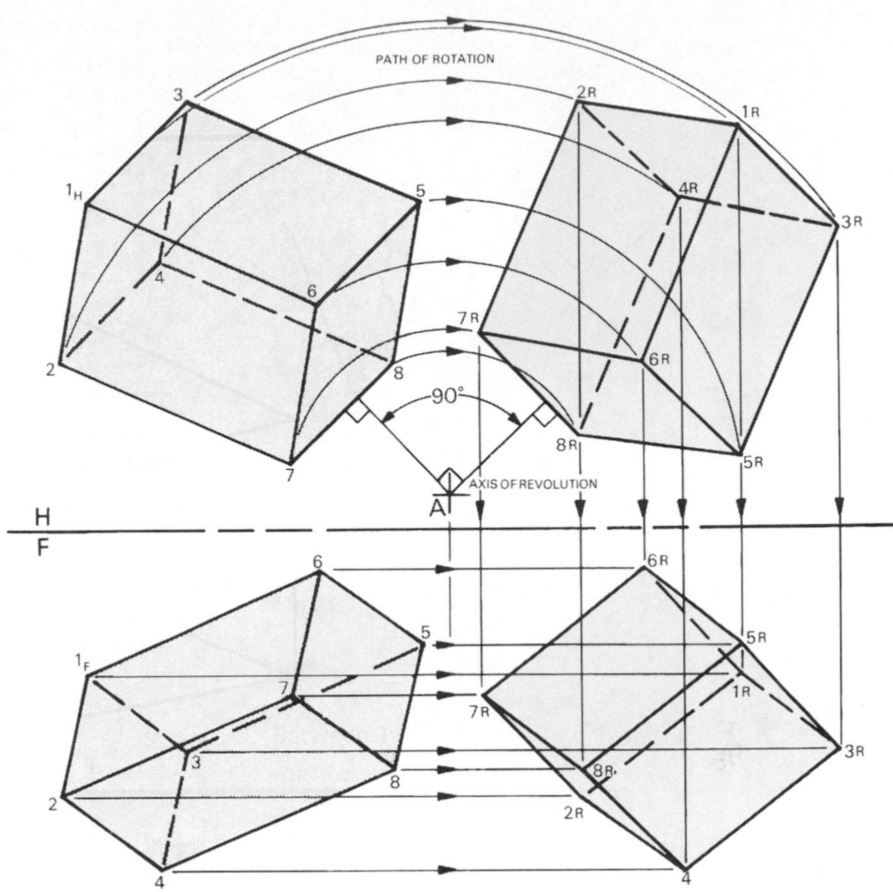

FIGURE 26.20 Revolution of a Solid at a Specified Angle

figure is a wireframe 3D model, which displays all edges as visible. The proper visibility is not established for this illustration. CAD systems offer a hidden line removal capability that would show the part with the correct visible and hidden lines. In Figure 26.23, the solid model is displayed. Here the assembly can be ratated about its clevis and shown in both its retracted and its extended operation positions.

After the original 3D model has been created, the designer can establish an unlimited number of views. The

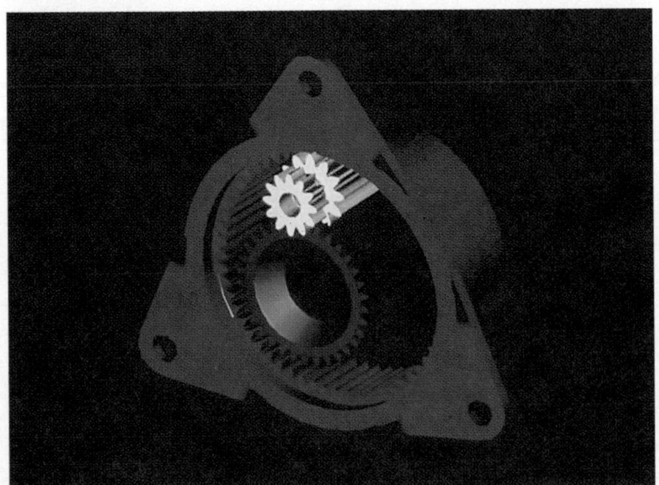

FIGURE 26.21 Planetary Gear System

rotated views in Figure 26.22 were created quickly and with a minimum of effort. The manual projection of the six rotated views would have required many hours of effort.

In AutoCAD, the **ROTATE** command will rotate objects 2D. The **ROTATE3D** or the **ROTATE** command rotates three-dimensional parts in space. In Figure 26.24 the assembly is being rotated about a specified axis. The axis can be specified by picking either two points, an existing object, the **X, Y,** or **Z** axis, or the **Z** direction of the current view. In this example the command was given and then the object was selected (1). The axis was then picked with a start point and an endpoint (2, 3). The angle of rotation was then specified. The following is AutoCAD's command sequence for **ROTATE3D**:

```
Command: ROTATE3D
Select Objects: Pick items to rotate
Axis by Entity/Last/View/Xaxis/Yaxis/
Zaxis/<2points>: pick start point and endpoint of
axis
Rotational Angle>/Reference: type angle (360
here)
```

The **3DARRAY** command in AutoCAD can rotate and copy 3D features. With the **3DARRAY** you can create a **polar** array or a **rectangular** array of the objects in 3D. Give the **3DARRAY** command, and choose polar or rectangular.

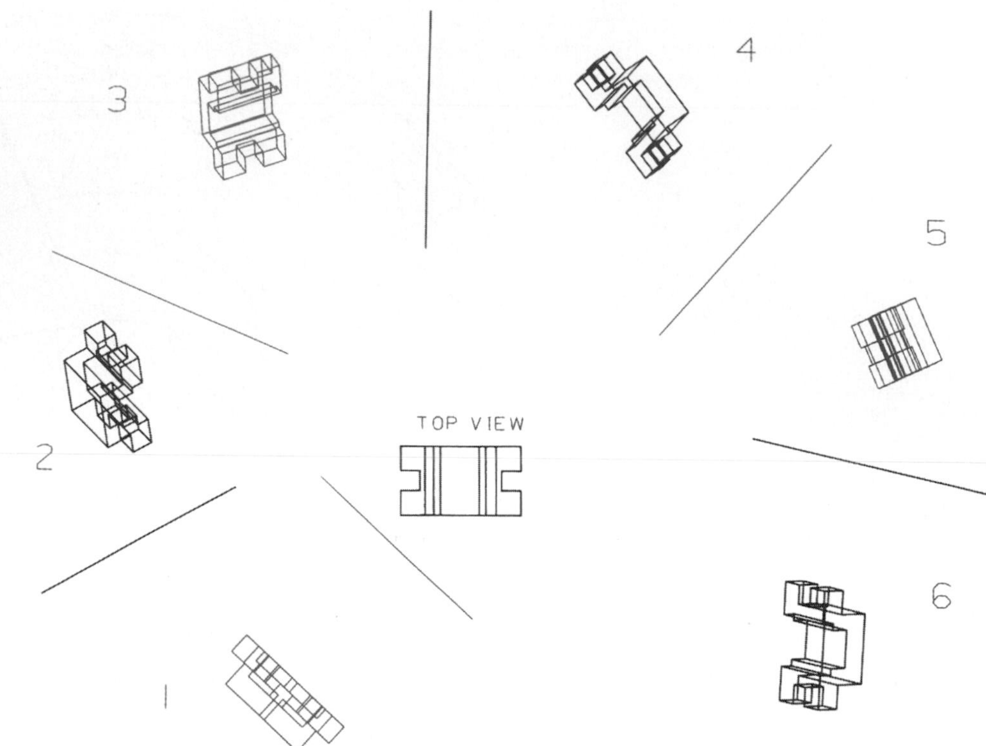

FIGURE 26.22 Revolution of a Part Using 3D CAD

(In Figure 26.25 the **polar** option was selected.) Then select the object or feature. Enter the number of items to array.

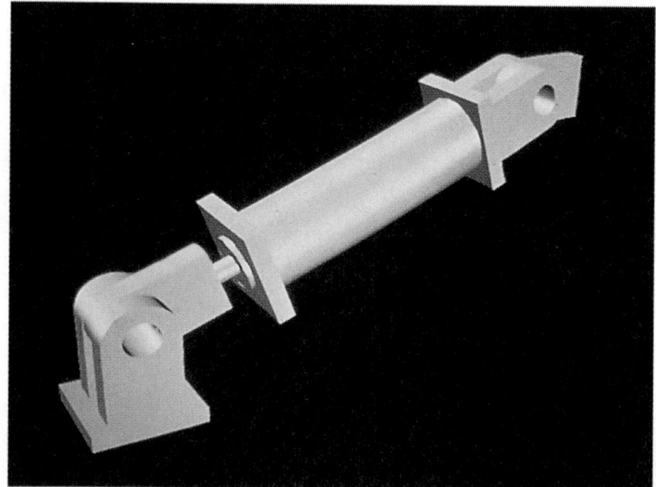

FIGURE 26.23 Solid Model

Specify the angle of rotation the features are to fill. Then press Enter to rotate the objects as they are arrayed, or enter **n** to retain their orientation. Specify the start point and the endpoint of the axis of rotation. The feature will then be rotated and copied as shown. The following AutoCAD command sequence is used with the **3DARRAY** command.

`Command:` 3DARRAY
`Select Objects:` Pick the objects to array
`Rectangular or Polar Array (R/P):` **P** or **R** (here it is R)
`Number of Items:` type number of items
`Angle to Fill` <`360`>: <Enter> for **360**
`Rotate Objects as they are copied?` <`Y`>: **Y**
`Center of Array:` give center position and <Enter>
`Second Point on Axis of Rotation:` give point and <Enter>

You May Complete Exercises 26.3 and 26.4 at This Time

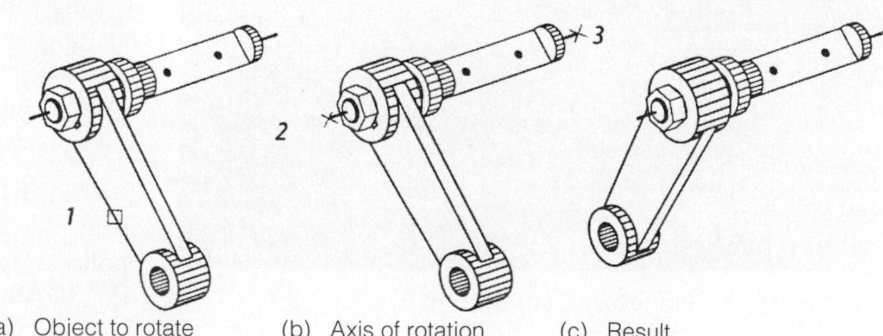

FIGURE 26.24 Using the ROTATE3D Command to Revolve a Part Feature

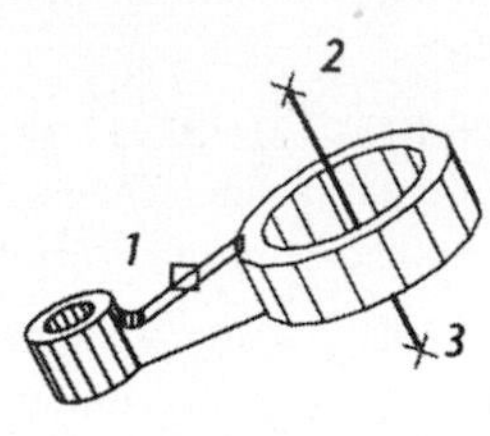

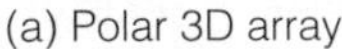
(a) Polar 3D array

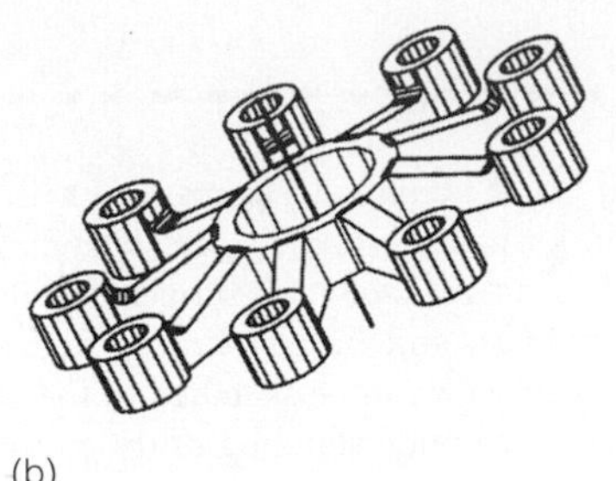
(b)

FIGURE 26.25 Using AutoCAD's 3DARRAY Command

QUIZ

True or False

1. With double revolution, the axis of rotation for each revolution will be in the same view.
2. **ROTATE** and **ROTATE3D** can both rotate a part or feature in 3D.
3. The dihedral angle is formed by the intersection of a surface and a projection plane in the horizontal view.
4. Revolutions will in many cases eliminate the need for an auxiliary view.
5. The slope is the angle an inclined line makes with the horizontal plane (in elevation).
6. The path of rotation is seen in the same view as the true-length axis line.
7. Revolution of parts and part features is an important aspect of mechanical design.
8. When a line revolves about another line, it generates a cone if the lines are parallel.

Fill in the Blanks

9. The ________ ________ of a plane is found in a view in which a ________ in the plane shows as a ________.
10. When an ________ ________ is revolved about an axis line, a hyperboloid of revolution is formed.
11. The ________ ________ ________ is generated by revolving a line about an axis line, and passes through an endpoint of the axis.
12. Revolution/rotation requires that the ________ be revolved or rotated and that the observer remain ________.
13. ________ ________ systems enable the designer to revolve a part into any position by executing the appropriate command.
14. The ________ ________ of a plane can be determined by revolving the plane about a ________ ________ axis line that lies on the plane.
15. The ________ of a line can be measured in an ________ ________ in which the line appears true length and the ________ plane shows as an edge.
16. The path of a point as it is revolved about an ________.

Answer the Following

17. What are three shapes that can be created when a line is revolved about a line axis?
18. What is the path of revolution/rotation?
19. What is the function of an axis line when drawing a revolved projection of a part?
20. Define *axis of revolution.*
21. What is the cone locus of a line?
22. What are the slope angle and the bearing of a line?
23. Explain *double revolution.*
24. Describe the difference between using 3D CAD for a revolution and drawing one manually or with a 2D CAD system.

EXERCISES

Exercises may be assigned as sketching, instrument, or CAD projects. Transfer the given information to an "A"-size sheet of .25 in. grid paper. Complete all views, and solve for proper visibility, including centerlines, object lines, and hidden lines. Exercises that are not assigned by the instructor can be sketched in the text to provide practice and to enhance understanding of the preceding instructional material.

After Reading the Chapter Through Section 26.4.3 You May Complete Exercises 26.1 and 26.2

Exercise 26.1(A) Rotate the point 200° clockwise around the frontal line. Show in all views.

Exercise 26.1(B) Rotate the point around the line 100° counterclockwise.

Exercise 26.1(C) Project an auxiliary view to establish a true length of the given line. Then solve for a point view of the line and rotate the given point 180°. Show in all views.

Exercise 26.2(A) Using revolution, determine the true length of the line and the angle the line makes with the horizontal plane. Verify by projection of an auxiliary view.

Exercise 26.2(B) Determine the angle between the line and the profile plane.

Exercise 26.2(C) Using revolution, project and measure the true lengths of the sides of the given figure.

Exercise 26.2(D) Using revolution, solve for both the angle the line makes with the frontal view and its true length.

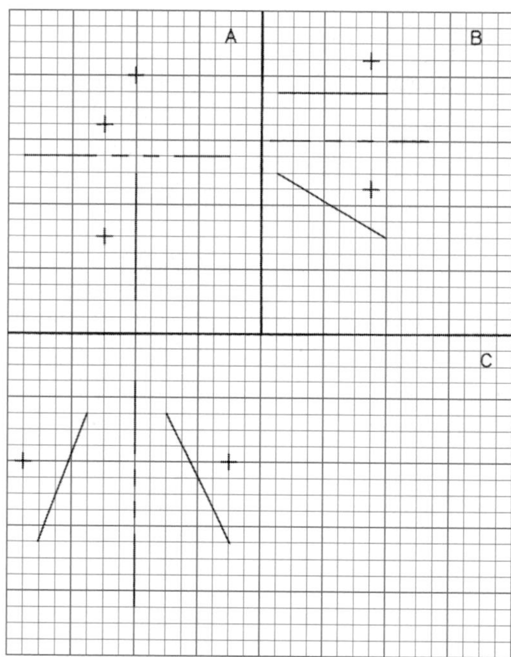

EXERCISE 26.1

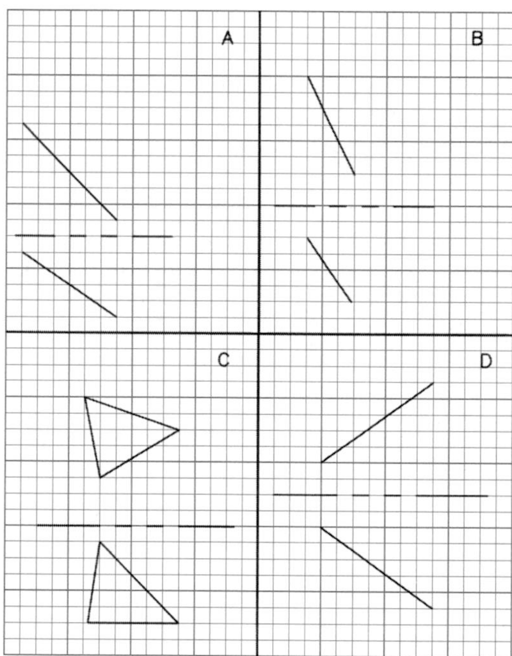

EXERCISE 26.2

After Reading the Chapter Through Section 26.7 You May Complete the Following Exercises

Exercise 26.3(A) Solve for the true shape of the plane by double revolution. The edge view will show in the view on the left (frontal view).

Exercise 26.3(B) Using double revolution, solve for the true shape of the plane. The edge view appears in the frontal view. Construct the largest circle that can be inscribed in the triangle using geometric construction.

Exercise 26.4 Project a point view of the true-length line, and revolve the plane 90° downward around the line. Show the revolved position in all views.

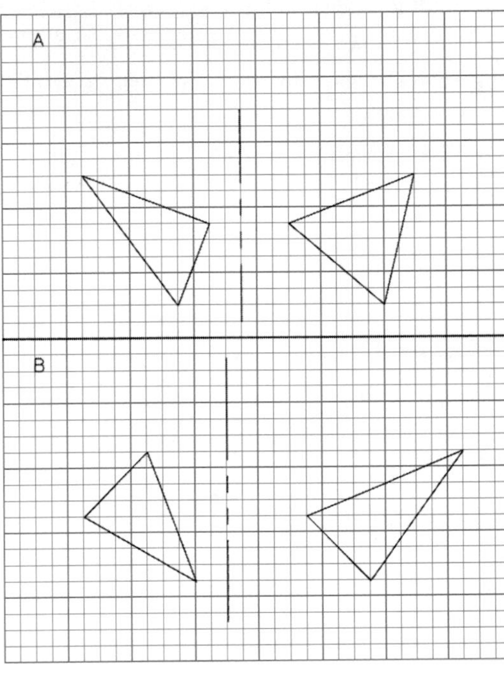

EXERCISE 26.3

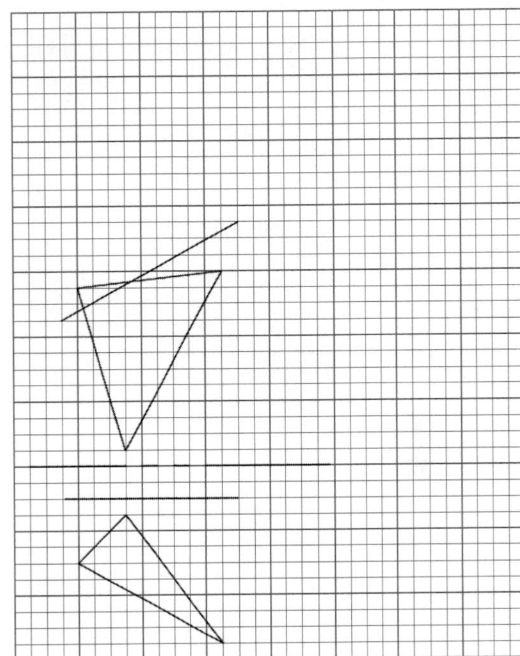

EXERCISE 26.4

PROBLEMS

Problems may be assigned as sketching, instrument, or CAD projects. For Problems 26.1 and 26.5, transfer the given problem to a separate "A"-size sheet. Complete all views, and solve for proper visibility, including centerlines, object lines, and hidden lines. Use dividers to transfer the positions of the points and lines. A 1.5/1 scale is suggested but a 2/1 scale could also be used. Make a rough trial sketch of the problem and the solution before finalizing its position on the paper.

Problem 26.1(1) Using revolution, determine both the true length of line 1-2 and the angle it makes with the horizontal plane. Scale: 1 in. = 50 ft

Problem 26.1(2) Determine the angle between line 1-2 and the profile plane using revolution.

Problem 26.1(3) Using revolution, solve for the sides of the figure. Scale: 1 in. = 50 ft

Problem 26.1(4) Determine the true length, bearing, and slope angle of line 4-5.

Problem 26.2 Use double revolution to solve for the true shape of the plane. Show the triangular plane in all views.

Problem 26.3(1) Solve for the edge view and the true shape using double revolution.

Problem 26.3(2) Solve for the largest-diameter circle that will fit within the plane. Use revolution.

Problem 26.4(1) Determine the true angle between the two planes using revolution.

Problem 26.4(2) Solve for the true angle between the two planes using rotation.

Problem 26.5 Project a point view of line 1-2, and revolve plane 3-4-5 105° clockwise (downwards). Show the revolved plane in all views.

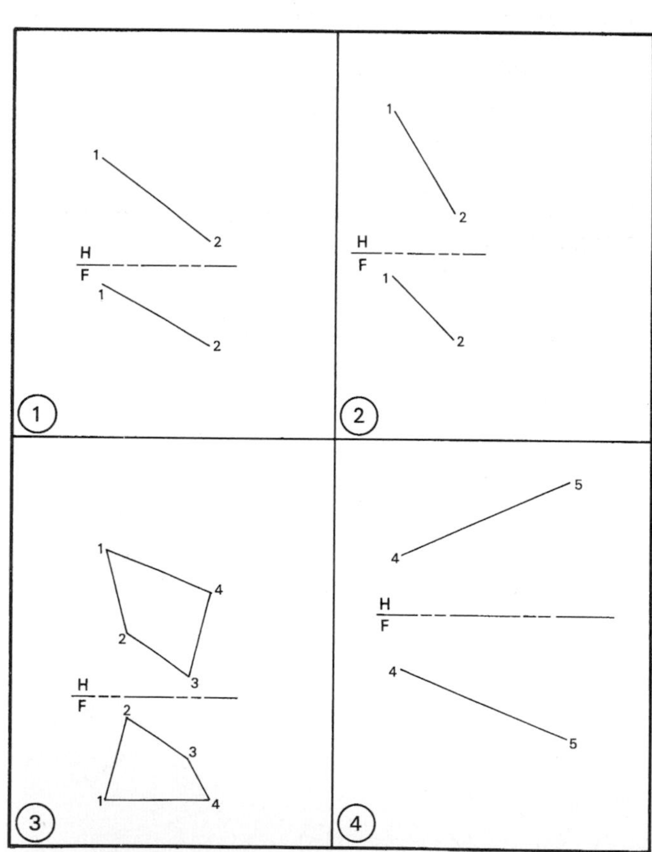

PROBLEM 26.1

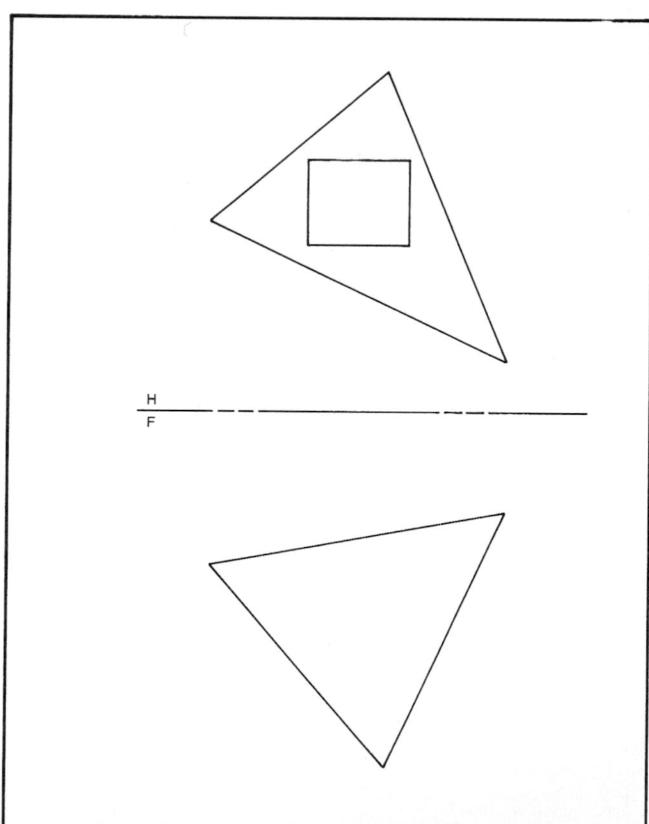

PROBLEM 26.2

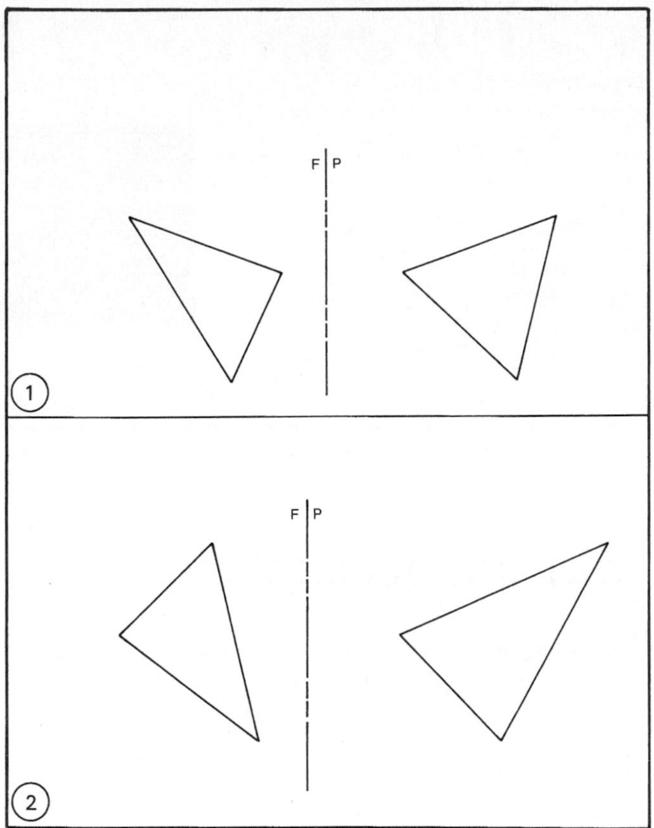

PROBLEM 26.3

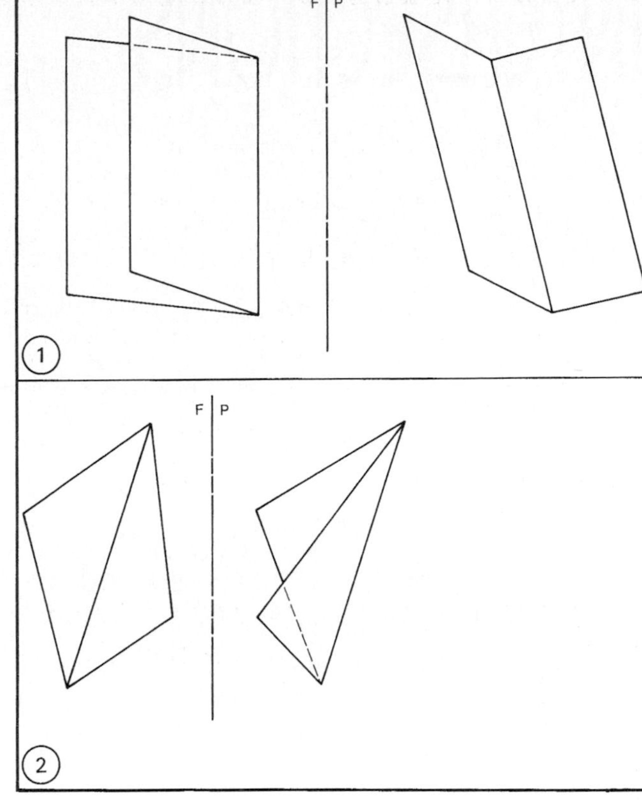

PROBLEM 26.4

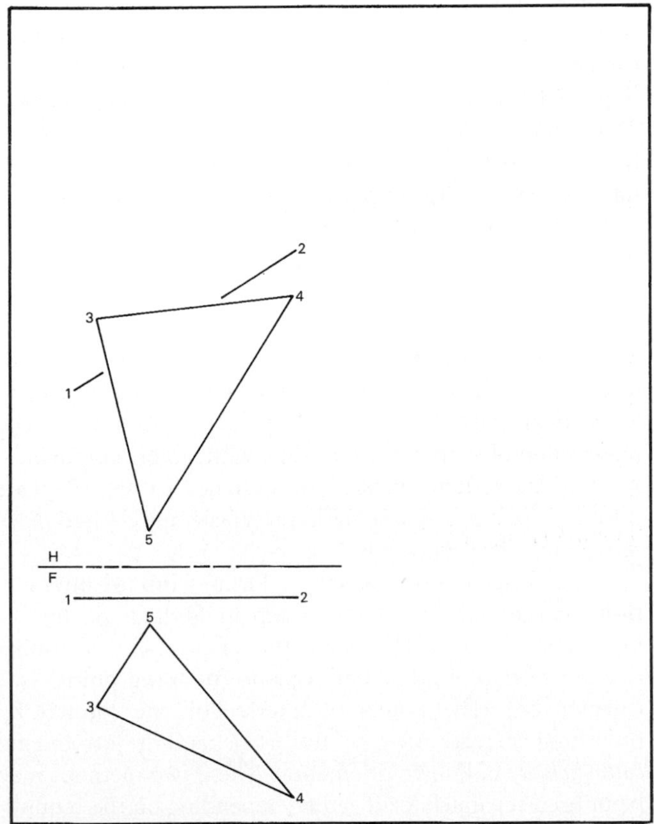

PROBLEM 26.5

INTERSECTIONS

Chapter 27

LEARNING OBJECTIVES

Upon completion of this chapter you will be able to:

1. Determine the line of intersection or common line of joined shapes so that they may be described graphically and produced economically.
2. Utilize edge view and cutting plane methods to locate points of intersection.
3. Appreciate the importance of auxiliary views in solving for intersections.
4. Produce conic sections while identifying resulting shapes.
5. Understand the CAD system's capacity for surface and solid modeling to produce solutions to intersection problems.
6. Demonstrate familiarity with CAD commands for generating intersections.

27.1 INTRODUCTION

The design and engineering of products and systems will involve lines, planes, and solids that intersect. Cubes, prisms, pyramids, cylinders, cones, spheres, and their intersecting variations are just a few of the many forms used in engineering design work. Part of the responsibility of a designer is to establish both simple and complex forms that can yield a functional, producible product. A necessary step in this process is the determination of the intersection of the various shapes so that they can be described graphically and manufactured economically.

Piping systems [Fig. 27.1(a)] include a vast array of intersecting shapes and forms. A piping system for a refinery can be created in 3D via a solid modeling CAD/CAM system [Fig. 27.1(b)]. Intersecting pipes, nozzle and vessel intersections, and a wide variety of equipment intersections are all found on the typical process piping project. Besides piping, intersections are also important in other engineering fields. The scale model of the clean room in Figure 27.2 includes a number of intersections. The air filtration system is composed of intersecting HVAC sheet metal ducting, and the ducting system intersects walls and floors.

Intersections can be solved through manual or automated methods, or via construction techniques developed for manual drafting but applied by a 2D CAD system. The intersection of shapes is established with simple commands. A 3D CAD system enables the designer to pass a plane through a part at any orientation to create any desired cross section for detail drawings.

The intersection of two shapes forms a **line of intersection**, or *common line*. A basic step in finding the line of intersection between two geometric shapes is to determine the intersection of a line and a plane **(piercing point)** (see Chapter 26). The points of intersection are located by projecting an *edge view* of the plane and/or introducing *cutting planes* of known orientation. These two methods may be utilized separately or together, depending on the requirements of the problem.

FIGURE 27.1(a) Petrochemical Refinery

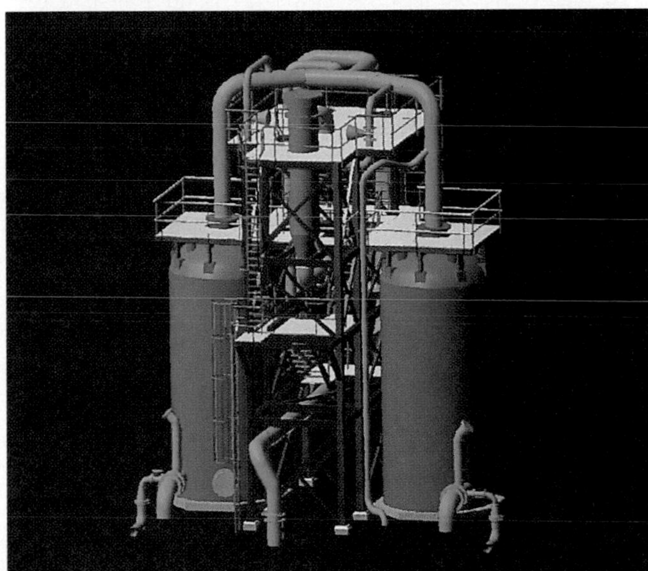

FIGURE 27.1(b) Complex Piping Substation

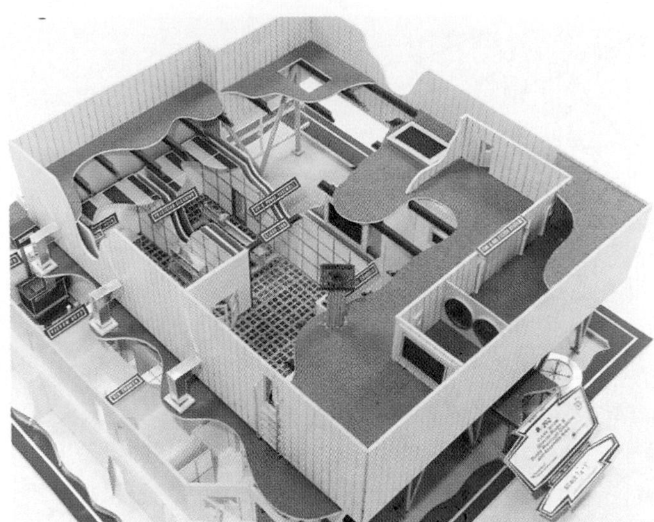

FIGURE 27.2 Scale Model of Clean Room

27.2 INTERSECTION OF PLANES

The intersection of two or more planes can be determined by finding the edge view of one of the planes. Where any two lines on one plane pierce the edge view of any plane, they will determine the endpoints of the line of intersection. Because both lines and planes can be considered unlimited in size or extent for construction purposes, both given planes and their line of intersection can be extended as required. The actual intersection of two defined planes will have a limited line of intersection that must be common to both planes.

27.2.1 Intersection of Two Planes

To establish the intersection of two planes, it is necessary to find two points common to both. These points of intersection form a straight line. In Figure 27.3, the line of intersection and correct visibility are required. The following steps were used to solve the intersection.

1. Plane 1-2-3-4 and plane 5-6-7 are given. Plane 1-2-3-4 appears as an edge in the frontal view [Fig. 27.5(a)].
2. Lines 5-6 and 5-7 pierce the edge view of plane 1-2-3-4 at points 8 and 9, respectively [Fig. 27.5(b)]. Project these two piercing points to the horizontal view, where they form line 8-9, which is the line of intersection. Visibility is determined by inspection.

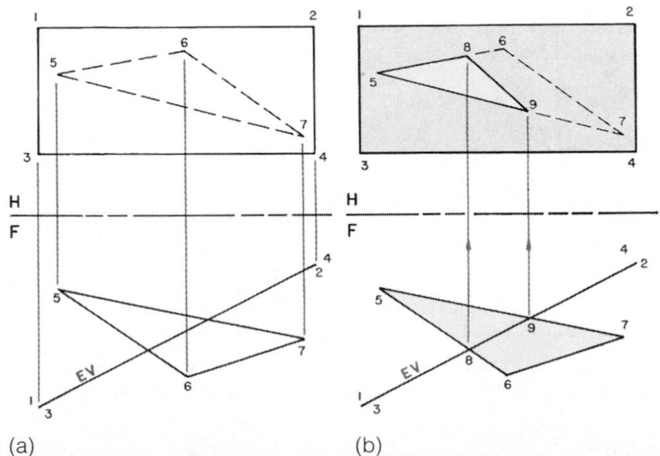

FIGURE 27.3 Intersection of Two Planes Using the Edge View Method

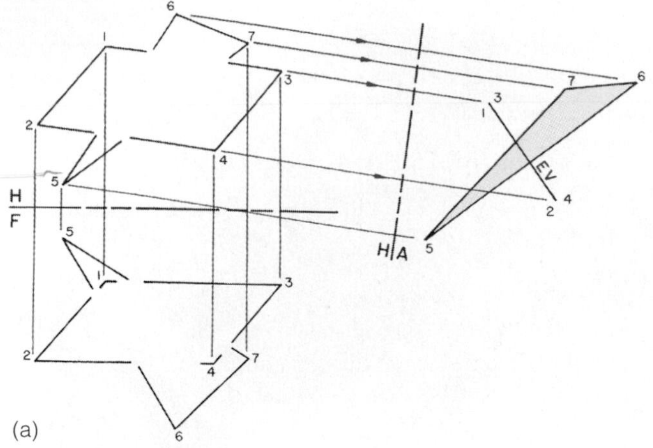

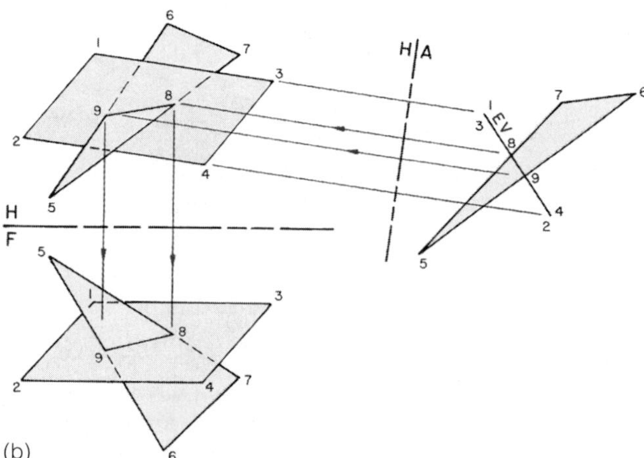

FIGURE 27.4 Intersection of Two Oblique Planes Using the Edge View Method

1. Lines 1-3 and 2-4 are horizontal lines [Fig. 27.4(a)]. Draw H/A perpendicular to line 2-4 and project auxiliary view A. In view A, plane 1-2-3-4 appears as an edge view and plane 5-6-7 is oblique.
2. Line 5-7 pierces the edge view of plane 1-2-3-4 at point 8 [Fig. 27.4(b)]. Line 5-6 pierces plane 1-2-3-4 at point 9. Project points 8 and 9 to the horizontal view, where they form the common line of intersection between the two planes, line 8-9.
3. Locate intersection line 8-9 in the frontal view by projection. The portion of the plane formed by line 8-9 and point 5 is in general above and in front of plane 1-2-3-4; therefore, it appears visible in the frontal and horizontal views.

27.2.2 Intersection of Two Oblique Planes (Edge View Method)

When the intersection of two oblique planes is required, an auxiliary projection showing one of the planes as an edge is needed. In Figure 27.4, oblique planes 1-2-3-4 and 5-6-7 are given. The following steps were used in the solution.

27.2.3 Intersection of Two Planes (Cutting Plane Method)

The **cutting plane method** for finding the intersection of a line and a plane can establish two common piercing points. Each piercing point is found individually and then projected to the adjacent view. Using cutting planes to solve for the piercing point of a line and a plane *in each view*, instead of projecting located points from view to view, is called the **individual line method.**

In Figure 27.5, oblique planes 1-2-3 and 4-5-6-7 are given. Their line of intersection is to be determined by the cutting plane method. Note that some lines make better cutting planes than others. Suitability is determined by trial and error. Some lines obviously will not cross the other plane and, therefore, cannot be used (unless extended). Others cross only very small parts of the other plane and may not be adequate. It may be necessary to extend a line in some cases. Also, cutting planes can be established using lines of different planes in the same view. In Figure 27.5, cutting planes are passed through different lines on the same plane. The following steps were used to solve the problem.

1. Pass a vertical cutting plane through line 1-2 in the horizontal view [Fig. 27.5(a)]. Line 1-2 represents the edge view of CP1. CP1 cuts line 4-7 at point 8 and line 5-6 at point 9. Project points 8 and 9 to the frontal view, where they form line 8-9. Line 8-9 crosses (intersects)

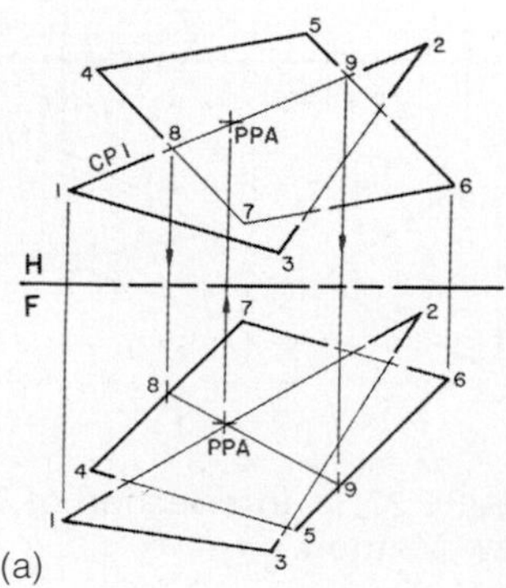

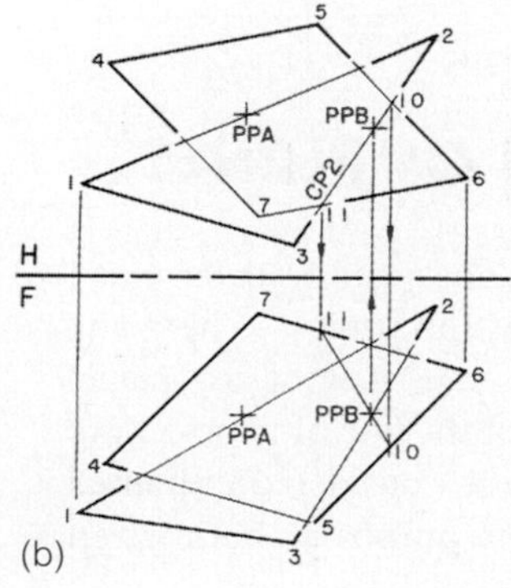

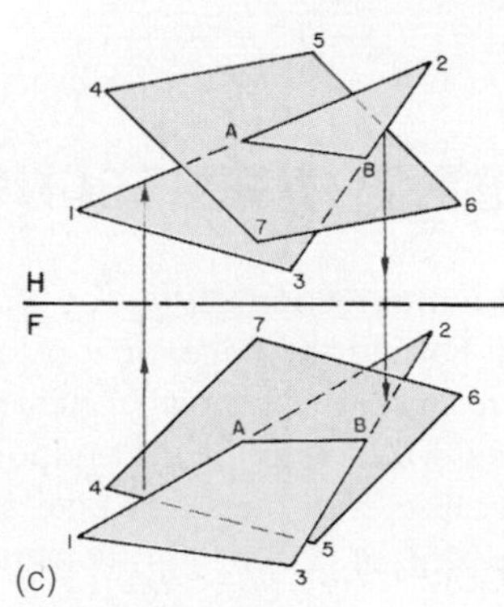

FIGURE 27.5 Intersection of Two Planes Using the Cutting Plane Method

line 1-2 at PPA. PPA is the piercing point of line 1-2 and plane 4-5-6-7. Project piercing point PPA back to the horizontal view.

2. Pass vertical cutting plane CP2 through line 2-3, in the horizontal view [Fig. 27.5(b)]. Line 2-3 represents the edge view of CP2. CP2 crosses line 5-6 and line 6-7 at points 10 and 11, respectively. Project points 10 and 11 to the frontal view, where they form line 10-11. Line 10-11 crosses (intersects) line 2-3 at piercing point PPB. Project PPB back to the horizontal view.
3. Connect point PPA and point PPB to form intersection line A-B [Fig. 27.5(c)]. Visibility is determined by applying the visibility test as shown.

27.3 INTERSECTION OF A PLANE AND A PRISM (EDGE VIEW METHOD)

The intersection of a prism and a plane requires an auxiliary view showing the plane as an edge if the plane is oblique in the given views. In Figure 27.6, the horizontal view shows the plane as an edge; therefore the piercing points of each line (each edge of the prism) pierce the plane and establish the points along the line of intersection.

In Figure 27.7, plane 1-2-3-4 and prism 5-6-7 are both *oblique* in the given frontal and horizontal views. The solution to this problem requires the projection of a view showing the plane as an edge. The intersection and correct visibility are required. The following steps were used to solve the problem.

1. Lines 1-2 and 3-4 are horizontal lines (true length in the horizontal view). Draw H/A perpendicular to line 1-2. Complete auxiliary view A.
2. Plane 1-2-3-4 represents the edge view of a cutting plane in view A. Plane 1-2-3-4 intersects the prism at points 8, 9, and 10. In other words, the edge lines of the prism pierce the plane at points 8, 9, and 10. Project all three piercing points to the horizontal view. The horizontal view of the piercing points determines the plane section cut from the prism, which in turn corresponds to the intersection of the plane and the prism.
3. Project points 8, 9, and 10 to the frontal view. The frontal location of each piercing point can also be fixed by transferring distances from auxiliary view A along projection lines drawn from each point in the horizontal view. This method will ensure the accurate location of the intersecting points, and should be used to check the placement of the piercing points.
4. Visibility is determined by inspection of auxiliary view A and/or the visibility test.

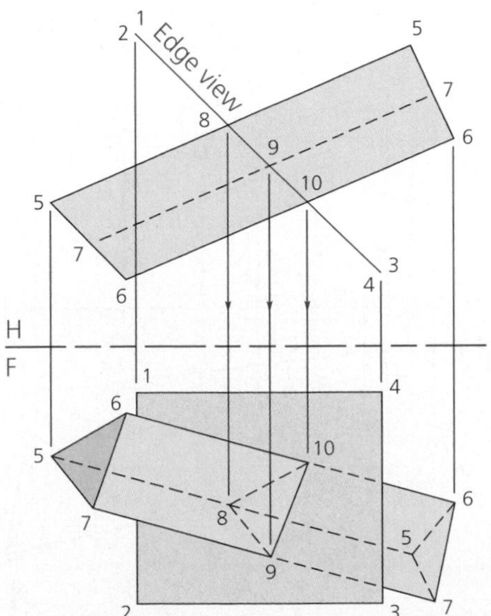

FIGURE 27.6 Intersection of a Plane and a Prism

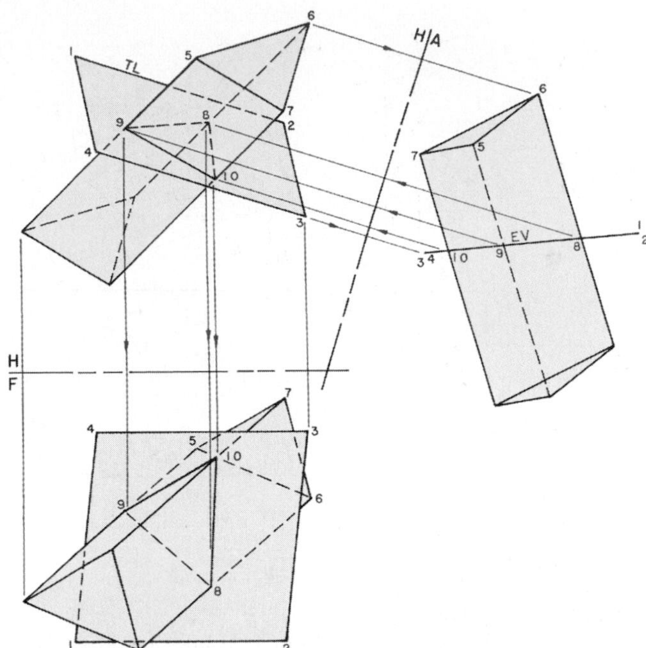

FIGURE 27.7 Intersection of an Oblique Plane and an Oblique Prism Using the Edge View Method

27.3.1 Intersection of a Plane and a Right Prism (Cutting Plane Method)

The line of intersection between two surfaces is a common line defined by connected piercing points located by introducing cutting planes. In Figure 27.8, the intersection of plane 1-2-3-4 and a right prism is required. The following steps were used to solve the problem.

1. Plane 1-2-3-4 and a prism defined by edge lines 5, 6, 7, and 8 are given [Fig. 27.8(a)].
2. Pass a vertical cutting plane (CP1) through the vertical

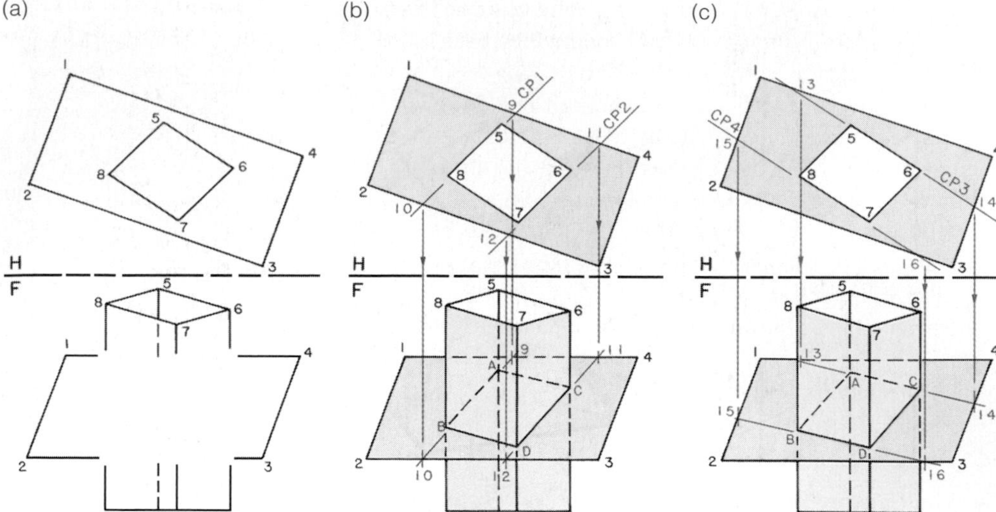

FIGURE 27.8 Intersection of a Plane and a Right Prism Using the Cutting Plane Method

plane represented by edge lines 5 and 8, and CP2 through edge lines 6 and 7 [Fig. 27.8(b)]. CP1 intersects lines 1-4 and 2-3 at points 9_H and 10_H, respectively. CP2 intersects line 1-4 at point 11 and line 2-3 at point 12. Project all four points to the frontal view, where they form lines 9-10 and 11-12. Line 9-10 intersects edge lines 5 and 8 at points A and B, and line 11-12 intersects edge lines 6 and 7 at points C and D. A, B, C, and D are the piercing points of the edge lines of the prism and the plane. Connect piercing points A, B, C, and D to establish the lines of intersection between the plane and the prism.

3. Vertical cutting planes CP3 and CP4 could be used instead of CP1 and CP2 or as a check [Fig. 27.8(c)].

27.3.2 Intersection of an Oblique Plane and an Oblique Prism (Cutting Plane Method)

The line of intersection of an oblique prism and oblique plane can be located by the cutting plane method. Cutting planes can be introduced at any angle, in any view. Vertical, horizontal, and front-edge-view cutting planes passed through existing lines are the most convenient. In Figure 27.9, the plane and the prism are given; the line of intersection is required. The following steps were used in the solution.

1. Pass vertical cutting plane CP1 through line 4 in the horizontal view.
2. CP1 intersects line 1-2 at point 8 and line 2-3 at point 7. Project points 7 and 8 to the frontal view, where they form line 7-8.
3. Line 7-8 intersects line 4 at point 14. Point 14 is the piercing point of line 4 and plane 1-2-3.
4. Project piercing point 14 to the horizontal view.
5. Pass vertical cutting planes CP2 and CP3 through line 5 and 6, respectively.
6. CP2 intersects line 2-3 at point 9 and line 1-2 at point 10. CP3 intersects lines 2-3 and 1-2 at points 11 and 12, respectively. Project points 9 and 10 and points 11 and 12 to the frontal view, where they form lines 9-10 and 11-12.
7. Line 9-10 intersects line 5 at piercing point 13. Line 11-12 intersects line 6 at piercing point 15. Project piercing points 13 and 15 to the horizontal view.
8. Connect all three piercing points in both views to establish the line of intersection between the plane and the prism and solve for visibility.

Note that all three vertical cutting planes are parallel in the horizontal view and, therefore, cut parallel lines on the plane in the frontal view.

You May Complete Exercises 27.1 Through 27.4 at This Time

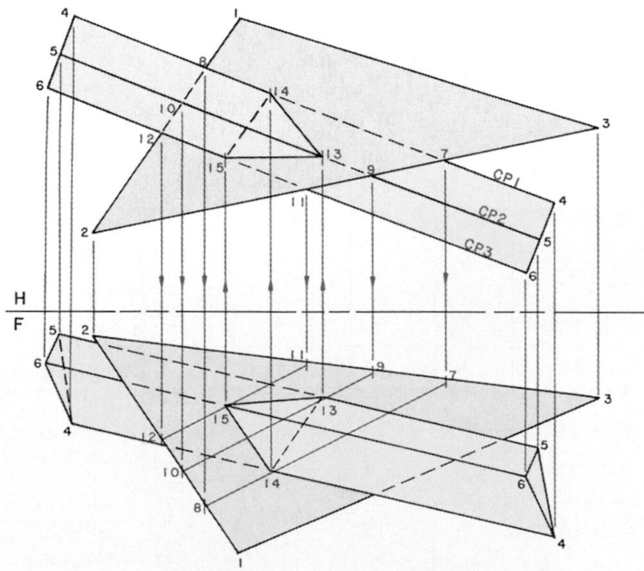

FIGURE 27.9 Intersection of an Oblique Plane and an Oblique Prism Using the Cutting Plane Method

Focus On . . .

SOUND, LIGHTS, CAMERA

Mechanical designers have always struggled with the problem of representing parts composed of different geometric shapes joined to produce required forms. Since precision fit is often critical for proper function, correct representation of these intersecting surfaces is very important. Intersection drawings must ensure that the components will join together and function properly, before being manufactured. CAD systems that calculate these intersections automatically have replaced time-consuming manual techniques.

Camera design is an example of where a CAD system has made it possible to join intersecting parts graphically before they are made. The camera lens may have as many as twenty housing elements joined on top of each other. By means of the layer function in CAD, the designer can clearly visualize how these elements join together. Interferences can be checked with other components without creating a physical model. Since each camera may have as many as twenty lenses, generating intersections graphically saves a lot of time and money.

Camera design is only one example of the need for intersection calculations. Farm equipment design relies heavily on these capabilities to represent joints, couplers, and power train transitions. HVAC (heating, ventilation, and air conditioning) ductwork and turbine design are other examples. CAD systems that generate these complex intersections automatically save development time and ultimately reduce other costs, such as for rework. No doubt, CAD systems will play an increasingly important role in this type of design work.

Camera design requires intersection calculations.

27.4 CYLINDERS

A **cylinder** is a tubular form generated by moving a straight-line element around and parallel to a straight-line axis. A cylinder is considered to be composed of an infinite number of elements. *A right section cut perpendicular to the axis line shows the true shape of the cylinder.* Most cylinders are **cylinders of revolution,** that is, cylinders generated by an element moving in a circle, parallel to the axis line. Cylinders are represented by their axis line and two extreme elements.

27.4.1 Intersection of a Plane and a Cylinder (Cutting Plane Method)

The line of intersection of a plane and a cylinder can be determined by passing a series of cutting planes parallel to the axis of the cylinder. Each CP cuts elements on the cylinder, which pierce the plane to form an elliptical line of intersection. Accuracy increases with the number of cutting planes employed.

In Figure 27.10, a series of vertical cutting planes is passed parallel to the axis and through the cylinder. Each cutting plane establishes two elements on the cylinder and a line on the plane. Where these related lines and elements intersect, they establish the required piercing points. The following steps were used to solve the problem.

1. Draw CP1 and CP2 parallel to the axis line (and parallel to the H/F fold line) [Fig. 27.10(a)]. CP1intersects line 1-3 at point 4 and line 2-3 at point 5. CP2 intersects line 1-2 at point 6 and line 2-3 at point 7. Both cutting planes establish an element on the cylinder. Project the elements to the frontal view along with lines 4-5 and 6-7. Line 4-5

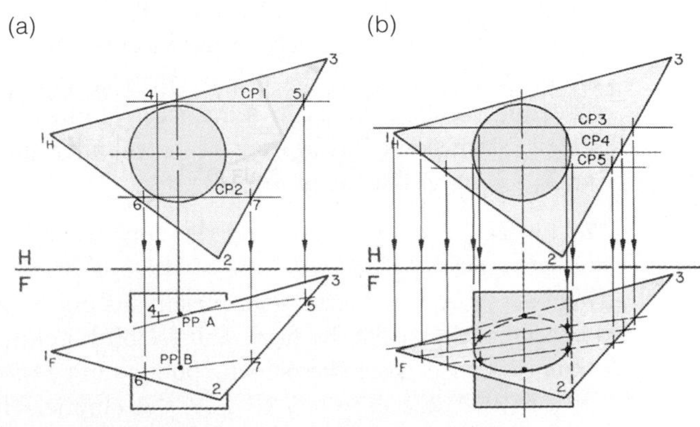

FIGURE 27.10 Intersection of an Oblique Plane and a Right Cylinder Using the Cutting Plane Method

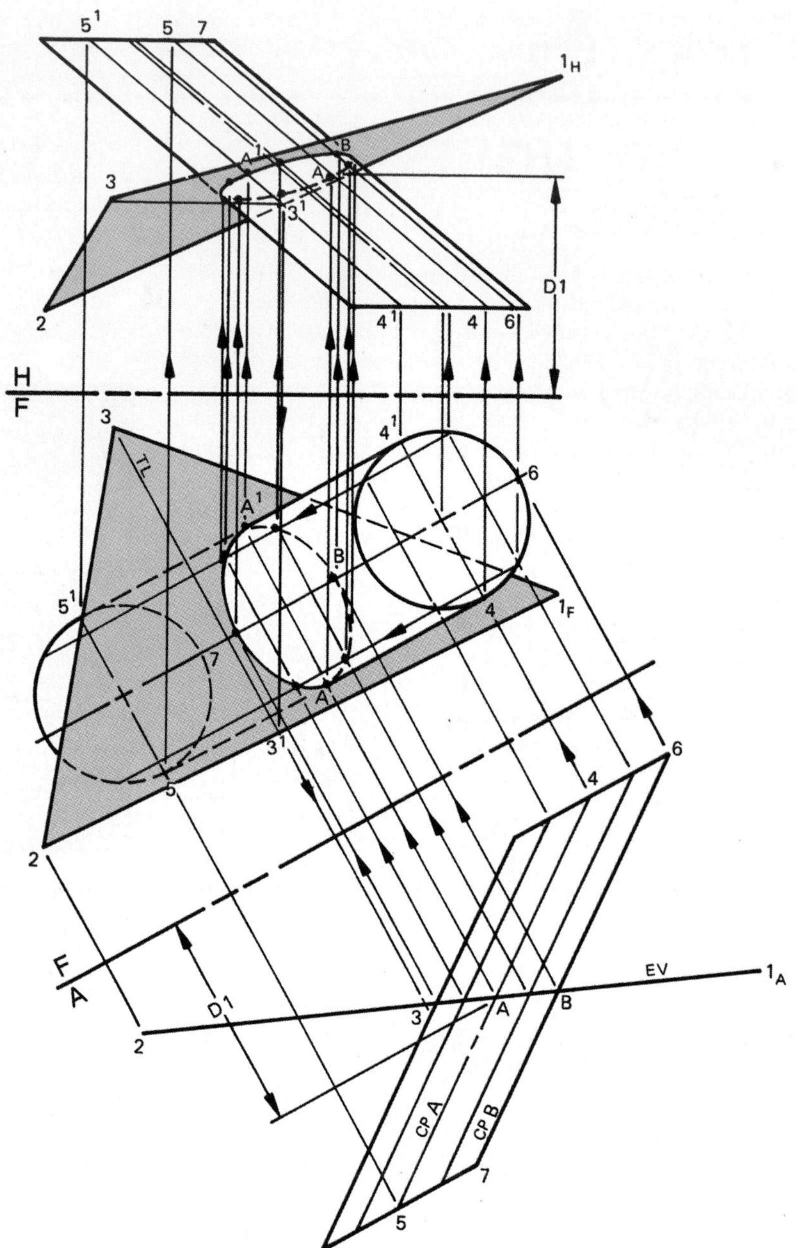

FIGURE 27.11 Intersection of an Oblique Prism and an Oblique Plane

intersects its element at piercing point A and line 6-7 intersects its corresponding element at point B.

2. Repeat step 1 using CP3, CP4, and CP5 [Fig. 27.10(b)]. Note that each of these cutting planes cuts two elements on the cylinder, so each locates two piercing points. Connect the piercing points in sequence to form a smooth curve. Since point 2 is in front of the cylinder, lines 1-2 and 2-3 are visible, as is point B.

In Figure 27.11 the plane and the cone are oblique. A view in which the plane shows as an edge is projected. In auxiliary view A, the intersection of elements on the surface of the cylinder intersect the plane and establish points along the line of intersection. The piercing points can be projected back into the adjacent view to find the elliptical line of intersection.

27.5 CONES

A **cone** is a single-curved surface formed by line segments/elements connecting the vertex with all points on the perimeter of the base. A cone is generated by the movement of a straight-line element passed through the vertex and moving around the boundary of the base. A cone generated by a right triangle rotating about one of its legs is a **right cone**, or **cone of revolution.** If a right section cut from the cone is an ellipse, the cone is an **elliptical cone.** A cone with a circular base whose right section is an ellipse is sometimes referred to as an **oblique circular cone.** If a cone is cut below its vertex, it is termed a **truncated cone.**

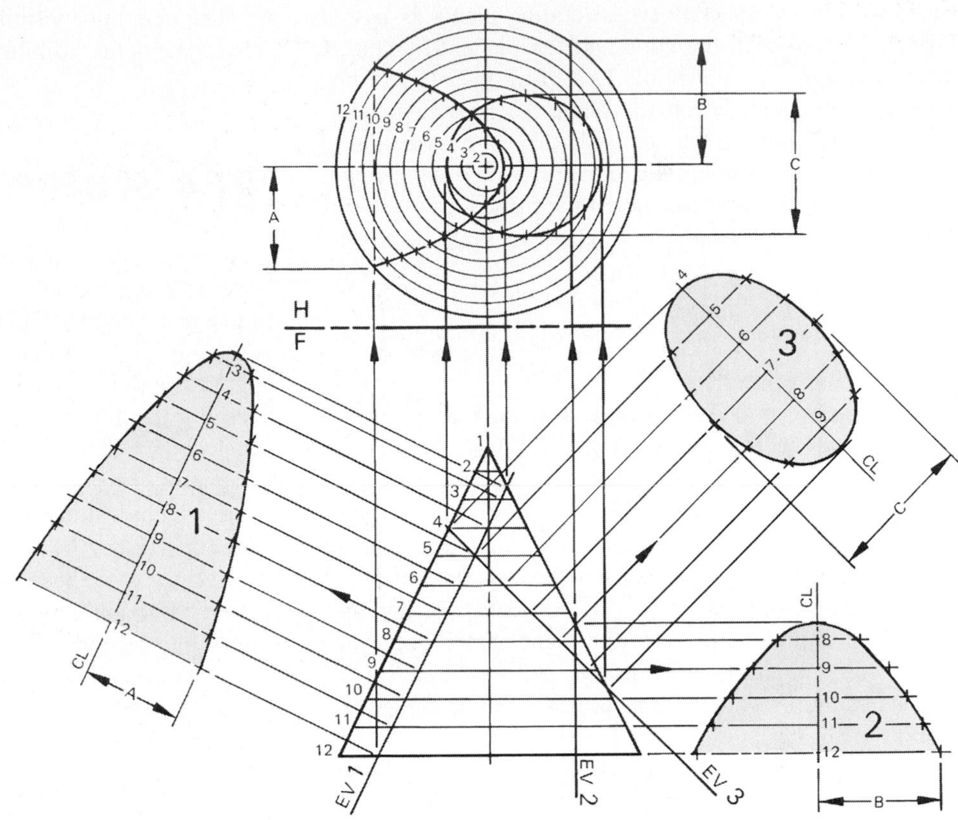

FIGURE 27.12 Conic Sections. The intersection of a plane and a right cone forms one of the following: (1) parabola, (2) hyperbola, and (3) ellipse.

27.5.1 Conic Sections

The intersection of a plane and a right cone is called a **conic section.** Five types of shapes can result from this intersection (Fig. 27.12).

Parabola A plane parallel to an extreme element of the cone (and therefore forming the same base angle) cuts a parabola (1).

Hyperbola A plane passed through the cone at a greater angle than the base angle results in a hyperbola (2).

Ellipse A plane that cuts all the elements of the cone but that is not perpendicular to the axis forms a true ellipse (3).

Isosceles triangle A plane passed through the vertex cuts an isosceles triangle (the frontal view).

Circle A plane passed perpendicular to the axis forms a circular intersection. A series of horizontal cutting planes has been in introduced in the frontal view, which project as circles in the horizontal view (Fig. 27.12).

The intersection of a cone and a plane is established by passing a series of horizontal cutting planes perpendicular to the axis of the cone. In Figure 27.12, the frontal and horizontal views of the cone are given, along with the edge view of three theoretical unlimited planes that intersect the cone. The horizontal view and the true shape of each intersection are required. The following steps were used to solve the problem.

1. Pass a series of evenly spaced horizontal cutting planes through the cone, CP1 through CP12.
2. Each cutting plane projects as a circle in the horizontal view.
3. EV1 intersects CP3 through CP12 in the frontal view. Project each intersection point to the horizontal view. The intersection of EV1 and the cone forms a parabola.
4. The true shape of the parabola is seen in a view projected parallel to EV1. The centerline of the parabola is drawn parallel to EV1, and the intersection points of the plane (EV1) and each cutting plane are projected from the frontal view. Distances are transferred from the horizontal view, as is dimension A.
5. Repeat steps 3 and 4 to establish the intersection of EV2 and EV3 with the cone. EV2 projects as a line in the horizontal view and as a hyperbola in a true-shape view (2). EV3 forms an ellipse in the horizontal view and projects as a true ellipse in a true-shape view (3).

27.5.2 Intersection of an Oblique Plane and a Cone (Cutting Plane Method)

The cutting plane method can determine the intersection of a plane and a cone if the plane is oblique in its given views.

A series of evenly spaced vertical cutting planes is passed through the vertex of the cone and the plane. The cutting planes intersect the cone and the plane as straight-line elements (lines) that lie on the plane. Each element intersects its corresponding line along the line of intersection of the plane and the cone. The point at which an element intersects its corresponding line on the plane locates a point on the line of intersection. This intersection point lies on the plane and on the cone's surface.

In Figure 27.13, oblique plane K-L-M-N and the right cone are given and their intersection line is required. The following steps were used in the solution.

1. Pass a series of evenly spaced vertical cuffing planes through the cone's vertex [Fig. 27.13(a)]. Project the elements to the frontal view and label as shown.
2. Each element corresponds to a cutting plane that intersects the cone and the plane [Fig. 27.13(b)]. As an example, a cutting plane passed through the cone and intersecting the plane forms elements O_H-2_H and O_H-10_H, and also intersects the plane at points A_H and B_H. Points A_H and B_H form line A_H-B_H, which lies on the plane and represents the intersection of the cutting plane and the given plane.
3. Project Line A-B to the frontal view, where it intersects element O_F-2_F at piercing point A^1. Each line formed by the intersection of the cutting plane and the plane intersects two corresponding elements on the cone.
4. Determine the line of intersection by connecting the piercing points with a smooth curve.
5. Project the piercing points to the horizontal view to locate the line of intersection in that view.
6. Then determine visibility for both views by using inspection or by the visibility check.

27.6 SPHERES

A **sphere** can be defined as a geometric form bounded by a surface containing all possible points at a given distance from a given point. A sphere is generated by rotating a circle around an axis line that passes through the sphere's center. Spheres are **double-curved surfaces** and contain no straight lines. In all projections, spheres are represented as circles equal to their diameter.

Spheres or portions of spheres are found in the design of a variety of industrial products, consumer goods, toys, buildings, and vessels.

A plane passed through the center of a sphere and at an angle to the adjacent projection plane creates an elliptical line of intersection [A and B in Fig. 27.14(a)]. This type of intersection is known as a **great circle** of a sphere. A plane passed parallel to the adjacent projection plane and not through its center cuts a **small circle** [C and D in Fig. 27.14(b)].

27.6.1 Intersection of a Plane and a Sphere

The intersection of a plane and a sphere results in a circular line of intersection. If the plane is inclined, the line of intersection appears as an ellipse (Fig. 27.15). The extreme piercing points and, therefore, the major and minor axes

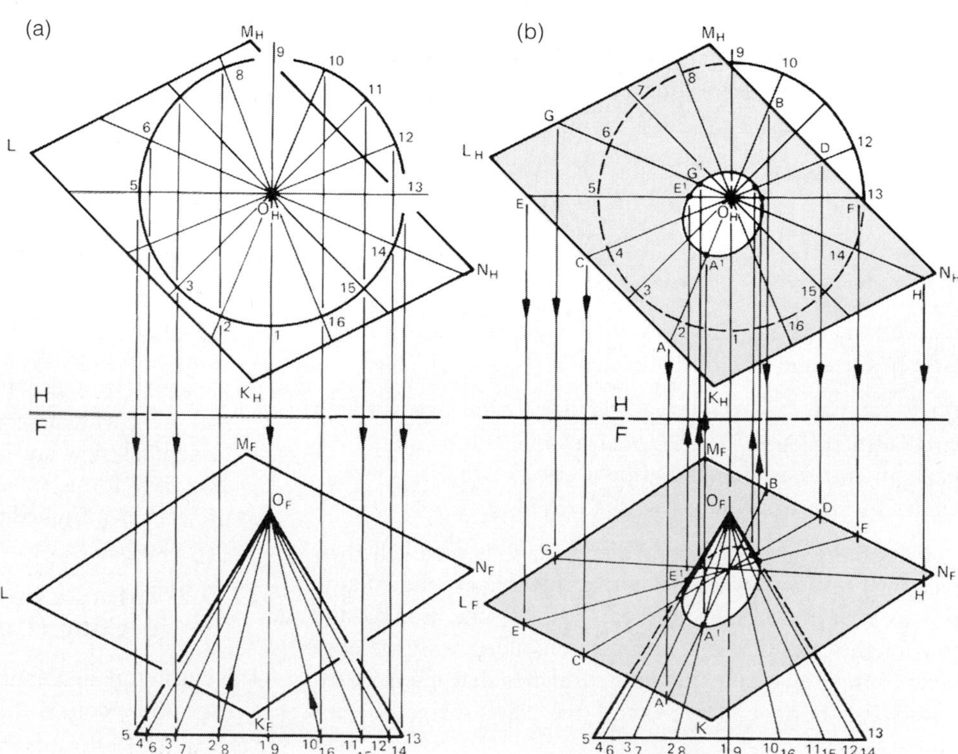

FIGURE 27.13 Intersection of an Oblique Plane and a Right Cone Using the Cutting Plane Method

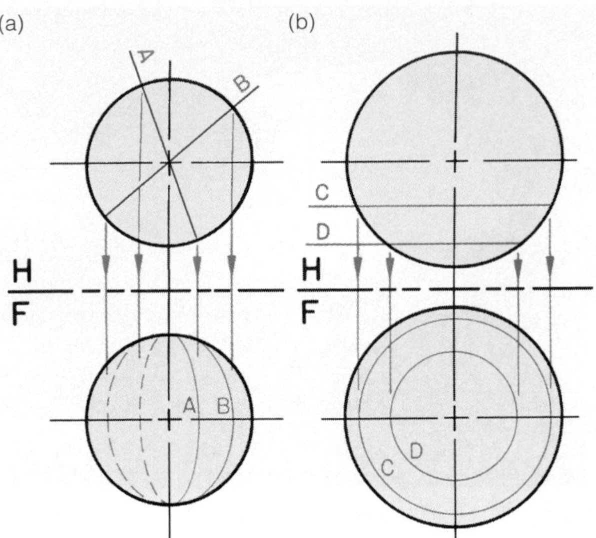

FIGURE 27.14 Great and Small Circles of a Sphere

must first be found by the edge view or cutting plane method. The actual ellipse can be constructed by means of an ellipse template using the major and minor axes. Another method involves plotting a series of piercing points established by cutting planes in a view showing the plane as an edge.

In Figure 27.15, the intersection of the sphere and the plane is required. The following steps were used to solve the problem.

1. Pass a series of evenly spaced horizontal cutting planes through the sphere and project to the horizontal view. Each cutting plane cuts a small-circle section.
2. Each cutting plane intersects the edge view of the plane and locates two piercing points, which you then project to the horizontal view to establish the line of intersection. Finally, determine visibility.

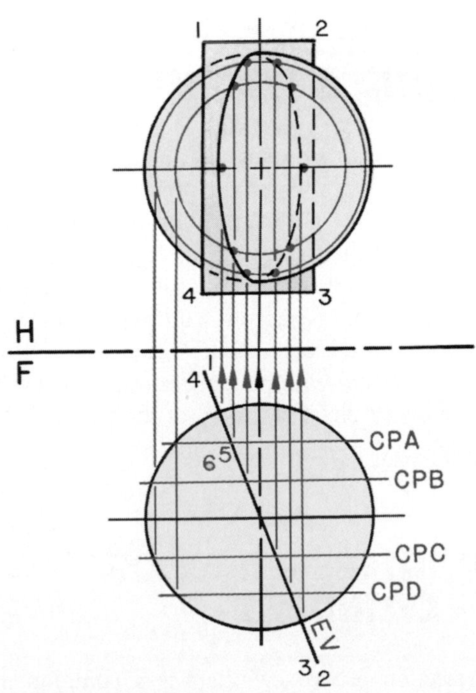

FIGURE 27.15 Intersection of a Plane and a Sphere Using Cutting Planes

27.7 INTERSECTION OF PRISMS

The intersection of two prisms can be determined by the edge view method. The piercing point of an edge line of one prism and a surface of the other prism can be established in a view in which one of the prisms is an edge view. This type of problem can be reduced to finding the piercing point of a line and a plane. Where each edge line of a prism pierces a surface (plane) of the other prism, a point (piercing point) on the line of intersection is established. The line of intersection includes only surface lines of intersection, not those that will be "inside" the prisms.

In Figure 27.16, two right prisms intersect at right angles. The horizontal view shows the edge view of the rectangular prism, and the profile view shows the triangular prism as an edge view. The following steps were used in the solution.

1. The edges of the triangular horizontal prism pierce the vertical prism in the horizontal view at points 1 through 6. Edge line A pierces the surface bounded by lines D and G at piercing point 1, and at piercing point 2 on the surface bounded by lines D and E.
2. Project points 1 and 2 to the frontal view until they intersect line A.
3. Repeat this procedure to locate piercing points 3, 4, 5, and 6 in both views.
4. The edges of the vertical rectangular prism pierce the surfaces of the horizontal prism in the profile view at

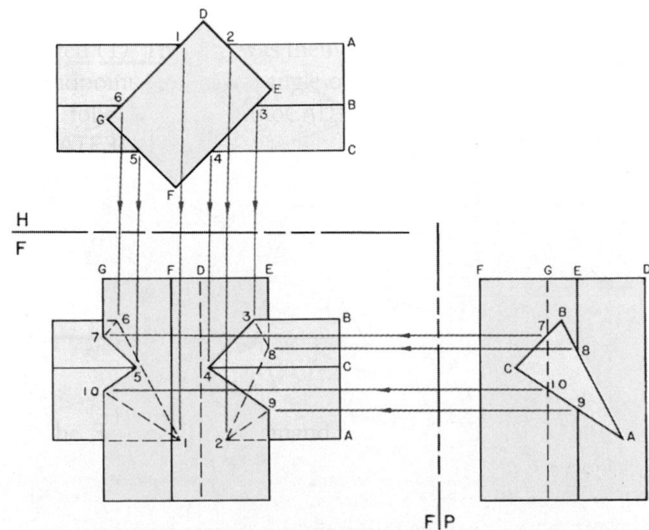

FIGURE 27.16 Intersection of Two Prisms

points 7, 8, 9, and 10. Edge line G pierces the surface bounded by lines B and C at piercing point 7.

5. Project point 7 to the frontal view until it intersects line G.
6. Repeat step 5 to locate piercing points 8, 9, and 10.
7. Determine visibility, and connect the piercing points to form the line of intersection.

27.7.1 Intersection of Two Prisms (Edge View Method)

The line of intersection of two prisms is established by finding the piercing points of the edge lines of one prism with each surface of the other prism. This process is repeated using the lines of the second prism and is theoretically the intersection of individual lines and planes or the intersection of two planes. Each prism must be shown as an edge view. If only one prism is given as an edge view, an auxiliary view must be projected showing the other prism as an edge view.

In Figure 27.17, the horizontal and frontal views of the two prisms are given; the line of intersection is required. The following steps were used to solve the problem.

1. Draw an auxiliary view showing the triangular prism as an edge view. Each of the edge lines of the triangular prism is a frontal line (true length in the frontal view). Therefore draw F/A perpendicular to line 1 and project auxiliary view A.
2. In the horizontal view, edge line 1 pierces the surfaces bounded by lines A and D at point 1. The surface bounded by line A and B is pierced by line 2 at point 2 and by line 3 at point 3.
3. Project points 1, 2, and 3 to the frontal view to establish the endpoints of lines 1-1, 2-2, and 3-3.
4. In auxiliary view A, corner line A intersects two of the surfaces of the triangular prism at points 4 and 5.

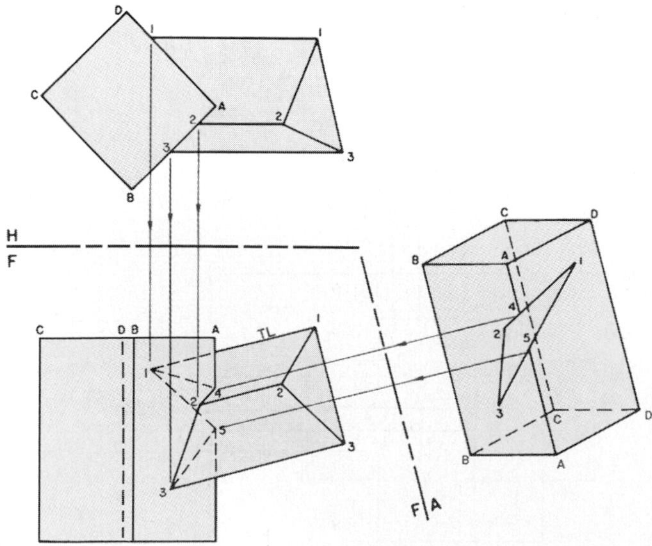

FIGURE 27.17 Intersection of Two Prisms Using the Edge View Method

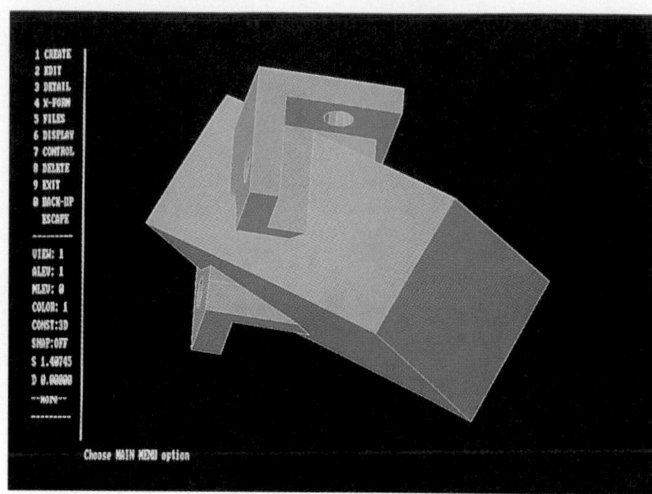

FIGURE 27.18 Solid Intersection

5. Project piercing points 4 and 5 to the frontal view until they intersect corner line A.
6. Determine visibility by inspection of the profile and horizontal views. Connect the piercing points in the proper sequence. In the frontal view, intersection lines 3-2 and 2-4 are visible; all others are hidden.

The intersection of prisms is shown on a CAD system in Figure 27.18.

You May Complete Exercises 27.5 Through 27.8 at This Time

27.8 INTERSECTION OF A PRISM AND A PYRAMID

The intersection of a prism and a pyramid requires the projection of a view in which the prism shows as an edge. In Figure 27.19(a), the right prism intersects the pyramid. After the edge view of the prism is projected (auxiliary view A), the intersection is solved for by locating the piercing points of the shapes. In this example, cuttings planes were introduced to solve for the line of intersection, since the solution could not be derived with piercing points exclusively. Figure 27.19(b) shows a physical model of the project.

27.9 INTERSECTION OF CYLINDERS

The intersection of two cylinders is a common industrial problem in piping and vessel design and in duct design for HVAC. Two intersecting perpendicular right cylinders of the

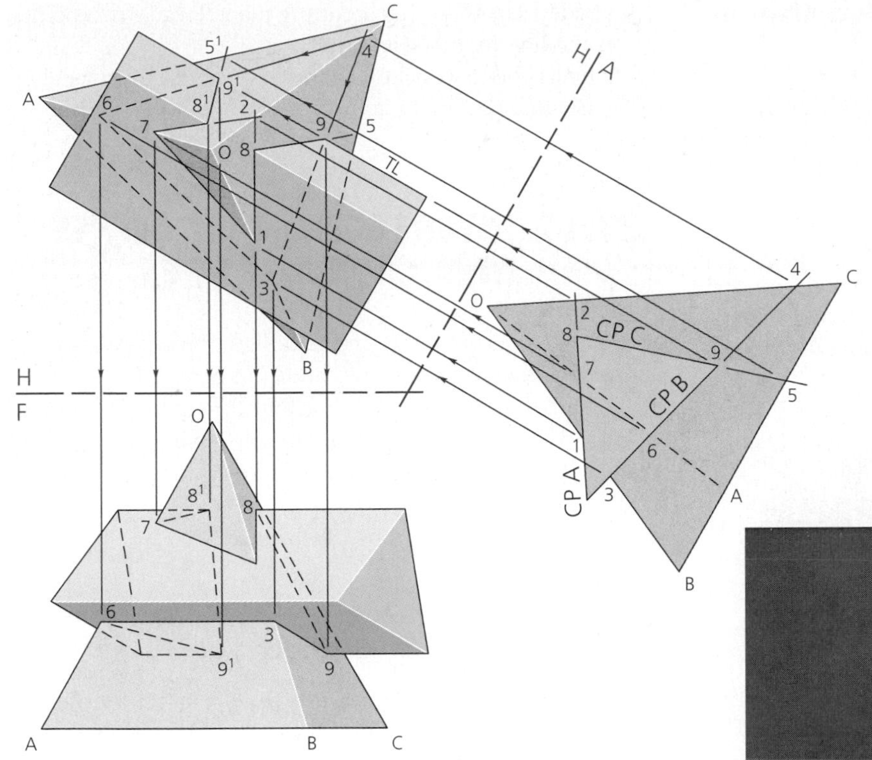

(a) Intersection of a pyramid and a prism

FIGURE 27.19 Intersections

(b) Model of the intersection of a pyramid and a prism

same diameter intersect as shown in Figure 27.20. The line of intersection can be determined by showing each cylinder as an edge view and passing a series of equally spaced cutting planes through both cylinders. Each cutting plane intersects a cylinder as an element on its surface. The intersection of related elements determines the line of intersection. Each intersection point is actually the piercing point of an element of one cylinder and the surface of the other cylinder.

In Figure 27.20, both cylinders are the same diameter and intersect one another at right angles. The resulting **curved lines of intersection** appear as straight lines in the frontal view. Therefore, in this case the line of intersection could have been determined by simply drawing the straight lines from point 1 to point 4 to point 7.

To solve for the perpendicular intersection of two cylinders, regardless of their diameters, a series of elements is drawn on the surface of one cylinder by equally dividing the edge view of the vertical cylinder (Fig. 27.20). Each vertical cutting plane passes parallel to the cylinder's axis and cuts a straight-line element on both surfaces. Points 1 through 7 represent the intersection of related elements established by the intersection of a cutting plane and each cylinder. The profile view can also serve to divide the horizontal cylinder equally and establish vertical cutting planes, as shown.

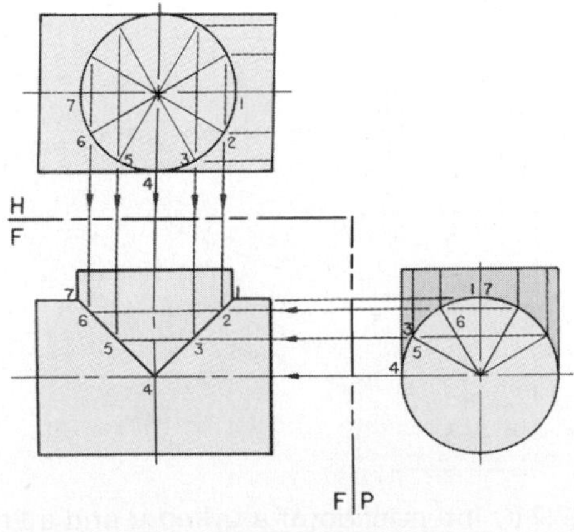

FIGURE 27.20 Intersection of Two Cylinders at 90°

27.9.1 Intersection of Two Cylinders (Not at Right Angles)

To find the intersection of two cylinders not at right angles, an edge view of both cylinders is necessary. Project an edge view of the cylinder, if it does not appear as an edge in a given view. Pass a series of cutting planes; each cutting plane intersects both cylinders as elements on their surface. Related elements intersect along the line of intersection of the two cylinders. Accuracy increases proportionally to the number of cutting planes and therefore piercing points. Connect piercing points by means of a smooth curve.

27.10 INTERSECTION OF A CYLINDER AND A PRISM AT AN ANGLE

In Figure 27.21, the vertical right cylinder and the inclined prism are given in the frontal and horizontal views. A series of cutting planes is drawn through an end view of the prism (right section) and parallel to the axis of the cylinder. The following steps were used to solve the problem.

1. Draw F/A perpendicular to the true-length lines of the prism in the frontal view. Project auxiliary view A. The cylinder need not be shown.
2. Pass a series of evenly spaced vertical cutting planes through the right section of the prism in auxiliary view A. Show the cutting planes in the horizontal view.
3. The edge lines of the prism intersect the cylinder in the horizontal view. Project piercing points A, B, C, and D to the frontal view.
4. Project to the frontal view the elements established on the prism in auxiliary view A and the elements established on the cylinder in the horizontal view. Note that each cutting plane cuts two elements on the prism and one on the cylinder. Therefore, each cutting plane locates two points on the line of intersection.
5. Connect the intersection points in proper sequence after determining visibility.

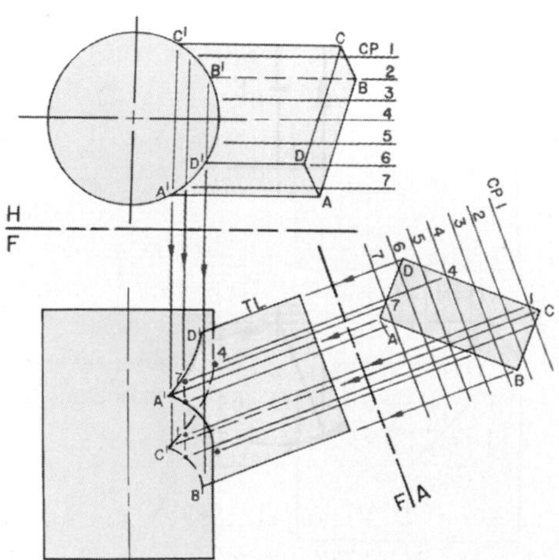

FIGURE 27.21 Intersection of a Cylinder and a Prism at an Angle

27.11 INTERSECTION OF CONES AND OTHER SHAPES

Conical shapes are found in the design of a wide variety of industrial products, structures, and commercial applications. In general, the right circular cone and the frustum of a right circular cone are the most common. Oblique cones with circular bases sometimes serve as transition pieces and in ducting HVAC designs. In Figure 27.22, a number of conical and cylindrical intersections can be seen.

27.11.1 Intersection of a Cone and a Horizontal Cylinder

The intersection of a cone and a cylinder can be determined by passing a series of cutting planes through the cylinder's axis in a view in which the cylinder appears as a right circular section. In Figure 27.23, the intersection of a cone and a cylinder is required. The following steps were used in the solution.

1. Project the profile view to show the right section of the cylinder.

FIGURE 27.22 Electronic Testing of Top Hat and Probe

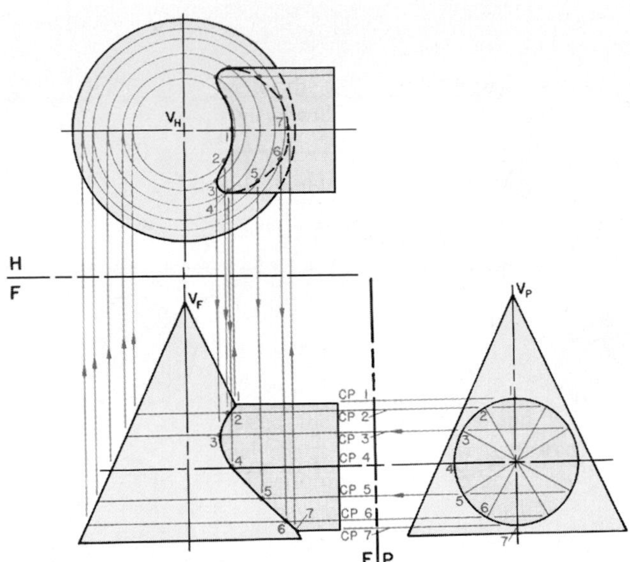

FIGURE 27.23 Intersection of a Cone and a Horizontal Cylinder

2. Evenly divide the cylinder as shown. Each division corresponds to a horizontal cutting plane, CP1 through CP7. Extend the cutting planes to the frontal view.
3. The highest and lowest points of the intersection are established in the frontal view, where CP1 and CP7 intersect the cone at points 1 and 7, respectively. Project points 1 and 7 to the horizontal view.
4. Project the cutting planes to the horizontal view. Each cutting plane appears as a *circle element* on the cone and as a straight-line element on the surface of the cylinder.
5. The intersection of related elements determines a point on the line of intersection. Locate the points in both views.
6. Except for points 1 and 7, each common point is used to plot a line of intersection that is symmetrical to the axis of the cylinder in the horizontal view.
7. Determine visibility, and connect the points as a smooth curve representing the line of intersection.

Figure 27.24 shows the intersection of the right cone and a vertical cylinder. A series of evenly spaced vertical cutting planes is introduced through the cone's vertex. Each cutting plane cuts related elements on the surface of the cone and the cylinder. The intersection of related elements establishes points of intersection. Figure 27.25(a) shows a similar intersection created on AutoCAD as a solid model. The top, front, right side, and pictorial views of the intersection are shown in Figure 27.25(b). [This is a good example of Problem 27.1(I).]

27.11.2 Intersection of a Cone and a Cylinder at an Angle

A vertical cutting plane passed through the vertex of a cone and parallel to its axis intersects both the cone and cylinder

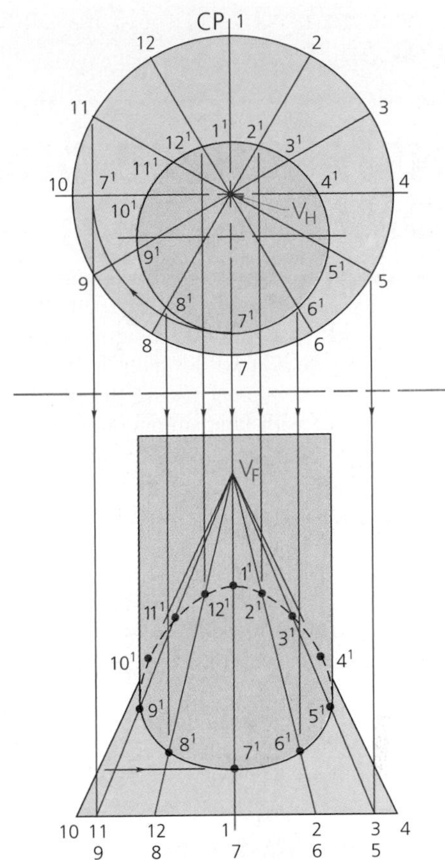

FIGURE 27.24 Intersection of a Cone and a Vertical Cylinder

as straight-line elements on their surfaces. A right section view of the cylinder is required to fix the position of the elements along its surface. In Figure 27.26 the intersection of a cone and a cylinder is required. The following steps were used to solve the problem.

1. Project auxiliary view A perpendicular to the cylinder. The cylinder appears as a right section.
2. Evenly divide one-half of the circumference of the cone's base in the horizontal view. Since the intersection is symmetrical about the cylinder's axis, only the front divisions need be used as cutting planes. Each division corresponds to a vertical cutting plane passed through the vertex of the cone.
3. Each cutting place cuts a straight-line element along the surface of the cone. Locate the cutting planes in each view by projecting the elements of the cone.
4. The intersection of the cutting planes and the cylinder in auxiliary view A establish related elements along the surface of the cylinder. Project the cylinder's elements to the frontal view.
5. The intersection of related elements in the frontal view determines points along the line of intersection. CP1 locates points 1 and 6 at the extremes of the intersection line. CP2 locates points 2 and 5.

Focus On . . .

CONSTRUCTIVE SOLID GEOMETRY (CSG)

Cameras are developed and designed by a variety of modeling methods. The camera shown here was modeled with constructive solid geometry. **Constructive solid geometry (CSG)** modeling is a powerful technique that allows flexibility both in the way primitives are defined and combined. The relationships between the primitives are defined with **Boolean operations**, of which there are three types: **union** (∪), **difference** (−), and **intersection** (∩).

The camera design shows how union and difference operations can create different forms. The critical area is the place where two objects overlap. This is where the differences between the Boolean operations are evident. The union operation is essentially additive, with the two primitives being combined. However, in the final form, the volume where the two primitives overlap is represented only once; otherwise, there would be twice as much material in the area of overlap, which is not possible in a real object. With a difference operation, the area of overlap is not represented at all. The final form resembles one of the original primitives with the area of overlap removed. With the intersection operation, *only* the area of overlap remains; the remainder of the primitive volumes is removed.

In the figure, Boolean operations are shown in their mathematical form. The union (∪) operation, like the mathematical operation of addition, is not sensitive to the order of the primitive operands (e.g., 11 + 4 = 4 + 11 = 15). On the other hand, the difference (−) operation *is* sensitive to order (e.g., 11 − 4 = 7, but 4 − 11 = −7). For a Boolean difference operation, the overlapping volume is removed from the primitive listed *first* in the operation.

With Boolean operations, it is possible to have a form that has no volume (a *null* object). If the second primitive of the difference operation completely encompasses the first primitive, the result will be a null object, since negative geometry cannot be represented in the model.

Primitives that adjoin but do not overlap are also a special case. Performing a union operation on such primitives will simply fuse them together. A difference operation will leave the first primitive operand unchanged. An intersection operation results in a null object, since such an operation only shows the volume of overlap and there is no overlap for the adjoining primitives.

The final form of a model can be developed in several ways. As with pure primitive instancing, you can begin by defining a number of primitive forms. The primitives can then be located in space such that they are overlapping or adjoining. Boolean operation can then be applied to create the resulting form. The original primitives may be retained in addition to the new form, or they may be replaced by the new form. More primitives can be created and used to modify the form, until the final desired shape is reached. The camera sequence shows how the union and difference operations result in a solid model.

As with pure primitive instancing, the person doing the modeling must have a clear idea of what the final form will look like and develop a strategy for the sequence of operations needed to create that form. The use of *sweeping operations* to create primitives can lend even more flexibility in modeling.

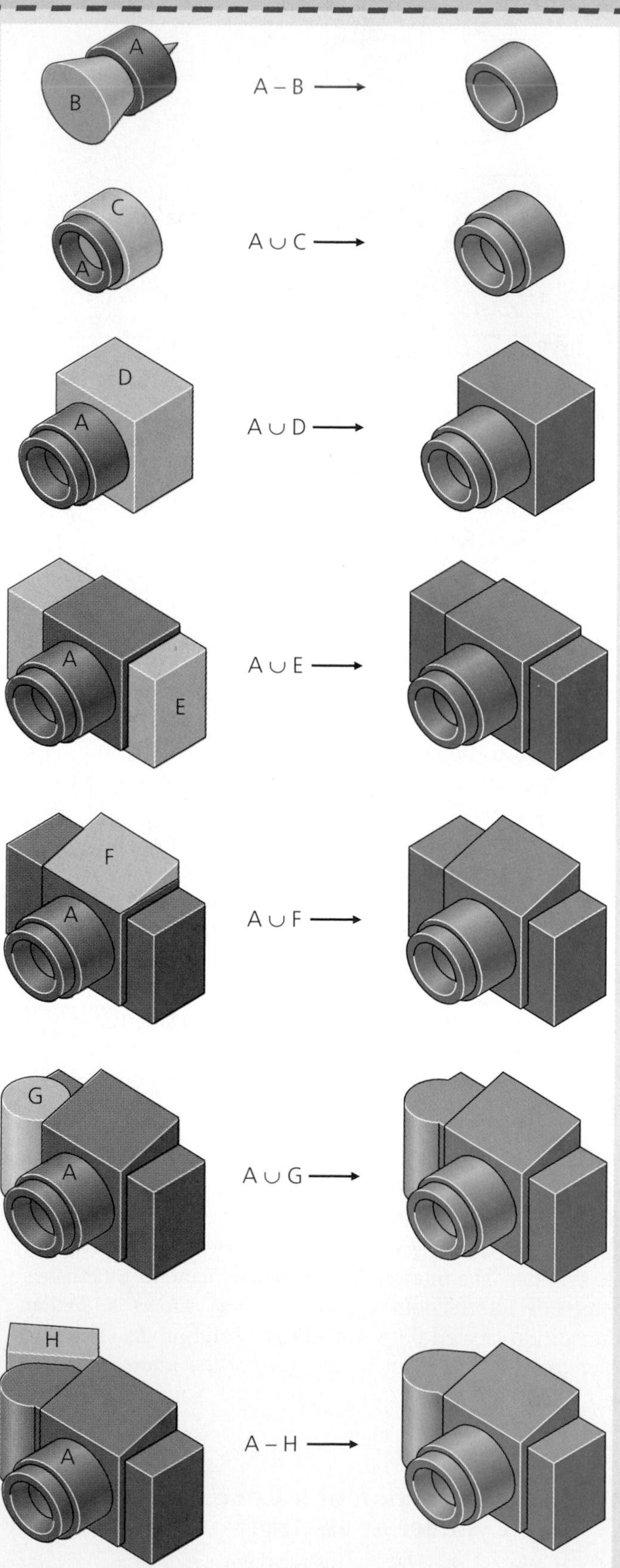

Constructive solid geometry (CSG) modeling of a camera.

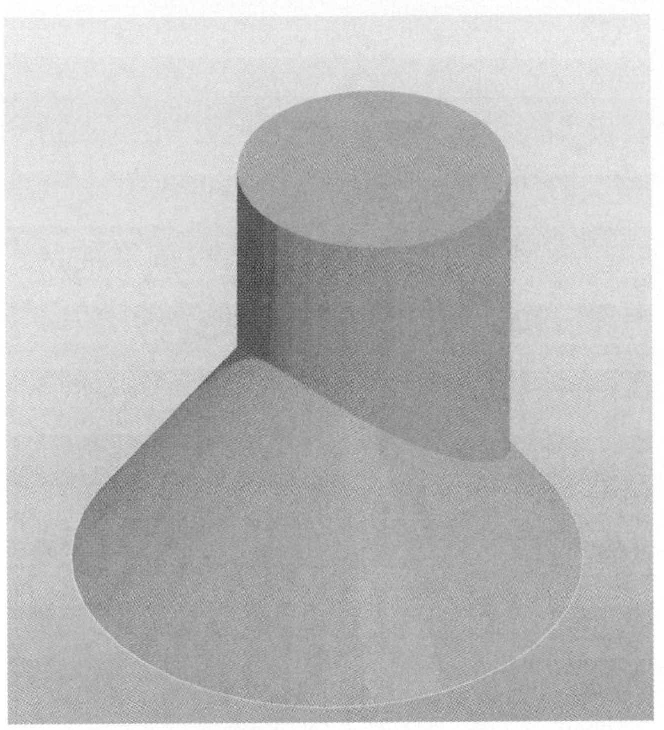

(a) Solid intersection on a shaded model using AutoCAD

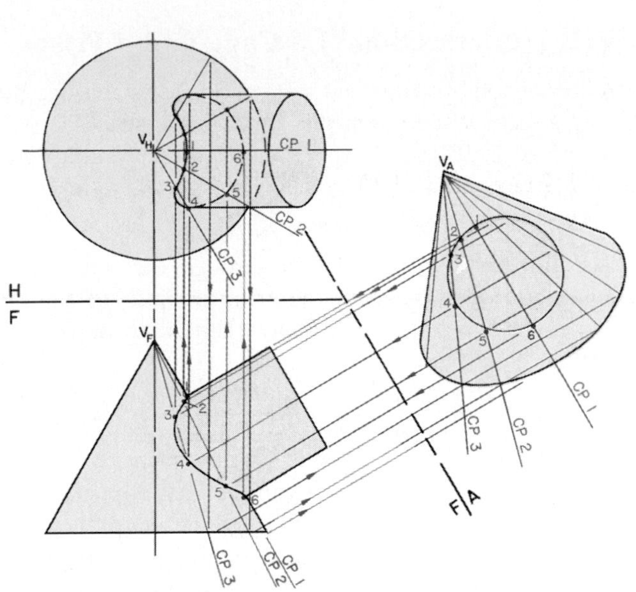

FIGURE 27.26 Intersection of a Cone and a Cylinder at an Angle

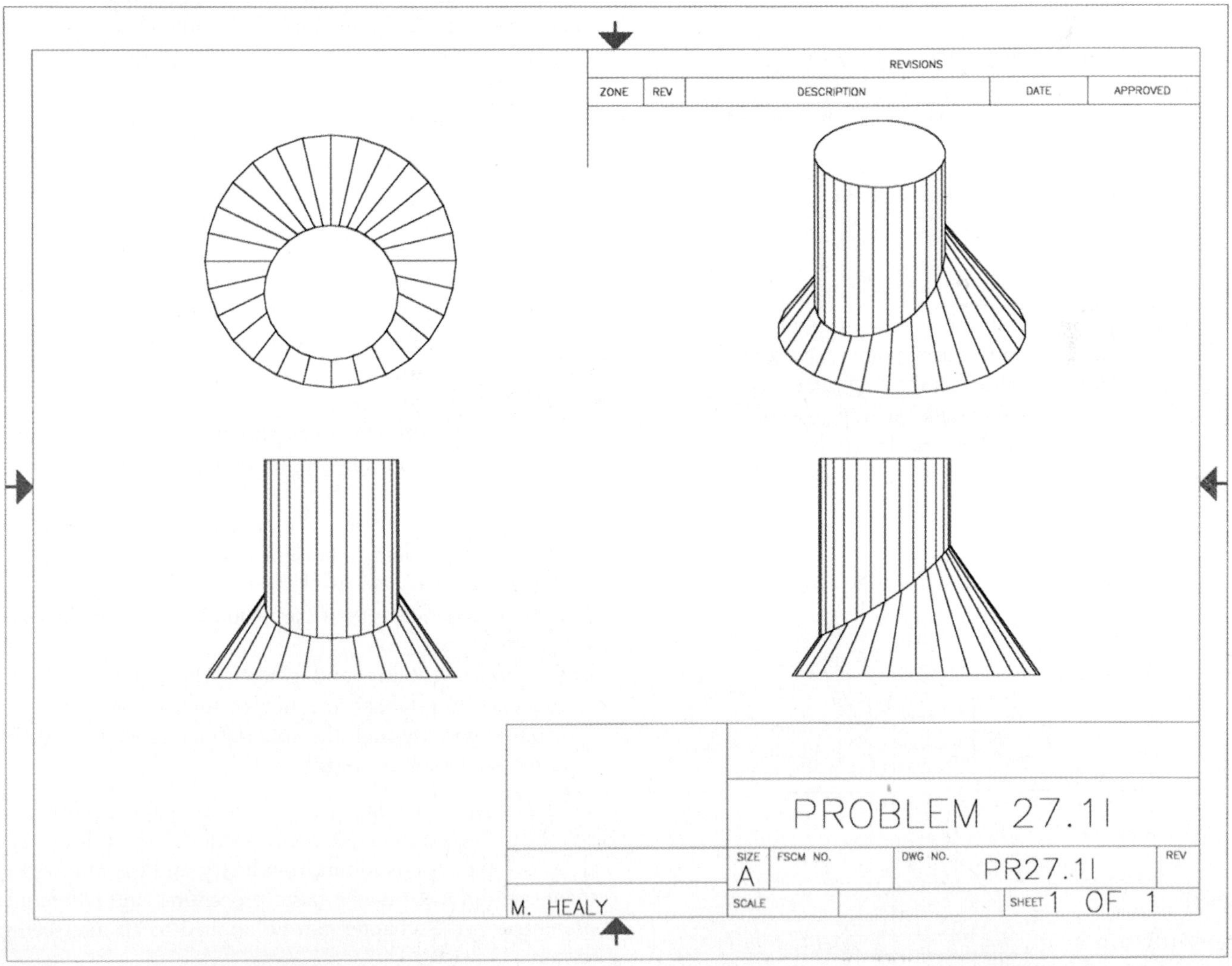

REVISIONS

ZONE	REV	DESCRIPTION	DATE	APPROVED

PROBLEM 27.1I

SIZE A | FSCM NO. | DWG NO. PR27.1I | REV

M. HEALY | SCALE | SHEET 1 OF 1

(b) Four views of solid intersection using AutoCAD

FIGURE 27.25 Intersections Using AutoCAD

27.11.3 Intersection of a Cone and a Prism

The intersection of a cone and a prism can be established by passing a series of cutting planes through the shapes.

In Figure 27.27, the intersection of a prism and a right circular cone is required. The following steps were taken to solve the problem.

1. Pass horizontal CP1 and CP2 through the upper and lower horizontal planes of the prism. Project the cutting planes to the horizontal view, where they appear as circular elements.
2. Since the upper and lower surfaces of the prism are horizontal planes, the line of intersection coincides with the circular elements cut by the cutting planes.
3. When the prism's surfaces are not horizontal planes, use vertical cutting planes passed through the axis of the cone in the horizontal view. CPs 3, 4, 5, and 6 cut elements along the cone's surface. Their intersection with the prism in the frontal view cuts two elements, each on the prism.
4. Intersecting elements determine the line of intersection in the horizontal view.

27.12 INTERSECTION OF A SPHERE AND A CYLINDER

By passing a series of cutting planes parallel to the axis of a cylinder and through a sphere, points along the line of intersection can be determined. A cutting plane drawn parallel to the axis of a cylinder will cut straight-line elements along its surface. Therefore, the intersection of a related circle and straight-line elements establishes points on the line of intersection. Each point represents a point common to both the sphere and the cylinder. Cutting planes are conveniently passed parallel to the axis of a cylinder, where the cylinder appears as an edge (right section). A right section shows the cylinder's axis line as a point.

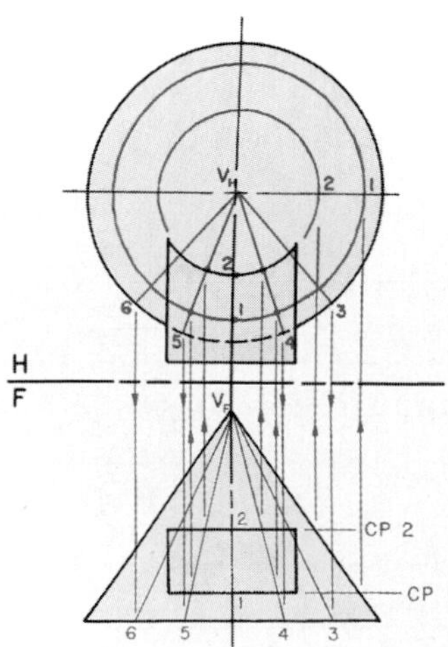

FIGURE 27.27 Intersection of a Cone and a Horizontal Prism

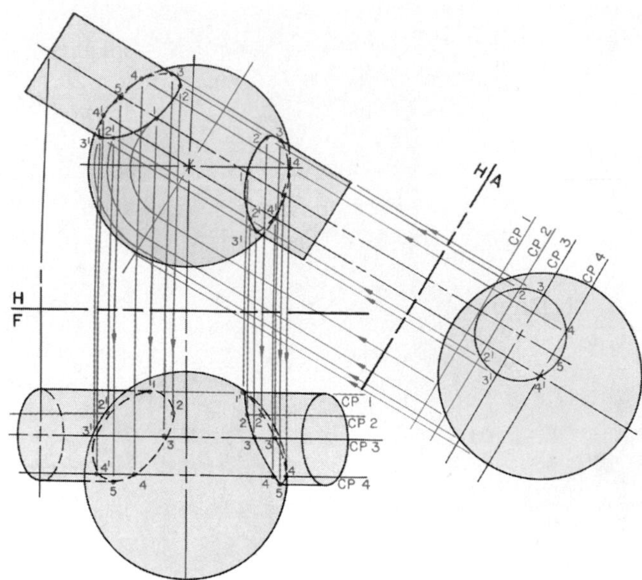

FIGURE 27.28 Intersection of a Sphere and a Horizontal Cylinder

Figure 27.28 gives the frontal and horizontal views of a sphere and a horizontal cylinder. The line of intersection is required. The following steps were used in the solution.

1. Draw H/A perpendicular to the cylinder's axis, and project auxiliary view A. The cylinder appears as a right section with its axis line as a point view.
2. Pass a series of conveniently spaced horizontal cutting planes through the edge view of the cylinder and the sphere in auxiliary view A. Show the cutting planes in the frontal view. Project the cutting planes to the horizontal view, where they appear as circles on the sphere.
3. CP1 cuts a straight-line element along the upper surface of the cylinder and a circular element on the surface of the sphere. The intersection of the sphere's circular element and the cylinder's straight-line element in the horizontal view locates a point on the line of intersection, point 1.
4. CP2 and CP3 intersect the sphere as circular elements and cut two straight-line elements, each on the surface of the cylinder.
5. Project all points to their corresponding cutting planes on the frontal view.
6. Determine visibility, and connect the points in proper sequence to establish the line of intersection. Since the cylinder goes through the sphere (pierces it), two curved lines of intersection result.

This chapter so far has provided many examples of simple as well as complex intersections of surfaces. The types of intersections found in industry, and the numbers of them, are infinite, but the basic procedures and techniques presented in this chapter can be applied to all intersecting forms.

You May Complete Exercises 27.9 Through 27.12 at This Time

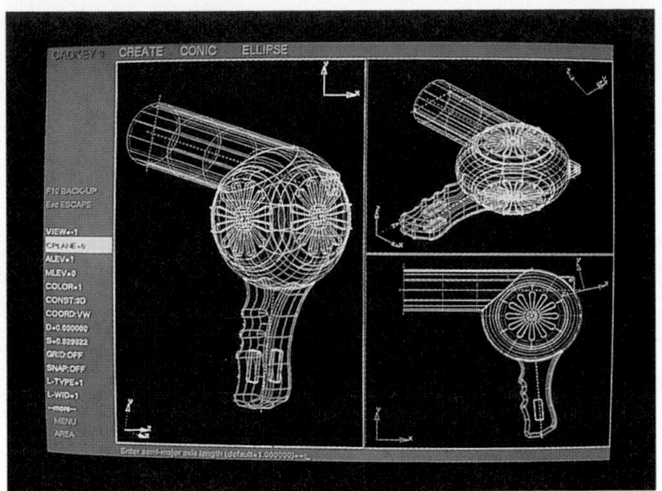

FIGURE 27.29 3D Surface Model of Hair Dryer

27.13 INTERSECTION SOLUTIONS USING CAD

On a CAD system, intersections of surfaces can be determined by a number of different techniques. The basic primitives are combined automatically by the system, without the need to create descriptive geometry drawings. Both surface modeling (Fig. 27.29) and solid modeling provide complete capabilities for intersection problems.

Piercing points and intersections of lines, planes, and solid shapes can be generated automatically with 3D CAD via commands such as **CUT SURFACE**, **INTERSECT SURFACE**, **CUT PLANE** (Computervision), and **UNION** (AutoCAD).

Figure 27.30 shows an example of a solid modeling system used to solve for the union of two solids (CADKEY). The figure displays the two solids both together and separately. Figure 27.31 (CADKEY) shows an example of a complex shape and its intersection with a solid cylindrical shape. This type of modeling uses the power of the computer to merge the two solids automatically.

The intersection of two planes (Fig. 27.32) requires a minimum of two views for the cutting plane method and three views with the edge view method. The CAD solution requires that a **CUT PLANE** command (Computervision and Personal Designer) be given and the two planes picked. The system automatically generates the intersection points. However, depending on the system, the line of intersection may need to be put in with a command to draw a line. The system may also require the operator to give a **HIDE** command in order to show proper visibility.

The intersection of a plane and a pyramid is shown in Figure 27.33. The **CUT PLANE** command (Computervision and Personal Designer) was used and correct visibility was established.

27.13.1 Intersection Using CAD Solid Modeling

When completed manually, the intersection of two solids is one of the most difficult problems encountered in descrip-

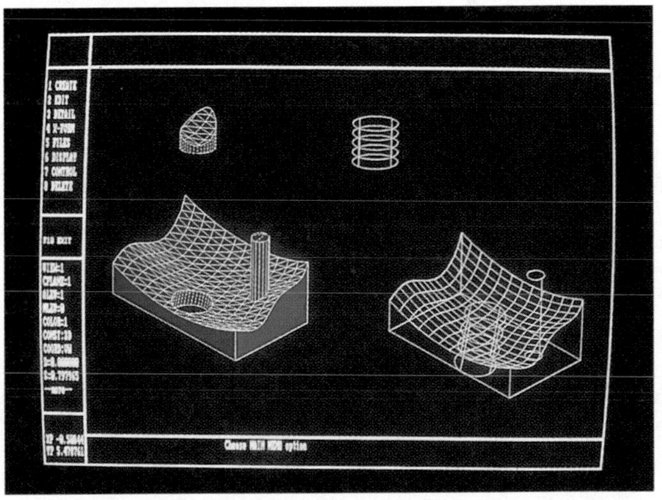

FIGURE 27.31 Solid Intersection of a Sculpted Surface and a Cylinder

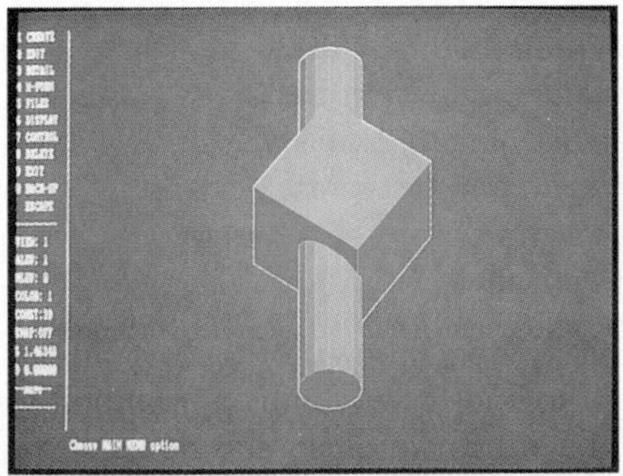

(a) Solid model of an intersection cylinder and block

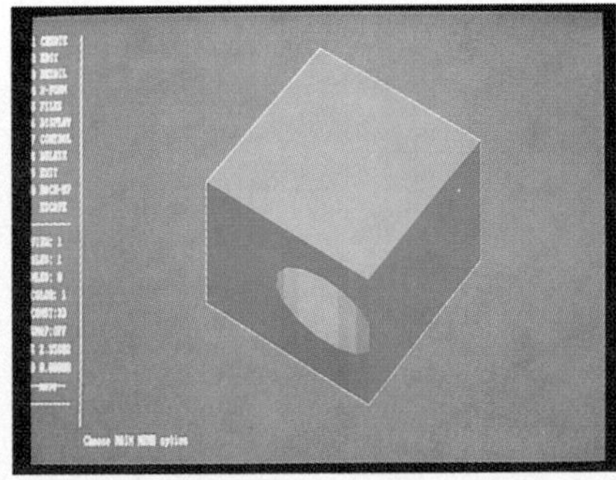

(b) Solid model of a block with the cylinder removed, thereby creating a hole

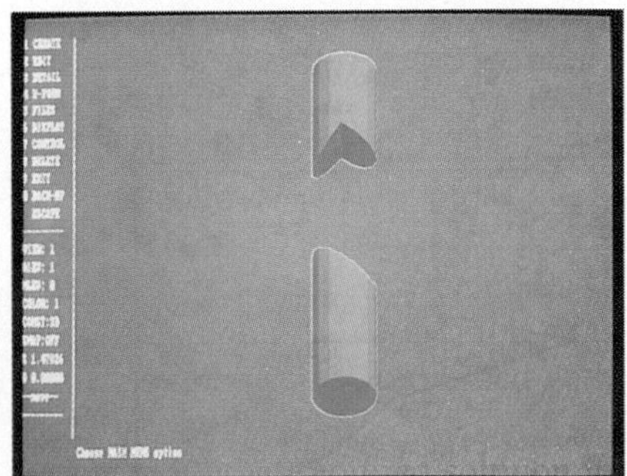

(c) Solid model of cylinder, with block removed

FIGURE 27.30 Solid Intersections

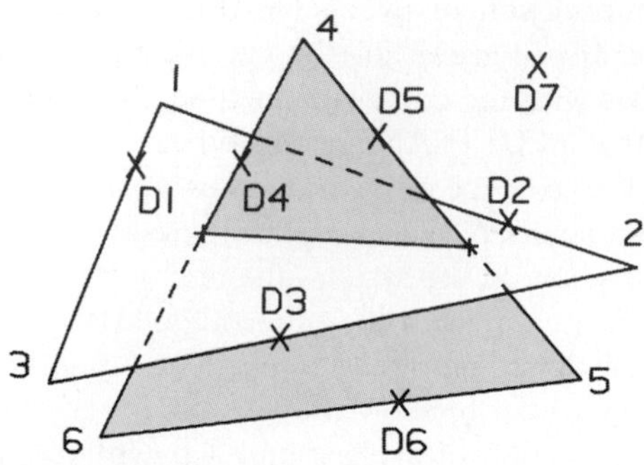

CUT PLANE :D1 D2 D3,D4 D5 D6
HIDE PART :D7

FIGURE 27.32 CAD-Generated Solution for the Intersection of Two Planes

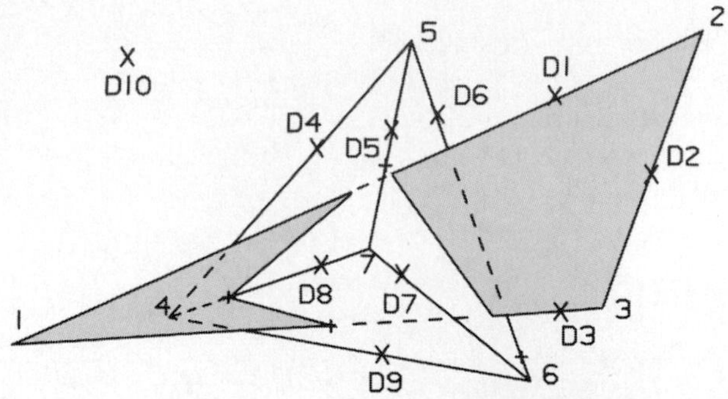

CUT PLANE :D1 D2 D3, D4 D5 D6 D7 D8 D9
HIDE PART :D10

FIGURE 27.33 CAD-Generated Solution for the Intersection of a Plane and a Pyramid

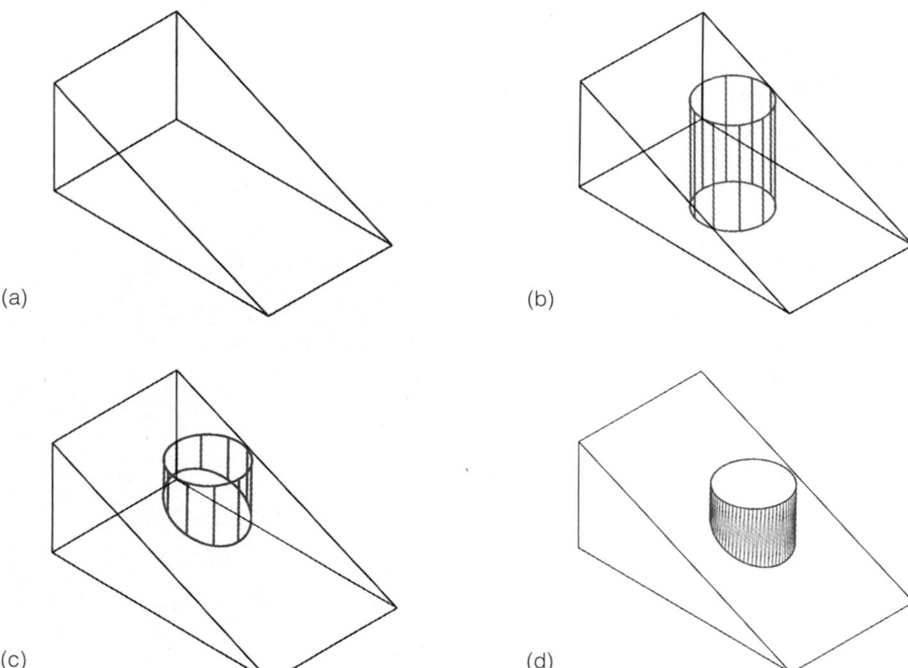

FIGURE 27.34 Union of a Cylinder and a Wedge Using AutoCAD

```
Command: VPOINT
Rotate/<View point> <0.0000, 0.0000,
1.0000>: 1, -1, 1
Command: PAN
Displacement: 0,0
Second point: 5,4
Command: ISOLINES
New value for Isolines <4>: 10
Command: WEDGE
Center/<Corner of wedge> <0,0,0>: Press
Enter
Cube/Length/<Other corner>: 7,4,3
Command: COLOR
New object color <BYLAYER>: Blue
Command: CYLINDER
Elliptical/<Center point> <0,0,0>: 3,2,0
Diameter/<Radius>: 1
Center of other end/<Height>: 3
Command: UNION
Select objects: Pick the wedge and the cylinder
Command: ZOOM
All/Center/Dynamic/Extents/Left/Previous/
Vmax/Window/<Scale(X/XP)>: All
Command: HIDE
Command: SHADE (not shown)
```

tive geometry. With a solid modeling program, the same intersections are simple and easy to construct. The following examples were modeled on AutoCAD using solid modeling.

Figures 27.34 through 27.38 present a series of projects involving AutoCAD solids. These figures illustrate how to input the commands to create the solids and how to solve for their intersection using a **UNION** command. The **HIDE** and **SHADE** commands complete the examples. The results of the **SHADE** commands are not shown. If you have an AutoCAD system, try each of the commands and plot the illustrations as required. These AutoCAD commands represent Release 13 of the software.

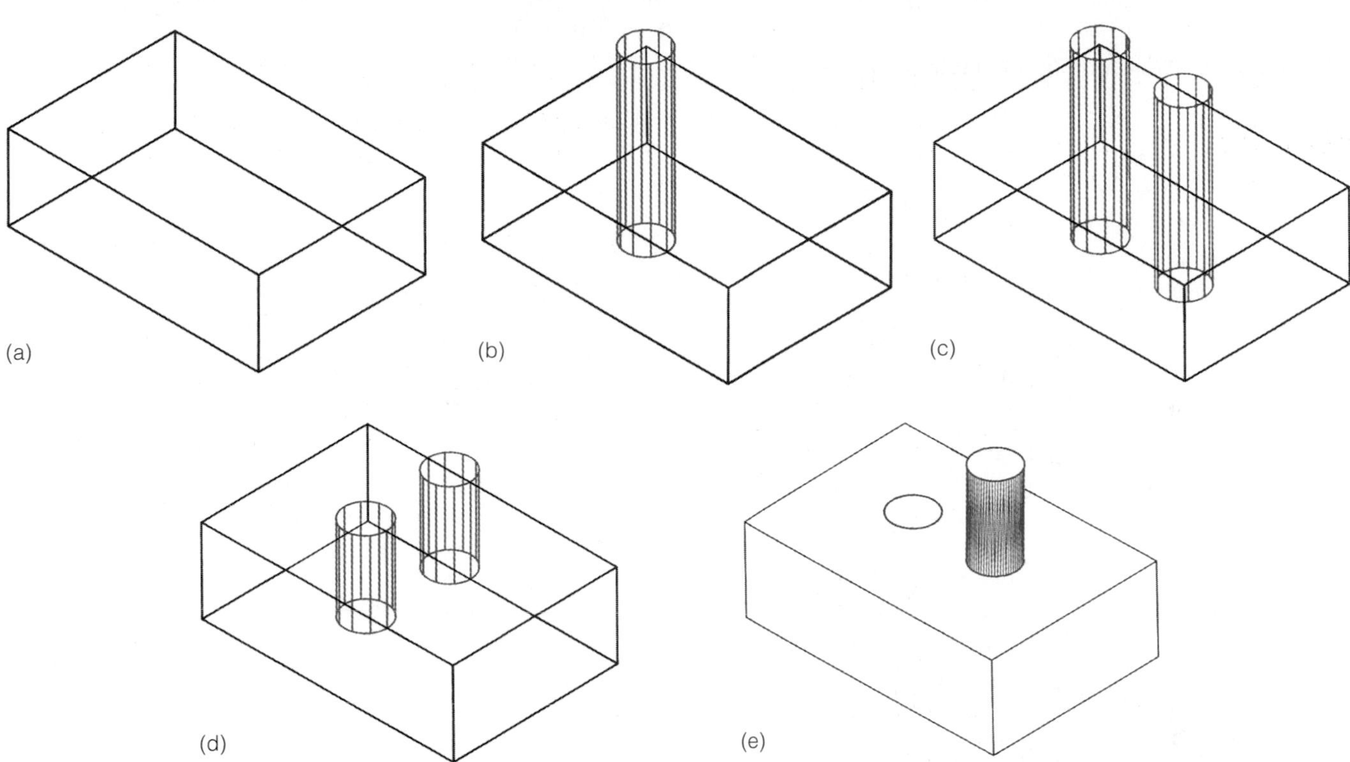

FIGURE 27.35 Union of Two Cylinders and a Box Using AutoCAD

```
Command: VPOINT
Rotate/<View point> <0.0000, 0.0000,
1.0000>: 1, -1, 1
Command: PAN
Displacement: 0,0
Second point: 5,4
Command: ISOLINES
New value for Isolines <4>: 10
Command: BOX
Center/<Corner of box> <0,0,0>: Press Enter
Cube/Length/<other corner>: 6,4,2
Command: COLOR
New object color <BYLAYER>: Blue
Command: CYLINDER
Elliptical/<Center point> <0,0,0>: 2,2,0
Diameter/<Radius>: .5
Center of other end/<Height>: 4
Command: CYLINDER
Elliptical/<Center point> <0,0,0>: 4,2,0
Diameter/<Radius>: .5
Center of other end/<Height>: 4
Command: SUBTRACT
Select solids and regions to subtract from . . .
Select objects: Pick the box
Select objects to subtract from them . . .
Select objects: Pick the first cylinder
Command: UNION
Select objects: Pick the box and the second cylinder
Command: ZOOM
All/Center/Dynamic/Extents/Left/Previous/
Vmax/Window/<Scale(X/XP)>: All
Command: HIDE
Command: SHADE (not shown)
```

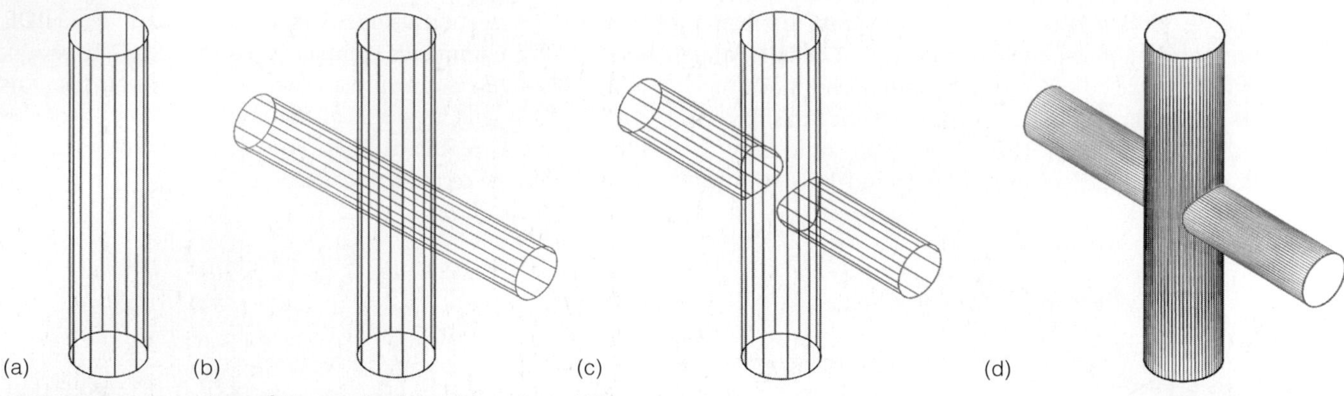

FIGURE 27.36 Union of Two Cylinders Using AutoCAD

```
Command: VPOINT
Rotate/<View point> <0.0000, 0.0000,
1.0000>: 1, -1, 1
Command: PAN
Displacement: 0,0
Second point: 5,4
Command: ISOLINES
New value for Isolines <4>: 10
Command: CYLINDER
Elliptical/<Center Point><0,0,0>: 0,0,-5
Diameter/<Radius>: 1
Center of other end/<Height>: 10
Command: COLOR
New object color <BYLAYER>: Blue
Command: UCS
Origin/ZAxis/3point/Object/View/X/Y/Z/
Prev/Restore/Save/Del/?/<World>: Y
Rotation angle about Y axis <0>: 90
Command: CYLINDER
Baseplane/Elliptical/<Center Point>
<0,0,0>: 0,0,-5
Diameter/<Radius>: .75
Center of other end/<Height>: 10
Command: UNION
Select objects: Pick the two cylinders
Command: ZOOM
All/Center/Dynamic/Extents/Left/Previous/
Vmax/Window/<Scale(X/XP)>: All
Select objects: Pick the object
Command: HIDE
Command: SHADE (not shown)
```

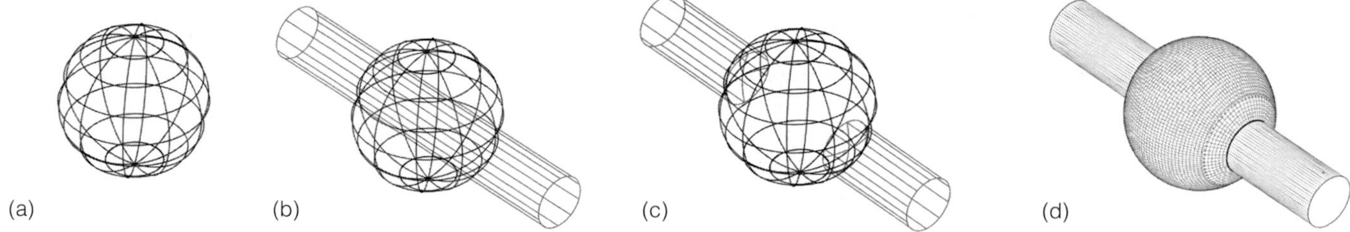

FIGURE 27.37 Union of a Cylinder and a Sphere Using AutoCAD

```
Command: VPOINT
Rotate/<View point> <0,0000, 0.0000,
1.0000>: 1, -1, 1
Command: PAN
Displacement: 0,0
Second point: 5,4
Command: ISOLINES
New value for Isolines <4>: 10
Command: SPHERE
Center of sphere <0,0,0>: Press Enter
Diameter/<Radius> of sphere: 2
Command: COLOR
New entity color <BYLAYER>: Blue
Command: UCS
Origin/ZAxis/3point/Object/View/X/Y/
Z/Prev/Restore/Save/Del/?/<World>: Y
Rotation angle about Y axis <0>: 90
Command: CYLINDER
Elliptical/<Center point><0,0,0>: 0,0,-5
Diameter/<Radius>: .75
Center of other end/<Height>: 10
Command: UNION
Select objects: Pick the sphere and the cylinder
Command: ZOOM
All/Center/Dynamic/Extents/Left/
Previous/Vmax/Window/<Scale(X/XP)>: All
Command: HIDE
Command: SHADE (not shown)
```

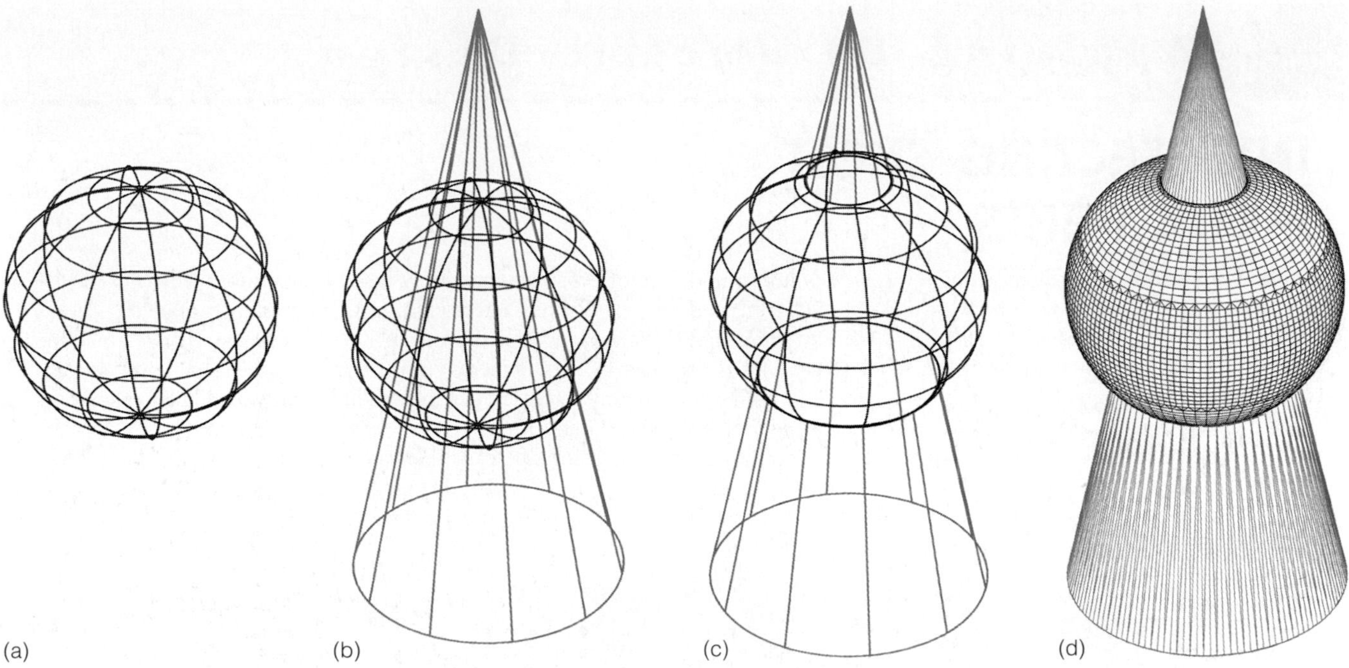

FIGURE 27.38 Union of a Cone and a Sphere Using AutoCAD

```
Command: VPOINT
Rotate/<View point> <0.0000, 0.0000,
1.0000>: 1, -1, 1
Command: PAN
Displacement: 0,0
Second point: 5,4
Command: ISOLINES
New value for Isolines <4>: 10
Command: SPHERE
Center of sphere <0,0,0>: Press Enter
Diameter/<Radius> of sphere: 2
Command: COLOR
New entity color <BYLAYER>: Blue
Command: CONE
Elliptical/<Center point> <0,0,0>: 0,0,-5
Diameter/<Radius>: 2
Apex/<Height>: 10
Command: UNION
Select objects: Pick the sphere and the cone
Command: ZOOM
All/Center/Dynamic/Extents/Left/Previous/
Vmax/Window/<Scale(X=XP)>: All
Command: HIDE
Command: SHADE (not shown)
```

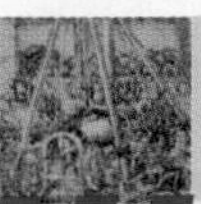

Applying Parametric Design . . .

INTERSECTING SHEET METAL PARTS

Intersections can be created with a variety of modes and commands. The Sheet Metal Mode created the 270° truncated cone in Figure A. The **Slot** command and the **Cut** command were used to remove two portions of the cone (Fig. B). The cut was sketched first to create the slice that was removed from the cone's surface (Fig. C). This is the same as intersecting a prism with a cone. The **Slot** command was used to create the slot with the differing radii (Fig. D). The completed part has two cutouts (intersections) (Fig. E). A flat pattern can be generated automatically from the cone part by unbending (Fig. F). An unbent part design can be used in manufacturing (Fig. G).

The cone's intersections can be modified after the part is completed. The dimensions of the cut are changed per the design requirements (Fig. H), and the slot's size is also modified (Fig. I). The regenerated part shows the new cutouts (Figs. J and K).

A solid part can be created, intersected, and then shelled (hollowed) (Fig. L). The part can be converted into sheet metal

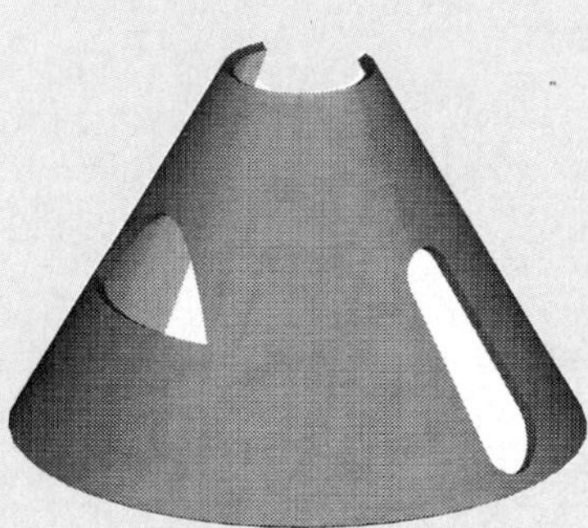

FIGURE A Shaded Image of Cone

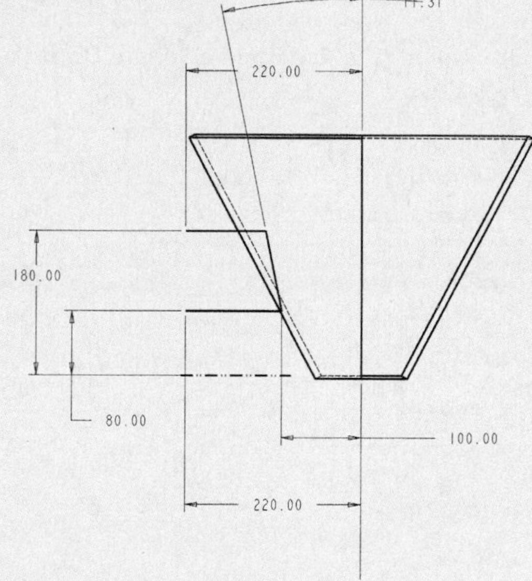

FIGURE C Sketched Section of Cut

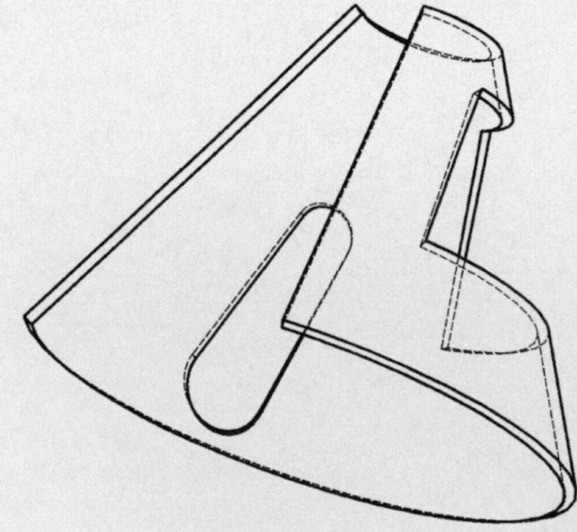

FIGURE B Intersected Cone

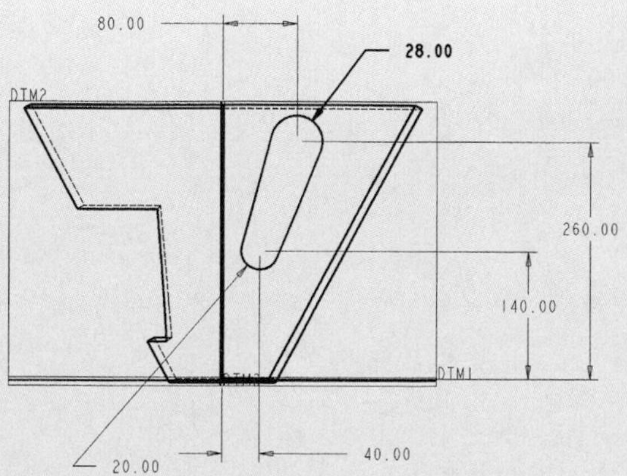

FIGURE D Sketched Section of Slot

FIGURE G Flat Pattern of Cone

after it has been shelled. The following commands create a solid cone from a revolved section (Fig. M). The cone part (Fig. N) will be intersected by a solid protrusion:

Feature---**Create**---**Solid**---**Protrusion**---**Revolve**---**Solid**--- **360**---(pick DTM3)---**Okay**---**Top**---(pick DTM2)---**Sketch**---**Line**--(sketch section and centerline)---(dimension, alignment, modify, and regenerate)---**Done** (see Fig. O)

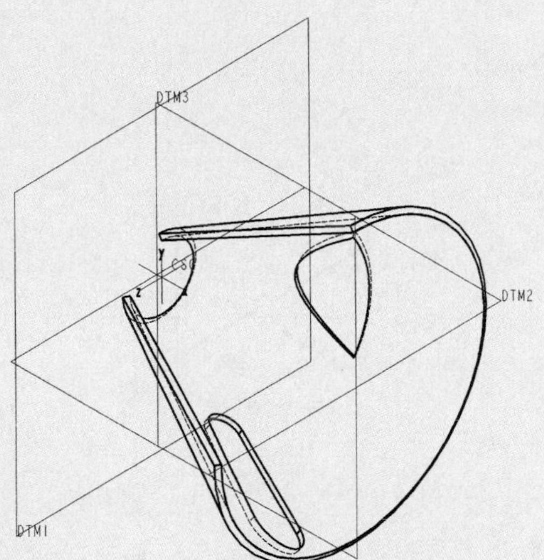

FIGURE E Datum Planes and Cone

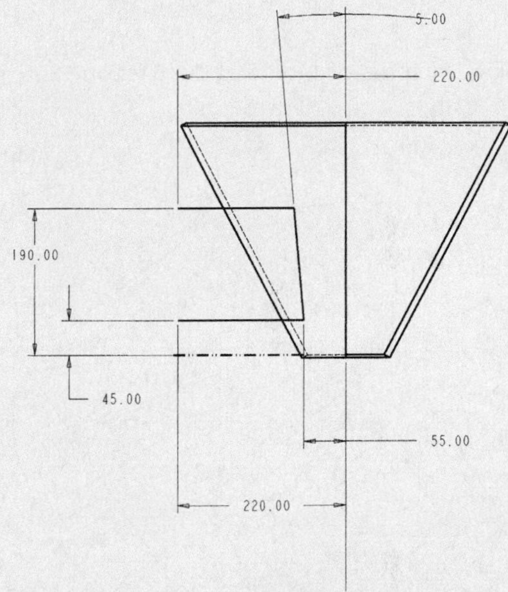

FIGURE H Modified Cut

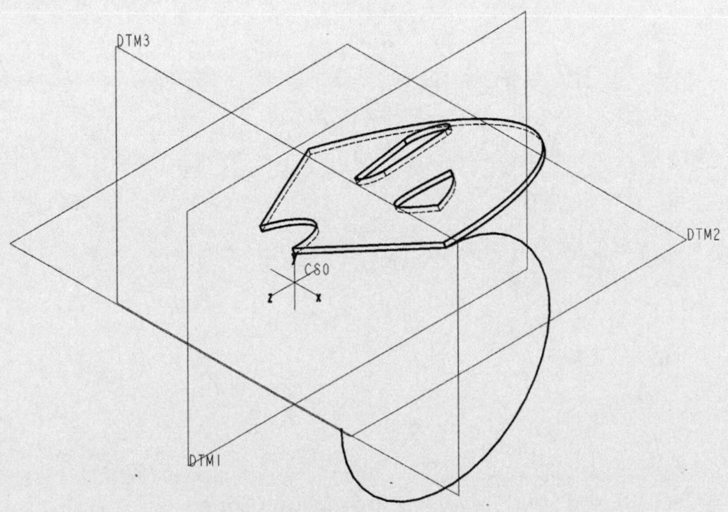

FIGURE F Unbent Cone

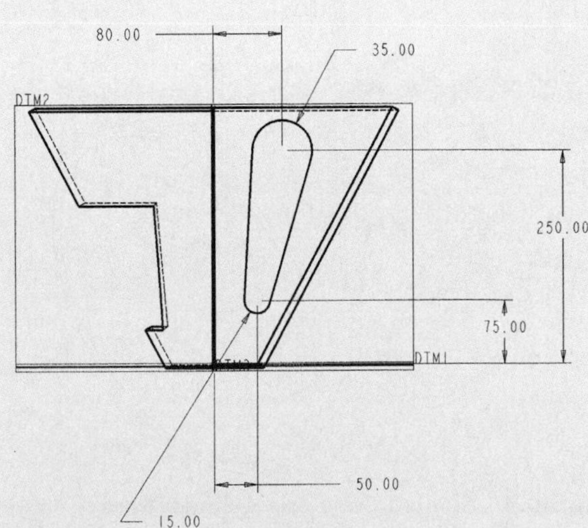

FIGURE I Modified Slot

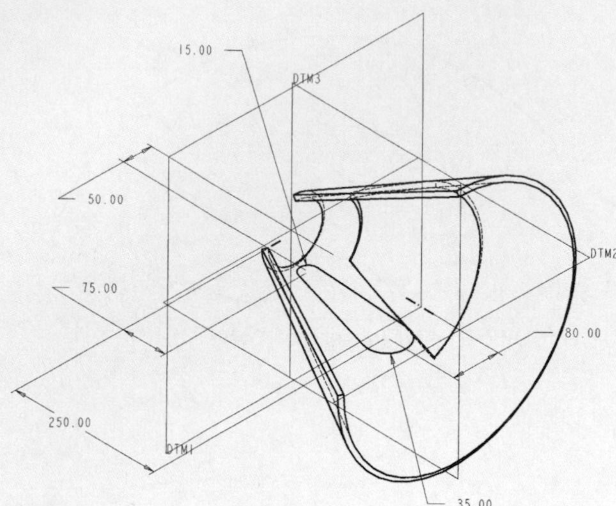

FIGURE J Pictorial of Modified Cut Section Sketch

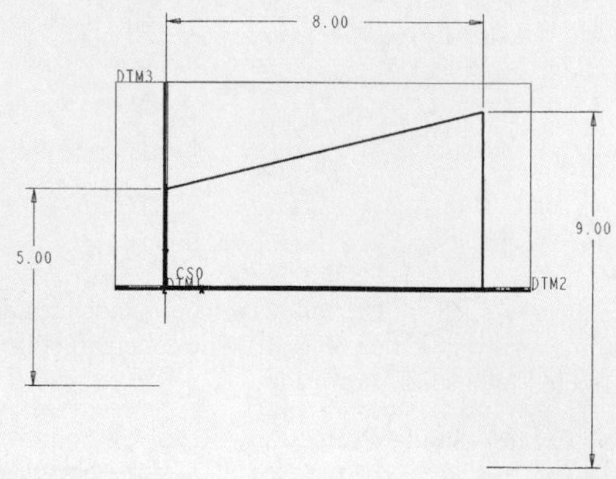

FIGURE M Section Sketch

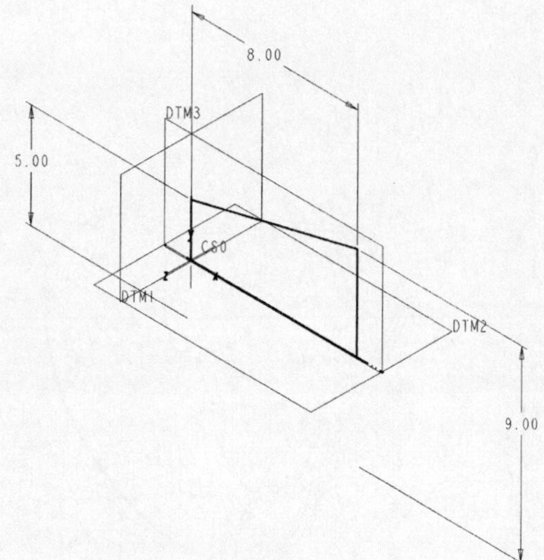

FIGURE N Pictorial of Section Sketch of Revolved Protrusion

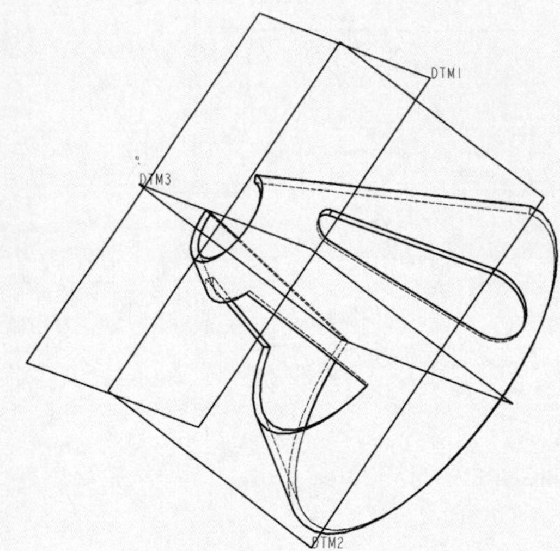

FIGURE K Completed Cone Part

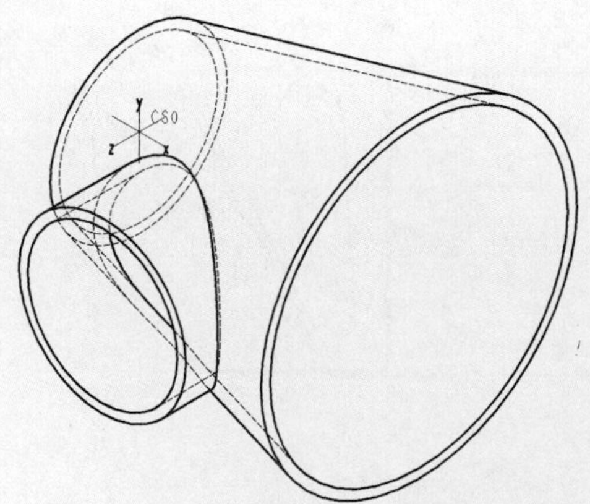

FIGURE L Shelled Cone and Cylinder Part

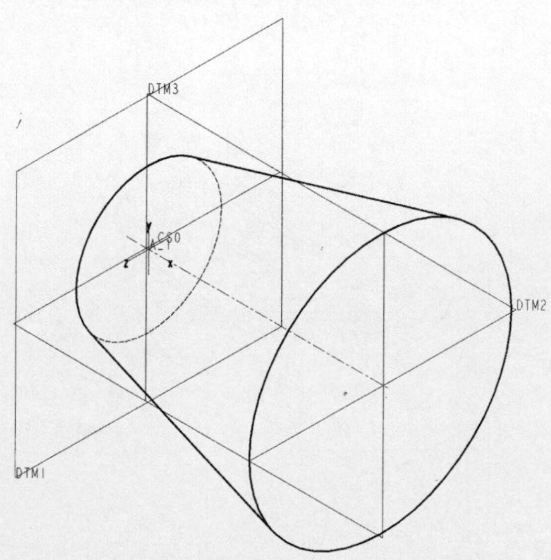

FIGURE O Solid Revolved Protrusion (Cone Base Feature)

Create a datum plane offset from DTM1 to use in the construction of the solid cylindrical protrusion (Fig. P):

Feature---Create---Datum---Plane---Default---Single---Offset---(4.00 from DTM1)

Using DTM4, create the solid protrusion:

Feature---Create---Solid---Protrusion---Extrude---Solid---Single---One Side---Blind---Plane---(pick DTM3)---Okay---Top---(pick DTM2)---(sketch circle with center at intersection of DTM2 and DTM4)---(dimension, alignment, modify, and regenerate)---Done---(enter depth of 5.00)---(see Fig. Q)

The part will now be hollowed out using the **Shell** command (Fig. R).

Feature---Create---Shell---(select all of the circular surfaces)---(enter the thickness of .25)---Done

The completed part (Fig. S) is composed of a truncated cone intersected by a cylinder.

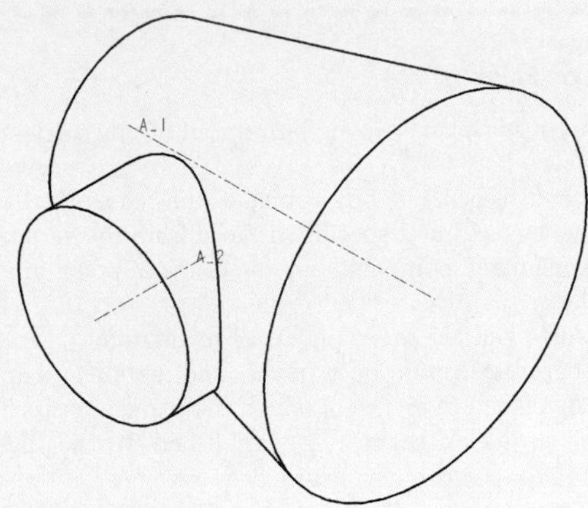

FIGURE Q **Solid Part**

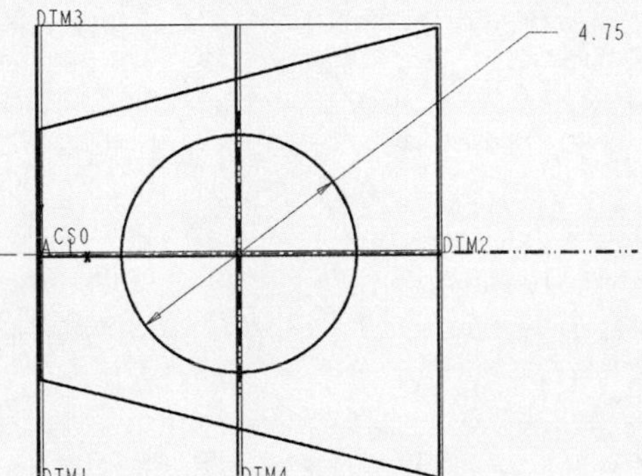

FIGURE P **Sketch of Circular Protrusion**

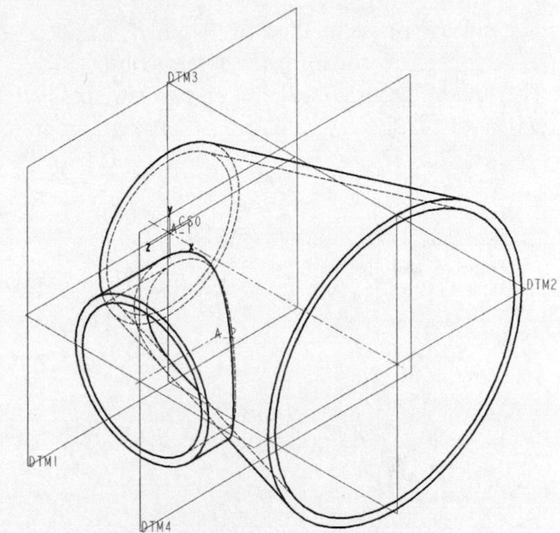

FIGURE R **Shelled Part**

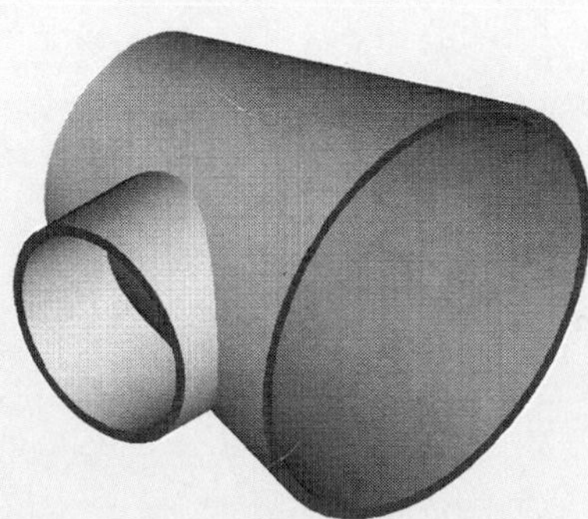

FIGURE S **Shaded Image**

QUIZ

True or False

1. A cutting plane can be introduced at any angle and in any view.
2. A cone is generated by a straight-line element passed through the axis and at a specific distance from the vertex.
3. A piercing point and an intersection point are the same thing.
4. Most cylinders are cylinders of revolution.
5. The intersection of a plane and another shape can be established in a view in which the plane appears as an edge.
6. An isosceles triangle is established by passing a plane through a triangular prism.
7. A plane passed parallel to the adjacent projection plane and not through its center cuts a small circle from a sphere.
8. The intersection of a sphere and a plane results in a circular line of intersection.

Fill in the Blanks

9. The cutting plane method needs only __________ adjacent __________ to solve for the intersection.
10. The line of intersection between two surfaces is defined by a series of __________ __________ representing the __________ of __________.
11. A cylinder is a __________ __________ surface.
12. A sphere is a __________ __________ surface.
13. Passing a plane through a sphere's center results in a __________.
14. A right cone is generated by revolving a __________ about one of its legs.
15. An __________ is the result of a plane cutting all the elements of a cone.
16. A double curved surface contains no __________ __________.

Answer the Following

17. Define *conic section.*
18. Describe the cutting plane method and the edge view method of solving for intersections.
19. Name three specific engineering applications for intersecting shapes.
20. When a plane intersects a circular cylinder at an angle to the cylinder's axis, the resulting intersection makes what type of shape?
21. Explain what is meant by *common line,* or the *line of intersection.*
22. What is a cylinder of revolution?
23. Name the five types of sections resulting from a plane intersecting a cone.
24. What is a sphere, and how is it generated?

EXERCISES

Exercises may be assigned as sketching, instrument, or digitizing CAD projects. Transfer the given information to an "A"-size sheet of .25 in. grid paper. Complete all views, and solve for proper visibility, including centerlines, object lines, and hidden lines. Exercises that are not assigned by the instructor can be sketched in the text to provide practice and to enhance understanding of the preceding instructional material.

After Reading the Chapter Through Section 27.3.2 You May Complete Exercises 27.1 Through 27.4

Exercises 27.1(A) Through (C) Solve for the intersection of the two planes.

Exercise 27.2(A) Use the edge view method to solve for the intersection of the plane and the prism.

Exercise 27.2(B) Determine the intersection between the oblique plane and the oblique prism.

Exercises 27.3(A) Through (C) Using the cutting plane method, determine the intersection between the oblique plane and the right prism.

Exercise 2.4(A) Solve for the intersection of the pyramid and the plane by the edge view method.

Exercise 27.4(B) Determine the intersection of the oblique plane and the pyramid via the cutting plane method.

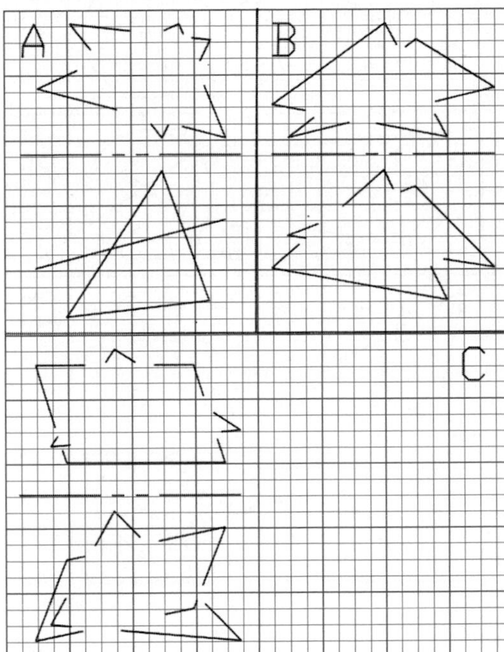

EXERCISE 27.1

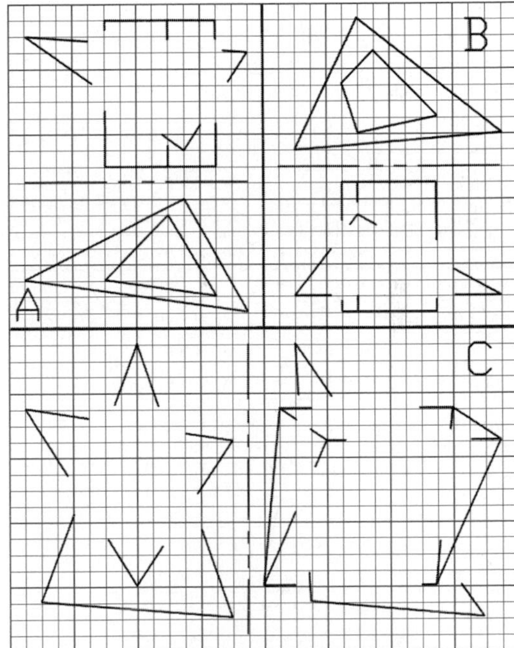

EXERCISE 27.3

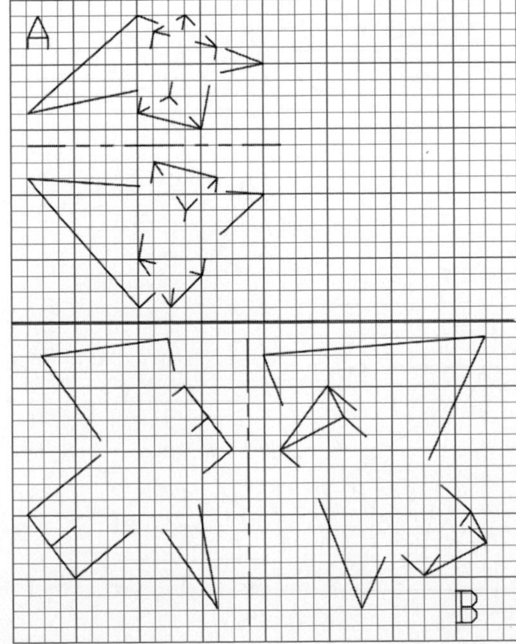

EXERCISE 27.2

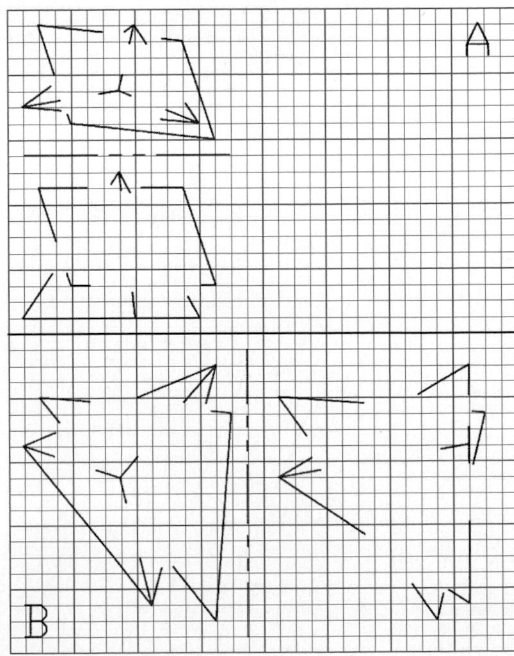

EXERCISE 27.4

After Reading the Chapter Through Section 27.7.1 You May Complete Exercises 27.5 Through 27.8

Exercise 27.5(A) Complete the two views of the intersecting plane and cylinder.

Exercise 27.5(B) Solve for the intersection of the plane and the cone. Use the cutting plane method.

Exercise 27.6 The front view of the right cone is cut by three separate planes. Show the resulting true-shape conic sections and the intersection lines in the horizontal view.

Exercises 27.7(A) and (B) Solve for the intersection of the plane and the sphere.

Exercise 27.7(C) Complete the views, and determine the intersection of the two prisms.

Exercise 27.8(A) Using the edge view method, complete the views and solve for the intersection of the two prisms.

Exercise 27.8(B) Solve for the intersection of the pyramid and the prism. Use the cutting plane method.

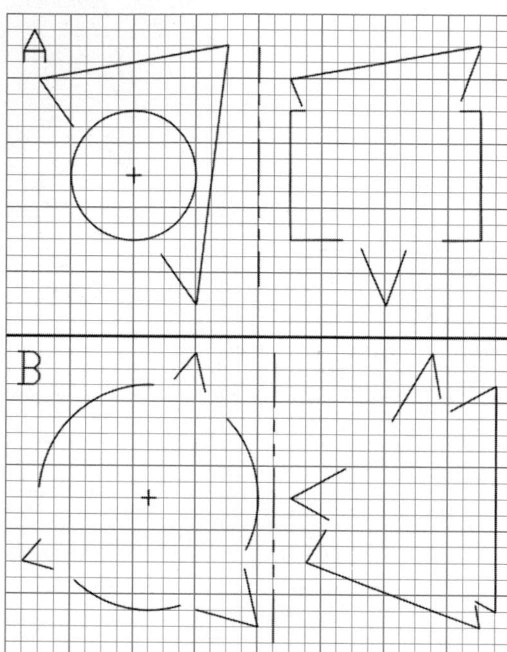

EXERCISE 27.5

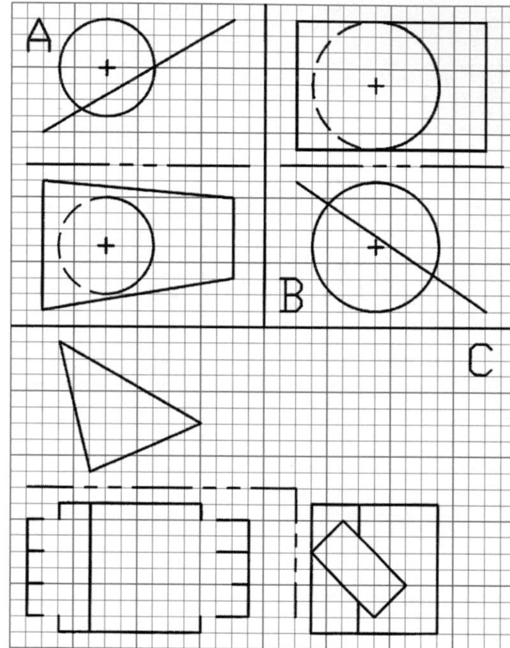

EXERCISE 27.7

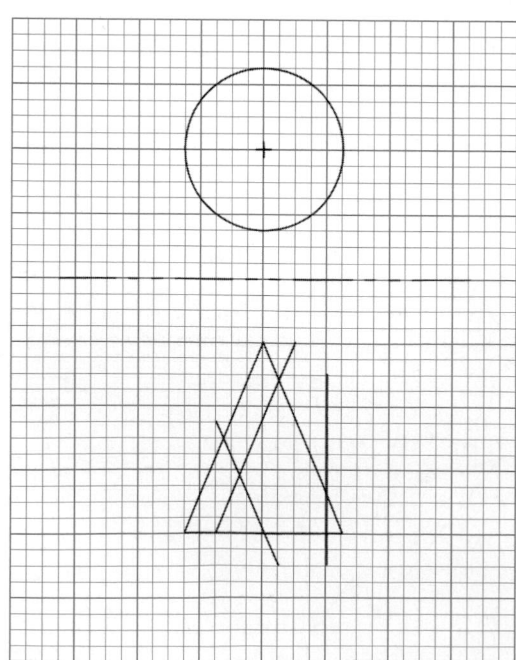
EXERCISE 27.6

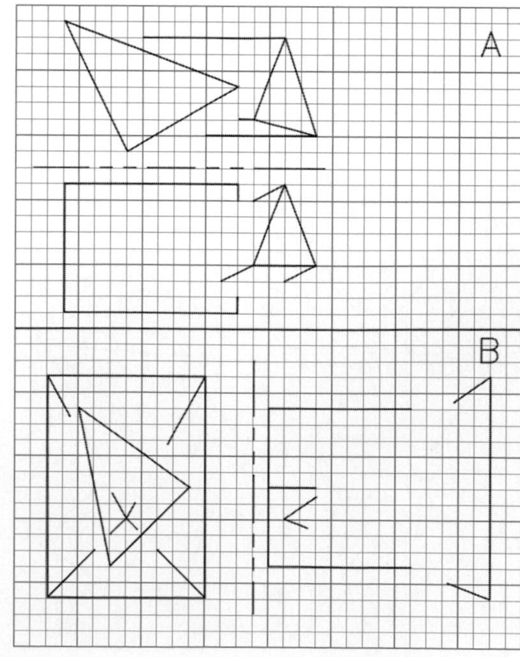

EXERCISE 27.8

After Reading the Chapter Through Section 27.12 You May Complete the Following Exercises

Exercise 27.9 Complete the given views, and solve for the intersection by means of an edge view.

Exercise 27.10(A) Solve for the intersection between the given cylinders.

Exercise 27.10(B) Determine the intersection between the prism and the cylinder.

Exercise 27.11 Complete the three views of the cone intersected by the cylinder.

Exercises 27.12(A) and (B) Complete the views of the intersecting shapes.

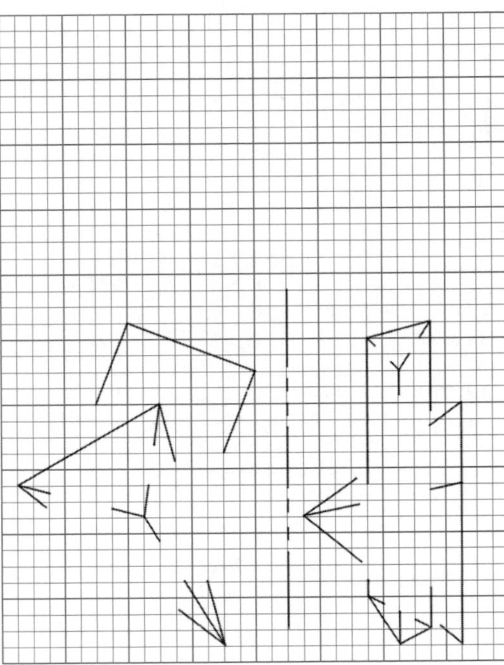

EXERCISE 27.9

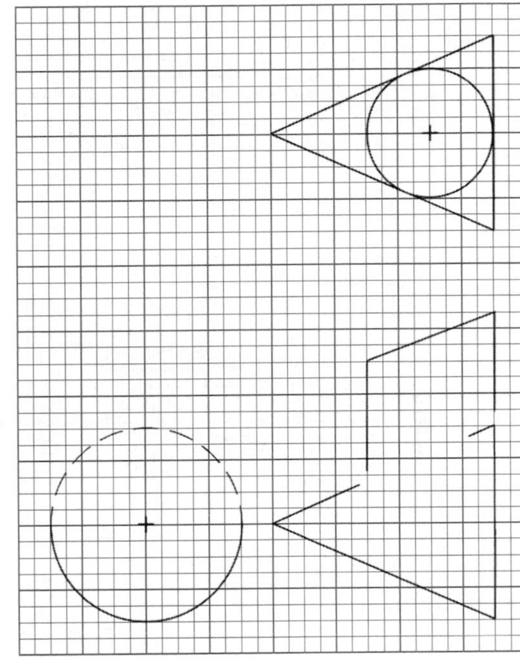

EXERCISE 27.11

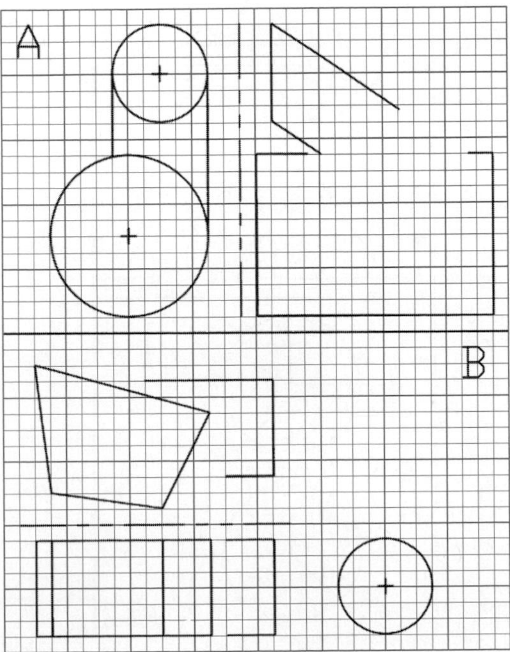

EXERCISE 27.10

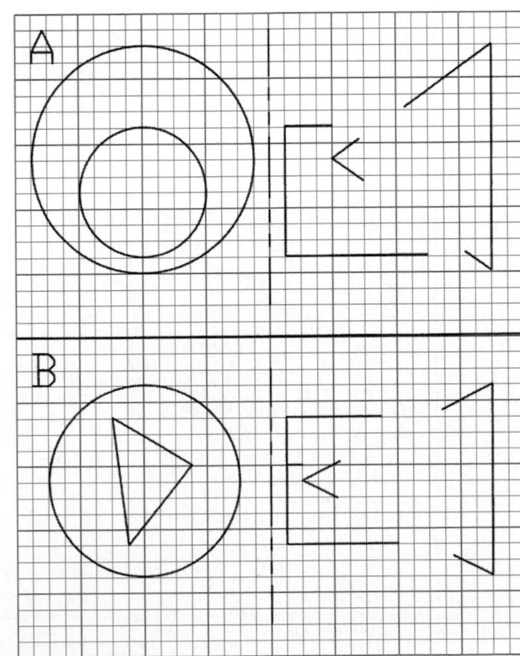

EXERCISE 27.12

PROBLEMS

Problems may be assigned as sketching, instrument, or CAD projects.

Problems 27.1(A) Through (L) Transfer each problem to another sheet. Most problems will fit on an "A"-size drawing format. Complete the views of each intersection project. Add any view needed to complete the project. Use the edge view or the cutting plane method. Instructor may assign some projects for development problems after Chapter 28 is completed. Models of any of the problems can also be assigned.

Example solutions to Problems 27.1(A) and (B) are provided on the following pages.

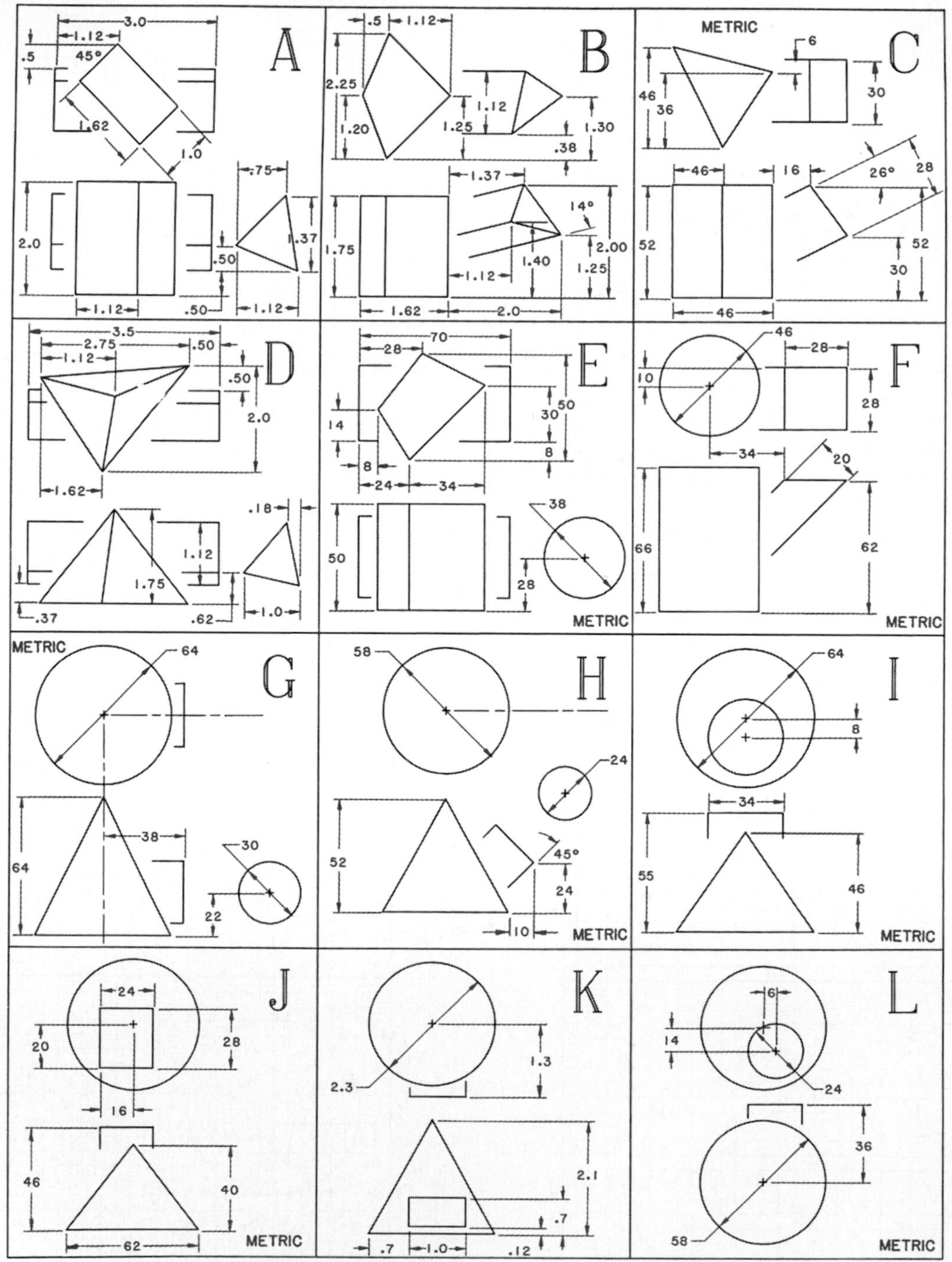

PROBLEMS 27.1(A) THROUGH 27.1(L) Intersection Problems

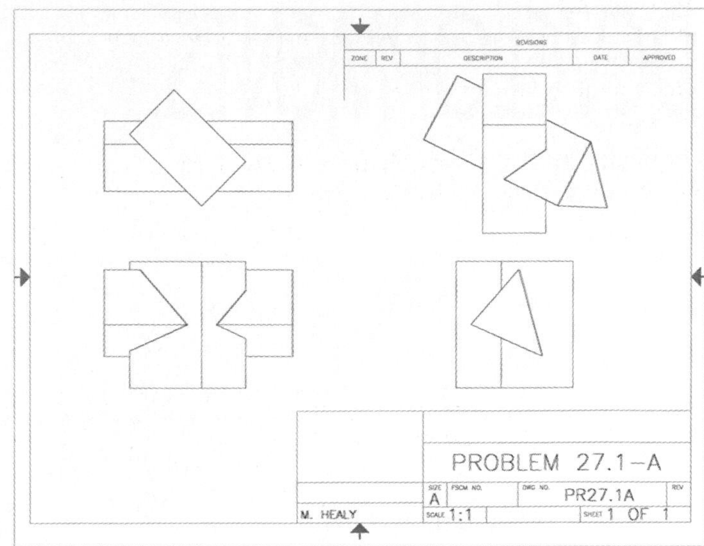

PROBLEM 27.1 Example Solution for Problem 27.1(A)

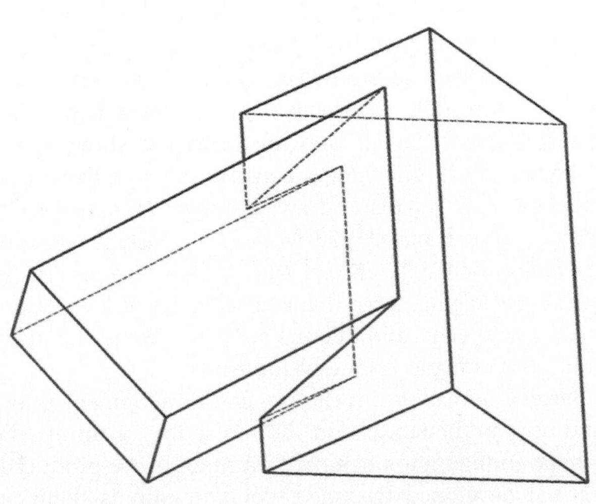

PROBLEM 27.1 Example Solution for Problem 27.1(B)

DEVELOPMENTS

Chapter 28

LEARNING OBJECTIVES

Upon completion of this chapter you will be able to:

1. Appreciate the significance of development and pattern drawings in the manufacturing and packaging industries.
2. Identify and define basic development classifications.
3. Become familiar with models, flat pattern developments, and joining techniques.
4. Become proficient in producing developments for prisms, pyramids, cylinders, cones, and their intersections.
5. Render true-length diagrams in order to develop surfaces with numerous edges.
6. Demonstrate knowledge of transition pieces and triangulation techniques.
7. Produce developments of spheres by the zone and gore methods.
8. Use CAD to create 2D and 3D models for developments.
9. Understand how to use automated unfold programs on 3D systems.

28.1 INTRODUCTION

Various industrial structures, products, packaging, and manufactured parts are made from flat sheet stock material. Electronic component **packaging** is one of the most common areas of engineering and design that utilizes sheet metal developments. The electronic product in Figure 28.1(a) consists of a circuit board, electronic components, cabling-wiring, and packaging employing sheet metal. The electronics were designed by means of an advanced CAD/CAM program called Pro/ECAD (Pro/ENGINEER's optional electronic component software); the sheet metal package was designed with Pro/SHEETMETAL. The assembly of the components and the package was completed with Pro/ASSEMBLY. The sheet metal package is created in its folded state and then unfolded to detail the flat pattern. A CAM program then sets up and manufactures the sheet metal forms.

The turbine in Figure 28.2(a) is an example of a complex industrial application that incorporates a sheet metal development into its design. The air intake housing was created from a sheet of metal by means of a pattern. The sheet metal enclosure for the bake-out oven in Figure 28.2(b) is composed of interlocking and welded sheet metal parts.

Parts designed to be produced from flat materials are cut from a pattern that is drawn as a **development**. The complete unfolded layout drawing of a part showing the total surface area in one view is constructed from *true-length* dimensions. This flat plane drawing shows each surface of the part as *true shape*. All surfaces of the object are connected along their adjacent *bend lines*. Sheet metal objects, cardboard packaging, large-diameter cylindrical vessels and piping, funnels, cans, and ducting are just a few of the many types of objects made from developments.

A **pattern** is made from the original development drawing and used in the fabrication shop to scribe, or set up, the true-shape configuration of a part, plus tabs, to be produced. The actual developed flat sheet configuration is then cut according to its pattern. The final operations include bend-

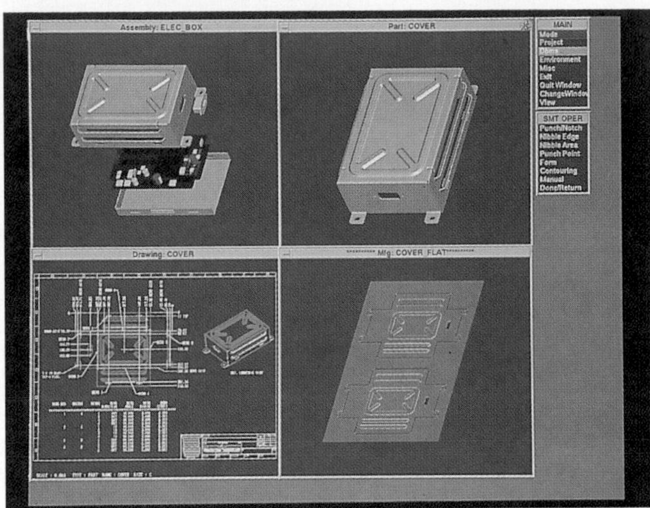

(a) Pro/ECAD used to design an electronic product

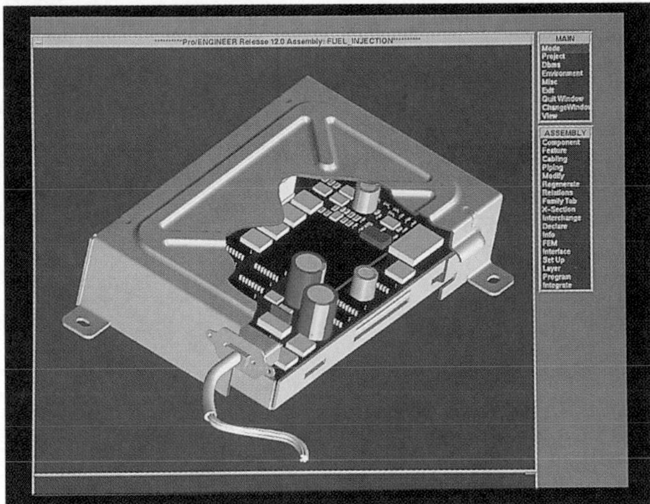

(b) Pro/SHEETMETAL used to package electronic components

FIGURE 28.1 **Electronic Component Assembly Using Sheet Metal Packaging**

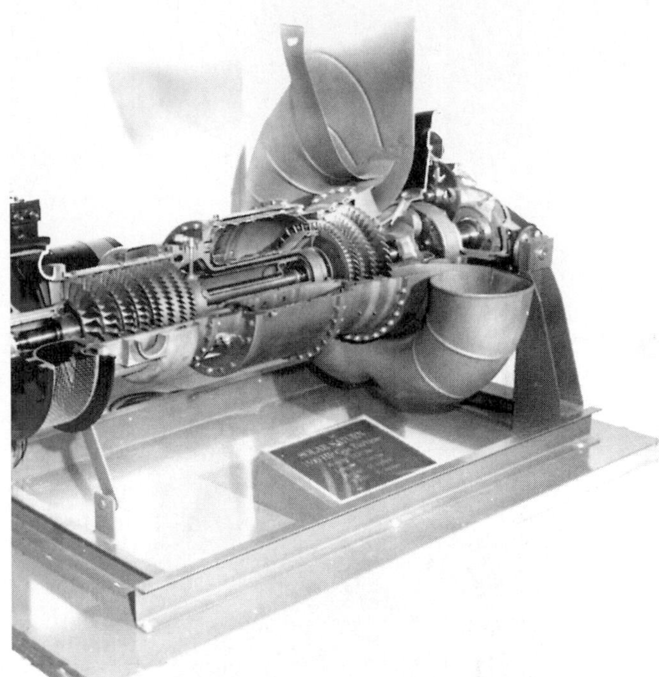

(a) Turbine and sheet metal air intake housing

(b) Bake-out oven with sheet metal enclosure

FIGURE 28.2 **Sheet Metal Application**

ing, folding or rolling, and stretching the part to its required design. Welding, gluing, soldering, bolting, seaming, or riveting can be used to join the piece's seam edge.

28.1.1 Basic Developments

The four most common shapes that can be accurately developed include the **prism**, the **pyramid**, the **cylinder**, and the **cone**, plus their variations (Fig. 28.3). An object is normally developed by unfolding or unrolling its surfaces onto the plane of the paper. The actual drawing of the object consists of showing each successive surface as true shape and connected along common edges. One edge line serves as a **seam** for a shape composed of plane surfaces. The seam, or **break line**, for a curved shape will be along a line/element on its surface.

Each of the parts is developed as an **inside-up** pattern drawing. That is to say, it is unfolded/unrolled so that the inside surface is face up. In some cases a pattern may be required to show an outside-up development. The difference in drawing this variation is shown in the representation of the bend lines.

The prism and the pyramid in Figure 28.3(a) and (b) have been unfolded inside up so that each surface is laid flat and connected along common edges. The first line and the last line of any development represent the same line (edge),

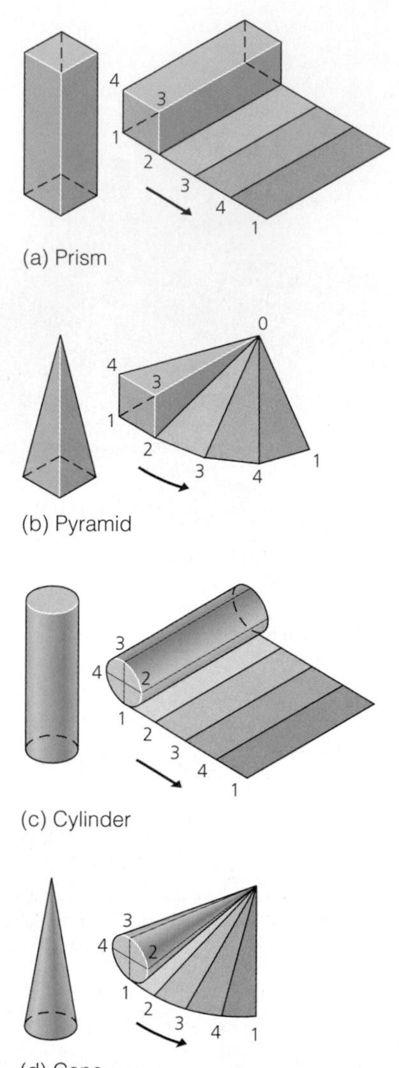

FIGURE 28.3 Basic Developments

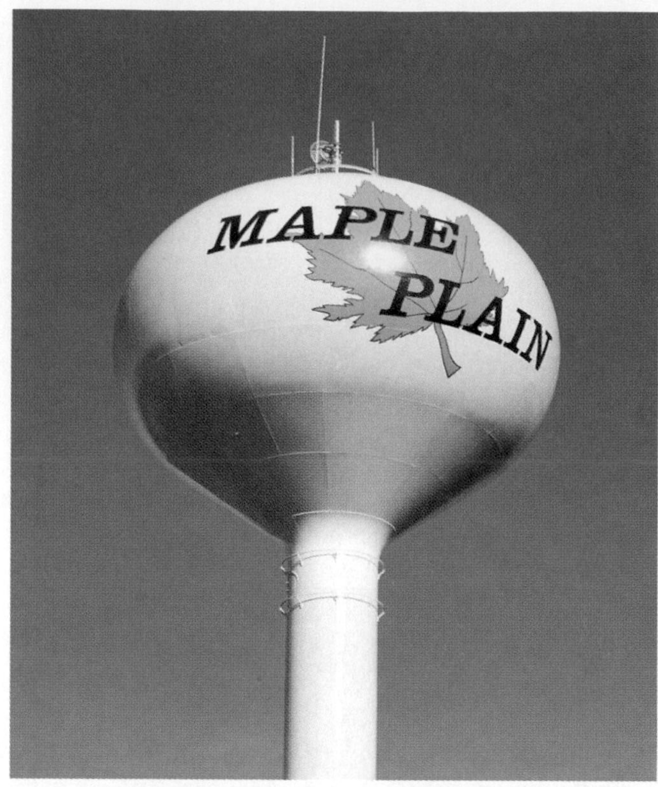

FIGURE 28.4 Ellipsoidal-Shaped Water Tower

because they will be joined together along the seam. A right prism unfolds as a rectangle. The length of the rectangle is equal to the perimeter of the base, and its width is equal to its altitude.

The cylinder and the cone in Figure 28.3(c) and (d) have been unrolled (inside up). A seam edge for these figures is along a specified line or element on their surface. A cylinder unfolds/unrolls as a rectangle, with its length equal to its circumference ($\pi \times$ **diameter**) and its height equal to its altitude. A cone develops as a portion of a circle (*sector*).

The edges of a prism and a pyramid correspond to the bend lines of the development. For a cylinder and a cone, **elements** are established along the surface, and bend lines are not required.

Parts that are composed of flat surfaces, such as prisms [Fig. 28.3(a)] and pyramid shapes, along with single-curved surfaces, such as cylinders and cones, are *developable*. In other words, they can be laid flat and constructed from a single piece of material. Double-curved and warped surfaces, on the other hand, are considered to be *undevelopable*. **Spheres**, **paraboloids**, **ellipsoids**, **oblique helicoids**, and **cylindroids** are examples of undevelopable surfaces. However, these types of surfaces can be developed adequately by *approximate methods*.

28.2 TYPES OF DEVELOPMENTS

There are four types of developments. This classification of developments is based on the shape of the surface and/or the method employed to construct its development.

Parallel line Forms that are composed of parallel straight-line elements or edges: cylinders, prisms.

Radial line Forms whose edges or elements define triangular surface areas: pyramids, cones.

Triangulation Forms whose surfaces must be broken into triangular areas to be developed. Transition pieces are the most common type of development for this category.

Approximate Forms whose surfaces cannot be truly developed, such as warped and double-curved surfaces (spheres). The water tower in Figure 28.4 is an example.

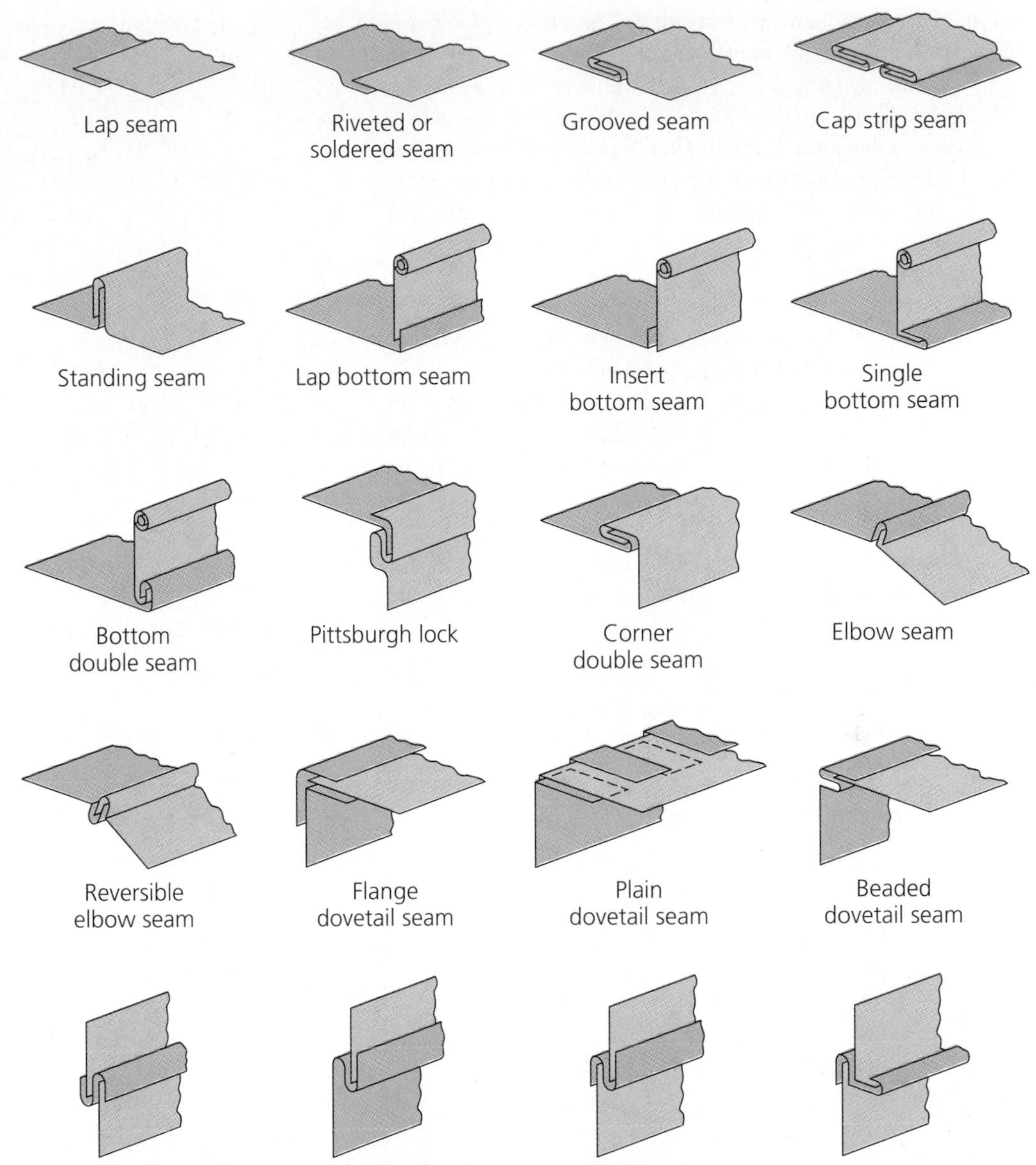

FIGURE 28.5 Standard Types of Seams Used in Sheet Metal Fabrication

28.2.1 Sheet Metal Developments

A variety of complex three-dimensional shapes are fabricated from flat sheet materials. The shape to be formed is subdivided into its simplest elements, which individually have the shapes of prisms, cylinders, cones, pyramids, or spheres. All of these shapes can be formed from a flat sheet of material by first cutting to the proper pattern and then folding or rolling the material into the three-dimensional form. Sheet metal is a typical material for developable products or parts. HVAC ducting, transition pieces, and aircraft and spacecraft bodies are made from sheet metal developments.

The fabricator, working from drawings and specifications, develops pattern drawings of each component to be produced in the fabrication shop. These patterns are usually made to the full size of the object and can only be made after the true lengths of all lines that will lie on the pattern have been determined. Because a pattern is a drawing composed entirely of true-length lines, all patterns are true shape/size. Each development must be drawn accurately so that the final product is of the correct shape within given tolerance limits.

A **bend allowance** is usually added to the pattern drawing to accommodate the space taken by the bending process. A **tab** or **lap** is added to the pattern so that the two adjoining edges that form the seam may be attached. The width of this tab/lap depends on the type of joining process. The length of the lap is normally established along the *shortest edge* so as to limit the amount and length of the seam and the cost of the joining process. Throughout this chapter a bend allowance and a lap have been eliminated from the problems and example illustrations so as not to confuse the beginner. Each development will be a *true development*, that is, one without bend allowances.

Typical seams for sheet metal are shown in Figure 28.5.

Seams can be mechanical or welded. The choice of seam is determined by the thickness and the type of metal, along with the cost of fabrication. Welded and riveted seams are considered *permanent* and are found in applications where the pieces to be joined are thicker and are of heavier-gage metals. Metal thickness is designated by gage number. From .25 in. and above, the thickness is designated by inches or metric sizes. See Appendix C for sheet metal sizes of common-gage metals.

Much of electronics packaging involves the fabrication of sheet metal parts to be used for chassis, panels, mounting plates, and a variety of enclosures and envelopes (Fig. 28.6). Sheet metal parts are typically made from a **blank** of sheet metal. Panels, mounting plates, and other parts are normally flat sheets of metal cut to the functional outline, with the proper slots and holes punched or machined per the design requirements

Sheet metal configurations such as enclosures, chassis, cages, and some cabinets are laid out as developments of the

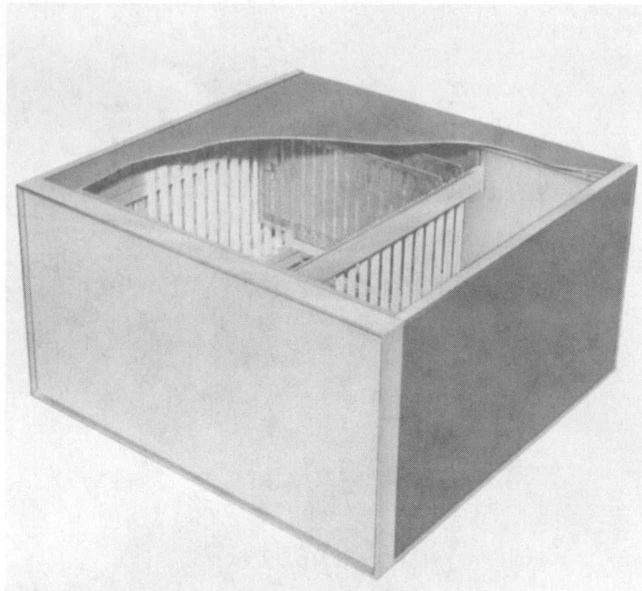

FIGURE 28.6 Sheet Metal Enclosure Used for Electronics Packaging

FIGURE 28.7 Sheet Metal Chassis for Electronic Equipment. This item was developed from a single sheet of metal shown as a pattern in Figure 28.8.

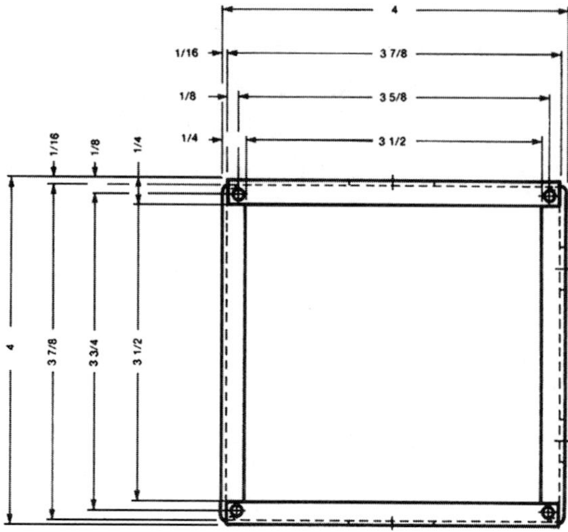

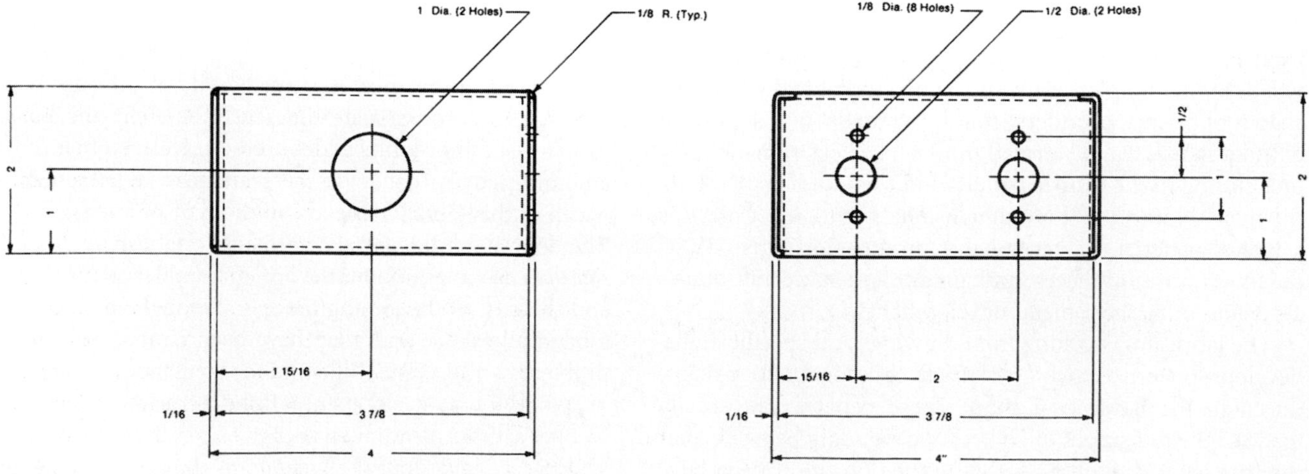

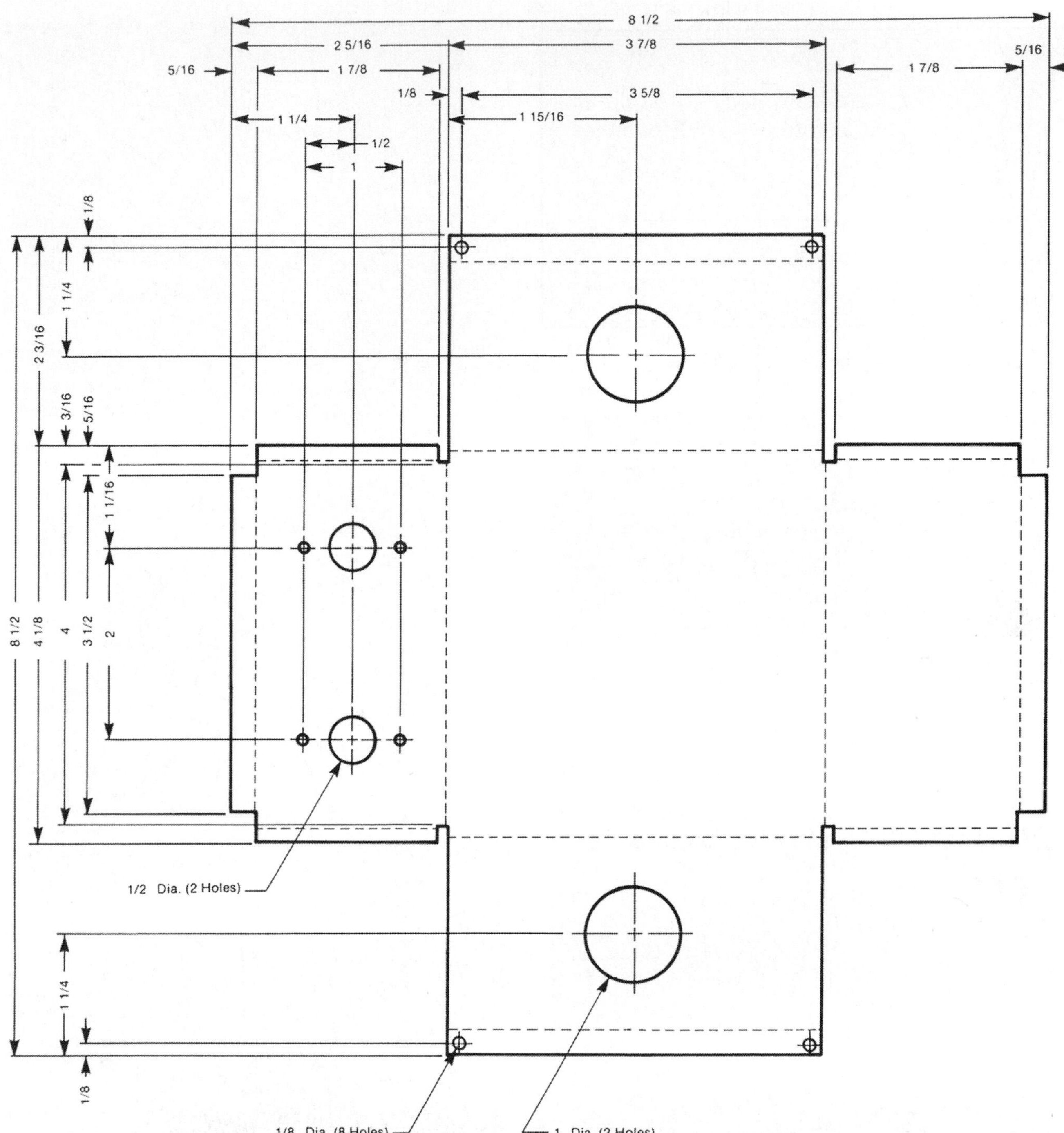

FIGURE 28.8 Pattern Development Used to Fabricate the Enclosure Shown in Figure 28.7

original design. The industrial drawing of the chassis enclosure shown in Figure 28.7 has been developed as an inside-up pattern in Figure 28.8. The dashed lines on the pattern development are bend lines, lines along which the flat sheet metal will be bent.

28.2.2 Automated Flat Pattern Development

CAD software programs are available for flat pattern developments. Flat pattern development on a CAD system improves the speed and accuracy of transferring 3D part models into developed flat patterns. Such programs allow the designer to unfold the planes of the 3D part model on the screen of a graphics workstation.

The series of screen displays in Figure 28.9 was generated on a CAD system. This software package includes dimensioning and programmed manufacturing. Figure 28.9 shows the sheet metal form as a 3D part model during the first stage of unbending (originally a U-shape) (a), as a finished flat pattern pictorial view (b), and as a dimensioned flat pattern shop drawing (c). The resulting flat pattern with hole requirements can be positioned in any orientation on the CRT. The pattern can be copied any number of times by means of a nesting technique. **Nesting** (see Chapter 3)

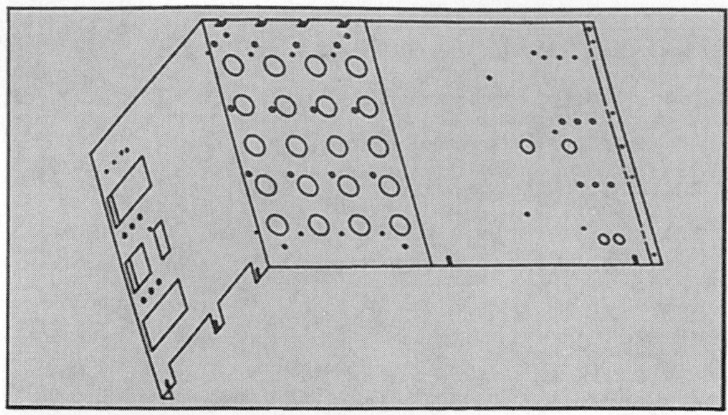

(a) The first stage of unbending is complete

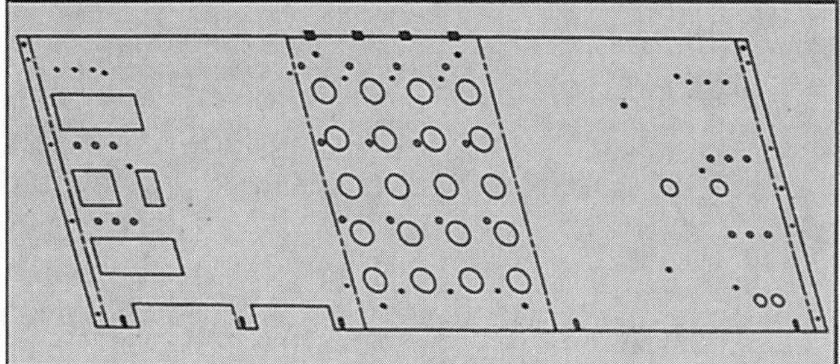

(b) The finished flat pattern can be displayed in an auxiliary view

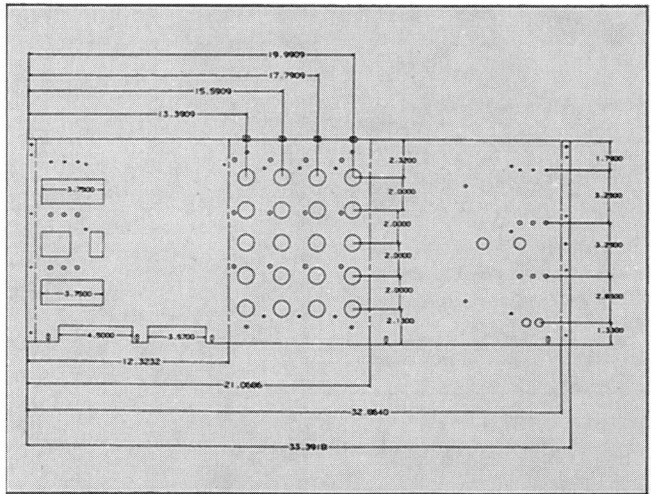

(c) The system automatically dimensions the flat pattern by incorporating the bending data

FIGURE 28.9 CAD Systems Allow the Designer/Drafter to Unfold the Design Automatically

allows the designer to create more parts with the best possible utilization of the sheet metal stock. This is done by repeating a flat pattern on the stock and replicating the punch tool positions. Outlines of any stock size and shape can be graphically represented on the display. This nesting feature minimizes the percentage of excess scrap and reduces material costs. (Chapter 3 covers CAD software used for flat pattern packaging design.)

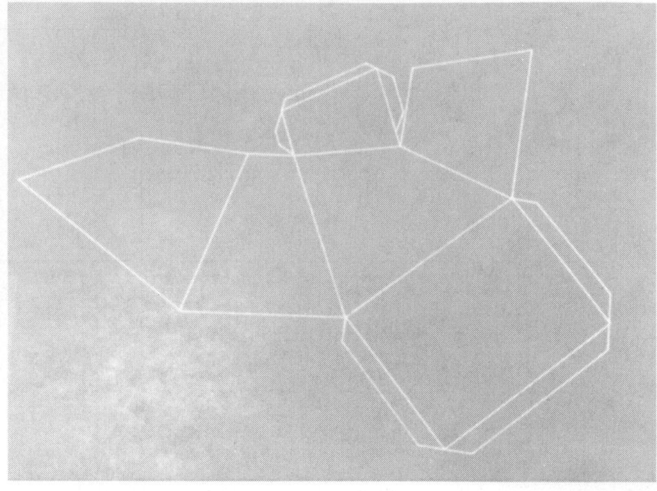

(a) Drawing of cardboard model pattern

(b) Cutout pattern before gluing part

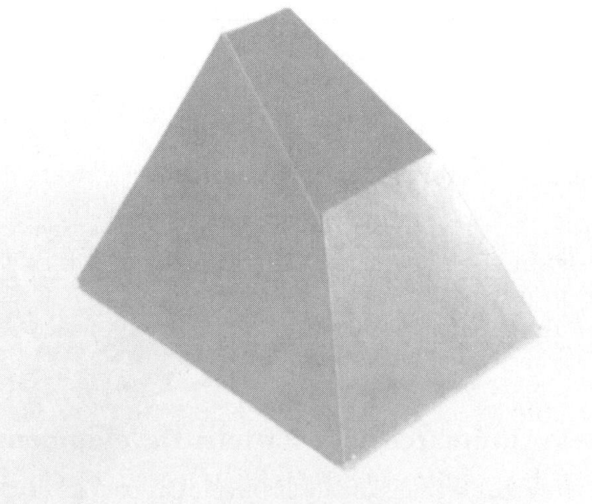

(c) Cardboard model

FIGURE 28.10 Development Model

Focus On . . .

PACKAGING

Most of us don't pay attention to packaging cartons. The cartons merely contain some valuable item and are meant to be thrown away. However, millions of dollars are spent each year to develop new, more attractive, and convenient food containers.

Each carton is designed not only to protect its contents, but to attract the consumer. Fold lines must be symmetrical to produce precise corners, and edge flaps must be cut precisely so the package can be opened and closed. Seals must be applied to keep the product fresh and free from tampering.

Carton design, from cereal boxes to display stand items, requires several sets of drawings. Producing a full-size drawing or template for the manufacturer is the first step. These templates contain cut lines along which the carton is cut or stamped from stock material. Complex curved cuts require a cutting die. Score or fold lines are also on the template. Specification drawings or scale drawings provide precise dimensions, material type, and finish. These drawings must be accurate to $\frac{1}{32}$ in. The manufacturer makes a full-size model of the carton for changes before it goes to production.

Companies such as Procter & Gamble, Pillsbury, and General Mills continually research and develop new ways to package products. Consider the importance of these developments to the packaging industry and how the package was produced the next time you open one of these attractive, disposable food containers. Regardless of how much attention we do or do not pay to packaging, many companies will continue to spend millions convincing us to pick a particular package.

Unfolded cereal box.

28.2.3 Development of Models

Though a pattern is normally drawn full size, a reduced **scale model** may also be made by the designer to check the design. Small-scale, accurate models are constructed for design analysis and to explain design variations to the fabricator or purchaser.

Models can be constructed for any of the problems in this chapter. The pattern is needed before a development and model is constructed [Fig. 28.10(a)]. The pattern is cut out [Fig. 28.10(b)] and the model completed as in Figure 28.10(c). Lightweight cardboard, such as file folder material, works well for making small models. The pattern outline and bend lines are easily transferred onto it, and it folds well, making sharp corners. Note in Figure 28.10(a) that tabs were added along seam edges so as to be able to join the form by gluing or taping. The pattern is transferred onto the cardboard from a carefully executed projection by small pin pricks at controlling points (endpoints of edge/bend lines) or by the use of carbon paper. The pattern is then transferred onto the cardboard and the outline cut. The resulting cardboard pattern is then folded along bend lines and joined along the tabs [Fig. 28.10(c)].

28.2.4 Development of a Truncated Right Prism

The first step in drawing a **parallel-line development** is to find the true length of each edge line and the width of each face plane. A **right section view** shows the perimeter of the object. *The length of the development is equal to the perimeter of the prism as measured in the right section view.* A right section view is always taken perpendicular to the true-length edge lines of a prism or the axis line of a cylinder (end view). The distance between each edge line/element is measured where they appear as points on the right section. The width of each lateral surface is equal to the distance between points on the right section and is transferred directly to the stretch-out line.

In Figure 28.11, the distance between points 1 and 2 in the right section view is transferred to the stretch-out line to establish the width of the first plane face. A **stretch-out line**

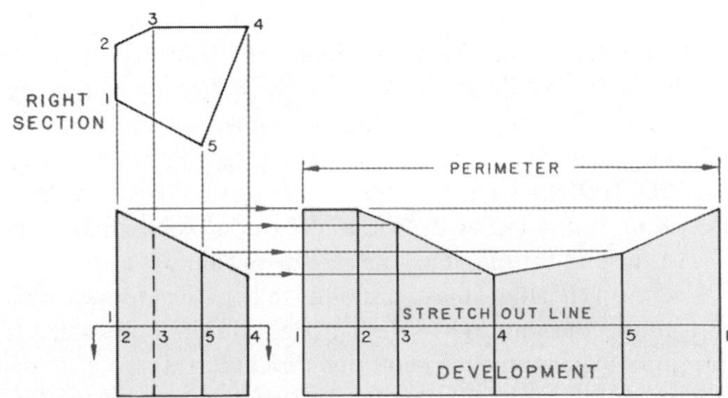

FIGURE 28.11 Development of a Truncated Right Prism

is a construction line along which all perimeter dimensions are laid off. The prism is unfolded clockwise, using the shortest edge as the seam when it is required. In Figure 28.11, edge line 1, not the shortest edge, is the seam line. The stretch-out line is drawn perpendicular to the edge lines as shown. The edge lengths are projected from the frontal view. The outline of the development is then completed by connecting the endpoints of the edge lines. Edge lines in both the front view and the development are true length. Because the development itself is made completely of true-length lines, each lateral surface (plane face) is true shape/size, as is the total development. The length of the development can be checked by measuring the perimeter of the prism (the distance around the right section view). *The development length must equal the perimeter.*

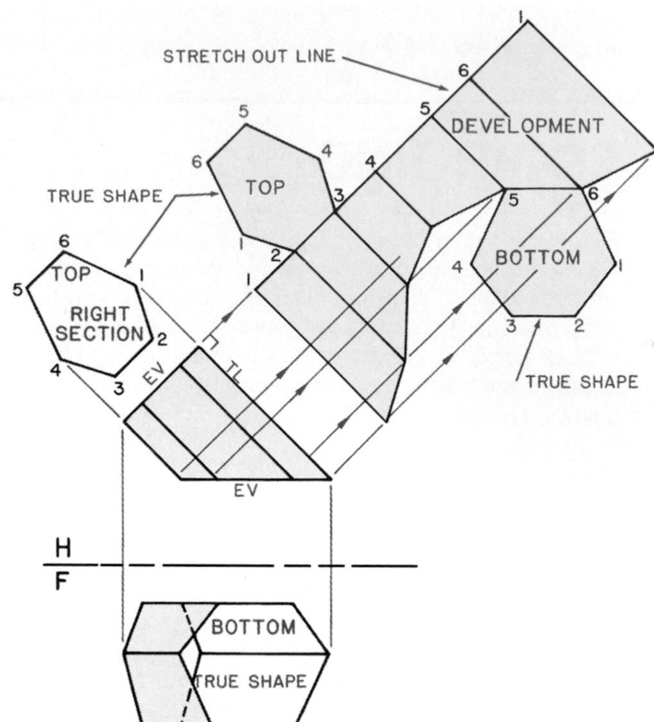

FIGURE 28.12 Prism Development Including End Surfaces

28.2.5 Development of a Prism (Top Face and Lower Base Included)

When one end face of a prism is perpendicular to edge lines, a true-shape end view is a right section. The stretch-out line is projected parallel to the edge view of an end surface, if that surface is perpendicular to the edge lines of the prism. The stretch-out line forms one complete edge of the development outline.

When the lower base and the upper face are required, a view showing these surfaces as true shape must be completed. The true shape of an end surface is established by projecting an auxiliary view perpendicular to the edge view of the base or top face. Each end surface is attached to an appropriate upper or lower border line of the development. A development's stretch-out line can be established at any convenient location on or off the paper. When this procedure is used, distances above and below the stretch-out line are transferred from the true-length view to establish edge line (bend line) lengths on the development. The face widths are, as before, taken from the right section (or true-shape end view).

In Figure 28.12, the development of the prism is required. The bottom surface and the top face are to be included as part of the development. Line 1 is the seam. The following steps were taken to solve the problem.

1. The edge lines of the prism are frontal lines (true length in the frontal view). The prism is laid on its side. Therefore, draw the stretch-out line parallel to the edge view of the top face, as shown. The bottom view is given instead of a top view for this example.
2. Project a true-shape view of the top face (labeled **RIGHT SECTION**).
3. Transfer the face widths from the true-shape/right section view, and set off along the stretch-out line.
4. Project the edge line's endpoints to the development, and connect them to form the outline. The stretch-out line is an edge of the outline on this development.
5. Attach the top face and the bottom base, as shown. The base plane appears as true shape in the bottom view. The upper and lower surfaces can be attached along any related line on the development's outline.

28.2.6 Development of a Right Pyramid

Developments of surfaces that are composed of triangular planes, such as pyramids, or that can be divided into small triangular areas, such as cones, are considered **radial-line developments**. Each lateral edge of a pyramid, or element of a cone, *radiates* from the vertex point.

To develop a pyramid, it is necessary to establish the true length of each of its lateral edges and baselines. The development of a pyramid consists of laying out the true shape of each lateral surface in successive order. If the pyramid is a right pyramid, all of its lateral edges will be of equal length and therefore the true length of only one lateral edge is necessary.

In Figure 28.13, the perimeter of the base is true length in the horizontal (top) view. Revolve an edge line until parallel to the frontal plane to obtain its true length in the frontal view. Use this true-length edge line as the **true-length radius**. To start the development, locate vertex point 0 at a convenient location. Swing an arc from point 0 using the true-length radius. Starting with point 1, lay off the true-length distances transferred from the base edges in the horizontal view. Lines 1-2, 2-3, 3-4, and 4-1 are true length in the top view. Connect each point with vertex point 0, and draw straight-line chords between the points to establish the base perimeter on the development.

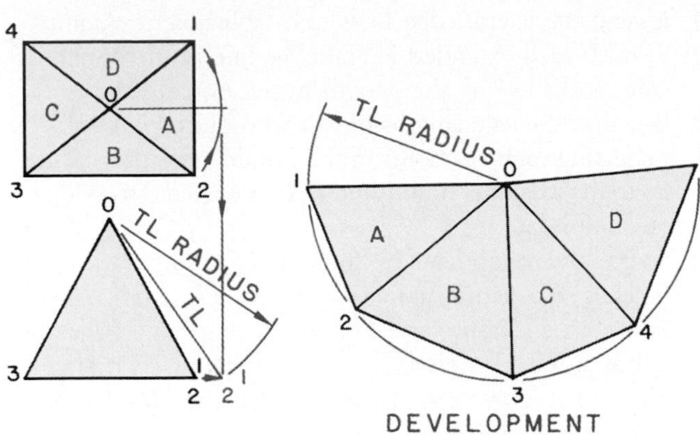

FIGURE 28.13 Development of a Right Pyramid

28.2.7 Development of a Truncated Right Pyramid

Figure 28.14 gives the frontal and horizontal views of a truncated right pyramid. A development, including its upper face (truncated surface), is required. The following steps were used in the solution.

1. Draw the F/A folding line parallel to the edge view of the truncated face, and complete auxiliary view A. The upper/top face is true shape here.
2. Establish the true length of edge line 0-1 by revolution. The true length of 0-1 is equal to all other edge lines and is used as the TL radius.
3. Solve for the true length of the distances from vertex point 0 to where each edge line has been cut. Points 1^1, 2^1, 3^1, 4^1, etc., represent the points at which the lateral edge lines have been cut. True-length distances 0-1^1, 0-2^1, 0-3^1, etc., are used to establish the upper outline of the development.
4. Locate vertex point 0 at a convenient location. Swing the TL radius (radius 0-1) an indefinite length.
5. Line 1-1^1 is the shortest edge; therefore, it is used as the seam. Draw line 0-1 on the development and step off the baseline distances along the arc. Distances 1-2, 2-3, 3-4, 4-5, 5-6, 6-7, 7-8, and 8-1 (taken from the horizontal view) are laid off along the arc. All base lengths are equal since the base plane is an octagon; therefore, distance 1-2 is used for the chord lengths.
6. Connect the base points to vertex point 0. Draw these lines as construction lines only. The actual bend lines include the distance from the base points to the cut points.
7. Connect the base points in sequence as straight-line chords to establish the lower outline of the development.
8. Transfer distance 0-1^1 to line 0-1 on the development. Repeat this procedure to locate the cut points on the development. Connect points 1^1, 2^1, 3^1, 4^1, etc., to form the development's upper outline.
9. Attach the true shape of the top surface to the development if along a common line.

28.2.8 Development of an Oblique Pyramid

The development of an oblique pyramid is similar to that of a right pyramid, except that the lateral edges of an oblique pyramid are unequal. Hence, a radius cannot be used to

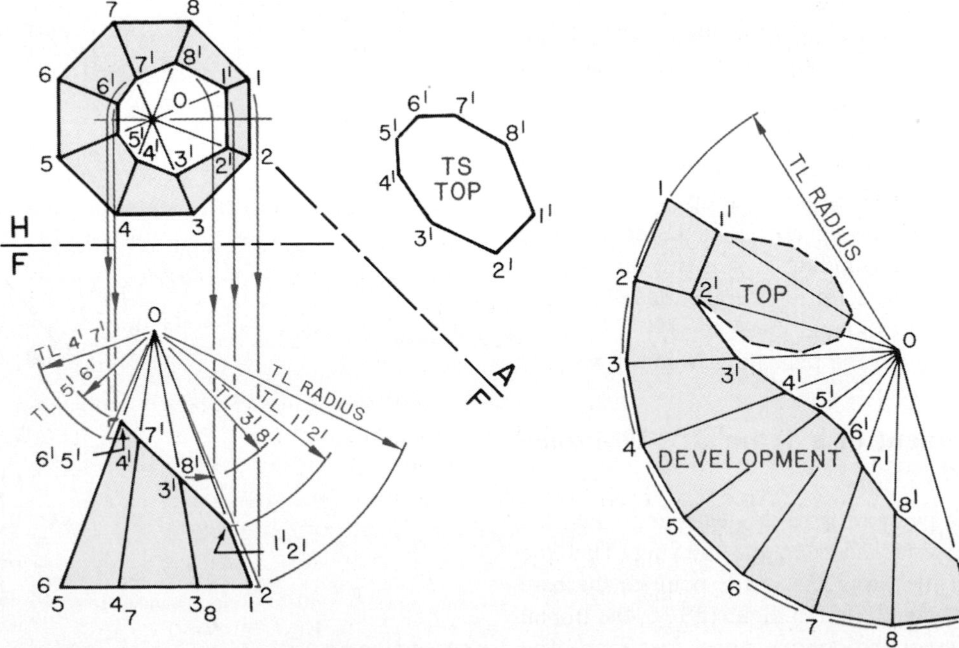

FIGURE 28.14 Development of a Truncated Pyramid

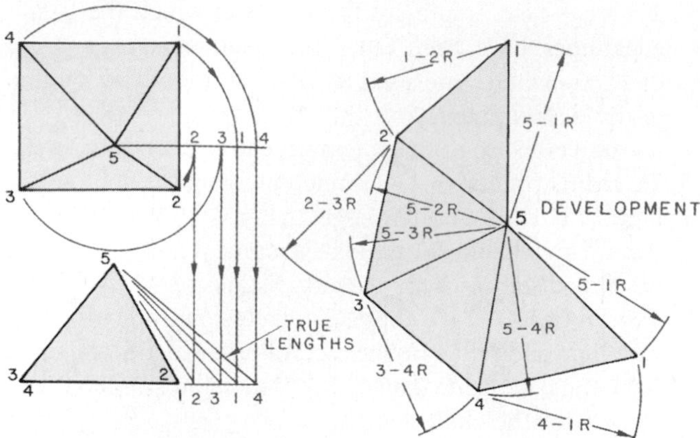

FIGURE 28.15 Development of an Oblique Pyramid

speed the development process. The true length of each lateral edge must be determined separately. Two methods are in common use: the *true-length diagram* and the *revolution method*. In this section the revolution method has been employed.

The base plane normally appears as an edge in the frontal view and parallel to the horizontal plane. When this is the case, the true shape of the base plane shows in the horizontal view. A true-shape view provides the true length of the base's perimeter. The development is constructed by drawing each triangular lateral surface as true shape with common edges joined. In Figure 28.15, the development of the oblique prism is required. The following steps were taken to solve the problem.

1. Revolve each lateral edge line about vertex point 5 in the horizontal view, and show in the frontal view as true-length measurements. On the development, each of these lines serves as a true-length radius.
2. Start the development by swinging radius 5-1R to establish line 5-1. From point 5, swing arc 5-2R. From point 1, swing arc 1-2R (this is the true length of baseline 1-2, taken from the horizontal view) until it intersects arc 5-2R at point 2. The lateral surface bounded by points 5, 1, and 2 is true shape, with its inside up.
3. From vertex point 5, swing arc 5-3R. Using the true length of baseline 2-3 as radius 2-3R, swing an arc until it intersects arc 5-3R at point 3. Lateral surface 5-2-3 is true shape. Line 5-2 is a bend line.
4. Repeat step 3 to lay out the remaining two surfaces.

28.2.9 Development of a Truncated Oblique Pyramid

A truncated oblique pyramid is easily developed when the vertex point can be established on the drawing. The true lengths of the edge lines from the vertex point to the base points must be determined first. In Figure 28.16, the frontal and horizontal views of the oblique prism are given. The following steps were used to develop the part.

1. Extend the lateral edge lines to establish vertex point 0.
2. Revolve each extended lateral edge line in the horizontal view, and show as true length in the frontal view.
3. Establish the true lengths of the bend lines (cut edges) by projecting each cut point in the frontal view, perpendicular to the axis line, until it intersects its related true-length revolution.
4. Start the development by drawing edge line 0-1. Using baseline 1-2 as the radius, swing arc 1-2 from point 1. Swing an arc from vertex point 0 using line 0-2 as the radius, until it intersects arc 1-2 at point 2. Triangular plane 0-1-2 is one panel/face of the development. Complete the remaining triangular faces.
5. Complete the layout by establishing the cut edges to form the upper edge of the development.

You May Complete Exercises 28.1 Through 28.4 at This Time

28.3 CURVED SURFACES

In the preceding sections the developments of geometric forms were straight lines and plane surfaces. The development of forms whose surfaces are curved is also an impor-

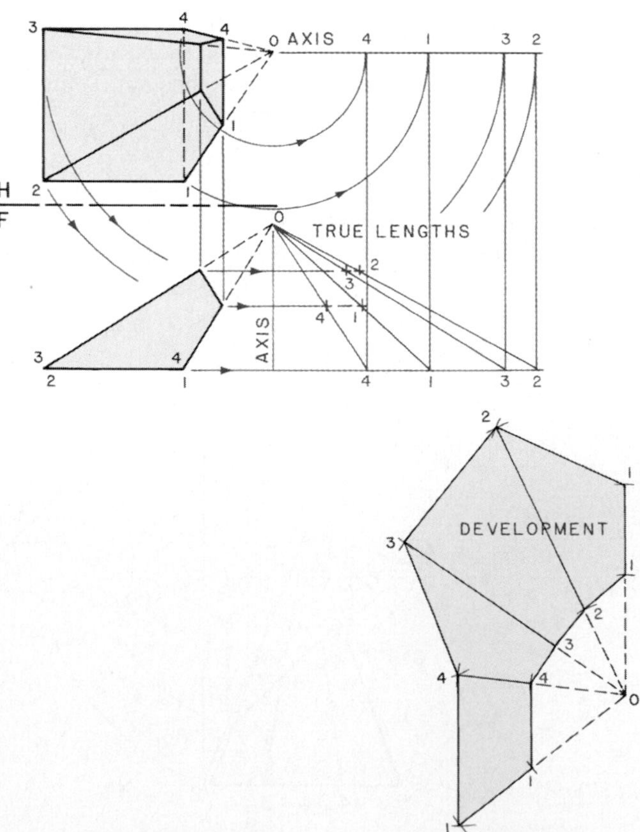

FIGURE 28.16 Development of a Truncated Oblique Pyramid

tant part of engineering design work. **Curved surfaces** fall into two basic categories: single-curved and double-curved.

A **single-curved surface** is a **ruled surface**, since it can be generated by the movement of a straight line. Cylinders, cones, and convolutes are the three types of single-curved surfaces. In Figure 28.4, the base support of the water tower is cylindrical. Single-curved surfaces are the most common and can be accurately developed.

A **double-curved surface** is generated by the movement of a curved line. The sphere, spheroid, torus, paraboloid, and hyperboloid are examples of double-curved surfaces. Double-curved surfaces can be developed only approximately. The water tank in Figure 28.4 is an example of a double-curved surface.

All curved surfaces are generated by the movement of a curved or a straight line. The line that generates a surface is called a **generatrix**. Any one position of the generatrix is an **element** of the surface. The generatrix moves according to the **directrix**, which is a line (or lines) that defines the direction and motion of the generatrix.

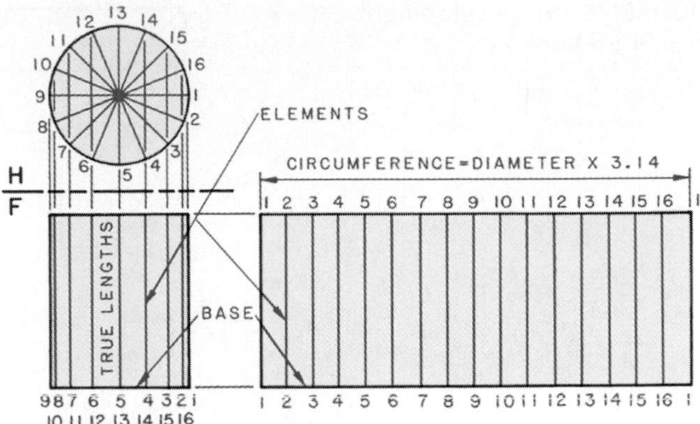

FIGURE 28.17 Development of a Right Cylinder

28.3.1 Development of Single-Curved Surfaces

Cylinders, cones, and convolutes are the three types of **single-curved surfaces**. A single-curved surface is generated by the movement of a straight line so that each of its two closest positions is in the same plane. Any two consecutive positions (elements) are parallel (as in a cylinder) or intersect (as in a cone or a convolute).

A **cylinder** is generated by a straight-line generatrix moving around a curved directrix. The directrix is normally a closed curve (ellipse, circle, etc.). All positions of the generatrix (elements) are parallel to one another. A cylinder develops as a parallel-line development.

A **cone** is generated by the movement of one end of a straight-line element (generatrix) around a curved directrix (normally closed). The other end of the generatrix is fixed at one point: the vertex/apex. The positions of the generatrix establish elements on the surface of the cone. A development of a cone is a *radial-line development,* since each of its elements radiates from the vertex point.

A **convolute** is generated by a straight-line generatrix, which moves in accordance and tangent to a double-curved line (directrix). Two (*never* three) consecutive elements intersect. Aircraft wings and fuselages, piping and ducting transition pieces, and automobile bodies are a few examples of the use of convolutes in industry.

28.3.2 Development of a Right Circular Cylinder

A cylinder is developed by unrolling its surface, normally inside up. A right circular cylinder has a stretch-out line equal to its circumference: diameter × 3.141 (π), as in Figure 28.17. A right section (axis as a point) and a view showing the axis as true length are necessary to develop a cylinder. The edge view/right section determines the shape of the cylinder and provides a view in which elements can be established on its surface. A true-length view of the cylinder's axis shows all elements on its surface as true length. A development is made by rolling the lateral surface of the cylinder onto a plane

In Figure 28.17, the right section of the cylinder is shown in the horizontal view. Elements are established along its surface by dividing the right section view into a number of equal parts. The elements are located by evenly dividing the circumference of the circular section as shown; twelve, sixteen, or twenty-four radial divisions are common. Each division is projected to the true-length view (frontal view) to establish the elements on the lateral surface. The stretch-out line is drawn perpendicular to the true-length view. The base perimeter may be used as the stretch-out line if it is perpendicular to the cylinder's axis, as in the example. The stretch-out line is divided into the same number of equally spaced parts as the right section and labeled accordingly. The true length of each element is projected to the development, from the true-length view, to establish its outline. In Figure 28.17, both bases are perpendicular to the axis and so all elements are the same length and the development unrolls as a rectangle, with its height equaling the altitude of the cylinder and its length equal to the circumference. Cylinders are a single surface; therefore, the elements are drawn as thin construction lines in all views and on the development.

28.3.3 Development of Intersecting Cylinders

Figure 28.18 shows the development of two cylinders intersecting with a 90° **miter bend.** The following steps were taken to solve the problem.

1. Draw a half circle and divide into equal parts. The half section corresponds to the end view (right section) of the cylinder. Label the intersection of the division lines from 1 to 7.

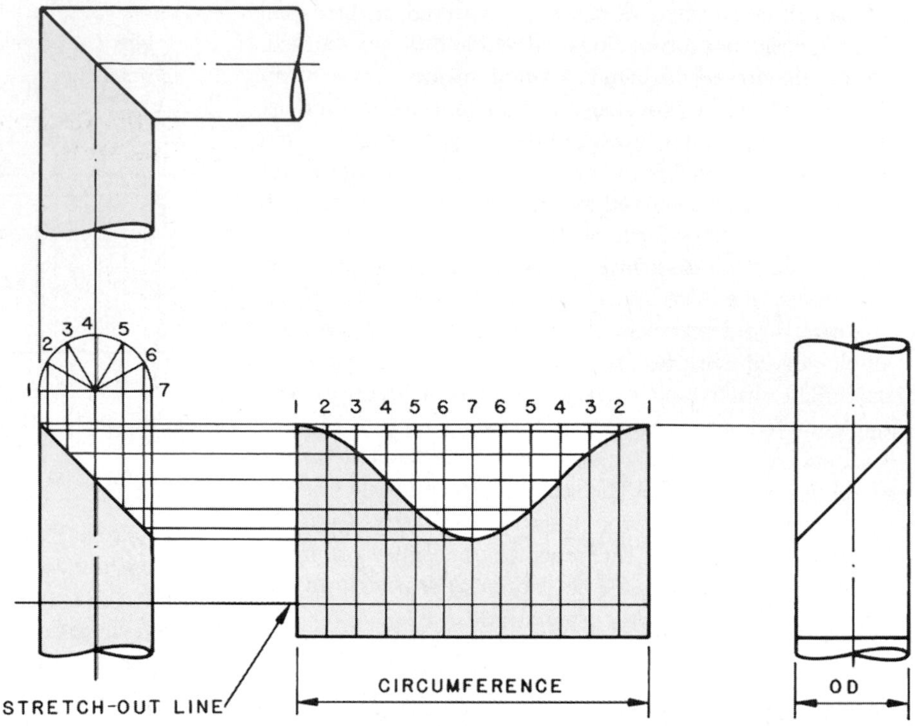

FIGURE 28.18 Development of a 90° Elbow

2. Project points 1 through 7 to the front view, where they intersect the miter line.
3. Extend a stretch-out line perpendicular to the front view of the pipe (axis line), and lay off the length of the development using the calculated circumference (or set off the chord distances, 1-2, 2-3, etc.).
4. Divide the circumference into equal parts (twelve here) along the stretch-out line, and label.
5. Project the height dimension of each element from the front view to the development.
6. Connect points on the development with a smooth curve.
7. The development can now be transferred to a pattern and cut out to serve as a wrap-around template on a pipe or cylinder.

In Figure 28.19 two cylinders of different diameters are intersecting at 90° to form a tee. The following steps were taken to solve the problem.

1. Draw the front and side views of the intersecting pipes (excluding the line of intersection).

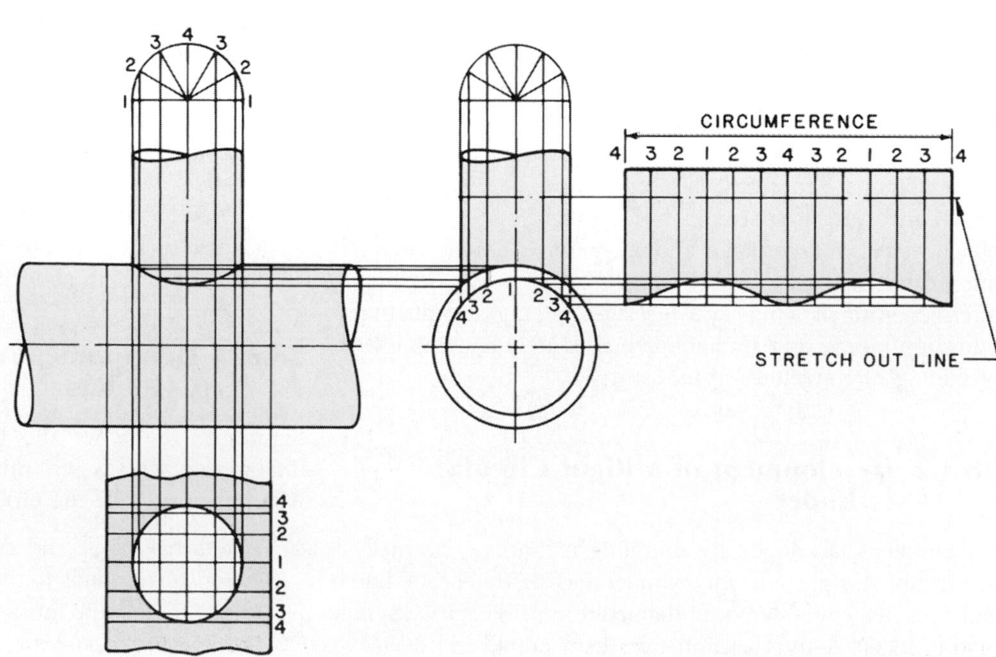

FIGURE 28.19 Development of a 90° Tee with Pipes of Differing Diameters

2. Draw half circles (above each view) corresponding to the branch pipe circumference, and divide it into equal parts.
3. Project the points into the views as shown. Where the points intersect the header (main larger pipe) in the side view, label the intersection points as shown and project to the front view.
4. Project the numbered points from the half circle to the front view. Where they intersect corresponding points extended from the side view, points along the line of intersection are established. If the pipes are the same diameter, the lowest point is established by calculating the distance from the head centerline (2 × pipe wall thickness of the branch pipe). This method is used because the branch will fit inside the hole cut from the header.
5. Calculate the circumference of each pipe, and lay off the length of the developments. Divide the circumferences into twelve equal parts, and establish the element lengths by projecting the points from the front view.

Figure 28.20 describes how to establish a development for two pipes intersecting at something other than 90°. Here the pipes intersect at 45°. The following steps were used in the solution.

1. After drawing the front and side views, construct half-circle end sections and divide into equal parts.
2. Project the end-section divisions (points) to the front view to establish the line of intersection.
3. Draw the stretch-out lines perpendicular to the pipes, and calculate their respective circumferences.

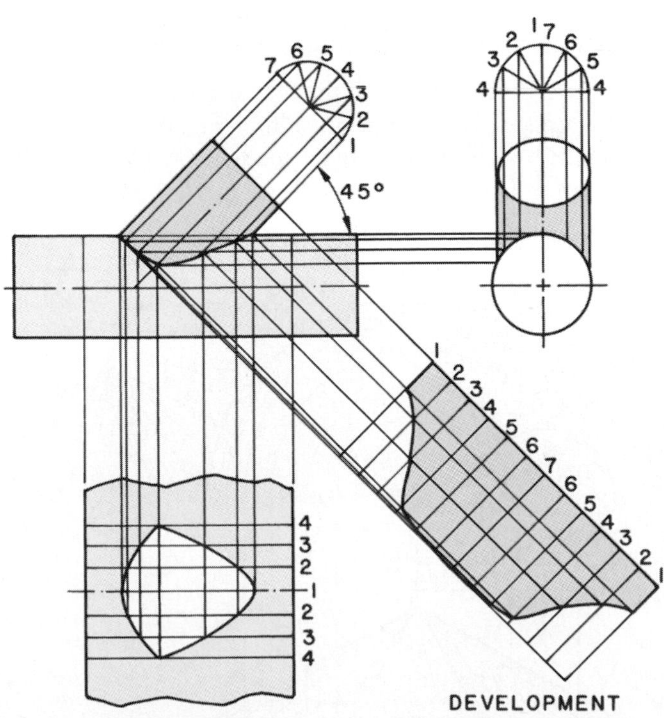

FIGURE 28.20 Pipe Lateral Pattern

4. Divide the circumference length into twelve equal parts, project the related points to the development.
5. Connect the points with a smooth curve.

You May Complete Exercises 28.5 Through 28.8 at This Time

28.3.4 Development of Cones

Cones are found in the design of a variety of industrial products, airplane configurations, storage tanks, ducting and piping transitions, and numerous structural, architectural, and mechanical designs. A **cone** is a single-curved surface generated by the movement of a straight-line generatrix, fixed at one end and intersecting a curved directrix. The fixed point is the vertex, and the directrix is normally a closed curve (usually a circle or ellipse). Each position of the generatrix establishes an element on the surface of the cone. Because all elements of a cone terminate at the vertex point, the development of a cone is a radial-line development. The generatrix of a cone is a straight line.

There are three general types of cones: right circular, oblique, and open. A **right circular cone** is a cone of revolution generated by revolving the generatrix about an axis line with a circle as a directrix and an axis perpendicular to the base plane (directrix plane). An **oblique cone** has an axis that is not perpendicular to its base plane; its directrix is a closed curve. An **open cone** has an open single-curved or double-curved line as a directrix.

28.3.5 Development of a Right Circular Cone

A right circular cone develops as a sector of a circle whose radius equals the **slant height** of the cone and with an arc length equal to the circumference of the cone. The development of a right circular cone involves one of two methods. The *graphical* method involves dividing the base circle of the cone into equal parts. In Figure 28.21 the base circle is radially divided into sixteen equal parts. An element on the cone's surface is drawn at each division. All elements are of

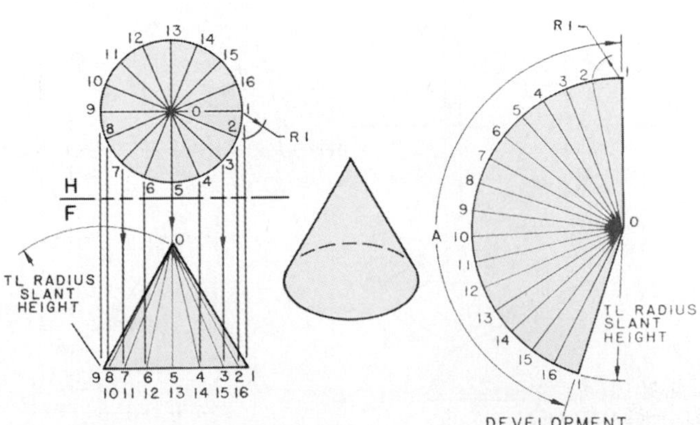

FIGURE 28.21 Development of a Right Circular Cone

the same length. The true length of an element equals the slant height of the cone. For the development, the slant height is used as the TL radius, which is swung an indefinite length. Distances between the base divisions (chord measurements) are stepped off along the development arc, R1. This method produces a development pattern with an arc length (A) slightly smaller than a true development since the chord distance between base divisions is smaller than the arc distance.

When an accurate development of a right circular cone is required, the arc angle (*A*) can be calculated. Angle *A* is the sector angle of the development. The sector angle (angle *A*) equals the radius of the cone's base divided by the slant height, multiplied by 360° [Angle A = (radius of base/slant height) × 360°]. The development is drawn using the computed sector angle to establish the length of the arc of the development.

28.3.6 Development of a Truncated Right Circular Cone

The development of a truncated right circular cone can be established by drawing the sector as in Figure 28.21. The upper outline of the development, corresponding to the truncated surface, is determined by the same general method as for a truncated right pyramid. A right circular cone will have equal elements (Fig. 28.22).

In Figure 28.22, a development of the truncated right circular cone is required. The following steps were taken to solve the problem.

1. Divide the cone's circular base into twelve evenly spaced parts to establish the surface elements and project to the frontal view.
2. Label the elements and the cut points along the elements.
3. All elements are true length; therefore, the cut points (A through G) may be moved perpendicular to the axis until they intersect element 1 or 7 (both of which appear true length in the frontal view). This procedure is simply the revolution of each cut point in the horizontal view and its true-length projection in the frontal view.
4. Using element 0-1 as the slant height, swing an arc from vertex 0 to start the development. Establish the sector of the development by the graphical method, stepping off the cone's base chord distances on the sector's arc, 1-2, 2-3, 3-4, etc.
5. Transfer the true lengths of the upper portions of the elements to their related elements on the development, and connect the cut points to form the upper outline. 0-A is transferred to element 0-1. 0-B is transferred to elements 0-2 and 0-12. 0-C is transferred to elements 0-3 and 0-11.

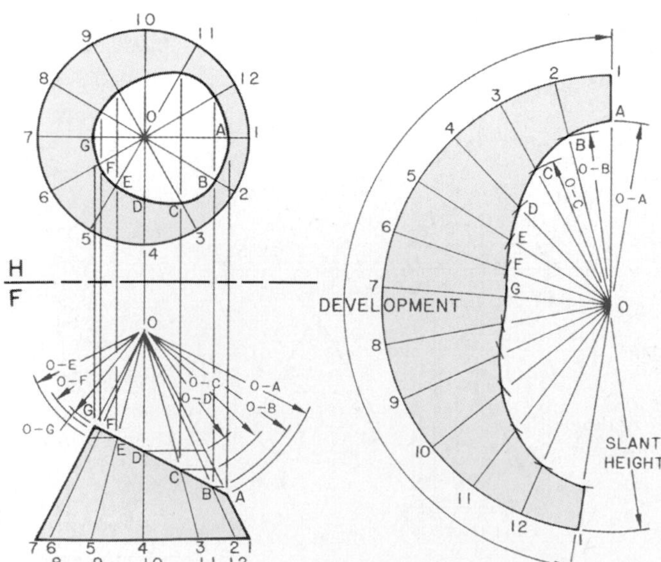

FIGURE 28.22 Development of a Truncated Cone

28.3.7 Development of an Oblique Cone

The development of an oblique cone is similar to the development of an oblique pyramid. Elements are established on the cone's surface by evenly dividing the base curve (Fig. 28.23). Since the cone is oblique, the elements are of different lengths and the development is not a sector of a circle. Two adjacent elements and their corresponding **chordal distances** define a series of triangular planes on the cone's surface. The development of the cone involves laying out each successive triangle with common edges joined. The true length of each element is determined before the development is started. Revolution establishes the true length of the elements

In Figure 28.23, a development of the oblique cone is required. The following steps were used in the solution.

1. Divide the cone's base in the horizontal view into twelve equal parts. Draw elements from vertex 0 to each point on the base. Show the frontal and horizontal views of the elements.

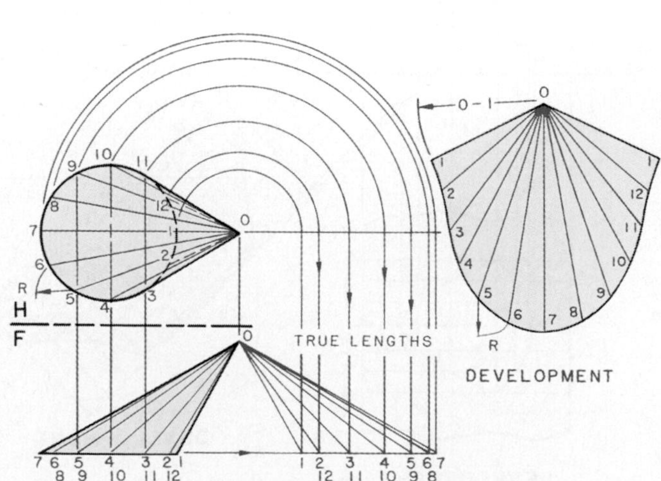

FIGURE 28.23 Development of an Oblique Cone

2. Determine the true length of each element.
3. Use the shortest element as the seam, and draw the development inside up. Start the development by drawing element 0-1.
4. From point 1 on the development, swing an arc (1-2) equal to the chordal distance R. All chords equal R
5. Using the true length of element 0-2, swing an arc from vertex 0 until it intersects arc 1-2 (R) and locates point 2. Triangular plane 1-0-2 is the first of twelve successive planes representing the unrolled surface of the cone. Continue laying out the triangular planes. Connect the endpoints of the elements with a smooth curve to complete the outline of the development.

28.3.8 True-Length Diagrams

To develop a surface composed of numerous edges, a **true-length diagram** (TL) is drawn. Since the true length of each edge is necessary, the revolution method may not be adequate. The revolution method takes more room and requires that the given views be used to revolve the lines. A true-length diagram, however, can be constructed anywhere, on or off the paper. One or more TL diagrams can be employed as required for clarity if the edge lengths are very similar in length or too numerous.

The TL diagram establishes the true length of each edge surface element by creating a right triangle. The height dimension is drawn representing a vertical line dropped from the vertex point to the base plane. The base dimension is measured in the top view (H) as a straight-line distance from the vertex (0) to one of the points on the curve's edge (0-8, 0-9, 0-10, etc.). The **hypotenuse** equals the true length of a corresponding edge line on the TL diagram, and is used to lay out the development (0-1, 0-2, etc.) (Fig. 28.24).

28.3.9 Development of a Conical Offset

A **conical offset** sometimes serves as a transition between two circular pipes of different diameters on different axes. This type of **transition piece** is actually a frustum of an oblique cone. In order for the offset piece to be a frustum, the upper and lower base planes must be parallel. Therefore, the two given pipes are intersected by parallel planes, as shown in Figure 28.24.

Figure 28.24 gives the frontal and horizontal views of the conical offset. Since the offset is symmetrical, only a half development needs to be drawn. The vertex is located by extending the edge lines of the offset until they intersect at vertex 0. Elements are established on the surface of the offset, where it appears as a circle. The elements are drawn from the vertex through each division. The elements are then projected to the frontal view. A true-length diagram is constructed in order to establish the true lengths and the frustum (all points) of each element. Since the lower base of the offset is at an angle to the horizontal plane, the base end of the elements on the true-length diagram will be at different elevations. The height dimensions can be projected from the frontal view.

The true-length chordal distance between divisions on the offset's base cannot be determined in the given views. The lower base is revolved in the frontal view until parallel to the horizontal plane. A true-shape view of the offset base is projected as shown. The true chordal distances, as represented by R, can now be used to lay out the approximate base outline of the development.

Start the development by locating the vertex point and drawing the shortest element 0-1, as shown. The lower leg of each thin triangular plane (representing the surface to be developed) is equal to the base divisions, e.g., 1-2, 2-3, 3-4, etc. Lay out the development using the true lengths from the TL diagram and the base divisions.

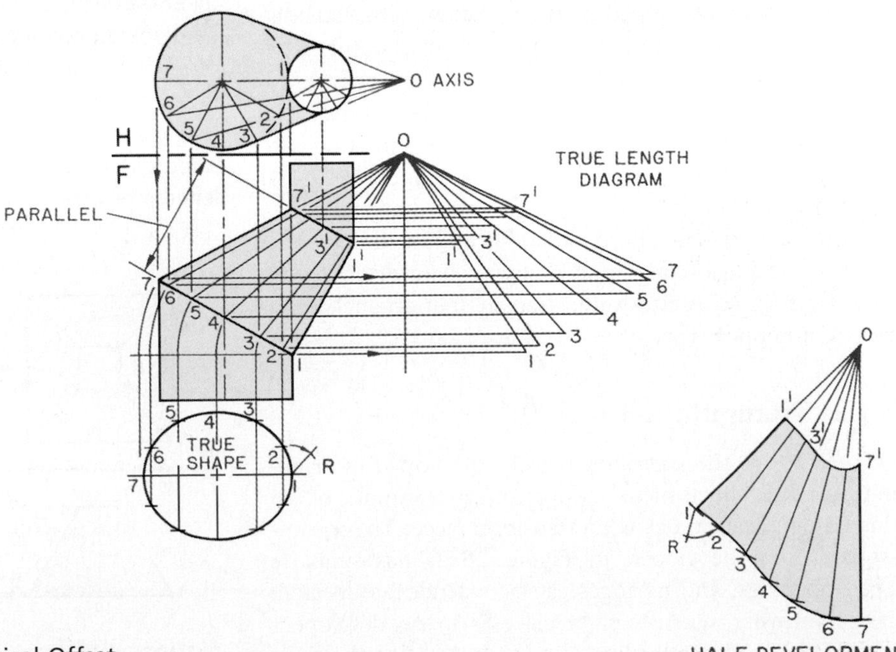

FIGURE 28.24 Development of a Conical Offset

28.4 TRANSITION PIECES

A general definition of a **transition piece** would include all shapes that connect two or more forms of different size. This broad definition would thus include types of developments already covered under cones and pyramids.

Transition pieces are developed by **triangulation**—that is, by dividing the surface of the piece into triangles. Triangulation has already been used to develop a variety of shapes in preceding sections. Elements are drawn on the surface of the form to bedeveloped and connected by diagonals if adjacent elements do not intersect. The development is laid out as a series of joined triangular areas.

Because a transition piece joins two or more geometric forms, each opening of the transition piece will be a different configuration. In general, transition pieces are designed to be formed from sheet metal or other materials and connected along a common seam. Transition pieces join a variety of materials and objects. Pipe shapes and HVAC ducting utilize transition pieces throughout their design. Hoppers, warped funnels, and vessel bottoms of all types have transition pieces integrated into their design. The conical, convolute, or warped surface configuration of an aircraft's forward section is a transition piece between the nose and the fuselage.

In Figure 28.25, eleven possible variations of transition pieces are provided. The possibilities of shapes and sizes are limited only by the designer's imagination and the financial and production feasibilities. Types (a) and (b) are both a symmetrical square-to-round transition, one of the more common variations. Type (c), a rectangle-to-round transition, is developed by the same general method as (a) and (b). Type (d), a square-to-rectangle transition, is composed of plane surfaces and can therefore be accurately developed. Note, this type is really a frustum of a right pyramid. Its given surfaces are developed by triangulation if the vertex is unavailable. The next three examples all involve the connecting of two or more circular or elliptical shapes: Type (e) is a conical offset connecting two separate pipes of differing diameters and axes; type (f) is a WYE fitting, connecting two round pipes to one pipe of a larger diameter; and type (g) is a three-stream transition into a single large-diameter pipe. The remainder are specialized variations of transition pieces: type (h), round to oblong; type (i), two square ducts to one round; type (j), square-to-round transition at an angle; and type (k), a hopper type.

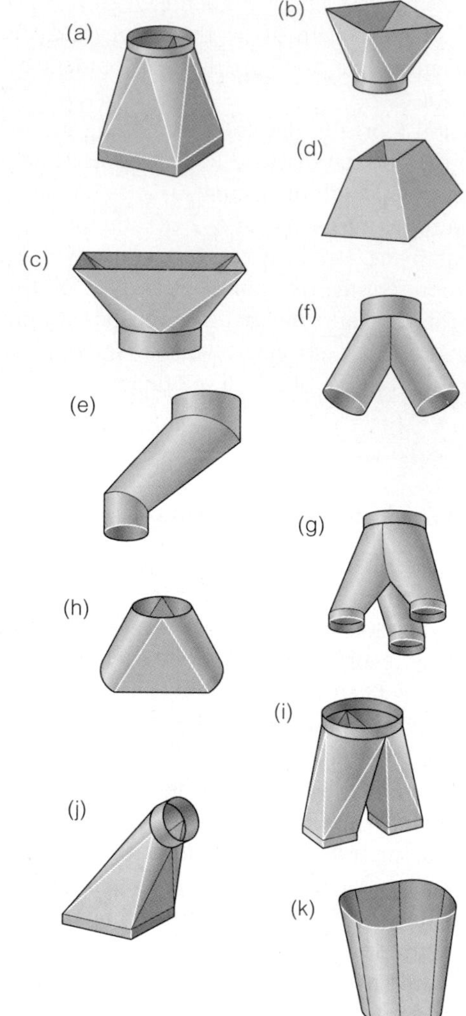

FIGURE 28.25 Examples of Transition Pieces

28.4.1 Triangulation

In Figure 28.26, the transition piece is developed by **triangulation**. The sheet metal hopper is an example of an industrial application of such a transition piece. The square-to-square form developed in Figure 28.26 has similarly shaped openings, and its edges can be extended to locate a vertex. Normally, when such a piece is to be developed, methods are used that utilize the vertex, and the development is constructed as a frustum of a pyramid. This form is here only to provide a simple illustration of the triangulation of a surface. Because all surfaces of the object are identical, only one surface need be divided into a triangular area. A diagonal, 4-5, is drawn so as to divide one of the equal trapezoidal shapes into two triangular planes. The true lengths of the hopper's edges and diagonals are established

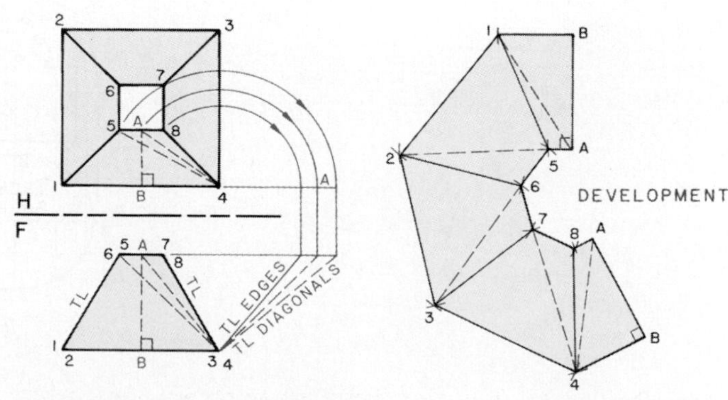

FIGURE 28.26 Triangulation

by revolution. The true lengths of the upper and lower openings appear in the horizontal view and can be transferred directly to the development.

To establish the shortest seam, divide the front surface in half. Line A-B will become the seam edge. This placement of the seam makes the joining method easier, quicker, and along the shortest line. This area must also be divided into triangles: Draw a diagonal from point A to point 4 and establish its true length by revolution.

Start the development by drawing line A-B longer than required. Using the true lengths of the edges, diagonals, and upper and lower opening edge lines as arc lengths, complete the development. Triangle A-B-4 is a right triangle. Swing arcs B-4 and 4-A to locate point A. Arcs A-8 and 4-8 intersect at point 8.

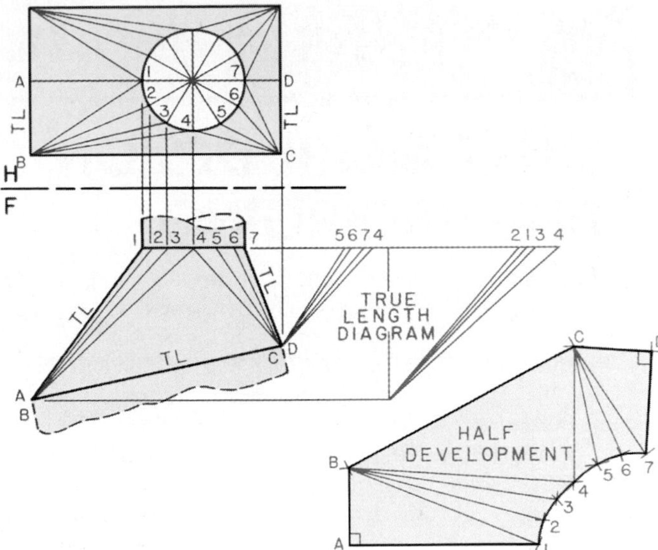

FIGURE 28.28 Transition Piece Development

28.4.2 Development of a Transition Piece: Circular to Rectangular

A transition piece connecting a circular to a rectangular geometric form is developed by dividing its surface as in Figure 28.27. The surface of the transition piece is composed of four isosceles triangles and four conical surfaces.

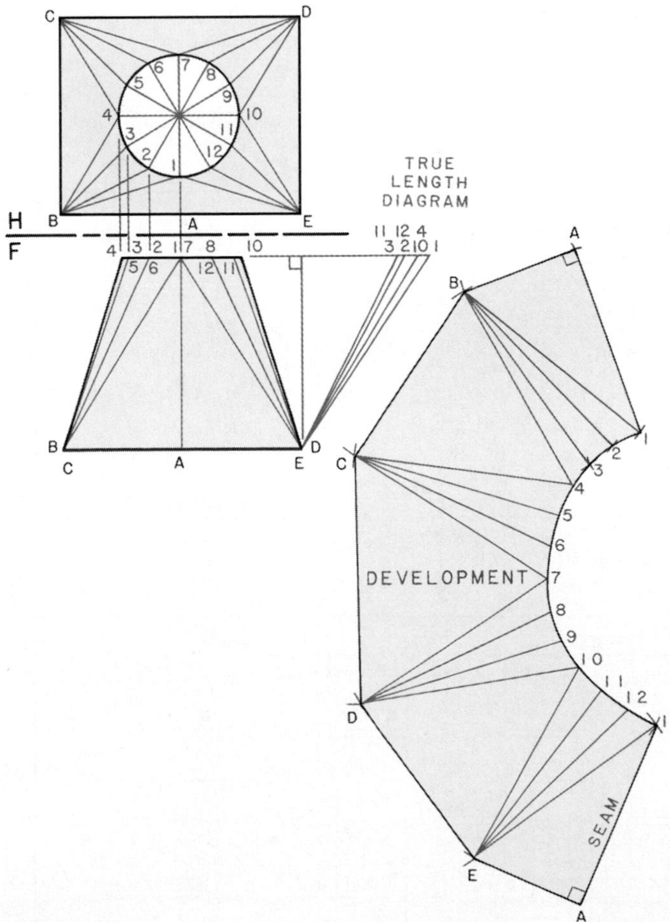

FIGURE 28.27 Transition Piece Development: Circular to Rectangular

The bases of the isosceles triangles form the lower base of the transition piece. The four conical surfaces are portions of an oblique cone.

The first step in the development of a circular-to-rectangular transition is to divide the conical surfaces into triangular areas. In Figure 28.27, the circumference of the circular base is divided into twelve equal parts. Points 1, 4, 7, and 10 already exist as divisions, since they correspond to the vertex points of the isosceles triangular areas of the piece's surface. All other points divide the conical surfaces into three separate areas. Since the transition piece is symmetrical, all of the four conical surfaces and their triangular divisions are identical, and so the true lengths of only one set of elements need be established.

A true-length diagram is constructed as shown to establish the true lengths of the four elements. The true lengths of the lower rectangular base can be found in the horizontal view, as can the chord distances between divisions on the upper circular base. The seam line is established by dividing the frontal triangular surface in half. Line 1-A will become the seam line.

Start the development by laying out triangle A-B-1. Draw line A-1 longer than the final length. Construct the triangle by drawing line A-B perpendicular to construction line A-1. Length A-B can be taken directly from the top view of the part, since the baseline is true length there. A-B is one-half of baseline B-E. Lengths B-1 and E-1 are the same; therefore, use the TL diagram to establish the true length, and swing an arc (radius B-1) from B on the development to where it crosses construction line A-1 at point 1. Use the true lengths of the elements, the chord distances, and the lower base lengths as arc lengths. Triangle 1-B-2 is laid out next. Each successive triangle is constructed so that the transition piece is unrolled clockwise, inside up.

The rectangular-to-circular transition piece shown in Figure 28.28 has an angled base edge. This figure is

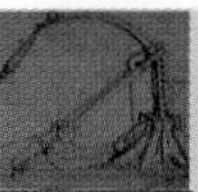

Applying Parametric Design . . .

SHEET METAL DESIGN AND PACKAGING

Developments can be created via a program called **Pro/SHEETMETAL.** The design can be created as a flat pattern and then bent into the required shape, or it can be created in the required design shape and unfolded into a flat pattern (Fig. A). The flat pattern can then be nested in a workpiece for manufacturing (Fig. B).

Pro/SHEETMETAL is an optional module for Pro/ENGINEER for designing a sheet metal part. A variety of capabilities are provided with this software, including the following:

- Designing the sheet metal parts by defining the volume and support for the components of an assembly
- Adding sheet metal features such as walls, bends, cuts, punches, notches, and forms to the part in an unbent or bent condition (Fig. C)
- Creating bend tables that provide the developed length of material for bends of different radii and material thicknesses
- Creating the flat pattern of the part
- Creating a bend order table that specifies the order, bend radius, and bend angle needed for manufacturing
- Creating a drawing that contains the "flat pattern" and "as designed" sheet metal part, and the bend order table for manufacturing

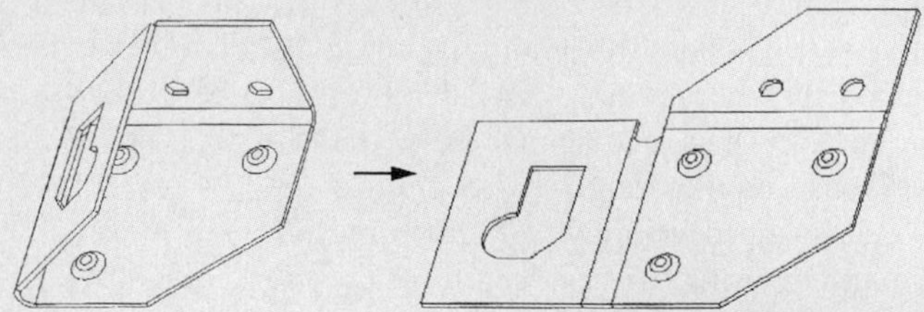

FIGURE A Sheet Metal Part in Its Designed Condition and As an Unfolded Flat Pattern

A sheet metal part can be created in Sheet Metal mode or in Assembly mode as a sheet metal component, or it can be a constant-thickness regular part that is converted to a sheet metal part.

Typical sheet metal structures that will be designed with Pro/SHEETMETAL are cabinets and supporting structures for electrical and mechanical equipment (Figs. D and E). In these instances, you will want to design the cabinet and support structures around the internal components. As with regular parts created in Assembly mode, a sheet metal part can be dimensioned to the component parts that it is supporting. A possible design approach to follow for creating sheet metal part is as follows.

1. Create the basic sheet metal parts in Sheet Metal mode.

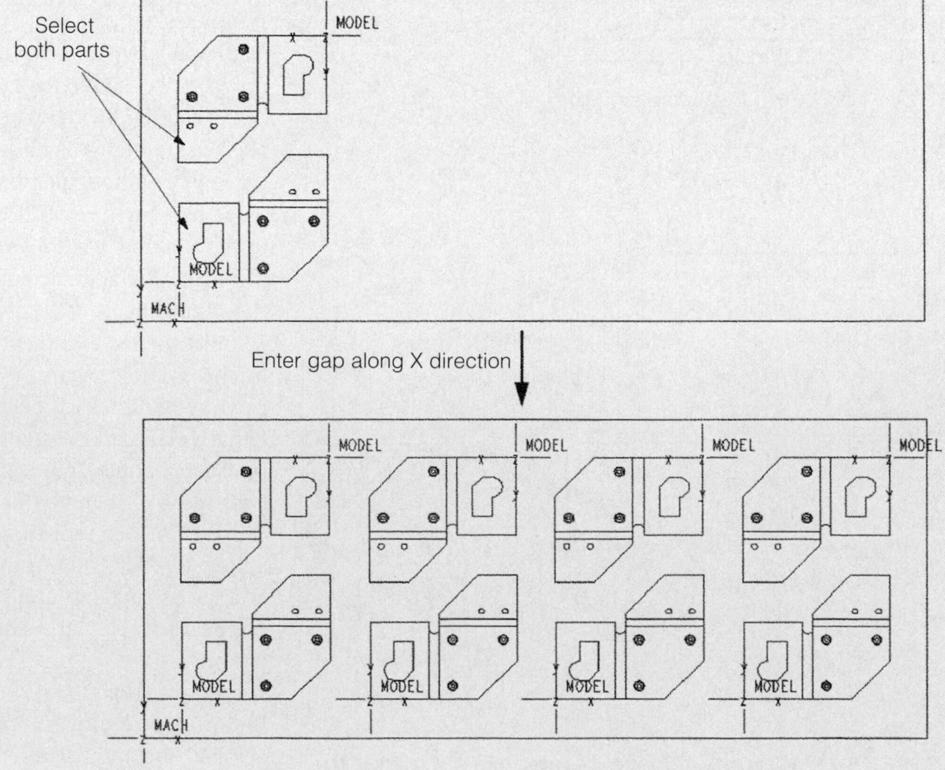

FIGURE B Nesting a Flat Pattern for Manufacturing

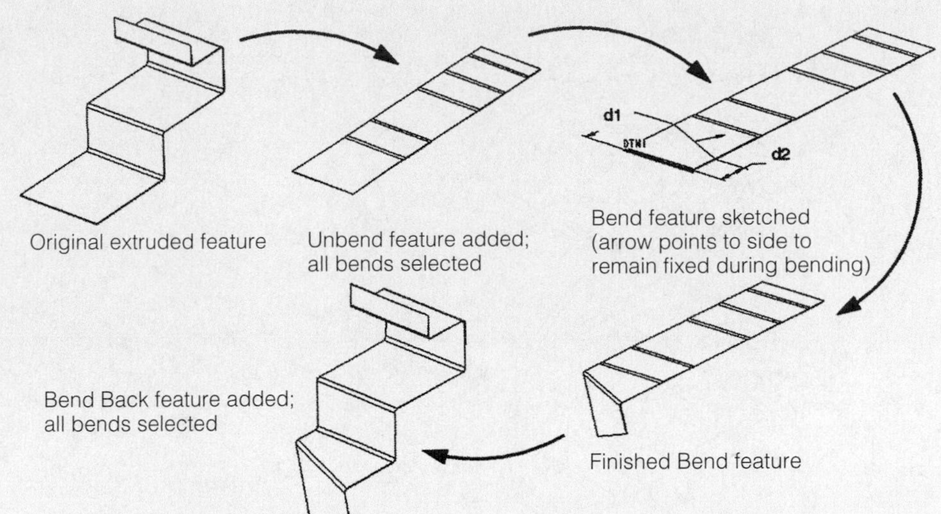

FIGURE C Adding Unbends and Bends to an Extruded Feature

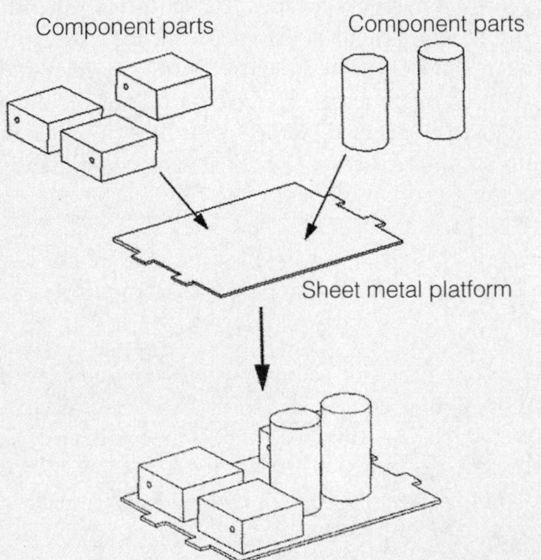

FIGURE D Designing Around Component Parts

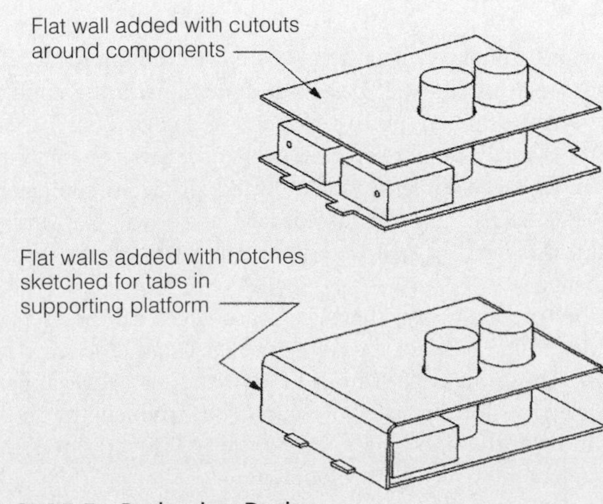

FIGURE E Packaging Design

Since many of the components will be held in place with screws or bent tabs, you might want to leave the creation of these features for later, when the components are assembled.

2. Create the assembly by assembling all major internal components relative to each other. Include simple supporting structures, or sheet metal parts that are not completely defined at this time, to place the components. Less important components can also wait.
3. Create or modify the sheet metal parts in Assembly mode using the internal components as references. This will aid you in adding supporting walls, form features for stiffening panels, and punches and notches for fastening the components.
4. After the cabinet and supporting structures are defined relative to the internal components and each other, add any remaining components, sheet metal, or assembly features.
5. Create and/or select a bending table to provide material allowances when unbending the part.
6. In Sheet Metal mode, create a bend order table to define the bending sequences for each part.
7. Add a **Flat Pattern** feature. This will create your flat pattern for drawing and manufacturing.
8. Create a family table for each sheet metal part, including at least two instances: the unbent flat pattern instance, and the "as designed" instance. The bend table data will ensure accurate flat pattern geometry of the unbent part.
9. Document the part by creating drawings; you can include both instances (multimodel drawing). Show the dimensions for the "as designed" part, and show/create dimensions for the flat pattern part. Add the bend order table as a note.

Pro/SHEETMETAL has a set of features unique to sheet metal parts. Sheet metal features can be added to a sheet metal part when the part is completely unbent or completely bent in its design condition, or at any stage of bend/unbend in between.

Design the part in the "as defined" condition, not as a flat pattern, unless you know all flat pattern details and dimensions. Add as many bends to the part as possible before adding

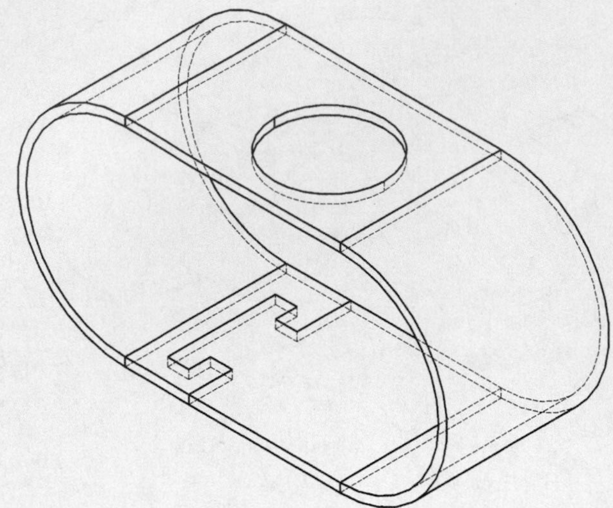

FIGURE F Part with Rip Feature

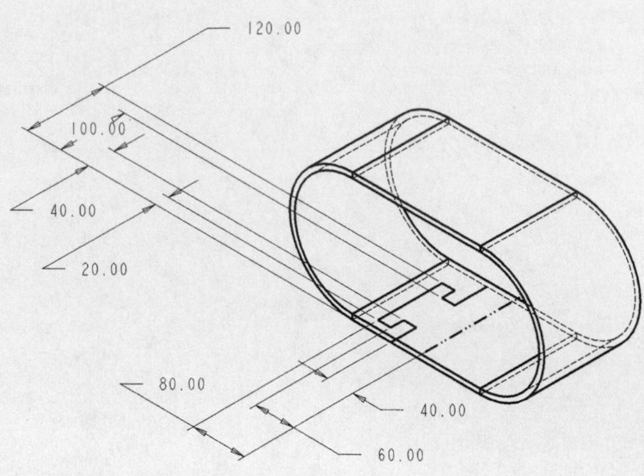

FIGURE H Interlocking Rip Feature

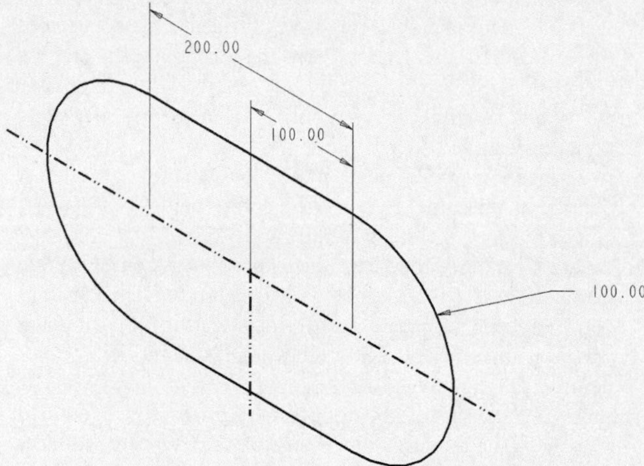

FIGURE G Sketched Base Feature (Slot-Shaped)

other features, since cuts at an angle or through bend areas might require larger dimensions for proper clearance.

Bends are added with the bend features, or when adding a wall. Bends can be dimensioned to the inside or the outside of the bend, or to a specified surface regardless of which side of the bend it is. Zero-radius bends create a sharp edge on whichever side they are dimensioned to.

The base sheet metal feature can only be a wall. There are several options for creating a base feature that are not available when adding more walls to the part. The feature forms include the following:

Extrude Sketch the side section of the wall and extrude it a specified depth.

Revolve Sketch the side section of the wall and revolve about the axis.

Bend Create a sheet metal wall by blending several sections sketched in parallel planes.

developed by the same general method as in the previous example. The transition piece is composed of four triangular lateral surfaces whose baselines form the lower base edge of the figure. The corners of the piece are portions of oblique cones. The development is constructed by dividing the surface into triangular areas that approximate the surface of the piece. Each triangle is then laid out in successive order with common elements joined. Note that this and the development in Figure 28.27 are *approximate developments,* since the given forms are basically warped surfaces.

The circumference of the upper base circle is divided into equal parts. Elements that define triangular areas on the conical surface are drawn through the division points and connected to one of the lower base corners. The elements correspond to bend lines when the piece is formed by rolling a flat piece of sheet metal that was cut to the outline of the pattern. Since the lower base is at an angle and the circular base is not centered left to right, as was Figure 28.27, there will be a total of eight separate element lengths to establish before the development can be started. To avoid confusion, two true-length diagrams are drawn, as shown. Revolution could also have helped determine the true lengths of the elements.

The true lengths of the lower base edges can be seen in the horizontal view for the right edge (C-D) and the left edge (A-B). The front edge (line B-C) and the rear edge appear true length in the frontal view. The true-length chord distances of the upper base are transferred directly from the horizontal view to the development.

In Figure 28.28, a half development is constructed, since

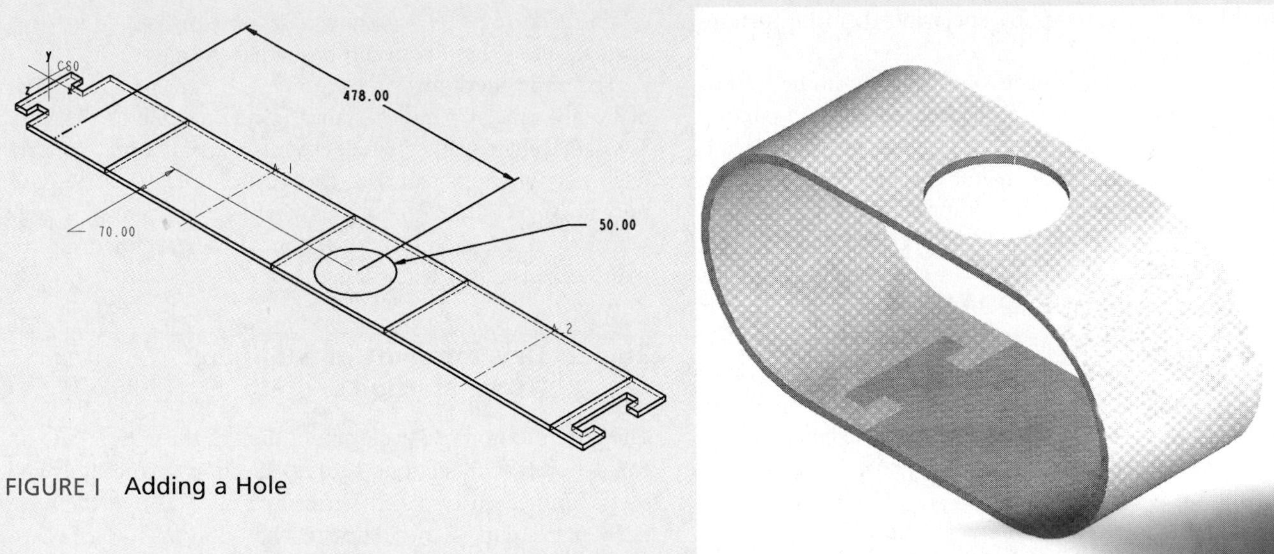

FIGURE I **Adding a Hole**

FIGURE K **Shaded Illustration**

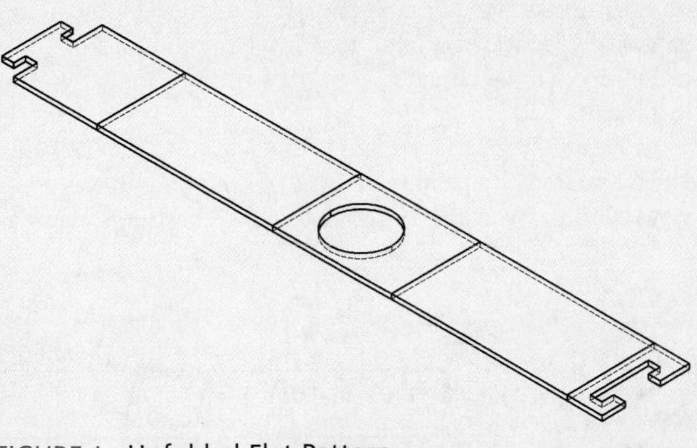

FIGURE J **Unfolded Flat Pattern**

Flat Sketch the boundaries of the wall.
Advanced Create a sheet metal wall using datum curves, multiple trajectories, etc.

Figure F shows an oblong part that was created as a loop and later ripped to establish a starting edge for unfolding. The 100 × 400 mm slotlike feature was sketched first (Fig. G). The **rip**, designed as an interlocking tab, was then sketched on the appropriate surface (Fig. H). Rips create a zero gap between two edges, as if a saw cut the part but no material was removed in the process. The hole is added last. The sketched hole is placed on the appropriate surface after the part is unfolded (Fig. I). The completed flat pattern is then used for manufacturing (Fig. J). The shaded illustration is shown in Figure K.

the piece is symmetrical. The half development can be flipped over to complete the full pattern. Line D-7 becomes the seam edge line since it is the shortest line. The true lengths of the elements, baselines, and chord distances are used to lay out the development.

Start the development by drawing line A-1. Line A-B is drawn perpendicular to line A-1 to form the first triangular area, A-1-B. Triangle 1-B-2 is laid out next. Complete the half development by laying out each successive triangular area as shown.

You May Complete Exercises 28.9 Through 28.12 at This Time

28.5 DOUBLE-CURVED SURFACES

Double-curved surfaces are divided into two basic types: surfaces of revolution and double-curved surfaces of the general type. General types of double-curved surfaces are composed of curved lines or contours drawn at predetermined spacings. Contour maps, topographic models, and fairing surfaces of ships, airplanes, automobiles, and spacecraft are examples of the general type of double-curved surfaces. **Double-curved surfaces of revolution** are generated by the movement of a curved-line generatrix about a straight-line axis (directrix). Because a double-curved surface is composed solely of curved lines, it is theoretically undevelopable. Approximate developments are constructed from double-curved surfaces by enclosing them in portions of cones and cylinders.

Double-curved surfaces of revolution include the following shapes: sphere, annular torus, spheroid/ellipsoid paraboloid, and the serpentine (spring). A double curved surface is made by stretching flat sheet metal that has been cut to a specific set of patterns until it approximates the desired form. Surfaces of revolution can also be turned on a lathe if the finished piece is to be a solid. In general, the sphere is the most common form of double-curved surface that is developed.

There are no straight lines on a double-curved surface. The intersection of a plane and a double-curved surface, perpendicular to its axis line, cuts a curved element on its surface. A plane passed parallel to its axis cuts a section showing the outline of the piece.

28.5.1 Spheres

Spheres are double-curved surfaces of revolution that are generated by a revolving curved-line (circle) generatrix about a straight-line axis (directrix). Spheres can be developed by many methods. The **gore method** (*meridian method*) divides the surface of the sphere into a number of meridians. A **meridian** is established by passing a plane through the axis of the sphere. Two adjacent radial meridians define a section/panel. Meridians are evenly spaced (radially), so all panels of the development are identical. Since it can serve as a pattern for the remaining sections, only one panel need be established. A panel is really a section of a cylinder that encloses the sphere between two adjacent meridians.

The **zone method** of developing a sphere passes a series of evenly spaced parallel planes perpendicular to the axis. Two adjacent cutting planes establish a horizontal section. Each section approximates the surface of the sphere. A horizontal section can be thought of as a frustum of a cone whose vertex is at the intersection of the extended chords that define the frustum's sides.

28.5.2 Development of a Sphere (Gore Method)

The **gore method** of development divides the sphere into an equal number of sections (**gores**). Sections are established by passing equally spaced vertical planes through the axis. Each plane cuts a meridian on the sphere's surface. Two adjacent meridians form a section. Each section can be considered a section of a cylinder. Because one section can serve as a pattern for the remaining sections, the development of one section is all that is necessary. The greater the number of sections, the more accurate the development and spherically perfect the final piece, but the number of sheet metal pieces to be cut and seams that need be joined will be increased.

In Figure 28.29, the sphere is divided into sixteen evenly spaced sections by passing vertical planes through the point view of the axis in the horizontal view. The frontal view is

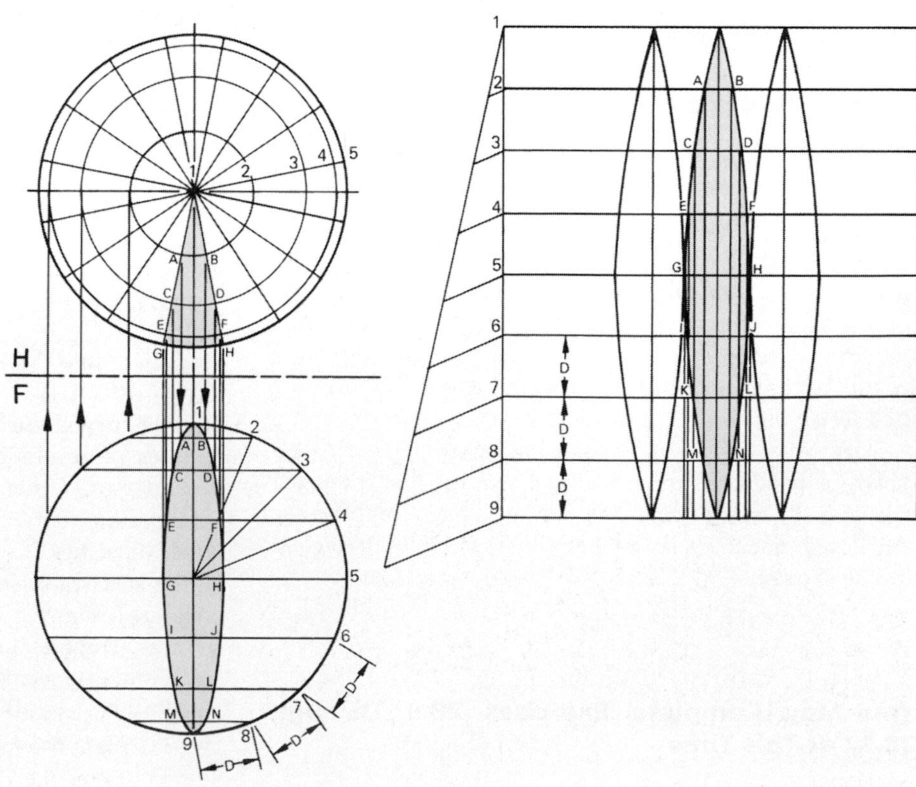

FIGURE 28.29 Sphere Development Using the Gore Method

similarly divided into equal divisions, as shown. Horizontal planes are passed through divisions in the frontal view, 1 through 9. Each horizontal plane appears as an edge in the frontal view and projects as a small-circle element on the sphere in the horizontal view. The chord distance between horizontal planes, dimension D, is equal for all frontal divisions. The vertical planes (meridian elements) and the circle elements intersect in the horizontal view, points A through N. Each intersection point is projected to the frontal view, as shown, to establish the gore (meridian) section.

The development is constructed by unfolding one section/panel. Start the development by drawing the stretch-out line equal to one-half of the sphere's circumference. Divide the stretch-out line into eight equal spaces and label 1 through 9, corresponding to the horizontal divisions. Each division should be equal to dimension D. Points A through N can be transferred to the development along related horizontal lines. The widest part of the section is at the equatorial line (5). Points G and H are transferred from the frontal view by measuring their distance from the axis line, which is the centerline of the section/panel.

Figure 28.30 shows a spherical tank constructed from gore sections. Because the spherical shape provides equal pressure distribution of the vessel's contents, spheres are frequently used in the design of pressure vessels.

28.5.3 Development of a Sphere (Zone Method)

The **zone method** of developing a sphere divides the surface of the sphere into horizontal zones. This procedure approximates the surface of a sphere by enclosing each horizontal zone in a right circular cone. Each zone is really a frustum of a cone. The development consists of developing successive frustums.

FIGURE 28.30 Vessel Constructed of Welded Gore Sections

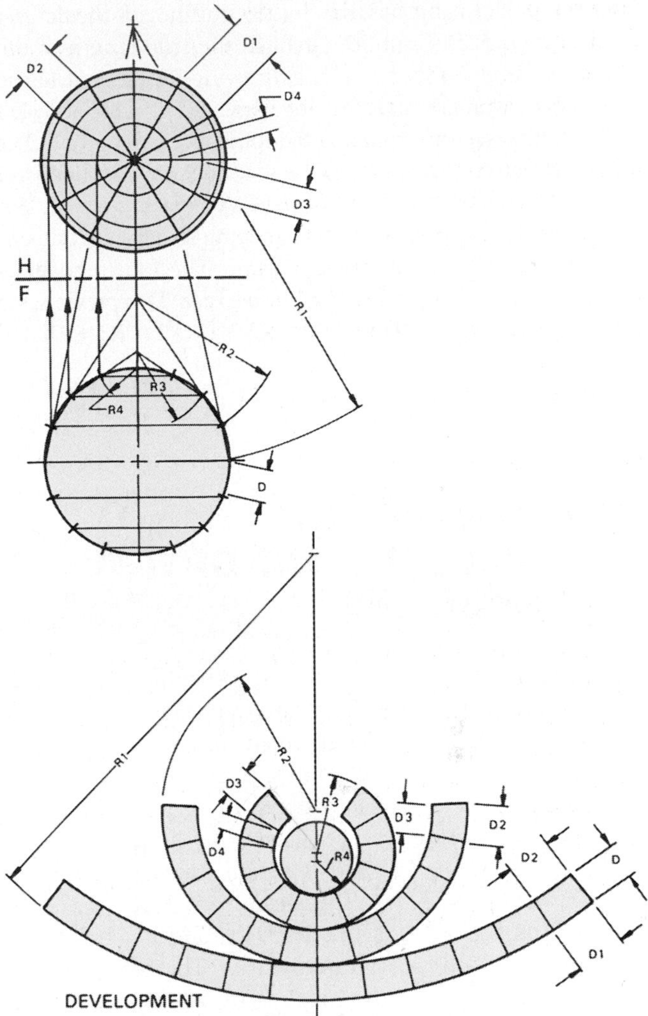

FIGURE 28.31 Development of a Sphere Using the Zone Method

In Figure 28.31, the sphere is divided into sixteen equal spaces along its circumference. Horizontal planes are passed through the divisions to define the upper and lower bases of the frustum. The horizontal projection of the plane sections are small-circle elements on the sphere's surface. Two adjacent parallel plane sections define a zone. Dimension D is the chord distance between divisions. Related chords are extended to locate the vertex of their respective cones. R1, R2, R3, and R4 are the slant heights of the cones. Slant heights are used to swing a true-length arc when drawing the development.

In the horizontal view, the sphere is divided into equal parts by passing vertical cutting planes through the point view of the axis line. Each vertical plane cuts an element on the sphere's surface. The intersection of straight-line elements and the circle elements in the horizontal view determines dimensions D1, D2, D3, and D4.

Start this development by drawing the centerline from which all true-length radii are swung. Swing arc R1 to locate the development outline for the largest frustum (zone).

Dimension D establishes the inside outline of the largest frustum (zone). D1 and D2 establish the true length of the zone's arc. Repeat this procedure, drawing R2 tangent to the inside development line of the first zone. D2 and D3 establish the second zone's development arc length. R3 is swung tangent to the inside of the second zone's outline, and D3 and D4 determine the total development arc length. R4 completes the development, being swung so as to be tangent to the inside of the third zone's outline. The fourth zone, as defined by R4, is a circle. *Note: Dimension D represents the thickness for all zones; that is, R1 − R2 = D, R2 − R3 = D, and R3 − R4 = D.*

28.6 CAD AND THE DEVELOPMENT OF FLAT PATTERNS

CAD systems were originally limited to parallel-line, radial-line, and transition pieces requiring triangulation for development of flat patterns. Development programs now allow you to create a 3D model and to request the system to develop the piece as a flat pattern. In Figure 28.32(a), a sheet metal enclosure was designed with a parametric 3D CAD/CAM program. The part is designed using the dimensions in Figure 28.32(b). The shaded image of the sheet metal part is shown in Figure 28.32(c), and its shaded flat pattern is provided in Figure 28.32(d). The enclosure has been redesigned in Figure 28.33(a) by adding side walls, top, and vent holes for cooling and by changing the side tab sizes [Fig. 28.33(b)]. A opening has been added by cutting out the side panel [Fig. 28.33(c)]. The completed project is shown in Figure 28.33(d). The next step in documenting the

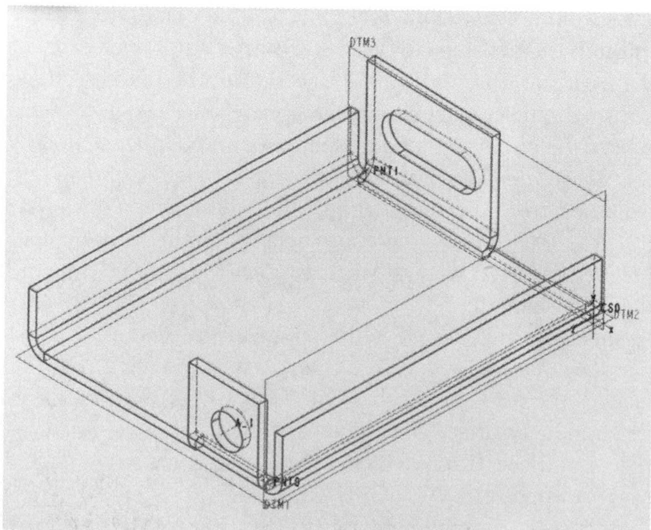

(a) Parametric 3D model of sheet metal enclosure

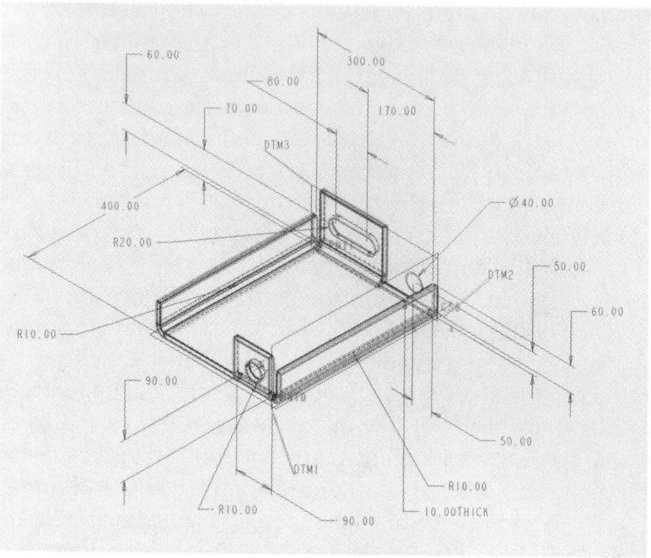

(b) Parametric dimensions

(c) Shaded model of final part

(d) Unfolded plate pattern

FIGURE 28.32 **Sheet Metal Design**

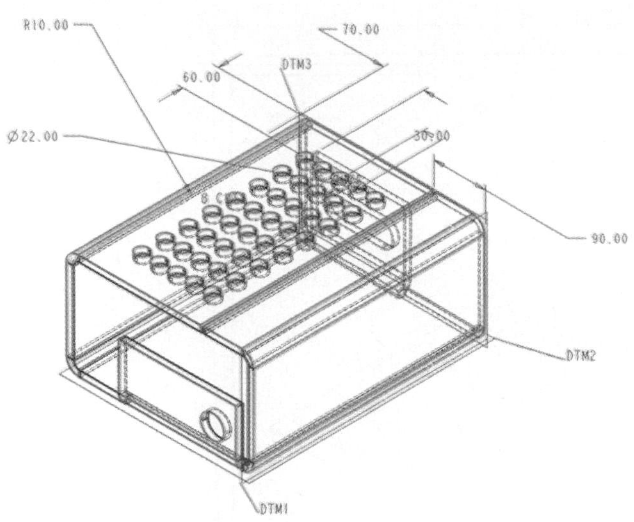

(a) Variation of sheet metal enclosure with additional sides, top, ventilation holes, and tabs

(b) Shaded image of design

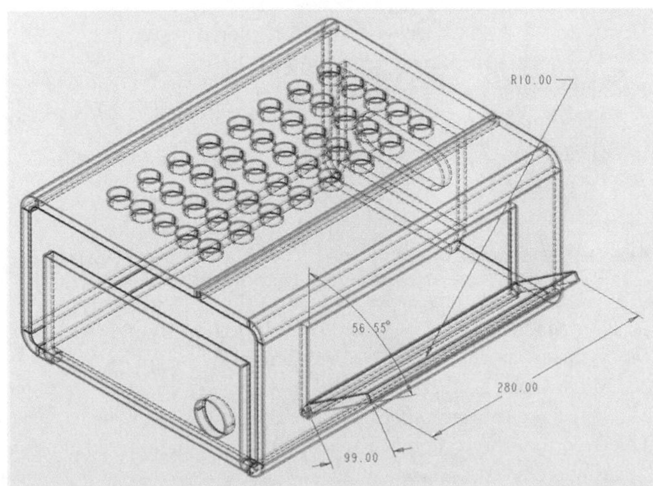

(c) Modified side panel

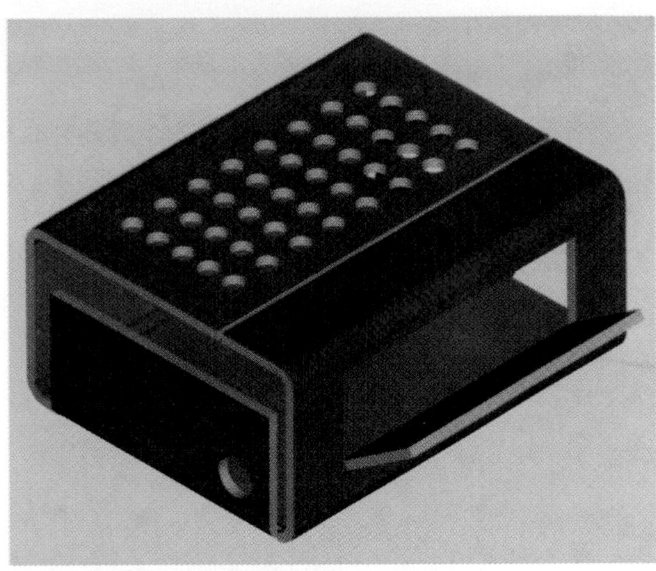

(d) Shaded image of completed design

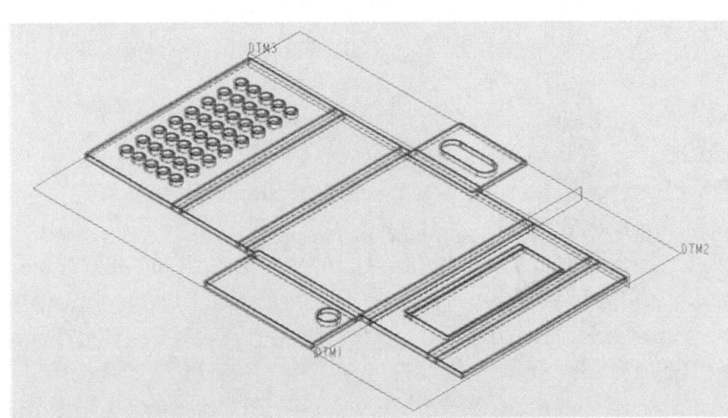

(e) Unfolded flat pattern

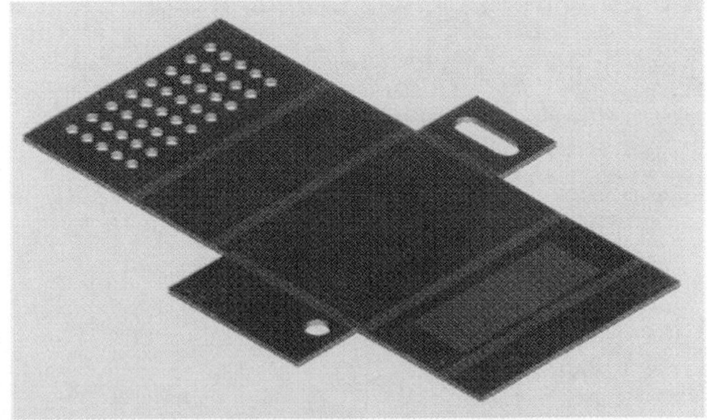

(f) Shaded image of flat pattern

FIGURE 28.33 Modified Sheet Metal Design—*Continues*

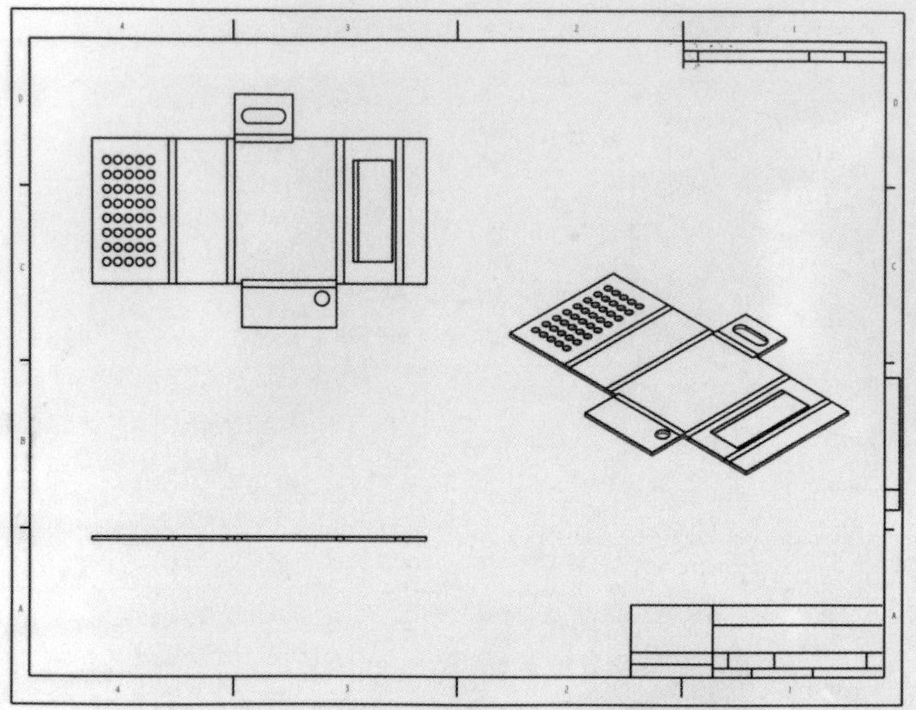

(g) Flat pattern shown in views on "C"-size sheet

FIGURE 28.33 Modified Sheet Metal Design—*Continued*

design is requesting a flat pattern [Figs. 28.33(e) and (f)]. The part is shown on a "C"-size format in Figure 28.33(g), and is now ready for detailing.

Two-dimensional development programs are also available, but either they require the construction techniques found in manual drafting or the pattern is assembled from polygon elements. Both 2D and 3D CAD flat pattern programs can calculate bend allowances. 3D systems additionally can create bend tables in which the part is bent sequentially according to defined bend angles.

QUIZ

True or False

1. The stretch-out line should always be drawn perpendicular a the object's lateral true-length edges.
2. Developments of spheres and warped surfaces are true developments.
3. A pattern is composed of true-length lines.
4. Cylinders and cones are considered single-curved surfaces.
5. An oblique cone has an axis that is perpendicular to its base.
6. Spheres are double-curved surfaces and must be developed approximately.
7. The gore method divides the sphere into a number of zones for laying out the development.
8. The first step in drawing a parallel-line development is to find the true lengths of each face and edge.

Fill in the Blanks

9. Most developments should be unfolded with the ________ ________.
10. The length of a cylindrical development is ________ to its ________.
11. Transition pieces join ________ or ________ geometric forms of ________ ________.
12. A cylinder is generated by a ________ ________ generatrix.
13. Curved surfaces fall into two general categories: ________ and ________.
14. ________ surfaces are also considered ruled ________.
15. The generatrix moves according to the ________.
16. Sheet metal is designated by ________ ________ for sizes smaller than ________.

Answer the Following

17. Name six different types of seams.
18. Describe the types of shapes developed by triangulation.
19. What is an approximate development?
20. What is a TL diagram?
21. What are the four types of developments?
22. Describe the difference between a double-curved and a single-curved surface.
23. Why is a right section required for parallel-line developments?
24. What is a transition piece?

EXERCISES

Exercises may be assigned as sketching, instrument, or CAD projects. Transfer the given information to an "A"-size sheet of .25 in. grid paper. Complete all views, and solve for proper visibility, including centerlines, object lines, and hidden lines. Exercises that are not assigned by the instructor can be sketched in the text to provide practice and to enhance understanding of the preceding instructional material.

After Reading the Chapter Through Section 28.2.9 You May Complete Exercises 28.1 Through 28.4

Exercises 28.1(A) and (B) Develop the inside pattern of the prism. Use the given element to start the roll-out.

Exercise 28.2 Develop the inside pattern of the prism. Use the given element to start the roll-out.

Exercise 28.3 Develop the inside pattern of the prism. Use the given element to start the roll-out.

Exercises 28.4(A) and (B) Develop the inside pattern of each pyramid. Complete the top view of the intersected pyramid for Exercise 28.4(A).

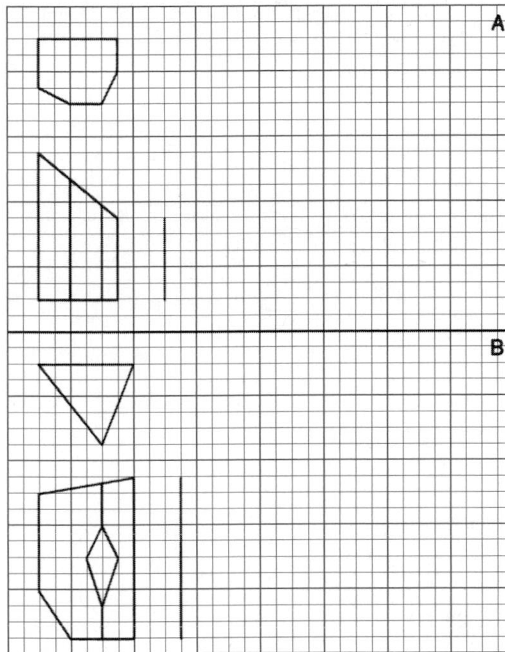

EXERCISE 28.1

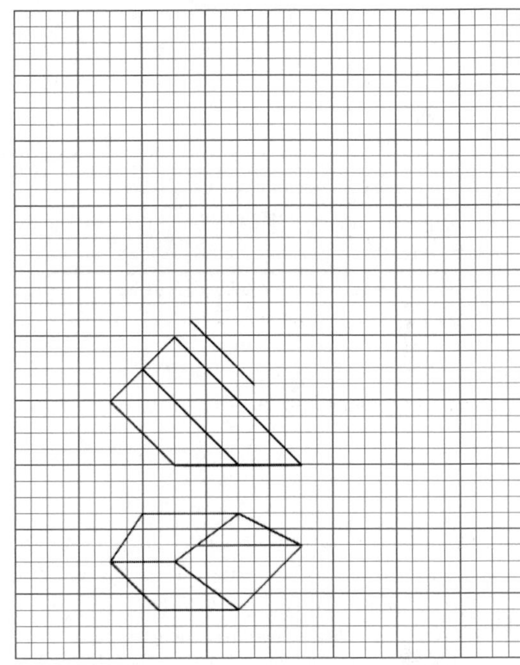

EXERCISE 28.3

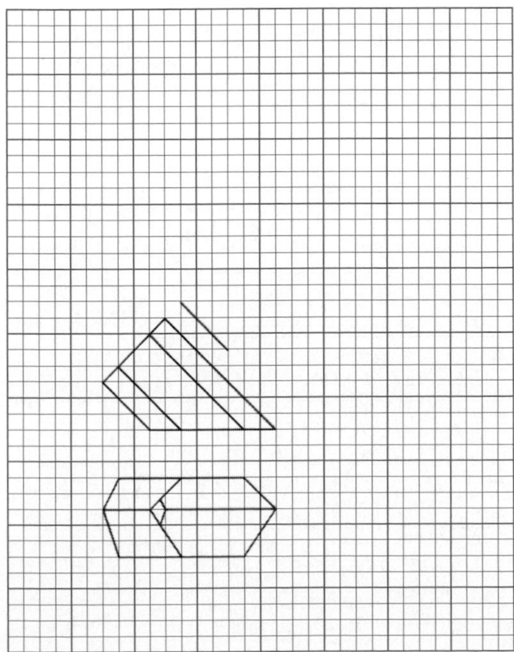

EXERCISE 28.2

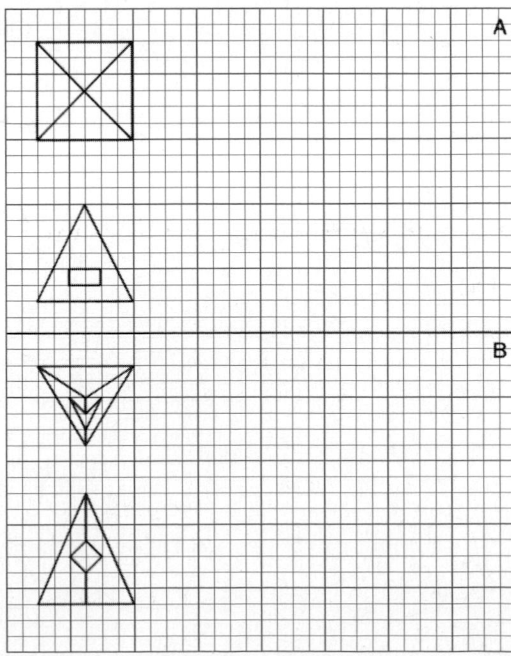

EXERCISE 28.4

After Reading the Chapter Through Section 28.3.3 You May Complete Exercises 28.5 Through 28.8

Exercises 28.5(A) and (B) Develop the inside pattern of each pyramid. Complete the top view for Exercise 28.5(B).

Exercise 28.6(A) Develop one-half of the inside pattern of the pyramid. Extend the edges to locate the vertex.

Exercise 28.6(B) Develop the inside pattern of the cylinder.

Exercise 28.7 Determine the intersection of the two cylinders on the given views, and develop each of the two different patterns in the space provided.

Exercise 28.8(A) Develop the inside pattern of the center piece of the mitered elbow.

Exercise 28.8(B) Develop the inside pattern of the 45° WYE. Develop the header and one branch.

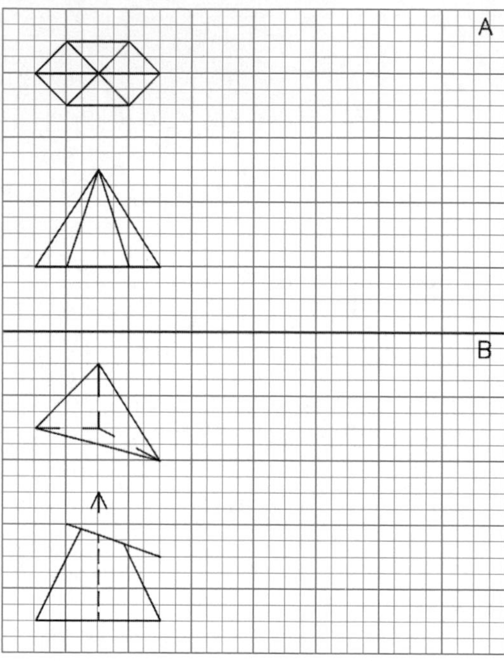

EXERCISE 28.5

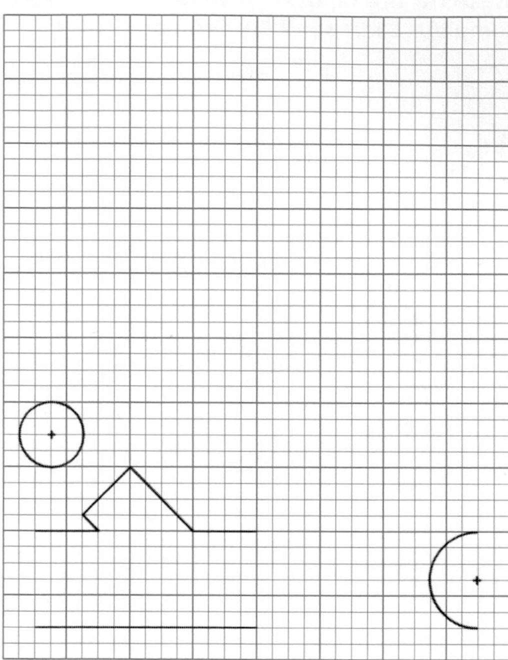

EXERCISE 28.7

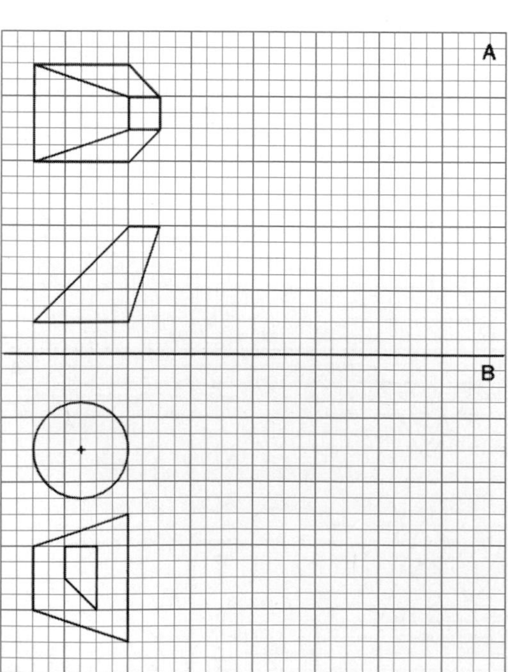

EXERCISE 28.6

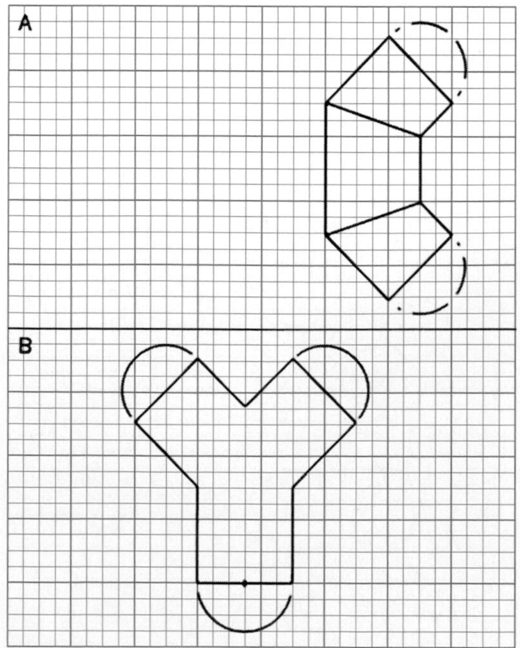

EXERCISE 28.8

After Reading the Chapter Through Section 28.4.3 You May Complete the Following Exercises

Exercise 28.9(A) Develop one-half of the inside pattern of the oblique cone.

Exercise 28.9(B) Establish the top view of the intersected cone, and develop its inside pattern.

Exercise 28.10(A) Develop the inside pattern of one-half of the truncated cone.

Exercise 28.10(B) Complete the top view of the truncated oblique cone. Develop one-half of the inside pattern of the cone.

Exercise 28.11(A) Develop the inside pattern of the conical offset.

Exercise 28.11(B) Develop the inside pattern of the transition piece.

Exercise 28.12(A) Develop one-half of the inside pattern of the transition piece.

Exercise 28.12(B) Develop the inside pattern of the transition piece.

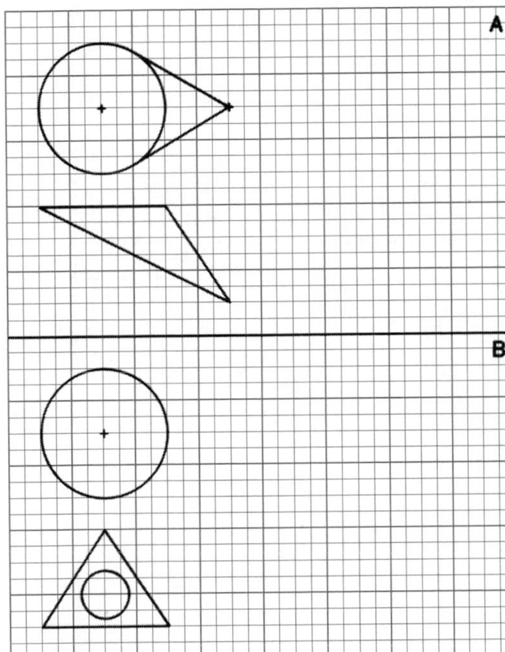

EXERCISE 28.9

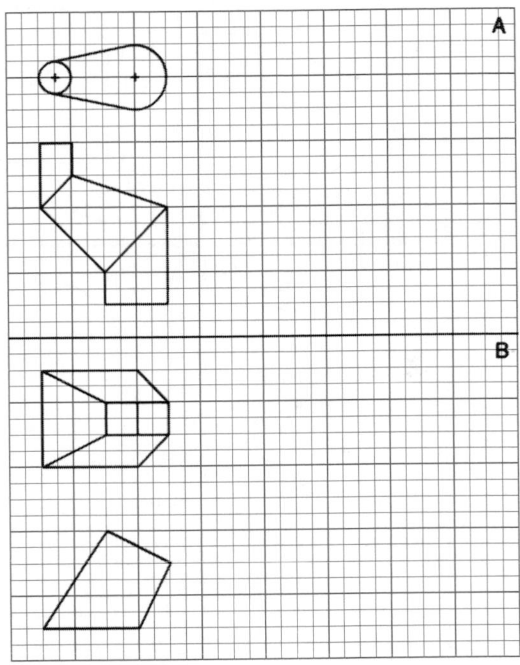

EXERCISE 28.11

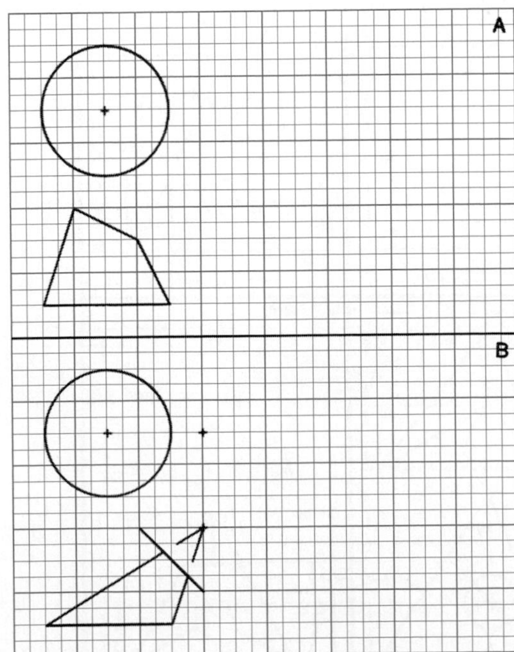

EXERCISE 28.10

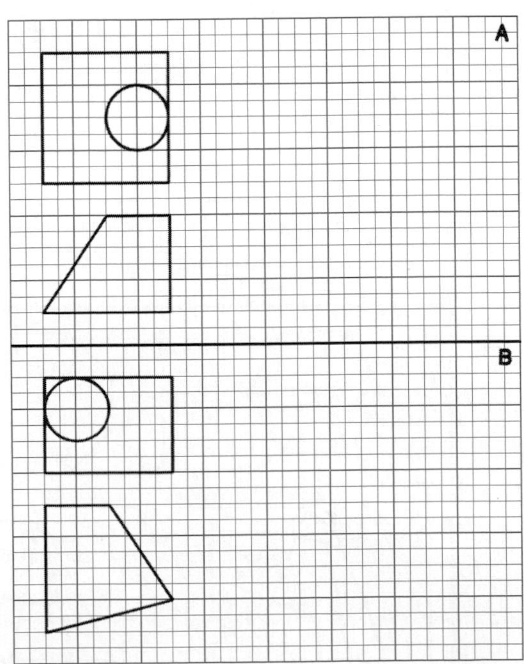

EXERCISE 28.12

PROBLEMS

Problems may be assigned as sketching, instrument, or CAD projects.

Problem 28.1 Transfer each problem to another sheet. All problems will fit on a "B"-size sheet. Develop each part as an inside-up pattern. Instructor may assign some projects as half patterns. Models of any of the problems can also be completed as assigned.

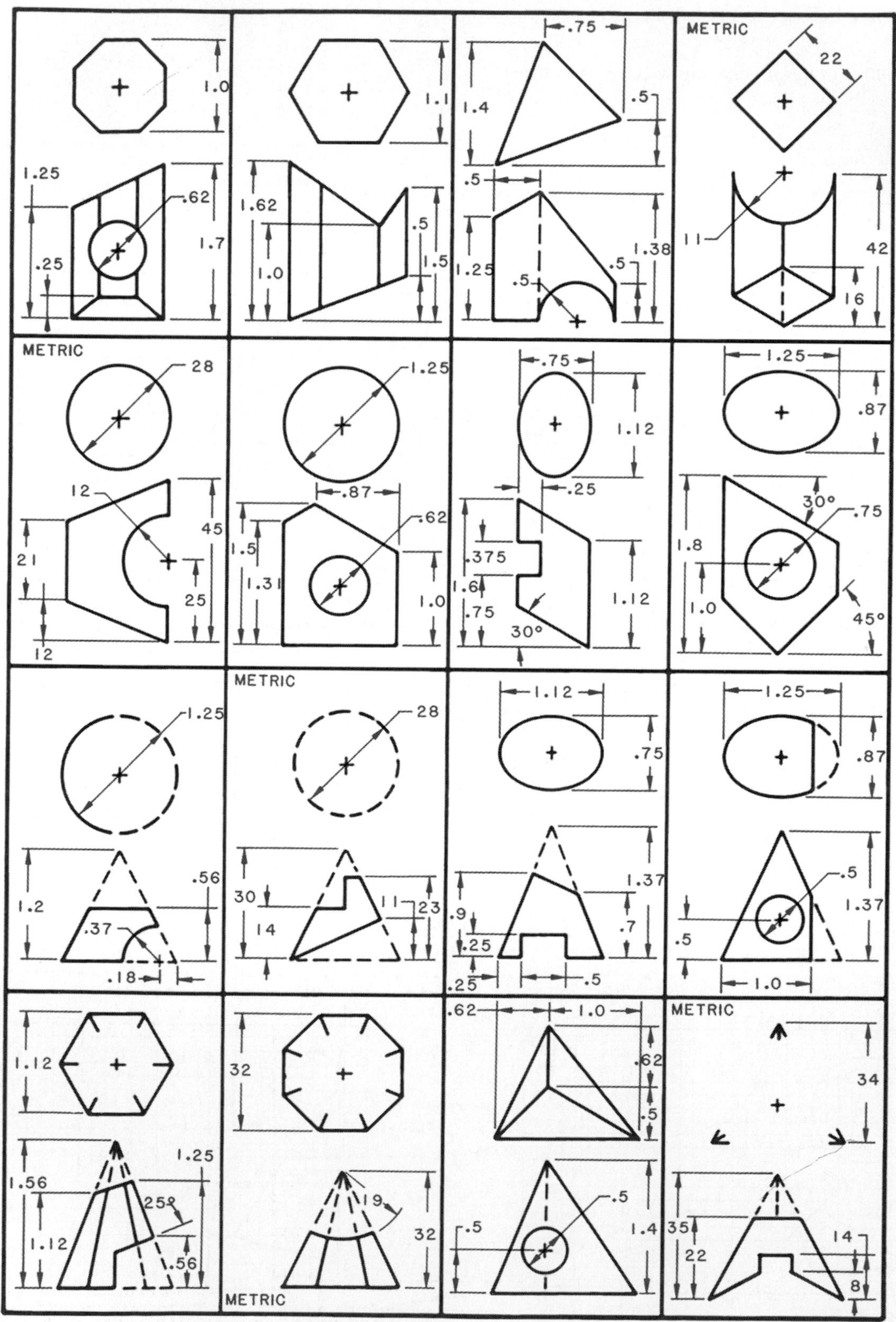

Problem 28.2 Transfer each problem to another sheet. All problems will fit on a "B"-size sheet. Develop each part as an inside-up pattern. Instructor may assign some projects as half patterns. Models of any of the problems can also be completed as assigned.

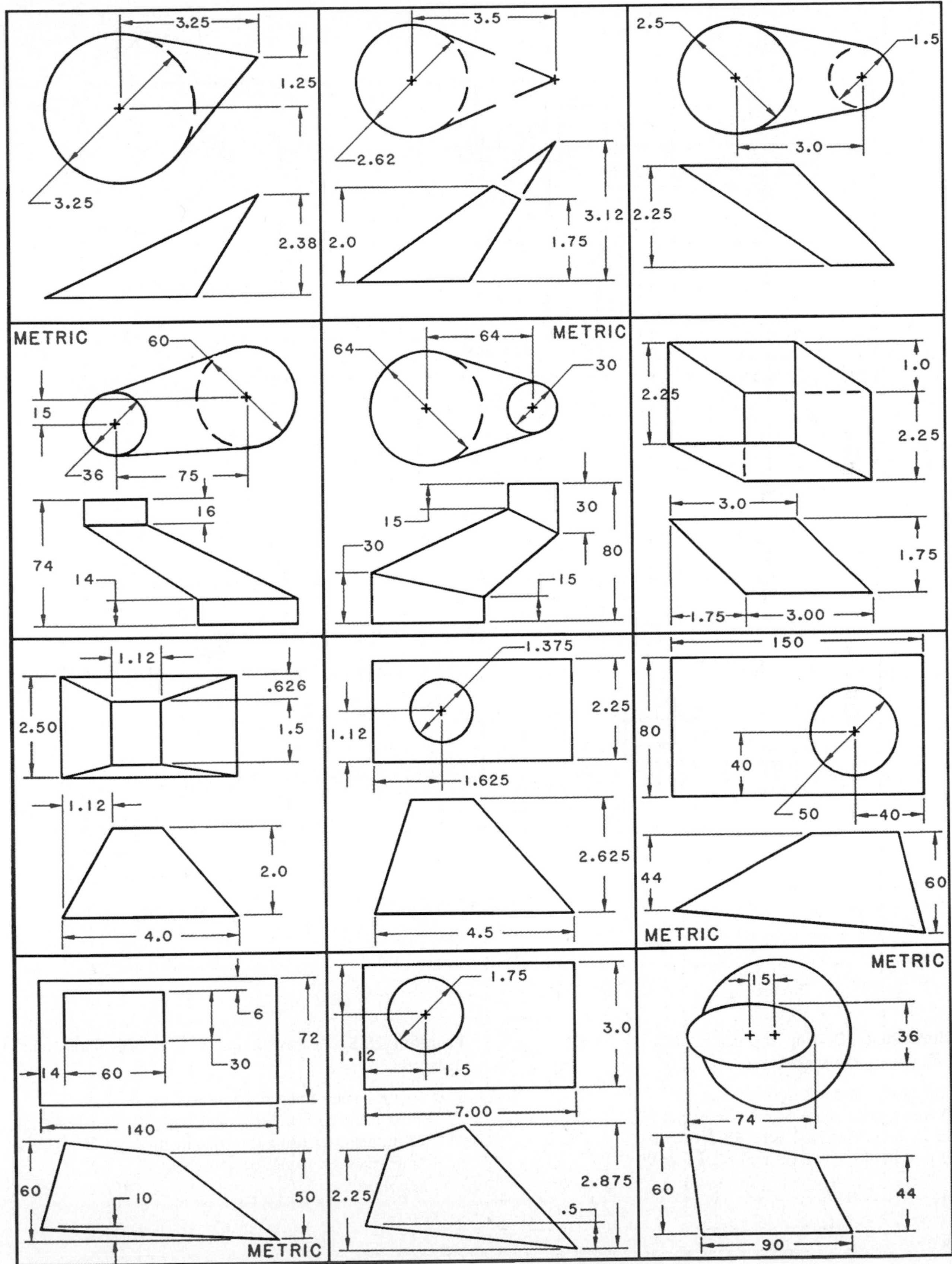

Problem 28.3 Draw and dimension the mounting bracket detail as shown. On a separate sheet, lay out and develop the part.

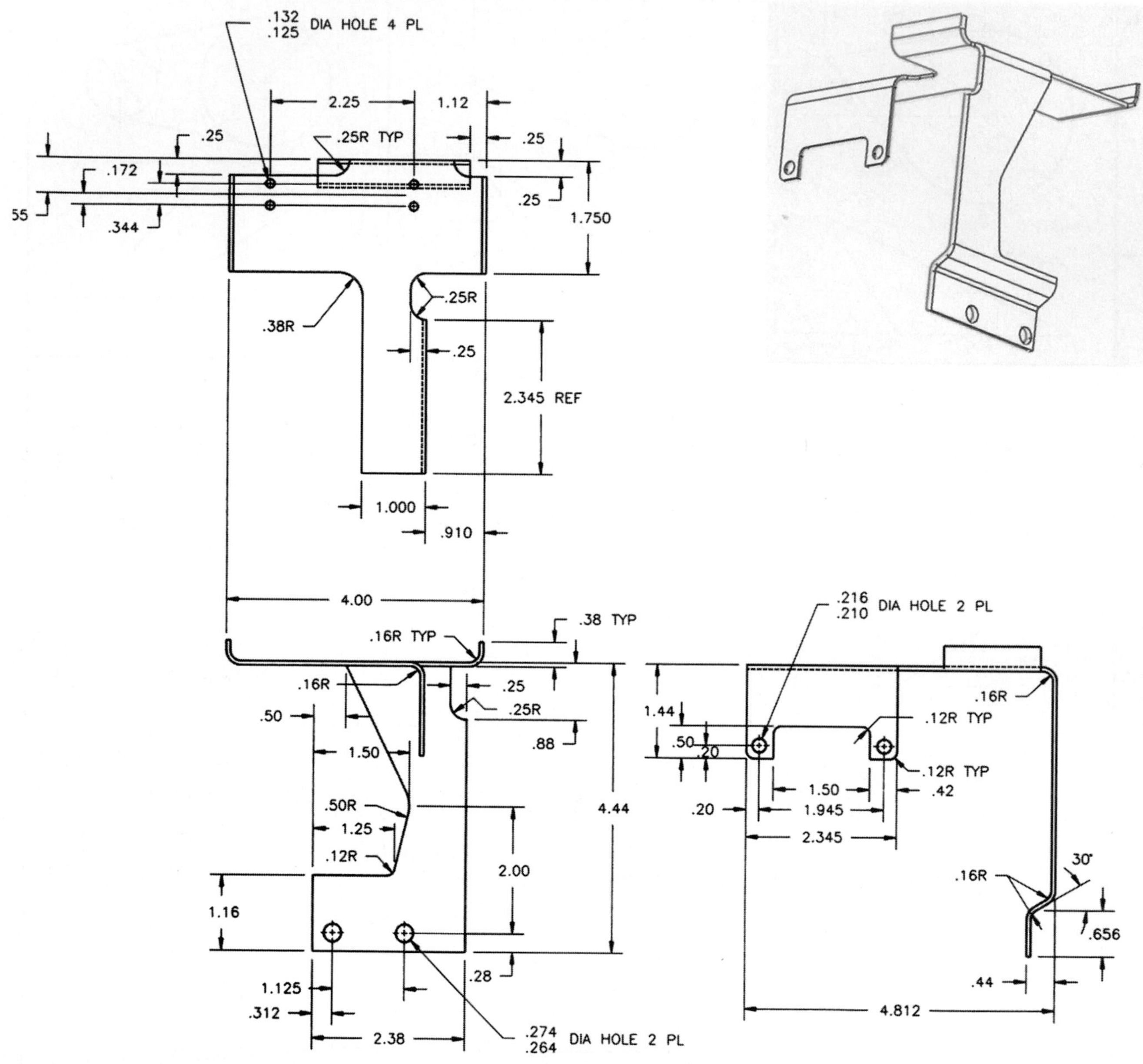

Problem 28.4 Develop the header and the branch for the following intersecting pipes:

1. 3 in. header and a 2 in. branch at 45°
2. 55 mm header and a 35 mm branch at 60°
3. 2.5 in. header and a 1.5 in. header at 40°
4. 45 mm header and a 38 mm branch at 90°

Problem 28.5 Develop a sphere with one of the following diameters:

1. 2.5 in. diameter using the gore method
2. 38 mm diameter using the zone method
3. 3.25 in. diameter using the zone method
4. 44 mm diameter using the gore method

VECTOR ANALYSIS

Chapter 29

LEARNING OBJECTIVES

Upon completion of this chapter you will be able to:

1. Understand the four components of a force.
2. Find the resultant of a force system by the parallelogram method, the polygon method, and the mathematical method.
3. Find the forces in members in coplanar force systems.
4. Find the reaction forces for beams under various loading conditions.
5. Find the forces and reaction forces in the members of a truss.
6. Find the member forces for non-coplanar force systems.

29.1 INTRODUCTION

The design of any structure such as a bridge, a transmission tower (Fig. 29.1), a roof truss, a crane boom, a space station, a machine, or a building requires a complete analysis and understanding of the forces acting on each member and

FIGURE 29.1 A Truss Transmission Tower

connection involved in the assemblage. In fact, mechanics, the study of these forces, is one of the oldest and most fundamental of the physical sciences. A force can cause a member to deform or to move if it is at rest. In **vector analysis,** only structures that are in static equilibrium are studied. Simply stated, these structures are not moving and will remain at rest. This branch of physical science is usually called **statics.** A different branch of science, **dynamics,** studies bodies in motion. In statics, all the parts of the structure or machine are called rigid bodies, and it is assumed that these parts are perfectly rigid and do not deform, even under large loads.

In order for these forces to be analyzed (either graphically or mathematically), the forces on these bodies must be described completely. The graphical representations of these forces are known as **vectors.** A complete definition of a force must include a **magnitude** (the size of the force—1000 pounds, for example) and a direction (the path of the line of action of the force—vertical, for example). The **point of application** and the **sense** of the vector must also be described. A graphical solution that is completed via drafting skills will provide a solution that is equal in usefulness to the mathematical solution in most cases. Graphical and mathematical solutions complement each other. One solution can serve as an accuracy check of the other. The structures in Figures 29.2 and 29.3 can be analyzed by graphical methods.

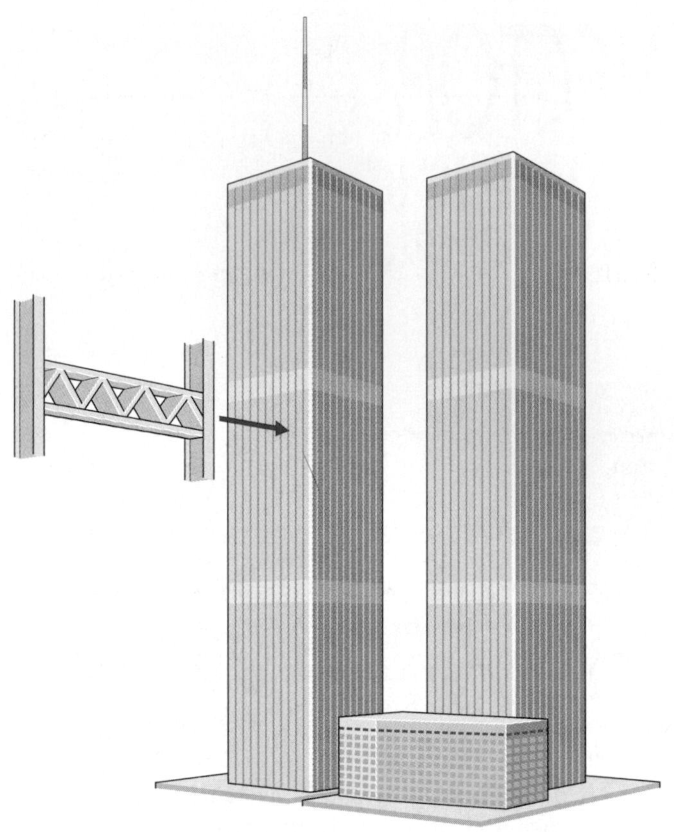

FIGURE 29.3 Buildings Contain Truss Assemblies

29.2 DEFINITION OF TERMS

Before the techniques of graphical vector analysis can be utilized to solve a problem, the new terms and concepts that are used in vector geometry must be understood. The following concepts are used throughout this chapter.

Force A push or a pull exerted on one body by another that attempts to cause motion or a change of motion. There are four characteristics of a force:

- *Magnitude* The amount of the force measured in standard units, such as pounds or newtons
- *Point of application* The place on or in an object where the force is applied to the object
- *Line of action (direction)* The path of the line that positions the force as it acts at the point of application
- *Sense* The tendency of motion along the line of action caused by the force, either toward the point of application (*compression*) or away from the point of application (*tension*)

Direction of force A combination of the point of application, line of action, and sense of a force.

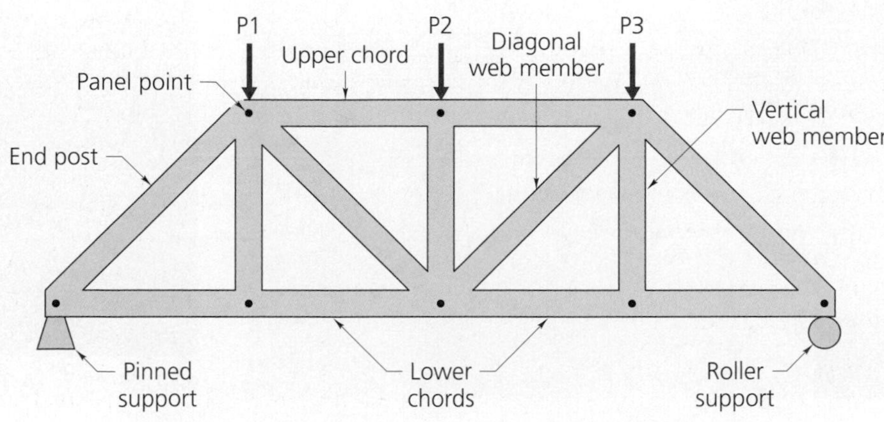

FIGURE 29.2 A Truss Can Be Analyzed by Graphical Methods

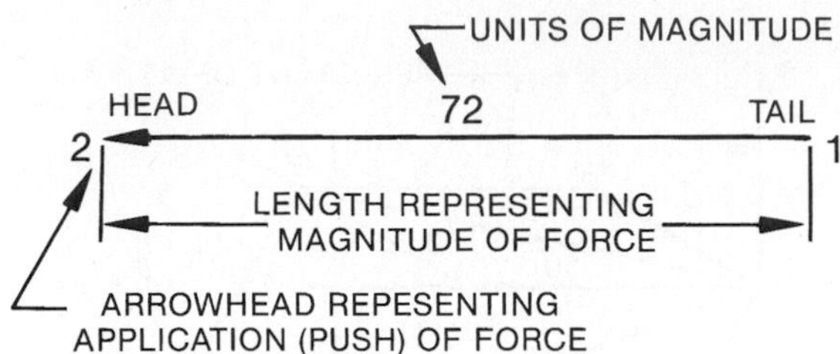

FIGURE 29.4 Graphical Representation of a Vector

Vector The graphical representation of a force. It is a straight line, with an arrowhead at one end (Fig. 29.4). Vectors are drawn to scale, with length units representing force units (1 mm = 10 N, for example). This scale length is the magnitude of the vector. The arrowhead indicates the application of the force along its length and is determined from the sense of the force. Labeling gives the vector's tail-to-head relationship. For example, vector 1-2 in Figure 29.4 acts from tail end 1 to head end 2. Vector 2-1 would act from 2 to 1 and would represent a force opposite to that shown.

Resultant force The summation of the several individual forces.

Equilibrium When the summation of all forces is equal to zero.

Equilibrant force A force equal in magnitude but opposite in action to the resultant force; the force that will counteract all of the other forces acting on an object, to create equilibrium.

Component forces Two or more forces that will produce the same effect as a single force. The summation of the two or more individual forces is equal to the given force. Component forces that are parallel to the Cartesian coordinates are called the X component, Y component, and Z component.

Bow's notation A systematic method for notating a structural diagram and the associated force diagram. The spaces between structural members are numbered, and these numbers serve to label vectors (permitting their consecutive labeling).

Pin connection A connection of structural members that does not restrain the movement of the members around the connection (a loose bolt, for example); also called a *pin-connected joint* or *pin joint.*

Collinear forces Forces that act along a common line of action. These forces have parallel lines of action, although their actions may be opposed. A two-force system in equilibrium is always collinear, with the two forces being equal in magnitude and opposite in action.

Coplanar forces Forces that all lie in one plane (two-dimensional space). The number of forces is not limited as long as they lie in a single plane. A three-force system in equilibrium is always coplanar.

Noncoplanar forces Forces that lie in more than one plane (three-dimensional space). A noncoplanar force system in equilibrium has a minimum of four forces.

Concurrent forces Forces whose lines of action pass through a common point. These force systems may be coplanar or noncoplanar. Nonparallel three-force systems in equilibrium are always concurrent coplanar force systems.

Nonconcurrent forces Forces whose lines of action do not pass through a common point. Forces with lines of action that are parallel or skewed or have multiple intersections are nonconcurrent. These force systems may be coplanar or noncoplanar.

Structural diagram A view, drawn to scale, of a body that accurately shows the position of all structural parts, the connections of these parts, and the external forces acting on the object. Often a structural diagram is simplified by showing only the centerlines of each member. In 2D systems, only one view (the true-size view) is used. In 3D systems, a minimum of two adjacent views are necessary to show the space relationships and the true lengths.

Free body diagram A view of an isolated connection or part of a body; used in the analysis of all forces acting at a single connection or part of the object.

Force diagram (vector diagram) A view of the vectors, drawn to scale, of the forces acting on an object and of the forces acting in each part of the object. The length unit represents a unit of force.

String diagram (funicular diagram) A diagram that is defined and used in coplanar nonconcurrent force systems.

29.3 GRAPHICAL VECTOR ANALYSIS

The accuracy of any graphical solution to a vector analysis is a direct result of the accuracy of the drafting procedures. Careful layout and sharp linework and lettering will produce a solution that is visually easy to check for procedure and accuracy. These solutions will be as useful as a mathematical solution. A CAD system will, of course, increase the accuracy correspondingly.

These graphical solutions must stand up to the rigors of accepted engineering practice, design, and code review by governing agencies and to contract law. It is not possible to overemphasize the value of good design documentation. Remember, graphical solutions and mathematical solutions complement each other.

The primary item of significance is quality equipment. Graphical problem solutions require precision drafting of exact line lengths and angles. Lines must be drawn exactly parallel to other lines, and line lengths must be measured with precision. Therefore, a CAD system will greatly increase the accuracy of your solutions.

Employ a systematic procedure during the solution of graphical problems. There is a systematic sequence of steps for the solution of each force problem, just as there is for any other descriptive geometry or drafting problem.

Always summarize your solution and the parameters that were given as a basis for the design. The solution must be explicit in presenting the given design parameters and the results of the analysis. This is effectively done by summarizing all forces acting on the structural system. The summary lists both the *given* forces and the forces that were *determined*.

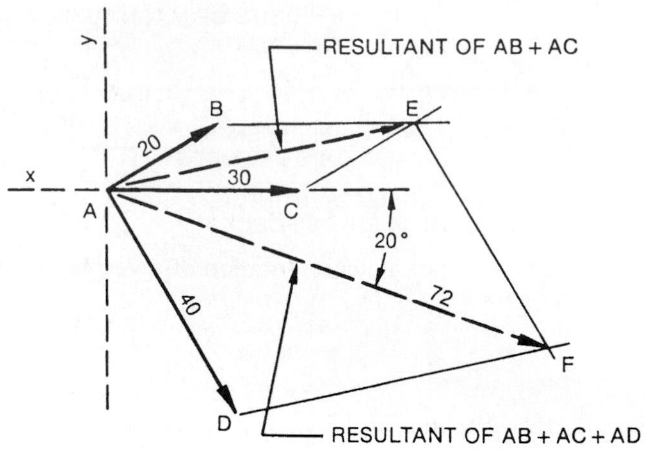

FIGURE 29.6 Parallelogram Method

29.4 COPLANAR VECTOR SUMMATION

The summation of two or more vectors is their resultant vector. Coplanar vectors appear true length in a single view, and their true-length projections serve to determine the resultant vector. Three structural members connected by a loose pin at point A are shown in Figure 29.5. The force acting in each member and the angles between members are given. An X axis and Y axis have been superimposed through the pin at point A. Two graphical methods—the parallelogram method and the polygon method—will be illustrated along with the mathematical method.

The **parallelogram method** is shown in Figure 29.6. Vectors AB, AC, and AD are drawn exactly parallel to members AB, AC, and AD; their lengths represent their respective magnitudes, and the arrowheads indicate the direction of their respective actions on the pin at point A. In this method, only two vectors can be summed into a resultant vector in each step. The first step is to determine the resultant of vectors AB and AC. Parallelogram ABCE is drawn to find point E, and vector AE is the resultant of vectors AB and AC. Next, parallelogram AEFD is drawn to find point F. Because vector AF is the resultant of resultant vector AE and vector AD, vector AF is also the resultant vector of vectors AB, AC, and AD. Its magnitude and its angle with the positive X axis can now be measured. It is good drafting practice to draw given vectors and resultant vectors so they look different, for easy visualization. Here, broken-line vector AF is the resultant vector.

The **polygon method**, shown in Figure 29.7, is the method for drawing force diagrams. To make a systematic identification of the vectors possible, in the sequence of their summation, use **Bow's notation.** A simplified sketch of the centerlines of members AB, AC, and AD is drawn and labeled. Then the spaces between pairs of members are numbered. These numbers give automatic labeling so that

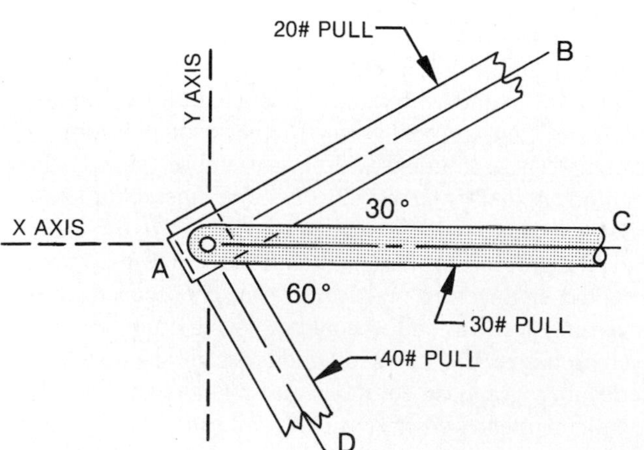

FIGURE 29.5 Coplanar Vector Summation Problem

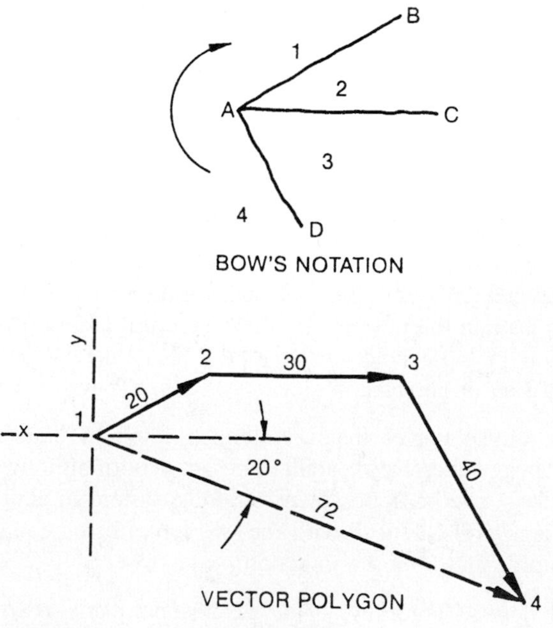

FIGURE 29.7 Polygon Method

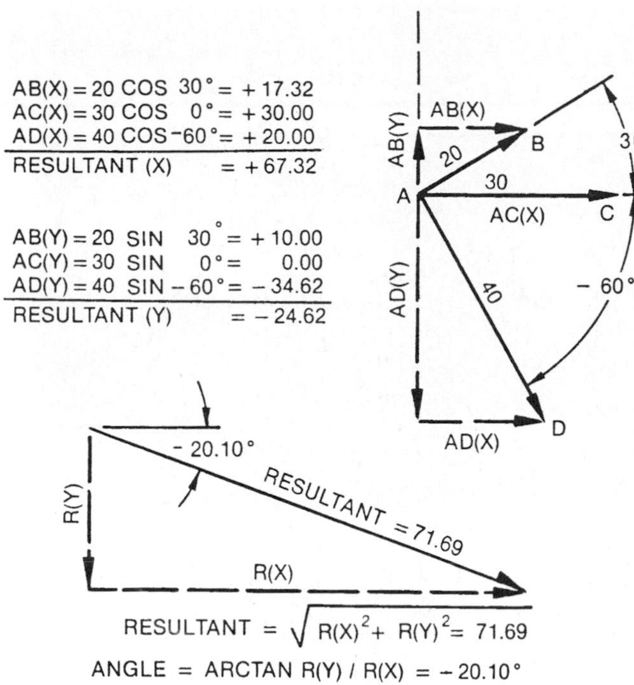

FIGURE 29.8 Mathematical Method

vector 1-2 acts in member AB, vector 2-3 acts in member AC, and vector 3-4 acts in member AD. The great advantage to this is that the label of the tail of one vector is the same as the label of the head of the succeeding vector polygon. Bow's Notation gives a logical and consistent sequence to vector summation and simplifies vector labeling.

The **vector polygon** is constructed by drawing vector 1-2 exactly parallel to member AB. Next, vector 2-3 (parallel to member AC) is drawn, starting at point 2 of vector 1-2. Finally, vector 3-4 (parallel to member AD) is drawn, starting at point 3 of vector 2-3. The resultant of vectors 1-2, 2-3, and 3-4 is vector 1-4.

The **mathematical method** illustrated in Figure 29.8 uses the summation of forces parallel to the horizontal X axis and to the vertical Y axis. The X component and the Y component of each force acting in members AB, AC, and AD are individually calculated and summed. These sums are the X and Y components of the resultant force. While this method gives as many decimals of accuracy as the calculator will permit, accuracy to three significant figures (obtainable in graphic solutions) is all that is required for most professional engineering practice.

You May Complete Exercises 29.1 Through 29.4 at This Time

29.5 COPLANAR FORCE SYSTEMS

Examples of coplanar force systems include equipment such as mobile constrution cranes and towers, earthmoving loaders and backhoes, forklifts, and tow trucks, highways, building beams, and trusses. Even though these objects are physically three dimensional, the main loads acting on these bodies as a result of the work being done (working loads) form coplanar force systems. Analyses of the strength of the materials, stability, and buckling require the three-dimensional shape.

29.5.1 Two Force Members

Two methods of supporting a 10 lb block are shown in Figure 29.9—a column under the block, and a chain suspending the block. These two systems are also presented as drawings in Figure 29.10(a) and (c). The column and the chain are both considered weightless here so that the weight of the block and the readings of the two scales can all be considered equal.

In Figure 29.10(a), the forces acting on the column are shown collinear with the centerline of the column. If this were not true and the column were not otherwise supported, the system would collapse. The push of the block at point A must be counteracted by an equal and opposite push by the column [Newton's third law, Fig. 29.10(b)]. A similar equal and opposite push is transmitted from grain to grain along

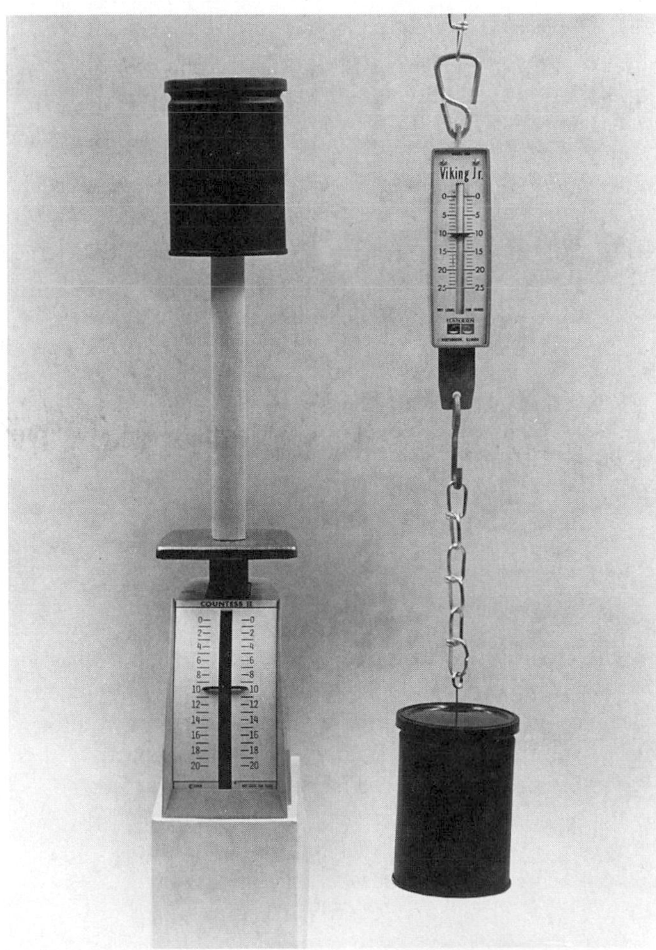

FIGURE 29.9 Two Methods of Supporting a Block

Focus On . . .

MAGNIFICENT IRON BRIDGES

Iron was truly the miracle material of the nineteenth century. Suddenly a material that was strong, inexpensive, fire-resistant, and easy to obtain was available for engineering structures. It served the period between wood and steel and was perfect for an era hungry for a material to build canals, roadways, railroads, bridges, and beams and columns for buildings. Between 1840 and 1880, thousands of iron bridges were built in the United States, and several still survive, mainly in New York, Ohio, and Pennsylvania. After 1880, a new miracle material, steel, replaced iron in engineering structures.

The beauty that iron brought to bridges of the time may never be matched. Cast iron was chosen for compression members in these bridges, and wrought iron was only for tension members, since it was twice as expensive as cast iron.

In the early nineteenth century, several designers—Burr, Town, Long, Howe, Pratt, and Warren—created the triangular patterns called trusses to distribute stresses in bridges safely. Trusses make these roads spanning rivers or ravines stronger and stiffer by helping them resist the weight of the loads against them. Early truss designs were for wooden structures; later designs were for iron and steel structures. In 1847, Squire Whipple published the world's first book on mathematical truss analysis, *An Essay on Bridge Building.*

Truss bridge.

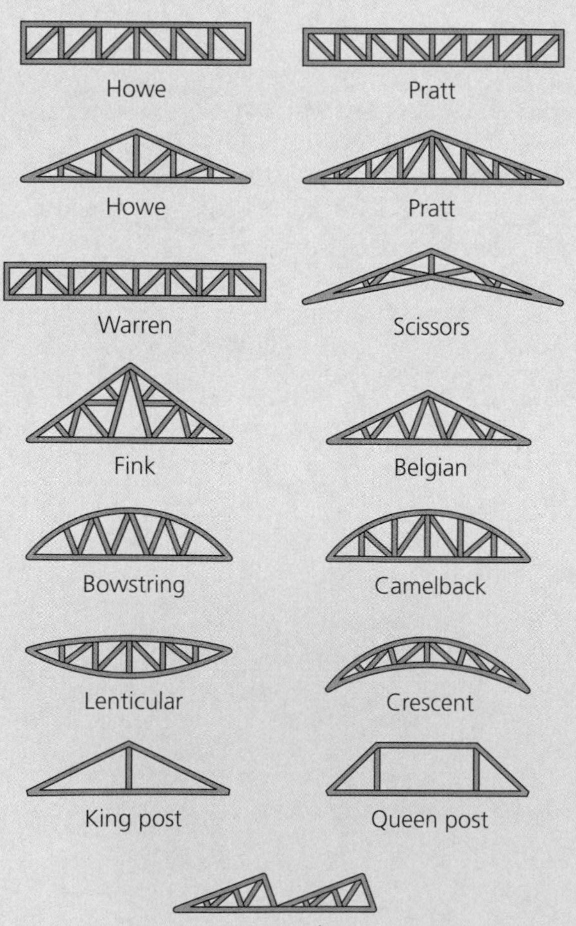

Truss designs.

The first real move away from wood came in 1840, when William Howe patented the Howe truss design, which had vertical wrought-iron tension members and heavy wood diagonal compression members. (William was the uncle of Elias Howe, designer of the sewing machine.) The simple designs of Warren and Pratt survived the transition to cast iron and steel and have endured into the twentieth century.

As the country expanded west, formidable rivers like the Ohio and the Mississippi required more mathematical contributions to bridge design. The Mississippi was spanned in 1874. But 1876 saw a terrible disaster on the Ashtabula Bridge: On a cold winter night, the Ohio cast-iron and wrought-iron bridge built in 1865 collapsed, plunging a passenger train into the river below and killing six people. The report by the American Society of Civil Engineers condemned the combination cast- and wrought-iron design and recommended an all wrought-iron construction with riveted rather than pinned connections. A similar collapse in Britain in 1879 was blamed on a lack of understanding of metallurgy, bad manufacturing techniques, defective castings, and instability under wind loads.

After the Ashtabula disaster, railroads launched design competitions based on specifications and performance rather than off-the-shelf or in-house designs. Written specifications for bridges were new in this era. The first set of specifications was written in 1871 by George Morison and required successful bidders to submit stress diagrams, calculations, and plans and to inspect materials and workmanship during construction. By 1880, bridge consultants were the first specialists in civil engineering.

Bridge building had at first been the province of frontiersmen with instincts for design. It evolved into a precise science in which structural analysis, manufacturability, knowledge of metallurgy, and practical construction techniques became absolutely essential skills for the bridge designer. The iron bridges that survive to this day are a tribute to the time when we were discovering the true beauty of bridge design.

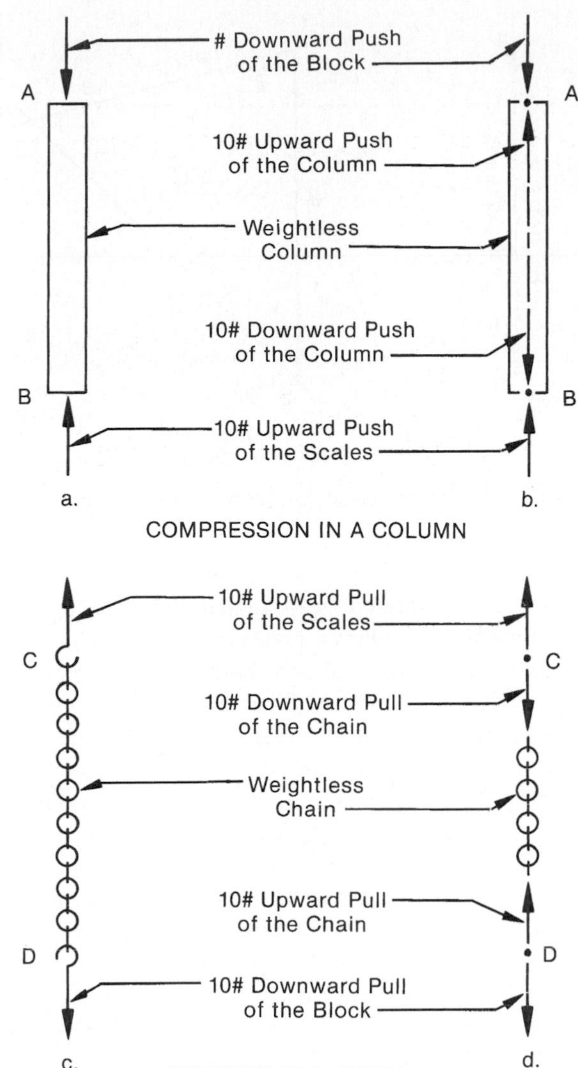

FIGURE 29.10 Graphical Representations of the Support Methods

the length of the column to the end at point B. Here the column now exerts a push on the scale, and the scale pushes back with an equal force, as indicated by the dial reading.

In Figure 29.10(c), the forces acting on the chain are shown collinear with the taut chain. This collinearity is easily demonstrated with a simple string model. The downward pull of the hook on the block at point D must be counteracted by an equal and opposite upward pull by the chain [Fig. 29.10(d)]. A similar equal and opposite pull is transmitted from link to link of the chain until the top link exerts a downward pull equal to the weight of the block. This example demonstrates two-force structural members in compression or in tension.

When two forces act on a member in equilibrium, the lines of action of the two forces are collinear, equal in magnitude, and opposite in action. A member in compression exerts a pushing force at each end of the member; a member in tension exerts a pulling force at each end of the member.

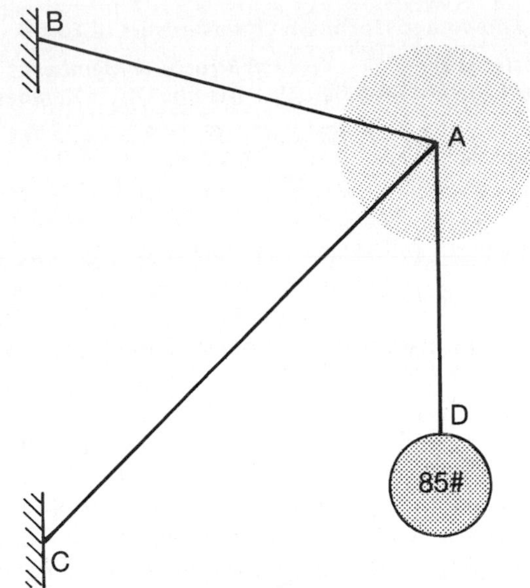

FIGURE 29.11 Three-Force-Member Support Bracket

29.5.2 Three Force Members

A **three-force**-member support bracket is presented in Figure 29.11. This bracket has pin connectors at each end and supports the gravity load shown. The force acting in each member of the bracket when the system is in equilibrium is to be determined.

The **structural diagram** must reproduce accurately the shape of the support bracket. It is the source of the line of action of the force (and of the vector) acting in each member. Graphical accuracy in this diagram is mandatory. The members are identified as AB, AC, and AD (Fig. 29.12). The bracket is assumed to be in **static equilibrium.** Point A is the connection that is common to all three members; therefore, solving for equilibrium at joint A will provide the required answers.

The technique for solving the problem is first to consider joint A as an isolated part of this structure (a **free body**) that is in equilibrium and then to find the magnitude and sense of the force in each member common to point A.

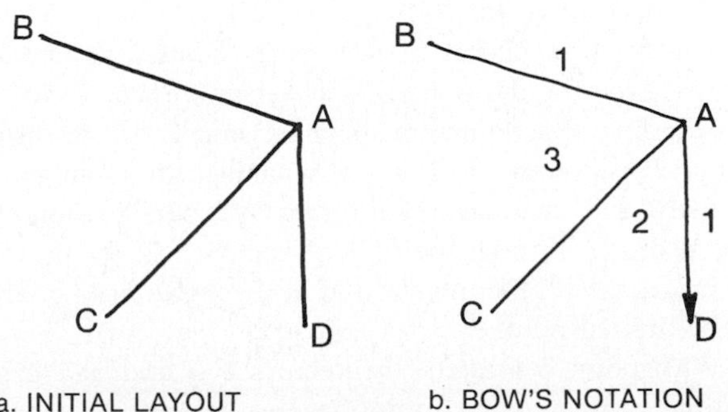

FIGURE 29.12 Layout and Bow's Notation for the Three Force Members

Known and Unknown Characteristics of Forces			
Characteristics of Each Force	***Force in Structural Members***		
	Member AB	***Member AC***	***Member AD***
Point of Application	Point A	Point A	Point A
Line of Action	Parallel to Member AB	Parallel to Member AC	Parallel to Member AD
Magnitude	Unknown	Unknown	85 pounds
Sense	Unknown	Unknown	Tension (−)

FIGURE 29.13 Summary of Problem Parameters

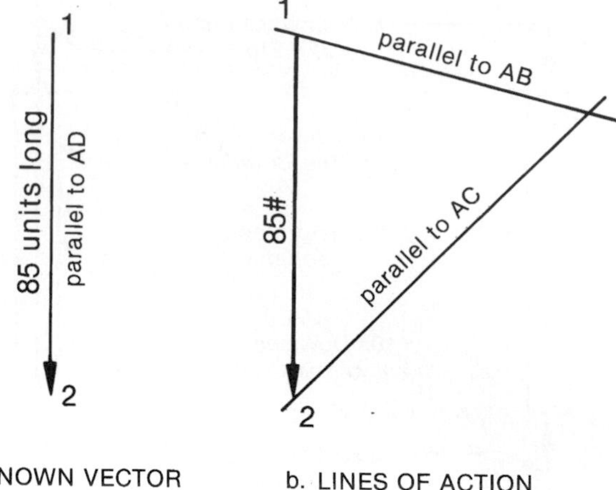

FIGURE 29.14 Vector Description of the Problem

A concise summary of the given problem parameters is given in Figure 29.13. A tabulation like this is helpful to plan strategies for the solution to the problem and to ensure that significant facts are not overlooked. It is a worksheet that may not be included with the design documentation, but it will be a of substantial help in efficient problem solving.

Examination of the selected joint starts with a **free body diagram.** This may be drawn freehand, but should approximate closely the angles of the members (and of the lines of action of their forces). Figure 29.12(a) shows the initial layout and labeling of the free body diagram. An arrowhead is added to indicate how the known force acts on point A. The gravity force attached at point D of member AD causes a tension force to act in member AD and, in turn, to apply a tension force pulling away from point A along the line of member AD.

Next, **Bow's notation** is added to give logical sequence and notation to the vectors of the force diagram. Numbering of spaces should always allow vector 1-2 to represent the known force. The force diagram in Figure 29.14(a) is started by drawing the known vector 1-2 exactly parallel to member AD. This is its correct line of action. The length is scaled accurately to represent the known magnitude.

Vector names are taken from Bow's notation in the free body diagram in a continuous order of rotation. In the solution in Figure 29.14, the rotation around point A is clockwise. The labeling places 1 at the vector tail and 2 at the vector head so that reference to vector 1-2 shows that the push of the force is from 1 to 2. Bow's notation will cause point 2 also to be the tail of vector 2-3 and point 1 also to be the head of vector 3-1.

The lines of action of vectors 2-3 and 3-1 are now drawn, even though point 3 is as yet unknown. Vector 2-3 has the line of action of member AC and is drawn through point 2 of vector 1-2 exactly parallel to member AC. Similarly, the line of action of vector 3-1, parallel to member AB, is drawn through point 1 of vector 1-2. As shown in Figure 29.14(b), the intersection of these two lines of action is the desired point 3.

With point 3 located, the vectors 2-3 and 3-1 can be completed by drawing appropriate arrowheads, as shown in Figure 29.15. Equilibrium requires that the summation of all of the vectors in the force diagram be zero. This means that all vectors are connected head to tail (also the result of correct application of Bow's notation). The magnitude of each vector is now measured and should be recorded on the diagram. The sense (motion direction) of these forces is unknown at this moment, but is determined by completing the free body diagram. The arrowhead indicates the push of the force along the line of action of its corresponding member as it acts on joint A. If the implied motion (sense) is toward point A, the member is in compression. If the implied motion (sense) is away from point A, the member is in tension. If 2-3 must be in compression, then its head is at 3, and 3-1 must be in tension. To improve readability, the arrowheads on lines AB and AC are placed in the middle of their length.

The free body diagram and the force diagram now show the answers to the problem statement. However, it takes considerable searching by another reader or reviewer to find them. Thus, although the free body diagram and the force diagram are necessary for the solution of the problem, they are difficult to sort through to find the required information.

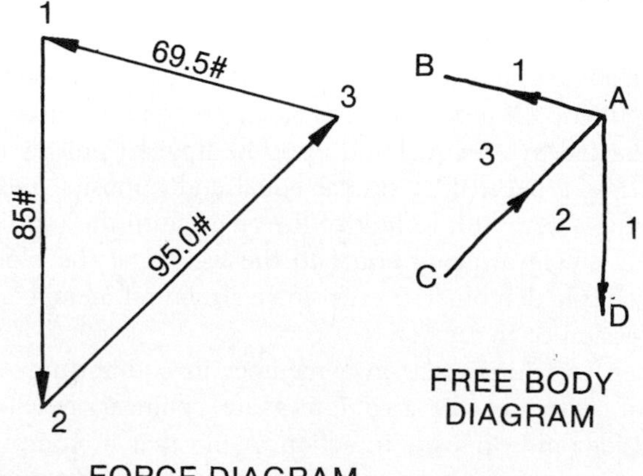

FIGURE 29.15 Force Diagram and Free Body Diagram of the Problem

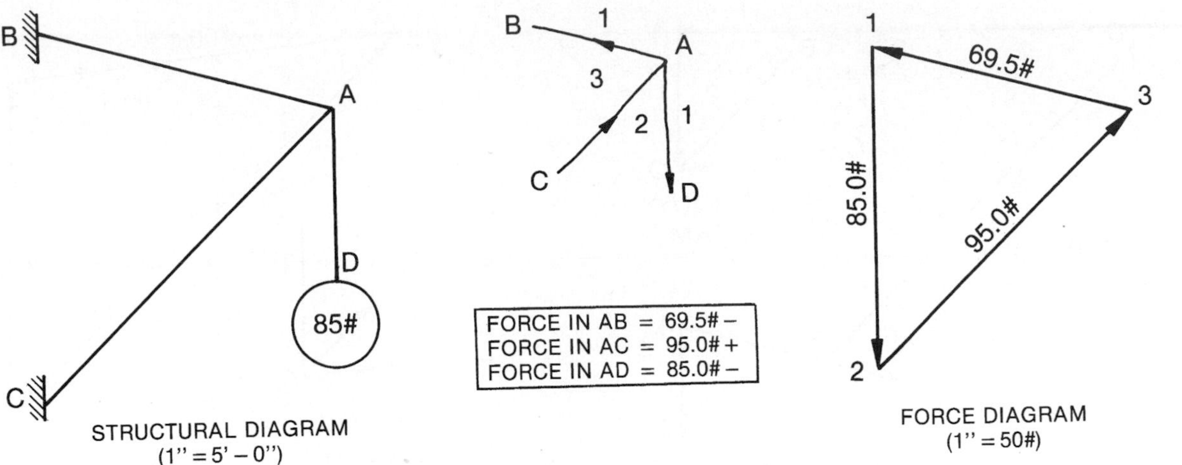

FIGURE 29.16 Complete Solution to the Problem

The complete solution of this problem is shown in Figure 29.16 and should be examined carefully. Note the following:

- The natural sequence of diagrams is left to right.
- The structural diagram is drawn to scale and the scale is noted.
- The scale of the force diagram is noted.
- The free body diagram, as a link between members in the structural diagram and vectors in the force diagram, is positioned between these diagrams.
- Values are recorded where they are found: magnitude in force diagram, and sense in free body diagram. This is valuable for visual checking.
- The summary of values is boxed.

29.5.3 Three Forces Acting on a Beam

A stiff member (a beam) capable of resisting bending is often used in simple lifting applications. This beam may be combined with two force members to make a useful mechanism. Figure 29.17 shows an application in which a beam is supporting a gravity load at one end and is also supported both at its opposite end and at an intermediate point. It is necessary to determine the forces acting in the two force members and to determine the force acting at each of the three connections of the beam. It is assumed that the system is in equilibrium.

Figure 29.17 is a simplified structural diagram of this system. The real problem is to determine what happens at points A, B, and C. The force acting in member AE is already known, and the force acting in member BD will be known when the conditions at point B are determined. However, the forces in the three separate connections to beam ABC are not discoverable by the methods used with the last problem. Figure 29.18 is a tabulation of the forces acting on beam ABC.

As in the last problem, the magnitudes and senses of two of the forces are unknown. In addition, the line of action of the force at point C is only partially known (it passes through point C). Consider the necessary conditions of a three-force system: A three-force system is coplanar and concurrent. Members AE and BD are both two-force members, and forces carried by them must have lines of action through their respective connections. Extending these lines of action until they intersect (Fig. 29.19) establishes the point of concurrency at point O. Drawing line OC gives the desired line of action at point C.

The tangent method is recommended for measuring the

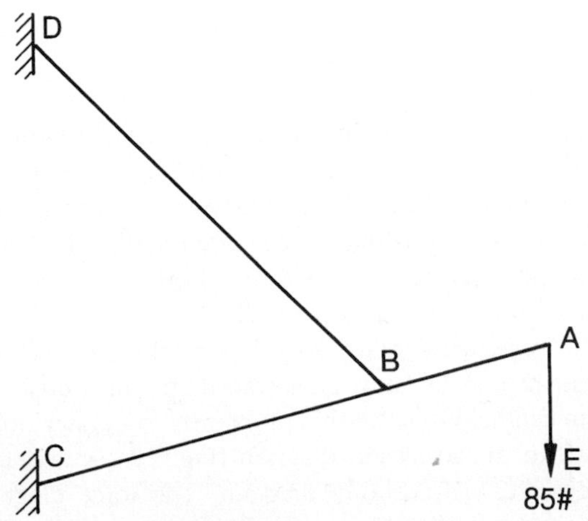

FIGURE 29.17 A Simple Beam Mechanism

Known and Unknown Characteristics of Forces			
Characteristics of Each Force	***At Point A***	***At Point B***	***At Point C***
Point of Application	Point A	Point B	Point C
Line of Action	Parallel to Member AE	Parallel to Member BD	Through Point C
Magnitude	85 pounds	Unknown	Unknown
Sense	Downward	Unknown	Unknown

FIGURE 29.18 Tabulation of Data for the Problem

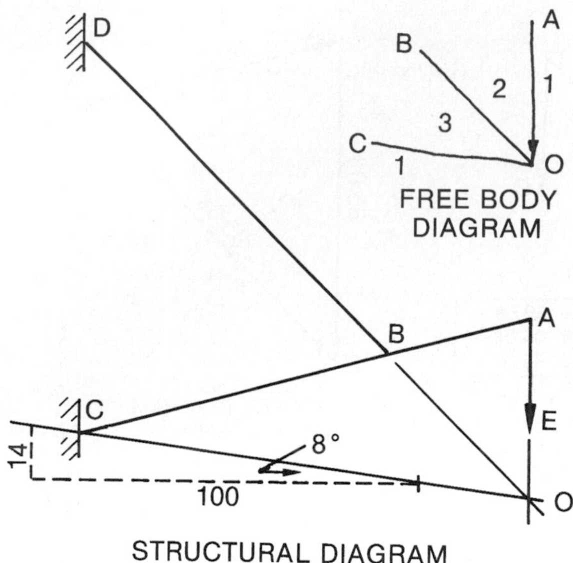

FIGURE 29.19 Free Body Diagram and Structural Diagram

angle of the force acting at point C (and all other angles). One side of the triangle should always be drawn 100 units long (Fig. 29.19). Then the other side of the triangle, divided by 100, is the tangent of the angle. Angles of forces acting on members are measured from the positive X axis, with clockwise measurements as minus degrees and counterclockwise measurements as plus degrees. This is consistent with mathematical practice.

The free body diagram is similar in form to the one in the last problem, but involves some slightly different concepts. It has point O (the point of concurrency) as the free body and then projects the forces as they act on the beam. Note that Bow's notation will make vector 1-2 the known force. The rotation around point O is counterclockwise in this example. A clockwise rotation would give identical values, but the force diagram would have vector 1-2 on the left side.

The force diagram is begun by drawing vector 1-2 and the lines of action of vectors 2-3 and 3-1 to position point 3 (Fig. 29.20). The force diagram is then completed and the

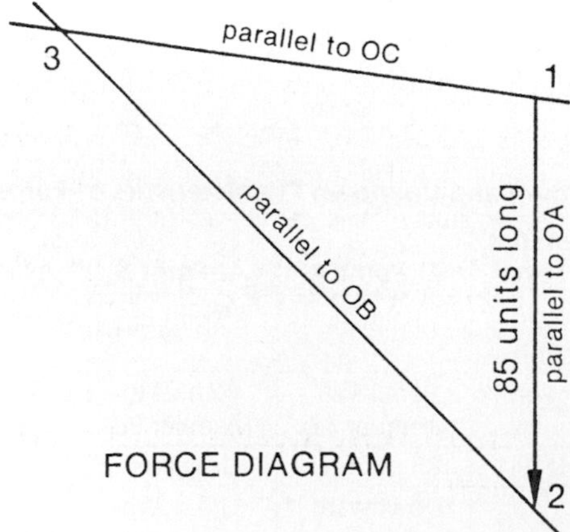

FIGURE 29.20 Force Diagram

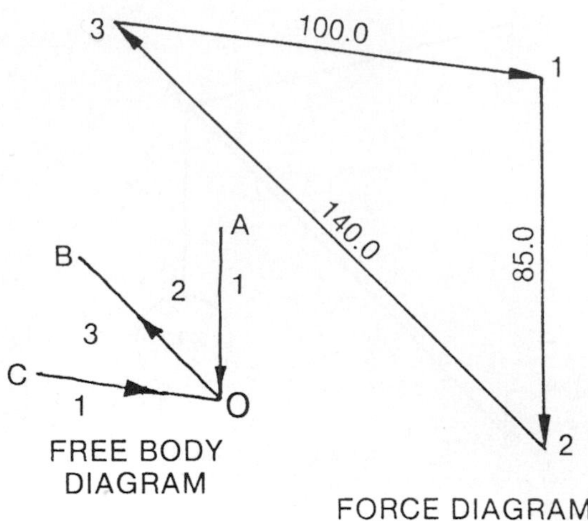

FIGURE 29.21 Completed Free Body Diagram

magnitudes of the forces recorded. The free body diagram is completed, with the push arrowheads of the found forces drawn in the middle of lines OB and OC, as shown in Figure 29.21. Remember that these indicate how the forces at points B and C act on the beam. Figure 29.22 shows the three diagrams of this solution and the necessary tabulation of results.

29.5.4 Three Parallel Forces Acting on a Beam

Beams that carry gravity loads frequently have forces acting along parallel lines of action (Fig. 29.23). The known load is a gravity load and acts vertically; the support at one end of the beam is also known to act vertically. The magnitude and angle of the force acting at each support are to be determined. The system is in static equilibrium.

The simplified structural diagram for this system is shown in Figure 29.23 with a pin-connected support at point A, a known vertical-line-of-action support at point C, and a known vertical load acting at point B. The known and unknown characteristics of the forces are summarized in Figure 29.24. The line of action at point A is given as "through point A" because a fixed-pin connection is capable of accepting a force acting in any direction. In this case, however, the force at A acts with a vertical line of action. The forces at points B and C, having vertical lines of action, cannot exert any horizontal force components; therefore, the force at point A cannot have any horizontal component either and necessarily acts vertically.

If the forces are parallel, they do not intersect and there is no point of concurrency. However, a special kind of force diagram can help to solve this problem. First, Bow's notation is added to the structural diagram (Fig. 29.25) and it now also serves as a free body diagram. The force diagram is begun by duplicating the position of points of application and lines of action of the space diagram. Then known vector

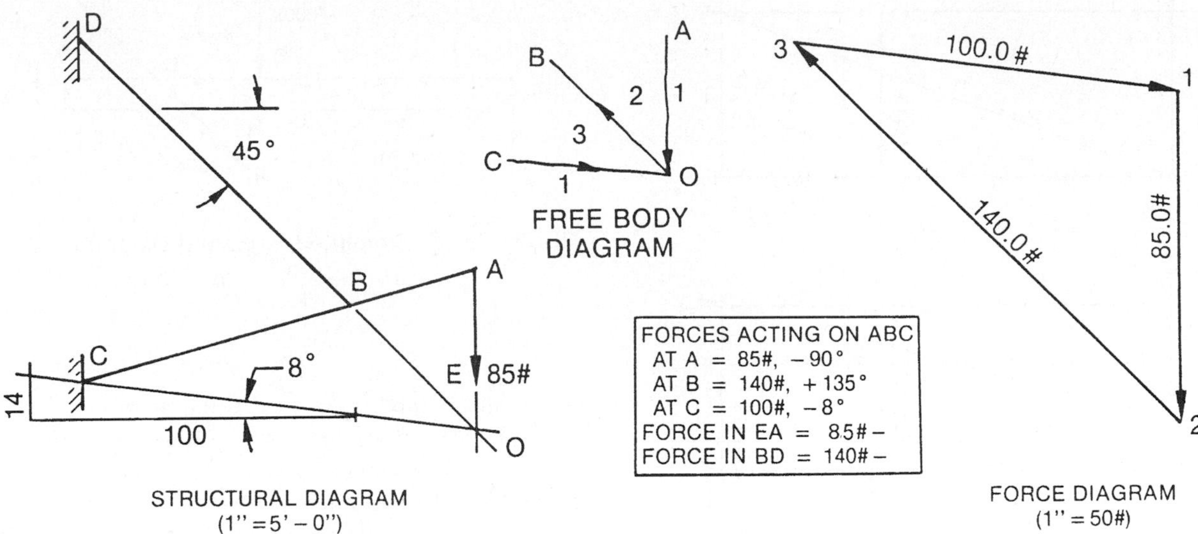

FIGURE 29.22 Completed Problem

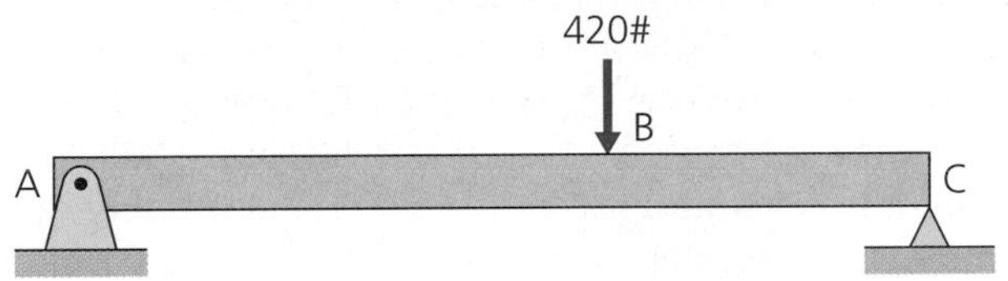

FIGURE 29.23 Simplified Structural Diagram

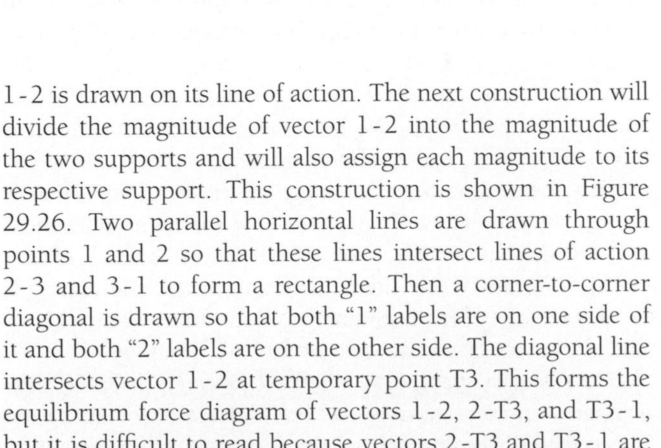

Known and Unknown Characteristics of Forces			
Characteristics of Each Force	***Forces on Member ABC***		
	At Point A	***At Point B***	***At Point C***
Point of Application	Point A	Point B	Point C
Line of Action	Through Point A	Vertical	Through Point C
Magnitude	Unknown	420 pounds	Unknown
Sense	Unknown	Downward	Unknown

FIGURE 29.24 Table Summarizing Data

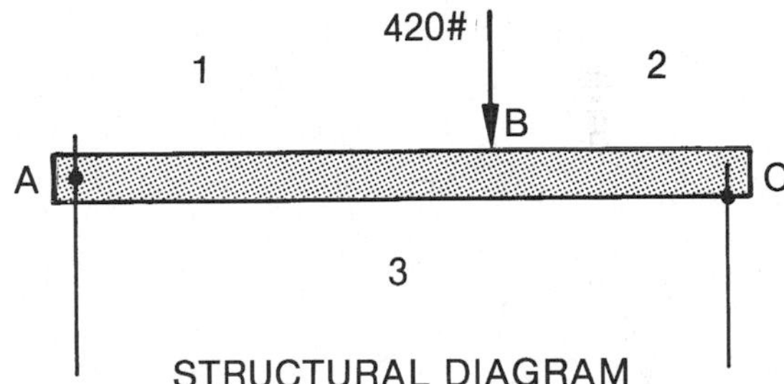

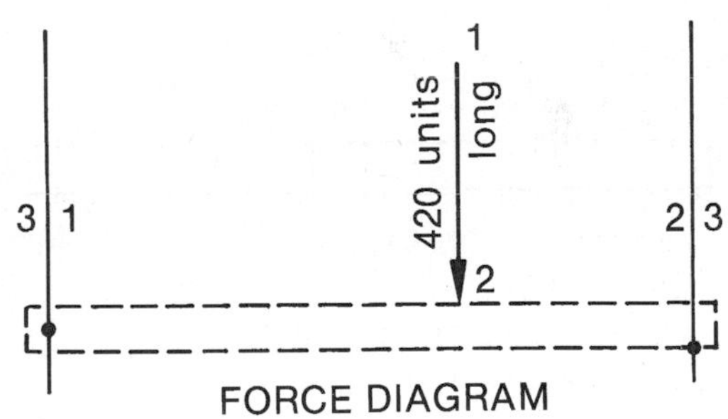

FIGURE 29.25 Structural Diagram and Force Diagram

1-2 is drawn on its line of action. The next construction will divide the magnitude of vector 1-2 into the magnitude of the two supports and will also assign each magnitude to its respective support. This construction is shown in Figure 29.26. Two parallel horizontal lines are drawn through points 1 and 2 so that these lines intersect lines of action 2-3 and 3-1 to form a rectangle. Then a corner-to-corner diagonal is drawn so that both "1" labels are on one side of it and both "2" labels are on the other side. The diagonal line intersects vector 1-2 at temporary point T3. This forms the equilibrium force diagram of vectors 1-2, 2-T3, and T3-1, but it is difficult to read because vectors 2-T3 and T3-1 are superimposed over vector 1-2 . To make the diagram easier to read, vector 2-T3 is superimposed over vector 1-2 and vector 2-T3 is moved to line of action 2-3 and vector T3-1 to line of action 3-1, by drawing a horizontal line through point T3. Arrowheads and labels complete the force diagram. The structural diagram and force diagram of the complete solution are shown in Figure 29.27.

29.5.5 Four or More Forces Acting on a Beam

Beams are used in building construction and in mechanical equipment to carry combinations of loads that may act along

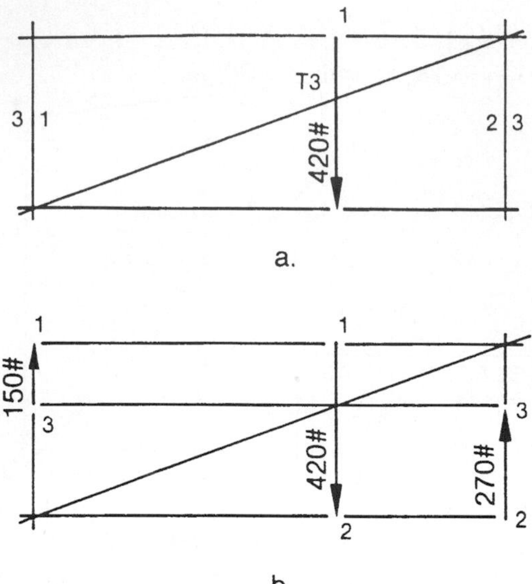

FIGURE 29.26 Support Reactions

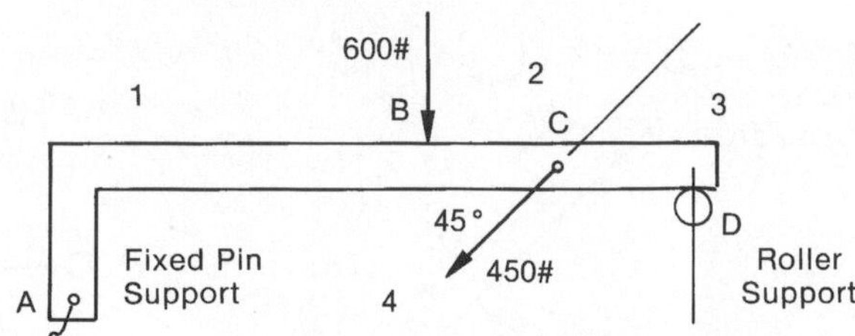

FIGURE 29.28 Simplified Structural Diagram

many lines of action. The beam in Figure 29.28 is supported with a fixed-pin joint at the left end and a roller support at the right end. This kind of support is common with beams because it allows for thermal expansion and contraction in the beam. The fixed-pin support can accept a force acting along any line of action, whereas the roller support can do so only along a line of action that is normal (perpendicular) to the supporting surface. Mechanical equipment uses beams with similar supports except that the beam may pivot at the fixed-pin support and be supported by a two-force member at the moveable support, with the force acting along the line of action of the two-force member.

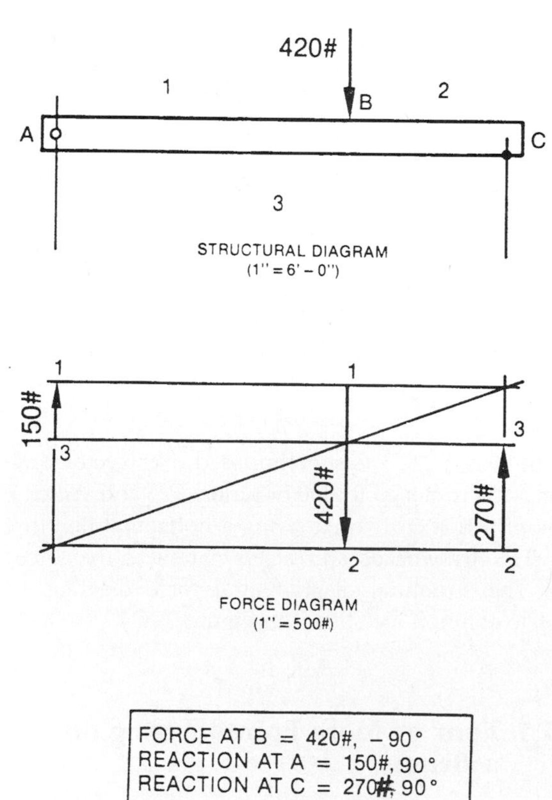

FIGURE 29.27 Completed Solution

Several important features of the lines of action in this structural diagram must be examined (Fig. 29.28). The fixed-pin support at A has an unknown line of action, as indicated by the wavy line. The box on the beam exerts its gravity force vertically through its center of mass onto the beam. This is represented by the force arrow (and line of action) at B. The block and tackle attached at the hole in the beam pulls downward and to the left. The force arrow at C shows this relationship. The roller support at D can only act normal to the supporting surface (bottom face of the beam) and therefore has a vertical line of action.

Bow's notation is placed on the structural diagram in nonconcurrent beam problems (the structural diagram then also serves as a modified free body diagram). The construction of a force diagram dictates that the known force vectors be graphically summed first, before the reaction vectors (supports) can be determined. This means that the spaces adjacent to the forces must be numbered first. They must also occur sequentially. That is why the line of action at C has been extended above the beam. The last restriction on Bow's notation is that only one space be permitted between the lines of action of the two reactions. A summary of the known and unknown characteristics of the four forces acting on the beam is tabulated in Figure 29.29. Of the four forces, two act vertically, one acts diagonally, and the other has an unknown line of action. This a nonconcurrent system of forces.

One solution method for this problem could be first to combine the known applied forces into one resultant applied force and then to use a three-force solution method. Determining the magnitude and angle of the resultant force is graphically easy. However, determining the point of application of this resultant force requires an additional diagram (a **string diagram**). The method given will avoid making a determination of a resultant applied force and will go directly for the determination of the two reactions.

The string diagram, also called the *funicular diagram,* is an accurate representation of the lines of action of all of the forces in the system and is constructed from an expanded force diagram. The steps of this construction are as follows.

Known and Unknown Characteristics of Forces				
Characteristics of Each Force	***Forces Acting on the Beam***			
	At Point A	***At Point B***	***At Point C***	***At Point D***
Point of Application	Point A	Point B	Point C	Point D
Line of Action	Through Point A	Vertical	45° Diagonal	Vertical
Magnitude	Unknown	600 pounds	450 pounds	Unknown
Sense	Unknown	Downward	Downward	Unknown

FIGURE 29.29 Summary of Known and Unknown Forces

1. Locate the points of application [Fig. 29.30(a)] in their exact space relationship. It is recommended that the shape of the beam be drawn lightly (to scale) and then the points of application located and labeled. This will provide for easy visual checking against the structural diagram. The line of action of each force is drawn through its respective point of application, and the lines of action are labeled according to Bow's notation. Because the line of action at point of application A is unknown, it is indicated with a wavy line. The strings of the string diagram will be drawn between these lines of action based on information from the force diagram.
2. The force diagram is begun graphically [Fig. 29.30(b)] by summing vectors 1-2 and 2-3 of the known forces acting at points B and C. The line of action of the reaction at point C is known, and its corresponding vector line is drawn through point 3. All that is known about point 4 is that it lies somewhere on this line.
3. The force diagram is expanded to include rays (used to give information about the strings of the string diagram). These rays are lines extending from the ends of the vectors to a pole point, labeled 0 in Figure 29.30(b). The positioning of pole point 0 is arbitrary and does not affect the results of the solution, but it does affect the shape (and the ease of drawing) of the string diagram.
4. Once the rays from point 0 to the ends of all of the

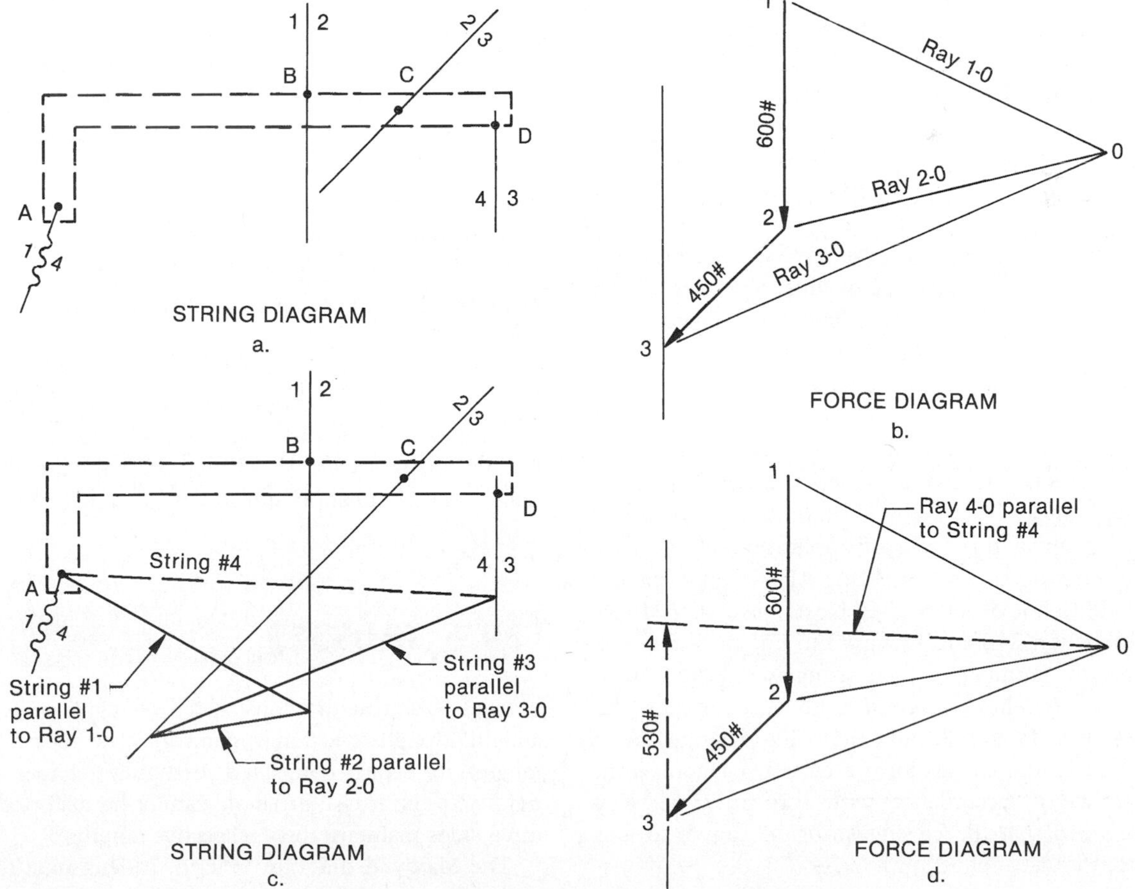

FIGURE 29.30 Constructing a String Diagram and a Force Diagram

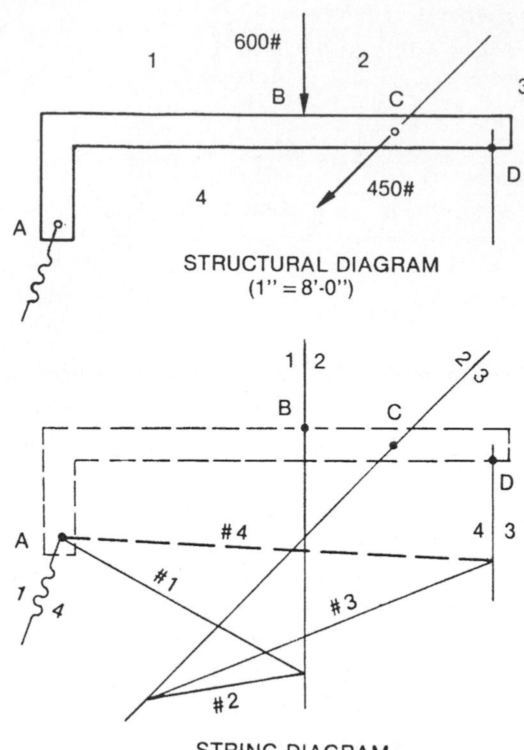

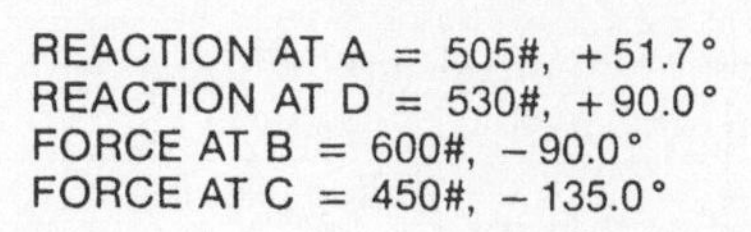

REACTION AT A = 505#, +51.7°
REACTION AT D = 530#, +90.0°
FORCE AT B = 600#, −90.0°
FORCE AT C = 450#, −135.0°

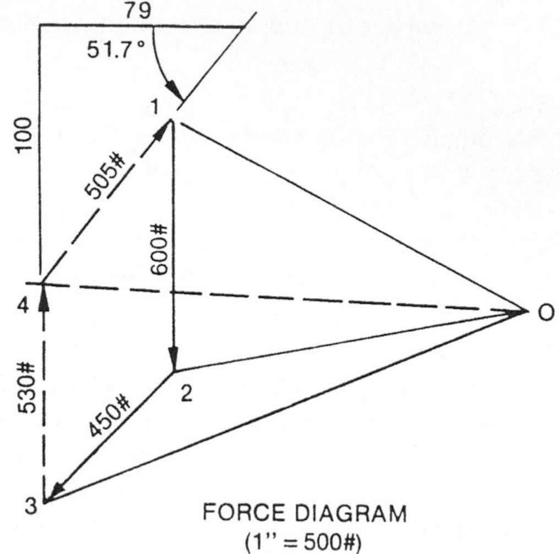

FIGURE 29.31 Completed Problem Solution

known vectors are established in the force diagram, they are used to give direction to corresponding strings in the string diagram. Note that ray 2-0 is common to vectors 1-2 and 2-3. Also, ray 3-0 is common to vectors 2-3 and 3-4, even though point 4 is not yet located. It follows that ray 1-0 is common to vector 1-2 and to the unknown vector 4-1 and that a ray 4-0 will be common to vectors 3-4 and 4-1. The determination of ray 4-0 will position point 4 on vector line 3-4 and permit completing the force diagram. Ray 4-0 is determined after finding its string in the string diagram.

5. The strings are drawn sequentially between their lines of action [Fig. 29.30(c)] and parallel to their corresponding rays. Point A is on line of action 4-1, regardless of its angular position, because it must pass through point A. Thus, it is always necessary to start the strings of the string diagram at the point of application of the fixed reaction. Starting at point A, string #1 is drawn (parallel to ray 1-0) to line of action 1-2. Next, string #2 is drawn to line of action 2-3 and string #3 to line of action 3-9. Note that the number of each string is reflected in the names of the two lines of action it intersects. Because this force system is in equilibrium, the string diagram always closes; that is, the strings form a closed polygon. String #4 is drawn in accordance with this principle. It is recommended that the closing string be drawn to look different (for visual checking).
6. The necessary information is now available to complete the force diagram. Ray 4-0 [Fig. 29.30(d)] is drawn parallel to string #4 and intersects vector line 3-4, giving position to point 4 and allowing completion and measuring of vector 3-4. Close the equilibrium force diagram with vector 4-1, and measure the magnitude and angle of vector 4-1.

The completed solution is shown in Figure 29.31, along with the required tabulation of all forces acting on the beam. Note that the angles of the forces reflect how they act on the beam, not how the beam acts on the imposing loads and the reactions.

Problems with three or more known loads (five or more forces, including the two reactions) are solved in accordance with the same principles that are illustrated here, remembering that the vectors of all known forces must occur sequentially in Bow's notation and in the force diagram.

29.6 TRUSSES

A **truss** is a structure constructed of many relatively short and lightweight two-force members. The members are arranged to create connected triangular shapes that give rigidity to the truss (a triangle cannot be distorted when its three sides maintain their respective lengths).

The **Maxwell diagram** is used to determine the magnitude and sense of the forces acting in the members of a truss. The complete analysis of a truss requires that the magnitude

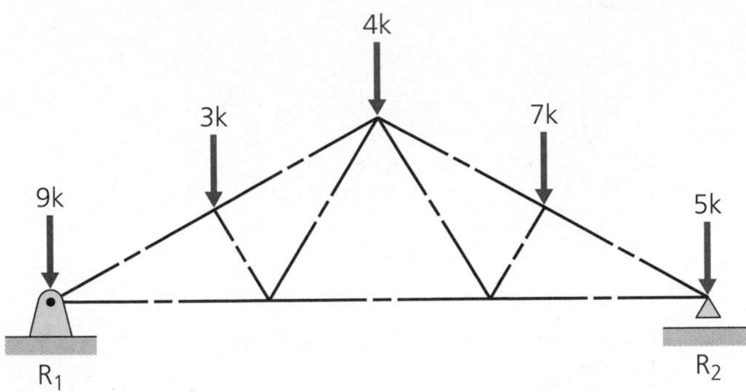

FIGURE 29.32 Structural Diagram of a Truss

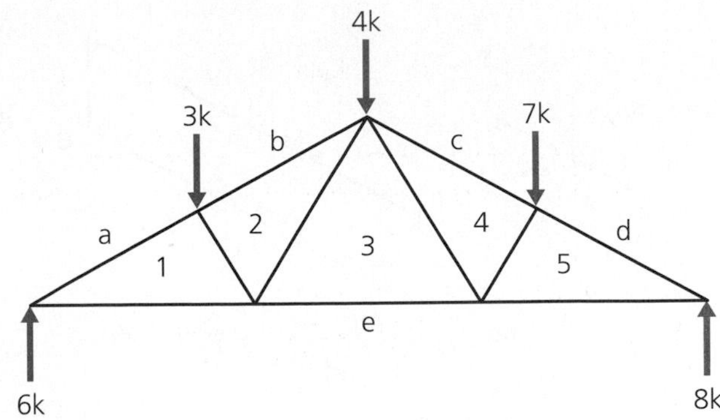

FIGURE 29.33 Simplified Structural Diagram of Truss

and direction of each reaction be determined. Then the magnitude and sense of the force acting in each member of the truss can be determined. The method to find reactions of trusses is exactly the same as that in the last section.

After the reactions are determined, the next step in the analysis of a truss is to determine the stress acting in each member of the truss. The method here requires that each connection of the truss be connected with pins (the centerlines of all members act through a common point). Each member carries only axial loads in tension or compression.

The analysis of a truss requires that each connection of the truss be examined independently to determine the magnitude and sense of the forces acting at that connection. As forces in individual members are determined, they become known forces and can be used to determine the forces acting in the adjacent connection. The order of examination of each connection is determined by the number of unknown forces acting at any connection. Only *two* unknown forces can be resolved at each connection.

The first step in the solution is to reduce the problem to its simplest form. This is accomplished with a structural diagram in which all structural members are represented by centerlines and all imposing forces are represented by force arrows (Fig. 29.32). Before proceeding further, imposing forces are examined to determine if any of these forces do not contribute to the forces acting in the members of the truss. In this example, the 9k force acting vertically over the support at R_1 and the 5k force acting vertically over the other support at R_2 act directly on the supports and do not contribute to forces acting in the truss. Therefore, they are eliminated from this analysis. The structural diagram shown in Fig. 29.33 shows only those forces that contribute to the stresses in the truss members. Also, the magnitude and direction of the reactions have been determined.

In Figure 29.33, Bow's notation has been added by labeling the external spaces between the imposing loads and the reactions with letters and the internal spaces of the truss with numbers. The labeling of external spaces is clockwise and starts between the left reaction force and a loading force. The labeling of internal spaces is from left to right, taking each space in order. This is usually the only labeling on trusses, and each member is named for the two spaces it is between. The connections are *not* labeled as in other vector solutions. This system of identification means that all external truss members (chord members) are identified by a letter and a number, all internal truss members (web members) by two numbers, and all imposing loads and reactions by two letters. This systematic identification system gives immediate information about each member. The vector for each member will be identified in the same manner.

The force acting at each joint (connection) is now found for those joints that do not have more than two unknown forces. The only joints having this condition are at the two ends of the truss. Selecting the joint at the left end, a free body diagram and a force diagram [Fig. 29.34(a)] are started. The known force (vector EA) is drawn parallel to its known line of action and at a selected force scale [Fig. 29.34(b)]. It is labeled according to the clockwise sequence of the structural diagram so that its tail is at E and its head at A [Fig. 29.34(c)]. Then the line of action of vector A-1 is drawn through point A of vector EA (parallel to member A-1), and the line of action of vector 1-E is drawn through point E of vector EA (parallel to member 1-E). The intersection of these two lines of action locates point 1, and this force diagram is completed [Fig. 29.34(c)] by drawing the vectors so that the joint is in equilibrium (all vectors in the diagram are head to tail and the diagram is closed). Knowing the direction of "push" of the forces as they act on this joint,

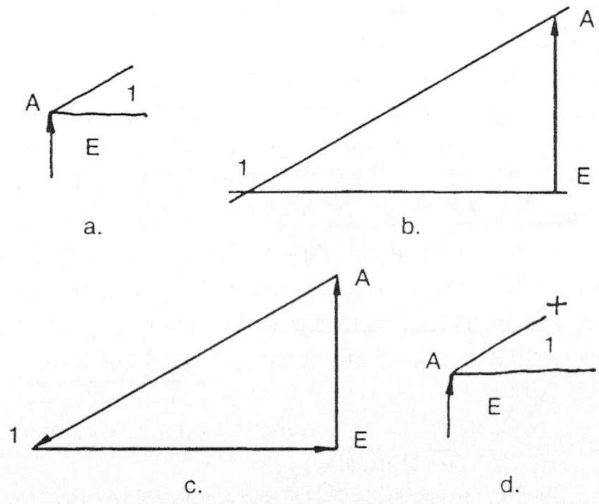

FIGURE 29.34 Partial Free Body Diagram

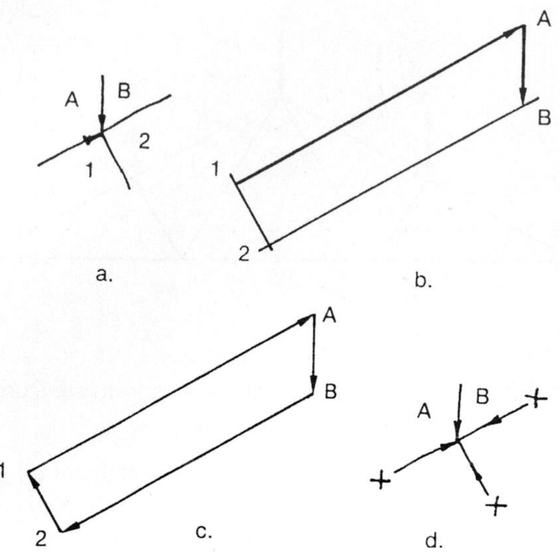

FIGURE 29.35 Next Free Body Diagram

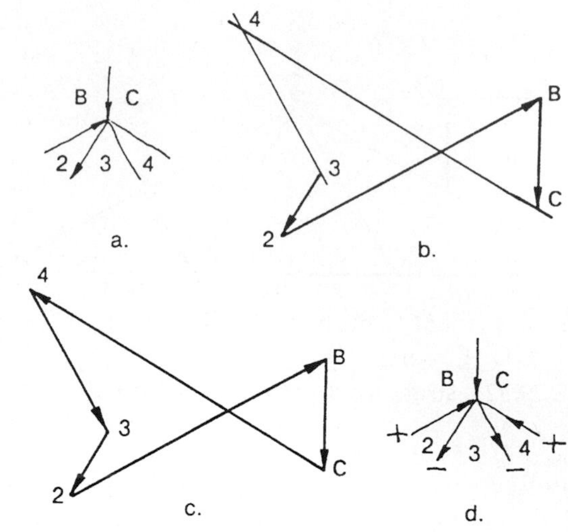

FIGURE 29.37 Joint 3-2-B-C-4 Free Body Diagram

the free body diagram can be completed and the sense of each force noted [Fig. 29.34(d)]. The solution of this joint now makes the forces in members A-1 and 1-E known, so they can be used in the solution of the next joints.

A new free body diagram of this joint is started showing the lines of action for the four forces acting on this joint and the direction given for the two known forces [Fig. 29.35(a)]. Note that the direction for the "push" of the force in member 1-A is now opposite the direction in the free body diagram of joint E-A-1 (compression members "push" at each end of the member). Then the force diagram is started by first drawing the two known forces (1-A and A-B, in this order) and by drawing the lines of action of B-2 and 2-1 [Fig. 29.35(b)]. Completion of the force diagram [Fig. 29.35(c)] and the free body diagram [Fig. 29.35(d)] determines the forces in members B-2 and 2-1. Joints E-1-2-3 and 3-2-B-C-4 are solved by these same procedures, as shown in Figures 29.36 and 29.37, respectively.

A comparison of the force diagrams for joints E-A-1, 1-A-B-2, E-1-2-3, and 3-2-B-C-4 shows that the force vector for each truss member in the left half of the truss has appeared twice, identical in line of action and length (magnitude) but acting in opposite directions. If these force diagrams were stacked one over the other, some drawing could be eliminated, and in addition a more concise solution for all of the joints could be made. This is the basis for drawing a **Maxwell diagram.** A series of individual force diagrams is drawn for each joint so that each is over the previous diagram. Thus, each force diagram for a joint can use vectors determined at a preceding joint. The imposing loads and the reactions must form an equilibrium force diagram before starting the individual-joint force diagrams.

Figure 29.38 shows the resulting stack of equilibrium force diagrams for all joints of the truss. When the force

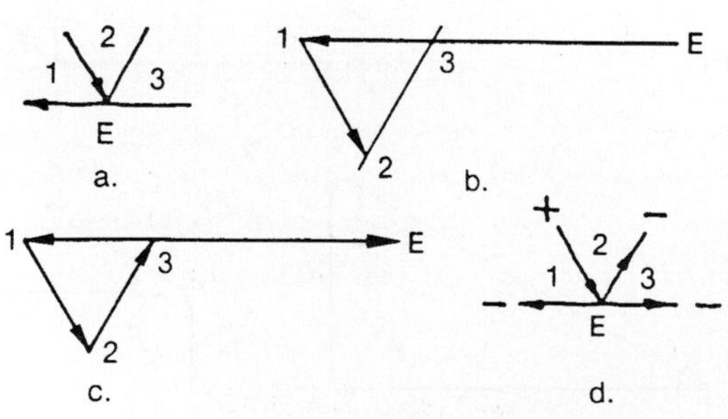

FIGURE 29.36 Joint E-1-2-3 Free Body Diagram

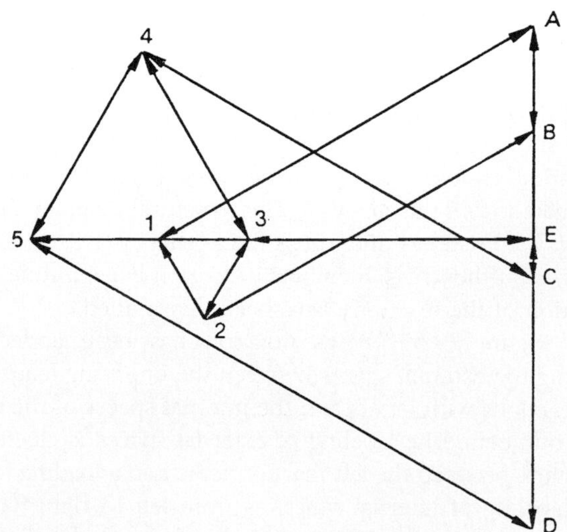

FIGURE 29.38 Stack of Equilibrium Diagrams

diagrams are superimposed in this manner, the vectors of every force in every member in a truss would have an arrowhead at each end. To avoid this, the arrowheads are not drawn on vectors for truss members in the Maxwell diagram, but the arrowheads for all imposing loads and reactions are drawn as shown in Figure 29.39. However, the arrowheads on each vector acting through a joint under investigation are assumed and are necessary to determine the sense of the force in that member. Also, a free body diagram is usually not drawn for each joint, although the structural diagram can be marked to serve this purpose.

Figure 29.40 shows a complete Maxwell diagram solution to the original problem. The final step in completing the problem is the tabulation of the values determined. List the external truss members (chords) first, in alphabetical order, followed by the internal (web) members, in numerical order. Give the sense of each force after the magnitude.

The solution for a similar truss having two vertical

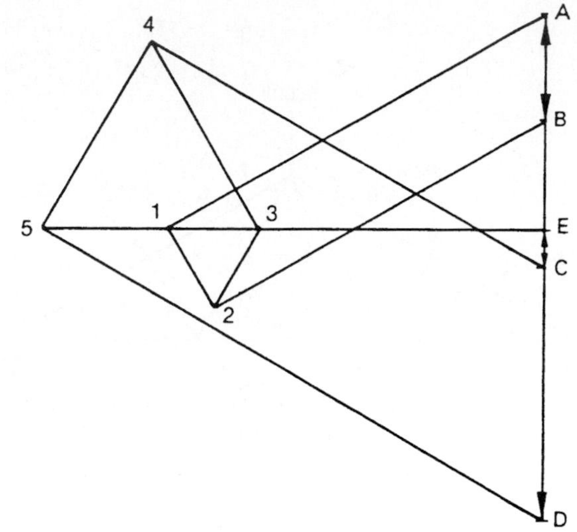

FIGURE 29.39 Maxwell Diagram

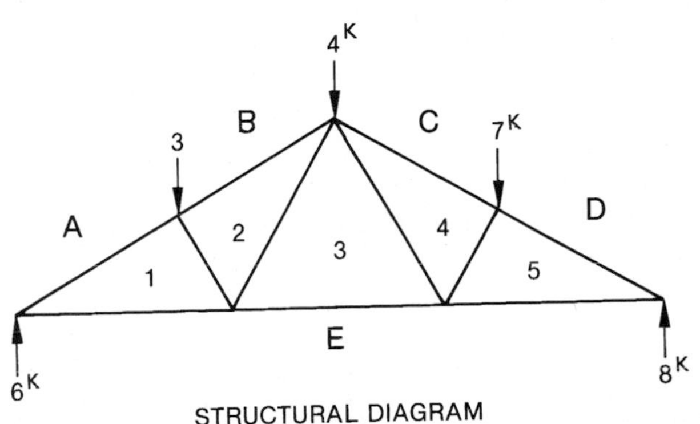

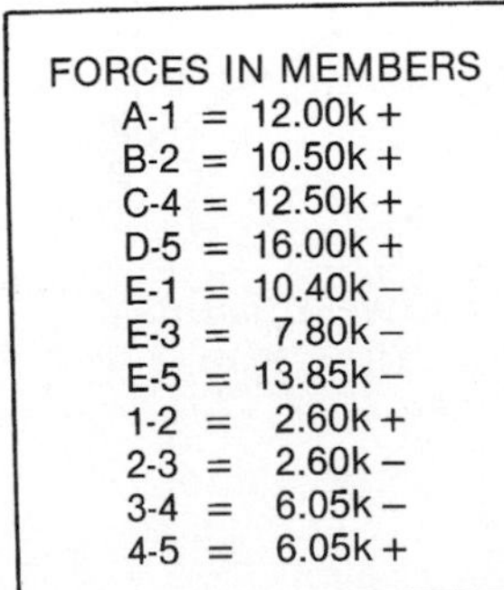

FORCES IN MEMBERS

A-1	=	12.00k +
B-2	=	10.50k +
C-4	=	12.50k +
D-5	=	16.00k +
E-1	=	10.40k –
E-3	=	7.80k –
E-5	=	13.85k –
1-2	=	2.60k +
2-3	=	2.60k –
3-4	=	6.05k –
4-5	=	6.05k +

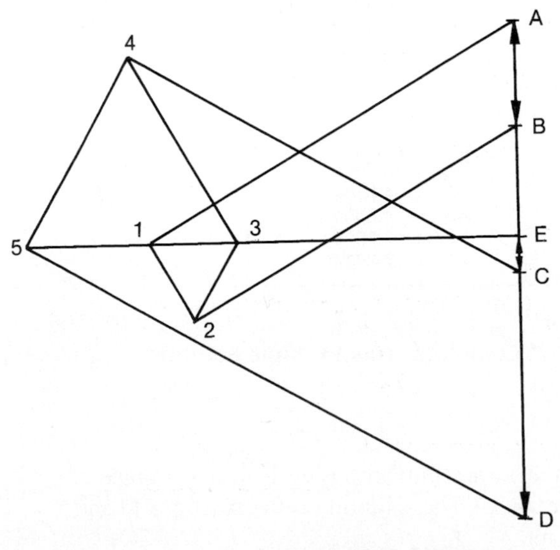

FIGURE 29.40 Complete Maxwell Solution

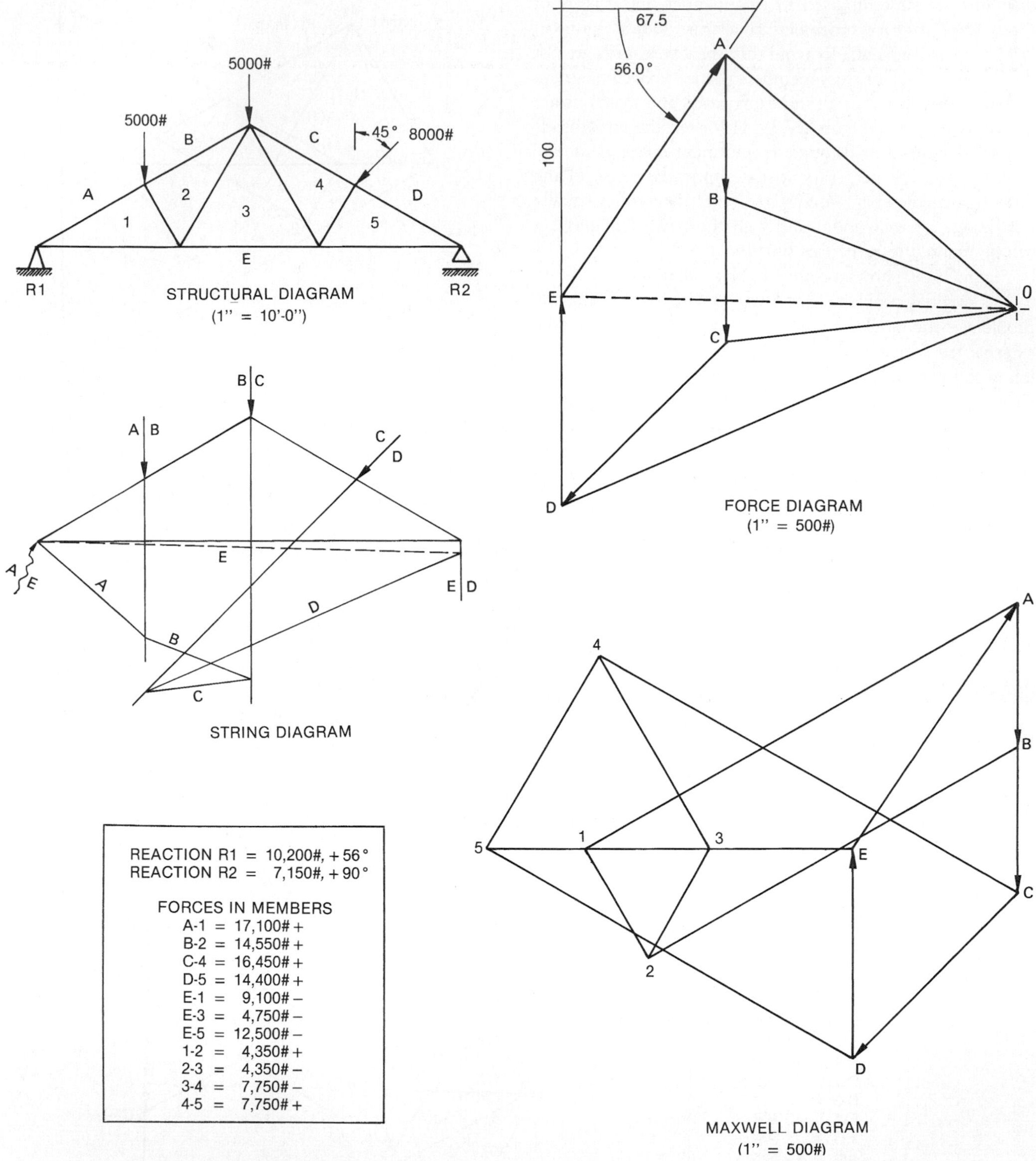

FIGURE 29.41 A Complete Truss Example Solution

imposing loads and the third imposing load at an angle is shown in Figure 29.41. The solution for the reactions Rl and R2 is the first step.

Graphical solutions provide adequate results for the design of these equilibrium structural systems if appropriate techniques are used. The principal requirements are that the design conditions be accurately known, that each vector be drawn exactly parallel to its line of action, that all vectors be scaled carefully (both drawing and reading), and that all force diagrams close.

You May Complete Exercises 29.5 Through 29.8 at This Time

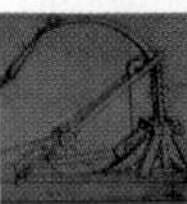

Applying Parametric Design . . .

FINITE-ELEMENT MODELING AND FINITE-ELEMENT ANALYSIS

Finite-element modeling (FEM) is the creation of a mathematical model representing a mechanical part or assembly that is under design. The FEM model is created via a program to subdivide the design model into a mesh of smaller, simpler, interconnected components known as finite elements.

In addition to creating the mesh, **Pro/MESH** defines the FEM model's attributes (such as **structural** and **thermal loading**).

After the FEM model is meshed, it is output to a **finite-element analysis (FEA)** program. The FEA program creates a mathematical simulation of the part or assembly and its **boundary conditions** and **loads.** It then analyzes the structural integrity of the part or assembly based on this simulation.

The results of the FEA are displayed in a variety of graphical and tabular formats.

FEM Procedure

1. Design a part or assembly.
2. While working in part, sheet metal, or assembly mode, prepare the part or assembly for meshing:
   - Simplify the part's geometry.
   - Add coordinate systems for specifying the vector components of loads and constraints.
   - Add datum points to position loads, mesh constraints, and bar elements on part surfaces.
   - Define materials.
3. Define the FEM model.
   - Assign material properties to the model.
   - Create regions on the model that divide the model's surface to allow for partial loading, constraining, and pairing of its components areas.
   - If required, create bar elements to represents struts, supports, or other features on a model that is to be modeled with shell mesh elements.
   - Specify a thickness for surfaces features that are defined as quilts.
   - If the model is to be modeled with shell mesh elements, define how its surfaces are to be prepared.
   - Apply loads and constraints to the model.
   - Apply mesh controls to the model.
4. Mesh the model.
5. Output the FEM model to the FEA program for analysis.
6. Display and evaluate the analysis results.

The steps completed prior to analyzing the FEM model are referred to as *preprocessing.*

A mesh is a representation of the FEM model consisting of a two- or three-dimensional arrangement of smaller, simpler, interconnected elements. The process of generating this mesh automatically is referred to as *meshing the model.*

After you have defined the FEM model, applied all required loads and constraints to it, and specified desired mesh controls, you are ready to generate the mesh. **Pro/MESH** uses two different mesh elements types.

Tetrahedral (tet) Solid three-dimensional elements
Triangular (shell) Two-dimensional surface elements

Once a mesh has been generated successfully, you can improve the mesh quality, refine the mesh locally, change the model geometry, modify the applied loads and constraints, or store the mesh data to a database file for later retrieval. You can also have mixed mesh types on the same part (Fig. A) or assembly (Fig. B).

To access the meshing functionality, choose **Make Model** from the FEM menu and follow the menu structure. To ensure the successful generation of a finite-element mesh, complete the following task prior to meshing a part or an assembly. In part, sheet metal, or assembly mode, make sure you do the following:

- Simplify the part(s) or assembly to remove features unnecessary for finite element analysis.
- Assign a material file to the part(s).
- Add all required load and boundary conditions to the part(s).
- Apply the appropriate amount of mesh control to the part(s) to control the fineness of the mesh.
- Create the appropriate shell model by defining all surface pairs.
- Assign a material file to shell pairs and solid chunks.

The mesh program uses tetrahedral elements to mesh solid parts. The meshing process attempts to create an optimal model of the solid volume of the meshed part or assembly with a network of three-dimensional tetrahedral elements.

How to Generate a Tet Mesh

1. Choose **Tet Mesh** from the FEM MESH menu.
2. In response to the displayed prompt, accept the default global min mesh control value or enter a new one.
3. The mesh generator creates the tetrahedral mesh using the specified global min mesh control value.

When the mesh has finished generating, the meshed model displays. After the FEM model's mesh has been solved via an online finite-element analysis program, the results of the analysis can be displayed. Postprocessing capabilities allow the thermal or structural analysis results to be displayed on screen in a variety of graphical formats.

To display the results of a model's structural analysis, choose the **Visualize** option from the RESULTS menu, and access the menu structure.

To display the results of a model's thermal analysis (Fig. C), choose the **Visualize** option from the RESULTS menu, and access the menu structure.

Once the structural or thermal analysis of your model is complete, there are many options to control how to display the analysis results. With these options, you can do the following:

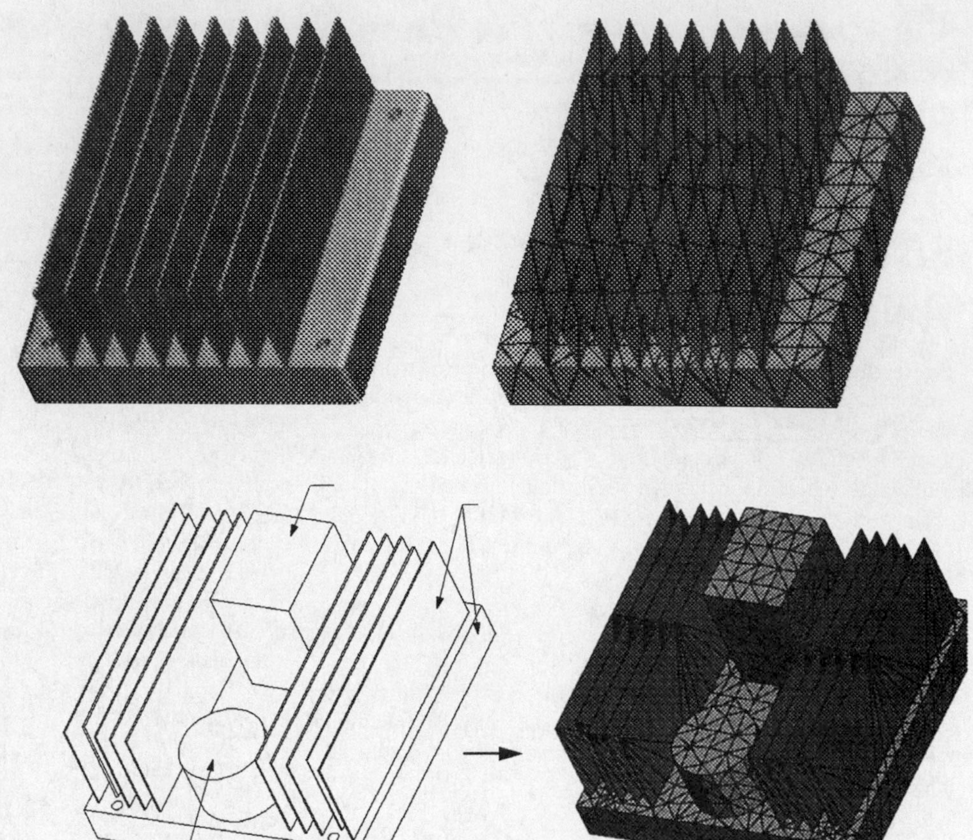

FIGURE A
Mixed Mesh on Part

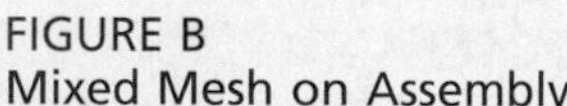

FIGURE B
Mixed Mesh on Assembly

- Specify any of the following color shading methods for representing analysis results on the model: smooth shading, stepped shading, above-value shading, and wireframe (suppressed shading).
- Represent analysis results on the model by user-defined isolines or isosurfaces (Fig. D).
- Compare the model in its undeformed state to its deformed state by means of superimposition.
- Display the entire model or only selected surfaces.
- Display the exterior or interior of the model.
- Display the outline of the mesh elements on the model.
- Display applied loads and constraints on the model.
- Cut the model so that it is not shown in its entirety. The model may be cut along a user-defined plane or at a user-specified level.
- Reorient and spin the displayed model by choosing **View** from the MAIN menu.
- Plot the display model by selecting **Interface** from the RESULTS menu.

When evaluating structural or thermal analysis results on the FEM model, it is often helpful to display the actual loads and boundary constraints that brought about the results.

How to display the FEM Model's Applied Loads and Constraints

1. Chose **Disp Options** from the VISUALIZE menu.
2. Choose **Loads/BC** from the DISP OPTIONS menu.
3. Choose any other desired options from the DISP OPTIONS menu.
4. Choose **Done** from the DISP OPTIONS menu.

The FEM model with its applied loads and constraints is displayed as in Figure E.

FIGURE C Thermal Analysis of Part

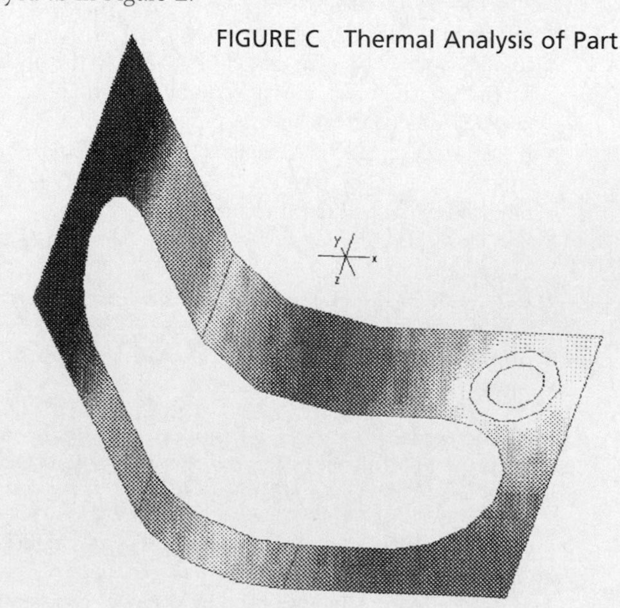

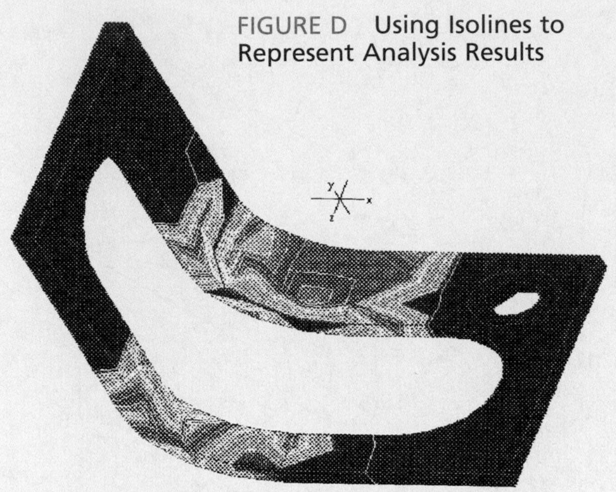

FIGURE D Using Isolines to Represent Analysis Results

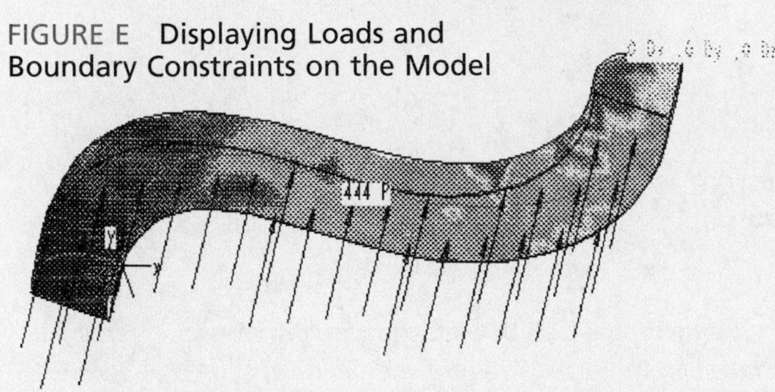

FIGURE E Displaying Loads and Boundary Constraints on the Model

Statistics can be gathered from the "top" and "bottom" sides of shell elements. The top side of a shell element is defined as the surface facing in the direction of the element's positive normal vector (Fig. F). The shell element's positive normal vector is calculated by applying the right-hand rule to the shell element's nodes.

Analysis statistics can be generated for the entire model or for only a selected surface, edge, vertex, or point. When evaluating analysis statistics generated for a model's edge, you have the option of displaying the statistics as a graph (Fig. G). This graph may then be output to a plotter.

How to Generate an Edge Graph

1. Choose **Info** from the RESULTS menu. The POSTPROCINFO menu opens.
2. Choose the analysis data to evaluate **Stress, Strain, Temperature,** etc.
3. If the model's mesh is comprised of shell elements, specify which side of the shell elements to generate statistics on:

   Top Side Generate statistics based on the bottom side shell elements.

   Bottom Side Generate statistics based on the bottom side shell elements.

   Average Val Generate statistics based on the average value of the top and bottom sides of the shell elements.

   Both Sides Generate statistics based on both the top and bottom sides of the elements.

4. Choose **Constr Cases** and specify which of the model's applied constraint cases to base the analysis statistics on. Multiple constraint cases may be represented on a single graph.

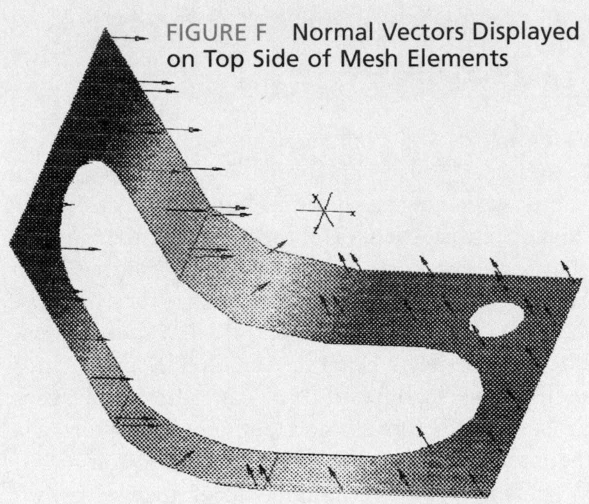

FIGURE F Normal Vectors Displayed on Top Side of Mesh Elements

5. Choose **Select.** Using the options provided in the GET SELECT menu, specify which of the model's edges to generate analysis statistics along.
6. Choose **Edge Graph.** The edge graph displays in a graph window.
7. If you wish to output the edge graph to a plotter, create a plot file by choosing an option from the PLOTTERS menu:

   colorpaste Create a plot file in color PostScript format.

   screen Display the edge graph plot in a graph window.

   list Display a list of supported plotting devices.

   others Create a plot file for a plotter other than the default plotter. Enter the name of the plotting device in response to the prompt.

   default Create a plot file for the default printer.

   postscript Create a plot file in standard PostScript format.

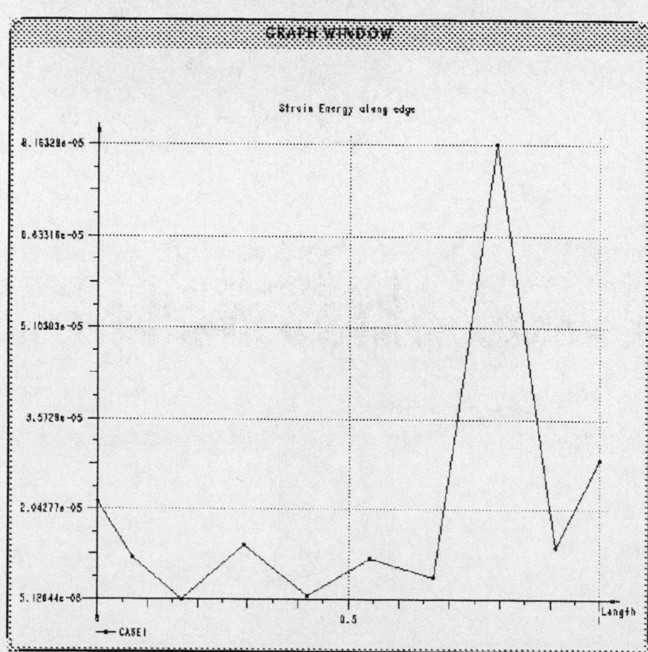

FIGURE G Displaying an Edge Graph

29.7 NONCOPLANAR FORCE SYSTEMS

The 2D principles from the previous sections can be extended to noncoplanar concurrent systems (3D). These systems are all in the general form of a tripod supporting a fourth member that exerts a known force at the point of concurrency. Applications of noncoplanar concurrent force systems occur in stationary support structures that are designed to carry loads applied from various three-dimensional directions. Examples are found in electrical transmission towers, ship and dockside cranes, tow trucks, portable shop floor cranes, and automobile jack stands. Only the forces as a result of working loads are considered. The equipment and structural members themselves will again be considered weightless and infinitely strong.

The principal difference between the analysis of 2D and 3D systems is the introduction of depth into the views. In coplanar analysis, a structural view is selected that projects all members true length, meaning all vectors project true length. In noncoplanar (three-dimensional) analysis, two structural views are required to establish the space relationships of the members. From two given views, it may be necessary to project auxiliary views to find necessary true lengths for the force analysis.

FIGURE 29.42 A Transmission Tower

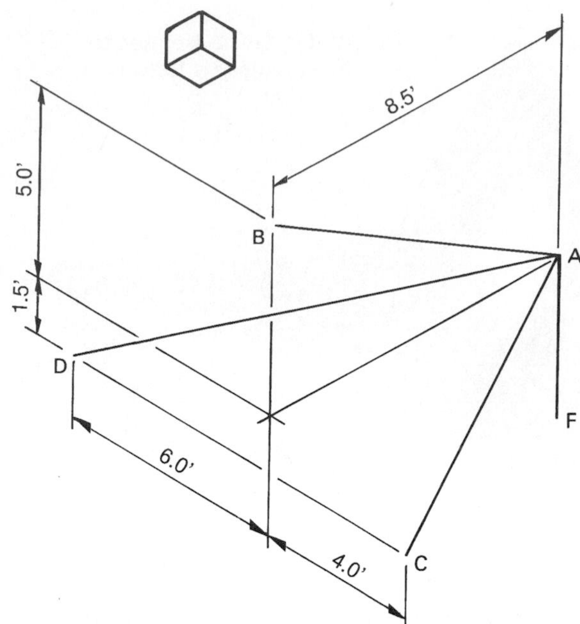

FIGURE 29.43 Space Relationships for a Noncoplanar Truss

A **special-case** solution is possible when the given structural diagram views provide the necessary lines of action to draw the force diagram views. Keep in mind that the force diagram is 3D and the space relationships of the structural diagram views are reflected in the force diagram views.

The previous coplanar problem solutions have all been based on the ability to draw a unique triangle when two angles and the included side are known. This same principle is applied to each of the views in the solution of noncoplanar problems and must satisfy these two general conditions:

1. No more than three lines of action are projected in each view.
2. One measurable force vector can be drawn along one of the projected lines of action.

For example: A transmission line tower supports an electrical cable with an insulator (Fig. 29.42). The force acting in each of the three members that provide support for the insulator must be determined. The space relationships for a similar problem are given in Figure. 29.43. This problem is nonsymmetrical. The force applied at point F is 1000 lb, acting vertically downward.

Structural views should be selected that will satisfy the conditions for lines of action and for a projectable force vector. The first condition of three lines of action for four members (AB, AC, AD, and AF) is satisfied easily if any one member is projected into point projection (its line of action is a point and disappears in that view). It will also be true length in the adjacent view. The condition is also met if two members are projected so that they coincide—that is, so that their force vectors share the same line of action in that projection. If a frontal view is drawn so that the plane ACD

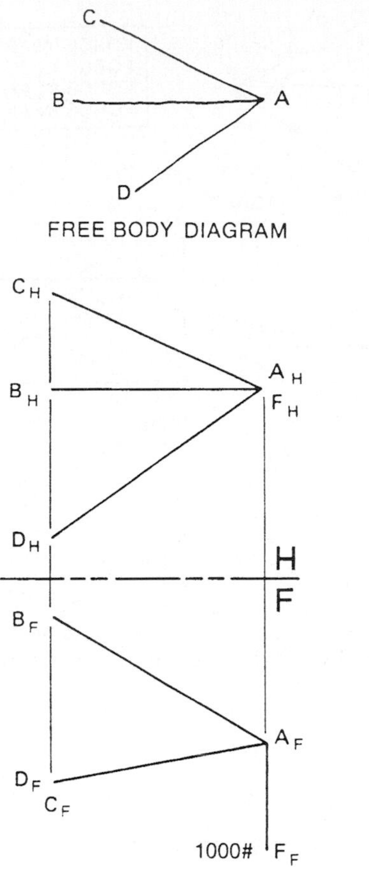

FIGURE 29.44 Frontal and Horizontal Projections in the Structural Diagram

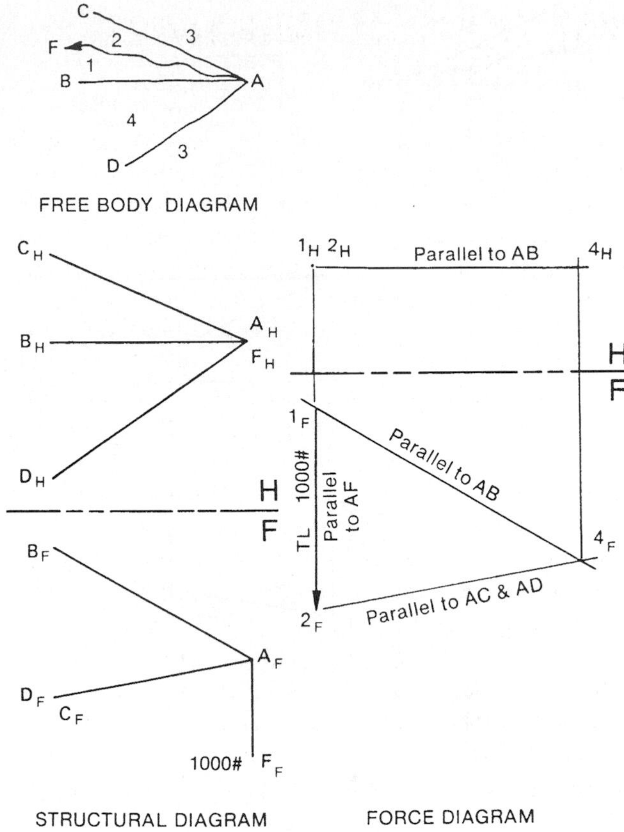

FIGURE 29.45 Start of the Force Diagram

is in edge view by putting the line DC in point projection, this condition is satisfied. At the same time, member AF, which carries the given load, is projected true length and satisfies the second condition of a known projectable length for the known force vector. Note: The member carrying the given load must not have the same line of action as another member.

This frontal projection and the horizontal projection are drawn in the structural diagram of Figure 29.44. The horizontal view also meets the requirement that no more than three lines of action be projected in it, and a "projectable vector length" will be obtained from the frontal view. These two projections provide all of the information needed to solve the problem. This is called the **special case.**

Before drawing the 3D force diagram, it is necessary to decide the order of summation of the force vectors and to ensure that this order will be followed in each view of the force diagram. A free body diagram serves this purpose; it also helps determine the sense of each of the forces. The start of the free body diagram is shown in Figure 29.45. The free body diagram (one view) is sketched parallel to one of the space views, with the space view usually having one member in point projection. This allows us to put this point projection member into whichever of three positions yields the most desirable vector sequence. This sequence requires that each view of the force diagram form a triangular shape. This in turn means that the vectors of members that coincide in a space view must occur sequentially. In this problem, this requirement prohibits placing line AF between lines AC and AD. Either of the other two choices is acceptable, the only difference is in how the force diagram will appear. In Figure 29.45, member AF is placed between members AB and AC, and Bow's notation is added to complete the free body diagram. Bow's notation assigns the known force in member AF to vector 1-2, which necessarily is drawn first in the force diagram.

The force diagram has frontal and horizontal projections that parallel the structural diagram projections. These will be drawn and completed by using lines of action from the structural diagram and by drawing the known vector to scale length. The force diagram is started (Fig. 29.45) by drawing the frontal view of vector 1-2 true length. The horizontal view of vector 1-2 is drawn in point projection. Then, in the frontal view, the line of action of vector 2-3 is drawn, parallel to member AC through point 2_F . Vector 3-4 is collinear with vector 2-3 (in the frontal view only) because members AC and AD are combined in the frontal structural view. All that is known now is that both points 3_F and 4_F lie

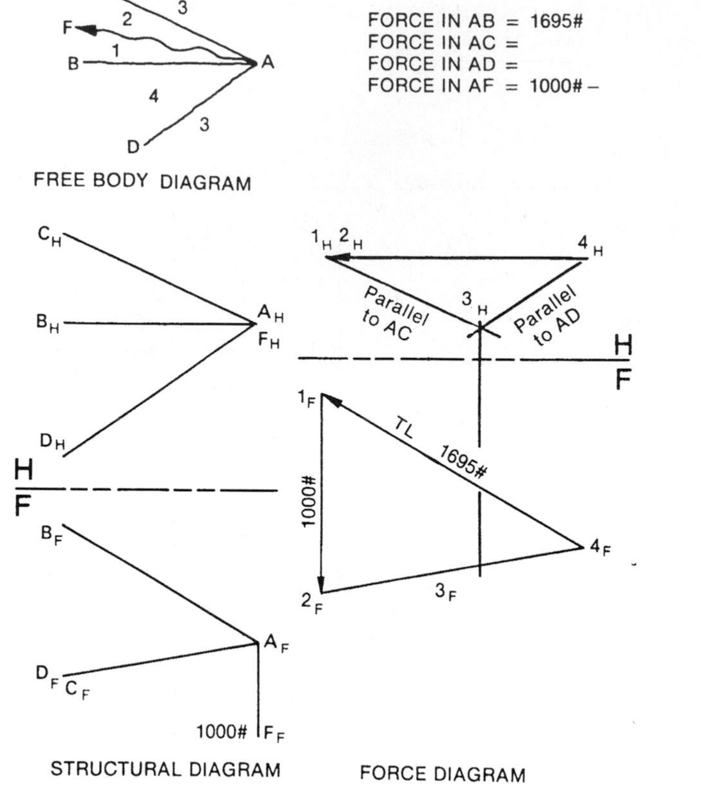

FIGURE 29.46 Completing the Special Case

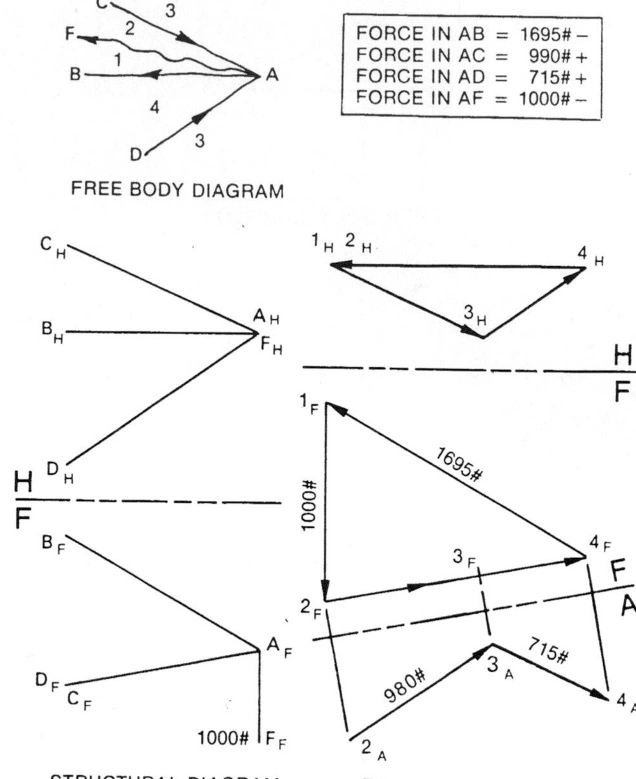

FIGURE 29.47 Completed Solution

on this line. The line of action of vector 4-1 is drawn through point 1_F, and the intersection of these two lines of action is point 4_F. This must be point 4_F and not 3_F because point 4 is common to both lines of action. Point 4_H is located by projecting from point 4_F across the fold line onto the line of action of vector 4-1 in the horizontal view. Vector 4-1 is completed, and, being true length in the frontal view, it is measured.

Locating point 4_H now gives a projected length of vector 4-1 in the horizontal view, making it possible to find point 3_H by projecting the line of action of vector 2-3 in the horizontal view through point 2_H and of vector 3-4 through point 4_H (Fig. 29.46). Their intersection is point 3_H, which can be projected into the frontal view to locate point 3_F on line 2_F -4_F. The horizontal and frontal views of the force diagram are now completed by adding arrowheads to the vectors. The arrowheads must agree (project) in both views.

The free body diagram is now completed by transferring arrowheads from the horizontal force diagram view onto the corresponding member lines (Fig. 29.47). The sense of each force can now be determined from its action on point A. The magnitude of vector 4-1 is measurable directly in the frontal view since it is true length. Vectors 2-3 and 3-4 are foreshortened in both views. Their true lengths are determined in an auxiliary view, by rotation, or by true-length diagram. It is convenient in this problem to use the auxiliary view method. The problem is completed with the customary summary of results.

Another special-case problem is presented in Figure 29.48, where a pole of height 16 ft is supported by three nonsymmetrically positioned guy wires. It is known that the force acting in guy wire AB is 140 lb. The complete solution to this problem is given in Figure 29.49, and the reader is encouraged to examine it carefully. Note that the known

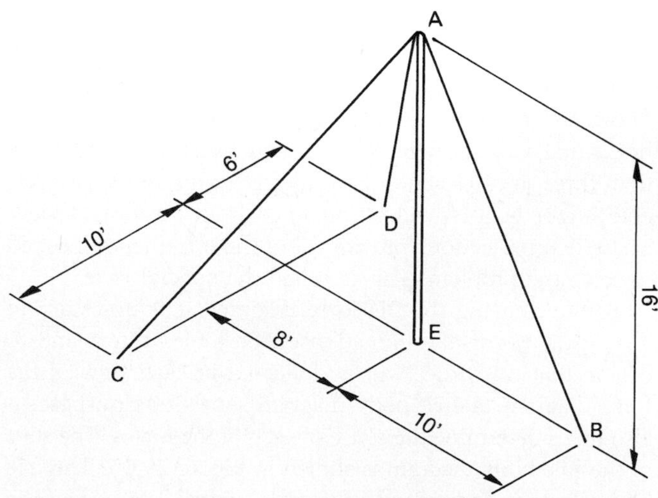

FIGURE 29.48 Another Special-Case Problem

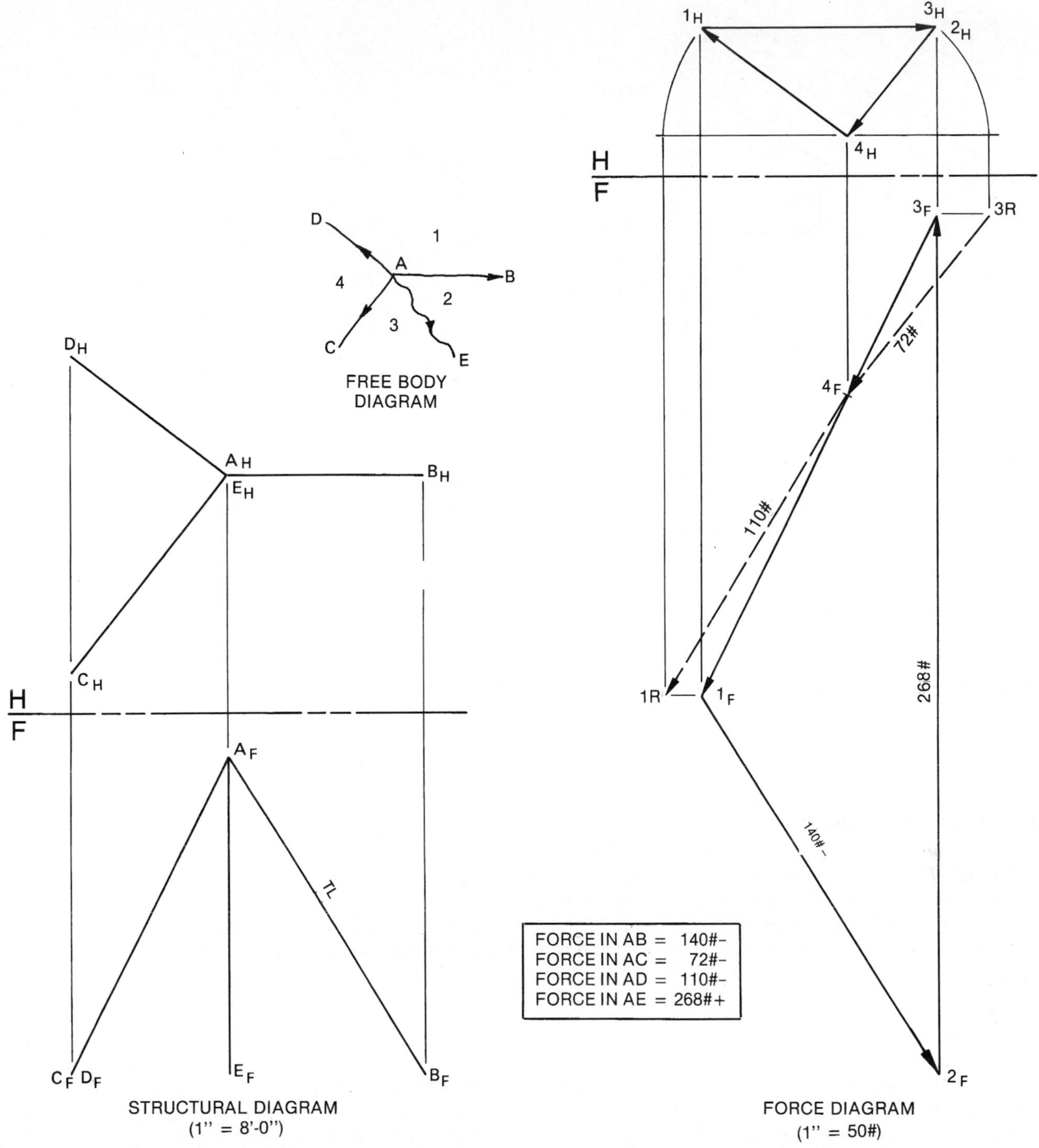

FIGURE 29.49 **Solution to the Special-Case Problem**

force in member AB is projectable in both views of the force diagram and that one of the unknown force members appears in point projection in the structural diagram.

The **general-case** solution is necessary whenever the given structural views project more than three lines of action from the members in one or both views. Such views cannot be used directly for drawing a force diagram view. The first steps of the general-case solution are to project an auxiliary view (or views) until two adjacent structural diagram views meet the following two conditions:

1. No more than three lines of action are projected in each (adjacent) view.
2. One measurable force vector can be drawn along one of the projected lines of action.

When two adjacent structural diagram views meet these

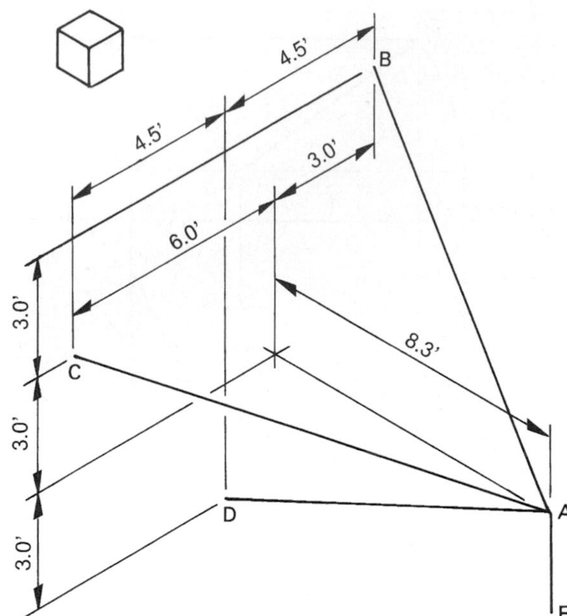

FIGURE 29.50 General-Case Noncoplanar Problem

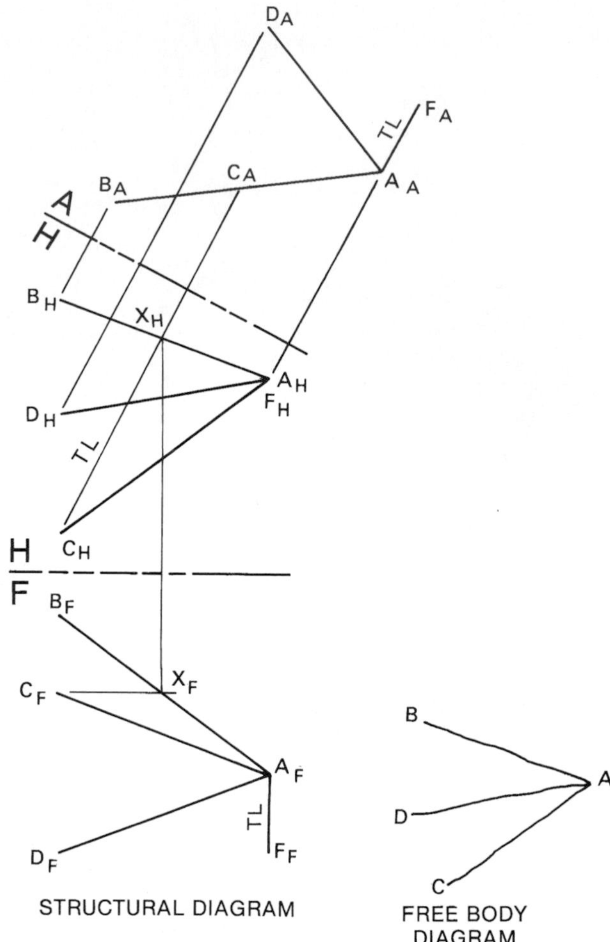

FIGURE 29.51 Horizontal and Frontal Views

requirements, the force diagram is drawn in the same way as in the special case, except that the vector projections in the force diagram are drawn parallel to the member projection of these two adjacent views.

A bracket with nonsymmetrically positioned members is shown in Figure 29.50. This bracket is supporting a vertical gravity load of 1200 lb at point F. Frontal and horizontal views are given in Figure 29.51. The frontal view projects a separate line of action for each of the four members and so cannot be used (condition 1). The horizontal view does satisfy condition 1 and can be used if an adjacent first auxiliary view can be projected that will satisfy both conditions. Because the known force member, AF, is in point projection in the horizontal view, it will project true length in any adjacent view. Therefore, an auxiliary view that projects any two other members with a common line of action will satisfy the conditions. The auxiliary view shown is drawn by projecting an edge view of the plane defined by members AB and AC. (Horizontal line CX, lying on plane ABC, is projected into point projection.) The horizontal view and this first auxiliary view now satisfy both conditions and will provide the lines of action and a measurable vector length projection necessary to complete the force diagram.

Before starting the force diagram, the free body diagram is drawn to establish the vector names and the vector sequence for the force diagram. The free body diagram (Fig. 29.52) is drawn so that the vectors 3-4 and 4-1 (acting in members AB and AC that are combined in the auxiliary view) occur sequentially. Now the force diagram can be drawn parallel to the horizontal and auxiliary views. The frontal view is not used for any lines of action. Now vector 1-2 is drawn, and the position of point 3 is found by the special-case method. Point 4 is then found (Fig. 29.53) and the two views of the force diagram are completed by adding arrowheads to show equilibrium.

Because the vectors 2-3, 3-4, and 4-1 are all foreshortened in both views of the force diagram, true-length projections of the vectors must be completed to determine their magnitudes. In the special-case problem, it was convenient to project an auxiliary view. Here, space limitations made rotation a desirable method (Fig. 29.54). Also, the free body diagram is completed to determine the sense of each force. Finally, the results of the solution are summarized and boxed.

The horizontal and frontal views of Figure 29.55 show the space relationships of a tripod structure that supports a tension force of 1250 lb at point F. The line of action of the force is collinear with member AF. To satisfy the two conditions for drawing a force diagram, it is necessary first to project member AF into true length in auxiliary view A. Then auxiliary views B and C are projected so that no more than three lines of action are represented in either view, and these views are used to draw the force diagram.

FIGURE 29.52 Free Body Diagram

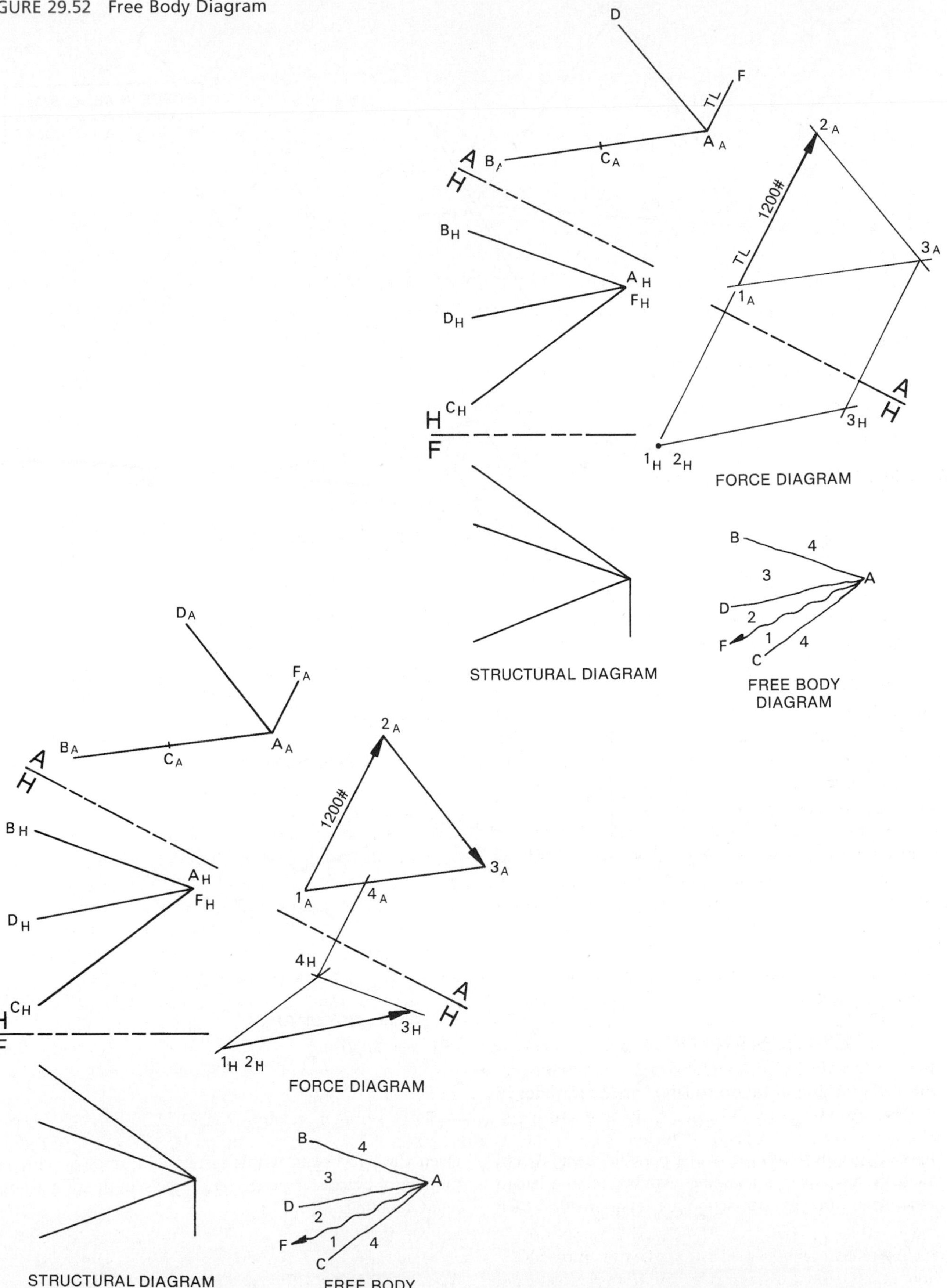

FIGURE 29.53 Point 4 and the Force Diagram

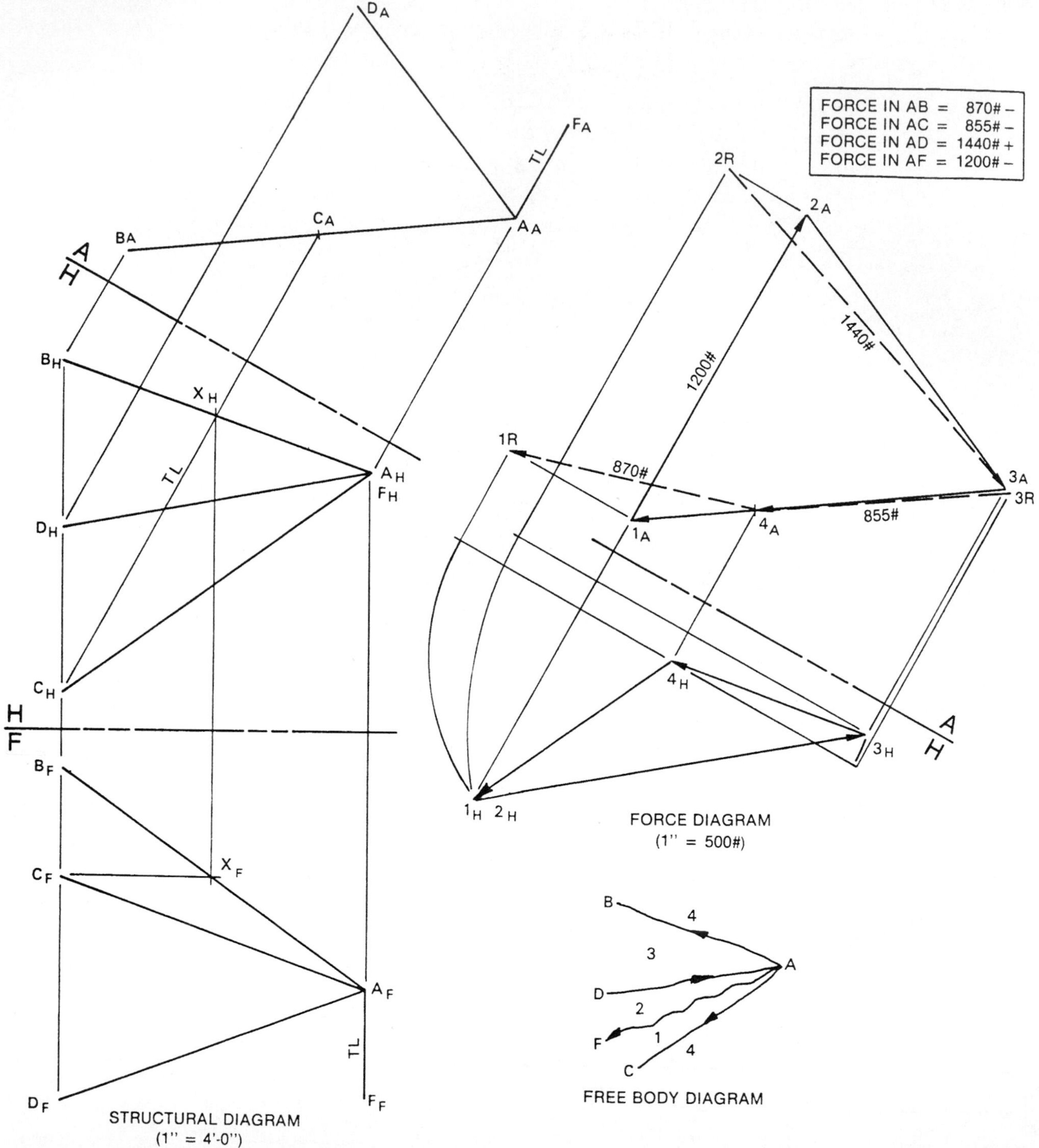

FIGURE 29.54 **Using Rotation to Find the Magnitudes**

This example illustrates the "worst possible" general case, in which the given views show no member in true length and more than three lines of action are represented in each given view. To obtain usable results in a problem with this number of successive projections, precision drafting is absolutely required.

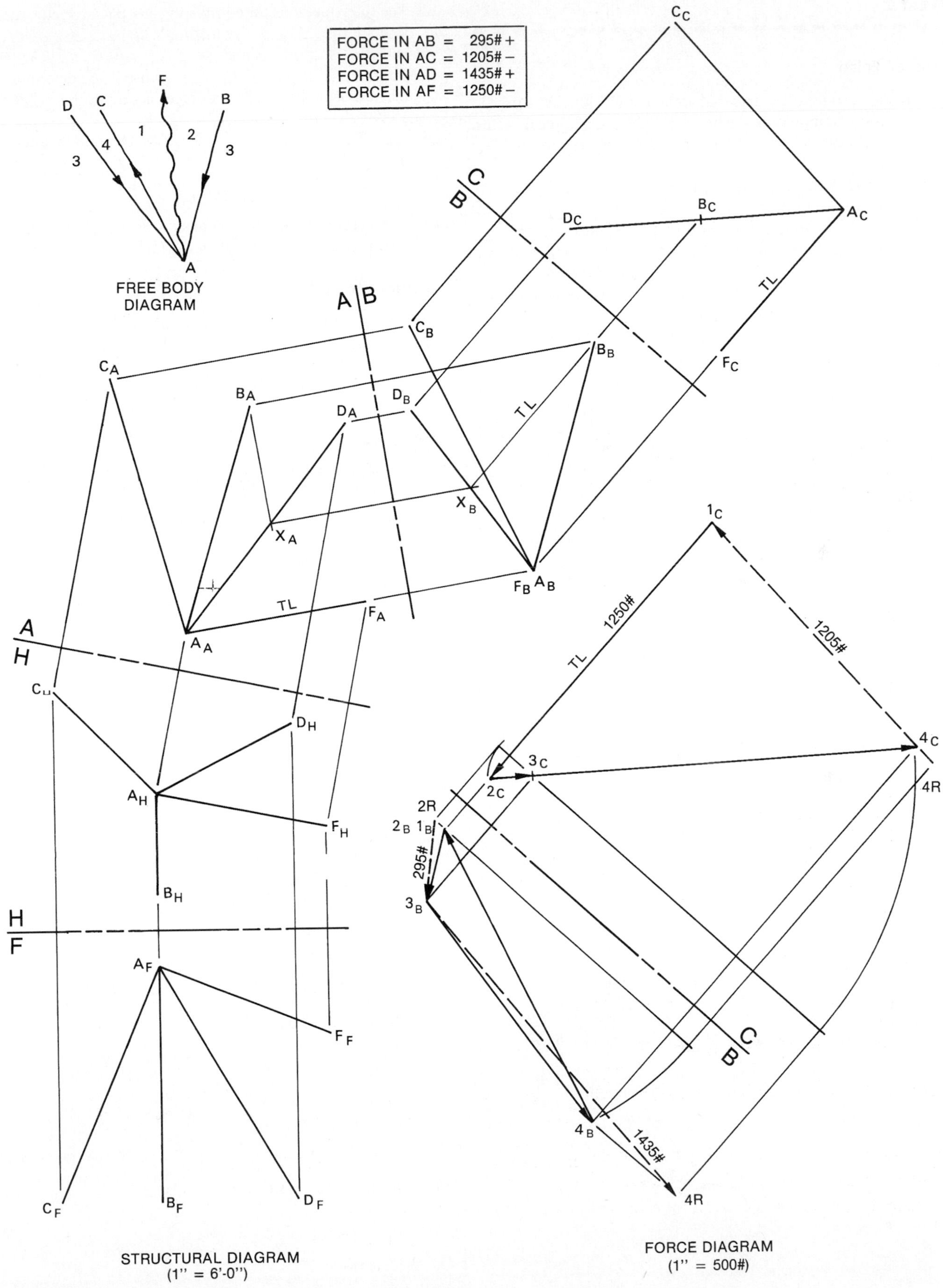

FIGURE 29.55 The Most General 3D Noncoplanar Problem

QUIZ

True or False

1. In statics, only structures that are in equilibrium are studied.
2. Precision is unnecessary when completing a graphical vector analysis because only three decimal places are required for the answer.
3. Coplanar forces lie in three dimensions.
4. A structural diagram is also called a free body diagram because both diagrams perform the same function.
5. A pin connection resists rotation and movement in all directions.
6. You can solve for the reaction forces on a beam when three parallel forces act on the beam.
7. It is not possible to solve noncoplanar force systems graphically.
8. The Maxwell diagram helps solve for the forces in a truss.

Fill in the Blanks

9. The four characteristics of a force are __________, __________, __________, and __________.
10. A __________ is a graphical representation of a force.
11. The systematic method for notation of a structural diagram and its associated force diagram is called__________ __________.
12. The three methods for completing a coplanar vector summation are the __________ method, the __________ method, and the __________ method.
13. The __________ __________ is used to determine the magnitude and sense of the forces acting in the members of a truss.
14. __________ __________ act along a common line of action.
15. A __________ __________ is also called a funicular diagram.
16. A structure constructed of many relatively short and lightweight two-force members is called a __________.

Answer the Following

17. List the four characteristics of a force.
18. Describe the difference between a coplanar force system and a noncoplanar force system.
19. Describe the difference between the polygon method and the parallelogram method in coplanar vector analysis.
20. Describe the difference between a two-force member and a three-force member.
21. What are the differences between collinear forces and coplanar forces?
22. What is the purpose of a string diagram?
23. Describe how a string diagram is used in coplanar nonconcurrent force systems.
24. Explain how to solve for the member forces in the most general case in 3D noncoplanar problems.

EXERCISES

Exercises may be assigned as sketching, instrument, or CAD projects. Transfer the given information to an "A"-size sheet of .25 in. grid paper. Complete all views, and solve for proper visibility, including centerlines, object lines, and hidden lines. Exercises that are not assigned by the instructor can be sketched in the text to provide practice and to enhance understanding of the preceding material.

After Reading the Chapter Through Section 29.4 You May Complete Exercises 29.1 Through 29.4

Exercise 29.1 By the parallelogram method, find the resultant of the given vectors. Also solve for the resultant vector mathematically.

Exercise 29.2 Use the parallelogram method to find the resultant of the given vectors. Also solve for the resultant vector mathematically.

Exercise 29.3 By the polygon method, find the resultant of the given vectors. Also solve for the resultant vector mathematically.

Exercise 29.4 Use the polygon method to find the resultant of the given vectors. Also solve for the resultant vector mathematically.

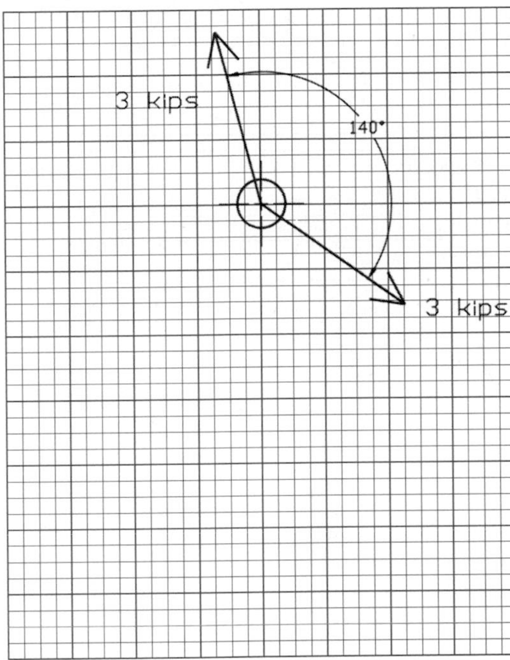

EXERCISE 29.1

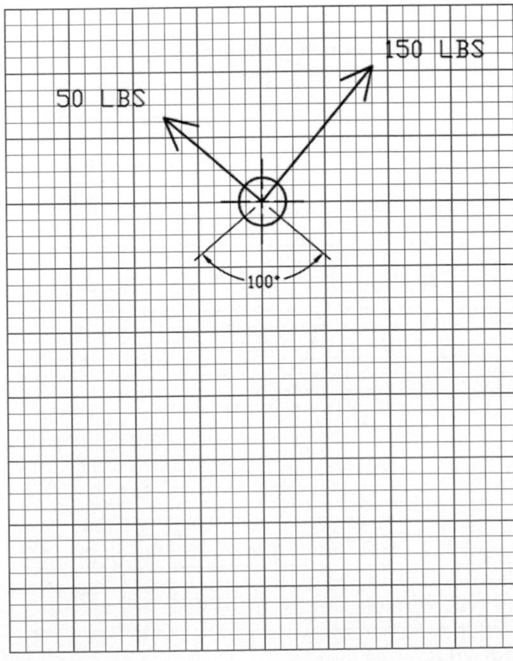

EXERCISE 29.2

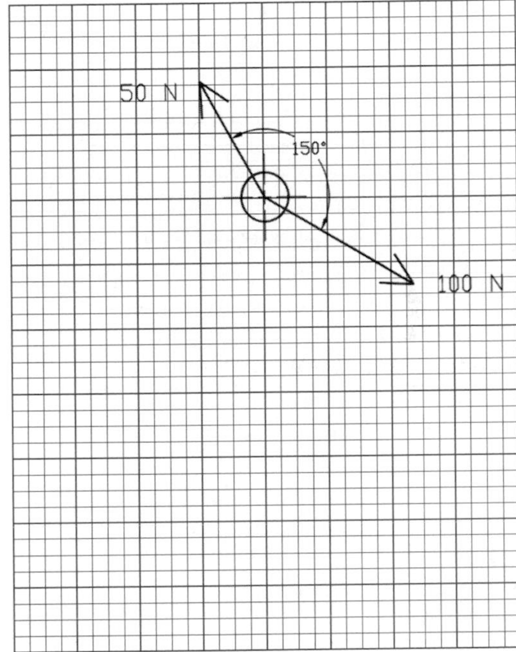

EXERCISE 29.3

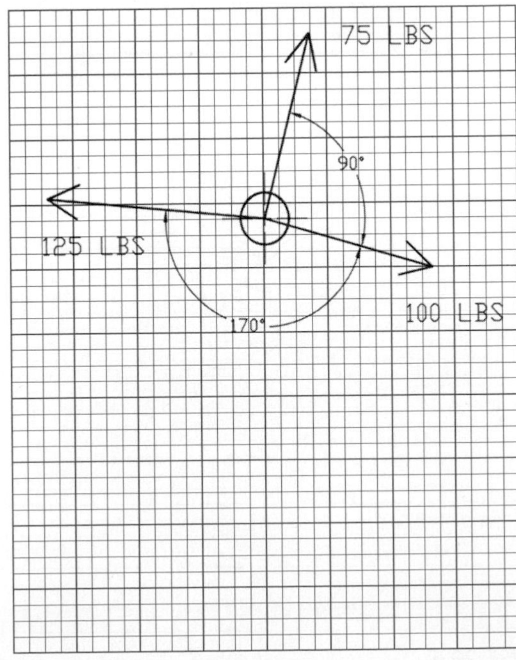

EXERCISE 29.4

After Reading the Chapter Through Section 29.6 You May Complete the Following Exercises

Exercise 29.5 For the given truss, first solve for the reaction forces and then find the force in each member.

Exercise 29.6 For the given truss, first solve for the reaction forces and then find the force in each member.

Exercise 29.7 For the given truss, first solve for the reaction forces and then find the force in each member.

Exercise 29.8 For the given truss, first solve for the reaction forces and then find the force in each member.

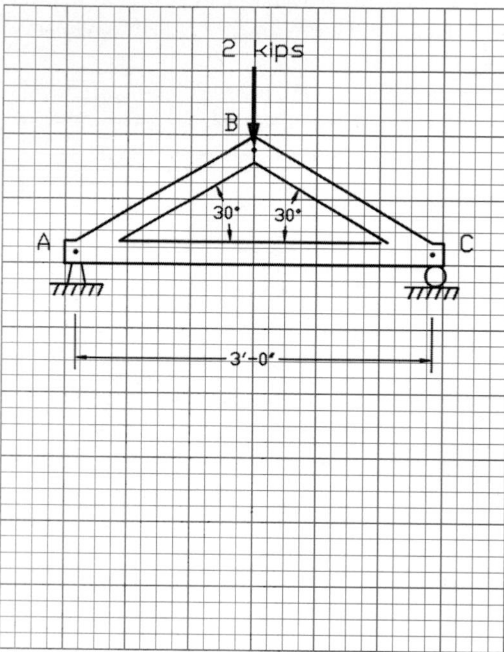

EXERCISE 29.5

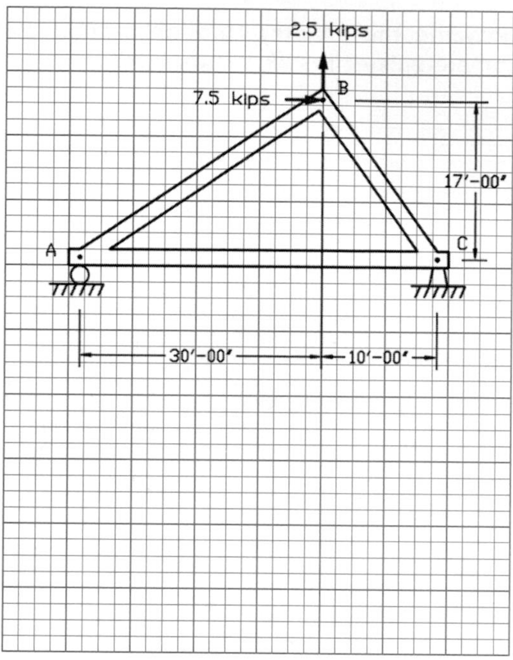

EXERCISE 29.7

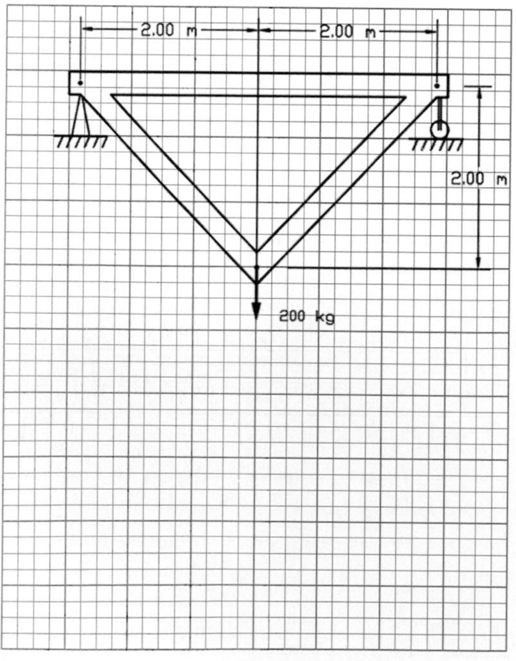

EXERCISE 29.6

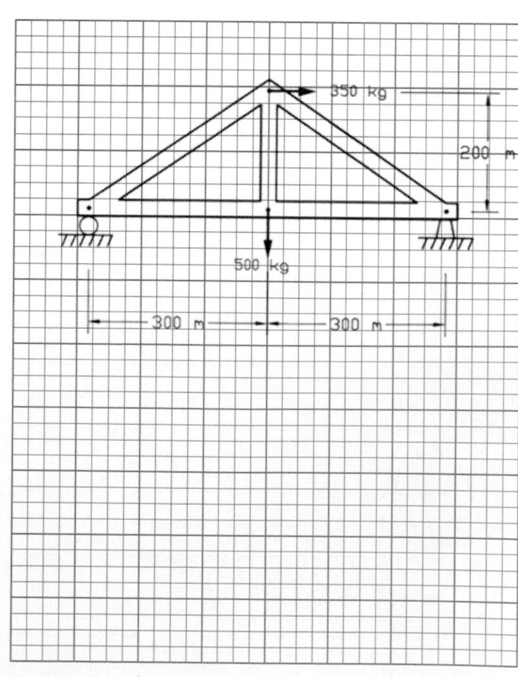

EXERCISE 29.8

PROBLEMS

Problem 29.1 Use the parallelogram method to solve for the resultant of the given vectors.

Problem 29.2 By the polygon method, solve for the resultant of the given vectors.

Problem 29.3 Use the mathematical method to solve for the resultant of the given vectors.

Problem 29.4 By the parallelogram method, solve for the resultant of the given vectors.

Problem 29.5 By the polygon method, solve for the resultant of the given vectors.

Problem 29.6 Use the mathematical method to solve for the resultant of the given vectors.

Problem 29.7 Assume that the weight at point F is 120 lb and that the other measurements are in inches. Determine the forces in all the members of the structure. B and C are pin connections.

Problem 29.8 Assume that a weight of 300 lb is attached to point H and that all the other measurements are in inches. Determine the forces in all the members of the structure. C and D are pin connections.

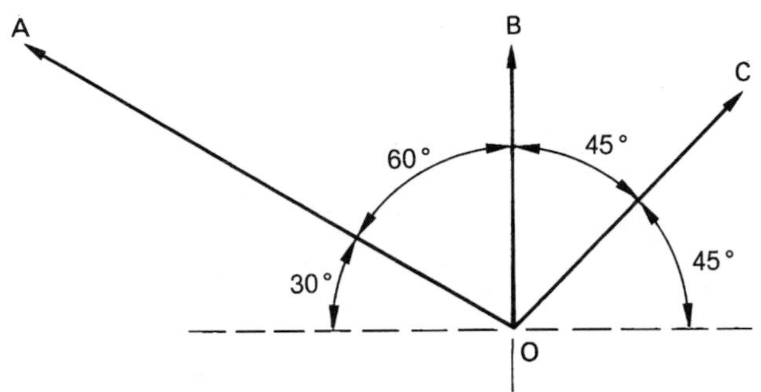

PROBLEMS 29.1, 29.2, 29.3

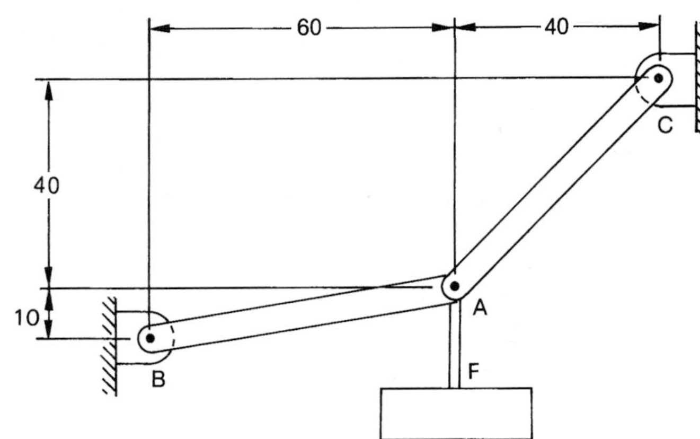

PROBLEM 29.7

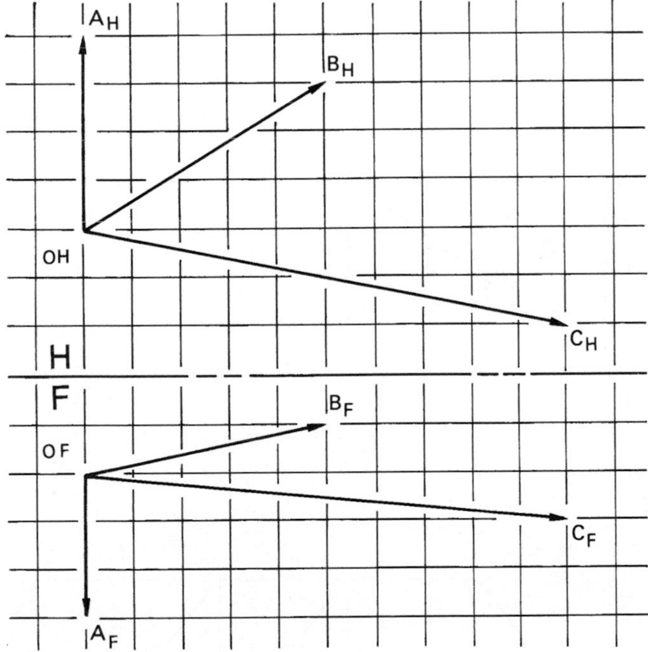

PROBLEMS 29.4, 29.5, 29.6

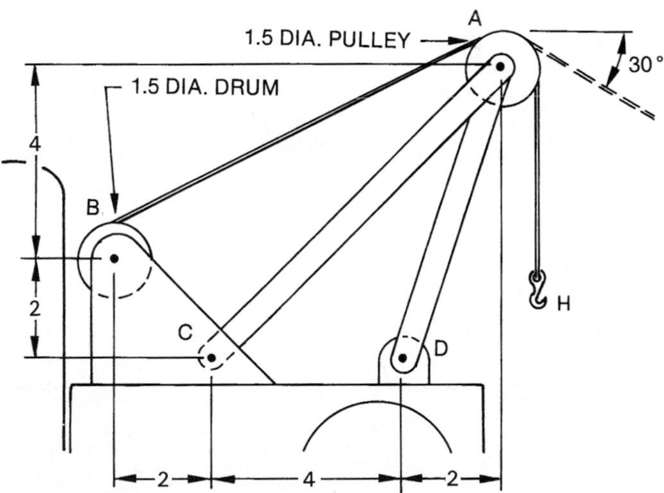

PROBLEM 29.8

Problem 29.9 Assume that a force of 250 lb pulls along the line of action of AE and that all the other measurements are in inches. Determine the forces in all the members of the structure. C and D are pin connections.

Problem 29.10 Assume that a force of 120 lb is attached to point F and that all the other measurements are in inches. Determine the forces in all the members of the structure. All the connections are pin connections.

Problem 29.11 Find the reactions R1 and R2.

Problem 29.12 Find the reactions R1 and R2. Find the forces in each of the truss members. X, Y, and Z are 100 lb each.

Problem 29.13 Find the reactions R1 and R2. Find the forces in each of the truss members. X and Y are each 50 lb and Z is 75 lb.

Problem 29.14 Find the reactions R1 and R2. Find the forces in each of the truss members. X, Y, and Z are 50 lb each.

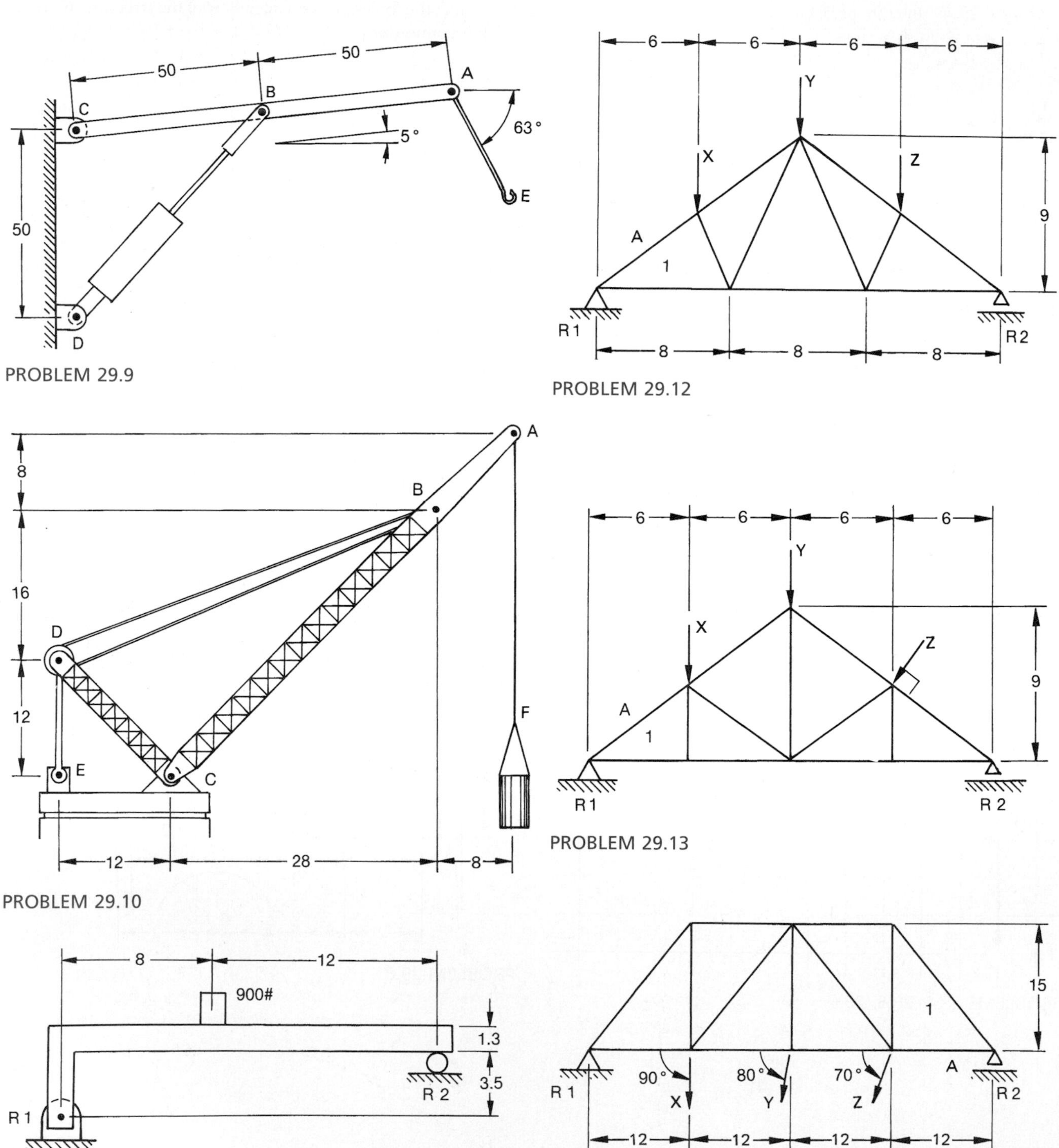

PROBLEM 29.9

PROBLEM 29.12

PROBLEM 29.10

PROBLEM 29.13

PROBLEM 29.11

PROBLEM 29.14

Problem 29.15 Find the reactions R1 and R2. Find the forces in each of the truss members. X and Y are each 75 lb and Z is 50 lb.

Problem 29.16 Find all the members' forces if a gravity load of 1000 lb is supported at F.

Problem 29.17 Find all the members' forces if a gravity load of 1250 lb is supported at F.

Problem 29.18 Find all the members' forces if there is a tensile load of 750 lb in member AE.

Problem 29.19 Find all the members' forces if a gravity load of 500 lb is supported at F.

Problem 29.20 Find all the members' forces if a gravity load of 1500 lb is supported at E.

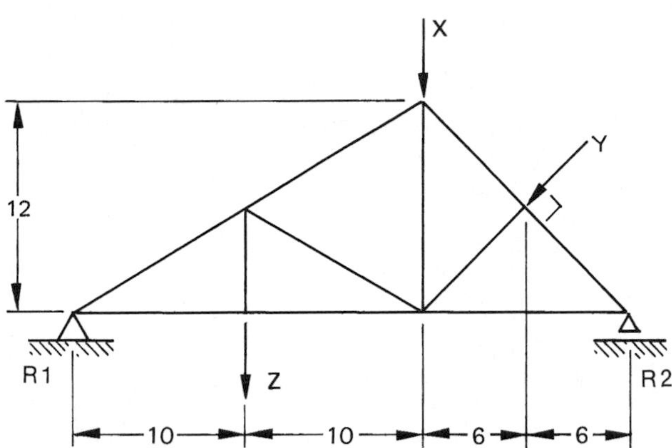

PROBLEM 29.15

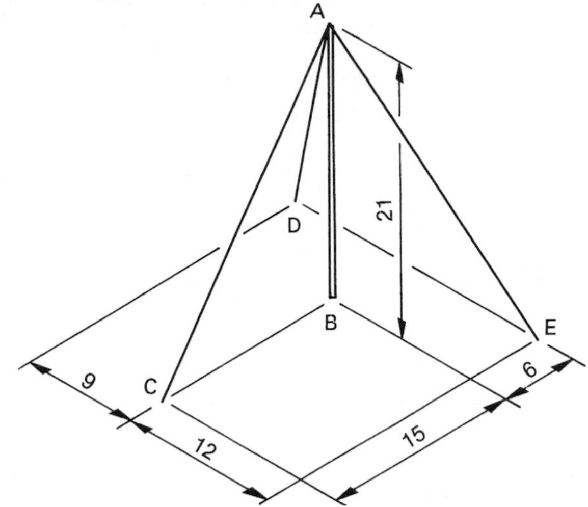

PROBLEM 29.18

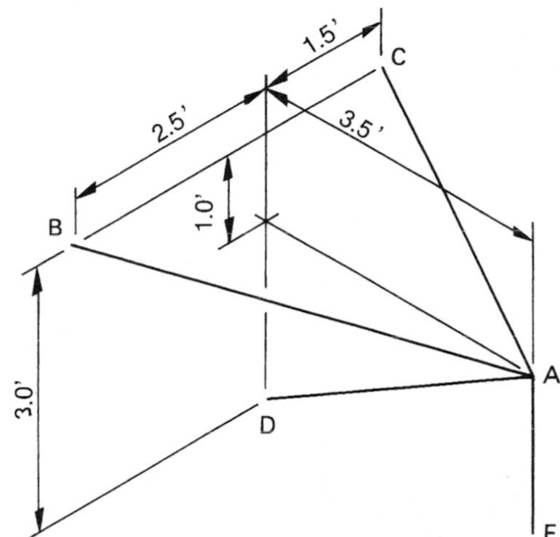

PROBLEM 29.16

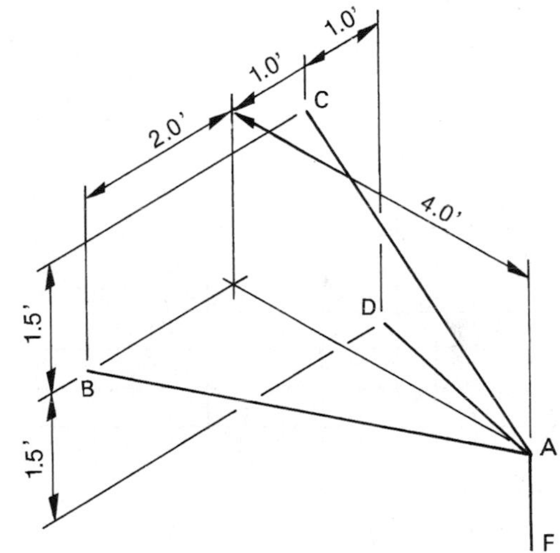

PROBLEM 29.19

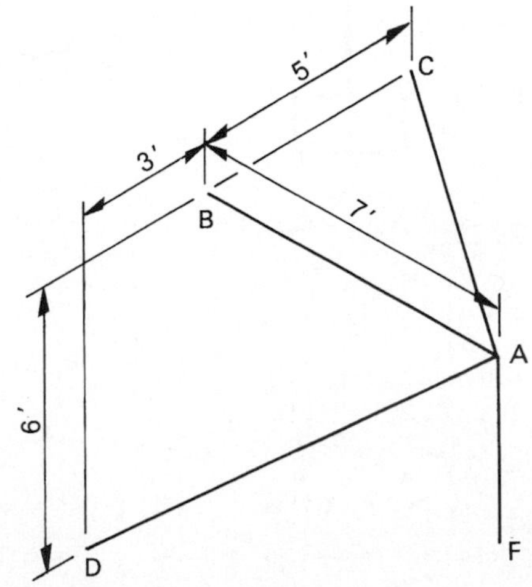

PROBLEM 29.17

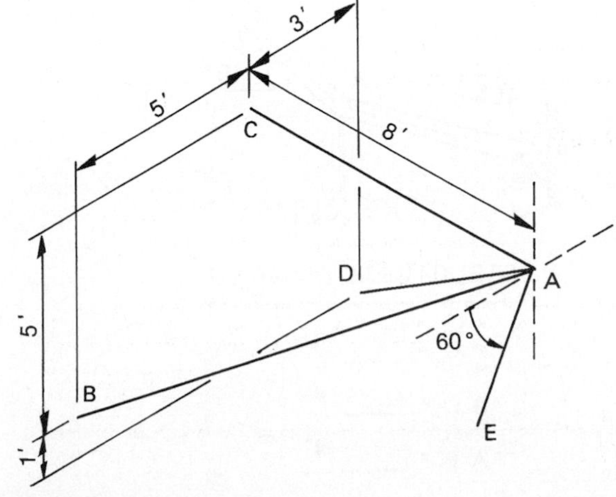

PROBLEM 29.20

Problem 29.21 Find the resultant force by the parallelogram method.

Problem 29.22 Find the resultant force by the polygon method.

Problem 29.23 Find the resultant force by the mathematical method.

Problem 29.24 Find the resultant force by the parallelogram method.

Problem 29.25 Find the resultant force by the polygon method.

Problem 29.26 Find the resultant force by the mathematical method.

Problem 29.27 Find the forces in the members in this coplanar system.

Problem 29.28 Find the forces in the members in this coplanar system.

Problem 29.29 Find the forces and directions in the members in this coplanar system.

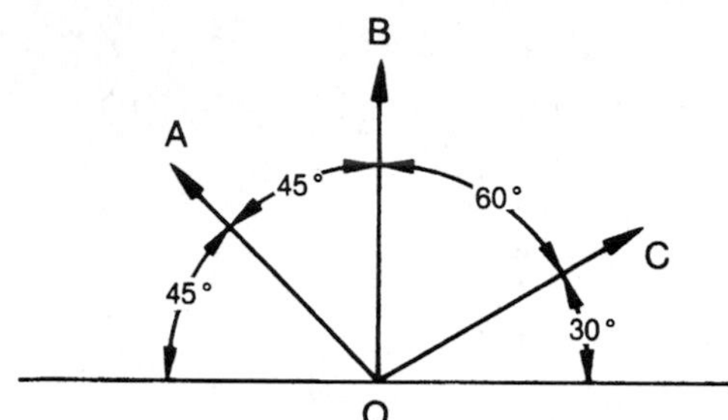

PROBLEMS 29.21, 29.22, 29.23

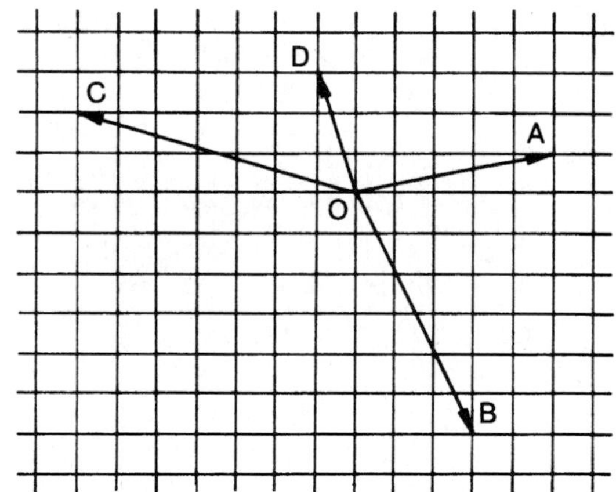

PROBLEMS 29.24, 29.25, 29.26

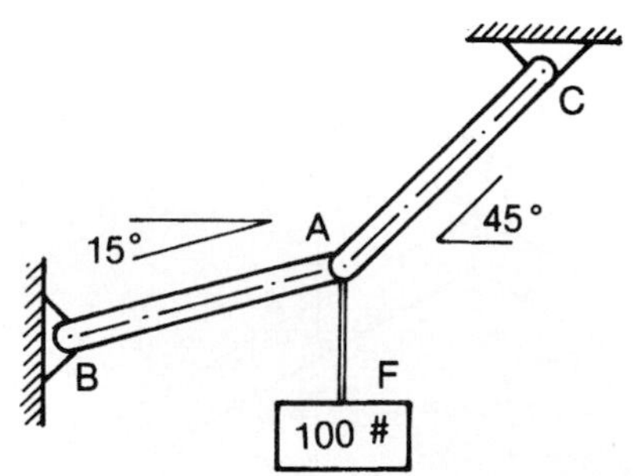

AB = ____ #

AC = ____ #

AF = ____ #

PROBLEM 29.27

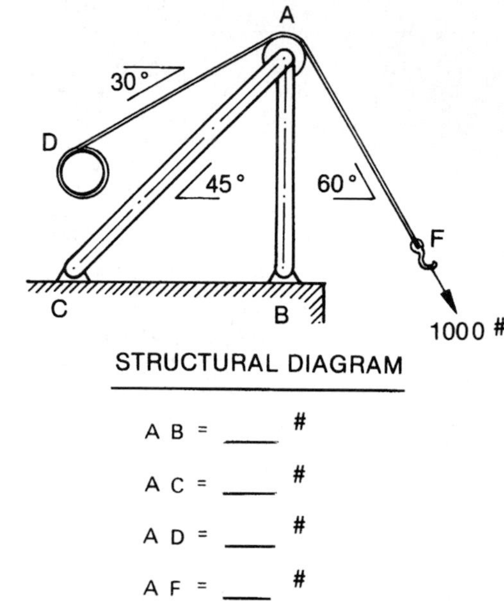

AB = ____ #

AC = ____ #

AD = ____ #

AF = ____ #

PROBLEM 29.28

MAGNITUDE AT A = ________

MAGNITUDE AT B = ________

ANGLE AT B = ________

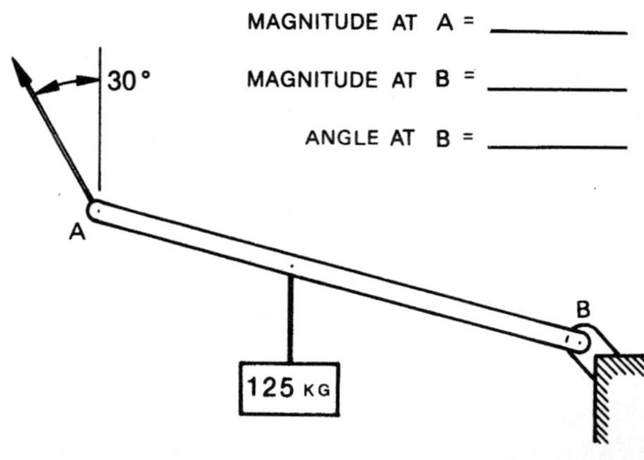

PROBLEM 29.29

Problem 29.30 Find the forces and directions in the members in this coplanar system.

Problem 29.31 Find the reaction forces for this beam.

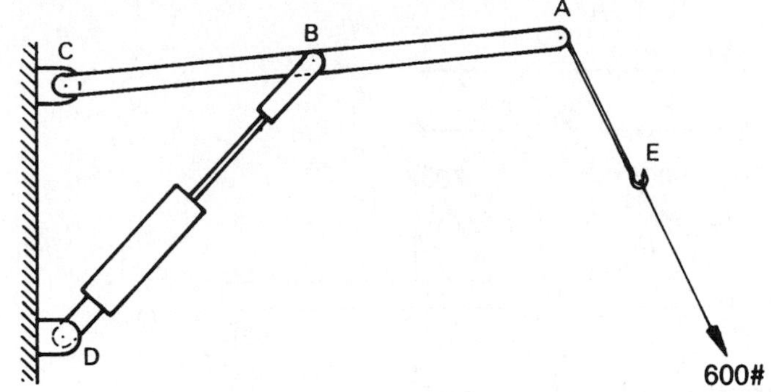

FORCE IN BD = ________

MAGNITUDE AT C = ________

ANGLE AT C = ________

PROBLEM 29.30

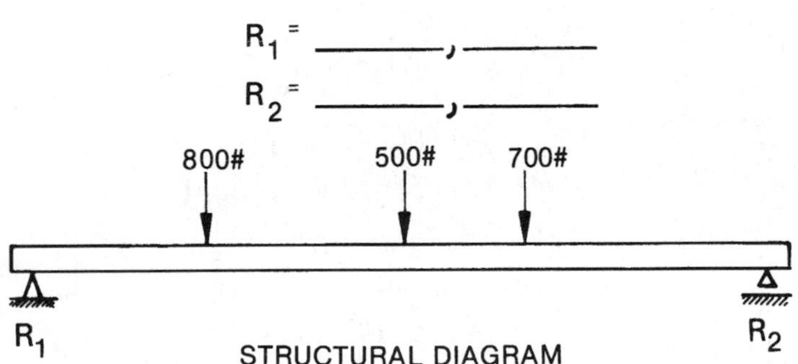

STRING DIAGRAM

FORCE DIAGRAM

PROBLEM 29.31

Problem 29.32 Find the reaction forces for this beam.

Problem 29.33 Find the reaction forces and the forces in each member for this truss.

Problem 29.34 Find the reaction forces and the forces in each member for this truss.

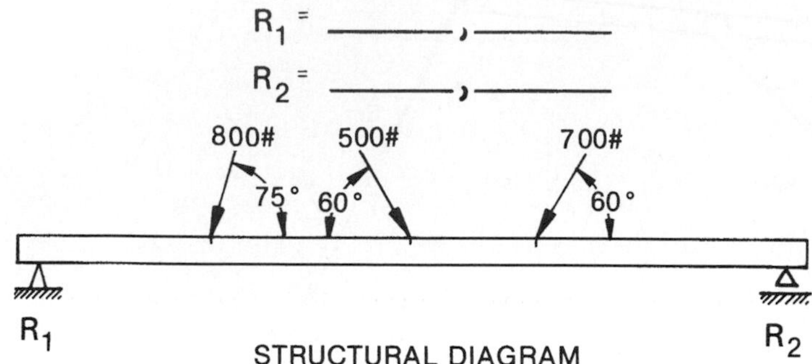

STRING DIAGRAM

FORCE DIAGRAM

PROBLEM 29.32

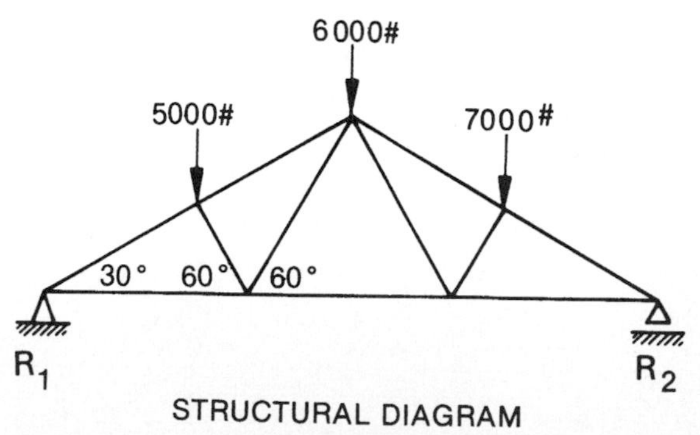

PROBLEM 29.33

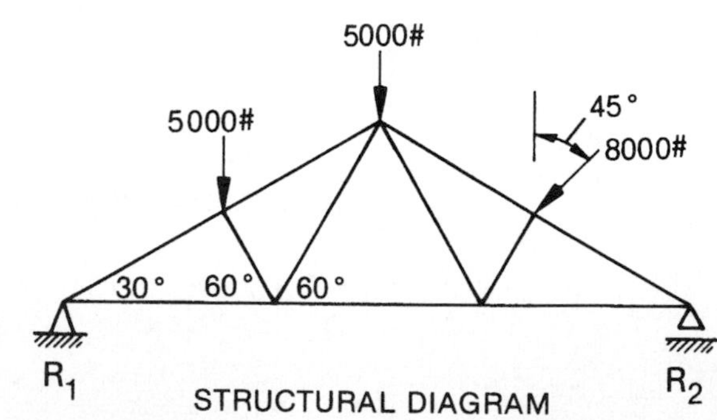

PROBLEM 29.34

Problem 29.35 Complete the horizontal and frontal views.

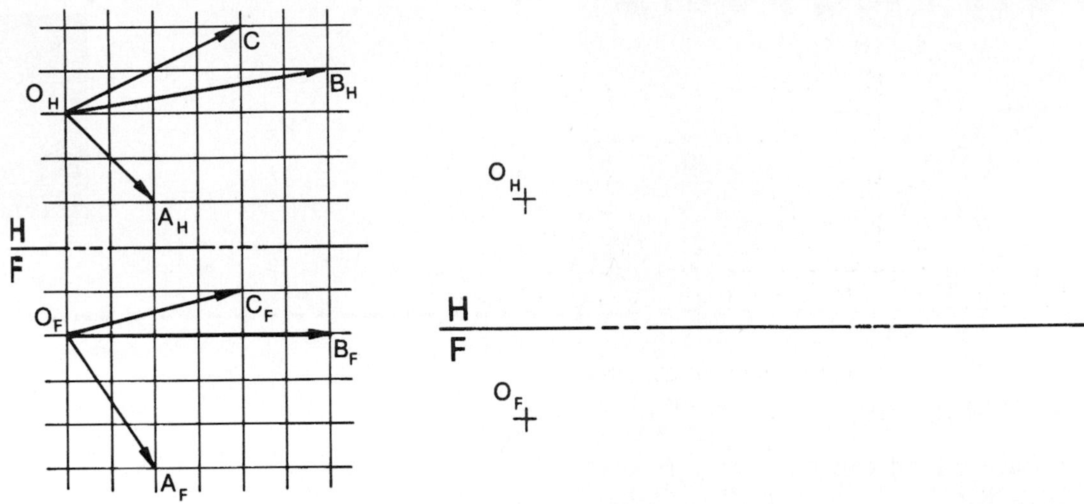

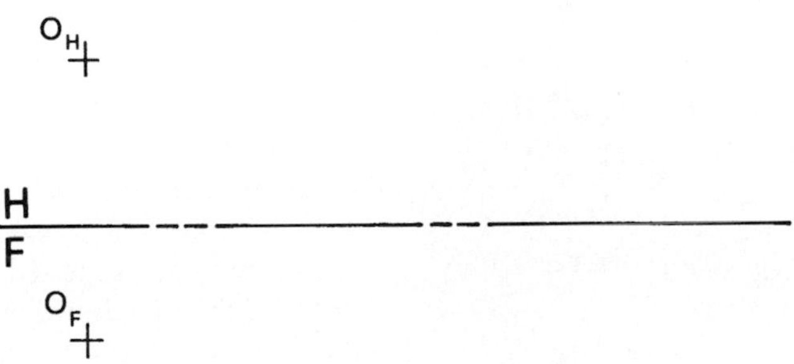

PROBLEM 29.35

DESIGN PROJECTS

Chapter 30

LEARNING OBJECTIVES

Upon completion of this chapter you will be able to:

1. Understand the role of the engineer and design teams in the design process.
2. Analyze the stages of the design process and follow them while completing projects.
3. Have a deeper understanding of design, tooling, and production concepts.
4. Gain a deeper understanding of the efficient design of a manufactured product.
5. Understand product design parameters more completely.
6. Know the fundamentals of product design.
7. Develop a working knowledge of the design tree.

30.1 INTRODUCTION

Student design projects involve teams of students or individual students working with professionals to develop skills in the practical aspects of engineering design (Fig. 30.1). There is no substitute for the rigors involved in creating and designing "real" devices and products. Design work is challenging and exciting. You will learn valuable lessons in teamwork and the importance of communication. Concurrent engineering and design for manufacturability should always be considered when completing design projects. Design team members may include working professionals, company representatives, students in other programs, older students from your program, or fellow classmates.

The projects suggested in this chapter are certainly not intended to teach design or to be in any way comprehensive; they are only ideas for projects. The projects may be limited to the design stage, or they may be comprehensive, starting with design and finishing with the completed project. The tooling by which the product will be manufactured may also be designed or produced (Fig. 30.2). Your instructor will help you define the goals for your project. The Mono-Ski in Figure 30.1 was designed and produced by a team of university students from manufacturing engineering technology and industrial design programs working with professionals from skiing schools and sporting equipment manufacturers. (A Mono-Ski is a device that allows differently abled skiers to enjoy the sport of downhill skiing.) Basic design parameters included: adaptability to individual physical limitations; ability to accommodate a range of individuals, from a 4 ft, 70 lb child to a 6 ft, 180 lb adult; self-loading features for access to the chair lift, device weight under 30 lb; interchangeability from Mono-Ski to Bi-Ski; straightforward production methods; low maintenance costs; and low production costs.

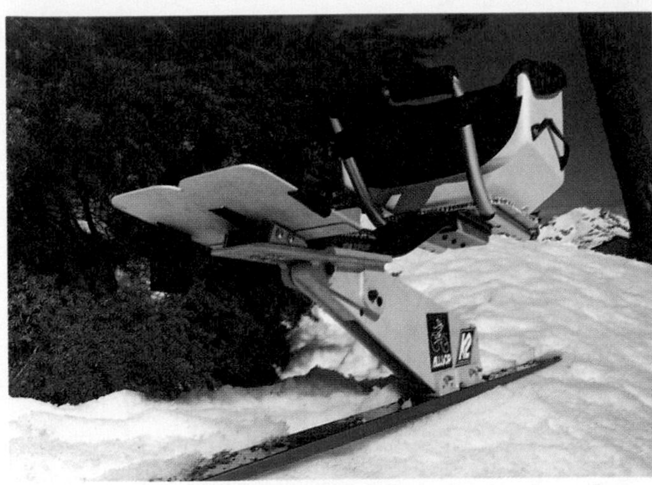

FIGURE 30.1 Mono-Ski Designed by a Student Team to Help Differently Abled Skiers Enjoy Recreational Skiing

FIGURE 30.2 Tooling Designed and Produced by a Student Design Team for a Robotic Workcell

30.2 DESIGN PROJECT EXAMPLES

So that you may gain a practical appreciation of the design process for student design projects, an example will be given here that illustrates design project phases. These phases were covered in detail in Chapters 2 and 3; you may wish to refer back to those chapters while reviewing this section.

The project example in this section is the student team's design and producibility plan for a weight-lifting machine for the differently abled (Fig. 30.3). The stated purpose of the team was to design a weight-lifting machine capable of offering a wheelchair athlete four different exercise options while the wheelchair itself remains stationary. The central feature of the design was that the machine rotates 360° to bring each of the four exercises to the athlete. Upper-body exercises that stimulate muscle strength are emphasized.

The students first investigated the principals of weight training (Fig. 30.4). They also identified a number of goals at the inception of the project (Fig. 30.5). The team identified a set of management functions, which included planning, organizing, direction, control, decision making, and presentation arrangements. The six team members picked a team leader and created team assignments for each member (Fig. 30.6). Assignments included written documentation, detail drawings, documentation control, CAD drawings, major subassemblies, and assembly drawings.

The design process itself began with brainstorming sessions. Recall that there are usually many possible solutions to a particular design situation and that no one solution is likely to offer everything the designers want. The chosen design must be producible at a cost that consumers are willing to pay.

Compromise is important in team design projects or concurrent engineering teams. Usually, the design selected is a combination of a number of good design ideas. Incorporating all the best ideas in the final design is an important goal. Team members must be willing to listen to other ideas in the initial design stages and to compromise. The team leader often has to facilitate open communication among team members and give all team members an equal chance to contribute to the brainstorming. Some student team members may be reluctant to participate at first, but a good brainstorming facilitator brings out the best in all participants. Often, everyone gets caught up in the excitment and ideas flow freely. But selecting the best compromises from the long list of ideas can be more difficult. Team members must be willing to compromise during that selection process. They should keep in mind that design decisions are professional decisions that must never be taken personally.

Recall the basic questions a designer or design team should ask at the inception of a project: *Who* needs it? *What* is needed? *Where* is it needed? *When* is it needed? *Why* is it needed? *How many* are needed?

Also recall the list of design elements from Chapter 3:

Design Elements

1. Define the *basic design problems* relevant to the solution.
2. Define the *secondary design problems* that are not the designer's concern but still need to be solved.
3. Identify *perceived problems* that are not really important. This alleviates false concerns.
4. Identify *obstructions* to the design, i.e., significant obstacles to the design solution that must be avoided or circumvented.
5. Find and discuss all *hidden difficulties,* i.e., obstructions to the solution that are not clearly seen or understood.
6. Scrutinize any *hindrances* to the design that are really not important enough to justify much time.

Recall the following from Chapter 2:

Characteristics of a Good Design Engineer

- Intuition
- Good communication skills—written, verbal, graphic

(a) Design

FIGURE 30.3 Weight-Lifting Machine for Differently Abled Individuals

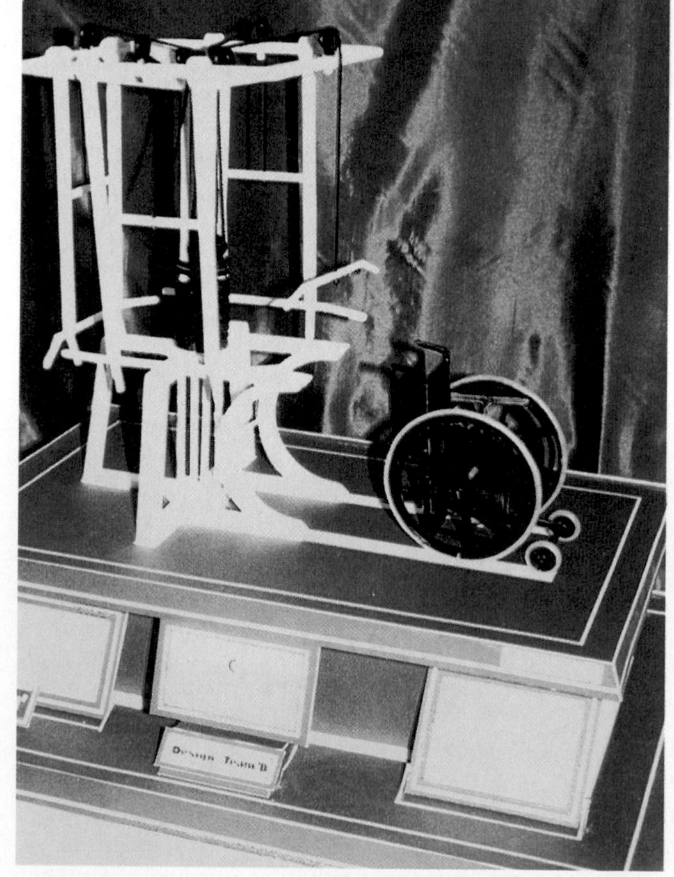

(b) Design model

- Open mind to problem-solving
- Inquisitive mind
- Understanding of fundamental design principles
- Ability to integrate and balance several ideas and solutions
- Ability to do self-evaluation
- Concentration skills
- Visualization skills
- Ability to think and communicate in 3D
- Mathematical skills

Design sketches are often drawn to communicate initial design concepts to team members (Figs. 30.7 through 30.9). Once the sketches are discussed, design refinement begins. Off-the-shelf parts are identified. New mechanisms are designed. Design details are worked out and final designs

Progressive Resistance

- Muscles grow when they are subjected to overload, at the same time internal organs grow healthier.
- Your strength and size progressively get larger by adding on weight to keep pace with growing strength.
- To tone muscles and stay in generally good shape, you lift *light* weights with ten to twenty repetitions, three days a week.
- To increase the size of muscles, weight-lifting athletes must lift heavy weights four to five times a week, no more than eight repetitions.
- Repetitions mean continuing to do the exercise until the point of exhaustion or until you are unable to continue lifting the weight.
- Sets equal volume of work done in repeating the motion of moving weights at least a minimum of five sets.
- In general, (physically challenged) people lift weights to gain upper-body strength.
- Average length of each workout session is one and one-half hours.
- Diet and rest are an important part of training.

FIGURE 30.4 Principals of Weight Training Identified by the Design Team

A comprehensive paradigm has been outlined for all design team members' participation. The following reflect our company goals:

- Presentation of three product design concepts, choosing one product to evaluate its potential market.
- Ongoing field research and contacts will be undertaken to add to our resources materials.
- Generate detailed 3D drawings on AUTOCAD and PERSONNEL DESIGNER, in the lab and on our home computers.
- Research patents and comparable exercise equipment found in magazines, books, and brochures.
- Our design team will participate in field trips and research at physical fitness centers.
- Comprehensive review of machining, fabrication, and manufacturing of our design concepts.
- Make a scale model, approximately 24 in. high, with accompanying photos.
- Marketing and promotional materials.
- Final presentation with handouts to all class members.

FIGURE 30.5 Goals for the Design Project

decided on by the group. A working prototype of the product is often produced at this time (Fig. 30.10). The number of refinements and design iterations depends on the complexity of the design and on previous experience with the particular product.

In our example, the cable pulley system was redesigned

Generate Research

1. Go to hardware companies to research off-the-shelf clamps.
2. Look into details on off-the-shelf weight plates.
3. Research bearing and pulley devices.
4. List references to patent details.
5. Redraw his design in 3D mechanical drawings with black line drawings.
6. Research spring-loaded mechanism.
7. Hand sketch of window cleaning device.
8. Drawing upper carousel workstation handle structure and rubber handle grip.
9. Drawing upper ring bearing detail for workstation.

FIGURE 30.6 A Typical Assignment List for an Individual Team Member at Fitness for All

repeatedly. The features added were: triceps extensions, cable reverse press-downs, incline curls, one-arm cross cables, cable pullovers, reverse curls, behind-the-neck shoulder presses, chin-ups, hanging abdominal exercises, seated cable rows, lat and grip pull-downs, and cable crossovers.

The manufacturing costs included those for steel channel and tubing, thrust bearings, pulleys, cables, weight disks,

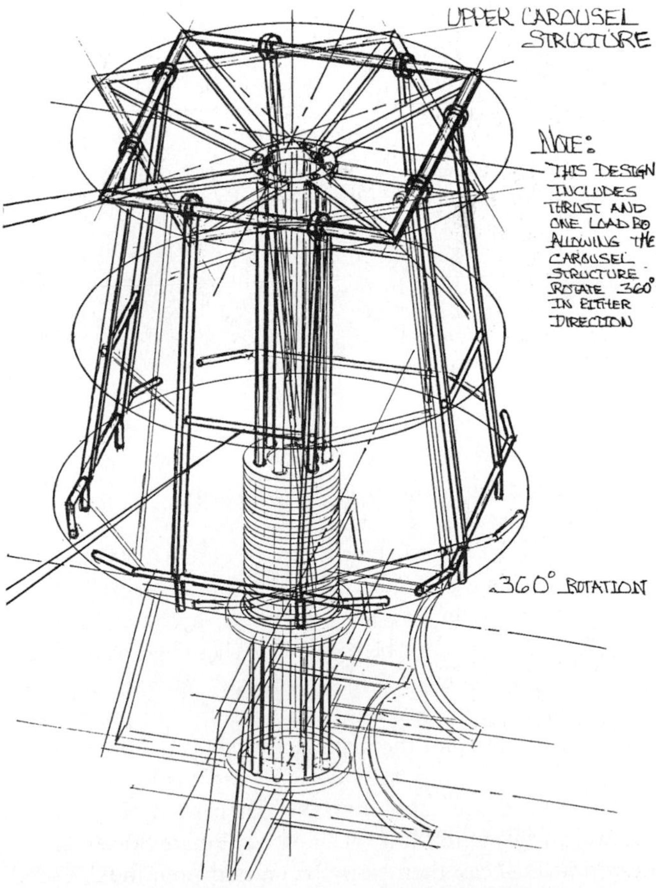

FIGURE 30.7 Sketch of Preliminary Design for Weight-Lifting Machine—Upper Carousel Structure

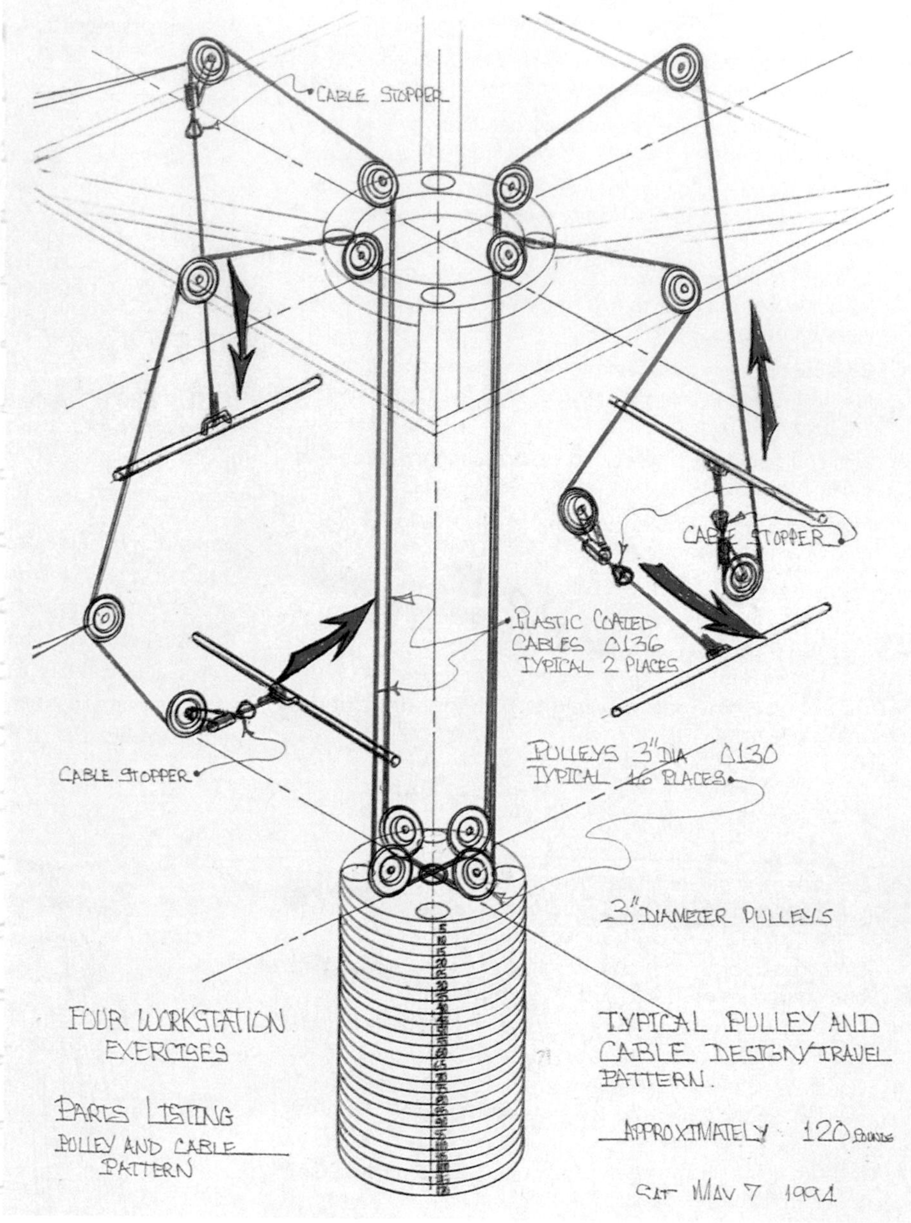

FIGURE 30.8 Pulley and Cable Design

workstation framing, and carousel cross members. Specifications for bearings were created at this stage (Fig. 30.11), as was a parts list (Fig. 30.12).

Assembly drawing sketches help the design team work out the final details for manufacturing the product (Fig. 30.13).

After the design has been finalized, a complete set of working drawings must be produced. These may also consist of solid models from which working drawings can be produced. Solid models have the advantage of providing a complete database for the manufacturing team. For example, computer numerical control (CNC) toolpaths for machining of parts can be generated from this database. A 3D model of the weight-lifting machine is shown in Figure 30.14. Multiview drawings can then easily be created from the 3D solid models (Fig 30.15).

Good communication among team members is essential for a productive and creative design team. When team members do not communicate effectively, the teams simply do not produce good designs easily. Team members must act professionally and must not take design decisions personally. All team members must work toward one goal—making the best possible product in the shortest possible time given the design constraints. A product too late to market is often useless, a financial failure. For instance, should a design team that produces children's toys miss important deadlines, the new toys might not be produced in time for the Christmas season.

After you complete a design project, you will often understand the design process better and view the importance of each of the listed characteristics in a new light.

The interaction among design parameters—weight, texture, material, color, symmetry, size, balance—also gains new meaning. Every design parameter affects the other parameters. For instance, the weight of a product is influ-

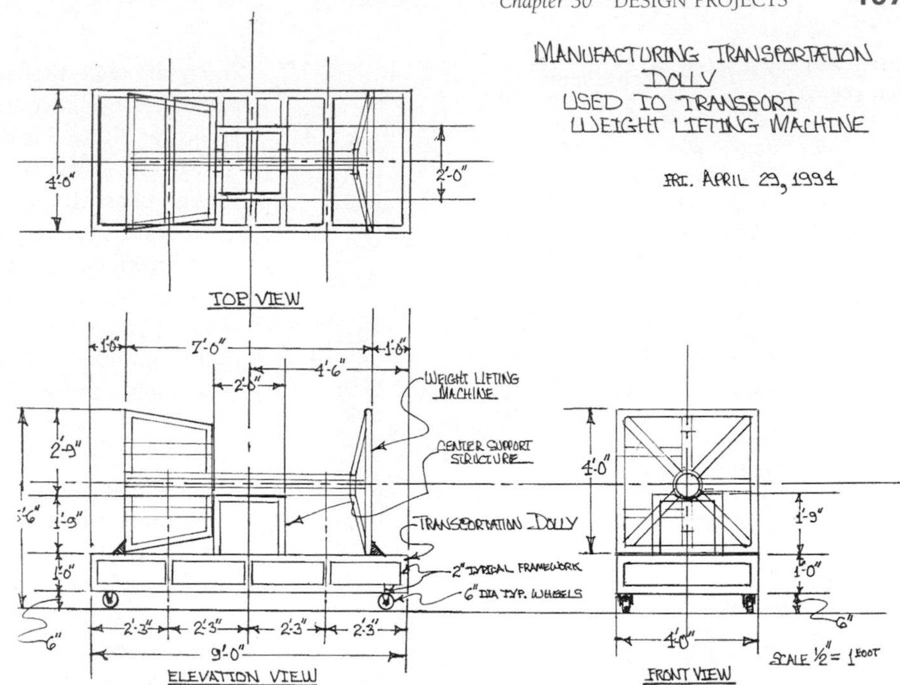

FIGURE 30.9 Design for Manufacturing Transportation Dolly

enced by its material and size; the color will be influenced by the material; the weight and size will affect ease of use (Fig. 30.1).

No one solution can satisfy all the design criteria perfectly. Material selection is often influenced by the *availability*

FIGURE 30.10 Prototype Weight-Lifting Machine

- 2-dimensional and 3-dimensional drawings have been generated to show upper and lower bearing and rotation of 360°, on 12 inch diameter support.
- Roller bearings used in these configurations distinguished by the design of rollers and raceways to handle axial, combined axial, and thrust loads.
- The free rings on these roller bearings are designed with a flange to provide some restraint to end-wise movements in one direction. Bearing rings may be displaced axially with respect to each other.
- These rolling contact bearings are made with all load-carrying members of full-hard steel or case-hardened.
- Tolerance limits for cylindrical roller thrust bearing

  Heavy series—types TP and TR
- Selection of roller bearings:

  Starting friction is low.
  Less axial space required.
  Accurate shaft alignment can be maintained.
  Both radial and axial loads can be carried easily.
  Angle of load application is not restricted.
  Heavy overloads can be carried easily.
  Lubrication is simple.
  Simplicity of design offers off-the-shelf supply.
- Load and fatigue life:

  Under ideal conditions, repeated stresses developed in contact areas of the rollers and raceways eventually result in fatigue, but last longer than most bearings.
- Lubricating oils:

  The most versatile and best-known lubricant for roller bearings in mineral oil.
- Tapered roller bearings:

  Specially designed for medium to heavy loads at low speeds, these tapered poller bearings have up to four times the load capacity of ball bearings.

FIGURE 30.11 Specification Sheet for Bearings (Off-the-Shelf Standard Parts)

Main Frame	
■ Upper Carousel Framework	
A. Tube 2″ dia	0080
B. Tube 2″ dia	0081
C. Tube 2″ dia	0082
D. Tube 2″ dia	0083
Upper Carousel Ring Support	0085
16 pulleys	0090
Four Crossmember Supports	
A. Support Crossmember Frames	0096
B. Support Crossmember Frames	0097
C. Support Crossmember Frames	0098
D. Support Crossmember Frames	0099
Exercise Arm Station (E)	0100
Exercise Arm Station (F)	0101
Exercise Arm Station (G)	0102
Exercise Arm Station (H)	0103
Rotating Handles	0104
Rubber Handle Grips	0105
■ Center Supports	0106
Cable Attachment	0107
Cable Attachment	0108
Cable Attachment	0109
■ Center Tubular Structure $1\frac{1}{2}$ dia × 7′	
Tube (A)	0110
Tube (B)	0111
Tube (C)	0112
Tube (D)	0113
Main Thrust Bearing	0120
Cast-iron Weight Plate	0121
Lower Support Bearing	0122
Center Pin	0125
■ Pulley and Cable, plastic-coated	
16 Pulley 3″ dia	0130
Two Plastic-coated Cables	0136
■ Lower Support Structure	
Steel Frame, size 4″ × $1\frac{1}{2}$″	
Right-Side Framework	0140
Bottom	0141
Top	0142
Right side	0143
Left-Side Framework	0150
Bottom	0151
Top	0152
Left side	0153
Center Framework	0160
Bottom	0161
Top	0162
End Unit	0163
Wheelchair Securing Framework	0170
Right-side bottom	0171
Right-side top	0172
Right-side wheel	0173
Left-side bottom	0174
Left-side top	0175
Left-side wheel	0176

FIGURE 30.12 **Parts List for Weight-Lifting Machine**

of the material in the desired price range; materials that are unavailable or not cost effective must be eliminated. The texture and the final color of the product will then be affected as well. Sometimes, the processes available at your manufacturing facilities will govern material selection, and therefore will determine weight, texture, and color. The processes available to you will limit material selection: If a process you need is not at your manufacturing facilities, you must find alternative sources and plants for them during the design phase. If these facts are not identified early, manufacture of the product could be too costly or even impossible.

Remember, too, that the *best-selling* product is not always the *best* product. A reliable, functional, long-lasting product will not necessarily sell if it is unappealing in color or shape. Many products for differently abled individuals are functional but, unfortunately, not attractive. A good designer determines the proper mix of factors based on their relative importance to the project.

Recall the list of design considerations from Chapter 2: **function, constraints, materials, appearance, effect of environment on product and of product on environment, product life, reliability, safety requirements, interchangeability and standardization of components, maintenance and service requirements,** and **costs.**

Finally, recall the design comparisons that should be made during the design stage:

- Capability of satisfying the original statement of the design intent and project definition
- Cost, manufacturability, and reliability
- Design requirements for precision (which will affect cost), operating efficiency/flexibility, maintenance projections, and environmental impact
- Material and manufacturing processes
- Effect of configuration and complexity on manufacturing costs

Project management must play an important part in your project or it will not be successful—in school or in industry. There is no substitute for good, effective leadership. There is no substitute for effective team communication. A leader guides the team and helps everyone on the team finish their assigned tasks. A good team leader respects everyone and assists everyone. If a team member is not completing his or her part of the project, it is up to the team leader to help that member fulfill his or her responsibilities.

You may also wish to establish a Gantt chart to complete your design project. The team leader should create a project timeline, with input from the design team. Critical dates should be identified early in the process. Gantt charts are extremely useful in project management, especially in classroom projects. Projects that are to be completed in ten or fifteen weeks have very short product lead times. Team leaders should identify critical issues early. An example of a Gantt Chart for project management is shown in Figure 30.16. Daily or weekly oral reports on activities to team members may help everyone finish their tasks on time. If an important deadline is missed, the team, with guidance from the leader, must figure out a new plan to get the project completed on time.

A summary of the design process is given here for you to review before you begin your own projects. The design process starts with the **identification** of a problem, an

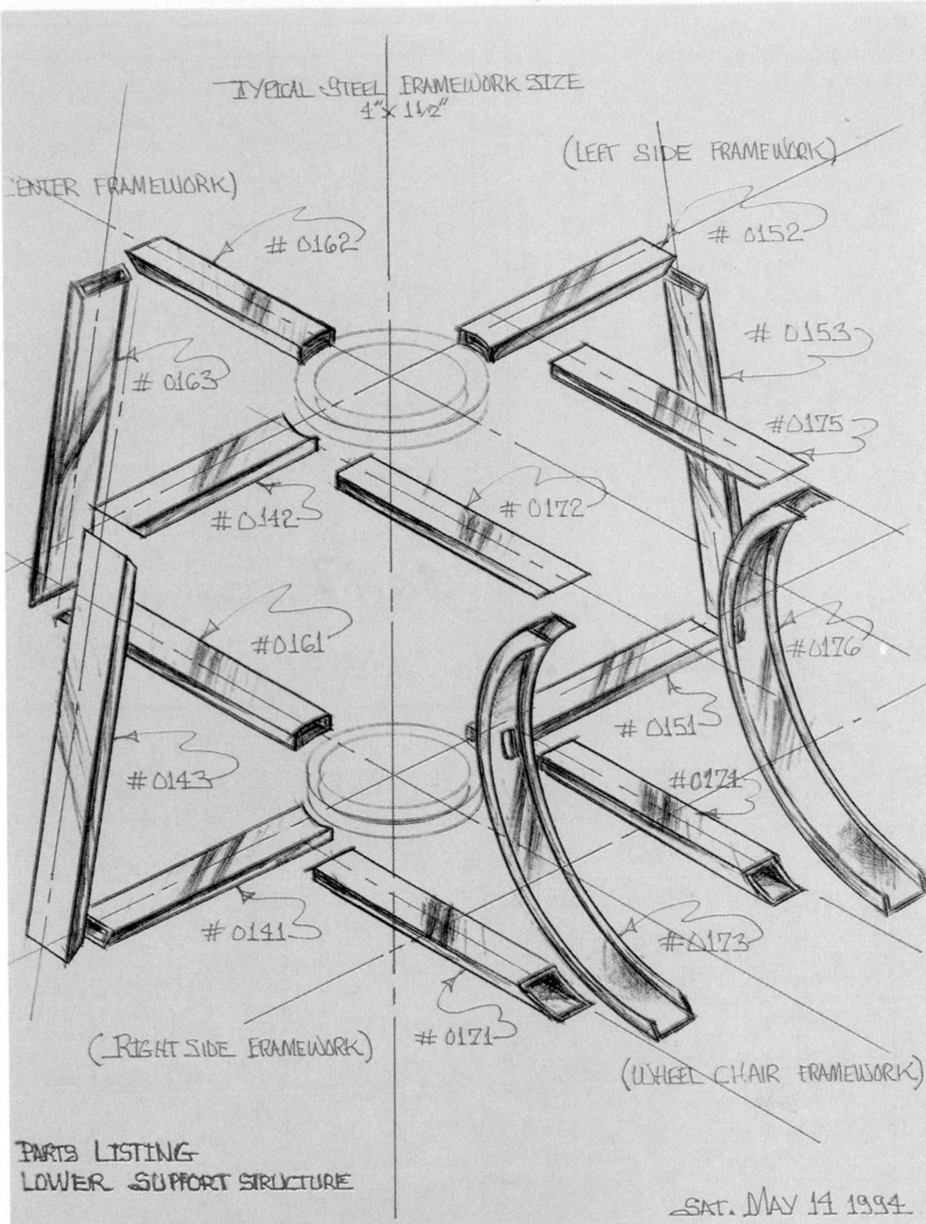

FIGURE 30.13
Assembly Drawing Sketches

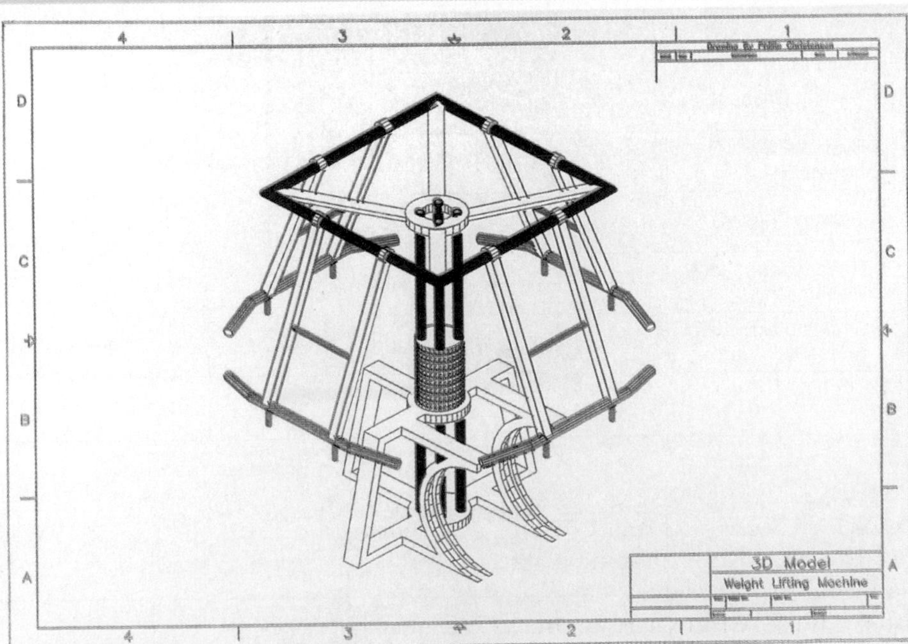

FIGURE 30.14 3D Model of Weight-Lifting Machine

FIGURE 30.15 Multiview Drawing of Pulley Detail

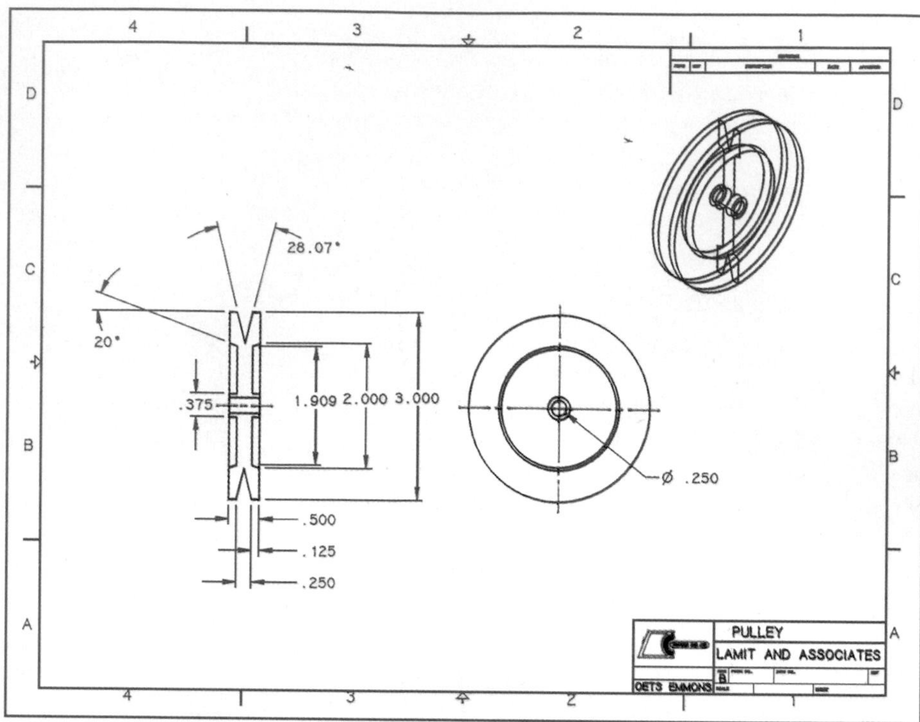

ID	Task Name	Duration	Start	Finish
1	Evaluate Test Apparatus Design	8d	3/28/96	4/4/96
2	Assemble Apparatus	1w	4/5/96	4/11/96
3	Build Jig for Test Bed Apparatus	1w	4/12/96	4/18/96
4	Machining of Test Bed	1w	4/19/96	4/25/96
5	Evaluate Test Bed Air System	3d	4/26/96	4/28/96
6	Assemble Test Bed Air System	4d	5/1/96	5/4/96
7	Evaluate Test Procedure	5d	5/5/96	5/9/96
8	Testing Phase 1	2w	5/10/96	5/23/96
9	Testing Phase 2	1w	5/24/96	5/30/96
10	Evaluate Control Potential	3d	5/31/96	6/2/96
11	Testing Phase 3	1w	6/5/96	6/11/96
12	Recommendations/ Report	4d	6/12/96	6/15/96
13	Evaluate Additional Sensors	2w	6/16/96	6/29/96

April May June
3/26 4/2 4/9 4/16 4/23 4/30 5/7 5/14 5/21 5/28 6/4 6/11 6/18 6/25

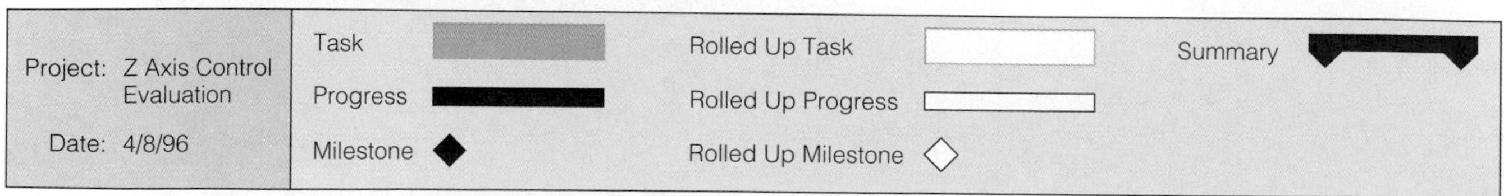

FIGURE 30.16 Gantt Chart for Project Management

observed need, or a potential new idea for a product or system. The **background** of the project is presented to the design team by a concerned party: the company management, an outside client, or a company inventor who has a new idea. The **general description** and possible solutions to the problem flow from a series of meetings conducted with the design team. The economics of a particular solution must be understood early. Before the design process goes any further, **creative possibilities** for a solution to the design problem should be investigated. The identification and classification of design elements helps to clarify and separate important or vital elements from minor or nonvital ones. A creative choice for a design solution must flow from a deep understanding of the design elements related to the project. Sketches and layouts help refine the design. They also isolate physical aspects of the problem and help spin off creative or new solutions. Many aspects of the design background must be understood *before* the brainstorming session if it is not to be a useless exercise. Brainstorming may help bring to light a unique or unthought-of set of possibilities. Multiple products or variations of one product or solution should be thoroughly investigated.

After the brainstorming session, all notes, sketches, surveys, marketing analysis, and research data should be reviewed. Any ideas that show no merit are filed at this point. The **evaluation** of possible solutions and their **refinement** into an end product is then completed. Refinement of a design is more restrictive at this juncture. More than one solution is still pursued, but the basic parameters of the project have helped to control the breadth of the design effort. To be successful, the analysis of a problem must include both its requirements and its limitations. Product design includes consideration of human engineering requirements. **Hidden factors** must be considered: Have any factors been overlooked in the design? Are there any aspects that are suspect? If these or other pertinent questions are not answered satisfactorily, the design team needs to go back to the beginning of the design process and review each step. The design proposal cannot be accepted without the consensus of the total team and all departments in the company. Solutions to any problems must be solved here, not later, when they could prove very costly.

The **analysis and evaluation** of possible design solutions is normally done through a thorough investigation of the data that pertains to it. Technical reports containing design data on each possible solution must be generated at this point in the process. A project may even be abandoned now, or more than one product or solution may be accepted. Sometimes the design concept exceeds the known capabilities of science and technology. A complete technical report on each solution must be submitted by the design group. The management decision team, which includes members from the design, manufacturing, and marketing departments, evaluates the merits of each solution and reaches a decision on the design choice or choices. The design team then proceeds to the next stage, **optimizing** the selected design. The selection of materials, processes, and other design requirements can be further refined at this stage. Each feature and capability of the design should be analyzed and evaluated. After the solutions have been chosen, every concern of all team members must be addressed and a consensus reached.

The project work schedule is determined once the final design is chosen. The development-and-implementation stage of the design process includes the drawing, modeling, testing, analysis, and refinement of the design. Actual full-scale prototypes are developed from design drawings to test for strength and design flaws. **Design, layout, and working drawings** are then completed. No major modifications are expected here. Modeling with a 3D CAD system allows the design team to evaluate multiple options for a design and to generate working drawings automatically. **Stereolithography** may be used to create conceptual models, plastic prototypes, soft tooling for silicone and sand molds, and patterns for metal castings. The finalization of a design then begins.

Once the final design is complete, it is evaluated for potential new technology, innovation, and patent possibilities. A patent can be granted for a process or a unique invention or discovery. Patent drawings may be generated at this point. Manufacturing tooling and process selection is included at this stage.

Tooling design can be emphasized in an academic project as well. In fact, if you are to go beyond the prototype stage, the design and production of tooling is as essential as the product design. As an illustration we next present a student project that emphasized tooling and fixturing design.

The student team was asked to design and produce fifty switches that could be used by physical therapists while they worked with individuals with various motor function problems (Fig. 30.17). The big-button switch for turning on and off DC and AC electric devices was made from polycarbonate, for toughness. Individuals with cerebral palsy, for example, can break their own bones with the force generated

FIGURE 30.17 Production Run of Big-Button Switches and Control Boxes

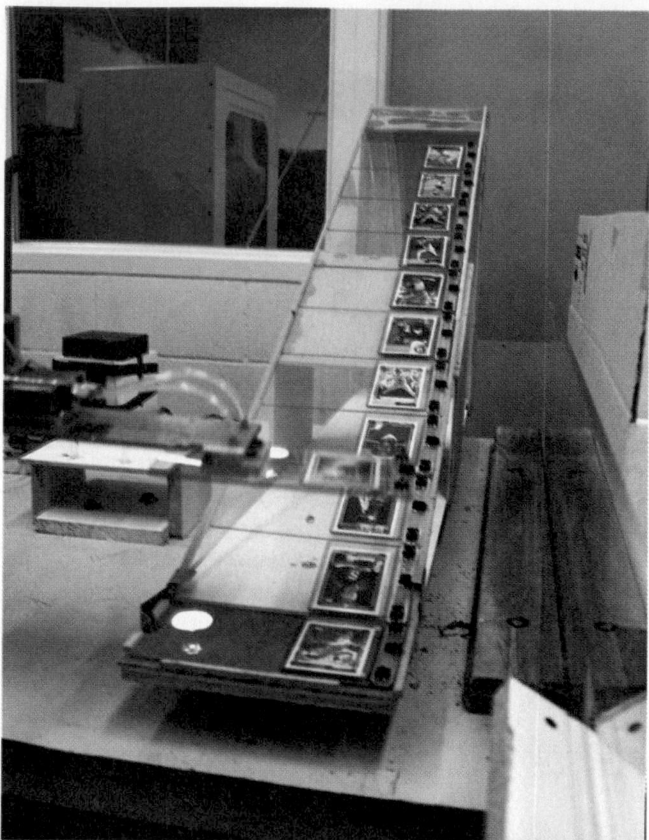

FIGURE 30.18 Polycarbonate Switch Blank Presentation

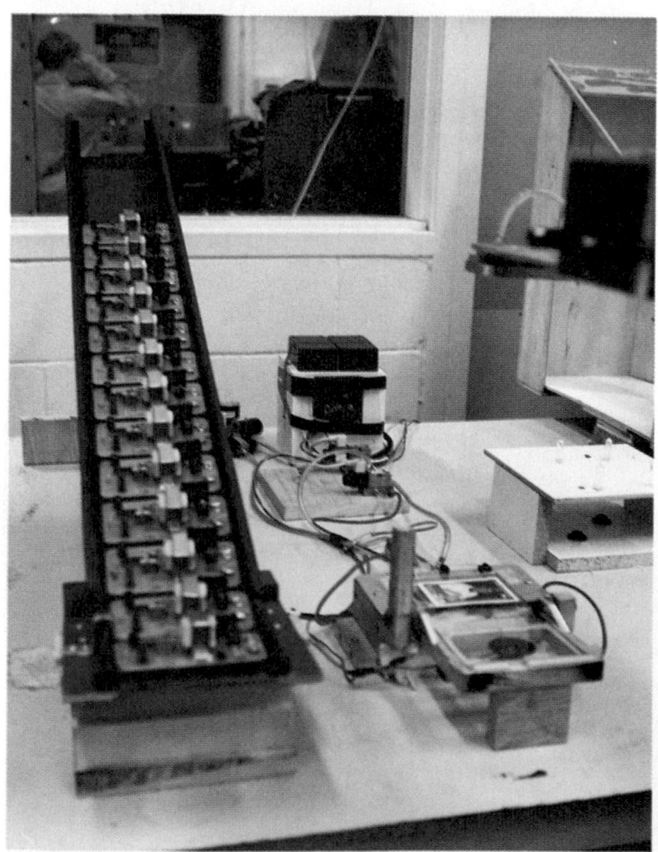

FIGURE 30.19 AC Control Circuit Presentation

FIGURE 30.20 Polycarbonate Blank Bending Fixture

from a muscle spasm. On the other hand, stroke victims may have limited mobility and may lack the force needed to push a switch. (The electrical control box for AC devices is contained in the blue plastic box in the photos.)

The student team was designing tooling for an automated workcell consisting of two robots, an ultrasonic welder, and a tabletop CNC vertical mill. In any automated workcell, all product components must be presented to the workcell (Figs. 30.18 and 30.19) so that the robots can perform the appropriate operations. In this case, simple gravity feeding and ramps were selected by the design team. Gravity-fed ramps are often used in industrial settings as well.

The end-effector tooling for the robots was designed by the student team. A vacuum end-effector was used to pick up the polycarbonate blank and place it in the bending fixture (Fig. 30.20). The same vacuum end-effector functioned to pick up the AC switch-box circuit assembly (Fig. 30.21).

The tooling needed to complete the CNC milling was more complex, and it required a stiffer material, 6061-T6 aluminum alloy, to resist the cutting forces during milling (Fig. 30.22). The fixture itself was actuated by a pneumatic cylinder (Fig. 30.23). The students produced the milling fixtures on an industrial-size CNC vertical turning center.

The tooling needed to weld the plastic box together ultrasonically also required a stiff material (6061-T6 aluminum again) and a pneumatic actuator (Fig. 30.24). The box was welded in two places. The tool for the robot is also visible in this photo. As shown in Figure 30.25, the tooling for the second part of the assembly operation employed a wide range of materials and actuation methods. Wood, polymers, aluminum, steel, and composites are often chosen for tooling and fixturing. Stiff materials may be more difficult to produce, but they are essential when rigidity plays a key role.

Marketing, sales, and **distribution** are also important to the total design effort. A product that is not marketed correctly will not sell. The sales distribution network is an

FIGURE 30.21 Vacuum End-Effector Picks Up AC Switch-Box Cover

FIGURE 30.22 Aluminum Fixture for CNC Milling

essential part of the process. A customer will not wait forever, even for a good product. If a product is unavailable, sales are often lost. The costs for advertising, marketing, packaging, shipping, and distribution greatly affect the cost to bring the product to market. And appropriate packaging is critical. For consumer goods, packaging should be attrac-

FIGURE 30.23 Pneumatic Actuator for CNC Milling Fixture

tive and well conceived. Even when the packaging for a product is less important, the package must still protect the product during shipping and distribution. Packaging considerations also include the new concepts of "green" packaging (environmental packaging)—that is, using biodegradable

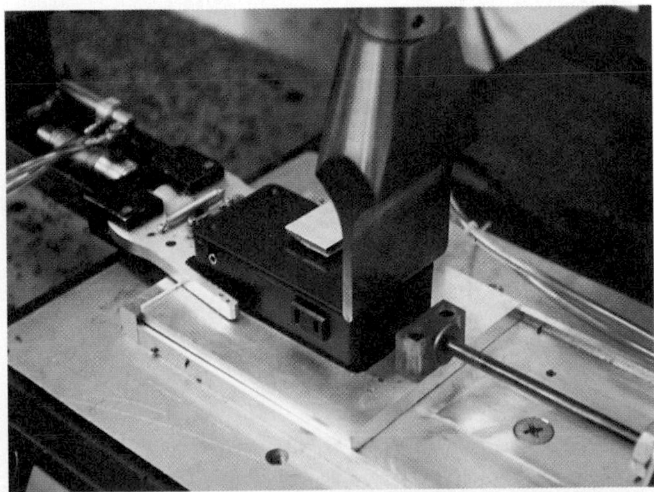

FIGURE 30.24 Aluminum Fixture for Ultrasonic Welding. The robot tool for holding the part is also visible.

FIGURE 30.25 Tabletop Tooling for Workcell

materials and eliminating overpackaging, which creates unnecessary amounts of waste.

The design process summary from Chapter 3 is again presented here. You may wish to refer to it as a check-off list or as a guide through your own design projects.

Design Process Summary

1. *Identification*: Defining the design objective
   a. Make a list of known facts and existing information.
   b. Ask the following questions: What? Why? Where? Who? How? When?
2. *Conceptualization*: Brainstorming, creative solutions
   a. How many ways can it be solved?
   b. Thought starters: make a list of values.
   c. Determine similarities, environmental requirements.
   d. Checklist, brainstorming, material options.
   e. Is there a simpler way?
3. *Evaluation*: Application, functional requirements, synthesis
   a. What makes the design good—economy, simplicity, reliability, durability, usefulness, attractiveness, manufacturability, easy to promote in sales, easy to service?
   b. What are the alternatives to the design?
4. *Decision*: Design optimization
   a. What materials should be used?
   b. Should the parts be interchangeable?
   c. Should standard parts be used?
   d. Is the manufacturing process economical?
   e. How easy to operate is the product?
5. *Development*: Implementation of design
   a. Create working drawings and details.
   b. Model the part—CAD, physical, types, number of models.
   c. Check the design.
   d. Testing and analysis—modeling, debugging.
   e. Improve and redesign for aesthetic or functional refinements.
6. *Production*: Manufacturing, packaging, handling the product
   a. Facility needs
   b. Personnel requirements
   c. Materials and processes for manufacturing
   d. Packaging design
   e. Material handling and product handling
7. *Marketing*: Sales and distribution
   a. Staff training
   b. Servicing the product
   c. Low maintenance costs, customer acceptance
   d. Sales strategy on how to present
   e. Product and main features
   f. Distribution of the product: Who? How?

30.3 SUGGESTED DESIGN PROJECTS

Following are some suggestions for design projects. Your instructor will help you define the scope of your project. Study Chapters 2 and 3 again. Make sure your design team follows the design process carefully. Elect team leaders who are good facilitators and communicators. Make sure you have a good management plan in place before you begin. Identify critical design goals early in the project. Consult often with your instructor during the design process. Make all team members feel like valuable contributors, and emphasize team goals.

Always document your project carefully. Keep initial concept sketches and ideas from early brainstorming sessions. After the final design is selected, for most projects your team should produce a set of working drawings. A manufacturing plan should also be included. You may expand the project to include tooling and fixturing. You may also want to complete the project using solid modeling and then generate a set of working drawings from the solid model database. Keep communication open during the project. Discuss concurrent engineering and design for manufacturability often. Don't forget to plan the completion of the project with a Pert or Gantt chart.

Yard Toy for Children Design a child's backyard play toy. Include a slide, a ladder, a swing, a tunnel, a rope climb, and a tire walk. Design for safety, strength, and creative play situations. Make sure that all aspects of the design are sized for the child.

Small Hand Tools Do a short survey on the variety of small tools, such as screwdrivers, pliers, and saws. Attempt to redesign an existing product to suit the needs of the user better. Improve the design; attempt to find creative and aesthetically pleasing alternatives. Also, redesign them for use by individuals with small hands.

Packaging Machine Take a small household product and design a packaging machine to load and box the item.

Garbage Dumper Design a garbage can and a lift device that could empty different cans into a dump truck. Expand on this idea by designing stackable recycling containers for glass, cans, plastic, and paper products. Redesign the trash collection system for your college or university.

Fishing Rod Holder Create a series of fishing rod holders that will accommodate all sizes and shapes of handles. One version should be for a boat-mounted holder, another for a shore fishing model.

Face Guard Design a face guard for baseball players to use while batting. Do a study on the typical human face and how to protect it without reducing visibility or inhibiting the batter.

Trailer Hitch Design an interchangeable hitch that could be used for all ball sizes and every class of hitch, if possible. Research should include the ball sizes, weight limits, classifications, and materials of existing hitches.

Easy CD Storage Container Design a storage container for compact disks for either your stereo or your computer that allows for easy access and sorting of the CD's. Make sure the container can fit into a small space, such as that available in most apartments and homes.

Portable Computer Security Device Design a locking docking station for a portable or laptop computer. The device should allow a business traveler to lock the computer into a secure location while on a business trip. Consider available locations in motel or hotel rooms, as well as business spaces.

Portable Coin Sorter Design a portable coin sorter so that market or street vendors can easily sort their coins into rolls at the close of each business day. Consider an alternative design to help them remove any Canadian money from the rolled coins.

Ergonomic Computer Workstation Design an ergonomic computer workstation for individuals who have developed carpel tunnel syndrome from repetitive keyboard motions. (Many secretaries and computer professionals have developed repetitive trauma injuries as a result of improper computer workstation design.) Consult with medical professionals while completing this project.

Toy Solar-Powered RC Vehicle Design a toy solar-powered radio-controlled (RC) vehicle that will be able to navigate an obstacle course. Limit the weight of the vehicle to under 0.5 lb.

Toy Solar-Powered RC Boat Design a toy solar-powered radio-controlled (RC) boat that will be able to navigate a course in a small lake. Consider designing more than one boat and having them compete in a race or obstacle course.

Weed Puller Design a weed puller for older people who no longer have the mobility to bend repeatedly to pull weeds from their gardens and lawns. The device should be adjustable and simple to operate. It should store in a small amount of space.

Pepper Grinder Design a pepper grinder for freshly ground pepper that operates by squeezing handles rather than by rotating the grinder parts. Make the grinder adjustable so that it can produce fine- medium- and course-ground pepper.

Hot-Beverage Holder Design a hot-beverage holder for an automobile that will help prevent children from spilling the contents on themselves or on surfaces in the car. Develop an alternative design for cold items, like ice cream cones and snow cones.

Big-Button Remote Control Design a big-button remote control for a TV and VCR for individuals with limited mobility in their hands. Limit the number of buttons so that only essential features are controlled. (Older individuals with arthritis often have difficulty using remotes with very small buttons, and a large number of buttons is often confusing to everyone.)

Portable Communicator for Nonverbal Children Design a portable communicator device (portable tape player size) for nonverbal children. The device should be reprogrammable and feature changeable icons over the buttons.

Multimedia Computer Design a multimedia computer that features integrated speakers, a CD-ROM player, a joystick, a microphone, headphones, and a mouse. Ideally, all components should be in one multifunctional container.

Portable 3.5″ Disk Holder Design a 3.5″ disk holder (1) that a student can pack inside a notebook or in a backpack and (2) that is lightweight and protects the diskettes (up to five) from the wear and tear of a typical college student's backpack. The package should be waterproof.

Automatic Feeder for a Cat Design an automatic feeder for a cat that can feed a cat for up to seven days while the owner is on vacation. It should accommodate both canned food and dry food as well as liquids.

Car Seat Toy Design an interesting toy for a child to play with while the child is confined in a car seat. Be sure to consider the safety issues involved.

Easy-Turn Light Switch Design a light switch for a lamp

that is easier to turn for those with limited hand mobility. Reconsider the design for individuals in a wheelchair.

Computer Mouse/Joystick Design a multifunctional device that a computer operator could use equally well as a pointing device (mouse) or as a joystick (game interface). Consider designing a different device for a child and for an adult.

Ergonomic Keyboard Design an alternative keyboard for computers that takes into account human factors and ergonomics. Consider the number of individuals using a keyboard and the fact that reports of carpel tunnel syndrome and other repetitive trauma injuries are rising.

Emergency-Exit House Lighting Design an emergency-exit house lighting system similar to those found in emergency aircraft exit systems. The strips of light should lead a person to an exit when the house is filled with smoke and flames. Design a modular system that can be installed in a typical home. Make sure the system is easy enough for children to understand and follow.

Emergency Ladder or Chute Design an emergency ladder or chute to provide a safe exit from the second story of a home during a house fire. Consider the safety, security, and aesthetics of such a system.

Earthquake Safety Kit Container Design a container for a safety kit for use in a major metropolitan area after a major earthquake. The container should be easy to locate and should be able to survive the earthquake itself.

Cellular Phone Safety Clip Design a general-purpose clip for car cellular phones. The clip should be able to secure a portable cellular phone in the car while the phone is not in operation. (An unsecured cellular phone can become a weapon during a car crash.)

Small-Tool Holder for Garage Design a general-purpose holder to hold and sort small tools normally found in home garages. (Often, small tools such as screwdrivers, pliers, and wrenches are difficult to find in a garage because they are not organized.) Make the system easy to install for all home owners.

Portable Home Recycling Container Storage Design a storage device for home recycling containers that makes the containers easy to store and easy to move to the curbside for weekly pickup. (Home owners often make multiple trips to the curbside with multiple containers for recycling pickup.)

Door Lock Portable Safety Device Design an improved portable locking mechanism for motel and hotel doors that provides increased security for travelers. Consider the safety issues involved regarding both forced room entry and emergency exit.

Portable Steering Wheel Lock Design a portable steering wheel lock that helps prevent automobile theft. The device should be as light and as small as possible so that it can be stored in small spaces when not in use.

Door Bell Alert for the Hearing Impaired Design a system that alerts a hearing-impaired individual to a visitor who is waiting for a response to a doorbell. Design the system so that it can distinguish between two different doors and so that it can alert the person in any room of the house.

Rollerblade Gear Container Design a portable container for a pair of rollerblades and the various pads that a typical rollerblade skater wears. The device should hold the gear and then be useful to the rollerblader after the gear is put on. (Rollerblade skaters seldom want to return to the parking lot to store the container after they put on the gear.)

All-Terrain Wheelchair Design a wheelchair that can function in snow conditions and on ice. (Students using conventional wheelchairs typically have a difficult time maneuvering on campus in snow and ice conditions.)

Mouse for Portable Computers Design a computer mouse (pointing device) for small, portable computers. The mouse should be usable in small, confined spaces, such as on a tray table on an airplane.

Portable Wheelchair for Air Travel Design a collapsible wheelchair that a customer on an airplane can take on the flight. Keep in mind the weight and space restrictions on a typical airplane.

One-Handed Paper Towel Dispenser Design a new paper towel dispenser that will dispense single sheets of paper towels when only one hand is free to operate the device. Design it for home use. It should be easy to load and inexpensive.

Design Projects for the Differently Abled Most colleges and universities have services devoted to helping the differently abled. An excellent design project would include the research and analysis of how the life of a physically challenged student is affected by the man-made items found in daily life. Contact your disabled-student services program and request to interview a number of wheelchair-bound students, staff, or faculty. Other types of physical limitations could also be studied. Consider, for example, design projects for the blind, the hearing impaired, or the seeing impaired. Designing real applications for real people is often the most exciting and challenging of all projects.

Since differently abled individuals use many of existing facilities, this is an excellent area in which to research, analyze, and design products and fixtures. Do some research and tabulate your findings as in Figure 30.26, where the number of fixtures and the number of users of a facility are displayed on a graph. Figure 30.27 is an example of a sketch

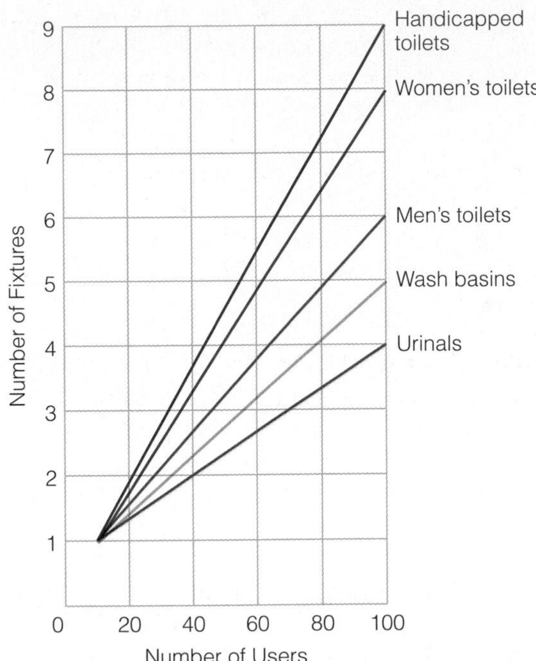

FIGURE 30.26 **Graphical Analysis of Research Data on Restroom Facility Use**

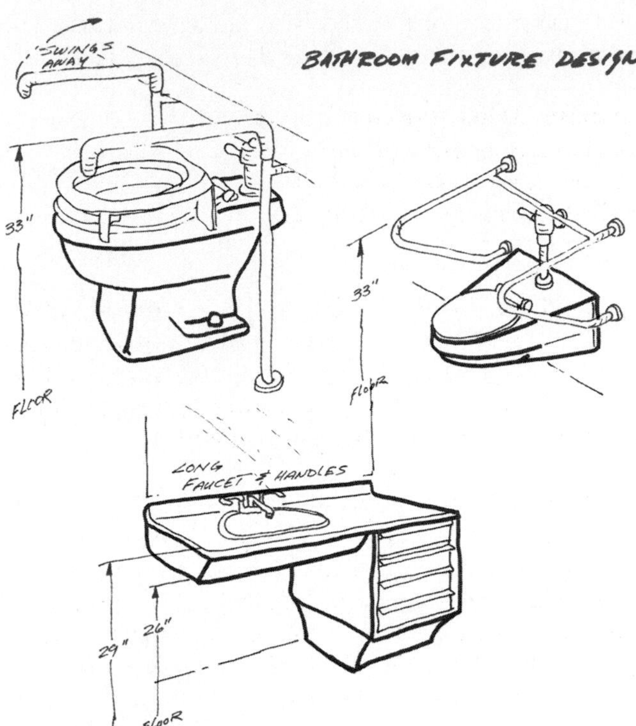

FIGURE 30.27 **Bathroom Fixture Design for the Differently Abled**

for determining the proper heights of restroom facilities for the physically limited. Your problems should have rough sketches, development layouts, and accurate CAD or manual assemblies and details.

Many products will require studies of human factors and ergonomics. Researchers might consult *Human Factors Design Handbook* by Wesley E. Woodson (McGraw-Hill) and *Ergonomic Design for People at Work* (Eastman Kodak Co., Lifetime Learning Publications). Both of these volumes contain pertinent data on designs for the differently abled.

APPENDIXES

GLOSSARIES

Appendix A

A.1 MECHANICAL GLOSSARY

Accurate Manufactured within the specified tolerances.

Acme thread A screw thread similar to the square thread. The acme has in most cases replaced the square thread because it is stronger and easier to manufacture. It is widely used as a feed screw.

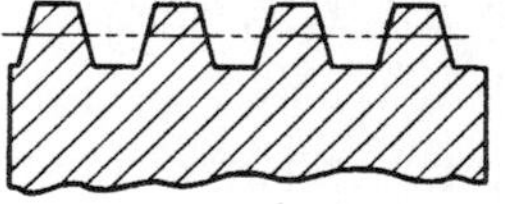

Acme thread

Addendum The radial distance between the top of the tooth and the pitch circle of a gear.

Aging A change in a metal or alloy by which its structure recovers from an unstable condition produced by quenching (quench aging) or by cold working (strain aging).

Air hardening Full hardening of a metal or alloy during cooling in air or some other gaseous medium from a temperature above its transformation range.

Air-set process No-bake sand-casting process; molds and cores made with a mix of sand and a resin-based chemical binder that hardens without baking.

Allen screw Special set screw or cap screw with hexagon socket in head.

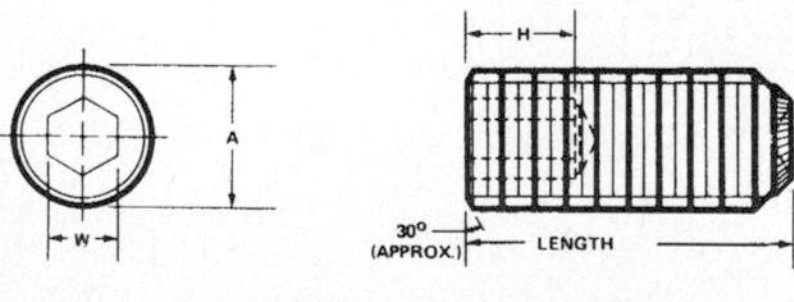

Allen screw

Allowance The intentional difference between the MMC limits of size of mating parts; the minimum clearance (positive allowance) or maximum interference (negative allowance) between such parts.

Alloy A mixture of two or more metals to obtain characteristics similar to the individual metals or different from any displayed by the individual components. See also **binary alloy.**

Alloying Adding elements other than those usually comprising a metal or alloy to change its engineering performance characteristics and mechanical properties.

Aluminum A lightweight but strong metal. Principle commercial source is bauxite ore.

Annealing A process of heating steel above the critical range, holding it at that temperature until it is uniformly heated and the grain is refined, and then cooling it very slowly.

Anodizing Usually refers to the formation of a conversion coating on the surface of aluminum by a process of electrolytic oxidation.

ANSI American National Standards Institute. A nongovernmental organization that proposes, modifies, approves, and publishes drafting and manufacturing standards for voluntary use in the United States.

Antioch process Plaster molding process using a mixture of sand, gypsum, and fibrous talc mixed with water. The mold is air set, subjected to steam pressure, rehydrated, and baked for several hours before pouring off the mold.

Arc A continuous portion (as of a circle or ellipse) of a curved line.

Arc

Arc welding A process of joining two or more metal parts together by fusing them by means of an electric arc. The arc melts the welding rod and fuses the parts together.

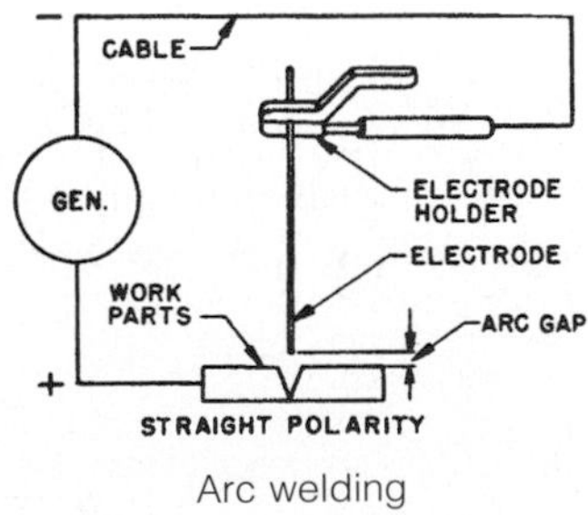

Arc welding

Artificial aging An aging treatment at a temperature somewhat above room temperature. See also **aging.**

As-cast condition Referring to newly produced, unmachined castings that have not been subjected to any form of finishing operations (beyond gate removal or shot-blast cleaning) or treatment of any kind, including heat treatment.

Assembly drawing A drawing representing a group of parts constituting a major subdivision of the final product.

Austempered ductile iron A relatively new family of ductile iron materials that are comparable in engineering performance to steel forgings.

Auxiliary view Any view that lies in a projection plane other than the horizontal (top), frontal (front), or profile (side) plane.

Axis A straight line (centerline) about which a feature of revolution revolves, or about which opposite-hand features are symmetrical.

Axonometric One of several forms of single-plane projections giving the pictorial effect of perspective, with the possibility of measuring the principal planes directly.

Back draft A reverse taper from the design direction of draw on a pattern or corebox that prevents removal of the pattern from the mold or removal of the core from the corebox.

Basic dimension A numerical value used to describe the theoretically exact size, profile, orientation, or location of a feature or datum target. It is the basis from which permissible variations are established by tolerances on other dimensions, in notes, or in feature control frames.

Bearing A machine part in which another part turns or slides.

Bend allowance The amount of sheet metal required to make a bend of a specific radius.

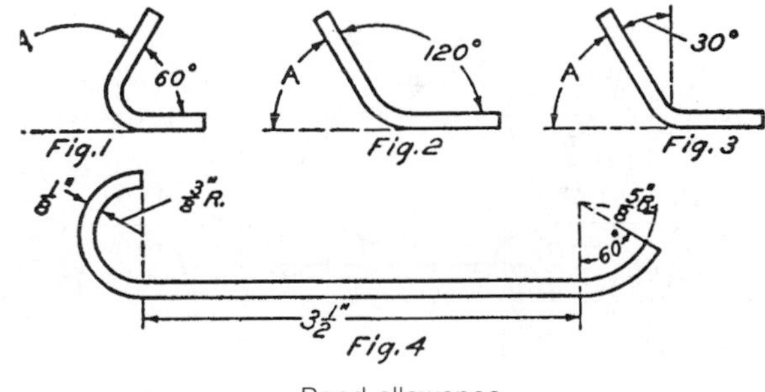

Bend allowance

Bevel The angle that one surface or line makes with another when they are not at right angles.

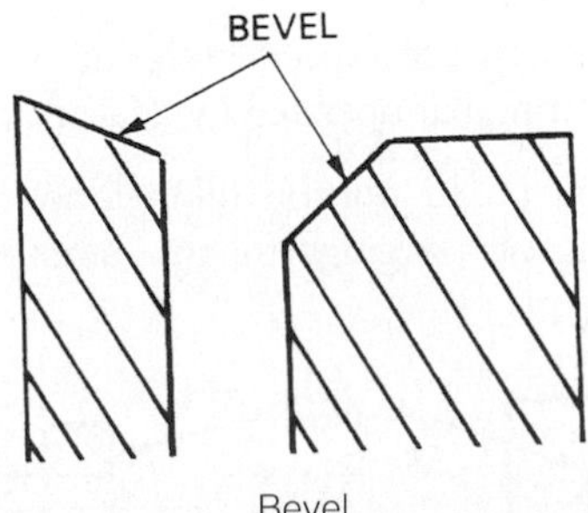

Bevel

Bilateral tolerance A tolerance in which variation is permitted in both directions from the specified dimension.

Binary alloy An alloy of two metals.

Binder A material used to hold the grains of foundry sand together to form a mold or core. It can be a cereal, an oil, clay, or natural/synthetic resins.

Biscuit Excess metal left at the end of the ejection cylinder of a cold-chamber die-casting machine. Also called a *slug*.

Black heart An American type of malleable iron. Normal fracture shows a mouse-gray rim around a velvety-black interior.

Blanking A punch press operation that consists of shearing from sheet metal stock a part having a definite contour determined by the punch and die.

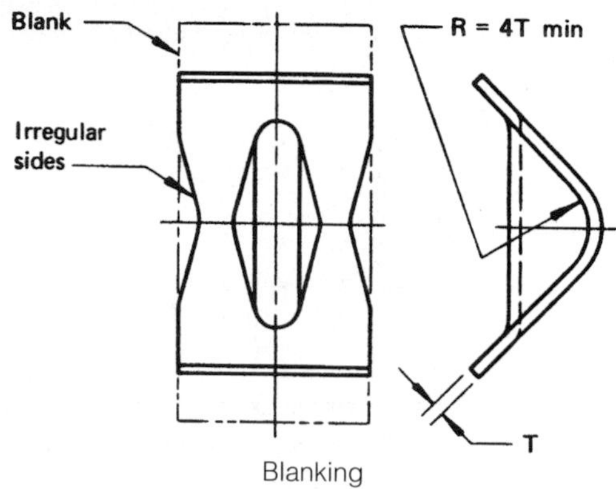

Blanking

Blast cleaning A process to clean or finish castings by use of an air blast or airless centrifugal wheel that throws abrasive particles or metal shot against the surface of castings.

Bolt A headed and externally threaded mechanical device designed for insertion through holes in assembled parts. It mates with a nut and is normally intended to be tightened or released by turning that nut.

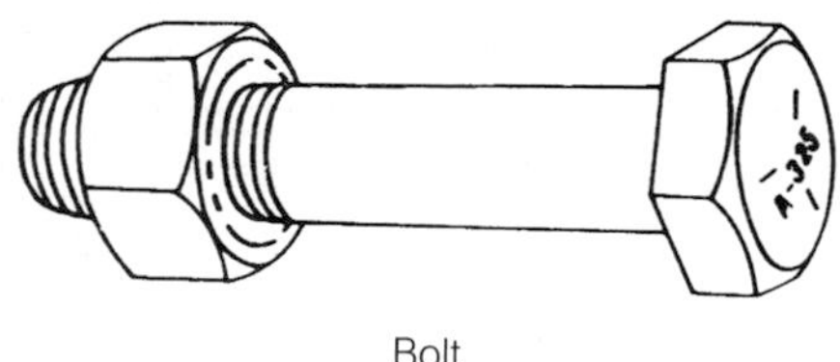
Bolt

Bolt circle A circular centerline on a drawing; contains the centers of holes about a common center.

Bore To enlarge a hole to a specified size by employing a point tool held in a boring bar operated by a lathe or a boring mill.

Boss A circular raised portion of material added around holes in castings or forgings to give strength or bearing surface to the part.

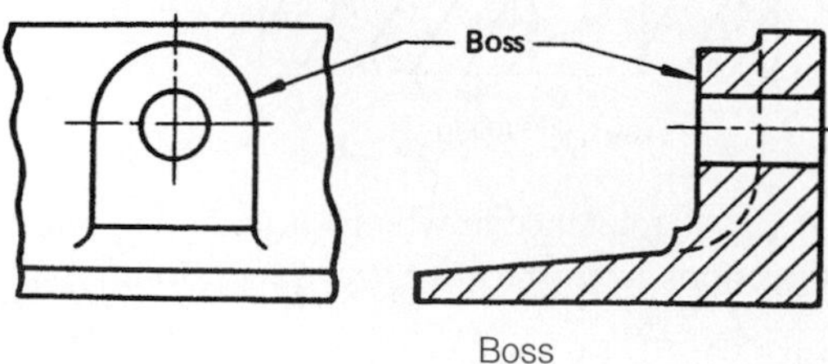

Boss

Brass An alloy of copper and zinc.

Brazing A group of welding processes wherein coalescence is produced by heating to a temperature above 800°F and by using a nonferrous filler metal (solder) having a melting point below that of the base metals (zinc or brass).

Brinell hardness A measure of the hardness of a metal or alloy. It is determined by measuring the diameter of an indentation formed by a hardened steel ball of given diameter applied under a known load.

Brittleness The tendency of a material to fracture with little or no plastic deformation.

Broaching To machine a hole to a desired shape by planing it with a transverse cutting tool (a *broach*) moved in a straight line so that each tooth removes a definite amount of stock.

Broach

Bronze A copper-base alloy with tin as the major alloying element.

Buffing A polishing operation using a fine abrasive wheel made of discs of cotton or wool impregnated with very fine abrasive, bonded with wax or grease.

Burnishing Smoothly finishing surfaces by compressing with the use of highly polished rolls or by the use of steel balls in rolling contact with the surface.

Burr A rough edge raised on metal along the path of a cutting tool.

Bushing A removable cylindrical sleeve used as a lining of low-friction material that provides a bearing surface. It is either press fitted or removable and provides accurate and quick location of the drilling operation when used in a drill jig.

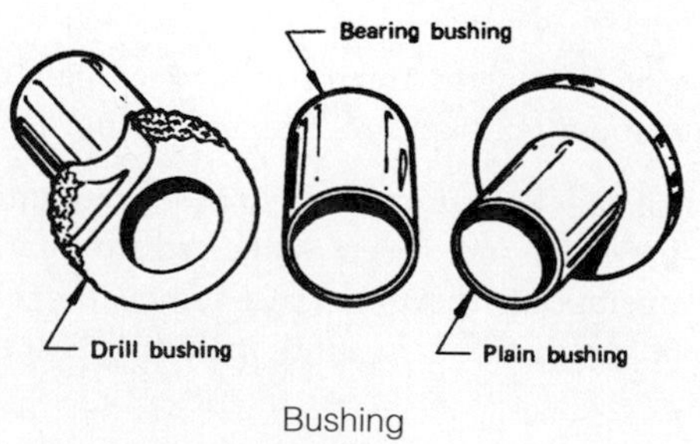

Bushing

Caliper A measuring tool for checking outside or inside measurements.

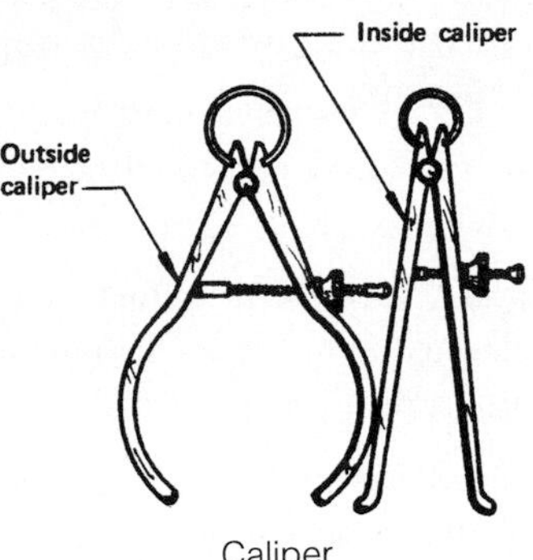

Caliper

Callout A note on a drawing giving a dimension, specification, or manufacturing process.

Cam A mechanical device on a rotating shaft that transforms rotary motion into lateral motion. A *face cam* is designed so that the follower travels in a groove cut in the face of the cam. A *barrel cam* has a groove cut in the outer surface of a cylinder to give motion in a direction parallel to the axis of rotation. A *disc cam* is designed so that the follower travels along its periphery.

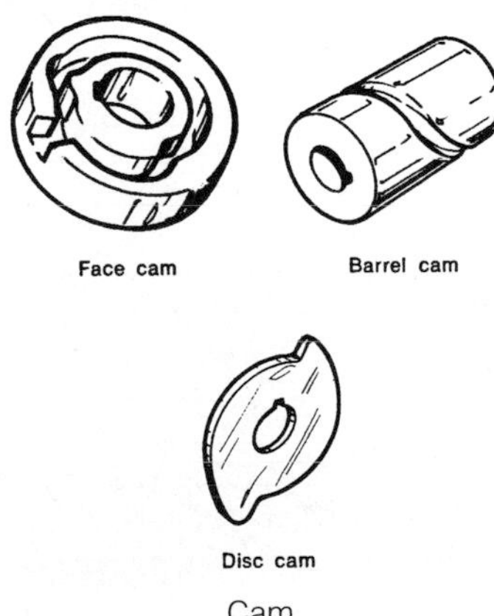

Cam

Carbonitriding A process for case-hardening an iron-base alloy by the simultaneous absorption of carbon and nitrogen.

Carbon steel Steel that has carbon as the major alloying element. Also known as ordinary straight carbon steel or plain carbon steel.

Carburize To harden the surface of iron-based alloys by heating the metal below its melting point in contact with solids, liquids, or gases that have a high carbon content. Carburizing is best performed on steels with less than 0.25% carbon content.

Case-harden To harden a surface either by carburizing or through the use of potassium cyanide.

Cast iron Generic term for alloys of iron, carbon, and silicon in which the amount of carbon is greater than what can be retained in solid solution in austenite at the eutectic. Common types of cast iron are gray, ductile, white, malleable, and austempered.

Casting (*noun*) An object formed by pouring, pumping, or sucking molten metal into a mold or set of dies and allowing it to solidify. (*verb*) The act of pouring, pumping, or sucking molten metal into a mold (made of sand, metal, ceramic, or graphite) or a set of metal dies.

Casting

Casting strains Strains in a cast metal component resulting from internal stresses created during cooling. Heat treatment and other processes can remove these strains.

Casting yield The weight of casting or castings divided by the total weight of metal poured into the mold, expressed as a percentage.

Center drill A drill to produce bearing holes in the ends of a workpiece. Also called a *countersink*.

Centrifugal casting A casting process in which molds are filled by pouring molten metal into a sand or metal mold that is revolving rapidly about either a horizontal or a vertical axis or by pouring the metal into the mold, then revolving the mold rapidly before the metal can solidify.

Chamfer A small, angular surface on an external edge corner for purposes of easy assembly or to remove sharp edges. The most frequent application is on shafts and cylinders.

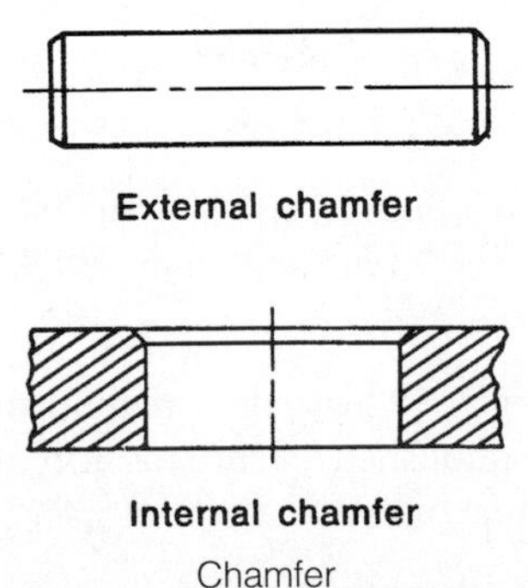

Chamfer

Chaplet An inset in a mold cavity used to support a core. If metal, it becomes part of the casting.

Charpy test A pendulum type of impact fracture test in which a specimen is supported at both ends and then broken by the impact of a swinging pendulum.

Chill A metal insert placed in a mold to increase the speed of cooling. Internal chills are placed in the mold cavity and become integral parts of the casting.

Chilled iron Cast iron poured against a chill to produce an extremely hard, abrasion- and wear-resistant surface.

Chuck A mechanism for holding a rotating tool or workpiece on a lathe.

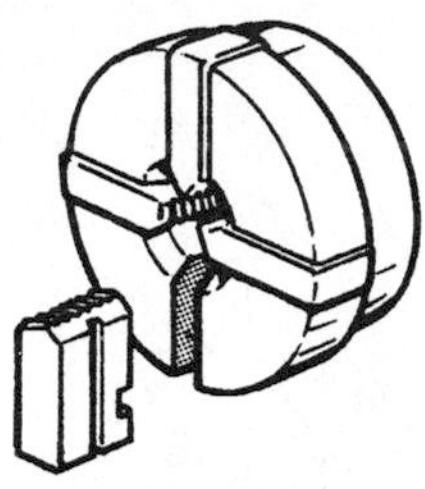

Chuck

Cleaning Removal of (a) sand and excess metal from a sand casting, (b) ceramic and excess metal from an investment casting, or (c) excess metal from a diecasting.

Code identification number A five-digit number, assigned to each design activity, used in conjunction with a part or identity number in a parts list [also referred to as a *Federal Supply Code for Manufacturers (FSCM)*].

Coining A method of cold-forging parts to desired size and shape by compressing them under heavy pressure between coining dies.

Cold-rolled steel (CRS) Open hearth or Bessemer steel containing 0.12% to 0.20% carbon that has been rolled while cold to produce a smooth, accurate stock.

Collar A cylindrical ring or round flange fitted on a shaft to prevent a sliding movement.

Collar

Combination die (multiple-cavity die) In diecasting practice, a die with two or more different cavities for different castings.

Commercial fastener A fastener manufactured to the requirements of published standards or documents and stocked by manufacturers or distributors.

Commercial item A supply or service that is (a) regularly used for other-than-government purposes and (b) sold or traded in the course of conducting normal business operations.

Compressive strength The maximum stress in compression that a material can withstand without fracturing, shattering, or deforming permanently.

Conductivity The ability of a material to conduct or transmit heat or electricity.

Controlled cooling A process by which a metal object is cooled from an elevated temperature in a manner that avoids hardening, cracking, or internal damage.

Conversion coating A coating consisting of a compound of the surface metal that is produced by chemical or electrochemical treatment such as a chromate coating on zinc, cadmium, magnesium, or aluminum, or an oxide or phosphate coating on iron or steel.

Cope The top half of a sand mold or pattern.

Cope-and-drag patterns Pattern equipment in which the cope-and-drag pattern sections are mounted on separate pattern boards so that the cope-and-drag sand mold sections can be made at the same time.

Core A solid form made of sand that is shaped in a core box and baked and used to shape the interior of a hollow casting.

Core print A projection on a pattern that forms an opening in the sand to hold the end of a core.

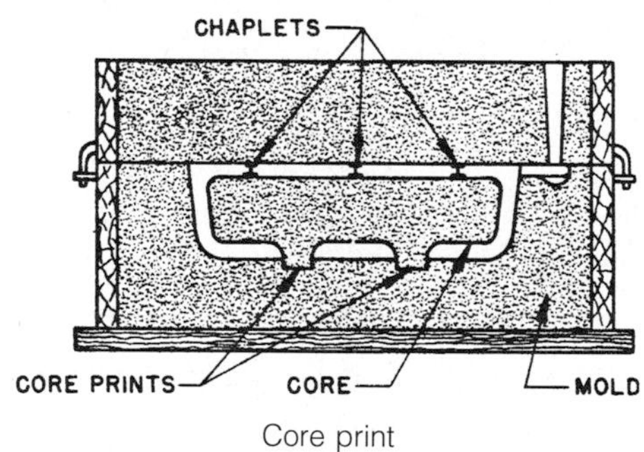

Core print

Core shift A deviation from specified dimensions of a cored section caused by a change in position of the core or a misalignment of cores in the core-setting procedures.

Cotter pin A half-round stock that is bent so as to have an eye at one end and that forms a round split pin when compressed together (used to lock parts of an assembly together).

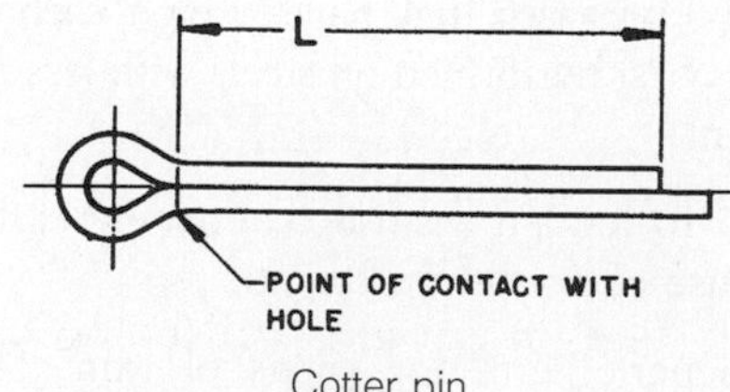

Cotter pin

Counterbore To enlarge the end of a cylindrical hole to a given depth with a flat shoulder; also the name of the tool used to produce such a hole.

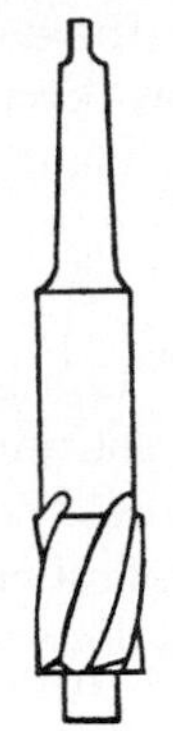

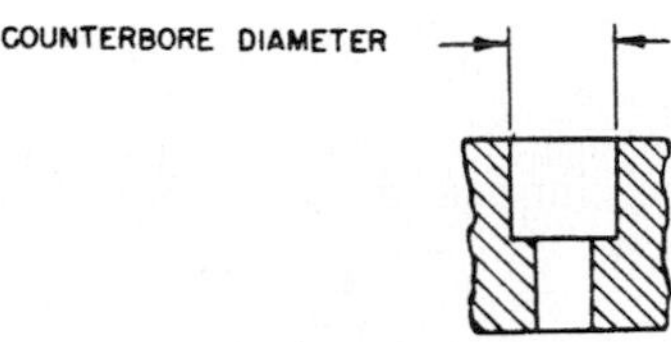

Counterbore

Counterdrill To form a conical shoulder in a drilled hole by enlarging it with a larger drill.

Countersink To recess a hole with a cone-shaped tool to provide a seat for a flathead screw or rivet; also the name of the tool used to make such a hole.

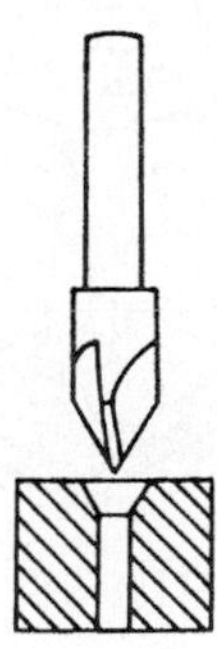

Countersink

Crosshatching Filling in an outline with a series of symbols to highlight part of a design.

Cut off To remove gates, risers, and other excess metal from a casting.

Cyaniding Surface-hardening of a ferrous alloy by heating at a suitable temperature in contact with a cyanide salt, followed by quenching.

Datum A theoretically exact point, axis, or plane derived from the true geometric counterpart of a specified datum feature. The origin from which the location or geometric characteristics of features of a part are established.

Dedendum The distance from the pitch circle to the bottom of the tooth space on a gear.

Degate To remove gating-system metal from castings.

Design activity An activity having responsibility for the design of an item; may be a government activity or a contractor, a vendor, or others.

Despruing Removing gates and risers from castings after the metal has solidified and cooled sufficiently.

Detail drawing A drawing of a single part that provides all the information necessary in the production of that part.

Dewaxing The process of melting out the wax pattern from an investment (ceramic shell) mold.

Diameter The length of a straight line running through the center of a circle.

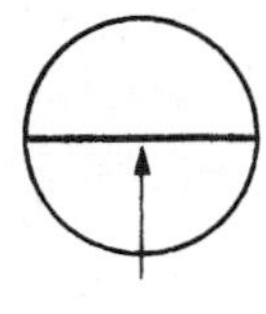

Diameter

Diametral pitch The number of gear teeth per inch of pitch diameter.

Dichromate treatment A chromate conversion coating that resists corrosion produced on magnesium alloys. Castings are immersed in a boiling solution of sodium chromate.

Die A hardened metal piece shaped to cut or form a required shape in a sheet of metal by pressing it against a mating die.

Diecasting (verb) Injecting molten metal under pressure into a mold chamber formed by metal dies. (*noun*) A casting produced by the diecasting process, which nowadays is most suitable for high-volume production of aluminum, zinc, and magnesium alloy castings. In Europe, any casting produced in a metal mold.

Diecasting, cold-chamber The diecasting process in which the metal injection mechanism is *not* submerged in molten metal.

Diecasting, gravity In Europe, the term means producing a casting by pouring molten metal (gravity pouring) into a metal mold, with no application of pressure. In the United States, this is the permanent mold casting process.

Diecasting, hot-chamber The diecasting process in which the metal injection mechanism is submerged in the molten metal.

Diecasting, pressure In Europe, a casting made in a metal mold (set of metal dies) in which the metal is injected under high pressure, by either cold-chamber or hot-chamber diecasting machines. In the United States, this is simply diecasting. *High-pressure diecasting* and *low-pressure diecasting* are terms commonly used in Europe to differentiate between what in the United States would be called, respectively, *diecasting* and *low-pressure permanent molding.*

Diecast skin The metal on the surface of a diecasting, to a depth of approximately .020 in. (0.8 mm), characterized by fine-grain structure and freedom from porosity.

Die stamping A part that has been cut or formed from sheet metal by the use of dies.

Differential hardening The hardening method in which different areas of a casting are subjected to different heating and quenching treatments, resulting in different hardnesses.

Dimension, basic A numerical value for describing the theoretically exact size, shape, or location of a feature or datum target. It is the basis from which permissible variations are established by tolerances on other dimensions, in notes, or by feature control symbols.

Dimension, coordinate Rectangular coordinate dimensioning is where all dimensions are measured from two or three mutually perpendicular datum planes.

Dimensional stability The ability of a casting to remain unchanged in size and shape under ordinary atmospheric conditions.

Dog A small auxiliary clamp for preventing work from rotating in relation to the face plate of a lathe.

Downsprue (downgate sprue) The first channel, usually vertically oriented, through which molten metal flows down into a mold.

Dowel A pin that serves to prevent sliding (and for location) between two contacting flat surfaces.

Draft The taper on the sides of a pattern that allow it to be removed easily from the sand mold; the taper on the sides of a forging die that permit the forging to be removed easily.

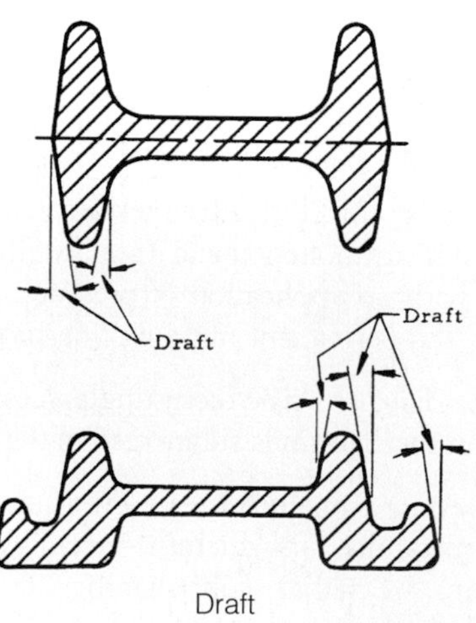

Draft

Drag The bottom half of a sand mold or pattern.

Draw To form a metal, which may be either hot or cold, by distorting or stretching; to temper steel by gradual or intermittent quenching.

Drawing format The standardized form, usually preprinted, on which various constant information (design activity identification, standard tolerance block, etc.) is provided, together with spaces for variable information (drawing number, title, etc.).

Drawing number Consists of letters, numbers, or a combination of letters and numbers, which may or may not be separated by dashes. The number is assigned to a particular drawing for identification and file retrieval.

Drawing type The name applied to a drawing, descriptive of its design and end use.

Drill (verb) To form a cylindrical hole with a drill. *(noun)* One of a variety of revolving cutting tools designed for cutting at the point.

Drill press A machine used for hole-forming operations.

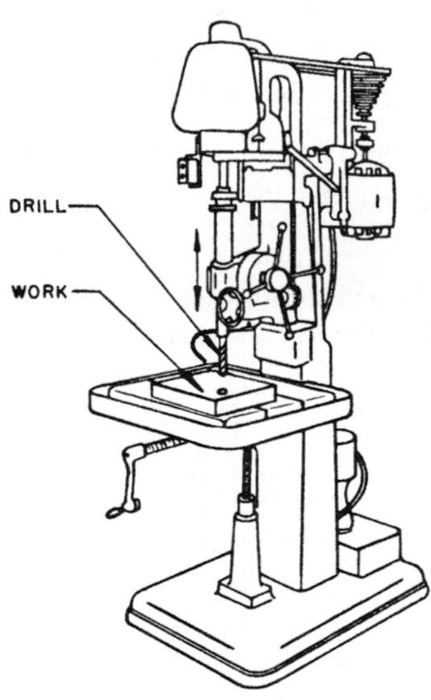

Drill press

Drop-forge To form a piece while hot by placing it between dies in a drop hammer.

Ductile iron Cast iron with nodular or spheroidal graphite shapes produced in iron after addition of magnesium or cerium in the ladle.

Ductility A mechanical property that permits permanent deformation of a casting by stress in tension without rupture.

Ejector marks The marks left on a hot diecasting from the impact of ejector pins in the diecasting machine.

Elastic limit The highest stress that a casting can withstand without permanent deformation after complete release of the stress. For casting application purposes, elastic limit is the yield strength.

Elongation The amount of permanent stretch before rupture, usually expressed as a percentage of the original gage length, such as 15% in 2 in.

Emboss To raise patterns or letters by impressing with matching punch and die; to form projections in sheet metal prior to projection welding.

Embrittlement The reduction in the normal ductility of a metal or alloy caused by a physical or chemical change.

Engineering data Drawings, associated lists, accompanying documents, manufacturer specifications, and standards, or other information relating to the design, manufacture, procurement, testing, or inspection of items or services.

Engineering definition A description expressed in engineering terms in sufficient detail to enable meeting the requirements of design, development, engineering, production, procurement, or logistic support.

Engineering document release The process of transferring custody of an engineering document, or change thereto, from the preparing activity to a control activity, which is responsible for its reproduction, distribution, storage, and the maintenance of history records.

Engineering drawing An engineering document that discloses, by means of pictorial and/or textual presentations, the form and function of a part.

Expendable pattern casting A metal casting process that employs a foam plastic pattern-and-sprue assembly that is usually robot positioned in a metal flask. Loose sand is poured into the flask and vibrated in and around the pattern-and-sprue assembly. Molten metal, poured into the sprue, vaporizes the sprue and the foam pattern instantly and replaces the shape with what becomes the casting when the metal solidifies. The process is also popularly called *lost foam casting.*

Extruding Forming a continuous cross section by forcing material through openings designed to a desired shape.

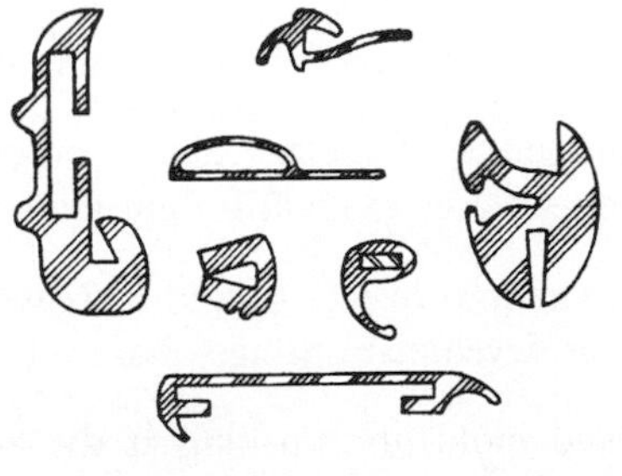

Extruding

Face To machine a flat surface on a part, using a lathe, by turning the surface perpendicular to the axis of rotation.

Facing sand Sand that touches or faces a pattern; when a sand mold is made, facing sand comes in direct contact with the molten metal and greatly affects the texture or smoothness of the casting surface.

Fastener A mechanical device designed specifically to hold, join, couple, assemble, or maintain equilibrium of single or multiple components.

Fatigue The tendency for a metal to break under conditions of repeated cyclic stressing considerably below its rated ultimate tensile strength.

Fatigue crack or failure A fracture starting from a nucleus where there is an abnormal concentration of cyclic stress.

Feather A rectangular sliding key that permits a pulley to move along the shaft parallel to its axis.

Feather edge A sharp point on a pressed metal stamping.

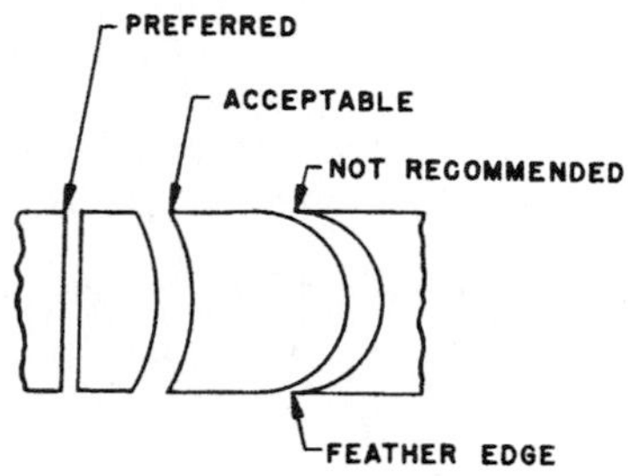

Feather edge

Feather key A flat key, which is partly sunk in a shaft and partly in a hub, permitting the hub to slide lengthwise on the shaft.

Federal supply code for manufacturers (FSCM) Five codes applicable to all activities that have produced or are producing items used by the federal government; also applies to government activities that control design or are responsible for the development of certain specifications, drawings, or standards that control the design of items.

Ferritic steels Steels with an alpha iron (ferrite) structure; they are magnetic.

File To shape, finish, or trim with a fine-toothed metal cutting tool, either in a rotating arbor or by hand.

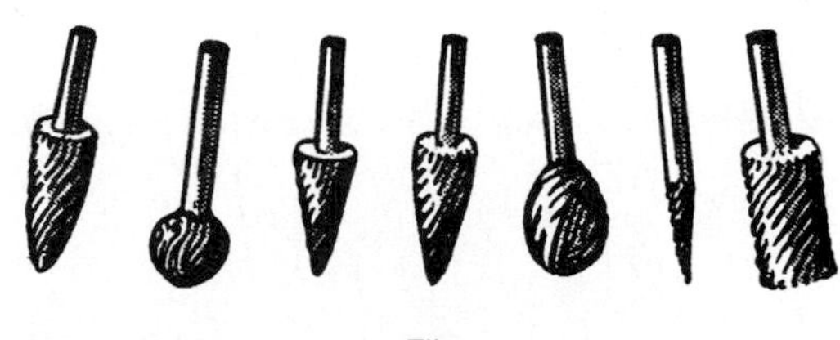

File

Fillet A curved inside corner that increases the strength at the junction of two intersecting surfaces of a part.

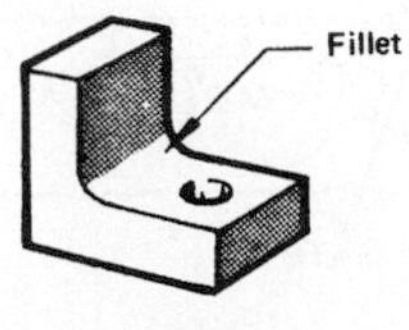

Fillet

Fin A thin extrusion of metal at the intersection of dies or sand molds.

Finish The degree of smoothness or roughness of a surface; the covering applied to a surface, such as plating or painting.

Fit The degree of tightness or looseness between two mating parts.

Fixture A tool for holding a part on which machining operations are being performed.

Flame annealing Softening the surface of an iron-base alloy via localized heat applied by a high-temperature flame.

Flame hardening A process of heating the surface of a casting to a high temperature with a flame, then quenching.

Flange A rim extending from the main section of a part, such as the top and bottom members of a beam or a projecting rim added at the end of a pipe or fitting for making a connection.

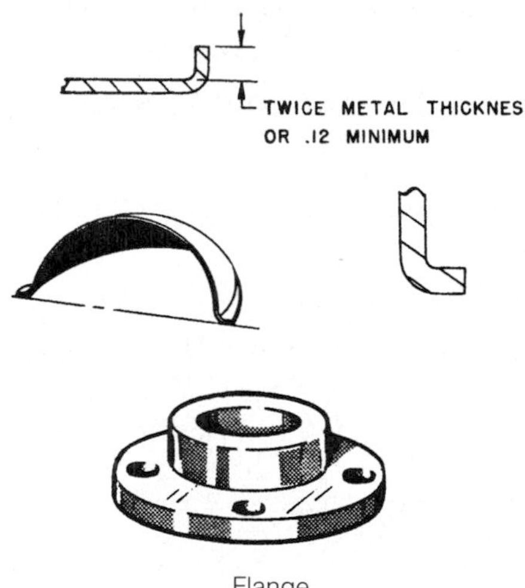

Flange

Flash Thin film or web of metal extending from a casting along the parting line because of poor contact between mating cope-and-drag molds or metal dies.

Flask The container in which sand molds are made; consists of two sections—the *cope* (upper section) and the *drag* (lower section). Any midsection is called a *cheek*.

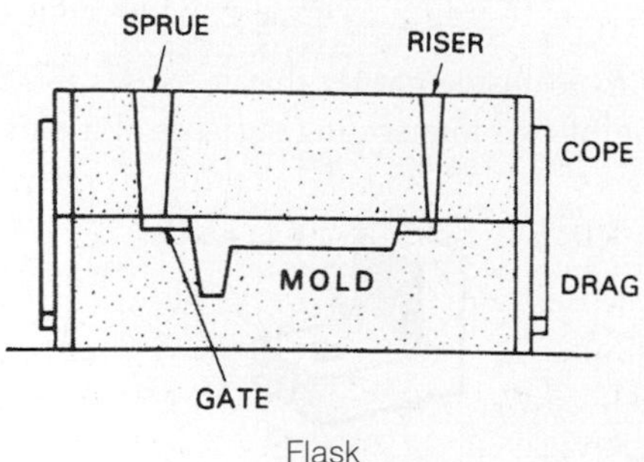

Flask

Flat pattern A layout (development) showing true dimensions of a part before bending.

Flute A groove, as on twist drills, reamers, and taps.

Forge To force metal while hot to take on a desired shape by hammering or pressing it.

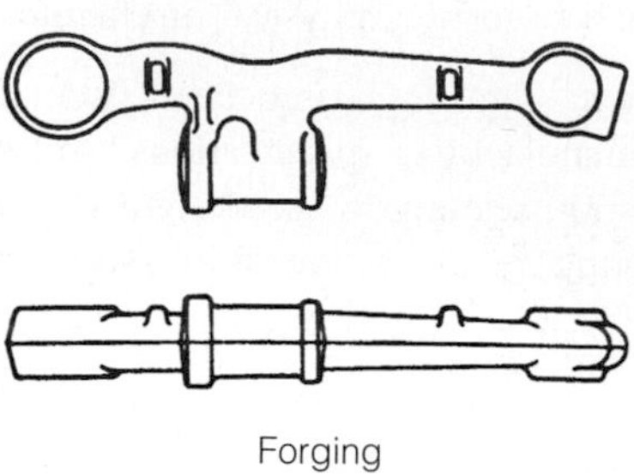

Forging

Gage An instrument for determining correctness of size or strength of manufactured parts within specified limits, such as depth gage, dial gage, plug gage, ring gage, snap gage, surface gage, thread gage, and wire gage.

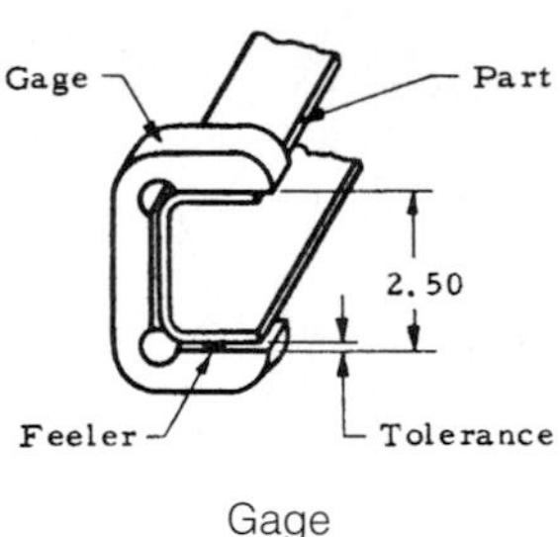

Gage

Galvanize To coat metal parts by immersing in a zinc bath.

Gasket A thin piece of metal, rubber, or other material placed between surfaces to make a tight joint.

Gas porosity Casting defects caused by gases trapped in molten metal or developed during solidification.

Gate In a sand mold, the opening at the bottom of the sprue through which the molten metal passes to enter the cavity or mold.

Gated patterns One or more patterns with gates or channels attached.

Gated system The complete assembly of sprues, runners, and gates in a mold through which metal flows to enter the casting cavity.

Gears Cylindrical or conical-shaped parts having teeth and used in gear trains that transmit power between shafts, such as spur gear, helical gear, herringbone gear, bevel gear, gear and rack, and internal spur gear.

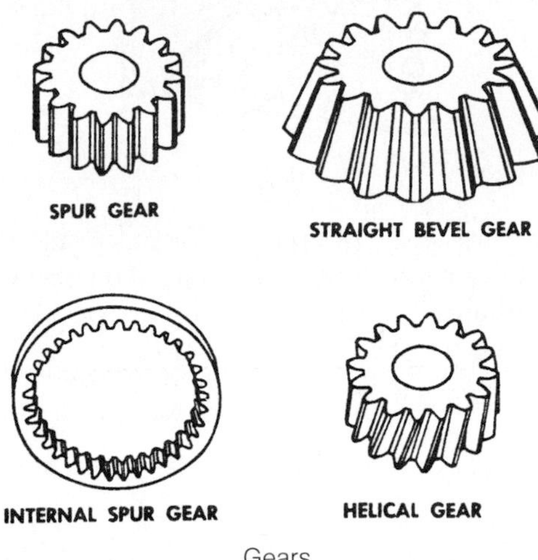

Gears

Green sand Moist clay-bonded molding sand ready for making molds.

Grinding Finishing a surface by means of a revolving abrasive wheel. Abrasive wheels are available in various grades, from fine to coarse.

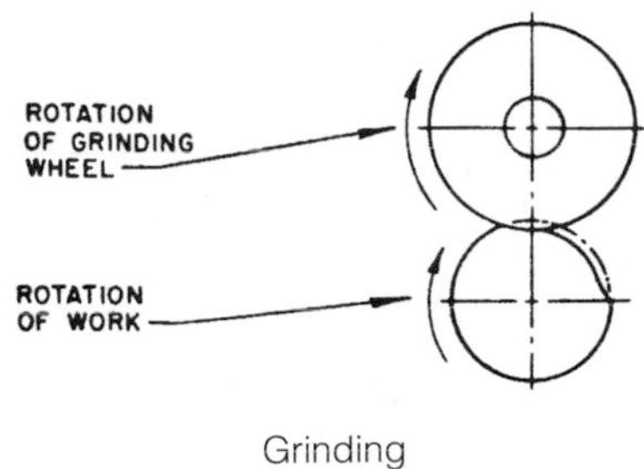

Grinding

Gusset A small plate for reinforcing assemblies.

Hardening To heat steel or aluminum above a critical temperature and then to quench it in water or oil.

Hardness That property of a metal that resists indentation. The value obtained is a measure of either the impression diameter (Brined) or the impression depth (Rockwell) under controlled loading and penetrator geometry.

Hardness, Vickers An indentation hardness test in which a diamond-pyramid indenter, with a 136° angle between opposite faces, is forced into the surface of a test specimen, under a known load.

Heat treatment A series of operations that improves the physical properties of a material.

High-pressure molding A term applied to certain types of high-production sand molding machines in which high-pressure air is released instantly from a large pressure vessel to produce extremely hard, high-density molds from green sand.

Hot isostatic pressing (HIPping) A process that uses high pressures at elevated temperatures to close interior voids in castings.

Hot quenching A process of quenching iron-base alloys in a medium that has a temperature substantially higher than ambient temperature.

Impact test A test in which one or more blows are applied to a cast test specimen. Results usually are expressed in terms of energy absorbed or the number of blows of a given intensity needed to break the specimen. Izod impact or Charpy impact are common types of tests.

Impregnation A process for making castings fluid tight by pressure injecting them with liquid synthetic resins or other sealers. The injected liquid is solidified in place by heating or baking. Media used include silicate of soda, drying oils with or without styrenes, plastics, and proprietary compounds.

Impression A cavity in a die. A multiple-cavity die has two or more duplicate impressions.

Injection The process of forcing molten metal or plastic into a die cavity.

Ingot Metal cast to size and shape for remelting.

Inoculant Material that, when added to molten metal, modifies the structure, and thereby changes the physical and mechanical properties to a degree not explained on the basis of the change in composition resulting from its use.

Insert A metal component (plug or stud) that is placed in a diecasting die or a sand mold, allowing molten metal to be cast around it. The component becomes an integral part of the casting.

Interchangeability A number of similar parts manufactured so that any one can be used in place of another in an assembly and still function properly.

Investment casting A process in which a wax pattern is invested (dipped in a slurry then sprinkled with loose sand). This process is repeated several times, making a thick "green pottery" mold. After the mold dries, the wax pattern is melted out, and the mold is baked, producing a ceramic shell or mold. Molten metal is poured into the mold to make a casting.

Iron, hard or white Iron that is highly abrasion resistant. Iron to be malleablized is initially white iron.

Iron, malleable A mixture of iron and carbon, including smaller amounts of silicon, manganese, phosphorus, and sulfur, which, after being cast as white iron, is converted structurally by heat treatment into malleable iron.

Jig A special type of fixture for holding and accurately locating, as well as guiding, the tools used in manufacture, such as in drilling operations.

Jolt-squeezer molding machine A combination green-sand molding machine that employs a jolt action followed by a squeezing action to compact the sand around the pattern, to make molds.

Key A part employed between a shaft and a hub to prevent movement of one relative to the other.

Keyseat or keyway A groove cut parallel to the axis of a shaft or hub to receive a key. A key rests in a keyseat and slides in a keyway.

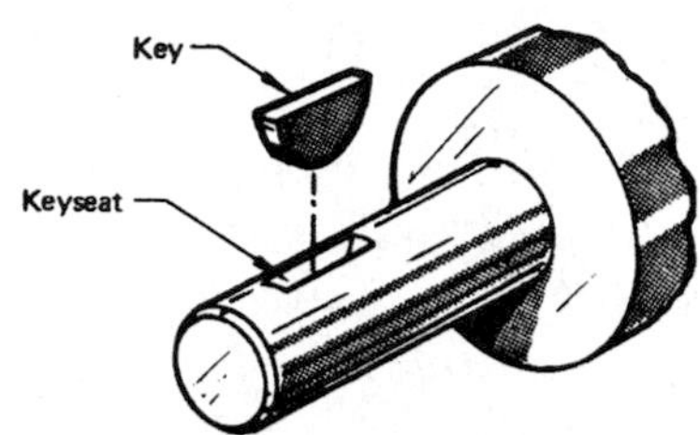

Key and keyseat

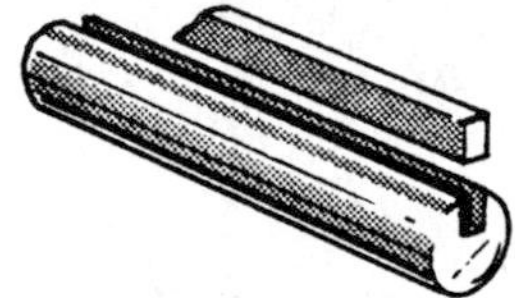
Keyseat or keyway

Knurling The forming of a series of fine ridges to roughen a cylindrical surface and provide a firmer grip for the fingers.

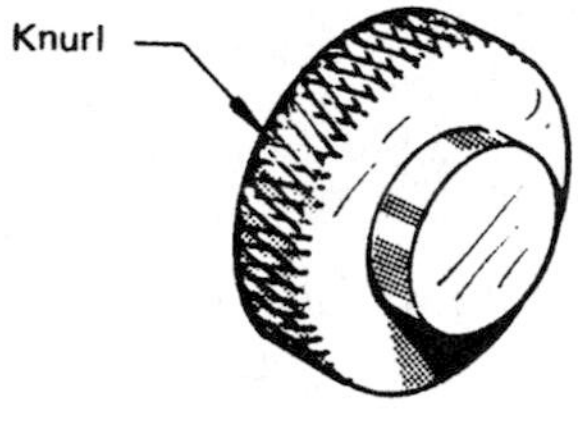

Knurling

Ladle A special vessel for transferring molten metal from a foundry's melt shop to the mold pouring area.

Lapping To finish or polish a surface with a piece of soft metal, wood, or leather impregnated with abrasive compound.

Lead The axial distance a point will travel on a screw thread when turned one complete revolution of the thread.

Light metal castings Castings made from low-density, lightweight metals and alloys of aluminum, lithium, magnesium, beryllium, and titanium.

Limited production Manufactured under model-shop conditions, as opposed to mass production under factory production line conditions.

Lug A projection or ear that is cast or forged as a portion of a part to provide support or attachment facility with another part.

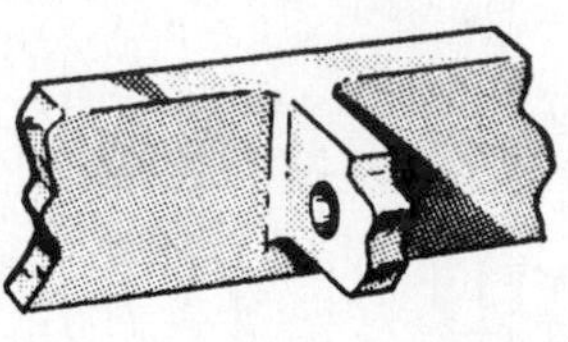
Lug

Machining allowance Extra metal or stock added in the design of a casting to permit machining of the part to precise final dimensions.

Malleability The property of being permanently deformed by compression or bending without rupture.

Malleable casting A casting that has been annealed to provide extra strength.

Manufacturer A person or firm that owns, operates, or maintains a factory or establishment that produces on the premises the materials, supplies, articles, or equipment required under the contract or of the general character described by specifications, standards, and publications.

Matched parts Those parts, such as special application parts, that are machine matched, or otherwise mated, and for which replacement as a matched set or pair is essential.

Matchplate pattern A plate of metal or other material on which patterns, split along the parting line and mounted back to back, form a single integral pattern unit. This pattern is used in a matchplate molding machine to form the casting cavity in a sand mold.

Material allowance Extra material provided for machining to achieve close accuracy and smooth surfaces.

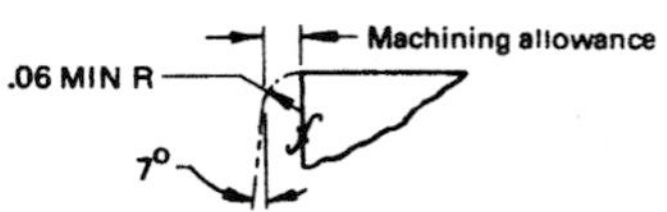

Material allowance

Mechanical properties Characteristics of an engineering material, such as hardness and tensile strength, that describe how it will behave when force is applied.

Metallurgy The science of metals, their alloys, and their ores; also, the technology of their production, fabrication, and processing.

Micrometer caliper A caliper with a micrometer screw attached, for making accurate measurements.

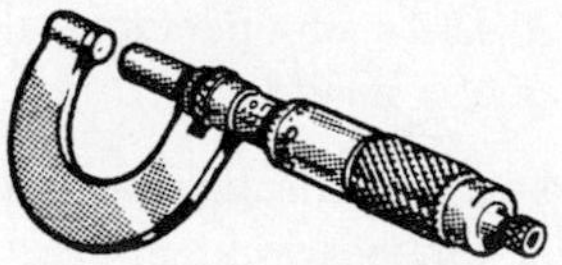
Micrometer caliper

Microporosity In castings, extremely fine porosity caused by shrinkage or gas evolution, apparent on radiographic film as mottling.

Microstructure The structure of polished and etched metal and alloy specimens as revealed by the microscope.

Milling Removing material from a part by means of a revolving cutter. Various cutters are available: end mill, form cutter, straddle milling, and hollow cutter.

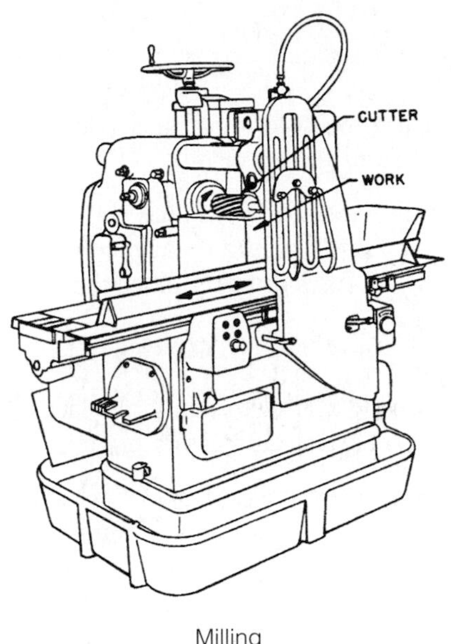

Milling

Mold The form provided for, or the act of, forming by pouring molten metal into a hollow during a casting operation to give the part a desired shape when the material solidifies. A mold can be made of sand, plaster, or metal, as long as the mold will withstand the temperature required for the part's material.

Neck To cut a circular groove around a shaft to provide firm fitting between the shaft and its mating part in assembly.

Nesting The arrangement of sheet metal parts on strip stock to provide the least scrap per blanks.

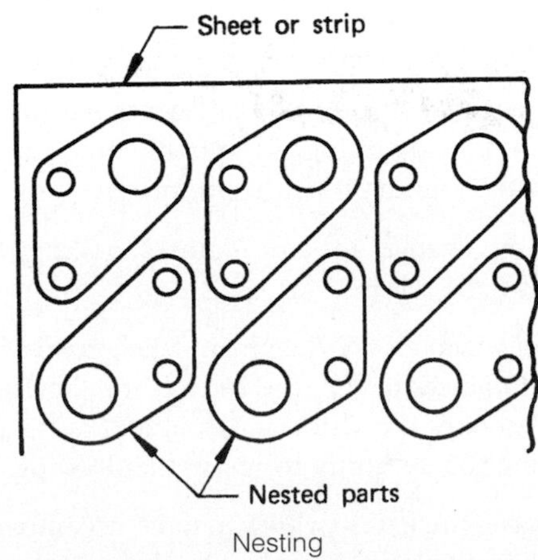

Nesting

Ni-hard cast iron Hard white cast iron containing 4% nickel and 2% chromium.

Nitriding A process for hardening ferrous alloys in which nitrogen is added by heating the object in ammonia gas or some other source of atomic nitrogen.

Nodular iron Another name for *ductile iron,* still used primarily in the automotive industry.

Nondestructive testing Testing or inspection procedure that does not destroy the casting being tested.

Normalize To heat steel above its critical temperature and then to cool it in air.

Nut A perforated block (usually of metal) possessing an internal, or female, screw thread, intended for use on an external, or male, screw thread, such as a bolt, for the purpose of tightening, adjusting, or holding two or more parts in definite relative positions.

Oil core or mold A core or mold in which the sand is bonded by an oil binder.

Open sand casting Pouring off a mold that has no cope or other covering.

Pack-harden To carburize, then to case-harden.

Pad A low projection surface, usually rectangular, as contrasted with a boss.

Part drawing An engineering drawing that defines an item and assigns it a part or control number to identify its configuration.

Part number A number (or combination of numbers and letters) assigned to identify uniquely a specific part. The part number includes the design activity drawing number.

Parting line The line along which a pattern is divided for molding; the line along which the sections of a mold or die separate.

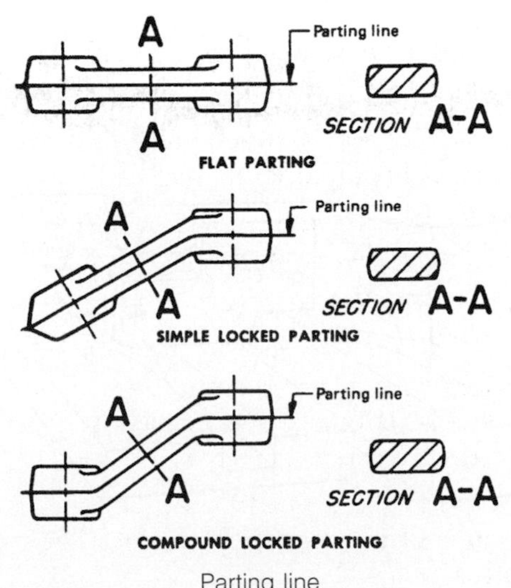

Parting line

Pattern The form used to make the cavity in a mold and that duplicates the shape of the part to be cast, except that it is made proportionately larger to compensate for shrinkage due to the contraction of the metal when cooled.

Pattern draft The taper on vertical elements in a pattern that allows easy separation of the pattern from the mold or the core from the corebox.

Patternmaker's shrinkage The allowance made in the design and construction of all patterns to compensate for the volumetric change in dimensions as the solidified casting cools from the metal's freezing temperature to room temperature.

Peening Stretching metal by battering it with the peen end (ball end) of a hammer.

Permanent-mold casting A casting process that uses a long-life mold, usually metal, into which molten metal is poured by gravity. Metals cast are usually aluminum alloys, although a few producers pour iron into water-cooled metal dies.

Pickling Removing scale and rust from a casting or forging by immersing it in an acid bath.

Plane (verb) To finish a flat surface on a planer machine with a fixed cutter and reciprocating bed on which the part is securely attached. (*noun*) A geometric description of a flat surface.

Polishing The finishing of a surface to a smooth and lustrous condition by means of a fine abrasive as a basis for plating, etc.

Porosity Holes or nonspecific cavities in a casting from insufficient feed metal during solidification, or numerous other causes.

Precipitation hardening Hardening an alloy in which a constituent precipitates from a supersaturated solid solution.

Profiling Using a pattern as a guide to make a similar part in a vertical milling machine operation in which the tool spindle is guided by the master plate made to the required shape of the part.

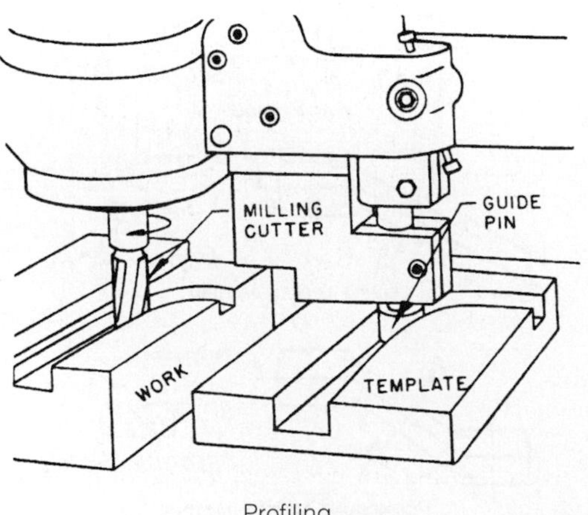

Profiling

Punch That part of a tool that pierces holes in stock or shapes the inside contour of a part in a forming die.

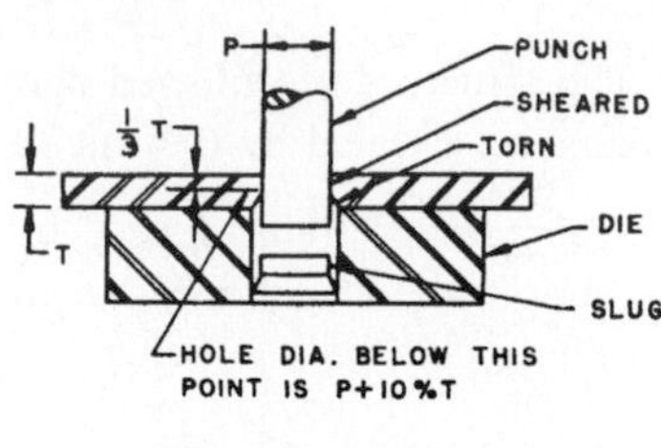

Punch

Quenching The process of cooling a part rapidly by immersing it in liquids, gases, or oil.

Quenching crack A fracture caused by thermal stresses induced during rapid cooling or quenching or by stresses caused by delayed transformation after the object has been fully quenched.

Rack A bar having gear teeth cut on the face so that rotary motion is converted to reciprocating motion or vice versa.

Radiography The use of radiant energy in the form of X rays or gamma rays for nondestructive examination of opaque objects, such as castings, to produce graphic records that indicate the comparative soundness of the object being tested.

Radiographic inspection The examination of the soundness of a casting by radiography.

Reamer A fluted cutting tool for finishing a hole to a desired size within specified limits.

Reamer

Relief A groove on a part, such as a cut next to a shoulder.

Returns Metal in the form of cutoff gates, sprues, runners, risers, and scrapped castings of known composition that is returned to the foundry's melt shop for remelting.

Revision Any change to an original drawing after that drawing has been released for use.

Revision authorization A document such as a "Notice of Revision," "Engineering Change Notice," or "Revision Directive" that describes a revision in detail and is issued by the source having the authority to revise the drawing.

Revision symbol A letter (which may be accompanied by a suffix number) that serves to identify particular revisions on the face of the drawing or in a revision description block.

Rib A ridge cast into thin sections of a part to make it stronger.

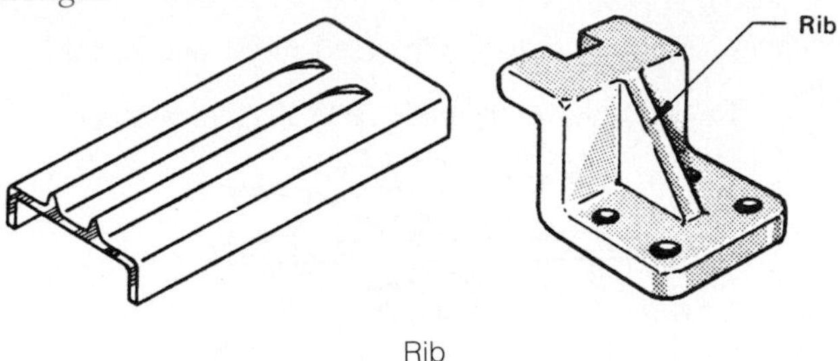

Rib

Riser Sometimes referred to as a *head* or a *feeder.* 1. A chamber that forms the reservoir for feed metal necessary to compensate for losses caused by shrinkage as a casting solidifies. 2. The pattern part that forms the riser and the metal solidified in it.

Riser gating A gating system in which molten metal from the sprue enters a riser close to the mold cavity and then flows into the mold cavity.

Rivet A headed and unthreaded mechanical device for assembling two or more components by an applied force, which deforms the plain rivet end to develop a completed mechanical joint.

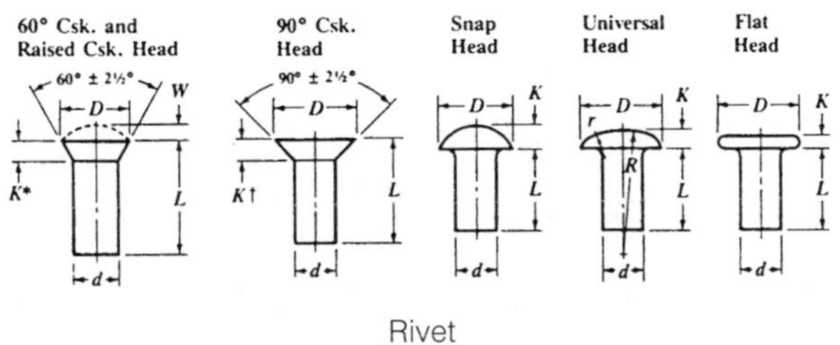

Rivet

Riveting A hammering process by which a rivet is made to fasten two or more parts by passing the shank through mating holes and then peening or pressing down the plain end to form a second head.

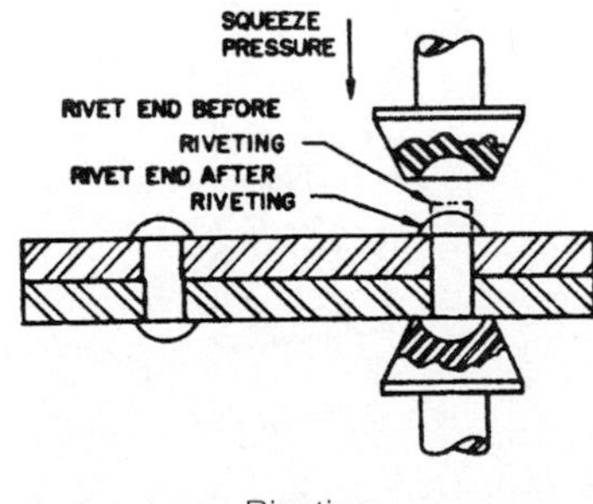

Riveting

Round A rounded external corner on a casting or forging.

Runner That portion of a gate assembly connecting the downgate or sprue with the casting.

Runner system Also called *gating;* the set of channels in a mold through which molten metal travels to the mold cavity; includes sprues, runners, gates, and risers.

Sample casting A casting made to check overall quality and dimensional accuracy prior to production.

Sandblasting The cleaning of the surface of a part by means of sand forced from a nozzle at high velocity.

Sand castings Metal castings produced in sand molds.

Scrap Rejected castings, parts, or assemblies.

Screw A headed and externally threaded mechanical device possessing capabilities that permit it to be inserted into holes in assembled parts; it is meant to be mated with a preformed internal thread or to form its own thread.

Set screw A screw used in a hub that bottoms against a shaft to prevent relative motion between two parts. Made either headless or with different types of heads as well as points.

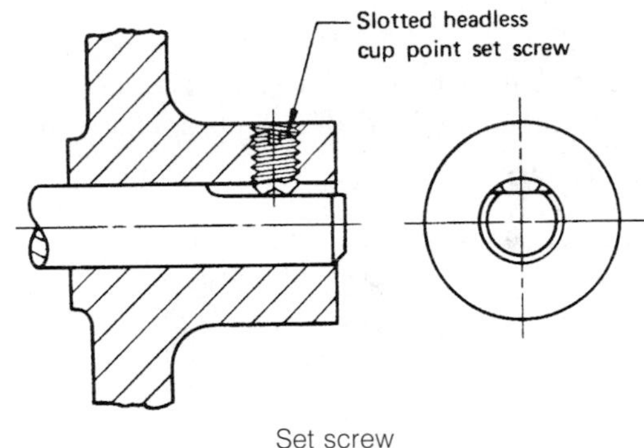

Set screw

Shakeout The process of separating a solidified casting from its mold materials (sand, cores, binders, etc.).

Shaper A machine tool with a sliding ram used to finish parts and flat surfaces. The workpiece is clamped in a stationary vise during the cutting stroke.

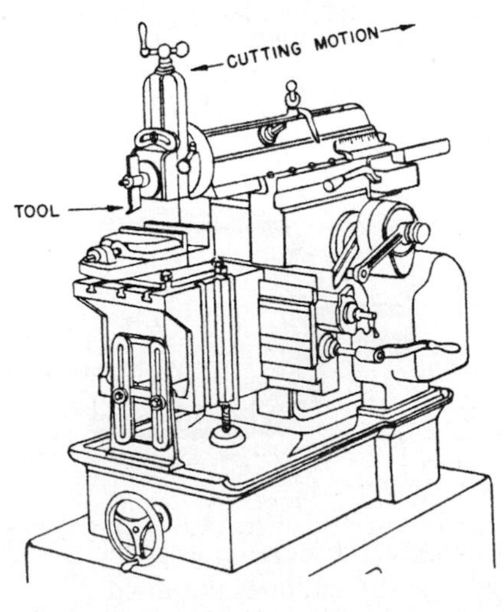

Shaper

Shear To cut off sheet or bar metal with the shearing action of two blades.

Shift A casting defect caused by a misalignment of cope-and-drag molds.

Shim A thin metal strip inserted between two parts for the purpose of adjustment.

Shot A die filling or that part of the diecasting cycle in which molten metal is forced into the die.

Shrinkage 1. Volume change of metal during solidification. 2. A void caused by insufficient feed metal during solidification. 3. Dimensional change during cooling to room temperature after solidification.

Slurry Refractory sand particles mixed with a liquid binder to form the ceramic mold in the investment process.

Slush casting A casting made by pouring a metal alloy into a metal mold, slushing the liquid metal around long enough to form a thin, solid shell, and then pouring out the remaining liquid metal.

Spline A key for inserting into a slot in a shaft, or a rib that has been machined on the shaft and fits another part having a mating slot.

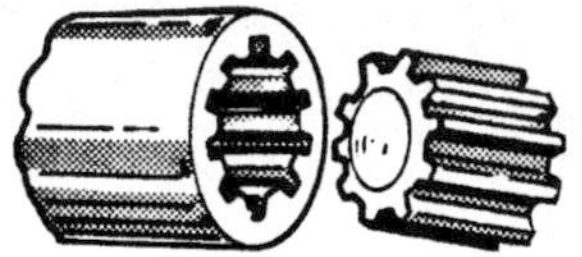

Spline

Spot weld To weld two overlapping sheet metal parts in spots by means of the heat generated by resistance to an electric current between a pair of electrodes.

Spotfacing (verb) Finishing the rough surface around a round hole using a counterbore tool to smooth and square the surface to allow a bolt or screw head to seat properly. (*noun*) A shallow counterbore.

Sprocket A gear made for chain-driven rotating mechanisms.

Sprocket

Sprue The vertical portion of a gating system through which molten metal first enters the mold.

Squeeze casting Also known as *liquid metal forging.* A casting process by which molten metal (ferrous or nonferrous) solidifies under pressure within closed dies positioned between the plates of a hydraulic press.

Stainless steel A wide range of steels containing chromium or chromium and nickel, exhibiting high resistance to corrosion.

Stamping Any part made by pressed-metal operations.

Staple To assemble by means of a U-shaped fastener.

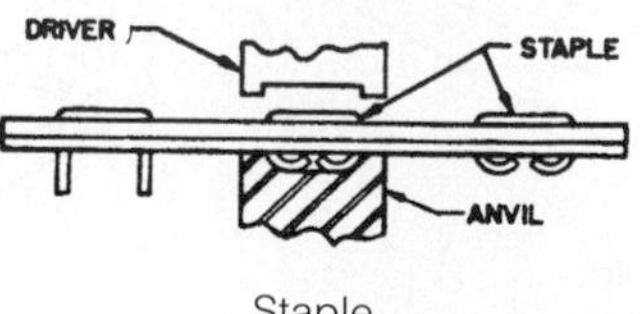

Staple

Stock allowance Material added to a part to allow for surface preparation or precise dimensioning by machining.

Stripper The plate used in a die that strips the part from the die.

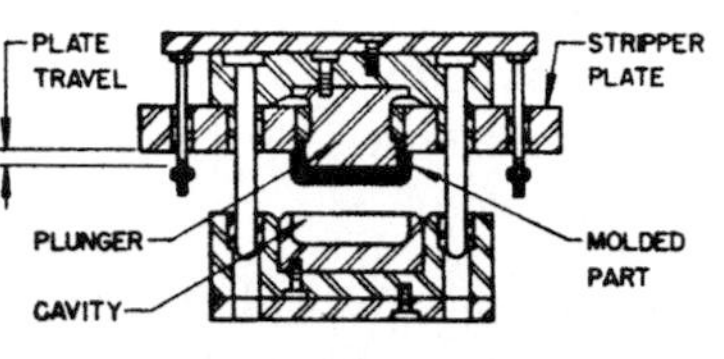

Stripper

Stud A stationary shaft, one end of which is fastened to the body of a part and receives a nut for fastening on the other.

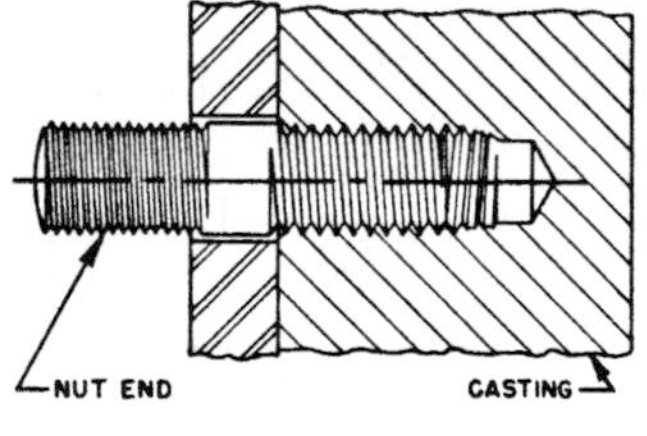

Stud

Surface gage A flat block of steel carrying an adjustable, upright spindle with which a scriber is mounted for layout work or for use as an indicator for transfer readings.

Surface gage

Surface plate A plate with a flat surface used to check parts for flatness.

Surface plate

Swage To form metal while cold by drawing or squeezing or by submitting to a number of blows sufficient to shape to desired form.

Sweat To solder together by first clamping the parts in contact with soft solder between them and then heating.

Tack weld The welding of short intermittent sections.

Tap To cut an internal thread by screwing a fluted tapered cutting tool into the hole.

Taper A gradual and uniform increase or decrease in size.

Tapered pin A pin requiring a taper-reamed hole at assembly and depending only on a taper lock, which can totally disengage when minor displacement occurs.

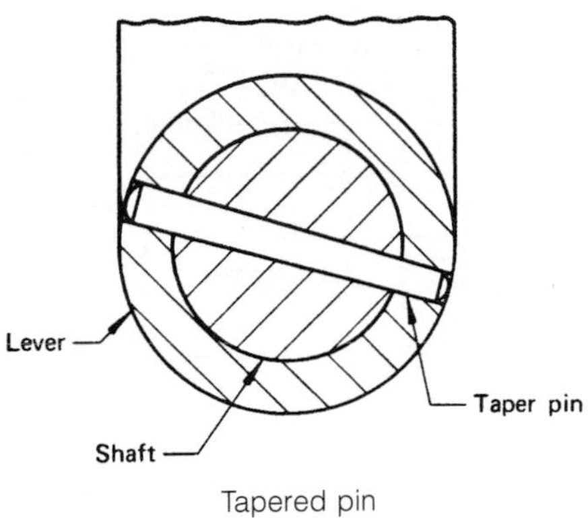

Tapered pin

Temper To reheat hardened steel to some temperature below critical temperature, followed by the desired rate of cooling; also called *drawing.*

Template A pattern or guide for laying out duplicate parts or guiding the tools while machining.

Tensile strength (U.T.S.) The maximum tensile load per square inch that a material can withstand. It is computed by dividing the maximum load obtained in a tensile tester by the original cross-sectional area of the test specimen.

Thread pitch The distance between corresponding points on adjacent threads, measured parallel to the axis.

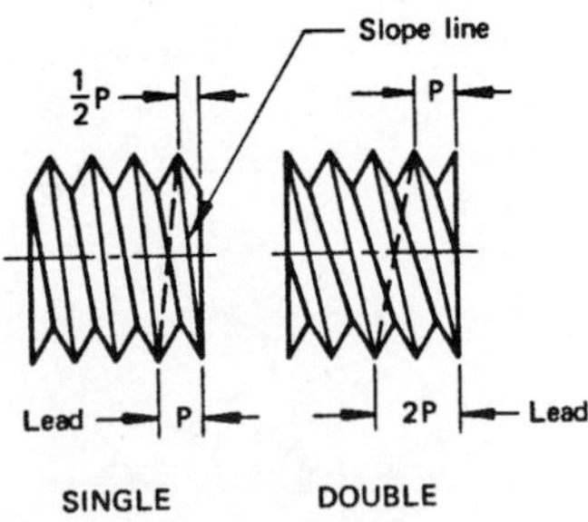

Thread pitch

Tolerance The permissible variation from the basic dimension of a part, expressed either unilaterally (one side given) or bilaterally (a summation at both ends).

Truncate To cut off a geometric solid at an angle to its base.

T-slot A slot machined in a part having a sectional shape resembling the capital letter T.

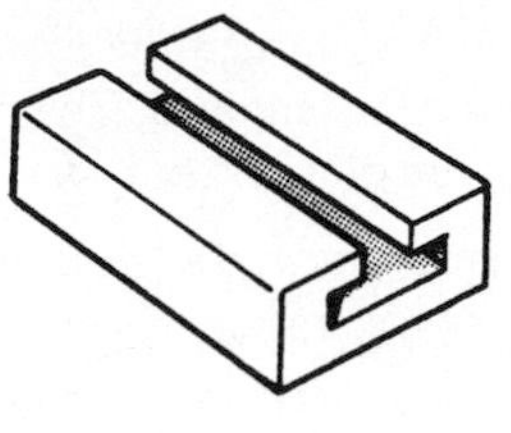

T-slot

Turning A process for removing material to produce relatively smooth and dimensionally accurate external and internal surfaces by turning the workpiece against the cutting tool, as in a lathe.

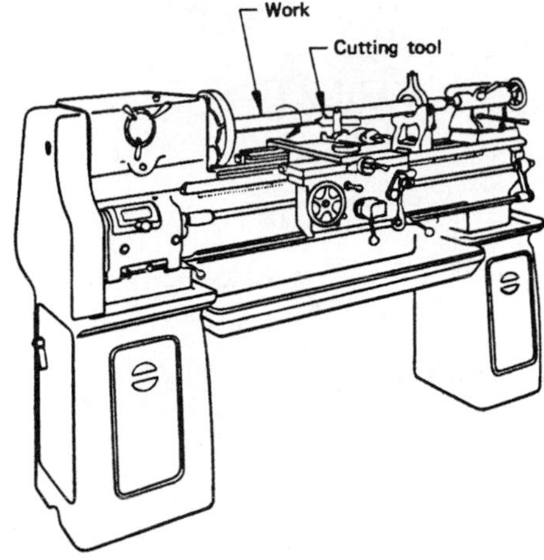

Lathe used for turning

Ultrasonic testing Using ultrasonic-frequency sound waves to detect flaws in metals.

Undercut A recessed cut that permits a firm fitting of one part with another.

Union A tube or pipe fitting for connecting lines that carry either gases or liquids at relatively high pressures and that are not subjected to excessive vibration or movement.

Upset To increase the sectional area of a part in order to form a shoulder during forging.

Vacuum casting process A process in which a special-design sand mold or a permanent (metal) mold with a bottom opening is lowered into a molten metal bath of a "casting" furnace. A vacuum is then placed on the mold, and the metal is drawn into the mold through gates in the bottom of the mold. Used by some foundries to make intricate, thin-wall castings.

Vacuum molding process Popularly known as the V-process; a sand molding process in which a sheet of thin plastic film is placed over a special metal pattern with many small vent holes. The pattern is heated, a vacuum is applied, and the plastic film assumes the shape of the pattern. A special flask is set over the film-covered pattern, and dry, loose sand is vibrated in place to make each half of the mold. A piece of plastic is placed over the top of the loose sand in the flask, and a vacuum is pulled through the loose sand to retain its shape after the pattern is removed. The mold halves, which are under vacuum, are closed, ready for pouring.

Vernier caliper A small, moveable scale on measuring instruments for determining a fractional part of one of the equal divisions of a graduated scale. The vernier caliper yields high accuracy because it is, in effect, one scale on another scale.

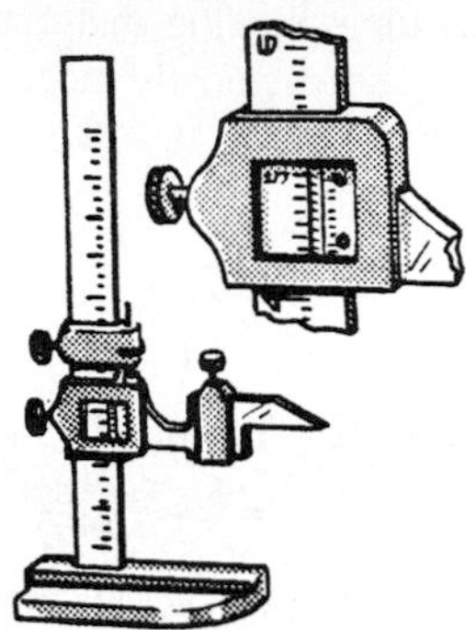

Vernier caliper

Wash A liquid coating applied to sand molds and cores used in sand casting as well as to foam plastic patterns used in the lost-foam casting process.

Washer A round piece of metal (usually steel), either flat or spring type, with a hole in the center and placed on a bolt or screw ahead of the nut to provide a positive clamping, bearing surface or to lock the nut in position.

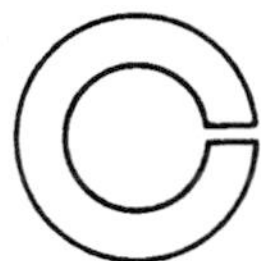

Washer

Web A thin section of a casting between the ribs, bosses, and flanges to provide additional strength.

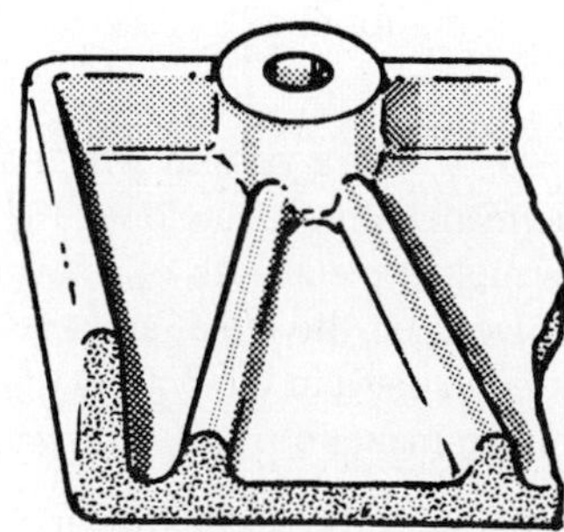

Web

Welding Any one of several methods of permanent assembly whereby parts are joined together by heating the joint to material fusion temperature, such as by arc welding, gas welding, projection welding, or spot welding.

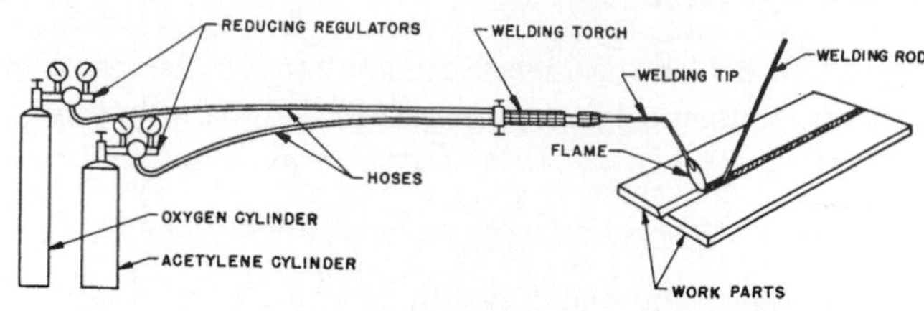

Gas welding

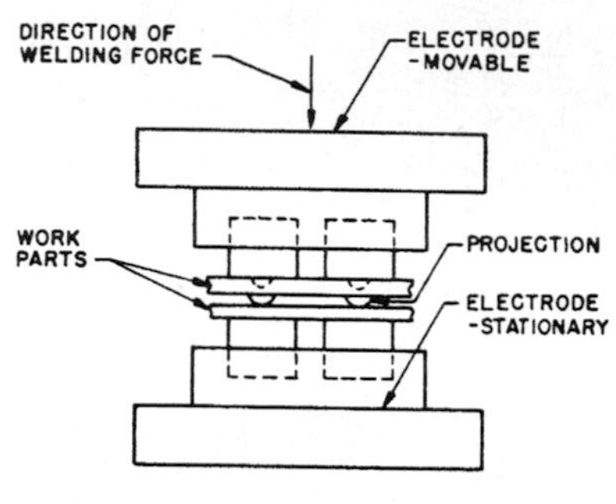

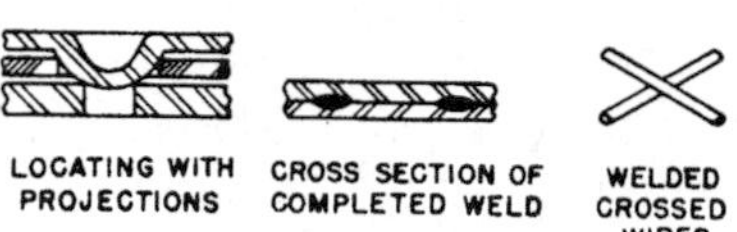

Projection welding

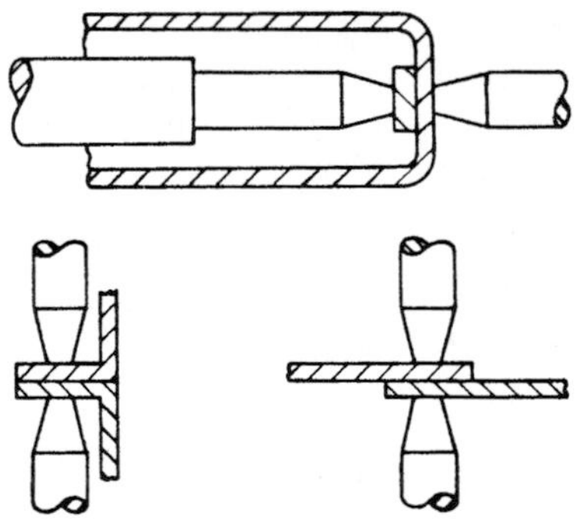

Spot welding

White iron A very hard iron with a whitish interior; used in abrasive product applications.

Wing nut Screw fastener especially designed with extensions on the internal threaded part for the convenience of tightening by hand.

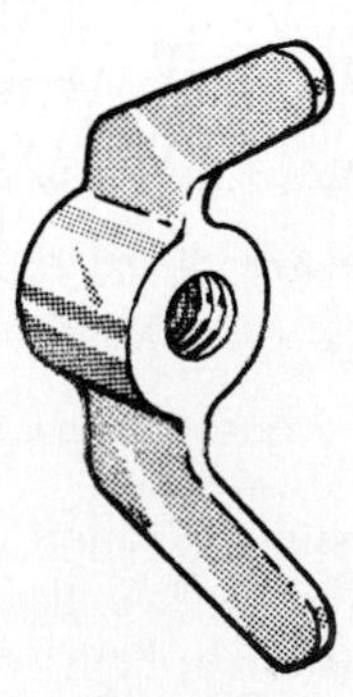

Wing nut

Worm A gear in the form of a screw used to transmit motion parallel to the axis of the shaft and that provides large reduction of velocity.

Worm wheel The gear that meshes with the worm in an installation and that may be combined with the worm; provides 90° transmission of revolving forces and increases torque and smoothness of action.

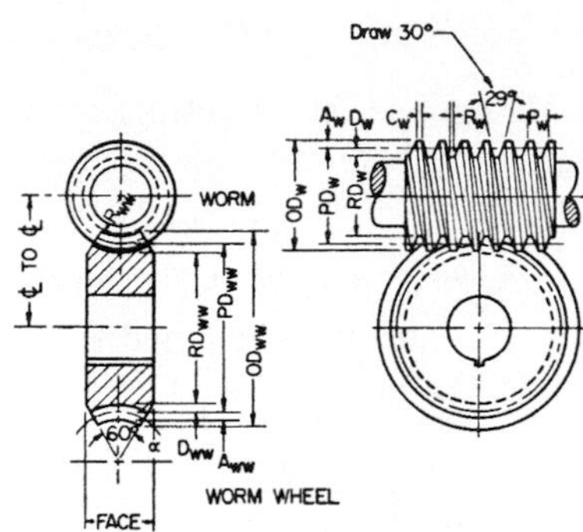

Worm and worm wheel

Yield Comparison of casting weight to total weight of metal poured into a mold or set of dies.

Yield strength The maximum stress that a metal can withstand without a predefined amount of permanent deformation.

ZA A designation followed by a number (ZA-8, ZA-12, or ZA-27) that serves to identify a group of three zinc-base casting alloys. The number indicates the approximate nominal percentage of aluminum content.

Zamak An acronym for zinc, aluminum, magnesium, and copper, used to designate the zinc alloys 2, 3, 5, and 7.

A.2 CAD/CAM GLOSSARY

Absolute coordinates The values of the X, Y, or Z coordinates with respect to the origin of the coordinate system.

Absolute data Values representing the absolute coordinates of a point or other geometric entity on a display surface. The values may be expressed in the units of the display or of the engineering drawing.

Acceptance test A test for evaluating newly purchased hardware or software. The hardware or software must conform to predefined specifications.

Access To retrieve and use a specific program or data.

Access time One measure of system response: the time interval between when data is requested from storage and when this data is displayed on the screen.

Accuracy Generally denotes the number of digits to the right of the decimal point that can be used by a particular algorithm or system.

Acronym A word made from the first letters of words in a phrase (e.g., CAD is the acronym for computer-aided design).

Address The location of data or a program in storage.

Addressability A measure of picture resolution: the number of points that can be displayed on the screen.

Addressable point A position on the screen that can be specified by absolute coordinates.

Aiming device A pattern of light activated by a light pen on the display surface to assist positioning of the pen and to describe the pen's field of view. See *Cursor.*

ALGOL ALGorithmic-Oriented Language. A high-level programming language.

Algorithm A set of well-defined rules or procedures for solving a problem.

Aliasing The raster display condition in which straight lines appear as jagged lines if the display has low resolution.

Alphanumeric display A display that shows letters, numbers, and special characters. It allows the designer to enter commands and to receive messages from the system.

Alphanumeric keyboard A typewriter-like keyboard that allows a designer to communicate with the system.

Analog The representation of data by linear movement rather than by the numbers 0 and 1, as with digital.

Annotation The process of adding text, notes, or identification to a drawing, map, or diagram.

ANSI American National Standards Institute. An association formed by industry and the U.S. government to produce and disseminate drafting and manufacturing standards.

Application software A computer program that assists a user to perform a specific task.

APT (automatically programmed tools) A computer language for programming numerically controlled machine tools.

Archive To place infrequently used data in auxiliary storage.

Array A set of elements or components arranged in a pattern (e.g., a matrix).

Artificial intelligence The ability of a computer to perform tasks normally associated with human intelligence, such as reasoning, learning, and self-improvement.

Artwork A photoplot, photomask, pen plot, electrostatic copy, or positive or negative photographic transparency used to manufacture an IC, PC board, or other product.

ASCII American Standard Code for Information Interchange. A standard for representing characters in the computer.

Assembler The computer program that converts mnemonic instruction into equivalent machine language instructions.

Assembly language A computer-dependent language that corresponds one-to-one with the computer machine language instructions.

Associative dimensioning The means by which a CAD dimensioning program automatically updates the dimensions as the geometry changes.

Associativity The linking of parts, components, or elements with their attributes or with other geometric entities.

Attribute A nongraphic characteristic of a part, component, or element (e.g., length, diameter, name, volume, use, creation date).

Automated design system (ADS) Another term for computer-aided design system.

Automated drafting system Another term for computer-aided drafting system.

Automatic dimensioning The CAD system's capability to compute dimensions and automatically to place dimensions, extension lines, and arrowheads where required.

Autoplacement (TM) A Computervision software option that automatically packages IC elements and optimizes the layout of components on a PC board.

Autoroute (TM) A Computervision software option that automatically determines the placement of copper on a printed circuit board to connect part pins of the same signal.

Auxiliary storage Storage devices other than the main memory; also called peripheral storage (e.g., disk drives or magnetic tape).

Back annotation The automatic extraction of data from a completed PC board for the purpose of updating the schematic. Information can also be back-annotated into piping drawings and three-dimensional models.

Backup copy A copy of a file that is kept for reference in case the original file is destroyed (i.e., for safekeeping).

BASIC Beginner's All-purpose Symbolic Instruction Code. A high-level algebraic programming language.

Batch processing The running of a program or set of programs in a noninteractive mode.

Baud rate A measure, in bits per second, of the speed of signal transmission between a computer and workstations.

Benchmark A set of standards for testing a software or hardware product or system from which a measurement can be made. Benchmarks are often run on a system to verify that it performs according to specifications.

Beta site A CAD site selected for testing a new hardware or software enhancement before its sale to other customers of the vendor.

Bill of materials (BOM) A listing of all the subassemblies, parts, materials, and quantities required to manufacture an assembly or to build a plant.

Binary code The representation of all characters through combinations of 0 and 1.

Bit A binary digit. The smallest unit of information that can be stored and processed by a digital computer. It can only be a 0 or a 1. Computers are often classified by word size in bits, such as a 16-bit or 32-bit computer.

Bits per inch (BPI) The number of bits of binary code that 1 in. of magnetic tape can store.

Boot up To start up a computer.

Bootstrap A routine whose first few instructions load the rest of the routine into the computer from storage.

Buffer A software program or hardware device for holding data, when transferring data from one device to another, if there is a difference in the time it takes the devices to process the data.

Bug A flaw in a software program or hardware design that leads to erroneous results or malfunctions.

Bus A circuit or group of circuits that provides a communications path between two or more devices.

Byte A sequence of eight bits that are operated on as a unit.

CAD (computer-aided design) A process by which a computer assists in creating or modifying a design.

CAM (computer-aided manufacturing) A process in which computer technology assists in managing and controlling the operations of a manufacturing facility.

Cartesian coordinates The distance of a point from any of three intersecting perpendicular planes; X, Y, Z coordinates.

Catalog The directory of files contained in computer storage.

Cathode-ray tube (CRT) A display device that creates images with a beam of electrons striking a screen.

Central processing unit (CPU) The brain of a CAD system that controls the processing of information.

Character A letter, number, or other symbol used to represent data. Symbols include the letters A through Z, the numbers 0 through 9, punctuation marks, logical symbols, relational operators, and any other single symbol that may be interpreted by computer languages. A character is represented as a byte in the computer.

Characters per second (CPS) The speed at which a device, such as a printer, can process data.

Chip See *Integrated circuit.*

CL file (cutter location file) Output of an APT or graphics system that provides X, Y, and Z coordinates and NC information for machine tool processing.

COBOL Common Business-Oriented Language. A high-level programming language oriented to business applications.

Code A set of programming instructions that may be in machine language, assembly language, or a high-level language. Also may refer to an industry standard, such as ANSI or ASCII.

COM See *Computer output microfilm.*

Command An instruction given to a computer processor via a menu and tablet, a stylus, or an alphanumeric keyboard.

Command language The language used by designers and drafters to operate a CAD system; it varies with each system.

Communication link The physical connection, such as a telephone line, from one system to another or from one component to another.

Communications network A number of systems linked together to exchange data.

Compatibility The ability of a hardware module or software program to be used in a CAD system without modification.

Compiler A program that translates high-level language instructions to machine language instructions that can be understood by the CPU.

Component A subassembly or part that goes into higher-level assemblies.

Computer A data processor that can perform arithmetic and logical operations.

Computer architecture The internal design of the parts of a computer system.

Computer graphics Any discipline or activity that uses computers to generate, process, and display pictorial images.

Computer-integrated manufacturing (CIM) A totally automated factory in which all manufacturing processes are integrated and controlled by a computer system.

Computer literacy A basic understanding of computers and their use.

Computer network Two or more interconnected computers.

Computer numerical control (CNC) Using a computer to store numerical control instructions, generated by a CAD system, to control a machine.

Computer output microfilm The image of a drawing plotted on 35mm film at a small scale by a beam of light. Microfilm containing computer-generated data; also, to place computer-generated data on microfilm.

Computer program A set of software commands that instructs the computer to perform specific operations. Often called a *software program* or *software package.*

Computer word A sequence of bits or characters treated as a unit.

Configuration A particular combination of computer software, hardware, and peripherals at a single installation.

Connect node An attachment point for lines or text.

Connection The lines between pins, components, contacts, or circuits in printed circuit boards and writing diagram construction.

Construction plane A predefined or operator-defined plane on which digitized points are projected.

Conversational mode A mode of operation for a data processing system in which each unit of input entered by the user elicits a prompt response from the computer.

Coordinate dimensioning A system of dimensioning in which points are defined as being a specified distance and direction from a reference point.

Copy To reproduce a design in a different location on a computer screen or to duplicate a file and its contents.

CPU See *Central processing unit.*

Crosshairs A horizontal line intersected by a vertical line to indicate a point on a display whose coordinates are desired.

Cursor A special character, such as a small cross, on a computer screen that follows every movement of the stylus, light pen, or joystick.

Cut plane A plane intersected with a three-dimensional object to derive a sectional view.

Data Elements of information.

Data bank The total collection of information used by an organization.

Data entry Data entered by an operator from an input device such as a card reader, keyboard, or disk.

Data extract The capability to obtain information from a database.

Data management The control of access to information, information storage conventions, and the use of input and output devices.

Data processing system A system that accepts information, processes it in a specific manner, and produces the desired results.

Data tablet A graphical input device consisting of a board area capable of monitoring the position of a pen-shaped stylus.

Database An organized collection of standard parts libraries, completed designs, documentation, and computer programs.

Debugging Detecting and removing programming errors (bugs) from programs.

Dedicated Assigned to a single function, such as a workstation used exclusively for engineering calculations.

Default The predetermined value of a parameter that is supplied automatically by a system whenever that value is not specified by the user.

Delete To erase information from a computer's memory or from storage.

Delimiter A space, slash, asterisk, or other mark that separates data within a continuous string.

Design automation (DA) Using a computer to automate portions of the design process.

Design file The information in a CAD database that relates to a design project.

Detail drawings The drawing of a single part with all the dimensions and annotations necessary to define the part completely for manufacturing and inspection.

Device A hardware item such as a cathode-ray tube, plotter, printer, or hard-copy unit.

Diagnostics Computer programs that test a system or its key components to detect and isolate malfunctions.

Digit Either 0 or 1 in binary notation; 0 through 9 in decimal notation.

Digital The representation of data as combinations of the numbers 0 and 1.

Digitize To convert lines and shapes into digital form.

Digitizer A table or tablet on which a designer moves a puck or stylus to selected points and enters coordinates for lines and shapes by pressing down the input button on the puck or stylus.

Direct numerical control (DNC) Using a shared computer to distribute part program data to change machine tools.

Directory The location on a disk where the names of files and information about them are stored.

Disk A circular plate of magnetic media on which information is stored.

Disk drive The device that reads data from or writes data onto magnetic disks.

Disk storage The use of magnetic disks as a storage device.

Display The part of a workstation that shows the image of the data; usually refers to a cathode-ray tube.

Display elements Points, line segments, and characters used to describe an object on a display.

Display group A collection of display elements that can be manipulated as a unit and that may be further combined to form larger groups.

Display image The collection of display elements shown together on the display device.

Display menu A display option that allows an operator to select the next action by indicating one or more choices with an input device.

Display parameters Data that controls the appearance of graphics (e.g., choice of solid or dashed lines).

Display space The usable area of a display surface that includes all addressable points.

Documentation The general description, user's manual, and maintenance manual necessary to operate and maintain a system.

Down Not working; describes a computer or device.

Drum plotter An electromechanical pen plotter that draws a picture on paper or film mounted on a drum through a combination of plotting-head movement and drum rotation.

Dumb terminal A computer terminal that can only communicate with a host computer and cannot function in a stand-alone mode.

Dump To transfer to permanent storage all the data accumulated on a system during a given period.

Dynamic movement The ability to zoom, scroll, and rotate an image on a screen interactively.

Edit To change, add, or delete data.

Electrical schematic A diagram of the logical arrangement of hardware in an electrical system that uses standard component symbols.

Electrostatic plotter Wire nibs, spaced 100 to 200 nibs per inch, that place dots where needed on a piece of paper to generate a drawing.

Element The lowest-level design entity with an identifiable logical, electrical, or mechanical function; a basic geometric unit (e.g., a point, line, arc, or circle).

Emulation The use of a computing system to execute programs written for another system.

Enhancements Software or hardware improvements, additions, or updates.

Entity Any one of the fundamental building blocks by which a designer represents a product (e.g., arc, circle, line, text, point, line, figure, nodal line).

Ergonomic Designed with the needs of the user in mind.

Error file File generated during data processing to retain information about errors during the process.

Execute, Of a computer program, to carry out an instruction or perform a routine.

Family of parts A collection of previously designed parts with similar geometric characteristics but different physical measurements.

Fetch To locate data in storage and load it into a computer.

Field A specific area in a string of characters or a record.

Figure A symbol or a part that may contain other figures, attributes, and associations.

File (*noun*) A named set of data on magnetic disk or tape. (*verb*) To transfer the contents of working storage to permanent storage.

File management system A software system that provides control of input, output, physical storage, and logical relationships for data files.

File protection The control of access to a file to only those with proper authority, and the prevention of accidental erasure of data within a file.

Fillet A rounded corner or arc that blends together two intersection curves, lines, or surfaces.

Finite-element analysis (FEA) The determination of the structural integrity of a part by mathematical simulation of the part and of the forces acting on the part.

Finite-element modeling (also method) (FEM) The creation of a mathematical model of a part for input to a finite-element analysis program.

Finite elements The subdivision of a complex structure into small pieces.

Firmware Sets of instructions built into user-modifiable hardware.

Flatbed plotter An electromechanical pen plotter that draws a picture on paper, glass, or film mounted on a flat table. The plotting head moves in both axial directions.

Flicker The flashing on and off of the image on a screen.

Flip The same as mirror-image projection.

Floppy disk A flexible magnetic disk for storing data.

Flowchart A graphical representation of the solution of a problem in which symbols represent operations, data flow, and equipment.

Font, line Repetitive patterns used to make a line easier to recognize (e.g., a solid, dashed, or dotted line).

Font, text An assortment of characters of a given size and style.

Form flash To project a constant pattern, such as a report form, grid, or map, as background for a display. Synonymous with *form overlay*.

Format The specific arrangement of data for a list or report; a preprinted drawing border (e.g., title block and zones).

FORTRAN FORmula TRANslation. A high-level programming language, primarily for scientific applications, that uses mathematical formulas.

Full frame A display image scaled to maximize use of the viewing surface of the area of a display device.

Function key An area on a digitizing tablet or a key on a box or terminal by which to enter a command.

Function keyboard A part of a workstation that contains a number of function keys.

Function menu The display or list of commands available to a user for performing a task.

Glitch A minor, often temporary, malfunction of computer hardware or software.

Graphic primitives Simple geometric shapes such as lines, circles, cones, cylinders, ellipses, and rectangles that can be used to construct more complex shapes.

Graphics Pictorial data such as points, lines, shapes.

Graphics tablet A surface through which coordinate points can be transmitted by means of a cursor or stylus. Another term for *digitizing tablet*.

Grid A matrix of uniformly spaced points displayed on a screen for approximately locating and digitizing a position or placing symbols in the creation of a schematic.

Hard disk A hard metal disk that is sealed in a disk drive and used for storage.

Hardcopy A copy on paper of what is shown on screen; generated with an online printer or plotter.

Hardware The computer, disk, magnetic tape, cathode-ray tube, and other physical components that comprise a system.

Hidden lines Line segments that would ordinarily be hidden from view in a three-dimensional display of a solid object because they are behind other items in the display.

Hierarchy A data structure consisting of different levels in which certain objects are subdivisions of an object on a higher level.

High-level language A programming language that is independent of any given computer and permits the execution of a number of subroutines through a simple command (e.g., BASIC, FORTRAN, Pascal, and COBOL).

Host computer The computer attached to a network providing services such as computation, database management, and special programs; the primary computer in a multiple computer operation.

Inches per second (IPS) The number of inches of magnetic tape that can be recorded or read per second, or the speed of a pen plotter.

In-house Within an organization or company.

Initialize computer To set counters, switches, or addresses to zero or to other starting values at the beginning of a program or routine.

Initialize disk To prepare a disk to store information in the format of the particular operating system being used.

Input To enter data or a program into a system.

Input device A device such as a graphic tablet or keyboard that allows the user to input data into the CAD system.

Input/output (I/O) Communications devices and the process by which communication takes place in a CAD system.

Input/output channel The path for transmitting data in and out of a central processing unit.

Inquiry A request for information from a computer.

Insert To enter entities, figures, or information into a design that is on the display.

Instruction Line of computer programming telling the computer what to do.

Instruction set All the commands to which a computer will respond.

Integrated circuit (IC) An electronic component that may vary in complexity from a simple logic gate to a microprocessor. An IC is usually packaged in a single substrate as a slice of silicon. Also called a *chip*.

Integrated system A CAD system that integrates the entire product development cycle—analysis, design, and fabrication—into a single system.

Intelligent robot A robot that can make decisions by using its sensing and recognizing capabilities.

Intelligent terminal A terminal with local processing power whose characteristics can be changed under program control.

Interactive Providing two-way instantaneous communication between a CAD system and its operators.

Interactive display terminal A terminal consisting of one or more display devices and one or more input devices such as tablets, control balls, light pens, alphanumeric keyboards, function keys, and tape readers.

Interactive graphics The capability to perform graphics operations directly on a computer, with immediate feedback.

Interactive graphics system A CAD system in which the workstations are utilized interactively for computer-aided design and drafting; often synonymous with CAD.

Interconnection The connection between one display entity or connection point on a component and another. On schematic drawings, interconnections are lines that connect elements.

Interface A hardware or software link that enables two systems or a system and its peripherals to operate as a single, integrated system.

Interference checking A CAD capability that allows plant or mechanical designers to examine a three-dimensional model and automatically pinpoint interfaces between pipes, equipment, structures, or machinery.

Interpreter A software program that converts high-level language instructions to machine language instructions.

Isometric A drawing in which the object is rendered from an oblique view so that it appears to be solid.

Jaggies The jagged (sawtooth) appearance of lines on a screen when the screen has low resolution.

JCL Job control language. A problem-oriented language for expressing job requirements to an operating system.

Job All necessary computer programs, linkages, files, and instructions for a unit of work.

Joystick A CAD data entry device involving a hand-controlled lever that moves the cursor on the screen to enter coordinates' various points.

k 1,024, as in 1 kbyte.

Keyboard A typewriter-like device for entering instructions or coordinates into a computer.

Keypunch A keyboard-actuated device that punches holes in cards.

Kinematics A process for simulating the motion of mechanisms to study interference, acceleration, and forces.

Large-scale computer A computer with large internal memory capacity and multiple input/output channels. Such computers can process many programs concurrently.

Layer A logical concept for distinguishing subdividable groups of data within a given drawing. Layers may be thought of as a series of transparencies overlayed in any order, without any depth.

Layer discrimination The selective assignment of colors to a layer or the highlighting of entities to distinguish among data on different layers displayed on a screen.

Layout A to-scale drawing of the physical components and the mechanical and electrical arrangements of a part, product, or plant.

Library A collection of symbols, components, shapes, or parts stored in a CAD database as templates for future design work on the system.

Light pen A penlike device used in conjunction with a vector-refresh screen that identifies displayed elements from the light sources on the screen.

Line printer A peripheral device that prints alphanumeric data one line at a time.

Line speed The rate at which signals can be transmitted over a communications line, usually measured in bauds, or bits per second.

LIS Large interactive surface. An automated drafting table for plotting and/or digitizing drawings. Also called a *digitizer table.*

Load To enter data into computer memory, for later processing on the system.

Local area network (LAN) A communications network in which all of the computers and workstations are in the same general area or building.

Log-off To follow the procedure by which a user ends a workstation session.

Log-on To follow the procedure by which a user begins a workstation session.

Loop A sequence of instructions that is executed repeatedly in a computer until stopped by an operator or some predetermined condition.

Machine A computer.

Machine instruction An instruction that a computer can recognize and execute.

Machine language The set of instructions, in combinations of the numbers 0 and 1, used directly by a computer.

Macro A combination of commands executed from a single command.

Magnetic disk A flat, circular plate with a magnetic surface on which data can be recorded and from which data can be read. The data can be randomly accessed.

Magnetic drum A cylinder with a magnetic surface on which data can be recorded and from which data can be read.

Magnetic tape A tape with a magnetic surface on which data can be recorded and from which data can be read. The data can only be accessed sequentially. The access speed is constrained by the location and density of the data on the tape and the speed of the tape drive.

Main memory The principal storage device of a computer system—an integral part of the computer. Generally, just called *memory.*

Main storage The general-purpose storage of a computer, program addressable, from which instructions can be executed and from which data can be loaded directly into registers.

Mainframe In general, the central processing unit of a large-scale computer configuration.

Management information system (MIS) A system that can store, retrieve, process, and output data to help management in its decision-making functions.

Mass storage device Auxiliary or bulk memory that can store large amounts of data readily accessible to the computer (e.g., a disk or magnetic tape).

Matrix A two- or three-dimensional rectangular array of identical symbols or entities.

Megabyte Approximately 1 million bytes.

Menu A table of available commands, either on a digitizing tablet or on screen, that can be selected instead of typing in commands on the keyboard.

Merge To combine two or more sets of related data into a single set.

Microcomputer A small, relatively low-cost computer that includes a microprocessor, memory, and all necessary interface circuits. Home or personal computers such as Apple, IBM-PC, and TRS-80 are examples of microcomputers.

Microprocessor A single integrated circuit that is the central processing unit of a microcomputer.

Minicomputer A computer that is between a mainframe computer and a microcomputer in size, power, complexity, and cost; generally, a 32-bit computer.

Mirror-image projection In computer graphics, the reflection of display elements or groups with respect to a specific straight line or plane. Synonymous with *flip* and *reflect.*

Mnemonic Short words that represent complete sentences or phrases of instructions, e.g., **ADD SUM**, **INV** (inverse), **SHIFTL** (shift left).

Model An accurate three-dimensional representation of a part, assembly, or plant designed on a CAD system and stored in its database.

Modeling Constructing a mathematical or analytical model of a physical object or system for analysis.

MODEM MOdulator-DEModulator. A device that converts digital signals into analog signals for transmission over telephone lines. The analog signals are converted back to digital signals at the other end by another modem.

Modularity The method of assembling a system from components that can be replaced individually.

Monitor A display for computer output, either monochrome or full color, that is usually a cathode-ray tube.

Motherboard The large printed circuit board at the bottom of a computer to which chips, other boards, and components are attached.

Mouse A hand-held data entry device, about the size of a cigarette pack, that can be used like a puck, without a digitizing pad.

Multiprocessor Computer architecture that can execute one or more computer programs using two or more processing units simultaneously.

Nesting Embedding data in levels of other data so that certain routines or data can be executed or accessed continuously in loops.

Network Two or more central processing facilities that are interconnected.

Node A computer or workstation connected to a local area network.

Numeric keypad A calculator-type numeric input device that is generally part of a keyboard.

Numerical control (NC) The control of machine tools, drafting machines, and plotters by punched paper or magnetic tape encoded with the proper information to cut a part or draw a figure.

Off-line Describes equipment or devices in a system that are not under direct control of the system's computer.

On-line Describes equipment or devices in a system that are directly connected to and under the control of the system's computer.

Operating system The software that controls the execution of computer programs and all hardware activity. Also called *system software.*

Operation An action that a computer is instructed to perform, such as add, subtract, store, read, or write.

Operator The person who performs input and output functions at a workstation.

Order To place in sequence according to rules or standards.

Origin An X-Y or X-Y-Z coordinate from which all figures and entity locations are referenced.

Orthographic The method of making a layout, drawing, or map in which the projecting lines are perpendicular to the plane of the drawing or map.

Output The end result of a process or series of processes, such as artwork, hard copy, reports, and drawings.

Output device Hardware, such as a printer or plotter, for producing a copy of the results of a computer's processing operations.

Overlay To position one or more drawings on top of another and view them simultaneously on screen.

Pad An area of plated copper on a PC board to which leads of components are soldered.

Paint To fill in a bounded figure on a display by means of a combination of repetitive patterns or line fonts.

Pan To scroll the view of an object on screen.

Paper tape punch/reader A peripheral device that can punch or read perforated components.

Parallel interface An interface that transfers several signals at once.

Parameter A variable that controls the effect and usage of a command.

Part A product, assembly, subassembly, or component.

Part programming language A language that describes machining operations so that they are understood by computers or controllers.

Pascal A high-level programming language frequently preferred by computer scientists for its more logical structure and greater power.

Passive graphics The use of a display terminal in a noninteractive mode, usually through such devices as plotters and microfilm viewers.

Passive mode A method of operating a display device that allows no online interaction or alteration.

Password A unique string of characters that a programmer, computer operator, or user must enter to gain access to data.

Path The route that an interconnection takes between connections in printed circuit board design.

Pattern generation The transformation of CAD integrated circuit design information into a format for use by photobeam or electron-beam machines in producing a reticle.

PC Printed circuit; more commonly, personal computer.

Pen plotter An electromechanical CAD output device that draws a picture on paper or film using a ballpoint pen or liquid ink.

Perforated tape An input or output medium that employs punched holes along a continuous strip of nonmagnetic tape to record and store data.

Performance, CRT How well a cathode-ray tube meets specifications such as screen resolution, display writing speed, internal intelligence, working area, accuracy, and precision.

Performance, system How well a system meets specifications such as speed, capacity, accuracy, and the productivity ratio of CAD versus manual methods.

Peripherals Devices connected to a computer, such as tape drives, disks, workstations, and plotters.

Permanent storage The location, outside the central processing unit, where completed data is stored (e.g., a disk or tape).

Photoplotter A device for generating artwork photographically for PC boards.

Pixels PICture ELements. Individual dots on a display screen that are illuminated to create an image. Pixels are evenly spaced on the display.

PL/1 Programming Language/1. A high-level programming language used in a wide range of commercial and scientific applications.

Plot To draw a design on paper or film by means of pen, pencil, or electrostatics; to create a drawing.

Plotter An automated device that produces accurate drawings. Plotters include electrostatic, photoplotter, and pen types.

Point An element that represents a single X-Y-Z coordinate.

Polar coordinates The two numbers that locate a point by (a) its radial distance from the origin and (b) the angle that a line through this point makes with the X axis.

Postprocessor A software program or procedure that interprets graphical data and formats it for use by an NC machine or by other computer programs.

Power supply A transformer that reduces voltage and changes AC to DC to provide electrical power to a computer.

Preprocessor A method of converting data into computer-usable form for processing and output.

Processor The hardware components that perform arithmetic and logic operations, often called the *computer.*

Program The complete sequence of instructions to a computer to perform a task.

PROM Programmable read-only memory. A read-only integrated circuit that can be programmed.

Prompt A message or symbol appearing on screen that informs the user of a procedural error, incorrect input to the program being executed, or the next expected action.

Properties Nongraphic entities that may be associated. Properties in electrical design may include component name and identification, color, wire size, pin number, lug type, and signal values.

Protocol The format of signals between two computer systems or between a computer and its peripherals that allows them to communicate.

Puck A hand-held device that enables the user to digitize a drawing placed on a digitizer surface.

Quality control The establishment and maintenance of standards to ensure well-made products.

Quality engineering The performance and interpretation of tests to measure product quality.

Queue A waiting list of tasks to be performed or messages to be transmitted.

Random-access memory (RAM) A main memory storage unit that provides direct access to the stored information; memory from which data can be retrieved regardless of input sequence.

Raster The geometric coordinate grid dividing the display area of a display device.

Raster display A CAD workstation display in which the entire screen surface is a matrix of pixels and the image is scanned at a constant refresh rate. The bright, flicker-free image can be selectively written and erased.

Raster scan A line-by-line sweep across an entire screen surface to generate an image. The device can display a large amount of information without flicker.

Rasterize The process of converting an image into a corresponding pattern of dots.

Read-only memory (ROM) A storage device (memory), generally for controlling programs, whose content is not alterable.

Real time Immediate feedback to the user from tasks or functions executed by a CAD system. Immediate feedback through the workstation makes interactive operation of a CAD system possible.

Record Related data processed as a unit.

Reflect The same as *mirror-image projection.*

Refresh CRT display technology requiring continuous redrawing of the display image.

Refresh rate The rate at which an image on a screen is redrawn (e.g., 30 times per second, or 30 Hz).

Reliability The amount of time a system is running without problems versus the downtime.

Remote terminal An input or output peripheral located at a distance from its computer.

Repaint To redraw a display image on a CRT to reflect its updated status.

Repeatability (of display device) A measure of the hardware accuracy or the coincidence of successive retraces of a display element.

Replicate To generate an exact copy of a design on screen at any location or scale desired.

Resolution The smallest spacing between points on a graphic device at which the points can be detected as distinct.

Response time The elapsed time from the completing of a command at a workstation to the display of the results at that workstation.

Restart To resume execution of an interrupted computer program.

Restore To return a design to its original configuration after editing or modification.

Robotics The use of computer-controlled robots to automate manufacturing processes such as welding, material handling, painting, and assembly.

Rotate To turn a displayed image about an axis through a predefined angle.

Router A program that determines automatically the routing path for the component connections on a PC board.

Routine A computer program; a set of instructions arranged in proper sequence to cause a computer to perform a desired operation.

Routing Placing the interconnects between components on a printed circuit board or integrated circuit.

Rubberbanding A technique for displaying a straight line with one end fixed and the other end attached to the movable cursor.

Run To execute a program.

Satellite A remote system, connected to a host system, that contains processors, memory, and mass storage to operate independently from the host.

Save To transfer the data created at a workstation to a storage device.

Scale To enlarge or shrink an image without changing its shape.

Schematic A not-to-scale diagram of an electrical circuit.

Scissor To trim a drawing in a database so that it can be viewed on a CRT screen.

Screen A computer display device. Also called a *monitor* or *cathode-ray tube.*

Scroll To roll up automatically on a screen, as on a spool, a message or drawing too large to be displayed all at once.

Section To cut an object with an intersecting plane, and then to request generation and display of the total intersection geometry on a display surface.

Security Safeguards and procedures that can be applied to computer hardware, programs, and data to ensure that access to the system is controlled.

Selective erase The deletion of portions of a design on screen without repainting the entire screen.

Semiconductor A material (e.g., silicon) that conducts electricity and is used for the storage and transfer of computer data.

Serial interface A connection that transfers data sequentially, one bit at a time.

Shape fill The automatic shading of an area on screen.

Silicon The basic material used in the manufacture of computer chips. See *Semiconductor.*

Silk screen Artwork used in print component placement and identification information on a printed circuit board.

Simulate To imitate the behavior of a finished part under various structural and thermal loading conditions.

Software The computer programs, procedures, rules, and instructions that control the computer hardware.

Solid model A way to represent the mass and the boundary of a complete form.

Sort To segregate items into groups according to specified criteria (e.g., to alphabetize).

Source User-written instruction statements prior to translation by a computer into a form that can be executed by machine.

Spline A smooth curve between a sequence of points in one place.

Storage The physical device or location that contains all of the information on a CAD system.

Storage device or storage unit A peripheral component in which data can be stored and later retrieved.

Storage tube A CRT that retains an image for a considerable period of time without redrawing. It allows no selective editing or erasing.

String A sequence of characters such as a word or a sentence.

Stylus A hand-held instrument that provides coordinate input to a display device.

Surface machining The ability to output 3-, 4-, and 5-axis NC toolpaths by means of three-dimensional surface definition capabilities (e.g., ruled surfaces, tabulated cylinders, and surfaces of revolution).

Surface of revolution The surface generated when a curve is rotated around an axis through a specified angle.

Symbol A set of primitive graphic entities, lines, points, arcs, circles, and text that are grouped together as a unit. Symbols may be combined or nested to form larger symbols or drawings.

Syntax The set of rules that describes the structure of statements in a computer language.

System All of the people, machines, and methods needed to perform a specific task.

Tablet An input device through which a designer can digitize coordinate data or enter commands into a CAD system by means of a stylus or a puck. Also called a *digitizing pad.*

Tape drive The peripheral device that records and reads magnetic tape.

Telecommunications The transmission of signals over long distances between a computing system and remotely located devices by telephone, microwave, infrared link, or coaxial cable.

Telewriter A typewriter-like keyboard device for entering commands or printing system messages.

Template A commonly used component or part that serves as a design aid and that can be subsequently traced instead of redrawn whenever needed. The CAD equivalent of a designer's template is a symbol in the symbol library.

Temporary storage A location in memory for temporarily storing results of a program on a system until they can be transferred to permanent storage. Also called *working storage.*

Terminal A device equipped with a keyboard and some kind of display that sends and receives information over a communication channel to and from a computer.

Text Letters, numbers, and special characters.

Text editor A program for creating and modifying text on a system.

Text file A file stored in a system that consists entirely of text.

Throughput The work performed by a CAD system or workstation during a given period of time; a quantitative measure of system productivity.

Thumbwheels A CAD input device that uses a manually controlled vertical wheel for locating a coordinate on the Y axis and a horizontal wheel for locating a coordinate on the X axis.

Timesharing The concurrent use of a computing system in which two or more users can execute computer programs simultaneously, usually from remote terminals.

Tolerance The allowed variance from a given nominal dimension.

Toolpath A trace of the movement of the tip of a numerical control cutting tool, used to guide or control machining equipment.

Tracking Moving a cursor across the surface of a screen with a light pen, stylus, or puck.

Tracking symbol A symbol, such as a cross, dot, angle, or square, for indicating the position of a stylus.

Transistor An electronic switch that transmits a signal of either 0 or 1 to communicate information in binary machine language. A semiconductor device often made of silicon.

Translate To change data from one language to another.

Transportability The ability to execute a program on different computers without major changes.

Tree A method of file storage in which the file structure has a top level and one or more sublevels, which in turn may contain additional sublevels.

Turnaround time The elapsed time between the start and finish of a task or project.

Turnkey system A CAD system for which the vendor assumes total responsibility for building, installing, and testing all the hardware and software required to do a specific application or applications; a computer system sold in a ready-to-use state.

Tutorial A message displayed to show a user how to perform a task.

Up Working properly, as for a computer.

Updating Changing a file by adding, modifying, or deleting information.

User-friendly Easy to understand and operate, as for a CAD system (both hardware and software).

Utility program A specific system software program, such as a diagnostic program, a plot program, or a sort program.

Vector A directed line segment that has magnitude and direction.

Vector generation The process that determines all intermediate points between two endpoints of a line segment.

Verification The feedback message to a display device acknowledging that an input was detected (e.g., the brightening of a display element selected by a light pen).

Version A configuration control identifier that is changed whenever there are modifications or enhancements.

Via A hole in a printed circuit board through which a path from one layer or side is transferred to the other.

View port A user-selected viewing area on screen that frames the contents of a window.

Wafer A slice of silicon from which a larger number of integrated circuit chips are produced.

Winchester drive A combination of a disk drive and one or more hard disks permanently sealed in a case.

Window A portion or view of a design that is framed by a view port.

Windowing Proportionally enlarging a figure or portion of a figure so that it fills the screen or view port.

Wireframe A picture of a three-dimensional object displayed on screen as a series of lines that represent the edges of its surfaces. This picture looks as if it were made from coat hangers.

Wiring diagram A schematic representation of all circuits and devices that shows their interconnectivity.

Word processing (WP) The use of a special program to create, edit, store, display, and print text.

Working drawing A detailed layout of components with complete dimensions and notes.

Workstation The hardware by which a designer interacts with a computer. Also called a *terminal.*

Write To copy information from main memory to a storage device.

Write protect A security feature that prevents existing data from being erased by new data.

Z clipping The ability to specify depth parameters for a three-dimensional drawing such that all elements above or below the specified depths become invisible. No change is made to the database of the part or drawing; useful in viewing cluttered or complex part geometry.

Zoom To successively enlarge or shrink an image on screen.

ABBREVIATIONS AND STANDARDS

Appendix B

B.1 GENERAL ABBREVIATIONS

B.2 ANSI AND CANADIAN STANDARDS

B.1 GENERAL ABBREVIATIONS

TABLE B.1 Examples of Terms and Corresponding Abbreviations or Symbols

Term	Abbreviation or Symbol
And	&
Across flats	A/F
American National Standards Institute	ANSI
Angular	ANG
Approximate	APPROX
Assembly	ASSY
Basic	BSC
Bill of materials	B/M or BOM
Bolt circle	BC
Brass	BR
Brown and Sharpe gage	B & S GA
Bushing	BUSH
Canada Standards Institute	CSI
Casting	CSTG
Cast iron	CI
Centimeter	cm
Centerline	℄
Center to center	C to C
Chamfered	CHAM
Circularity	CIR
Cold-rolled steel	CRS
Concentric	CONC
Counterbore	⌴ or CBORE
Countersink	⌵ or CSK
Cubic centimeter	cm^3
Cubic meter	m^3
Datum	DATUM { ISO & ANSI [A]
Deep	↧
Degree (angle)	° or DEG
Diameter	⌀ or DIA
Diametral pitch	DP
Dimension	DIM
Drawing	DWG
Eccentric	ECC
Figure	FIG
Finish all over	FAO
Gage	GA
Heat treat	HT TR
Head	HD
Heavy	HVY
Hexagon	HEX
Hydraulic	HYD
Inside diameter	ID
International Standards Organization	ISO
Iron pipe size	IPS
Kilogram	kg
Kilometer	km
Large end	LE
Least material condition	Ⓛ or LMC
Left hand	LH

Term	Abbreviation or Symbol
Liter	L
Machined	√or ∀
Machine steel	MS or MACH ST
Material	MATL
Maximum	MAX
Maximum material condition	Ⓜ or MMC
Meter	m
Metric thread	M
Micrometer	μm
Millimeter	mm
Minimum	MIN
Minute (angle)	MIN
Newton	N
Nominal	NOM
Not to scale	____ or NTS
Number	NO
On center	OC
Outside diameter	OD
Parallel	PAR
Pascal	Pa
Perpendicular	PERP
Pitch	P
Pitch circle diameter	PCD
Pitch diameter	PD
Plate	PL
Radian	rad
Radius	R
Reference or reference dimension	( ) or REF
Regardless of feature size	Ⓢ or RFS
Revolutions per Minute	rev/min
Right hand	RH
Second (arc)	(")
Second (time)	SEC
Section	SECT
Slotted	SLOT
Socket	SOCK
Spherical	SPHER
Spotface	⌴ or SFACE
Square	□ or SQ
Square centimeter	cm^2
Square meter	m^2
Steel	STL
Straight	STR
Symmetrical	‡ or SYM
Thread	THD
Through	THRU
Tolerance	TOL
True profile	TP
Undercut	UCUT
U.S. sheet metal gage	USS GA
Watt	W
Wrought iron	WI

B.2 ANSI AND CANADIAN STANDARDS

TABLE B.2.1 ANSI Standards

Column A	Column B	Column A	Column B
Abbreviations	Y1.1-1972	Mechanical and Acoustical Element as Used in Schematic Diagrams	Y32.18-1972(R1978)
American National Standard Drafting Practices		Pipe Fittings, Valves, and Piping	Z32.2.3-1949(R1953)
Size and Format	Y14.1-1980	Heating, Ventilating, and Air Conditioning	Z32.2.4-1949(R1953)
Line Conventions and Lettering	Y14.2M-1979	Heat Power Apparatus	Z32.2.6-1950(R1956)
Multi- and Sectional View Drawings	Y14.3-1975(R1980)	Letter Symbols for:	
Pictorial Drawing	Y14.4-1957	Glossary of Terms Concerning Letter Symbols	Y10.1-1972
Dimensioning and Tolerancing	Y14.5M-1982	Hydraulics	Y10.2-1958
Screw Threads	Y14.6-1978	Quantities Used in Mechanics for Solid Bodies	Y10.3-1968
Screws Threads (Metric Supplement)	Y14.6aM-1981	Heat and Thermodynamics	Y10.4-1982
Gears and Splines		Quantities Used in Electrical Science and Electrical Engineering	Y10.5-1968
Spur, Helical, and Racks	Y14.7.1-1971	Aeronautical Sciences	Y10.7-1954
Bevel and Hyphoid	Y14.7.2-1978	Structural Analysis	Y10.8-1962
Forgings	Y14.9-1958	Meteorology	Y10.10-1953(R1973)
Springs	Y14.13M-1981	Acoustics	Y10.11-1953(R1959)
Electrical and Electronic Diagram	Y14.15-1966(R1973)	Chemical Engineering	Y10.12-1955(R1973)
Interconnection Diagrams	Y14.15a-1971	Rocket Propulsion	Y10.14-1959
Information Sheet	Y14.15b-1973	Petroleum Reservoir Engineering and Electric Logging	Y10.15-1958(R1973)
Fluid Power Diagrams	Y14.17-1966(R1980)	Shell Theory	Y10.16-1964(R1973)
Digital Representation for Communication of Product Definition Data	Y14.26M-1981	Guide for Selecting Greek Letters Used as Symbols for Engineering Mathematics	Y10.17-1961(R1973)
Computer-Aided Preparation of Product Definition Data		Illuminating Engineering	Y10.18-1967(R1977)
Dictionary of Terms	Y14.26.3-1975	Mathematical Signs and Symbols for Use in Physical Sciences and Technology	Y10.20-1975
Digital Representation of Physical Object Shapes	Y14 Report	Unified Screw Threads	ANSI B1.1
Guideline—User Instructions	Y14 Report No. 2	Square and Hex Bolts and Screws	ANSI B18.2.1
Guideline—Design Requirements	Y14 Report No. 3	Square and Hex Nuts	ANSI B18.2.2
Chassis Frames	Y14.32.1-1974	Socket Cap, Shoulder, and Setscrews	ANSI B18.3
Parts Lists, Data Lists, and Index Lists	Y14.34M-1982	Slotted-Head Cap Screws, Square-Head Setscrews, Slotted-Headless Setscrews	ANSI B18.6.2
Surface Texture Symbols	Y14.36-1978	Machine Screws and Machine Screw Nuts	ANSI B18.6.3
Illustrations for Publication and Projection	Y15.1M-1979	Woodruff Key and Keyslot Dimensions	ANSI B17.2
Time Series Charts	Y15.2M-1979	Keys and Keyseats	ANSI B17.1
Process Charts	Y15.3M-1979	Lock Washers	ANSI B18.21.1
Graphic Symbols for:		Plain Washers	ANSI B27.2
Electrical and Electronics Diagrams	Y32.2-1975	Surface Texture	ANSI B46.1
Plumbing	Y32.4-1977		
Use on Railroad Maps and Profiles	Y32.7-1972(R1979)		
Fluid Power Diagrams	Y32.10-1967(R1974)		
Process Flow Diagrams in Petroleum and Chemical Industries	Y32.11-1961		

AMERICAN NATIONAL STANDARDS INSITUTE, INC.
1430 BROADWAY,
NEW YORK, N.Y. 10018

THE AMERICAN SOCIETY OF MECHANICAL ENGINEERS
UNITED ENGINEERING CENTER
345 EAST 47TH STREET,
NEW YORK, N.Y. 10017

TABLE B.2.2 CSA—Canadian Standards

Column A	Column B	Column A	Column B
Unified and American Screw Threads	CSA B1.1	Surface Texture	CSA B95
Plain Washers	CSA B19.1	Limits and Fits for Engineering and Manufacturing	CSA B97.1
Square and Hexagon Bolts and Nuts, Studs and Wrench Openings	CSA B33.1	Abbreviations for Scientific and Engineering Terms	CSA Z85
Machine Screws, Stove Bolts and Associated Nuts	CSA B35.1	Architectural Drawing Practices (National Research Council, Ottawa, Canada)	33-GP-7
Drawing Standard—General Principles	CSA B78.1		
Drawing Standard—Dimensioning and Tolerancing	CSA B78.2		

CANADIAN STANDARDS ASSOCIATION
178 REXDALE BOULEVARD
REXDALE, ONTARIO, CANADA, M9W 1R3

STANDARD CATALOG PARTS AND REFERENCE MATERIALS

Appendix C

C.1 THREADS

C.2 METRIC TWIST DRILLS

C.3 BOLTS, NUTS, AND SCREWS

C.4 WASHERS

C.5 RIVETS

C.6 RETAINING RINGS

C.7 PINS

C.8 BUSHINGS

C.9 WOODRUFF KEYS

C.10 STANDARD SHEET METAL GAGES

C.11 STRUCTURAL SHAPES AND SIZES

C.12 FITS AND TOLERANCES

C.1 Threads

TABLE C.1.1 Standard Unified Thread Series*

Present Unified Thread Nominal Size—diameter			Coarse (NC) (UNC)		Fine (NF) (UNF)		Extra-fine (NEF) (UNEF)	
Inch		*Metric equiv.*	*Threads per inch*	*Tap drill*†	*Threads per inch*	*Tap drill*†	*Threads per inch*	*Tap drill*†
.060	0	1.52	—	—	80	$\frac{3}{64}$	—	—
.073	1	1.85	64	No. 53	72	No. 53	—	—
.086	2	2.18	56	No. 50	64	No. 50	—	—
.099	3	2.51	48	No. 47	56	No. 45	—	—
.112	4	2.84	40	No. 43	48	No. 42	—	—
.125	5	3.17	40	No. 38	44	No. 37	—	—
.138	6	3.50	32	No. 36	40	No. 33	—	—
.164	8	4.16	32	No. 29	36	No. 29	—	—
.190	10	4.83	24	No. 25	32	No. 21	—	—
.216	12	5.49	24	No. 16	28	No. 14	32	No. 13
.250	$\frac{1}{4}$	6.35	20	No. 7	28	No. 3	32	No. 2
.3125	$\frac{5}{16}$	7.94	18	*F*	24	*I*	32	*K*
.375	$\frac{3}{8}$	9.52	16	$\frac{5}{16}$	24	*O*	32	*S*
.4375	$\frac{7}{16}$	11.11	14	*U*	20	$\frac{25}{64}$	28	*Y*
.500	$\frac{1}{2}$	12.70	13	$\frac{27}{64}$	20	$\frac{29}{64}$	28	$\frac{15}{32}$
.5625	$\frac{9}{16}$	14.29	12	$\frac{31}{64}$	18	$\frac{33}{64}$	24	$\frac{17}{32}$
.625	$\frac{5}{8}$	15.87	11	$\frac{17}{32}$	18	$\frac{37}{64}$	24	$\frac{19}{32}$
.6875	$\frac{11}{16}$	17.46	—	—	—	—	24	$\frac{41}{64}$
.750	$\frac{3}{4}$	19.05	10	$\frac{21}{32}$	16	$\frac{11}{16}$	20	$\frac{45}{64}$
.8125	$\frac{13}{16}$	20.64	—	—	—	—	20	$\frac{49}{64}$
.875	$\frac{7}{8}$	22.22	9	$\frac{49}{64}$	14	$\frac{13}{16}$	20	$\frac{53}{64}$
.9375	$\frac{15}{16}$	23.81	—	—	—	—	20	$\frac{57}{64}$
1.000	1	25.40	8	$\frac{7}{8}$	12	$\frac{59}{64}$	20	$\frac{61}{64}$
1.0625	$1\frac{1}{16}$	26.99	—	—	—	—	18	1
1.125	$1\frac{1}{8}$	28.57	7	$\frac{63}{64}$	12	$1\frac{3}{64}$	18	$1\frac{5}{64}$
1.1875	$1\frac{3}{16}$	30.16	—	—	—	—	18	$1\frac{9}{64}$
1.250	$1\frac{1}{4}$	31.75	7	$1\frac{7}{64}$	12	$1\frac{11}{64}$	18	$1\frac{3}{64}$
1.3125	$1\frac{5}{16}$	33.34	—	—	—	—	18	$1\frac{17}{64}$
1.375	$1\frac{3}{8}$	34.92	6	$1\frac{13}{64}$	12	$1\frac{19}{64}$	18	$1\frac{5}{16}$
1.4375	$1\frac{7}{16}$	36.51	—	—	—	—	18	$1\frac{3}{8}$
1.500	$1\frac{1}{2}$	38.10	6	$1\frac{21}{64}$	12	$1\frac{27}{64}$	18	$1\frac{29}{64}$
1.5625	$1\frac{9}{16}$	39.69	—	—	—	18	1	$\frac{1}{2}$
1.625	$1\frac{5}{8}$	41.27	—	—	—	18	1	$\frac{9}{16}$
1.6875	$1\frac{11}{16}$	42.86	—	—	—	18	1	$\frac{5}{8}$
1.750	$1\frac{3}{4}$	44.45	5	$1\frac{35}{64}$	—	—	16	$1\frac{11}{16}$
2.000	2	50.80	$4\frac{1}{2}$	$1\frac{25}{32}$	—	—	16	$1\frac{15}{16}$
2.250	$2\frac{1}{4}$	57.15	$4\frac{1}{2}$	$2\frac{1}{32}$	—	—	—	—
2.500	$2\frac{1}{2}$	63.50	4	$2\frac{1}{4}$	—	—	—	—
2.750	$2\frac{3}{4}$	69.85	4	$2\frac{1}{2}$	—	—	—	—
3.000	3	76.20	4	$2\frac{3}{4}$	—	—	—	—
3.250	$3\frac{1}{4}$	82.55	4	3	—	—	—	—
3.500	$3\frac{1}{2}$	88.90	4	$3\frac{1}{4}$	—	—	—	—
3.750	$3\frac{3}{4}$	95.25	4	$3\frac{1}{2}$	—	—	—	—
4.000	4	101.60	4	$3\frac{3}{4}$	—	—	—	—

*Adapted from ANSI B1.1, 1960.
Unified Standard—Classes 1A, 2A, 3A, 1B, 2B, and 3B.
For recommended hole-size limits before threading, see Tables 38 and 39, ANSI B1.1-1960.
†Tap drill for a 75% thread (not Unified—American Standard).

TABLE C.1.2 Thread Sizes and Dimensions: Fraction/Decimal/Metric

Nominal Size		Diameter (Major)		Diameter (Minor)		Tap Drill (for 75% Th'd.)			Threads per Inch		Pitch (mm)		T.P.I. (Approx.)	
Inch	***mm***	***Inch***	***mm***	***Inch***	***mm***	***Drill***	***Inch***	***mm***	***UNC***	***UNF***	***Coarse***	***Fine***	***Coarse***	***Fine***
—	M1.4	.055	1.397	—	—	—	—	—	—	—	.3	.2	85	127
0	—	.060	1.524	.0438	1.092	3/64	.0469	1.168	—	80	—	—	—	—
—	M1.6	.063	1.600	—	—	—	—	—	—	—	.35	.2	74	127
1	—	.073	1.854	.0527	1.320	53	.0595	1.499	64	—	—	—	—	—
1	—	.073	1.854	.0550	1.397	53	.0595	1.499	—	72	—	—	—	—
—	M.2	.079	2.006	—	—	—	—	—	—	—	.4	.25	64	101
2	—	.086	2.184	.0628	1.587	50	.0700	1.778	56	—	—	—	—	—
2	—	.086	2.184	.0657	1.651	50	.0700	1.778	—	64	—	—	—	—
—	M2.5	.098	2.489	—	—	—	—	—	—	—	.45	.35	56	74
3	—	.099	2.515	.0719	1.828	47	.0785	1.981	48	—	—	—	—	—
3	—	.099	2.515	.0758	1.905	46	.0810	2.057	—	58	—	—	—	—
4	—	.112	2.845	.0795	2.006	43	.0890	2.261	40	—	—	—	—	—
4	—	.112	2.845	.0849	2.134	42	.0935	2.380	—	48	—	—	—	—
—	M3	.118	2.997	—	—	—	—	—	—	—	.5	.35	51	74
5	—	.125	3.175	.0925	2.336	38	.1015	2.565	40	—	—	—	—	—
5	—	.125	3.175	.0955	2.413	37	.1040	2.641	—	44	—	—	—	—
6	—	.138	3.505	.0975	2.464	36	.1065	2.692	32	—	—	—	—	—
6	—	.138	3.505	.1055	2.667	33	.1130	2.870	—	40	—	—	—	—
—	M4	.157	3.988	—	—	—	—	—	—	—	.7	.35	36	51
8	—	.164	4.166	.1234	3.124	29	.1360	3.454	32	—	—	—	—	—
8	—	.164	4.166	.1279	3.225	29	.1360	3.454	—	36	—	—	—	—
10	—	.190	4.826	.1359	3.429	26	.1470	3.733	24	—	—	—	—	—
10	—	.190	4.826	.1494	3.785	21	.1590	4.038	—	32	—	—	—	—
—	M5	.196	4.978	—	—	—	—	—	—	—	.8	.5	32	51
12	—	.216	5.486	.1619	4.089	16	.1770	4.496	24	—	—	—	—	—
12	—	.216	5.486	.1696	4.293	15	.1800	4.572	—	28	—	—	—	—
—	M6	.236	5.994	—	—	—	—	—	—	—	1.0	.75	25	34
1/4	—	.250	6.350	.1850	4.699	7	.2010	5.105	20	—	—	—	—	—
1/4	—	.250	6.350	.2036	5.156	3	.2130	5.410	—	28	—	—	—	—
5/16	—	.312	7.938	.2403	6.096	F	.2570	6.527	18	—	—	—	—	—
5/16	—	.312	7.938	.2584	6.553	I	.2720	6.908	—	24	—	—	—	—
—	M8	.315	8.001	—	—	—	—	—	—	—	1.25	1.0	20	25
3/8	—	.375	9.525	.2938	7.442	5/16	.3125	7.937	16	—	—	—	—	—
3/8	—	.375	9.525	.3209	8.153	Q	.3320	8.432	—	24	—	—	—	—
—	M10	.393	9.982	—	—	—	—	—	—	—	1.5	1.25	17	20
7/16	—	.437	11.113	.3447	8.738	U	.3680	9.347	14	—	—	—	—	—
7/16	—	.437	11.113	.3726	9.448	25/64	.3906	9.921	—	20	—	—	—	—
—	M12	.471	11.963	—	—	—	—	—	—	—	1.75	1.25	14.5	20
1/2	—	.500	12.700	.4001	10.162	27/64	.4219	10.715	13	—	—	—	—	—
1/2	—	.500	12.700	.4351	11.049	29/64	.4531	11.509	—	20	—	—	—	—
—	M14	.551	13.995	—	—	—	—	—	—	—	2	1.5	12.5	17
9/16	—	.562	14.288	.4542	11.531	31/64	.4844	12.3031	12	—	—	—	—	—
9/16	—	.562	14.288	.4903	12.446	33/64	.5156	13.096	—	18	—	—	—	—

Continues

TABLE C.1.2 Thread Sizes and Dimensions: Fraction/Decimal/Metric–*Continued*

Nominal Size		Diameter (Major)		Diameter (Minor)		Tap Drill (for 75% Th'd.)			Threads per Inch		Pitch (mm)		T.P.I. (Approx.)	
Inch	*mm*	*Inch*	*mm*	*Inch*	*mm*	*Drill*	*Inch*	*mm*	*UNC*	*UNF*	*Coarse*	*Fine*	*Coarse*	*Fine*
$\frac{5}{8}$	—	.625	15.875	.5069	12.852	$\frac{17}{32}$	.5312	13.493	11	—	—	—	—	—
$\frac{5}{8}$	—	.625	15.875	.5528	14.020	$\frac{37}{64}$	.5781	14.684	—	18	—	—	—	—
—	M16	.630	16.002	—	—	—	—	—	—	—	2	1.5	12.5	17
—	M18	.709	18.008	—	—	—	—	—	—	—	2.5	1.5	10	17
$\frac{3}{4}$	—	.750	19.050	.6201	15.748	$\frac{21}{32}$	.6562	16.668	10	—	—	—	—	—
$\frac{3}{4}$	—	.750	19.050	.6688	16.967	$\frac{11}{16}$	.6875	17.462	—	16	—	—	—	—
—	M20	.787	19.990	—	—	—	—	—	—	—	2.5	1.5	10	17
—	M22	.866	21.996	—	—	—	—	—	—	—	2.5	1.5	10	17
$\frac{7}{8}$	—	.875	22.225	.7307	18.542	$\frac{49}{64}$	.7656	19.446	9	—	—	—	—	—
$\frac{7}{8}$	—	.875	22.225	.7822	19.863	$\frac{13}{16}$	.8125	20.637	—	14	—	—	—	—
—	M24	.945	24.003	—	—	—	—	—	—	—	3	2	8.5	12.5
1	—	1.000	25.400	.8376	21.2598	$\frac{7}{8}$	.8750	22.225	8	—	—	—	—	—
1	—	1.000	25.400	.8917	22.632	$\frac{59}{64}$	.9219	23.415	—	12	—	—	—	—
—	M27	1.063	27.000	—	—	—	—	—	—	—	3	2	8.5	12.5

TABLE C.1.3 Unified Screw Thread Standard Series

Nominal Size			Graded Pitch Series*			Constant Pitch Series*								
			Coarse UNC	Fine UNF	Extra fine UNEF	4 UN	6 UN	8 UN	12 UN	16 UN	20 UN	28 UN	32 UN	
Primary	Secondary	Basic Major Diameter	Threads per Inch											Nominal Size
0		0.0600	—	80	—	—	—	—	—	—	—	—	—	0
	1	0.0730	64	72	—	—	—	—	—	—	—	—	—	1
2		0.0860	56	64	—	—	—	—	—	—	—	—	—	2
	3	0.0990	48	56	—	—	—	—	—	—	—	—	—	3
4		0.1120	40	48	—	—	—	—	—	—	—	—	—	4
5		0.1250	40	44	—	—	—	—	—	—	—	—	—	5
6		0.1380	32	40	—	—	—	—	—	—	—	—	UNC	6
8		0.1640	32	36	—	—	—	—	—	—	—	—	UNC	8
10		0.1900	24	32	—	—	—	—	—	—	—	—	UNC	10
	12	0.2160	24	28	32	—	—	—	—	—	—	UNF	UNEF	12
$\frac{1}{4}$		0.2500	20	28	32	—	—	—	—	—	UNC	UNF	UNEF	$\frac{1}{4}$
$\frac{5}{16}$		0.3125	18	24	32	—	—	—	—	—	20	28	UNEF	$\frac{5}{16}$
$\frac{3}{8}$		0.3750	16	24	32	—	—	—	—	UNC	20	28	UNEF	$\frac{3}{8}$
$\frac{7}{16}$		0.4375	14	20	28	—	—	—	—	16	UNF	UNEF	32	$\frac{7}{16}$
$\frac{1}{2}$		0.5000	13	20	28	—	—	—	—	16	UNF	UNEF	32	$\frac{1}{2}$
$\frac{9}{16}$		0.5625	12	18	24	—	—	—	UNC	16	20	28	32	$\frac{9}{16}$
$\frac{5}{8}$		0.6250	11	18	24	—	—	—	12	16	20	28	32	$\frac{5}{8}$
	$\frac{11}{16}$	0.6875	—	—	24	—	—	—	12	16	20	28	32	$\frac{11}{16}$
$\frac{3}{4}$		0.7500	10	16	20	—	—	—	12	UNF	UNEF	28	32	$\frac{3}{4}$
	$\frac{13}{16}$	0.8125	—	—	20	—	—	—	12	16	UNEF	28	32	$\frac{13}{16}$
$\frac{7}{8}$		0.8750	9	14	20	—	—	—	12	16	UNEF	28	32	$\frac{7}{8}$
	$\frac{15}{16}$	0.9375	—	—	20	—	—	—	12	16	UNEF	28	32	$\frac{15}{16}$
1		1.0000	8	12	20	—	—	UNC	UNF	16	UNEF	28	32	1
	1-$\frac{1}{16}$	1.0625	—	—	18	—	—	8	12	16	20	28	—	1-$\frac{1}{16}$
1-$\frac{1}{8}$		1.1250	7	12	18	—	—	8	UNF	16	20	28	—	1-$\frac{1}{8}$
	1-$\frac{3}{16}$	1.1875	—	—	18	—	—	8	12	16	20	28	—	1-$\frac{3}{16}$
1-$\frac{1}{4}$		1.2500	7	12	18	—	—	8	UNF	16	20	28	—	1-$\frac{1}{4}$
	1-$\frac{5}{16}$	1.3125	—	—	18	—	—	8	12	16	20	28	—	1-$\frac{5}{16}$
1-$\frac{3}{8}$		1.3750	6	12	18	—	UNC	8	UNF	16	20	28	—	1-$\frac{3}{8}$
	1-$\frac{7}{16}$	1.4375	—	—	18	—	6	8	12	16	20	28	—	1-$\frac{7}{16}$
1-$\frac{1}{2}$		1.5000	6	12	18	—	UNC	8	UNF	16	20	28	—	1-$\frac{1}{2}$
	1-$\frac{9}{16}$	1.5625	—	—	18	—	6	8	12	16	20	—	—	1-$\frac{9}{16}$
1-$\frac{5}{8}$		1.6250	—	—	18	—	6	8	12	16	20	—	—	1-$\frac{5}{8}$
	1$\frac{11}{16}$	1.6875	—	—	18	—	6	8	12	16	20	—	—	1-$\frac{11}{16}$
1-$\frac{3}{4}$		1.7500	5	—	—	—	6	8	12	16	20	—	—	1-$\frac{3}{4}$
	1$\frac{13}{16}$	1.8125	—	—	—	—	6	8	12	16	20	—	—	1-$\frac{13}{16}$
1-$\frac{7}{8}$		1.8750	—	—	—	—	6	8	12	16	20	—	—	1-$\frac{7}{8}$
	1$\frac{15}{16}$	1.9375	—	—	—	—	6	8	12	16	20	—	—	1-$\frac{15}{16}$
2		2.0000	4$\frac{1}{2}$	—	—	—	6	8	12	16	20	—	—	2
	2$\frac{1}{8}$	2.1250	—	—	—	—	6	8	12	16	20	—	—	2-$\frac{1}{8}$
2-$\frac{1}{4}$		2.2500	4$\frac{1}{2}$	—	—	—	6	8	12	16	20	—	—	2-$\frac{1}{4}$

Continues

TABLE C.1.3 Unified Screw Thread Standard Series–*Continued*

Nominal Size			Graded Pitch Series*			Constant Pitch Series*								
			Coarse UNC	***Fine UNF***	***Extra fine UNEF***	***4 UN***	***6 UN***	***8 UN***	***12 UN***	***16 UN***	***20 UN***	***28 UN***	***32 UN***	
Primary	***Secondary***	***Basic Major Diameter***	***Threads per Inch***											***Nominal Size***
	$2\frac{3}{8}$	2.3750	—	—	—	—	6	8	12	16	20	—	—	2-$\frac{3}{8}$
2-$\frac{1}{2}$		2.5000	4	—	—	UNC	6	8	12	16	20	—	—	2-$\frac{1}{2}$
	$2\frac{5}{8}$	2.6250	—	—	—	4	6	8	12	16	20	—	—	2-$\frac{5}{8}$
2-$\frac{3}{4}$		2.7500	4	—	—	UNC	6	8	12	16	20	—	—	2-$\frac{3}{4}$
	$2\frac{7}{8}$	2.8750	—	—	—	4	6	8	12	16	20	—	—	2-$\frac{7}{8}$
3		3.0000	4	—	—	UNC	6	8	12	16	20	—	—	3
	3-$\frac{1}{8}$	3.1250	—	—	—	4	6	8	12	16	—	—	—	3-$\frac{1}{8}$
3-$\frac{1}{4}$		3.2500	4	—	—	UNC	6	8	12	16	—	—	—	3-$\frac{1}{4}$
	3-$\frac{3}{8}$	3.3750	—	—	—	4	6	8	12	16	—	—	—	3-$\frac{3}{8}$
3-$\frac{1}{2}$		3.5000	4	—	—	UNC	6	8	12	16	—	—	—	3-$\frac{1}{2}$
	3-$\frac{5}{8}$	3.6250	—	—	—	4	6	8	12	16	—	—	—	3-$\frac{5}{8}$
3-$\frac{3}{4}$		3.7500	4	—	—	UNC	6	8	12	16	—	—	—	3-$\frac{3}{4}$
	3-$\frac{7}{8}$	3.8750	—	—	—	4	6	8	12	16	—	—	—	3-$\frac{7}{8}$
4		4.0000	4	—	—	4	6	8	12	16	—	—	—	4
	4-$\frac{1}{8}$	4.1250	—	—	—	4	6	8	12	16	—	—	—	4-$\frac{1}{8}$
4-$\frac{1}{4}$		4.2500	—	—	—	4	6	8	12	16	—	—	—	4-$\frac{1}{4}$
	4-$\frac{3}{8}$	4.3750	—	—	—	4	6	8	12	16	—	—	—	4-$\frac{3}{8}$
4-$\frac{1}{2}$		4.5000	—	—	—	4	6	8	12	16	—	—	—	4-$\frac{1}{2}$
	4-$\frac{5}{8}$	4.6250	—	—	—	4	6	8	12	16	—	—	—	4-$\frac{5}{8}$
4-$\frac{3}{4}$		4.7500	—	—	—	4	6	8	12	16	—	—	—	4-$\frac{3}{4}$
	4-$\frac{7}{8}$	4.8750	—	—	—	4	6	8	12	16	—	—	—	4-$\frac{7}{8}$
5		5.0000	—	—	—	4	6	8	12	16	—	—	—	5
	5-$\frac{1}{8}$	5.1250	—	—	—	4	6	8	12	16	—	—	—	5-$\frac{1}{8}$
5-$\frac{1}{4}$		5.2500	—	—	—	4	6	8	12	16	—	—	—	5-$\frac{1}{4}$
	5-$\frac{3}{8}$	5.3750	—	—	—	4	6	8	12	16	—	—	—	5-$\frac{3}{8}$
5-$\frac{1}{2}$		5.5000	—	—	—	4	6	8	12	16	—	—	—	5-$\frac{1}{2}$
	5-$\frac{5}{8}$	5.6250	—	—	—	4	6	8	12	16	—	—	—	5-$\frac{5}{8}$
5-$\frac{3}{4}$		5.7500	—	—	—	4	6	8	12	16	—	—	—	5-$\frac{3}{4}$
	5-$\frac{7}{8}$	5.8750	—	—	—	4	6	8	12	16	—	—	—	5-$\frac{7}{8}$
6		6.0000	—	—	—	4	6	8	12	16	—	—	—	6

Courtesy of American National Standards.

TABLE C.1.4 Drill and Counterbore Sizes for Socket-Head Cap Screws (1960 Series)

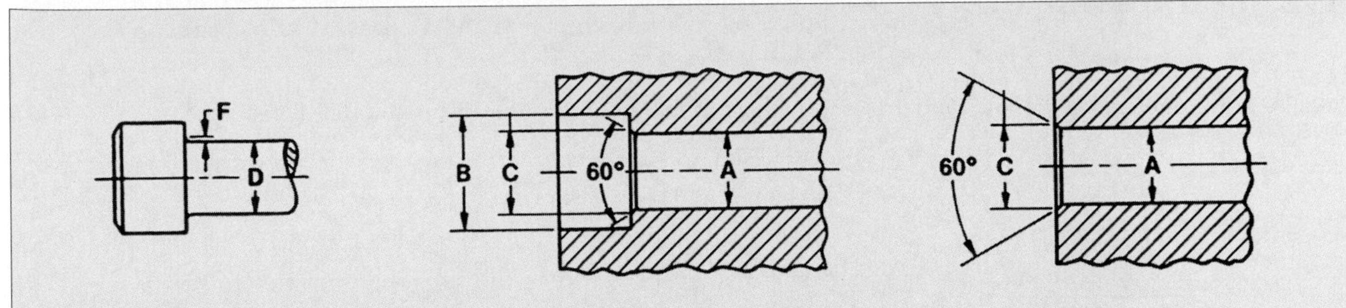

		A				B	C
		Nominal Drill Size					
		Close Fit		Normal Fit			
Nominal Size or Basic Screw Diameter		Number or Fractional Size	Decimal Size	Number or Fractional Size	Decimal Size	Counterbore Diameter	Countersink Diameter D (Max) + 2F (Max)
0	0.0600	51	0.067	49	0.073	$\frac{1}{8}$	0.074
1	0.0730	46	0.081	43	0.089	$\frac{5}{32}$	0.087
2	0.0860	$\frac{3}{32}$	0.094	36	0.106	$\frac{3}{16}$	0.102
3	0.0990	36	0.106	31	0.120	$\frac{7}{32}$	0.115
4	0.1120	$\frac{1}{8}$	0.125	29	0.136	$\frac{7}{32}$	0.130
5	0.1250	$\frac{9}{64}$	0.141	23	0.154	$\frac{1}{4}$	0.145
6	0.1380	23	0.154	18	0.170	$\frac{9}{32}$	0.158
8	0.1640	15	0.180	10	0.194	$\frac{5}{16}$	0.188
10	0.1900	5	0.206	2	0.221	$\frac{3}{8}$	0.218
$\frac{1}{4}$	0.2500	$\frac{17}{64}$	0.266	$\frac{9}{32}$	0.281	$\frac{7}{16}$	0.278
$\frac{5}{16}$	0.3125	$\frac{21}{64}$	0.328	$\frac{11}{32}$	0.344	$\frac{17}{32}$	0.346
$\frac{3}{8}$	0.3750	$\frac{25}{64}$	0.391	$\frac{13}{32}$	0.406	$\frac{5}{8}$	0.415
$\frac{7}{16}$	0.4375	$\frac{29}{64}$	0.453	$\frac{15}{32}$	0.469	$\frac{23}{32}$	0.483
$\frac{1}{2}$	0.5000	$\frac{33}{64}$	0.516	$\frac{17}{32}$	0.531	$\frac{13}{16}$	0.552
$\frac{5}{8}$	0.6250	$\frac{41}{64}$	0.641	$\frac{21}{32}$	0.656	1	0.689
$\frac{3}{4}$	0.7500	$\frac{49}{64}$	0.766	$\frac{25}{32}$	0.781	1-$\frac{3}{16}$	0.828
$\frac{7}{8}$	0.8750	$\frac{57}{64}$	0.891	$\frac{29}{32}$	0.906	1$\frac{3}{8}$	0.963
1	1.0000	1-$\frac{1}{64}$	1.016	1-$\frac{1}{32}$	1.031	1-$\frac{5}{8}$	1.100
1-$\frac{1}{4}$	1.2500	1-$\frac{9}{32}$	1.281	1-$\frac{5}{16}$	1.312	2	1.370
1-$\frac{1}{2}$	1.5000	1-$\frac{17}{32}$	1.531	1-$\frac{9}{16}$	1.562	2$\frac{3}{8}$	1.640
1-$\frac{3}{4}$	1.7500	1-$\frac{25}{32}$	1.781	1-$\frac{13}{16}$	1.812	2-$\frac{3}{4}$	1.910
2	2.0000	2-$\frac{1}{32}$	2.031	2-$\frac{1}{16}$	2.062	3-$\frac{1}{8}$	2.180

C.2 Metric Twist Drills

TABLE C.2.1 American National Standard Combined Drills and Countersinks—Plain and Bell Types (ANSI B94.11M-1979)

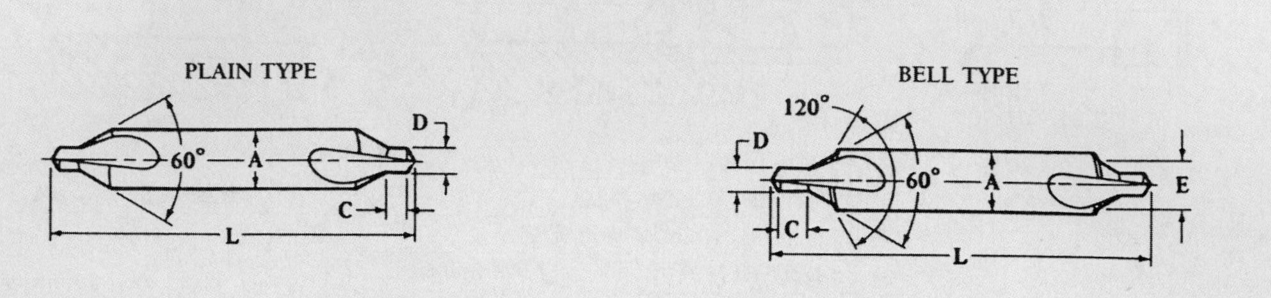

Size Designation	Body Diameter A		Drill Diameter D		Drill Length C		Overall Length L	
	Inches	Millimeters	Inches	Millimeters	Inches	Millimeters	Inches	Millimeters
00	$\frac{1}{8}$	3.18	.025	0.64	.030	0.76	$1\frac{1}{8}$	29
0	$\frac{1}{8}$	3.18	$\frac{1}{32}$	0.79	.038	0.97	$1\frac{1}{8}$	29
1	$\frac{1}{8}$	3.18	$\frac{3}{64}$	1.19	$\frac{3}{64}$	1.19	$1\frac{1}{4}$	32
2	$\frac{3}{16}$	4.76	$\frac{5}{64}$	1.98	$\frac{5}{64}$	1.98	$1\frac{7}{8}$	48
3	$\frac{1}{4}$	6.35	$\frac{7}{64}$	2.78	$\frac{7}{64}$	2.78	2	51
4	$\frac{5}{16}$	7.94	$\frac{1}{8}$	3.18	$\frac{1}{8}$	3.18	$2\frac{1}{8}$	54
5	$\frac{7}{16}$	11.11	$\frac{3}{16}$	4.76	$\frac{3}{16}$	4.76	$2\frac{3}{4}$	70
6	$\frac{1}{2}$	12.70	$\frac{7}{32}$	5.56	$\frac{7}{32}$	5.56	3	76
7	$\frac{5}{8}$	15.88	$\frac{1}{4}$	6.35	$\frac{1}{4}$	6.35	$3\frac{1}{4}$	83
8	$\frac{3}{4}$	19.05	$\frac{5}{16}$	7.94	$\frac{5}{16}$	7.94	$3\frac{1}{2}$	89

(Table subheading: Plain Type)

TABLE C.2.2 Twist Drill Sizes: Decimal/Metric

Number Sizes								Letter Sizes			
No. Size	***Decimal Eqivalent***	***Metric Equivalent***	***Closest Metric Drill (mm)***	***No. Size***	***Decimal Equivalent***	***Metric Equivalent***	***Closest Metric Drill (mm)***	***Size Letter***	***Decimal Equivalent***	***Metric Equivalent***	***Closest Metric Drill (mm)***
1	.2280	5.791	5.80	41	.0960	2.438	2.45	A	.234	5.944	5.90
2	.2210	5.613	5.60	42	.0935	2.362	2.35	B	.238	6.045	6.00
3	.2130	5.410	5.40	43	.0890	2.261	2.25	C	.242	6.147	6.10
4	.2090	5.309	5.30	44	.0860	2.184	2.20	D	.246	6.248	6.25
5	.2055	5.220	5.20	45	.0820	2.083	2.10	E	.250	6.350	6.40
6	.2040	5.182	5.20	46	.0810	2.057	2.05	F	.257	6.528	6.50
7	.2010	5.105	5.10	47	.0785	1.994	2.00	G	.261	6.629	6.60
8	.1990	5.055	5.10	48	.0760	1.930	1.95	H	.266	6.756	6.75
9	.1960	4.978	5.00	49	.0730	1.854	1.85	I	.272	6.909	6.90
10	.1935	4.915	4.90	50	.0700	1.778	1.80	J	.277	7.036	7.00
11	.1910	4.851	4.90	51	.0670	1.702	1.70	K	.281	7.137	7.10
12	.1890	4.801	4.80	52	.0635	1.613	1.60	L	.290	7.366	7.40
13	.1850	4.699	4.70	53	.0595	1.511	1.50	M	.295	7.493	7.50
14	.1820	4.623	4.60	54	.0550	1.397	1.40	N	.302	7.671	7.70
15	.1800	4.572	4.60	55	.0520	1.321	1.30	O	.316	8.026	8.00
16	.1770	4.496	4.50	56	.0465	1.181	1.20	P	.323	8.204	8.20
17	.1730	4.394	4.40	57	.0430	1.092	1.10	Q	.332	8.433	8.40
18	.1695	4.305	4.30	58	.0420	1.067	1.05	R	.339	8.611	8.60
19	.1660	4.216	4.20	59	.0410	1.041	1.05	S	.348	8.839	8.80
20	.1610	4.089	4.10	60	.0400	1.016	1.00	T	.358	9.093	9.10
21	.1590	4.039	4.00	61	.0390	0.991	1.00	U	.368	9.347	9.30
22	.1570	3.988	4.00	62	.0380	0.965	0.95	V	.377	9.576	9.60
23	.1540	3.912	3.90	63	.0370	0.940	0.95	W	.386	9.804	9.80
24	.1520	3.861	3.90	64	.0360	0.914	0.90	X	.397	10.084	10.00
25	.1495	3.797	3.80	65	.0350	0.889	0.90	Y	.404	10.262	10.50
26	.1470	3.734	3.75	66	.0330	0.838	0.85	Z	.413	10.491	10.50
27	.1440	3.658	3.70	67	.0320	0.813	0.80				
28	.1405	3.569	3.60	68	.0310	0.787	0.80				
29	.1360	3.454	3.50	69	.0292	0.742	0.75				
30	.1285	3.264	3.25	70	.0280	0.711	0.70				
31	.1200	3.048	3.00	71	.0260	0.660	0.65				
32	.1160	2.946	2.90	72	.0250	0.635	0.65				
33	.1130	2.870	2.90	73	.0240	0.610	0.60				
34	.1110	2.819	2.80	74	.0225	0.572	0.55				
35	.1100	2.794	2.80	75	.0210	0.533	0.55				
36	.1065	2.705	2.70	76	.0200	0.508	0.50				
37	.1040	2.642	2.60	77	.0180	0.457	0.45				
38	.1015	2.578	2.60	78	.0160	0.406	0.40				
39	.0995	2.527	2.50	79	.0145	0.368	0.35				
40	.0980	2.489	2.50	80	.0135	0.343	0.35				

Fraction-size drills range in size from one-sixteenth to 4 in. and over in diameter, by sixty-fourths.

C.3 Bolts, Nuts, and Screws

Socket Flat Countersunk Head Cap Screws (ANSI/ASME B18.3, 1986)

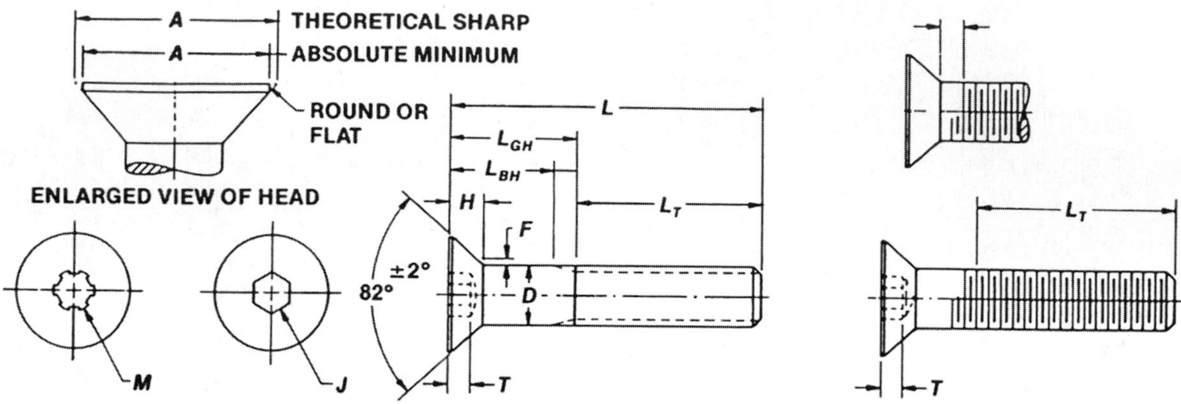

TABLE C.3.1 Dimensions of Hexagon and Spline Socket-Flat-Countersunk-Head Cap Screws

		D		*A*		*H*		*M*	*J*		*T*	*F*
Nominal Size or Basic Screw Diameter		Body Diameter		Head Diameter		Head Height		Spline Socket Size	Hexagon Socket Size		Key Engage-ment	Fillet Ext. Above *D* Max
		Max	*Min*	*Theoretical Sharp Max*	*Abs Min*	*Reference*	*Flushness Tolerance*		*Nom*		*Min*	*Max*
0	0.0600	0.0600	0.0568	0.138	0.117	0.044	0.006	0.048		0.035	0.025	0.006
1	0.0730	0.0730	0.0695	0.168	0.143	0.054	0.007	0.060		0.050	0.031	0.008
2	0.0860	0.0860	0.0822	0.197	0.168	0.064	0.008	0.060		0.050	0.038	0.010
3	0.0990	0.0990	0.0949	0.226	0.193	0.073	0.010	0.072	$\frac{1}{16}$	0.062	0.044	0.010
4	0.1120	0.1120	0.1075	0.255	0.218	0.083	0.011	0.072	$\frac{1}{16}$	0.062	0.055	0.012
5	0.1250	0.1250	0.1202	0.281	0.240	0.090	0.012	0.096	$\frac{5}{64}$	0.078	0.061	0.014
6	0.1380	0.1380	0.1329	0.307	0.263	0.097	0.013	0.096	$\frac{5}{64}$	0.078	0.066	0.015
8	0.1640	0.1640	0.1585	0.359	0.311	0.112	0.014	0.111	$\frac{3}{32}$	0.094	0.076	0.015
10	0.1900	0.1900	0.1840	0.411	0.359	0.127	0.015	0.145	$\frac{1}{8}$	0.125	0.087	0.015
$\frac{1}{4}$	0.2500	0.2500	0.2435	0.531	0.480	0.161	0.016	0.183	$\frac{5}{32}$	0.156	0.111	0.015
$\frac{5}{16}$	0.3125	0.3125	0.3053	0.656	0.600	0.198	0.017	0.216	$\frac{3}{16}$	0.188	0.135	0.015
$\frac{3}{8}$	0.3750	0.3750	0.3678	0.781	0.720	0.234	0.018	0.251	$\frac{7}{32}$	0.219	0.159	0.015
$\frac{7}{16}$	0.4375	0.4375	0.4294	0.844	0.781	0.234	0.018	0.291	$\frac{1}{4}$	0.250	0.159	1.015
$\frac{1}{2}$	0.5000	0.5000	0.4919	0.938	0.872	0.251	0.018	0.372	$\frac{5}{16}$	0.312	0.172	0.015
$\frac{5}{8}$	0.6250	0.6250	0.6163	1.188	1.112	0.324	0.022	0.454	$\frac{3}{8}$	0.375	0.220	0.015
$\frac{3}{4}$	0.7500	0.7500	0.7406	1.438	1.355	0.396	0.024	0.454	$\frac{1}{2}$	0.500	0.220	0.015
$\frac{7}{8}$	0.8750	0.8750	0.8647	1.688	1.604	0.468	0.025	. . .	$\frac{9}{16}$	0.562	0.248	0.015
1	1.0000	1.0000	0.9886	1.938	1.841	0.540	0.028	. . .	$\frac{5}{8}$	0.625	0.297	0.015
1-$\frac{1}{8}$	1.1250	1.1250	1.1086	2.188	2.079	0.611	0.031	. . .	$\frac{3}{4}$	0.750	0.325	0.031
1-$\frac{1}{4}$	1.2500	1.2500	1.2336	2.438	2.316	0.683	0.035	. . .	$\frac{7}{8}$	0.875	0.358	0.031
1-$\frac{3}{8}$	1.3750	1.3750	1.3568	2.688	2.553	0.755	0.038	. . .	$\frac{7}{8}$	0.875	0.402	0.031
1-$\frac{1}{2}$	1.5000	1.5000	1.4818	2.938	2.791	0.827	0.042	. . .	1	1.0000	0.435	0.031

Countersunk Bolts and Slotted Countersunk Bolts (ANSI/ASME B18.5, 1978)

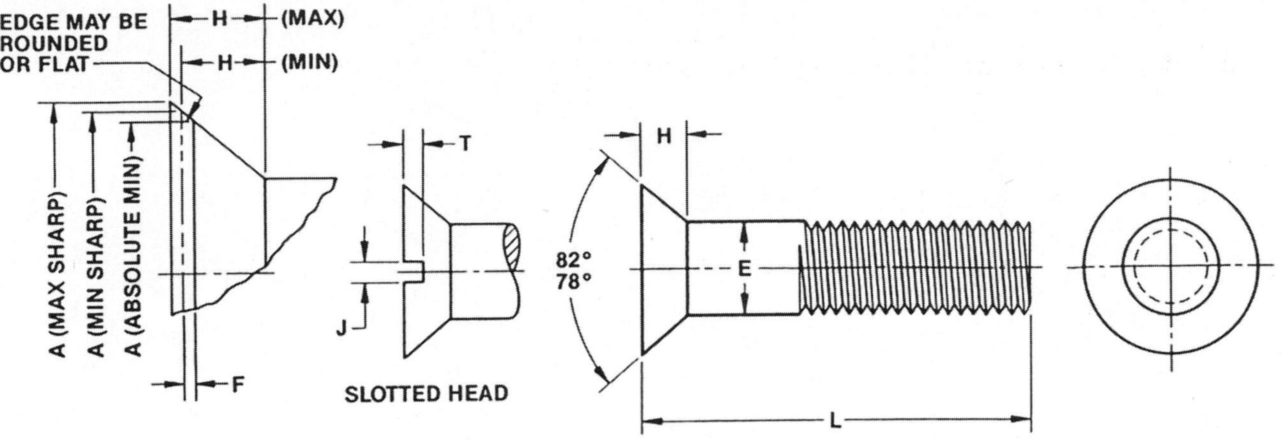

TABLE C.3.2 Dimensions of Countersunk Bolts and Slotted Countersunk Bolts

Nominal Size or Basic Bolt Diameter		*E* Body Diameter		*A* Head Diameter			*F* Flat on Min Dia Head	*H* Head Height		*J* Slot Width		*T* Slot Depth	
		Max	*Min*	*Max Edge Sharp*	*Min Edge Sharp*	*Absolute Min Edge Rounded or Flat*	*Max*	*Max*	*Min*	*Max*	*Min*	*Max*	*Min*
$\frac{1}{4}$	0.2500	0.260	0.237	0.493	0.477	0.445	0.018	0.150	0.131	0.075	0.064	0.068	0.045
$\frac{5}{16}$	0.3125	0.324	0.298	0.618	0.598	0.558	0.023	0.189	0.164	0.084	0.072	0.086	0.057
$\frac{3}{8}$	0.3750	0.388	0.360	0.740	0.715	0.668	0.027	0.225	0.196	0.094	0.081	0.103	0.068
$\frac{7}{16}$	0.4375	0.452	0.421	0.803	0.778	0.726	0.030	0.226	0.196	0.094	0.081	0.103	0.068
$\frac{1}{2}$	0.5000	0.515	0.483	1.935	1.905	0.845	0.035	0.269	0.233	0.106	0.091	0.103	0.068
$\frac{5}{8}$	0.6250	0.642	0.605	1.169	1.132	1.066	0.038	0.336	0.292	0.133	0.116	0.137	0.091
$\frac{3}{4}$	0.7500	0.768	0.729	1.402	1.357	1.285	0.041	0.403	0.349	0.149	0.131	0.171	0.115
$\frac{7}{8}$	0.8750	0.895	0.852	1.637	1.584	1.511	0.042	0.470	0.408	0.167	0.147	0.206	0.138
1	1.0000	1.022	0.976	1.869	1.810	1.735	0.043	0.537	0.466	0.188	0.166	0.240	0.162
1-$\frac{1}{8}$	1.1250	1.149	1.098	2.104	2.037	1.962	0.043	0.604	0.525	0.196	0.178	0.257	0.173
1-$\frac{1}{4}$	1.2500	1.277	1.223	2.337	2.262	2.187	0.043	0.671	0.582	0.211	0.193	0.291	0.197
1-$\frac{3}{8}$	1.3750	1.404	1.345	2.571	2.489	2.414	0.043	0.738	0.641	0.226	0.208	0.326	0.220
1-$\frac{1}{2}$	1.5000	1.531	1.470	2.804	2.715	2.640	0.043	0.805	0.698	0.258	0.240	0.360	0.244

Hex Cap Screws (Finished Hex Bolts) (ANSI/ASME B18.2.1, 1981)

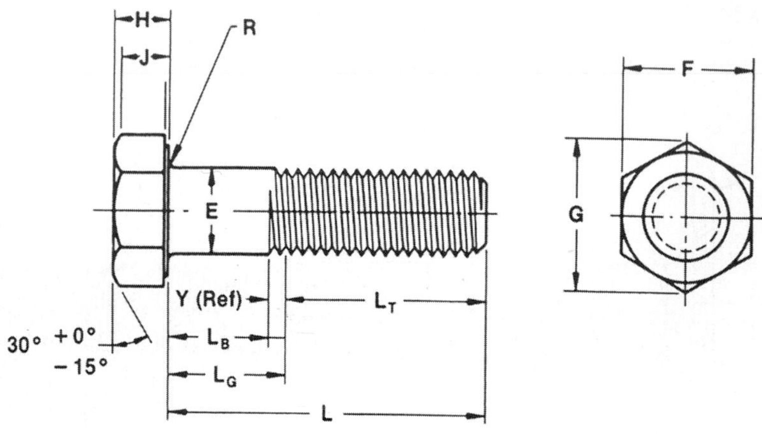

TABLE C.3.3 Dimensions of Hex Cap Screws

	E		*F*			*G*		*H*			*J*	L_T		*Y*	
Nominal Size or Basic Product Diameter	Body Diameter		Width Across Flats			Width Across Corners		Height			Wrenching Height	Thread Length for Screw Lengths: 6 in. & shorter	Thread Length for Screw Lengths: Over 6 in.	Transition Thread Length	Runout of Bearing Surface FIM
	Max	*Min*	*Basic*	*Max*	*Min*	*Max*	*Min*	*Basic*	*Max*	*Min*	*Min*	*Basic*	*Basic*	*Min*	*Max*
1/4 0.2500	0.2500	0.2450	7/16	0.438	0.428	0.505	0.488	5/32	0.163	0.150	0.106	0.750	1.000	0.250	0.010
5/16 0.3125	0.3125	0.3065	1/2	0.500	0.489	0.577	0.557	13/64	0.211	0.195	0.140	0.875	1.125	0.278	0.011
3/8 0.3750	0.3750	0.3690	9/16	0.562	0.551	0.650	0.628	15/64	0.243	0.226	0.160	1.000	1.250	0.312	0.012
7/16 0.4375	0.4375	0.4305	5/8	0.625	0.612	0.722	0.698	9/32	0.291	0.272	0.195	1.125	1.375	0.357	0.013
1/2 0.5000	0.5000	0.4930	3/4	0.750	0.736	0.866	0.840	5/16	0.323	0.302	0.215	1.250	1.500	0.385	0.014
9/16 0.5625	0.5625	0.5545	13/16	0.812	0.798	0.938	0.910	23/64	0.371	0.348	0.250	1.375	1.625	0.417	0.015
5/8 0.6250	0.6250	0.6170	15/16	0.938	0.922	1.083	1.051	25/64	0.403	0.378	0.269	1.500	1.750	0.455	0.017
3/4 0.7500	0.7500	0.7410	1-1/8	1.125	1.100	1.299	1.254	15/32	0.483	0.455	0.324	1.750	2.000	0.500	0.020
7/8 0.8750	0.8750	0.8660	1-5/16	1.312	1.285	1.516	1.465	35/64	0.563	0.531	0.378	2.000	2.250	0.556	0.023
1 1.0000	1.0000	0.9900	1-1/2	1.500	1.469	1.732	1.675	39/64	0.627	0.591	0.416	2.250	2.500	0.625	0.026
1-1/8 1.1250	1.1250	1.1140	1-11/16	1.688	1.631	1.949	1.859	11/16	0.718	0.658	0.461	2.500	2.750	0.714	0.029
1-1/4 1.2500	1.2500	1.2390	1-7/8	1.875	1.812	2.165	2.066	25/32	0.813	0.749	0.530	2.750	3.000	0.714	0.033
1-3/8 1.3750	1.3750	1.3630	2-1/16	2.062	1.994	2.382	2.273	27/32	0.878	0.810	0.569	3.000	3.250	0.833	0.036
1-1/2 1.5000	1.5000	1.4880	2-1/4	2.250	2.175	2.598	2.480	1-5/16	0.974	0.902	0.640	3.250	3.500	0.833	0.039
1-3/4 1.7500	1.7500	1.7380	2-5/8	2.625	2.538	3.031	2.893	1-3/32	1.134	1.054	0.748	3.750	4.000	1.000	0.046
2 2.0000	2.0000	1.9880	3	3.000	2.900	3.464	3.306	1-7/32	1.263	1.175	0.825	4.250	4.500	1.111	0.052
2-1/4 2.2500	2.2500	2.2380	3-3/8	3.375	3.262	3.897	3.719	1-3/8	1.423	1.327	0.933	4.750	5.000	1.111	0.059
2-1/2 2.5000	2.5000	2.4880	3-3/4	3.750	3.625	4.330	4.133	1-17/32	1.583	1.479	1.042	5.250	5.500	1.250	0.065
2-3/4 2.7500	2.7500	2.7380	4-1/8	4.125	3.988	4.763	4.546	1-11/16	1.744	1.632	1.151	5.750	6.000	1.250	0.072
3 3.0000	3.0000	2.9880	4-1/2	4.500	4.350	5.196	4.959	1-7/8	1.935	1.815	1.290	6.250	6.500	1.250	0.079

Metric Hex Cap Screws (ANSI B18.2.3.1M, 1979)

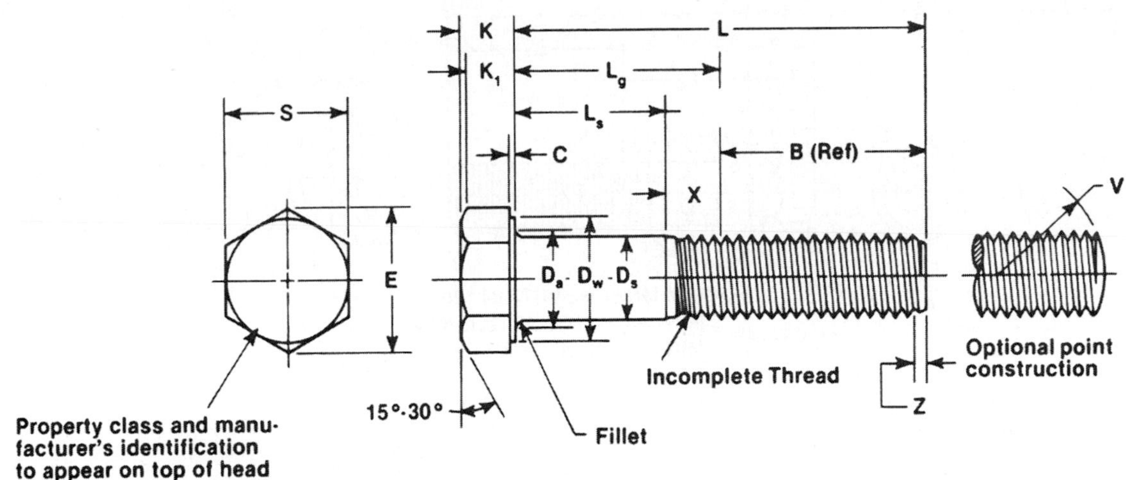

TABLE C.3.4 Dimensions of Hex Cap Screws

D	D_S		*S*		*E*		*K*		K_i	*C*		D_W	Runout
Nominal Screw Diameter and Thread Pitch	Body Diameter		Width Across Flats		Width Across Corners		Head Height		Wrenching Height	Washer Face Thickness		Washer Face Dia	of Bearing Surface FIM
	Max	*Min*	*Max*	*Min*	*Max*	*Min*	*Max*	*Min*	*Min*	*Max*	*Min*	*Min*	*Max*
M5 × 0.8	5.00	4.82	8.00	7.78	9.24	8.79	3.65	3.35	2.4	0.5	0.2	6.9	0.22
M6 × 1	6.00	5.82	10.00	9.78	11.55	11.05	4.15	3.85	2.8	0.5	0.2	8.9	0.25
M8 × 1.25	8.00	7.78	13.00	12.73	15.01	14.38	5.50	5.10	3.7	0.6	0.3	11.6	0.28
M10 × 1.5	10.00	9.78	16.00	15.73	18.48	17.77	6.63	6.17	4.5	0.6	0.3	14.6	0.32
M12 × 1.75	12.00	11.73	18.00	17.73	20.78	20.03	7.76	7.24	5.2	0.6	0.3	16.6	0.35
M14 × 2	14.00	13.73	21.00	20.67	24.25	23.35	9.09	8.51	6.2	0.6	0.3	19.6	0.39
M16 × 2	16.00	15.73	24.00	23.67	27.71	26.75	10.32	9.68	7.0	0.8	0.4	22.5	0.43
M20 × 2.5	20.00	19.67	30.00	29.16	34.64	32.95	12.88	12.12	8.8	0.8	0.4	27.7	0.53
M24 × 3	24.00	23.67	36.00	35.00	41.57	39.55	15.44	14.56	10.5	0.8	0.4	33.2	0.63
M30 × 3.5	30.00	29.67	46.00	45.00	53.12	50.85	19.48	17.92	13.1	0.8	0.4	42.7	0.78
M36 × 4	36.00	35.61	55.00	53.80	63.51	60.79	23.38	21.62	15.8	0.8	0.4	51.1	0.93
M42 × 4.5	42.00	41.38	65.00	62.90	75.06	71.71	26.97	25.03	18.2	1.0	0.5	59.8	1.09
M48 × 5	48.00	47.38	75.00	72.60	86.60	82.76	31.07	28.93	21.0	1.0	0.5	69.0	1.25
M56 × 5.5	56.00	55.26	85.00	82.20	98.15	93.71	36.20	33.80	24.5	1.0	0.5	78.1	1.47
M64 × 6	64.00	63.26	95.00	91.80	109.70	104.65	41.32	36.68	28.0	1.0	0.5	87.2	1.69
M72 × 6	72.00	71.26	105.00	101.40	121.24	115.60	46.45	43.55	31.5	1.2	0.6	96.3	1.91
M80 × 6	80.00	79.26	115.00	111.00	132.72	126.54	51.58	48.42	35.0	1.2	0.6	105.4	2.13
M90 × 6	90.00	89.13	130.00	125.50	150.11	143.07	57.74	54.26	39.2	1.2	0.6	119.2	2.41
M100 × 6	100.00	99.13	145.00	140.00	167.43	159.60	63.90	60.10	43.4	1.2	0.6	133.0	2.69
*M10 × 1.5	10.00	9.78	15.00	14.73	17.32	16.64	6.63	6.17	4.5	0.6	0.3	13.6	0.31

Socket-Head Cap Screws (1960 Series) (ANSI/ASME B18.3, 1986)

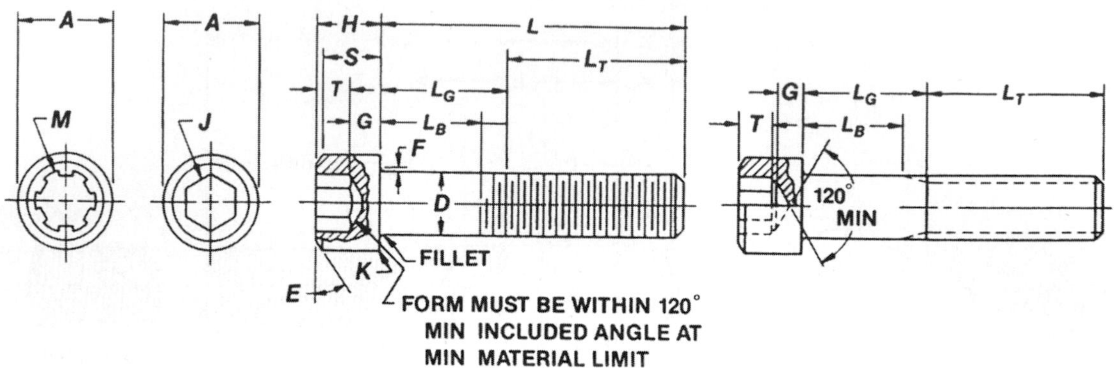

TABLE C.3.5 Dimensions of Hexagon and Spline Socket-Head Cap Screws (1960 Series)

Nominal Size or Basic Screw Diameter		*D* Body Diameter		*A* Head Diameter		*H* Head Height		*S* Head Side Height	*M* Spline Socket Size	*J* Hexagon Socket Size		*T* Key Engagement	*G* Wall Thickness	*K* Chamfer or Radius
		Max	*Min*	*Max*	*Min*	*Max*	*Min*	*Min*	*Nom*	*Nom*		*Min*	*Min*	*Max*
0	0.0600	0.0600	0.0568	0.096	0.091	0.060	0.057	0.054	0.060		0.050	0.025	0.020	0.003
1	0.0730	0.0730	0.0695	0.118	0.112	0.073	0.070	0.066	0.072	1/16	0.062	0.031	0.025	0.003
2	0.0860	0.0860	0.0822	0.140	0.134	0.086	0.083	0.077	0.096	5/64	0.078	0.038	0.029	0.003
3	0.0990	0.0990	0.0949	0.161	0.154	0.099	0.095	0.089	0.096	5/64	0.078	0.044	0.034	0.003
4	0.1120	0.1120	0.1075	0.183	0.176	0.112	0.108	0.101	0.111	3/32	0.094	0.051	0.038	0.005
5	0.1250	0.1250	0.1202	0.205	0.198	0.125	0.121	0.112	0.111	3/32	0.094	0.057	0.034	0.005
6	0.1380	0.1380	0.1329	0.226	0.218	0.138	0.134	0.124	0.133	7/64	0.109	0.064	0.047	0.005
8	0.1640	0.1640	0.1585	0.270	0.262	0.164	0.159	0.148	0.168	9/64	0.141	0.077	0.056	0.005
10	0.1900	0.1900	0.1840	0.312	0.303	0.190	0.185	0.171	0.183	5/32	0.156	0.090	0.065	0.005
1/4	0.2500	0.2500	0.2435	0.375	0.365	0.250	0.244	0.255	0.216	3/16	0.188	0.120	0.095	0.008
5/16	0.3125	0.3125	0.3053	0.469	0.457	0.312	0.306	0.281	0.291	1/4	0.250	0.151	0.119	0.008
3/8	0.3750	0.3750	0.3678	0.562	0.550	0.375	0.368	0.337	0.372	5/16	0.312	0.182	0.143	0.008
7/16	0.4375	0.4375	0.4294	0.656	0.642	0.438	0.430	0.394	0.454	3/8	0.375	0.213	0.166	0.010
1/2	0.5000	0.5000	0.4919	0.750	0.735	0.500	0.492	0.450	0.454	3/8	0.375	0.245	0.190	0.010
5/8	0.6250	0.6250	0.6163	0.938	0.921	0.625	0.616	0.562	0.595	1/2	0.500	0.307	0.238	0.010
3/4	0.7500	0.7500	0.7406	1.125	1.107	0.750	0.740	0.675	0.620	5/8	0.625	0.370	0.285	0.010
7/8	0.8750	0.8750	0.8647	1.312	1.293	0.875	0.864	0.787	0.698	3/4	0.750	0.432	0.333	0.015
1	1.0000	1.0000	0.9886	1.500	1.479	1.000	0.988	0.900	0.790	3/4	0.750	0.495	0.380	0.015
1-1/8	1.1250	1.1250	1.1086	1.688	1.665	1.125	1.111	1.012	...	7/8	0.875	0.557	0.428	0.015
1-1/4	1.2500	1.2500	1.2336	1.875	1.852	1.250	1.236	1.125	...	7/8	0.875	0.620	0.475	0.015
1-3/8	1.3750	1.3750	1.3568	2.062	2.038	1.375	1.360	1.237	...	1	1.000	0.682	0.523	0.015
1-1/2	1.5000	1.5000	1.4818	2.250	2.224	1.500	1.485	1.350	...	1	1.000	0.745	0.570	0.015
1-3/4	1.7500	7.7500	1.7295	2.625	2.597	1.750	1.734	1.575	...	1-1/4	1.250	0.870	0.665	0.015
2	2.0000	2.0000	1.9780	3.000	2.970	2.000	1.983	1.800	...	1-1/2	1.500	0.995	0.760	0.015
2-1/4	2.2500	2.2500	2.2280	3.375	3.344	2.250	2.232	2.025	...	1-3/4	1.750	1.120	0.855	0.031
2-1/2	2.5000	2.5000	2.4762	3.750	3.717	2.500	2.481	2.250	...	1-3/4	1.750	1.245	0.950	0.031
2-3/4	2.7500	2.7500	2.7262	4.125	4.090	2.750	2.730	2.475	...	2	2.000	1.370	1.045	0.031
3	3.0000	3.0000	2.9762	4.500	4.464	3.000	2.979	2.700	...	2-1/4	2.250	1.495	1.140	0.031
3-1/4	3.2500	3.2500	3.2262	4.875	4.837	3.250	3.228	2.925	...	2-1/4	2.250	1.620	1.235	0.031
3-1/2	3.5000	3.5000	3.4762	5.250	5.211	3.500	3.478	3.150	...	2-3/4	2.750	1.745	1.330	0.031
3-3/4	3.7500	3.7500	3.7262	5.625	5.584	3.750	3.727	3.375	...	2-3/4	2.750	1.870	1.425	0.031
4	4.0000	4.0000	3.9762	6.000	5.958	4.000	3.976	3.600	...	3	3.000	1.995	1.520	0.031

Metric Socket-Head Cap Screws (ANSI/ASME B18.3.1M, 1982)

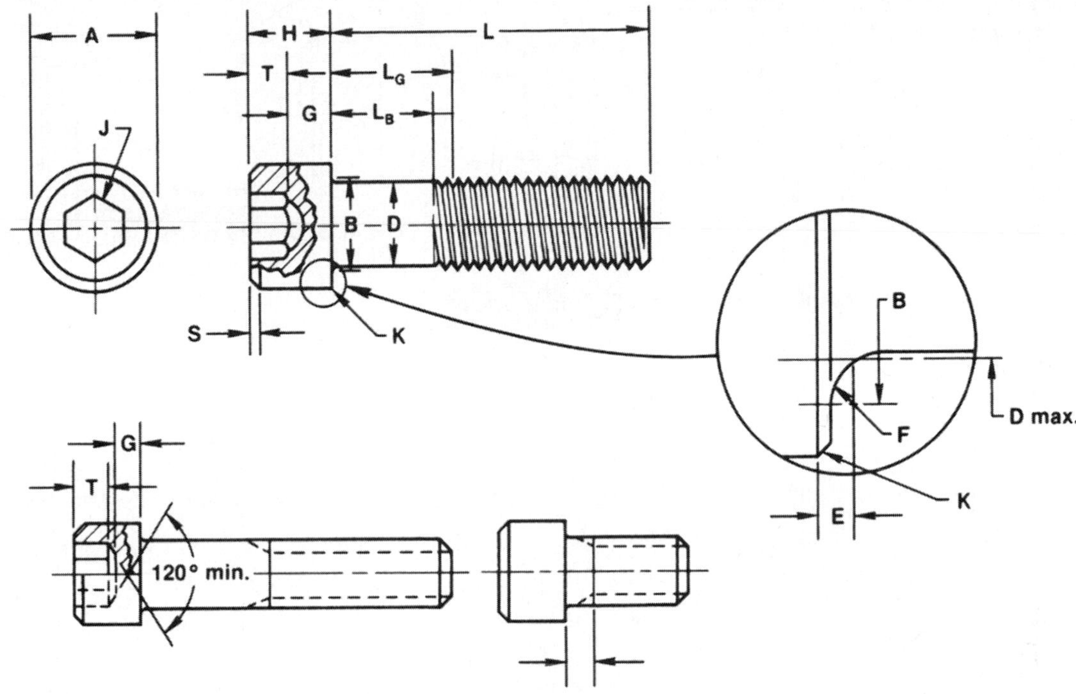

TABLE C.3.6 Dimensions of Metric Socket-Head Cap Screws

Nominal Screw Diameter and Thread Pitch	*D* Body Diameter		*A* Head Diameter		*H* Head Height		*S* Chamfer or Radius	*J* Hex-agon Socket Size	*T* Key Engage-ment	*G* Wall Thick-ness	*B* Under Head Fillet: Transi-tion Diameter		*E* Under Head Fillet: Transi-tion Length	*F* Under Head Fillet: Junc-ture Radius	*K* Chamfer or Radius
	Max	*Min*	*Max*	*Min*	*Max*	*Min*	*Max*	*Nom*	*Min*	*Min*	*Max*	*Min*	*Max*	*Min*	*Max*
M1.6 × 0.35	1.60	1.46	3.00	2.87	1.60	1.52	0.16	1.5	0.80	0.54	2.0	1.8	0.34	0.10	0.08
M2 × 0.4	2.00	1.86	3.80	3.65	2.00	1.91	0.20	1.5	1.00	0.68	2.6	2.2	0.51	0.10	0.08
M2.5 × 0.45	2.50	2.36	4.50	4.33	2.50	2.40	0.25	2.0	1.25	0.85	3.1	2.7	0.51	0.10	0.08
M3 × 0.5	3.00	2.86	5.50	5.32	3.00	2.89	0.30	2.5	1.50	1.02	3.6	3.2	0.51	0.10	0.13
M4 × 0.7	4.00	3.82	7.00	6.80	4.00	3.88	0.40	3.0	2.00	1.52	4.7	4.4	0.60	0.20	0.13
M5 × 0.8	5.00	4.82	8.50	8.27	5.00	4.86	0.50	4.0	2.50	1.90	5.7	5.4	0.60	0.20	0.13
M6 × 1	6.00	5.82	10.00	9.74	6.00	5.85	0.60	5.0	3.00	2.28	6.8	6.5	0.68	0.25	0.20
M8 × 1.25	8.00	7.78	13.00	12.70	8.00	7.83	0.80	6.0	4.00	3.20	9.2	8.8	1.02	0.40	0.20
M10 × 1.5	10.00	9.78	16.00	15.67	10.00	9.81	1.00	8.0	5.00	4.00	11.2	10.8	1.02	0.40	0.20
M12 × 1.75	12.00	11.73	18.00	17.63	12.00	11.79	1.20	10.0	6.00	4.80	14.2	13.2	1.87	0.60	0.25
(1)M14 × 2	14.00	13.73	21.00	20.60	14.00	13.77	1.40	12.0	7.00	5.60	16.2	15.2	1.87	0.60	0.25
M16 × 2	16.00	15.73	24.00	23.58	16.00	15.76	1.60	14.0	8.00	6.40	18.2	17.2	1.87	0.60	0.25
M20 × 2.5	20.00	19.67	30.00	29.53	20.00	19.73	2.00	17.0	10.00	8.00	22.4	21.6	2.04	0.80	0.40
M24 × 3	24.00	23.67	36.00	35.48	24.00	23.70	2.40	19.0	12.00	9.60	26.4	25.6	2.04	0.80	0.40
M30 × 3.5	30.00	29.67	45.00	44.42	30.00	29.67	3.00	22.0	15.00	12.00	33.4	32.0	2.89	1.00	0.40
M36 × 4	36.00	35.61	54.00	53.37	36.00	35.64	3.60	27.0	18.00	14.40	39.4	38.0	2.89	1.00	0.40
M42 × 4.5	42.00	41.61	63.00	62.31	42.00	41.61	4.20	32.0	21.00	16.80	45.6	44.4	3.06	1.20	0.40
M48 × 5	48.00	47.61	72.00	72.27	48.00	47.58	4.80	36.0	24.00	19.20	52.6	51.2	3.91	1.60	0.40

Socket-Head Shoulder Screws (ANSI/ASME B18.3, 1986)

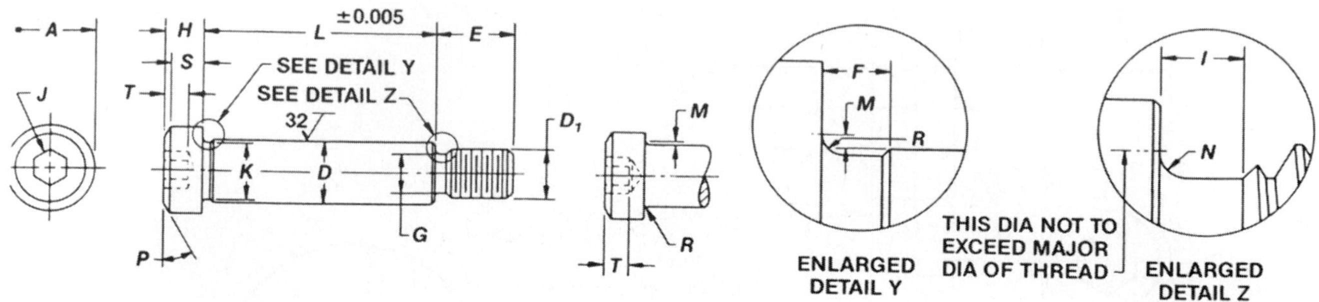

TABLE C.3.7 Dimensions of Hexagon Socket-Head Shoulder Screws

Nominal Size or Basic Shoulder Diameter		D Shoulder Diameter		A Head Diameter		H Head Height		S Head Side Height	J Hexagon Socket Size		T Key Engagement	M Head Fillet Extension Above D	R Head Fillet Radius
		Max	Min	Max	Min	Max	Min	Min	Nom		Min	Max	Min
1/4	0.250	0.2480	0.2460	0.375	0.357	0.188	0.177	0.157	1/8	0.125	0.094	0.014	0.009
5/16	0.312	0.3105	0.3085	0.438	0.419	0.219	0.209	0.183	5/32	0.156	0.117	0.017	0.012
3/8	0.375	0.3730	0.3710	0.562	0.543	0.250	0.240	0.209	3/16	0.188	0.141	0.020	0.015
1/2	0.500	0.4980	0.4960	0.750	0.729	0.312	0.302	0.262	1/4	0.250	0.188	0.026	0.020
5/8	0.625	0.6230	0.6210	0.875	0.853	0.375	0.365	0.315	5/16	0.312	0.234	0.032	0.024
3/4	0.750	0.7480	0.7460	1.000	0.977	0.500	0.490	0.421	3/8	0.375	0.281	0.039	0.030
1	1.000	0.9980	0.9960	1.312	1.287	0.625	0.610	0.527	1/2	0.500	0.375	0.050	0.040
1-1/4	1.250	1.2480	1.2460	1.750	1.723	0.750	0.735	0.633	5/8	0.625	0.469	0.060	0.050
1-1/2	1.500	1.4980	1.4960	2.125	2.3095	1.000	0.980	0.842	7/8	0.875	0.656	0.070	0.060
1-3/4	1.750	1.7480	1.7460	2.375	2.345	1.125	1.105	0.948	1	1.000	0.750	0.080	0.070
2	2.00	1.9980	1.9960	2.750	2.720	1.250	1.230	1.054	1-1/4	1.250	0.937	0.090	0.080

Nominal Size or Basic Shoulder Diameter		K Shoulder Neck Diameter	F Shoulder Neck Width	D_1 Nominal Thread Size or Basic Thread Diameter		Threads per Inch	G Thread Neck Diameter		I Thread Neck Width	N Thread Neck Fillet		E Thread Length
		Min	Max				Max		Max	Min		Basic
1/4	0.250	0.227	0.093	10	0.1900	24	0.142	0.133	0.083	0.023	0.017	0.375
5/16	0.312	0.289	0.093	1/4	0.2500	20	0.193	0.182	0.100	0.028	0.022	0.438
3/8	0.375	0.352	0.093	5/16	0.3125	18	0.249	0.237	0.111	0.031	0.025	0.500
1/2	0.500	0.477	0.093	3/8	0.3750	16	0.304	0.291	0.125	0.035	0.029	0.625
5/8	0.625	0.602	0.093	1/2	0.5000	13	0.414	0.397	0.154	0.042	0.036	0.750
3/4	0.750	0.727	0.093	5/8	0.6250	11	0.521	0.502	0.182	0.051	0.045	0.875
1	1.000	0.977	0.125	3/4	0.7500	10	0.638	0.616	0.200	0.055	0.049	1.000
1-1/4	1.250	1.227	0.125	7/8	0.8750	9	0.750	0.726	0.222	0.062	0.056	1.125
1-1/2	1.500	1.478	0.125	1-1/8	1.1250	7	0.964	0.934	0.286	0.072	0.066	1.500
1-3/4	1.750	1.728	0.125	1-1/4	1.2500	7	1.089	1.059	0.286	0.072	0.066	1.750
2	2.000	1.978	0.125	1-1/2	1.5000	6	1.307	1.277	0.333	0.102	0.096	2.000

Square Bolts (ANSI/ASME B18.2.1, 1981)

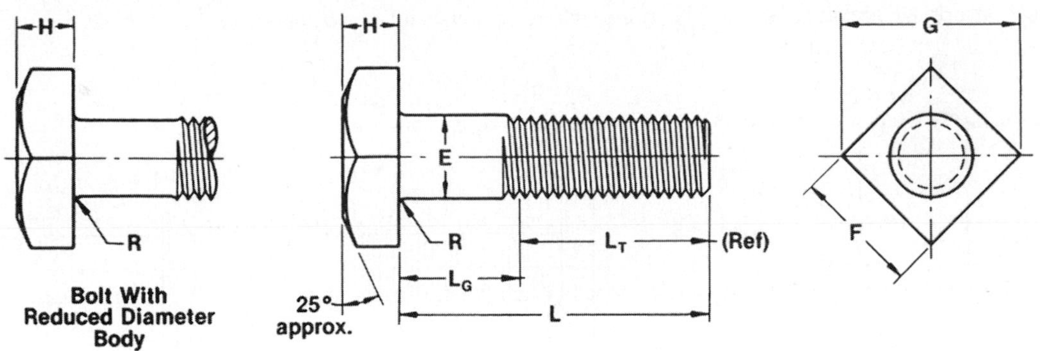

TABLE C.3.8 Dimensions of Square Bolts

Nominal Size or Basic Product Diameter		E: Body Dia	F: Width Across Flats			G: Width Across Corners		H: Height			R: Radius of Fillet		L_T: Thread Length for Bolt Lengths	
		Max	Basic	Max	Min	Max	Min	Basic	Max	Min	Max	Min	6 in. and Shorter Basic	Over 6 in. Basic
1/4	0.2500	0.260	3/8	0.375	0.362	0.530	0.498	11/64	0.188	0.156	0.03	0.01	0.750	1.000
5/16	0.3125	0.324	1/2	0.500	0.484	0.707	0.665	13/64	0.220	0.186	0.03	0.01	0.875	1.125
3/8	0.3750	0.388	9/16	0.562	0.544	0.795	0.747	1/4	0.268	0.232	0.03	0.01	1.000	1.250
7/16	0.4375	0.452	5/8	0.625	0.603	0.884	0.828	19/64	0.316	0.278	0.03	0.01	1.125	1.375
1/2	0.5000	0.515	3/4	0.750	0.725	1.061	0.995	21/64	0.348	0.308	0.03	0.01	1.250	1.500
5/8	0.6250	0.642	15/16	0.938	0.906	1.326	1.244	27/64	0.444	0.400	0.06	0.02	1.500	1.750
3/4	0.7500	0.768	1-1/8	1.125	1.088	1.591	1.494	1/2	0.524	0.476	0.06	0.02	1.750	2.000
7/8	0.8750	0.895	1-5/16	1.312	1.269	1.856	1.742	19/32	0.620	0.568	0.06	0.02	2.000	2.250
1	1.0000	1.022	1-1/2	1.500	1.450	2.121	1.991	21/32	0.684	0.628	0.09	0.03	2.250	2.500
1-1/8	1.1250	1.149	1-11/16	1.688	1.631	2.386	2.239	3/4	0.780	0.720	0.09	0.03	2.500	2.750
1-1/4	1.2500	1.277	1-7/8	1.875	1.812	2.652	2.489	27/32	0.876	0.812	0.09	0.03	2.750	3.000
1-3/8	1.3750	1.404	2-1/16	2.062	1.994	2.917	2.738	29/32	0.940	0.872	0.09	0.03	3.000	3.250
1-1/2	1.5000	1.531	2-1/4	2.250	2.175	3.182	2.986	1	1.036	0.964	0.09	0.03	3.250	3.500

Socket-Button-Head Cap Screws (ANSI/ASME B18.3, 1986)

General Note: This product is designed and recommended for light fastening applications such as guards, hinges, etc. It is not suggested for use in critical high-strength applications, where socket-head cap screws should normally be used.

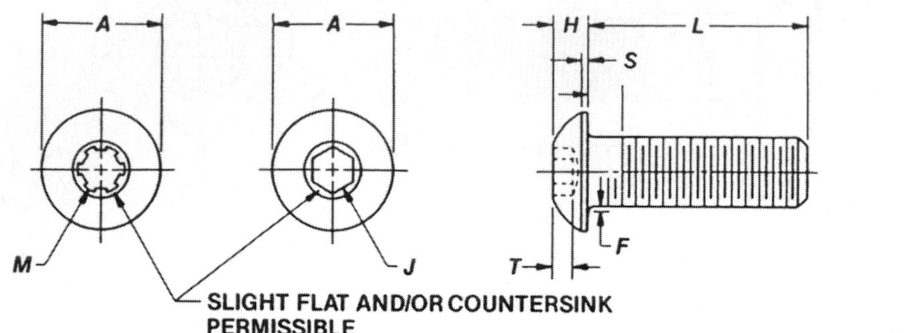

TABLE C.3.9 Dimensions of Hexagon and Spline Socket-Button-Head Cap Screws

Nominal Size or Basic Screw Diameter		A Head Diameter		H Head Height		S Head Side Height	M Spline Socket Size	J Hexagon Socket Size		T Key Engagement	F Fillet Extension		L Max Standard Length
		Max	Min	Max	Min	Ref	Nom	Nom		Min	Max	Min	Nom
0	0.0600	0.114	0.104	0.032	0.026	0.010	0.048		0.035	0.020	0.010	0.005	0.50
1	0.0730	0.139	0.129	0.039	0.033	0.010	0.060		0.050	0.028	0.010	0.005	0.50
2	0.0860	0.164	0.154	0.046	0.038	0.010	0.060		0.050	0.028	0.010	0.005	0.50
3	0.0990	0.188	0.176	0.052	0.044	0.010	0.072	$\frac{1}{16}$	0.062	0.035	0.010	0.005	0.50
4	0.1120	0.213	0.201	0.059	0.051	0.015	0.072	$\frac{1}{16}$	0.062	0.035	0.010	0.005	0.50
5	0.1250	0.238	0.226	0.066	0.058	0.015	0.096	$\frac{5}{64}$	0.078	0.044	0.010	0.005	0.50
6	0.1380	0.262	0.250	0.073	0.063	0.015	0.096	$\frac{5}{64}$	0.078	0.044	0.010	0.005	0.63
8	0.1640	0.312	0.298	0.087	0.077	0.015	0.111	$\frac{3}{32}$	0.094	0.052	0.015	0.010	0.75
10	0.1900	0.361	0.347	0.101	0.091	0.020	0.145	$\frac{1}{8}$	0.125	0.070	0.015	0.010	1.00
$\frac{1}{4}$	0.2500	0.437	0.419	0.132	0.122	0.031	0.183	$\frac{5}{32}$	0.156	0.087	0.020	0.015	1.00
$\frac{5}{16}$	0.3125	0.547	0.527	0.166	0.152	0.031	0.216	$\frac{3}{16}$	0.188	0.105	0.020	0.015	1.00
$\frac{3}{8}$	0.3750	0.656	0.636	0.199	0.185	0.031	0.251	$\frac{7}{32}$	0.219	0.122	0.020	0.015	1.25
$\frac{1}{2}$	0.5000	0.875	0.851	0.265	0.245	0.046	0.372	$\frac{5}{16}$	0.312	0.175	0.030	0.020	2.00
$\frac{5}{8}$	0.6250	1.000	0.970	0.331	0.311	0.062	0.454	$\frac{3}{8}$	0.375	0.210	0.030	0.020	2.00

Socket Set Screws (ANSI/ASME B18.3, 1986)

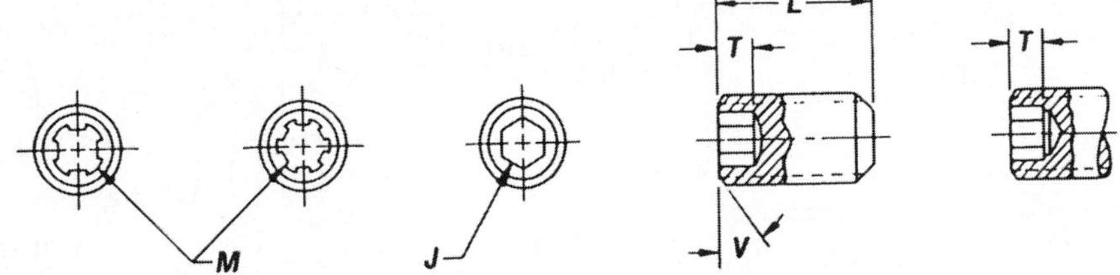

TABLE C.3.10 Dimensions of Hexagon and Spline Socket Set Screws

Nominal Size or Basic Screw Diameter		J		M	T		C		R	Y
		Hexagon Socket Size		Spline Socket Size	Min Key Engagement to Develop Functional Capability of Key		Cup and Flat Point Diameters		Oval Point Radius	Cone Point Angle 90° ± 2° for for These Nominal Lengths or Longer; 118° ± 2° for Shorter Nominal Lengths
		Nom		Nom	*Hex Socket T_H Min*	*Spline Socket T_S Min*	*Max*	*Min*	*Basic*	
0	0.0600		0.028	0.033	0.050	0.026	0.033	0.027	0.045	0.09
1	0.0730		0.028	0.033	0.060	0.035	0.040	0.033	0.055	0.09
2	0.0860		0.035	0.048	0.060	0.040	0.047	0.039	0.064	0.13
3	0.0990		0.050	0.048	0.070	0.040	0.054	0.045	0.074	0.13
4	0.1120		0.050	0.060	0.070	0.045	0.061	0.051	0.084	0.19
5	0.1250	$\frac{1}{16}$	0.062	0.072	0.080	0.055	0.067	0.057	0.094	0.19
6	0.1380	$\frac{1}{16}$	0.062	0.072	0.080	0.055	0.074	0.064	0.104	0.19
8	0.1640	$\frac{5}{64}$	0.078	0.096	0.090	0.080	0.087	0.076	0.123	0.25
10	0.1900	$\frac{3}{32}$	0.094	0.111	0.100	0.080	0.102	0.088	0.142	0.25
$\frac{1}{4}$	0.2500	$\frac{1}{8}$	0.125	0.145	0.125	0.125	0.132	0.118	0.188	0.31
$\frac{5}{16}$	0.3125	$\frac{5}{32}$	0.156	0.183	0.156	0.156	0.172	0.156	0.234	0.38
$\frac{3}{8}$	0.3750	$\frac{3}{16}$	0.188	0.216	0.188	0.188	0.212	0.194	0.281	0.44
$\frac{7}{16}$	0.4375	$\frac{7}{32}$	0.219	0.251	0.219	0.219	0.252	0.232	0.328	0.50
$\frac{1}{2}$	0.5000	$\frac{1}{4}$	0.250	0.291	0.250	0.250	0.291	0.270	0.375	0.57
$\frac{5}{8}$	0.6250	$\frac{5}{16}$	0.312	0.372	0.312	0.312	0.371	0.347	0.469	0.75
$\frac{3}{4}$	0.7500	$\frac{3}{8}$	0.375	0.454	0.375	0.375	0.450	0.425	0.562	0.88
$\frac{7}{8}$	0.8750	$\frac{1}{2}$	0.500	0.595	0.500	0.500	0.530	0.502	0.656	1.00
1	1.0000	$\frac{9}{16}$	0.562	...	0.562	...	0.609	0.579	0.750	1.13
1-$\frac{1}{8}$	1.1250	$\frac{9}{16}$	0.562	...	0.562	...	0.689	0.655	0.844	1.25
1-$\frac{1}{4}$	1.2500	$\frac{5}{8}$	0.625	...	0.625	...	0.767	0.733	0.938	1.50
1-$\frac{3}{8}$	1.3750	$\frac{5}{8}$	0.625	...	0.625	...	0.848	0.808	1.031	1.63
1-$\frac{1}{2}$	1.5000	$\frac{3}{4}$	0.750	...	0.750	...	0.926	0.886	1.125	1.75
1-$\frac{3}{4}$	1.7500	1	1.000	...	1.000	...	1.086	1.039	1.312	2.00
2	2.0000	1	1.000	...	1.000	...	1.244	1.193	1.500	2.25

Metric Socket Set Screws (ANSI B18.3.6M, 1979)

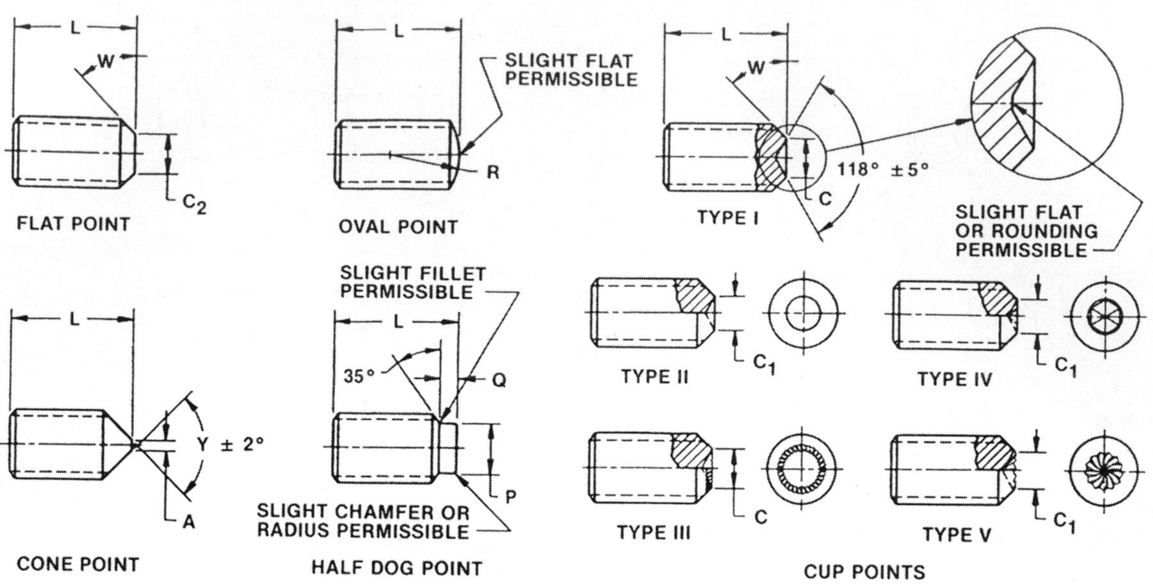

TABLE C.3.11 Dimensions of Points for Metric Socket Set Screws

D	*C*		C_1		C_2		*R*		*Y*	*A*		*P*		*Q*	
Nominal Size of Basic Screw Diameter	Cup Point Diameter for Types I and III		Cup Point Diameter for Types II, IV, and V		Flat Point Diameter		Oval Point Radius		Cone Point Angle 90° for These Lengths and over; 118° for Shorter Lengths	Flat of Truncation on Cone Point		Half Dog Point Diameter		Half Dog Point Length	
	Max	*Min*	*Max*	*Min*	*Max*	*Min*	*Max*	*Min*		*Max*	*Min*	*Max*	*Min*	*Max*	*Min*
1.6	0.80	0.55	0.80	0.64	0.80	0.55	1.60	1.20	3	1.16	0	0.80	0.55	0.53	0.40
2	1.00	0.75	1.00	0.82	1.00	0.75	1.90	1.50	3	0.2	0	1.00	0.75	0.64	0.50
2.5	1.20	0.95	1.25	1.05	1.50	1.25	2.28	1.88	4	0.25	0	1.50	1.25	0.78	0.63
3	1.40	1.15	1.50	1.28	2.00	1.75	2.65	2.25	4	0.3	0	2.00	1.75	0.92	0.75
4	2.00	1.75	2.00	1.75	2.50	2.25	3.80	3.00	5	0.4	0	2.50	2.25	1.20	1.00
5	2.50	2.25	2.50	2.22	3.50	3.20	4.55	3.75	6	0.5	0	3.50	3.20	1.37	1.25
6	3.00	2.75	3.00	2.69	4.00	3.70	5.30	4.50	8	1.5	1.2	4.00	3.70	1.74	1.50
8	5.00	4.70	4.00	3.65	5.50	5.20	6.80	6.00	10	2.0	1.6	5.50	5.20	2.28	2.00
10	6.00	5.70	5.00	4.60	7.00	6.64	8.30	7.50	12	2.5	2.0	7.00	6.64	2.82	2.50
12	8.00	7.64	6.00	5.57	8.50	8.14	9.80	9.00	16	3.0	2.4	8.50	8.14	3.35	3.00
16	10.00	9.64	8.00	7.50	12.00	11.57	12.80	12.00	20	4.0	3.2	12.00	11.57	4.40	4.00
20	14.00	13.57	10.00	9.44	15.00	14.57	15.80	15.00	25	5.0	4.0	15.00	14.57	5.45	5.00
24	16.00	15.57	12.00	11.39	18.00	17.57	18.80	18.00	30	6.0	4.8	18.00	17.57	6.49	6.00

Hex Nuts and Hex Jam Nuts (ANSI/ASME B18.2.2, 1986)

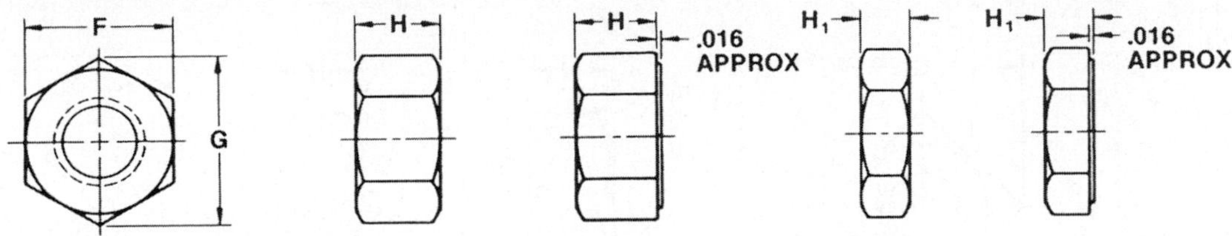

TABLE C.3.12 Dimensions of Hex Nuts and Hex Jam Nuts

Nominal Size or Basic Major Diameter of Thread		F Width Across Flats			G Width Across Corners		H Thickness, Hex Nuts			H_1 Thickness, Hex Jam Nuts			Runout of Bearing Face, FIM — Hex Nuts, Specified Proof Load: *Up to 150,000 psi*	Runout of Bearing Face, FIM — Hex Nuts, Specified Proof Load: *150,000 psi and Greater*	Runout of Bearing Face, FIM — Hex Jam Nuts: *All Strength Levels*
		Basic	*Max*	*Min*	*Max*	*Min*	*Basic*	*Max*	*Min*	*Basic*	*Max*	*Min*	*Max*	*Max*	*Max*
1/4	0.2500	7/16	0.438	0.428	0.505	0.488	7/32	0.226	0.212	5/32	0.163	0.150	0.015	0.010	0.015
5/16	0.3125	1/2	0.500	0.489	0.577	0.557	17/64	0.273	0.258	3/16	0.195	0.180	0.016	0.011	0.016
3/8	0.3750	9/16	0.562	0.551	0.650	0.628	21/64	0.337	0.320	7/32	0.227	0.210	0.017	0.012	0.017
7/16	0.4375	11/16	0.688	0.675	0.794	0.768	3/8	0.385	0.365	1/4	0.260	0.240	0.018	0.013	0.018
1/2	0.5000	3/4	0.750	0.736	0.866	0.840	7/16	0.448	0.427	5/16	0.323	0.302	0.019	0.014	0.019
9/16	0.5625	7/8	0.875	0.861	1.010	0.982	31/64	0.496	0.473	5/16	0.324	0.301	0.020	0.015	0.020
5/8	0.6250	15/16	0.938	0.922	1.083	1.051	35/64	0.559	0.535	3/8	0.387	0.363	0.021	0.016	0.021
3/4	0.7500	1-1/8	1.125	1.088	1.299	1.240	41/64	0.665	0.617	27/64	0.446	0.398	0.023	0.018	0.023
7/8	0.8750	1-5/16	1.312	1.269	1.516	1.447	3/4	0.776	0.724	31/64	0.510	0.458	0.025	0.020	0.025
1	1.0000	1-1/2	1.500	1.450	1.732	1.653	55/64	0.887	0.831	35/64	0.575	0.519	0.027	0.022	0.027
1-1/8	1.1250	1-11/16	1.688	1.631	1.949	1.859	31/32	0.999	0.939	39/64	0.639	0.579	0.030	0.025	0.030
1-1/4	1.2500	1-7/8	1.875	1.812	2.165	2.066	1-1/16	1.094	1.030	23/32	0.751	0.687	0.033	0.028	0.033
1-3/8	1.3750	2-1/16	2.062	1.994	2.382	2.273	1-11/64	1.206	1.138	25/32	0.815	0.747	0.036	0.031	0.036
1-1/2	1.5000	2-1/4	2.250	2.175	2.598	2.480	1-9/32	1.317	1.245	27/32	0.880	0.808	0.039	0.034	0.039

Square Nuts (ANSI/ASME B18.2.2, 1986)

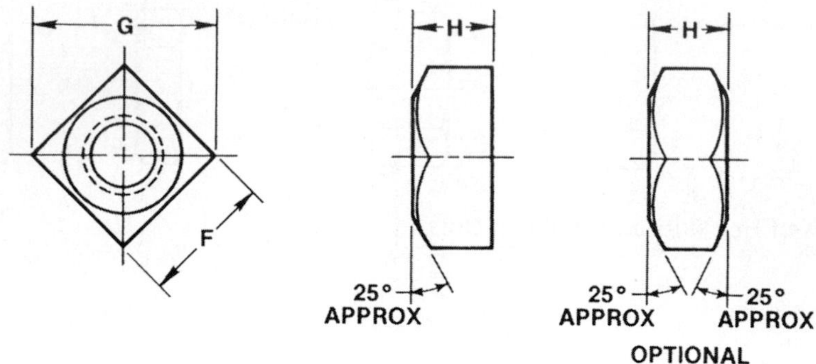

TABLE C.3.13 Dimensions of Square Nuts

Nominal Size or Basic Major Diameter of Thread		F Width Across Flats			G Width Across Corners		H Thickness		
		Basic	*Max*	*Min*	*Max*	*Min*	*Basic*	*Max*	*Min*
$\frac{1}{4}$	0.2500	$\frac{7}{16}$	0.438	0.425	0.619	0.554	$\frac{7}{32}$	0.235	0.203
$\frac{5}{16}$	0.3125	$\frac{9}{16}$	0.562	0.547	0.795	0.721	$\frac{17}{64}$	0.283	0.249
$\frac{3}{8}$	0.3750	$\frac{5}{8}$	0.625	0.606	0.884	0.802	$\frac{21}{64}$	0.346	0.310
$\frac{7}{16}$	0.4375	$\frac{3}{4}$	0.750	0.728	1.061	0.970	$\frac{3}{8}$	0.394	0.356
$\frac{1}{2}$	0.5000	$\frac{13}{16}$	0.812	0.788	1.149	1.052	$\frac{7}{16}$	0.458	0.418
$\frac{5}{8}$	0.6250	1	1.000	0.969	1.414	1.300	$\frac{35}{64}$	0.569	0.525
$\frac{3}{4}$	0.7500	1-$\frac{1}{8}$	1.125	1.088	1.591	1.464	$\frac{21}{32}$	0.680	0.632
$\frac{7}{8}$	0.8750	1-$\frac{5}{16}$	1.312	1.269	1.856	1.712	$\frac{49}{64}$	0.792	0.740
1	1.0000	1-$\frac{1}{2}$	1.500	1.450	2.121	1.961	$\frac{7}{8}$	0.903	0.847
1-$\frac{1}{8}$	1.1250	1-$\frac{11}{16}$	1.688	1.631	2.386	2.209	1	1.030	0.970
1-$\frac{1}{4}$	1.2500	1-$\frac{7}{8}$	1.875	1.812	2.652	2.458	1-$\frac{3}{32}$	1.126	1.062
1-$\frac{3}{8}$	1.3750	2-$\frac{1}{16}$	2.062	1.994	2.917	2.708	1-$\frac{13}{64}$	1.237	1.169
1-$\frac{1}{2}$	1.5000	2-$\frac{1}{4}$	2.250	2.175	3.182	2.956	1-$\frac{5}{16}$	1.348	1.276

Metric Hex Nuts, Style 1 (ANSI B18.2.4.1M, 1979)

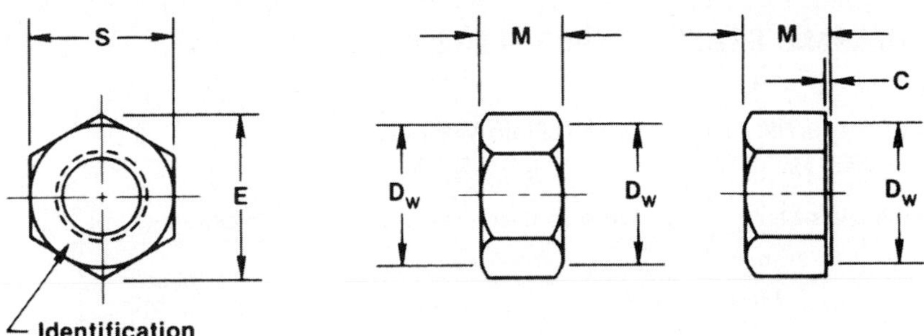

TABLE C.3.14 Dimensions of Hex Nuts, Style 1

Nominal Nut Diameter and Thread Pitch	*S* Width Across Flats		*E* Width Across Corners		*M* Thickness		D_W Bearing Face Diameter	*C* Washer Face Thickness		Total Runout of Bearing Surface FIM
	Max	*Min*	*Max*	*Min*	*Max*	*Min*	*Min*	*Max*	*Min*	*Max*
M1.6 × 0.35	3.20	3.02	3.70	3.41	1.30	1.05	2.4	—	—	—
M2 × 0.4	4.00	3.82	4.62	4.32	1.60	1.35	3.1	—	—	—
M2.5 × 0.45	5.00	4.82	5.77	5.45	2.00	1.75	4.1	—	—	—
M3 × 0.5	5.50	5.32	6.35	6.01	2.40	2.15	4.6	—	—	—
M3.5 × 0.6	6.00	5.82	6.93	6.58	2.80	2.55	5.1	—	—	—
M4 × 0.7	7.00	6.78	8.08	7.66	3.20	2.90	5.9	—	—	—
M5 × 0.8	8.00	7.78	9.24	8.79	4.70	4.40	6.9	—	—	0.30
M6 × 1	10.00	9.78	11.55	11.05	5.20	4.90	8.9	—	—	0.33
M8 × 1.25	13.00	12.73	15.01	14.38	6.80	6.44	11.6	—	—	0.36
M10 × 1.5	16.00	15.73	18.48	17.77	8.40	8.04	14.6	—	—	0.39
M12 × 1.75	18.00	17.73	20.78	20.03	10.80	10.37	16.6	—	—	0.42
M14 × 2	21.00	20.67	24.25	23.35	12.80	12.10	19.6	—	—	0.45
M16 × 2	24.00	23.67	27.71	26.75	14.80	14.10	22.5	—	—	0.48
M20 × 2.5	30.00	29.16	34.64	32.95	18.00	16.90	27.7	0.8	0.4	0.56
M24 × 3	36.00	35.00	41.57	39.55	21.50	20.20	33.2	0.8	0.4	0.64
M30 × 3.5	46.00	45.00	53.12	50.85	25.60	24.30	42.7	0.8	0.4	0.76
M36 × 4	55.00	53.80	63.51	60.79	31.00	29.40	51.1	0.8	0.4	0.89
*M10 × 1.5	15.00	14.73	17.32	16.64	9.1	8.7	13.6	—	—	0.39

C.4 Washers

Plain Washers (ANSI/ASME B18.22.1 1965, 1981)

TABLE C.4.1 Dimensions of Preferred Sizes of Type A Plain Washers

Nominal Washer Size			*A* Inside Diameter			*B* Outside Diameter			*C* Thickness		
			Basic	*Tolerance Plus*	*Tolerance Minus*	*Basic*	*Tolerance Plus*	*Tolerance Minus*	*Basic*	*Max*	*Min*
—	—		0.078	0.000	0.005	0.188	0.000	0.005	0.020	0.025	0.016
—	—		0.094	0.000	0.005	0.250	0.000	0.005	0.020	0.025	0.016
—	—		0.125	0.008	0.005	0.312	0.008	0.005	0.032	0.040	0.025
6	0.138		0.156	0.008	0.005	0.375	0.015	0.005	0.049	0.065	0.036
8	0.164		0.188	0.008	0.005	0.438	0.015	0.005	0.049	0.065	0.036
10	0.190		0.219	0.008	0.005	0.500	0.015	0.005	0.049	0.065	0.036
3/16	0.188		0.250	0.015	0.005	0.562	0.015	0.005	0.049	0.065	0.036
12	0.216		0.250	0.015	0.005	0.562	0.015	0.005	0.065	0.080	0.051
1/4	0.250	N	0.281	0.015	0.005	0.625	0.015	0.005	0.065	0.080	0.051
1/4	0.250	W	0.312	0.015	0.005	0.734	0.015	0.007	0.065	0.080	0.051
5/16	0.312	N	0.344	0.015	0.005	0.688	0.015	0.007	0.065	0.080	0.051
5/16	0.312	W	0.375	0.015	0.005	0.875	0.030	0.007	0.083	0.104	0.064
3/8	0.375	N	0.406	0.015	0.005	0.812	0.015	0.007	0.065	0.080	0.051
3/8	0.375	W	0.438	0.015	0.005	1.000	0.030	0.007	0.083	0.104	0.064
7/16	0.438	N	0.469	0.015	0.005	0.922	0.015	0.007	0.065	0.080	0.051
7/16	0.438	W	0.500	0.015	0.005	1.250	0.030	0.007	0.083	0.104	0.064
1/2	0.500	N	0.531	0.015	0.005	1.062	0.030	0.007	0.095	0.121	0.074
1/2	0.500	W	0.562	0.015	0.005	1.375	0.030	0.007	0.109	0.132	0.086
9/16	0.562	N	0.594	0.015	0.005	1.156	0.030	0.007	0.095	0.121	0.074
9/16	0.562	W	0.625	0.015	0.005	1.469	0.030	0.007	0.109	0.132	0.086
5/8	0.625	N	0.656	0.030	0.007	1.312	0.030	0.007	0.095	0.121	0.074
5/8	0.625	W	0.688	0.030	0.007	1.750	0.030	0.007	0.134	0.160	0.108
3/4	0.750	N	0.812	0.030	0.007	1.469	0.030	0.007	0.134	0.160	0.108
3/4	0.750	W	0.812	0.030	0.007	2.000	0.030	0.007	0.148	0.177	0.122
7/8	0.875	N	0.938	0.030	0.007	1.750	0.030	0.007	0.134	0.160	0.108
7/8	0.875	W	0.938	0.030	0.007	2.250	0.030	0.007	0.165	0.192	0.136
1	1.000	N	1.062	0.030	0.007	2.000	0.030	0.007	0.134	0.160	0.108
1	1.000	W	1.062	0.030	0.007	2.500	0.030	0.007	0.165	0.192	0.136
1-1/8	1.125	N	1.250	0.030	0.007	2.250	0.030	0.007	0.134	0.160	0.108
1-1/8	1.125	W	1.250	0.030	0.007	2.750	0.030	0.007	0.165	0.192	0.136
1-1/4	1.250	N	1.375	0.030	0.007	2.500	0.030	0.007	0.165	0.192	0.136
1-1/4	1.250	W	1.375	0.030	0.007	3.000	0.030	0.007	0.165	0.192	0.136
1-3/8	1.375	N	1.500	0.030	0.007	2.750	0.030	0.007	0.165	0.192	0.136
1-3/8	1.375	W	1.500	0.045	0.010	3.250	0.045	0.010	0.180	0.213	0.153
1-1/2	1.500	N	1.625	0.030	0.007	3.000	0.030	0.007	0.165	0.192	0.136
1-1/2	1.500	W	1.625	0.045	0.010	3.500	0.045	0.010	0.180	0.213	0.153

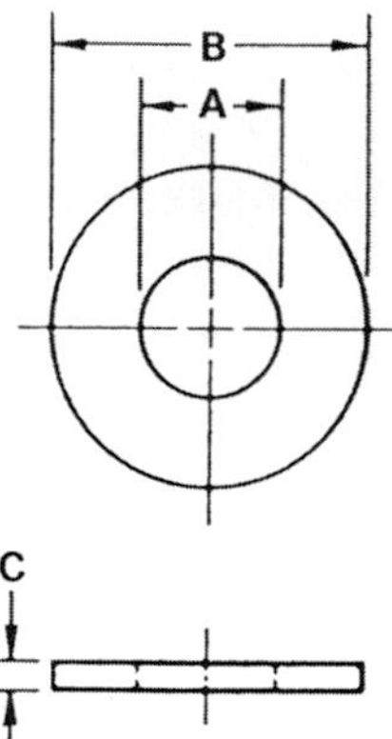

TABLE C.4.1 Dimensions of Preferred Sizes of Type A Plain Washers — *Continued*

Nominal Washer Size		A Inside Diameter			B Outside Diameter			C Thickness		
			Tolerance			*Tolerance*				
		Basic	*Plus*	*Minus*	*Basic*	*Plus*	*Minus*	*Basic*	*Max*	*Min*
1-$\frac{5}{8}$	1.625	1.750	0.045	0.010	3.750	0.045	0.010	0.180	0.213	0.153
1-$\frac{3}{4}$	1.750	1.875	0.045	0.010	4.000	0.045	0.010	0.180	0.213	0.153
1-$\frac{7}{8}$	1.875	2.000	0.045	0.010	4.250	0.045	0.010	0.180	0.213	0.153
2	2.000	2.125	0.045	0.010	4.500	0.045	0.010	0.180	0.213	0.153
2-$\frac{1}{4}$	2.250	2.375	0.045	0.010	4.750	0.045	0.010	0.220	0.248	0.193
2-$\frac{1}{2}$	2.500	2.625	0.045	0.010	5.000	0.045	0.010	0.238	0.280	0.210
2-$\frac{3}{4}$	2.750	2.875	0.065	0.010	5.250	0.065	0.010	0.259	0.310	0.228
3	3.000	3.125	0.065	0.010	5.500	0.065	0.010	0.284	0.327	0.249

Metric Plain Washers (ANSI B18.22M, 1981)

TABLE C.4.2 Dimensions of Metric Plain Washers (General Purpose)

Nominal Washer Size	Washer Series	A Inside Diameter		B Outside Diameter		C Thickness	
		Max	*Min*	*Max*	*Min*	*Max*	*Min*
1.6	Narrow	2.09	1.95	4.00	3.70	0.70	0.50
	Regular	2.09	1.95	5.00	4.70	0.70	0.50
	Wide	2.09	1.95	6.00	5.70	0.90	0.60
2	Narrow	2.64	2.50	5.00	4.70	0.90	0.60
	Regular	2.64	2.50	6.00	5.70	0.90	0.60
	Wide	2.64	2.50	8.00	7.64	0.90	0.60
2.5	Narrow	3.14	3.00	6.00	5.70	0.90	0.60
	Regular	3.14	3.00	8.00	7.64	0.90	0.60
	Wide	3.14	3.00	10.00	9.64	1.20	0.80
3	Narrow	3.68	3.50	7.00	6.64	0.90	0.60
	Regular	3.68	3.50	10.00	9.64	1.20	0.80
	Wide	3.68	3.50	12.00	11.57	1.40	1.00
3.5	Narrow	4.18	4.00	9.00	8.64	1.20	0.80
	Regular	4.18	4.00	10.00	9.64	1.40	1.00
	Wide	4.18	4.00	15.00	14.57	1.75	1.20
4	Narrow	4.88	4.70	10.00	9.64	1.20	0.80
	Regular	4.88	4.70	12.00	11.57	1.40	1.00
	Wide	4.88	4.70	16.00	15.57	2.30	1.60
5	Narrow	5.78	5.50	11.00	10.57	1.40	1.00
	Regular	5.78	5.50	15.00	14.57	1.75	1.20
	Wide	5.78	5.50	20.00	19.48	2.30	1.60
6	Narrow	6.87	6.65	13.00	12.57	1.75	1.20
	Regular	6.87	6.65	18.80	18.37	1.75	1.20
	Wide	6.87	6.65	25.40	24.88	2.30	1.60
8	Narrow	9.12	8.90	18.80	18.37	2.30	1.60
	Regular	9.12	8.90	25.40	24.48	2.30	1.60
	Wide	9.12	8.90	32.00	31.38	2.80	2.00
10	Narrow	11.12	10.85	20.00	19.48	2.30	1.60
	Regular	11.12	10.85	28.00	27.48	2.80	2.00
	Wide	11.12	10.85	39.00	38.38	3.50	2.50
12	Narrow	13.57	13.30	25.40	24.88	2.80	2.00
	Regular	13.57	13.30	34.00	33.38	3.50	2.50
	Wide	13.57	13.30	44.00	43.38	3.50	2.50
14	Narrow	15.52	15.25	28.00	27.48	2.80	2.00
	Regular	15.52	15.25	39.00	38.38	3.50	2.50
	Wide	15.52	15.25	50.00	49.38	4.00	3.00
16	Narrow	17.52	17.25	32.00	31.38	3.50	2.50
	Regular	17.52	17.25	44.00	43.38	4.00	3.00
	Wide	17.52	17.25	56.00	54.80	4.60	3.50
20	Narrow	22.32	21.80	39.00	38.38	4.00	3.00
	Regular	22.32	21.80	50.00	49.38	4.60	3.50
	Wide	22.32	21.80	66.00	64.80	5.10	4.00
24	Narrow	26.12	25.60	44.00	43.38	4.60	3.50
	Regular	26.12	25.60	56.00	54.80	5.10	4.00
	Wide	26.12	25.60	72.00	70.80	5.60	4.50
30	Narrow	33.02	32.40	56.00	54.80	5.10	4.00
	Regular	33.02	32.40	72.00	70.80	5.60	4.50
	Wide	33.02	32.40	90.00	88.60	6.40	5.00
36	Narrow	38.92	38.30	66.00	64.80	5.60	4.50
	Regular	38.92	38.30	90.00	88.60	6.40	5.00
	Wide	38.92	38.30	110.00	108.60	8.50	7.00

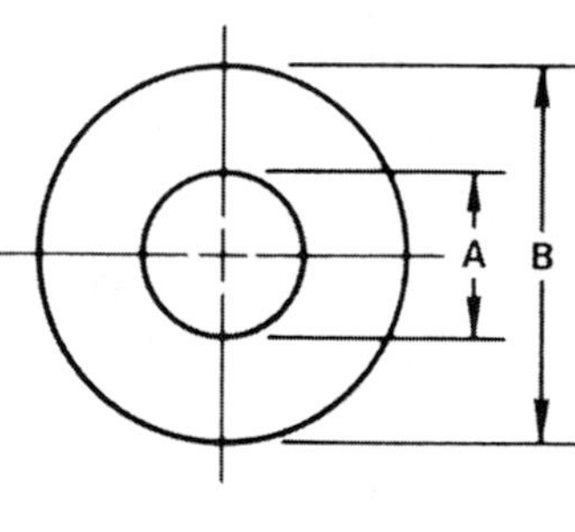

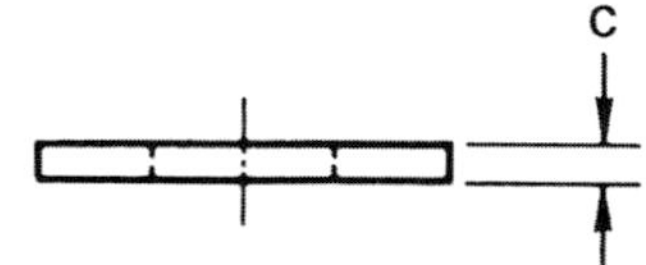

NOTES:
1. Nominal washer sizes are intended for use with comparable nominal screw or bolt sizes.
2. The 18.80/18.37 and 25.40/24.88 mm outside diameters avoid washers that could be used in coin-operated devices.

C.5 Rivets

Flat-Head Rivets and Flat-Countersunk-Head Rivets (ANSI/ASME B18.1.1 1972, R1981)

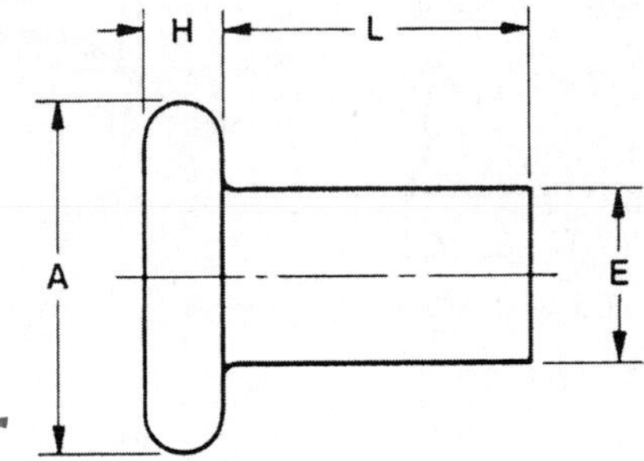

TABLE C.5.1 Dimensions of Flat-Head Rivets

Nominal Size or Basic Shank Diameter		*E* Shank Diameter		*A* Head Diameter		*H* Head Diameter	
		Max	***Min***	***Max***	***Min***	***Max***	***Min***
$\frac{1}{16}$	0.062	0.064	0.059	0.140	0.120	0.027	0.017
$\frac{3}{32}$	0.094	0.096	0.090	0.200	0.180	0.038	0.026
$\frac{1}{8}$	0.125	0.127	0.121	0.260	0.240	0.048	0.036
$\frac{5}{32}$	0.156	0.158	0.152	0.323	0.301	0.059	0.045
$\frac{3}{16}$	0.188	0.191	0.182	0.387	0.361	0.069	0.055
$\frac{7}{32}$	0.219	0.222	0.213	0.453	0.427	0.080	0.065
$\frac{1}{4}$	0.250	0.253	0.244	0.515	0.485	0.091	0.075
$\frac{9}{32}$	0.281	0.285	0.273	0.579	0.545	0.103	0.085
$\frac{5}{16}$	0.312	0.316	0.304	0.641	0.607	0.113	0.095
$\frac{11}{32}$	0.344	0.348	0.336	0.705	0.667	0.124	0.104
$\frac{3}{8}$	0.375	0.380	0.365	0.769	0.731	0.135	0.115
$\frac{13}{32}$	0.406	0.411	0.396	0.834	0.790	0.146	0.124
$\frac{7}{16}$	0.438	0.443	0.428	0.896	0.852	0.157	0.135

TABLE C.5.2 Dimensions of Flat-Countersunk-Head Rivets

Nominal Size or Basic Shank Diameter		E		A		H
		Shank Diameter		Head Diameter		Head Height
		Max	*Min*	*Max*	*Min*	*Ref*
$\frac{1}{16}$	0.062	0.064	0.059	0.118	0.110	0.027
$\frac{3}{32}$	0.094	0.096	0.090	0.176	0.163	0.040
$\frac{1}{8}$	0.125	0.127	0.121	0.235	0.217	0.053
$\frac{5}{32}$	0.156	0.158	0.152	0.293	0.272	0.066
$\frac{3}{16}$	0.188	0.191	0.182	0.351	0.326	0.079
$\frac{7}{32}$	0.219	0.222	0.213	0.413	0.384	0.094
$\frac{1}{4}$	0.250	0.253	0.244	0.469	0.437	0.106
$\frac{9}{32}$	0.281	0.285	0.273	0.528	0.491	0.119
$\frac{5}{16}$	0.312	0.316	0.304	0.588	0.547	0.133
$\frac{11}{32}$	0.344	0.348	0.336	0.646	0.602	0.146
$\frac{3}{8}$	0.375	0.380	0.365	0.704	0.656	0.159
$\frac{13}{32}$	0.406	0.411	0.396	0.763	0.710	0.172
$\frac{7}{16}$	0.438	0.443	0.428	0.823	0.765	0.186

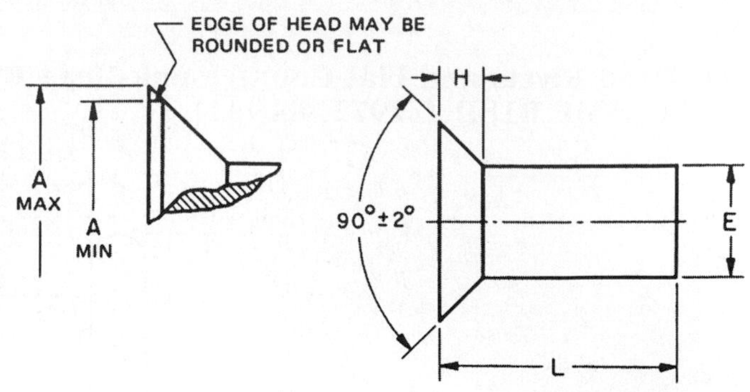

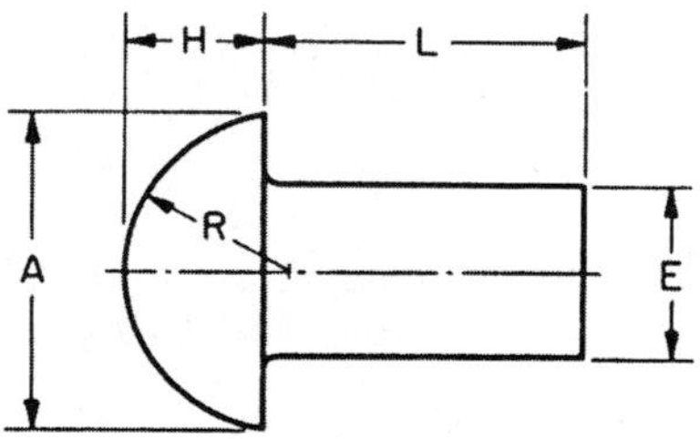

TABLE C.5.3 Dimensions of Button-Head Rivets

Nominal Size or Basic Shank Diameter		E		A		H		R
		Shank Diameter		Head Diameter		Head Height		Head Radius
		Max	*Min*	*Max*	*Min*	*Max*	*Min*	*Approx*
$\frac{1}{16}$	0.062	0.064	0.059	0.122	0.102	0.052	0.042	0.055
$\frac{3}{32}$	0.094	0.096	0.090	0.182	0.162	0.077	0.065	0.084
$\frac{1}{8}$	0.125	0.127	0.121	0.235	0.215	0.100	0.088	0.111
$\frac{5}{32}$	0.156	0.158	0.152	0.290	0.268	0.124	0.110	0.138
$\frac{3}{16}$	0.188	0.191	0.182	0.348	0.322	0.147	0.133	0.166
$\frac{7}{32}$	0.219	0.222	0.213	0.405	0.379	0.172	0.158	0.195
$\frac{1}{4}$	0.250	0.253	0.244	0.460	0.430	0.196	0.180	0.221
$\frac{9}{32}$	0.281	0.285	0.273	0.518	0.484	0.220	0.202	0.249
$\frac{5}{16}$	0.312	0.316	0.304	0.572	0.538	0.243	0.225	0.276
$\frac{11}{32}$	0.344	0.348	0.336	0.630	0.592	0.267	0.247	0.304
$\frac{3}{8}$	0.375	0.380	0.365	0.684	0.646	0.291	0.271	0.332
$\frac{13}{32}$	0.406	0.411	0.396	0.743	0.699	0.316	0.294	0.358
$\frac{7}{16}$	0.438	0.443	0.428	0.798	0.754	0.339	0.317	0.387

C.6 Retaining Rings

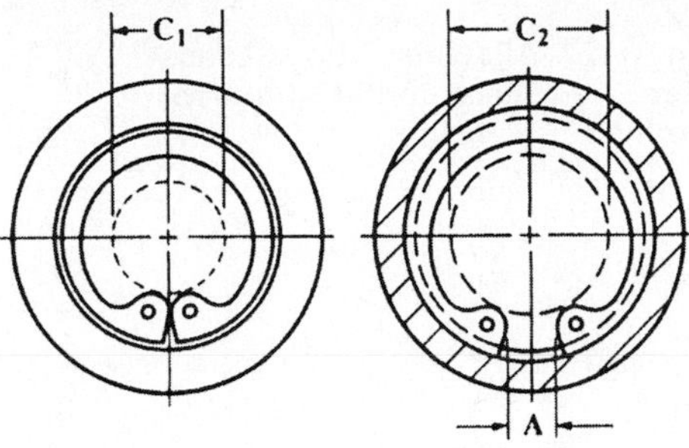

Ring Compressed in Bore

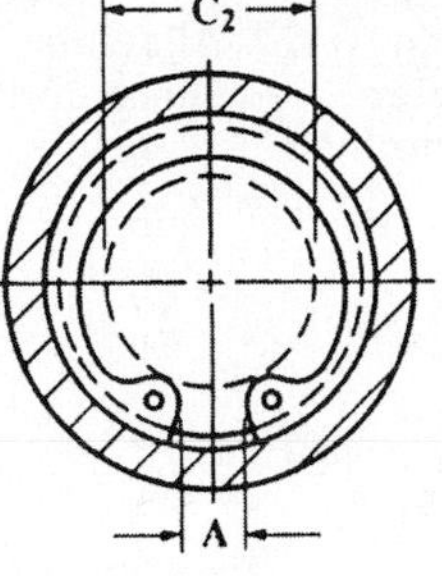

Ring Seated in Groove

Max. Allowable Radius of Retained Part

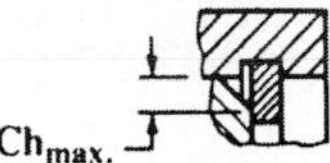

Max. Allowable Chamfer of Retained Part

TABLE C.6.1 Dimension of Internal Retaining Rings

Ring Series and Size No.	Clearance Diameter: Ring in Bore	Clearance Diameter: Ring in Groove	Gaging Diameter	Allowable Thrust Loads Sharp Corner Abutment		Maximum Allowable Corner Radii and Chamfers	
BM No.	C_1 **(mm)**	C_2 **(mm)**	A_{min}**(mm)**	P_r **(kN)**	P_g **(kN)**	R_{max} **(mm)**	Ch_{max} **(mm)**
−8	4.4	4.8	1.40	2.4	1.0	0.4	0.3
−9	4.6	5.0	1.50	4.4	1.2	0.5	0.35
−10	5.5	6.0	1.85	4.9	1.5	0.5	0.35
−11	5.7	6.3	1.95	5.4	2.0	0.6	0.4
−12	6.7	7.3	2.25	5.8	2.4	0.6	0.4
−13	6.8	7.5	2.35	8.9	2.6.	0.7	0.5
−14	6.9	7.7	2.65	9.7	3.2	0.7	0.5
−15	7.9	8.7	2.80	10.4	3.7	0.7	0.5
−16	8.8	9.7	2.80	11.0	4.2	0.7	0.5
−17	9.8	10.8	3.35	11.7	4.9	0.75	0.6
−18	10.3	11.3	3.40	12.3	5.5	0.75	0.6
−19	11.4	12.5	3.40	13.1	6.0	0.8	0.65
−20	11.6	12.7	3.8	13.7	6.6	0.9	0.7
−21	12.6	13.8	4.2	14.5	7.3	0.9	0.7
−22	13.5	14.8	4.3	22.5	8.3	0.9	0.7
−23	14.5	15.9	4.9	23.5	8.9	1.0	0.8
−24	15.5	16.9	5.2	24.8	9.7	1.0	0.8
−25	16.5	18.1	6.0	25.7	11.6	1.0	0.8
−26	17.5	19.2	5.7	26.8	12.7	1.2	1.0
−27	17.4	19.2	5.9	33	14.0	1.2	1.0
−28	18.2	20.0	6.0	34	14.6	1.2	1.0
−30	20.0	21.9	6.0	37	16.5	1.2	1.0
−32	22.0	23.9	7.3	39	17.6	1.2	1.0
−34	24.0	26.1	7.6	42	20.6	1.2	1.0
−35	25.0	27.2	8.0	43	22.3	1.2	1.0
−36	26.0	28.3	8.3	44	23.9	1.2	1.0
−37	27.0	29.3	8.4	45	24.6	1.2	1.0
−38	28.0	30.4	8.6	46	26.4	1.2	1.0
−40	29.2	31.6	9.7	62	27.7	1.7	1.3

Continues

TABLE C.6.1 Dimension of Internal Retaining Rings — *Continued*

Ring Series and Size No.	Clearance Diameter		Gaging Diameter	Allowable Thrust Loads Sharp Corner Abutment		Maximum Allowable Corner Radii and Chamfers	
	Ring in Bore	Ring in Groove					
BM No.	C_1 ***(mm)***	C_2 ***(mm)***	A_{min}***(mm)***	P_r ***(kN)***	P_g ***(kN)***	R_{max} ***(mm)***	Ch_{max} ***(mm)***
−42	29.7	32.2	9.0	65	30.2	1.7	1.3
−45	32.3	34.9	9.6	69	33.8	1.7	1.3
−46	33.3	36.0	9.7	71	36	1.7	1.3
−47	34.3	37.1	10.0	72	38	1.7	1.3
−48	35.0	37.9	10.5	74	40	1.7	1.3
−50	36.9	40.0	12.1	77	45	1.7	1.3
−52	38.6	41.9	11.7	99	50	2.0	1.6
−55	40.8	44.2	11.9	105	54	2.0	1.6
−57	42.2	45.7	12.5	109	58	2.0	1.6

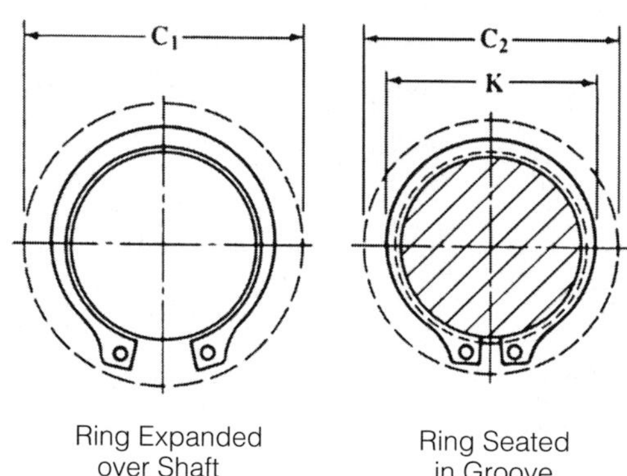

Ring Expanded over Shaft

Ring Seated in Groove

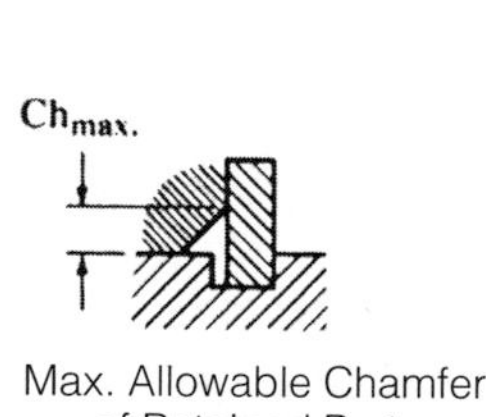

Max. Allowable Radius of Retained Part

Max. Allowable Chamfer of Retained Part

TABLE C.6.2 Dimensions of External Retaining Rings

Ring Series and Size No.	Clearance Diameter		Gaging Diameter	Allowable Thrust Loads Sharp Corner Abutment		Maximum Allowable Corner Radii and Chamfers		Allowable Assembly Speed
	Ring over Shaft	Ring in Groove						
AM (No.)	C_1 ***(mm)***	C_2 ***(mm)***	K_{max} **(mm)**	P_r ***(kN)***	P_g ***(kN)***	R_{max} ***(mm)***	Ch_{max} ***(mm)***	***(rpm)***
−4	7.0	6.8	4.90	0.6	0.2	0.35	0.25	70 000
−5	8.2	7.9	5.85	1.1	0.3	0.35	0.25	70 000
−6	9.1	8.8	6.95	1.4	0.4	0.35	0.25	70 000
−7	12.3	11.8	8.05	2.6	0.7	0.45	0.3	60 000
−8	13.6	13.0	9.15	3.1	1.0	0.5	0.35	55 000
−9	14.5	13.8	10.35	3.5	1.2	0.6	0.35	48 000
−10	15.5	14.7	11.50	3.9	1.5	0.7	0.4	42 000
−11	16.4	15.6	12.60	4.3	1.8	0.75	0.45	38 000
−12	17.4	16.6	13.80	4.7	2.0	0.8	0.45	34 000
−13	19.7	18.8	15.05	7.5	2.2	0.8	0.5	31 000
−14	20.7	19.7	15.60	8.1	2.6	0.9	0.5	28 000
−15	21.7	20.6	17.20	8.7	3.2	1.0	0.6	27 000
−16	22.7	21.6	18.35	9.3	3.5	1.1	0.6	25 000
−17	23.7	22.6	19.35	9.9	4.0	1.1	0.6	24 000

C.7 Pins

Clevis Pins (ANSI/ASME B18.8.1, 1972, R1983)

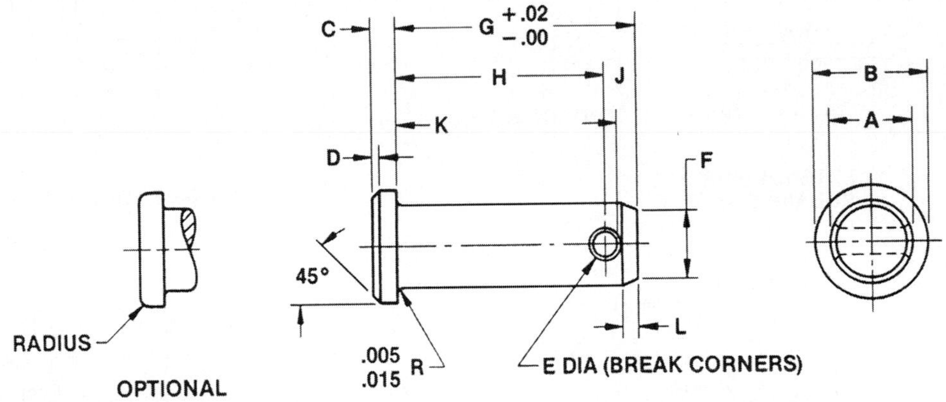

TABLE C.7.1 Dimensions of Clevis Pins

Nominal Size or Basic Pin Diameter	A Shank Diameter		B Head Diameter		C Head Height		D Head Chamfer	E Hole Diameter		F Point Diameter		G Pin Length	H Head to Center of Hole		J End to Center Ref	K Head to Edge of Hole Ref		L Point Length		Recommended Cotter Pin Nominal Size
	Max	*Min*	*Max*	*Min*	*Max*	*Min*	*±0.01*	*Max*	*Min*	*Max*	*Min*	*Basic*	*Max*	*Min*	*Basic*	*Min*	*Max*	*Min*	*Max*	
$\frac{3}{16}$ 0.188	0.186	0.181	0.32	0.30	0.07	0.05	0.02	0.088	0.073	0.15	0.14	0.58	0.504	0.484	0.09	0.548	0.520	0.055	0.035	$\frac{1}{16}$ 0.062
$\frac{1}{4}$ 0.250	0.248	0.243	0.38	0.36	0.10	0.08	0.03	0.088	0.073	0.21	0.20	0.77	0.692	0.672	0.09	0.736	0.708	0.055	0.035	$\frac{1}{16}$ 0.062
$\frac{5}{16}$ 0.312	0.311	0.306	0.44	0.42	0.10	0.08	0.03	0.119	0.104	0.26	0.25	0.94	0.832	0.812	0.12	0.892	0.864	0.071	0.049	$\frac{3}{32}$ 0.093
$\frac{3}{8}$ 0.375	0.373	0.368	0.51	0.49	0.13	0.11	0.03	0.119	0.104	0.33	0.32	1.06	0.958	0.938	0.12	1.018	0.990	0.071	0.049	$\frac{3}{32}$ 0.093
$\frac{7}{16}$ 0.438	0.436	0.431	0.57	0.55	0.16	0.14	0.04	0.119	0.104	0.39	0.38	1.19	1.082	1.062	0.12	1.142	1.114	0.071	0.049	$\frac{3}{32}$ 0.093
$\frac{1}{2}$ 0.500	0.496	0.491	0.63	0.61	0.16	0.14	0.04	0.151	0.136	0.44	0.43	1.36	1.223	1.203	0.15	1.298	1.271	0.089	0.063	$\frac{1}{8}$ 0.125
$\frac{5}{8}$ 0.625	0.621	0.616	0.82	0.80	0.21	0.19	0.06	0.151	0.136	0.56	0.55	1.61	1.473	1.453	0.15	1.548	1.521	0.089	0.063	$\frac{1}{8}$ 0.125
$\frac{3}{4}$ 0.750	0.746	0.741	0.94	0.92	0.26	0.24	0.07	0.182	0.167	0.68	0.67	1.91	1.739	1.719	0.18	1.830	1.802	0.110	0.076	$\frac{5}{32}$ 0.156
$\frac{7}{8}$ 0.875	0.871	0.866	1.04	1.02	0.32	0.30	0.09	0.182	0.167	0.80	0.79	2.16	1.989	1.969	0.18	2.080	2.052	0.110	0.076	$\frac{5}{32}$ 0.156
1 1.000	0.996	0.991	1.19	1.17	0.35	0.33	0.10	0.182	0.167	0.93	0.92	2.41	2.239	2.219	0.18	2.330	2.302	0.110	0.076	$\frac{5}{32}$ 0.156

Cotter Pins (ANSI/ASME B18.8.1, 1972, R1983)

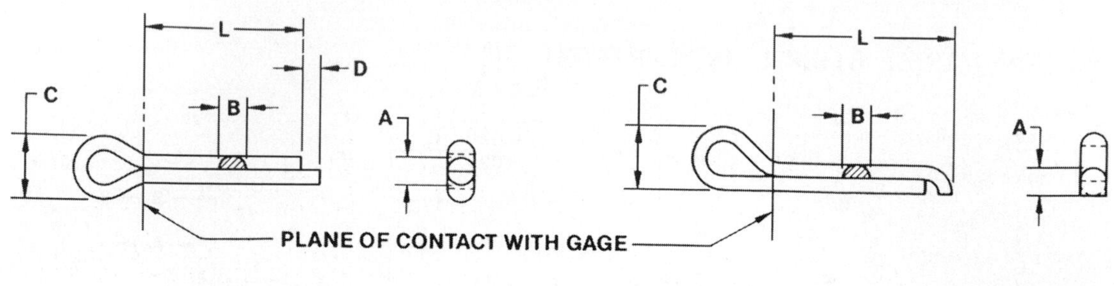

TABLE C.7.2 Dimensions of Cotter Pins

Nominal Size or Basic Pin Diameter		*A* Total Shank Diameter		*B* Wire Width		*C* Head Diameter	*D* Extended Prong Length	Recom-mended Hole Size
		Max	*Min*	*Max*	*Min*	*Min*	*Min*	
$\frac{1}{32}$	0.031	0.032	0.028	0.032	0.022	0.06	0.01	0.047
$\frac{3}{64}$	0.047	0.048	0.044	0.048	0.035	0.09	0.02	0.062
$\frac{1}{16}$	0.062	0.060	0.056	0.060	0.044	0.12	0.03	0.078
$\frac{5}{64}$	0.078	0.076	0.072	0.076	0.057	0.16	0.04	0.094
$\frac{3}{32}$	0.094	0.090	0.086	0.090	0.069	0.19	0.04	0.109
$\frac{7}{64}$	0.109	0.104	0.100	0.104	0.080	0.22	0.05	0.125
$\frac{1}{8}$	0.125	0.120	0.116	0.120	0.093	0.25	0.06	0.141
$\frac{9}{64}$	0.141	0.134	0.130	0.134	0.104	0.28	0.06	0.156
$\frac{5}{32}$	0.156	0.150	0.146	0.150	0.116	0.31	0.07	0.172
$\frac{3}{16}$	0.188	0.176	0.172	0.176	0.137	0.38	0.09	0.203
$\frac{7}{32}$	0.219	0.207	0.202	0.207	0.161	0.44	0.10	0.234
$\frac{1}{4}$	0.250	0.225	0.220	0.225	0.176	0.50	0.11	0.266
$\frac{5}{16}$	0.312	0.280	0.275	0.280	0.220	0.62	0.14	0.312
$\frac{3}{8}$	0.375	0.335	0.329	0.335	0.263	0.75	0.16	0.375
$\frac{7}{16}$	0.438	0.406	0.400	0.406	0.320	0.88	0.20	0.438
$\frac{1}{2}$	0.500	0.473	0.467	0.473	0.373	1.00	0.23	0.500
$\frac{5}{8}$	0.625	0.598	0.590	0.598	0.472	1.25	0.30	0.625
$\frac{3}{4}$	0.750	0.723	0.715	0.723	0.572	1.50	0.36	0.750

Spring Pins (ANSI/ASME B18.8.2, 1978)

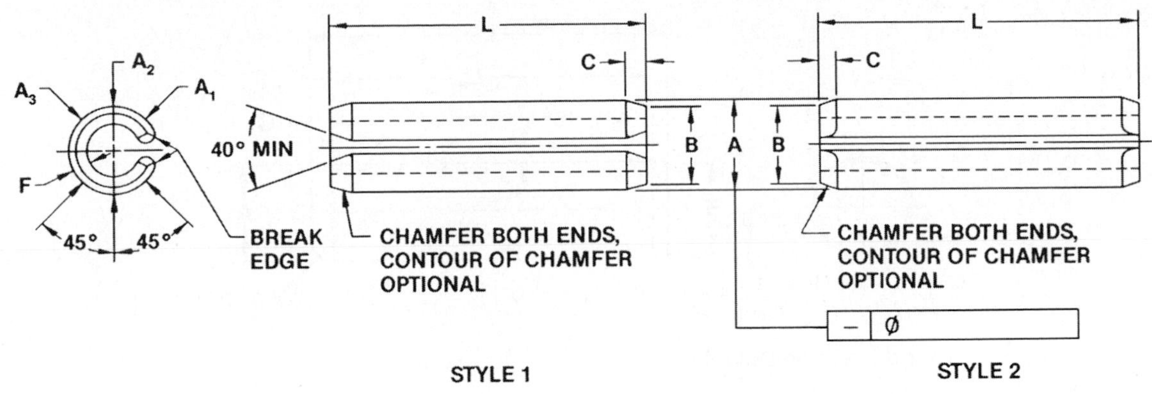

TABLE C.7.3 Dimensions of Slotted-Type Spring Pins

Nominal Size or Basic Pin Diameter		A Pin Diameter		B Chamfer Diameter	C Chamfer Length		F Stock Thickness	Recommended Hole Size		Double Shear Load, Min, lb — Material		
		Max	Min	Max	Max	Min	Basic	Max	Min	AISI 1070–1095 and AISI 420	AISI 302	Beryllium Copper
1/16	0.062	0.069	0.066	0.059	0.028	0.007	0.012	0.065	0.062	425	350	270
5/64	0.078	0.086	0.083	0.075	0.032	0.008	0.018	0.081	0.078	650	550	400
3/32	0.094	0.103	0.099	0.091	0.038	0.008	0.022	0.097	0.094	1,000	800	660
1/8	0.125	0.135	0.131	0.122	0.044	0.008	0.028	0.129	0.125	2,100	1,500	1,200
9/64	0.141	0.149	0.145	0.137	0.044	0.008	0.028	0.144	0.140	2,200	1,600	1,400
5/32	0.156	0.167	0.162	0.151	0.048	0.010	0.032	0.160	0.156	3,000	2,000	1,800
3/16	0.188	0.199	0.194	0.182	0.055	0.011	0.040	0.192	0.187	4,400	2,800	2,600
7/32	0.219	0.232	0.226	0.214	0.065	0.011	0.048	0.224	0.219	5,700	3,550	3,700
1/4	0.250	0.264	0.258	0.245	0.065	0.012	0.048	0.256	0.250	7,700	4,600	4,500
5/16	0.312	0.328	0.321	0.306	0.080	0.014	0.062	0.318	0.312	11,500	7,095	6,800
3/8	0.375	0.392	0.385	0.368	0.095	0.016	0.077	0.382	0.375	17,600	10,000	10,100
7/16	0.438	0.456	0.448	0.430	0.095	0.017	0.077	0.445	0.437	20,000	12,000	12,200
1/2	0.500	0.521	0.513	0.485	0.110	0.025	0.094	0.510	0.500	25,800	15,500	16,800
5/8	0.625	0.650	0.640	0.608	0.125	0.030	0.125	0.636	0.625	46,000	18,800	. . .
3/4	0.750	0.780	0.769	0.730	0.150	0.030	0.150	0.764	0.750	66,000	23,200	. . .

Dowel Pins (ANSI/ASME B18.8.2, 1978)

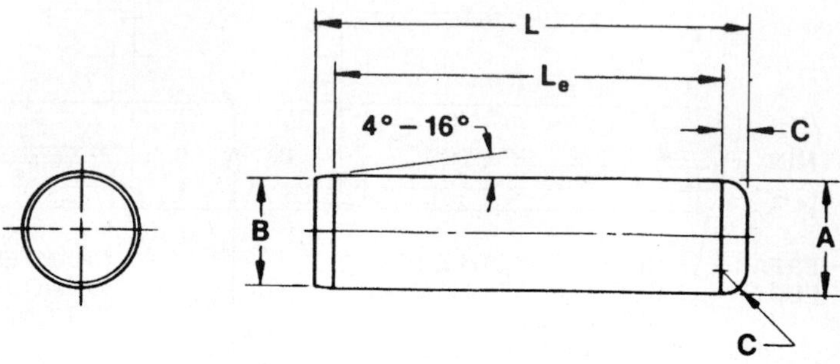

TABLE C.7.4 Hardened Ground Machine Dowel Pins

Nominal Size or Nominal Pin Diameter	Pin Diameter, *A*						Point Diameter, *B*		Crown Height or Radius, *C*		Range of Preferred Lengths, *L*	Double Shear Load, Min, lb for Carbon or Alloy Steel	Suggested Hole Diameter	
	Standard Series Pins			*Oversize Series Pins*										
	Basic	*Max*	*Min*	*Basic*	*Max*	*Min*	*Max*	*Min*	*Max*	*Min*			*Max*	*Min*
$\frac{1}{16}$ 0.0625	0.0627	0.0628	0.0626	0.0635	0.0636	0.0634	0.058	0.048	0.020	0.008	$\frac{3}{16}$ – $\frac{3}{4}$	800	0.0625	0.0620
$\frac{5}{64}$ 0.0781	0.0783	0.0784	0.0782	0.0791	0.0792	0.0790	0.074	0.064	0.026	0.010	. . .	1,240	0.0781	0.0776
$\frac{3}{32}$ 0.0938	0.0940	0.0941	0.0939	0.0948	0.0949	0.0947	0.089	0.079	0.031	0.012	$\frac{5}{16}$–1	1,800	0.0937	0.0932
$\frac{1}{8}$ 0.1250	0.1252	0.1253	0.1251	0.1260	0.1261	0.1259	0.120	0.110	0.041	0.016	$\frac{3}{8}$–2	3,200	0.1250	0.1245
$\frac{5}{32}$ 0.1562	0.1564	0.1565	0.1563	0.1572	0.1573	0.1571	0.150	0.140	0.052	0.020	. . .	5,000	0.1562	0.1557
$\frac{3}{16}$ 0.1875	0.1877	0.1878	0.1876	0.1885	0.1886	0.1884	0.180	0.170	0.062	0.023	$\frac{1}{2}$–2	7,200	0.1875	0.1870
$\frac{1}{4}$ 0.2500	0.2502	0.2503	0.2501	0.2510	0.2511	0.2509	0.240	0.230	0.083	0.031	$\frac{1}{2}$–$2\frac{1}{2}$	12,800	0.2500	0.2495
$\frac{5}{16}$ 0.3125	0.3127	0.3128	0.3126	0.3135	0.3136	0.3134	0.302	0.290	0.104	0.039	$\frac{1}{2}$–$2\frac{1}{2}$	20,000	0.3125	0.3120
$\frac{3}{8}$ 0.3750	0.3752	0.3753	0.3751	0.3760	0.3761	0.3759	0.365	0.350	0.125	0.047	$\frac{1}{2}$–3	28,700	0.3750	0.3745
$\frac{7}{16}$ 0.4375	0.4377	0.4378	0.4376	0.4385	0.4386	0.4384	0.424	0.409	0.146	0.055	$\frac{7}{8}$–3	39,100	0.4375	0.4370
$\frac{1}{2}$ 0.5000	0.5002	0.5003	0.5001	0.5010	0.5011	0.5009	0.486	0.471	0.167	0.063	$\frac{3}{4}$,1–4	51,000	0.5000	0.4995
$\frac{5}{8}$ 0.6250	0.6252	0.6253	0.6251	0.6260	0.6261	0.6259	0.611	0.595	0.208	0.078	$1\frac{1}{4}$–5	79,800	0.6250	0.6245
$\frac{3}{4}$ 0.7500	0.7502	0.7503	0.7501	0.7510	0.7511	0.7509	0.735	0.715	0.250	0.094	$1\frac{1}{2}$–6	114,000	0.7500	0.7495
$\frac{7}{8}$ 0.8750	0.8752	0.8753	0.8751	0.8760	0.8761	0.8759	0.860	0.840	0.293	0.109	2,$2\frac{1}{2}$–6	156,000	0.8750	0.8745
1 1.0000	1.0002	1.0003	1.0001	1.0010	1.0011	1.0009	0.980	0.960	0.333	0.125	2,$2\frac{1}{2}$–5,6	204,000	1.0000	0.9995

Metric Spring Pins (IFI 512-S, 1982)

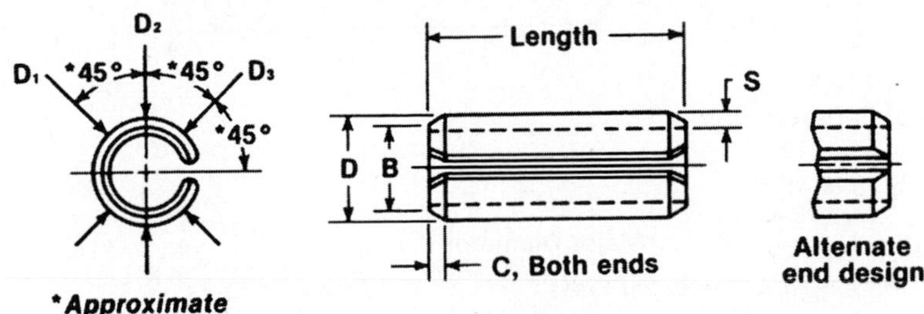

TABLE C.7.5 Dimensions of Unhardened Ground Dowel Pins

Nominal Size or Nominal Pin Diameter		A Pin Diameter		C Chamfer Length		Double Shear Load Min, lb Material	
		Max	Min	Max	Min	Carbon Steel	Brass
$\frac{1}{16}$	0.0625	0.0600	0.0595	0.025	0.005	350	220
$\frac{3}{32}$	0.0938	0.0912	0.0907	0.025	0.005	820	510
$\frac{7}{64}$	0.1094	0.1068	0.1063	0.025	0.005	1,130	710
$\frac{1}{8}$	0.1250	0.1223	0.1218	0.025	0.005	1,490	930
$\frac{5}{32}$	0.1562	0.1535	0.1530	0.025	0.005	2,350	1,470
$\frac{3}{16}$	0.1875	0.1847	0.1842	0.025	0.005	3,410	2,130
$\frac{7}{32}$	0.2188	0.2159	0.2154	0.025	0.005	4,660	2,910
$\frac{1}{4}$	0.2500	0.2470	0.2465	0.025	0.005	6,120	3,810
$\frac{5}{16}$	0.3125	0.3094	0.3089	0.040	0.020	9,590	5,990
$\frac{3}{8}$	0.3750	0.3717	0.3712	0.040	0.020	13,850	8,650
$\frac{7}{16}$	0.4375	0.4341	0.4336	0.040	0.020	18,900	11,810
$\frac{1}{2}$	0.5000	0.4964	0.4959	0.040	0.020	24,720	15,450
$\frac{5}{8}$	0.6250	0.6211	0.6206	0.055	0.035	38,710	24,190
$\frac{3}{4}$	0.7500	0.7548	0.7453	0.055	0.035	55,840	34,900
$\frac{7}{8}$	0.8750	0.8705	0.8700	0.070	0.050	76,090	47,550
1	1.0000	0.9952	0.9947	0.070	0.050	99,460	62,160

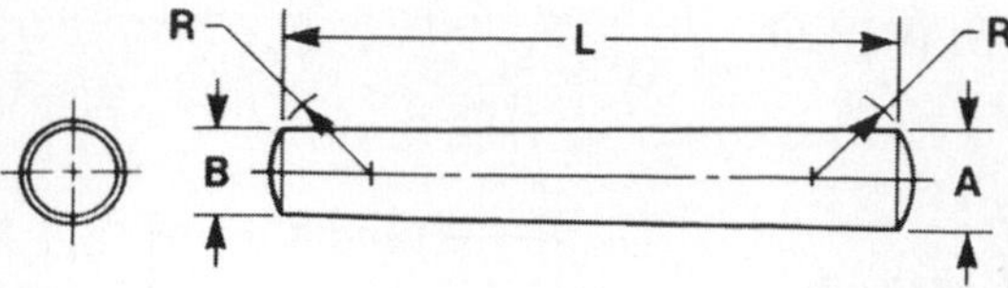

TABLE C.7.6 Dimensions of Tapered Pins

Pin Size Number and Basic Pin Diameter		A Major Diameter (Large End)				R End Crown Radius	
		Commercial Class		Precision Class			
		Max	*Min*	*Max*	*Min*	*Max*	*Min*
7/0	0.0625	0.0638	0.0618	0.0635	0.0625	0.072	0.052
6/0	0.0780	0.0793	0.0773	0.0790	0.0780	0.088	0.068
5/0	0.0940	0.0953	0.0933	0.0950	0.0940	0.104	0.084
4/0	0.1090	0.1103	0.1083	0.1100	0.1090	0.119	0.099
3/0	0.1250	0.1263	0.1243	0.1260	0.1250	0.135	0.115
2/0	0.1410	0.1423	0.1403	0.1420	0.1410	0.151	0.131
0	0.1560	0.1573	0.1553	0.1570	0.1560	0.166	0.146
1	0.1720	0.1733	0.1713	0.1730	0.1720	0.182	0.162
2	0.1930	0.1943	0.1923	0.1940	0.1930	0.203	0.183
3	0.2190	0.2203	0.2183	0.2200	0.2190	0.229	0.209
4	0.2500	0.2513	0.2493	0.2510	0.2500	0.260	0.240
5	0.2890	0.2903	0.2883	0.2900	0.2890	0.299	0.279
6	0.3410	0.3423	0.3403	0.3420	0.3410	0.351	0.331
7	0.4090	0.4103	0.4083	0.4100	0.4090	0.419	0.399
8	0.4920	0.4933	0.4913	0.4930	0.4920	0.502	0.482
9	0.5910	0.5923	0.5903	0.5920	0.5910	0.601	0.581
10	0.7060	0.7073	0.7053	0.7070	0.7060	0.716	0.696
11	0.8600	0.8613	0.8593			0.870	0.850
12	1.0320	1.0333	1.0313			1.042	1.022
13	1.2410	1.2423	1.2403			1.251	1.231
14	1.5210	1.5223	1.5203			1.531	1.511

C.8 Bushings

TABLE C.8.1 Jig Bushings

Range of Hole Sizes in Renewable Bushings	Inside Diameter *A*			Body Diameter *B*					Overall Length *C*	Radius *D*	Head Diam. *E*	Head Thick. F_{max}	Number
				Unfinished			*Finished*						
	Nom	*Max*	*Min*	*Nom*	*Max*	*Min*	*Max*	*Min*					
0.0135 to 0.1562	0.312	0.3129	0.3126	0.500	0.520	0.515	0.5017	0.5014	0.312	0.047	0.625	0.094	HL-32-5
									0.500				HL-32-8
									0.750				HL-32-12
									1.000				HL-32-16
0.1570 to 0.3125	0.500	0.5005	0.5002	0.750	0.770	0.765	0.7518	0.7515	0.312	0.062	0.875	0.094	HL-48-5
									0.500				HL-48-8
									0.750				HL-48-12
									1.000				HL-48-16
									1.375				HL-48-22
									1.750				HL-48-28
0.3160 to 0.5000	0.750	0.7506	0.7503	1.000	1.020	1.015	1.0018	1.0015	0.500	0.062	1.125	0.125	HL-64-8
									0.750				HL-64-12
									1.000				HL-64-16
									1.375				HL-64-22
									1.750				HL-64-28
									2.125				HL-64-34
0.5156 to 0.7500	1.000	1.0007	1.0004	1.375	1.395	1.390	1.3772	1.3768	0.500	0.094	1.500	0.125	HL-88-8
									0.750				HL-88-12
									1.000				HL-88-16
									1.375				HL-88-22
									1.750				HL-88-28
									2.125				HL-88-34
									2.500				HL-88-40
0.7656 to 1.0000	1.375	1.3760	1.3756	1.750	1.770	1.765	1.7523	1.7519	0.750	0.094	1.875	0.188	HL-112-12
									1.000				HL-112-16
									1.375				HL-112-22
									1.750				HL-112-28
									2.125				HL-112-34
									2.500				HL-112-40
1.0156 to 1.3750	1.750	1.7512	1.7508	2.250	2.270	2.265	2.2525	2.2521	1.000	0.094	2.375	0.188	HL-144-16
									1.375				HL-144-22
									1.750				HL-144-28
									2.125				HL-144-34
									2.500				HL-144-40
									3.000				HL-144-48
1.3906 to 1.7500	2.250	2.2515	2.2510	2.750	2.770	2.765	2.7526	2.7522	1.000	0.125	2.875	0.188	HL-176-16
									1.375				HL-176-22
									1.750				HL-176-28
									2.125				HL-176-34
									2.500				HL-176-40
									3.000				HL-176-48

All dimensions are in inches.

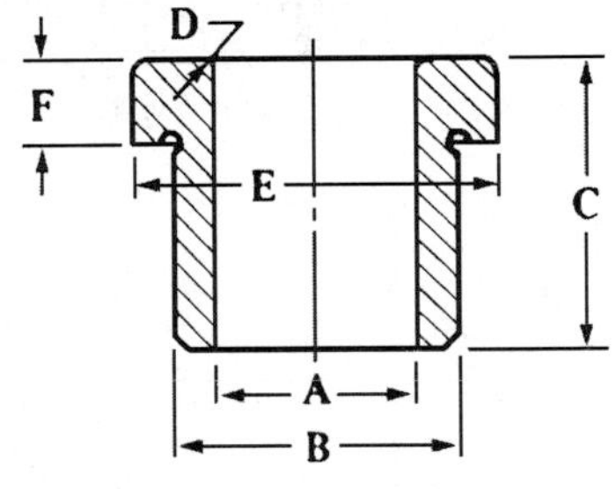

TABLE C.8.2 Headless-Type Press Fit Wearing Bushings Type-P

Range of Hole Sizes *A*	Body Diameter *B*					Body Length *C*	Radius *D*	Number
		Unfinished		*Finished*				
	Nom	*Max*	*Min*	*Max*	*Min*			
0.0135 up to and including 0.0625	0.156	0.166	0.161	0.1578	0.1575	0.250	0.016	P-10-4
						0.312		P-10-5
						0.375		P-10-6
						0.500		P-10-8
0.0630 to 0.0995	0.203	0.213	0.208	0.2046	0.2043	0.250	0.016	P-13-4
						0.312		P-13-5
						0.375		P-13-6
						0.500		P-13-8
						0.750		P-13-12
0.1015 to 0.1405	0.250	0.260	0.255	0.2516	0.2513	0.250	0.016	P-16-4
						0.312		P-16-5
						0.250		P-16-6
						0.500		P-16-8
						0.750		P-16-12
0.1406 to 0.1875	0.312	0.327	0.322	0.3141	0.3138	0.250	0.031	P-20-4
						0.312		P-20-5
						0.375		P-20-6
						0.500		P-20-8
						0.750		P-20-12
						1.000		P-20-16
0.1890 to 0.2500	0.406	0.421	0.416	0.4078	0.4075	0.250	0.031	P-26-4
						0.312		P-26-5
						0.375		P-26-6
						0.500		P-26-8
						0.750		P-26-12
						1.000		P-26-16
						1.375		P-26-22
						1.750		P-26-28
0.2570 to 0.3125	0.500	0.520	0.515	0.5017	0.5014	0.312	0.047	P-32-5
						0.375		P-32-6
						0.500		P-32-8
						0.750		P-32-12
						1.000		P-32-16
						1.375		P-32-22
						1.750		P-32-28

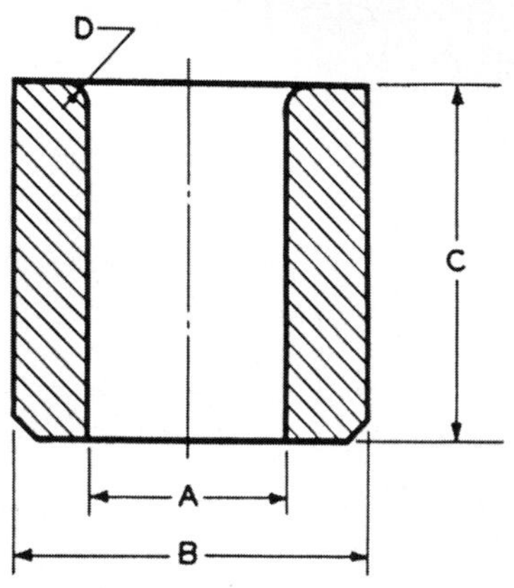

C.9 Woodruff Keys

Keys and Keyseats

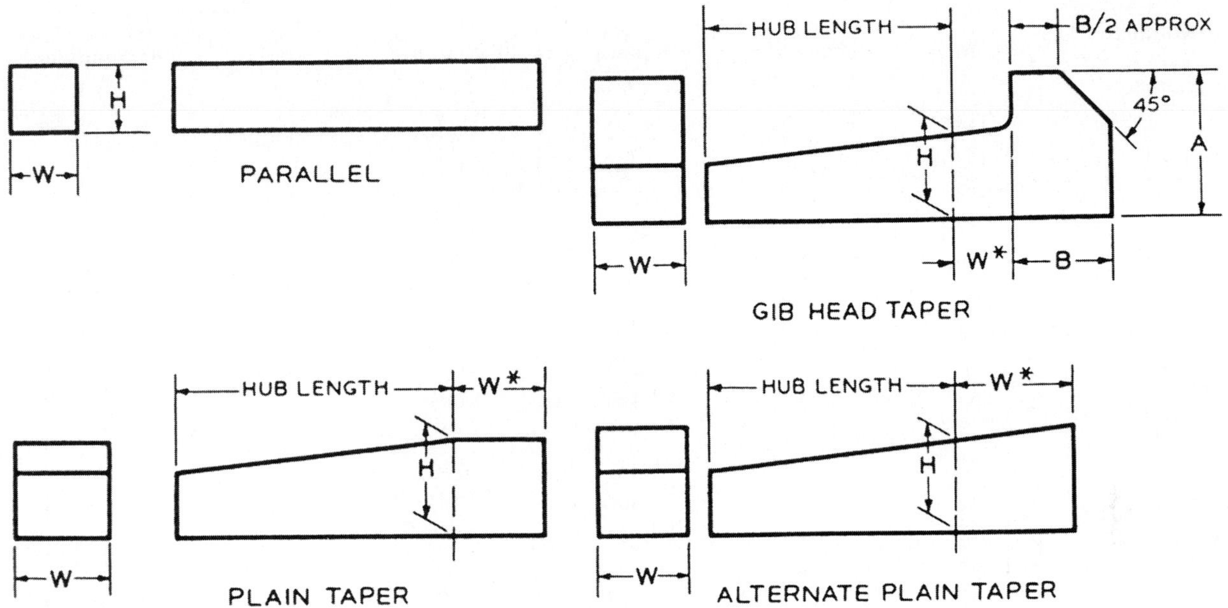

Plain and Gib Head Taper Keys Have a 1/8" Taper in 12"

TABLE C.9.1 Key Dimensions and Tolerances

KEY			NOMINAL KEY SIZE Width, W		TOLERANCE			
			Over	To (Incl)	Width, W		Height, H	
Parallel	Square	Bar Stock	—	$\frac{3}{4}$	+0.000	−0.002	+0.000	−0.002
			$\frac{3}{4}$	$1\frac{1}{2}$	+0.000	−0.003	+0.000	−0.003
			$1\frac{1}{2}$	$2\frac{1}{2}$	+0.000	−0.004	+0.000	−0.004
			$2\frac{1}{2}$	$3\frac{1}{2}$	+0.000	−0.006	+0.000	−0.006
		Keystock	—	$1\frac{1}{4}$	+0.001	−0.000	+0.001	−0.000
			$1\frac{1}{4}$	3	+0.002	−0.000	+0.002	−0.000
			3	$3\frac{1}{2}$	+0.003	−0.000	+0.003	−0.000
	Rectangular	Bar Stock	—	$\frac{3}{4}$	+0.000	−0.003	+0.000	−0.003
			$\frac{3}{4}$	$1\frac{1}{2}$	+0.000	−0.004	+0.000	−0.004
			$1\frac{1}{2}$	3	+0.000	−0.005	+0.000	−0.005
			3	4	+0.000	−0.006	+0.000	−0.006
			4	6	+0.000	−0.008	+0.000	−0.008
			6	7	+0.000	−0.013	+0.000	−0.013
		Keystock	—	$1\frac{1}{4}$	+0.001	−0.000	+0.005	−0.005
			$1\frac{1}{4}$	3	+0.002	−0.000	+0.005	−0.005
			3	7	+0.003	−0.000	+0.005	−0.005
Taper	Plain or Gib Head Square or Rectangular		—	$1\frac{1}{4}$	+0.001	−0.000	+0.005	−0.000
			$1\frac{1}{4}$	3	+0.002	−0.000	+0.005	−0.000
			3	7	+0.003	−0.000	+0.005	−0.000

*For locating position of dimension H. Tolerance does not apply.
All dimensions given in inches.

TABLE C.9.2 Depth Control Values (Three Values for S and T)

Nominal Shaft Diameter	Parallel and Taper		Parallel		Taper	
	Square *S*	**Rectangular** *S*	**Square** *T*	**Rectangular** *T*	**Square** *T*	**Rectangular** *T*
$\frac{1}{2}$	0.430	0.445	0.560	0.544	0.535	0.519
$\frac{9}{16}$	0.493	0.509	0.623	0.607	0.598	0.582
$\frac{5}{8}$	0.517	0.548	0.709	0.678	0.684	0.653
$\frac{11}{16}$	0.581	0.612	0.773	0.742	0.748	0.717
$\frac{3}{4}$	0.644	0.676	0.837	0.806	0.812	0.781
$\frac{13}{16}$	0.708	0.739	0.900	0.869	0.875	0.844
$\frac{7}{8}$	0.771	0.802	0.964	0.932	0.939	0.907
$\frac{15}{16}$	0.796	0.827	1.051	1.019	1.026	0.994
1	0.859	0.890	1.114	1.083	1.089	1.058
$1\frac{1}{16}$	0.923	0.954	1.178	1.146	1.153	1.121
$1\frac{1}{8}$	0.986	1.017	1.241	1.210	1.216	1.185
$1\frac{3}{16}$	1.049	1.080	1.304	1.273	1.279	1.248
$1\frac{1}{4}$	1.112	1.144	1.367	1.336	1.342	1.311
$1\frac{5}{16}$	1.137	1.169	1.455	1.424	1.430	1.399
$1\frac{3}{8}$	1.201	1.232	1.518	1.487	1.493	1.462
$1\frac{7}{16}$	1.225	1.288	1.605	1.543	1.580	1.518
$1\frac{1}{2}$	1.289	1.351	1.669	1.606	1.644	1.581
$1\frac{9}{16}$	1.352	1.415	1.732	1.670	1.707	1.645
$1\frac{5}{8}$	1.416	1.478	1.796	1.733	1.771	1.708
$1\frac{11}{16}$	1.479	1.541	1.859	1.796	1.834	1.771
$1\frac{3}{4}$	1.542	1.605	1.922	1.860	1.897	1.835
$1\frac{13}{16}$	1.527	1.590	2.032	1.970	2.007	1.945
$1\frac{7}{8}$	1.591	1.654	2.096	2.034	2.071	2.009
$1\frac{15}{16}$	1.655	1.717	2.160	2.097	2.135	2.072
2	1.718	1.781	2.223	2.161	2.198	2.136
$2\frac{1}{16}$	1.782	1.844	2.287	2.224	2.262	2.199
$2\frac{1}{8}$	1.845	1.908	2.350	2.288	2.325	2.263
$2\frac{3}{16}$	1.909	1.971	2.414	2.351	2.389	2.326
$2\frac{1}{4}$	1.972	2.034	2.477	2.414	2.452	2.389
$2\frac{5}{16}$	1.957	2.051	2.587	2.493	2.562	2.468
$2\frac{3}{8}$	2.021	2.114	2.651	2.557	2.626	2.532
$2\frac{7}{16}$	2.084	2.178	2.714	2.621	2.689	2.596
$2\frac{1}{2}$	2.148	2.242	2.778	2.684	2.753	2.659
$2\frac{9}{16}$	2.211	2.305	2.841	2.748	2.816	2.723
$2\frac{5}{8}$	2.275	2.369	2.905	2.811	2.880	2.786
$2\frac{11}{16}$	2.338	2.432	2.968	2.874	2.943	2.849
$2\frac{3}{4}$	2.402	2.495	3.032	2.938	3.007	2.913
$2\frac{13}{16}$	2.387	2.512	3.142	3.017	3.117	2.992
$2\frac{7}{8}$	2.450	2.575	3.205	3.080	3.180	3.055
$2\frac{15}{16}$	2.514	2.639	3.269	3.144	3.244	3.119
3	2.577	2.702	3.332	3.207	3.307	3.182
$3\frac{1}{16}$	2.641	2.766	3.396	3.271	3.371	3.246
$3\frac{1}{8}$	2.704	2.829	3.459	3.334	3.434	3.309

All dimensions given in inches.

Woodruff Keys and Keysets

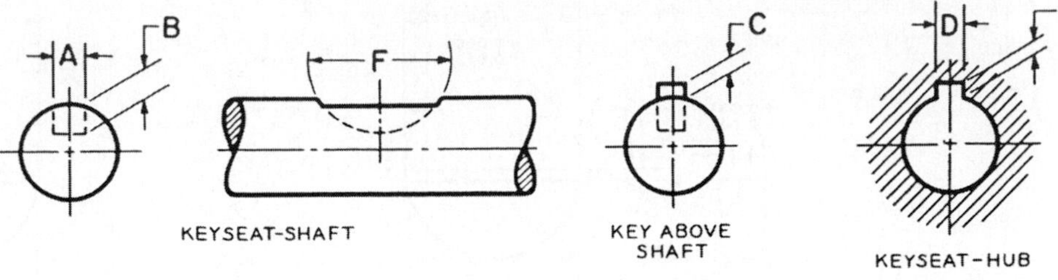

TABLE C.9.3 Keyseat Dimensions

Key No.	Nominal Size Key	Keyseat—Shaft Width A Min	Width A Max	Depth B +0.005 −0.000	Diameter F Min	Diameter F Max	Key Above Shaft Height C +0.005 −0.005	Keyseat—Hub Width D +0.002 −0.000	Keyseat—Hub Depth E +0.005 −0.000
202	$\frac{1}{16} \times \frac{1}{4}$	0.0615	0.0630	0.0728	0.250	0.268	0.0312	0.0635	0.0372
202.5	$\frac{1}{16} \times \frac{5}{16}$	0.0615	0.0630	0.1038	0.312	0.330	0.0312	0.0635	0.0372
302.5	$\frac{3}{32} \times \frac{5}{16}$	0.0928	0.0943	0.0882	0.312	0.330	0.0469	0.0948	0.0529
203	$\frac{1}{16} \times \frac{3}{8}$	0.0615	0.0630	0.1358	0.375	0.393	0.0312	0.0635	0.0372
303	$\frac{3}{32} \times \frac{3}{8}$	0.0928	0.0943	0.1202	0.375	0.393	0.0469	0.0948	0.0529
403	$\frac{1}{8} \times \frac{3}{8}$	0.1240	0.1255	0.1045	0.375	0.393	0.0625	0.1260	0.0685
204	$\frac{1}{16} \times \frac{1}{2}$	0.0615	0.0630	0.1668	0.500	0.518	0.0312	0.0635	0.0372
304	$\frac{3}{32} \times \frac{1}{2}$	0.0928	0.0943	0.1511	0.500	0.518	0.0469	0.0948	0.0529
404	$\frac{1}{8} \times \frac{1}{2}$	0.1240	0.1255	0.1355	0.500	0.518	0.0625	0.1260	0.0685
305	$\frac{3}{32} \times \frac{5}{8}$	0.0928	0.0943	0.1981	0.625	0.643	0.0469	0.0948	0.0529
405	$\frac{1}{8} \times \frac{5}{8}$	0.1240	0.1255	0.1825	0.625	0.643	0.0625	0.1260	0.0685
505	$\frac{5}{32} \times \frac{5}{8}$	0.1553	0.1568	0.1669	0.625	0.643	0.0781	0.1573	0.0841
605	$\frac{3}{16} \times \frac{5}{8}$	0.1863	0.1880	0.1513	0.625	0.643	0.0937	0.1885	0.0997
406	$\frac{1}{8} \times \frac{3}{4}$	0.1240	0.1255	0.2455	0.750	0.768	0.0625	0.1260	0.0685
506	$\frac{5}{32} \times \frac{3}{4}$	0.1553	0.1568	0.2299	0.750	0.768	0.0781	0.1573	0.0841
606	$\frac{3}{16} \times \frac{3}{4}$	0.1863	0.1880	0.2143	0.750	0.768	0.0937	0.1885	0.0997
806	$\frac{1}{4} \times \frac{3}{4}$	0.2487	0.2505	0.1830	0.750	0.768	0.1250	0.2510	0.1310
507	$\frac{5}{32} \times \frac{7}{8}$	0.1553	0.1568	0.2919	0.875	0.895	0.0781	0.1573	0.0841
607	$\frac{3}{16} \times \frac{7}{8}$	0.1863	0.1880	0.2763	0.875	0.895	0.0937	0.1885	0.0997
707	$\frac{7}{32} \times \frac{7}{8}$	0.2175	0.2193	0.2607	0.875	0.895	0.1093	0.2198	0.1153
807	$\frac{1}{4} \times \frac{7}{8}$	0.2487	0.2505	0.2450	0.875	0.895	0.1250	0.2510	0.1310
608	$\frac{3}{16} \times 1$	0.1863	0.1880	0.3393	1.000	1.020	0.0937	0.1885	0.0997
708	$\frac{7}{32} \times 1$	0.2175	0.2193	0.3237	1.000	1.020	0.1093	0.2198	0.1153
808	$\frac{1}{4} \times 1$	0.2487	0.2505	0.3080	1.000	1.020	0.1250	0.2510	0.1310
1008	$\frac{5}{16} \times 1$	0.3111	0.3130	0.2768	1.000	1.020	0.1562	0.3135	0.1622
1208	$\frac{3}{8} \times 1$	0.3735	0.3755	0.2455	1.000	1.020	0.1875	0.3760	0.1935
609	$\frac{3}{16} \times 1\frac{1}{8}$	0.1863	0.1880	0.3853	1.125	1.145	0.0937	0.1885	0.0997
709	$\frac{7}{32} \times 1\frac{1}{8}$	0.2175	0.2193	0.3697	1.125	1.145	0.1093	0.2198	0.1153
809	$\frac{1}{4} \times 1\frac{1}{8}$	0.2487	0.2505	0.3540	1.125	1.145	0.1250	0.2510	0.1310
1009	$\frac{5}{16} \times 1\frac{1}{8}$	0.3111	0.3130	0.3228	1.125	1.145	0.1562	0.3135	0.1622

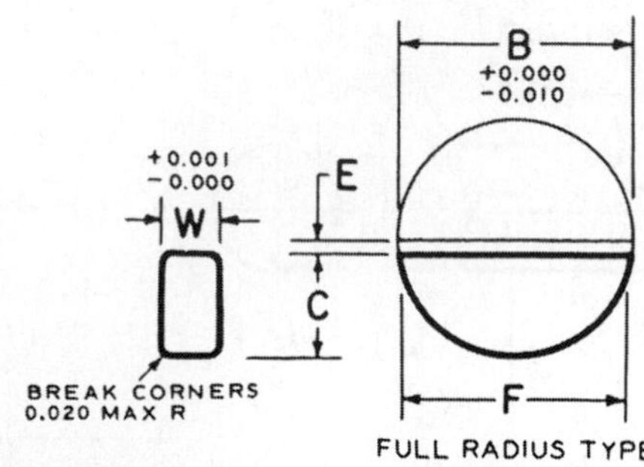

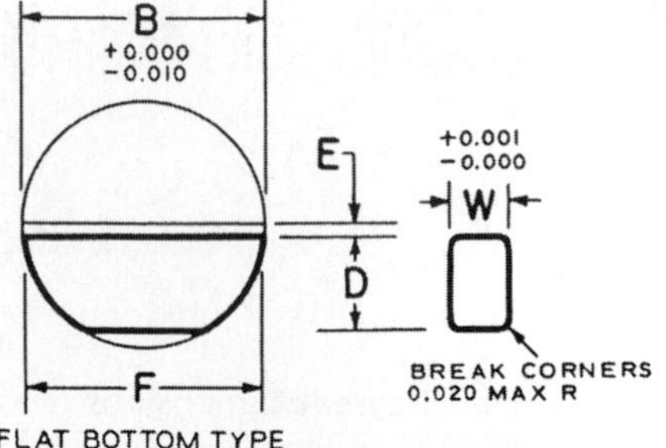

TABLE C.9.4 Woodruff Keys

Key No.	Nominal Key Size $W \times B$	Actual Length F +0.000 −0.010	Height of Key C Max	C Min	D Max	D Min	Distance Below Center E
202	$\frac{1}{16} \times \frac{1}{4}$	0.248	0.109	0.104	0.109	0.104	$\frac{1}{64}$
202.5	$\frac{1}{16} \times \frac{5}{16}$	0.311	0.140	0.135	0.140	0.135	$\frac{1}{64}$
302.5	$\frac{3}{32} \times \frac{5}{16}$	0.311	0.140	0.135	0.140	0.135	$\frac{1}{64}$
203	$\frac{1}{16} \times \frac{3}{8}$	0.374	0.172	0.167	0.172	0.167	$\frac{1}{64}$
303	$\frac{3}{32} \times \frac{3}{8}$	0.374	0.172	0.167	0.172	0.167	$\frac{1}{64}$
403	$\frac{1}{8} \times \frac{3}{8}$	0.374	0.172	0.167	0.172	0.167	$\frac{1}{64}$
204	$\frac{1}{16} \times \frac{1}{2}$	0.491	0.203	0.198	0.194	0.188	$\frac{3}{64}$
304	$\frac{3}{32} \times \frac{1}{2}$	0.491	0.203	0.198	0.194	0.188	$\frac{3}{64}$
404	$\frac{1}{8} \times \frac{1}{2}$	0.491	0.203	0.198	0.194	0.188	$\frac{3}{64}$
305	$\frac{3}{32} \times \frac{5}{8}$	0.612	0.250	0.245	0.240	0.234	$\frac{1}{16}$
405	$\frac{1}{8} \times \frac{5}{8}$	0.612	0.250	0.245	0.240	0.234	$\frac{1}{16}$
505	$\frac{5}{32} \times \frac{5}{8}$	0.612	0.250	0.245	0.240	0.234	$\frac{1}{16}$
605	$\frac{3}{16} \times \frac{5}{8}$	0.612	0.250	0.245	0.240	0.234	$\frac{1}{16}$
406	$\frac{1}{8} \times \frac{3}{4}$	0.740	0.313	0.308	0.303	0.297	$\frac{1}{16}$
506	$\frac{5}{32} \times \frac{3}{4}$	0.740	0.313	0.308	0.303	0.297	$\frac{1}{16}$
606	$\frac{3}{16} \times \frac{3}{4}$	0.740	0.313	0.308	0.303	0.297	$\frac{1}{16}$
806	$\frac{1}{4} \times \frac{3}{4}$	0.740	0.313	0.308	0.303	0.297	$\frac{1}{16}$
507	$\frac{5}{32} \times \frac{7}{8}$	0.866	0.375	0.370	0.365	0.359	$\frac{1}{16}$
607	$\frac{3}{16} \times \frac{7}{8}$	0.866	0.375	0.370	0.365	0.359	$\frac{1}{16}$
707	$\frac{7}{32} \times \frac{7}{8}$	0.866	0.375	0.370	0.365	0.359	$\frac{1}{16}$
807	$\frac{1}{4} \times \frac{7}{8}$	0.866	0.375	0.370	0.365	0.359	$\frac{1}{16}$
608	$\frac{3}{16} \times 1$	0.992	0.438	0.433	0.428	0.422	$\frac{1}{16}$
708	$\frac{7}{32} \times 1$	0.992	0.438	0.433	0.428	0.422	$\frac{1}{16}$
808	$\frac{1}{4} \times 1$	0.992	0.438	0.433	0.428	0.422	$\frac{1}{16}$
1008	$\frac{5}{16} \times 1$	0.992	0.438	0.433	0.428	0.422	$\frac{1}{16}$
1208	$\frac{3}{8} \times 1$	0.992	0.438	0.433	0.428	0.422	$\frac{1}{16}$
609	$\frac{3}{16} \times 1\frac{1}{8}$	1.114	0.484	0.479	0.475	0.469	$\frac{5}{64}$
709	$\frac{7}{32} \times 1\frac{1}{8}$	1.114	0.484	0.479	0.475	0.469	$\frac{5}{64}$
809	$\frac{1}{4} \times 1\frac{1}{8}$	1.114	0.484	0.479	0.475	0.469	$\frac{5}{64}$
1009	$\frac{5}{16} \times 1\frac{1}{8}$	1.114	0.484	0.479	0.475	0.469	$\frac{5}{64}$

C.10 Standard Sheet Metal Gages

Gage	Thickness		Weight per Sq Ft		Gage
10	.1406 in.	3.571 mm	5.625 lb	2.551 kg	10
11	.1250 in.	3.175 mm	5.000 lb	2.267 kg	11
12	.1094 in.	2.778 mm	4.375 lb	1.984 kg	12
13	.0938 in.	2.383 mm	3.750 lb	1.700 kg	13
14	.0781 in.	1.983 mm	3.125 lb	1.417 kg	14
15	.0703 in.	1.786 mm	2.813 lb	1.276 kg	15
16	.0625 in.	1.588 mm	2.510 lb	1.134 kg	16
17	.0563 in.	1.430 mm	2.250 lb	1.021 kg	17
18	.0500 in.	1.270 mm	2.000 lb	0.907 kg	18
19	.0438 in.	1.111 mm	1.750 lb	0.794 kg	19
20	.0375 in.	0.953 mm	1.500 lb	0.680 kg	20
21	.0344 in.	0.877 mm	1.375 lb	0.624 kg	21
22	.0313 in.	0.795 mm	1.250 lb	0.567 kg	22
23	.0280 in.	0.714 mm	1.125 lb	0.510 kg	23
24	.0250 in.	0.635 mm	1.000 lb	0.454 kg	24
25	.0219 in.	0.556 mm	0.875 lb	0.397 kg	25
26	.0188 in.	0.478 mm	0.750 lb	0.340 kg	26
27	.0172 in.	0.437 mm	0.687 lb	0.312 kg	27
28	.0156 in.	0.396 mm	0.625 lb	0.283 kg	28
29	.0141 in.	0.358 mm	0.563 lb	0.255 kg	29
30	.0120 in.	0.318 mm	0.500 lb	0.227 kg	30

C.11 Structural Shapes and Sizes

Structural Steel Shapes

Structural steel shapes are manufactured in a wide variety of shapes, sizes and weights per linear foot. Steel mills roll these sections in six basic steel materials. The following are most common materials.

American standard beams (S) Generally called I-beams because of their resemblance to that capital letter. Used as columns and struts.

American standard channels (C) Used as struts and in trusses when light loadings are required. They are often found in steel platforming load-bearing members.

Wide-flange shapes (W) Used as both beams and columns and furnished with constant-thickness flanges.

Miscellaneous shapes (M) Similar in shape to W shapes.

Structural tees (WT, MT, and ST) Made by splitting S, W, and M shapes, usually at mid-distance of their webs. Most structural steel fabricators order S, W, and M shapes and cut the webs themselves to form tees.

Angels (L) Used for struts, platforms, to add framing strength and for many other items. They have two legs set at right angles to each other. These legs may be equal or unequal widths.

Flat bars (Bar) Have a rectangular cross section, and are rolled in many widths and thicknesses, but widths are normally limited to 6″ or 8″ depending on the thickness. If wider bars are needed, a sheet of plate is cut to form it.

Plate (PL or PL) Rectangular in cross section and comes in varied widths and thicknesses, but in larger pieces than bars. Plate widths start at 10″ and are rolled up to 200″ wide depending on thickness. Lengths are as long as shipping will allow.

Common Structural Steel Shapes Used on Pipe Supports

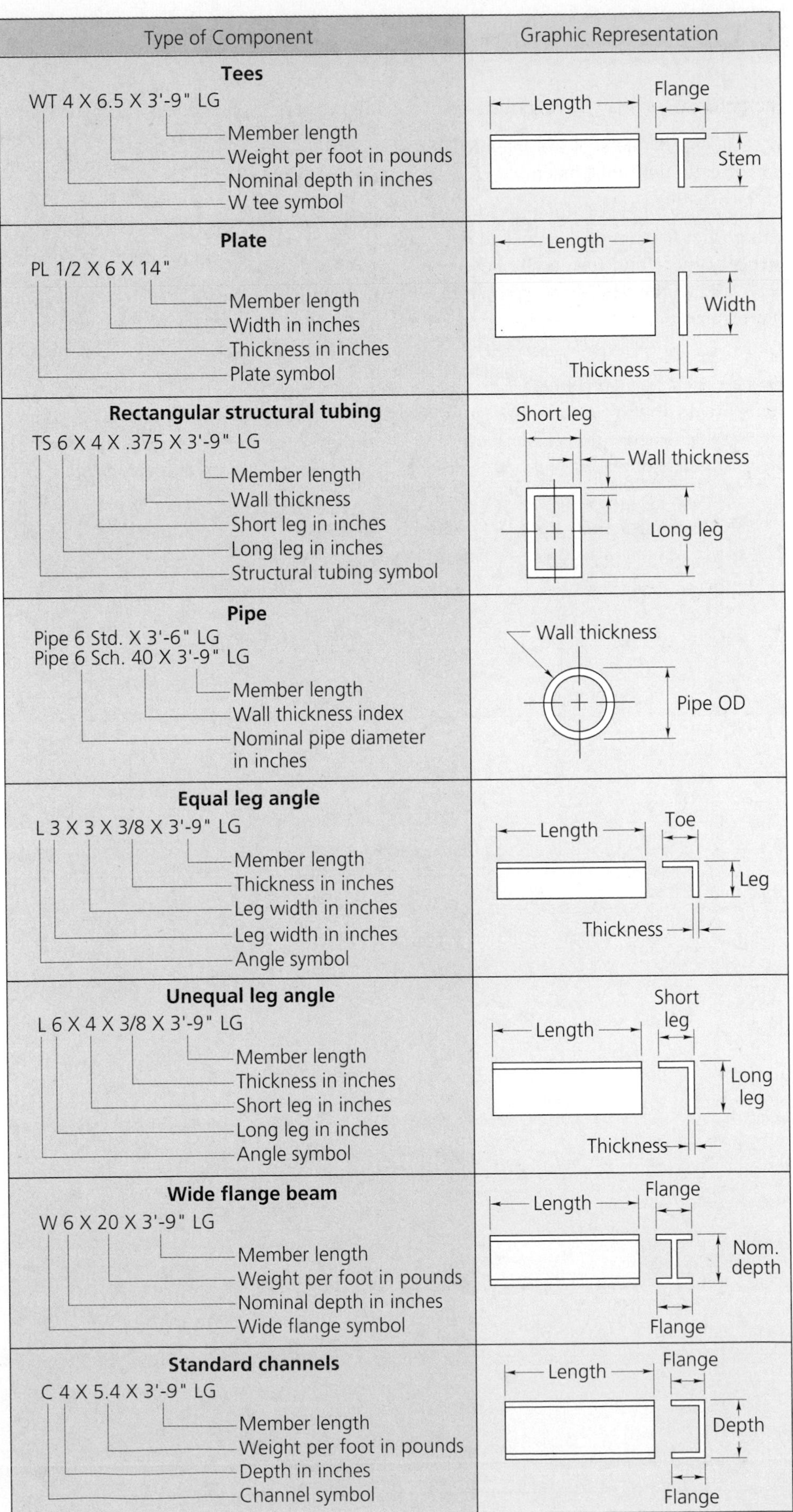

Type of Component	Graphic Representation
Tees WT 4 X 6.5 X 3'-9" LG Member length Weight per foot in pounds Nominal depth in inches W tee symbol	Length Flange Stem
Plate PL 1/2 X 6 X 14" Member length Width in inches Thickness in inches Plate symbol	Length Width Thickness
Rectangular structural tubing TS 6 X 4 X .375 X 3'-9" LG Member length Wall thickness Short leg in inches Long leg in inches Structural tubing symbol	Short leg Wall thickness Long leg
Pipe Pipe 6 Std. X 3'-6" LG Pipe 6 Sch. 40 X 3'-9" LG Member length Wall thickness index Nominal pipe diameter in inches	Wall thickness Pipe OD
Equal leg angle L 3 X 3 X 3/8 X 3'-9" LG Member length Thickness in inches Leg width in inches Leg width in inches Angle symbol	Length Toe Leg Thickness
Unequal leg angle L 6 X 4 X 3/8 X 3'-9" LG Member length Thickness in inches Short leg in inches Long leg in inches Angle symbol	Length Short leg Long leg Thickness
Wide flange beam W 6 X 20 X 3'-9" LG Member length Weight per foot in pounds Nominal depth in inches Wide flange symbol	Length Flange Nom. depth Flange
Standard channels C 4 X 5.4 X 3'-9" LG Member length Weight per foot in pounds Depth in inches Channel symbol	Length Flange Depth Flange

C.12 Fits and Tolerances

The types of fits may be described briefly as follows:

RC 1 Close sliding fits are intended for the accurate location of parts that must assemble without perceptible play.

RC 2 Sliding fits are intended for accurate location but with greater maximum clearance than class RC 1. Parts made to this fit move and turn easily but are not intended to run freely, and in the larger sizes may seize with small temperature changes.

RC 3 Precision running fits are about the closest fits that can be expected to run freely. They are intended for precision work at slow speeds and light journal pressures, but are not suitable where appreciable temperature differences are likely to be encountered.

RC 4 Close running fits are intended chiefly for running fits on accurate machinery with moderate surface speeds and journal pressures, where accurate location and minimum play is desired.

RC 5 and RC 6 Medium running fits are intended for higher running speeds or heavy journal pressures or both.

RC 7 Free running fits are intended for use where accuracy is not essential or where large temperature variations are likely to be encountered or under both of these conditions.

RC 8 and RC 9 Loose running fits are intended for use where wide commercial tolerances may be necessary, together with an allowance, on the external member.

TABLE C.12.1 Running and Sliding Fits

Nominal Size Range, Inches	Class RC 1			Class RC 2			Class RC 3			Class RC 4		
	Limits of Clearance	Standard Limits		Limits of Clearance	Standard Limits		Limits of Clearance	Standard Limits		Limits of Clearance	Standard Limits	
Over To		Hole H5	Shaft g4		Hole H6	Shaft g5		Hole H7	Shaft f6		Hole H8	Shaft f7
0 – 0.12	0.1	+0.2	− 0.1	0.1	+ 0.25	− 0.1	0.3	+ 0.4	− 0.3	0.3	+ 0.6	− 0.3
	0.45	0	− 0.25	0.55	0	− 0.3	0.95	0	− 0.55	1.3	0	− 0.7
0.12 – 0.24	0.15	+0.2	− 0.15	0.15	+ 0.3	− 0.15	0.4	+ 0.5	− 0.4	0.4	+ 0.7	− 0.4
	0.5	0	− 0.3	0.65	0	− 0.35	1.12	0	− 0.7	1.6	0	− 0.9
0.24 – 0.40	0.2	+0.25	− 0.2	0.2	+ 0.4	− 0.2	0.5	+ 0.6	− 0.5	0.5	+ 0.9	− 0.5
	0.6	0	− 0.35	0.85	0	− 0.45	1.5	0	− 0.9	2.0	0	− 1.1
0.40 – 0.71	0.25	+0.3	− 0.25	0.25	+ 0.4	− 0.25	0.6	+ 0.7	− 0.6	0.6	+ 1.0	− 0.6
	0.75	0	− 0.45	0.95	0	− 0.55	1.7	0	− 1.0	2.3	0	− 1.3
0.71 – 1.19	0.3	+0.4	− 0.3	0.3	+ 0.5	− 0.3	0.8	+ 0.8	− 0.8	0.8	+ 1.2	− 0.8
	0.95	0	− 0.55	1.2	0	− 0.7	2.1	0	− 1.3	2.8	0	− 1.6
1.19 – 1.97	0.4	+0.4	− 0.4	0.4	+ 0.6	− 0.4	1.0	+ 1.0	− 1.0	1.0	+ 1.6	− 1.0
	1.1	0	− 0.7	1.4	0	− 0.8	2.6	0	− 1.6	3.6	0	− 2.0
1.97 – 3.15	0.4	+0.5	− 0.4	0.4	+ 0.7	− 0.4	1.2	+ 1.2	− 1.2	1.2	+ 1.8	− 1.2
	1.2	0	− 0.7	1.6	0	− 0.9	3.1	0	− 1.9	4.2	0	− 2.4
3.15 – 4.73	0.5	+0.6	− 0.5	0.5	+ 0.9	− 0.5	1.4	+ 1.4	− 1.4	1.4	+ 2.2	− 1.4
	1.5	0	− 0.9	2.0	0	− 1.1	3.7	0	− 2.3	5.0	0	− 2.8
4.73 – 7.09	0.6	+0.7	− 0.6	0.6	+ 1.0	− 0.6	1.6	+ 1.6	− 1.6	1.6	+ 2.5	− 1.6
	1.8	0	− 1.1	2.3	0	− 1.3	4.2	0	− 2.6	5.7	0	− 3.2
7.09 – 9.85	0.6	+0.8	− 0.6	0.6	+ 1.2	− 0.6	2.0	+ 1.8	− 2.0	2.0	+ 2.8	− 2.0
	2.0	0	− 1.2	2.6	0	− 1.4	5.0	0	− 3.2	6.6	0	− 3.8
9.85 – 12.41	0.8	+0.9	− 0.8	0.8	+ 1.2	− 0.8	2.5	+ 2.0	− 2.5	2.5	+ 3.0	− 2.5
	2.3	0	− 1.4	2.9	0	− 1.7	5.7	0	− 3.7	7.5	0	− 4.5
12.41 – 15.75	1.0	+1.0	− 1.0	1.0	+ 1.4	− 1.0	3.0	+ 1.8	− 3.0	3.0	+ 3.5	− 3.0
	2.7	0	− 1.7	3.4	0	− 2.0	6.6	0	− 4.4	8.7	0	− 5.2
15.75 – 19.69	1.2	+1.0	− 1.2	1.2	+ 1.6	− 1.2	4.0	+ 1.6	− 4.0	4.0	+ 4.0	− 4.0
	3.0	0	− 2.0	3.8	0	− 2.2	8.1	0	− 5.6	10.5	0	− 6.5
19.69 – 30.09	1.6	+1.2	− 1.6	1.6	+ 2.0	− 1.6	5.0	+ 3.0	− 5.0	5.0	+ 5.0	− 5.0
	3.7	0	− 2.5	4.8	0	− 2.8	10.0	0	− 7.0	13.0	0	− 8.0
30.09 – 41.49	2.0	+1.6	− 2.0	2.0	+ 2.5	− 2.0	6.0	+ 4.0	− 6.0	6.0	+ 6.0	− 6.0
	4.6	0	− 3.0	6.1	0	− 3.6	12.5	0	− 8.5	16.0	0	−10.0
41.49 – 56.19	2.5	+2.0	− 2.5	2.5	+ 3.0	− 2.5	8.0	+ 5.0	− 8.0	8.0	+ 8.0	− 8.0
	5.7	0	− 3.7	7.5	0	− 4.5	16.0	0	−11.0	21.0	0	−13.0
56.19 – 76.39	3.0	+2.5	− 3.0	3.0	+ 4.0	− 3.0	10.0	+ 6.0	−10.0	10.0	+10.0	−10.0
	7.1	0	− 4.6	9.5	0	− 5.5	20.0	0	−14.0	26.0	0	−16.0
76.39–100.9	4.0	+3.0	− 4.0	4.0	+ 5.0	− 4.0	12.0	+ 8.0	−12.0	12.0	+12.0	−12.0
	9.0	0	− 6.0	12.0	0	− 7.0	25.0	0	−17.0	32.0	0	−20.0
100.9 – 131.9	5.0	+4.0	− 5.0	5.0	+ 6.0	− 5.0	16.0	+10.0	−16.0	16.0	+16.0	−16.0
	11.5	0	− 7.5	15.0	0	− 9.0	32.0	0	−22.0	36.0	0	−26.0
131.9 – 171.9	6.0	+5.0	− 6.0	6.0	+ 8.0	− 6.0	18.0	+ 8.0	−18.0	18.0	+20.0	−18.0
	14.0	0	− 9.0	19.0	0	−11.0	38.0	0	−26.0	50.0	0	−30.0
171.9 – 200	8.0	+6.0	− 8.0	8.0	+10.0	− 8.0	22.0	+16.0	−22.0	22.0	+25.0	−22.0
	18.0	0	−12.0	22.0	0	−12.0	48.0	0	−32.0	63.0	0	−38.0

Limits are in thousandths of an inch. Limits for hole and shaft are applied algebraically to the basic size to obtain the limits of size for the parts. Symbols H5, g5, etc. are hole and shaft designations in the ABC System.

Continues

TABLE C.12.1 Running and Sliding Fits—*Continued*

Class RC 5			Class RC 6			Class RC 7			Class RC 8			Class RC 9			Nominal Size Range, Inches	
Limits of Clearance	Standard Limits		Limits of Clearance	Standard Limits		Limits of Clearance	Standard Limits		Limits of Clearance	Standard Limits		Limits of Clearance	Standard Limits			
	Hole H8	*Shaft e7*		*Hole H9*	*Shaft e8*		*Hole H9*	*Shaft d8*		*Hole H10*	*Shaft c9*		*Hole H11*	*Shaft*	*Over*	*To*
0.6 1.6	+ 0.6 − 0	− 0.6 − 1.0	0.6 2.2	+ 1.0 − 0	− 0.6 − 1.2	1.0 2.6	+ 1.0 0	− 1.0 − 1.6	2.5 5.1	+ 1.6 0	− 2.5 − 3.5	4.0 8.1	+ 2.5 0	− 4.0 − 5.6	0	0.12
0.8 2.0	+ 0.7 − 0	− 0.8 − 1.3	0.8 2.7	+ 1.2 − 0	− 0.8 − 1.5	1.2 3.1	+ 1.2 0	− 1.2 − 1.9	2.8 5.8	+ 1.8 0	− 2.8 − 4.0	4.5 9.0	+ 3.0 0	− 4.5 − 6.0	0.12	0.24
1.0 2.5	+ 0.9 − 0	− 1.0 − 1.6	1.0 3.3	+ 1.4 − 0	− 1.0 − 1.9	1.6 3.9	+ 1.4 0	− 1.6 − 2.5	3.0 6.6	+ 2.2 0	− 3.0 − 4.4	5.0 10.7	+ 3.5 0	− 5.0 − 7.2	0.24	0.40
1.2 2.9	+ 1.0 − 0	− 1.2 − 1.9	1.2 3.8	+ 1.6 − 0	− 1.2 − 2.2	2.0 4.6	+ 1.6 0	− 2.0 − 3.0	3.5 7.9	+ 2.8 0	− 3.5 − 5.1	6.0 12.8	+ 4.0 0	− 6.0 − 8.8	0.40	0.71
1.6 3.6	+ 1.2 − 0	− 1.6 − 2.4	1.6 4.8	+ 2.0 − 0	− 1.6 − 2.8	2.5 5.7	+ 2.0 0	− 2.5 − 3.7	4.5 10.0	+ 3.5 0	− 4.5 − 6.5	7.0 15.5	+ 5.0 0	− 7.0 − 10.5	0.71	1.19
2.0 4.6	+ 1.6 − 0	− 2.0 − 3.0	2.0 6.1	+ 2.5 − 0	− 2.0 − 3.6	3.0 7.1	+ 2.5 0	− 3.0 − 4.6	5.0 11.5	+ 4.0 0	− 5.0 − 7.5	8.0 18.0	+ 6.0 0	− 8.0 − 12.0	1.19	1.97
2.5 5.5	+ 1.8 − 0	− 2.5 − 3.7	2.5 7.3	+ 3.0 − 0	− 2.5 − 4.3	4.0 8.8	+ 3.0 0	− 4.0 − 5.8	6.0 13.5	+ 4.5 0	− 6.0 − 9.0	9.0 20.5	+ 7.0 0	− 9.0 − 13.5	1.97	3.15
3.0 6.6	+ 2.2 − 0	− 3.0 − 4.4	3.0 8.7	+ 3.5 − 0	− 3.0 − 5.2	5.0 10.7	+ 3.5 0	− 5.0 − 7.2	7.0 15.5	+ 5.0 0	− 7.0 − 10.5	10.0 24.0	+ 9.0 0	− 10.0 − 15.0	3.15	4.73
3.5 7.6	+ 2.5 − 0	− 3.5 − 5.1	3.5 10.0	+ 4.0 − 0	− 3.5 − 6.0	6.0 12.5	+ 4.0 0	− 6.0 − 8.5	8.0 18.0	+ 6.0 0	− 8.0 − 12.0	12.0 28.0	+ 10.0 0	− 12.0 − 18.0	4.73	7.09
4.0 8.6	+ 2.8 − 0	− 4.0 − 5.8	4.0 11.3	+ 4.5 0	− 4.0 − 6.8	7.0 14.3	+ 4.5 0	− 7.0 − 9.8	10.0 21.5	+ 7.0 0	− 10.0 − 14.5	15.0 34.0	+ 12.0 0	− 15.0 − 22.0	7.09	9.85
5.0 10.0	+ 3.0 0	− 5.0 − 7.0	5.0 13.0	+ 5.0 0	− 5.0 − 8.0	8.0 16.0	+ 5.0 0	− 8.0 − 11.0	12.0 25.0	+ 8.0 0	− 12.0 − 17.0	18.0 38.0	+ 12.0 0	− 18.0 − 26.0	9.85	12.41
6.0 11.7	+ 3.5 0	− 6.0 − 8.2	6.0 15.5	+ 6.0 0	− 6.0 − 9.5	10.0 19.5	+ 6.0 0	− 10.0 − 13.5	14.0 29.0	+ 9.0 0	− 14.0 − 20.0	22.0 45.0	+ 14.0 0	− 22.0 − 31.0	12.41	15.75
8.0 14.5	+ 4.0 0	− 8.0 −10.5	8.0 18.0	+ 6.0 0	− 8.0 −12.0	12.0 22.0	+ 6.0 0	− 12.0 − 16.0	16.0 32.0	+10.0 0	− 16.0 − 22.0	25.0 51.0	+ 16.0 0	− 25.0 − 35.0	15.75	19.69
10.0 18.0	+ 5.0 0	−10.0 −13.0	10.0 23.0	+ 8.0 0	−10.0 −15.0	16.0 29.0	+ 8.0 0	− 16.0 − 21.0	20.0 40.0	+12.0 0	− 20.0 − 28.0	30.0 62.0	+ 20.0 0	− 30.0 − 42.0	19.69	30.09
12.0 22.0	+ 6.0 0	−12.0 −16.0	12.0 28.0	+10.0 0	−12.0 −18.0	20.0 36.0	+10.0 0	− 20.0 − 26.0	25.0 51.0	+16.0 0	− 25.0 − 35.0	40.0 81.0	+ 25.0 0	− 40.0 − 56.0	30.09	41.49
16.0 29.0	+ 8.0 0	−16.0 −21.0	16.0 36.0	+12.0 0	−16.0 −24.0	25.0 45.0	+12.0 0	− 25.0 − 33.0	30.0 62.0	+20.0 0	− 30.0 − 42.0	50.0 100	+ 30.0 0	− 50.0 − 70.0	41.49	56.19
20.0 36.0	+10.0 0	−20.0 −26.0	20.0 46.0	+16.0 0	−20.0 −30.0	30.0 56.0	+16.0 0	− 30.0 − 40.0	40.0 81.0	+25.0 0	− 40.0 − 56.0	60.0 125	+ 40.0 0	− 60.0 − 85.0	56.19	76.39
25.0 45.0	+12.0 0	−25.0 −33.0	25.0 57.0	+20.0 0	−25.0 −37.0	40.0 72.0	+20.0 0	− 40.0 − 52.0	50.0 100	+30.0 0	− 50.0 − 70.0	80.0 160	+ 50.0 0	− 80.0 −110	76.39	100.9
30.0 56.0	+16.0 0	−30.0 −40.0	30.0 71.0	+25.0 0	−30.0 −46.0	50.0 91.0	+25.0 0	− 50.0 − 66.0	60.0 125	+40.0 0	− 60.0 − 85.0	100 200	+ 60.0 0	−100 −140	100.9	131.9
35.0 67.0	+20.0 0	−35.0 −47.0	35.0 85.0	+30.0 0	−35.0 −55.0	60.0 110.0	+30.0 0	− 60.0 − 80.0	80.0 160	+50.0 0	− 80.0 −110	130 260	+ 80.0 0	−130 −180	131.9	171.9
45.0 86.0	+25.0 0	−45.0 −61.0	45.0 110.0	+40.0 0	−45.0 −70.0	80.0 145.0	+40.0 0	− 80.0 −105.0	100 200	+60.0 0	−100 −140	150 310	+100 0	−150 −210	171.9	200

TABLE C.12.2 Locational Clearance Fits

Nominal Size Range, Inches		Class LC 1			Class LC 2			Class LC 3			Class LC 4			Class LC 5		
		Limits of Clearance	Standard Limits		Limits of Clearance	Standard Limits		Limits of Clearance	Standard Limits		Limits of Clearance	Standard Limits		Limits of Clearance	Standard Limits	
Over	**To**		**Hole H6**	**Shaft h5**		**Hole H7**	**Shaft h6**		**Hole H8**	**Shaft h7**		**Hole H10**	**Shaft h9**		**Hole H7**	**Shaft g6**
0	0.12	0 0.45	+0.25 −0	+0 −0.2	0 0.65	+0.4 −0	+0 −0.25	0 1	+0.6 −0	+0 −0.4	0 2.6	+1.6 −0	+0 −1.0	0.1 0.75	+0.4 −0	−0.1 −0.35
0.12	0.24	0 0.5	+0.3 −0	+0 −0.2	0 0.8	+0.5 −0	+0 −0.3	0 1.2	+0.7 −0	+0 −0.5	0 3.0	+1.8 −0	+0 −1.2	0.15 0.95	+0.5 −0	−0.15 −0.45
0.24	0.40	0 0.65	+0.4 −0	+0 −0.25	0 1.0	+0.6 −0	+0 −0.4	0 1.5	+0.9 −0	+0 −0.6	0 3.6	+2.2 −0	+0 −1.4	0.2 1.2	+0.6 −0	−0.2 −0.6
0.40	0.71	0 0.7	+0.4 −0	+0 −0.3	0 1.1	+0.7 −0	+0 −0.4	0 1.7	+1.0 −0	+0 −0.7	0 4.4	+2.8 −0	+0 −1.6	0.25 1.35	+0.7 −0	−0.25 −0.65
0.71	1.19	0 0.9	+0.5 −0	+0 −0.4	0 1.3	+0.8 −0	+0 −0.5	0 2	+1.2 −0	+0 −0.8	0 5.5	+3.5 −0	+0 −2.0	0.3 1.6	+0.8 −0	−0.3 −0.8
1.19	1.97	0 1.0	+0.6 −0	+0 −0.4	0 1.6	+1.0 −0	+0 −0.6	0 2.6	+1.6 −0	+0 −1	0 6.5	+4.0 −0	+0 −2.5	0.4 2.0	+1.0 −0	−0.4 −1.0
1.97	3.15	0 1.2	+0.7 −0	+0 −0.5	0 1.9	+1.2 −0	+0 −0.7	0 3	+1.8 −0	+0 −1.2	0 7.5	+4.5 −0	+0 −3	0.4 2.3	+1.2 −0	−0.4 −1.1
3.15	4.73	0 1.5	+0.9 −0	+0 −0.6	0 2.3	+1.4 −0	+0 −0.9	0 3.6	+2.2 −0	+0 −1.4	0 8.5	+5.0 −0	+0 −3.5	0.5 2.8	+1.4 −0	−0.5 −1.4
4.73	7.09	0 1.7	+1.0 −0	+0 −0.7	0 2.6	+1.6 −0	+0 −1.0	0 4.1	+2.5 −0	+0 −1.6	0 10	+6.0 −0	+0 −4	0.6 3.2	+1.6 −0	−0.6 −1.6
7.09	9.85	0 2.0	+1.2 −0	+0 −0.8	0 3.0	+1.8 −0	+0 −1.2	0 4.6	+2.8 −0	+0 −1.8	0 11.5	+7.0 −0	+0 −4.5	0.6 3.6	+1.8 −0	−0.6 −1.8
9.85	12.41	0 2.1	+1.2 −0	+0 −0.9	0 3.2	+2.0 −0	+0 −1.2	0 5	+3.0 −0	+0 −2.0	0 13	+8.0 −0	+0 −5	0.7 3.9	+2.0 −0	−0.7 −1.9
12.41	15.75	0 2.4	+1.4 −0	+0 −1.0	0 3.6	+2.2 −0	+0 −1.4	0 5.7	+3.5 −0	+0 −2.2	0 15	+9.0 −0	+0 −6	0.7 4.3	+2.2 −0	−0.7 −2.1
15.75	19.69	0 2.6	+1.6 −0	+0 −1.0	0 4.1	+2.5 −0	+0 −1.6	0 6.5	+4 −0	+0 −2.5	0 16	+10.0 −0	+0 −6	0.8 4.9	+2.5 −0	−0.8 −2.4
19.69	30.09	0 3.2	+2.0 −0	+0 −1.2	0 5.0	+3 −0	+0 −2	0 8	+5 −0	+0 −3	0 20	+12.0 −0	+0 −8	0.9 5.9	+3.0 −0	−0.9 −2.9
30.09	41.49	0 4.1	+2.5 −0	+0 −1.6	0 6.5	+4 −0	+0 −2.5	0 10	+6 −0	+0 −4	0 26	+16.0 −0	+0 −10	1.0 7.5	+4.0 −0	−1.0 −3.5
41.49	56.19	0 5.0	+3.0 −0	+0 −2.0	0 8.0	+5 −0	+0 −3	0 13	+8 −0	+0 −5	0 32	+20.0 −0	+0 −12	1.2 9.2	+5.0 −0	−1.2 −4.2
56.19	76.39	0 6.5	+4.0 −0	+0 −2.5	0 10	+6 −0	+0 −4	0 16	+10 −0	+0 −6	0 41	+25.0 −0	+0 −16	1.2 11.2	+6.0 −0	−1.2 −5.2
76.39	100.9	0 8.0	+5.0 −0	+0 −3.0	0 13	+8 −0	+0 −5	0 20	+12 −0	+0 −8	0 50	+30.0 −0	+0 −20	1.4 14.4	+8.0 −0	−1.4 −6.4
100.9	131.9	0 10.0	+6.0 −0	+0 −4.0	0 16	+10 −0	+0 −6	0 26	+16 −0	+0 −10	0 65	+40.0 −0	+0 −25	1.6 17.6	+10.0 −0	−1.6 −7.6
131.9	171.9	0 13.0	+8.0 −0	+0 −5.0	0 20	+12 −0	+0 −8	0 32	+20 −0	+0 −12	0 8	+50.0 −0	+0 −30	1.8 21.8	+12.0 −0	−1.8 −9.8
171.9	200	0 16.0	+10.0 −0	+0 −6.0	0 26	+16 −0	+0 −10	0 41	+25 −0	+0 −16	0 100	+60.0 −0	+0 −40	1.8 27.8	+16.0 −0	−1.8 −11.8

Limits are in thousandths of an inch. Limits for hole and shaft are applied algrebraically to the basic size to obtain the limits of size for the parts. Symbols H6, h5, etc. are hole and shaft designations in the ABC System.

Continues

TABLE C.12.2 Locational Clearance Fits—*Continued*

Class LC 6			Class LC 7			Class LC 8			Class LC 9			Class LC 10			Class LC 11			Nominal Size Range, Inches	
Limits of Clearance	Standard Limits Hole *H9*	Standard Limits Shaft *f8*	Limits of Clearance	Standard Limits Hole *H10*	Standard Limits Shaft *e9*	Limits of Clearance	Standard Limits Hole *H10*	Standard Limits Shaft *d9*	Limits of Clearance	Standard Limits Hole *H11*	Standard Limits Shaft *c10*	Limits of Clearance	Standard Limits Hole *H12*	Standard Limits Shaft	Limits of Clearance	Standard Limits Hole *H13*	Standard Limits Shaft	*Over*	*To*
0.3 1.9	+ 1.0 0	− 0.3 − 0.9	0.6 3.2	+ 1.6 0	− 0.6 − 1.6	1.0 3.6	+ 1.6 − 0	− 1.0 − 2.0	2.5 6.6	+ 2.5 − 0	− 2.5 − 4.1	4 12	+ 4 − 0	− 4 − 8	5 17	+ 6 − 0	− 5 − 11	0	0.12
0.4 2.3	+ 1.2 0	− 0.4 − 1.1	0.8 3.8	+ 1.8 0	− 0.8 − 2.0	1.2 4.2	+ 1.8 − 0	− 1.2 − 2.4	2.8 7.6	+ 3.0 − 0	− 2.8 − 4.6	4.5 14.5	+ 5 − 0	− 4.5 − 9.5	6 20	+ 7 − 0	− 6 − 13	0.12	0.24
0.5 2.8	+ 1.4 0	− 0.5 − 1.4	1.0 4.6	+ 2.2 0	− 1.0 − 2.4	1.6 5.2	+ 2.2 − 0	− 1.6 − 3.0	3.0 8.7	+ 3.5 − 0	− 3.0 − 5.2	5 17	+ 6 − 0	− 5 − 11	7 25	+ 9 − 0	− 7 − 16	0.24	0.40
0.6 3.2	+ 1.6 0	− 0.6 − 1.6	1.2 5.6	+ 2.8 0	− 1.2 − 2.8	2.0 6.4	+ 2.8 − 0	− 2.0 − 3.6	3.5 10.3	+ 4.0 − 0	− 3.5 − 6.3	6 20	+ 7 − 0	− 6 − 13	8 28	+ 10 − 0	− 8 − 18	0.40	0.71
0.8 4.0	+ 2.0 0	− 0.8 − 2.0	1.6 7.1	+ 3.5 0	− 1.6 − 3.6	2.5 8.0	+ 3.5 − 0	− 2.5 − 4.5	4.5 13.0	+ 5.0 − 0	− 4.5 − 8.0	7 23	+ 8 − 0	− 7 − 15	10 34	+ 12 − 0	− 10 − 22	0.71	1.19
1.0 5.1	+ 2.5 0	− 1.0 − 2.6	2.0 8.5	+ 4.0 0	− 2.0 − 4.5	3.0 9.5	+ 4.0 − 0	− 3.0 − 5.5	5 15	+ 6 − 0	− 5 − 9	8 28	+ 10 − 0	− 8 − 18	12 44	+ 16 − 0	− 12 − 28	1.19	1.97
1.2 6.0	+ 3.0 0	− 1.2 − 3.0	2.5 10.0	+ 4.5 0	− 2.5 − 5.5	4.0 11.5	+ 4.5 − 0	− 4.0 − 7.0	6 17.5	+ 7 − 0	− 6 − 10.5	10 34	+ 12 − 0	− 10 − 22	14 50	+ 18 − 0	− 14 − 32	1.97	3.15
1.4 7.1	+ 3.5 0	− 1.4 − 3.6	3.0 11.5	+ 5.0 0	− 3.0 − 6.5	5.0 13.5	+ 5.0 − 0	− 5.0 − 8.5	7 21	+ 9 − 0	− 7 − 12	11 39	+ 14 − 0	− 11 − 25	16 60−	+ 22 −0	− 16 − 38	3.15	4.73
1.6 8.1	+ 4.0 0	− 1.6 − 4.1	3.5 13.5	+ 6.0 0	− 3.5 − 7.5	6 16	+ 6 − 0	− 6 −10	8 24	+ 10 − 0	− 8 − 14	12 44	+ 16 − 0	− 12 − 28	18 68	+ 25 − 0	− 18 − 43	4.73	7.09
2.0 9.3	+ 4.5 0	− 2.0 − 4.8	4.0 15.5	+ 7.0 0	− 4.0 − 8.5	7 18.5	+ 7 − 0	− 7 −11.5	10 29	+ 12 − 0	− 10 − 17	16 52	+ 18 − 0	− 16 − 34	22 78	+ 28 − 0	− 22 − 50	7.09	9.85
2.2 10.2	+ 5.0 0	− 2.2 − 5.2	4.5 17.5	+ 8.0 0	− 4.5 − 9.5	7 20	+ 8 − 0	− 7 −12	12 32	+ 12 − 0	− 12 − 20	20 60	+ 20 − 0	− 20 − 40	28 88	+ 30 − 0	− 28 − 58	9.85	12.41
2.5 12.0	+ 6.0 0	− 2.5 − 6.0	5.0 20.0	+ 9.0 0	− 5 −11	8 23	+ 9 − 0	− 8 −14	14 37	+ 14 − 0	− 14 − 23	22 66	+ 22 − 0	− 22 − 44	30 100	+ 35 − 0	− 30 − 65	12.41	15.75
2.8 12.8	+ 6.0 0	− 2.8 − 6.8	5.0 21.0	+10.0 0	− 5 −11	9 25	+10 − 0	− 9 −15	16 42	+ 16 − 0	− 16 − 26	25 75	+ 25 − 0	− 25 − 50	35 115	+ 40 − 0	− 35 − 75	15.75	19.69
3.0 16.0	+ 8.0 0	− 3.0 − 8.0	6.0 26.0	+12.0 − 0	− 6 −14	10 30	+12 − 0	−10 −18	18 50	+ 20 − 0	− 18 − 30	28 88	+ 30 − 0	− 28 − 58	40 140	+ 50 − 0	− 40 − 90	19.69	30.09
3.5 19.5	+10.0 0	− 3.5 − 9.5	7.0 33.0	+16.0 − 0	− 7 −17	12 38	+16 − 0	−12 −22	20 61	+ 25 − 0	− 20 − 36	30 110	+ 40 − 0	− 30 − 70	45 165	+ 60 − 0	− 45 −105	30.09	41.49
4.0 24.0	+12.0 0	− 4.0 −12.0	8.0 40.0	+20.0 − 0	− 8 −20	14 46	+20 − 0	−14 −26	25 75	+ 30 − 0	− 25 − 45	40 140	+ 50 − 0	− 40 − 90	60 220	+ 80 − 0	− 60 −140	41.49	56.19
4.5 30.5	+16.0 0	− 4.5 −14.5	9.0 50.0	+25.0 − 0	− 9 −25	16 57	+25 − 0	−16 −32	30 95	+ 40 − 0	− 30 − 55	50 170	+ 60 − 0	− 50 110	70 270	+100 − 0	− 70 −170	56.19	76.39
5.0 37.0	+20.0 0	− 5 −17	10.0 60.0	+30.0 − 0	−10 −30	18 68	+30 − 0	−18 −38	35 115	+ 50 − 0	− 35 − 65	50 210	+ 80 − 0	− 50 −130	80 330	+125 − 0	− 80 −205	76.39	100.9
6.0 47.0	+25.0 0	− 6 −22	12.0 67.0	+40.0 − 0	−12 −27	20 85	+40 − 0	−20 −45	40 140	+ 60 − 0	− 40 − 80	60 260	+100 − 0	− 60 −160	90 410	+160 − 0	− 90 −250	100.9	131.9
7.0 57.0	+30.0 0	− 7 −27	14.0 94.0	+50.0 − 0	−14 −44	25 105	+50 − 0	−25 −55	50 180	+ 80 − 0	− 50 −100	80 330	+125 − 0	− 80 −205	100 500	+200 − 0	−100 −300	131.9	171.9
7.0 72.0	+40.0 0	− 7 −32	14.0 114.0	+60.0 − 0	−14 −54	25 125	+60 − 0	−25 −65	50 210	+100 − 0	− 50 −110	90 410	+160 − 0	− 90 −250	125 625	+250 − 0	−125 −375	171.9	200

TABLE C.12.3 Locational Transition Fits

Nominal Size Range, Inches	Class LT 1			Class LT 2			Class LT 3			Class LT 4			Class LT 5			Class LT 6		
		Standard Limits			Standard Limits			Standard Limits			Standard Limits			Standard Limits			Standard Limits	
Over To	Fit	*Hole H7*	*Shaft js6*	Fit	*Hole H8*	*Shaft js7*	Fit	*Hole H7*	*Shaft k6*	Fit	*Hole H8*	*Shaft k7*	Fit	*Hole H7*	*Shaft n6*	Fit	*Hole H7*	*Shaft n7*
0 – 0.12	−0.10	+0.4	+0.10	−0.2	+0.6	+0.2							−0.5	+0.4	+0.5	−0.65	+0.4	−0.65
	+0.50	−0	−0.10	+0.8	−0	−0.2							+0.15	−0	+0.25	+0.15	−0	+0.25
0.12 – 0.24	−0.15	+0.5	+0.15	−0.25	+0.7	+0.25							−0.6	+0.5	+0.6	−0.8	+0.5	+0.8
	+0.65	−0	−0.15	+0.95	−0	−0.25							+0.2	−0	+0.3	+0.2	−0	+0.3
0.24 – 0.40	−0.2	+0.6	+0.2	−0.3	+0.9	+0.3	−0.5	+0.6	+0.5	−0.7	+0.9	+0.7	−0.8	+0.6	+0.8	−1.0	+0.6	+1.0
	+0.8	−0	−0.2	+1.2	−0	−0.3	+0.5	−0	+0.1	+0.8	−0	+0.1	+0.2	−0	+0.4	+0.2	−0	+0.4
0.40 – 0.71	−0.2	+0.7	+0.2	−0.35	+1.0	+0.35	−0.5	+0.7	+0.5	−0.8	+1.0	+0.8	−0.9	+0.7	+0.9	−1.2	+0.7	+1.2
	+0.9	−0	−0.2	+1.35	−0	−0.35	+0.6	−0	+0.1	+0.9	−0	+0.1	+0.2	−0	+0.5	+0.2	−0	+0.5
0.71 – 1.19	−0.25	+0.8	+0.25	−0.4	+1.2	+0.4	−0.6	+0.8	+0.6	−0.9	+1.2	+0.9	−1.1	+0.8	+1.1	−1.4	+0.8	+1.4
	+1.05	−0	−0.25	+1.6	−0	−0.4	+0.7	−0	+0.1	+1.1	−0	+0.1	+0.2	−0	+0.6	+0.2	−0	+0.6
1.19 – 1.97	−0.3	+1.0	+0.3	−0.5	+1.6	+0.5	−0.7	+1.0	+0.7	−1.1	+1.6	+1.1	−1.3	+1.0	+1.3	−1.7	+1.0	+1.7
	+1.3	−0	−0.3	+2.1	−0	−0.5	+0.9	−0	+0.1	+1.5	−0	+0.1	+0.3	−0	+0.7	+0.3	−0	+0.7
1.97 – 3.15	−0.3	+1.2	+0.3	−0.6	+1.8	+0.6	−0.8	+1.2	+0.8	−1.3	+1.8	+1.3	−1.5	+1.2	+1.5	−2.0	+1.2	+2.0
	+1.5	−0	−0.3	+2.4	−0	−0.6	+1.1	−0	+0.1	+1.7	−0	+0.1	+0.4	−0	+0.8	+0.4	−0	+0.8
3.15 – 4.73	−0.4	+1.4	+0.4	−0.7	+2.2	+0.7	−1.0	+1.4	+1.0	−1.5	+2.2	+1.5	−1.9	+1.4	+1.9	−2.4	+1.4	+2.4
	+1.8	−0	−0.4	+2.9	−0	−0.7	+1.3	−0	+0.1	+2.1	−0	+0.1	+0.4	−0	+1.0	+0.4	−0	+1.0
4.73 – 7.09	−0.5	+1.6	+0.5	−0.8	+2.5	+0.8	−1.1	+1.6	+1.1	−1.7	+2.5	+1.7	−2.2	+1.6	+2.2	−2.8	+1.6	+2.8
	+2.1	−0	−0.5	+3.3	−0	−0.8	+1.5	−0	+0.1	+2.4	−0	+0.1	+0.4	−0	+1.2	+0.4	−0	+1.2
7.09 – 9.85	−0.6	+1.8	+0.6	−0.9	+2.8	+0.9	−1.4	+1.8	+1.4	−2.0	+2.8	+2.0	−2.6	+1.8	+2.6	−3.2	+1.8	+3.2
	+2.4	−0	−0.6	+3.7	−0	−0.9	+1.6	−0	+0.2	+2.6	−0	+0.2	+0.4	−0	+1.4	+0.4	−0	+1.4
9.85 – 12.41	−0.6	+2.0	+0.6	−1.0	+3.0	+1.0	−1.4	+2.0	+1.4	−2.2	+3.0	+2.2	−2.6	+2.0	+2.6	−3.4	+2.0	+3.4
	+2.6	−0	−0.6	+4.0	−0	−1.0	+1.8	−0	+0.2	+2.8	−0	+0.2	+0.6	−0	+1.4	+0.6	−0	+1.4
12.41 – 15.75	−0.7	+2.2	+0.7	−1.0	+3.5	+1.0	−1.6	+2.2	+1.6	−2.4	+3.5	+2.4	−3.0	+2.2	+3.0	−3.8	+2.2	+3.8
	+2.9	−0	−0.7	+4.5	−0	−1.0	+2.0	−0	+0.2	+3.3	−0	+0.2	+0.6	−0	+1.6	+0.6	−0	+1.6
15.75 – 19.69	−0.8	+2.5	+0.8	−1.2	+4.0	+1.2	−1.8	+2.5	+1.8	−2.7	+4.0	+2.7	−3.4	+2.5	+3.4	−4.3	+2.5	+4.3
	+3.3	−0	−0.8	+5.2	−0	−1.2	+2.3	−0	+0.2	+3.8	−0	+0.2	+0.7	−0	+1.8	+0.7	−0	+1.8

Limits are in thousandths of an inch. Limits for hole and shaft are applied algebraically to the basic size to obtain the limits of size for the mating parts.
"Fit" represents the maximum interference (minus values) and the maximum clearance (plus values).
Symbols H7, js6, etc. are hole and shaft designations in the ABC System.

TABLE C.12.4 Locational Interference Fits

Nominal Size Range, Inches		Class LN 1			Class LN 2			Class LN 3		
		Limits of Intolerance	Standard Limits		Limits of Intolerance	Standard Limits		Limits of Intolerance	Standard Limits	
Over	***To***		***Hole H6***	***Shaft n5***		***Hole H7***	***Shaft p6***		***Hole H7***	***Shaft r6***
0	0.12	0 0.45	+ 0.25 − 0	+0.45 +0.25	0 0.65	+ 0.4 − 0	+ 0.65 + 0.4	0.1 0.75	+ 0.4 − 0	+ 0.75 + 0.5
0.12	0.24	0 0.5	+ 0.3 − 0	+0.5 +0.3	0 0.8	+ 0.5 − 0	+ 0.8 + 0.5	0.1 0.9	+ 0.5 0	+ 0.9 + 0.6
0.24	0.40	0 0.65	+ 0.4 − 0	+0.65 +0.4	0 1.0	+ 0.6 − 0	+ 1.0 + 0.6	0.2 1.2	+ 0.6 − 0	+ 1.2 + 0.8
0.40	0.71	0 0.8	+ 0.4 − 0	+0.8 +0.4	0 1.1	+ 0.7 − 0	+ 1.1 + 0.7	0.3 1.4	+ 0.7 − 0	+ 1.4 + 1.0
0.71	1.19	0 1.0	+ 0.5 − 0	+1.0 +0.5	0 1.3	+ 0.8 − 0	+ 1.3 + 0.8	0.4 1.7	+ 0.8 − 0	+ 1.7 + 1.2
1.19	1.97	0 1.1	+ 0.6 − 0	+1.1 +0.6	0 1.6	+ 1.0 − 0	+ 1.6 + 1.0	0.4 2.0	+ 1.0 − 0	+ 2.0 + 1.4
1.97	3.15	0.1 1.3	+ 0.7 − 0	+1.3 +0.7	0.2 2.1	+ 1.2 − 0	+ 2.1 + 1.4	0.4 2.3	+ 1.2 − 0	+ 2.3 + 1.6
3.15	4.73	0.1 1.6	+ 0.9 − 0	+1.6 +1.0	0.2 2.5	+ 1.4 − 0	+ 2.5 + 1.6	0.6 2.9	+ 1.4 − 0	+ 2.9 + 2.0
4.73	7.09	0.2 1.9	+ 1.0 − 0	+1.9 +1.2	0.2 2.8	+ 1.6 − 0	+ 2.8 + 1.8	0.9 3.5	+ 1.6 − 0	+ 3.5 + 2.5
7.09	9.85	0.2 2.2	+ 1.2 − 0	+2.2 +1.4	0.2 3.2	+ 1.8 − 0	+ 3.2 + 2.0	1.2 4.2	+ 1.8 − 0	+ 4.2 + 3.0
9.85	12.41	0.2 2.3	+ 1.2 − 0	+2.3 +1.4	0.2 3.4	+ 2.0 − 0	+ 3.4 + 2.2	1.5 4.7	+ 2.0 − 0	+ 4.7 + 3.5
12.41	15.75	0.2 2.6	+ 1.4 − 0	+2.6 +1.6	0.3 3.9	+ 2.2 − 0	+ 3.9 + 2.5	2.3 5.9	+ 2.2 − 0	+ 5.9 + 4.5
15.75	19.69	0.2 2.8	+ 1.6 − 0	+2.8 +1.8	0.3 4.4	+ 2.5 − 0	+ 4.4 + 2.8	2.5 6.6	+ 2.5 − 0	+ 6.6 + 5.0
19.69	30.09		+ 2.0 − 0		0.5 5.5	+ 3 − 0	+ 5.5 + 3.5	4 9	+ 3 − 0	+ 9 + 7
30.09	41.49		+ 2.5 − 0		0.5 7.0	+ 4 − 0	+ 7.0 + 4.5	5 11.5	+ 4 − 0	+11.5 + 9
41.49	56.19		+ 3.0 − 0		1 9	+ 5 − 0	+ 9 + 6	7 15	+ 5 − 0	+15 +12
56.19	76.39		+ 4.0 − 0		1 11	+ 6 − 0	+11 + 7	10 20	+ 6 − 0	+20 +16
76.39	100.9		+ 5.0 − 0		1 14	+ 8 − 0	+14 + 9	12 25	+ 8 − 0	+25 +20
100.9	131.9		+ 6.0 − 0		2 18	+10 − 0	+18 +12	15 31	+10 − 0	+31 +25
131.9	171.9		+ 8.0 − 0		4 24	+12 − 0	+24 +16	18 38	+12 − 0	+38 +30
171.9	200		+10.0 − 0		4 30	+16 − 0	+30 +20	24 50	+16 − 0	+50 +40

Limits are in thousandths of an inch. Limits for hole and shaft are applied algebraically to the basic size to obtain the limits of size for the parts. Symbols H7, p 6, etc. are hole and shaft designations used in the ABC System.

TABLE C.12.5 Force and Shrink Fits

Nominal Size Range, Inches	Class FN 1			Class FN 2			Class FN 3			Class FN 4			Class FN 5		
	Limits of Interference	Standard Limits		Limits of Interference	Standard Limits		Limits of Interference	Standard Limits		Limits of Interference	Standard Limits		Limits of Interference	Standard Limits	
Over To		*Hole H6*	*Shaft*		*Hole H7*	*Shaft s6*		*Hole H7*	*Shaft t6*		*Hole H7*	*Shaft u6*		*Hole H8*	*Shaft ×7*
0 – 0.12	0.05	+0.25	+0.5	0.2	+0.4	+0.85				0.3	+0.4	+ 0.95	0.3	+0.6	+ 1.3
	0.5	−0	+0.3	0.85	−0	+0.6				0.95	−0	+ 0.7	1.3	−0	+ 0.9
0.12 – 0.24	0.1	+0.3	+0.6	0.2	+0.5	+1.0				0.4	+0.5	+ 1.2	0.5	+0.7	+ 1.7
	0.6	−0	+0.4	1.0	−0	+0.7				1.2	−0	+ 0.9	1.7	−0	+ 1.2
0.24 – 0.40	0.1	+0.4	+0.75	0.4	+0.6	+1.4				0.6	+0.6	+ 1.6	0.5	+0.9	+ 2.0
	0.75	−0	+0.5	1.4	−0	+1.0				1.6	−0	+ 1.2	2.0	−0	+ 1.4
0.40 – 0.56	0.1	−0.4	+0.8	0.5	+0.7	+1.6				0.7	+0.7	+ 1.8	0.6	+1.0	+ 2.3
	0.8	−0	+0.5	1.6	−0	+1.2				1.8	−0	+ 1.4	2.3	−0	+ 1.6
0.56 – 0.71	0.2	+0.4	+0.9	0.5	+0.7	+1.6				0.7	+0.7	+ 1.8	0.8	+1.0	+ 2.5
	0.9	−0	+0.6	1.6	−0	+1.2				1.8	−0	+ 1.4	2.5	−0	+ 1.8
0.71 – 0.95	0.2	+0.5	+1.1	0.6	+0.8	+1.9				0.8	+0.8	+ 2.1	1.0	+1.2	+ 3.0
	1.1	−0	+0.7	1.9	−0	+1.4				2.1	−0	+ 1.6	3.0	−0	+ 2.2
0.95 – 1.19	0.3	+0.5	+1.2	0.6	+0.8	+1.9	0.8	+0.8	+ 2.1	1.0	+0.8	+ 2.3	1.3	+1.2	+ 3.3
	1.2	−0	+0.8	1.9	−0	+1.4	2.1	−0	+ 1.6	2.3	−0	+ 1.8	3.3	−0	+ 2.5
1.19 – 1.58	0.3	+0.6	+1.3	0.8	+1.0	+2.4	1.0	+1.0	+ 2.6	1.5	+1.0	+ 3.1	1.4	+1.6	+ 4.0
	1.3	−0	+0.9	2.4	−0	+1.8	2.6	−0	+ 2.0	3.1	−0	+ 2.5	4.0	−0	+ 3.0
1.58 – 1.97	0.4	+0.6	+1.4	0.8	+1.0	+2.4	1.2	+1.0	+ 2.8	1.8	+1.0	+ 3.4	2.4	+1.6	+ 5.0
	1.4	−0	+1.0	2.4	−0	+1.8	2.8	−0	+ 2.2	3.4	−0	+ 2.8	5.0	−0	+ 4.0
1.97 – 2.56	0.6	+0.7	+1.8	0.8	+1.2	+2.7	1.3	+1.2	+ 3.2	2.3	+1.2	+ 4.2	3.2	+1.8	+ 6.2
	1.8	−0	+1.3	2.7	−0	+2.0	3.2	−0	+ 2.5	4.2	−0	+ 3.5	6.2	−0	+ 5.0
2.56 – 3.15	0.7	+0.7	+1.9	1.0	+1.2	+2.9	1.8	+1.2	+ 3.7	2.8	+1.2	+ 4.7	4.2	+1.8	+ 7.2
	1.9	−0	+1.4	2.9	−0	+2.2	3.7	−0	+ 3.0	4.7	−0	+ 4.0	7.2	−0	+ 6.0
3.15 – 3.94	0.9	+0.9	+2.4	1.4	+1.4	+3.7	2.1	+1.4	+ 4.4	3.6	+1.4	+ 5.9	4.8	+2.2	+ 8.4
	2.4	−0	+1.8	3.7	−0	+2.8	4.4	−0	+ 3.5	5.9	−0	+ 5.0	8.4	−0	+ 7.0
3.94 – 4.73	1.1	+0.9	+2.6	1.6	+1.4	+3.9	2.6	+1.4	+ 4.9	4.6	+1.4	+ 6.9	5.8	+2.2	+ 9.4
	2.6	−0	+2.0	3.9	−0	+3.0	4.9	−0	+ 4.0	6.9	−0	+ 6.0	9.4	−0	+ 8.0
4.73 – 5.52	1.2	+1.0	+2.9	1.9	+1.6	+4.5	3.4	+1.6	+ 6.0	5.4	+1.6	+ 8.0	7.5	+2.5	+11.6
	2.9	−0	+2.2	4.5	−0	+3.5	6.0	−0	+ 5.0	8.0	−0	+ 7.0	11.6	−0	+10.0
5.52 – 6.30	1.5	+1.0	+3.2	2.4	+1.6	+5.0	3.4	+1.6	+ 6.0	5.4	+1.6	+ 8.0	9.5	+2.5	+13.6
	3.2	−0	+2.5	5.0	−0	+4.0	6.0	−0	+ 5.0	8.0	−0	+ 7.0	13.6	−0	+12.0
6.30 – 7.09	1.8	+1.0	+3.5	2.9	+1.6	+5.5	4.4	+1.6	+ 7.0	6.4	+1.6	+ 9.0	9.5	+2.5	+13.6
	3.5	−0	+2.8	5.5	−0	+4.5	7.0	−0	+ 6.0	9.0	−0	+ 8.0	13.6	−0	+12.0
7.09 – 7.88	1.8	+1.2	+3.8	3.2	+1.8	+6.2	5.2	+1.8	+ 8.2	7.2	+1.8	+10.2	11.2	+2.8	+15.8
	3.8	−0	+3.0	6.2	−0	+5.0	8.2	−0	+ 7.0	10.2	−0	+ 9.0	15.8	−0	+14.0
7.88 – 8.86	2.3	+1.2	+4.3	3.2	+1.8	+6.2	5.2	+1.8	+ 8.2	8.2	+1.8	+11.2	13.2	+2.8	+17.8
	4.3	−0	+3.5	6.2	−0	+5.0	8.2	−0	+ 7.0	11.2	−0	+10.0	17.8	−0	+16.0
8.86 – 9.85	2.3	+1.2	+4.3	4.2	+1.8	+7.2	6.2	+1.8	+ 9.2	10.2	+1.8	+13.2	13.2	+2.8	+17.8
	4.3	−0	+3.5	7.2	−0	+6.0	9.2	−0	+ 8.0	13.2	−0	+12.0	17.8	−0	+16.0
9.85–11.03	2.8	+1.2	+4.9	4.0	+2.0	+7.2	7.0	+2.0	+10.2	10.0	+2.0	+13.2	15.0	+3.0	+20.0
	4.9	−0	+4.0	7.2	−0	+6.0	10.2	−0	+ 9.0	13.2	−0	+12.0	20.0	−0	+18.0

Limits are in thousandths of an inch. Limits for hole and shaft are applied algebraically to the basic size to obtain the limits of size for the parts. Symbols H7, s6, etc. are hole and shaft designations used in the ABC System.

Continues

TABLE C.12.5 Force and Shrink Fits—*Continued*

Nominal Size Range, Inches		Class FN 1			Class FN 2			Class FN 3			Class FN 4			Class FN 5		
		Limits of Interference	Standard Limits		Limits of Interference	Standard Limits		Limits of Interference	Standard Limits		Limits of Interference	Standard Limits		Limits of Interference	Standard Limits	
Over	*To*		*Hole* *H6*	*Shaft*		*Hole* *H7*	*Shaft* *s6*		*Hole* *H7*	*Shaft* *t6*		*Hole* *H7*	*Shaft* *u6*		*Hole* *H8*	*Shaft* *×7*
11.03	12.41	2.8 4.9	+ 1.2 − 0	+ 4.9 + 4.0	5.0 8.2	+ 2.0 − 0	+ 8.2 + 7.0	7.0 10.2	+ 2.0 − 0	+ 10.2 + 9.0	12.0 15.2	+ 2.0 − 0	+ 15.2 + 14.0	17.0 22.0	+ 3.0 − 0	+ 22.0 + 20.0
12.41	13.98	3.1 5.5	+ 1.4 − 0	+ 5.5 + 4.5	5.8 9.4	+ 2.2 − 0	+ 9.4 + 8.0	7.8 11.4	+ 2.2 − 0	+ 11.4 + 10.0	13.8 17.4	+ 2.2 − 0	+ 17.4 + 16.0	18.5 24.2	+ 3.5 + 0	+ 24.2 + 22.0
13.98	15.75	3.6 6.1	+ 1.4 − 0	+ 6.1 + 5.0	5.8 9.4	+ 2.2 − 0	+ 9.4 + 8.0	9.8 13.4	+ 2.2 − 0	+ 13.4 + 12.0	15.8 19.4	+ 2.2 − 0	+ 19.4 + 18.0	21.5 27.2	+ 3.5 − 0	+ 27.2 + 25.0
15.75	17.72	4.4 7.0	+ 1.6 − 0	+ 7.0 + 6.0	6.5 10.6	+ 2.5 − 0	+ 10.6 + 9.0	9.5 13.6	+ 2.5 − 0	+ 13.6 + 12.0	17.5 21.6	+ 2.5 − 0	+ 21.6 + 20.0	24.0 30.5	+ 4.0 − 0	+ 30.5 + 28.0
17.72	19.69	4.4 7.0	+ 1.6 − 0	+ 7.0 + 6.0	7.5 11.6	+ 2.5 − 0	+ 11.6 + 10.0	11.5 15.6	+ 2.5 − 0	+ 15.6 + 14.0	19.5 23.6	+ 2.5 − 0	+ 23.6 + 22.0	26.0 32.5	+ 4.0 − 0	+ 32.5 + 30.0
19.69	24.34	6.0 9.2	+ 2.0 − 0	+ 9.2 + 8.0	9.0 14.0	+ 3.0 − 0	+ 14.0 + 12.0	15.0 20.0	+ 3.0 − 0	+ 20.0 + 18.0	22.0 27.0	+ 3.0 − 0	+ 27.0 + 25.0	30.0 38.0	+ 5.0 − 0	+ 38.0 + 35.0
24.34	30.09	7.0 10.2	+ 2.0 − 0	+10.2 + 9.0	11.0 16.0	+ 3.0 − 0	+ 16.0 + 14.0	17.0 22.0	+ 3.0 − 0	+ 22.0 + 20.0	27.0 32.0	+ 3.0 − 0	+ 32.0 + 30.0	35.0 43.0	+ 5.0 − 0	+ 43.0 + 40.0
30.09	35.47	7.5 11.6	+ 2.5 − 0	+11.6 +10.0	14.0 20.5	+ 4.0 − 0	+ 20.5 + 18.0	21.0 27.5	+ 4.0 − 0	+ 27.5 + 25.0	31.0 37.5	+ 4.0 − 0	+ 37.5 + 35.0	44.0 54.0	+ 6.0 − 0	+ 54.0 + 50.0
35.47	41.49	9.5 13.6	+ 2.5 − 0	+13.6 +12.0	16.0 22.5	+ 4.0 − 0	+ 22.5 + 20.0	24.0 30.5	+ 4.0 − 0	+ 30.5 + 28.0	36.0 43.5	+ 4.0 − 0	+ 43.5 + 40.0	54.0 64.0	+ 6.0 − 0	+ 64.0 + 60.0
41.49	48.28	11.0 16.0	+ 3.0 − 0	+16.0 +14.0	17.0 25.0	+ 5.0 − 0	+ 25.0 + 22.0	30.0 38.0	+ 5.0 − 0	+ 38.0 + 35.0	45.0 53.0	+ 5.0 − 0	+ 53.0 + 50.0	62.0 75.0	+ 8.0 − 0	+ 75.0 + 70.0
48.28	56.19	13.0 18.0	+ 3.0 − 0	+18.0 +16.0	20.0 28.0	+ 5.0 − 0	+ 28.0 + 25.0	35.0 43.0	+ 5.0 − 0	+ 43.0 + 40.0	55.0 63.0	+ 5.0 − 0	+ 63.0 + 60.0	72.0 85.0	+ 8.0 − 0	+ 85.0 + 80.0
56.19	65.54	14.0 20.5	+ 4.0 − 0	+20.5 +18.0	24.0 34.0	+ 6.0 − 0	+ 34.0 + 30.0	39.0 49.0	+ 6.0 − 0	+ 49.0 + 45.0	64.0 74.0	+ 6.0 − 0	+ 74.0 + 70.0	90.0 106	+10.0 − 0	+106 +100
65.54	76.39	18.0 24.5	+ 4.0 − 0	+24.5 +22.0	29.0 39.0	+ 6.0 − 0	+ 39.0 35.0	44.0 54.0	+ 6.0 − 0	+ 54.0 + 50.0	74.0 84.0	+ 6.0 − 0	+ 84.0 + 80.0	110 126	+10.0 − 0	+126 +120
76.39	87.79	20.0 28.0	+ 5.0 − 0	+28.0 +25.0	32.0 45.0	+ 8.0 − 0	+ 45.0 + 40.0	52.0 65.0	+ 8.0 − 0	+ 65.0 + 60.0	82.0 95.0	+ 8.0 − 0	+ 95.0 + 90.0	128 148	+12.0 − 0	+148 +140
87.79	100.9	23.0 31.0	+ 5.0 − 0	+31.0 +28.0	37.0 50.0	+ 8.0 − 0	+ 50.0 + 45.0	62.0 75.0	+ 8.0 − 0	+ 75.0 + 70.0	92.0 105	+ 8.0 − 0	+105 +100	148 168	+12.0 − 0	+168 +160
100.9	115.3	24.0 34.0	+ 6.0 − 0	+34.0 +30.0	40.0 56.0	+10.0 − 0	+ 56.0 + 50.0	70.0 86.0	+10.0 − 0	+ 86.0 + 80.0	110 126	+10.0 − 0	+126 +120	164 190	+16.0 − 0	+190 +180
115.3	131.9	29.0 39.0	+ 6.0 − 0	+39.0 +35.0	50.0 66.0	+10.0 − 0	+ 66.0 + 60.0	80.0 96.0	+10.0 − 0	+ 96.0 + 90.0	130 146	+10.0 − 0	+146 +140	184 210	+16.0 − 0	+210 +200
131.9	152.2	37.0 50.0	+ 8.0 − 0	+50.0 +45.0	58.0 78.0	+12.0 − 0	+ 78.0 + 70.0	88.0 108	+12.0 − 0	+108 +100	148 168	+12.0 − 0	+168 +160	200 232	+20.0 − 0	+232 +220
152.2	171.9	42.0 55.0	+ 8.0 − 0	+55.0 +50.0	68.0 88.0	+12.0 − 0	+ 88.0 + 80.0	108 128	+12.0 − 0	+128 +120	168 188	+12.0 − 0	+188 +170	230 262	+20.0 − 0	+262 +250
171.9	200	50.0 66.0	+10.0 − 0	+66.0 +60.0	74.0 100	+16.0 − 0	+100 + 90	124 150	+16.0 − 0	+150 +140	184 210	+16.0 − 0	+210 +200	275 316	+ 2.5 − 0	+316 +300

TABLE C.12.6 Preferred Metric Hole Basis Clearance Fits

Basic Size		Loose Running			Free Running			Close Running			Sliding			Locational Clearance		
		Hole H11	*Shaft c11*	*Fit*	*Hole H9*	*Shaft d9*	*Fit*	*Hole H8*	*Shaft f7*	*Fit*	*Hole H7*	*Shaft g6*	*Fit*	*Hole H7*	*Shaft h6*	*Fit*
1	Max	1.060	0.940	0.180	1.025	0.980	0.070	1.014	0.994	0.030	1.010	0.998	0.018	1.010	1.000	0.016
	Min	1.000	0.880	0.060	1.000	0.955	0.020	1.000	0.984	0.006	1.000	0.992	0.002	1.000	0.994	0.000
1.2	Max	1.260	1.140	0.180	1.225	1.180	0.070	1.214	1.194	0.030	1.210	1.198	0.018	1.210	1.200	0.016
	Min	1.200	1.080	0.060	1.200	1.155	0.020	1.200	1.184	0.006	1.200	1.192	0.002	1.200	1.194	0.000
1.6	Max	1.660	1.540	0.180	1.625	1.580	0.070	1.614	1.594	0.030	1.610	1.598	0.018	1.610	1.600	0.016
	Min	1.600	1.480	0.060	1.600	1.555	0.020	1.600	1.584	0.006	1.600	1.592	0.002	1.600	1.594	0.000
2	Max	2.060	1.940	0.180	2.025	1.980	0.070	2.014	1.994	0.030	2.010	1.998	0.018	2.010	2.000	0.016
	Min	2.000	1.880	0.060	2.000	1.955	0.020	2.000	1.984	0.006	2.000	1.992	0.002	2.000	1.994	0.000
2.5	Max	2.560	2.440	0.180	2.525	2.480	0.070	2.514	2.494	0.030	2.510	2.498	0.018	2.510	2.500	0.016
	Min	2.500	2.380	0.060	2.500	2.455	0.020	2.500	2.484	0.006	2.500	2.492	0.002	2.500	2.494	0.000
3	Max	3.060	2.940	0.180	3.025	2.980	0.070	3.014	2.994	0.030	3.010	2.998	0.018	3.010	3.000	0.016
	Min	3.000	2.880	0.060	3.000	2.955	0.020	3.000	2.984	0.006	3.000	2.992	0.002	3.000	2.994	0.000
4	Max	4.075	3.930	0.220	4.030	3.970	0.090	4.018	3.990	0.040	4.012	3.996	0.024	4.012	4.000	0.020
	Min	4.000	3.855	0.070	4.000	3.940	0.030	4.000	3.978	0.010	4.000	3.988	0.004	4.000	3.992	0.000
5	Max	5.075	4.930	0.220	5.030	4.970	0.090	5.018	4.990	0.040	5.012	4.996	0.024	5.012	5.000	0.020
	Min	5.000	4.855	0.070	5.000	4.940	0.030	5.000	4.978	0.010	5.000	4.988	0.004	5.000	4.992	0.000
6	Max	6.075	5.930	0.220	6.030	5.970	0.090	6.018	5.990	0.040	6.012	5.996	0.024	6.012	6.000	0.020
	Min	6.000	5.855	0.070	6.000	5.940	0.030	6.000	5.978	0.010	6.000	5.988	0.004	6.000	5.992	0.000
8	Max	8.090	7.920	0.260	8.036	7.960	0.112	8.022	7.987	0.050	8.015	7.995	0.029	8.015	8.000	0.024
	Min	8.000	7.830	0.080	8.000	7.924	0.040	8.000	7.972	0.013	8.000	7.986	0.005	8.000	7.991	0.000
10	Max	10.090	9.920	0.260	10.036	9.960	0.112	10.022	9.987	0.050	10.015	9.995	0.029	10.015	10.000	0.024
	Min	10.000	9.830	0.080	10.000	9.924	0.040	10.000	9.972	0.013	10.000	9.986	0.005	10.000	9.991	0.000
12	Max	12.110	11.905	0.315	12.043	11.950	0.136	12.027	11.984	0.061	12.018	11.994	0.035	12.018	12.000	0.029
	Min	12.000	11.795	0.095	12.000	11.907	0.050	12.000	11.966	0.016	12.000	11.983	0.006	12.000	11.989	0.000
16	Max	16.110	15.905	0.315	16.043	15.950	0.136	16.027	15.984	0.061	16.018	15.994	0.035	16.018	16.000	0.029
	Min	16.000	15.795	0.095	16.000	15.907	0.050	16.000	15.966	0.016	16.000	15.983	0.006	16.000	15.989	0.000
20	Max	20.130	19.890	0.370	20.052	19.935	0.169	20.033	19.980	0.074	20.021	19.993	0.041	20.021	20.000	0.034
	Min	20.000	19.760	0.110	20.000	19.883	0.065	20.000	19.959	0.020	20.000	19.980	0.007	20.000	19.987	0.000
25	Max	25.130	24.890	0.370	25.052	24.935	0.169	25.033	24.980	0.074	25.021	24.993	0.041	25.021	25.000	0.034
	Min	25.000	24.760	0.110	25.000	24.883	0.065	25.000	24.959	0.020	25.000	24.980	0.007	25.000	24.987	0.000
30	Max	30.130	29.890	0.370	30.052	29.935	0.169	30.033	29.980	0.074	30.021	29.993	0.041	30.021	30.000	0.034
	Min	30.000	29.760	0.110	30.000	29.883	0.065	30.000	29.959	0.020	30.000	29.980	0.007	30.000	29.987	0.000
40	Max	40.160	39.880	0.440	40.062	39.920	0.204	40.039	39.975	0.089	40.025	39.991	0.050	40.025	40.000	0.041
	Min	40.000	39.720	0.120	40.000	39.858	0.080	40.000	39.950	0.025	40.000	39.975	0.009	40.000	39.984	0.000
50	Max	50.160	49.870	0.450	50.062	49.920	0.204	50.039	49.975	0.089	50.025	49.991	0.050	50.025	50.000	0.041
	Min	50.000	49.710	0.130	50.000	49.858	0.080	50.000	49.950	0.025	50.000	49.975	0.009	50.000	49.984	0.000
60	Max	60.190	59.860	0.520	60.074	59.900	0.248	60.046	59.970	0.106	60.030	59.990	0.059	60.030	60.000	0.049
	Min	60.000	59.670	0.140	60.000	59.826	0.100	60.000	59.940	0.030	60.000	59.971	0.010	60.000	59.981	0.000
80	Max	80.190	79.850	0.530	80.074	79.900	0.248	80.046	79.970	0.106	80.030	79.990	0.059	80.030	80.000	0.049
	Min	80.000	79.660	0.150	80.000	79.826	0.100	80.000	79.940	0.030	80.000	79.971	0.010	80.000	79.981	0.000
100	Max	100.220	99.830	0.610	100.087	99.880	0.294	100.054	99.964	0.125	100.035	99.988	0.069	100.035	100.000	0.057
	Min	100.000	99.610	0.170	100.000	99.793	0.120	100.000	99.929	0.036	100.000	99.966	0.012	100.000	99.978	0.000
120	Max	120.220	119.820	0.620	120.087	119.880	0.294	120.054	119.964	0.125	120.035	119.988	0.069	120.035	120.000	0.057
	Min	120.000	119.600	0.180	120.000	119.793	0.120	120.000	119.929	0.036	120.000	119.966	0.012	120.000	119.978	0.000
160	Max	160.250	159.790	0.710	160.100	159.855	0.345	160.063	159.957	0.146	160.040	159.986	0.079	160.040	160.000	0.065
	Min	160.000	159.540	0.210	160.000	159.755	0.145	160.000	159.917	0.043	160.000	159.961	0.014	160.000	159.975	0.000
200	Max	200.290	199.760	0.820	200.115	199.830	0.400	200.072	199.950	0.168	200.046	199.985	0.090	200.046	200.000	0.075
	Min	200.000	199.470	0.240	200.000	199.715	0.170	200.000	199.904	0.050	200.000	199.956	0.015	200.000	199.971	0.000
250	Max	250.290	249.720	0.860	250.115	249.830	0.400	250.072	249.950	0.168	250.046	249.985	0.090	250.046	250.000	0.075
	Min	250.000	249.430	0.280	250.000	249.715	0.170	250.000	249.904	0.050	250.000	249.956	0.015	250.000	249.971	0.000
300	Max	300.320	299.670	0.970	300.130	299.810	0.450	300.081	299.944	0.189	300.052	299.983	0.101	300.052	300.000	0.084
	Min	300.000	299.350	0.330	300.000	299.680	0.190	300.000	299.892	0.056	300.000	299.951	0.017	300.000	299.968	0.000
400	Max	400.360	399.600	1.120	400.140	399.790	0.490	400.089	399.938	0.208	400.057	399.982	0.111	400.057	400.000	0.093
	Min	400.000	399.240	0.400	400.000	399.650	0.210	400.000	399.881	0.062	400.000	399.946	0.018	400.000	399.964	0.000
500	Max	500.400	499.520	1.280	500.155	499.770	0.540	500.097	499.932	0.228	500.063	499.980	0.123	500.063	500.000	0.103
	Min	500.000	499.120	0.480	500.000	499.615	0.230	500.000	499.869	0.068	500.000	499.940	0.020	500.000	499.960	0.000

TABLE C.12.7 Preferred Metric Hole Basis Transition and Interference Fits

		Locational Transition			Locational Transition			Locational Interference			Medium Drive			Force		
Basic Size		***Hole H7***	***Shaft k6***	***Fit***	***Hole H7***	***Shaft n6***	***Fit***	***Hole H7***	***Shaft p6***	***Fit***	***Hole H7***	***Shaft s6***	***Fit***	***Hole H7***	***Shaft u6***	***Fit***
1	Max	1.010	1.006	0.010	1.010	1.010	0.006	1.010	1.012	0.004	1.010	1.020	−0.004	1.010	1.024	−0.008
	Min	1.000	1.000	−0.006	1.000	1.004	−0.010	1.000	1.006	−0.012	1.000	1.014	−0.020	1.000	1.018	−0.024
1.2	Max	1.210	1.206	0.010	1.210	1.210	0.006	1.210	1.212	0.004	1.210	1.220	−0.004	1.210	1.224	−0.008
	Min	1.200	1.200	−0.006	1.200	1.204	−0.010	1.200	1.206	−0.012	1.200	1.214	−0.020	1.200	1.218	−0.024
1.6	Max	1.610	1.606	0.010	1.610	1.610	0.006	1.610	1.612	0.004	1.610	1.620	−0.004	1.610	1.624	−0.008
	Min	1.600	1.600	−0.006	1.600	1.604	−0.010	1.600	1.606	−0.012	1.600	1.614	−0.020	1.600	1.618	−0.024
2	Max	2.010	2.006	0.010	2.010	2.010	0.006	2.010	2.012	0.004	2.010	2.020	−0.004	2.010	2.024	−0.008
	Min	2.000	2.000	−0.006	2.000	2.004	−0.010	2.000	2.006	−0.012	2.000	2.014	−0.020	2.000	2.018	−0.024
2.5	Max	2.510	2.506	0.010	2.510	2.510	0.006	2.510	2.512	0.004	2.510	2.520	−0.004	2.510	2.524	−0.008
	Min	2.500	2.500	−0.006	2.500	2.504	−0.010	2.500	2.506	−0.012	2.500	2.514	−0.020	2.500	2.518	−0.024
3	Max	3.010	3.006	0.010	3.010	3.010	0.006	3.010	3.012	0.004	3.010	3.020	−0.004	3.010	3.024	−0.008
	Min	3.000	3.000	−0.006	3.000	3.004	−0.010	3.000	3.006	−0.012	3.000	3.014	−0.020	3.000	3.018	−0.024
4	Max	4.012	4.009	0.011	4.012	4.016	0.004	4.012	4.020	0.000	4.012	4.027	−0.007	4.012	4.031	−0.011
	Min	4.000	4.001	−0.009	4.000	4.008	−0.016	4.000	4.012	−0.020	4.000	4.019	−0.027	4.000	4.023	−0.031
5	Max	5.012	5.009	0.011	5.012	5.016	0.004	5.012	5.020	0.000	5.012	5.027	−0.007	5.012	5.031	−0.011
	Min	5.000	5.001	−0.009	5.000	5.008	−0.016	5.000	5.012	−0.020	5.000	5.019	−0.027	5.000	5.023	−0.031
6	Max	6.012	6.009	0.011	6.012	6.016	0.004	6.012	6.020	0.000	6.012	6.027	−0.007	6.012	6.031	−0.011
	Min	6.000	6.001	−0.009	6.000	6.008	−0.016	6.000	6.012	−0.020	6.000	6.019	−0.027	6.000	6.023	−0.031
8	Max	8.015	8.010	0.014	8.015	8.019	0.005	8.015	8.024	0.000	8.015	8.032	−0.008	8.015	8.037	−0.013
	Min	8.000	8.001	−0.010	8.000	8.010	−0.019	8.000	8.015	−0.024	8.000	8.023	−0.032	8.000	8.028	−0.037
10	Max	10.015	10.010	0.014	10.015	10.019	0.005	10.015	10.024	0.000	10.015	10.032	−0.008	10.015	10.037	−0.013
	Min	10.000	10.001	−0.010	10.000	10.010	−0.019	10.000	10.015	−0.024	10.000	10.023	−0.032	10.000	10.028	−0.037
12	Max	12.018	12.012	0.017	12.018	12.023	0.006	12.018	12.029	0.000	12.018	12.039	−0.010	12.018	12.044	−0.015
	Min	12.000	12.001	−0.012	12.000	12.012	−0.023	12.000	12.018	−0.029	12.000	12.028	−0.039	12.000	12.033	−0.044
16	Max	16.018	16.012	0.017	16.018	16.023	0.006	16.018	16.029	0.000	16.018	16.039	−0.010	16.018	16.044	−0.015
	Min	16.000	16.001	−0.012	16.000	16.012	−0.023	16.000	16.018	−0.029	16.000	16.028	−0.039	16.000	16.033	−0.044
20	Max	20.021	20.015	0.019	20.021	20.028	0.006	20.021	20.035	−0.001	20.021	20.048	−0.014	20.021	20.054	−0.020
	Min	20.000	20.002	−0.015	20.000	20.015	−0.028	20.000	20.022	−0.035	20.000	20.035	−0.048	20.000	20.041	−0.054
25	Max	25.021	25.015	0.019	25.021	25.028	0.006	25.021	25.035	−0.001	25.021	25.048	−0.014	25.021	25.061	−0.027
	Min	25.000	25.002	−0.015	25.000	25.015	−0.028	25.000	25.022	−0.035	25.000	25.035	−0.048	25.000	25.048	−0.061
30	Max	30.021	30.015	0.019	30.021	30.028	0.006	30.021	30.035	−0.001	30.021	30.048	−0.014	30.021	30.061	−0.027
	Min	30.000	30.002	−0.015	30.000	30.015	−0.028	30.000	30.022	−0.035	30.000	30.035	−0.048	30.000	30.048	−0.061
40	Max	40.025	40.018	0.023	40.025	40.033	0.008	40.025	40.042	−0.001	40.025	40.059	−0.018	40.025	40.076	−0.035
	Min	40.000	40.002	−0.018	40.000	40.017	−0.033	40.000	40.026	−0.042	40.000	40.043	−0.059	40.000	40.060	−0.076
50	Max	50.025	50.018	0.023	50.025	50.033	0.008	50.025	50.042	−0.001	50.025	50.059	−0.018	50.025	50.086	−0.045
	Min	50.000	50.002	−0.018	50.000	50.017	−0.033	50.000	50.026	−0.042	50.000	50.043	−0.059	50.000	50.070	−0.086
60	Max	60.030	60.021	0.028	60.030	60.039	0.010	60.030	60.051	−0.002	60.030	60.072	−0.023	60.030	60.106	−0.057
	Min	60.000	60.002	−0.021	60.000	60.020	−0.039	60.000	60.032	−0.051	60.000	60.053	−0.072	60.000	60.087	−0.106
80	Max	80.030	80.021	0.028	80.030	80.039	0.010	80.030	80.051	−0.002	80.030	80.078	−0.029	80.030	80.121	−0.072
	Min	80.000	80.002	−0.021	80.000	80.020	−0.039	80.000	80.032	−0.051	80.000	80.059	−0.078	80.000	80.102	−0.121
100	Max	100.035	100.025	0.032	100.035	100.045	0.012	100.035	100.059	−0.002	100.035	100.093	−0.036	100.035	100.146	−0.089
	Min	100.000	100.003	−0.025	100.000	100.023	−0.045	100.000	100.037	−0.059	100.000	100.071	−0.093	100.000	100.124	−0.146
120	Max	120.035	120.025	0.032	120.035	120.045	0.012	120.035	120.059	−0.002	120.035	120.101	−0.044	120.035	120.166	−0.109
	Min	120.000	120.003	−0.025	120.000	120.023	−0.045	120.000	120.037	−0.059	120.000	120.079	−0.101	120.000	120.144	−0.166
160	Max	160.040	160.028	0.037	160.040	160.052	0.013	160.040	160.068	−0.003	160.040	160.125	−0.060	160.040	160.215	−0.150
	Min	160.000	160.003	−0.028	160.000	160.027	−0.052	160.000	160.043	−0.068	160.000	160.100	−0.125	160.000	160.190	−0.215
200	Max	200.046	200.033	0.042	200.046	200.060	0.015	200.046	200.079	−0.004	200.046	200.151	−0.076	200.046	200.265	−0.190
	Min	200.000	200.004	−0.033	200.000	200.031	−0.060	200.000	200.050	−0.079	200.000	200.122	−0.151	200.000	200.236	−0.265
250	Max	250.046	250.033	0.042	250.046	250.060	0.015	250.046	250.079	−0.004	250.046	250.169	−0.094	250.046	250.313	−0.238
	Min	250.000	250.004	−0.033	250.000	250.031	−0.060	250.000	250.050	−0.079	250.000	250.140	−0.169	250.000	250.284	−0.313
300	Max	300.052	300.036	0.048	300.052	300.066	0.018	300.052	300.088	−0.004	300.052	300.202	−0.118	300.052	300.382	−0.298
	Min	300.000	300.004	−0.036	300.000	300.034	−0.066	300.000	300.056	−0.088	300.000	300.170	−0.202	300.000	300.350	−0.382
400	Max	400.057	400.040	0.053	400.057	400.073	0.020	400.057	400.098	−0.005	400.057	400.244	−0.151	400.057	400.471	−0.378
	Min	400.000	400.004	−0.040	400.000	400.037	−0.073	400.000	400.062	−0.098	400.000	400.208	−0.244	400.000	400.435	−0.471
500	Max	500.063	500.045	0.058	500.063	500.080	0.023	500.063	500.108	−0.005	500.063	500.292	−0.189	500.063	500.580	−0.477
	Min	500.000	500.005	−0.045	500.000	500.040	−0.080	500.000	500.068	−0.108	500.000	500.252	−0.292	500.000	500.540	−0.580

TABLE C.12.8 Preferred Metric Shaft Basis Clearance Fits

Basic Size		Loose Running			Free Running			Close Running			Sliding			Locational Clearance		
		Hole C11	*Shaft h11*	*Fit*	*Hole D9*	*Shaft h9*	*Fit*	*Hole F8*	*Shaft h7*	*Fit*	*Hole G7*	*Shaft h6*	*Fit*	*Hole H7*	*Shaft h6*	*Fit*
1	Max	1.120	1.000	0.180	1.045	1.000	0.070	1.020	1.000	0.030	1.012	1.000	0.018	1.010	1.000	0.016
	Min	1.060	0.940	0.060	1.020	0.975	0.020	1.006	0.990	0.006	1.002	0.994	0.002	1.000	0.994	0.000
1.2	Max	1.320	1.200	0.180	1.245	1.200	0.070	1.220	1.200	0.030	1.212	1.200	0.018	1.210	1.200	0.016
	Min	1.260	1.140	0.060	1.220	1.175	0.020	1.206	1.190	0.006	1.202	1.194	0.002	1.200	1.194	0.000
1.6	Max	1.720	1.600	0.180	1.645	1.600	0.070	1.620	1.600	0.030	1.612	1.600	0.018	1.610	1.600	0.016
	Min	1.660	1.540	0.060	1.620	1.575	0.020	1.606	1.590	0.006	1.602	1.594	0.002	1.600	1.594	0.000
2	Max	2.120	2.000	0.180	2.045	2.000	0.070	2.020	2.000	0.030	2.012	2.000	0.018	2.010	2.000	0.016
	Min	2.060	1.940	0.060	2.020	1.975	0.020	2.006	1.990	0.006	2.002	1.994	0.002	2.000	1.994	0.000
2.5	Max	2.620	2.500	0.180	2.545	2.500	0.070	2.520	2.500	0.030	2.512	2.500	0.018	2.510	2.500	0.016
	Min	2.560	2.440	0.060	2.520	2.475	0.020	2.506	2.490	0.006	2.502	2.494	0.002	2.500	2.494	0.000
3	Max	3.120	3.000	0.180	3.045	3.000	0.070	3.020	3.000	0.030	3.012	3.000	0.018	3.010	3.000	0.016
	Min	3.060	2.940	0.060	3.020	2.975	0.020	3.006	2.990	0.006	3.002	2.994	0.002	3.000	2.994	0.000
4	Max	4.145	4.000	0.220	4.060	4.000	0.090	4.028	4.000	0.040	4.016	4.000	0.024	4.012	4.000	0.020
	Min	4.070	3.925	0.070	4.030	3.970	0.030	4.010	3.988	0.010	4.004	3.992	0.004	4.000	3.992	0.000
5	Max	5.145	5.000	0.220	5.060	5.000	0.090	5.028	5.000	0.040	5.016	5.000	0.024	5.012	5.000	0.020
	Min	5.070	4.925	0.070	5.030	4.970	0.030	5.010	4.988	0.010	5.004	4.992	0.004	5.000	4.992	0.000
6	Max	6.145	6.000	0.220	6.060	6.000	0.090	6.028	6.000	0.040	6.016	6.000	0.024	6.012	6.000	0.020
	Min	6.070	5.925	0.070	6.030	5.970	0.030	6.010	5.988	0.010	6.004	5.992	0.004	6.000	5.992	0.000
8	Max	8.170	8.000	0.260	8.076	8.000	0.112	8.035	8.000	0.050	8.020	8.000	0.029	8.015	8.000	0.024
	Min	8.080	7.910	0.080	8.040	7.964	0.040	8.013	7.985	0.013	8.005	7.991	0.005	8.000	7.991	0.000
10	Max	10.170	10.000	0.260	10.076	10.000	0.112	10.035	10.000	0.050	10.020	10.000	0.029	10.015	10.000	0.024
	Min	10.080	9.910	0.080	10.040	9.964	0.040	10.013	9.985	0.013	10.005	9.991	0.005	10.000	9.991	0.000
12	Max	12.205	12.000	0.315	12.093	12.000	0.136	12.043	12.000	0.061	12.024	12.000	0.035	12.018	12.000	0.029
	Min	12.095	11.890	0.095	12.050	11.957	0.050	12.016	11.982	0.016	12.006	11.989	0.006	12.000	11.989	0.000
16	Max	16.205	16.000	0.315	16.093	16.000	0.136	16.043	16.000	0.061	16.024	16.000	0.035	16.018	16.000	0.029
	Min	16.095	15.890	0.095	16.050	15.957	0.050	16.016	15.982	0.016	16.006	15.989	0.006	16.000	15.989	0.000
20	Max	20.240	20.000	0.370	20.117	20.000	0.169	20.053	20.000	0.074	20.028	20.000	0.041	20.021	20.000	0.034
	Min	20.110	19.870	0.110	20.065	19.948	0.065	20.020	19.979	0.020	20.007	19.987	0.007	20.000	19.987	0.000
25	Max	25.240	25.000	0.370	25.117	25.000	0.169	25.053	25.000	0.074	25.028	25.000	0.041	25.021	25.000	0.034
	Min	25.110	24.870	0.110	25.065	24.948	0.065	25.020	24.979	0.020	25.007	24.987	0.007	25.000	24.987	0.000
30	Max	30.240	30.000	0.370	30.117	30.000	0.169	30.053	30.000	0.074	30.028	30.000	0.041	30.021	30.000	0.034
	Min	30.110	29.870	0.110	30.065	29.948	0.065	30.020	29.979	0.020	30.007	29.987	0.007	30.000	29.987	0.000
40	Max	40.280	40.000	0.440	40.142	40.000	0.204	40.064	40.000	0.089	40.034	40.000	0.050	40.025	40.000	0.041
	Min	40.120	39.840	0.120	40.080	39.938	0.080	40.025	39.975	0.025	40.009	39.984	0.009	40.000	39.984	0.000
50	Max	50.290	50.000	0.450	50.142	50.000	0.204	50.064	50.000	0.089	50.034	50.000	0.050	50.025	50.000	0.041
	Min	50.130	49.840	0.130	50.080	49.938	0.080	50.025	49.975	0.025	50.009	49.984	0.009	50.000	49.984	0.000
60	Max	60.330	60.000	0.520	60.174	60.000	0.248	60.076	60.000	0.106	60.040	60.000	0.059	60.030	60.000	0.049
	Min	60.140	59.810	0.140	60.100	59.926	0.100	60.030	59.970	0.030	60.010	59.981	0.010	60.000	59.981	0.000
80	Max	80.340	80.000	0.530	80.174	80.000	0.248	80.076	80.000	0.106	80.040	80.000	0.059	80.030	80.000	0.049
	Min	80.150	79.810	0.150	80.100	79.926	0.100	80.030	79.970	0.030	80.010	79.981	0.010	80.000	79.981	0.000
100	Max	100.390	100.000	0.610	100.207	100.000	0.294	100.090	100.000	0.125	100.047	100.000	0.069	100.035	100.000	0.057
	Min	100.170	99.780	0.170	100.120	99.913	0.120	100.036	99.965	0.036	100.012	99.978	0.012	100.000	99.978	0.000
120	Max	120.400	120.000	0.620	120.207	120.000	0.294	120.090	120.000	0.125	120.047	120.000	0.069	120.035	120.000	0.057
	Min	120.180	119.780	0.180	120.120	119.913	0.120	120.036	119.965	0.036	120.012	119.978	0.012	120.000	119.978	0.000
160	Max	160.460	160.000	0.710	160.245	160.000	0.345	160.106	160.000	0.146	160.054	160.000	0.079	160.040	160.000	0.065
	Min	160.210	159.750	0.210	160.145	159.900	0.145	160.043	159.960	0.043	160.014	159.975	0.014	160.000	159.975	0.000
200	Max	200.530	200.000	0.820	200.285	200.000	0.400	200.122	200.000	0.168	200.061	200.000	0.090	200.046	200.000	0.075
	Min	200.240	199.710	0.240	200.170	199.885	0.170	200.050	199.954	0.050	200.015	199.971	0.015	200.000	199.971	0.000
250	Max	250.570	250.000	0.860	250.285	250.000	0.400	250.122	250.000	0.168	250.061	250.000	0.090	250.046	250.000	0.075
	Min	250.280	249.710	0.280	250.170	249.885	0.170	250.050	249.954	0.050	250.015	249.971	0.015	250.000	249.971	0.000
300	Max	300.650	300.000	0.970	300.320	300.000	0.450	300.137	300.000	0.189	300.069	300.000	0.101	300.052	300.000	0.084
	Min	300.330	299.680	0.330	300.190	299.870	0.190	300.056	299.948	0.056	300.017	299.968	0.017	300.000	299.968	0.000
400	Max	400.760	400.000	1.120	400.350	400.000	0.490	400.151	400.000	0.208	400.075	400.000	0.111	400.057	400.000	0.093
	Min	400.400	399.640	0.400	400.210	399.860	0.210	400.062	399.943	0.062	400.018	399.964	0.018	400.000	399.964	0.000
500	Max	500.880	500.000	1.280	500.385	500.000	0.540	500.165	500.000	0.228	500.083	500.000	0.123	500.063	500.000	0.103
	Min	500.480	499.600	0.480	500.230	499.845	0.230	500.068	499.937	0.068	500.020	499.960	0.020	500.000	499.960	0.000

TABLE C.12.9 Preferred Metric Shaft Basis Transition and Interference Fits

		Locational Transition			Locational Transition			Locational Interference			Medium Drive			Force		
Basic Size		***Hole K7***	***Shaft h6***	***Fit***	***Hole N7***	***Shaft h6***	***Fit***	***Hole P7***	***Shaft h6***	***Fit***	***Hole S7***	***Shaft h6***	***Fit***	***Hole U7***	***Shaft h6***	***Fit***
1	Max	1.000	1.000	0.006	0.996	1.000	0.002	0.994	1.000	0.000	0.986	1.000	−0.008	0.982	1.000	−0.012
	Min	0.990	0.994	−0.010	0.986	0.994	−0.014	0.984	0.994	−0.016	0.976	0.994	−0.024	0.972	0.994	−0.028
1.2	Max	1.200	1.200	0.006	1.196	1.200	0.002	1.194	1.200	0.000	1.186	1.200	−0.008	1.182	1.200	−0.012
	Min	1.190	1.194	−0.010	1.186	1.194	−0.014	1.184	1.194	−0.016	1.176	1.194	−0.024	1.172	1.194	−0.028
1.6	Max	1.600	1.600	0.006	1.596	1.600	0.002	1.594	1.600	0.000	1.586	1.600	−0.008	1.582	1.600	−0.012
	Min	1.590	1.594	−0.010	1.586	1.594	−0.014	1.584	1.594	−0.016	1.576	1.594	−0.024	1.572	1.594	−0.028
2	Max	2.000	2.000	0.006	1.996	2.000	0.002	1.994	2.000	0.000	1.986	2.000	−0.008	1.982	2.000	−0.012
	Min	1.990	1.994	−0.010	1.986	1.994	−0.014	1.984	1.994	−0.016	1.976	1.994	−0.024	1.972	1.994	−0.028
2.5	Max	2.500	2.500	0.006	2.496	2.500	0.002	2.494	2.500	0.000	2.486	2.500	−0.008	2.482	2.500	−0.012
	Min	2.490	2.494	−0.010	2.486	2.494	−0.014	2.484	2.494	−0.016	2.476	2.494	−0.024	2.472	2.494	−0.028
3	Max	3.000	3.000	0.006	2.996	3.000	0.002	2.994	3.000	0.000	2.986	3.000	−0.008	2.982	3.000	−0.012
	Min	2.990	2.994	−0.010	2.986	2.994	−0.014	2.984	2.994	−0.016	2.976	2.994	−0.024	2.972	2.994	−0.028
4	Max	4.003	4.000	0.011	3.996	4.000	0.004	3.992	4.000	0.000	3.985	4.000	−0.007	3.981	4.000	−0.011
	Min	3.991	3.992	−0.009	3.984	3.992	−0.016	3.980	3.992	−0.020	3.973	3.992	−0.027	3.969	3.992	−0.031
5	Max	5.003	5.000	0.011	4.996	5.000	0.004	4.992	5.000	0.000	4.985	5.000	−0.007	4.981	5.000	−0.011
	Min	4.991	4.992	−0.009	4.984	4.992	−0.016	4.980	4.992	−0.020	4.973	4.992	−0.027	4.969	4.992	−0.031
6	Max	6.003	6.000	0.011	5.996	6.000	0.004	5.992	6.000	0.000	5.985	6.000	−0.007	5.981	6.000	−0.011
	Min	5.991	5.992	−0.009	5.984	5.992	−0.016	5.980	5.992	−0.020	5.973	5.992	−0.027	5.969	5.992	−0.031
8	Max	8.005	8.000	0.014	7.996	8.000	0.005	7.991	8.000	0.000	7.983	8.000	−0.008	7.978	8.000	−0.013
	Min	7.990	7.991	−0.010	7.981	7.991	−0.019	7.976	7.991	−0.024	7.968	7.991	−0.032	7.963	7.991	−0.037
10	Max	10.005	10.000	0.014	9.996	10.000	0.005	9.991	10.000	0.000	9.983	10.000	−0.008	9.978	10.000	−0.013
	Min	9.990	9.991	−0.010	9.981	9.991	−0.019	9.976	9.991	−0.024	9.968	9.991	−0.032	9.963	9.991	−0.037
12	Max	12.006	12.000	0.017	11.995	12.000	0.006	11.989	12.000	0.000	11.979	12.000	−0.010	11.974	12.000	−0.015
	Min	11.988	11.989	−0.012	11.977	11.989	−0.023	11.971	11.989	−0.029	11.961	11.989	−0.039	11.956	11.989	−0.044
16	Max	16.006	16.000	0.017	15.995	16.000	0.006	15.989	16.000	0.000	15.979	16.000	−0.010	15.974	16.000	−0.015
	Min	15.988	15.989	−0.012	15.977	15.989	−0.023	15.971	15.989	−0.029	15.961	15.989	−0.039	15.956	15.989	−0.044
20	Max	20.006	20.000	0.019	19.993	20.000	0.006	19.986	20.000	−0.001	19.973	20.000	−0.014	19.967	20.000	−0.020
	Min	19.985	19.987	−0.015	19.972	19.987	−0.028	19.965	19.987	−0.035	19.952	19.987	−0.048	19.946	19.987	−0.054
25	Max	25.006	25.000	0.019	24.993	25.000	0.006	24.986	25.000	−0.001	24.973	25.000	−0.014	24.960	25.000	−0.027
	Min	24.985	24.987	−0.015	24.972	24.987	−0.028	24.965	24.987	−0.035	24.952	24.987	−0.048	24.939	24.987	−0.061
30	Max	30.006	30.000	0.019	29.993	30.000	0.006	29.986	30.000	−0.001	29.973	30.000	−0.014	29.960	30.000	−0.027
	Min	29.985	29.987	−0.015	29.972	29.987	−0.028	29.965	29.987	−0.035	29.952	29.987	−0.048	29.939	29.987	−0.061
40	Max	40.007	40.000	0.023	39.992	40.000	0.008	39.983	40.000	−0.001	39.966	40.000	−0.018	39.949	40.000	−0.035
	Min	39.982	39.984	−0.018	39.967	39.984	−0.033	39.958	39.984	−0.042	39.941	39.984	−0.059	39.924	39.984	−0.076
50	Max	50.007	50.000	0.023	49.992	50.000	0.008	49.983	50.000	−0.001	49.966	50.000	−0.018	49.939	50.000	−0.045
	Min	49.982	49.984	−0.018	49.967	49.984	−0.033	49.958	49.984	−0.042	49.941	49.984	−0.059	49.914	49.984	−0.086
60	Max	60.009	60.000	0.028	59.991	60.000	0.010	59.979	60.000	−0.002	59.958	60.000	−0.023	59.924	60.000	−0.057
	Min	59.979	59.981	−0.021	59.961	59.981	−0.039	59.949	59.981	−0.051	59.928	59.981	−0.072	59.894	59.981	−0.106
80	Max	80.009	80.000	0.028	79.991	80.000	0.010	79.979	80.000	−0.002	79.952	80.000	−0.029	79.909	80.000	−0.072
	Min	79.979	79.981	−0.021	79.961	79.981	−0.039	79.949	79.981	−0.051	79.922	79.981	−0.078	79.879	79.981	−0.121
100	Max	100.010	100.000	0.032	99.990	100.000	0.012	99.976	100.000	−0.002	99.942	100.000	−0.036	99.889	100.000	−0.089
	Min	99.975	99.978	−0.025	99.955	99.978	−0.045	99.941	99.978	−0.059	99.907	99.978	−0.093	99.854	99.978	−0.146
120	Max	120.010	120.000	0.032	119.990	120.000	0.012	119.976	120.000	−0.002	119.934	120.000	−0.044	119.869	120.000	−0.109
	Min	119.975	119.978	−0.025	119.955	119.978	−0.045	119.941	119.978	−0.059	119.899	119.978	−0.101	119.834	119.978	−0.166
160	Max	160.012	160.000	0.037	159.988	160.000	0.013	159.972	160.000	−0.003	159.915	160.000	−0.060	159.825	160.000	−0.150
	Min	159.972	159.975	−0.028	159.948	159.975	−0.052	159.932	159.975	−0.068	159.875	159.975	−0.125	159.785	159.975	−0.215
200	Max	200.013	200.000	0.042	199.986	200.000	0.015	199.967	200.000	−0.004	199.895	200.000	−0.076	199.781	200.000	−0.190
	Min	199.967	199.971	−0.033	199.940	199.971	−0.060	199.921	199.971	−0.079	199.849	199.971	−0.151	199.735	199.971	−0.265
250	Max	250.013	250.000	0.042	249.986	250.000	0.015	249.967	250.000	−0.004	249.877	250.000	−0.094	249.733	250.000	−0.238
	Min	249.967	249.971	−0.033	249.940	249.971	−0.060	249.921	249.971	−0.079	249.831	249.971	−0.169	249.687	249.971	−0.313
300	Max	300.016	300.000	0.048	299.986	300.000	0.018	299.964	300.000	−0.004	299.850	300.000	−0.118	299.670	300.000	−0.298
	Min	299.964	299.968	−0.036	299.934	299.968	−0.066	299.912	299.968	−0.088	299.798	299.968	−0.202	299.618	299.968	−0.382
400	Max	400.017	400.000	0.053	399.984	400.000	0.020	399.959	400.000	−0.005	399.813	400.000	−0.151	399.586	400.000	−0.378
	Min	399.960	399.964	−0.040	399.927	399.964	−0.073	399.902	399.964	−0.098	399.756	399.964	−0.244	399.529	399.964	−0.471
500	Max	500.018	500.000	0.058	499.983	500.000	0.023	499.955	500.000	−0.005	499.771	500.000	−0.189	499.483	500.000	−0.477
	Min	499.955	499.960	−0.045	499.920	499.960	−0.080	499.892	499.960	−0.108	499.708	499.960	−0.292	499.420	499.960	−0.580

Index

A page number in italics indicates that a photograph or an illustration appears on that page.

The following illustrations were rendered by artists at Precision Graphics:

Figure 1.03
1.11–1.13
2.05
2.13
2.21
2.24
3.02
3.04
3.06–3.08
3.11
3.13–3.14
3.16
3.20–3.21
3.23–3.24
3.26–3.32
3.36
3.41
3.56
3.58
3.62
5.05
5.16
5.17a (flow chart)
5.28
6.12
6.16
6.19–6.21
6.24–6.25
6.28–6.33
6.42–6.43
6.53–6.69
7.03–7.04
7.07
7.10–7.18
7.33–7.36
Chapter 7 Applying Parametric Design . . . Text and Notes on Models and Drawings, page 193 (Figures D and E)
8.02–8.04
8.06–8.45
8.46a
8.47–8.64
Chapter 8 Focus On . . . Geometry, page 210 (both figures)
9.05–9.12
9.15
9.18–9.19
9.21
9.23–9.25
9.30
9.33–9.34
9.37–9.38
9.44–9.46
10.04–10.11
10.17–10.21
10.23–10.39
10.41–10.57
10.63
10.65
11.07
11.15–11.17
11.25
11.29–11.33
11.36 (top diagrams)
11.37–11.38
12.03–12.09
12.15
12.21–12.22
13.09
13.13–13.16
13.18–13.26
13.29–13.31
13.33–13.42
13.49–13.50
13.56–13.57
13.59
13.63
13.66–13.73
13.75–13.76
14.04–14.05
14.07
14.13
14.24c
14.26
14.27b
14.27c
14.32
14.38
14.46
14.47
15.51
15.86–15.90
15.99–15.100
15.102–15.105
15.107
16.02–16.30
16.34–16.37
16.49–16.52
Chapter 16 Applying Parametric Design . . . Tolerancing and Parametric Features, pages 622, 624, and 626 (Figures A, B, C, J, N, and O)
Problems 16.05– Problem 16.12
17.11
17.14–17.20
17.26
17.31
17.85
Chapter 17 Applying Parametric Design . . . Standard Part Families and Cosmetic Fastener Threads, page 677 (Figures L and M)
18.02–18.03
18.05
18.08
18.11
18.13
18.15
Chapter 18 Focus On . . . Spring Designs Drawn from Tooling Libraries, page 697 (top left)
19.02
19.04–19.07
19.09–19.10
19.13–19.14
19.17
19.23–19.24
19.29–19.31
19.37
19.39–19.40
20.07–20.19
21.01–21.11
21.13–21.24
22.03–22.05
22.07–22.08
22.11
23.26
23.33
24.03–24.04
24.07
24.09
24.13
24.24
25.06
25.08
26.01c and d
27.06
27.19a
27.24
Chapter 27 Focus On . . . Constructive Solid Geometry (CSG), page 980
28.03
28.05
28.25
29.02–29.03
29.23
29.32–29.33
Chapter 29 Focus On . . . Magnificent Iron Bridges, page 1036
30.16
30.26
Appendix C, page A-79

Photo and Illustration Credits

Figure numbers precede each credit line. Materials credited to Autodesk are reprinted with the permission from and under the copyright of Autodesk, Inc. Copyright © 1995 Autodesk, Inc.

Chapter 1. *Figure 1.01* Hewlett Packard
1.02 Hewlett Packard
1.04 Computervision
1.05 Lockheed
1.07 Parametric Technology Corp.
1.09 Gary Donaldson
1.10 Lockheed
1.14 Lockheed
1.17 J. I. Case Corporation
1.20 Chicago Bridge and Iron Co.
1.22 NASA
1.23 © Richard R. Hansen/Photo Researchers
1.24 American Switch Business
1.25 Adage, Inc.
1.29 Evolution Engineering
1.30 Lockheed
1.31 Aero Gear
1.32 Autodesk
Chapter 1 Focus on . . . The Design Process, page 8 (left), courtesy of Levi-Strauss, and (right) © Tony Freeman/PhotoEdit

Chapter 2. *2.01a* Autodesk
2.01b Drawn with AutoCAD© 3D Studio
2.02 Parametric Technology Corp.
2.03a Logitech
2.03b–2.03c Parametric Technology Corp.
2.06 Stanford Physics Lab, Palo Alto
2.07 Lockheed
2.10 © Tony Freeman/PhotoEdit
2.11 Autodesk
2.17 © Tony Freeman/PhotoEdit
2.18 © Photri
2.19 NASA (1977)
2.25–2.28 Lockheed
2.30–2.32 Lockheed
2.33–2.34 Gary Donaldson/Lockheed
2.35–2.36 Lockheed

Chapter 3. *3.01* Autodesk
3.09–3.10 Grove Valve and Regulator Company
3.15 Macola, Inc.
3.17 NASA
3.18 Engineering Model Associates, Inc.
3.19 Magee-Bralla, Inc.
3.35 © UPI/Bettmann
3.37–3.38 © Photri
3.39 NASA
3.40a Silverscreen
3.40b © Ross Harrison Koty/Tony Stone Images
3.42–3.44 NASA
3.46 Model by Continental Engineering
3.48 Megatek Corp.
3.49 CADKEY, Inc.
3.50 Gibbs and Associates
3.52 Computervision
3.53 © Calma, a division of Prime Computer
3.59 Computervision
3.63c Innovative Design Systems Corp.
3.64a © 1994 Logitech, Inc.
Chapter 3 Focus On . . . Stereolithography in the Design Process, page 57, courtesy of Motorola

Chapter 4. *4.01* Hewlett Packard Co.
4.02 Cincinnati Milacron
4.03 CADKEY, Inc.
4.04 Lockheed
4.05 Cincinnati Milacron
4.06 CADKEY, Inc.
4.07–4.08 Hewlett Packard Co.
4.09 Control Data Systems, Inc.
4.10 © Apple Computer, Inc. All rights reserved. Used with permission. Apple® and the Apple logo are registered trademarks of Apple Computer, Inc.
4.11–4.12 Hewlett Packard Co.
4.13 ISICAD, Inc.
4.17 © 1994 Logitech, Inc.
4.18 Hewlett Packard Co.
4.19 Computervision
4.20–4.24 Hewlett Packard Co.
4.25 IBM
4.26 Computervision
4.27 Intergraph Corp.
4.28 Autodesk
4.30 McDonnell Douglas
4.31 Drawn using American Small Business Computers' DesignCAD 3D
4.32a Vector Automation
4.32b Macola, Inc.
4.33a Drawn using American Small Business Computers' DesignCAD 3D
4.34 Hewlett Packard
4.36 IBM
4.37 Drawn using American Small Business Computers' DesignCAD 3D
4.38 CADKEY, Inc.
4.39a Drawn using American Small Business Computers' DesignCAD 3D
4.39b CADKEY, Inc.
4.40 CAMAX Systems, Inc.
4.41–4.43 Cincinnati Milacron
4.44 Ford Motor Co.
4.45 © Simon Fraser, Newcastle Library/Photo Researchers
4.46 Evans & Sutherland Computer Corp.

Chapter 5. *5.01* Parametric Technology Corporation
5.02–5.04 Parametric Technology Corp.
5.12–5.13 Parametric Technology Corp.
5.18 Parametric Technology Corp.
5.25–5.27 Parametric Technology Corp.
5.29 Parametric Technology Corp.
5.36–5.39 Parametric Technology Corp.

Chapter 6. *6.01* Koh-I-Noor
6.02 © The Image Works
6.03 © Peter Menzel/Stock Boston
6.04–6.05 3M Company
6.07 Koh-I-Noor
6.08 Staedtler, Inc.
6.09 VEMCO
6.10 Staedtler, Inc.
6.13 Berol RapiDesign
6.14–6.15 Koh-I-Noor
6.17 Staedtler, Inc.
6.18 Koh-I-Noor
6.22–6.23 Staedtler Inc.
6.26 © J. Pickerell/The Image Works
6.27 Koh-I-Noor
6.35 © Bob Daemmrich/Stock Boston
6.36 Hearlihy & Co.
6.37–6.38 Koh-I-Noor
6.39 Staedtler, Inc.
6.40 VEMCO
6.41 Koh-I-Noor
6.44 K & E

6.45 Staedtler, Inc.
6.46–6.49 Koh-I-Noor
6.50–6.52 ANSI
6.70 Staedtler, Inc.
6.71 Koh-I-Noor

Chapter 7. *7.09* Koh-I-Noor
7.21 Staedtler, Inc.
7.23 Staedtler, Inc.
7.26 Arnold & Brown
7.27–7.28 Kroy, Inc.
Chapter 7 Focus On . . . The Alphabet, page 186 and page 187 (left) © North Wind Picture Archives, and page 187 (right) © Michael Newman/PhotoEdit

Chapter 8. *8.01a* Lockheed
8.01b © Joseph Nettis/Photo Researchers
8.01c Intergraph

Chapter 9. *9.51* Computervision
Chapter 9 Focus On . . . Leonardo Da Vinci, The Sketcher, page 256 (left and right), © North Wind Picture Archives

Chapter 10. *10.01* Lockheed
10.02 Autodesk
Chapter 10 Focus On . . . Evinrude, page 303 (left and right), courtesy of Outboard Marine Company

Chapter 11. *11.02a* Lunkenheimer Corp.
11.45 Control Data Corp.
11.46 © Alan Levenson/Tony Stone Images
Chapter 11 Focus On . . . Ultrasound, page 352, courtesy of Techsonic Industries

Chapter 12. *Focus On . . . Hand Tools and Devices,* page 389, © Michael Newman/Photo Edit

Chapter 13. *13.04* Lockheed
13.05–13.06 Autodesk
13.07–13.08 Parametric Technology Corporation
13.64 SmartCAM/CAMAX Manufacturing Technologies
13.79 Parametric Technology Corporation
13.84 Autodesk
Chapter 13 Focus On . . . Pictorials, page 433 (top right), © North Wind Picture Archives, and (bottom left, middle, and right) © Autodesk

Chapter 14. *14.03* Lockheed
14.06a Lockheed
14.06b Cogsdill Tool Products, Inc.
14.08 Lockheed
14.10 Cogsdill Tool Products, Inc.
14.11 © Michael Rosenfeld/Tony Stone Images
14.14 Cogsdill Tool Products, Inc.
14.16 © Photri
14.17 © Will & Deni McIntyre/Photo Researchers
14.18 © Holt Confer/The Image Works
14.20 © 1995 Terry Wild Studios
14.21 Aero Gear
14.22 Mitutoyo/MTI Corp.
14.23 © 1995 Terry Wild Studios
14.28 Parametric Technology Corporation
14.37 Aero Gear
14.39 Parametric Technology Corporation
14.42 Cogsdill Tool Products, Inc. of Camden, SC
14.43 Control Data Systems Inc.
14.44 Vericut by CGTECH
14.45 D. P. Technology Corp.
14.48 D. P. Technology Corp.
14.49–14.50 SmartCAM/CAMAX Manufacturing Technologies
14.52a Cincinnati Milicron
14.54 Evans & Sutherland
Chapter 14 Focus On . . . Computers in Manufacturing, page 489 (top right), courtesy of Ford Motor Company, and (bottom left) © Benelux/Photo Researchers
Chapter 14 Applying Parametric Design . . . Parametric Models and Machining, page 500, courtesy of Parametric Technology Corporation

Chapter 15. *15.01a and b* D. P. Technology Corporation
15.01c Lockheed-California Co.
Chapter 15 Focus On . . . The History of the Metric Standard, page 533, © The Bettmann Archive

Chapter 17. *17.04* D. P. Technology Corporation
17.34 Federal Screw Products
17.47 Holo-Krome©

Chapter 19. *19.01* Aero Gear
19.03 D. P. Technology Corp.
19.08 Aero Gear
19.35 Hewlett-Packard Co.
19.38 FAG Bearing Corp.
19.41–19.42 The Timken Company
19.43–19.44 FAG Bearing Corp.
Chapter 19 Focus On . . . Elevators, page 718 (left) © The Bettmann Archive, and (right) © Robert Brenner/PhotoEdit

Chapter 20. *20.02a* © Tony Freeman/PhotoEdit
20.03 Commercial Cam Company, Inc. (CAMCO)
Chapter 20 Focus On . . . Engine Camshafts, page 747, © D. Miliano/Photri

Chapter 21. *Chapter 21 Focus On . . . Piping Systems,* page 766 (left), © The Bettmann Archive, and (right) © Copyright 1994 George Haling/Photo Researchers/All rights reserved

Chapter 22. *22.01* © Bruce Forster/Tony Stone Images
Chapter 22 Focus On . . . Using the Laser to Weld, page 783 (bottom left) © James Holmes/Rover/Science Photo Library, and (top right) © Photri

Chapter 23. *23.01* Parametric Technology Corporation
23.03 NASA
23.06 Grove Valve and Regulator Company
23.09 FAG Bearing Corp.
23.12 IBM
23.23 © Tom Hollyman 1979/Photo Researchers
23.24–23.25 3M
23.27 IBM
23.28 Autodesk
23.29 CADKEY, Inc.
23.32 IBM
23.35 Gerber Systems Technology, Inc.
23.37 Carr Lane
23.38 Wedge Innovations
Chapter 23 Focus On . . . America's First Automobile, page 820, courtesy of Ford Motor Company
Chapter 23 Applying Parametric Design . . . Assemblies, Exploded Assembly Models, and Reports (BOM), page 832 (Figures A and B), courtesy of Parametric Technology Corporation

Chapter 24. *24.34* Louis Gary Lamit

Chapter 26. *26.01* © SERAPID, Inc.
26.21 PATRAN, a division of PDA Engineering/MacNeal-Schoendler Corporation
26.23 PATRAN, a division of PDA Engineering/MacNeal-Schoendler Corporation
Chapter 26 Focus On . . . The Gyrocompass, page 947, courtesy of Sperry Marine

Chapter 27. *27.01b* IBM
27.02 Lockheed
27.18 CADKEY, Inc.
27.22 Lockheed
27.30–27.31 CADKEY, Inc.

Chapter 28. *28.02b* Lockheed
28.30 © John Coletti/Stock Boston
Chapter 28 Focus On . . . Packaging, page 1005, © Michael Newman/PhotoEdit

Chapter 29. *29.01* © David R. Frazier Photolibrary/Photo Researchers
29.42 © John Keating 1981/Photo Researchers
Chapter 29 Focus On . . .Magnificent Iron Bridges, page 1036 (top right), © Brian Yarvin 1994/Photo Researchers

ANSI TITLE BLOCK DIMENSIONS

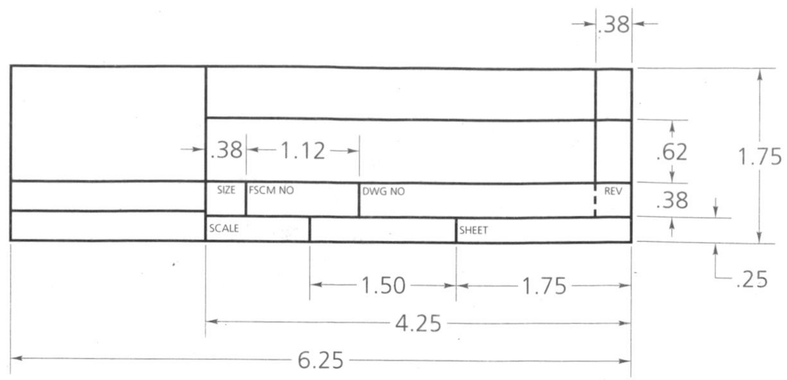

TITLE BLOCK FOR SIZES A, B, C, AND G

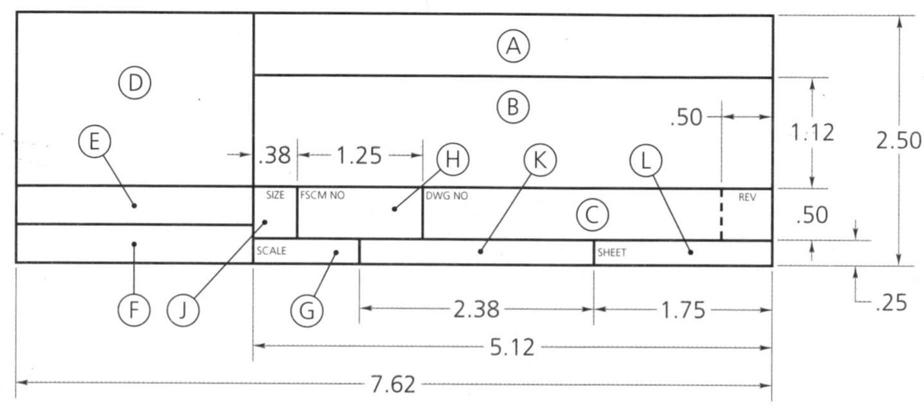

TITLE BLOCK FOR SIZES D, E, F, H, J, AND K

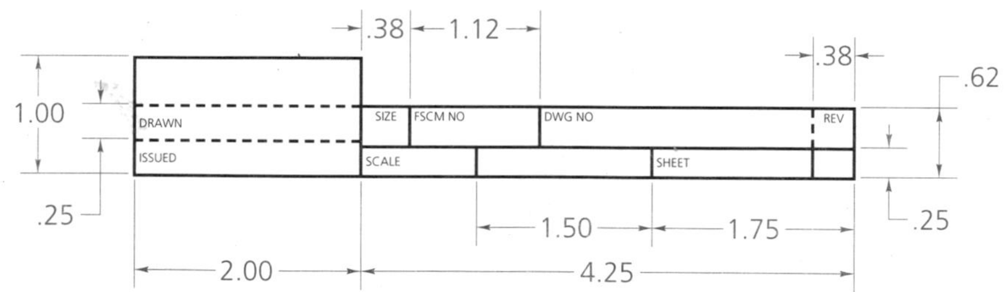

CONTINUATION SHEET TITLE BLOCK FOR SIZES A, B, C, AND G

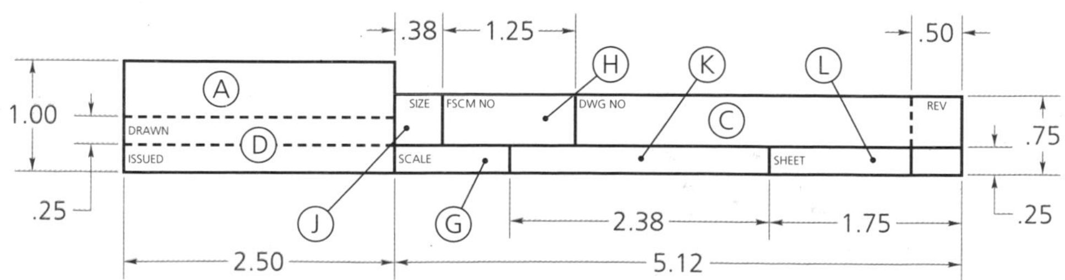

CONTINUATION SHEET TITLE BLOCK FOR SIZES D, E, F, H, J, AND K